Competition Page

Have You Sharp Eyes: How Many Mistakes Can You See?

THE MECCANO MAGAZINE ANTHOLOGY

Edited by Allen Levy

FRANK HORNBY
1863–1936

New Cavendish Books
LONDON

Dedicated to Royston Carss who many years ago dreamt up the notion of a book called 'The Hornby Companion'. Royston's idea of a single book was expanded to this series.

First edition published in Great Britain by New Cavendish Books—1991.

Specification: 1072 pages.
With rigid slipcase.
280 × 209 mm.

Acknowledgements
The publishers wish to thank Anthony Bianco and Jim Gamble for generously allowing us access to their original Meccano Magazine collections. We also acknowledge Dr C. J. Stratmann's original selection of material.

The Hornby Companion Series

Design—John B. Cooper
Editor—Allen Levy
Production—Narisa Chakra

Phototypesetting and mono illustrations by Wyvern Typesetting Ltd, Bristol.

Printed and Bound in Hong Kong under the supervision of Mandarin Offset, London.

New Cavendish Books, 3 Denbigh Road, London W11 2SJ

ISBN 1 872727 80 8

PREFACE

One of the tributes that can be paid to 'The Meccano Magazine' is that it was thought important enough by the authorities to allow publication throughout the second world war.

Few readers of the other volumes of this series would not have come into contact with this extraordinary publication. In volume 7 the Editors tackled one part of the presentation of the Magazine's history, namely a massive index of sixty five years of almost unbroken publishing together with reproductions of all the covers – over 600 of them. In this volume over 400 articles and features are reproduced in their entirety thus completing our aim to give the owner of The Hornby Companion series one of the most complete reviews of a Company's products and promotional material ever published.

Part of this anthology was compiled by Dr C. J. Stratmann who wrote several articles in the Magazine under the name H.G. Forsythe.

Some typical advertisements, which were so much a part of the original Magazine have been included to give extra flavour to this retrospective anthology.

This anthology contains a cross section of articles published in 'The Meccano Magazine' from the 1920's through to the 1960's, this period being considered the Magazine's prime years.

By the very nature of an anthology the choice of material is subjective but the Editors aims have been to give the reader a broad cross section of articles that the original Editors thought would be of interest to 'Meccano Boys'.

In some cases page layouts have been amended from the originals to ensure that all articles are complete within the new pagination, but in a few cases the continuation of articles not reproduced in their entirety may appear. In those cases the relevant text is indicated with a light grey tint. In the case of the year 1936 all the editorial and features for the whole year together with the annual index for that year have been reproduced with all the advertisements that appeared within the editorial sections. Furthermore all 1936 articles have been reproduced with a light yellow tint.

The year 1939 in particular has been excluded as an excellent annual of that year's magazines was published some years ago.

CONTENTS

Month, year and page of original *MM* article in parenthesis.

Editorial (11/23 p. 141) **5**
The Men Who Gave Us Radio (11/23 p. 151) **6**
The Heaviest Dragline in the World (4/24 p. 88 & 89) .. **7**
Electricity (4/24 p. 94 & 95) **9**
Bridging the Atlantic (5/24 p. 129 & 131) **11**
Handling Goods on the Docks (2/25 p. 90 & 91) **14**
Engineering News of the Month (4/25 p. 192 & 193) .. **17**
From our Readers (8/25 p. 404) **19**
In the Land of the Rising Sun (8/25 p. 406 & 407) **20**
Electric Trains and their Story (11/25 p. 567 & 569) **22**
The Story of the Forth Bridge (11/25 p. 580, 581 & 584) **24**
Railway News of the Month (1/26 p. 18 & 19) **27**
Air News of the Month (1/26 p. 46 & 47) **29**
Jackie Coogan's Visit to the American Meccano Factory (2/26 p. 102 & 103) **31**
Jackie Coogan's Visit to the American Meccano Factory (3/26 p. 154 & 155) **33**
Cleaning a Giant Locomotive (5/26 p. 290, 291, 293 & 328) **35**
A Giant Planing Machine (7/26 p. 463) **39**
Largest Arch Bridge in the World (12/26 p. 722, 723 & 724) **40**
With the "Flying Scotsman" (8/26 p. 522 & 523) **43**
Britain's Most Powerful Loco (2/27 p. 98 & 99) **46**
Southern Railway 4-4-0 Type Locomotives (2/27 p. 111 & 183) **48**
Famous Trains and the Routes over which they run (2/27 p. 120, 121, 122, 123 & 183) **49**
Over 200 Miles an Hour (5/27 p. 392, 393 & 453) **55**
Why the Martians Declared War (6/27 p. 534 & 535) ... **58**
How Engines Pick Up Water (7/27 p. 630, 631 & 632) **60**
A New Miniature Railway (9/27 p. 799, 800 & 801) **63**
Famous Canals of the World (12/27 p. 1043, 1044 & 1045) **66**
Monster Canadian Locomotives (12/27 p. 1046 & 1047) **69**
The Conquest of the Air (7/28 p. 546, 547, 548 & 549) **73**
Producing the "Meccano Magazine" (7/28 p. 550 & 551) **77**
Driving an Electric Locomotive (7/28 p. 571, 572, 573 & 574) **79**
Stories of Famous Inventions (7/28 p. 575, 576, 577 & 618) **83**
"The Flagship of the U.S. Lines Fleet" (8/28 p. 628 & 629) **87**
Producing the "Meccano Magazine" (8/28 p. 636, 637 & 694) **89**
Wonderful Seadrome Scheme (1/29 p. 2 &3) **92**
A Run on the "Twentieth Century Limited" (2/29 p. 98, 99 & 133) **94**
New York Central Railroad (2/29 p. 100 & 101) **96**
The New Channel Tunnel Scheme (2/29 p. 130, 131 & 133) **98**
The "D.O.X"—A Leviathan of the Air (12/29 p. 922, 923 & 960) **102**
Bridging the English Channel (12/29 p. 952, 953 & 954) **105**
The New High-Pressure Locomotives (1/30 p. 102, 103 & 92) **108**
Light Power Units for Railways (2/30 p. 454, 455, 456 & 462) **111**
Building a Giant Locomotive (3/30 p. 178 & 179) **115**
Exciting Moments on an Express (11/30 p. 862 & 863) **117**
Stamp Collecting (11/30 p. 909) **120**
The Cierva "Autogiro" (5/31 p. 362, 363 & 437) **121**
Our Busy Inventors (5/31 p. 388 & 389) **124**
Birds Take Their Own Photographs! (5/31 p. 400 & 401) **126**
Lives of Famous British Admirals (10/32 p. 742, 743 & 748) **128**
How Wireless Waves Curve Round the Earth (10/32 p. 749) **131**
Air News (10/32 p. 750 & 751) **132**
Famous Air Line Companies (10/32 p. 752 & 753) **134**
Fireworks: Preparing for "The Fifth" (10/32 p. 758 & 759) **136**
Railway News (10/32 p. 760 & 761) **138**
The Story of the Flexible Locomotive (10/32 p. 762, 763, 764 & 770) **140**
The Life Story of Meccano (10/32 p. 772, 773 & 818) **144**
Building Your Own Motor Cars! (10/32 p. 776 & 777) **147**
Road & Track (11/34 p. 852 & 853) **149**
Our Busy Inventors (11/34 p. 858 & 859) **151**
Machines Used by Imperial Airways (11/34 p. 866 & 867) **153**
Six-Engined "Sentinel" Locomotives (11/34 p. 872 & 873) **155**
Railway News (11/34 p. 874 & 875) **157**
Mixed Traffic Locomotives (11/34 p. 877) **159**
The Planning of a New Railway (11/34 p. 878 & 879) **160**
Chemical Magic At Home (11/34 p. 882 & 883) **162**
With The Modelbuilders (11/34 p. 893) **164**
Junior Section, Hornby Railway Company (11/34 p. 910, 911 & 901) **165**
The Fastest Four-Engined Air Liner (12/34 p. 970 & 971) **168**
The Railways of Switzerland (12/34 p. 976 & 977) **170**
A Minute I Shall Never Forget (12/34 p. 989) **172**
Editorial (10/35 p. 561) **173**
Giant Creeper Cranes at Work (10/35 p. 570 & 571) **174**

Footplate Runs on the L.N.E.R.
(10/35 p. 586, 587 & 588) 176
How to Get More Fun from Hornby Trains
(10/35 p. 614 & 615) 179
1936 January to December 181
Index for 1936 930
Portsmouth to Waterloo on the Footplate
(7/37 p. 396 & 397) 934
From Our Readers (7/37 p. 404 & 405) 936
"Riding The Cab" of a U.S. Freight Engine
(7/37 p. 406 & 407) 938
Fireside Fun (7/37 p. 439) 940
114 m.p.h. on the L.M.S. (8/37 p. 442 & 443) 942
Inventions of the Future (8/37 p. 452 & 453) 944
Hornby "Princess Elizabeth" in Service
(8/37 p. 492 & 493) 946
A Hornby "Schools" Class Locomotive
(8/37 p. 494) 948
Stamp Gossip (8/37 p. 499 & 501) 949
Electrifying the Pennsylvania Railroad
(10/37 p. 590 & 591) 952
Some Railway Engineering Feats
(10/37 p. 596 & 597) 954
Preparing a Railway Timetable (10/37 p. 624) 956
A Famous Streamlined Locomotive
(10/38 p. 544 & 545) 959
Photography. Tricks to amuse your Friends
(1038 p. 550 & 551) 961
The New "Twentieth Century Limited"
(11/38 p. 608) 964
How Geographical Globes Are Made (11/38 p. 609) .. 965
How the Locomotive Works. 1.
(11/38 p. 610 & 611) 966
Railway News (11/38 p. 614 & 615) 968
The World's Giant Silk Moths (11/38 p. 616 & 617) .. 970
Stamp Collecting (11/38 p. 659) 972
How the Locomotive Works. 2.
(12/38 p. 670 & 671) 975
More Conjuring for Christmas Parties
(12/38 p. 672 & 673) 977
Fun With Hornby Dublo Clockwork Trains
(12/38 p. 704) 979
With The Model Builders (12/38 p. 717) 980
Photography. Lakes and Ponds (5/43 p. 157) 985
A Polish Officer's Dublo Layout (5/43 p. 170 & 171) 986
Forty-Five Years of Railway Photography
(6/43 p. 184, 185 & 214) 988
The "Methuen Park Railroad"
(6/43 p. 208 & 209) 991
In the Cab of "The Flying Scotsman"
(3/45 p. 76, 77 & 78) 993
Engineering Notes (4/45 p. 122) 997
"The International Limited"
(9/45 p. 292, 293 & 294) 998
The Short "Shetland" (9/45 p. 295) 1001
The Atomic Bomb (12/45 p. 412, 413 & 434) 1002
The Gallant Malta Convoy (3/46 p. 107) 1007
Photography. Action Portraits (3/46 p. 111) 1008
Photography. Moving Trains (7/46 p. 289) 1009
"Queen Mary" in Service Again (10/47 p. 389) 1010
Helicopters At Work (5/48 p. 146 & 147) 1011
Oil Burners in the Western Region (5/48 p. 148) 1013
Oil for Britain (5/48 p. 158, 159, 160 & 176) 1014
The "Mammoth" Merseyside's Giant Floating Crane
(5/49 p. 182 & 183) 1018
Electric Power from Volcanic Steam
(4/52 p. 152 & 153) 1020
Boeing's Atom-Bombers (4/52 p. 154, 155 & 156) ... 1022
Riding a Southern Main Line Diesel
(7/52 p. 290 & 291) 1025
A Talk with Stirling Moss (1/53 p. 10, 11 & 52) 1027
Engine Nicknames (1/53 p. 22, 23 & 24) 1030
Two Bells (6/55 p. 308, 309, 310 & 342) 1033
"The Deltic" (4/56 p. 203 & 189) 1037
"The Overland" (12/56 p. 610, 611 & 612) 1039
Farewell to Flying Boats
(5/57 p. 216, 217, 218 & 259) 1042
Space Notes (8/58 p. 364 & 365) 1046
Back from the Sea (1/60 p. 5, 6 & 7) 1049
Living on a Railway Tunnel (1/60 p. 15) 1052
A Railway Miscellany (1/60 p. 25) 1053
A Giant of the Seas (9/60 p. 450, 451 & 452) 1054
The House That Downing Built (3/61 p. 74 & 75) ... 1057
Roads—From a Lake (5/61 p. 162 & 163) 1059
Photographers' Page (12/61 p. 439) 1061
Ram Jets (1/62 p. 6 & 7) 1062
The Mile-A-Second Aeroplane (1/62 p. 10 & 11) 1064
"The Friendliest Line in The World"
(5/63 p. 198, 199 & 217) 1066
Railway Notes: Engine With A Wonderful History
(5/63 p. 204 & 205) 1069
Fireside Fun (5/63 p. 229) 1071

EDITORIAL OFFICE
Binns Road,
LIVERPOOL

PUBLISHED IN THE
INTERESTS OF BOYS
on the
15th of each month

The Growing "M.M."

It is a pleasure for me to acknowledge letters from hundreds of enthusiastic readers, with congratulations on the increased number of pages, and the improved appearance of the recent issues of the "*M.M.*" Some time ago I mentioned that it was my intention to make this the brightest and best paper for boys, and now scores of boys tell me that I have done that already. This does not mean that we have arrived at the end, however, for the "*M.M.*" will continue to improve with every issue.

Increase in Price

For our future issues I have a number of good things and several surprises in store. At the moment I am not able to disclose the preparations that are being made for your interest in the forthcoming numbers. For many months past there have been two insistent demands from our readers. One has been that we add more literary pages and increase the price to 2d., and the other that we publish fortnightly, or even weekly! After careful consideration I have decided to adopt the former course—the latter demand will be further considered later. The increased price will come into operation next month, with a special large Xmas number.

Increased Subscription Rates

The "*M.M.*" is considerably heavier than it was in the old days, when we had only 12 pages, and the postage is now 1d. It will, therefore, be necessary to increase the subscription rates for Magazines mailed from Liverpool to 1/6 for six months or 3/- for twelve months. From the date of this notice the subscription for copies to be mailed direct will be at the above-mentioned rates, but we shall keep faith with our existing subscribers and execute all orders on our books at the old rates until the subscriptions expire. This remark does not apply to the Xmas number, for which each subscriber will be debited 3d. The "*M.M.*" is now included in Messrs. W. H. Smith & Son's wholesale list and is thus available to newsagents. It may be ordered from all regular Meccano dealers and also from any newsagent or bookstall, price 2d. Should any reader have difficulty in obtaining the "*M.M.*" from his Meccano dealer or newsagent, he should write to me, giving full particulars.

Special Xmas Number

And now just a word in connection with the special Christmas number that is being prepared. This will appeal to all my readers, both at home and abroad, and will have more pages than the "*M.M.*" has ever had before. It will contain a host of good things. There will be articles on Meccano Model Building, Radio, Stamps, Books, Presents to Buy, and some new features including a Puzzle and Joke Column that will appeal very strongly to Guild Members. New Competitions will be announced, and there will be a special splendid article on a proposed new structure that, when completed, will be one of the world's largest bridges. Be sure that you order your copy of the December "*M.M.*" in good time.

Do you Sketch?

In this issue I am announcing a new competition, the subject of which is "Drawing the Editor." During the past twelve months I have received thousands of requests from all over the world for copies of my photograph. Some of my readers imagine me with a long grey beard, and others have guessed that I have red hair! Many readers have asked whether the little sketch at the head of this column shows me as I really am. To tell the truth, I am not able to answer this conundrum, for I have never seen myself! My friends tell me that the sketch is not at all like me, and that I am not nearly so good-looking as the young gentleman depicted there! It has occurred to me that it would be rather interesting to ask those who enter our first drawing competition to send sketches of the Editor as they imagine him to be. I expect we shall have some very humorous entries, and I am looking forward with interest to seeing the efforts of those of my readers who are fond of sketching! Of course, the winning sketches will be printed in the "*M.M.*"! Full particulars on page 161.

Motor Cars to Run on Railways

The New York, New Haven, and Hartford Railway has recently introduced a new type of vehicle, consisting of a kind of motor 'bus that runs on railway lines. The cars seat 35 passengers, carry 2,000 lbs. of luggage and travel at a speed of 45 miles per hour. A driver and a conductor constitute the crew.

The mechanical construction, which is practically the same as that of a motor car in use on roads, includes petrol-engine, clutch, gear-box, propeller shaft and bevel-gear rear-end drive. No differential is necessary, however, and reverse is obtained by a separate set of levers and gears, the cars having four speeds forward and four speeds reverse. They are worked much more severely than a road car, however, because their engines must operate at high speed, hour after hour

(*Continued on page* 168)

The New Railway Motor 'Bus

The Men Who Gave Us Radio:

VI. HUGHES, HERTZ, ONESTI, and BRANLEY.

In previous instalments of this article we have described the work of those scientists, who, in the nineteenth century and previously, contributed to the discovery of the principles of wireless telegraphy.

As will be seen from these articles, the invention of wireless telegraphy was not solely due to Marconi, although he was the first to put into operation a practical system. Many boys are surprised to find that Radio is the result of researches that extend over the past century. Progress may be traced by studying the lives of those men who devoted themselves to the science. The manner in which they overcame difficulties and step by step gained the desired end, is a splendid object lesson for every Meccano boy. In this series of articles we are outlining the development of Radio by briefly describing the researches of those scientists who, before Marconi's time, laid the foundation of communication without wires.

Hughes

UNTIL the end of the nineteenth century two methods had been used to transmit messages from one place to another without wires. These were (1) Conduction, or the use of the conductive properties of the earth and of water for conveying the electric force, and (2) Induction by which the electric impulse is transferred from one circuit to another, without there being connection between the two circuits.

Towards the end of the century, however, these two methods were superseded by the discovery that electro-magnetic waves may be *radiated* through space, and it is upon this fact that present-day Radio depends. Credit for this discovery is generally accorded to a German named Hertz, but—although Hertz certainly was the first to publicly make known the existence of these waves—we now know that they were first discovered by a British scientist, Professor D. E. Hughes.

Hughes, who was the inventor of the microphone and of the printing telegraph, had been engaged in a study of wireless telegraphy from 1879 to 1886. He discovered that when a current passing through a coil of wire was interrupted it caused such intense currents at the exact instant of interruption in a second coil near by that the atmosphere was momentarily disturbed. Solid objects did not seem to present any obstacle to these disturbances, which seemed to be able even to pass through walls with ease.

HERTZ

Heinrich Rudolph Hertz was born at Hamburg on 22nd February, 1857. He determined to enter the Engineering profession, but devoted his attention to Physical Science. He studied successively at Munich, Berlin, and Keil, where he commenced his investigations on Clerke-Maxwell's Electro-Magnetic theory. He died at Bonn on 1st January, 1894.

Using this discovery, Hughes devised a means of transmitting signals to a considerable distance, and several leading scientists witnessed his demonstrations. In 1892 Sir William Crookes wrote that: "Even now, telegraphing without wires is possible within a restricted radius of a few hundred yards. Messages may be transmitted from one part of a house to another, without intervening wires."

Professor Hughes believed his success was made possible by electric waves. He did not announce his results, however, because three eminent scientists expressed the opinion that his achievement did not involve any new discovery. They stated that the results could all be explained by known electro-magnetic induction effects, and that therefore Professor Hughes's view, that there existed unknown electric waves, could not be accepted. In the face of this discouraging report, Hughes did not devote further time to the matter and the great opportunity passed him.

Hertz

Although the secret of wireless communication had not yet been solved, the triumph of science was rapidly drawing near, for a new era was to commence with the notable discoveries of Heinrich Hertz, of Munich. Hertz greatly advanced the science of electricity, taking up the subject at the point to which it had been advanced by Faraday and Clerke-Maxwell.

Hertz studied at Berlin, where in 1880 he became assistant to Helmholtz, a notable physicist. He was particularly attracted by Clerke-Maxwell's theory regarding light and electro-magnetic waves in the ether, and (in 1888) commenced to investigate the subject at the suggestion of Helmholtz. His object was to establish the existence of the waves by actual experiment, and at last, after considerable work and study, he succeeded in doing so.

In these experiments Hertz used an apparatus, called an "oscillator," consisting of two metal discs each mounted at the end of a rod. Metal knobs were fixed at the opposite end of these rods and when these were connected to an induction coil they became charged. This caused a spark to jump across the small gap that separated the two balls. When this occurred, electric waves were radiated from the apparatus, each oscillation causing, as it were, a ripple in the ether.

Hertz next bent a wire into a circular shape, cut it and placed a small metal knob at the end of each wire. This part of the apparatus, called the "resonator," was placed a short distance away from the oscillator. When the latter was set in action, sparks were seen to jump across the gap in the resonator, although the latter was not connected in any way with the oscillator.

Hertz showed that the waves in the ether caused by the oscillation closely resemble waves of light. He showed also that they might be reflected, refracted and even polarised, just as may light. He thus brilliantly demonstrated beyond doubt Clerke-Maxwell's theory that light and electricity are identical in their essential details.

Onesti

Before wireless telegraphy could become possible, some more delicate apparatus than a resonator spark-gap was necessary for the detection of the Hertzian waves. In 1885 Professor Galzecchi Onesti, an Italian, introduced a more sensitive detector. He used a small quantity of iron filings, enclosed in a glass tube, between two corks. Through each cork there passed a wire, projecting into the space occupied by the filings, but not touching each other. To ordinary electric currents, these filings were a bad conductor, but when subjected to high frequency currents, such as the spark from an induction coil, they instantly became a good conductor. By connecting them in the circuit of a battery and a Morse recorder it was thus possible to make them record signals from a distance.

BRANLEY

Edouard Branley was born at Amiens in 1846 and was educated at St. Quentin College and Henry IV. College, Paris.

(Continued from last month)

The bucket of a Dragline is of simple construction, and being open at the front and the top, to a certain extent resembles a coal-scuttle. The digging rope is connected to a cross-bar, above the front of the bucket, the hoisting rope being fixed to the body of the bucket furthest away from the machine. The bucket is emptied by holding it up on the hoisting rope, and releasing the digging rope. This allows the bucket to tilt forward, and so discharges the contents from the open mouth.

In the cycle of operations of a Dragline the bucket is first lowered, at its extreme radius, to the foot of the excavation. By placing the winding drum in gear, the digging rope is then wound in, and hauling the bucket towards the machine, drags it into the material to be excavated. The thickness of the cut, or the depth to which the bucket is allowed to sink into the material, is regulated by the tension on the hoisting rope. If the depth is correct, the hoisting rope is allowed to unwind freely, or the cut may be made thinner by braking the drum around which it is wound.

Emptying the Bucket

When the bucket is full, the clutch is thrown out of the digging drum, and the hoisting gear engaged. The bucket is then lifted by the hoisting rope and the digging rope allowed to run freely, the bucket thus swinging towards the front of the jib. On the machine being slewed over the dumping point, the bucket is discharged in the manner already described.

When necessary, the bucket may be swung out beyond the radius of the jib head, so as to take a larger radius of cut, by drawing in the bucket on the digging line and allowing it to run out as rapidly as possible, so that it swings beyond the jib head.

The Heaviest Dragline in the World

The illustration at the head of this article, which we print by courtesy of the manufacturers, Messrs. Ruston & Hornsby Ltd., shows the No. 250 Dragline. This is by far the largest excavator ever built in this country. In fact, we believe it is the heaviest of its type ever built by any-one in the world. It weighs 250 tons nett and upwards of 300 tons when fully equipped and in working order. The bucket has a capacity of 8 cubic yards and would nearly fill an 8-ton coal wagon in one cut. The jib is 120 ft. in length and the drag-rope from the bucket 1¼ in. in diameter. A cutting power of 30 tons is exerted on the bucket teeth.

The machine's coal bunker has a capacity of 4 tons and is filled by means of a special steam-operated hoist. The main engines are upwards of 400 h.p. and, in addition, separate engines of about 200 h.p. are fitted for slewing the machine.

Designed for India

The cycle of operations is completed in 45 to 55 seconds, including digging, slewing round, discharging, slewing back again and dropping the bucket in readiness for another cut.

The machine is being supplied for work in connection with the Indian irrigation schemes, which, by the way, will be the largest in the world. Some of the channels are to be over 200 ft. in width, and 12 ft. in depth, the excavated material being deposited upon the sides to form banks.

As a crane the machine will lift a load of 22 tons at 125 ft. radius, and although so large and heavy it is very easily controlled by means of steam clutches and steam brakes to all the motions.

This is the second instalment of an article describing a remarkable machine that will play an important part in the history of engineering. A splendid competition with a cash prize of £5 has been arranged in connection with this article. For full particulars see the concluding paragraph on the next page.

Dragline does Work of 300 Men

For travelling the machine on rails, special swivelling bogies are used, all the wheels being driven. In less than one minute the machine digs 7 to 8 cubic yards of material and deposits it 200 ft. away from the point where the material was taken out. In other words, this great excavator is capable of digging 300 to 400 cubic yards of material in an hour, and will deposit the material over 120 ft. from the centre of the machine, equalling the work of over 300 men.

£5 for Best Model Dragline

The giant Dragline illustrated in these pages forms such an excellent subject for a model that we suggested to Messrs. Ruston & Hornsby Limited, the makers of the original appliance, that they should offer a prize for the best Meccano model of their Dragline. They readily agreed to our suggestion, and we announce, therefore, a special Competition for the best model of this great Dragline, built with Meccano.

The bucket of a Dragline digs its way into the material to be excavated. It is dragged towards the machine and is emptied by releasing the dragging rope. Its contents are then discharged through the open end

Eight Tons in 45 Seconds—(*cont.*)

The first prize will be a cheque for £5 awarded by Messrs. Ruston & Hornsby Limited. Second and third prizes of Meccano products to the value of £3 3s. 0d. and £2 2s. 0d. respectively, to be chosen by the winner, will be awarded by Messrs. Meccano Limited.

There will be no age limit and any size Meccano Outfit may be used. Entrants should, however, state their age and the number of Outfit used, as this will be taken into consideration in making the awards. The Competition will close on the 30th September next. Actual models should not be submitted, but drawings or photographs should be sent, together with a description of the special features of the model entered, and on these the awards will be made. We shall illustrate a Meccano model of the Dragline, when announcing the results of this Competition in our November issue.

We hope that our readers will set to work and evolve a model worthy of the subject.

A near view of the mechanism that operates the heaviest Dragline in the world

In this column the Editor replies to letters from his readers, from whom he is always pleased to hear. He receives hundreds of letters each day, but only those that deal with matters of general interest can be dealt with here

Correspondents will help the Editor if they will write neatly in ink and on one side of the paper only.

R. Kirkwood (Bath).—We are glad you like the "*M.M.*" so much. Your suggestion that we start a column for animals and domestic pets, is no doubt a good one, but we require all our space at present to do full justice to our already numerous features. Perhaps we shall be able to arrange it a little later.

M. Vaccard (Milan).—We are always pleased to have letters from you in your own language, and there is no need for you to have them translated into English. Your suggestion that we publish several new models each month, one for each Meccano Outfit, makes us gasp a little!

J. Judge (Midsomer Norton).—

"Yes, we have some Meccanos
We've lots of Meccano to-day,
We've long strips and short strips,
And bent strips and flat strips,
And all kinds of strips, I say."

Sorry we cannot find room for all your verses, James, but this one is certainly a good effort. We experienced no difficulty in finding a suitable tune for it! We hope your father will soon be in harness and hard at work again.

T. McKelvie (Auckland, N.Z.).—We have heard of your "little country," as you call it. In fact, it happens to be a country in which we take an intensely keen interest. We know many people who live there; we know it geographically, commercially and ethnologically, and all we know of it is good! We will find a suitable English correspondent for you. Don't wait to be asked to join a Meccano Club—start one yourself and put your back into the work.

L. O'Brien (Johannesburg, S.A.).—We read your letter with much pleasure, and we congratulate you on your school successes. We hope you will enter your new model in our big competition. Write us again.

J. Sears (Watford).—

"There was an old lady of Clewer,
Who rode on a bike and it threw 'er.
A butcher came by
Said 'Missis, don't cry!'
And fastened her on with a skewer!"

A Meccano boy would, of course, have fixed her up in a much more secure fashion with nuts and bolts and strips.

Kenneth Haynes (Maidenhead).—Your suggestions for running a Meccano Field and Nature Club are both interesting and useful. The requests for a Nature Section are numerous, and we are seriously considering the matter.

W. G. Hartley (Birchington).—

"Life is mostly froth and bubble;
Two things stand like stone—
Building models with Meccano,
Letting work alone."

We were much impressed with your poetry, Walter, until we came to the last line, which made us elevate our eyebrows a little. Perhaps some of our readers can think of a better line to replace the offending one. We will give half-a-crown for the best effort.

E. V. Corps (Northampton).—First let us congratulate you on your success in your Chemistry exam. Your suggestion for a "Readers' Own Corner" in which letters from Meccano boys would be the principal feature is good, and we may adopt it later. We note you liked the tongue-twisters in our Xmas number, and shall give some more of these in a future number. We agree that a man in the condition you name might have some difficulty in saying "Agricultural statistics!"

G. H. B. Stafford (Pitsmoor).—We are pleased to receive your first letter, although, as you have been a keen Meccano boy for eight years, you really should have written to us long ago! You are both wise and fortunate in having so many enjoyable hobbies. We have read with interest the programmes of the two organ recitals which you have given at your church, and are glad to have a copy of the music which you have composed.

H. Hurdle (Hornsey).—We are writing to you separately about the nearest Meccano Clubs, and we hope you will have joined one of them by this time. Thanks for your suggestion that we provide Meccano flags for decorating models; this we may consider later.

II. FURTHER EXPERIMENTS WITH STATIC ELECTRICITY

IN our article last month we showed how a glass rod that is electrically charged (by rubbing it with a silk handkerchief or piece of flannel) attracts or repels pith balls. We mentioned also that electricity is of two kinds, "negative" and "positive," and that the kind of electricity with which a glass rod becomes charged depends upon the material used for rubbing it. Glass rubbed with silk takes a positive charge; sealing-wax rubbed with flannel takes a negative charge.

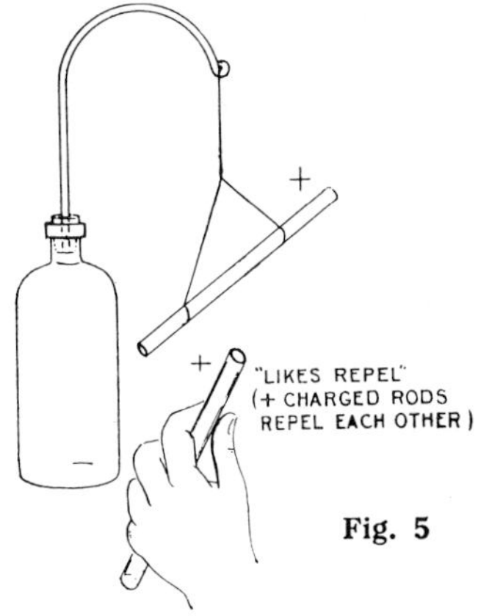

Fig. 5

We may demonstrate this more clearly by suspending a glass rod in place of the pith ball. This may be done by arranging two loops of silk thread, or by hanging a stirrup of wire by a silk thread from our support. Before suspending the rod in this manner we first electrify it by rubbing briskly with a piece of flannel. Then, by slipping it through the loops, we leave it hanging in a charged state. We then charge another glass rod in a similar manner, and on holding it near the suspended rod we find that the latter is repelled by it (Fig. 5). On the other hand, if the rod we hold is charged by rubbing it with a silk handkerchief, we find that it does not repel the hanging glass rod, but attracts it (Fig. 6). When performing this experiment remember that the hanging rod should be recharged, if the other rod touches it at any time.

Curious Behaviour of Pith Balls

The same experiment may be repeated with two pieces of sealing-wax, in place of the glass rods, rubbing them with a silk handkerchief, a piece of fur, or with flannel. Many other interesting experiments on similar lines may be devised. For instance, having observed the effect on the pith balls, first of the glass rod and then of the sealing wax, we may learn what happens when the glass and sealing-wax are used together. Having first presented the sealing-wax—excited with flannel—to the balls, rub the glass rod with the silk handkerchief and hold it near to the **balls.** They will at once be attracted by it, although they had been previously repelled by the sealing-wax. Allow the glass rod to touch them until they become fully charged and they will then be repelled by it. On presenting the excited sealing-wax to them again, however, they will now be attracted by it.

Electricity, the greatest force in the Universe, is a good servant but a bad master. When imprisoned and under control it serves man, giving light and power. Unfettered—as in the lightning flash—it may do great damage, setting fire to a warehouse or wrecking a building.

Attraction and Repulsion

Another extension of the original experiment may be performed by using two pairs of pith balls, suspending them by silk threads from separate supports. Hang each pair some distance apart and, rubbing the glass rod with the silk handkerchief, electrify one pair. Now rub the sealing wax and electrify the other pair, having done which move the two pairs near each other. A surprising condition immediately arises, for one pair will be attracted by the other. All trace of electrification will promptly disappear if they are allowed to touch.

From these experiments we prove to our own satisfaction that there are two kinds of static electricity, as Dufay discovered. We also see that unelectrified bodies are strongly attracted by either kind of electricity, whether + or —. At the same time we learn that two bodies charged with the same kind of electricity, no matter whether positive or negative, repel each other. Having thus mastered the meaning of positive and negative electricity, we shall have less difficulty in understanding and making other experiments of a more advanced nature, later on.

Electrified Paper

We may generate static electricity by several methods other than by rubbing with silk or flannel. For example, a piece of writing paper warmed before the fire, laid on a wooden table, and rubbed briskly with a dry hand adheres to the table (Fig. 8).

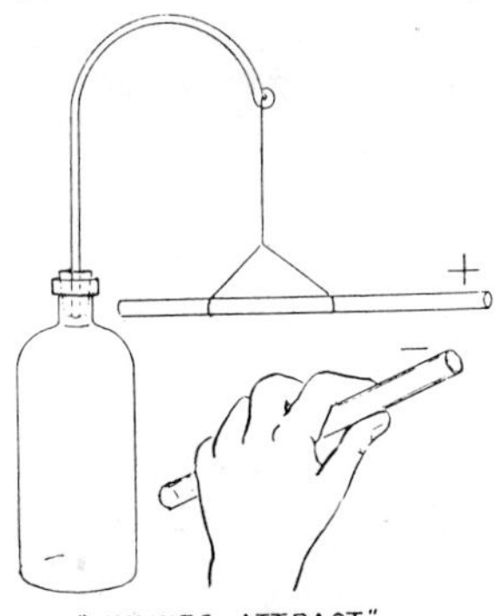

Fig. 6

Ordinarily the paper is easily moved about on the surface of the table, but after being rubbed it is difficult to move. If one corner be lifted, the paper will curl up and will cling to the hands or clothing. If held to the face a tickling sensation is experienced.

Those of my readers who are photographers will, perhaps, have experienced a similar phenomenon when drying their prints. In order to obtain a high glaze, photographic prints are pressed with a rubber roller (known as a "squegee") on to a metal plate. After having been dried by the fire the corners of the prints are lifted and the dried prints peel off the plates. Often they will be found to be electrically charged and adhere to the plate, to the hand of the photographer, or to any portion of his clothing on which they may be placed. If they are lifted to the face there is a tickling sensation as though a very feeble electric current is passing.

All these phenomena are due to the fact that in each case the paper is electrified with a charge of static electricity. In obedience to the law mentioned in our last instalment ("unlikes attract") the paper adheres to other objects because they are not electrically charged.

Constructing an Electroscope

The presence of a charge of electricity is demonstrated by an electroscope, a simple form of which may be made as indicated in our illustration (Fig. 9). This consists of a fold of paper balanced on the point of a needle, the head of which is embedded in a cork.

METAL DISC
GLASS TUBE
WAX
CORK
GOLD LEAF

Fig. 7
A Simple Electroscope

Electricity—(*cont.*)

Actually this simple electroscope is a kind of paper compass, and it will move around when the charged glass rod is brought near it, just as a compass needle will move when a bar-magnet is brought near it.

Another form of electroscope, which is sensitive to less powerful electrical charges, may be made from gold-leaf, which may be obtained from a picture-

Fig. 8. Experiment with Paper

framer or artist's colourman. If gold-leaf cannot be obtained, very fine tissue paper will serve the purpose, but is not so sensitive. First obtain a glass jar with a wide neck, and then hang the strips of gold-leaf from a piece of wire passed through the neck of the bottle. The gold leaf is suspended by bending the lower end of the wire at right-angles as shown in our illustration (Fig. 7). The bottle is closed by a cork through the centre of which a narrow glass tube passes. The glass tube is used to completely insulate the wire and an additional precaution may be taken by coating the cork with wax to insulate it more completely from the bottle. A metal disc of two or three inches in diameter is soldered to the upper end of the copper wire and the electroscope is ready for work.

If we bring an electrified glass rod to the metal disc of the electroscope we find that the strips of gold-leaf repel each other in a marked degree. If the electroscope has been well made, the gold-leaf will begin to separate even whilst the charged rod is some distance from the disc. The gold-leaf electroscope is one of the most sensitive means of detecting small charges of electricity and has been used in most of the important electrical experiments by leading scientists. This form of electroscope may be made so sensitive that the strips may be caused to diverge simply by the electrical charges generated in the chips formed by sharpening a pencil.

A Surprise for the Cat

Summer is not the best time for performing experiments with static electricity. These are more successful when the air is cool and clear. In summer the atmosphere contains a large proportion of moisture, and this conducts the electricity away from the apparatus almost as quickly as it is produced.

An interesting experiment in static electricity may be performed with your cat on a cold, dry day in winter. Choose a time when the cat is near a fire and stroke it rapidly with the hand. If you listen carefully you will notice a faint crackling noise as your hand passes over the cat's fur. If you perform this experiment in a dark room you will be able to see small sparks passing between your hand and the cat, and it is these sparks that cause the crackling noise. After you have been stroking the cat for a short time, place your knuckle near the cat's nose. A spark will then jump from the cat to your knuckle (Fig. 10), much to the surprise of the cat, who will probably not be at all pleased with your experiment! The experiment is an interesting one, but we hope that—for the cat's sake at any rate—our readers will not perform it on more than one occasion, even if they are able to persuade pussy to come along and oblige them a second time!

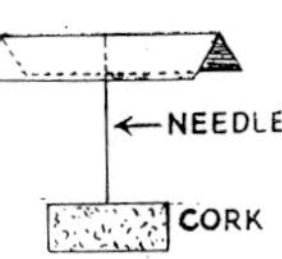

Fig. 9

Electrified Sand

Before concluding this article we may mention another exceedingly interesting experiment, which illustrates the mutual repulsion of bodies charged with the same kind of electricity. If we pour fine, dry sand into a funnel, the sand runs through the funnel in a steady narrow stream. Now let us connect the reservoir of the funnel by means of a wire to a glass rod, which may be conveniently electrified by rubbing with flannel. If now the funnel be filled with sand, and the rod electrified, it will be seen that, at each stroke of the flannel on the rod, the sand stream breaks and the particles fall, not in a narrow stream, but in a wide one, something like an open umbrella in shape. The explanation of this is that the tiny particles of sand, all being charged with the same kind of electricity, repel one another, and in their efforts to get away from one another they spread out into a wide stream.

NEXT MONTH

In our next issue we shall tell how Franklin brought an electric current from the sky to earth by means of a kite. We shall also describe an interesting experiment called "the jumping frogs."

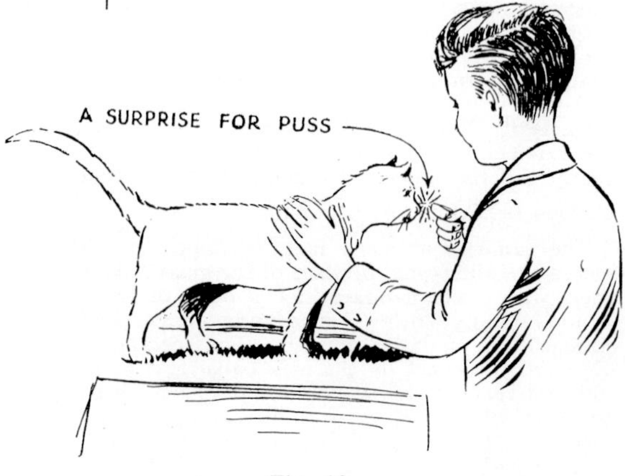

Fig. 10
Making a spark between the cat and your knuckle

BRIDGING THE ATLANTIC

Schoolboy Transmits to America

THE Radio Society of Great Britain recently organised a series of trans-Atlantic tests for amateur wireless enthusiasts, with a view to experimenting in transmission to and reception from America. About 60 British amateurs entered for these tests, including several well-known English amateur stations. One of these was the station of the great public school at Mill Hill, near London (2SZ). The operator of this station was Mr. C. W. Goyder, a pupil at the school who has been interested in radio for some time.

Choosing a Site

In order to take part in the tests it was necessary to use a higher-powered transmitting set than is allowed under the usual transmitting licence. The Mill Hill Station was fortunate in obtaining a 250-watt transmitting licence from the Postmaster-General and permission to use a wavelength of 100 metres, a wavelength that has been found to be the most suitable for long distance work.

The obstacles which confronted Mr. Goyder were considerable and would have deterred any less enthusiastic amateur. One great difficulty was the fact that the new science buildings, which were chosen as being the only suitable site for an aerial, were still in the process of erection. Walls and ceilings were unplastered, the floor was unlaid, and the window frames had to be stuffed with newspapers to keep out the draught. Even the staircase had not been built, and the room could only be reached by a ladder! It could scarcely be termed an ideal room in which to spend the twenty nights required for the tests. It had one possible advantage, however, that the operator was unlikely to be troubled by curious visitors during one of the critical tests!

Aerial Details

After several narrow escapes from disaster the set was at last installed in the half-built science room, and a cable laid for current to the chapel nearby. Readers of the "*M.M.*" will be interested to learn that our familiar advertisers, the Mullard Radio Valve Co., kindly loaned two Mullard Valves of the 0 250/C type for the tests, and it must be satisfactory to the manufacturers to know that their products enabled the operator to make wireless history. One of the Mullard valves is to be seen in the illustration, while above it is the cage-lead to the aerial and counterpoise. The 5-wire aerial, 55 ft. in length and 22 ft. above the roof, was fitted with 10 ft. spreaders. The lead-in, which was of the cage type, was fitted with rings of 3-ply wood, and was brought in through the roof. Eight wires were stretched between two cross wires below the aerial for the counterpoise, and were attached to the roof by hooks, with another lead-in, also of the cage type.

Mr. C. W. Goyder, the Wireless Amateur, and the apparatus with which he succeeded in transmitting to America

Two Aerials Used

A single wire aerial—the type most suitable for reception—was also erected, pointing in the direction of America. The "earth" consisted of a copper earthing mat ("borrowed" from the school O.T.C.), buried under the window to a depth of 3 ft.

The inductance used consisted of ¼" cable wound on the frame above the transformer, the clips fastened to it being adjustable for varying the wave-length. In the centre of our illustration is to be seen the transformer, which lights the transmitting valve. A reading of the amount of current passing is obtained from the ammeter shown to the left of the valve. The two panels on the right of the photograph are transformers for supplying current to the valve plate. The current used was rectified alternating current, at 2,500 volts potential.

First Night of the Test

While this set was being assembled the school term was still in progress. On December 18, however, Mill Hill "broke up" and Goyder was left in sole possession. The official tests were due to start on December 22, but on the night of the 21st Goyder decided to try his set. Working on a wave-length of 200 metres he was successful in picking-up several American stations, but no reply was received to messages sent out.

The first night of the test was unlucky, for at the very moment when officially due to transmit, the radiation of the set suddenly dropped to half normal. The reason for this mysterious occurrence was not discovered until two days later, when the trouble was traced to a piece of wet string hanging on the counterpoise and causing a leakage to earth! Troubles have an unpleasant habit of never coming singly, particularly in wireless, and on a subsequent night a valve was ruined through permitting an external wire to touch the valve, and spark through the glass. Also another leakage was caused by workmen leaving a piece of loose wire over the counterpoise!

First American Two-way Communication

At last the station was in working order, however, and on December 31 an American amateur living in New Jersey (2AGB) was plainly heard calling all stations. Goyder immediately called him up on the 100 metre wavelength and succeeded in getting his message across the Atlantic, for he received a reply from 2AGB shortly afterwards. Communication between the two stations was continued for some time, and Goyder took down three New Year messages for France. Arrangements were then made to carry on the next morning if possible, and before closing down, 2AGB sent "*You are the only European station heard here to-night.*"

At 6 a.m. on January 8 Goyder established communication with an American amateur (1XW) at Hartford, Conn., and worked with him for two hours. Conditions were particularly favourable that night, and signals were so loud and clear that when Goyder called his friend 2AGB, the latter was able to hear Goyder's signals at a distance of even 4 ft. from his phones and 75 to 100 ft. from the loud speaker! The next night a Canadian (1BQ) at Halifax, Nova Scotia, was picked up on 110 metre wavelength and signals were exchanged.

Reports of the reception of Goyder's signals soon began to come in from U.S.A.

(*Continued on page 131*)

A radio station is shortly to be installed in Vancouver. The cost is expected to be in the neighbourhood of 2,000,000 dollars.

* * *

A taxi-cab company in Paris has applied for permission to equip its vehicles with receiving apparatus.

* * *

An enterprising Lincoln barber has installed a radio receiver in his saloon for the use of customers.

* * *

The control of a steam locomotive by radio was recently accomplished in America.

* * *

Messrs. Harland and Wolff Ltd., are building life-boats equipped with wireless installations in the forecastle. The first of these boats has just been delivered to one of the largest British Steamship Companies.

* * *

A message from the Birmingham broadcasting station has been picked up at Ontario, Canada. Birmingham was distinctly heard calling " This is the broadcasting station at Birmingham, England. We are testing for the benefit of continental and American cities, which we hope to pick up our station."

A scheme is under consideration whereby it is proposed to grant a licence to an Indian Company to broadcast. The decision on this matter is anxiously awaited by Radio enthusiasts in India, who have long felt the need for some such organisation.

* * *

More than a square mile of land has recently been purchased by the Post Office authorities at Hillmorton, near Rugby. This land is to be used for the erection of the largest wireless station in the world, the construction of which will take several years to complete.

* * *

Several railway coaches in this country have had wireless apparatus installed. This has proved an exceedingly popular innovation, and will help considerably to while away the tedium of long journeys.

Bridging the Atlantic—*(cont. from p. 129)*

and Canada, where the signals had been heard strongly as far inland as Denver* (Colorado), Chicago, and Atlanta (Georgia). Other interesting reports came from various parts of the world, including Lisbon and Algeria, and it was soon evident that Goyder's transmissions had been heard every night he had sent during the tests—i.e., nineteen times in all.

Regular Transatlantic Transmissions

Owing to the activities of the workmen on the new building, Goyder was not able to again connect up his set until February 9. Getting up at 5 o'clock next morning, he almost immediately got into touch with 2BN (Montreal), 3OT (Pittsburgh), 1XAR (Massachusetts), 1BQ (Nova Scotia), and finally his old friend BD1 (Maine University). An exchange of messages was carried on with this station for over an

(Continued in next column)

* Denver is a distance of about 5,000 miles from Mill Hill!

hour, and Goyder gave him messages for several other amateurs whose signals he had received. This work was done with one Mullard O250c. Valve.

Wonderful Progress

We wonder how many of our readers can appreciate how pleased Mr. Goyder felt when he established communication with America, thus linking up the Old and New Worlds with invisible bonds. It was a very great achievement, and we gladly take this opportunity, on behalf of Meccano boys all over the world, of congratulating him on his achievement. It is indeed a wonderful and rapid advance from the time when Marconi first endeavoured to send messages over a few yards distance. At the present day a schoolboy is able to exchange messages with friends several thousands of miles across the Atlantic!

We are indebted to Mr. C. W. Goyder (who, by the way, is an old reader of the "*M.M.*"), for the photograph reproduced on page 129. He tells us that in the near future he intends to take up telephony in addition to telegraphy, although this will necessitate several additions and alterations to the apparatus. In the meantime, radio enthusiasts who are able to read Morse should listen for the call sign 2SZ between broadcasting hours and send their reports of reception to Mr. Goyder at Mill Hill.

Kevin Dinneen (Limerick).—We are sure that you will derive as much fun from the Meccano Crystal Set as from the other Meccano products that you already possess. Write us if at any time you are in difficulties.

W. Melville-Arnott (Scotland).—The fact that you have received telephony with a Meccano Crystal Receiver at a distance of 50 miles from the Glasgow Broadcasting Station is certainly an accomplishment. We shall be interested to hear of your further experiences in this connection.

Messrs. Bradley (London) Ltd.—The manufacture of a Meccano Valve Receiving Set will not be proceeded with at the moment.

W. T. Samuels (Birmingham).—We are pleased to know that you are acquiring useful knowledge in connection with Radio. You will find that the Meccano Receivers are of great assistance to you.

William Blackie (Melbourne).—I would like you to let me have some first-hand information about the prevailing conditions governing Radio in Australia. There seem to be considerable restrictions.

T. Browne (Doncaster).—You are too far distant from the nearest broadcasting station (Manchester) to receive telephony with a Crystal Receiver.

Wm. Duckworth (Blackburn).—Instruction Leaflets for the Meccano No. 2 Crystal Receiver are still available, price 4d., post free.

William Epy (Saskatchewan).—Our Depôt at 11, Colborne Street, Toronto, will always be very pleased to answer any enquiry you may direct to them.

E. J. Neame (London, W.).—A special constructor's licence is issued for those who construct their own Radio Receiving Sets from Meccano or other parts. I trust you will spend many happy hours with your apparatus when it is completed.

V. Govett (London, W.2).—The Meccano Receiving Sets are No. 1 Radio Receiver (Non-Constructional), No. 2 Radio Receiver (Constructional). Presumably it is the latter to which you refer, and instructions for building this have already been forwarded to you.

J. Fogarty (South Dunedin).—The Meccano Depôt, 379, Kent Street, Sydney, will always be pleased to give you any information you may require in regard to the Meccano Receiving Sets.

Jack MacDonald (Dumfries).—I much regret that it is impossible to supply you with an earth wire separately, but you could obtain the necessary wire for this purpose from any electrician. The Meccano Aerial is only listed in its complete state.

Just like Dad's...
PRICE
25/-
A PERFECT WORKING
• MODEL OF THE •
WORLD'S STANDARD
WIRELESS LOUD
SPEAKER
The
AMPLION
DRAGONFLY
A real "Baby" Loud Speaker
The Amplion name-plate guarantees a genuine product of the House of Graham
AMPLION
LOUD
SPEAKER
DRAGONFLY

Handling Goods on the Docks

Labour-Saving Machines in Warehouses

EVERYBODY knows that goods from foreign countries are brought to this country by sea, landed at one of the great ports and then distributed to their various destinations. Probably, however, very few people know the vast amount of organisation necessary to carry on the work of the docks.

Handling Explosives

Let us start at the moment when a steamer has been safely berthed and when the great dockside cranes—electric, steam, or hydraulic—are at work discharging her cargo. A certain quantity of the goods landed is taken away at once in special vehicles waiting for that purpose, but by far the greater proportion of the cargo has to remain on the quay. Goods are not allowed to be kept on the quay for an indefinite time, however, otherwise the congestion would become very serious, and usually, if merchandise is not removed within about 48 hours, a special charge called "penalty rent" or some similar name, comes into force.

Certain kinds of traffic, however, are never allowed to touch the quay at all. These include explosive goods, which either have a vehicle waiting to receive them and take them away or they are carried off by the dock authorities to a place of safety, at the expense of the owners of the traffic. The same thing applies to any kind of goods that would be likely to contaminate other goods lying near.

All docks have ample railway sidings giving direct connection with the main railway lines, and also with the large warehouses standing near by. Traffic that is ready for immediate despatch is carefully stowed into trucks, and if these trucks are open and the traffic is of a perishable or fragile nature it must be properly sheeted to protect it from the weather. Some traffic, of course, is not sent by rail, but by horse vans or motor lorries.

Bonded Warehouses

For various reasons, however, it is not always convenient for goods to be sent forward direct. For instance, the goods may not have been consigned to any particular buyer, and the shippers may be relying on the consignees to find a buyer after the goods reach this country. Again, it may be that the buyers are not ready to receive the goods. In all such cases storage in a warehouse is necessary.

Warehouses may be of one or more storeys, but a single-storey warehouse is better, not only because it costs less to build but also because the goods it contains can be handled more easily, and it can be better lighted by means of a glazed roof.

In all warehouses special attention is given to the prevention of fire. Most warehouses have a sprinkler or other system installed, so that if at any time the temperature rises above a certain point water is automatically turned on.

A certain number of warehouses at all docks are "Bonded," that is, they are buildings approved by the Customs Authorities for the storage of dutiable goods. Whereas in the ordinary way duty must be paid on goods immediately on arrival at the docks, goods stored in Bonded warehouses are not liable for duty until they leave the warehouse for final delivery.

Making Gravity Help

At the warehouses, goods are unloaded from trucks by cranes of all types. Some of these cranes travel about and do their work so cleverly that they appear almost human when in action. Whenever possible, goods are stacked by means of "stackers," which usually consist of square-shaped rollers fixed in a frame and turned by electric or other power. The traffic to be stacked is fed to the end of a series of these rollers, and these carry the packages to the top of the stack and place them in the desired position. Bale lifters, on the same principle as the Meccano model No. 443, are used for handling the larger bales of wool, cotton, etc.

Delivery of traffic from the warehouse is often effected by means of "gravity runways," which consist of a number of rollers fixed in a frame down which gradually run the goods to be delivered. Delivery can also be effected by the same cranes that were used to receive the goods into the warehouse, but the special advantage of gravity runways is that they require no power to work them. Generally speaking, in all warehouses man-handling is reduced to its lowest possible limit in order to keep down costs and to speed-up the work.

So far we have spoken of traffic handling in general, and it will be interesting now to say a few words on the treatment of various individual traffics.

Photo courtesy] *[Messrs. Henry Simon Ltd.*

Portable Combined Piler Stacking Sacks

Handling Cotton and Wool

Cotton, for instance, is packed in huge bales, and contrary to what might be expected, the worst-packed bales are the American. They are, therefore, extremely difficult to handle, as when they arrive they have often burst in various places and the raw cotton is protruding. On the other hand Egyptian cotton is carefully press-packed, enabling a larger quantity to be packed into one bale and rendering the handling of the bales very much easier.

Wool also arrives in large bales, and in this traffic what are known as "extra services" are often required. These services include mending bales and setting out for show, the latter involving the removal of one corner from each bale in order that prospective buyers may examine the contents.

Precautions against fire must be redoubled in the case of inflammable merchandise like cotton and wool. Warehouses intended for the storage of this class of traffic are generally divided into fire-tight sections, so that in the event of one part of the warehouse catching fire the other portions may be saved. Also an ample supply of water must be kept at hand, and this may be provided for by means of a large tank on the roof.

Tobacco, Canned Goods and Grain

Tobacco is usually packed in great barrels called "tierces," weighing about 7,800 lb. each. The Customs Authorities require that this traffic should be weighed, and large scales are therefore provided. The hoops are slipped off the barrels by means of machinery, leaving the tobacco standing up in its own bulk, and the barrels are re-fixed after weighing. Tobacco is often kept for years in store in order that it may mature.

Wines and spirits also often remain in store for a long period. This traffic is usually stored by means of barrel racks which make the removal of casks an easy matter.

Canned goods are imported from America and other countries in huge quantities, and a large amount of this traffic usually goes into warehouses. The "extra services" commonly required on this class of goods include opening of cases, examining for damaged tins, removal of blown tins, labelling, etc.

Grain, which is packed in bags, has to be carefully stored to prevent bursting. Before the war there was a tradition that it should never be piled more than five bags high. This, of course, involved a great loss of space, and during the war, when all available space was required, this convention came to an end, and in some cases the grain was stored over 80 bags high! If the piling is done by machinery under expert supervision, there is no real risk of danger.

Photo courtesy] [*Messrs. Henry Simon Ltd.*

Loading Railway Wagons

Cold Storage

A detailed description of all the many classes of goods dealt with in docks and warehouses would take up a great deal of space and be very monotonous, but our article would not be complete without some mention of cold storage. Varying degrees of low temperature are required for different kinds of traffic. Meat usually requires a temperature of about 15° or 16°, while bacon, butter, cheese, etc., may have temperatures ranging from 26° to 45°, the storing of goods at this latter temperature being known as cool storing. All such goods, of course, require special handling. Refrigerated meat, for instance, has to be transported in insulated vans, either railway or motor. The interior of these vans is entirely covered with cork to prevent a rise in temperature, and the vans are specially locked.

The Meccano Model (No. 443) of a Bale Lifter

The cold storage of eggs is a specially difficult problem. A temperature of a little over 30° is required, and only a margin of about one-eighth of a degree can be allowed either way. If the eggs are kept at too low a temperature they crack, while if the temperature is too high they go bad. In order, therefore, to keep a close watch on the temperature, an electric alarm is installed which automatically gives warning by means of a bell whenever the safe limits are exceeded.

All the various services carried out at docks and in warehouses have, of course, to be paid for. The first charge incurred is that for port dues payable on all goods entering the particular port. Next is the landing charge, which at some ports is charged on all goods and at others only on goods that actually touch the quay. This charge also covers rent for the use of the quay during the few hours the traffic remains there.

A further charge is made for the hauling or cartage of goods from quay to warehouse.

As for the actual warehousing, a charge is made for receiving, storing and re-delivery to vehicles at the proper time, with an additional sum per week, usually a few pence, for rent while the goods are in store. In the case of tobacco and other traffics which may be stored for years, the rent charge is often considerably reduced after the first year. Extra services are charged in addition, usually at cost plus a small percentage for profit, but in some traffics such as wool, where extra services are more often performed than not, most of these extras are included in one rate called a consolidated rate.

It is not easy in a short article to give an adequate idea of the intensely interesting methods and mechanism employed in handling goods at docks and in warehouses, but it is hoped that enough has been said to encourage Meccano boys to take the first opportunity that comes along to see these things for themselves.

The New Meccano Manual

There are three Manuals, the 0 Manual for simple models built with the 00 and 0 Outfits, the 0–3 Manual comprising models built with any of the Outfits up to and including No. 3, and the Complete Manual, which comprises a selection of models that may be built with every Outfit up to a No. 7.

This latter Manual is a very fine publication and should be in the hands of every Meccano boy. It includes instructions for building 389 models, including most of the models shown in the former No. 3 Manual, the publication of which is now discontinued. The new edition (No. 24) of the Complete Manual is beautifully illustrated in half-tone and most of the models have recently been revised, and very greatly improved by the introduction of new parts that have been added to the Meccano system during the past year. Several new models have been included for the first time, including some of those published in recent numbers of the "*M.M.*"

Prices of Manuals.

0 Manual	(postage free)	6d.
0–3 ,,	,,	1/2
Complete Manual	,,	2/10

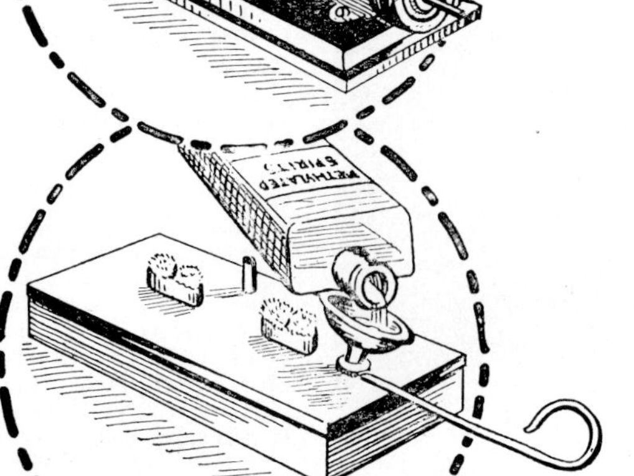

British Model Launches
made for
Speed, Service, Beauty

Here's a lovely Launch for you—one of which you will be proud and the other boys envious. She has a real engine which generates a nice turn of speed and keeps the boat going for 20 or 25 minutes with one filling. You can't get such splendid value anywhere else—it beats the German boats hollow.

Hours of joy for any boy!

MISS AMERICA

Painted three colours enamel, totally enclosed firebox, well-made brass boiler, engine, and twin bladed propeller. Power to drive 20 minutes.

12/6

31 inches Long. 3¼ inch Beam.

Post 9d. extra.

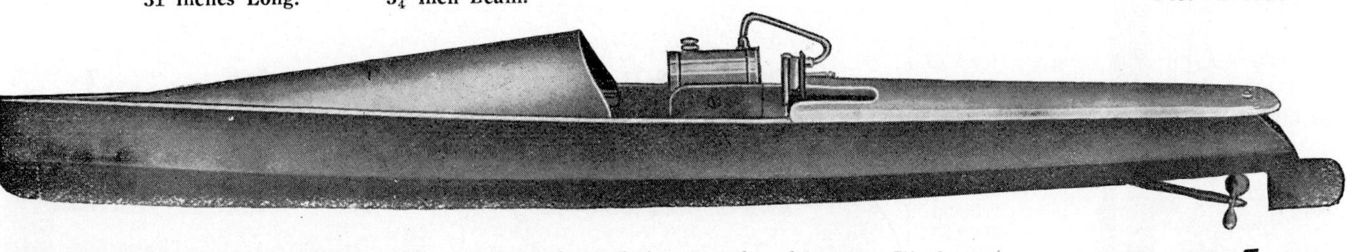

PEGGY

32½ inches Long. 3½ inch Beam.

A Boat of superlative strength and beauty. The larger power unit gives greater driving energy, and keeps the boat at good speed for over 25 minutes to cover a mile on the straight at one filling. The "tuff-tuff" of the steam carried out astern is a delightful piece of realism.

22/6

Post 9d. extra.

FREE TO ANY MECCANO BOY

Every reader of Meccano Magazine should write for free lists giving full details of these Launches. Write to Peggy Dept., or if you live near a Branch call for the lists there.

You can order safely by post

HOBBIES LIMITED (PEGGY DEPT.) DEREHAM, NORFOLK

Branches : 65, New Oxford St., W.C. ; 79, Walworth Rd., S.E. ; 147, Bishopsgate, E.C. ; 326, Argyle St., Glasgow ; 10a, Piccadilly, Manchester ; 9a, High St., Birmingham ; 15, County Arcade, Leeds ; 11, Bridge St., Southampton ; 68, London Rd., Brighton ; 214, West St., Sheffield. Stores and Agencies everywhere. And 45, Colborne St., Toronto, Canada.

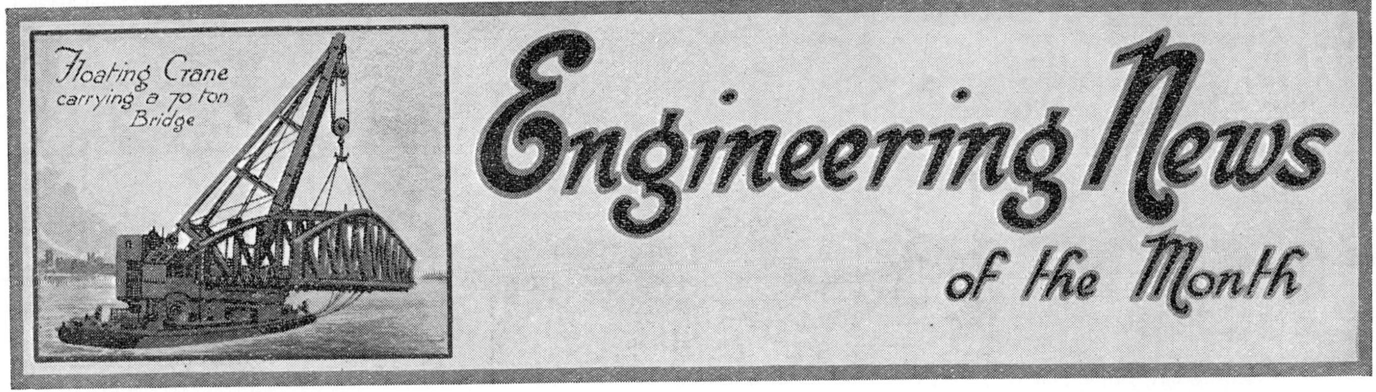

World's Largest Airship

Rapid progress is being made with the construction at Cardington, Bedford, of the R101, the world's largest airship, which will fly on the Empire air route to India. The engines, seven in number, will burn heavy gas oil fuel, and will produce a total horse power of 4,210. It is expected that the airship's maximum speed will be about 70 miles per hour.

* * * *

London's Oldest Machine

A steam-driven beam-engine at King's Cross (L.N.E.R.) is on the verge of its 120th birthday. It is believed to be the oldest piece of machinery in London still regularly developing power. Every day the old engine is hard at work providing power for the " shop " machinery. " Her action has been much admired by modern engineers," an official said recently, " and never in 120 years has the piston worked more than 1/32nd of an inch out of the vertical." The Company bought her second-hand from a wood sawyer in 1850 for £500, and since then she has always kept up at least a 48-hours' week.

* * * *

New Cement Works

Portland cement is playing such a great part in engineering that it will be of interest to all our readers to learn that the foundation stone of the largest Portland cement works in the United Kingdom was laid at Bevans, Northfleet, last month. The new factory will have a productive capacity of 10,000 tons of cement a week, or 500,000 tons a year—nearly one-sixth the total cement production of Great Britain. The installation of modern plant and the fact that the raw materials are on the spot, will, it is claimed, enable cement to be produced more cheaply at Bevans than at any other works in the country.

* * * *

No Palace of Engineering this Year

We feel sure that all our readers will read with regret the announcement that pride of place in the Palace of Engineering at Wembley is this year to be given to a display of housing, which is being organised by a special Committee. The exhibit will show the practical uses for the various new methods and materials now recommended for the building of houses and side by side with the display of houses will be exhibits devoted to such details as heating, lighting, ventilating, etc.

However interesting a Housing Exhibit may be—and no doubt it will be very attractive in its way—it cannot approach in interest the magnificent display of British engineering products that occupied the same space last year. It is doubtful, indeed, if there has ever been such an exhibit and it will certainly be a long time before we are privileged to see another like it.

It is pleasing to learn, at the same time, that this year the railway companies hope to show in some part of the Palace of Engineering large transport exhibits, which will illustrate the results of 100 years' progress. It is also hoped that there will be a representative display of water transport, in which the most important of the big steamship companies will take part. Further details will be announced on this page as soon as they are available.

* * * *

Four new steamers are being laid down at the Baltic Shipbuilding Yards, Leningrad. They will be used by the Soviet Government for the export of timber.

* * * *

Tunnelling on Mountain

Work will shortly be begun on a tunnel 16 ft. in diameter and 15 miles in length under Ben Nevis. This tunnel is being cut to carry the waters of Lochs Treig and Laggan to a new powerhouse at Fort William, for the Lochaber hydro-electric project of the North British Aluminium Company. The tunnel will cost something like £1,750,000, and the scheme will find employment for between 2,000 and 3,000 men for over three years. Large works for the production of aluminium, in connection with which extensive electrical energy is utilised, will ultimately be built at Fort William.

* * * *

Unroofing a Tunnel

A difficult engineering task is being carried out in the demolition of Chevet Tunnel, on the L.M.S. railway between Leeds and Sheffield. The tunnel, which is over 700 yards in length, is now being unroofed to allow another two sets of metals to be laid between Chevet and Snydale Junction in order to eliminate a very awkward " bottle neck."

The line is one of the busiest on the system, tapping the heart of the Yorkshire coalfield and some 240 trains pass through the tunnel every day. The total length of tunnel that is being widened is three and three-quarter miles.

The work entails the cutting of a passage through nearly 80 ft. of solid sandstone, as the rail level is about 94 ft. below the surface. Giant shields are placed beneath the arched roof to prevent bricks from falling on to the metals.

Flooded Under-Sea Mine

About half-a-million gallons of fresh water have been flowing daily into the Ellington Colliery, Northumberland, from some mysterious source beneath the North Sea. The inrush is completely under control, and, except that 40 men who were in the district when the burst occurred have been removed to other districts, the colliery is working as usual, and output is being fully maintained. Twelve hundred men and boys are employed in the pit, which belongs to the Ashington Coal Company.

It is supposed that this vast quantity of water has been stored in some huge receptacle existing in the strata between the sea and the mine galleries.

* * * *

Mammoth Water Tower

A notable scheme now in hand at Goole, in Yorkshire, is the construction of a ferro-concrete water tower, which will be the largest of its kind in the country. It will have a capacity of 750,000 gallons, against the capacity of 30,000 gallons of the town's present tower.

The new tower is part of a big undertaking to provide new waterworks at Pollington, where three connected wells will be augmented by a new bore-hole, 500 ft. in depth, and 3 ft. in diameter.

The height of the new tower will be about 147 ft. from the ground, and the tank 20 ft. in depth and 90 ft. in diameter. In the base alone there will be 30 tons of ironwork, the total weight being about 4,000 tons.

* * * *

A Sliding Hill

Following on the news of the moving mountain in Wales, it is now announced that two villages—Feetham and Low Row—in Swaledale, North Yorkshire, are in danger of being carried into the valley by the slipping of the hill-side above them.

The main road from Reeth to Kirkby Stephen is threatened, although at present it is still possible to use it. In some places the earth coming down the hill-side to the road resembles waves rolling on to the beach.

The movement is said to have been going on for 35 years, but has only recently become threatening. Perhaps some explanation is to be found in the fact that in Swaledale lead mines are believed to have existed in the reign of King John and the district where the landslide has occurred is riddled with mines.

Britain's New Submarine

Recently there arrived at Portsmouth the submarine X.1, reputed to be the largest and fastest submarine in the world. She is of an entirely new type, and having been built at Chatham in secret, has recently been engaged on tests.

Her dimensions are:—Length 350 ft., Beam 39¾ ft., Draft 17 ft. Her displacement is 2,780 tons on the surface and 3,600 tons submerged. Details as to the construction and performance of the submarine have not been published, but we understand she has a high turn of speed. She is said to have been designed as a commerce-raider, but she would be equally serviceable for many other purposes. She carries a crew of 100, each member of which has been specially chosen for proficiency, because submarines of such length and enormous weight as the X.1 require very careful handling.

Apart from her imposing size, there are several remarkable features, including two turrets, each containing a pair of guns so mounted as to be clear of the water even in stormy weather. The number of her torpedo tubes, and other details, have not yet been officially announced. She is the first submarine to have a canteen on board.

The building of the X.1 is particularly interesting in view of the fact that a German, Professor Flamm, some time ago took occasion to cast doubt on the skill of British submarine designers, alleging that they were baffled by the problem of the construction of large submarines. Professor Flamm himself designed two submarines, one of 4,000 tons and the other—which he called a "diving cruiser"—of over 7,000 tons—neither of which have yet been built.

Other countries are also building large submarines, as for instance the V2, recently built for the United States. This vessel is 341½ ft. in length and of 2,164 tons displacement on the surface. Her speed is 21 knots, and armament one 5″ gun and six torpedo tubes. She carries a crew of 80. France is also building two large submarines, "*Vengeur*" and "*Redoubtable*," each of which has a displacement of 3,000 tons.

Proposed New Bridges

Several new bridges are proposed in the London area, the most important of which is necessitated by the present condition of Waterloo Bridge, to which further reference is made below.

One proposal is for a new bridge at Aldwych, whilst another is for a bridge at St. Paul's. There has been some talk, too, of the possibility of moving Charing Cross Station to the south side of the River. This scheme, which is entirely in the air at present, would be a gigantic engineering task and the expense involved would be colossal. Its completion would, however, make way for a new bridge at Charing Cross, the approaches for which would pass either under or over the Strand. A plan has been put forward for a bridge over the Strand with approaches reaching ground level near the National Gallery. The reason that makes it necessary for any new Charing Cross bridge to pass under or over the Strand is that the influx of cross-river traffic into the Strand would hold up the east and west traffic to such an extent that a bridge on any other plan would be impossible.

* * * *

Waterloo Bridge

The special Committee appointed to report on the bridges of the Thames have recently stated that in their opinion Waterloo Bridge should be demolished. This decision has given rise to considerable discussion, as Waterloo Bridge is one of the best known bridges in the world. The Committee state that they "would have been willing to make sacrifices in traffic improvements to save so famous and beautiful a bridge, but this would be useless. It must now be held as established that the old bridge is worn out and must be taken down to prevent it from falling down."

Waterloo Bridge was built by the famous engineer Rennie, and the special Committee recommend the construction of a new bridge with not more than five arches and of a sufficient width to carry six lines of vehicular traffic.

The Chief Engineer of the London County Council has ordered the closing of Waterloo Bridge entirely from the 1st May to the 30th June to permit the launching of the girders for the large span of the temporary bridge.

* * * *

Coal Transporters for the Sudan

Large engineering projects are being commenced shortly in the Sudan. These include a bridge over the Nile, tramway and waterworks schemes, and the erection of an important coal-handling plant. This latter structure at Port Sudan will comprise four of the largest electrically-driven travelling and slewing bridge transporters in the world. Erected on the "Temperley" principle, they will each have a length of 425 ft., span 215 ft. and lift of 45 ft. above the ground. The transporters will be fitted with high-speed grabs of 2 tons capacity, and will be used for loading and unloading steamers and barges, the coal being either distributed over the storage ground or delivered into the wagons of the Sudan Government Railways. It is claimed that the equipment will form one of the most important modern coaling installations.

* * * *

Berengaria's New Record

During the voyage from New York which finished at Southampton on the 6th March, the Cunard Liner Berengaria accomplished the fastest day's steaming of her career. From noon on the previous Sunday to noon the next day she covered a distance of 579 miles at an average speed of over 25 knots. She made the whole crossing at an average speed of over 23½ knots.

* * * *

Canal Drained Dry

In the construction of a culvert through the Trent and Mersey Canal, between Burton and Wellington, an old water-course was disturbed, and started a leakage in the bottom of the canal. In spite of the efforts of workmen, hastily summoned, the leakage rapidly increased until the bottom of the canal gave way. The surrounding fields were flooded and the whole length of the canal was drained dry. The borough surveyor, in conjunction with the canal engineer, at once grasped the importance of the situation (which entailed a fine of £50 a day for each day the canal was closed), and by great energy built up a concrete retaining wall well past the danger zone and thus enabled the canal to be used again.

This page is reserved for articles from our readers. Contributions not exceeding 500 words in length are invited on any subject of general interest. These should be written neatly on one side of the paper only, and they may be accompanied by photographs or sketches for use as illustrations. Articles that are published will be paid for at our usual rates. Statements contained in articles submitted for this page are accepted as being sent in good faith, but the Editor takes no responsibility for their accuracy.

From a West Indian Reader

I have been asked by the Editor to write a short description of the island of St. Vincent, where I live. This island, which owes its name to being discovered by Columbus on St. Vincent's day 22nd January 1498, is one of the lesser Antilles and is only 18 miles in length and 11 miles in breadth.

When discovered it was in the hands of the Caribs, and it remained so until 1627. In 1773 a treaty was concluded by which the Caribs acknowledged themselves to be British subjects, and in return were granted a large tract of land in the north-east of the island. In 1779 the island was surrendered to the French, but it was restored to the British four years afterwards by the Treaty of Versailles. The Caribs overran the island in 1795, but this rising was suppressed by Sir Ralph Abercromby in the following year. Afterwards most of the Caribs were taken to the Island of Balliceaux—one of the Grenadines, away to the South—and then sent to the Island of Ruatan in the Bay of Honduras.

View of Kingstown, showing Fort Charlotte in the distance

St. Vincent is very far behind the times and the capital Kingstown, where I live, is a quiet little town situated at the head of Kingstown Harbour and surrounded by a magnificent ring of mountains, dominated by Mount St. Andrew. It has three main streets running parallel to each other and intersected by smaller ones, and in spite of its small size it possesses the finest cathedral in the West Indies.

I spend most of my spare time, when not building Meccano models, in bathing, rowing, fishing and sailing. The bathing is specially glorious, and those of you who have read R. M. Ballantyne's book, "*Coral Island,*" will understand what it is like. My chums and I have a special place for bathing called "Flat Rock." The main rock consists of a number of ledges off which we dive and try to reach bottom, which no one has yet succeeded in doing. The rock cannot be reached by land, so we often hire a boat and row over to spend a day there, and it may be guessed what a fine time we have!

There are many points of interest about our island. The most prominent is the crater of the volcano "Soufrière," which erupted in 1902 and caused much damage and loss of life, especially among the Caribs who lived just under the mountain. The Caribs, of whom there are now only a few left, are most interesting to talk to, and the men for the most part are handsome. At our public library may be seen many of the stones that the Caribs used in their warfare. They are all shapes and sizes and are highly polished, with one side ground to the shape of a hatchet with a sharp cutting edge.

There are many small islands and rocks around the coast of St. Vincent. One of them, Fort Duvernette, a large rock situated on the south side of the island not far from Kingstown, was fortified in the reigns of George II. and George III., and the old guns are still to be seen there.

Whale fishing is carried on extensively among the Grenadines and St. Vincent, and it is interesting to watch the native fishermen at work. It is a dangerous sport and one gets quite excited while looking on. The natives live largely on fish, which they catch from their little "catamarans," or rafts.

G. Blencowe, Kingstown.

An Early Iron Bridge

I was very interested to read a reference to the Iron Bridge across the River Severn at Broseley, in a recent number of the "*M.M.*," and I think that some readers will like to have some further details regarding this bridge. I should therefore like to give a description from a book, called "*The Wilkinsons,*" by John Randall, in which this bridge is described. Here it is:—

"On the abutments of the stone work are placed iron plates, with mortices, in which stand two upright pillars of the same. Against the foot of the inner pillar the bottom of the main rib bears on a base plate. This rib consists of two pieces connected by a dovetail joint in an iron key and fastened by screws. Each piece is 70 ft. in length. The shorter ribs pass through the pillar, the back rib in like manner, without coming down to the plate. The cross-stays, braces, circle in the spandrils, and the brackets connect the larger pieces so as to keep the bridge perfectly steady, while diagonal and cross-stays and top-plates connect the pillars and ribs together in opposite directions.

"The whole bridge is covered with top-plates, projecting over the ribs at each side, and on this projection stands the balustrade of cast iron. The road over the bridge, made generally of iron slag, is 24 ft. in width and 1 ft. in depth. The span of the arch is 100 ft. 6 in. and the height from the base line to the centre is 40 ft. The weight of iron in the whole is 378 tons 10 cwt.

"On the largest or exterior rib is inscribed in capitals 'This bridge was cast at Coalbrookdale, and erected in the year 1779.'"

A toll is still taken (½d.) but the bridge is but little used because of the erection of what is known as the "Free Bridge."

It is interesting to note that the first iron barge was built at Broseley in 1787 and that the first iron railway lines were made and laid down at Coalbrookdale about 1760. The first iron pot was made in this district, although I regret I do not know the date of this latter achievement. E. L. Bray, Horsehay, Salop.

A Chat About Caves

Nearly all boys, like myself, are interested in caves. By caves I do not mean miserable little holes in the side of a cliff, but grand caves such as the Adelsberg Cave in Austria and Fingal's Cave on the Island of Staffa.

Many caves are very beautiful, especially those hollowed out of limestone rock by the action of water. Carbonic acid in the water dissolves the limestone, and thus the constant dripping into the cave forms stalactites which hang downwards from the roof, and stalagmites which rise up from the floor below. Sometimes after a great number of years the two meet and form pillars of the most marvellous shapes, which sometimes defy even the cleverest sculptor to copy. The caves in the Cheddar Cliffs are like this.

Our British caves, however, cannot rival the caves on the Continent and elsewhere abroad. The cave of Adelsberg, for instance, mentioned above, is such a wonderful place that it is impossible for a boy like myself to give a good description of it. Close to the entrance it is of a dull stone colour, but further in the pillars are of the purest white. Some of the stalagmite beds have been tinged red, and the crystalline fragments produce the effect of diamonds on a red cushion. In some places the stalactites take the form of thin sheets which, when struck, give forth a musical sound. The chain of vaults extends several miles underground. The great beauty of it all is very bewildering, and you are constantly going into different vaults each of which seems to be more beautiful than the last.

The cave of Adelsberg is in fact one of the wonders of the world.

W. H. Waters, Clapham, London.

In the Land of the Rising Sun

Greetings to "*M.M.*" Readers from the East

MOST of our readers know that the Meccano Manuals and other publications are printed in 16 languages, and that Meccano depôts are to be found in all parts of the world. We wonder how many of our readers understand exactly what this means, and if they realise how wide-spread the Kingdom of Meccano really is.

When you sit in your home in England, or Canada, or Australia, or wherever it is that you live, do you ever think of the boys of other nations who are also building Meccano models? Many of these boys are situated in vastly different surroundings, and play under very different conditions from your's—yet you all enjoy the same hobby, face the same mechanical difficulties, and learn the same lessons.

From time to time we have published photographs of Meccano boys in the Argentine, in New Zealand, in Australia, and in other distant parts of the world. This month we are pleased to be able to reproduce some photographs of two of our young friends in Japan.

TWO HAPPY MECCANO BOYS IN THE LAND OF THE RISING SUN

Masters Sakurai. of Nakayamate-dori Japan.

Kenichi, aged nine, & his young brother spend many hours enjoying MECCANO Fun. Our photographs show that they are as clever at model-building as western boys

These photographs reached us from the "Land of the Rising Sun" at a time when it was cold and wet in England, and they brought a ray of joyous sunshine into the Editorial office. They made us realise there is a land where the sun often shines, and if it is not shining out-of-doors, we feel confident it shines wherever the smiling faces of our two happy little friends may be!

Some time ago Mr. S. Sakurai wrote us a very interesting letter from Nakayamate-dori, Japan, telling us how his two sons spent many happy hours with Meccano; how they thought out new models; and how they endeavoured to improve upon the models shown in our Manuals, as all true Meccano boys should!

Kenichi, the elder of the two boys, is nine years of age, and he has been a Meccano boy for eighteen months. He is already quite a clever young engineer and has built many fine models, Ships, Locomotives, Swing-Bridges, Pit Head Gears—but the models in which he is most interested are Cranes of all types.

Kenichi's younger brother (aged six) caught "Meccano-itis" while watching him at work, and now the brothers have great fun seeing who can invent and build the finest model without assistance!

Mr. Sakurai very kindly sent us several photographs, five of which are reproduced here in a group. The top left-hand photograph shows Kenichi on his bicycle outside his home in Nakayamate-dori. It is interesting to note that although he is riding his bicycle, Kenichi is wearing the little wooden Japanese sandals. In the centre photograph our young friends are shown together in the sunshine, having been persuaded to leave their Meccano for a few moments in order to be photographed out of doors. The other three photographs are typical of several, which show Kenichi and his brother at work on their models.

But what pleased us nearly as much as the charming photographs was a letter from Kenichi himself. Although we have become fairly expert in deciphering Meccano boys' letters—in all kinds of bad writing and in all manner of languages—we must confess that we couldn't make head or tail of Kenichi's message.

It really was fortunate that his father had expected this, and enclosed a translation, as otherwise there would have been some considerable delay in our discovering the meaning of the letter!

This is what Kenichi wrote to us, reproduced exactly as it appears, each letter and each word a work of art in itself.

お手紙ありがたう僕は今年の夏休みをメッカノの組立で非常に愉快に暮したことをよろこんで居ます。
尚此後も弟と色々と工夫して組立て見やうと思つて居ります。宅へ来られる父のお友達に見せますと皆さん好いおもちやだと感心されて居ります。
私共は一人でもメッカノ黨のふえる様心がけたいと思つて居ます。
大正十三年十一月廿二日
櫻井憲一
メッカノヲヂサマ

Kenichi Sakurai's Letter to the Editor of the "M.M."

" Dear Uncle Meccano,

" I thank you for your letter. I am delighted to say that I have had most pleasant times throughout my last summer vacation in working up your Meccano models. And from now on I am going to continue this interesting work, together with my brother, making interesting structures to the best of our ability.

" I always show the models to the friends of my father when they call, and am very pleased to hear their admiration of the excellent toy.

" To increase the number of Meccano engineers is our wish, and we are always keeping it in our mind."

Yours truly,

Kenichi Sakurai.

We know that Meccano boys in all parts of the world will join in extending the hand of good-fellowship to our little friends, thousands of miles away in Sunny Japan. We welcome them to Meccanoland and hope that there are many happy days in store for them.

FAMOUS BRIDGES—No 4

Washington Bridge and High Bridge, New York

Our cover this month shows two famous bridges, Washington Bridge in the foreground and High Bridge in the distance beyond.

Washington Bridge, to which a brief reference was made in our article last month, was constructed at a cost of over £600,000 and required two years to complete. Work was commenced in July 1886 and the Bridge opened for traffic in December 1888.

The Bridge crosses the River Hudson from Manhattan to New York, at a point where the river is 400 ft. in width. It is built in two tremendous steel arches, the span of each being 508 ft. One arch spans the river and the other bridges the land adjoining the water's edge. There is a clearance of 133 ft. under the bridge at high water, the length of the whole structure from end to end—including the masonry approaches—being 2,375 ft. and the width 86 ft. 7 in.

The accompanying photograph, published by the courtesy of the Department of Plant and Structures City of New York, gives an excellent idea of the unusual grace and beauty of this bridge and of the length of the two steel arches. The Bridge is, indeed, an excellent instance showing how nothing of beauty and grace of line need be sacrificed to gain requisite strength.

High Bridge, New York

The many-arched bridge in the background on our cover design is the High Bridge. This bridge was built in 1848, as part of the old Croton Aqueduct and carries three water mains with a water-carrying capacity of 90,000,000 gallons of water per day.

The Federal Government consider this bridge a menace to navigation, and plans have now been made for the removal of four of the masonry piers. These will be substituted by a steel cantilever arch of 420 ft. span with a rise of 103 ft., leaving an unobstructed waterway and removing the menace to navigation.

A depth of 15 ft. of water is provided at low water and the estimated cost of remodelling the Bridge is £200,000. The new steel arch, a cantilever, will be sprung from rock to rock, and will eliminate any danger of the future settling of High Bridge.

Electric Trains and Their Story

The Development of Electric Traction from 1885 to the Present Day

ALTHOUGH for many years the steam locomotive must continue to be the prime mover for main-line railway working, recent developments seem to indicate that for practically every form of railway haulage, electric traction will ultimately displace steam. There is little doubt that the general use of electricity will be a great advantage to the railways.

It is difficult to say which of the many attributes of electrical traction are the most important. Economy in working should certainly take a leading place for, apart from the heavy initial outlay for track and power equipment, electric railways are more economical to operate than steam railways. Another favourable factor is the greater cleanliness and consequent increased pleasure in travelling by electric trains, which are capable of sustained high speed working and smooth and noiseless running.

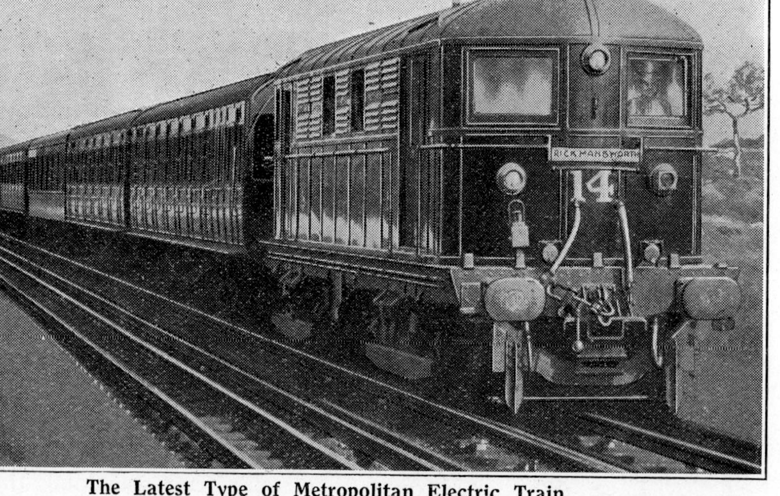

The Latest Type of Metropolitan Electric Train

Up to the present time, electric trains have been used chiefly for suburban services, because of their quick acceleration from the numerous stops, and general convenience on such services, for the multiple-unit system of electric trains has solved the problems of high-pressure work at busy terminal stations. The use of automatic signalling in conjunction with electric trains represents the high water mark of railway efficiency, and enables a set of metals to carry the utmost number of passengers, with complete safety, in a given time and at the highest speed.

Express working by electric trains over long distances has not yet been attempted in this country, although interesting developments undoubtedly lie ahead. Abroad the experiment has in many instances developed into a successful and permanent arrangement, however, whilst the handling of goods traffic by electric locos is said to show a saving of 40% in working expenses.

The Four Systems in General Use

There are four systems of electric traction in ordinary use (1) Direct Current (low tension) (2) Direct Current (high tension) (3) the Three-phase (4) the Single-phase.

The first on the list was the earliest system to be developed and is the one in most general use for short railways. In its simplest form the D.C. system does not require much apparatus. Current is supplied direct to an insulated overhead wire or conductor rail, from which it is collected by the locomotive or electric train by means of some form of sliding contact. It then passes through a suitable regulating apparatus to the motors, and returns either through the wheels and running rails, or through a specially-insulated conductor rail back through a short cable to the generator.

The Largest Power Station in Europe

Where high pressure current is generated at a power station, special sub-stations must be arranged in order to reduce it to low-pressure current suitable for direct use on the train motors.

A most interesting example of this system is to be found in the supply of power from Lots Road Power Station in Chelsea—one of the largest in Europe. Electric power is there generated on the three-phase system at a pressure of 11,000-volts, and supplied to the Metropolitan District Railway and its extensions, also to the most recently constructed Tube Railways. Current is transmitted through the tunnels to the sub-stations, where by means of rotary converters it is transformed into direct current at 600-volts ready for use by the trains.

Transformers Eliminate Sub-stations

The Single-phase system is the latest development, and although its possibilities have been known for many years, difficulties of construction and equipment have prevented its use until comparatively recently. In this system, high tension current at pressures up to 15,000-volts is collected directly by the train, no stationary sub-stations with rotating machinery being necessary. Although the train motors are only suitable for low pressure, each electric train carries its own sub-station in the form of a static transformer. The current is generally collected from an overhead wire and is then passed through a main switch, circulated through the high-tension coils of the main transformer and returned by way of the wheels to the rails, and thus back to the power house. All the current used for the propulsion, brake-operating and lighting of the train is taken from the low-tension side of the transformer.

(*Continued on page* 569

Photo courtesy] [Southern Railway

One of the New Motor Coaches built by the Metropolitan Carriage, Wagon, and Finance Co., Birmingham, for the South Eastern Suburban Services of the Southern Railway

Electric Trains and Their Story—(continued from page 567)

An interesting example of the three-phase current system is found in the haulage of heavy trains through the Simplon Tunnel. The high-tension direct current system is being adopted with great success in the United States and on the Continent.

The First Electric Tramway

The pioneer applications of electricity to traction purposes were made in Ireland in 1885, tramways at Newry and Portrush being run off a 250-volt third rail. In 1890 the City and South London Railway adopted electricity and in 1893 the Liverpool Overhead Railway installed electrically driven trains, whilst at the close of the century, several other lines were being equipped. Greater progress was made in the United States, and several short lines had been electrified at this time, the usual system being the D.C. third rail.

In 1900 a great impetus was given to electricity for railways by the opening of the Central London Railway and by the conversion in 1904-5 of the Metropolitan and District Railway after a long enquiry at which the respective merits of three-phase and direct current were hotly debated.

The next five years saw the electrification of the Mersey Railway, the Liverpool and Southport (L.&Y.R.), North Eastern Tyneside lines, and Great Western and Metropolitan Joint. Across the Atlantic a law was passed to minimise the smoke nuisance in New York, and several of the great trunk railways abandoned the use of steam locomotives for their approach lines to that city.

The direct current system with two conductor rails was favoured in this country, but two lines in 1908 and 1909 tried the alternating current method with overhead collection. These were the Midland, who had an experimental section between Lancaster and Heysham, and the Brighton Railway with their suburban lines in the London area.

Electric Railway across the Rockies

In 1913 a further advance was made, a section of the Lancashire and Yorkshire Railway between Bury and Holcombe Brook being electrified at 3,500-volts direct current. This was an immediate success, although overhead equipment problems in the congested Manchester area caused a reversion to a 1,300-volt third rail system when other lines were brought up-to-date in 1916. The rolling-stock, constructed entirely of steel and aluminium, was the first all-metal stock to be built in Britain.

In 1915 the Chicago, Milwaukee, and St. Paul Railway commenced to electrify some 650 miles of their main line across the Rocky Mountains on a 3,000-volt D.C. system with a 100,000-volt A.C. transmission to the sub-stations, which contained motor-generators in place of rotary converters.

Further developments in this country of the D.C. system were the electrification during the years of the War of the L. & N.W.R. North London and Watford suburban lines, and the change-over of 47 miles of track on the old London and South Western.

In 1915 the only section of goods railway so far to be electrified in this country was commenced between Newport and Shildon, on the North Eastern Railway, and proved to be a very advantageous turn-over from steam. The first mineral line in the world to be worked entirely by electric locomotives was the Butte, Anaconda, and Pacific Railroad in America. It was twenty-five miles in length and was worked by D.C. at 2,400-volts.

Since the War, the electrification of suburban lines has proceeded apace, and the new suburban services of the Southern Railway probably represents its highest standard, although there is nowhere to be found an electric railway that can be criticised adversely.

The First Electric Locomotive

Of the various systems of electric traction that most closely akin to steam working is, of course, the employment of an electric locomotive. The comparatively short history of this steed is a story of almost incredible advancement and increase in power and size.

The earliest electric locomotive of which any record remains was designed by a Mr. Davidson, an eminent Scots scientist, and was tried on the Edinburgh and Glasgow Railway as long ago as December 1842. It was self-contained, of course, the current being derived from primary batteries consisting of zinc and iron corrugated plates immersed in acid. The motor was of the simplest type, working on the principle of the attraction of iron bars on a revolving cylinder to fixed electro-magnets. These bars were energised and de-energised at correct intervals by brush and commutator.

(To be continued)

FAMOUS BRIDGES VI.

The Story of the Forth Bridge

Part II.

LAST month we outlined the history of the great cantilever bridge across the Forth and gave a description of the completed bridge. In the following article we deal with an even more interesting topic—the actual building of the bridge.

Preliminary Operations

Work was commenced in January 1883, and on the rising ground at the south side several acres of land were secured and here offices, workshops and stores were erected. Lines were laid down throughout the various yards and workshops and by means of a siding the whole was brought into direct communication with the North British Railway.

In addition to all this, steamers, barges and boats of all kinds; cranes, steam and hydraulic, and a bewildering amount of machinery for drilling, lighting, pumping, riveting, etc., had to be provided. Many of these machines were specially designed for the work by the contractors. Temporary cottages had to be built for the workmen, as the accommodation afforded by the local villages of Dalmeny and Kirkliston was insufficient.

Foundation of the Piers

The first task was to secure the foundation of the piers, which were fixed into bed-rock and boulder clay. The masonry work necessarily had to be very substantial and was carried out in cofferdams.

The engineers drove into the ground a circle of heavy piles, filled up the space between the piles with clay, and inside the palisade thus formed erected a framework of timber to strengthen it and to resist the pressure of the water. The water inside was then pumped out and the workmen were able to dig the foundations.

Many difficulties were encountered in this work owing to the sloping nature of some of the foundations on which the piers had to rest, and also because the tides had to be waited for, as much of the work in the centre of the river could only be carried out at low-water of big tides.

The Platforms, after building out the first strut

The cofferdams were about 70 ft. in length and 40 ft. in width, and averaged in depth between 30 ft. and 40 ft. below high water. The whole area of the bottom of the cofferdams was covered with concrete a few feet thick, upon which the masonry was constructed.

The foundations of the Fife piers, which stood on the mainland, demanded nothing further than straightforward excavation and rock levelling.

Constructing the Caissons

The two southern piers on the island and the four southern or Queensferry piers were constructed by the aid of caissons, huge cylindrical structures closely resembling an ordinary gasometer. They were built in a small bay to the east of the bridge. The structural material was mainly wrought iron, with the exception of the lower or cutting edge which was made of steel.

Each caisson had a floor which formed the roof of the air chamber and was supported from above by a series of girders. Upon this floor and about 7 ft. from the outer skin was an internal skin, the two being braced together in such a manner that the space between them was converted into a series of chambers which, when filled with concrete, were utilised for weighting the caisson at any given point. The caissons were built to a certain height and were then towed into position, where they sank into the boulder clay by pressure.

With one exception all the caissons were built, launched and sunk without any serious mishap, which was a great tribute to the skill and care of all concerned in the operations. This will be realised when it is learned that the average weight of each caisson was about 400 tons, and

Photo by permission of] **The Forth Bridge from the south-west before the cantilevers were built out** [*Messrs. Baker and Hurtzig, Westminster*

when loaded with concrete this weight was increased to about 15,000 tons.

Working by Compressed Air

The height of the permanent caissons was not sufficient to keep out the water at high tide and to serve this purpose temporary iron segments were bolted on. On a level with the top of these segments a platform was erected from which most of the operations were carried out. From the floor of the caisson to this platform three shafts were constructed. Two of these were for the purpose of handling materials and the third provided the means by which the men entered and left the air chamber.

The lower chamber had no bottom, and therefore as the shafts by which it was connected with the air were open, it is obvious that, until steps were taken to prevent it, water would rise in them to the level at which it stood outside. Before the men could descend to work, this water had to be expelled, and this was carried out by compressed air.

When the compressors had provided the pressure necessary to drive out and keep out the water from the air chamber, the men descended into an air lock and found themselves in a chamber containing an inner door leading directly to the compressed air. This inner door was held fast by a pressure of many tons from within, and before it could be opened the pressure in the two chambers had to be equalised. This was effected by closing the outer door and admitting compressed air through a valve until the outer door was held fast by the increased pressure. At this stage the pressure in the two chambers was the same, the inner door swung open and the workmen were able to continue their descent by means of iron ladders.

Caisson Disease

Working in compressed air has certain decided disadvantages. The large supply of oxygen enables the men to work with unusual energy, but the strain is severe and only men of thoroughly strong physique are able to withstand it for long. The density of the air produces many curious effects, such as exaggerating noises to an almost alarming extent. Voices too, sound harsh and quite different from their normal tones. The worst feature of all, however, is the trouble known as "Caisson Disease." The symptoms of this disease, usually intensely severe pains in the joints, are felt when the air pressure is reduced to normal, and the mischief is caused by an excessive amount of nitrogen being absorbed by the blood. If the transition from high pressure to normal pressure is performed very slowly and gradually there is little inconvenience, but if the process is hurried the results are extremely unpleasant.

The main difficulty experienced was to make the men stay in the air locks while the pressure was gradually reduced and the unwanted nitrogen expelled by means of the lungs. When a man had neglected the necessary precautions and on reaching the open air was attacked by caisson disease, the only method of affording him relief was to carry him back into one of the air locks and increase the pressure again, subsequently reducing it very slowly and gradually. It is stated, whether truly or not, that some of the men employed in the Forth Bridge caissons suffered so much from caisson disease that they were only too glad to spend their Sundays in the air locks in order to obtain relief!

Photo by permission of] [*Messrs. Baker and Hurtzig, Westminster*

The main pier at Fife

The one exception to the successful sinking of the caissons was due mainly to the slope of the river bed at that particular point. This particular caisson was watched with anxiety from the first, and although every possible care was taken it heeled over so far as to permit the rising tide to create an amount of damage that took some months to repair.

Viaduct Piers

The rail level of the bridge having been fixed at 150 ft. above high water, it was necessary that the viaducts connecting the cantilevers with the two shores should also be at a considerable height. The piers were built up to a certain level and the girders were put together on a sort of stage a few feet above each pier. The steelwork was then raised by hydraulic jacks, each capable of lifting some 200 tons if necessary. Each jack was connected with pumping engines in such a manner that all worked together. When pressure was applied to the jacks the girders were raised and packings of

(*Continued on page 584*)

CHOOSE YOUR OWN CHRISTMAS PRESENT

An opportunity for "*M.M.*" readers

It is a wonderful sensation to sit down and study illustrations and descriptions, and select your own Christmas present. Try it! The Special Christmas Number of the "*M.M.*" will contain advertisers' announcements of all kinds of splendid toys, books, and all manner of articles for giving pleasure to boys at Christmas. We are going to make at least one boy happy by giving him the very thing he wants, from amongst the articles advertised in our columns.

Let us know what you want—

On a Postcard

Obtain a copy of the Christmas number of the *Meccano Magazine*, which will be ready on 9th December, look at *all* the articles advertised and then decide which you would like the postman to hand to you on Christmas morning. Write the name of it on the top of your postcard, marking it No. 1. Then write the name of the article that you would like second best and mark it No. 2. Do this with six articles altogether, write your name and address at the bottom in very plain letters, and send the postcard to "Christmas Presents, *Meccano Magazine*, Binns Road, Liverpool."

To the boy whose list corresponds most nearly in order of merit with the total voting we will post the article that heads his list, to reach him on Christmas morning.

"Christmas Presents" postcards must reach us not later than 18th December.

Lives of Famous Engineers—

(*Continued from page* 559)

degree upset there was always the danger of a splash of hot metal, which frequently set the men's clothes on fire or caused terrible scalds and burns.

Nasmyth's safety ladle was designed to prevent these accidents. He applied a screw wheel keyed to the trunnions of the ladle, which was acted upon by an endless screw attached to the sling of the ladle. By this arrangement one man could move on its axis the largest ladle and pour out its contents with perfect safety, at the same time securing better castings by means of the increased steadiness of the flow of metal into the mould.

Another improvement brought about by Nasmyth was the fixing of a skimmer to the edge of the ladle to keep back the dross or slag floating on the surface of the molten metal. This process also was previously done by hand and many accidents occurred in consequence. Nasmyth did not patent these inventions, but preferred to make them over to the public.

The Story of the Forth Bridge—

(*Continued from page* 581)

hard wood were placed beneath them to hold them in position while the jacks were moved to a new bearing, when a second lift was made. By repeating this process the lifting of the girders and the building of the masonry proceeded until the required height was attained. The building of the masonry between each lift, including the time required for setting of the work on one half of the pier before the other was commenced, was carried upward at the rate of about 9 ft. on each pier per month. As the girders were ultimately raised to 150 ft. above high water, and as each lift was only about 3 ft. 6 in., the time occupied in the process was considerable. The first lift was made in April 1886 and the last in April 1887. The steel girders used were of the ordinary lattice type having a depth of 22 ft. 6 in.

The Conquest of the Air—(*cont. from p.* 585)

The petrol tank is fitted in rather a novel position, it being incorporated in the upper wing of the machine. It will be clearly seen from our illustration that part of the upper wing above the fuselage is a metal tank, and it is here that the petrol is stored, being fed to the engine by gravity.

An improvement has been made in the tail skid, so that better control on the ground is obtained, and any sudden stress on the rudder bar prevented.

The machine is fitted with a seaplane undercarriage for use with either normal or large wings. The undercarriage is interchangeable and special provision is made in the fuselage for hoisting so that the machine may be lifted by crane or derrick from the sea without damage.

Dimensions of the

Fokker C.V Aeroplane

	Normal	*Small*	*Large Wings*
Wing Area ...	48.68 sq. yds.	43.65 sq. yds.	55 sq. yds.
Span ...	42.04 ft.	40.55 ft.	48.25 ft.
Length ...	30.35 ,,	30.35 ,,	30.64 ,,
Height ...	10.86 ,,	10.77 ,,	11.09 ,,
Weight empty	3,160 lbs.	3.050 lbs.	3.271 lbs.
,, laden	4,928 ,,	4,376 ,,	5,481 ,,
,, per h.p.	10.0 ,,	9.72 ,,	12.16 ,,
Speed (max.)	137.4 m.p.h.	143.7 m.p.h.	131.2 m.p.h.

Meccano Platform Scales—

(*Continued from page* 565)

suspended by means of Flat Brackets 20 and Hook 21, connects with the levers 23 in the base of the model (Fig. C, page 565). These levers are pivoted on Hooks 24 and carry a central 3″ Rod 25 from which hangs a link 26 consisting of a Double Bracket and ¾″ Bolt. This link supports a further Rod 27 carried in the ends of another pair of levers 28 pivoted to the Hooks 28A. The 6½″ Rods 29 and 30, on which the Hooks are mounted, are journalled in the framework of the base.

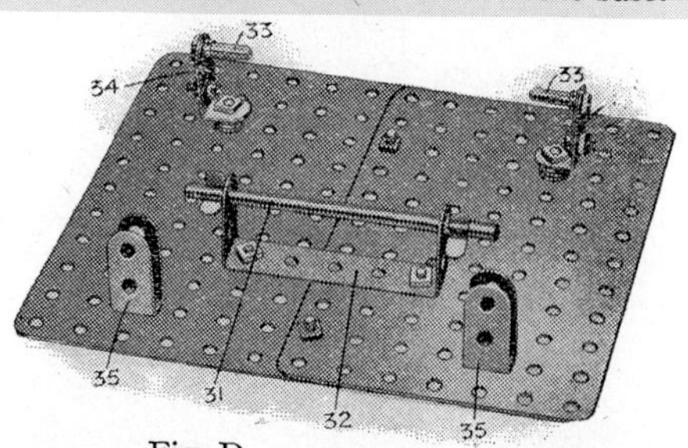

Fig. D

The platform, shown inverted in Fig. D, is composed of two large Flat Plates overlapped one hole and secured together; the Axle Rod 31 carried in a Double Angle Strip 32 rests upon the levers 23, while the Threaded Pins 33 bolted in 1″ by ½″ Angle Brackets 34 rest upon the levers 28. Two Washers are placed on the bolts underneath each end of the Double Angle Strip 32 and four Washers are placed beneath each of the brackets 34. Single Bent Strips 35 form guides for the platform and fit over the Rod 30 in the base.

A weight 36 consisting of a Strip Coupling, short Rod, and ¾″ Pinion slides along the steelyard 1 and carries a small pointer, cut from cardboard, which indicates the load being weighed by means of the graduated rule 37. A piece of cardboard 38 cut in the form of an arrow may be bolted to a 1″ Reversed Angle Bracket 39 and arranged to rest against the cardboard indicator 40 when the scales are exactly balanced.

When the model is complete, and before commencing to weigh, care should be taken in balancing the steelyard by means of the weight 11 and adjustment 15, so that the arrow 38 rests on the line at 40 when the sliding weight 36 is at the "O" mark in the rule 37.

The graduated scale may be prepared by placing known weights on the platform, and accurately marking the position at which the sliding weight 36 must point in order to maintain the arrow 38 dead on the line at 40.

The model should be oiled at frequent intervals, and all working parts must be perfectly free to move. The fulcrum 7, especially, should not be allowed to make contact with the suspended 3½″ Strips.

Parts required:
(Revised List)

3 of No. 1	1 of No. 15	6 of No. 57
2 ,, ,, 2	3 ,, ,, 16	20 ,, ,, 59
2 ,, ,, 3	2 ,, ,, 16B	2 ,, ,, 62
2 ,, ,, 4	1 ,, ,, 17	8 ,, ,, 63
3 ,, ,, 5	2 ,, ,, 18A	1 ,, ,, 63B
2 ,, ,, 6	1 ,, ,, 18B	1 ,, ,, 64
6 ,, ,, 6A	8 ,, ,, 20	2 ,, ,, 65
4 ,, ,, 8	1 ,, ,, 25	1 ,, ,, 81
2 ,, ,, 9	2 ,, ,, 26	4 ,, ,, 90
4 ,, ,, 10	8 ,, ,, 35	3 ,, ,, 100
1 ,, ,, 11	78 ,, ,, 37	2 ,, ,, 102
2 ,, ,, 12	14 ,, ,, 38	2 ,, ,, 108
1 ,, ,, 12A	1 ,, ,, 46	1 ,, ,, 111
3 ,, ,, 12B	3 ,, ,, 48	1 ,, ,, 111A
2 ,, ,, 13	4 ,, ,, 48D	2 ,, ,, 115
2 ,, ,, 14	2 ,, ,, 52A	2 ,, ,, 126A

A Long Trip on the Buffers

A young apprentice baker of Budapest, wishing to visit Paris without payment of the fare, crawled on to the buffers of a railway carriage and remained in that position until the train, which was not a through express, reached Toulon, when the carriage was detached. He was then observed by the railway police and charged with travelling for four and a half days with no ticket. The sentence was twenty days' imprisonment!

* * * *

Oil-Burning Locos for Peru

The Yorkshire Engine Co. Ltd. have recently completed and shipped five large 4–8–2 type locos built to the standard gauge for the Central Railway of Peru.

The section over which these locos will operate rises from sea level to a height of nearly 16,000 ft., and for a distance of 75 miles there is a continuous gradient of 1 in 25 with many sharp curves. The nature of the line necessitates a very flexible wheelbase, and flanged tyres have been omitted from both the leading and intermediate coupled wheels, which have a diameter of 4 ft. 4 in. Two outside cylinders are employed and the general arrangement of both cylinders and loco frames is in accordance with American practice. The cylinders are 20 in. in diameter and of 28 in. stroke, and the motion rods, of special high-tensile nickel chrome steel, are of light construction.

All fittings are of the most up-to-date design, and include electric head and cab lamps, with a dynamo driven from one of the tender axles. The total weight of each loco and tender is 123 tons 8 cwt., oil fuel apparatus is installed, and the locos are handsomely finished with polished metal bands adorning the boiler and cylinders.

* * * *

S.R. Notes

It was recently stated in these columns that many tank locos of the Southern Railway which were formerly engaged in suburban passenger services, have become unemployed as electrification has been extended. It is now officially announced that a number of the 0–4–4 tankers are for sale.

* * * *

Since the various railways of the Isle of Wight have been taken over by the Southern Railway, the older locos of various types have been largely replaced by more powerful tank locos. These locos were transported from Southampton on lighters and were accompanied across the Solent by the 150-ton floating crane from the port. No difficulty was experienced in performing the interesting tasks of loading and unloading the locos, which are of 0–4–4 type, L. & S.W.R. design.

* * * *

What Railways Carry Each Year

Under the title " What Railways Carry for the Nation Every Year," the L.N.E.R. recently published a very interesting list of figures. Some extracts are given :—

1. Railways employ 700,573 persons, or 1 in every 19 who are able to work.
2. Trains journeys : 1,745,802,000 passengers are carried by rail each year, equal to every person making 44 journeys.
3. Trains travel 398,417,000 miles a year, or two journeys to the sun and back.
4. Railway wagons number 718,610, or a train 2,722 miles long.
5. Railways carry each year 99,398 horses, 3,744,760 cattle, 11,263,357 sheep, 2,347,400 pigs.
6. Coal and Coke : 225,454,000 tons carried each year. Equal to a train of wagons 24,750,000 in number, and 93,749 miles long.

* * * *

Chinese Railway Survey Corps

A Survey Corps is being formed by the Chinese Government to undertake a complete investigation of all the Chinese railway systems. It is intended that the reports shall review all the factors contributing to the success or failure of any line or section, and to enable this to be done the geological and geographical features of every district will be examined. The growth of towns, location of populations, industrial, agricultural and mineral resources, and the general living conditions of the people will each be examined to determine the financial possibilities of opening up new branch lines and providing additional freight facilities.

* * * *

New Pullmans

The Pensylvania Company has ordered fifty all-steel sleeping cars from the Pullman Company of America. The equipment specified by the contract includes shower baths in the dressing compartments, writing desks, telephones and a library. A fully equipped tailor's shop will be added to carry out any necessary repairs to travellers' clothing.

Luxury travel in America is fast reaching the conceivable maximum and almost every possible aid to comfort is installed.

Railway Renewals

Much of the evidence given before the Railway Rates Tribunal was concerned with renewals of stock and material, and we glean many interesting facts.

Mr. Walter Lloyd told the Tribunal that on the Great Western Railway, of which he is Joint Chief Engineer, it was the custom to renew the main and principal lines with new material and employ the serviceable material thus recovered on the secondary and branch lines. Of a total mileage of 6,915 miles, 4,194 are regarded as principal and require new material for renewals, the cost of which is estimated at £3,000 per mile.

Mr. George Ellsom, Deputy Chief Engineer to the Southern Railway, stated that the average life of a single rail is twenty years, but that some of the rails at suburban line junctions last only three months. Maintenance costs are seriously affected by wet weather, which impairs the earthworks and gives rise to disintegration of the permanent way. Landslides are a formidable problem and, at the present time, the Southern Railway is engaged in dealing with over one hundred of them.

Mr. H. N. Gresley, Chief Mechanical Engineer to the L.N.E.R., dealing with the upkeep costs of locomotives and rolling stock, said that the average life of a loco was 33 years and during that period two boilers would be required.

* * * *

Sheffield Station Alterations

Considerable alterations are in hand at the L.N.E.R. Darnall station, Sheffield. The present track, consisting of three double lines, is being supplemented by another track, thus enabling a pair of lines on each side of the station to be used solely by mineral and goods traffic. A subway is to take the place of the existing passenger footbridge and a central island platform will be substituted for the two platforms hitherto in use. The platform booking offices are to be demolished and a new range of buildings erected at the station entrance. The cost of the work will be £36,000.

* * * *

Irish Mail Stop

In future the Irish Mail from Holyhead to Euston will stop at Bletchley each morning to pick up 100 gallons of cream for London. There is no previous record of this famous passenger train stopping to take up dairy produce. No alteration is being made in the running time.

South African News

Three experimental types of locomotives have recently been delivered to the Union of South Africa Railways and are now being tested on the "Union Limited" and "Union Express." These two expresses are booked to cover the 965 miles between Capetown and Johannesburg in 29 hours. The north-bound expresses on this run have to attain an altitude of 5,735 ft., traversing very severe gradients. In some sections inclines are as steep as 1 in 40.

Two of the new types are of American design and were built at the Baldwin Works, Philadelphia. They are of the 4–8–2 (Mountain) and 4–6–2 (Pacific) types and are among the largest locos ever designed for the 3 ft. 6 in. gauge. Each representative has two large outside cylinders. The "Mountain" weighs 227,100 lbs. and the Pacific 192,650 lbs. in working order without the tenders, which are of the well-known American bogie type, not previously used in South Africa. A special feature of each loco is grease lubrication for the coupled wheel axle boxes and crank pins. This method has made possible the extremely long runs now common in America, and it is anticipated that equally good results will be obtained in South Africa.

One of the "Pacific" class has already established what is claimed by the Union of South Africa Railways to be a world's record for the 3 ft. 6 in. gauge. It completed the distance of 965 miles between Johannesburg and Capetown in 27 hours 35 min. actual running time.

The third experimental loco has been built in England and is of the "Garratt" design which is now extending in use very rapidly. It is of the 2–6–2 : 2–6–2 type and is a development of previous "Garratts" supplied by the same builders, Messrs. Beyer, Peacock & Co. Ltd., Gorton. It is to be tested between Capetown and Beaufort West, a distance of 339 miles which includes the Hex River Bank of 16 miles at 1 in 40.

The loco is designed for express work at speeds up to 60 m.p.h., and has coupled wheels 4 ft. 9 ins. in diameter. The four cylinders are 18 ins. diameter by 26 ins. stroke, and the steam pressure is 180 lbs. per sq. in. Total weight of the "Garratt" loco is 147 tons 13¾ cwt., and its greatest width over buffer beams 10 ft. All three locos are fitted with the latest pattern L.M.S. superheater.

* * * *

Progress on the Southern

In addition to the Company's extensive electrification of London suburban lines, the Southern Railway has made notable progress in other directions during 1925.

The advent of the new express locos of the famous "King Arthur" class has resulted in greatly-improved time keeping and the running of considerably heavier trains than ever before on the South Eastern.

During the summer months 13 complete new corridor trains, with six new dining-cars, were placed in service, and several new steamers added to the Company's cross-channel fleet, including the fast new ships "Maid of Kent" and "Isle of Thanet."

The holiday season made great demands upon the Company's resources, and it is computed that no less than 26,000 main line seaside expresses ran to or from London, besides ordinary stopping trains, during the ten weeks of the "rush" season.

An Unusual Load

Photo courtesy] [*L.N.E.R.*

Our photograph shows a train load of 20 "Marshall" steam road rollers, each of which is carried on a special type of wagon, leaving Gainsborough by the L.N.E. Railway for shipment to Hull. These rollers are part of an order for 100 steam road rollers placed by the Greek Government for the great road reconstruction scheme in that country.

* * * *

New Locos for Central Section. Southern Railway

Fourteen new engines of the "King Arthur" class are being built at Eastleigh for use next summer in the South Coast passenger expresses of the Central Section, including the "Southern Belle," etc. The tenders of these locomotives will be the same as those of the No. 810 class Maunsell Mixed Traffic engines. They will be named after the following Knights of the Round Table :—

Sir Ontzlake, Sir Ector de Maris, Sir Dinadan, Sir Dodinas le Savage, Sir Blamor de Ganis, Sir Hectimere, Sir Ironside, Sir Meleaus de Lile, Sir Meliot de Logres, Sir Durnore, Sir Harry le Fise Lake, Sir Cador of Cornwall, Sir Constantine, Sir Galleron.

The name of locomotive No. 788, at present "*Sir Beaumains,*" will be changed to "*Sir Urre of the Mount.*"

* * * *

A Gramophone Record

A Gramophone disc recording the departure of the "Flying Scotsman" from King's Cross has been prepared and includes the sounds of the station bell, the guard's and locomotive whistles and the clatter and rattle of the signals.

Diesel-Electric Locomotives

The Canadian National Railways have been testing new types of cars operated by electricity, produced by a generator placed in the body of the car. Two types have been tried out, one consisting of an articulated body, 102 ft. in length, really made up of two bodies placed on three four-wheel trucks; the other is of a lighter type with a body 60 ft. in length over all and capable of hauling a trailer. One of the lighter cars made the Toronto - Montreal run, 335 miles, in only a slightly longer time than that taken by the regular trains drawn by steam locos.

These experiments with Diesel - electric cars represent an attempt to escape the high fuel cost of coal-burning locos. The first attempts were made with petrol driven cars and, later, storage battery cars were tested over the shorter lines with not altogether satisfactory results. The Diesel-electric was the next step and the Canadian National Railway engineers state that it represents an economical and serviceable type of motive power, well suited to suburban and branch line traffic.

In recent tests these cars averaged one gallon per 4.6 miles, this being about 10 per cent. of the full costs of a steam loco over the same run.

* * * *

Locos Seen at Manchester

During a recent afternoon spent at London Road Station, Manchester (L.M.S. and L.N.E. Railways) the locos seen were of a great variety of designs, as was much of the rolling-stock. Among the former working to and from the L.M.S. side of the station, were "Claughtons," "Princes," and "Georges," while the earlier 4–6–0 and 4–4–0 classes were also represented. An 0–6–0 mixed traffic loco of Midland type, though built this year at Crewe, worked out with a local train, and an express from the Potteries came in behind a North Stafford 0–6–4 tanker. A Midland compound passenger engine was also in evidence.

On the L.N.E. side a heavy express left for London drawn by a Great Central 4–6–0 of the "Sir Sam Fay" class, while the same section of the L.N.E.R. was represented as well by 4–4–0 "Directors," 0–6–0's, and very many 4–4–2 and 2–4–2 tanks which work suburban trains. One of the new 0–6–2 tanks of Great Eastern design, but with standard funnel and fittings, also left with a stopping train.

Amongst interesting combinations of rolling-stock there was a former Highland Railway bogie coach working on the Buxton (L.M.S.) expresses.

Aeroplane as Disinfector

American farmers do not hesitate to adopt new methods in order to obtain more satisfactory results. Disinfecting crops by means of insect killing dust sprayed from aeroplanes is the latest "stunt." This idea was first used in the cotton fields but in the spring of this year it was carried out with great success over a peach orchard consisting of more than 10,000 trees. The "dust" consisted of hydrated lime and arsenated lead and the whole process was completed in just under two hours, this time including landings for fresh supplies of disinfectant.

* * * *

Interesting New Type of Flying Machine

In appearance somewhat like a windmill, but with horizontal sails, a machine that is probably the strangest flying machine ever invented has reached this country from Spain, to undergo Air Ministry trials. The 'plane is the result of considerable research by Don Juan de la Cierva, who has thirty-three previous aeroplanes to his building record. It embodies an attempt to combine the principal properties of the helicopter, the ordinary monoplane and the ornithopter, so called because it flaps its wings in imitation of a bird. This "flying windmill" has already undergone extensive tests in Madrid, and a prominent British pilot has stated that it possesses big possibilities. (Full description on page 48).

* * * *

Aerial Scouting

The Eastman Kodak Research Laboratories issue details of a remarkable development in aerial photography that will increase both the value and speed of the camera scout under the conditions of modern warfare. Dr. C. E. Kenneth Mees, the eminent photographic research worker, has evolved a reversible film, known technically as "Ana-positive." The film has now been tested by officers of the United States Army Air Service and Dr. Burka, a scientist employed by the U.S. Government.

The striking feature of the film is that it exhibits, after development, a negative image when viewed by transmitted light and a positive when seen by reflected light. Thus for immediate use in wartime a positive picture is available and ordinary prints may be made later. Apparatus for developing, fixing and washing is provided in the observer's compartment of the aeroplane and the drying of the film is also completed while the machine is in the air.

It is claimed that, using this film, the air scout of the future will not be obliged to return to his headquarters before his exposed plates and films will be of use, but the new film will enable photographs of enemy positions to be taken, completed and dropped at pre-arranged points, leaving the airman free to carry on his reconnoitring without landing.

Our readers will understand the idea of this film better if they will examine any badly under-exposed negative they may possess. When viewed from certain angles by light reflected from the surface, a positive can be seen. Only the negative image is seen when the film is viewed by being placed between the eye and the source of the light, i.e., by transmitted light. It must not be inferred, however, that the reversed image of Dr. Mees' film is obtained in the same way. The process is of course secret and under-exposed negatives have no place in the aerial photographer's scheme of things.

* * * *

Aero-Insurance

The International Air Congress, which met recently at Lyons, discussed many points of legal interest to aviation in its commercial aspect. The question of compulsory insurance of passengers by the carrying companies came under review, but was voted against. The position remains that the passenger must effect his own insurance—the risk from air travel is fast becoming a normal risk—if he specially desires so to do.

The Congress decided, however, that the personnel engaged on the machine should be insured compulsorily, save in those countries where the laws provide for compensation for injury arising out of employment.

* * * *

The "Postal" Napier-Bodmin

This new all-metal machine, which underwent its trial flights in August, will probably be the first machine for use on the proposed Karachi-Kantara mail route. The machine is an entirely new design as the two 450 h.p. Napier engines are placed in an engine room situated in the fuselage, each engine driving a propeller on either side of the fuselage through gears. The twelve cylinders are fitted on the broad arrow principle, in three rows of four, the weight per horse power developed of each engine being slightly less than 2 lbs.

Should one engine fail, the other will be able to maintain the aeroplane in flight.

Intended for mail and passenger carrying the 'plane, which is to be known as the "Postal" type, can be quickly converted for use as a bombing machine for military purposes.

* * * *

Night Flying

Last year several experiments were conducted at Croydon Aerodrome with the object of increasing and improving the landing arrangements for night flying. Further official experiments are shortly to be made to improve upon the present arrangements, which include two series of red neon tube lights mounted on towers and several stationary and flashing lights. The neon lights have displayed excellent fog-piercing properties and it is proposed to lay lines of similar lights across the aerodrome.

A further interesting improvement will be the electric ring cable that is to be laid around the boundary of the aerodrome. Signals radiated from the cable will affect a special instrument mounted in the 'plane, and the pilot will be enabled to verify his height above the ground from moment to moment. These electric signals will indicate the machine's position in relation to the landing ground, so that even in mist or fog it can glide down continuously until the aerodrome lights are clearly visible.

* * * *

Aircraft Inspection

The importance of the Commercial Air Industry is reflected in a statistical table given elsewhere in these notes and it is therefore not altogether surprising to learn that the Bureau Veritas, a French Association corresponding with the British Association of underwriters known as Lloyds, has decided to include aircraft within the scope of its operations.

As is well known, both Lloyds and Bureau Veritas have been in existence for over a hundred years, rendering incalculable service to maritime interests particularly and commerce generally. Their operations consist of registering the details of all new ships, classifying and keeping track of them and making periodical inspections for the purpose of certifying their state of fitness for sea. So great is their authority that no company will insure an uncertified ship and the shipping authorities would decline to permit such a vessel to carry passengers.

This brief review of the functions performed by the two associations will enable our readers to grasp the importance of the first Aeronautical Register issued by the Bureau Veritas for the year 1925. In this register are entered the details of the civil aircraft inspected, together with general information of importance to aviators. A certificate of fitness for flight is issued in respect of all machines and airships registered, and each will be required to undergo periodical inspection.

The institution of this inspection marks an important forward step in commercial aviation and should prove of vast importance both to passengers and insurance companies.

Dutch 'Planes and British Engines

With the exception of four Fokker III. monoplanes, which are to be held in reserve, the whole of the machines owned by one of the most important lines in Holland are to be offered for sale. The new machines ordered for replacement purposes are Fokker VII. passenger aeroplanes, all of which will be equipped with British Jupiter 400 h.p. air-cooled engines.

* * *

Propellerless Aeroplane

An aeroplane that will dispense with propellers and rely for its motive power upon the discharge of highly compressed gas is in course of construction by a French inventor. Briefly stated, propulsion is effected by a powerful charge of gas, generated in a specially devised chamber and passed through a compressor. It will be emitted through three nozzles at the rear of the machine with such force as to send the machine forward. It is claimed that speeds of 380 m.p.h. will be possible, as compared with the maximum of 300 m.p.h. forecasted for the latest racing machine of the orthodox type.

* * * *

Indian Airship Shed

The Armstrong Construction Company, a subsidiary of Messrs. Armstrong Whitworth Co., is commencing a contract for the erection of a new airship shed on a site near to the present station of the Royal Air Force at Karachi. The shed is intended to be the terminal station for the proposed England-India Air Service.

The Karachi shed will be one of the largest structures in the world, being 850 ft. in length and 180 ft. in width, with a total height of nearly 200 ft. For the purpose of comparison it is interesting to note that the shed will be twice the length of the Crystal Palace and considerably higher and wider. The Cardington airship shed, at present the largest building of the kind, is 40 ft. shorter and about 15 ft. less in height.

* * * *

Rescued by Air

Two French commercial aeroplanes recently were instrumental in saving the lives of the crew of a Bordeaux tug who had been cast ashore on the West African Coast and were in danger of attack by turbulent natives. Part of the crew had been picked up by a passing schooner, but four had been left behind and were surrounded by hostile Moors. The two pilots landed near the scene of the attack and each succeeded in rescuing two of the men.

An Aerial Stowaway

A Los Angeles report states that the first instance of an aerial stowaway was recorded there recently, when a boy attempted to steal a ride by clutching the wings of an aeroplane as it started up. The boy was carried several miles before he was noticed by the occupants, in endeavouring to trace the cause of the machine's continual deviation from an even keel. He was motioned to work his way along the wing to the fuselage and finally hauled aboard.

* * *

More Records

A new world's record for seaplanes has been established by Lieut. J. H. Doolittle of the American Army Air Service over the 3 kilometres course at Bay Shore Park, while flying the Curtiss Racer with which he won the Schneider Cup Race. The speed attained was 245.713 m.p.h., which is 17 m.p.h. faster than the record set up by Supermarine-Napier S.4.

* * * *

Light Aeroplane Costs

The results of the first few months' flying by the light aeroplane clubs show that the cost of upkeep is very little more than that of the average motor car. Altogether 7,000 miles have been flown for instructional purposes, including approximately 1,200 landings, and replacement costs have been practically non-existent.

* * * *

Aviation in Australia

Australian aviation continues to develop speedily and new commercial routes are being mapped out. With these in operation there will be 53 aerodromes and 85 emergency service landing stations dotted up and down 4,700 miles of recognised flying routes. The most important of these routes is that maintained by Western Australian Airways Ltd., between Perth and Derby, a distance of approximately 700 miles, over which a weekly service is maintained.

World's Largest Aeroplane

Photo courtesy] *[Messrs. Vickers Aviation Dept.*

The Vickers Rolls-Royce "Vanguard," recently handed over for service with Imperial Airways, is the largest passenger-carrying aeroplane in the world. We hope to fully describe this wonderful machine in the near future.

Duration Trials

Experiments are in progress in America to investigate the possibility of relieving the fatigued pilot and mechanic of a machine and replacing them by a fresh crew while in the air. The transfer from one machine to another will be made by means of a flexible wind-shielded ladder, the two machines meanwhile flying at the lowest possible speed.

Tests are also being carried out to ascertain how long an aeroplane can remain in flight provided that its fuel tanks are replenished from another machine. In early experiments a big army biplane was refueled fifteen times by aircraft flying immediately overhead and feeding it through flexible tubes.

* * *

Submarine Hangar

A marvellous little seaplane that can be folded up and stored in a submarine has recently passed trials at St. Raphael. The machine is fitted with a 40 h.p. Radial engine and carries a small wireless set with which it can be in constant communication with its parent ship while in flight. Its chief duty in war would be scouting when the submarine was operating at a distance from its base and, if necessary, it would be able to attack hostile craft. At the completion of its flight the machine alights on the water alongside the submarine and is lifted on board, folded and stowed away in a small water-tight compartment below deck.

Aircraft manufacturers in this and other countries have been attempting to produce an efficient submarine-carried aeroplane but, owing to Air Ministry restrictions, very little is known of British progress.

The Air Ministry's "Hush Hush" policy is the cause of a neat joke going the rounds. An inventor of a tailless 'plane presented it for the Ministry's inspection. Now it's a "tale"-less 'plane!

* * * *

Body-less Aeroplane

A young engineer named De Monge is the inventor of a body-less aeroplane that was successfully tried out at Villacoublay recently. Except for the forepart in which the engines are located, and to which sections of the single wing are attached, the machine has no body, the tail being connected to the motors and wings by two light metal "girders." The machine is driven by two 9 h.p. engines, which propel it at a speed of approximately 90 m.p.h., the petrol consumption being roughly one gallon per 25 miles. The inventor is designing a 20-passenger machine embodying the same principles in which he hopes to cross the Atlantic.

Jackie Coogan's Visit
to the American Meccano Factory

by Frank Hornby

During a visit to America, Mr. Hornby, the inventor of Meccano and Managing-Director of Meccano Ltd., was able to show Jackie Coogan over the Meccano factory at Elizabeth, New Jersey, U.S.A., and below he gives an interesting account of his chat with this " great little " film star. Jackie Coogan is undoubtedly the world's most popular boy, and I feel sure that many thousands of our readers who have witnessed his clever acting on the screen will be interested to read of the happy " off " hours that Jackie spends with Meccano and other boyish hobbies. On completing his tour of the American factory, Jackie was surprised to learn that there was a still bigger factory at Liverpool, and another at Paris, and he has made up his mind that he will certainly visit the Head Office of Meccanoland on his next trip to Europe.—EDITOR.

MOST of us, I suppose, enjoy spending an occasional evening at the cinema and I must confess that this is one of my favourite forms of recreation. The films I like best are those that deal with children and their doings, and I suppose that is quite natural, as most of my life has been spent in caring for boys and studying and providing for their well-being and enjoyment.

Once or twice during the last few years I have experienced the very pleasant surprise of discovering in some little domestic scene depicted on the screen, a boy or a number of boys playing with Meccano models. When this has happened I have felt an almost irresistible, and, of course, ridiculous desire to step around to the back of the stage and have a little talk with them.

The films that have given me a very real and genuine pleasure are those that depict that wonderful little genius Jackie Coogan, going through all manner of extraordinary experiences in that daring, clever, and lovable way with which we are familiar. The first picture that I saw him in was " The Kid," and I remember wondering at that time if he had ever heard of Meccano and if he enjoyed playing with it like all the other millions of boys do. I decided that no doubt he had had so busy a life thrust upon him, that he would not have much time for any form of recreation and that his companions would be much older people who would have no sympathy with regular boyish pursuits. I remember thinking what a pity it was that we could not get hold of him and pitch him in among a bunch of boys of his own age and give him a great time playing Meccano and trains and football and fishing.

I have seen Jackie Coogan on the screen a number of times since then and each time the same thoughts have run through my head, so you can imagine the keen pleasure I experienced when I received a very kindly and appreciative letter from Jackie's father telling me how much his son enjoyed playing with Meccano. I wrote back to Mr. Coogan at once telling him how glad I was to receive his letter and telling him also of the great interest with which I had followed the work of his clever son. Very shortly he sent me another letter telling me more about the fine models that Jackie had made. He also gave me full permission to reproduce his first letter and to tell all the other Meccano boys that Jackie was one of them. Better still came a letter from Jackie himself, which I am printing here, and I am sure Jackie will be very proud to see his letter reproduced in the *Meccano Magazine.*

The Meccano Tractor is one of Jackie Coogan's favourite models. He is seen above "putting it through its paces"

Jackie Wants to be an Engineer

Like all other keen Meccano boys Jackie naturally wants to become an engineer. That is one of his wishes that I hope will not be gratified because, although we might discover in him a great engineer, we should certainly lose one of the most lovable laughter-makers the world has ever known.

In one of his letters Jackie expressed the hope that

some day, in some part of the world, we might meet, because there were a lot of things concerning Meccano that he wanted to ask me about. Whilst I entertained the same wish perhaps even more keenly than Jackie himself, I thought it very unlikely that he and I would ever be within a thousand miles of each other. A month or so later I was on a visit to the offices of the Meccano Co. Inc.—an associate company of Meccano Ltd.—and to my great surprise, I received a letter saying that Jackie was in New York and that he wanted to come over to Elizabeth, New Jersey, to inspect the Meccano Factory with me, if it could be managed.

Jackie arrives at the Meccano Factory

It did not take long to fix up arrangements and within a day or two I had the pleasure of welcoming both Jackie and his father at my American office. Jackie got to work at once with his questions, and I soon realised that there was very little I could tell him about Meccano models or Meccano parts and their uses. He was thoroughly familiar with them all and could intelligently discuss the construction of an Auto Chassis, the Meccano Loom, the Clock, and he could tell me the functions of various cranes and discuss the details with me. What I liked best about him, though, was his keen imagination. He told me he had been to Paris and that when he saw the Eiffel Tower he felt sure it had been designed from Meccano. He said he had a notion that he could build an exact model of the Eiffel Tower himself every bit as big, if only he had enough parts and enough time, and then he added, "Wouldn't it be fine if Meccano boys could run it, and operate the elevators, and let all the other Meccano boys who came, examine the machinery and explain it all to them!"

"And what would your part in the matter be, Jackie," I asked.

"Oh!" he replied, "I would be the elevator boy and I would say 'Step right in; this is free day to Meccano boys, and it's all quite safe, everything's made of Meccano.'"

I could tell by the look of pleasure on Mr. Coogan's face, that while the idea amused him, he was proud of his boy's intelligence.

JACKIE COOGAN PRODUCTIONS, INC.

OFFICE OF THE PRESIDENT.

JACK COOGAN, PRESIDENT
LILLIAN R. COOGAN, SEC'Y & TREAS.

HOLLYWOOD, CALIFORNIA.

March,
Twenty-fifth,
1 9 2 5.

Mr. Frank Hornby, Pres.,
Meccano Company, Inc.,
Elizabeth, N. J.

My dear Mr. Hornby:-

I think you will be interested to know that my boy, Jackie, is a Meccano enthusiast. He loves to build models and then to operate them and what a range of models he has built with Meccano.

I like him to play with it and I have noticed that whilst Jackie is amusing himself with Meccano, he is at the same time acquiring a good knowledge of engineering. As a father, I am a firm believer in the modern idea of learning while playing.

Jackie has had unusual opportunities of satisfying his toy wants and I think it very much to his credit that he selected Meccano.

If other boys are getting as much pleasure from Meccano as Jackie is - what a host of boy friends you must have!

Wishing you every success,

Cordially yours,
Jack Coogan

P.S. I am glad to tell you that recently Jackie, only nine years old, passed with honors an examination for boys of thirteen.

A letter from Jackie's Father—

JACKIE COOGAN PRODUCTIONS, INC.

OFFICE OF THE PRESIDENT.

JACK COOGAN, PRESIDENT
LILLIAN R. COOGAN, SEC'Y & TREAS.

HOLLYWOOD, CALIFORNIA.

Mar. 31, 1925.

Mr. Frank Hornby,
Elizabeth, N.J.
My dear Mr. Hornby.

I have many good times playing with my Meccano. I have been a Meccano fan since the first set was given to me, and like it so well that some day I may be an engineer.

Your friend,
Jackie Coogan.

—and Jackie Coogan's own letter to Mr. Hornby

"Jackie has been drumming this kind of stuff into me ever since he came back from his recent visit to Europe," he said, "Everyone in Hollywood knows of Jackie's keenness on building Meccano models. He has asked our art director next time they need a miniature bridge to use Meccano to make it. The art director tells me that many of his suggestions are on really practical lines, and he will be able to make use of them. Jackie has read somewhere that architects and builders use Meccano parts for modelling out their structures in the first place, and that a big engineering firm build up special models of anything new they may be designing, with Meccano parts, and so try out the various movements and mechanical details first in this way; and he sees no reason why we in our business should not make similar good use of Meccano."

(To be continued)

Jackie Coogan's Visit

to the American Meccano Factory

by Frank Hornby

During a visit to America, Mr. Hornby, the inventor of Meccano and Managing-Director of Meccano Ltd., was able to show Jackie Coogan over the Meccano factory at Elizabeth, New Jersey, U.S.A., and he concludes below an account of a pleasant chat with this " great little " film star. Jackie Coogan is undoubtedly the world's most popular boy, and I feel sure that many thousands of our readers who have witnessed his clever acting on the screen will be interested to read of the happy " off " hours that Jackie spends with Meccano and other boyish hobbies. On completing his tour of the American factory, Jackie was surprised to learn that there was a still bigger factory at Liverpool, and another at Paris, and he has made up his mind that he will certainly visit the Head Office of Meccanoland on his next trip to Europe.—EDITOR.

(Concluded from last month)

JACKIE'S suggestions concerning the possible applications of Meccano to the film industry were most original, and I was especially pleased to see that he was so familiar with the many commercial uses to which Meccano has been applied.

" Jackie is very keen on a plan for making slow motion pictures of a boy building models with Meccano," said his father. " He thinks it would be an excellent means of showing other boys how easy and delightful the work is. Don't you think, Mr. Hornby, that something like that would be useful ? "

I agreed that the suggestion was a good one and that it might be worth planning out something of the kind.

All the while Mr. Coogan was speaking there was a grave expression on Jackie's face as he looked at us, glancing from one to the other, that showed he was anxious that his ideas should be taken very seriously. The long talk that we had together gave me all the clues I needed to his strong character and showed me plainly enough why his personality and genius have impressed themselves in so marked a fashion on his audiences all over the world.

Jackie Coogan at work on his Hammerhead Crane. The pulley block, apparently, calls for some serious thinking

How Jackie got his Start

I expressed the wish to know something of his short and wonderful career, and his father told me, with a twinkle in his eye, that his first appearance in a theatre was when he was twenty months old. Mr. Coogan himself was on the stage at the time, when he noticed that the audience was laughing, applauding something at the back of him. He looked round and beheld Jackie toddling towards him. It appears that his mother had taken Jackie to the theatre that day and as he was standing in the wings he evidently felt that he would like to have a talk with his father, so he walked out to him.

He Meets Charlie Chaplin

Mr. Coogan made the best of the situation, introduced his son to the laughing audience, and set him doing some of the dance steps which he had learned at home.

At the age of four he appeared on the stage with Annette Kellerman and it was while he was doing some of his dance steps in this performance that he attracted the attention of Charlie Chaplin.

For four years the comedian had wanted to film the story eventually called " The Kid," but he had postponed production time after time because he could not find the right child to play the name part. And here he recognised in Jackie Coogan the boy whom he had sought so long. A week or so later Chaplin called upon the Coogans in Los Angeles, and had himself introduced to Jackie by Sid Grauman, a well-known theatrical impresario who had known the Coogans in San Francisco.

The history of the production of " The Kid " and Jackie's instantaneous success is no doubt common knowledge. Jackie's pictures since then are as follows : " Peck's Bad Boy," " My Boy," " Trouble," " Daddy,"

"Circus Days," "Oliver Twist," "Long Live the King," "A Boy of Flanders," "Little Robinson Crusoe," and "The Ragman."

Undoubtedly he occupies an unique place in the public's heart all over the world. Perhaps never in history has there been an individual, in any walk of life, so universally beloved as this youngster.

Putting the finishing touches to a Meccano Steam Shovel

Jackie Inspects the Factory

We went through the Meccano factory and Jackie revelled in all that he saw. The giant power presses, noisily blanking out Rectangular and Sector Plates, filled him with wonder, and he was fascinated by the working of the safety guards with which they are all equipped. These guards are designed to prevent accidents to the operators of the presses and are so arranged that they automatically push the operator's hands out of danger as the ram of the press descends.

From the presses we turned to the Automatic Department, and here the steady hum of the screw-cutting machines was in marked contrast to the clanking of the presses. Jackie marvelled at the automatic screw machines. To see a brass rod fed into the machine at one end and a completely fashioned worm wheel drop out at the other end every few seconds, seemed like a piece of magic, and I assured him that many people much older than he found the sight just as mystifying. For myself, I must confess that to this day these wonderful machines fascinate me.

The drilling and tapping machines proved to be hardly less interesting and even the machines that assemble the set screws into the wheels so rapidly were not overlooked.

The Meccano Factory at Elizabeth, New Jersey, U.S.A.

Jackie becomes a Nickel-Plater

In the Nickel-Plating Department Jackie felt like a little chemist and he plated a complete batch of work himself. He was handed a rack of parts ready for plating and, having immersed them in the hot cleaning vat, which not only removes dirt but adds a deposit of copper before the parts are plated with nickel, he exclaimed with glee at the quick change in the appearance of the parts. When he immersed them they were a dull steel colour; when he took them out they had a bright copper tint. Then he put the rack of parts in the nickel bath, rinsed them afterwards, dried them in heated sawdust, and with a roguish smile, turned to me and said, "That's easy, isn't it."

Jackie would have liked to linger a while in each department but time was pressing and we were able to make only a brief visit to the Packing Department. Here, however, Jackie saw to it that we stopped long enough to enable him to pack up a Meccano Outfit all by himself, from start to finish — a performance of which he was exceedingly proud. Like all other visitors to our factory, Mr. Coogan and Jackie were amazed at the precision and accuracy with which each little part of the Meccano system is produced.

Jackie was a little surprised to learn we have several other factories besides the one in Elizabeth and that the real home of Meccano is in Liverpool, where an enormous staff is employed by the firm, and that there is another large factory in Paris. On his next trip to Europe he intends visiting both of these factories.

I mentioned that at Liverpool he would be able to watch the manufacture of Hornby Trains, in addition to that of Meccano. Then I told him the story of Hornby Trains and explained how they had grown in popularity until to-day they vie with Meccano for first place as the world's most popular toy.

"Say!" he exclaimed. "They must be dandy trains to do that!"

As we said good-bye, he told me that, although he had met kings and princes, had been entertained as no visiting potentate is entertained, had had gifts of all kinds lavished upon him, his greatest thrill had come to him on his visit to the Meccano factory.

THE END

Cleaning a Giant Locomotive:

The "*Flying Scotsman's*" Four Hours' Toilet

WE all generally think of such fine locomotives as the "*Flying Scotsman*," "*The Centenary*" and other famous members of the L.N.E.R. "Pacifics," only as speeding between King's Cross and Edinburgh. We picture them in our mind's-eye hauling trains of enormous length, and being turned round at their destination to start off on the return journey without loss of time.

There is another side to the picture, however, and this is the "toilet" of these giant locomotives—that is the preparation they have to undergo before every long-distance run. They receive this attention in the Locomotive Depôts of which the one at King's Cross is typical of many other similar Locomotive Depôts scattered all over the country.

The "Flying Scotsman" at Home

It is always interesting to visit the King's Cross Depôt, for here some of the "Pacifics" are housed after their return from Scotland. A scene of great activity prevails. Engines are to be seen almost everywhere, some coming in, others going out. The difference between those coming off and those going on duty is as remarkable as, and quite equal to, the difference between workmen going to their work and workmen after the day's toil.

Some of the engines crawling about the yard, just off duty after racing to King's Cross from York or Leeds, seem so tired as to be almost falling asleep. They pause only to report themselves at the yard foreman's office, and whistling a sleepy "good-night" to everybody, contentedly steam off for a well-earned rest. Before leaving the depôt again they will receive attention from many attendants.

In these depôts the monster "Pacifics" are very submissive creatures. The "*Flying Scotsman,*" generally seen hissing and snorting with ill-concealed impatience at the head of his train, now stands humbly in his shed, with a small bar-boy in his fire-box and two men beneath him with a flickering lamp. Here we may climb into the cab or even crawl beneath the monster boiler. Standing in front of this towering mass of steel, we may imagine with a shudder what would happen to us if this 150-ton loco were approaching at 60 miles an hour!

Courtesy] [*L.N.E.R.*
The Driver screws home the fastener of the smoke-box cover (L.N.E.R. No. 2544 "Lemberg.") If this is not fastened tightly, the engine loses efficiency

Barrow-loads of Scale

Over four hours' preparation by a host of workmen is required to get the "*Flying Scotsman*" ready for his race to the north. In the giant locomotive's toilet, and in the attention necessary to get the best possible effect, not even the most particular sister of any reader of the "*M.M.*" could be more careful before going to a dance!

The loco first receives attention from boiler-smiths, fire-boys, and fire-lighters. To set the fire going, two or three scoops of live coal, each weighing 40 or 50 lbs., are thrown into the fire-box, and by the time the driver comes on duty the boiler has a head of 80 lbs. of steam. When the driver and his mate arrive they oil up, take water, and put on the finishing touches.

In addition to the regular routine, as outlined above, the boiler must be thoroughly cleaned every 2½ days. Barrow loads of scale (or fur something like that found in the ordinary household kettle) are removed. There are 3,800 ft. of internal pipes on a "Pacific" and soot and scale quickly collect, considerably reducing the power and also causing a greater consumption of coal per mile than is the case when the pipes are clean.

At King's Cross the cleaning of the pipes is done by an ingenious washing-out appliance consisting of a system of pipes, filters and pumps. The appliance is actuated by the steam remaining in the boiler after a long run, the steam being condensed into water and used under pressure. On the average, about 20 minutes is required to clean out the pipes by this washing appliance. Every day scores of locomotives are cleaned in this manner, and the use of this washing appliance results in a considerable saving of time, as before it was installed it was necessary to wait until the locos had cooled before the pipes could be dealt with.

The Importance of Lubrication

The oiling of these hard-working locomotives is, of course, a most important part of their preparation for a long run. All railway companies are large consumers of oil of all kinds, but two kinds of oil are principally used for the "Pacific" locos. One is for lubricating the axle boxes, valve motions and other working parts and consists of a mixture of rape oil and mineral oil. The other, for lubricating the interior of the valve chests and cylinders, has to stand a very high temperature and is a heavy mineral oil containing a certain proportion of fats. Rape oil is the most expensive ingredient, and, as might be expected, the amount used is much greater in express passenger engine lubrication than in the case of other locomotives.

The oil is delivered in bulk to the Locomotive Depôt by contract. There it is stored in large tanks, being drawn off and carefully measured as required, each driver receiving a certain ration according to his day's run.

Courtesy] [L.N.E.R.

Cleaning the outside of the boiler of the "*Flying Scotsman*"

Lubrication: Old and New Style

On the L.N.E.R. passenger engines the consumption of lubricating oil for axle boxes works out at about 5 pints to every 100 miles. The consumption of lubricating oil for the cylinders is approximately $1\frac{3}{4}$ pints for every 100 miles.

In the early days of railways when there was considerably more play in the working parts, cotton waste and sacking soaked in oil were often used to assist in lubrication. It was often necessary for the oil-can to be freely applied during a journey and if necessary the train was pulled up for the purpose of allowing the driver to lubricate the working parts!

The task of the driver of the present day in the matter of lubrication is very different from that of the drivers of the earliest engines, such as "*Locomotion No. 1.*" Although automatic lubricators relieve him of a good deal of anxiety with regard to oiling, it continues to be necessary for every working part to constantly be examined in order to ensure steady running.

Reclaiming Oil from Waste

Climbing round the frame while the engine is in motion has, of course, now been done away with—much to the disappointment of many small boys whose sole ambition in life was to climb along the frame of the Scotch Express, when travelling at over 60 miles an hour, with an oil-can in one hand and a handful of cotton waste in the other!

The modern driver still carries a handful of waste but this is used to remove surplus oil. At the end of the shift, the waste is collected with other waste rags and sent to the oil rag laundries. Here centrifugal oil extractors, working on the principle of the steam turbine, reduce the viscosity of the oil. A mixture, which consists principally of oil and matter, is thrown out and carried through pipes into tanks. Approximately 50% of the oil is extracted by this first process. Should by any chance a drop of oil escape the centrifugal action of the machine and remain in the cloth, it will then have to face a solution of caustic soda and boiling water.

It is surprising to learn that every year the L.N.E.R. oil rag laundries save 40,000 gallons of valuable oil in this manner! The reclaimed liquid is not wasted but is placed in catch-pits and tallow is added to give consistency, the mixture then forming wagon grease.

From Cleaner to Driver

Although the cleaning of locomotives may appear to be a dirty and decidedly unromantic occupation, yet it is from the ranks of cleaners that the first-class passenger express drivers are recruited. During his engine-cleaning period the future driver lays the foundation of the expert knowledge that is necessary to all drivers in order that they may run to time and yet with perfect safety. The engine cleaner works his way up through the various grades of shunting fireman, local goods fireman, main line fireman and express passenger train fireman, and before attaining the

Cleaning the inside of the smoke-box of L.N.E.R. No. 4474, "*Victor Wild*"

grade of driver has to pass quite a severe examination in regard to the mechanism and working of the engine.

In a large engine shed it is obviously necessary to lay down strict regulations in order to avoid accidents. These regulations vary to some extent on different lines, but in the main they are the same. When a locomotive has to enter a shed it is first brought to a standstill outside and is not allowed to enter until all men who may be working on the road on which it will run have been warned of its arrival. When adequate warning has been given a loco must not enter at more than a crawling speed, an alarm whistle being sounded in the meantime.

Once inside the shed the loco is not immediately left to its own devices, but the cylinder cocks must be opened, the hand brakes must be put on hard, the regulator shut and the reversing ever put out of gear. Cleaners are expressly forbidden to move engines in steam, and this can only be done by a driver, or by a fireman instructed and accompanied by a driver, or by the shed foreman, shed shunter or other specially authorised men.

Without regulations of this kind accidents in engine sheds undoubtedly would occur very frequently, but as it is, mishaps are comparatively rare and when they do occur it is almost always as the result of neglect of some rule.

Cleaning and Oiling the Giant's Wheels

Inside an Engine Shed

The engine shed bears the same relation to the locomotive as the stable to the horse or the garage to the motor car. Roughly speaking engine sheds are of two types, "straight road," having several parallel roads passing through the building, or "turn-table," containing turn-tables from which lead roads connecting the tables together and also leading from each table outside the shed. Just as in the case of a garage, pits are excavated between the metals in order to enable men to work below the locos when required. An interesting feature of an engine shed is the smoke troughs in the roof. These are arranged in such a manner that the smoke from any engine within the shed, no matter in what position this may be standing, is carried away.

The actual sequence of engine shed operations varies in different places but as a rule the loco, having arrived at the shed, is taken charge of by an authorised man and the driver and fireman book off duty. The loco is taken towards the coal stage pit to be filled up in its turn and during the waiting period the smoke-box ashes are shovelled out and dropped alongside or removed by a pneumatic ejector. When the loco has received its due amount of coal it is taken over a "fire-dropping" pit where the fire is either cleaned or dropped. If the fire is to be cleaned, the clinker and dirt is shovelled out and dumped alongside and the ashes are raked from the ashpan into the pit. When this process is complete a small fire is kept burning so that the engine may be ready for service quickly when required. If, on the other hand, the boiler is to cool down before the next spell of duty, the fire is dropped, which means that it is shovelled out entirely. Subsequently the boiler is washed out as already described.

All locos are apt to develop slight defects. Whenever a driver becomes aware that any part of his engine is not working as it should he makes a note of the fact and during its stay in the shed the engine is taken in hand by fitters, boiler smiths, etc., who have been informed of the defect and promptly proceed to remove it. In addition, all locos go through more extensive examinations at stated intervals. For instance, smoke-boxes, water gauges, brake gear and pressure gauges may be examined monthly and safety valves yearly. The boiler will be examined monthly by the shed staff and at longer intervals by an inspector of the running department, while pistons and valves are examined after runs of from 12,000 to 20,000 miles, according to the nature of the loco and its work. These periodical examinations are carried out to schedule whether a loco has developed any obvious defects or not.

Newcomers Require Most Attention

The locomotive superintendent at King's Cross Depôt has 90 engines to look after, and they require each day 600 tons of coal and thousands of gallons of water.

"I wouldn't mind if they all thrived on it," he told the writer recently, "but like most human beings they suffer now and then from indigestion! No. 4444 over there came home stuffed-up on Tuesday, but she is better now and may go out for a little exercise to-morrow."

"But the new arrivals, such as the '*Flying Scotsman,*' surely don't need much attention?" I asked.

"Don't they though!" replied the superintendent. "I'd like to tell you that it takes a loco about three months to get into its stride. Look at 2736 in the corner there. She was new only 10 weeks ago and has been a real handful ever since."

"What about your 'oldest inhabitants?'" I asked.

"Oh! they don't give us much trouble. They require very little attention on the whole, but after they have knocked off 90,000 miles or so we give them a thorough overhaul. They're just going to start on one over there."

(*Continued on page 328*)

little thought to realise that with a shutter speed of 1/25th of a second snapshots of rapidly moving objects, at anything like close quarters, are impossible.

Moving Objects and Slow Shutters

Assuming that we are confined to such a shutter and that we are determined to obtain snaps of moving objects, there is only one way out of the difficulty. This is to snap the moving object from a distance and subsequently enlarge the tiny image thus obtained. By adopting this method some quite surprisingly sharp snapshots of objects moving at considerable speed may be obtained with the cheapest cameras, even when fitted with the most rudimentary lenses.

A further point to remember is that a longer exposure may be given for objects moving directly towards the operator than for objects moving obliquely towards or from the camera. Unless our shutter is capable of extremely high speeds a broadside view should not be attempted. Certain subjects are, of course, practically impossible in any circumstances with a slow speed shutter.

Some readers may like to try the following experiment when taking objects that are moving across the field of view. Hold the camera firmly at about waist height and with your finger on the shutter-release, move your body and the camera in the direction in which the object is travelling, at the same time releasing the shutter. The effect will be that although the background will come out blurred, owing to the movement of the camera during the exposure, the main object of the photograph is much less likely to be blurred than if the exposure were made in the ordinary manner. The faster the object is travelling, and the nearer it is to the camera, the quicker should be the turning movement at the moment of exposure.

Next month we shall consider another extremely important and interesting point—depth of focus.

26th Photographic Contest

The subject of this month's contest will be "Reflections." One of the most fascinating photographic subjects to a beginner—or for that matter to many camera enthusiasts who have left behind the novitiate stage—is a silent pool of water with a placid mirror-like surface, reflecting brilliantly the images of surrounding trees and buildings, and there are few scenes, taken as a class, that can yield such delightful photographs.

Reflections however are not confined to motionless meres; more often the most pleasing effects are those obtained from a pool, the surface of which is just ruffled by a lightly moving breeze; or from the surface of a town pavement just after rain. But best of all is the stretch of wet sand photographed as the sun is sinking. Then the sand gleams with reflected glories of the sky. A sky screen used with the lens is a necessity for work of this type but the beauty of a successful attempt amply repays the additional care required.

The usual two sections will be held, A for those over 16, B for those under 16 and prizes of photographic material or Meccano products (to be chosen by the winners) to the value of £1-1s. and 10/6 respectively will be awarded to the first and second best entries in each section. Closing date, 31st May. Overseas, 30th September.

Cleaning a Locomotive—
(*Continued from page* 292)

I walked over to the place indicated and watched whilst mechanics penetrated the inner recesses of the smoke-box. Meanwhile a loud hammering commenced in the very vitals of the engine—the firebox—and to crown all the loco was being weighed at the same time!

Weighing a Giant Loco

No giant scales are necessary for this. Instead the work is done by a wonderfully sensitive hydraulic jack, to which is attached an indicator dial.

Placing this compact instrument in a square pit alongside the line, the giant monster of the rail, now steamless and without power, was slowly pushed back towards the waiting lifter until one of the main driving wheels was directly opposite the weigher. "A bit more," shouted the foreman, and the pushing tank loco strained again to push the inert engine an inch or two further.

"Stop!"

The wheel was directly opposite the weigher, and with a quick movement of a handle the giant was made to lift its wheel as a bear would lift its paw. A workman quickly passed a steel rod between the wheel and the rail to make sure that it was clear.

"Nineteen tons. Next wheel!" shouted the foreman. The tanker came again into action and the operation was repeated. Each wheel was weighed in turn, the total making up the exact weight of the engine as a whole—nearly 150 tons.

Weighing each wheel of a locomotive separately is a valuable guide to the railwaymen, for if the weight is not distributed correctly on the individual wheels the engine will "ride badly" and lose time, or in extreme cases even become derailed.

Electricity—(*continued from page* 305)

Immediately the connection is completed the director is cut out of the circuit and is available for use in putting through another connection on another line. It will be seen from the diagram, where the speaking connections are shown across the upper portion, that the director does not enter into the speaking portion of the circuit in any way. It merely takes the place of the human operators and, like them, when the call is completed it is no longer required and is therefore available for use by other subscribers. This, of course, greatly reduces the amount of equipment required to deal with a given volume of traffic.

* * * *

In the last seven issues of the "*M.M.*" we have traced the invention, progress and working of the telephone from the early days of Bell and Edison. We have seen how the receiver and the microphone were developed from their first forms and we have seen exactly how the subscriber's circuits, and the exchange circuits, both manual and automatic, are arranged and how they operate. It is interesting to notice that in 1910 there were 10½ million telephones in the world, in 1914 14¾ millions, and in 1920 19¾ millions. This is an increase of nearly one million a year, so that if this rate has been maintained during the last six years, that is from 1920 to 1926, there will in all probability be about 25 million telephones in the world to-day.

A Giant Planing Machine

For Sydney Harbour Bridge Work

We are able to illustrate an unusually large plate-edge planing machine, which has been built by Messrs. Smith Brothers & Co. Ltd., Glasgow, to the order of Messrs. Dorman, Long & Co. Ltd., for use in connection with the Sydney Harbour Bridge contract.

As our readers know, this bridge is now under construction. It is to be the largest arch bridge in the world, the total length of the arch and approach spans being 3,770 ft. Necessarily, there is a great amount of steel work in it, and the plates, girders, etc., are generally of massive proportions. In order to facilitate the work, special machines, of which this giant planing machine is one, have had to be designed.

The machine is designed to plane the edges of high tensile steel plates up to 66 ft. in length by 2¼ in. in thickness. A direct-coupled motor provides the drive and one of the most remarkable features of the machine is the simplicity of the control and the rack drive.

The motor, of 40 brake horse-power at 480 revolutions per minute, is fixed to the saddle that carries the tool, as also is the stop and start switch. Attached to the saddle is a platform from which the operator can start up, stop, and reverse the motor in either direction. Within easy reach are the hand wheels for the vertical and horizontal feeds, and a hand lever for tilting the tool-box, so that the operator has full control of the machine without having to leave the platform. The master-switch is fitted inside one of the large housings at the end of the machine, and is operated through a kicker bar—to be seen at the front of the bed—by a foot lever on the saddle platform.

The tool has two cutting edges, and is carried in a box which is tilted by hand horizontally at each end of the plate, so that the tool is able to cut on the forward as well as on the backward stroke.

Current to the motor is supplied from wires running along the top front side of the girder with which roller collectors make contact. The motor drives through three trains of gear-wheels on to a large pinion. This meshes with a rack fixed to the underside and running practically the full length of the table.

All the gearing, including the rack, are made of steel, the teeth being machine-cut from the solid. Change gearing is provided to give two cutting speeds, namely, 25 ft. and 40 ft. per minute. The machine is arranged in such a manner that, in the event of the trip gear failing to operate properly, or should the current supply fail when the saddle is nearing one of the housings, there is no danger of a smash as a result of overrun. The saddle in these circumstances would simply travel on until it left the rack and came to rest about 2 in. short of the housing.

Each housing is 24 in. in depth and the overall length of the machine is 78 ft. 10 in. The motor traversing the saddle is larger than is necessary, but the size adopted was chosen for the sake of standardisation and interchangeability purposes. In some recent tests, the tool was fed downwards, and cuts ¾ in. in depth by ⅛ in. feed, were easily carried continuously at a cutting speed of 40 ft. per minute.

For holding the plate down on the table, 22 hydraulic cylinders are provided on the top side of the built steel girder. This girder, 7 ft. 2 in. in depth, is jointed in the middle. In addition to the hydraulic cylinders, 21 hand screws are fitted to the under side of the beam alternately with the cylinders, but these screws are only used when water is not available.

It is interesting to learn that for the same contract, Messrs. Smith Bros. & Co. Ltd., recently shipped to Sydney a large single-ended machine with adjustable centres for bending and straightening rolled steel H-beams, measuring up to 24 in. by 7½ in. and 100 lb. in section.

No doubt at a later date we shall hear something more of the performance of these machines and of the important part they are to play in the construction of the world's greatest bridge.

Largest Arch Bridge in the World

Over 50,000 Tons of Steel to Span Sydney Harbour

As it would have been with the original design for a cantilever bridge

THE suggestion to bridge Sydney Harbour seems to have been made first in 1815—the year of Waterloo—when Francis H. Greenway, then Government Architect, brought a scheme before the notice of Governor Macquarie. Some years later, in a letter to the press, Greenway wrote :—" . . . in the event of the bridge being thrown across from Dawes' Battery to the North Shore, a town would be built on that shore, and would have formed with these buildings a grand whole that would have indeed surprised anyone on entering the harbour, and have given an idea of strength and magnificence that would have reflected credit and glory on the Colony and the Mother Country."

It is evident that the idea was the subject of a good deal of discussion even in those early days, for there is preserved in the Government Records at Sydney a minute of 1875 in which the Under Secretary for Works expresses the opinion that "No doubt the bridge would soon be an accomplished fact." Obviously this gentleman was an optimist!

Many times since then politicians and statesmen have not only hoped that the bridge would soon be an "accomplished fact," but in their election speeches have even gone to the extent of promising their supporters its immediate construction!

The first recorded design seems to have been prepared in 1857 by one Peter Henderson and at a more favourable time it is possible that his bridge might have been built. His scheme could not survive the local opposition, however, based upon the fear that if two bullock wagons happened to meet in the centre the structure might collapse!

Shall it be a Bridge or a Tunnel?

The question of a bridge was brought up repeatedly at intervals as the years went on, but always without practical result. From time to time engineers were consulted and architects prepared drawings, but the actual bridge remained as far off as ever. Year by year the city of Sydney was developing at an enormous rate and the necessity of doing something in regard to improving cross-harbour communication became increasingly evident.

In 1912 a Public Works Committee was appointed to consider the whole question of connecting the two shores either by bridge or tunnel, and to ascertain the estimated cost of whichever undertaking they decided to be the best. The idea of a tunnel or sub-

As it would have been with the cantilever bridge. The south approach, showing piers and abutments

As it will be—the alternative arch bridge in position, and dominating the Harbour

way was very popular at first, but it was abandoned when it was realised that a tunnel beneath the harbour would mean that no vessels having a draught of more than 38 or 39 ft. would be able to enter the roadstead. On the other hand the lie of the surrounding land, which rises rapidly on both sides of the harbour, was particularly suited to the construction of a bridge, and in addition the distance would be three-quarters of a mile less by bridge than by subway and the inevitable gradients would be much easier.

Finally on 18th July 1913, the Committee, having examined carefully all the schemes submitted to them, passed a resolution advising the construction of a cantilever bridge to join Sydney and North Sydney. The plans recommended for the proposed bridge were those prepared by Dr. J. J. C. Bradfield, M.E., M.I.C.E., who at that time was Chief Engineer of the Metropolitan Railway Construction, Public Works Department, New South Wales. Subsequently the New South Wales Government appointed Dr. Bradfield to be Chief Engineer for the Sydney Harbour Bridge.

The Suggested Cantilever Bridge

The original plans for this cantilever bridge, afterwards superseded by the arch bridge now under construction, were for steel cantilevers spaced 98 ft. 6 in. apart, centre to centre, with shore and harbour arms each 500 ft. in length. The harbour arms were to support a 600 ft. central span and the clear span from centre to centre of main piers was to be 1,600 ft.

The clear and suspended spans were to be " M " braced, with each main panel divided into four, the cross girders being pitched 37 ft. 6 in. and 50 ft. apart, and cantilevered beyond the main girders to carry the railway and the footways. Wind-bracing and sway-bracings were also to be provided.

The three spans of the southern approach were to consist of four " M " type deck trusses with subdivided panels, 204 ft. in length, centre to centre, and spaced 33 ft. apart transversely. The three spans of the northern approach were to have been similar to those on the southern, except that the former were to be on a curve of eight chains radius. The total length of the main bridge and approaches was to have been 3,810 ft.

Thus the matter stood on the outbreak of war. The scheme had then perforce to be postponed, and the ferry boat remained as before the only means of crossing the harbour.

By 1921 the traffic across the harbour had increased from 16½ million to 42 million passengers, and it was admitted on all sides that something must be done at once. The bridge question was reopened and in the following year the Government of New South Wales passed an Act authorising the construction of a bridge to cross the harbour in one span, at a height sufficient to allow the passage of the largest ocean liners.

Already Meccano enthusiasts are building models of the Sydney Harbour Bridge. This one, built by Everard J. Earl of Sydney, is strong enough to bear the weight of its builder, his sister and his father, showing that the model is constructed on correct engineering principles

Decision to Build an Arch Bridge

The general design and exact position of the bridge, together with the dimensions, etc., were defined by a specification drawn up by Dr. Bradfield, and competitive tenders were invited from a number of engineering firms in all parts of the world. Two British firms—Sir Wm. Arrol & Co. Ltd., the builders of the Forth Bridge, and Dorman, Long & Co. Ltd., of Middlesbrough—were given a 10 per cent. preference over any foreign rivals, but in spite of this the competition was very keen. After careful examination of the tenders and designs, and after repeated Cabinet meetings, the Government came to a decision and in February 1924 it was announced that the contract had been awarded to Dorman, Long & Co. Ltd., who had submitted seven alternative tenders, both for arch and cantilever bridges.

The successful tender was for an arch bridge with a central suspended span to extend across the harbour from Dawes' Point to Milson's Point. As has already been mentioned, the Government had leaned very much towards the idea of a cantilever bridge—in fact, the original specifications called for a cantilever solely. The suggestion for an arch bridge was advanced partly on the ground that the cost would be appreciably less, and also because it was believed that the arch type would present a more pleasing appearance. This, of course, is certainly an important factor to our Australian cousins, who proudly claim that Sydney Harbour is the most beautiful in the world.

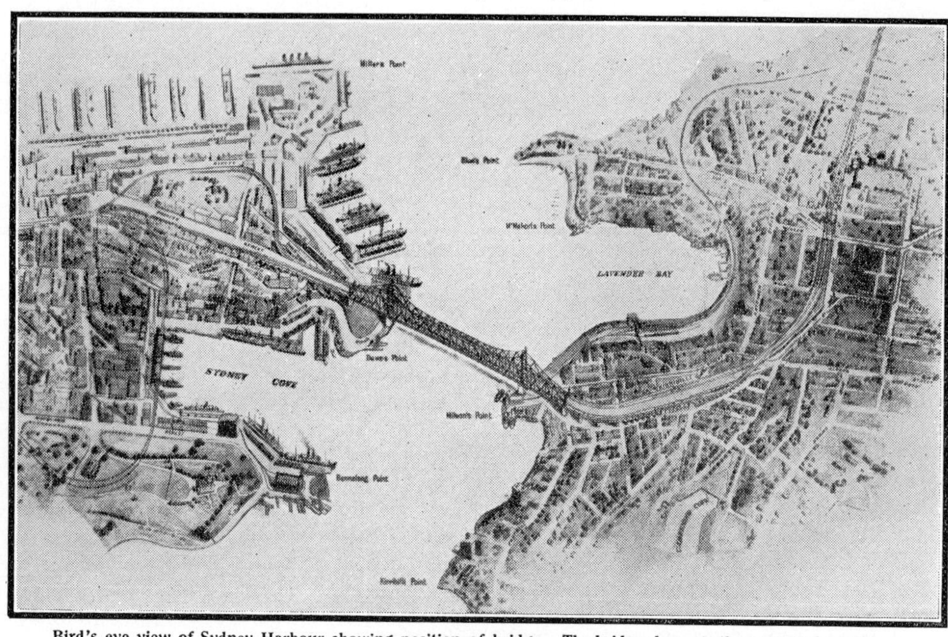

Bird's eye view of Sydney Harbour showing position of bridge. The bridge shown is the suggested cantilever, now superseded by an arch bridge

To be Completed in 1931

As the highest point of the arch will be 450 ft. above high-water level, some idea may be gained of how enormously the bridge will dominate the harbour. In selecting the arch type the authorities have ensured that the traveller entering Sydney Harbour from the sea will be met by the sight of a giant bridge well worthy to rank with the finest of any other country in the world.

The Sydney Harbour Bridge will be by far the largest arch bridge in the world, its nearest rival (Hell Gate Bridge, New York) having a span of about 1,000 ft. It will, indeed, be the third largest bridge in the world, irrespective of type, the two larger being, of course, the Quebec and the Forth cantilever bridges.

The contract stipulates that constructional operations are to be carried on simultaneously on both sides of the harbour, and the time limit for the work is fixed at six years from the date of notification of acceptance of the tender, unless, of course, a special extension of time is granted by the Australian Government.

Materials to be Used

The question of a steady and assured supply of materials is invariably of first importance in the carrying out of so vast an undertaking. In this respect Dorman, Long & Co. Ltd. are particularly fortunate, for some years ago they established constructional works at Sydney and Melbourne. Although the greater part of the heavy steel plates used will be manufactured at the contractors' own works in England, the terms of the contract require that certain of the lighter materials shall be of Australian origin. In all there will be over 50,300 tons of steelwork.

The bridge will have a total width of 150 ft. and will carry four lines of railway of 4 ft. $8\frac{1}{2}$ in. gauge, a road 57 ft. in width, and two footpaths each 10 ft. in width. It will consist of two hinged spandrel braced main trusses, set in vertical plane and spaced 98 ft. 6 in. apart from centre to centre, the clear span, centre to centre, being 1,650 ft. The web system will consist of verticals and diagonals forming 50 ft. panels, the cross girders being pitched 50 ft. apart and cantilevered beyond the main trusses to carry one railway track and a 10 ft. pathway.

Granite to come from Australian Quarries

The total length of the arch and bridge spans is to be 3,770 ft., and the height to the top of the arch will be 450 ft. above high water. The central 600 ft. span will have a clearance of 170 ft. above the water at mean high tides, so that practically all large ships—with the exception of such vessels as the "*Olympic,*" whose masts are 202 ft. in height—will be able to pass beneath the bridge on their way to the docks. On each side of the central span the headway will be less, as it follows the railway grade.

The foreshores have been reclaimed and 40,000 cubic yards of earth are now being excavated to make room for the piers, the foundations for which are being laid on the solid rock. These piers, as well as the anchor piers and abutments of the approach spans, are to be constructed of concrete or re-inforced concrete, faced with granite ashlar masonry. Ornamental portals are to be built at each end of the main bridge.

The masonry pylons are to be 93 ft. by 50 ft. at deck level, tapering to 75 ft. at their summit which will reach 285 ft. above high-water level.

For the pylons, piers and abutments, granite is being obtained from Moruya, on the South Coast of New South Wales. Here the quarries, which are being worked by the contractors, will produce 30,000 cubic yards of granite for facings and will keep 150 men employed for five years. The southern approaches of the bridge will absorb 50,000 cubic yards of sand and 100,000 cubic yards of granite material. Over 1,000,000 ft. super. of ironbark, grey gun and Oregon pine will be required, and also 30,000 tons of cement.

The deck of the bridge will be very firmly laid as it has to stand very heavy strains from both road and railway traffic. The roadway will consist of $\frac{3}{8}$ in. buckled plates, and the footway of $\frac{5}{16}$ in. buckled plates, supported on transverse rolled steel joists resting on steel stringers. Coke concrete will then be laid to a thickness of 3 in. from the top of the buckled plates.

(*To be continued*)

With the "*Flying Scotsman*"

A Short Account of a Ride on the Footplate of this Famous Locomotive

As our readers no doubt know, permission to ride on the footplate of a passenger locomotive is only given in very exceptional circumstances. More particularly is this the case with the main line expresses, so the writer regarded himself as particularly fortunate in being able to make a trip behind the "*Flying Scotsman*" a short time ago. This article is a short account of his experiences.

* * *

"Good morning, Mr. Driver!"

There was such a difference in our ages and such a steely look in his eye that I felt the "Mr." was very necessary! We were standing at the end of the platform where it slopes down to the rails. The fireman was on top of the tender slogging away and hammering the largest lumps of coal to make them small enough to go into the firebox of the giant "Pacific."

The "Flying Scotsman" at Speed

Away along the platform the guard's whistle shrilled its starting message, and thrusting a clean rag into my hand, "Mr. Driver" positively bundled me on to the magic carpet that was to travel over 100 miles without a stop. "Carpet," did I say? Rather a steel shelf, bounded by a wonderful arrangement of wheels and levers, a very hot furnace, several look-out windows, and five tons of coal.

I quickly grasped a projection, which action caused the driver to eye me suspiciously, for it so happened I had taken hold of the knob of his private locker! As we majestically drew out of the station my first impression was that of an irresistible power suddenly released. "Pulse!... Pulse!!... Pulse!!!... Throb!... Throb!!... Throb!!!..." The steam was doing its work, as the driver with his hand on the regulator handle coaxed the mechanism into motion.

Nor was the fireman idle, for the hungry furnace already demanded to be fed. It seemed to me to be quite hot enough, but steadying himself with a firm stance, the fireman swung shovelfuls of coal from the tender through the firebox door, where it was instantly engulfed. Six, seven, eight times the shovel went backwards and forwards, while the train gradually gathered speed.

What a depth of understanding there is between driver and fireman! Isolated from the rest of the world—even from the comfortable carriages behind they are separated by tons of coal—they live in a world of their own. A nod indicates the important fact that some specially vital signal or particular position on the line is clear. A wave of the hand conveys a wealth of meaning that makes words superfluous, even were they possible amid the steadily rising roar of the engine.

Interior of Cab of "Flying Scotsman"

Fields flash by and bridges whip overhead. We enter a wonderfully straight piece of line that no doubt has something to do with the driver's sudden sociability. I am still holding the knob of the driver's locker like grim death! He crosses the cab to where I am standing, comes close beside me and takes out a large bottle containing a dark looking liquid. Quickly taking a drink, he hands the bottle to me, and I am thankful to moisten my already parched lips with cold tea. Driving is a dry business and cold tea has been proved to be the best thirst quencher obtainable.

By this time our speed was approaching 65 miles an hour and low overhead was a continual stream of smoke and steam from the funnel.

To put one's face or hand outside the sheltering cab was like cutting it with a knife, and yet the driver and his fireman went about their accustomed tasks as if we had been standing still.

Motioning me from my protecting corner, the fireman shouted the one word "Water." Far ahead on the track, I caught a glimpse of two narrow ribbons of water between the rails —the water troughs from which we were to pick up water. Rapidly turning a handle, without slacking speed in any way, the driver lowered a scoop below the tender into the trough which had now been reached. In far less time than it takes to write, we had picked up over 2,000 gallons of water and the tender and footplate, to say nothing of the outside of the first carriage were drenched. It was cooling, but uncomfortable. Reversing the wheel, the driver completed his task and turned to his accustomed crouching attitude beside the window, peering ahead.

The "Flying Scotsman" from the roof of King's Cross Station

The fireman, after coaling again, turned the water injector handle, but the steam pressure indicator dial would not keep up. So he produced a tremendously long poker and began to poke the very vitals of the throbbing mass ahead of us. Returning this long poker to its place on the tender, I noticed that although only in the furnace about 30 seconds, the tip was white-hot.

Stretching his hand upward the driver pulled a chain. The whistle shrieked, incidentally covering us with steam and spray, and we roared into a tunnel.

It was pitch darkness, except for the searchlight glow from the firebox. Steam, fumes, smoke, coal dust swirled round us until it was almost impossible to see across the cab. Surely this must be the end of all things, I thought. After what seemed interminable minutes, we rushed out into sunshine again as quickly as we had plunged into the darkness. Once again the driver passed the cold tea round, and I took a deep draught, after which I felt better!

Seizing the regulator handle with both hands, the driver swung it over to the shut position. A sound of hissing air—the brakes were being applied—and slowly, very slowly, we slackened speed. Far ahead on the horizon was my destination station, and rapidly we approached it. The battle was over—the race against time was won. The wild throbbing monster was tamed, as we carefully came to a stop just beyond a crowd of people who were waiting to board the train.

With a smile the driver turned to me and asked me how I had enjoyed it. At least I think that is what he said, but for 10 minutes I could hear nothing, so sudden was the silence after the noise and throbbing of the run. Bidding me a hasty adieu as I stood on the platform, he turned to his regulator again and soon steamed out of sight.

Searching out an adjacent wash and brush-up I caught sight of a strange figure in the looking glass, for all the world like a nigger minstrel. Three pieces of soap, two towels, one scrubbing brush soon made a difference, but it will be weeks before I can get rid of every trace of my footplate run. I had covered only 100 miles, and the driver and fireman do hundreds of miles almost every day of their lives! "Hats off" to these splendid fellows!

Lives of Famous Engineers—

(*Continued from page* 485)

commencing the preliminary operations, and very soon he had nearly 400 men engaged upon the work at six different points. The main difficulty lay in making the road practicable for heavy vehicles, and his plan was as follows. He had great quantities of heather pulled from the surrounding ground and bound up into small bundles of a size that could be conveniently grasped with the hand. These bundles were placed close together in rows in the direction of the line of road, and afterwards other similar bundles were laid down transversely upon them, and the whole was well pressed down. Stones and gravel were then led on in wagons and spread over the bundles, thus producing a firm and level road.

The operations were watched with keen interest by a crowd of spectators who had come in full expectation of seeing both horses and wagons disappear in the bog. These expectations were not realised, however, and when the horses drawing the first wagon reached firm ground again in safety, they were greeted with loud cheers. The whole length across the marshes was completed in the same manner, and this section proved one of the best and driest parts of the whole road.

Those who read our story of the life of George Stephenson (*"M.M."* January, March, April and May, 1924) will notice that Metcalf's method of building this road across the marshes was the same as that subsequently adopted by Stephenson in carrying the Manchester and Liverpool railway across Chat Moss.

Road-making for 30 years

Metcalf continued road-making for over 30 years. His last road was between Haslingden and Accrington, with a branch road to Bury. This proved one of the most difficult works he had undertaken, and when he brought it to a successful conclusion, after two strenuous years, he found himself a loser on the contract by exactly £40. He completed this road in 1792 at the age of 75, and afterwards retired to Spofforth, near Wetherby, where he spent his remaining years on a small farm. He died peacefully in 1810 in his 93rd year, leaving behind him a wonderful record of triumph over one of the most terrible of all physical disabilities.

BRITISH TOYS FOR BRITISH BOYS

Size of Car : 11 ins. × 5 ins. × 4½ ins.

The ROLLS-ROYCE OF TOYLAND

Car only 10/-, carriage paid U.K.
"Brenco" Garage only 2/6, carriage paid U.K.

SPECIFICATION :— Chassis built of heavy sheet metal. Unbreakable Clockwork Movement under Bonnet wound up by Starting Handle as in a Real Car. Transmission by propeller shaft driving direct on the back axle by Gear and Pinion. Steering and Brake Control operated from Driving Position. Body of beautifully enamelled sheet metal finished Red. Adjustable Wind Screen. Plated Bonnet hinged to open correctly. Wheels detachable at hub. Spare on Running Board. Detachable rubber tyres. Garage of Sheet Metal with double doors enamelled in colours. All parts replaceable. Driving Licence and Spare Parts. List with each Car.

Entirely British and built to last for years.

CAR COMPLETE WITH GARAGE - - 12/6 Post Free U.K.

OVERSEAS EXPORT PACKED IN STRONG BOX. CAR COMPLETE WITH GARAGE £1 CARRIAGE PAID THE WORLD OVER.

Telegrams: "Brenco" Manchester.

THE NEW BRENCO MANUFACTURING CO.
(Dept. M.M.), 63-67, Great Jackson Street, Hulme, MANCHESTER, England

Telephone: City 5090

A REAL FLYING MODEL
British Patents, G.B. 171,499—G.B. 188,523
United States Patent 1377867.

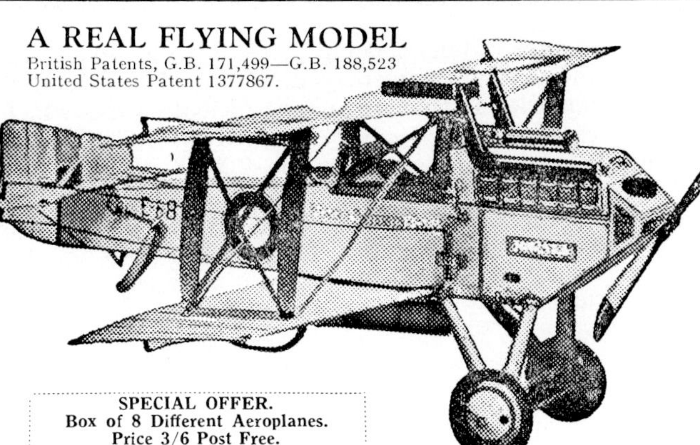

SPECIAL OFFER.
Box of 8 Different Aeroplanes.
Price 3/6 Post Free.

Build This Fine Model Aeroplane

Boys ! Here is the very thing for you. This model has all the parts and controls that you'll find on the big planes. Elevators, ailerons, machine-guns, pitot tubes, windscreens and even a miniature dashboard with dummy instruments, gauges, etc. Real elastic shock absorbers are fitted to the landing wheels and tail skid.

When you have built up the model you can make it do everything that a real plane can do.

Size of Model 12″, Span 13″ Long.

Complete Set of Cardboard Parts printed in colours, together with all necessary Elastic, Wood, Wire and Book of Instructions.

PRICE 1/- (Post 4d. extra)

Catalogue of other Models. Price 2d., post free.

Send P.O. off to-night to

WILLIAM E. APPLEBY (N/C) & CO.
(Dept. K.), 217, Jesmond Road, Newcastle-on-Tyne.

BOYS! Buy Your Meccano FROM

ODD & SONS

111, HIGH STREET, SUTTON, Surrey
(Corner of West Street)

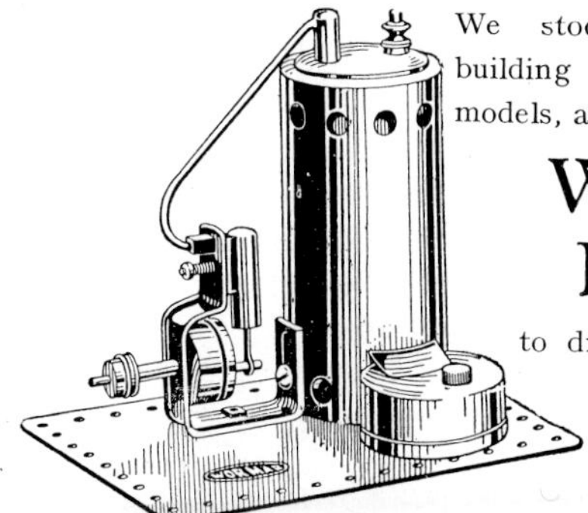

We stock every part for building all the new Meccano models, also the wonderful little

Wormar Engine

to drive your models.

Prices from

5/11

FULL RANGE OF

HORNBY TRAINS

(CLOCKWORK AND ELECTRIC)

Be sure to call at ODD'S to inspect the New Control System

Britain's Most Powerful Loco

For Express Passenger Traffic:—The "*Lord Nelson*"

IN order to cope with the steadily increasing weight of express passenger traffic on the Southern Railway, a new locomotive, designed by Mr. R. E. L. Maunsell, Chief Mechanical Engineer for the Southern Railway, has been built at the Eastleigh, Hants, locomotive works. This engine is No. 850E, named "*Lord Nelson*," and is the first of a new series of 4–6–0 four-cylinder simple superheater engines with double bogie tenders, slightly heavier and possessing more power than the famous "King Arthur" class. The new type will be known as the "Nelson" class.

The "*Lord Nelson*" has been built to haul trains of 500 tons at an average speed of 55 miles per hour, but since the heaviest passenger trains on the Southern Railway at present rarely exceed 450 tons, the locomotive will possess considerable reserve power.

Remarkable Increase in Power

Most of our readers will be aware that some two years ago Mr. Maunsell conducted a number of experiments with one of the Drummond four-cylinder engines, No. 449. This engine had two inside and two outside cylinders, whose drive was divided between two axles, the angle of the cranks being arranged to give four impulses per revolution. In the experiments mentioned the drive was re-arranged to turn the cranks of the inside engine through 45° and the wheels were re-balanced to suit this arrangement, which resulted in eight separate impulses being given in each revolution.

The increase in power secured by this alteration was so remarkable that a similar order of cranks which, for reference purposes, can be termed the 135° arrangement, has been embodied in the "*Lord Nelson*." In this case, while the crank pins on each of the two driving axles are placed at 90°, one pair is arranged 135° in advance of the second pair. Thus are the eight equally-spaced exhaust impulses secured. The remarkable effect of this arrangement upon the steaming power of the boiler has made it necessary to enlarge the blast nozzle in three successive steps.

Boiler barrel	
Outside diameter at fire-box ...	5 ft. 9 in.
Length	13 ft. 9 in.
Length between tube plates ...	14 ft. 2 in.
Fire-box shell	
Width	4 ft. 0½ in.
Length	10 ft. 6 in.
Heating Surface	
Fire-box	194 sq. ft.
Small tubes	1,282 sq. ft.
Large tubes	513 sq. ft.
Total	1,989 sq. ft.
Superheater surface	376 sq. ft.
Grate area	33 sq. ft.
Cylinders ...	(four) 16½ in. dia. by 26 in. stroke
Coupled wheels	6 ft. 7 in. dia.
Bogie wheels	3 ft. 1 in. dia.
Tractive effort at 85 per cent. boiler pressure	14.95 tons
Weight of engine in working order	83 tons 10 cwt.
Weight of tender in working order ...	56 tons 14 cwt.
Total weight	140 tons 4 cwt.

Special Skill for Reciprocating Parts

Walschaerts' valve gear is employed for both inside and outside cylinders and the revolving and reciprocating parts have been made extremely light by the use of a special high-tensile steel known as "*Vibrac.*" This patent steel is manufactured by Sir W. G. Armstrong Whitworth & Co. Ltd., and is of the nickel-chromium class, its specially high quality being obtained by substituting molybdenum for a portion of the chromium. The comparative lightness of the balance weights used on the wheels is, of course, a resultant advantage, and the use of this special steel will be watched with considerable interest by all locomotive engineers.

The fire-box is of the Belpaire pattern—a new feature

Side view of the new Southern Railway Locomotive No. 850, "*Lord Nelson*"

for engines built at Eastleigh—and is of extremely liberal proportions. The fire-box stays are of steel in the fire area and ordinary riveted copper in the other parts. The tubes are of moderate length, there being 173 small tubes each of 2 in. external diameter, and 27 large tubes of 5¼ in. external diameter. The super-heater header is of the Maunsell type, with air relief valves, while safety valves of the Ross patent "pop" type are mounted above the fire-box. Included among the other fittings are a soot blower, exhaust injector, and a four-feed sight-feed lubricator with a separate condenser for the cylinders and valve chests.

Miles			Schedule min.	Actual Times min.	Actual Times sec.	Speeds Noted m.p.h.	Notes
0.0	Salisbury	dep.	0	0	0	—	8½ min. late
1.1	Tunnel Jctn. ...	pass	—	4	14	38	
5.5	Porton	,,	—	11	20	37	At top of 1 in 140
8.1	Amesbury Jctn. ...	,,	—	15	20	41½	At top of 1 in 245
11.0	Grateley	,,	—	19	5	50	At summit
17.4	Andover	,,	22	24	45	74	11¼ min. late
21.3	Mile-post 62½ ...	,,	—	28	15	59	
22.6	Hurstbourne ...	,,	—	29	30	66	
24.5	Whitchurch ...	,,	—	31	20	61	
28.1	Overton	,,	—	34	55	60	
31.3	Oakley	,,	—	38	5	60	
33.4	Worting Jctn. ...	,,	39	40	5	—	9½ min. late
35.9	Basingstoke ...	,,	41½	42	10	75	9¼ min. late
36.7	Barton Mill ...	,,	—	—	—	77½	
41.5	Hook	,,	—	46	40	71½	
43.9	Winchfield ...	,,	—	48	35	—	
47.2	Fleet	,,	—	51	15	77½	
50.5	Farnborough ...	,,	—	54	0	—	
51 5	Sturt Lane Jctn.	,,	—	54	55	—	
52.8	Mile-post 31 ...	,,	—	56	0	69	
55.7	Brookwood ...	,,	—	58	20	76½	
59.4	Woking	,,	62½	61	15	80½	7¼ min. late
62.1	Byfleet	,,	—	63	20	79	
64.6	Weybridge ...	,,	—	65	20	71½	
66.7	Walton	,,	—	67	5	71½	
69.4	Esher	,,	—	69	20	71½	Engine 'eased' here
70.5	Hampton Ct. Jctn.	,,	73	70	15	68	5¾ min. late
71.7	Surbiton	,,	—	71	25	64	
74.0	Malden	,,	—	73	40	62½	
75.1	Raynes Park ...	,,	—	74	40	64	
76.5	Wimbledon ...	,,	—	76	0	65	
78.2	Earlsfield	,,	—	77	30	68	
79.9	Clapham Jctn. ...	,,	84	79	5	40	Service slack
81.0	Queen's Rd. ...	,,	—	80	30	47½	3½ min. late
82.4	Vauxhall	,,	88	82	30	—	3 min. late
83.8	Waterloo	arr.	92	85	30	—	2 min. late

Load: 10 corridor coaches and two dining cars=388 tons empty and approximately 415 tons with passengers and luggage.

Brakes Act on Tender's Wheels

The cab follows generally the design of Mr. Maunsell's latest 4–4–0 type engine cabs and has side windows of glass and tip-up seats for the driver and fireman. All the controls are arranged so that they can be reached with a minimum of effort. The double bogie tender is similar to that used with the "King Arthur" engines with the exception that it has straight flat sides with no overhanging coping. It has a capacity for 5,000 gallons of water and five tons of coal. The three steel cylinders that are just discernible in the illustrations at the rear of the tender are auxiliary reservoirs used in connection with the automatic vacuum brake and are specially connected to act on the tender wheels.

The overall dimensions of the "*Lord Nelson*" permit of its being worked on any main line section of the Southern Railway, and the leading particulars are as shown in the accompanying table.

"Castles" and "Pacifics" Surpassed!

When it is recalled that the complete weight of the "King Arthur" class engine with tender is only 34 cwt. less than that of the "*Lord Nelson*," it will be seen that the considerable increase in power has been achieved only by close attention to detail. The tractive effort, 33,500 lb. (14.96 tons), is calculated on the usual basis of 85 per cent. of the boiler pressure and is greater than that of either the G.W. "Castle" engines or the L.N.E.R. Pacifics, the tractive efforts of which are 14.12 and 13.32 tons respectively. The "King Arthurs" on the Southern Railway have a tractive effort of 11.31 tons.

The "*Lord Nelson*" has already worked the Waterloo-Bournemouth and "Atlantic Coast" expresses and at present is being tried on the Eastern Section's Continental service, being temporarily stationed at Nine Elms, where it has been fitted with a shelter for indicating purposes.

First Test Run

The first official run of the "*Lord Nelson*" took place on 12th October last when the down "Atlantic Coast Express," 11 a.m. out of Waterloo, was hauled as far as Salisbury, the engine making the return trip from Salisbury on the "up" "Atlantic Coast Express." The approximate weight of the train in each case was 420 tons.

Leaving Waterloo punctually at 11 a.m., the train consisted of twelve well-filled coaches, and made an excellent run into Salisbury, arriving 35 secs. ahead of schedule, after covering the distance of 83.8 miles in 89.25 secs. The fastest recorded speed was 82 m.p.h. attained at Andover, while the 75.4 miles between Wimbledon and Tunnel Junction were run in exactly 75 minutes.

The return journey provided a greater test of the engine's capabilities, however, for the start was made 8½ minutes after time and the run throughout was accompanied by a very steady drizzle of rain. Despite this, the train arrived at Waterloo only 2 mins. behind time, having covered the run in 85 mins. 30 secs. From Worting Junction to Esher, 36 miles, the average speed was 73.85 m.p.h., the speed falling below 70 m.p.h. only momentarily to 69 m.p.h. when passing the mile post 31 miles out from Waterloo; while from Grately to Earlsfield, 67 miles, the speed only once dropped below 60 m.p.h.

Southern Railway 4-4-0 Type Locomotives

For Express Service on the Eastern Section

FIFTEEN 4-4-0 type express engines have been built by the North British Locomotive Company, Glasgow, for service on the Eastern Section of the Southern Railway. In general design the engines are duplicate with the "L" class introduced in 1914, but improvements have been made by Mr. R. E. L. Maunsell, the Chief Mechanical Engineer of the Southern Railway, in various details.

One of the 4-4-0 type Express Locomotives of the Southern Railway

The boiler pressure has been increased from 160 to 180 lb. per sq. inch, and the cylinder diameter reduced from $20\frac{1}{2}$ in. to $19\frac{1}{2}$ in., so that the tractive effort is not appreciably affected.

The Stephenson link motion has been entirely remodelled and the valve travel increased to $5\frac{3}{8}$ in. in full gear, the lap being increased from $\frac{7}{8}$ in. to $1\frac{3}{16}$ in.

The engines have the "Maunsell" type superheater with shifting valves and the hydrostatic sight feed lubricator having separate condenser for cylinder and valves.

The smoke-box arrangement has been re-designed and a standard chimney fitted. The flat-sided tender with enhanced brake power is also duplicate with the 2-6-0 type engines of Mr. Maunsell's design.

Particular care has been taken with the rearrangement of the cab and footplate, resulting in improvement for the comfort and convenience of the enginemen. The cab roof has been extended backwards, side windows provided, and the large tool boxes behind the splashers have been replaced by tip-up seats.

The lighting in the cab is excellent and the look-out improved. Such fittings as the vacuum brake ejector, steam reversing gear control and sight feed lubricator have been carefully located in the most convenient positions for observation and operation. Hand sanding gear is provided to each pair of coupled wheels. The Davies & Metcalfe exhaust steam injector is fitted on the left-hand side.

7' 7" OVER CAB
8' 4"
End View

These engines, which are numbered A.753 to A.759 and A.782 to A.789, are mainly intended for the Charing Cross, Folkestone and Deal, and the Charing Cross and Hastings services.

The accompanying diagram gives an elevation and also shows the dimensions of these locos. The leading particulars are as follows.

The boiler, which is of the Belpaire type, has a working pressure of 180 lbs. per sq. in. Its barrel diameter outside the front ring is 4 ft. $10\frac{7}{8}$ in. and the barrel diameter outside the back ring is 5 ft. The length of the barrel is 11 ft. 5 in. and the width of the fire-box shell 4 ft. $\frac{1}{2}$ in. its length being 7 ft. 5 in.

There are 169 tubes of $1\frac{3}{4}$ in. diameter and twenty-one tubes of $5\frac{1}{4}$ in. diameter.

The total heating surface of 1,407 sq. ft. is made up as follows: Fire-box

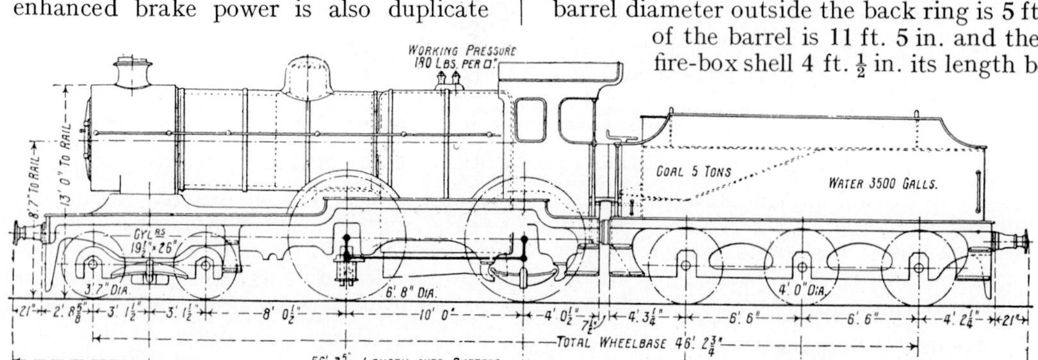

Diagram and Leading Dimensions of Southern Railway 4-4-0 Type Express Locomotive

(Cont. on p. 183)

A RECORD-BREAKER of no mean order is the "*Cornish Riviera Express*" of the Great Western Railway, for daily it makes the longest non-stop railway run in the whole world! Before the first halt is made, at the North Road Station at Plymouth, this famous "flyer" has bridged the gap between the Thames and the Tamar, travelling westward and southward for 225¾ miles.

Even across the vast spaces of the American continent no actual run can be found of greater length than 183 miles, made by the west-bound "*Twentieth Century Limited*" between Buffalo and Cleveland; while the longest European run, outside our own country, is over the 193 miles between Paris and Brussels.

Thus, by the enterprise of the Great Western Railway, Great Britain takes a handsome lead over the rest of the world in the matter of non-stop train running, just as she does in high-scheduled train-speeds with the 75-minute run over the 77¼ miles from Swindon to Paddington.

Formation of the "Limited"

A British record is also very nearly established by the weight to which the "*Limited*"—as she is affectionately known all over the Great Western system—is made up at the busier times of the year. In the height of summer this famous train runs in two parts, but in the spring and the autumn the formation is run up to fourteen of the biggest and heaviest 70-foot steel-panelled cars, weighing empty all but 500 tons, and with the full complement of passengers and luggage quite 530 tons behind the engine tender. "Unlimited" would, I think, be a more suitable title than "Limited" for a train of this character!

Like its near neighbour, the 11 a.m. out of Waterloo, the "*Cornish Riviera Express*" is a train of many portions. Next to the engine you find the real "Cornishman," destined to travel as far westward as the iron trail has yet been laid—to Penzance, 305 miles away. This section consists of three coaches and a restaurant car. The St. Ives through coach will keep these company to St. Erth Junction, and the Falmouth coach or coaches as far as the cathedral city of Truro. Then comes the Newquay coach, which parts company with the main train at Plymouth and is taken on from there to the Newquay branch junction, at Par, by a slower train.

But what of the six coaches on the rear of the train? We shall find them labelled successively Torquay (two), Ilfracombe, Minehead and Weymouth (two). How are these to reach their destinations, if the "*Limited*" does not stop before reaching Plymouth? It is obvious that they are not destined to travel to Plymouth and then back again to their various junction stations! No; they are going to be "slipped." The two hindmost will be quietly dropped off at Westbury, 95½ miles from London. Then the Minehead and Ilfracombe coaches will come off together as the "*Limited*" flies through Taunton, 142¾ miles out; and last of all the Torquay coaches will be slipped at Exeter.

Thus the engine will have been relieved of half-a-dozen of her fourteen coaches ere she draws up at her first stopping-place, and one might quite easily get into the middle of the train at Paddington and, to one's astonishment, find oneself in the last coach on arrival at Plymouth, without having stopped anywhere in between!

Leading Dimensions of G.W.R. 4-6-0 Engines, "Castle" Type

Cylinders (4) Diameter	16 in.
" Stroke	26 in.
Driving Wheels, Diameter	6 ft. 8½ in.
Heating Surface, Tubes	1,886 sq. ft.
" " Firebox	164 "
" " Superheater (14 elements) ...	262 "
" " Total	2,312 "
Firegrate Area	30¼ "
Working Steam Pressure ...	225 lb. per sq. in.
Tractive Effort (at 85% wkg. press.)	31,625 lb.
Water Capacity of Tender ...	4,000 gallons
Coal " "	6 tons
Adhesion Weight of Engine	58¾ "
Total Weight of Engine (in working order)	79¾ "
Total Weight of Engine and Tender (full)	126½ "
Length of Engine and Tender (over buffers)	65 ft. 2 in.

"Slip" Coaches

Just a word here about this business of slipping. The advantage, of course, is that it is possible to set down passengers at any intermediate station without the loss of time occasioned by stopping the express for the purpose. But against it, from the railway point of view, are the expense—for each slip portion must have its own guard—and the trouble of providing specially-fitted slip vehicles in the train formation. On the Great Western Railway, to which line with but few exceptions all the slip coaches of to-day are confined, "safety first" is always the main consideration, and in order that no one shall interfere with the slip guard in the performance of his responsible duties the slip portions are not connected by vestibule with the main train. So one may be travelling as far as Exeter in the "*Limited*" and yet find it impossible to get lunch on the journey, although the restaurant car is only a few coaches away!

The mechanism of slipping is quite simple. At the "business" end of the vehicle is a special form of coupling, by which the slip portion is attached to the main train. At this end also is the compartment in which the slip guard rides, with a good look-out window in front. The hook of the coupling just referred to is hinged in the middle and is held securely in position by means of a sliding bar of steel, which can be withdrawn at the right moment by a lever, worked from inside the guard's compartment. Provision is made, too, for the guard to "seal up the vacuum" in his slip portion. On the main train an appliance is carried that automatically seals the vacuum; otherwise, when the flexible brake-pipe joining the coaches was severed, both halves of the train would come to an unpleasantly sudden stop! In the winter, steam-heat connections are arranged to sever automatically as they are pulled apart, and to seal themselves up in order to prevent escape of steam.

Phot.] [F. E. Mackay

G.W.R. "Cornish Riviera Express" leaving Paddington, hauled by "Builth Castle"

How the Slipping is Effected

As the train nears the slipping station the guard makes his preparations. First of all he seals up the vacuum of the brake. Then he applies his hand-brake, lightly pressing the wheels of the slip-coach. Finally, at the right place—usually about half a mile from the station, but governed in exact distance by the gradients, the customary speed of the express, and other factors—he pulls over his slipping lever. The wedge is withdrawn, the coupling from the last coach of the main train falls out, brake and steam-heat pipes pull apart and the severance is complete.

The light pressure of the brake soon draws the slip well behind the main train. The hand-brake is then taken off and the slip is allowed to roll into the station, where the guard applies his vacuum brake and brings it to rest. Immediately after slipping he has waved a green flag out of his side window in order that the engine crew may know that the slip is safely "off."

Needless to say, the working of the slips is hedged about with the most careful restrictions, owing to the possible danger of the slip running into the main train after the severance if the latter should be stopped for any reason before it is clear of the station. In fog or thickly falling snow all slipping is suspended, and the express stops instead to detach the slip.

A special horn is fixed to the front of the slip brake, so that the guard may warn any railwaymen, who might be tempted unthinkingly to step on to the line after the passage of the express, that the slip is coming just behind. Special tail-signals, too, are carried by slip portions, consisting of red and white lamps encircled with red and white discs, arranged in various ways. You will find that the innermost, or Exeter slip on the "*Limited*" carries on its back a pair of red and white lamps, side by side. The second or Taunton slip carries the red lamp above the white; while the outermost, or Westbury slip, has an imposing array of three lamps, two red and one white, carried in a triangle. The object of these special indications is to inform signalmen and others that no slip portion has become detached before reaching its rightful destination.

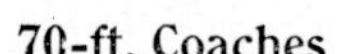

70-ft. Coaches

The Great Western Railway use the longest coaches in England. For many years now their standard for long-distance work has been 70 ft., and occasionally as much as 73 ft. 6 in. over buffers. This allows of third-class corridor coaches being made with no less than ten compartments, as well as lavatories at both ends, so that each coach of this type thus seats 80 passengers. Every seat in the "*Limited*," by the way, is numbered, and may be reserved in advance. The latest Great Western coaches, in their handsome chocolate and cream livery, are panelled with thin steel plates, both at the sides and ends and over the roofs as well, steel being found to wear better than wood.

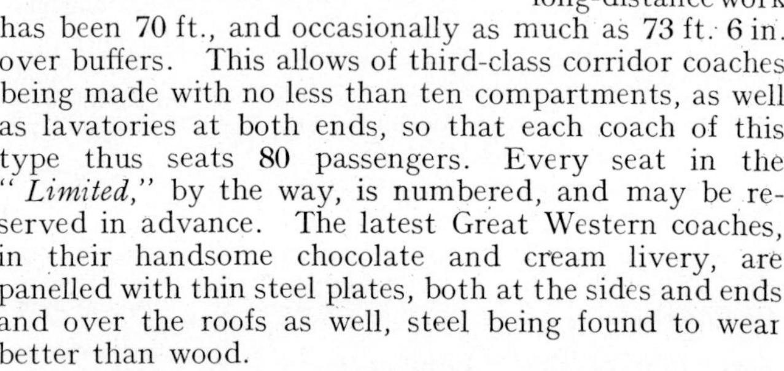

Another recent Great Western innovation has been the use of one combined central coupling and buffer, like two hands coming together in a firm grip, which helps the train to ride more steadily, in addition to being a valuable safeguard against the dreaded "telescoping" of coaches in the unlikely event of a derailment. This is not a new idea, however, having been introduced on the East coast trains of the L.N.E.R. as far back as 1897, and having since become standard on that line. The "*Limited*" is coupled up in this manner except, of course, the slip portions. These newest coaches are tremendously heavy, scaling from 35 to 37 tons apiece.

So, at last, when we have walked up the whole length of this vast train at No. 1 platform at Paddington—the 14 coaches alone measure all but 1,000 ft. in length and the extreme front of the train is probably out of sight round the curve at the outward end of the station—we come to the engine. There is no question as to what type it will be. There is only one class of locomotive on the line capable of keeping time with the "*Limited*," and that is the famous "Castle" class. It is safe to say that no other type of locomotive in the world has done more wonderful work, in proportion to its weight and size, than the Great Western "Castles." It is not only the haulage of enormous loads at high speeds that is in question here, but the low consumption of fuel and water on which these feats are carried out.

In the exchange of locomotives between the G.W.R. and the L.N.E.R. in 1925 it was proved that, although the L.N.E.R. "Pacific" could work the down "*Cornish Riviera Express*" to time without difficulty, yet the G.W. "Castle," of 12 tons less weight, burned less coal on exactly the same duty. Last year, again, on the L.M.S. line, "*Launceston Castle*" succeeded in gaining time with 500-ton trains, whereas L.M.S. engines are limited to a maximum of 360 tons. Moreover, she did her work on a lower coal consumption per horse-power developed than had ever been recorded previously on L.M.S. metals.

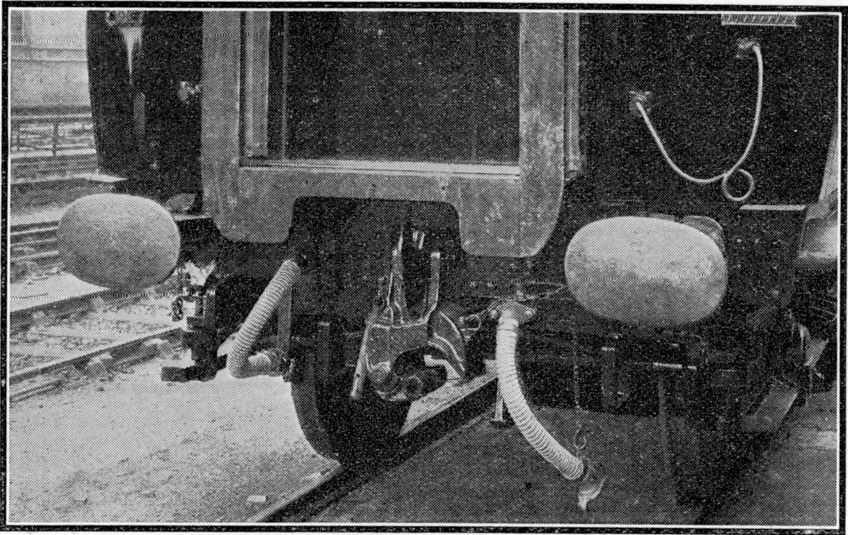

End View of lower portion of G.W. 70 ft. Restaurant Car, showing Automatic Coupler, swung out of position for coupling coach by ordinary screw coupling

"Castle" Class Engines of the G.W.R.

The Great Western "Castle" class engine has the 4–6–0 wheel arrangement and weighs, without tender, 79¾ tons in working order. The latest type of six-wheeled tender, with accommodation for six tons of coal and 4,000 gallons of water, brings the total weight up to 126½ tons. Many reasons have been advanced for the extraordinary capabilities of these Great Western locomotives, but there is little doubt that their success lies largely in the high working pressure that they carry, namely, 225 lb. per sq. in. The force of this pressure, acting on the pistons of the four cylinders, contributes largely to the high tractive power of the engines. The long travel of the piston-valves, which enables their drivers constantly to work the "Castles" in short cut-offs, is probably the chief agent in their efficiency. But this is rather too technical a subject to go into here, and it is now time for us to take our places in the train, as it is just on the starting time of 10.30 a.m.

On the stroke of the half-hour the guard's whistle blows, or the whistle of one of the guards as four of them are travelling with the train. The driver opens his regulator and we are off!

We have a finer start than exists out of any other London terminus. Other lines have to rise out of the valley of the Thames, but Brunel carried his line westward up the Thames Valley and, by his old route—via Reading, Didcot, Swindon Bath and Bristol—barely a grade worth mention exists for the whole of the way to Taunton. So by about Southall we attain the mile-a-minute rate, and by Slough we are ticking off the level quarter-miles every thirteen seconds or so, meaning a speed of just under 70 miles an hour. If we are running dead to time we should pass through Reading, 36 miles out of Paddington, in 37 minutes.

Photos courtesy] [G.W.R.

As above, but with Automatic Coupler in position, and side buffers swung out of use

Cutting Off the Corners

Here we must reduce our speed to 40 miles an hour for the curve at the west end of the station, for we are now to leave Brunel's old main line in order to take the more recent short cut by Westbury. After the opening of the 20 miles shorter London and South Western route to Exeter and Plymouth, the old main line by Bristol, beautifully graded though it was, was found too circuitous, and it became imperative to curtail the distance. This was done by bringing the old "Berks and Hants" line up to main line standards, cutting a great corner out of it by linking Patney and Westbury with a new direct route, 15½ miles in length, and then joining Castle Cary, where the Weymouth line bends southward, with the West of England line at Cogload, near Taunton, by another new stretch of line 24½ miles in length.

By this means, costly but effective, the Great Western cut exactly 20 miles from their journey to Taunton and all points west of that town. In the earliest year that the "*Limited*" ran it travelled via Bristol, and so made the even longer non-stop journey of 245¾ miles daily.

The Westbury route is not difficult in its grades, but it has some long stretches of "collar-work" for the engine. Up the valley of the Kennet it gradually rises, past Newbury and Hungerford, steepening then to the summit at Savernake, 70 miles from Paddington. At Aldermaston, 45 miles out of Paddington, occur the first track-troughs, notable by the provision of one of the first water-softening plants erected in England for treating locomotive water. To Savernake we probably shall have taken just about 1¼ hours. Possibly we may be a minute or two behind time, especially if the weather is at all windy, but we may pick up a minute or so on the glorious racing stretch down to Westbury, on which we shall probably touch 80 m.p.h., while descending the 1 in 222 from Patney to Lavington.

A severe brake application heralds the approach to Westbury, owing to the sharp curve into the station, and if we follow the reprehensible practice of leaning out of the carriage window we shall see the two coaches of the outermost "slip" neatly drop off the back of the train. An interesting sight at Westbury, by the way, is the most southerly blast-furnace plant in England, on the north side of the line just beyond the station.

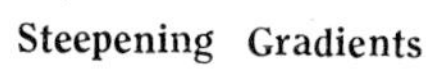

Steepening Gradients

Immediately after Westbury, passed in 97 minutes from Paddington if we have kept time over this initial stretch of 95½ miles, comes another installation of track-troughs, where our thirsty steed takes a second long drink. We have barely recovered from the 30 m.p.h. slack through Westbury when there comes another restriction to the same limit over the Frome curve. From here follow rising grades to the summit known as Brewham or, in the working time-tables, "milepost 122¾," the actual distance mentioned being the old one by Swindon and Chippenham. The last couple of miles up to this point are as steep in parts as 1 in 107.

Once over Brewham we have in front of us a further high-speed stretch down to Castle Cary, 120 miles from Paddington. The grade

Saltash Bridge, joining Devon with Cornwall

here is mostly 1 in 98, but exceptionally high speeds are rarely run owing to the winding character of the line. Then we pass over the "cut-off" to Cogload and Taunton. From Castle Cary to Taunton is, perhaps, the one easily-timed stretch of the whole journey, and the timing is greatly prized by drivers as giving them a little chance of recovering a few minutes that may have been dropped on the arduous earlier stages. Water is taken from troughs just after the old main line has been joined at Cogload.

Taunton, 142¾ miles from Paddington, should be passed in 148 minutes. Here our steed is thankful to be rid of the burden of two more coaches, as the stiff ascent to Whitehall, where the train crosses the watershed separating the Severn basin from the rivers running southward to the English Channel, is now immediately in prospect. First the ascent steepens during four miles from 1 in 220 to 1 in 163, and then for three miles it increases from the formidable figure of 1 in 90 to 1 in 81. The final three-quarter mile through the summit tunnel is at 1 in 126. With the 530 tons that our "Castle" drew out of Paddington it would not be possible to climb this bank unaided. The load is now four coaches less, however, and with 385 tons our engine finds no difficulty in making the ascent.

Once over Whitehall we have a downhill run of 20 miles to Exeter, which is passed slowly in one minute under three hours from Paddington, our average speed to this point having been no less than 58.2 m.p.h. This, however, is the end of high speed achievement.

Photo] [F. E. Mackay

Down "Cornish Riviera," passing Kensal Green, hauled by "Prince George"

Among the "Mountains" of South Devon

The line now has to wind round the coast past Starcross—where we pass over the fourth set of track-troughs—Dawlish and Teignmouth to Newton Abbot whence, as it skirts the southern slopes of Dartmoor and has to cross one by one the deep river valleys finding their way to the sea, it stretches out before our engine the steepest main line gradients in the whole of Great Britain. Fortunately two more coaches were dropped off at Taunton, leaving only eight, of a total weight of 310 tons, which is the maximum that even the powerful locomotives of the "Castle" class are allowed to take unaided over Dainton and Rattery Summits.

The ascent from beyond Newton Abbot to Dainton Tunnel is only two miles long, but its steepest pitch is no less severe than 1 in 36, and if we top the summit at anything much over 20 m.p.h. we shall do well. Then follows an almost equally precipitate and very sharply winding descent to the valley of the Dart at Totnes, whence we are faced with Rattery Bank, five miles long, 2½ of which are at 1 in 51 or but slightly less steep, and another 1½ at 1 in 90. From Rattery we go away over a "tableland" past Brent and Ivybridge, finishing with another terrific drop, for two miles at 1 in 42, from Hemerdon Box down to Plympton. This is the terror of drivers in the reverse direction, coming so soon after the Plymouth start, with no chance of taking a "rush" at it.

So, probably on the stroke of 2.37 p.m., our "Castle" brings the "*Limited*"—or what is left of it !—to rest at North Road Station at Plymouth. Even after so strenuous a task as this, however, her day is not done, for, in charge of another crew, she has yet to retrace her tracks over that last formidable stretch of line, by making a trip from Plymouth to Exeter and back before nightfall.

On to the seven coaches of the "*Limited*"—the Newquay coach is to follow—another engine has now been hitched. Until recently the handy "Moguls" were responsible for most of the Cornish work, but 4-6-0 engines, even up to and including "Castles," now work freely right through to Penzance, and quite likely we shall have a four-cylinder 4-6-0 "Star" for the rest of the journey. The ups-and-downs of the Cornish main line are so terribly steep and the curves so sharp that we must not expect much in the way of speed. To Truro, our next stop, 80 minutes are allowed for the 53¾ miles.

Saltash Bridge

Chief interest in this part of the run centres in the crossing of Brunel's magnificent Saltash Bridge, which takes us over the Tamar from Devon into Cornwall, four miles after leaving North Road. The river here is 1,100 ft. wide, and the difficulty of spanning the waterway was the greater in that its depth in the centre was some 80 ft. This difficulty Brunel overcame by the use of caisson construction, and he managed to "fly" (*Continued on page* 183)

Can You Locate These Words?

Fourth Stamp Competition

THIS month's Stamp Competition is, perhaps, a little more difficult than those we have had before, but our readers have proved themselves so successful in solving our problems, that we are sure they will be able to tackle this one quite well.

In the accompanying panel there are 20 words or phrases that appear on twenty postage stamps and you must try to find out what countries issued the various stamps.

None of the words is taken from stamps issued since 1924 nor is any taken from very old or rare stamps, so that all will have an equal chance of being able to solve the problems. Also none of the words is in particularly small type on its stamp and all are quite easily readable in the illustrations in the writer's catalogue. As usual, catalogues may be used in solving any difficulties that arise, but no other help, either from other books or people, is allowed.

1. **Justice, Commerce, Freedom.**
2. **Puerte y Casa de los Virreyes.**
3. **Niet bestellen op Zondag.**
4. **Nadie la apagara.**
5. **Freie Stadt ——.**
6. **Droits de l'homme.**
7. **Centenario de la incorporacion del partido de N——.**
8. **Lord Byron.**
9. **III. Centenario di propaganda fide.**
10. **Commission Interalliée.**
11. **Beira.**
12. **Pro Juventute.**
13. **Signing of the compact.**
14. **Republica Mayor de Centro America Estado de el ——.**
15. **Batalla de Ayacucho.**
16. **Him that found the new isle.**
17. **IIe Centenaire —— (British colony).**
18. **The love of liberty brought us here.**
19. **Tercentenary of establishment of representative institutions.**
20. **1822, Pioneers landing, 1922.**

The first prize, which will be awarded to the sender of the correct or most nearly correct solution, consists of stamps to the value of one guinea to be chosen from advertisements in this issue of the "*Meccano Magazine.*" The second prize is stamps to the value of half a guinea, and the third, stamps to the value of five shillings.

When you have solved the competition to the best of your ability, make a list of the countries in the correct order, add your name and address and the list of stamps you choose, and post so as to arrive here before 28th February.

In locating the countries of issue it will be a considerable help if readers try to decide to what languages the various phrases belong. There are a number of British phrases, of course, but this does not necessarily mean that these are from stamps of the British Empire, in the same way as a foreign phrase is by no means necessarily from a foreign stamp.

In the cases of mottoes, etc., a foreign language is normally used, but in the cases of statements concerning the use, etc. of the stamps the native language will probably be used.

You will notice that a dash figures in Nos. 5, 7, 14 and 17 and this indicates that here a word has been omitted, that, if it were inserted, would probably locate the origin of the phrase immediately. In the case of No. 7 we give the initial letter of this word as a little help, and in No. 17 we note that the government of a certain British Colony is responsible for its issue, although, we may add, it is not the name of the colony that is the omitted word.

We think, personally, that Nos. 3, 5, 8, 11, and 16 will be found the easiest to solve, for these are perhaps the best known in the list to stamp collectors generally.

Care should be taken with No. 5, however, for there is another country with a somewhat similar inscription. By the way, No. 14 has nothing to do with mayors, nor has No. 4 anything to do with asparagus!

Stamps Valued at £3,000,000

One of the most interesting and valuable collection of stamps ever shown under one roof was admired by philatelists from all over the world at the International Stamp Exhibition held recently in New York. The value of the stamps exhibited may be gauged from the fact that they were insured for £3,000,000.

The Sudan, Russia, the Irish Free State, Baghdad, Barum and Togo all contributed most interesting and beautiful specimens, which aroused widespread interest among visitors. Several Governments exhibited stamps at this Exhibition, among them being Austria, Sweden, Russia and the United States.

It may here be mentioned that American collectors are acquiring many of the most beautiful and valuable stamps of the world. One of their possessions is the unique one cent British Guiana stamp of 1856 (owned by Mr. Alfred Hind). This stamp realised the huge sum of £7,400 at the Ferrari sale and was exhibited in London three years ago.

Southern Railway 4-4-0 Type Locos— (*Continued from page* 111)

154.5 sq. ft., small tubes 914 sq. ft., large tubes 338.5 sq. ft.

There are twenty-one elements in the superheater, the area of which is 235 sq. ft., the grate area being 22.5 sq. ft.

The wheels are 19½ in. in diameter and the stroke 26 in.

The diameter of the piston valves, inside admission, is 9 in. At 75% cut off the travel of the valves is 5⅝ in. and their lap 1$\frac{3}{16}$ in.

The coupled wheels are 6 ft. 8 in. in diameter and the bogie wheels 3 ft. 7 in. in diameter.

The weight on the coupled wheels is 38 tons, the total weight of the loco in working order being 58 tons 10 cwts. The tractive effort at 85% boiler pressure is 8.44 tons.

The tender has a coal capacity of 5 tons and a water capacity of 3,500 gallons. Its total weight in working order is 40 tons 10 cwts.

December Stamp Contest

We cannot, unfortunately, comment at any great length on the competition as the Overseas Section is still open and any slight hint given now might materially influence some of the entries from European competitors to the disadvantage of competitors from the more distant parts of the world.

On the whole the competition proved even more popular than that held in September, although the second and last items presented difficulty to a considerable number of entrants.

The prizes were awarded to the following competitors:—1. Colin McCaig (Willaston, Birkenhead); 2. N. G. Pearl (Enfield); 3. D. Rathie (Bradford).

Famous Trains—(*continued from page* 123)

over the river by two vast spans resting on the one central pier. The chief strength of the bridge lies in the great curved tubes of wrought iron, elliptical in section and hollow, from which the floor of the bridge is suspended by vertical tie-rods. It is a tribute both to the genius and to the foresight of Brunel that this unique structure, opened in 1859, is still in use, carrying the vastly heavier locomotives and trains of to-day.

So the "*Limited*" forges westward past Liskeard, Par and St. Austell to Truro, over stone viaducts that until recently were wooden trestle bridges, through cuttings and tunnels and over reverse curves which, from the footplate, seem almost bewildering in their frequency. Then on through Redruth and Camborne, famous for their connection with Watt and Trevithick, to Gwinear Road, where connection is made to Helston and the Lizard; St. Erth, where the St. Ives coach is jettisoned; and last of all round the margin of Mount's Bay across a causeway from Marazion into Penzance, where we draw up at 5 p.m., exactly as far from London as is the Scottish border north of Carlisle.

So another day's journey of the "*Cornish Riviera Limited*" express has been successfully completed.

The Story of Coal—(*continued from page* 102)

It contains a very small amount of gas and a very large proportion of carbon, and its name is derived from the Greek word *anthrax*, meaning carbon. Anthracite is difficult to ignite and this fact hindered its general adoption for a considerable time. It is perhaps best known for its remarkable steam-raising qualities.

There is also another curious kind of coal known as "*Cannel*" coal. The name is probably a corruption of the word "candle," on account of the fact that it burns with a bright, clear candle-like flame. It is said that at one time pieces of this coal were used as a substitute for candles and torches. In Scotland it is known as "Parrot" coal on account of the crackling sound it makes while burning.

On distillation, cannel coal gives off a large quantity of gas of high illuminating power and it is therefore greatly used in gasworks. This coal has come into greater prominence during recent years on account of the considerable quantity of valuable oils that can be extracted from it by the process known as low-temperature carbonisation, to which we shall refer later.

An interesting form of cannel coal is that known as Jet. This substance is very hard and can be cut and polished with great success. At one time a considerable amount of jet was extracted near Whitby in Yorkshire, and cut into brooches, ear-rings, beads and other ornaments, which were largely used as mourning jewellery. Jet has been out of favour for many years in this country, although it is still more or less popular in Spain and Turkey.

Published by MECCANO Ltd., Binns Rd., Liverpool.
Printed by Stembridge & Co. Ltd., Albion Street Leeds.

Over 200 Miles an Hour

Major Segrave's Great Feat

ON Tuesday, 29th March, the world's motoring speed record was not merely beaten, but shattered, by Major H. O. D. Segrave, who drove a Sunbeam car along Daytona Beach, Florida, at the amazing speed of 207.015 miles per hour.

The new record was the climax to a series of attempts to secure the honour that have been made by three great drivers. First Captain Malcolm Campbell succeeded in reaching the speed of 174.224 miles per hour on Pendine Sands, South Wales, in February last, then Mr. J. G. Parry Thomas was unfortunately killed in an accident to his car on the same track while trying to beat this record; and now the third of the famous trio, Major Segrave, has exceeded the previous record by no less than 30 miles per hour.

Major Segrave's World Records

1 mile ...	... 203.841	miles per hour
1 kilometre ...	202.541	,, ,, ,,
5 ,,	... 203.616	,, ,, ,,

A British-made Car

It is interesting to note that the new record was set up with a British-made car, and the accomplishment of the feat is greatly to the credit of the British motor industry in general and of the Sunbeam Motor Car Co. Ltd., Wolverhampton, the makers of the car, in particular. The car was designed to reach the speed of 200 miles per hour, and makers and driver alike were confident that this speed would be attained. Unfortunately there is no track in England long and safe enough to give such a car a fair run, and so Major Segrave was compelled to take his huge red car to the famous Daytona beach.

In one of the preliminary attempts the car reached the speed of 166 miles an hour and it was decided to make a further trial on 29th March. On that date the weather conditions were better than they had been previously, as a brisk north-east wind and high tides had combined to smooth the beach to fine condition. No vehicles were allowed to ruin the surface, the only cars on the beach being the lorry that towed the racer to the course, the touring cars of the officials—and, ominously, an ambulance car! Fortunately the last-named was not needed.

A Mile in Seventeen Seconds!

Finally the car was started over the nine mile course. The first run was in the northerly direction against the wind. The huge car gathered speed quickly in the preliminary four miles and covered the measured mile in 17.94 seconds, which works out at an average of 200.668 miles per hour. The remaining four miles were required to bring the car to a stop. The car was then turned round while the timing device was being re-adjusted, and again it swept along the course. This time, with the wind behind him, Major Segrave covered the measured distance in 17.39 seconds, reaching the amazing speed of 207.015 miles per hour!

The machine shot like a projectile past the 7,000 spectators, who caught only a momentary glimpse of the strained features of the driver. One account of the attempt describes the passage of the thousand horse-power monster as "a rushing blur enshrouded in a cloud of sand."

Conditions for Records

The actual figures of the records established are of great interest. It must be remembered that no record is accepted unless the measured distance has been covered in both directions and the speed is calculated from the average time for the two runs. This is done to prevent advantage being taken of such accidental circumstances as high wind or a sloping course. Electrical timing apparatus is always used as no human being is able to record the moment of the passing of a "rushing blur in a cloud of sand" with sufficient accuracy. It was under these conditions, then, that the Sunbeam made the world's records shown on the previous page.

These figures do not show the greatest speed at which the car travelled. As already mentioned the car actually covered the course in one direction at 207.015 miles per hour. This works out at more than 100 yards per second, and one way to realise what a speed of 200 miles per hour means is to measure out the distance of 100 yards, take out your watch—and think!

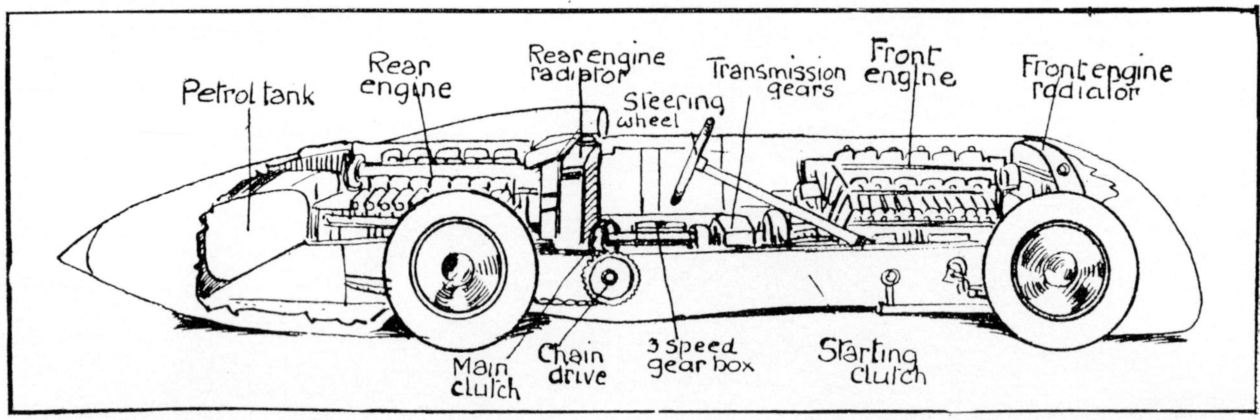

Courtesy] [*"Liverpool Echo"*

Diagram to illustrate the arrangement of the main parts of the car

Major Segrave's Career

Major Segrave is an experienced racing motorist. He is of Irish descent, was born in America, and received his education and training in England. He adopted a military career and during the war became a member of the Royal Air Force. Later he began to take an active interest in motor racing. Since his first appearance at Brooklands in 1920, his career has been eventful. He has won numerous races on the track at Brooklands, and in addition has been successful in the great road races, the French and the Spanish Grand Prix, to win which is the ambition of every racing motorist. Most of his successes have been obtained in association with the famous designer Mr. Louis Coatalen, who is responsible for the Sunbeam car with which the great feat has been accomplished.

After the trial Major Segrave confessed that he had practically no control over the car at the speed of 200 miles per hour, as the wind pressure created by such a speed in the face of the head wind was so great that it made steering almost impossible. New steering gear, a new braking system, and a different distribution of weight will be necessary if cars to travel at this speed are desired, as the present equipment answers so slowly as to make the controls inadequate.

Features of the 100 h.p. Sunbeam Racer

The racer itself is the most amazing motor car ever devised. It is very striking in appearance, as a glance at the illustration shows, and gives a fine impression of power and capacity for speed. Two engines are used. Each is a 500 h.p. Aero engine of the "Matabele" class, manufactured by the Sunbeam Company, and modified in various ways for use on the road. One of them is mounted at the front of the chassis in the conventional position, while the other is placed in the rear of the car, behind the driver.

Each engine has 12 cylinders mounted in "V" fashion upon the crankcase. The bore and stroke is 122×160 m.m. and the total volume swept by the 24 pistons is 44,888 cubic centimetres which, by the way, is over 58 times the capacity of the "Baby Austin"—one of the smallest cars made. As each cylinder has four valves and two sparking plugs, 96 valves, 48 sparking plugs, 8 magnetos and 4 carburetters are used to attend to the needs of the giant power units.

The two engines are connected by a shaft and behind the foremost engine there is a clutch. The front engine is started first and then the clutch is engaged to set the rear engine in motion. The shaft connecting the engines carries a gear which meshes with another on the front end of the gearbox, but interposed between this gear and the gearbox is the multi-plate clutch used for driving the car.

On an ordinary car the gearbox shaft is direct driven by the engine and runs at engine speed, but on this machine it is geared up to rotate at 2½ times engine speed. The reason for this unusual feature is that the increase in speed results in a proportional reduction in torque and consequently the size and weight of the box can be reduced. Three speeds are provided.

Aft of the gearbox is a bevel-driven countershaft which is connected at each end to the rear wheels by Coventry roller chains. The use of chain drive may strike the reader as curious, but it must not be forgotten that the mounting of an engine at the rear makes the fitting of a conventional type of axle extremely difficult. Apart from this a live axle capable of bearing the weight of the car in addition to transmitting the thrust of 1,000 horse power would, in any case, be prohibitively heavy. The arrangement chosen has the advantage of minimum unsprung weight.

The Unusual Shape a Safety Measure

The frame side members are very deep in section and the axles pass through suitable slots in them. Several powerful cross members render the frame inordinately stiff and under it there is a punt-shaped steel cover which extends the complete length of the car. A small ground clearance is given so that in the event of a tyre burst the car can slide along on its steel-clad stomach and so come to rest without the risk of turning over or being jarred to pieces. (*Continued on page* 453)

Buying Heavy Engineering Plant—

(Continued from page 445)

feet to get the necessary head for the pump to work against, the same effect is obtained by partially closing the throttle valve in the discharge pipe until the pressure-gauge reads the required head. In order that the customer may see that the pump is delivering the quantity of water required, a venturi-meter, which is an instrument which shows the rate at which water is flowing through it, is placed in the discharge pipe.

After the pump has passed its tests it is partly taken down, the bearings are examined, and it is given a good clean, after which it goes to the paint shop, where it is painted and has all its bright parts well greased to prevent corrosion.

The packing department receives it next and prepares it for the journey to its destination, packing also all spare parts, tools and other gear that belong to it. When it is all ready, the despatch department send it off and advise the customer that it is on the way.

On the arrival of the pump at the mine, some of the outside erecting staff of the works will take it in hand, installing it on its foundations, coupling it to its driving source and probably installing any necessary pipework, and finally testing it to see that everything is all right. If this is the case, it is officially handed over to the customer, and after he has checked over the specification to see that it is correct, the contract is discharged.

It will be seen, therefore, that buying heavy machinery is not quite as simple as buying a model engine, and that, except in rare cases, it is not possible to buy engineering plant "over the counter!"

Over 200 Miles an Hour—

(Continued from page 393)

The tyres, it may be noted, are special plain Dunlops. They were tested prior to leaving the works by rotating them at a speed of 190 miles an hour with the actual load that they were designed to carry. The same test applied to an older type of racing tyre resulted in the tread being ripped off with a noise like an explosion and hurled through the door of the test hut!

Each power unit has its own independent radiator mounted directly in front of it. The forward one obtains its cooling draught from a large rectangular hole cut in the nose of the car, while two scoops feed the rear one. The wheel base is 11 ft. 9 in., track 5 ft. 2 in., but by careful design the height has been reduced to under 4 ft. When seated in the car the driver is actually nearer the ground than he would be in an ordinary household chair. In the tail there is mounted a 28-gallon petrol tank which, however, does not hold enough to drive the car for more than 63 miles.

New Zealand (1927) Model-Building Competition

We again take the opportunity to draw the attention of all readers who reside in New Zealand to the splendid new competition that has been organised by our agents for that country, Browning, Ifwersen Ltd. Entries in the competition will be divided into several sections according to the ages of the competitors. Many handsome prizes, consisting of Meccano or Hornby Train goods to be chosen by the winners, are offered for entries showing particular merit. The contest is limited to New Zealand Meccano boys, and all entries must be received not later than 4.30 p.m., June 30th next. Would-be competitors may obtain their entry forms and all necessary particulars from their Meccano dealers or direct from Browning, Ifwersen Ltd., P.O. Box 129, Auckland, N.Z.

Why the Martians Declared War

A Peep into 4000 A.D.

By B. J. Bowyer

ZIP! Bang! "Your breakfast, sir."

"Oh, it's you, Carruthers! Please prepare the automatic bath for me, Lever 49."

"Yes, sir."

I finished my breakfast in bed on the first morning of January, 4000, feeling very satisfied with things in general. I had bought a new helicopter on the previous day and was looking forward to giving it a trial. Impatiently I pulled over Lever 49 and was shot, somewhat violently, into Room 90—the bathroom.

In fifteen seconds I was automatically washed and dressed and then, pulling over Lever 47, I stepped into a chute and descended to the ground floor at the aggravatingly slow rate of 40 miles per minute—the monthly current supply was beginning to fail.

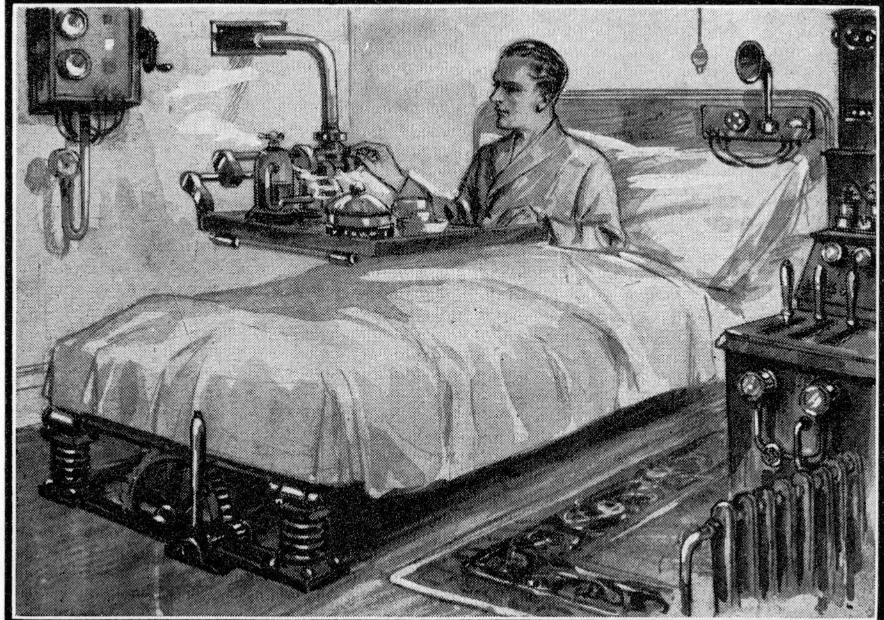

I finished my breakfast in bed . . .

Carruthers helped me into my fur coat and I stepped in the "Springmeup." This is a bullet-shaped lift to convey people to a height of at least 500 ft. at an average speed of 100 miles per minute. Carruthers pulled over the lever and in a flash I was seated in my helicopter which, in accordance with my instructions, had been placed conveniently on the flat roof.

Once inside I pressed the speed button, let go the clutch and was whirled upward to 2,000 ft., at which altitude I changed into horizontal movement. I continued to press the speed button until the speedometer registered 200 miles per minute, and five minutes later I saw the shimmering coast of Italy. I live in Norfolk, 75th State, England, so that I was then some 1,000 miles from home.

I alighted on the roof of the house of my friend Signor Murphius. Then things began to happen.

I garaged my helicopter safely and stepped on to the moving pavement, which there is on a level with the roofs of all the houses. I intended to switch off on to the ground chute and enter at the front door of the house. The fates were against me, however. Just as I was about to switch over, the operator at the Office of Machinery took it into his head to accelerate my section and I was flung neck and crop on to the roof of another house. Worse still, this house had a revolving roof for ventilation purposes, and I felt as though someone was swinging me round his head.

At that moment the operators must have developed an absolute mania for accelerating, because a second later, before I could do anything to help myself, I was flung into a bath upon the next roof. To make matters worse this house was untenanted, and thus the bath contained a dirty accumulation of rainwater. When I climbed out I was covered from head to foot with mud and my appearance provided considerable amusement to a small crowd of interested onlookers.

My immediate necessity now was to reach the ground, but this was a serious problem because there was no machinery working in the house. Finally I succeeded by sliding down a drainpipe and then dropping on to a sloping roof, from which I was able to reach the ground by making a somewhat alarming jump.

* * * *

"Ah, that's better!" said Signor Murphius, after he had had me washed and dressed. I thanked him and soon we were spending a happy evening. Time passed so rapidly that it was midnight before I left his house and returned to my helicopter. In another five minutes I was warming myself before the radium radiator in my home.

* * * *

I had intended to keep the following day free for a trip in my flying "300" American Automobile. Business prevented me, however, and I travelled by the "Minute-and-a-half" train to London. Having transacted my business I paid a visit to the Main Stores Depôt to obtain some accessories that I required for my new 20-valve combined receiver and transmitter.

Returning home on the "Two-minute" train I switched in my set to America. I was promptly answered by the amateur station 2 GUY with the startling information that a message had just been received from Mars. The message said: "War has been declared on the Earth by the Elect Four for two reasons to be stated later. We give you 120 minutes in which to prepare."

In frantic excitement I instantly conveyed this information to the War Ministry, but it was known there already. In another 60 seconds all the world knew of the declaration of war.

Immediately I began to consider what part I could take in the coming war and I decided that the best thing I could do would be to operate a fighting helicopter. I was backed up in this decision by my faithful Carruthers, who offered to come with me as bomber. Quickly we fitted the armament plates on to my helicopter, shut up the house and flew to London, arriving there just as the steady drone of the Martian aeroships was heard in the distance.

At the end of 100 minutes the Earth's forces were all gathered together on the Siberian Steppes, ready for immediate action.

* * * *

The manœuvres of the advanced squadrons of the Martian aeroships quickly made it evident that their idea was to wipe out London as a preliminary to destroying the British Isles. We were directed therefore to concentrate most of our forces on London. The first indication we received that the Martians were at work was a terrific explosion apparently some miles away. It was evident that the Martian death-ray had destroyed some important building, and we learned later that this was a gigantic munitions factory at a small town in Middlesex.

We had plenty of ammunition but not a Death-ray Apparatus

Subsequently we found out that the Martian death-ray burned and destroyed everything with which it came in contact. We employed a similar method of bringing destruction to the enemy's forces, but in addition we used high-power explosive that could be shot to a height of 6,000 ft. by means of a steel catapult gun.

* * * *

When the fighting began in earnest it was fierce beyond description, the combatants on the whole being fairly evenly matched. Carruthers and I had some very narrow escapes. One night we were just about to land when a Martian aeroship came whizzing round us intent on destruction. We had plenty of ammunition but unfortunately we had not a death-ray apparatus with us. After frantic circling for a second or two, a deadly-looking metal object came flying towards us from the aeroship, but I quickly accelerated and soon had put 10,000 ft. between us and the enemy. Carruthers then commenced active bombing operations, but our luck was out as the bomber went wrong after three shots, none of which took effect on the enemy.

We now had no means of escape left but flight, and a race for life ensued. I never felt so hot in all my life. In spite of all our efforts the aeroship gained appreciably upon us and kept on throwing out scorching rays, some of which did a good deal of damage to our machine. Then our fuel began to give out and we should have met with a terrible fate but for the presence of mind of Carruthers, who whipped out his portable wireless transmitter and sent out an "S.O.S." The response was immediate. Five of our bombing machines came racing to our assistance and in turn the Martians had to fly for their lives.

On another occasion our engine failed when we were in the thick of a skirmish. To add to our troubles the tail-end of the machine got entangled among the remains of an aeroship that came crashing down upon us. Fortunately I was able to steer clear of the wreckage and glide down to the ground, although we received a nasty jar on landing as our shock absorbers had been broken by the impact of the wrecked aeroship.

* * * *

The war came to an end on the 31st January 4000, when peace terms were signed, and for the first time the Martians stated their reasons for making war.

The Peace Terms provided for:

(1) No more war with the Earth during the reign of George XI., and

(2) The disarmament of both worlds.

The announcement of the two reasons for the war caused the greatest excitement. The first was that the Martians were disturbed because our scientists were discovering too many things about Mars and its inhabitants. The second reason was still more extraordinary. It was that the Earth was becoming far too gay, and the noise the people were making was proving a great annoyance to the sensitive Martians!

* * * *

Feeling the need of rest after the excitement of the war I decided to have a month's holiday at the seaside and Carruthers and I left Norfolk on 4th February 4000, for the Cornish coast on the "Sixty-Minute" train.

To-day I am peacefully smoking my pipe in the cool refreshing breeze from the Atlantic Ocean, and wondering what is going to happen next!

How Engines Pick Up Water

The Troughs on British Railways

By R. D. Gauld, M.Eng., A.M.Inst. C.E.

THE announcement that the London, Midland and Scottish Railway are about to lay down additional water troughs on their two Anglo-Scottish routes served as a reminder of the useful part played by these appliances in modern railway working.

It was in 1860 that Mr. John Ramsbottom, at that time chief mechanical engineer of the London and North Western Railway, introduced the water trough and pick-up system. Twenty-five years passed before any other railway company adopted them, and then the Lancashire and Yorkshire Railway put down the first of several installations. Since then practically all the main routes in the country have been equipped, enabling engines to make long non-stop runs, and also reducing the work to be done at the terminus or next stopping place.

L.M.S. Down Royal Train Picking up Water near Bushey

Situation of Troughs

The troughs are always laid on a level portion of the line and generally on a straight portion. The well-known troughs at Bushey, near Watford, however, are on a curve. In this special situation the troughs are so supported that the cant on the rails is neutralised, but the troughs are a little deeper than usual on account of the engine and its scoop being inclined to the horizontal. Traffic considerations chiefly decide where the troughs are to be laid, but a site is always chosen where there is an ample supply of water of a suitable quality for boiler purposes.

The total length of the troughs varies, but it is usually about 500 yards, the ends gradually tapering out. Towards the end of the troughs the track is graded at 1 in 300, down at the entering end, and up at the leaving end, while the end portions have a gradient of 1 in 192. The rails are parallel to the surface of the bottom of the trough, so that if the fireman does not raise the scoop in time, it comes out of the water automatically.

The operation of picking-up water at speed splashes a good deal of water over everything in the neighbourhood, and special measures have to be taken to drain the permanent way at these places. Extra large ballast is used, with cross and side drains, and to give extra solidity to the track an extra two or three sleepers are put into each 45 ft. rail length.

The troughs consist of steel plate bent to the required shape, supplied in lengths and riveted together. They are about 1 ft. 6 in. in width and 6 in. in depth, and are placed on the middle of the sleepers and supported at the sides upon baulks of timber, cut to shape. The rim of the trough stands 3 in. above the level of the rails, and the water surface is at 2 in. above rail level. When the scoop is down it dips 2 in. into the water, being thus at rail level and, therefore, well clear of the trough bottom and any possible obstacles. Arrangements have to

The L.M.S. Troughs at Bushey

be made to keep the troughs full of water automatically, and as this must be done fairly rapidly, the water is fed to the troughs at several points, the flow being governed by float valves similar to the domestic ball cock in the cistern. The troughs require frequent cleaning out as small pieces of ballast get washed into them and also leaves and other small pieces of rubbish.

The Engine Apparatus

The apparatus required on the engine is quite simple in construction. There is a gun-metal scoop, which has a thin steel cutting edge, easily renewable and adjustable for wear and tear and for settlement of the engine due to spring weakening and tyre wear. The scoop is hinged to the lower end of an iron pipe that passes up through the tender, and is jointed to the vertical delivery pipe, which has a half-round bend at the top for discharging the water into the tank. In order to allow excess water to escape, there is a hinged lid above the box covering the delivery pipe, and this opens when the tank is full. This is very necessary, as the water enters at high speed and sets up great pressure. Some tenders are provided with a pipe that discharges excess water back into the trough.

Owing to the pressure set up by the water, it is not easy to raise the scoop when the engine is travelling fast, and it may be necessary to raise it before the end of the trough is reached. This is usually done nowadays by a small cylinder and piston, actuated by steam, compressed air or vacuum. A balance-weight keeps the scoop normally up, the cylinder being employed to push it down. On tank locomotives, which may run either chimney or bunker first, two scoops are required. They may be separate fittings, or made to lower together. In the latter arrangement one of the scoops simply trails idly in the water while the other is picking up. A hinged flap in the vertical pipe prevents the water escaping by way of the idle scoop.

The lowest speed for the locomotive at which the water will rise high enough in the delivery pipe to discharge into the tender tank is about 15 to 20 miles per hour, and the higher the speed the more water can be picked up. When a train has two engines drawing it, the leading or pilot engine dips in first, and about half-way along the trough the train engine dips in and the pilot takes out his scoop. Many of the late Midland Railway engines, on account of the extensive piloting resorted to on that line, had steel shields fitted in front of the leading wheels to prevent small stones being thrown up into the motion by the water-splash created by the pilot engine. This refinement is not in general use however.

L.M.S. Down 11.10 a.m. non-stop at Bushey. Engine "*Rupert Guiness*" No. 668

Troughs on British Railways

In order that readers may be able to look out for these troughs whenever they are travelling, we give below a list of all those on the British railways. They are invariably laid in both the up and the down lines.

L.N.E.R.

Between Lucker and Belford; between Northallerton and Danby Wiske; near Charwelton and Killamarsh stations; between Bentley and Ipswich; between Burston and Tivetshall; at Langley; between Knebworth and Stevenage; at Werrington Junction, N. of Peterborough; between Newark and Carlton, N. of the Trent; between Scrooby and Bawtry; at Hatch End, between Pinner and Bushey.

Third part of L.M.S. 10 a.m. Scotch Express (4–6–0 Loco No. 2427) at Bushey

L.M.S.R.

Between the following places:—Wolverton and Castlethorpe; Rugby and Brinklow; Rugby and Brandon and Wolston; Tamworth (*Continued on next page*)

How Engines Pick Up Water—

(*Continued from previous page*)

and Lichfield; Whitmore and Madeley; Preston Brook and Moore; Brock and Garstang; Hest Bank and Bolton-le-Sands; Low Gill and Tebay; Waverton and Chester; Connah's Quay and Flint; Prestatyn and Rhyl; Llanfairfechan and Aber; Diggle and Marsden; Eccles and Weaste; Halebank and Ditton; Horbury Junction and Wakefield; Hoscar and Burscough Bridge; Kirkby and Fazakerley; Lea Road and Salwick; Lostock Junction and Bolton; Rufford and Burscough Junction; Rochdale and Smithy Bridge; Sowerby Bridge and Luddendenfoot; Moorside and Wardley and Walkden; Knottingley and Whitley Bridge; Oakley and Sharnbrook; Loughborough and Hathern; at Melton Mowbray; at Tamworth; at Hawes Junction.

G.W.R.

Near Goring; near Keynsham, between Bath and Bristol; near Creech, between Bridgwater and Taunton; at Exminster; near King's Sutton, between Oxford and Banbury; near Lapworth, between Warwick and Birmingham; between Charlbury and Ascott-under-Wychwood; between Aldermaston and Midgham; at Westbury; at Chipping Sodbury; near Severn Tunnel Junction; between Ferryside and Carmarthen; near Ludlow; at Denham.

There are no water troughs on the Southern Railway or on the Irish railways.

A Day in a Running Shed—

(*Continued from page 625*)

arrange for their work to be carried on, and then proceed to the vans.

The tool van train consists of the large steam crane with runner to carry the jib in its running position, a van containing wood packing, another with an ample supply of tools for tackling jobs where the crane cannot be used, and lastly the vehicle in which the staff ride. In this coach there is a cooking range for providing hot meals, and, of course, a supply of food is carried.

Amongst the tools carried are hydraulic jacks for heavy lifts, block and wire rope tackle for very heavy pulls, and an oxy-acetylene cutting plant for rapidly cutting through any metal.

Out on the line each of the gang takes a pride in helping to clear the wreckage in record time. After a big job, when gathered at the table in the riding van for their well-earned meal, tired out, none are too tired to compare their recent job with what they did at the same spot on a previous occasion. Whilst not doubting their veracity, you must grant them the proverbial fisherman's licence for yarning!

The yard of a main line locomotive shed is one of the busiest areas of the line, for at a shed like York it is a common matter for over 150 engines to enter, and also leave, the shed every 24 hours. This is at the rate of an engine either entering, or leaving, at less than 5 min. intervals throughout the day.

Nearly all these engines clean their fires, and the ballast thus obtained, amounting to about 250 tons per week, has to be cleared away daily.

Readers' Sales and Wants

If you have anything to sell or wish to buy anything, take advantage of the service offered by a small advertisement in the columns of the "*M.M.*" (see page 664).

Advertisers please note that advertisements of Meccano goods cannot be inserted.

The rates are one penny per word, with a minimum of 1/- (cash with order).

Your advertisement must be received before the 10th of the month for insertion in the following month's issue.

A British "Ljungström" Turbine Loco

(*Continued from page 621*)

Among these engines may be mentioned the "Reid-MacLeod" geared turbine condensing locomotive, built by the North British Locomotive Co. Ltd., of Glasgow, in 1924. This engine differs from the "Ljungström" turbo-condensing locomotive in many respects, notably in that its turbines are placed longitudinally. The driving wheels are actuated directly from the turbines and there is a complete absence of reciprocative motion.

In Germany also a good deal of experimental work has been carried out in regard to this type of engine. In 1924 Messrs. Krupp constructed at their Essen Works a turbine locomotive embodying many interesting features, and for this engine a reduction of 20 per cent. in fuel consumption was claimed. More recently, Messrs. J. A. Maffei of Munich constructed a turbine engine on somewhat similar lines to the Krupp locomotive. This engine, which was designed to develop 2,500 h.p. and to have a maximum speed of approximately 75 miles per hour, underwent extensive trials last year on the Bavarian section of the German State Railways.

A New Miniature Railway

Famous Motorist's Life Ambition Realised

On the way to Dymchurch. The top of the cab on the loco has been removed in this photograph

NEARLY every boy feels at some stage in his early days that the crowning experience of his life would be that of donning overalls and taking charge of a really big locomotive, but few ever realise that ambition. Nearly 40 years ago was born a boy whose ambition went beyond this, for he resolved that one day he would actually control a real railway. That bold ambition was realised on 28th May last when there was completed the final stretch of the fascinating 15 in. gauge railway that has been built to link up the ancient Cinque Port towns of Hythe and New Romney on the south-eastern coast of Kent.

The boy referred to is Captain J. E. P. Howey, who has formed an incorporated company under the Light Railways Act. He is the principal shareholder and is taking the leading part both in the construction and operation of the line. Capt. Howey is well known in motoring circles at Brooklands and other racing tracks and owns several famous cars.

The engineer and manager of the line is Mr. Henry Greenly, A.I.Loco. E., the famous designer of miniature locomotives, who has had a unique experience in every phase of miniature railway work.

The Romney, Hythe and Dymchurch Railway serves a district that for the past 40 years has desired a railway. The development has been promised time and time again, and when Captain Howey's scheme was mooted the populace almost to a man voted for it. Some 20 years ago the Southern Railway applied for powers to establish a similar scheme in this area, but this was to have been a standard gauge line with a single track at an estimated cost of £60,000. It was practically impossible for the district then to justify the expenditure of so large a sum and for that reason nothing came of the project. It is interesting to learn that the approximate total cost of building and equipping the new railway is rather less than half that of the Southern Railway's scheme, and that Sir Herbert Walker, the general manager of the Southern Railway, has given a considerable amount of practical support to Captain Howey in the development of the line.

A small gauge line, Captain Howey contends, is the ideal feeder scheme for country districts that could not economically support the standard gauge. The Romney, Hythe and Dymchurch line is in the midst of a popular holiday district, Hythe itself being wonderfully situated, with natural amenities equal to those of many considerably more famous seaside resorts. Dymchurch, hitherto practically isolated, has wonderful sands, while New Romney is an ancient medieval borough close to which is Dungeness, a name with which every boy is familiar. All these places are linked by the little R. H. & D. Railway.

The Romney Marsh is an interesting stretch of country, being land reclaimed from the sea. Its nominal level is low, but there is an excellent drainage system, and at no point will the line be at all waterlogged. The adoption of a small gauge has allowed roads to be tunnelled successfully, for a cutting can go down to 5 ft. 6 in. in depth without encountering water, and thus the 6 ft. 7 in.

headroom allowed by the Ministry of Transport has enabled the line to be taken under the main road at New Romney and the secondary road at Hythe, at a reasonable cost and with a reasonable alteration of road gradient.

Several main drainage canals and innumerable dykes have had to be crossed in the course of the 8¼ miles track, the largest of these being that adjacent to the Duke of York's Camp at Jesson. This bridge is a single span skew "N" type girder bridge 56 ft. in length, raised on reinforced concrete abutments. The road bridge at The Warren, New Romney, has two tunnels, each 50 ft. in length, and was built in reinforced concrete in 5½ weeks.

Inspecting the Locomotive at Romney Terminus

As already mentioned the gauge of the line is 15 in. This gauge was proposed many years ago by Sir Arthur Heywood, who adopted it for his own private line at Duffield Park in Derbyshire. Later he laid a 4½ mile system connecting Eaton Hall on the Duke of Westminster's estate with the neighbouring railway station at Balderton, and although Sir Arthur missed perfection in the design of locomotives he proved the usefulness of what he termed the "minimum gauge." The gauge was therefore adopted for several other pleasure park lines and some 25 years ago the first miniature or scale model locomotive was built. Designs were improved from time to time and in 1913 Captain Howey laid a private line at Stoughton Manor, Huntingdonshire, which was worked by a "Pacific" engine built to the designs of Mr. H. Greenly. In 1915 a narrow gauge (3 ft.) line at Eskdale in Cumberland was altered to 15 in. gauge and Captain Howey's "*Colossus*" was one of the locomotives tried out. Here the engine ran in direct competition with those of the Heywood type and showed a marked superiority in speed and efficiency. Another locomotive designed by Mr. Greenly, "*Green Goddess*," also was tried out on the Eskdale Railway, and a brief account of this line and "*Green Goddess's*" performance will do more than mere statistics to convey some idea of this engine's superlative efficiency.

Photos] [*W. H. Evernden*

The train standing in Romney Station

The Eskdale line abounds in steep gradients and sharp curves, and the principal goods traffic consists of stone quarried from the hills. It was in front of a 34-ton mineral train that this miniature locomotive put up its best performance in attaining a speed of 35 m.p.h. without difficulty. On a level and perfect track 40 m.p.h. could have been reached. It should be borne in mind that this load to "*Green Goddess*" represents 850 tons to its prototype, Mr. H. N. Gresley's "*Flying Scotsman*," which in practice is rarely called upon to tackle more than 550 tons.

The mechanism of "*Green Goddess*" is designed specially to meet the requirements of miniature railway work, and a very high degree of efficiency is obtained, the coal and water consumption being truly proportionate to the work done. The promoters of the R. H. & D. Railway believed that the miniature scheme could show a better performance than that achieved by the orthodox small gauge engine, and to prove their theory they purchased from the stock designs of an old-established firm of locomotive builders an engine built for use on contractors' small gauge lines. On runs of over six miles this engine failed dismally in comparison with Captain Howey's miniature engines. It possessed only half the power and burnt 2½ times as much coal.

From these beginnings the scale of 1/3rd (4 in. to the foot) was evolved, mainly with a view to obtaining increased power and speed, and providing for the better comfort of the engine driver. The disparity in size between the locomotives and coaches that must take "full size" passengers has been reduced, and the tenders arranged with a well seat that enables the driver to sit down and be sheltered by the "scale" cab.

The engines to be used on the R. H. and D. line will be eight in number and will be equipped with piston valves, superheaters, automatic vacuum brakes, pop safety valves, Wootten fireboxes, bogie tenders and every convenience that an engine driver could desire. All are miniatures of main-line types, built to a scale of 4 in. to the foot. Three of them—including the famous *"Green Goddess"* and the *"Northern Chief"* which are now at New Romney—are of the Great Northern (L.N.E.R.) "Pacific" type, and two express "Pacifics" with three cylinders have also been built. Two "Mountain" type (4–8–2) tender engines are on order and the locomotive stock is completed by a four-wheeled goods and shunting engine of special design. The standard passenger engines weigh over eight tons. They will haul in regular service a train of 20 carriages at 30 miles an hour with ease. The cylinders are $5\frac{1}{4}$ in. bore by $8\frac{1}{2}$ in. stroke. The driving wheels of the express "Pacific" type engines measure $25\frac{1}{2}$ in. diameter, and those of the eight-coupled engines are $19\frac{1}{2}$ in. In length the engines with tender total 25 ft. The valve gear is the complete Walschaerts' type, the prime motion being taken from a return crank on the driving crank. The reversing lever in the cab can be operated with a direct push and pull with a screw "vernier" adjustment, and at the Eskdale trials *"Green Goddess"* was able to haul a heavy train with the gear linked up to give a valve cut off of 35 per cent. of the stroke.

Dignity and Impudence! 3-cylinder "Pacifics," *"Typhoon No. 7"* and *"Flying Scotsman"*

Semi-open and closed carriages will be used. Sixty of the former, each capable of carrying eight adults have already been constructed, and for the winter traffic the closed cars will be installed. Goods wagons of various types according to the needs of the traffic are under consideration and already sixteen one-ton trucks have been delivered.

In the course of the $8\frac{1}{4}$ miles of the line there will be five stations and halts. In the layout of these stations the organisers have anticipated maximum requirements in order that the efficiency of the line may not be impaired in the future.

The stations are as follows :—

New Romney (the main terminus) with four passenger roads, locomotive and works buildings, turntable, a carriage shed and an extensive goods yard. The Southern Railway have extended their line into this yard for purposes of goods transfer.

Holiday Camp near Jesson Farm and adjacent to Messrs. Allnatt's famous children's holiday-camp. This camp is also known as the Duke of York's Summer Camp. H.R.H. the Duke of York has displayed considerable interest in Captain Howey's venture, and when visiting the camp last year he drove a train over the section from New Romney to Holiday Camp. Mr. H. N. Gresley, the L.N.E.R. Chief Mechanical Engineer, was among the party present, and when it was suggested that a collection be taken for the driver his was the hat that went round. It was quickly filled with small change and at the end of the run was handed to the Duke with due ceremony. The incident caused great amusement and in the end the Duke handed the proceeds to the regular driver of the engine.

Dymchurch (Marshlands), adjacent to the St. Mary's and Bonnington Roads and to the Marshlands Hotel near to the western end of this charming seaside resort. The R. H. and D. Railway thus brings Dymchurch into direct communication with London, and will enhance the popularity of its beautiful stretch of sand.

Dymchurch (Dymchurch Bay and Burmarsh). A halt on the eastern end of Dymchurch on the road to Burmarsh village. From here the line passes under the shadow of Lympne Castle close to the hills under the West Hythe Road to Hythe alongside the southern bank of the Military Canal.

Hythe (Ashford Road). This terminus is close to H.M. School of Musketry and near to the Folkestone omnibus terminus.

It is of interest to note here that the whole of the work of construction, including the permanent way and works buildings, bridges, locomotives, carriages, wagons, and equipment generally, has been carried out to the company's designs.

The directors of the R. H. and D. Railway think that their present proposals offer a reasonable chance of success, and that as the East Kent coast is a popular holiday centre, there will be sufficient summer traffic to allow the service to be continued during the winter. What they lose on the roundabouts will be made up on the swings! Therefore, in all probability, the inhabitants of the Marsh will be blessed with a service all the year round.

FAMOUS CANALS OF THE WORLD

VI.—PANAMA CANAL

IN last month's issue we showed how seriously de Lesseps had underestimated the engineering difficulties involved in cutting the Panama Canal, and how his miscalculations resulted in repeated revisions of his estimates of the time and money that would be required to complete the undertaking. To these purely engineering difficulties was added another that apparently had not been taken into consideration at all, and this was the havoc wrought by the fever-carrying mosquitoes that swarmed throughout large areas of the Isthmus.

The majority of the workpeople had been specially imported to carry out the scheme and, not having had time to adapt themselves to the new climatic conditions, they fell easy victims to the terrible epidemics of fever and cholera that swept at intervals through the camps of the Panama Canal Company. At Colon and Panama substantial hospitals had been built, but it was not long before every camp became a hospital. Desperate efforts were made to combat the ravages of the disease, but with little success, mainly on account of lack of knowledge of the manner in which the disease was spread and to a considerable extent also on account of a water supply that was very seriously contaminated.

The Gatun Locks (south end) in course of construction

Most of the unfortunate victims were French labourers who had been beguiled from the friendly climate of their own country to the tropical conditions of the Isthmus by visions of adventure and promises of big earnings. Their disillusionment was tragic. As the mosquitoes and insanitary conditions continued month after month to take heavy toll of life, fever became a dreaded spectre to engineers and workmen alike and the Isthmus became known as the "White man's grave-yard."

In the meantime work on the canal continued, but with painful slowness. A large amount of equipment was transported to the Isthmus and brought into use, including 72 excavators and 24 dredgers, in addition to steam cranes, locomotives and rolling stock. By the end of 1887 the canal had been wholly or partly excavated for a distance of about 10 miles inland at the Colon end and for nearly four miles at the Panama end, while some progress had been made in dredging a deep-water channel through each of the terminal harbours. In the Chagres Valley very little had been achieved, however, for there operations had been seriously delayed during the rainy seasons by the swamping of the works by the flood waters of the River Chagres. In the Culebra Hill locality also very little had been done. In short, in the course of 6½ years less than two-fifths of the canal had been constructed.

A feeling of hopelessness brooded over the whole enterprise, while the barely concealed discontent of the French labourers was a menacing undercurrent of which all were conscious. De Lesseps had to admit that, under the conditions then existing, it would be an almost insuperable task to cut a sea-level canal across the Isthmus and, realising that he must do something drastic to avert a complete collapse of his scheme, he regretfully gave up his original plan and decided to construct a canal having a series of four locks on each slope of Culebra Hill. The summit level of the canal through the Culebra cutting was to be 125 ft. above Atlantic level.

The immediate effect of this change of plan was to reduce the amount of necessary excavation through Culebra Hill by approximately 85,000,000 cubic yards, but against the substantial saving in labour and money that this represented had to be reckoned the necessity of constructing eight locks. This item in fact increased de Lesseps' estimate of the entire cost of the canal, and he now placed this at £65,500,000, as against his first estimate of £34,000,000.

The depressing reports that for a long time had been finding their way from the Isthmus to France had gradually weakened the French public's confidence in the famous engineer, and money was no longer liberally poured into the coffers of the Canal Company. The utter lack of enthusiasm with which de Lesseps' latest proposal was received must have given him warning of how slender had become the nation's trust in him. Worse was to follow, however, for a year later the inevitable happened and the Canal Company became bankrupt.

The financial collapse of the company created a painful sensation throughout France, where it brought utter ruin to thousands of families. On 2nd February, 1889, a City Tribunal at Paris declared the Canal Company to be officially dissolved and appointed a liquidator, who gradually closed down the activities at the Isthmus by withdrawing the workpeople in weekly batches. By May in the same year operations were brought to a complete standstill.

A public demand arose for the trial of de Lesseps and eventually he was arrested on a charge of having fraudulently used the funds of the Canal Company. The official inquiry into the affairs of the company lasted a considerable time and some startling disclosures were made. Of the enormous sum that had been sunk in the undertaking—approximately £100,000,000—only about one-third had been spent directly on the canal works. Of the remainder, one-third had been wasted and the other third misappropriated. Many of the officials had been paid utterly preposterous salaries and had lived on an almost incredible scale of extravagance. One official had a pigeon house built that cost the company £3,000 and another man erected a bath house costing £8,000. In addition, the huge consignments of goods sent out to the canal zone included a most amazing collection of utterly useless articles such as snowshoes, grand pianos, and a large cargo of hairpins!

In 1893 de Lesseps was sentenced to five years' imprisonment, but on account of his advanced age—he was then 88—and his past honourable record the sentence was never enforced. To some extent de Lesseps had been more sinned against than sinning, and the duplicity of some of his subordinates was reflected in the severe sentences passed upon them.

The collapse of the French enterprise brought about a revival of American interest in the canal project and in 1887 a survey party was sent from the United States to Nicaragua. So favourable was their report of the country through which it was proposed to construct a canal that in the following year a company was formed under the name of "The Maritime Canal Company," and it was not long before men and materials were being transported to the Nicaraguan Isthmus. Wharves and warehouses were erected at Greytown, where a breakwater for the protection of ships chartered by the company was also constructed. By taking advantage of Lake Nicaragua and adapting the San Juan River, the estimated amount of necessary excavation was reduced to 28 miles, out of a total length of canal of 170 miles. Work was commenced, but in 1894 the scheme collapsed, chiefly owing to lack of funds.

This American effort served to determine the French to complete their Panama scheme before the project was rendered of small importance by the construction of an oceanic canal across some other part of Central America. Thus it was that, in the year the American company failed at Nicaragua, a second or New Panama Canal Company was formed in France with an initial capital of £2,000,000.

The Colombian Government granted the New Panama Canal Company authority to complete the abandoned works, but stipulated that the canal must be finished within ten years after 1894. The company took over all the equipment of their predecessors, engaged considerable native labour in addition to European, and resumed operations at the Isthmus, but on a very reduced scale. Very little had been done by the old company in the way of constructing the eight locks planned by de Lesseps, and the entire canal scheme was now reconsidered and substantially altered.

The revised scheme comprised a canal with a sea-level section several miles in length at each end, and with the intermediate length of waterway constructed in two long sections elevated to different heights. The first altitude level was to be a large artificial lake created by erecting a dam at Bohio, and reached from the Atlantic level of the canal by a flight of two sets of locks. At Obispo the lake was to be terminated by a second similar flight of locks that would lead up to the summit level of the canal through Culebra Hill.

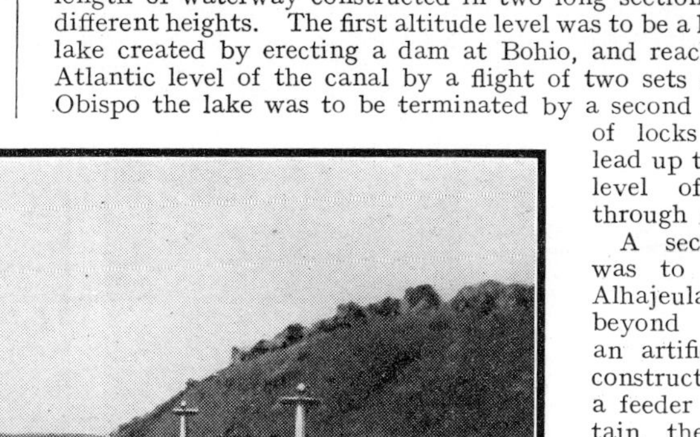

Miraflores Lock. Two pairs of locks, one for going up and one for coming down

A secondary dam was to be built at Alhajeula, nine miles beyond Obispo, and an artificial reservoir constructed from which a feeder would maintain the supply of water in the summit level. At the Panama end of this topmost section the canal was to be brought down to the level of the Pacific by means of four sets of locks situated at Paraiso, Pedro Miguel and Miraflores. The locks were each to have a clear length of 738 ft., a width of 82 ft., and a depth of 33 ft. 10 in. They were to be constructed two abreast, each set having a lifting range according to its situation. The depth of the canal proper was to be maintained throughout at 29 ft. 6 in. and the bottom width at 98 ft., except at certain points where the latter was to be increased for a short distance. It was estimated that this comprehensive scheme could be carried out for some £21,000,000, including the cost of diverting 31 miles of the Panama Railway from its route through the Chagres River to a course bordering the new lake.

From 1895 onward the New Panama Canal Company employed from 2,000 to 2,600 workpeople at the Isthmus. The company did not make any serious attempt to improve the conditions of living and the progress of the canal works proved slow and costly, although the native labourers principally employed did not succumb to disease as easily as Europeans.

Coaling Stage at Colon

The initial enterprise of the Maritime Company had reawakened the desire of the American people for their country to possess a State-owned and governed Atlantic-Pacific canal. Yielding to popular opinion, the Government ultimately had the Nicaraguan Isthmus re-surveyed, but without definite results. In 1899 President McKinley appointed a Commission to investigate the subject in detail, and two years later the Commission expressed themselves in favour of a canal via Lake Nicaragua, having a total length of 183⅝ miles and estimated to cost £40,000,000.

America had not lost interest in the chequered career of the Panama project and was aware that matters were not going well with the second French company. Before authorising the formation of a new American company to carry out the Nicaraguan scheme the United States Government therefore sought to purchase the Panama undertaking as it stood. The French company were only prepared to sell a half interest in their scheme, however, and the United States therefore declared their intention of pushing ahead with the Nicaraguan project.

The news of this decision was received with apprehension by the New Panama Canal Company, for if the Nicaraguan Canal were to become a reality—and backed by American enterprise and ample funds it had every prospect of doing so—the ultimate prosperity of the Panama Canal would suffer a severe blow. America was prepared to pay 40,000,000 dollars for the canal undertaking, which was barely one-sixteenth of the money so far expended on the scheme and considerably below the figure at which the French company were prepared to sell.

Then America learned that the concession granted to the company by the Colombian Government expired in October 1904, and that if the canal were unfinished at that time it would become the property of Colombia, unless the concession were renewed. America therefore decided to wait until that date in the hope of then being able to negotiate with Colombia, rather than continue the present haggling with the unwilling French owners.

The Panama Company now realised that unless they accepted America's offer they would not only ultimately lose the canal, for it was evident that this would not be completed before the concession expired, but would also lose the 40,000,000 dollars. They decided to make the best of a bad job therefore and, obtaining Colombia's permission to sell out to America, offered the canal undertaking to that country for 40,000,000 dollars. The offer was promptly accepted and in March 1903 the whole Panama scheme was officially signed over to the United States.

The H.M.S. "*Renown*," on which the Duke and Duchess of York toured the world, in the Gatun Locks at Panama

Complications now arose on account of the refusal of Colombia to agree to the United States assuming perpetual control of the three mile wide strip of land on each side of the canal that had been granted to the New Panama Canal Company. The difficult situation thus created was unexpectedly relieved in November of the same year, however, by Panama revolting from Colombian Government and declaring itself an Independent State.

The revolution was a very mild affair, as revolutions go. The trouble had been brewing in the Province of Panama for a long time and the revolutionists finally decided to strike their blow on 4th November, 1903. The Colombian Government authorities got wind of the affair, and on 3rd November a Colombian steamer arrived at Colon with five generals, all magnificently attired in full war regalia, and 450 soldiers, many of whom were accompanied by their wives! General Torves was left in charge of the troops, who camped out in the streets of the town, while General Tovar, the commander of the contingent, and three other generals entrained immediately for Panama, with the intention of creating awe in the hearts of the revolutionists.

Word was received at Panama that the four generals were on their way and preparations were hastily made to "welcome" them. On arrival at the barracks they were very courteously received but the warmth of the welcome died suddenly when General Huertas, one of the most stalwart of the revolutionists, stepped forward and ordered General Tovar to surrender his sword. The refusal of the latter was followed immediately by the arrest of himself and his fellow officers.

The die had now been cast and the revolutionists, feeling rather uneasy, realised that they must go through with their venture. Their nervousness was due partly to doubt as to the attitude of three Colombian gunboats stationed outside the harbour, and when the revolt was duly announced to the boats their reply was anxiously awaited. Two of the gunboats remained silent, but the third, named the "*Bogota*," replied that if the captive generals were not released by 10 o'clock the city would be bombarded. At 10 o'clock the generals were still locked up. The "*Bogota*" therefore manœuvred into position, fired three shells into the city—and then steamed away! A Chinese coolie near the barracks was killed, but he had the distinction of being the only fatality during the revolution!

On the following morning one of the two remaining gunboats decided to forsake the Colombian cause and hoisted the flag of the revolutionists; the other boat presumably steamed away.

When General Torves at Colon learned of the imprisonment of the four generals he immediately attributed it to American interference and announced that he would kill every American in Colon if General Tovar were not speedily released. So threatening did Torves become that 40 marines were landed from the American cruiser "*Nashville*," then anchored off Colon. Matters looked very ugly for a time. Torves demanded a special train to transport his troops across the Isthmus to Panama, and the superintendent of the line informed him that he would be pleased to provide a train—provided that the general would pay for it! The latter had not sufficient cash in his possession to pay the fares of 451 people, which would have amounted to about 2,000 dollars in gold, and he therefore retired defeated! On seeking to telephone and telegraph to his imprisoned comrades he was told that both systems were out of order.

Later the revolutionists offered Torves 8,000 dollars to remove himself and his men from Colon and he accepted the bribe. The contingent in due course left for home, embarking on the Royal Mail steamer "*Orinoco*." The general's negotiations with the revolutionists later became known to his troops and they expressed their contempt by forcibly relieving him of the money! Shortly after the party left Colon a special train drew up at the station and four very subdued-looking generals alighted. At Panama they had faithfully promised to be good and go home quietly and had thereupon been released!

A Republican Government of Panama was formed without delay. On 7th November Banau Varilla, an able French civil engineer who had been associated with the canal operations for many years and had also been one of the prime movers of the revolution, was appointed Envoy Plenipotentiary of Panama to the United States, and immediately took up his duties at Washington. Panama's new Government was, of course, wholly in favour of America taking over the canal enterprise and finishing it off in a prompt and efficient manner, and Varilla's appointment resulted in the signing of the Banau-Varilla Treaty on 18th November the same year. This treaty gave America perpetual occupation and control of a strip of land 10 miles in width—five miles on each side of the canal—extending the entire length of the canal and for three miles out to sea at the Atlantic and Pacific termini.

In May 1904 America took over from the French the actual control of the canal works, and thus France passed out of the affair completely.

The equipment purchased by America included of course, the Panama Railway, and this the American engineers found to be sadly disorganised. Upon its efficiency depended the quick transport of men and materials between the various scenes of operations, and therefore new rolling stock and a large quantity of rails were included among the necessary materials shipped to the Isthmus as a prelude to the campaign.

The preliminary operations were watched with keen interest by the people of the newly made Republic and it was quickly realised that this time the enterprise was being tackled in a really practical spirit, and that it would be carried through to a successful finish. Next month we shall describe how the difficulties that had proved too much for the French companies were overcome and the Panama Canal completed.

Monster Canadian Locomotives

Interesting Comparison with those of 60 Years Ago

Courtesy] [*C.N.R.*

The first of the Canadian National Railways' new "6100 Northern" type locomotives that have been introduced to celebrate the Jubilee of the Confederation of the Dominion of Canada

THE first of 40 giant 4–8–4 locomotives to be known as the "6100 Class, Northern Type" has been placed in service on the Canadian National Railways' line between Montreal and Toronto. This new monster, which pulls a steel train of 16 Pullman coaches at 90 miles an hour, is 15 ft. 3 in. in height and measures 39 ft. 10¾ in. from the tip of the "cow catcher" to the tail of the tender. The engine with its empty tender weighs 319 tons. Twenty of these engines are being built by the Canadian Locomotive Company, Kingston, and 20 by the Montreal Locomotive Works, both orders being identical with the exception of a few details. The engines are designed for either passenger or fast freight service.

The boiler is of the straight top type with radially stayed firebox and is built to carry a pressure of 250 lb. per sq. in. The cab is a short vestibule all-steel type, wood lined, with C.N. standard turrets placed ahead of the cab. The left-hand turret is supplied with superheated steam by a 3 in. pipe leading from a connection on the superheater header, while the right-hand turret is supplied with saturated steam from a direct connection to the boiler. Superheated steam is supplied to the air pump, feed water heater pump, stoker and headlight generator; while saturated steam is supplied to the inspirator, lubricator and other small auxiliaries.

An interesting feature is the location of the whistle, which had to be placed at the left-hand side of the smokestack as far from the cab as possible, in order to prevent the driver and the fireman being rendered deaf by its shriek when the train is travelling at high speed!

The "6100 type" engine has been designed by the Motive Power Department of the Canadian National Railways and represents an increase of 20 per cent. in tractive power over the "6000 type" engine which, at the time of its introduction, was the largest passenger locomotive in the world.

The leading dimensions and weights of these new engines are as follows:—

Cylinder	25½ in. × 30 in.
Driving Wheels—Dia.	73 in.
Boiler—Outside Dia.	90 in.
Working Pressure	250 lb.
Firebox	126⅛ in. × 96¼ in.
Wheelbase—Engine ...	43 ft. 10 in.
Wheelbase—Engine and Tender ...	82 ft. 0 in.
Weight of Engine (Booster fitted) in working order	388,000 lb.
Weight of Tender	260,000 lb.
Heating Surface :	
Tubes and Flues	3,814 sq. ft.
Firebox	315 "
Syphons and Arch Tubes ...	117 "
Total	4,256 "
Superheater	1,700 "
Grate Area	84.4 "
Max. Tractive Power, engines only	56,800 lb.
" " " with booster	69,700 lb.
Capacity of Tender—Water	11,300 Imp. Gals.
" " —Coal	20 tons

In designing the new locomotives the engineers of the C.N.R. have kept in mind the peculiar requirements of railway operation in Canada. Climatic conditions, ranging from intense summer heat to severe winter cold, create problems of considerable difficulty. The new engines therefore have been built to permit of their being worked with a high degree of efficiency throughout the complete range of weather, even in blizzards and heavy snowstorms.

These are the first Canadian engines to bear a distinctly Canadian name. Previously, Canadian-built engines have been based on the designs of some other well-known type, such as the "No. 6000," the "41000," and the "Santa Fé," but the "6100" is to be known as the "6100 Class, Northern Type," a name that clearly indicates the part of the American Continent in which it was developed.

The new engines are to be used on such important runs as that made by the "*International Limited*," from Montreal to Sarnia, a distance of 511 miles, in covering which a Canadian record will be set up for the longest run without a change of engine. To facilitate this long run special coal chutes have been built at various points along the line. Engines of the new type will also be used for the Grand Trunk Western lines and on the international trains running between the principal cities of Eastern Canada and the United States.

It is interesting to compare these huge locomotives with our own Great Western Company's "*King George V*," which, complete with tender, weighs 136 tons, 14 cwt. In spite of the extraordinary disparity in weight—nearly 150 tons in the booster-less type—there is a gain of only 16,500 lb. in tractive effort.

Another and in some respects even more interesting comparison is afforded by a study of our illustrations, the second of which shows a half-size model of the Canadian National locomotive "*Dorchester*." This was the first locomotive ever used in Canada and was constructed in England by Robert Stephenson & Co. It was shipped to Montreal for service on the Champlain and St. Lawrence Railway, the first Canadian line, built in 1835. This line, which was 16 miles in length, ran from Laprairie, on Lake Champlain, to St. Johns in Quebec, and now forms part of the Canadian National Railway system.

The original line was a "portage" road, designed to shorten the distance between Montreal and New York. The route, via the Richelieu River, was a natural artery of trade between the two countries in early days, and was first used by Indians. Later the French and other colonists used it for trade and war, while in revolutionary days it was followed by the Americans when they invaded Canada. The river of St. Johns is now spanned by several bridges, over one of which C.N.R. trains pass daily to and from New York, following a line that is practically parallel with the original water route.

Courtesy] [*C.N.R.*

A half-size model of the wood-burner "*Dorchester*," the first locomotive used in Canada

Our illustration shows a model of the "*Dorchester*" mounted on a lorry at an exhibition in Montreal. It will be seen that the locomotive was a wood-burner and carried its water in a barrel at the rear of the tender.

An interesting illustration of railway progress in Canada is furnished by a comparison between another wood-burning locomotive that ran on the Grand Trunk Railway 60 years ago, and the "6100" type of to-day. The boiler alone of the "6100" is almost equal in size to the complete engine of 1867. The latter could only haul four passenger coaches and from 10 to 15 freight cars on the level, whereas the new monster makes light work of 16 passenger coaches or 150 heavy freight cars.

Another interesting comparison is to be found in the smoke stacks of the two engines. That of the old wood-burner towered 14 ft. 10 in. above the track, flaring at the top like a glorified cement mixer; the new locomotive has a low and squat smoke stack, giving an impression of immense power and speed.

This new locomotive possesses the distinction of having been driven by Mr. Stanley Baldwin, the Prime Minister, during his recent visit to Canada.

Competition Results

No. 2 Outfit (Overseas Section)

The following are the results in the Overseas Section of the special Meccano Competition for models built from the contents of a No. 2 Outfit:—

First Prize (Meccano products to value of £3-3s.): Charles Roger, 55, rue de Turenne, Paris, III. Second Prize (Meccano products to value £2-2s.): Gordon H. F. Bartlett, Bowen Terrace, Brisbane, Queensland. Third Prize (Meccano products to value £1-1s.): I. K. Menon, Tellicherry, Malabar, S. India.

Six Prizes, each of Meccano products to value 10/6: F. J. A. Nash, Gibraltar; Salvatore Galdes, Valletta, Malta; J. W. M. Yorston, Dunedin, New Zealand; J. Sunderland, Newcastle, N.S.W.; C. Marchison, Melbourne, Australia; P. T. Hewitt, Geneva.

Specially Commended (Certificates of Merit): S. Wreford, South Canterbury, New Zealand; A. Sinclair, Toronto, Canada; M. Ruskjer, Alta, Canada; P. Grant, Johannesburg, S. Africa; W. L. Holcroft, East London, S. Africa; E. Holder, Port-of-Spain, Trinidad; D McDonald, Annotto Bay, Jamaica.

The First Prize-winning model represents a mobile crane—a particularly interesting subject for Meccano models. A crane of this type will travel anywhere where a petrol lorry can go, and it is used to a large extent in factories and engineering works on account of the considerable saving that it effects in handling costs. The crane may be run alongside a railway wagon, for example, and used to load a lorry, thereby obviating the necessity of shunting the wagon under a fixed crane.

G. H. F. Bartlett submitted a model vertical drill in which he has incorporated an ingenious method of lubrication, while I. K. Menon obtained Third Prize with a model railway velocipede. As most Meccano boys know, the latter apparatus resembles the frame of an ordinary bicycle mounted on four flanged wheels, which run on the railway lines. The machine is propelled either by pedals in the same way as in a bicycle, or by hand levers.

Meccano Bevel Gears

Readers are requested to note that part No. 30b, $\frac{3}{4}''$ diam. Bevel Gear, has been withdrawn from circulation in view of the fact that a right-angle drive giving a ratio of 1 : 1, for which this part was originally designed, may be obtained satisfactorily by using two of the existing $\frac{7}{8}''$ Bevel Gears, part No. 30.

The $1\frac{1}{2}''$ Bevel Gear (No. 30c), which was illustrated in the October "*M.M.*," is now supplied with eight holes punched in its face. This alteration adds considerably to the adaptability of the part.

The $1\frac{1}{2}''$ Bevel Gear is designed to mesh with the $\frac{1}{2}''$ Bevel Gear (No. 30a) only, and these wheels when used in this way provide a speed ratio of 3 : 1. Part No. 30a will not mesh correctly with a like part, nor will 30c; they are intended for use only with each other.

BUILD YOUR OWN MOTOR CAR

"STRUCTO" Motor Cars are everywhere accepted as the most perfect models of real motor cars made. The De Luxe Motor Car No. 12 here shown (which is supplied in parts, ready to build) will interest every boy and father who is keen on motor cars.

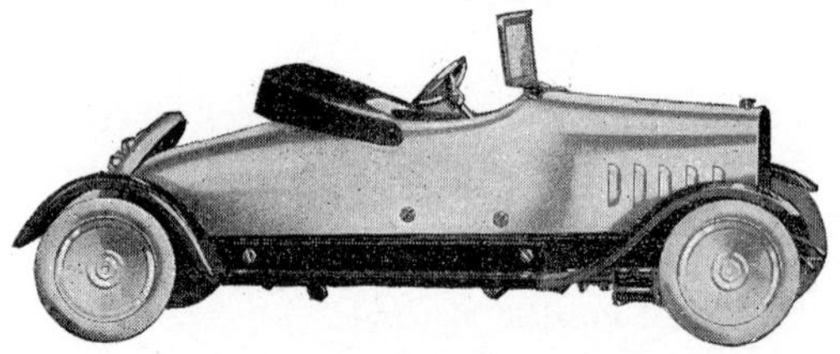

DE LUXE MOTOR. Set No. 12.

Sold in Construction Set ready to build

This is the most perfect reproduction of a real Motor Car ever produced. Notice the present day type of Motor Car design; the slanting wind shield, underslung body, spare wheel and other features. 16 in. long, $12\frac{1}{2}$ in. wheel base. Triple unit motor, sliding gear transmission, regular "big" car differential; two speeds, forward and reverse. Gear shift control lever. Complete in every respect. Finished in orange enamel, nickel trimmings and black mudguards. Separate winding crank.

Price 47/6

DE LUXE MOTOR. No. 12

In box ready to build

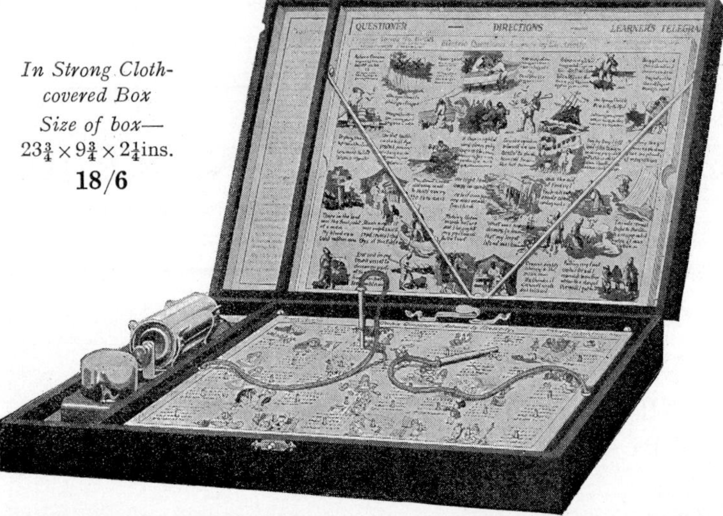

In Strong Cloth-covered Box

Size of box—

$23\frac{3}{4} \times 9\frac{3}{4} \times 2\frac{1}{4}$ ins.

18/6

The ELECTRIC QUESTIONER

Answers by Electricity

This is the greatest fun worker of the age. It is the game that asks you questions, puzzles you, teases you, and then with a loud B-U-Z-Z tells you the correct answer. Alice in Wonderland, Robinson Crusoe, Merchant Flags in Colour, Dogs in Colour, Conundrums, Questions from Wise Men, Characters in Literature, etc., etc., all are opened up to you in the Electric Questioner. As an entertainment it is incomparable. Also fitted with a Telegraph Key that enables anyone quite easily to learn the Morse Code.

Price 18/6

The ALFA-ROMEO Racing Car

Grand Prix of Europe 1924/5

World's Championship

Length 20 ins.

STRONG—FAST —SPORTY

There's a realism about this toy that will appeal to the boy who "wants the real thing." This miniature car—20 ins. in length—is an exact reproduction of the famous ALFA-ROMEO Racing Car.

An all-metal car, fitted with strong clockwork movement, large steering wheel, real front wheel steering gear and wire wheels fitted with balloon tyres. Beautifully finished in red, blue, or white enamel, the ALFA-ROMEO Racing Car is altogether a striking and speedy model. Each car packed in strong, attractive carton. A remarkable car at a remarkable price.

Price 25/-

Obtainable from all good Toy Departments and Toy Shops throughout the country

H. A. MOORE & CO. LTD., 150, Southampton Row, LONDON, W.C.1

The Conquest of the Air

DEVELOPMENT OF THE DIRIGIBLE

LAST month we described the construction of the British rigid airship R.34, and now we come to the historic flight across the Atlantic and back again made by this vessel in 1919. It was originally intended that the voyage should be "non-stop," but so great was the American interest in the project that it was finally arranged that the airship should remain in the United States for a few days before making the return trip to England. This having been decided, an advance party consisting of two officers and eight men was despatched to the United States to arrange for the provision and erection of a suitable mooring tower.

The flight began early in the morning of 2nd July, 1919. Twenty minutes after emerging from her shed at East Fortune, Scotland, the great airship was aloft, having on board a fuel supply of 4,900 gallons of petrol weighing 15.8 tons, and a specially selected crew of 32 with Major Scott in command. A 20 m.p.h. easterly wind was blowing and a misty rain falling at the time, and when only 1,000 ft. up the airship vanished above the low-lying clouds. At 1,500 ft. she re-appeared momentarily and was seen flying toward Edinburgh. Soon the western shore of Scotland was left behind, the northern coast of Ireland seen and passed, and the great expanse of the Atlantic opened out ahead.

The crew were relegated to four-hour turns of duty, while a useful "odd-job man" turned up in the person of a young stowaway who was found hiding amid the girders soon after the start of the flight. When he was discovered and hauled before the senior officer he was recognised as a mechanic who had begged to be included among the crew but whose application had been refused. By the time his presence became known it was impossible to drop him anywhere and he was therefore accommodated with the crew and as much use made of his services as possible.

During the greater part of the outward trip the R.34 flew at an altitude of 1,500 ft. and for a considerable period the crew had the strange experience of flying between two dense layers of clouds. Occasionally a rift in the bank of billowy vapour below gave them a glimpse of the sea, or a break in the cloud bank above gave them a brief sight of the sky. As they approached the Newfoundland coast they passed over innumerable icebergs. Dense fog was encountered as they passed over Newfoundland and they descended to 800 ft. in order to get their bearings. They were still 500 miles from their destination, and as Major Scott was becoming doubtful as to whether their supply of fuel would last out, he communicated by wireless with the United States authorities requesting them to despatch a destroyer to take the airship in tow. Happily this emergency measure proved unnecessary.

After the fog they encountered a severe thunderstorm, but eventually arrived safely at Long Island, New York, where a considerable landing party directed by United States airmen gave them a great welcome and assisted in anchoring the airship. The total time taken in making this momentous trip from East Fortune to Long Island, a distance of 3,520 miles, was 108 hours 12 mins.

The R.33 leaving the Aerodrome at Cardington, near Bedford

The weather did not improve much during the airship's sojourn on U.S. territory. On the evening of the 9th July, 1919, Major Scott decided to avail himself of the strong south westerly wind then blowing, and the crew were ordered to be at their posts at 10.30 p.m. that night. The gas-bags of the airship required partial re-inflation and this task was in hand almost up to the last moment. Hurried farewells were said to the many new friends the crew had made during their brief stay, the last of the necessary provisions were taken on board, the roll was called and a few minutes before midnight the airship was released. Although only three of the five engines were started up the airship rose quickly to a height of 2.000 ft. and headed toward New York.

News of the airship's departure had been flashed to New York immediately and naturally aroused the greatest interest. One of the officers of the R.34 in describing her passage over the great city wrote that "New York at midnight looks wonderful from above. Miles and miles of tiny twinkley lights—a veritable fairyland. We see thousands of upturned faces."

The return trip to England was accomplished in improving

The Giant Airship Shed at Howden, Yorkshire

weather and without any particular incidents. It was performed in much better time than the outer journey and Pulham airship station was reached at 6.20 p.m. on Sunday, 13th July, exactly 3 days, 3 hours, 3 minutes after the ascent from American territory.

A curious feature about this crossing of the Atlantic by the R.34 in 75 hours is that 75 years previously the famous writer Edgar Allan Poe published in an American newspaper a story in which an English airship was described as accomplishing a flight across the Atlantic in 75 hours!

Subsequently R.34 was flown from Pulham to East Fortune and her career came to a tragic end in 1921. The airship was being held down after a flight in foggy weather and in some manner the retaining party allowed her to swing with the result that she crashed into the cliffs. The forward and after cars were smashed but in spite of this damage she was able to fly to Howden. During the following night a strong wind arose and R.34 received such a severe buffeting that she became a total wreck.

The U.S.A. Army's "Blimp" T.C.5, about to land at East Boston, Mass., after a trial flight from Lakehurst, N.J.

A terrible fate awaited R.38 which was only partly completed at the time of the Armistice. An offer from the United States Government to purchase this airship when completed was accepted and the work was duly carried to a finish. It was intended to fly the airship across the Atlantic, and America sent a crew to England to take charge of her. A trial trip was made on 24th August, 1921, with a number of the American crew and many eminent British aeronautical experts included among the 49 persons on board.

Successful high-speed tests were made and a rudder test was then undertaken. As the airship floated above the River Humber, near Hull, at an altitude of 1,200 ft., the speed was reduced to 45 knots and the rudder put hard over and then reversed. The framework of the airship proved unequal to the severe strain imposed upon it and snapped near the stern. The break fractured some of the petrol tanks and a spark from a broken electric lead ignited the fumes of the escaping petrol. In a moment the hydrogen in the balloons also caught fire and the blazing airship dived into the Humber. Only five of the crew were rescued. This terrible catastrophe cast a gloom over this country and America, and a searching inquiry was held into the cause of the disaster. The information that came to light at this inquiry taught British aeronautical engineers more than they had ever learned before of the principles of airship construction.

Airship R.33 was built at Howden near Selby, Yorkshire, by Armstrong Whitworth & Co., and was 670 ft. in length, 79 ft. in diameter at the widest part and of almost 2,000,000 cub. ft. gas capacity. Accommodation was provided for a crew of 23. The five cars beneath the great hull accommodated five 250 h.p. motors and the combined power of the engines gave the airship a maximum speed of 65 m.p.h. The petrol and water ballast tanks were carried on a massive bridge girder that extended the length of a central gangway inside the hull. A ladder containing 130 rungs provided a means of passing from the bottom of the hull to a small roof platform, upon which an anti-aircraft gun could be mounted if necessary. The airship was steered to right or left by means of two rudders attached to two vertical fins at the stern, and movable elevators were attached to the two large horizontal fins also at the stern.

Several experimental flights were made with R.33, but it was deflated and stored away when airship activity in England was suspended in 1921, and it was not re-commissioned until May, 1924. The reconditioning of the airship was then put in hand at the Royal Aircraft factory at Bedford and was completed by 2nd April, 1925. The airship was then flown to Pulham, where she gained publicity a fortnight later by breaking away from the mooring tower during a gale. The gale sprang up on the evening of 15th April, 1925, and continued throughout the night and most of the following day. A careful inspection of the airship and its anchorage was made on the night of 15th April and everything appeared in order, but during the following morning a portion of the fitting on the mast-head fractured and freed the airship.

About two-thirds of the crew were aboard at the time, and as the R.33 was swung away from the mast by the wind a rush was made to start the engines, and water ballast was quickly released from a forward tank in order to lift the airship. Even so, she narrowly escaped trailing over some buildings in the neighbourhood. Although the engines were quickly got to work the 50 m.p.h. wind rapidly drove the airship eastward, in which direction the commanding officer wisely kept her directed in order to avoid further damage.

Airship R.34 starting out on a trial flight

The severe wrench given by the tower-head fitting as it broke away had crushed in the nose of the airship and ripped open and deflated the foremost gas bag. The officer in command ascended the ladder to the roof platform and struggled along against the wind to the nose and inspected the damage. Subsequently four of the crew made their way along the narrow gangway in the bottom of the hull and laced the deflated gas bag to the frame so that it formed a sort of bulkhead to protect the second gas bag.

The east coast of England was soon left behind and the airship still being hustled by the wind crossed the North Sea to the coast of Holland. From immediately after the break-a-way at Pulham until her subsequent return she was in constant wireless communication with the Air Ministry. At four o'clock in the afternoon of the 16th April, she reported that she was 25 miles W.N.W. of Texel, and was stationary in a wind computed to be blowing about 32 miles per hour. A message transmitted 2½ hours later stated that she was then passing over Ymuiden and was making eight knots sternway in a 40 m.p.h. wind. The wind subsequently decreased steadily and at 8.30 p.m. on the same day R.33 wirelessed that she had commenced to make her way back home. Progress was very slow, however, and she did not arrive at Pulham until 3.20 p.m. on the afternoon of the 17th April.

The hazardous voyage of R.33 was followed anxiously by the public of all countries interested in airship development, and the slight damage incurred was considered a testimony to the excellence of the materials and workmanship embodied in her.

The airship R.36 like R.38 was not completed when the Great War came to an end and her internal arrangements were then re-designed to enable her to be finished as a commercial airship. This change of plan gave the R.36 the distinction of being the first British airship to be equipped with a saloon. This was situated below the keel and contained a kitchen, tables and chairs, etc., accommodation being provided for 30 passengers. The airship was built by William Beardmore and Company Limited, and was 672 ft. in length, 78 ft. 9 in. in diameter at the widest part and was of 2,101,000 gas capacity. She had a maximum speed of 65 m.p.h. No flights of any outstanding merit are recorded of this airship.

The completion of England's latest rigid airships R.100 and R.101 is awaited with great interest. Details of these great dirigibles have been given in the "Air News" columns of the "*M.M.*" from time to time. The R.100 is being constructed at Howden and R.101 at Cardington. Work upon R.100 is now almost completed. This airship is 709 ft. in length, 130 ft. in diameter at the widest part and has a total lifting force of 158 tons. The combined power of the six 700 h.p. Rolls-Royce engines will enable the airship to attain a maximum speed of 82 m.p.h. The control cabins, and accommodation for both crew and passengers are inside the main hull framing.

Our survey of the great airships of the past 20 years would be incomplete without some mention of America's part in developing huge rigid airships. America's first rigid airship was built in 1923 by the Construction Corps of the U.S. Navy. The parts of the airship were made at the Naval Aircraft Factory at Philadelphia, and the airship was erected in a huge hangar at Lakehurst, New Jersey. The "*Shenandoah*," as the airship was named, was of cigar shape and was 680 ft. in length and 79 ft. in diameter at the middle. The six 6-cylinder engines, each housed in a separate car beneath the hull, were each capable of 300 h.p. at 3,000 ft. and gave to the airship a maximum speed of 65 m.p.h. The pilot and the various navigating instruments were accommodated in the foremost and largest of the cars, which was 20 ft. in length. The airship carried a crew of 22.

At the conclusion of a four-days' test the "*Shenandoah*" was moored to a tower at Lakehurst Station on 16th January, 1924. A gale of 75 m.p.h. velocity developed during the afternoon and in the evening tore the great airship from her mooring. The nose was left fastened to the mast head and a long strip of the envelope was torn from the starboard bow, while two forward gasbags were torn and deflated. Sufficient of the crew were on board to enable the airship to be efficiently handled, and as she swung away from the tower they dropped two of the forward fuel tanks through the canvas bottom in order to restore the buoyancy lost by the damaged gas-bags. By careful navigation the airship safely rode out the storm and very early the following morning returned to Lakehurst where she was safely housed before daybreak.

During a flight in September, 1925, the "*Shenandoah*" unexpectedly encountered a terrific storm and was completely wrecked. The storm was of the kind known as a "line" storm, which the designers of the airship had declared would probably prove fatal to her if ever she encountered one. A line storm is a vast wall of upward rushing air, and the one that the "*Shenandoah*" ran into shot her upward from her altitude of 3,000 ft. to a height of 7,000 ft. as though she were a mere toy. A severe vertical bending stress was at once set up in the forward part of the framework of the airship. The commander ordered the valves to be opened and, with gas escaping freely and engines running, the airship was canted nose downward. Thrust out of the stream of upward rushing air the "*Shenandoah*" descended so rapidly that the gas tanks had to be hurriedly dropped and large quantities of water ballast discharged in order to stay her plunge. By the time she had regained the 3,000 ft. level she was restored to an even keel and all seemed well again.

The terrific blow dealt by the line storm had taken effect, however, for hardly had the airship recovered her equilibrium when she broke in two about 250 ft. from the bow. As the two portions of the great airship fell, the forward one snapped into two pieces, shearing off the control car, which met the earth with a terrific impact, killing every occupant. The long after section of the airship fell stern first, the tail crushing up on coming into contact with the earth and forming a cushion that softened the fall of the broken framework and cars so that the crew housed in cars attached to this section were saved. The loss of the vessel and of several of its personnel created dismay throughout America and for a time confidence in rigid airships wavered.

The U.S. airship "*Los Angeles*" is of almost the same dimensions as the "*Shenandoah.*" She was built for the U.S. Navy by the Zeppelin Company in Germany, under the designation "*ZR.3,*" and was delivered by air, achieving the long flight of 5,060 miles from Friedrichshafen to Lakehurst in 81 hours. She has five 12-cylinder Maybach engines, specially designed for airship service, and each capable of 400 b.p.h. at 1,400 revs. per min., and has a maximum speed of 78 m.p.h.

When not in flight airships are either anchored to special structures known as airship mooring towers or are housed in huge sheds. Mooring towers were invented after the loss of the British airship R.34, which was wrecked during a gale owing to being inadequately anchored to the ground, as already related.

An airship mooring tower has recently been completed at Cardington, Bedfordshire, in preparation for the handling of the new British airships R.100 and R.101. This tower is an octagonal structure having an overall height of 200 ft. and tapers from a width of 70 ft. at the base to about 27 ft. across the top. A spiral staircase 3 ft. in width and an electrically operated passenger lift are accommodated up the centre of the tower. The power-house and winding-shed, for operating the lift and the cable for hauling in the airship, are situated at the base.

The tower is surmounted by a turret in which is accommodated a wonderful machine, weighing some 10 tons, the purpose of which is to respond to the pull of a moored ship upon the cable that holds it to the mast. The machine is free to move in all directions and thus adjust itself instantly to any changes in the pull of the ship, due to variations in the direction of the wind. The ship is held to the mast by its "nose," on which there is a fitting that is hauled by means of the cable into a cup-shaped recess at the extreme top of the mast. Around the mast at a distance of about 100 yards are ring-bolts set in concrete, to which is anchored the stern cable of the ship.

The passengers enter the ship by means of a gangway in the bow. This gangway is lowered to the top platform and fits into a circular rail running round the mast, thus enabling it to move in any direction in accordance with the movements of the ship, caused by changes in the direction of the wind.

The shed built by Count Zeppelin to house his first rigid airship was a timber structure erected upon pontoons on Lake Constance. This shed had the great advantage of being movable so that it could be swung round to face any particular direction according to the prevailing wind.

The airship sheds in England are built on land and, of course, are not movable in this manner. The most notable of them is the gigantic shed at Cardington. This consists of a massive steel framework of latticed girders built upon a concrete foundation. The walls are formed of corrugated iron sheeting while special protective material has been used for the roof. The shed is 812 ft. in length and has a maximum height of 180 ft. Its floor area is 4¾ acres and it will accommodate two airships of the R.33 type or one of the size of R.100.

BACK FROM HER 23,000 MILE TRIP

Courtesy] [Messrs. Short Bros. Ltd.

An interesting photograph showing the "Singapore" back at her original moorings after her aerial survey flight around Africa.

This famous Flying Boat is fitted with two Rolls-Royce "Condor" engines and weighs, fully laden, 20,050 lbs. The dimensions of the "Singapore" are roughly the same as those of the "Calcutta" Flying Boat, described in the "M.M." last month.

Outdoor Recreation Books

An interesting new series of small books on sports and games has been commenced by Frederick Warne & Co. Ltd., under the general heading of "*Warne's Recreation Books.*" Eight volumes are already available, dealing respectively with motor-cycling, golf, bowls, cricket, rowing and sculling, lawn tennis, camping and swimming. The volume on camping (No. 2 of the series) will be of special interest to Meccano Clubs that are contemplating holding a camp during the summer.

Each book is written by an expert and contains sound practical advice on the essential features of each sport. The style is clear and simple and the book cannot fail to be of interest, not only to beginners but also to those of considerable experience. The written descriptions of the various points are supplemented by simple but expressive sketches, which leave no doubt in the mind of the reader as to the author's meaning. The general get-up of the books is attractive and they are published at the remarkably low price of 6d. in paper covers or 9d. in cloth.

The Making of a Cricket Bat—

(*Continued from page 609*)

from pieces of cane, the number employed varying from nine to sixteen according to the thickness of the cane that is being used. The most suitable cane for the purpose is grown in Sarawak in the East Indies. If, for instance, nine canes are to be used in the making of a handle, these are all planed singly and are then glued into three slips of three canes each. The three slips are then planed and rubber is inserted between them, the inner slip being cut down if treble insertion is required. The slips are then glued together and after the glue has set the handle is turned and pointed to correspond with the V cuts that have been made in the blade.

The handle is now fixed into the blade at the correct angle and the shaping of the bat is commenced. This shaping is entirely carried out by hand and is of great importance, as upon its accuracy depends the correct balance of the bat. The usual weight of a full-sized bat is from 2 lb. 4 oz. to 2 lb. 7 oz., but a badly-balanced bat of the lighter weight would feel heavier to handle than the heavier bat correctly balanced.

Finally the handles are wound with twine and the bats are rubber grip fitted, branded and finished off ready for sale.

The upper illustration on page 609 shows Herbert Sutcliffe, the great Yorkshire and England batsman, instructing a schoolboy in the art of holding the bat correctly. The lower photograph, showing Sutcliffe completing a stroke, is of unusual interest. One wonders how many readers could state exactly the nature of the stroke and the direction in which the ball has gone!

I.—WHAT PEOPLE THINK OF IT TO-DAY

We believe that the "*Meccano Magazine*" is unique among publications of its type, in the rapidity of its growth and development, and in the intense interest shown by its readers in "things that matter." For a long time we have been receiving large numbers of requests for some information about the Magazine—how it is prepared, printed and distributed, and where all the illustrations come from. Up to the present space has prevented us from complying with these requests, but an opportunity now occurs and we propose to take our readers into our confidence and show them something of what goes on "behind the scenes."

First of all let us say something about the development of the Magazine and the position it occupies to-day. The first issue of the Magazine appeared in September 1916, as the result of continued demands from Meccano boys for a publication of their own. This first issue consisted of only four pages and was devoted entirely to Meccano, its sole object being to show Meccano boys how to get more fun out of their hobby and in particular to encourage them to build new models of their own invention.

For some time the Magazine appeared once every two months and did not alter greatly in its scope. Later, readers began to ask for articles on various engineering subjects that interested them. The first two or three articles that appeared in response to these requests met with such an enthusiastic reception that they were incorporated as a regular feature, and their number and length steadily increased. From that time the size and the scope of the Magazine have developed year by year, until to-day it is recognised all over the world as the greatest of all non-fiction papers for boys.

The secret of the success of the "*Meccano Magazine*" lies in the fact that it deals with subjects that are of interest to all intelligent boys, and deals with these subjects seriously. Our whole object is to provide articles that are accurate from an engineering and scientific point of view, and at the same time are written in an interesting style, free from all unnecessary complications and technicalities. The result is that the publication day of the "*M.M.*" is eagerly anticipated month by month by boys all over the world.

Over 60,000 copies of the Magazine are printed every month and some 20 tons of paper are required for the job. If all the copies that are printed for one month's issue were stacked one upon another they would make a pile 675 ft. in height; that is rather more than two-thirds the height of the Eiffel Tower! If a month's magazines were placed end to end they would stretch for over 10 miles. The area of the paper used each month is over 76 acres in extent—in other words there would be sufficient to cover nearly 1,600 lawn tennis courts. If the printed pages in one month's issue were placed end to end they would form a continuous band over 916 miles in length—more than sufficient to lay a line the width of the "*M.M.*" page from Lands End to John o'Groats. If all the lines of reading matter in one complete issue could be placed side by side they would extend for roughly 30,000 miles—in other words Sir Alan Cobham could have laid a line of print all the way to Australia and back.

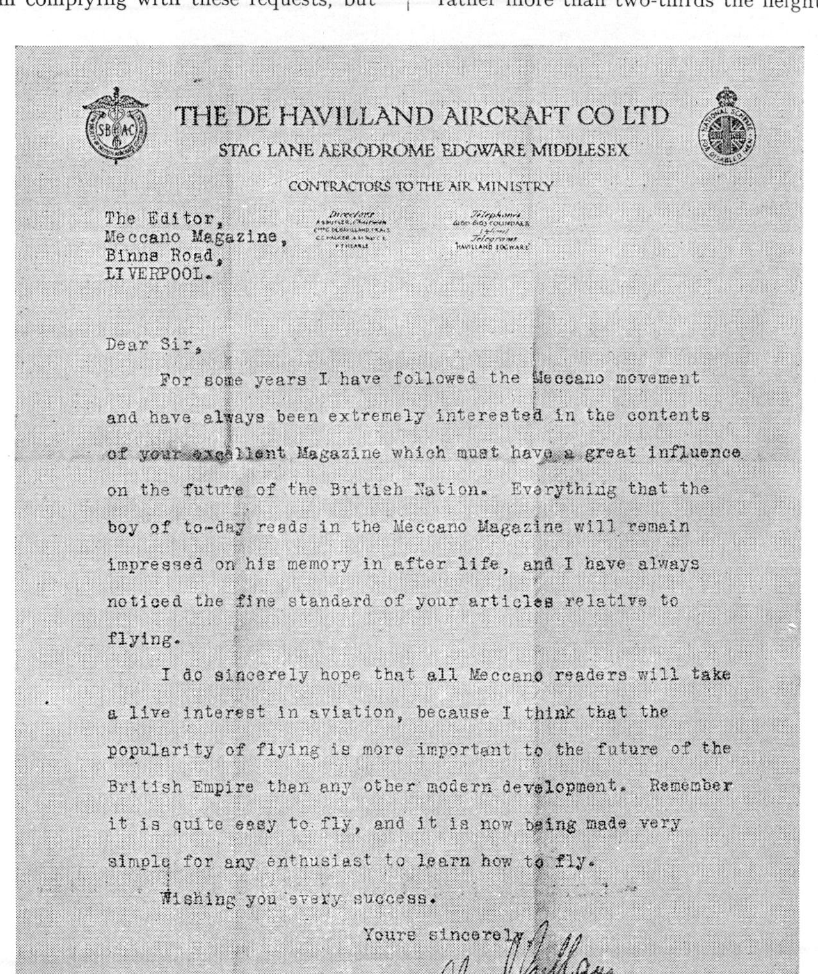
THE DE HAVILLAND AIRCRAFT CO LTD
STAG LANE AERODROME EDGWARE MIDDLESEX
CONTRACTORS TO THE AIR MINISTRY

The Editor,
Meccano Magazine,
Binns Road,
LIVERPOOL.

Dear Sir,

For some years I have followed the Meccano movement and have always been extremely interested in the contents of your excellent Magazine which must have a great influence on the future of the British Nation. Everything that the boy of to-day reads in the Meccano Magazine will remain impressed on his memory in after life, and I have always noticed the fine standard of your articles relative to flying.

I do sincerely hope that all Meccano readers will take a live interest in aviation, because I think that the popularity of flying is more important to the future of the British Empire than any other modern development. Remember it is quite easy to fly, and it is now being made very simple for any enthusiast to learn how to fly.

Wishing you every success.

Yours sincerely,

Alan J. Cobham

Although the bulk of the magazine circulates in the United Kingdom, many thousands of copies go overseas every month, in particular to Australia, New Zealand and South Africa. The magazine has, in fact, readers in every civilised country in the world, even in such far away places as Siberia, Labrador, Fiji and Tierra del Fuego.

Naturally the early issues of the "*M.M.*"—four pages unattractive in appearance, and devoted entirely to Meccano model-building—did not often attract "grown ups." Now, all that is changed and in many thousands of homes the "*M.M.*" is welcomed and appreciated as much—sometimes even more!—by adults as by the most enthusiastic Meccano boy. Indeed, we receive many letters from boys complaining that father gets hold of the Magazine first, and keeps it until he has read it from cover to cover! Others complain that on the first of the month they notice they are always sent to bed early, so that father can have the "*M.M.*"! In such cases we point out that as Dad usually pays the subscription he is entitled to "first whack" at the Magazine, and that in any case there is always a remedy for this state of affairs—to order two copies!

During the past few years the soundness of the information contained in the "*M.M.*" has attracted increasingly the attention of engineers, inventors, scientists and schoolmasters. Many have written us most encouraging letters, expressing their appreciation of the ideals and objects of the Magazine and congratulating us upon the success already achieved.

The commendation of engineers is especially encouraging to us because the "*M.M.*" is essentially an engineering paper for boys. We greatly appreciate, for instance, the following remark in the course of a letter from Dorman Long & Co. Ltd., the famous engineers who are now engaged in the colossal task of constructing the Sydney Harbour Bridge:—"We know your Magazine well and appreciate its educational value to those who, as you rightly remark, will become the engineers of the next generation."

Dr. H. S. Hele-Shaw, F.R.S.

Then, again, Dr. H. S. Hele-Shaw, F.R.S., formerly Professor of Engineering at Bristol University and Liverpool University, and the inventor of many successful mechanisms among which may be mentioned the Hele-Shaw clutch, wrote to us a short time back:—"Allow me to congratulate you on the whole Magazine which I, although an old man, read with interest. As Past President of the Institution of Mechanical Engineers I venture to say that your firm and you yourself are doing a great work for the youth of this country. When I remember that, on my first acquaintance with Mr. Hornby, he made his models in his own parlour, and now see the picture of his Meccano works, it makes me proud to think that the organisation is British."

We know that the heads of many engineering firms attach considerable importance to the value of Meccano model-building to the youth who intends to become an engineer. A particularly practical illustration of this belief was given at a recent exhibition at Bexhill-on-Sea, where the principal of a certain engineering firm, after examining the display of Meccano models, announced that he would be willing to reduce by six months the period of apprenticeship required at his works to any boy who could build successfully the Meccano Chassis model.

Sir William Crawford, K.B.E.

In regard to aviation, our aim is to do something towards the development of air-mindedness in the next generation, and here again our efforts have met with encouragement from famous pilots and from great commercial flying organisations, such as Imperial Airways. We regard with particular pride a letter from Sir Alan Cobham, the world-famous British pilot, in which he says:—"For some years I have followed the Meccano movement and have always been extremely interested in the contents of your excellent Magazine, which must have a great influence on the future of the British nation. Everything that the boy of to-day reads in the "*Meccano Magazine*" will remain impressed on his memory in after life, and I have always noticed the fine standard of your articles relative to flying."

We received an amusing letter from the Editor of "*The Aeroplane*" in reply to a letter of ours in which we said that, as far as aviation was concerned, we sometimes felt ourselves "a Voice crying in the Wilderness." The Editor replied:—"It strikes me that the '*Meccano Magazine*' can scarcely be called "a Voice crying in the Wilderness.' There does not seem to be much wilderness when you have a following as large as *you* have—unless of course you regard yourself as being like Moses with all the Children of Israel around him!"

Little by little during the past few years Meccano has made its way into schools all over the country. It has proved itself remarkably useful in the construction of models for teaching such a subject as mechanics, and in the fitting up of apparatus for chemical and other experiments. More recently Meccano has been followed by the "*Meccano Magazine*," and scarcely a week passes without our receiving appreciative letters from schoolmasters. The following letter, for example, comes from the master of a boys' school in London: "It may also interest you to know that I often make use of Meccano in the ordinary science lessons in which I specialise. I am sure that far too little time is given in present-day elementary science teaching to mechanical principles and in the teaching of these I find Meccano an unrivalled assistant. The last hour on Friday afternoons I often use in allowing the boys to bring their sets and make models and display their working to the less fortunate boys."

There is ample and welcome evidence that the "*M.M.*" appeals also to the shrewd business man, although he may have no direct connection with engineering or science. As an instance of this we may mention Sir William S. Crawford, K.B.E., Chairman and Governing Director of the well-known firm of advertising agents, W. S. Crawford Limited. The opinion of a man of such wide experience as Sir William, who stands in the forefront of his profession and is known all over the world, is of considerable value and for that reason we are glad to be able to quote the following passages from a recent letter from him. "I have read through the "*Meccano Magazine*" with the greatest interest. To my mind it fills a much-needed gap in boys' literature. You give them something better than hair-raising stories of adventure. You give them instructive information in a most attractive form, each subject being treated in the most interesting manner possible. It is a magazine to make boys think, and think on constructive lines. Congratulations on a fine effort well carried out."

As we have already stated, we endeavour to maintain the most scrupulous accuracy in our statements and descriptions, and every now and again comes along encouraging evidence that this labour is appreciated by experts. For example, some time ago we prepared an article on an electric arc produced by a pressure of one million volts in the experimental laboratories of Ferranti Limited, Hollinwood, Lancashire. This article involved a description of a somewhat complicated matter—"root-mean square" or, as usually expressed, "R.M.S." current values, and Ferranti Limited subsequently wrote:—"We must congratulate you on the lucid description for R.M.S. values. It is one of the simplest we have seen."

On another occasion, after the appearance of the article on "Silk" in our issue for October of last year, the Director of a large firm in the Midlands wrote to us:—"I must congratulate you especially on your October number containing the article on 'Silk.' This was shown to our Director in the Silk Department who is supposed to be the greatest authority on raw silk and manufacturing from same in Great Britain; so much so that when the new tax was being discussed the "*Daily Mail*" wired down for his opinion and his remarks were printed side by side with their article. He spoke of your article as being very fine indeed. Personally, I think for a boy, or a man who can think as a boy, the Magazine is the most interesting and attractive that could be produced."

In our next and subsequent issues we intend to describe in detail how the "*M.M.*" is produced. Starting with the troubles and trials of the Editor and his assistants, we shall show how the copy is prepared; how it is set up in type; how the blocks for the illustrations are made; how the paper is made; and finally how the complete Magazine is printed, folded and stitched, and distributed to its waiting readers all over the world, whose interest in its pages will no doubt be greatly stimulated by their knowledge of the organisation behind it.

Driving an Electric Locomotive

A Trip with a Driver on the "District" Railway

By D. Arnold-Forster

To judge by appearances only, the driving of an electric train is a much simpler affair than the driving of a steam locomotive. The electric train driver seems to have little more to do than to move two or three handles this way or that, and the results of these movements are seen only in a changed movement of the train, without the accompanying rush and roar of steam that makes the steam locomotive so attractive. Nevertheless the electric train is by no means a simple matter and the various operations involved have a special and peculiar interest of their own. The best method of realising this is to take a trip along with a driver, and we will suppose our driver to be in charge of a London Metropolitan District train running from Ealing Broadway terminus to Whitechapel.

Courtesy] [*London Underground Railways*

A typical Metropolitan District Train

This section of the line takes us from the west to the east end of London and covers a distance of 12 miles with 26 stations. The first part of the run is out in the open and the subsequent underground portion of it passes through the double-tracked tunnels constructed for the old steam trains.

On one of the many lines at the big depot at Acton is standing a train of six maroon-coloured cars all ready for running. The train is made up of three motor cars and three trailer cars. The motor cars, each of which carries beneath it two electric iron-clad motors, are arranged one at each end of the train and one in the middle. Before "taking over," the driver and the guard visit the inspector's office and examine the certificate of the mechanical department stating that the train is fit for service. They then proceed to make a brief examination of the train and prepare it for its journey. The driver walks quickly around the train in order to see for himself that the electrical and air connections between each car are properly made. He also makes sure that the main motor switches alongside each motor are cut "in" and that their big fuses are in position.

One of the principal electrical connections between the cars is a flexible double-connecting piece for the main cable, which carries the current picked up by the collecting shoes on each motor car from the two live rails on the track. By keeping down the collecting shoes on each of the three motor cars a complete break of current is avoided when one of them passes over points, where there are always gaps in the live rail. There is also a flexible connecting piece for the control circuit that runs along the whole of the train and enables all the motors to be controlled simultaneously from any driving cab.

Next, there are two flexible hose connections for the Westinghouse brake system. One of these connects the main air reservoir beneath each motor car, thus allowing the air compressor in any one of them to be used. The other connection serves to join up the "train-line pipe" which controls the brakes from the driver's brake valve in any cab, and charges the auxiliary air reservoirs under each car. The air-cocks for these pipes between cars must be open right along the train and closed at each end.

Other important outside fittings to be examined are the "trip-cocks." These are actuated if the train accidentally passes a signal at "danger," and they then immediately release air from the train-line pipe, thus applying the brakes and at the same time cutting off the current from the motors. The tripping is carried out by a short movable arm that rises close to the rail abreast the signal. The driver must make sure that the trip-cock in front and on the right of the leading motor car is set so that it is ready to come into operation.

Passing round the train the driver jumps in and out of each cab, starting with the front one where he switches on the air compressor and its governor, which then will automatically pump all the main reservoirs up to about 75 lb. pressure. In each cab he sees that the master controller used for driving is locked in its "off" position and that the small reverse handle, without which it cannot be unlocked, is removed. In order to make certain that no master controller can be moved by anyone but himself the driver always carries the reverse handle in his pocket and nobody else has one. He switches on the control circuit switch in his front cab and sees that it is off in the other cabs, and also makes sure that all driver's brake valves but his own are cut out by closing their isolating cocks. He also ascertains that all hand screw-down brakes are off—a matter that is easily overlooked. In addition, he switches on his proper distinctive headlights, and makes sure that all automatic circuit breakers are in by tripping and resetting them with his circuit breaker switch.

If all is correct so far, the driver is now ready to test the brakes. He gives two blasts on the whistle and the guard makes a full "emergency" application of the brakes by opening the guard's valves in the rear of the train. Having satisfied himself that all brakes are on, he signals to the driver, who takes them off by working his brake valve, the guard listening meanwhile to hear all brakes along the train release. Afterwards the driver makes an ordinary application of the brakes from his cab, releases them and moves his train a few yards to make sure that all brake blocks are off and that the main current is on to the motors.

Under the direction of the shunter the driver now pulls the train slowly out of the network of sidings on to the main line and takes it empty up the hill to Ealing Broadway. Before passing the "home" signal outside the terminus the brakes are tested and speed is reduced so that, in the event of the air brakes failing to act, the train could be stopped just short of the buffers by means of the hand brakes.

Courtesy] [*London Underground Railways*

The motorman's cabin, showing the driving mechanism

The driver now has to change ends. After making a full "emergency" application of the brakes he cuts out the driver's brake valve by closing its isolation cock; switches off the control circuit and headlights; removes the reverse handle from the master controller and puts it in his pocket; picks up his bag of tools and goes to the other end cab. There he immediately cuts in the driver's brake valve and releases the brakes; switches on his control circuit and headlights; puts on the small reverse handle and waits for the starting signal to drop.

The clear open run to Hammersmith provides a good opportunity of watching the method of driving. Immediately the starting signal drops, the driver blows the whistle by pressing a foot pedal, and as soon as the passengers are clear of the doors of the train the guard waves his green flag. The driver now takes hold of the controller and presses down with the palm of his right hand the safety button on the top of the handle. He then unlocks the controller by moving forward the reverse handle. After this he must keep the safety button pressed down the whole time; if he lets it go the brakes are applied with full force and the current is cut off from the motors—exactly the same effect as results from being "tripped" by the trip-cocks. The object of this is, of course, to stop the train quickly if from any cause the driver should become disabled and let go the controller handle.

Without loss of time the controller is moved to the first notch, which switches on each pair of motors in series but through a large resistance. The train begins to move and the controller is then moved step by step to the fifth notch, pausing about two seconds on each one. Each of these notches cuts out more resistance and the fifth cuts it all out, with the motors still in series and giving about half the full speed. The controller may be kept for any length of time on this fifth notch but if it is kept too long on any of the first four the resistance will heat up.

The controller is kept on the fifth notch while the train draws out and passes over the points and cross-overs of the terminus. Then, if the signals ahead are clear, it is moved gradually notch by notch up to the ninth. The sixth notch puts each pair of motors in parallel, through resistance, and at the ninth, the full speed notch, the motors are in parallel with all resistance cut out.

With the train "light" as it is at present, and on a level road, the controller can be notched up fairly quickly. Later, as the train fills up with passengers, or when starting anywhere on an incline, a longer pause is made on each notch. The driver's aim is always to get up speed as quickly as he can without any jerking and straining of the motors as he passes from one notch to another.

Just as the train begins to attain a good speed the line ahead is seen to curve sharply to the right over some bridges, and speed must be reduced. In order to do this the controller is moved smartly back to the "off" position and the train is allowed to run by its own momentum. In this manner, without any application of the brakes, the train is slowed down to a safe speed by the time the curve is reached. When the curve is passed the controller is notched up quickly to correspond with the speed of the train and then gradually notched up again to full speed.

After a mile run current is shut off for Ealing Common. In good time the driver gets the train in hand by moving his brake-valve to the service position to make a moderate application of the brakes, and holds it by moving his valve forward to the "lap" position. The train runs on into the station with brakes held on steadily and then at the proper moment, depending upon the speed and weight of the train and the gradient, the driver makes a stronger application and holds it again. Just before the train comes to rest he moves his valve right forward to the release position so as to ease the brakes and avoid a jar on stopping.

As the front cab pulls up opposite the proper place on the platform for a six-car train, the air compressor is heard to start up. What happens is this. The service position of the brake-valve lets air escape from the train-line pipe and the reduction of pressure causes the triple valves under the cars right along the train to move so as to admit air pressure from the auxiliary reservoirs into the brake cylinders. The lap position closes all air passages and holds the pressure in the brake cylinders; the release position lets air from the main cylinders into the train-pipe. This air pressure reverses the triple valves, which then admit air to the auxiliary reservoirs to re-charge them. The triple valves at the same time also release the pressure in the brake cylinders into the atmosphere, thus taking off the brakes. When pressure drops in the main reservoirs as the result of charging the auxiliary reservoirs, the air compressor starts automatically and pumps them up again.

Courtesy] [London Underground Railways

A close-up view of the "Deadman's Handle"

To make a clean non-jarring platform stop like this with only two "held" service applications is the ideal. Usually more than one additional application is found necessary, but a good driver will seldom have to "release" before the final stop and will avoid skidding, a practice that produces flats on the wheels. It is all a matter of judgment and experience.

As soon as the train-pipe has had time to recharge all auxiliary reservoirs the brake valve is put back into the running position. This is the normal position for running, and it allows a small make-up feed of air to pass into the train-pipe so as to ensure that the pressure does not drop in the auxiliary cylinders. There is still one more position—with the brake valve right back—called the "emergency" position. This makes a sudden full application of the brakes and it is rarely used by an experienced driver except for testing the system at rest.

The guard now waves his flag and the driver blows his whistle and starts up as before. There is a short quick run down into Acton Town and several strong service applications of the brake are made to bring up the train at the platform. Then follows a clear run, with slight gradients up and down, past Chiswick Park, Turnham Green and Stamford Brook to Ravenscourt Park. On this stretch a good speed is attained with plenty of "coasting"—that is running with the controller and brakes off.

Coasting saves current and drivers are encouraged to do it as much as they reasonably can without losing time. They are expected also to make as few unnecessary stops as possible between stations, because each starting-up again means a great expenditure of electrical energy and consequently a greater fuel consumption at the big power station at Lot's Road. If a driver sees a signal against him some way ahead he cuts off the current at once and coasts up to it. In the event of its clearing before he reaches it, as it very probably will, he can speed up again without much waste of power. If, on the other hand, the signal remains against him, at his reduced speed he can bring the train up close to it with the brakes, in a short space.

Signals at junctions and other special places are operated by signalmen from their boxes in the ordinary manner, but most of the signals along the line are automatic. They are normally at the "off" or clear position, but are set at danger when a train passes them and remain so until it clears the section beyond. Every automatic signal is repeated by a "repeater" signal in the section farther back, so that drivers have plenty of warning of what to expect. The arms of semaphore repeater signals are painted yellow and they are treated as "danger" signals. In the dark tunnels semaphores are replaced entirely by coloured lights close to the ground, and showing green in the clear position. An actual signal shows red at danger and a repeater shows orange. Most of the signals are in vertical pairs, the lower one being the repeater of the next signal farther on.

Just after leaving Ravenscourt Park comes the top of a steep bank, the bottom of which consists of a short tunnel on a sharp curve running down into Hammersmith. Coasting carefully down this bank, the brakes are applied lightly and held on to keep the train well in hand as it enters the tunnel and grinds round the curve into the station.

Now comes a fairly straight easy bit through Baron's Court with the queer squat-looking Tube trains running close alongside. A short drop to West Kensington is followed by a curly bit crossing another line, many signals, two junctions, a tunnel, and a short pull up to one of the long platforms at Earl's Court. Here in an office overhead is the Traffic Superintendent, who knows what every train on the line is doing and who quickly spots one that is delaying the punctual flow of traffic.

A broken-down train very soon means other trains being held up in all sections behind it and rapidly increasing crowds of passengers waiting on platforms of stations ahead of it. In the event of a breakdown a driver is expected to do whatever is likely to cause the least possible delay to traffic. If he is unable to make good the defect at once he usually can make some sort of temporary adjustment that will enable his train to crawl on to the next station where assistance is available. If, however, his train is badly stuck in the tunnel, the driver of the next train behind may be instructed to come on cautiously and push him out clear to a siding. But whenever a driver gets out of his cab on to the line, whether it is to attend to anything wrong or to shut off the rush of escaping air in front of his cab in the case of a "trip," he must always remember to step as carefully as a cat over the "live" rails and to look out and listen for passing trains.

After Earl's Court there is a sharp curve to the right and two sets of crossover points to the Inner Circle line that runs parallel through Gloucester Road and joins in just beyond South Kensington. Here the train plunges into the first and longest section of the black tunnel. There are no more semaphores and a sharp look-out is kept from the cab for red or orange lights among the double green ones seen along the ground at intervals in the gloom ahead.

The dull-looking old station at Sloane Square has a bad reputation among drivers. It lies at the bottom of a hill in either direction and is on a curve with the outer rail well raised to meet it. These conditions necessitate considerable skill to ensure a good stop, and even experienced drivers may occasionally make a bad shot.

The bright lights of Victoria are come upon very suddenly as the train rounds a curve in the tunnel; then St. James' Park, and Westminster with its sharply curving platform. In this level section of the line, with stations at half-mile intervals, very soon after the controller gets up to the ninth notch after one stop it is time to shut off current again and coast ready for the next stop. During the rush hours when passengers crowd into the train, much stronger braking is required to bring up the train correctly at the stations. If the brakes were worked as they were when running "light" out Acton way, the train would overshoot the mark every time.

At Charing Cross the driver looks out for a purple light that shows up if the leading trip-valve gear is in correct adjustment. If the light fails to show, the gear is adjusted at the first opportunity.

Now comes a straight, partly open run abreast the Thames Embankment to Temple and Blackfriars. The platforms of these old City stations are very short and care is necessary in order to avoid leaving the tail car partly in the tunnel. On clearing Blackfriars current is shut off and the train is run cautiously down to Mansion House, which has both terminal and through platforms with crossover points and whose signal lights can be seen at the bottom of the hill.

The gloomy part of the old City tunnel after Mansion House and beyond looks very weird and mysterious from the cab. Cannon Street, Monument and Mark Lane come at short intervals. Then the tunnel makes a long continuous curve to the left and signal lights keep appearing suddenly just around the corner. The line out of Fenchurch Street emerging from the mouth of another black tunnel is crossed at right angles. Then come junction lights and a sharp grinding curve to the right into Aldgate East and straight on to St. Mary's.

Here at last the train emerges from the long dark winding tunnels with their glimpses of the sky, and runs into steady daylight. There is a distinct feeling of relief. A clear run of a quarter of a mile in the open now brings us to Whitechapel, where we take leave of our driver, full of admiration not only of the efficiency with which he has piloted his train, but also of the engineering skill manifested in the numerous appliances that ensure the safety of the travelling public.

Turbo-Generators at Lots Road Power Station, Chelsea

Binding the "*M.M.*"

Binding cases for back numbers of the Magazine may be obtained from Messrs. O. H. Bateman and Co., 13, North John Street, Liverpool. These are supplied in two sizes (1) for six copies price 3/6 and (2) for twelve copies price 5/3 post free in each case. The binding cases are supplied in what is known as "Quarter Basil, full cloth"—that is to say three-quarters of the sides are dark crimson cloth and the back and a quarter of the sides are dark crimson leather as shown here. The case is tastefully embossed in gold with the name "Meccano Magazine," and on the back is the name and volume number.

Binding the "*M.M.*" These binding cases are supplied so that readers may have their Magazines bound locally, but where desired, the firm mentioned above will bind Meccano Magazines at a charge of 6/6 for six issues or 8/6 for twelve issues, including the cost of the binding and also return carriage. The covers of the Magazines may be included or omitted as required, but in the absence of any instructions to the contrary they will be included.

Whilst the binding of the twelve Magazines is quite satisfactory, they form a rather bulky volume and for that reason arrangements have been made to bind six months' Magazines where so desired, as explained above. Back numbers for any volume can be bound and the case will be embossed with the correct volume number.

Readers desiring to have their Magazines bound need only make a strong parcel of them, include a note of their name and address together with the necessary remit tance, and send the parcel direct to Messrs. O. H. Bateman and Co., 13, North John Street, Liverpool, by parcel post, carriage paid.

Bound Volumes of the "*M.M.*"

Will readers please note that all "*Meccano Magazines*" prior to December 1923 are out of print. Each of the 1924 issues is available, but only the May, June, July, September and December issues of 1925 are in stock. All of the 1926 and 1927 issues are available with the exception of January and February 1926.

Copies of back issues will be sent, post free, price 3d. for issues prior to 1925, 4d. for the issues of 1925 and 1926, with the exception of the December numbers. The December issues, 1925 and 1926, and all the issues of 1927, 8d. The number of copies is very limited and early application should be made.

We can supply a limited number of bound volumes of the "*M.M.*" at the following prices (carriage paid). January-December 1924, in one volume 10/–. July-December 1926, price 8/3. January-June 1927, 9/6. July-December 1927, 9/6.

IV.—THE SUBMARINE

ALTHOUGH the submarine in the sense of a vessel capable not only of remaining under water but also of travelling while submerged is modern, the idea of a submersible vessel is several centuries old. One of the earliest references to submersible boats occurs in the writings of Olaus Magnus, Archbishop of Upsala, Sweden. In an account entitled " Of Leather Ships Made of Hides Used by the Pyrats of Gruntland " he relates that these vessels were used by the pirates " for the purpose of going wherever they wish, either above or below water."

The Archbishop adds that " in 1505 I saw two of these leather boats or skiffs in the Cathedral church, Aslöe, in the western porch. They were dedicated to St. Haluard and placed there on exhibition and are said to have been taken by King Hakon while passing with his warships along the coast of Gruntland, when the pyrats tried to sink his vessels." The Gruntland referred to in this ancient record is generally assumed to mean Greenland, and although the Archbishop did not supplement his remarks with a description of the submersible boats used by the pirates, they are thought to have been simply Eskimo kyaks or canoes covered over with hide. This covering was drawn around the body of the occupant of the boat tightly enough to prevent any water from entering the craft.

Robert Fulton, inventor of the first practicable submarine

A similar dearth of information attaches to the record of a " diving vessel " that was exhibited to the Emperor Charles V at Toledo in 1538, and of a submersible boat that is said to have been used by the people of Venice 20 years later to salvage a sunken galleon.

About 1578 one of Queen Elizabeth's naval gunners named William Bourne proposed to construct a submersible vessel and gave details of his invention in a small book published in 1578, under the title of " Inuentions of Deuises—very necessary for all Generalles and Captaines, or Leaders of Men as wel by sea as by land." Bourne prefaced his description with the statement that " it is possible to make a shippe or boate that may goe vnder the water vnto the bottome and so come vp againe at your pleasure."

According to Bourne's description the vessel was to be of leather and to consist of three superimposed compartments. The top and bottom sections were to be water-tight while the intermediate one was to be " pierced with holes and provided with two longitudinal bulkheads." The vessel was only large enough to accommodate one person, who could cause the boat to sink by drawing inward the bulkheads and admitting sufficient water into the centre compartment, through the perforations in the side of the vessel, to reduce the buoyancy of the craft to the required degree. To raise the boat to the surface again the bulkheads were to be pushed outward, thus causing the water previously drawn into the compartment to be expelled. A hollow mast that projected above the surface of the water was the means of providing the occupant of the boat with a regular supply of fresh air. History does not record whether Queen Elizabeth ever availed herself of Bourne's inventive genius.

King James I was interested in the subject of submersible boats and he is said to have encouraged one Cornelius Van Drebbel to construct an efficient submarine. Drebbel first conceived the idea of a submarine in 1620, and during the ensuing four years he built three of these craft, one of which is said to have accommodated " 12 rowers besides passengers." Details of the construction of Drebbel's submarines are lacking, but a record dated 1645 informs us that the boat just mentioned successfully journeyed under water from Greenwich to Westminster, a distance of two Dutch miles and adds that the vessel could travel " even five or six miles, or as far as one please. In this boat a person could see under the water and without candle light as much as he needed to read in the Bible or any other book." It is recorded of King James that he was so interested in the results of Drebbel's genius that on one occasion he made a voyage in one of the submarines in the River Thames.

Drebbel discovered some means of replenishing the pure air in his closed submarine, but kept his method a close secret. When the air in the submarine became stuffy he is said to have resorted to a large bottle from which he withdrew a mysterious liquid that had the effect of purifying the air in the boat. After his death in 1634 his heirs endeavoured to obtain this secret for their own use and their efforts culminated in a lawsuit in the King's Court. A reference to this legal contest is made by Samuel Pepys in his famous diary, but nothing is known as to the outcome of the controversy.

A quaintly worded royal warrant dated 1626 reads: "His Majestie to the Master of the Ordnuance, for the makyng of dyvers water mines, water petards, fforged cases to be shot with fireworks, and boates to goe under water." A year later a royal warrant was also issued to the Duke of Buckingham in the following terms: "360 fforged iron cases with fireworks, 50 water mynes, 290 water petards, and two boates to conduct them under water for H.M. present services to goe with the fleete."

About this time several inventors both in this country and in France expounded schemes for constructing under-water craft. Among them were two French priests, Fournier and Mersenne, who in 1634 published a small book in which they detailed their ideas of how a practical submarine should be built. They stated that the submarine should have a metal hull and should be constructed as nearly fish-shaped as possible. Another inventor named Jean Barrie was granted a patent by the King of France in 1640 giving him authority to "fish at the bottom of the sea with his boat" at any time during the ensuing 12 years.

The first British submarine of the "A" class. These vessels were of 180 tons displacement and were capable of a speed of 12 knots on the surface and of 8 knots under water

About 1774 a wheelwright named Day, living in Suffolk, became interested in the subject of submersible boats. He obtained one of the small boats in common use on the Norfolk Broads and equipped it with a covering to render it totally enclosed and to prevent it from filling with water when submerged. In this improvised submarine he made several successful experiments and on one occasion he is said to have succeeded in remaining under water at a depth of 30 ft. for 24 hours.

Day was greatly encouraged by this success, but he lacked the funds necessary to cover the cost of building a larger and improved vessel. He endeavoured to raise the money among his friends but, although they were interested in his experiments they were loth to risk any capital in his ventures. There happened to be in the neighbourhood a man named Blake who had a reputation for making novel wagers, and by artful conversation Day interested Blake in the possibilities of a man being able to remain under water at a considerable depth for a long period without injury or discomfort. Blake then challenged any man to descend into the sea to a depth of 100 ft. in any contrivance and, after being continuously submerged for 12 hours, without any assistance from or connection with the outside world, to rise to the surface again none the worse for the adventure.

Day then accepted the challenge and it was arranged that the event should take place in Plymouth Sound. Day procured a small boat such as he had used during his experiments and in it he built a water-tight compartment. When all was ready Blake was sent for and in his presence a trial was carried out in shallow water. The vessel was submerged six hours before full tide and remained under water until six hours after the turn of the tide. Day remaining shut up in his tiny watertight compartment throughout the period. Having survived this preliminary ordeal he then prepared for the challenged demonstration.

On the appointed day the vessel was towed to an agreed place and special ballast placed on board in sufficient quantity to ensure that it would sink after a certain quantity of water was admitted. The ballast consisted in part of two heavy detachable weights connected with the watertight cabin in such a manner that, at the conclusion of the 12 hours' submersion, Day could detach them and cause the boat to rise to the surface.

An interesting account of the subsequent happenings is given in the "*Annual Register*" of 1774: "Mr. Day provided himself with whatever he thought necessary; he went into the vessel, let the water into her and with great composure retired to the room constructed for him and shut up the valve. The ship went gradually down in 22 fathoms of water at two o'clock on Tuesday, June 28th, in the afternoon, being due to return at two the next morning. He had thirteen buoys or messengers which he could send to the surface at option to announce his situation below; but none appearing, Mr. Blake, who was near at hand in a barge, began to entertain some suspicion. He kept a strict lookout, and at the time appointed neither the buoys nor the vessel coming up, he applied to the '*Orpheus*' frigate which lay just off the barge, for assistance."

In spite of prolonged efforts to locate and rescue Day and his submarine, neither was ever seen again. Probably the boat was too frail to withstand the pressure of the water at the depth to which it descended, and was crushed to pieces.

In the following year an American named David Bushnell completed the construction of a submersible boat that he had planned and commenced to build in 1771. During his school studies in chemistry Bushnell had become greatly interested in the problem of how to discharge effectively explosive powder under water, and had come to the conclusion that a submersible boat offered the best means of accomplishing this.

The vessel built to Bushnell's design resembled the upper halves of a pair of turtle shells joined together, the natural opening where the head of the turtle would be being occupied by a small conning tower by which entry was made into the boat. A false keel consisting of 200 lb. of lead was placed at the bottom of the boat to maintain it in a vertical position. The submarine only accommodated one person, and although there was no arrangement for renewing the supply of air, experiments proved that the occupant of the boat could remain under water for 30 minutes. The vessel was propelled backward and forward by means of a projecting oar situated near the front and rotated by the feet of the navigator manipulating a pedal arrangement. A rudder for steering purposes was fitted in the rear.

As in the case of Day's submarine, water was relied upon to start the boat sinking, and this was effected by opening a valve in the bottom of the vessel. When sufficient water had been admitted to achieve the desired object, downward progress was continued by an oar, functioning as a vertical screw, that was fitted in the top of the boat. To elevate the submerged boat the water was ejected by means of two force pumps. The compartments set aside for receiving the water corresponded to the water ballast tanks of a modern submarine. The extent to which the submarine descended or rose was registered by a water gauge, while a compass furnished the means of keeping the vessel on a desired course. As there was no means of illumination, this compass was treated with phosphorous so that the navigator could see it in the dark.

This vessel was designed to function as a war unit and was provided with a magazine charged with explosive powder, the idea being to silently approach the vessel selected as the submarine's prey, attach the magazine to the ship's hull and subsequently fire the charge. A device that resembled a huge screwdriver and carried a screw loosely attached to its upper end was fitted to the top of the submarine in such a manner that the occupant could manipulate the screw while the boat was submerged. The magazine of explosive, together with a clockwork mechanism by means of which the powder could be fired at a pre-arranged time, was attached to one end of a short cord, the other end of which was fastened to the screw.

Owing to ill health Bushnell was unable to operate his submarine when it was completed and his brother was trained to undertake this task. At this time the American War of Independence was in progress and Bushnell decided to test the efficiency of his craft at the expense of some of the British warships then in New York Harbour. He selected the Warship "*Eagle*" as his first victim and arrangements were made for his brother to utilise the submarine to torpedo the British vessel. Before the appointed time for the venture Bushnell's brother also became ill and his place was taken by a nam named Ezra Lee who had already had experience of the working of the submarine.

Boarding the submarine as it lay alongside the parent ship in the Hudson River, Lee began his hazardous exploit and skilfully navigated his boat until it was close to the unsuspecting warship. "When I rode under the stern of the ship," he afterwards related, "I could see the men on deck and hear them talk. I then shut down all the doors, sunk down and came up under the bottom of the ship." Lee then operated the screwdriving device and the screw began to pierce the wooden keel of the warship. A small iron plate or bolt fastening the ship's rudder in place prevented the screw from taking hold, however, and as the tide slowly carried the submarine away from the hull of the ship the screw came away from its socket. Lee endeavoured to locate a more vulnerable part of the hull for the screw, but in his manœuvres he eventually completely lost all trace of the warship.

One of the first five British submarines. These were built in 1901-2 and were of only 120 tons displacement

Rising to the surface again he was dismayed to find that dawn was breaking, and fearing that he would be observed by those on board the warships, or by the garrisons at the Forts, he made a hasty return to the parent ship. During his retreat he located the "*Eagle*" again, and while passing it he was seized by a sudden fear that he had been seen. He immediately discarded the magazine, which was at once carried away by the tide. The magazine had floated a considerable distance from the warship by the time the charge exploded an hour later, but the loud report and the great column of water that shot into the air caused considerable alarm on board the warship.

The "*Eagle*" incident roused the British to the need of greater watchfulness and the work of the submarine was thereby rendered more difficult and dangerous. Two further and unsuccessful attempts to blow up the warship were made before the British succeeded in tracing the submarine to its lair. The parent ship with the tiny under-water craft aboard was then pursued and sunk, but Bushnell later successfully salvaged the submarine.

If the navigator of Bushnell's vessel had achieved his object the submarine would have been proved an efficient weapon of war and its inventor hailed as a genius. As it was, the American authorities remained sceptical as to the merits of the invention. Bushnell became discouraged by their lack of faith and eventually he went to France, only to find that the French Government were equally unenthusiastic. Later he returned to America and, settling in Georgia under an assumed name, gave up his submarine experiments and practised medicine.

George Washington, the first president of the United States, wrote to Thomas Jefferson, who became the third president, regarding Bushnell's invention: "I thought, and still think, that it was an effort of genius, but that too many things were necessary to be combined to expect much from the issue against an enemy who are always on guard." Washington described Bushnell as a "man of great mechanical powers, fertile in genius, and master of execution."

The utility of the submarine as a weapon of war was realised by the famous American engineer Robert Fulton, who was one of the pioneers of steamships. In 1797 Fulton went to Paris and began to experiment with submersible boats and submarine torpedoes. His first submarine was of cigar shape and was called the "*Nautilus*." This vessel was launched on the Seine near Rouen on 30th July, 1800. It did not satisfy Fulton, however, and a second and improved submarine was constructed almost immediately afterward.

This vessel also was named the "*Nautilus*" and was completed in May 1801. It was 21 ft. 4 in. in length and 7 ft. in diameter amidships. The hull consisted of a framework of iron ribs covered with wood sheathed with copper, while a horizontal keel extended the whole length of the boat to give increased stability. The vessel could accommodate two men and entrance was effected by way of a small dome-shaped conning tower that surmounted the forepart of the hull. A short mast that could be laid flat on the deck when not in use was provided to enable the boat to travel on the surface of the water by sail when conditions were favourable.

When submerged, the boat travelled under the impulse of a small propeller at the stern, mounted at the end of a shaft that was rotated by a hand-wheel in the navigator's compartment. A rudder was fitted for steering, while compressed air was provided in sufficient quantity to enable the occupants to remain under water for several hours. Submersion was achieved by admitting water into special compartments, or ballast tanks, and the magazine of explosive carried was similar to that devised by Bushnell, as was also the method of discharge.

When the improved "*Nautilus*" was completed, Fulton tested it in the Seine near Paris and later journeyed in it to Brest. It is said that the gunners in the French forts that he passed were thrown into "fits of consternation" by the sight of the vessel periodically disappearing beneath the surface of the water and suddenly coming up again some distance ahead!

Fulton offered his submarine to France without success, but later Napoleon was sufficiently impressed by it to grant him £250 with which to continue experiments.

The tests carried out at Brest were witnessed by the authorities of the French Marine, and the manœuvres included the sinking of a pontoon by attaching to it a magazine and firing the explosive from an under-water position. Although the pontoon was successfully blown up, the authorities were not satisfied and they requested Fulton to carry out a similar exploit on a much larger scale. He then undertook to sink a British warship, but although he waited for a considerable time none appeared in the vicinity. As the days passed without the required feat taking place the authorities and Napoleon lost all interest in the submarine, and when Fulton subsequently applied for further funds for his experiments he met with a very cold reception.

If Napoleon had realised fully the capabilities of the submarine the outcome of the battles of the Nile and Trafalgar might have been very different. A touch of irony is given to the situation by the fact that when Napoleon was banished to St. Helena a submarine was built in America for the purpose of rescuing him, but he died before the vessel could set out on its mission.

After his failure to induce the French to adopt his submarine Fulton visited England and endeavoured to impress the British authorities with the merits of the (*Continued on page 608*)

Electricity Applied to Meccano—

(*Continued from page* 597)

along the wire 11 and Rod 3, through the particular switch and brush that are in contact, and so along the wire to the lamp. The current returns through the frame of the sign to the return wire 10.

As the insulated portion of each rotating switch is twice the length of the preceding one, an interval elapses before each lamp lights up. When the last brush has made contact the entire sign is illuminated and remains so until the insulated Angle Brackets lift the brushes one after the other, thereby causing the lamps to black out in rapid sequence, commencing from the end of the sign. Thus the "M" is the last letter to go out and the first to re-appear when the mechanism again starts to spell out the sign.

It is very important that plated parts be used in all parts of the model where good electrical contact is essential, as in the case of the brushes 6 and the switches 7. The Angle Girders 12 and 13 and the upright Girders to which they are bolted should be plated also, otherwise the Lamp Holders of all the lamps will have to be connected to the wire 10 by additional lengths of wire.

This model is sure to appeal to Club Secretaries and many others on account of its simplicity, reliability, and more particularly, its capacity for attracting immediate attention! It may be set working with the certain knowledge that there is nothing to get out of order. It will continue to tell the good news that "Meccano is Engineering for Boys" until the current is switched off, or all the lamps are destroyed!

"Christmas" Competition, Overseas Section)

(*Continued from page* 599)

hull and other principal features of the battleship have been designed most carefully, but it is the minute detail in the deck fittings that is the outstanding feature of Robinson's model. The model is built to scale and it is obvious that very few details have been omitted.

The construction of typewriters in Meccano is a somewhat difficult problem, but W. Sangers has succeeded in building a most interesting model of a machine of this kind. Naturally it would be very difficult, if not impossible, to construct a model that will include all the letters of the alphabet. Sangers therefore has fitted his machine with numbers in place of letters. The model is capable of typing on to a sheet of paper placed in the machine any number from 1 to 9 in any order whatsoever—certainly a remarkable piece of model-building!

An interesting effort was the motor dump lorry entered by T. C. Walker. The model incorporates a clutch mechanism consisting of two $\frac{3}{4}''$ Contrate Wheels mounted on separate shafts. One of the wheels may be brought in or out of engagement with the other, and the teeth of the Contrates form the clutch jaws.

Just as English Meccano boys have directed their attention recently to the construction of models of the Supermarine-Napier Seaplane, so Italian boys in accordance with patriotic instincts have attempted the building of the Italian machines which, though unsuccessful, put up an excellent performance in the Schneider Trophy Race. Enzo Bernardini's model of one of the Macci Fiat Machines is designed cleverly and although small is constructed very neatly.

Edward Holder submitted as his entry a model of a power hack saw. The eccentric motion imparted to the saw guides automatically alters the position of the saw blade as the material is cut. Holder's method of constructing the "feed motion" is very ingenious and the complete model is of a high standard.

Famous Inventions—

(*continued from page* 577)

invention, but his efforts met with a discouraging reception. Later he returned to America and designed and built a submarine capable of carrying 100 men. It was 80 ft. in length, 21 ft. in width and 14 ft. in depth, and travelled so silently that it became known as the "*Mute.*" Fulton died before this vessel was completed.

The "*Mute*" was used during the second American War of Independence and it is possible that it was the vessel that took part in the attempt to blow up the British warship "*Ramillies,*" anchored off New London. The attempt was a failure, and it resulted in so great a public outcry against this method of warfare that the use of submarines was abandoned.

(*To be continued*)

"The Flagship of the U.S. Lines Fleet"

The Romance of the S.S. "*Leviathan*": America's Largest Liner

FEW ocean liners have had as varied a history as the "*Leviathan*," the United States monster vessel that sails regularly between Southampton and New York.

The "*Leviathan*" was built in Hamburg and was originally named the "*Vaterland*." She was commissioned in 1914 as the world's largest liner. Her career under the German flag was very short, however, for she had only made three voyages across the Atlantic when she was cornered in New York in August 1914. There she remained until the United States came into the war in 1917 and she was then seized by the United States Government. The Germans did not smash the machinery of the "*Vaterland*" as they did that of many other of their vessels on the declaration of war, but when the United States Navy Department came to examine the turbines of the liner they found them to be in a very bad condition and considerable work had to be carried out before they could be made fit for service.

It was decided to use the vessel as a troop ship and she was therefore stripped of all her splendid passenger accommodation in order to adapt her to service under war conditions. She was then re-christened the "*Leviathan*."

During her term as a transport the "*Leviathan*" made ten trips across the Atlantic in the course of which she carried a total number of 119,511 United States troops. On one voyage she had 13,558 persons on board—the largest number ever carried across any ocean by any ship on any trip. Included in this number were no fewer than 11,470 soldiers, a figure that constituted a world record for troop transport during one single voyage.

Up the steps to the Winter Garden

On the conclusion of her war service it was decided that the "*Leviathan*" should be re-conditioned and put into the American Atlantic passenger service. In order to do this it was necessary to have plans of the vessel. These plans were, of course, in the hands of the Germans, who declined to sell them for less than £200,000. The American authorities rightly considered this sum to be excessive and therefore instructed their own engineers to survey the ship. This survey was duly carried out and within six months a complete set of plans was prepared at a total cost of only £50,000.

The "*Leviathan*" has an overall length of 950 ft., a width of 100 ft., and a gross tonnage of 59,956 tons. She has nine decks and her height from keel to bridge is 124 ft. In regard to gross tonnage she is the largest liner in the world, but in size she is exceeded by the White Star liner "*Majestic*," which, while of the same width, has an overall length of 956 ft.

In spite of her immense bulk the "*Leviathan*" can be steered as easily as a yacht. This was demonstrated very clearly while she was on her way to Newport News to be dry-docked for re-conditioning for passenger service. On this trip she was compelled to make a right-hand turn. At that time she was drawing 36 ft. of water as against her loaded draught of about 38 ft., and the depth of water between her keel and the bottom was only 6 in. In spite of this she swung about in perfect response to the helm. On this occasion the "*West Virginia*," the largest battleship of the United States Navy lay in dock a couple of hundred yards away from the "*Leviathan*" and from the decks of the latter she looked only about the size of a river steamer.

As might be expected, the anchors of the "*Leviathan*" are very massive affairs. The port and starboard bow anchors are each approximately 26,000 lb. in weight while the centre bow anchor weighs 33,000 lb.

The Lounge, with the Winter Garden beyond

In re-conditioning the liner for passenger service it would have been possible to make use of such of the German fittings that remained, supplementing them where necessary. After careful consideration, however, it was decided that such a course would not result in the ship presenting a uniformly harmonious appearance and therefore it was decided to make entirely new fittings. New steam radiators composed of coils of the finest copper tested to 600 lb. were installed in the state rooms, and the ventilating and cooking apparatus and the wiring and plumbing were all renewed. The original wiring of the ship did not satisfy the United States authorities and the wires installed by the Germans for the electric lighting system are now used only to connect up electric bells, the lighting system having been re-wired throughout. Altogether, nearly 250 miles of new wiring was installed and this, hidden away out of sight, forms a complex network through all the corridors and walls.

To describe in detail this gigantic floating palace, with its numerous state rooms ranging from the two-berth cabin to luxurious suites with spacious verandas looking out on the sea through thick plate glass windows, would require many pages of the "*M.M.*" The "*Leviathan*" can accommodate 976 first-class passengers, 548 second-class and 2,117 third-class, in addition to officers and crew numbering 1,150, making a total of 4,791 persons. The main dining saloon provides accommodation for 660 guests at small tables.

The beautiful Swimming Pool

The German scheme of decoration for the assembly halls was considered by the Americans too elaborate and it was replaced by a modern colour scheme embodying grey, green and buff. The first-class smoking room on "A" deck forward was originally decorated with the coats-of-arms of the German Empire and German States but these were removed and the United States coats-of-arms, including those of the thirteen original states, were substituted for them. Forward on the main deck is a library and a social hall which is used also as a theatre, being provided with modern stage equipment. An uninterrupted view of the stage may be obtained from any part of the hall as there are no pillars, the roof being supported by struts on the outside. The vessel has also a swimming bath arrangement. Gymnasiums fitted with elaborate and costly apparatus are provided for both first-class and second-class passengers.

The ship was constructed originally to burn coal but at the time of her re-conditioning she was converted to burn oil fuel, with a result of a saving of 10 per cent. in fuel consumption and a reduction in the engine room staff from 500 to 275 men. The storage capacity includes accommodation for 9,500 tons of fuel oil and 5,000 tons of fresh water. Six evaporators are installed each of which can transform 144 tons of sea water into fresh water every 24 hours, that is at the rate of six tons per hour.

Adequate precautions have been taken against any possible failure of the electric lighting system and a storage battery capable of running all the lights for three hours is installed. In addition, there are two Diesel engines either of which is capable of running the lighting plant until repairs can be made. Every day at sunset one of these engines is run for an hour in order to make certain that it is in good working order and ready for any emergency.

Very elaborate precautions have been taken against fire. If fire should break out in any part of the hold the smoke would reach the fire station on the bridge through pipes and the particular pipe from which the smoke was seen would identify the locality of the outbreak. Steam then would be turned into that part of the hold and the fire would quickly be smothered. In other spaces an automatic fire alarm warns the bridge immediately if fire breaks out. In addition, 57 fire stations where manual alarms can be sounded, are situated in various parts of the vessel and these stations are attended to by an equal number of firemen working in three-hour shifts. The whole ship, even to the remotest part, is inspected every half-hour night and day for any evidence of fire.

Protective devices innumerable have been installed in the endeavour to make the "*Leviathan*" as safe as is humanly possible and it is estimated that she is now 50 per cent. safer than when she was built. The self-closing doors have been re-distributed and they now divide the ship into a series of water-tight compartments. All these doors may be shut by a single operation on the bridge and an electric indicator shows instantly when any particular door fails to work. Alternatively, the doors may be closed individually by hand.

The wireless equipment of the "*Leviathan*" is exceptionally powerful and is supplemented by elaborate direction-finding apparatus.

Until recently it was commonly supposed that the economic limit in size in liners had been reached and that no more ships would be built as large as the "*Leviathan*," the "*Majestic*" or the "*Berengaria*." This supposition appears to have been wrong, however, for a White Star liner is being built that will exceed these vessels both in size and tonnage.

THE great difficulty in writing a description of the work of the Editor of the "*M.M.*" and his staff is to know where to begin. It would be comparatively simple if each issue of the Magazine were complete in itself, without connection with anything that has gone before or that will come afterwards. This is not the case, however, and the preparation of each individual issue is a task that begins months before the date of publication. For example, in order to understand how a Christmas issue is produced, it would be necessary to go back to the beginning of the previous summer, or even earlier.

A beginning has to be made somewhere, however, and so we will imagine that the Editor has before him what he calls a "dummy." This consists of an exact duplicate of the magazine, but with blank pages, and the task is to fill these pages with suitable articles and illustrations. First of all there are what might be called the "fixtures" to be considered. On the first page appear the Editor's notes, above which is the magazine heading with the number and date of the issue, and above that again a line drawing attention to the main feature of the succeeding issue. Then there are the continuations of serial articles to be inserted, the length of which is carefully worked out and the necessary number of pages in the dummy allotted to each. A rough note is made on the blank pages of the dummy accordingly.

Fig. 1. This is the rough layout, as sent to the printer, for the two pages 626-7 of this issue. The position and size of the blocks are shown and the lines around these spaces indicate to the printer where the type is to be set

These serial articles—such as "The Conquest of the Air"; "The Story of the Motor Car," etc.—frequently have the same heading block for two or three months in succession, but occasionally, as the articles progress, the heading block has to be changed to be in keeping with the current instalment, and due attention must be given to this. For other serial articles, such as those dealing with "Famous Aero Engines" and "Famous Trains," the heading may be changed entirely each month. Other fixtures are "Railway News"; "Air News"; "Engineering News"; "Books to Read"; "From Our Readers"; "Suggestions Section"; "In Reply"; "Competition Page"; "Stamp Notes"; "Fireside Fun"; and the pages devoted to New Meccano Models and Model-building Contests and their results.

When the necessary space has been allotted to each of these sections there is a number of pages left for other articles, and from the available material a selection is made to fill the space. In addition to this, the advertisement pages have to be filled. Most of the larger advertisements may be regarded as fixtures as the advertisers are so satisfied with the results they obtain from the "*M.M.*" that their notices are inserted month after month. Then there are the readers' sales and wants, and also the small advertisements that alter every month, their appearance often being determined by the season of the year according to whether the goods advertised are of summer or of winter interest.

All this sounds quite simple as we have outlined it, but the carrying-out of the scheme involves an almost incredible amount of detailed work. As we have already pointed out, it is absolutely necessary to plan ahead to a considerable extent and several months' issues are laid out well in advance of publication date. For instance, at the time this article is being written (early July) not only the August issue but also the September, October and November issues have been planned and exist in dummy form in the Editor's desk. The November dummy is a mere ghost of a *"M.M."*; the October one is more life-like, and that for September is practically in its final form. As soon as the August issue has gone to press the details of the September dummy will be finally settled and the October and November issues advanced a step further, while at the same time the December dummy will be taken in hand.

The articles come from a variety of sources. Many of them are prepared by the Editorial staff, the members of which are experts on the different topics dealt with. They also have the valuable faculty of being able to communicate their knowledge to readers in simple and interesting language, and without the inclusion of technicalities where these can be omitted without any loss of accuracy. Other articles are selected from the large numbers sent by outside contributors. Every article that is submitted to the Editor is given critical consideration, and only those are accepted that contain something of really outstanding interest.

THE MECCANO MAGAZINE

pieces of wood tied to a rope in such a manner that, if a caiman could be persuaded to swallow the "bait," the more he pulled the more the pieces would widen out and stick into his jaws. The other end of the rope was securely hitched to a stake driven into the ground and the bait was slung close to the water's edge. In due course a caiman came along, investigated the contrivance carefully and eventually swallowed it.

Having caught the caiman, the next thing was to get him out of the water without damaging his armour. At first the party refused to have anything to do with this part of the process, but by a combination of judicious bullying and persuasion—including the chasing of one man for a quarter of a mile over a sandbank—Waterton succeeded in getting them to make the attempt. The first effort only brought the caiman to the surface of the water, but on a second and more vigorous attempt he was hauled steadily to the bank. Waterton's account of the subsequent proceedings is interesting:—

"I took the mast of the canoe in my hand (the sail being tied round the mast) and sank down upon one knee about four yards from the water's edge, determined to thrust it down his throat in case he gave me an opportunity. This was an interesting moment. I kept my position firmly, with my eye fixed steadfastly on him. By this time the caiman was within two yards of me. I saw he was in a state of fear and perturbation; I instantly dropped the mast, sprang up, and jumped on his back, turning half round as I vaulted, so that I gained my seat with my face in a right position. I immediately seized his fore-legs, and by main force twisted them on his back; thus they served me for a bridle.

"He now seemed to have recovered from his surprise, and probably fancying himself in hostile company, he began to plunge furiously, and lashed the sands with his long and powerful tail.

"I was out of reach of the strokes of it, by being near his head. He continued to plunge and strike, and make my seat very uncomfortable. It must have been a fine sight for an unoccupied spectator.

"The people roared out in triumph, and were so vociferous that it was some time before they heard me tell them to pull me and my beast of burden further inland. I was apprehensive the rope might break, and then there would have been every chance of going down to the regions under water with the caiman. The people now dragged us above forty yards on the sand. It was the first and last time I was ever on a caiman's back. Should it be asked how I managed to keep my seat, I would answer, I hunted some years with Lord Darlington's foxhounds."

The caiman made desperate efforts to regain his liberty but after a while he became exhausted and was firmly secured.

Waterton was such a keen naturalist that he spent over £10,000 in building a high wall to convert his Yorkshire estate into a sanctuary for birds.

Incubator with baby alligators just emerging from the eggs. Above—their ultimate fate!

Conquest of the Air—(*continued from page*

less liable to oscillation. The diameter of the parachute was 34 ft. and it weighed about 400 lb.

The trial took place on 24th July, 1837. Green and a solicitor named Spencer occupied the car of the balloon, beneath which was suspended the open parachute having beneath it a small car in which Cocking was seated. The parachute greatly retarded the ascent of the balloon but eventually a height of about 5,000 ft. was attained, the balloon then being almost over Greenwich. Cocking signalled that he was about to free the parachute from the balloon and then manipulated the catch to effect this. For a few seconds the parachute descended rapidly and without oscillation, and then suddenly it was seen to collapse, crumple up, and fall at a greatly increased speed. At a height of about 20 ft. from the ground the car broke away from the parachute and crashed to earth, Cocking being literally dashed to pieces.

The sudden disengagement of the parachute caused the balloon to shoot upward at a great speed and it was with the utmost difficulty that Green and Spencer succeeded in checking its progress. Subsequently they effected a safe landing in the vicinity of Maidstone and then heard for the first time of Cocking's terrible death.

The Story of Oil—(*continued from page*)

companies struck oil at a depth of 1,820 ft., and so prolific was the output that Mexico's reputation as a territory rich in oil was established beyond dispute. The thrilling story of how this great well caught fire and provided one of the most terrible conflagrations ever witnessed upon an oilfield will be related in a subsequent article. In January 1910, an equally vast supply was tapped in another Mexican well, at a depth of 1,911 ft.

These great "strikes" were the signal for a rush of prospectors to the new oilfield. Companies were hastily financed to exploit large tracts of land and when the boom was at its height more than 120 organisations were operating oil wells in Mexico. Of these, about one half ultimately closed down. It is of interest to note that more oil is nowadays brought up in Mexico during 24 hours than 20 years ago was obtained in the course of one week.

This is a sufficient indication of the enormous progress made in drilling machinery.

(*To be continued*)

Fig. 2. Showing a page proof as received from the printer with certain blanks to be filled. The blank in the right hand column was not then filled, but later was filled with more copy, as will be seen on reference to page 143 in our February issue. The lower portion of the page has been filled with the continuations of other articles

In addition there are the articles that are written specially and exclusively for the *"M.M."* by recognised experts in their own particular line. As examples of these we may mention the series on *"Famous Trains"* by Mr. Cecil J. Allen, who is probably the most popular of all writers on railways; and the articles on running an aquarium by Mr. W. Coles-Finch, the well-known waterworks engineer and nature student. Other experts who contribute special articles from time to time are: Mr. R. D. Gauld, M. Eng., A.M. Inst. C.E., who writes fascinatingly on railway engineering; Mr. J. H. Shepstone, F.R.G.S., who tells of scenes and adventures in all parts of the world; and "Airman," a famous pilot, with whom we make imaginary flights in an aeroplane and learn exactly how the pilot handles his machine.

Galley No. 673

RAILWAY NEWS

"Pacifics" on the Waverley Route

The L.N.E.R. route from Carlisle to Edinburgh, which is 98 miles in length, is well known as being among the very hardest sections of main line in the country. There are many long and heavy gradients as the line crosses the Cheviot and Lammermoor Hills, and so sharp are the curves in many places that fast downhill running is out of the question. Long stretches as steep as 1 in 70 are common, and going north there is an unbroken bank of about nine miles at this gradient.

For many years the express services have been most ably performed by the large North British superheated "Atlantics," the ability of these fine engines to maintain a steady speed up the long banks having been remarked upon by many travellers over the "Waverley Route," so called because it traverses the beautiful Scott country. The maximum load for these engines, unassisted, is 290 tons, but the weight of the through trains to and from the Midland main line south of Carlisle very frequently range up to 400 tons or more. When the famous Gresley "Pacifics" were introduced on the L.N.E.R. they were tried on these services, but were found incapable of keeping time with train loads of 400 tons. One of the rebuilt engines of this class, "*Shotover*," has, however, successfully worked a test load of 400 tons between Carlisle and Edinburgh, and it is likely that the heaviest expresses will be taken by these high-pressure "Pacifics" in substitution for the "Atlantics."

* * * *

The Greatest Railway Centre

Many of our readers will be surprised to learn that Chicago is the greatest railway centre in the world. Actually 38 railways, including 23 main lines, have their termini in the city. The remarkable feature of Chicago's eminence is that no line passes through the city, which is, by reason of its geographical situation, a natural terminal point. The city is served by more than 120 railway yards providing reception accommodation for 200,000 freight cars.

* * * *

The Growth of Victoria's Railways

Since Victoria's first railway was opened in 1854 between Flinders Street, Melbourne, and Port Melbourne, the system has expanded very steadily, the average yearly increase in track mileage being 80. That rate of increase probably will be maintained for some years to come, for in addition to 112 miles of new lines that are already being laid, the construction of a further 50 miles was recently authorised.

Fig. 3. A galley proof from the printer showing some matter that could not be accommodated on the Railway News pages last month. Two of the paragraphs appear on page 646 of this issue

Practically every article that appears in the *"M.M."* is illustrated and the selection and preparation of these illustrations requires a considerable amount of skill and care. In the majority of cases the illustrations are prepared from photographs, but drawings are used in certain instances. In any case a "block" for the printer's use has to be made from the original. The making of these blocks is an extremely interesting process and in a subsequent article we shall deal with it in detail, and also with the preparation of the fine coloured covers that are one of the most striking features of the magazine.

When the Editor has before him the manuscript of an article and the necessary photographs or drawings, he prepares what is called a "layout." If, for example, the article is to fill three pages, he takes three blank sheets of paper the size of the magazine page. He thinks out suitable headlines for the article, and indicates at the top of the first page the position for these and the size and style of type to be used. As an alternative he may decide to have a heading made up partly from photographs and partly from type, and in this case the artist department makes a sketch and a block is made from this material. The block will be the full width of the page and of a depth that is in proportion.

Having arranged the title, the Editor has to decide on the position of the illustrations and the scale upon which they are to be reproduced. He then draws on the blank pages in the required position a rough outline of the illustrations with an indication of their size in inches; and finally, indicates by rough pencil lines that the manuscript is to be set by the printer to fill the space around the illustration (see Fig. 1). The "caption" for each illustration has then to be drafted out, its position is indicated and the size and style of type to be used. Generally the captions in the *"M.M."* are set in "Ludlow Bold" face of type, in 6 or 8 "point" size. (The "point" system of measuring type will be explained in a later instalment of this series).

Having drafted out the page and arranged the

(*Continued on page 694*)

Famous Aero Engines—

(*Continued from page* 663)

filter into which the oil drains from the engine. When the engine is stationary the surplus oil passes from the crankcase and collects in this sump, flooding of the crankcase and lower cylinders being thus prevented. Oil is drawn from the sump by a scavenge oil pump situated underneath the pressure pump, the scavenge oil pump then delivering the oil to the oil tank on the aircraft. On its way to the oil tank the oil passes through the jacketing of the carburetter and induction elbow, thereby imparting a positive degree of heating to the induction system.

A gear type petrol pump and relief valve of approved design are carried at the rear end of the engine, prolonged tests having proved this pump to be very successful.

A tachometer drive fitted to the engine is situated just above the petrol pump. The drive points towards the rear of the engine in order to avoid unnecessary bends in the tachometer flexible shaft.

Provision for priming is made by fitting a distributing ring at the rear of the engine, the ring having small branch pipes leading to each induction pipe. Each branch pipe terminates with a small atomising jet fitted to the induction pipes. The distribution ring is fed by means of a primer pump, filter and T piece, these parts being supplied loose with the engine.

Attached to the rear end of the engine is a conical bearer plate by means of which the engine is mounted in the aircraft.

Famous Trains—(*continued from page* 645)

our connecting train. The additional 45 miles of journey are booked to take 75 minutes, and Pretoria is reached at 6.25 p.m. But at Johannesburg, the headquarters of the South African Railway administration, the journey of the "*Union Express*" is at an end. It has covered 1,000 miles—all but a mere 44—and has risen from sea-level to an altitude of no less than 5,735 ft. in the course of the journey. Perhaps the most remarkable of the impressions that will remain with us when the memory of this trip has vanished into the past is that it should have been possible to travel for so great a length of time in such perfect comfort over so narrow a gauge.

Producing the "*M.M.*"

(*Continued from page* 637)

captions, the Editor has next to decide the size of type that he desires to be used for the article. If he writes "10 pt.," he requires the largest type that is used in the "*M.M.*" for articles; this is the type that is used every month for the "Reader's Page." More often the indication will be "8 pt.," a smaller type in which the Editorial notes are printed month by month. For certain purposes an even smaller type known as "6 pt." is used; "Our Mail Bag" is set in this type.

Having thus been provided with a layout that gives complete working instructions, the printer sets the type and submits proof sheets of his work. These proofs are scrutinised minutely by the editorial staff for any errors that may have crept in. As a further safeguard, proofs of articles that have been specially written are sent to the authors for examination and comment. Any necessary corrections are clearly marked in ink, and the corrected proofs are then returned to the printer, who afterwards submits a revised proof that usually requires no further alteration. When a corrected page is received, it is pinned or gummed in its pre-arranged position in the dummy, which gradually grows in to a completed dummy of the month's issue.

There yet remains the problem of dealing with "overset" matter—that is the small amount of matter that overflows from various articles. An article that was originally planned for, let us say, three pages, may, when it is set up in type, overflow its space by, say, 30 lines. Sometimes it is necessary to "edit" the end of this article and cut out sufficient lines to make the whole fit exactly the three pages. Very often, however, there are small spaces left here and there on other pages where the articles have not been long enough, and possibly this overset matter may be accommodated in one such space, with an indication at the foot of the main article as to where the continuation is to be found (see Fig. 2).

Finally, when all these details are attended to, the printer is given the word, and before long his machines are busily running, and in due course, when the printing is completed, the magazines are distributed by rail and steamship to their eager readers in all parts of the world.

In this column the Editor replies to letters from his readers, from whom he is always pleased to hear. He receives hundreds of letters each day, but only those that deal with matters of general interest can be dealt with here.

Correspondents will help the Editor if they will write neatly in ink and on one side of the paper only.

L. H. Stone (London, S.E.18).—We think our articles on the Motor Car will have interested you and we should be glad to hear your opinion of them. You are quite right in thinking that it is wrong to speak of a ship travelling so many knots an hour. A knot is a measure of speed not of distance, one knot being equivalent to a speed of one nautical mile per hour.

W. E. Waight (Weymouth).—We are glad to hear that the "*M.M.*" helps you and your friends to keep up to date in the latest developments in engineering. This, of course, is one of our main objects, and appreciation such as yours is of great encouragement to us. We have many good articles in store for the "Inventors" series.

N. Burgess (Tweed River, N.S.W.).—"I think I would rather lose my dinner than my '*M.M.*'"! This is the right spirit Norman, but judging by the enormous size of the bunches of bananas in your photograph we do not think that you are in danger of starving. We can imagine you with the "*M.M.*" in one hand and a banana in the other, enjoying both mental and physical refreshment at the same time! You would see your article on the "Readers' Page" for June, and we hope that you will send us others from time to time.

T. Harwood (Rondebosch, S.A.).—You send us quite cheery news about your examination success, and we are glad that your father has promised to buy you a bicycle in recognition of your good work. We wish you many pleasant rides and no punctures! The display of Meccano at the Rosebank Show must have been very attractive. We are glad to hear that you are bringing up your young cousin in the way he should go and that he is already a Hornby Train enthusiast.

Daphne Pooley (Victoria, B.C.).—Your enthusiasm for model-building is quite refreshing, and we are glad to hear that you have got your clockwork motor. We quite agree with you when you say that "it makes a wonderful difference when the models you construct can be worked without your having to turn a handle, and any trouble you have taken in completing your work seems very much more worth while when you look at the finished article working just right."

C. M. Grosett (Westcliff-on-Sea).—"It must be done with cold steel—a pen nib not a bayonet, so here you find me writing to you for the first time." You really ought to be ashamed of yourself, C.M., for not having written long ago. We are interested to hear that you caught the contagious Meccano disease in Jamaica, and that, so far from being cured, your model-building temperature is steadily rising!

K. Black (London, N.21).—We wish we could find space for your "*Song of Meccano*," but we are afraid this is impossible. Your first verse has just the right swing and spirit:—"Angles and girders, plates, pulleys and strips, for motors and engines, for lorries and ships. Clockwork, electric and tall derrick cranes, everything wanted to run Hornby trains. Collars and sprockets, grubs, bosses and worms, the language we talk is full of strange terms. Chorus—M..E..C..C..A..N..O, we are the fellows who make things GO!"

P. J. Acton (Birkenhead).—It is good news to hear that the information contained in the "*M.M.*" has been so helpful to you in your school work and that your physics master has complimented you. We agree that the "*M.M.*" should give first place to subjects of engineering or of a general scientific nature, but at the same time you must remember that we have many thousands of readers who, although keen on these subjects, at the same time have other interests, and we cannot afford to neglect them. If, for instance, we were to do away with the stamp pages we should raise a storm of protest.

N. E. Bagshaw (Wallasey, Ches.).—"I would like to say that you have realised your ambition to make the "*M.M.*" the brightest and best Magazine for boys." Many thanks, Norman. We hope that the articles on the production of the "*M.M.*" commenced last month, are what you desire. A little later we shall publish the story of Meccano. Articles on the exploration of the Antarctic are in course of preparation, but it may be a few months before we can find room to start this series.

Wonderful Seadrome Scheme

Aeroplane Landing Grounds in the Atlantic

THE few successful aeroplane flights that have been made across the Atlantic have shown that the crossing is feasible under ideal weather conditions but extremely hazardous in bad weather. Even in the most favourable circumstances, however, the crossing is not an economic proposition on account of the relatively enormous weight of petrol that must be carried to accomplish the distance. There is no doubt that the range of aeroplanes will increase considerably during the next few years but nevertheless it appears probable that the solution of the Atlantic crossing problem will be found only in the provision of intermediate landing grounds.

Until recently the idea of establishing a chain of floating aerodromes across the Atlantic appeared wildly fantastic, but a promising scheme has now been evolved by an American engineer, Mr. Edward R. Armstrong. This inventor has progressed so far as to have formed a company that intends to place a line of floating aerodromes across the Atlantic at intervals of 400 miles with smaller stations half way between them. If the scheme can be carried out successfully the year 1930 may see the establishment of a regular daily trans-Atlantic air service, maintained by amphibian aeroplanes of the Sikorski type. The operating range of these machines will be very greatly in excess of the distance between the seadromes, as the new structures may be called, and as a very detailed check upon weather conditions all along the route will then be possible, the Atlantic flight promises to become as safe as the journey by air from London to Paris.

For some years Mr. Armstrong was chief engineer of an American company and during this period he was called upon to design a floating factory to extract bromine from sea water for the purpose of manufacturing one of the constituents of ethyl petrol. One result of this work was to revive in his mind an idea that had occurred to him at least 20 years before—the possibility of placing a string of landing stages across the Atlantic to facilitate developments in aviation. Although he continued to turn over the idea in his mind he was too fully occupied with other work to make practical progress until 1926, when he reached the stage of constructing a model.

Subsequently the idea hung fire until the successful trans-Atlantic flights made by American pilots in 1927. A new model was then made and it was decided to proceed with the construction of a seadrome large enough to be placed at a point about 400 miles south-east of New York, in order to give the scheme a thorough test under service conditions. This particular position was chosen as the first stage of a route across the Atlantic that would be below the limit of drifting icebergs.

In planning his sea-raft Mr. Armstrong's chief aim has been to eliminate the effect of wave motion, and he claims to have accomplished this by taking advantage of the fact that oceanic disturbances are more limited in range than is generally supposed. The greatest waves seldom exceed 42 ft. in height, while the depth at which wave motion on the surface has any appreciable effect is considerably less than this. It seemed to the inventor, therefore, that a skeleton steel structure with its upper deck more than 45 ft. above water, and having its centre of gravity below the limit of under-water disturbance, would be practically free from the roll and pitch of surface vessels.

Experiments soon showed that this was the case. A structure was designed to have an upper deck 100 ft. above the water level, while its centre of equilibrium was to be lowered to the required depth by supporting the deck on telescopic steel tubes, the inner members of which could be extended to reach a depth of 185 ft. This method of construction was planned to make it possible to build the full scale seadrome in any shipyard, as it could be given a draft of less than 30 ft., which would be increased to the full amount after the giant raft had been towed to its anchorage. Discs of large area and weights were to be attached to the lower ends of the supports in order to keep the seadrome absolutely steady.

Courtesy] [Modern Transport

Sketch of one of the projected Armstrong Seadromes for trans-Atlantic air services, showing the landing deck, the hotels and the supporting "legs"

Interesting information with regard to the probable behaviour of the proposed structure was obtained by experiments with a scale model in a pond. It was found that waves corresponding to a height of 120 ft. at sea had no noticeable effect on the level of the deck of the model, while waves only half the height completely swamped a model of the "*Majestic*" on the same scale that was used for comparison purposes. The first reason for this difference in behaviour between the seadrome and the liner is that the open method of construction adopted in the case of the former presents practically no obstacle to the passing waves, while the slight force that is exerted on the supporting columns is more than counterbalanced by the effect of the damping discs. The second reason is that the centre of gravity of the seadrome model was well below the area of disturbance, whereas in the case of the model of the "*Majestic*" it was practically at the place where the disturbance was greatest.

The landing-deck of the Armstrong seadrome will be 900 ft. in length and 240 ft. in width. Towards the middle the width will be increased to 400 ft. to accommodate hotel buildings, offices and a meteorological station. It is anticipated that soon after the inauguration of the service from 2,000 to 3,000 people will pass through each seadrome daily and that many will stay for longer periods than the 15 minutes allowed for refuelling the aeroplanes. The staff required to carry out the necessary work in the hotels, offices and workshops, will be at least 150 for each seadrome.

A special deck below the landing is to be used for work on the aeroplanes and on the seadrome itself. The petrol, oil and water required for replenishing the supplies of the aeroplanes prior to despatching them to the next station will be stored in watertight compartments in the hollow portions of the supporting columns.

The area of the landing deck, exclusive of the space covered by buildings, will be about six acres, and it is possible that the main seadromes eventually will be given a deck area of not less than 12 acres. The hotels will provide accommodation for 250 people so that, with the 150 required for the various services, there will be a total population of 400. Eight main seadromes, 400 miles apart, and nine subsidiary stations are planned, so that when the scheme is completed the Atlantic will probably possess a semi-permanent population of 4,000!

Approximately 10,000 tons of steel and iron will be used in the construction of the seadromes. Heavy ballast will be necessary to keep the raft trimmed, and this probably will be in the form of iron ore stored in the lower portions of the cylindrical legs, bringing the total weight to approximately 50,000 tons. It is anticipated that the cost of each station will be somewhere about £300,000.

The greatest difficulty of the whole scheme undoubtedly lies in the securing of efficient anchorage. The bottom of the Atlantic ocean is at an average depth of some two miles. The length of an anchor cable in practice is three times the depth of the anchorage, which means that in order to anchor a seadrome a chain six miles in length will be required. The trouble lies in the fact that a heavy chain of this enormous length would have quite sufficient to do in preventing itself from snapping under its own weight, without having to undergo any additional strain.

Mr. Armstrong proposes to solve this problem by not anchoring the seadrome directly to the cable, but to a huge spar buoy about 60 ft. in length and of small diameter, to which the upper end of the anchor cable will be secured This buoy, like the seadrome itself, will offer very little resistance to the waves. Thus the heaving stresses due to surface movement of the water will not be transmitted to the anchor cable, which will be called upon to do very little more than support its own weight.

The scheme appears feasible and details of the behaviour of the trial seadrome will be awaited with great interest.

A Run on the "*Twentieth Century Limited*"

At the Throttle of a Giant "Pacific"

By H. W. Pontin
(Driver of Engine No. 596)

HAVE you ever wished that you could exchange places with one of the engine crew of a famous "Limited" express, in order to experience just for once the thrill of piloting one of these huge steel giants? Unfortunately it is given to few actually to stand at the throttle, but "second-hand is next best," and I want "*M.M.*" readers to come along with me in imagination. I want them to sit at my elbow on the footplate of No. 596, which is to pilot our portion of the "*Twentieth Century Limited,*" America's most famous train, from Boston, traversing the 200-mile main line of the Boston and Albany Railroad to join the New York portion at Albany, New York.

Now that we are all quite ready, let us go along to the engine-house and prepare our locomotive for the road. First of all, however, we must examine the bulletin board. On this board are shown plainly any changes in signals, notices concerning reconstruction work in progress, and any other running changes that affect the tracks over which we are to go. All these, of course, we must note carefully.

A few yards farther on and here we are! No. 596, one of the newest productions of the American Locomotive Works, is standing, bright and shiny, awaiting us. She—this engine of ours is too nearly human to be coldly termed "it"—incorporates everything new for securing economical power. She is a "Pacific" of phenomenal size, and to the trailer axle she has geared an auxiliary engine known as a "booster."

Now we climb aboard and start up the turbo-generator, which sets every cab light gleaming and energises the automatic train control apparatus. Next we start the air compressor and observe closely the gauges that indicate the pressure. Now, while you are watching the fireman as he inspects and oils the mechanical stoker, I will oil the valve motion connections and one or two other vital points, and then away we go!

Photograph] [Railway Photographs, Liverpool

The cab of one of the giant Pacifics that haul the "*Twentieth Century Limited.*" This photograph gives an excellent idea of the complexity of the controls, etc., as compared with those of a British locomotive

Backing slowly across the turntable, we stop to take water and coal and then move off to the Union Station, where on track four our train of nine 100-ton Pullmans is waiting. Coupling-up is the work of only a few minutes, and after charging the train air-brake pipes and cylinders we make a test, to ensure that everything is in perfect working order. If the weather conditions demand it, steam heat must be applied from the engine to the entire train. This steam is used also to heat water for the use of the barber and for various other purposes.

And now we have just a few minutes to spare in which to examine our "make up," so we will pass quickly along the platform and take a peep into the Pullmans. The first car is a combination baggage and buffet car. Here the chairs are arranged as in a club room, and every facility is provided for the business-man. A porter attends to the needs of the passengers and serves refreshments from a buffet located at one end of the car. The next three cars are of the regular Pullman drawing-room type. Then comes the diner, followed by four more Pullmans, the last of which bears a large illuminated sign that reads " *The Twentieth Century Limited.*" Now we must hurry back to the engine as time is getting short.

Just before we receive the starting signal let us take a look at the controls and gauges in the cab. Note how easily the engineer and the fireman can reach every lever and valve without leaving their cushioned seats. The gauges are all placed on one well-illuminated instrument panel, recalling the engine-room of an ocean liner. Where possible every steam pipe is placed outside the cab. Storm curtains to make the cab wind-tight and storm-proof in winter are coiled up ready for use.

Photograph] [Railway Photographs, Liverpool

The " *Twentieth Century Limited,*" hauled by locomotive No. 596

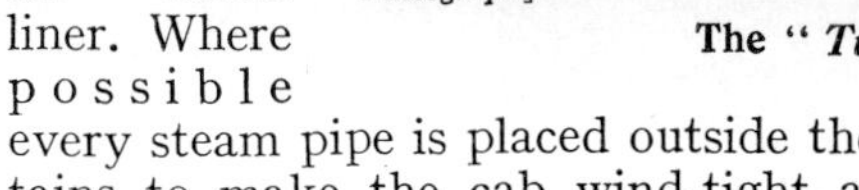

Now look into the firebox. All you can see is just a few live coals and some ashes, and you wonder what will happen when the engine starts to exhaust on that fire! Well, watch closely. You will see that when the fireman starts the stoker the fire gradually brightens until it becomes a snow-white sheet of flame all over. This, of course, would not be possible under the old system of hand firing.

Look, there is the starting light gleaming, and here comes the " Right Away." Open the throttle and we're off—12.30 p.m. on the dot! It is a smooth, easy start too, for we cut in the booster to provide us with the additional power that renders all jerks entirely unnecessary.

Photograph] [Railway Photographs, Liverpool

The east-bound " *Twentieth Century Limited*" at speed near Allston, Mass.; new Pacific locomotive, No. 596

Our engine soon settles down to business, and it is indeed surprising how easily these new engines handle in spite of their enormous size. The road ahead of us is very heavy and curves abound, so that here we shall have little time to watch the scenery. Our first stop is Worcester, 44 miles from Boston. Here we feel our bearings and prepare for the hard climb to Charlton Summit.

Now you will hear " 596 " bark! We are three minutes late, too, so that we must gather all the speed we can over the first couple of miles of level track in order to get a run at the hill. As the gradient gets steeper we feed the " notches " to our engine until the exhaust becomes a continuous roar. Peep into the firebox now; you see only the same snow-white flame and nothing more. The coal actually is consumed in mid-air as it falls from the elevators and all that remains on the grates is just ashes. No human fireman could keep pace with our engine now, but the mechanical stoker does all that is necessary quite easily.

Here is Charlton Summit, and we have picked up two minutes. From now on as far as Springfield the gradients are not so severe and the engine may be eased a little. With ordinary luck we shall make Springfield on time, which means 140 minutes for the 100 miles—quite lively enough when the heavy grades we have encountered are taken into consideration.

A few minutes later we swing into the New Station at Springfield exactly on schedule time. Water is running low so we must fill up our tank and, while the rod cups—which are lubricated by hard grease—are being filled, " 596 " is once more examined for warm bearings. We leave Springfield promptly to time and the next few miles take us along the banks of the Westfield River. From this point onward the scenery is wonderful. Here the famous Berkshire Hills start to rear their lofty heads and the booming exhaust of our engine echoes and re-echoes through the chasms. Climbing all the way to Chester, 26 miles from Springfield, we come to the foot of the famous Mount Washington. At this point we tackle our stiffest climb for the gradient rises 90 ft. to the mile—1 in 59. The steep rock cuttings through which we climb as they echo our roaring exhaust seem to be bellowing encouragement to the engine as she is (*Continued on page* 133)

New York Central Railroad

On Which Runs America's Most Famous Express

THIS month our coloured cover depicts a daily scene in La Salle St. Station, the palatial terminus at Chicago of the main line of the New York Central Railroad. Each of the three magnificent locomotives is waiting for the signal that will despatch it with its long train of luxurious cars on the 978 miles run to New York. The trains are sections of the "*Twentieth Century Limited,*" one of the world's most famous passenger expresses. It is not as old as our "*Flying Scotsman,*" and has only recently celebrated the 25th year of its existence, but in that time it has earned for the New York Central line a high reputation for punctuality and comfort.

The story of the growth of the great system on which the "*Twentieth Century Limited*" runs is one of the most fascinating romances in the railway history of America. The origin of the line may be traced back to 1812, when Geo. W. Featherstonhaugh, a scientist and explorer who lived in a town about 150 miles from New York, suggested that a steam locomotive running on iron rails would be an improvement on any system of transport then in operation. Although he had a great reputation, and numbered among his friends the most distinguished men of his time, Featherstonhaugh had great difficulty in making converts to his views, but in 1826 he succeeded in obtaining the necessary charter for the construction of the railroad that he wished to build.

Photograph] [Railway Photographs, Liverpool

Doing business! New "Lima" Super-Power Engine No. 1417, climbing Mount Washington, Mass.

Even then his difficulties were not at an end, and it was not until five years later that the line was completed. In the meantime the Baltimore and Ohio Railroad had been opened, and thus Featherstonhaugh was deprived of the distinction of being the actual railway pioneer of the American continent. The Mohawk and Hudson Rail Road, as his line was called, connected Albany and Schenectady, two small towns in the centre of the state of New York, and was only 17 miles in length. From this small beginning the system grew until it connected New York and Boston, on the shores of the Atlantic, with Chicago and the important cities on the Mississippi River a thousand miles away.

This growth was not achieved without a struggle. In its early days the Company had to contend with the strenuous opposition of those interested in the Erie Canal. This famous waterway connects the Hudson River with the great lakes, and was then the chief means of transport between New York and the growing communities of the West. Large sums of money had been expended in its construction, and for many years its supporters hindered very considerably the growth of the line that was the nucleus of the future New York Central Railroad.

By 1873, the line had grown until it reached from New York to Buffalo, a well-known city a few miles south of Niagara Falls. In that year was made the greatest step forward in the history of the Company. The principal figure in its management was Commodore Cornelius Vanderbilt, the first of the famous "Railway Kings" of North America. It was he who had been mainly responsible for the growth of the railway until it covered almost the whole of the State of New York, and in 1873, he acquired control of a company owning a line from Chicago to Buffalo. From that time onward the two railroads were worked in close alliance, and in fact, had the same principal executive officers. Finally on 23rd December, 1914, the two were consolidated into the extensive and remarkable system now known as the New York Central Railroad Company.

In the meantime progress has been continuous. Branches have been built and existing lines purchased until to-day a system of tracks 12,095 miles in length is under the control of a giant organisation called the New York Central Lines. Its nucleus is the New York Central Railroad and it includes what were originally about 560 smaller companies.

The magnitude of this great enterprise may be judged from the fact that during 1926 the total goods traffic over its lines amounted to more than 40 thousand million ton-miles. This was greater than the similar traffic in the same year on the whole of the railways of Great Britain and France combined.

Although its goods traffic is of such amazing proportions, it is chiefly as a passenger line that the New York Central has earned its great reputation. Over its lines run an astonishing number of luxurious and splendidly-equipped trains, on many of which the whole of the cars are Pullmans. The New York Central Lines transport more passengers in these comfortable cars than any other railroad in the world, but probably an equally important factor in the creation of its high reputation as a passenger line has been its wonderful main line track. This runs across low lying open country, and is practically at water level over the entire distance between New York and Chicago. There are no sharp curves or steep inclines, and unusually heavy trains may be operated on it.

The most famous of the many wonderful expresses that run over the lines of the New York Central Railroad is undoubtedly the "*Twentieth Century Limited.*" This train was first run on 15th June, 1902. It was planned to cover the distance between New York and Chicago in 20 hours at an average speed of almost 49 miles per hour. This startled many conservative people, and it was said that the experiment would soon be abandoned, as neither the track nor the rolling stock would be able to withstand the rough treatment they would undoubtedly receive. Prophecies of this kind not infrequently are made to appear ridiculous in later days, and this case was no exception. So far from being abandoned after pounding the track of the New York Central Railroad to pieces, the "*Twentieth Century Limited*" seized on public imagination and grew more and more popular. To-day its position as possibly the most remarkable long-distance express train in the world is unchallenged.

Even the railway officials who planned the running of this express can scarcely have foreseen the success that it would achieve. The train that left New York on that memorable day in 1902 carried only 27 passengers, and consisted of five cars. To-day an average of three trains, each consisting of ten cars, are required every day to maintain the service in each direction, and on rush days the express may be run in as many as seven sections!

New Tank Engines for Mountain Railway

Remarkable Hauling Power on Steep Gradients

THE interesting tank locomotive illustrated here has recently been built in Germany by the Hannoversche Maschinenbau A.G. for the Halberstadt-Blankenburg Railway. This railway owns a branch line from Blankenburg in the Hartz Mountains, climbing steadily to a height of some 3,740 ft., and having gradients up to as steep as 1 in 16½.

For a considerable time rack locomotives were used exclusively on this line but in 1921 the experiment was made of substituting ordinary adhesion locomotives. This obviously was a bold step to take, and it attracted considerable attention. The locomotives that were put into service were of the 2–10–2 goods type weighing 110 tons in running order. Their success was immediate. They tackled the steep mountain grades without difficulty while hauling quite considerable loads, and their only defect was that, owing to their small wheels, they were not equally suitable for passenger traffic on the more level sections of the system. In order to overcome this difficulty some lighter 2–8–2 locomotives were ordered last year and have recently been placed in service. These are constructed on the same principles as their heavier predecessors but are fitted with larger wheels.

Above is shown a general view of one of the 2-8-2 tank locomotives for a line in the Hartz Mountains that formerly was worked by rack locomotives. This photograph and the elevation shown below (dimensions in m.m.) are reproduced by courtesy of "*The Railway Engineer.*"

As our photograph shows, the new engines are quite distinctive in appearance. The boiler has been specially designed with reference to the heavy gradients, the diameter being relatively large and the tubes short. The result is to provide a high space above the top of the firebox that obviates any difficulty on account of the variations in water level on the gradients. As a further precaution the firebox top has been given an inclination of 1 in 16. The steam pressure is 235 lb. per sq. in.

The frame of the engine is of bar construction and has a fixed wheelbase of only 5 ft. 7 in. The two centre axles only are in fixed bearings, the others being in bogies; so that the engine is able to negotiate without difficulty the mountain curves. The steam cylinders are of unusually large size—25.2 in. diameter, 23.6 in. stroke—the object of this being to allow high tractive effort to be developed at the same time working economically with an early cut-off. Pneumatic sanding gear is provided on both sides of all the coupled wheels.

In the course of trial trips the new locomotives have hauled up the 1-in-16½ gradient coupled loads ranging up to as much as 200 tons, which is a very remarkable performance taking into consideration the fact that the available adhesive weight is only 70½ tons.

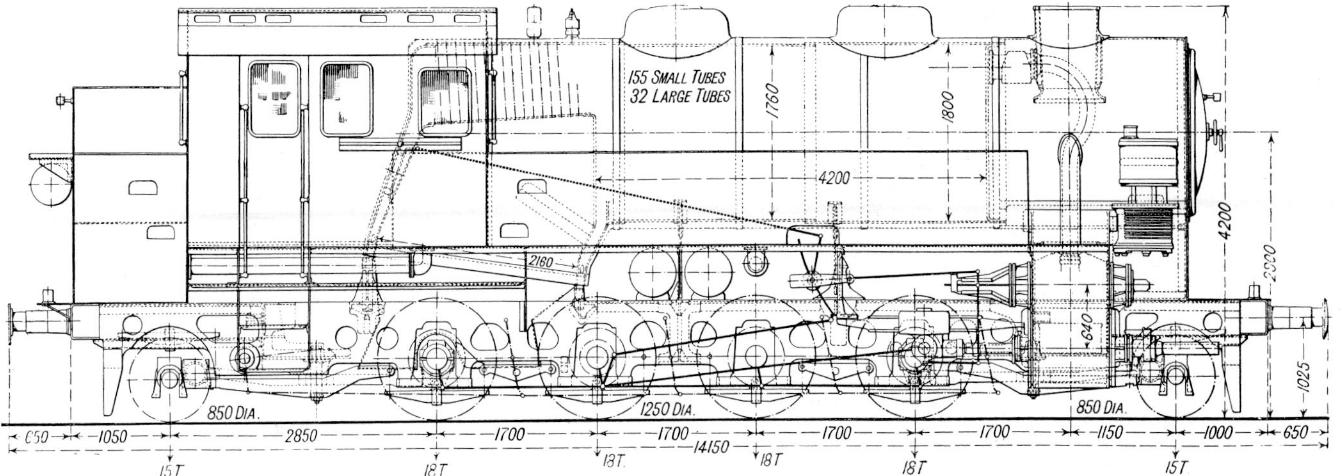

The New Channel Tunnel Scheme

Proposed High-Speed Broad Gauge Railway

FEW projected engineering schemes have been the subject of such protracted debate as the Channel Tunnel scheme.

It is almost 130 years since the idea was first put forward of linking up England and France by means of a submarine tunnel, and the matter has not yet passed beyond the discussion stage.

In 1802 a French mining engineer named M. Mathieu presented to the Emperor Napoleon a scheme for connecting England and France by means of a tunnel under the Strait of Dover. Mathieu proposed to build the tunnel in two sections each about 10 miles in length, one from the English coast and one from the French shore. Each section was to terminate on the Varnes Bank, which is situated about midway in the Strait. This submerged bank is only about 50 ft. below sea level and by means of strong embankments it was to be built up into a large island. The engineer suggested that an international town should be erected on the island, which was to be provided with a harbour of refuge for shipping. The two sections of the tunnel were to be lighted by oil lamps and ventilated by vertical shafts extending from the tunnel to the open air.

To us to-day this scheme appears crude, but it is undoubtedly ingenious. It had many strong supporters, including the famous British statesman Charles James Fox, but it did not come to maturity.

The site where the shaft on the English side was sunk for the old Tunnel Scheme

One of the most persistent advocates of closer communication between England and France was a French hydrographer and mining engineer named Thomas De Gamond, who dedicated his life and fortune to the subject. In 1834 he proposed the construction of a submarine tunnel composed of metallic tubes fitted one into the other in the manner of a telescope, but his plan was coldly received. Three years later he suggested that a train ferry service should be inaugurated, but although this idea attracted interest at the time it was soon forgotten.

In 1857 De Gamond drew up a scheme for spanning the Strait by means of a bridge that was to extend from a point near Dover to Calais. This scheme also met with no success for it was opposed very strongly by the naval and shipping authorities.

During the latter half of last century many schemes for establishing closer communication between the two countries were brought forward. Between 1862 and 1870 the idea of a train ferry service was revived and persistently advocated by the British engineer Sir John Fowler. Strong opposition from the Admiralty and from the Harbour Authorities effectually prevented any progress being made with the scheme, with the result that it had to be abandoned.

De Gamond's idea of a submarine tunnel was revived about this time and the British government proved to be more favourably inclined toward the subject than previously. Diplomatic communications were established with France on the matter and ultimately a joint Commission was appointed to consider the important and difficult details of a scheme for a tunnel between the two countries, and to decide upon the best means by which such a project could be carried out.

After investigation the Commission drew up a report embodying certain conditions that were to be the basis of a treaty between the two nations. When the problem of raising the necessary funds for the construction of a channel tunnel came to be considered, however, the interest of the British government waned, and eventually it was decided that existing financial conditions were unfavourable for giving support to the scheme. As a result of this decision the treaty was never signed.

In spite of this lack of government assistance a Channel Tunnel Company was formed in 1867 under the auspices of Lord Richard Grosvenor and Sir Edward Watkin, and investigations and surveys were carried out during the ensuing years. Nothing more was done until 1881, however, when preliminary plant was erected and the sinking of shafts commenced near Dover, in Kent, and at Sangatte, in France.

This definite move spurred opponents of the scheme to renewed and still more vigorous protests. The military authorities who, up to that time, had not displayed any particular hostility toward the idea, now suddenly woke up and opposed it tooth and nail. In addition, several prominent statesmen including the Duke of Cambridge, Lord Wolseley, and Lord Randolph Churchill, denounced the project on the ground that it would entirely destroy the security that Great Britain enjoyed from its situation as an island. "Fortifications," declared Lord Wolseley, on one occasion, "afford no adequate security of national safety and Dover in the possession of an enemy holding the tunnel, means England is at its mercy."

Admiral Sir Cooper Key, First Sea Lord of the Admiralty, addressed a letter to Lord Northbrook, First Lord of the Admiralty, couched in equally strong terms. He expressed the opinion that "Four hours' possession of the tunnel would enable 100,000 men to assemble and they would be joined in as many hours by as many more. What is to prevent an army from marching on London while our Navy, in all its pride and strength and power, looks on, a helpless spectator ? "

This cumulative opposition resulted in work on the Channel Tunnel being stopped in March 1883. The operations carried out up to that time included the sinking of the two shafts and the boring from each of a heading, or small tunnel. The two headings were to meet in mid-channel, so that the complete heading would form a passage by which the strata of the channel bed could be investigated.

On the English side a shaft had been sunk to the west of Shakespeare's Cliff, between Dover and Folkestone, and at the time that work was stopped the heading extended seaward from the base of the shaft for a distance of about 2,000 yds. The heading was 7 ft. in dia. and had been excavated on a descending gradient of 1 in 80. It was driven through a thick stratum of grey chalk and proved to be almost dry. Only 1½ gall. of water per min. penetrated into the tunnel, and this quantity gradually diminished. A 4 in. piston pump operating during one half-day per fortnight proved sufficient to drain the heading, which was not provided with any brick or iron lining to prevent percolation.

The heading from the base of the French shaft was driven seaward for about the same distance as the English heading. At the time when operations were stopped good progress was being made, and as much as 115 yds. of tunnel were bored out in six days. Like the Dover heading, the French one was unlined, and at one time water was leaking into the tunnel at the rate of about 400 gall. per min. Both headings were excavated by means of "Beaumont" boring machines, having two arms with steel teeth and driven by compressed air.

The tunnel scheme was revived once more in 1906, when British and French engineers inspected the old workings and drew up a joint report in which they recommended that communication between England and France should be established by means of two single track tunnels, 36 ft. apart from centre to centre, instead of by one double-track tunnel as contemplated in 1881. They advocated that the tunnels should be driven chiefly on a descending grade, but with a slight rise near mid-channel. The tunnels were to be driven by means of shields and were to be lined throughout with cast-iron segments, cement-grouted on the outside to prevent corrosion and to stop any leakage of water into the tunnels. When the segments were in position they were to be lined with concrete and lime-washed, so as to provide a smooth interior surface.

The engineers recommended that each of the tunnels should have an internal diameter of 18 ft., which would be large enough to accommodate the rolling stock of the British and French principal railways. Under this arrangement electric locomotives operating solely on the channel tunnel lines would take charge of trains at each terminus of the system. These locomotives were to be of sufficient power to cope with the heaviest trains running on the British and French main lines. It was further recommended that the two tunnels should be connected by cross passages equipped with air-tight doors.

This report attracted a great deal of attention and for some time was extensively discussed by engineers and others interested. Then once again the opposing influences prevailed and in spite of all efforts the scheme passed into oblivion.

During the War period and up till quite recently circumstances have made any fresh proposals impracticable, but now the subject is again attracting public attention in the form of a scheme put forward by a London engineer, Mr. William Collard.

Mr. Collard's scheme provides for a railway of 7 ft. gauge linking up London and Paris by way of a single tunnel under the Strait of Dover. The trains on this railway would be hauled by powerful electric locomotives operating on the third-rail system, and would travel at an average speed of 92 m.p.h., at which speed they would cover the 253 miles of line between the English and French termini in the short time of 2¾ hours.

The Channel tunnel would have an overall length of 44 miles and would consist of an 11-mile approach tunnel on the English side, a 24-mile length of tunnel under the Strait of Dover, and an exit tunnel on the French side nine miles in length. As trains would not be allowed to pass through the tunnel at a speed in excess of 60 m.p.h. the period of travel through the underground portion of the line would be about 45 minutes.

The tunnel would be large enough to accommodate a double track, while from the two termini to the respective approach tunnels four tracks would be laid. These would be supplemented by two additional tracks in the terminal suburban area—from London to Farningham, and from Paris to Beaumont-Persan. Both the London and the Paris terminals of the railway would be situated within easy reach of the principal thoroughfares of those cities, the London station being at Westminster and the Paris terminus in the Rue St. Lazare, between Gare St. Lazare and the Eglise de la Trinité. As a result of its location it would be proposed to give the Paris station the name of Paris-Trinité.

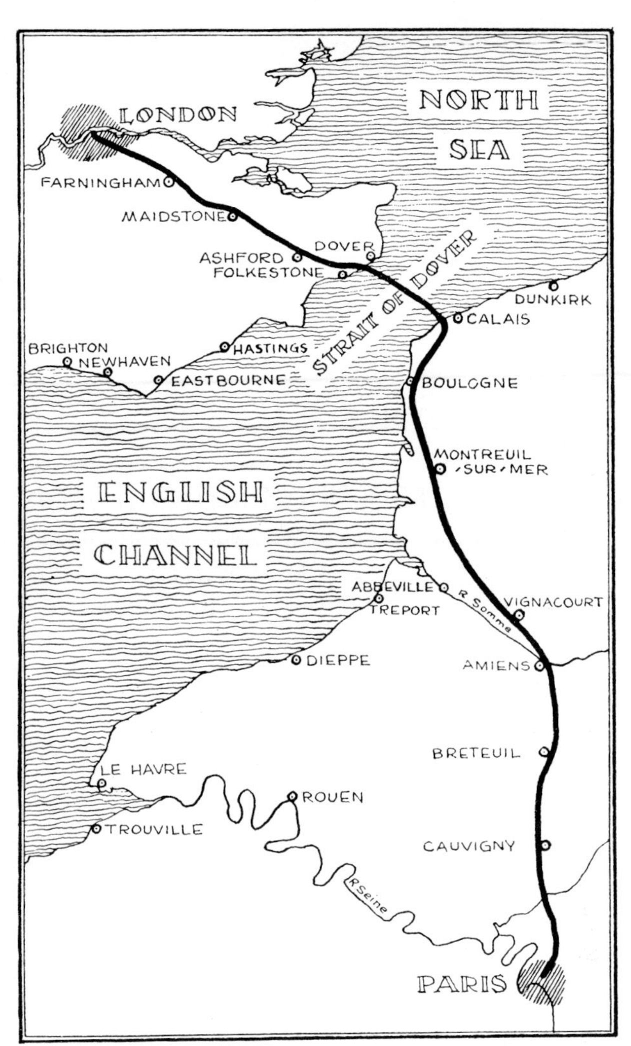

Map showing the route of the proposed tunnel and the London-Paris Railway

The accompanying map shows clearly the route of the proposed railway. The average gradient both ways over the entire route has been worked out at 1 in 746. The gradient of the "overland" section on the English side, that is from London to Monk's Horton station, would average 1 in 1,215. At Monk's Horton station the railway would enter the approach tunnel on a falling grade of 1 in 165, and the tunnel section would have an average gradient of 1 in 242. On the French side the average gradient of the overland section of the line would be 1 in 1,351.

The sharpest curve on the system would have a radius of one mile and would be at the entrance to the Paris terminus, while a curve having a radius of five miles would occur at St. Denis, near Paris. Other curves on the line have been planned for a minimum radius of seven miles.

On account of the broad gauge of the railway it would be impossible to link up with any of the existing railway systems in this country or in France in such a manner as to run through trains. This would appear to be a drawback but on the other hand it is pointed out that even if such linking up were possible, no advantage would be derived by passengers, because the compulsory customs examination in London and in Paris would necessitate their leaving the train at those places. Similarly, the necessary unloading of goods traffic for customs inspection would counteract any advantage of through conveyance and would entail elaborate precautions to keep track of loaded trucks passing through other countries on their way to or from remote places in Europe. A further advantage claimed for the broad gauge is that it would result in greater stability and would allow of increased freight accommodation on the trains.

The type of electric locomotives that would operate the system has not yet been definitely settled but probably they would be equipped with motors capable of at least 120 m.p.h. for short periods while hauling heavy loads. This high speed would be attained over certain portions of the journey through open country, the longest period of travel at the maximum speed being not more than 80 minutes. Two types of locomotive have been suggested. One is a recently designed gear-less locomotive equipped with six 1,000 h.p. motors and built by the General Electric Company, U.S.A. The other is the Brown-Boveri type, having four 1,500 h.p. motors set rigidly in the frames from the driving axles and transmitting their power to the driving wheels through two gear wheels. The locomotive would take direct current at 2,000 volts from a centre third rail.

The absence of curves of short radius would make practicable the use of unusually long coaches. It is anticipated that these would be 75 ft. in length, with a width of 13 ft. and a height of 14 ft. They would have 6-wheeled bogies of the Gresley articulated type with a wheelbase of 16 ft.

The first-class and third-class corridor coaches and the luggage vans each would weigh 50 tons, while *(Continued on page 133)*

A Run on the "*Twentieth Century Limited*"

(*Continued from page* 99)

"thrashed" to her utmost limit.

Upward we go until at last, after 62 miles' continuous climbing, we reach the summit of Mount Washington. From here after a sharp drop to Pittsfield, where we may touch 70 to 80 m.p.h. the scenery is just one beautiful panorama after another.

Through sleepy towns and villages we tear, the speedometer hanging steadily on at the 72 mark, until, as we start to cross the historic Hudson River we commence to decelerate in readiness for our entry into the great Union Station at Albany, N.Y. Here, two minutes to the good, we detach our train, leaving it to be taken forward to Chicago by one of the new "Hudson Speed" type of engines of the New York Central. Recrossing the Hudson River we reach our resting place where "596" will be thoroughly inspected and washed in preparation for the return on the morrow.

No doubt you feel ready now for a wash and a sleep but that does not prevent tongues from chattering. How, asks somebody, would that great "Hudson Speed" or even our gallant "596" look at the head of the "*Cornish Riviera*" express! That reminds me of an amusing little incident that occurred to me quite recently. That day I was driving "598" on the "*South Western Limited.*" We rolled into the terminal station of Boston and a few minutes later as I was looking over the engine a young fellow addressed me. It did my heart good to hear him speak. I am from England myself, you know, and he was from good old Lancashire! He was greatly interested in the engine and after a few moments' conversation he mentioned that he was an ex-Lancashire and Yorkshire Railwayman. I asked him how the engine would look running into Exchange Station, Liverpool. "By gum!" he replied, "I don't believe the beggar could get in!"

The New Channel Tunnel—

(*Continued from page* 131)

each dining car would be 55 tons in weight. A train unloaded would weigh 505 tons, and would consist of three first-class corridor coaches, each accommodating 100 passengers; two third-class corridor coaches seating 132 passengers each; one dining car; one luggage van and one locomotive. The passengers and luggage represent an additional 45 tons, so that a loaded train would weigh 550 tons.

The estimated total cost of the project is £189,177,094. Of this enormous sum the English "overland" section is estimated to cost £58,529,345, the Channel Tunnel £30,811,200, and the French "overland" section £99,836,549. It is calculated that the fare for the entire journey would be approximately £2; that for the journey to Boulogne £1, and the shorter journey from Ashford to Boulogne 10/-. Based on these figures, the gross receipts are estimated at £35,166,664 per annum, of which £23,209,998 would be required to meet working expenses, leaving a net profit of £11,956,666.

The interesting details of the proposed high-speed railway given in our article were published exclusively by "*Modern Transport.*" We have been able to reproduce them through the courtesy of the Editor of that paper.

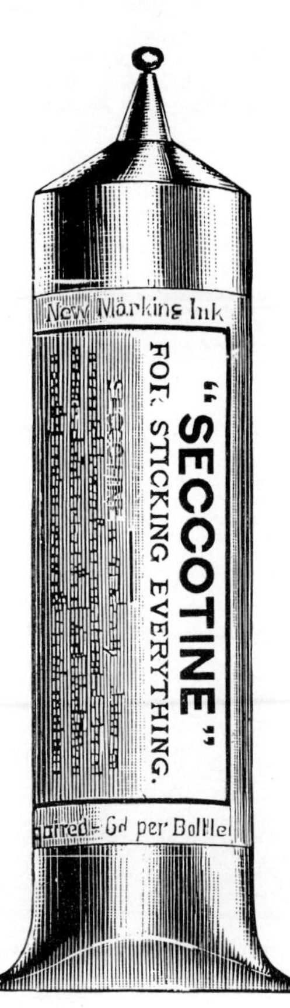

THE MECCANO BOY'S STAND-BY

THE TUBE OF

SECCOTINE

The World's Great Adhesive. Registered Trade Mark.

WITH it he can mend a thousand things—his bats, balls, boats, boxes, bags, books, &c. He can make numberless things that a boy likes. He can help his mother by mending breakages in house furniture, anything—everything.

NOTE. There is nothing messy about Seccotine. Use the spike or pin supplied to open a new tube—at top of cone—press gently at end of tube (at folded part) for as much adhesive as is needed—then replace spike or pin which acts as stopper. Keep folding tube end as contents are withdrawn. Give mended article adequate time for drying.

TUBES are 4½d. (vest pocket box), 6d. and 9d. each. Sold everywhere.

Mothers should know that cups, saucers, tumblers, etc. intended to hold liquids, hot or cold—should be mended with FIRMAS (Heat Seccotine). Tubes 6d. each.

McCAW, STEVENSON & ORR LTD.

The Linenhall Works BELFAST

The Best Gift! for every Boy

The Most Popular Flying Model

THE FAMOUS "SKISAIL"

Tractor Monoplane

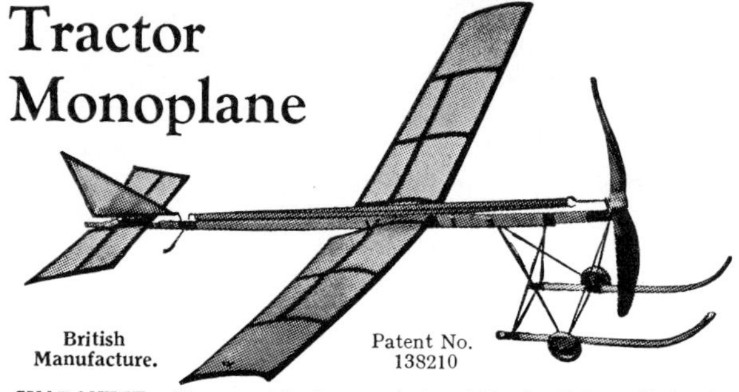

British Manufacture. Patent No. 138210

GUARANTEE.—These models show perfect stability in flight, will rise from the ground and fly from 150 to 450 yards according to size, in straight or circular flight.

SPECIFICATION.—Silver Spruce Fuselage, Silk-covered Planes, Aluminium Wheels, Polished Propeller. Nos. 0, 1, 2 and 3 fitted with our **Famous Patent Safety Chassis with Bamboo Runners.**

Wing Span of 18/6 Model 33 in. Length 31 in. Fitted with **Patent Safety Chassis with Landing Skids.** Wing span of our 4/6 model 21 in. Length 20 in.

The "Skisail Model de Luxe"

Wing Span 43 ins. Price 27/6 carr. paid.

No.		Price
0	Price	18/6
1	"	14/6
2	"	10/6
3	"	8/6
4	"	6/6
5	"	4/6

Carr. Paid U.K.

The "Skisail" Monoplanes are designed on correct aeronautical lines, constructed with highest quality materials and the prices are ranged to suit all pockets.

No other type can compare for **Design, Performance, or Price,** and our **Famous Patent Chassis** gives the "Skisail" a unique pre-eminence over any other make.

The "SKISAIL" PATENT MODELS are still the best. Purchase direct from the PIONEER INVENTORS.

PATENT MODEL MANUFACTURERS

159, Lymington Avenue, Wood Green, LONDON, N.22

A Book for Every Railway Enthusiast

200 pages and 58 Illustrations

Price

2/9

(post free)

This book tells the story of some of the most famous expresses of Great Britain. The author, Mr. Cecil J Allen, is one of the best-known writers on railway matters, and his lectures and B.B.C. talks are always popular, and his present contribution will be of great interest to all railway enthusiasts—young and old.

The book is beautifully printed on art paper, cloth bound, and is fully illustrated throughout. Now Ready. Price 2/9 (post free) from :—

MECCANO LTD. (Book Dept.), Old Swan, LIVERPOOL

The "DO.X"—A Leviathan of the Air

Giant Flying Boat to Carry 160 Persons

The Dornier "*DO.X*," the world's largest flying boat, on the slipway. We are indebted to the builders, the Dornier Metallbauten G.M.B.H., for permission to reproduce this and the other photographs illustrating this article

ON 21st October of this year the world of aviation was startled to learn that a "heavier than air" machine carrying no less than 169 people had made a flight of practically one hour's duration. The machine that performed this record-breaking feat is a huge 12-engined flying boat built by the Dornier Metallbauten G.M.B.H. of Friedrichshafen, Germany. The flight was made over Lake Constance, which already had become famous as the scene of the trials of Count Zeppelin's rigid airships.

The number of people on board the flying boat on this occasion easily constitutes a record for a flight in either an aeroplane or an airship, exceeding by 94 the number of persons carried on the preliminary flights of the great British airship "*R.101.*" The crew of the boat numbered ten and there were 150 passengers. The remaining nine were the inevitable stowaways, without whom it now seems impossible to make any flight of historic importance!

The designer of this great flying boat is Dr. Claudius Dornier, a well-known German engineer. Dr. Dornier had previously built monster flying boats, and before the flight of his latest boat the record for the number of passengers carried by a heavier-than-air machine was held by the "*Super-Wal*," which has made a flight with 60 passengers on board.

The rumours that Dr. Dornier had planned a "leviathan of the air" that would carry twice as many passengers as the "*Super-Wal*" had been greeted with scepticism, and some doubt of the ability of such a machine to rise from the water had been expressed. To a certain extent its designer also was a little uncertain. He was confident that eventually the great flying boat would be a success, but so many unknown factors were involved in its construction that to it he gave the name of "*DO.X.*" The first two letters are a contraction of his own name, and the "X" is the familiar algebraic symbol for an unknown quantity. Thus a literal rendering of the name by which the machine now is widely known is "Dornier's Unknown!"

As will be seen from the illustrations the machine is a monoplane. Immediately above the main plane is a smaller auxiliary aerofoil, which connects and supports the six nacelle turrets in which the engines are carried. The latter are "Jupiters"—a type that has brought and is bringing much fame to its British designers. There are twelve engines in all, developing a total of 6,300 horse power. They are placed in pairs end to end in the six nacelles, a form of distribution that is remarkable, for the six in front operate four-bladed tractor airscrews, while those behind are connected to airscrews of the pusher type. The fuel and oil tanks are situated on the lowest deck of the machine, and with full tanks and a complete crew the weight of the flying boat is about 35 tons.

An interesting feature of the machine is that minor alterations and repairs to the engines may be carried out while the boat is actually in the air. When a mechanic receives orders to attend to one of the engines that appears to be failing, he lies down on a small trolley that runs on rails laid inside the wing of the machine, and propels himself along until he is directly under the nacelle carrying the faulty engine. He then climbs up the turret and effects the necessary repairs, afterwards returning to the engine control room on the trolley to report to the engineer in charge.

The main body of the "*DO.X*" is of enormous size and has three decks. On the top deck is a cockpit for the two pilots and immediately behind this is a well-equipped navigation room. Thus the front part of the top deck may be regarded as equivalent to the bridge of an ocean-going liner. The engine control room, wireless cabin, and a room for mail also are situated on this deck.

Naturally a flying boat of such immense size cannot be controlled as easily as one of the ordinary type, and the *"DO.X"* therefore carries a crew of 12 men. This includes the captain, his assistant or first mate, two pilots, an engineer, four mechanics, a wireless operator, a cook and a steward. While in actual flight the boat is in charge of the captain, and the pilots merely act under his instructions exactly as the quarter-masters of Atlantic liners follow those of the officer in charge.

Passengers are accommodated on the middle deck. This contains a large lounge that is equipped with comfortable detached cushion chairs, and it is interesting to note that a wireless receiving outfit, complete with loud-speaker, is provided for the amusement of the passengers. The cabins also are situated on this deck. These are fitted up for 72 passengers, and it is intended to make this the maximum number to be carried on long flights. On flights of short duration the number may be increased and, as we have seen, the *"DO.X"* has accommodation for no fewer than 160 passengers in addition to the crew. In the bow there is a roomy smokeroom complete with bar, and the aft portion of the middle deck is occupied by cloakrooms, pantry and kitchen.

The Dornier "*DO.X*" in the water, with members of the crew standing by the engine nacelles

In the interests of the comfort of passengers efforts have been made to lessen the noise of the engines, and even in the earliest flights of this leviathan of the air it was noticed that the noise in the interior of the boat was not excessive. Further experiments are to be carried out in order to reduce this further, and to ensure that conversation between passengers may be carried on in an ordinary tone. At present passengers in airships are better situated in this respect, and generally accommodation on lighter-than-air vessels in more luxurious than on aeroplanes and flying boats. To many of the passengers in the *"DO.X"* the privilege of smoking no doubt will compensate for other deficiencies!

Putting the finishing touches to the giant Dornier flying boat prior to the launching ceremony. This view gives a good impression of the size of the machine

Electric lighting is provided throughout the machine, the current being generated by an auxiliary engine developing 4 h.p. This engine also provides the necessary current for the wireless outfit, the pumps and the engine-starting apparatus.

The giant flying boat was given a thorough trial over a period of ten weeks, during which 30 flights were made. Dr. Dornier was quite satisfied with its performance, and apart from trifling adjustments to the compensating surfaces of the rudder practically no modifications in design were necessary.

After several flights it was found that the rear engines were insufficiently cooled. This was a minor trouble and had not been unexpected, for never before had engines been carried in a similar position on a flying boat of this size, and the designer had little experience to guide him. A series of experiments were made in order to ascertain the manner in which the airstream passed around the cylinders of the rear engines, and the information obtained was sufficient to enable changes to be made in order to direct a cooling stream of air on them. This reduced their temperature to the correct level.

In spite of its size and weight the *"DO.X"* is said to be extraordinarily responsive to the pilot's touch. In anticipation of some difficulty in controlling the machine servo-motors had been provided, in order to minimise the strain on the pilot, but these proved to be quite unnecessary.

The *"DO.X"* already has some remarkable feats to its credit. Full details of its performance are not yet available, but on Lake Constance, with a total load amounting to 45 tons, it has taken off in little more than 60 seconds. The Lake is at an altitude of about 1,312 ft. above sea-level, and there is little doubt that from the latter, the machine would rise easily with loads of at least 52 tons, owing to the denser atmosphere.

During the trials the maximum speed attained was about 134 m.p.h., and it was found that the *"DO.X"* is capable of maintaining level flight *(Continued on page 960)*

Print Your Own Christmas Cards

(Continued from page 931)

speaking, the most effective scenes are those that lend themselves to treatment on similar lines. It is astonishing how much action may be put into a drawing consisting of a few bold lines only. The illustration of a calendar that accompanies this article is an excellent example of this, for the seaplane depicted on it appears to rise from the water in a very lively manner.

The two drawings at the foot of page 930 also are excellent specimens of the art of printing from linoleum blocks, that of a galleon being noteworthy for its particularly effective treatment of the sea. These and the other illustrations to the article will form useful guides to those who take up the fascinating hobby of linoleum block printing.

An interesting means of introducing variety is the use of colour, both in ink and paper. For instance, the calendar design already referred to, looks most effective when printed in dark blue ink on paper of a pale blue tint. A treatment of the same design that is almost equally effective is the use of black ink in conjunction with a pale grey card. The drawing of a galleon produces an excellent effect when black ink and blue paper are used, the change of the colour of the paper being to increase the effect produced by the simple representation of the sea. For the other designs illustrated, orange or red paper may be used to advantage. The interest of a black and white print may also be increased by tinting with water-colours the various sections enclosed by the lines of the design.

Dornier "*DO.X*"—*(Continued from page 923)*

with any four engines idle. The use of 12 engines gives the machine an ample reserve of power, and on one occasion, when carrying 25 passengers and having a total load of 36½ tons, take-off was successfully accomplished in 28 seconds with only eight engines running. So far all flights have been made with the same type of airscrew, but it is believed that a large increase of speed may be obtained by using other types. The landing speed is between 70 and 90 m.p.h., and the power-load ratio is 18.51 lb. per horse power.

The constructors of the "*DO.X*" intend to make efforts to secure a number of world's records. A series of longer flights are to be carried out over Lake Constance, and these will be followed by extensive flights to various points in Europe. Eventually the machine will make a trans-Atlantic flight and visit both North and South America. It is hoped to complete this programme by the end of January, 1930. No difficulty should be experienced in crossing the Atlantic Ocean, for the "*DO.X*" is expected to have a flying radius of more than 2,500 miles.

An order for two flying boats similar to the "*DO.X*" already has been placed by the Italian Government, and it is expected that the first of these machines will be completed and ready for delivery early in the New Year.

It is remarkable that the "*DO.X*" should appear at a time when interest in airships is reviving. To these the huge flying boat is a formidable rival. It is able to carry a large paying load and is much cheaper than an airship such as "*R.100*," for its cost was only £100,000, or less than a quarter of that of the British airship.

What Shall I Be—*(Continued from page 919)*

and young men living in the neighbourhood of their works. Of course their requirements are no less stringent than those of other electrical engineering firms, and those who hope to take up responsible positions with them must be fully trained.

Any boy who is attracted to the Electrical Engineering profession and wishes to enter it under one of the apprenticeship schemes above described should study the valuable information very carefully and should then write to suitable Electrical Engineering firms asking for full details of the systems followed. When the replies have been received, careful comparison, together with full consideration of other circumstances, will ensure that he is in a position to choose the one that is most advantageous. When this has been decided no time should be lost in making the necessary application for admission.

Engineering and student apprentices should take every opportunity of widening their general knowledge of engineering, and one admirable means of accomplishing this is to join the Institution of Electrical Engineers. Associate Membership and Full Membership of this Institution are the hall marks of the complete Electrical Engineer and carry with them the right to the use of the coveted letters " A.M.I.E.E." and " M.I.E.E."

This eminence is only attained after a period spent as a Student or Graduate, but those in the two last-named classes have the privilege of attending meetings of the Institution in London or in provincial centres. Full details may be obtained from the Secretary, The Institution of Electrical Engineers, Savoy Place, Victoria Embankment, London, W.C.2.

Bridging the English Channel

Famous Scientist's Amazing Scheme

By Our Special Correspondent: Frank Ellison

THE story of scientific discovery and invention is of enthralling interest to everybody, and it is only natural that all Meccano boys take a great delight in reading the lives of the great men who have helped to build up civilisation. Although it is wonderful to learn how these men achieved their successes, it is even more so when there is the added privilege of being associated with them throughout their careers. Actually to see inventors at work in their laboratories; to talk with them over their plans; and to follow the stages by which they overcome difficulty after difficulty—that indeed is an unforgettable experience! It was with such wonderful thoughts as these in my mind, and three fountain pens and six pencils in my pocket, that I arrived at Dozieville, a little village near Dover. Here it is that Professor Barmidotti, the world-famed scientist, has established his headquarters.

I had last seen the worthy Professor when I attended the sensational lecture in which he described the elaborate plans he had made for a journey by rocket to the Moon. A full report of this amazing scheme—the latest effort of post-war science—together with further details of the proposed flight, was given in the "*M.M.*" for January, 1928, to which interested readers will please refer. Since that time nothing had been heard of the learned Professor's activities, and as the Christmas number of the "*M.M.*" was going to press, the Editor asked me to undertake a special mission to enquire when the venerable scientist's plans were likely to be put into operation. Of course, a journey to the Moon is no light undertaking, but we all felt that some explanation of the delay was necessary—if the Professor was not to be classed as one of those preposterous imposters who at various times impose upon an unsuspecting public by claiming that they have solved the problem of journeying to other worlds by other than natural means.

After a long walk from Dozieville station I reached the Professor's house and was ushered into his laboratory by one of his assistants. Owing to the subdued light I could at first see nothing but retorts, batteries, wires, and formidable-looking pieces of apparatus of all descriptions. When my eyes became accustomed to the gloom, however, I descried the learned Professor bending over a metal pan on a specially designed stand in the furthest corner of the room. The whole attention of the great man was concentrated on his work. Naturally I hesitated to interrupt the world's foremost scientist—who was I, I thought, that I should intrude myself on an experimenter who was devoting his whole life to science . . . . . to the benefit of the great cause of humanity . . . . . . to uplifting the human race from the depths of despair to the heights of ecstasy? But remembering that I represented the "*M.M.*" and that I was, in fact, the chosen emissary of 100,000 of the finest boys in the world, I pulled myself together, and taking my courage in both hands, I coughed once . . . . . . twice and . . . . . . thrice. But without effect, for as is usual with all keen scientists, the world's greatest savant was completely absorbed in his work and was watching the contents of the metal pan so intently that he was totally unaware of my presence.

Obviously, any repetition of the expression of laryngital irritation of my epiglottis would be unavailing no matter how prolonged, so I gently tapped him on the shoulder. The howl of pain and the ejaculation of words in what was apparently a foreign tongue that followed, made me imagine for a moment that as the possessor of such an effective tap I should surely qualify for the world's heavyweight championship. But a slight smell of burning made me realise that the Professor's exclamation must be due to another cause.

When he had recovered his sangfroid, as our French readers would say, the Professor courteously explained that he was flooding a couple of sausages with ultra-violet rays in order to increase their vitamin content, before sending them to be cooked for his frugal meal. My tap on the shoulder had so startled him that accidentally he had placed his hand on the terminals of the mercury arc lamp that he was using to produce the violet rays, and had thus received a very purple shock. Being on the lookout for ideas myself, I decided that if ever I were called upon to tackle Phil Scott or Primo Carnera, I would arrange somehow to conceal a mercury arc lamp in each glove!

The latest portrait of Professor Barmidotti. Britain's greatest genius is showing—with commendable and touching pride—models of two of the most striking of his many wonderful inventions

When I had made myself known, Professor Barmidotti welcomed me with great enthusiasm. He is himself an old Meccano boy, it appears, being the proud owner of a complete 00 Outfit that he has built up by degrees from a beautiful No. 7 owned by his younger son!

I explained that the purpose of my visit was to enquire if any further progress had been made with the great scheme for visiting the Moon. Our readers particularly wanted to know, I said, if the full description of the Professor's amazing rocket published in the "*M.M.*" had resulted in any wealthy syndicate of financial magnates coming to his support. To my amazement I learned that the Professor had not been approached by a single individual, but in spite of this fact he was not disheartened. He is quite aware that men of genius usually are left to struggle alone and even to starve for lack of appreciation. He confided in me that he had determined to raise the necessary sum himself by means of a number of simpler inventions easily understood and generally useful. The first of these inventions certainly has been very successful, and promises to bring him a considerable sum of money. It is a wonderful self-starting tramcar and has already been adopted by the Tramways Department of the progressive town of Slushton, and without doubt will make an early appearance in other towns and cities at some remote date.

The principle of the invention is so surprisingly simple that I kick myself for not having thought of it myself. A wireless circuit including 15 or more valves is fitted to each car, and waves of a selected wave-length are broadcast from a central station. When the car is empty the circuit is not in tune with these waves, but when a body having large capacity is brought near the apparatus it receives them in full strength. In practice, this extra capacity is provided by the entrance of the passengers, matters being so arranged that when the car is full the capacity thus added is sufficient to bring the circuit exactly into tune, thereby causing it to operate a relay that starts the tramcar.

Thanks to the Professor's wonderful invention, in future every tramcar will carry a full paying load. The economy in running costs will be enormous—so great, indeed, as to be well worth off-setting against any irritation caused to those who at slack times will be compelled to sit for long periods while waiting for the car to fill up. The Professor is now at work devising subsidiary inventions covering special means of pacifying irate passengers. It has already been suggested by the Professor that gramophone reproductions of his University Extension lectures on " Dry Dust and Hot Air in the Palaeolithic-Ooglical Epoch " should be used for this purpose. It is believed that passengers will become so absorbed in listening to this discourse that they will forget the flight of time. Meantime, the Corporation have arranged to provide each tramcar with six sets of " Snakes and Ladders " boards and packs of " Happy Families " cards. Prizes will be offered from time to time in connection with these games, and the winner of the greatest number during Civic Week will qualify for admittance without fee in the first round of the West of England Ludo championship held every ten years.

In explaining his invention to me the Professor observed that occasionally a little complication must inevitably occur. For instance, the last person may be under average size, in which case the capacity added may be insufficient to start the car. To meet this emergency it is necessary to arrange to station permanently at each terminus a man weighing about 20 stone who carries the title of Official Car Starter. How the O.C.S. performs his important duties is clearly shown in the accompanying illustration, which shows one of the cars of the Slushton Corporation Tramways about to leave an outlying terminus.

The Professor informed me that the man on duty at this point has never failed to start a car, and that usually even a look from him is sufficient to galvanise the most obstinate vehicle into instant activity.

Whilst I was admiring this delightful photograph, the Professor was rummaging through several cabinets. Eventually he found the object of his search in his pocket, however, and this turned out to be a sheet of paper that, when unfolded, was about 15 ft. square. On it was a drawing of a mechanism or structure of which I could make nothing. This, of course, was not surprising, for naturally the products of such a genius as Professor Barmidotti are only comprehensible to ordinary individuals after prolonged study—and not always then !

As I gazed at the wonderful drawing, I seemed intuitively to sense that it represented some resemblance to a portion of an arch bridge—similar, perhaps, to the massive structure now being erected across Sydney Harbour. I decided, however, that if the drawing really was of a bridge, then it certainly was the queerest structure ever seen, for it appeared to be a combination of a suspension bridge and arch bridge. Heavy cables hung from the arch, and appeared to connect it with a curious structure that floated on the water under the bridge. Girders, struts, and ties were planned to stretch in every direction, and I was particularly impressed by the enormous size of the arch itself. The small portion of this that appeared on the drawing seemed huge enough to accommodate an airship as large as "*R.101.*"

In despair of ever being intelligent enough to understand the full purpose of the wonderful structure represented, I turned to the Professor and confessed that his work was entirely beyond me. Only then did he condescend to give me any explanation of his amazing scheme.

" This is a drawing of one end of a bridge to cross the English Channel," he said. " Naturally such a bridge must be stronger and larger than any yet built, and in planning it I have decided to combine the merits of all known types. It has always seemed rather futile to confine the design of any bridge to any particular type. Why should we always have Arch Bridges, Suspension Bridges, or Girder Bridges only ? Why not extract all that is best in each design and combine them into one glorious whole ? Do you follow me ? "

I said I did and thus reassured the Professor proceeded : " As you will see from the drawing, the structure is an arch bridge, but in order that it may carry heavy loads, the arch will be suspended from cables in exactly the same manner as the deck of a suspension bridge is suspended The whole thing is so perfectly simple that even a child can understand it."

The most amazing engineering structure the world has not yet seen ! This unique bridge across the English Channel has been designed by Professor Barmidotti, the world-famed scientist. It combines the merits of the arch and suspension types and has no middle, for very excellent reasons that are fully explained in this exclusive article

" But surely," I interrupted, " it will be necessary to carry to an enormous height the towers from which the cables are suspended ? "

With a pitying smile, the Professor told me that he had understood that from the beginning, and in order to secure the necessary height he proposed to make use of the cliffs at Dover. " The enormous towers that are necessary for every suspension bridge will be constructed at the top of the cliff and will be no less than 1,200 ft. in height. Thus, the top of each tower will be at a height of 1,550 ft. above the surface of the water of the Straits of Dover, for the cliffs themselves thereabouts are 350 ft. in height, and thus are suitable for my purpose."

I rapidly calculated that if this plan were followed, the centre of the bridge would be nearly 11 miles from shore, and judging from the angle at which it rose upward from the ground, the arch would reach the tremendous height of about 4½ miles. I began to think that either the Professor had misplaced a couple of decimal points or that unwearying study had at last turned his brain, for it was obvious that towers reaching only to a height of 1,550 ft. above the water would not be of much use for suspending an arch 4½ miles in height !

With fear in my mind of a terrible tragedy, I asked the great man if he thought that the towers on the cliffs would be sufficiently high to suspend the middle of the bridge. He looked at me in wonderment and then asked what I meant by the " middle of the bridge." Patiently I explained to him that the arch he had drawn apparently would rise to a height of 4½ miles, and that I did not understand how he expected cables from towers little more than a quarter of a mile in height to support it at this point. At last he grasped the idea in my feeble mind and to my amazement burst into a hearty laugh !

" Good heavens ! Are you so lacking in perception ! " he exclaimed. " Don't you understand that the bridge I propose to build has no " middle "—in my opinion it is a sinful waste of material to construct more than a few yards at each end of a bridge. Besides, bridges with middles are exceedingly dangerous, as has been proved on many occasions in history. For instance, where did the Quebec Bridge break—it certainly was not near the shore. The first break came when the southern cantilever had been extended for some distance from the main pier, and the second collapse was due to defects in the central span. And the Tay Bridge, where did that collapse ? Why—in the middle, of course ! "

" But how on earth do you expect anyone to cross a bridge that is not there ? " I asked, in bewilderment.

" You appear to have forgotten my rocket " he replied, in

a tone of severe reproof. He then proceeded to explain the wonderful project that he had thought out, and I saw what an ass I had been to have supposed even for a moment that a brain of my calibre could find a flaw in the Professor's plans. What I had taken to be the arch of the bridge is in reality a runway to accommodate a rocket! Actually, this will be a smaller edition of the amazing contrivance in which the Professor hopes to travel to the Moon. In the rear compartment will be carried a supply of explosives, adjusted to the exact amount necessary to carry the rocket across the Channel, where it will fall into a similar runway used subsequently for firing it in the reverse direction.

The chief modification in the design of the Channel rocket is that there will be a compartment for rockets at each end in order to avoid the necessity for reversing. The rocket used will be very roomy and comfortable in design, for of course, it will not be necessary on short trips to carry as many accessories as in the case of a rocket intended to travel to the Moon.

At first sight it may appear a little doubtful whether the rocket always will hit the runway on the portion of the arch erected on the further side of the channel. The Professor told me that he anticipated no difficulty on this score, however, for careful work on the part of the engineers who carry out his plans will enable them to place the two ends of the bridge exactly opposite each other. If the explosive charge is measured correctly it is thought that the rocket cannot fail to enter. In order to reassure timid people who may be unwilling to trust themselves to his guidance—there cannot be many, however, who do not place full confidence in him—he intends to widen out the ends of the arches into funnel-shaped openings in which a large number of powerful electro-magnets will be placed. In the unlikely event of any rocket deviating from its path, it will immediately be pulled into its correct position by the action of the magnets, and it must inevitably run down the arch and come to rest at the bottom.

It may be thought that the descent of a rocket will be extremely violent, and that on arrival at the bottom of the arch it will crash through the structure and demolish it. This cannot happen, however, for the retarding action of the magnets in the higher portion of the arch will reduce the speed of the projectile and hydraulic buffers eventually will bring it to rest.

The project is quite self-contained and nothing is forgotten. For instance, the power that will be required to produce the current for the electro magnets will be obtained from the rise and fall of the tides, and what I took to be cables descending from the bridge were really conducting wires from the floating power station established beneath. As the tide rises and falls it will operate turbines similar to those used in hydro-electric power stations and the current produced in generators connected with them will suffice not only to excite the coils of the electro-magnets, but also to provide the necessary current for lighting and heating the passenger station, waiting rooms, etc.

It is only a matter of time before this wonderful structure will make its appearance, for as soon as the Professor has made a fortune from his other inventions, he will begin with the construction of the cross-channel bridge, which will then provide funds for the Moon-rocket scheme. When the Channel Bridge is working, the visitor to the continent for the first time will be able to make use of an invention that combines the advantages of arch, suspension and transporter bridges with those of the rocket flying machines of the type that the Professor was the first to exploit. Sea-sickness will be completely avoided and nobody will have time to be airsick, for it must be clear to all our readers that the sensations of every passenger will certainly not last longer than a few seconds!

As I gazed in profound admiration at the drawing of the wonderful structure, I suddenly became aware that the Professor had ceased his explanations. Reluctantly tearing my gaze away from the fascinating plans of the Channel Bridge, I found that with a rapt expression on his face he was gazing through the window towards the French coast. I realised that a new idea had struck him and that in working it out he had totally forgotten my existence. I perceived that in my thirst for information I had taken up too much of the valuable time of Britain's greatest genius, and in awestruck silence I crept quietly from the room.

Another of the Professor's wonderful inventions—the Official Car Starter about to galvanise the self-starting tramcar into action

Famous Trains—(*Continued from page 915*)

Clapham Junction it becomes necessary to reduce speed. This point is little more than 104 miles from Bournemouth West, but we are due to pass it at 10.33, 113 min. after starting.

Through the maze of tracks of Clapham Junction we thread our way, and immediately after leaving the station itself we dive under the main line from Brighton. This joined us on our right immediately before reaching the station, and now climbs up to cross over on its way to Victoria. At this point there is an amazing area of tracks, and in all probability a greater number of parallel running lines, as distinct from sidings, exist here than anywhere else in Great Britain.

High speed over the busy stretch into Waterloo is impossible, and the immense volume of traffic makes very tight timing necessary. In order to fit in the expresses between the numerous electric trains entering the terminus it is necessary to use half-minute timings. For instance, at Vauxhall the booked passing time for the up "*Bournemouth Limited*" is 116½ minutes after leaving our starting point. When we reach Waterloo we have travelled 108 miles, and the manner in which our splendidly appointed train has made the journey over a road that is by no means easy, is highly creditable, even to our powerful locomotive and its capable crew.

Puzzle Your Sharp-Eyed Friends—

(*Continued from page 937*)

inside the tube in the manner clearly shown in Fig. 12 on page 937.

While the conjurer is talking about being able to turn the bran into anything he likes he lets the lower glass, which is the one containing the bran, slip unnoticed out of the tube into the box of bran. It falls into the hollow in the bran and therefore makes no sound. The paper tube containing the other glass is then brought forward, and in due course the chocolate doll is revealed, when both glass and tube may be examined by anyone.

This trick is simple, but extremely effective. It will be seen that for its success it depends very largely on the ability of the conjuror to cover up his movements by means of patter, and this is a convenient point to emphasise the importance of being able to talk well. Those who wish to embark on the career of amateur conjurer should not only become acquainted with tricks such as those described in this article, but also must cultivate what may be described as a platform manner. This is by no means difficult, and it will be found that a little ready wit in conjunction with suitable patter for each experiment will help to carry a conjurer successfully through his performance, and in many cases to extricate him from unexpected difficulties.

The New High-Pressure Locomotives

Bold Departure from British Practice

Courtesy] [L.N.E.R.
The L.N.E.R. experimental locomotive "No. 10000." This is an entirely new departure from British locomotive practice, and has a boiler of the water-tube type with a working pressure of 450 lb. per sq. in.

ONE of the most interesting recent events in the British railway world was the appearance shortly before the close of last year of two experimental locomotives employing high-pressure steam. In Germany and the United States considerable attention has been paid for some time to the possibilities of high boiler pressures. In this country, however, except in the case of one or two unusual types of goods engines, the maximum boiler pressure has been about 250 lb. per sq. in., as used in the G.W.R. "*King George*" and the L.M.S. "*Royal Scot.*" The new locomotives break away completely from previous British practice, and their trials will be watched with keen and widespread interest.

The first of the high-pressure locomotives to appear was "No. 10000," built at the Darlington Works of the London and North Eastern Railway. In outward appearance this new locomotive is an entire departure from previous practice in locomotive design in this country, and many of its constructional details are novel and extremely interesting. The design was finally arrived at as the result of tests that were made with a model of the locomotive in a wind flume with air currents of speeds up to 50 miles per hour.

Courtesy] [L.M.S.
The new L.M.S. high-pressure engine, which follows the design of the "Royal Scot" class with regard to the frame, but is fitted with a boiler designed on the Schmidt high-pressure system.

The boiler has been built to the extreme limits of the railway gauge, with the result that there is no room for a chimney to project above the boiler. This difficulty has been overcome by sinking the chimney within casing plates, which are arranged in such a manner as to throw the smoke upward in order to give the driver a clear view from his position on the footplate.

The locomotive has been designed for the unusually high working boiler pressure of 450 lb. per sq. in. This high pressure has necessitated the use of a boiler of the water tube type, which has never previously been applied to a locomotive in this country, although it is used to some extent in the latest American practice. The boiler, which has been designed jointly by Mr. H. N. Gresley and Mr. Harold Yarrow, was manufactured by Yarrow & Co. Ltd., of Glasgow.

The engine is a four-cylinder compound. The two high-pressure cylinders, which are made of cast steel—a new feature—are 12 in. in diameter by 26 in. stroke, driving on to the leading coupled wheels. The two low-pressure cylinders are situated outside the frames and drive the intermediate pair of coupled wheels. These cylinders have a diameter of 20 in. by 26 in. stroke, and they and the connecting rods,

Courtesy] [L.M.S.

A broadside view of the L.M.S. high-pressure locomotive "*Fury*," showing how the increased boiler demands have been satisfied without any sacrifice in outward appearance.

coupling rods, etc., conform to the standard type on the L.N.E.R. "Pacific" locomotives. Walschaerts valve gear is fitted to the outside cylinders, and the valves of the high-pressure cylinders are actuated by a rocking shaft in such a manner that the cut-off of the high-pressure cylinders can be varied independently of that of the low-pressure cylinders. An important feature of the design is that the whole of the air supplied to the firegrate is pre-heated, the supply being taken from the front of the smokebox, and passing down a space between the boiler and the casings.

A further interesting point about this locomotive is that it possesses the 4–6–4 or "Baltic" type wheel arrangement. "Baltic" tank engines are in use by the London Midland and Scottish and the Southern railways, but this is the first tender locomotive with this wheel arrangement to be constructed and operated in this country. The six coupled driving wheels are 6 ft. 8 in. in diameter. The tender is of the L.N.E.R. "*Flying Scotsman*" corridor type, and the total weight of engine and tender in working order is 166 tons.

"No. 10000" has been constructed to the designs and inventions of Mr. H. N. Gresley, C.B.E., Chief Mechanical Engineer of the London and North Eastern Railway Company. It has been built with the object of achieving higher all-round efficiency and fuel economy. After its preliminary trials the locomotive will be tested in actual service between London, King's Cross, and Edinburgh, Waverley.

Courtesy] [L.N.E.R.

A front view of the L.N.E.R. locomotive "No. 10000." The chimney has had to be sunk within casing plates.

Closely following upon Mr. Gresley's engine came the London Midland and Scottish high-pressure locomotive, No. 6399, "*Fury*." While this locomotive is less unorthodox in outward appearance than the L.N.E.R. "No. 10000," it is perhaps even more interesting in that it is fitted with a boiler designed on the Schmidt high-pressure system. It has been built by the North British Locomotive Company, Glasgow, under the supervision of Sir Henry Fowler, K.B.E., Chief Mechanical Engineer of the London Midland and Scottish Railway, in conjunction with the Superheater Company Ltd., London.

The design of the "*Fury*" follows that of the "Royal Scot" class with regard to the frame, but in this case the engine is a three-cylinder compound, the high-pressure cylinder being situated between the frames and the two low-pressure cylinders outside the frames. The design of the boiler is based upon that of the experimental Schmidt boiler that was built for one of the Continental railways, and which passed through a series of severe trials with complete success.

The Schmidt high-pressure boiler consists of three distinct systems or boilers, each carrying a different pressure. The system having the highest pressure—1,400 lb. to 1,800 lb. per sq. in., the variation in pressure depending upon the rate of firing—is in the form of a "closed circuit" consisting of a number of pipes that form the sides, roof, and back end of the firebox. These pipes are connected at the bottom to a foundation ring and at the top to equalising drums, into which they are expanded. From the equalising drums pipes are led to evaporating elements situated in the high-pressure drum. This closed circuit is initially filled to a predetermined level with pure water, and this latter is the medium by means of which heat is transmitted from the firebox to the evaporating elements in the high-pressure drum. This drum furnishes steam at 900 lb. per sq. in. for the high-pressure cylinder of the locomotive. The drum is of nickel steel, but is not in any way in contact with the fire. It is fed by water drawn as required from the low-pressure boiler by means of a pump.

The low-pressure boiler occupies the same position as the barrel of the normal locomotive boiler, and the water is evaporated by the gases passing through the boiler tubes. The barrel of this low-pressure boiler also is of nickel steel, but both tube plates are of mild steel.

An ordinary live steam injector is provided on the driver's side and an exhaust steam (*Continued on page 92*)

The New High-Pressure Locomotives—

(Continued from page 103)

injector on the fireman's side of the engine, to feed the low-pressure boiler.

As steam is raised much more quickly in the high-pressure drum than in the low-pressure boiler, arrangements are made to by-pass, by means of an intercepting valve, any excess steam from the high-pressure drum into the low-pressure boiler, thus avoiding waste through blowing-off.

The method of working this locomotive is more or less normal. The regulator handle operates both the high-pressure and the low-pressure regulator simultaneously. On opening the regulator steam is admitted into the high-pressure cylinder after passing through the high-pressure superheater situated in the lower boiler tubes. Exhausting from the high-pressure cylinder, the steam enters a mixing chamber, where it is met by low-pressure steam at 250 lb. pressure, which previously has passed through a low-pressure superheater situated in the upper boiler tubes. From the mixing chamber steam enters the two outside cylinders and goes thence to the exhaust.

It will be interesting to see how these two locomotives compare with high-pressure locomotives that have been tried in other countries. In the United States, for instance, the Delaware and Hudson Railroad put into service as far back as 1924 a locomotive with a special water-tube firebox and boiler design and a working steam pressure of 350 lb. to the sq. in. This locomotive gave such good results in heavy freight working that in 1927 another of similar design was introduced with a steam pressure of 400 lb. This engine also appears to have shown very high general efficiency.

An even more remarkable locomotive has been built in Switzerland by the Swiss Locomotive and Machine Company of Winterthur. In this locomotive a pressure of 850 lb. per sq. in. has been boldly adopted, in conjunction with a water-tube boiler of novel design.

Light Power Units for Railways

Development of the Steam Coach

ONE of the most interesting features of railway operation during the past few years has been the increasing use by the railway companies of the steam rail coach. The motor omnibus had begun to cut deeply into railway passenger receipts, and it was necessary for the railways to make a serious attempt, particularly on branch lines and in thinly-populated districts to win back some at least of the traffic that had been lost to them. The road vehicle possessed certain advantages over the train, prominent among which were its capacity for varying its route at will and its ability to pick up or set down passengers at any required point along the route. The railways on the other hand had the very important advantages of speed and comfort, and the problem with which the companies were faced was that of competing with their rivals in frequency and convenience of service at the lowest possible running cost.

Sentinel-Cammell geared steam rail coach "*Nettle,*" running on the L.N.E.R.

In 1902 the London and South Western Railway introduced a steam rail coach built at Nine Elms. This vehicle seated 10 first-class and 32 third-class passengers, and was capable of a speed of 30 m.p.h., which could be attained within half a minute of starting. It was provided with arrangements for driving from either end and was lighted by gas. In the following year the Great Western Railway introduced on various branches, and also in the neighbourhood of large centres of population, rail motor cars that performed circular trips or "shuttle" services. A policy of providing "halts" on or near the highway, at which passengers could alight or embark, was instituted, and this has been developed extensively throughout the system. Auto-trains consisting of two coaches with a small tank engine in between, or of one coach hauled by a tank engine, were also introduced and have been found of great service in many districts. Trailers are attached to these units as required.

Some of the companies that are now merged in one or other of the great groups formerly used rail motor coaches to some extent. In most cases this method of working was discontinued, however, probably because it was found that the power unit then in use showed little economy as compared with the local steam trains. Some five or six years ago, however, makers of steam road motor vehicles turned their attention to the steam rail coach. The first experiments gave remarkably promising results, and since that time rapid technical progress has been made. The best known of these new vehicles are the Sentinel-Cammell cars, built by the Sentinel Waggon Works Ltd., and Cammell Laird and Co. Ltd., and those built by Clayton Wagons Ltd.

Photos courtesy] [*"Sentinel" Waggon Works Ltd.*

Fitting seats and blinds in Sentinel-Cammell coach.

Among the first companies to experiment with steam rail coaches of this type was the L.N.E.R., which made some experimental runs from Pickering to Whitby, and thence to Scarborough by the coast line, in 1924. This test was a severe one from a gradient point of view and valuable experience was gained. Orders were placed for two vehicles, which were placed in service for East Anglia. Subsequent tests were made with a development of the Sentinel type and in 1927 two more cars were introduced in the Newcastle area, and later a Clayton car was employed.

At the beginning of 1928 a new design of Sentinel was introduced, this being a gear-driven, two-cylinder double bogie coach; and it was followed by the six-cylinder gear-driven Sentinel. Last year a considerable extension in the use of rail coaches took place, particularly on the north-east coast. Both Sentinel-Cammells and Claytons are employed, and the results in the case of both types have been perfectly satisfactory.

Steam rail coaches have their limitations, but they carry out successfully certain types of services that cannot be performed economically by the ordinary locomotive and train. It is stated that, working a double shift and covering some 200 miles per day, the cost per mile of a steam coach is about half that of the ordinary steam train. This economy enables services to be maintained in difficult areas, and it has happened that new services operated by rail coaches have proved so popular that a normal train service had to be set up to meet the needs of the traffic thus cultivated. Again owing to the low running costs, it has been found possible on some branch lines to double or even treble the existing services with very little increase in expense. The reduction in working costs that has been brought about by the use of the rail coach has a special value where train services are being run at a loss but must be continued; and where it is desired to give additional services although the traffic does not justify the running of extra steam trains.

An interesting feature of the adoption of rail coaches on the L.N.E.R. is that these have been given names borne by famous road coaches in the stage coach era; among them being "*Rapid,*" "*Comet,*" "*Chevy Chase,*" "*Transit,*" and "*Bang-up.*" A march thus seems to have been stolen on the road interests which, one

"Clayton" steam rail coach "*Wonder*," built for the L.N.E.R.

cannot help thinking, should have appropriated these titles for their own vehicles, as these are the direct and real successors of the stage coach.

The Sentinel-Cammell and the Clayton coaches differ considerably in design and construction and therefore it will be of interest to describe a typical example of each.

The standard Sentinel-Cammell gear-driven rail car has a six-cylinder single-acting engine with cylinders of 6 in. bore by 7 in. stroke, and the engine is suspended underneath the coach body behind the leading bogie. The designed output is about 130 b.h.p. at 500 r.p.m. Poppet type valves are used, actuated by cams; and lubrication to all surfaces is effected under pressure. Three running positions, corresponding to early, intermediate and late cut-off, are provided for in each direction of rotation, with in addition a central position in which all valves are held open. If adjustment becomes necessary, easy access to the engine is provided by means of removable floor boards in the luggage compartment, and the engine itself can be completely removed from the frame in about an hour. The cylinders, with the inlet and exhaust valve assemblies, are in clear view on one side of the coach. There are no flexible steam pipes or controls, the engine and the boiler both being firmly attached to the coach framework. Power is transmitted by universal joints splined on a cardan shaft from the engine to the gearbox, which is arranged on the front axle of the driving bogie. Any relative movement between the bogie axle and the engine is completely taken up by the universal joints and splines, no motion being transmitted to the engine itself.

The gear-box casing is carried on the axle by two bearings loaded to 150 lb. per sq. in., and flooded with oil thrown on to them by the gears. It incorporates a pair of bevel gears carried on roller bearings, and a pair of nickel chrome steel spur gears. Torque is dealt with by a stay bolted to the box and links suspended above the bogie frame. The boiler is of the latest Sentinel vertical water-tube type, and is designed for a working pressure of 300 lb. per sq. in. It has an output of about 2,350 lb. of steam per hour with Welsh coal. A cool driving compartment has been secured by adequate lagging of all heated parts, together with the provision of air casings over the boiler top and round the base of the funnel. Steam is taken through a superheater coil to the main valve, the total superheat temperature being from 650° to 700°F. The boiler is fed by a two-ram engine pump and two injectors are also provided. The boiler is so arranged that the whole of the firebox with the water tubes can be lowered out of the boiler for cleaning or repair. The wash-out plugs and the mechanism for dropping the hinged ashpan and half firegrate are readily accessible from the front of the car.

The bunker is completely enclosed in the body of the car and is designed to carry 30 cwt. of coal, sufficient for a run of about 300 miles. The coal is filled through flap doors in the roof. A 450-gallon water tank is arranged transversely at the back of the cab and can be filled from either side of the car. The water supply is sufficient for a run of about 60 miles. The driving compartment is roomy and comfortable, and the control levers are brought to a column in front of the driver's seat. An unobstructed view of the track ahead is provided by large glass windows, which are fitted with a mechanical wiper operated by suction.

Photos courtesy] [Clayton Wagons Ltd.

"Clayton" articulated steam coach, built for the Egyptian State Railways.

The coach body is divided into a third-class compartment to accommodate 59 passengers on reversible seats, a driver's cab at each end, and a luggage compartment next to the engine cab. Straps are provided for 20 standing passengers and there are parcel racks along the whole length of the compartment. Sliding doors give access from the luggage compartment to the driver's cab and the passenger compartment; and two large sliding doors are fitted at each side of the coach, those at the front end giving access to the luggage compartment. Steps are provided to allow of the car being entered from ground level. The car is steam heated and well ventilated, and lighted by a dynamo driven from the forward axle of the trailing bogie. A noteworthy feature is that the solebars of the underframe run from end to end of the car and the boiler and the engine are rigidly attached to them. This is a departure from the previous practice of articulating between the passenger accommodation and the power unit. The design of the bogies follows standard railway practice, and the upper parts of the car are painted cream and the lower portion bright green.

The length of the vehicle over buffers is 62 ft. 8 in., and the length over the body 58 ft. 6 in. The overall width of the car is 9 ft., and the height from rail to the top of the roof 12 ft. 4¼ in. The weight of the car in running order is 31 tons 15 cwt., and the car will maintain a speed of 50 m.p.h.

The latest Sentinel-Cammell development is a 200 h.p. rail car fitted with two engines each similar to the engine of the car just described. The second engine is placed in front of the rear bogie and drives the back axle of the car. The use of the two engines has the effect of distributing the weight and dispensing with the necessity of coupling the driving axles. An interesting feature of the design, particularly in view of recent locomotive developments in this country, is the boiler, which is of a three-drum, water-tube type, more usually associated with marine than with locomotive work. This boiler has proved capable of supplying steam to both engines in ample quantities for the most exacting work.

The first of the 200 h.p. cars was delivered to the North West Railway of Peru several months ago, and satisfactory reports have been received of its performance in that country. This car, however, was arranged for oil firing with a large boiler of the vertical type. In January of this year the first standard coal-fired car with the new boiler passed successfully through a severe test on the London and North Eastern Railway, for which company it was constructed. The route chosen for the test was from York to Whitby, and from there back by Scarborough, which includes the famous Ravenscar gradient of 1 in 39 for a distance of about three miles. A horsebox was attached in the rear over this part of the journey, and with this load the car covered the 3¼ miles between Flying Hall and Ravenscar in 12¼ minutes, as compared with the ordinary passenger timing of 13½ minutes. On the level a speed of 60 m.p.h. was obtained without vibration or undue sway, the riding throughout the trip being smooth and easy.

The forward driving compartment of the Sentinel-Cammell rail car, showing boiler, controls, feed-heaters, injectors, etc.

Other similar cars for the L.N.E.R. are now under construction in which a trailer car is incorporated, more than doubling the passenger-carrying capacity. This trailer is articulated with the driving car, the rear end of the latter and the front end of the trailer being carried on one bogie on the "Gresley" patent system.

The standard Clayton steam rail coach differs considerably in appearance from the Sentinel-Cammell coach, as is shown in the accompanying photographs. The difference is mainly due to the fact that while the engine of the Clayton coach is enclosed in the general body of the vehicle, the water tank and the coal bunker are detached from the main body and form an extension to the coach although they are mounted on the engine bogie.

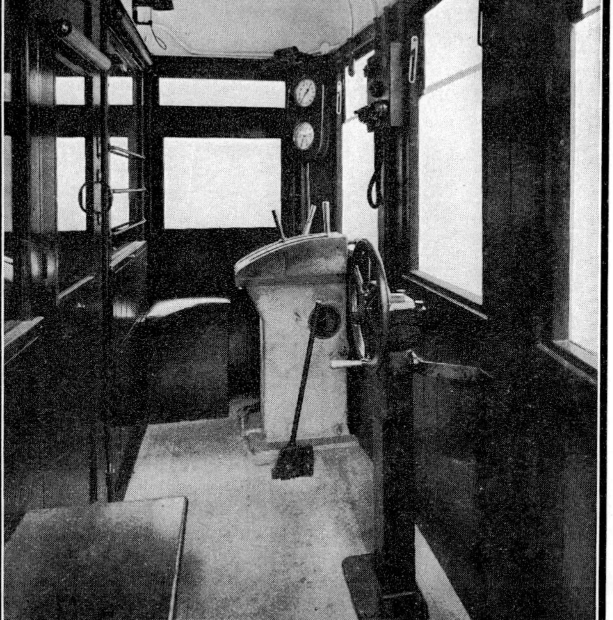

Photos courtesy] [*"Sentinel" Waggon Works Ltd.*

Rear driving compartment, showing controls.

The vehicle is of all-steel construction. The body and the underframe form one unit, and the former assists the latter in withstanding stresses. The body is mounted at each end on a swinging bolster disposed midway between the axles. Double-coil helical springs are fitted in the bolsters, and laminated springs are provided at each axle box. The suspension system is therefore identical with that of modern bogie carriage stock, and gives equal smoothness and comfort in running. The complete power equipment is mounted on one bogie, which is readily removable for overhaul. The water tank and the coal bunker are carried on the forward end of the power bogie, and are clear of the body; this permits standard coaling and water appliances to be used, and an ample supply of fuel and water to be carried. Provision is usually made for the carriage of 550 gallons of water and 15 cwt. of coal; that is, sufficient water for a run of from 100 to 120 miles and sufficient coal for 150 to 180 miles. The boiler is carried at the rear end of the power bogie, and the engine is mounted midway between the two axles on this bogie.

The Clayton engine as used in this car is a development of the one employed in the Clayton undertype steam wagon. It has two double-acting cylinders each 7 in. in diameter by 10 in. stroke. The valve gear is simple and quiet in operation, the piston valves used being operated by eccentrics mounted on a layshaft. The eccentrics run continually in the crankcase oil bath, and are therefore perfectly lubricated. A simple device is used to control the angle of advance and throw of the eccentrics, and to effect reversing. The engine is fully enclosed.

The boiler is of the vertical cylindrical type with cross water tubes and superheating coil. The tubes are inclined at about 12 degrees from the horizontal, so that the hot gases cross the tubes almost at right-angles, which is the condition for maximum heat transfer and for rapid circulation. The working pressure is 300 lb. per sq. in., and with good quality coal the boiler easily evaporates 2,400 lb. of water per hour. The boiler is fired from the front, and not from the top as in the original "Clayton" boiler. The firebox, complete with tubes, can be dropped for examination or cleaning. The joint faces are machined and asbestos gaskets are used. The boiler is fed from an independent steam-driven pump or by an injector; and a feed-water heater utilising exhaust steam is provided.

The engine is mounted on two bearings on the forward axle of the bogie, and drives a heavy spur wheel mounted on this axle through a pinion on the crankshaft. These gears are machine cut and oil-toughened; they are totally enclosed and run in an oil bath. The two axles of the engine bogie are coupled by side rods.

The bogies have a wheelbase of 7 ft., and are spaced 42 ft. 6 in. apart between the centres; although these dimensions may be varied to suit the special requirements of any particular railway. One bogie carries the complete driving unit and that end of the coach, while the other supports the opposite end of the coach body. The driver's cab is roomy and comfortable, and the windows provide a full view ahead. Covers are fitted to the coal bunker in order to prevent dust from being blown against the driver's windows. The controls are duplicated at each end of the body so that the driver can run the coach from either end as may be required.

The car has seating accommodation for 60 or more passengers; or if "bucket" seats are used, from 44 to 50 passengers can be accommodated. A good-sized luggage compartment is provided at the front end, and at the opposite end there is a driver's compartment for use when the car is running in the reverse direction. Suitable steps are furnished to enable passengers to mount or alight from ground level where it is not convenient for a stop to be made at a station. This standard type of coach is primarily intended to run as an independent unit, but it is always equipped with standard buffing and drawgear so that it may be run (*Continued on page 462*

Light Power Units—*(Continued from page 456)*

as part of a train if required. The coach is capable of speeds up to 50 m.p.h., and a point of interest is that it is able to draw a trailer, with a seating capacity practically equal to its own, without serious diminution of speed.

The foregoing details are descriptive of what may be termed the standard Clayton steam rail car; but in addition to this type articulated units also have been supplied. Cars of this type, supplied to the Egyptian State Railways, each consist of two separate coach bodies mounted on an individual bolster in the centre driving bogie, thus enabling either body to be removed without interfering with the other. These coaches contain seating accommodation for a total of 115 passengers, made up of 17 first-class, 20 second-class, and 70 third-class.

A driving compartment is provided at each end, while controls in the boiler compartment in the centre of the coach enable the vehicle to be manœuvred also from the footplate when required. The arrangement of the controls is simple, and care has been taken to ensure that unauthorised persons cannot interfere with them in any way. The driving compartments have ample look-out windows, arranged so that the top halves may be lowered if required, and collapsible gates protect the side openings. A driver's seat is provided, from which the regulator, reversing and brake levers may be operated conveniently.

The boiler, water tanks and coal bunker are mounted on the driving bogie underframes in the centre of the coach. A hinged flap covers the articulated joint. The boiler is of the latest standard vertical water-tube pattern, and the engine is of the standard Clayton rail coach type, carried horizontally between the two axles, and mounted on bearings on one axle. The overall length of the coach is 101 ft. 7 in.; the bogie centres are placed 41 ft. 10 in. apart, and each bogie wheelbase is 7 ft. The complete unit in working order weighs 45 tons 15 cwt.

World's Largest Vacuum Tube

The largest vacuum tube in the world is now being built in California by the scientists of Mount Wilson Observatory. It is being constructed of corrugated steel and when complete will be a mile in length. The tube is being made to enable the speed of light to be measured accurately. In recent experiments of this kind the atmosphere exerted a disturbing influence, and it is hoped that the use of the giant vacuum tube will give more satisfactory results.

Holidays Ahead!

Summer days! What many of us will be doing in a few weeks' time—bathing, lounging or playing games on the sands in the sunshine, and watching the passing of an occasional ship. This reader's photograph suggests the camera possibilities of the seaside.

Successful Meccano Contest at Lewisham

Meccano model-builders residing in the south-eastern district of London had the opportunity recently of competing in a special model-building competition organised by Mr. F. C. Cabeldu, the well known Meccano dealer of 371, High Street, Lewisham.

Local Meccanoites took great interest in the contest and submitted a fine collection of models. The entries were divided into three sections, Section 1 being for "Simplicity" models, Section 2 for "Original" models, while Section 3 was reserved solely for models of aeroplanes. It was decided to award the prizes according to public opinion and with this end in view the various models were displayed at Mr. Cabeldu's premises, where the public were invited to attend and cast votes for the prize-winning models. On the occasion of the prize-giving a great crowd assembled in the shop, and its capacity was so severely taxed that dozens of people had to be content with a place outside the windows while others crowded the doorway. The principal prizes were allocated according to the following list.

Section 1: First Prize (Meccano Clockwork Motor), L. J. Austin, Catford; Second Prize (Standard Mechanisms Manual), C. Deadman, Catford.

Section 2: First Prize (Meccano Steam Engine), J. D. Bedford, Catford; Second Prize (Miniature Tool Set), D. Cook, Catford; Third Prize (Speed Boat), S. Hedger, Catford; Fourth Prize (Aeroplane) H. Woodhead, Catford.

Section 3; First Prize (Aeroplane), E. C. D. Terry, Forest Hill; Second Prize (Speed Boat), G. Merrick, Catford.

The First Prize in Section 2 was awarded for a splendid model of the famous "Golden Arrow" racing car and the Second Prize for a very amusing model representing a grand piano together with pianist and violinist. L. J. Austin secured his prize in Section 1 with a seaplane and C. Deadman submitted a reciprocating engine. Other entries of considerable merit were H. Woodhead's motor cycle and sidecar, and a coupé motor car by S. Hedger. Models of biplanes secured awards for E. Terry and G. Merrick.

Mr. Cabeldu proposes to organise another competition in the early autumn of this year and local readers who would like to participate should send their names, addresses, and ages to 371, High Street, Lewisham, S.E.13, when they will be given full particulars of the contest in plenty of time to send in their entries.

Novel Use for Compressed Air

In the past great difficulty has been experienced in New England in keeping the entrances to the penstocks of hydro-electrical power stations clear of ice. In that portion of the United States, winter weather is very severe and when a dam freezes over, the pressure of the ice on its walls is liable to cause serious damage. The danger is greatest at the penstocks, for a steady current of water flowing down the huge tubes causes ice adhering to the walls to exert a steady pull on them, and this increases as the level in the dam falls.

The only means of dealing with the difficulty is to keep the ice away from the walls. In the past this could only be done by cutting channels along the intake side walls. This meant removing ice from a space, about eight feet in width, extending over a considerable length. The operation had to be carried out two or three times each winter and was costly.

At a station at Turner Falls, Massachusetts, an entirely new scheme has been introduced. There the engineer in charge hung a pipe along a wall at a depth of 12 ft. This was perforated at intervals and nozzles fitted into the holes. The pipe was then connected to a compressor that furnished air at a pressure of about 10 lb. per sq. in. The bubbles of air forced out from the jets rose to the surface and were found to be quite effective in preventing the formation of "shell" ice, as it is called, along the wall.

The experiment was so successful that compressed air is now used for the protection of each intake gate valve and sluice gate of the dams at Turner Falls.

The air is used at a pressure that does not usually exceed 20 lb. per sq. in., and as the machinery requires very little attention, the cost of preventing damage from ice is much less than that of the old method of laboriously cutting it out.

A Splendid Sports Catalogue

The new catalogue of A. G. Spalding and Bros. (British) Ltd., is the most interesting and best-produced publication of its type that we have seen. Its 127 pages cover outfits for every outdoor game that is worth consideration, and many indoor games also. It is indeed almost impossible for anyone to look through the catalogue without finding some piece of athletic equipment that is just exactly what he wants, and which he feels he must have immediately.

Commencing with golf clubs, we pass on to equipment of all kinds for tennis, cricket, football, hockey, baseball, lacrosse, badminton, croquet, bowls, and a variety of sports such as running, throwing the hammer, and hurdling. Indoor sports and games are also well represented, a particularly interesting section dealing with gloves, punchbags and other equipment for boxing. The different sections of the catalogue are arranged in such a manner as to make it easy to find quickly any desired item, and the excellent illustrations that are plentifully supplied on every page show clearly what the various items are like. Each article has been designed specially for its purpose by skilled experts of long experience in this class of work, and in every case the purchaser may be certain of sound British quality and workmanship.

We strongly advise those who are in want of equipment for any game or sport to write for this catalogue, which will be sent free on request if applicants mention the "*Meccano Magazine.*" (See advertisement on page 503).

Building a Giant Locomotive

THE enormous development of engineering during the past one hundred years or so has resulted, inevitably, in a process of subdivision and specialisation. At one time machines and mechanisms were so simple in design and so crude in construction that the village blacksmith could tackle, with reasonable prospect of success, almost any job of mending if not of making. Skilled mechanics in the present-day sense did not exist.

The result of this state of affairs was that when James Watt commenced his series of inventions that were to lead up to the wonderfully efficient steam engines of to-day he experienced the utmost difficulty in finding men capable of carrying out his ideas. On many occasions he was baffled and thrown into despair by the clumsiness of his workmen, and this is not to be wondered at when we learn that the cylinders cast for his engines were sometimes found to be more than one-eighth of an inch wider at one end than at the other!

No. 6100, the first of the famous C.N.R. class of passenger and fast freight locomotives. For this and the other illustrations to this article we are indebted to the courtesy of the Canadian National Railways.

Other inventors encountered similar difficulties, and it is probable that many a brilliant idea came to nothing from this cause. One striking example is provided by an American inventor, John Stevens, who as early as 1804 had devised a screw propeller for steamships. The failure of his plan was due almost entirely to the fact that at that time there were in America neither the tools nor the workmen to construct his engine. Stevens had to revert to the paddle wheel and thus the development of the screw propeller was put back for many years.

Gradually the need for more accurate workmanship became realised and engineers began to encourage their workmen to specialise in particular jobs, to take pride in their work, and to acquire the utmost possible manual skill. Then came the development of machine tools, which led up to the production of machines that not only could turn out work of an accuracy that could not be equalled by even the most skilful workmen, but also could repeat a job as often as required without the slightest variation. Finally there came into existence huge engineering works containing many different departments, in each of which a particular class of work was done by machinery specially designed for the purpose and working within limits of accuracy that would have truly amazed even the most expert mechanics of a previous generation.

A "6100" type locomotive in the early stages of construction.

In no branch of engineering has this specialisation become more prominent than in the building of locomotives, and this is particularly the case with the monster engines that have been developed in Canada and the United States, where the designer has not been hampered by narrow restrictions such as are imposed by bridges and tunnels in this country. Take, for instance, the "6100 Northern" type locomotives of the Canadian National Railways, one of which in process of construction is shown this month on our cover. These huge engines have been designed for either passenger or fast freight service, and they are capable of hauling a steel train of 16 Pullman coaches at a speed of 90 m.p.h. Some idea of the nature of the job of building them may be gained from the fact that they are 15 ft. 3 in. in height, 39 ft. $10\frac{3}{4}$ in. from the tip of the "cow catcher" to the tail of the tender, and weigh, with booster and empty tender, $289\frac{1}{4}$ tons!

The largest individual item in the make-up of a locomotive is the boiler; let us consider that of a "6100," which has an external diameter of 7 ft. 6 in. Both its inner and its outer casings are made of a special quality of silicon steel. The plates of which it is built up are curved to the required cylindrical form by passing them through bending rollers and are then assembled ready for drilling, which is carried out by machines working at very high speed. Then comes the riveting, for which hydraulic riveters are called into service. When the boiler is completely assembled the various mountings are placed on it and the ordinary and the superheater tubes are fitted in.

Then comes the question of strength. The boiler is intended to carry a pressure of 250 tons per sq. in., but it is not sufficient merely to test it to this pressure; a margin for safety must be allowed. The boiler is therefore given certain tests, first hydraulic and afterwards steam, at considerably higher pressures than those it is ever likely to be called upon to withstand. In boiler making there can be only one policy and that is "safety first."

When the boiler has passed safely through its various ordeals, and has been lowered on to the locomotive frames and secured in position, it is given a heat-resisting coat and then jacketted with special steel, which forms the outer covering that we see when we are admiring the finished locomotive. The heat-resisting coating, or "lagging" as it is called, protects this outer jacket from the heat of the boiler and also serves to retain heat in the boiler.

A broadside view of No. 6100, giving a good idea of its immense length and of the many details in which it differs from standard British practice.

The whole operation of boiler making is highly specialised and affords a good example of a series of processes that have been developed by the sheer necessity of having to produce bigger and still bigger boilers, and at the same time to produce them quickly and at the lowest possible cost.

So it is with the building of every portion of the locomotive. Manual labour is reduced to the minimum, every possible operation being carried out by specially devised machines that never tire, never become erratic or careless in their work—and never go on strike! In the old days heavy material had to be " man-handled " in the literal sense. Much hard labour was carried out with hammer and cold chisel, and setting-up operations involved the combined efforts of many men working with block and tackle and hand haul. Back-breaking work of this kind is now almost entirely eliminated in all well-equipped works.

When a locomotive has passed successfully her preliminary trials she returns to the sheds to receive her coats of paint and the various finishing touches that are necessary before she takes up active service. She already has a grey coat that has been applied to protect the metal from oxidization, and this coat forms the foundation of the final painting. In pre-war days British locomotives were famous the world over for their handsome livery and perfection of finish. Since the war, unfortunately, the urgent necessity of cutting down expenses in every possible direction has resulted in the substitution of much plainer painting schemes, and the days of such handsome locomotives as those of the old Caledonian Railway are a thing of the past.

A move in the reverse direction was made by the Canadian National Railways last year when they adopted a colour scheme of bright green, vermilion, and black for their locomotives of the " 6100 " class. This marked a new departure in Canadian railway practice. The first engine to appear in the new colours was No. 6138, which hauls the *"International Limited"* between Montreal and Chicago. The colour scheme is light green for the boiler, tender, tank and wheels; black for the cab, smoke box, coal hopper, and feed-water heater; and bright red for the buffer beams at each end, the wheel spokes, and the fluting of the driving rods. It will be interesting to watch the growth of this scheme.

In spite of their bulk and the strength of their component parts, even such monsters as the " 6100's " are subject to certain ailments and require periodical overhauling. Hospital treatment of a locomotive is clearly a serious undertaking. The work must be carried out with the utmost thoroughness, and yet at the same time it must be done as quickly as possible because every hour that a locomotive is out of action means loss to its owners. The repairing of a locomotive differs in certain important respects from the building of a new one, and in consequence railway companies have developed repair sections quite distinct from their constructing department. The Canadian National Railways do not build their own locomotives but, having received one from its builders, they tend it with the utmost care throughout its working life. In order to be able to deal promptly with all locomotive ailments the company have erected at Point St. Charles, Montreal, a series of huge repair shops lavishly equipped with the most up-to-date plant and machinery for all purposes.

The shops are grouped under one roof and the huge building that accommodates them is 1,056 ft. in length and 265 ft. in width. It is built in the form of a number of extensive bays in which the departments have been arranged in accordance with a carefully thought-out plan. The largest department, of course, is the locomotive erection shop which is 755 ft. in length, 85 ft. in width, and 56 ft. in height to the roof truss. It is served by a 200-ton overhead electric travelling crane and is provided also with one 10-ton auxiliary crane and two 15-ton overhead electric cranes, one of which serves an additional bay situated in front of the 34 locomotive pits. This bay is reserved for all locomotive front end work, such as repairs and rebuilding of boiler tubes; superheater equipments, feed water heaters, Westinghouse air brake work, etc.

The immense size of the boilers of the " 6100 " type locomotive may be seen from this photograph, which shows workmen fitting superheater tubes.

The blacksmith and forge shop at one end of the building extends across all the bays and is equipped with down draught forges, oil gas furnaces and powerful steam hammers. The furnaces and hammers are served by two 4,000 lb. and two 6,000 lb. self-supporting jib cranes, while the shop also contains a 10-ton overhead electric crane. Another important department is the boiler shop, which is a continuation of the two erecting shop bays. The main bay is 216 ft. in length and has a 40-ton overhead electric crane that is built on the same runways as the 200-ton crane in the erecting shop and, therefore, can pass from the boiler shop through the entire erecting shop without interruption to any other work in hand.

A feature of all the shops is the scientific manner in which the lighting has been arranged. The area of glass used amounts to over 119,000 sq. ft., and windows represent 39.5 per cent. of the entire side walls! The interior of the building is coated with aluminium paint to within 5 ft. of the floor, the remainder being finished in black.

Exciting Moments on an Express:

Making Motion Pictures of the "*Twentieth Century*"

By T. G. Price

LOCOMOTIVE 5222 and the twelve cars of the "*Motion Picture Limited*" stood on the siding at Chesterton, Ind. From the front coupler of the 300-ton Hudson type engine to the markers on the observation car the train was a mechanical counterpart of one section of the "*Twentieth Century*," except that it carried no dining car in the middle and no sign on the rear end.

The passenger list was unusual. John Smiley, Assistant General Superintendent, sat on the rear platform and consumed cigars. The other four passengers were holding a pow-wow with Mr. Vaniman, Road Foreman of Engines, in the cab of 5222. There was George Bainbridge, Assistant Director; the brothers, Oscar and Bill Ahbe, than whom there are no better motion picture cameramen in the city of Chicago, and the director of the piece.

"How do you want the engine run, Mr. Price?" asked Vaniman.

"Well," suggested the director, "you might run her to Englewood Station as fast as she'll go." The engine crew grinned expectantly.

"The speed limit is seventy miles an hour," stated Vaniman.

"All right, go the limit, as soon as you feel like it."

George Bainbridge squeezed his rotund bulk in behind the fireman on the left side of the cab. Oscar Ahbe crouched between the coal gates and adjusted the hand camera for the cab shots. Bill Ahbe and the director scrambled back over the coal to the flat deck of the tender. There stood the camera on its tripod, lashed down with steel cables to a complicated rigging of wood, rubber and springs to cushion the inevitable jarring.

There followed the rapid tolling of the bell. The world moved slowly backward. On their eerie perch Bill and the director pulled down their caps, leaned back on the safety ropes and prayed for sunshine.

The fake "*Century*" swung majestically on to the main line and headed for Chicago. The speed increased. The sound of the bell was drowned in the roar of the exhaust. The crossing at Porter swept by in a mad clatter. At forty miles an hour the director pointed ahead.

"Hit it!" he bawled, and the cameraman began to grind film. The speed mounted. Forty, forty-five, fifty—Bill and the director shielded their faces as best they could, stared ahead through clouded goggles and made unprintable remarks about red hot cinders. Breathing was becoming difficult.

As the train headed for Chicago, cameraman and director leaned back on the safety ropes and prayed for sunshine.

As the 5222 rolled to a long reverse curve Bill swung his lens backward as the director pointed. Behind them stretched the scimitar of twelve steel cars and the rushing roadbed, balanced for artistic composition by the flying smoke and the whole framed in the autumnal loveliness of the sand dunes along Lake Michigan.

The whistle was blaring continuously now for the Dunes Highway crossings. Evidently Vaniman and the engineman weren't going to be cheap about doing the limit. Fifty, fifty-five, sixty. Wind shrouded the men on the tender in a buffeting, smothering tumult. Dumbly the director thumped the cameraman on the back and pointed to where steel mills loomed ahead. Speech was impossible, but Bill understood the signals and cranked his camera.

Then speed mounted steadily. Sixty, sixty-five, seventy, seventy-five. The 5222 was stepping out. They descended on Gary like a falling planet. The station platform streaked by in a blurr of whirring lampposts and white, upturned faces of waiting passengers.

Dull foreground, towering black stacks, framed by streaking clouds of steam flew to meet them. "Here comes Buffington," thought the director, gulping lungfuls of coal gas and cinders. Again he thumped his companion and pointed. Indiana Harbour whirled by, kaleidoscopic with shifting switch engines and the abrupt thunder of the bridge with its whizzing beams and girders.

A brief rest for "5222" and the staff of the "*Motion Picture Limited*."

Heads down against the wind and smoke, Bill and the director strove to keep the camera on its legs and working. Fine grit sifted under the padding of their goggles. Whiting flew by, a ghostly line of white oil tanks. Then came the flat yards to the east across which they could see Lake Michigan rolling to the first November gale. State Line and Calumet Generating Stations moved by majestically, remote on far horizons.

The special bellowed through the Grand Calumet Bridge and tore pell-mell along the embankment paralleling South Chicago Avenue. Houses sprang up as if by magic. Then the speed slackened. Bill and the director were lowering the cameras as the 5222 rolled past Englewood Station and started down town at a respectable forty miles an hour.

They ducked the low bridge at Fortieth Street—only 17 ft. 2 in. from top of rail to bottom of lowest girders—raised the camera again and repeated the whole performance at Roosevelt Road. The camera was still going as the big Hudson slid under the train shed at La Salle Street.

"Everything all right, Mr. Price ?" asked Vaniman when the director and the cameraman had finally tumbled their equipment and themselves back to earth. Both admitted that the engine had been run satisfactorily. Then up came Alan Rogers and John Smiley and made pointed remarks about black-faced comedians who wore dungarees and rode on the tops of engines.

But the all-important question was " Did you get the pictures ? " and both Bill and Oscar stated that they had got them.

A few days later the New York Central men saw the opening episode of the Commonwealth Edison Company's new film, " Your Chicago." That part of the picture follows the subtitle, " Through Chicagoland on the Famous Twentieth Century Limited." And just before you get to Gary, in the picture, the director inserted a title that wasn't called for in the original script. It reads, " The first successful motion pictures to be made from a locomotive travelling seventy - five miles an hour."

Ever since that first showing the cameramen and the director have been shaking hands with themselves, for the pictures are sharp, bright and steady and there is enough footage to satisfy the most ardent railroad enthusiast.

Photograph] [*Railway Photographs, Liverpool*

The " *Twentieth Century Limited,*" hauled by locomotive No. 596.

But what is even more dear to the heart of the motion picture men is that the pictures are not faked or tricked in any respect, save only that they were not taken from the true *"Twentieth Century."* (*For this interesting article and photographs we are indebted to the courtesy of the Editor of the New York Central Lines Magazine*).

The New Hornby Book of Trains

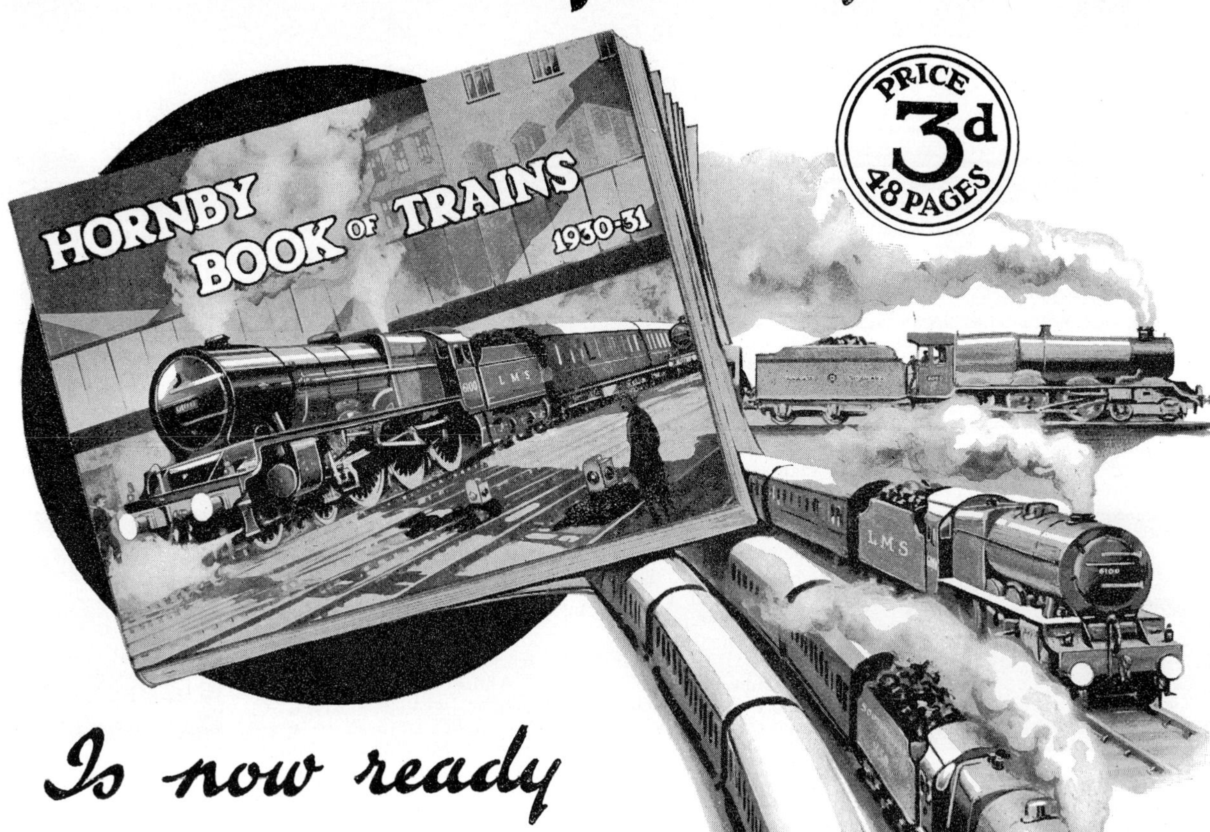

Is now ready

Here it is, boys! The 1930 Hornby Book of Trains—the biggest and best we have ever issued. Get your copy to-day!

This splendid new edition contains wonderful reading that will fascinate every boy who is keen on railways. A wide variety of subjects is dealt with in its pages, including interesting articles on famous locomotives and expresses, and descriptions of the wonderful high-pressure engines that may haul the trains of the future. All these subjects are dealt with under the following headings.

In Pre-Grouping Days: Some typical features of British Lines.
Recent Locomotive Progress: The use of High Pressure Steam.
Touring Britain by four Famous Expresses.
Some "Named" Locomotives that have made History.

The book also contains full details and many beautiful illustrations in full colour of the world-renowned Hornby Trains, together with descriptions and prices of all the items included in the Hornby System. Get your copy to-day!

How to Obtain the Book

You may obtain the Book from any Meccano dealer, price 3d., or direct from Meccano Ltd. (Dept. A.M.), Old Swan, Liverpool, price 4½d. post free. If you order direct, mention the names and addresses of two or three of your chums and we will send them some interesting Hornby Train literature. Write clearly and be sure to put the letters AM after your own name for reference.

Direct orders are not acknowledged. They are dealt with as soon as they are received, and every endeavour is made to send the book to the purchaser by return of post. It is desirable that a remittance in stamps should be sent and also that the name and address of the sender should be clearly written. There is no reduction if more than one copy is ordered.

Orders from Overseas

There is a special edition of the Hornby Book of Trains for Overseas, and copies have already been despatched to our agents to fill orders received. The price Overseas is 6d. post free (Canada 10 cents or 12 cents post paid). Readers in Australia, New Zealand, South Africa or Canada who require copies should address their orders to our agencies as detailed below.

Readers living in countries other than those mentioned should order from Meccano Ltd., Binns Road, Old Swan, Liverpool, sending a remittance for 6d. with their order.

AUSTRALIA.—E. G. Page & Co., 52, Clarence Street, Sydney. (P.O. Box 1832K).
NEW ZEALAND.—Models Ltd., Kingston Street, Auckland. (P.O. Box 129).
SOUTH AFRICA.—Arthur E. Harris, 142, Market Street, Johannesburg. (P.O. Box 1199).
CANADA.—Meccano Ltd., 34, St. Patrick Street, Toronto.

MECCANO LIMITED
OLD SWAN LIVERPOOL

GET YOUR COPY TO-DAY!

THE STORY OF THE PANAMA CANAL

GREAT engineering feats have ever been a profound source of inspiration for stamp designers, and most of the really important enterprises—and not a few of the unimportant—have figured on postage stamps. The Panama Canal probably can claim the distinction of providing the greatest number of designs, for in addition to providing the inspiration for two complete series issued by the Republic of Panama in 1915 and 1918 respectively, it has been featured extensively on U.S. General and Canal Zone issues.

In a short article such as this, it is, of course, impossible to relate the complete history of the Panama Canal, the greatest canal undertaking in the world, and readers who desire to delve fully into the subject are commended to the series of articles that commenced in the issue of the *"M.M."* for November, 1927. Nevertheless, the stamp story of the canal makes interesting reading, and for our first illustration we must take the 1c. stamp of the Panama 1915 issue, showing a relief map of the isthmus of Panama and the track of the canal across it.

The map makes clear how full advantage was taken of the natural features of the isthmus in driving the canal through. Commencing at the Atlantic seaboard, the canal is carried through Limon Bay near Colon, the coast-line of this bay being five miles from deep water, where the canal really begins and from which the measurements are taken. At the seventh mile the canal enters the Gatun Lake by the three Gatun Locks. From here to the Culebra Cut is 22 miles, and four miles beyond the cut is the Pedro Miguel Lock. After passing through this lock, Lake Miraflores is entered, at the far end of which are the Miraflores Locks that bring the canal back to sea-level. From the Miraflores Locks to deep water is another eight miles, the total distance between deep water in the Atlantic and deep water in the Pacific being very slightly less than 50 miles.

The early history of the canal really dates back to 1502, when Columbus endeavoured to discover a natural waterway from the Atlantic to the Pacific. On failing to find one, he appears to have become convinced that the coast line was in reality part of Asia. Subsequently, in 1513, the Spaniard, Vasco Nunes de Balboa, crossed the isthmus, and thenceforward throughout the 300 years of Spanish dominion, the canal project was continually under discussion, although it rarely advanced beyond the stage of dreams. It came to the front again in 1850, when an agreement was concluded between the U.S. and Great Britain, guaranteeing open passage for the ships of all nations in the event of the canal being constructed. In 1869, the opening of the Suez Canal gave it further prominence, and in 1879 the Colombian Government granted a concession to a French company actually to construct the canal. A start was made in 1881 with De Lesseps, the engineer of the Suez Canal, as the Chairman of the Company and Chief Engineer.

Progress was slow, for the difficulties were enormous, and eventually the company collapsed. A second company was formed and fared a little better, but in 1903 the U.S. Government bought up its rights and assets, and, having obtained a new concession from Colombia, took the completion of the work in hand.

Almost immediately, the scheme was jeopardised by Colombia's refusal to grant control of the territory bordering the canal, to the United States, but the inhabitants of Panama were determined that America should be given the chance to see the job through. They revolted, formed a republican government, and on 18th November granted the U.S. Government perpetual occupation and control of a ribbon of territory, ten miles in width, stretching across the isthmus. This extended five miles on each side of the route of the canal, and the area thus marked out forms the Canal Zone of to-day.

The political obstacles thus having been overcome, the Americans were able to turn their attention to the practical side of the job. The difficulties were stupendous. The cut through Culebra Hill, for example, involved the excavation and removal of nearly 80,000,000 cu. yds. of earth and rock.

An excellent impression of the enormous scale of the operations here is obtained from the 5c. stamp of the current Canal Zone issue, which shows small-gauge locomotives at work removing the material excavated from the canal bed. One of the great difficulties in the Culebra Cut was the constant collapse of the embankment sides, and it was found necessary to arrange a very gentle slope, although, where rock was encountered, the sides were cut almost perpendicular, of course. The 12c. value of the Panama 1918 issue makes this point clear. On it a steamer is shown passing through the completed canal, on one side of which the bank slopes gently away, while on the other it stands boldly upright.

It will be clear from the relief map that the making of the canal was not a mere matter of carving a way through the hills. The canal virtually goes over the hills, a feat that was accomplished by maintaining sea level over the first seven miles from Colon to Gatun, at which point a great dam was constructed across the River Chagres, creating a lake 22 miles in length extending to the Culebra Cut. Access to this lake—the summit point of the canal—is by means of a three-tier double flight of locks. The 5c. stamp of Panama's 1915 issue gives an excellent view of the locks, and of the runways, or ramps, at the side, along which run the electric locomotives that tow steamers through the locks.

The Cierva "Autogiro"

A Light Aeroplane that Cannot Stall or Spin

THE great majority of aeroplane accidents result from collision with another machine or with some obstacle when an aeroplane is landing or taking off, or from "stalling" or losing flying speed when the machine is near the ground, and consequently has not sufficient room to recover. Both these causes are the result of the necessity for a high speed to be attained before safety and stability can be achieved. In addition the correct use of the controls is essential to maintain this speed, for immediately the stalling point is approached, the controls of the average machine become quite ineffective. Generally speaking, therefore, the fundamental dangers of flight may be summed up as being due to the necessity of maintaining a high forward speed and to the lack of stability and control when this speed is lost.

An "Autogiro" landing at Hamble. The short space between the machine and the building should be noticed.

Many machines have been designed and constructed in the endeavour to eliminate these difficulties, but the only one that has achieved any real success is the "Autogiro," invented by Senor de la Cierva, a Spanish aircraft designer. This is claimed to be the safest aeroplane in existence. The problem has been solved in this machine by ensuring that when it has ceased to move forward there are still forces acting on the wings. These forces are provided by windmill-like blades that keep moving at a high speed, and give such support to the machine that it drops only at a rate that involves no danger. The actual speed at which the machine falls is less than the rate of descent of a parachute. The method in which the rotors are hinged to the rotating shaft also ensures that the machine will be perfectly stable at low speeds, and even if the controls are misused a stall or crash cannot result.

De la Cierva first turned his attention to the "Autogiro" after a machine that he had designed for the Spanish Air Force crashed through stalling. This convinced him that aeroplane flight in which safety depended on speed was by no means ideal. Careful consideration of possible alternative systems of flight led de la Cierva to eliminate in turn not only the conventional type of aeroplane, but also the helicopter, an aeroplane capable of rising and descending vertically, and the ornithopter, a machine that attempts to imitate bird flight by deriving its lift from flapping wings. He became convinced that the solution lay in a machine having wings in the form of blades capable of rotating round a vertical axis.

De la Cierva's first experiments were commenced early in 1920, and many varieties of revolving blades were tested on various aircraft, without any practical result being obtained. In the first type tested the revolving surface consisted of two four-bladed windmills mounted on a vertical axis and driven in opposite directions by the force of the wind; but this did not solve the problem. Shortly afterwards a second type was evolved, in which there was only a single windmill fitted with three cantilever blades. The blades were hinged so that their degree of incidence, that is the angle at which they face the airstream, could be varied at will by the pilot in order to alter the resultant lift to right or to left. The first attempts with this machine were encouraging, but after it had been damaged and modified and reconstructed nine times in the course of experiments it became clear that the solution of the problem had not been found.

The third type of "Autogiro" was fitted with a lifting windmill made up of five rigid blades heavily braced to the axis by steel wires. This machine appeared to be an improvement on the others, but after it had been damaged and repaired four times it was found to be unstable and was therefore put aside in favour of a fourth machine. This type embodied the principle of articulated blades, which eventually proved to be the main solution of de la Cierva's problem. The machine had a single windmill with four blades hinged at the root, so that they could move freely up and down in the vertical plane without any change in their angle to the airstream. Lateral control was provided for by tilting the axis to right or left, but this control proved to be too difficult for the pilot to operate, and many crashes resulted. This machine was reconstructed or modified no less than fifteen times.

Courtesy] *[Cierva Autogiro Co. Ltd.*

The latest model of the "Autogiro," the C.19 Mark III.

Eventually a better system of lateral control was provided, and in January 1923 a machine was completed that flew across the aerodrome at Getalfe, Spain. This machine subsequently carried out an officially observed and controlled four-minute flight over a closed circuit at the Guatro Vientos Aerodrome, Madrid.

Several other machines were produced after this, assistance being given to de la Cierva by the Spanish Government. One of these machines was demonstrated successfully at Farnborough in England, and at Villacoublay in France, and a similar machine constructed in 1925 by A. V. Roe & Co. Ltd. was demonstrated at the Hendon Air Pageant in 1926. The British Cierva Autogiro Co. Ltd. was formed in this country in that year, and now no less than twenty-one types of "Autogiros" have been constructed.

The modern "Autogiro" has a fuselage similar to that of any normal light aeroplane, but mounted above it on three supports rising over the front cockpit are four blades or rotors. These rotors are of aerofoil section and have a chord of 18.6 in. They are hinged at their attachments to the supporting pylon head to give them full freedom in both the vertical and the horizontal plane, and they provide 80 per cent. of the total lift of the machine when it is travelling at a high forward speed. When the machine is descending vertically this proportion of lift is increased to 100 per cent.

In early types of the machine the rotors were started to revolve by winding a rope round the axis and then setting six or eight men to haul on the rope. Later the rotors were started somewhat in the same manner as a top by means of a mechanical contrivance on the ground; and an attempt was made also to start them by attaching rockets to their tips. Subsequently it was found that the rotors could be started by taxi-ing the machine round and round until they were in operation. In the latest model the empennage or tail unit has been so constructed that the tail plane and the elevator can be brought together to deflect the engine slipstream to the rotors while the machine in held stationary by means of wheel brakes. With larger land machines and with seaplanes a mechanical self-starter is provided. This derives its power direct from the engine crankshaft through a mechanically-operated clutch, and brings the rotors up to speed in less than 30 seconds. When the machine is in flight the clutch is completely disengaged and has no connection whatever with the rotation of the blades, thus eliminating all the torque reaction found in helicopters. A simple braking arrangement similar to the familiar wheel brake stops the movements of the rotors after the "Autogiro" has landed.

This photograph shows how the elevator and the tail plane are brought together to start the rotors by deflecting the slipstream on to them.

The "Autogiro" has also a small fixed wing that is used mainly to provide lateral stability and control in addition to improving the aerodynamic efficiency of the machine. This wing is used also as a base for the wide-track landing gear. It is interesting to note that the fixed wing does not stall even when the machine is descending vertically, as it is always in the downwash from the rotor. This fact has been proved by attaching a series of threads to each part of the wing. When the machine was flown it was found that at all speeds from vertical descent to the maximum possible the threads showed a change in the angle of airflow of only a few degrees, and never approached an angle that would indicate that the fixed wing was in a stalled position.

The Cierva "Autogiro" in flight. For permission to reproduce the photographs on this page and the upper one on the opposite page we are indebted to the courtesy of "Flight."

In early models of the modern "Autogiro" it was found that the high centre of gravity, combined with the low fin area formed by the fuselage and vertical surfaces, rendered the machine laterally unstable at high speeds. This has been corrected in the present machine by setting the fixed wings at a substantial upward angle to the horizontal, and also by providing turned-up wing tips, giving the effect of high fin area.

The landing gear is of the wide-track divided axle type, and long-travel Oleo shock absorbers are used. The gear has been subjected to a great deal of strenuous service and has given complete satisfaction even after innumerable hard landings at the end of vertical descents with heavy loads. It is therefore considered as having been proved that the stresses on the landing gear of an "Autogiro" are less than those with ordinary aeroplanes of the same gross weight. These lower stresses make it possible to design parts of the fuselage and the fixed wing lighter than can be done in a normal aeroplane, with the result of a valuable saving in weight.

The "Autogiro" C.19 Mark III has a span and length of 35 ft., and is 10 ft. in height. The chord of the stabilising plane is 2 ft. 9 in., and it has an area of 42 sq. ft. The rotor blades have a total area of 91.25 sq. ft. The machine has a tare weight of 935 lb., and a loaded weight of 1,400 lb.; its maximum speed is 100 m.p.h. and its rate of climb 750 ft. per minute. It takes off in 30 yd., and there is no landing run or landing speed in still air.

The "Autogiro" is flown in a similar manner to an ordinary aeroplane. In order to take off the necessary revolutions of the rotor blades must first be obtained, and the brakes then released. The machine immediately begins to run forward in the normal manner, but takes off suddenly at a comparatively low horizontal speed, and maintains a fairly rapid climb at a slower forward speed than the conventional type of aeroplane. A notable feature when the machine is in flight is that bumps are hardly felt unless they are exceedingly strong; so that even in the worst weather there is little need to work the controls. When the pilot wishes to make a turn the rudder only need be used. The machine banks automatically unless the turn is very sharp, in which case the machine starts to turn flat before banking, and although the air speed drops there is no lack of lateral control. If the manœuvre has been too sudden, all that happens is the loss of a few feet in turning.

In a normal landing, when the engine is throttled down, the "Autogiro" glides at any speed desired until a height of from 3 ft. to 10 ft. above the ground is reached, and then the "stick" is pulled hard back. The nose rises and the machine stops at once, dropping very slowly to settle gently on the ground. If a forced descent from engine failure or any other cause necessitates a landing in a small field surrounded by high trees or similar obstructions, the machine can be made to drop slowly and vertically, but with perfect stability and still completely under control.

With the "Autogiro" there is no need for the delicate handling that is essential in a normal aeroplane. The machine actually looks after a pilot who, owing to inexperience, or lack of judgment, has mistaken his height when flattening out; and the pilot is free from any anxiety due to thoughts of forced landings or accidents due to engine failure. This makes it (*Continued on page 437*)

The "Autogiro"—(*Continued from page 363*)

possible for the "Autogiro" to be operated in regions that are unsuitable for ordinary aeroplanes. It is ideal also for deck landing purposes and for use with ships in general.

"Autogiros" have not only been constructed as landplanes, but a seaplane version also has been produced; and work is now being carried out by Short Bros. Ltd. on an "Autogiro" flying boat. The principle has attracted a great deal of attention in America, and recently the American branch of the Cierva Autogiro Company received a contract for supplying a machine to the Chief Fire Warden of the State of New Jersey. The Fire Warden intends to experiment with the machine to determine whether it is suitable for aerial fire-fighting purposes. The United States Navy have purchased an American-built "Autogiro" for experimental work in co-operation with sea-going vessels not fitted with launching and landing apparatus. The French Government authorities also are interested in the machine, and in England an "Autogiro Puss Moth" constructed by the de Havilland Aircraft Co. Ltd., is shortly to make its appearance.

Discussions have taken place recently between the Cierva Autogiro Company and the British railway authorities with regard to the possibility of constructing flat roofs over railway stations, from which "Autogiros" could operate. Nothing definite has yet been decided, but the scheme is full of interest, for it would enable travellers to make journeys between cities and their airports much more quickly than is at present possible.

It seems probable that the "Autogiro" is the machine of the future. Its safety and ease of operation will make flying possible for many people who are unable to develop the necessary skill to pilot an ordinary aeroplane. A beginner is able to take complete charge of an "Autogiro" after only a short period of dual tuition, for there is no danger of his getting into difficulties owing to loss of flying speed, or to a forced landing. The short space necessary for the "Autogiro" to take off is another feature of great value, for it means that the machine may be operated from a space no bigger than a good sized lawn.

Flying Boats—(*Continued from page 373*)

the Blackburn "Nile" and a six-engined monoplane which is taking shape at the Supermarine Aviation Works. The "Nile" is really the civilian counterpart of the Blackburn "Sydney." It has seats for fourteen passengers and will be fitted with three Bristol "Jupiter" engines developing a total normal power of 1,470 b.h.p. The machine will have a wing span of 100 ft., while its overall length will be 65 ft. 6 in. It will weigh 15,258 lb. empty, and 23,492 lb. when fully loaded. When near the ground its maximum speed will be about 125 m.p.h. while the cruising and stalling speeds will be 103 and 60 m.p.h. respectively. The duration of the machine will range from 4.5 to 8 hours.

The Supermarine six-engined flying boat will create a British record, for it will be the largest machine of the kind ever constructed in this country. It will not be so large as the Dornier "Do.X," the giant flying boat described fully on page 922 of the "*M.M.*" for December, 1929, but it will be capable of carrying 40 passengers in addition to a crew of seven, and sleeping accommodation for twenty passengers will be provided. The span of this machine is expected to be about 160 ft., or over 50 yards. The frames of the hull and the under water part will be planked with stainless steel. Six Rolls Royce "Buzzard" engines will be fitted, and at cruising speed the machine will have a designed endurance of about 12 hours.

The Supermarine Aviation Works also have produced the Supermarine "Sea Hawk Mark II," which is a civilian version of the "Southampton Mark X" already described. This machine has twelve seats and, like its prototype, is equipped with three Armstrong Siddeley "Panther" engines. It has a wing span of 78 ft. and an overall length of 60 ft. The empty and loaded weights are 11,290 lb. and 19,558 lb. respectively. The cabins and the mail and luggage accommodation have been designed in accordance with the requirements of air line companies.

A New Form of Transmitting Aerial

An entirely new type of aerial for wireless transmitting stations has been developed by the Westinghouse Electric Company and is now installed at its well-known station KDKA. Its purpose is to enable signals to be sent out that are powerful at a distance and comparatively weak nearby, thus making it possible for receiving sets near the station to tune in to distant programmes without suffering interference.

The aerial acts by repressing the wireless waves that travel along the ground, leaving those reflected from the Heaviside layer to affect distant receivers. In the case of short wave transmissions this effect is brought about by using eight vertical aerials arranged in a small circle. The ground wave from each aerial is absorbed by those from the others, and the result of this mutual interference is that only the sky wave travels outward. Thus the immediate vicinity of the station is free from overpowering radiation.

For longer waves a bird cage aerial erected on wooden poles arranged in a huge circle 800 ft. in diameter is used in order to give the same effect.

It is interesting to note that similar means may be adopted to cut out the sky wave and give a strong ground wave, and thus the method may be applied to stations that require only to provide radiation for reception within a limited area.

A new type of short-wave aerial installed at KDKA, the well-known Pittsburgh wireless station of the Westinghouse Electric Company, by courtesy of whom our photograph is reproduced. The aerial transmits signals that are powerful at a distance, but weak in the neighbourhood of the station.

Torpedo that Leaves No Visible Track

The latest development in naval warfare is an invisible torpedo. Those at present in use are driven by compressed air engines, and the air that bubbles to the surface of the water during the run of the torpedo betrays its track. This peculiarity often enables warships to avoid an oncoming torpedo or to explode it before it reaches its target.

The new weapon gives no indication of its approach, for it is driven by a small electric motor that takes current from light storage batteries. Torpedoes of the new type travel at speeds slightly less than those driven by compressed air, but it is believed that improvements to the batteries and motors will make them capable of a speed of 30 knots over a run of 12,000 yards.

Motor Driven by Sunlight

A problem that almost continuously attracts the attention of many scientists and inventors is that of deriving power direct from the Sun. In the usual form of plant the Sun's rays are concentrated by means of mirrors on cells containing water or oil, and the rise in temperature of the liquid is used as a source of energy. An entirely new direction has been given to these experiments by the invention of the photo-electric cell, for a German inventor has succeeded in constructing one that under the stimulus of daylight drives a half-volt motor.

In general appearance a photo-electric cell is similar to a wireless valve. It is evacuated or contains an inert gas at low pressure and has two electrodes, one of which is coated with sodium, potassium or some other substance that emits streams of electrons, or negatively-charged particles, when light falls upon it. The second electrode is usually given a positive charge in order to attract the electrons, and their passage across the cell constitutes an electric current. In the photo-electric cells now used in television and for other purposes, the current produced is very small. Apparently the German inventor has constructed a cell in which a larger current is obtained, and it is believed that the output may be increased far beyond the limits already attained.

Metal Bearing that Requires No Oil

A self-lubricating metal bearing has been produced in the research laboratories of the Westinghouse Electric Company. It is made by mixing metallic powders with materials that yield a soapy substance. The ingredients are subjected to a pressure of 40,000 lb. per sq. in., and the temperature is slowly raised to 400°F., or nearly twice that of boiling water. Half an hour later the pressure is increased to 200,000 lb. per sq. in. in order to complete the process.

Bearings made of the new metal may be mounted without oil or grease, and are particularly suitable for use in motors, such as the starting motors of cars, that are run intermittently, or in typewriters, calculating machines, microscopes and telescopes. They may also be employed in heavy machines. When used for this purpose they may be lubricated with oil in the usual manner, and have the advantage over ordinary bearings that they resist the heating effects of friction if the supply of lubricant becomes inadequate.

Tracer Pellets for Sporting Cartridges

Tracer bullets came into general use during the European War. In the base of one of these is a small proportion of combustible material that is ignited by the explosion of the cartridge, and this enables the course of the bullet to be traced almost to its destination.

The value of being able to follow the flight of a projectile is so great that the idea is now being applied to sporting cartridges. These contain a number of pellets, and of course, it is not so easy to apply the principle to them as to a single bullet. The problem has been solved by placing a special tracer pellet in the centre of the charge of shot. The combustible in this is ignited by the discharge and burns brilliantly for a distance of 75 yards from the muzzle of the gun. The pellet travels approximately along the axis of the cone formed by the spread of the shot in the charge, and thus serves as an indication of accuracy. The new cartridges are not intended for use in actual game shooting, but it is expected that they will prove useful for practice and in shooting at clay birds.

Electric Flash Lamp for Photography

One of the disadvantages of photography by flashlight is that the burning of the powders and sheets usually employed produces a considerable amount of smoke. This prevents their use in confined spaces such as the interiors of trains, airships or submarines, or in the operating theatres of hospitals. They also have the drawback that they cannot be used in such places as coal mines, where they may cause an explosion of fire damp, and in these and similar dangerous conditions photography is therefore almost impossible. Difficulties of this kind have now been overcome by the introduction of a glass bulb inside which a flash may be fired by electrical means. The device is silent, clean and safe in operation.

The bulb of the new photographic flash lamp contains oxygen and the filament is covered with a special preparation that is easily ignited and also with a quantity of thin aluminium foil. When the current is switched on, the heat produced by the burning of the filament brings about the combustion of the foil, which is accompanied by a flash of high actinic value that lasts for one hundredth of a second. The light produced has the advantage of being comparatively soft and diffused. Its efficiency for photographic purposes may be increased by means of a reflector and it is expected that photographs taken with its aid will not have the unnatural appearance that often results from the use of ordinary powders.

The current required for the operation of the lamp may be obtained from the mains, but an accumulator or a dry battery also may be used. A new lamp is required for each flash.

An impression of the Dover Road of the future, an elevated roadway along which great land liners will career to cross the Channel by means of an enormous bridge.

Testing Cans by Compressed Air

It is very important that tins used for preserving foodstuffs should be completely airtight, for admission of air would result in the deterioration of the fruit, vegetable, fish or meat contained in them. Testing the millions of cans used every year for this purpose is therefore a very important part of the work of producing them. A machine has now been introduced that enables the tins to be tested at high speed.

The machine is quite automatic in action. The tins to be tested reach it by means of a chute and are immediately clamped between cast iron plates and rubber discs on a large revolving wheel that dips under water in a large tank. Each can is filled with compressed air before reaching the water, and leaks are betrayed by the rise of escaping air bubbles. Immediately these are perceived the inspector in charge of the machine pulls down a lever that discharges the can through a separate chute. Tins that pass the test are automatically carried forward to the filling plant.

An Unbreakable Cinematograph Film

The breakage of films is a great cause of annoyance and waste in the cinematograph industry. Many efforts have been made to produce films that are unbreakable, and in the latest invention of this kind, the celluloid strip is sealed between pieces of thin steel in which are punched openings for the pictures and for the sprocket holes. The steel bindings are made in lengths of 4$\frac{3}{4}$ in. and they are large enough to accommodate sections of film carrying 16 pictures, a number that is sufficient for a run of one second.

The new cinematograph film is intended for use in an automatic projector that is set in motion by dropping a coin in a slot, or by merely pressing a button. In this projector the sections containing the film are stacked horizontally in a feed magazine, and are drawn electro-magnetically into contact with claws that move them through the gate of the machine, across which streams the beam of light. They fall into a take-up magazine, at the bottom of which is a horizontal conveyor that carries them back to the bottom of the feed magazine, where lifting mechanism brings them into their original position once more. Continuous circulation of what in effect is an endless film is thus provided for.

It will be seen that the film travels horizontally through the gate instead of vertically, as in the projectors used in picture theatres. The beam of light required is provided by a 100-watt lamp and is projected upward through the lenses and the film. A mirror placed at an angle of 45° to its path reflects it horizontally to a translucent section on the side of the box containing the mechanism.

Steel-bound films have shown practically no signs of wear after having been passed no fewer than 15,000 times in succession through the mechanism described.

Blowing Out Electric Lights

An American engineer has invented devices that enable electric lights to be blown out and to be relighted by striking a match. The first of these is called the "breath relay." It includes a special spring contact switch mounted in a small tube that has a mouthpiece like that of a telephone. Speaking into the mouthpiece or striking it produces no effect, but a minute puff of wind directed into it closes the contacts and completes an electric circuit. This acts through a relay to open a switch that cuts off the current supply of the light controlled by the device.

The breath relay is not a mere curiosity. Its purpose is to provide a switch that may be opened or closed when the hands or feet of the operator are otherwise occupied. It is expected to prove useful in the design of safety devices for use on motor cars, aeroplanes and many types of machines. Automatic devices to open doors, move the carriages of typewriters, turn pages of music, or carry out many tasks that normally involve interruption of other activities also may be brought into operation by the employment of the invention.

The second device makes use of an electric eye, or photo-electric cell, concealed in the base of the lighting fixture. When the rays from a lighted match fall on this cell a current flows between its electrodes, and this may be used through a relay to close the main circuit and thus to switch on the electric lights under its control.

Making Roads Safer for Foot Passengers

Many inventors have tried to construct devices that will reduce the number of deaths or serious injuries due to road accidents. The most recent of these is the "Clifford Auto-Saver," and its inventor claims that it will reduce by about 75 per cent. the risk of serious injury in accidents that involve pedestrians. There is great need for such an invention, for in 1929 no fewer than 4,035 foot passengers were killed, and 80,835 persons were injured in this country alone in street accidents.

The effective part of the Auto-saver is a roller with a corrugated surface that is carried in front of a motor car or lorry at a height of about 10 in. above the ground. Immediately it comes into contact with any obstacle, however slight in character, the roller is knocked down to a height of 3 in. and a contact switch brings into operation mechanism that causes it to rotate in the opposite direction to that of the road wheels. The result is that the obstacle is rolled along the road in front of the vehicle instead of being run over. It is said that injuries suffered by anyone rolled along in this manner are comparatively slight in character.

Birds Take Their Own Photographs!

Meccano Automatic Control for Camera Shutter

NATURE study with the aid of a camera is a most fascinating hobby, and a collection of photographs showing various aspects of plant and animal life is not only of great interest, but also of considerable value. The photography of plants is perhaps the easiest branch of nature photography, for whatever troubles we may have with the wind, we do know at any rate that the plant will not run away as soon as we approach it! Birds and small animals of the woods and fields are not only difficult to find when we want them, but still more difficult to photograph when we have found them, on account of their extreme nervousness and the rapidity of their movements.

The general procedure in taking photographs of such creatures as birds is first of all to find a place frequented by birds, and then to hide in bushes or bracken, or in a specially constructed shelter, and wait until a bird alights near by. Then arises the problem of making the exposure before the bird flies away. The Meccano device described in this article has been designed to remove much of the uncertainty of bird photography, and it enables excellent photographs to be obtained with comparatively little difficulty.

The device consists of a switch constructed in the form of a balance, at one end of which is secured a stout twig. The bird alights on the twig, and its weight causes the balance to pivot and close an electric circuit. A battery and an electro-magnet, the latter coupled to the shutter of the camera, are included in the circuit, and when the switch is closed by the bird the shutter is operated and the picture is taken. Thus the bird may truly be said to take its own photograph! The balance switch is also connected to a circuit containing an electric bell, so that immediately the photograph is taken the bell rings, informing the operator that it is necessary to re-set the switch and change the plate or film for the next exposure.

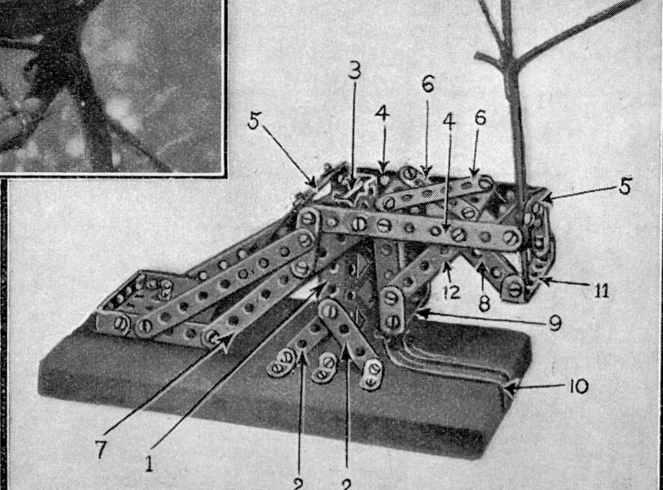

Fig. 1 (Below). The Meccano automatic camera shutter control switch removed from its covering box. (Above). A study of a robin obtained with the aid of the Meccano device.

The model is concealed in a wooden box covered with bark, and having a small hole at one end through which the twig is passed. This box is shown tilted back in Fig. 2, to show the device in position. A similar box is used to conceal the camera itself and the shutter operating gear.

If constructed carefully the complete system will be found to be very reliable in action. The photograph of the robin reproduced on this page, which was taken with a reflex-type camera controlled by the Meccano device, gives some idea of the excellent results that may be obtained.

The Meccano Model

The construction of the Meccano model may be followed from Fig. 1. The standard on which the balance portion of the switch pivots is mounted on a hardwood baseboard. Alternatively a base may be built up from Meccano Flat Plates and Angle Girders. The standard consists of two 3½″ × ½″ Double Angle Strips 1, between which is secured a 3½″ Braced Girder. The standard is secured to the baseboard by Angle Brackets and Wood-screws, and is held in an upright position by the 2″ Strips 2.

One arm of the balance consists of two 4½″ Strips 4, spaced apart by 2½″ × ½″ Double Angle Strips 5, and braced by 3″ Strips 6 secured diagonally between the Strips 4. To the underside of this arm two 2″ Strips 8 are fixed, and a 2½″ × ½″ Double Angle Strip 11 is secured between their ends. This last-mentioned Strip forms the lower support for the twig, the end of which is tapered so that it can fit into the centre hole in the Strip 11. The twig is clamped in position against the Double Angle Strip 5 by means of a 1½″ Strip and two ½″ Bolts.

Two 2½″ Strips 12 are secured to the Strips 4 in the position shown, and two 2″ Strips, also attached to the Strips 4, are joined to the ends of the Strips 12. Two Flat Brackets are also secured at this point. A 2½″ × ½″ Double Angle Strip 9, bolted between the Flat Brackets, forms the "shorting bar" of the switch, the downward movement of the balance arm 4 causing this Strip to bridge the two contacts 10, and thus complete the electro-magnet circuit.

The second arm of the balance is composed of two 4½″ Strips 7 secured to the Strips 4. Two 2½″ Strips are secured to the ends of the Strips 7, and a 2½″ × ½″ Double Angle Strip is bolted between them. A 2½″ × 2½″ Flat Plate is secured to the 2½″ Strip by means of Angle Brackets, and forms a tray on which small weights may be placed to obtain the correct balance. The contacts 10 consist of strips of brass ¼″ wide secured to the baseboard by small wood-screws. These strips should be bent at right angles below the Meccano Double Angle Strip 9, and their ends bent over so that the Double Angle Strip 9 can make sound electrical contact with them when the balance arm is depressed.

The complete balance arm is pivoted on a 3″ Axle Rod 3 journalled in the top holes of the Strips 1.

The electro-magnetic gear for operating the shutter of the camera should next be built. The actual design and arrangement of this mechanism will depend on the make and type of camera used, and no standard model can be described. The popular "box" pattern of camera is generally fitted with a shutter of the lever type, while the more expensive folding types incorporate a push release connected to the shutter by a flexible cable.

If the shutter of the camera is of the lever type, the simplest method of arranging the magnet release is as follows. A short length of Meccano Spring Cord is attached to the projecting end of the release lever and anchored to a framework composed of Meccano parts secured to the case of the camera. The tension of the Spring should be adjusted so that normally it pulls the shutter lever across the slot. An electro-magnet is next secured in the frame. A suitable magnet may be built up by winding a Meccano Bobbin to capacity with No. 26 S.S.C. wire, and connecting the ends of the winding to 6 B.A. Terminals mounted on the frame, but insulated from it by means of Insulating Bushes and Washers. The wound Bobbin should be clamped to the framework by Strips. The magnet should be mounted in such a position that an Axle Rod passed a short distance into the core of the Bobbin will act as a "catch" on the shutter lever, and prevent the tension spring from drawing it over and thus making an exposure. When a current is passed through the magnet winding, however, the Rod is drawn into the core of the Bobbin, thus releasing the shutter lever, which is immediately drawn over by the Spring and an exposure is made.

With a camera having a push release a different arrangement will be necessary. In this case the control push should be clamped in a vertical position and the electro-magnet arranged to release a small weight that presses on the push and thus operates the shutter.

To wire up the system, a length of thick insulated wire should be led from one of the contacts 10 of the balance switch to one end of the electro-magnet winding mounted on the case of the camera. A length of wire should be used to join the other end of the magnet coil to one pole of a 6-volt Accumulator, while the remaining pole of the accumulator should be connected to the second contact 10 of the balance switch. A length of twin flexible insulated wire should be attached at one end to the contacts 10 and at the other end to an electric bell and a dry battery. The bell must, of course, be placed at a considerable distance from the camera and switch. If the device is arranged in the garden the bell could be placed in a shed, or it might even be arranged to ring in the house. The further the bell is away, however, the more flex is required, and too great a length is not desirable.

Fig. 2. View of the control switch with covering box tilted back.

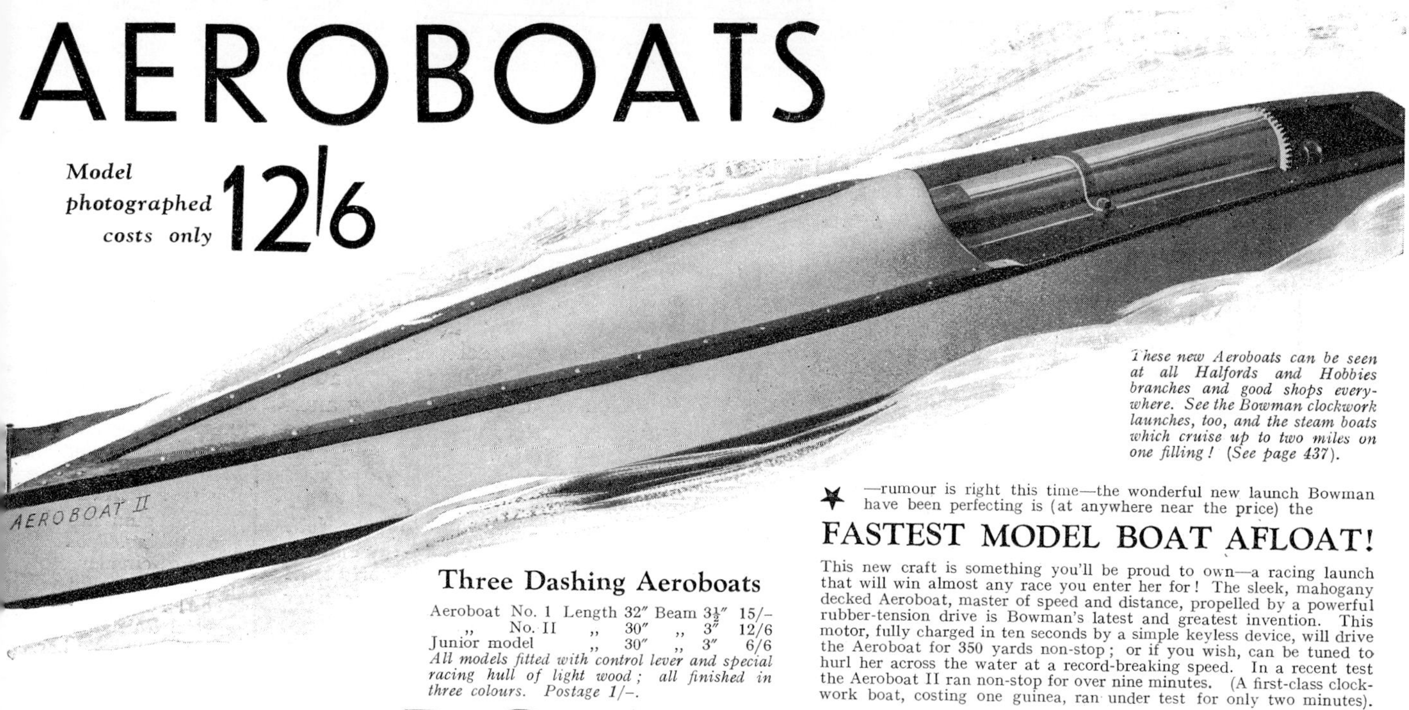

The balance switch is placed near some spot where birds are known to congregate, and the device wired up as already described. The camera is carefully focussed on the twig in the position in which this will be when the weight of the bird rests upon it. The catch of the shutter release mechanism is then set in the "on" position, and finally the bark-covered boxes are placed over the switch and the camera. All is now ready for the photograph, and the operator has only to retire to a suitable distance and wait patiently, and of course in perfect quietness. Presently, if circumstances are favourable, there will come the tinkle of the bell that proclaims the fact that one of our feathered friends has obligingly taken its own photograph!

II.—SIR FRANCIS DRAKE

When Queen Elizabeth succeeded to the throne of England in 1558 one of the first tasks she undertook was that of increasing the strength of the Navy, which had declined seriously since the time of Henry VIII. The war with France was brought to a close, and Spain now came into prominence as the great enemy. A remarkable wave of enthusiasm for the sea arose, and a host of privateers appeared in the Channel, attacking every Spanish ship they encountered, and making large profits out of their captures. Soon many of the more adventurous privateer captains extended their activities beyond the Channel. There is no doubt that Elizabeth secretly encouraged their marauding enterprises to the West, and had a financial interest in many of them. Among the outstanding figures in this company of "gentlemen adventurers" was Francis Drake.

Drake was born at Crowndale, a small village in Devonshire, in 1541. He was brought up in a seafaring atmosphere, for while he was still very young the family removed to Plymouth, where his father obtained a chaplaincy in the Royal Navy, and where they made their home in one of the old war hulks in the harbour. Unfortunately this appointment was terminated in 1553 when the Catholic Mary became Queen, and the family was soon reduced to such poverty that an opportunity was taken to apprentice the boy to the master of a coasting vessel trading with French, Spanish and Dutch ports. Life aboard such a ship in those days was rough even for hardened and experienced sailors, but the boy rose to the occasion and served so well and so faithfully that when his master died a few years later he bequeathed the ship to him. For some time Drake continued trading on the lines followed by his late master, and with considerable success.

In 1558 the Protestant Elizabeth succeeded to the throne, and the Catholic King of Spain, Philip II, in an excess of religious zeal closed all Spanish ports to English ships to keep the Protestant religion out of his country. This restriction seriously hindered Drake's trading activities, and selling his ship he engaged with John, afterwards Sir John Hawkins, and his brother. John Hawkins had just completed a successful voyage to the West Indies during which negro slaves had been collected and exchanged for Spanish treasure and merchandise, a form of trading that Philip II had strictly forbidden his American colonies to carry on with foreigners. Philip soon removed his restriction on English shipping, and Drake then sailed as purser in one of the Hawkins ships to St. Sebastian, Spain.

Meanwhile John Hawkins carried out a second successful slaving voyage that caused the King of Spain to protest to Elizabeth and resulted in Hawkins being forbidden to carry out a similar trip in the following year. The attitude of Spain met with little sympathy in this country, however, and a trading expedition led by Hawkins left England for the West Indies late in 1567. The expedition consisted of six vessels, one of which was under the command of Drake, and on the way to Guinea the fleet destroyed several Portuguese trading ships in revenge for similar treatment to some English ships. When about 500 negroes had been collected at Guinea Hawkins sailed for the Spanish Main, where he traded his unfortunate captives for treasure and then sailed for home.

A hurricane damaged his ships so much that he put into the harbour of San Juan de Ulloa, now known as Vera Cruz, for repairs. Hawkins obtained from the Spaniards an agreement not to molest him, but they treacherously attacked him. A desperate fight followed, Hawkins escaping with two of his ships. This conflict gave Drake his first taste of Spanish methods, and so great was his anger that he resolved to wage continual war against Spain.

Portrait of Drake from a contemporary print. This and the upper illustration on the opposite page are from prints in the possession of T. H. Parker Ltd., 28, Berkeley Square, London, by whose courtesy we are enabled to reproduce them.

Drake obtained from Queen Elizabeth a privateering commission, and gathering together a band of enthusiastic adventurers he made three voyages to the West Indies. The first two of these trips were chiefly to spy out the land and to enable him to form a plan of action. He decided to raid the town of Nombre de Dios, on the Caribbean side of the Isthmus of Panama, where the Spaniards periodically collected the mineral wealth obtained from the mines of Peru and Mexico for export to Spain; and he carried out this plan when on his third voyage in 1572.

The expedition consisted of two small ships with crews totalling 73 men and boys, and three collapsible pinnaces in which to row ashore. At Nombre de Dios the expedition was joined by a third ship, and the crew of this were left in charge of the three ships, while Drake and his men went ashore by moonlight. They took the Spaniards by surprise, and although Drake was wounded in the leg, the party succeeded in reaching the King's treasure house. As they stood before the entrance Drake told his men that he had brought them to the mouth of the "Treasure of the World," and that it was their own fault if they did not make the most of it. He then ordered them to break open the door, but had hardly given the command when he fainted from loss of blood. The uproar created in the town by the English invasion had somewhat unnerved Drake's men, and without risking an onslaught on the treasure house they carried him back to the boats.

The abandonment of the attack when victory was almost within grasp enraged Drake, and when he had recovered from his wound he consoled himself by attacking and burning Porto Bello, where he captured many Spanish ships and seized a great Spanish mule train of treasure. Before leaving the port Drake persuaded some friendly Indians to lead him to the highest point of the Isthmus where, by climbing a high tree, he obtained his first glimpse of the Pacific Ocean. It was a thrilling moment, for he was the first Englishman to view this sight, and his love of adventure stirred him to pray " Almighty God of His goodness to give him life and leave once to sail in an English ship in that sea." Laden with treasure the expedition returned home and reached Plymouth on 19th August, 1573. He landed at Plymouth on a Sunday morning, and we are told that the whole congregation left church in the middle of the sermon and rushed down to the waterside.

After four years of quiet life ashore Drake organised another expedition. He revealed to Elizabeth his plan to sail through the Strait of Magellan and raid Panama and the South Seas, and it is stated that the Queen gave him 1,000 crowns towards the expenses of the expedition on condition that her connection with the affair should be kept secret. At that time England was keenly interested in exploration, and Drake had no difficulty in raising the necessary funds and obtaining men and equipment. On 15th November, 1577, the expedition sailed from Plymouth, but bad weather damaged one of the ships and caused a return to port for repairs. A month later the expedition set out again on a voyage that was destined to bring its commander fame and fortune.

Drake's fleet consisted of his flagship the "*Pelican*," afterwards renamed "*Golden Hind*," a ship of 100 tons and armed with 18 guns; the "*Elizabeth*," 80 tons and 16 guns; the "*Swan*," 50 tons and 5 guns; the "*Marigold*," 40 tons and 16 guns, and the "*Benedict*," renamed "*Christopher*," 15 tons and one gun. The crews totalled about 160. The expedition encountered a series of violent storms that induced Drake to abandon the "*Swan*" and the "*Christopher*" in order to make his fleet more compact.

Drake's action off Gravelines during the Armada fight in 1588.

He forced his way through the Strait of Magellan, taking three weeks to make the passage, and then two disasters occurred. The "*Marigold*" sank with all on board, and the "*Elizabeth*" became separated from the "*Golden Hind*," and finally returned home alone. Drake was now left with only one ship. He did not allow this fact to worry him, however, and made straight for Valparaiso, and there had his first success in the capture of a large Spanish galleon laden with gold and wine. After raiding various towns along the coast he captured another treasure ship, and then made for home across the Indian Ocean and round the Cape of Good Hope. He arrived at Plymouth in September, 1580, thus being the first Englishman to circumnavigate the globe. In the following year Drake brought the "*Golden Hind*" to London, and on 4th April, after a great banquet on board, Elizabeth knighted him.

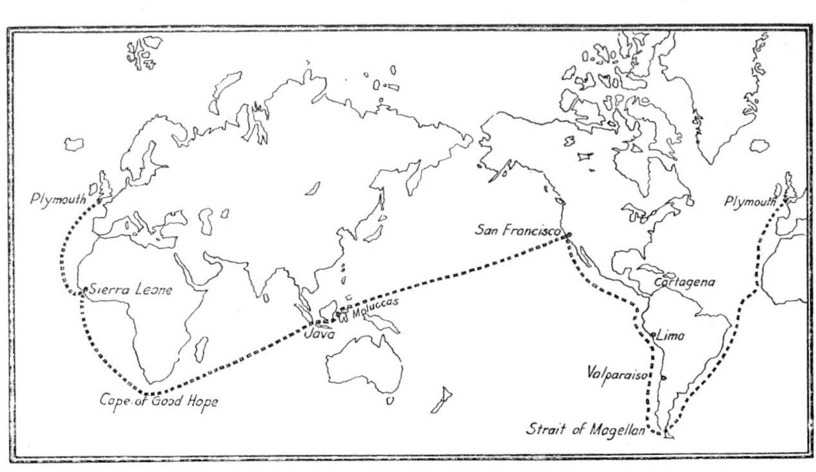

Map illustrating the route taken by Sir Francis Drake on his famous voyage round the World, 1577-1580.

An interesting glimpse of Drake aboard the "*Golden Hind*" is given in a letter written by a Spanish captain whom Drake captured and later released: "He is about 35 years old, of small size, with a reddish beard," writes the captain," and is one of the greatest sailors that exist, both from his skill and his power of commanding. He has with him nine or ten gentlemen, younger sons of the leading men in England, who form his council. He has, too, all possible luxuries, even to perfumes, many of which he told me were given him by the Queen. None of his gentlemen sits down or puts on his hat in his presence without repeated permission."

Relations between England and Spain became more and more strained, and the two countries rapidly drifted towards war. In 1585 Drake sailed again, this time with a commission from Elizabeth, and descended on the West Indies, captured San Domingo, held Cartagena to ransom, and returning home by way of Florida plundered the Spanish settlement of St. Augustine, and took on board the survivors of Raleigh's colony of Virginia.

By this time war with Spain was an actual fact, although it had never been formally declared. In 1587 Drake, with the rank of Admiral, was sent out to discover as much as possible of the Spanish preparations, and to do all he could to prevent the concentration of the fleet that Philip was collecting. He sailed on 2nd April and made for Cadiz, the chief Spanish naval base, where were assembled several big galleons and a number of storm-ships. After a fierce encounter the desperate resistance of the Spaniards was overcome, and Drake burned and destroyed to his heart's content. The Spanish losses amounted to some 12,000 tons of valuable shipping; Drake had indeed "singed the King of Spain's beard"! On his way home Drake captured the "*San Felipe*," Philip's own treasure ship, with a cargo of enormous value and documents regarding the Spanish East India trade that were of great importance in the subsequent decision to form an English East India Company.

Drake's devastating attack on the partly assembled Armada delayed its completion for a year, and matters were further complicated by the death of the Marquis of Santa Cruz, the most experienced of all the Spanish admirals. Philip appointed in his place as commander the Duke of Medina-Sidonia, who had little knowledge of military and less of naval warfare. The Duke persisted that he was unqualified to command the expedition, but for some extraordinary reason the king insisted on his taking the post. Finally the Armada sailed from Lisbon about the middle of May, but was forced to put into Corunna on account of a severe gale, coupled with bad provisions and shortage of water. It was not until 12th July that the fleet was able to set out once more.

The English fleet ready to oppose the Armada was under the command of Lord Howard of Effingham, with Drake as Vice-Admiral. It consisted of 197 ships made up of 34 royal ships of various sizes, 34 merchantmen, 30 ships and barques provided by the City of London, 33 barques and other ships, 43 coasting vessels provided by Elizabeth, and 23 voluntary ships. The number of men who actually took part in the engagement was probably about 10,000.

On 19th July the Armada was sighted off the Lizard. By this time there were only about 120 ships left of the 130 that had sailed from Lisbon with some 30,000 men; and of these vessels only about 60 could be considered real warships, the remainder being armed merchantmen. The news of the sighting of the Armada was brought to Lord Howard, who was playing bowls on Plymouth Hoe; and everyone is familiar with the story—which there is no reason to doubt—of how Drake waved the messenger aside, saying that there was plenty of time to finish the game and beat the enemy afterwards. The admirals then put to sea, each eager to be the first to tackle the Spaniards.

(*Continued on page 748*)

Famous British Admirals—*(Con. from page 743)*

Throughout the following day the Armada moved slowly up Channel towards Plymouth, while the English ships were coming out from the Sound against a stiff breeze and working to windward. On the 21st the English swept down with the wind to the attack, firing at a range at which the Spaniards could make no effective reply. Each ship after delivering her broadside swung round to take position astern while her guns were reloaded. Howard did not press his attack on this first day, but the Spanish fleet was thrown into confusion, so that collisions were frequent. As a result the "*Rosarie*" was captured, and the "*San Salvador*" was so badly damaged by an explosion of gunpowder that, although she escaped at the time, she was afterwards abandoned and captured.

The two fleets moved farther up Channel. On the 25th there was a sharp fight off the Isle of Wight, and subsequently, the wind having changed in their favour, the Spanish ships reached Calais and anchored in the Roads on the 27th. The English anchored well to windward, and on the following night Howard sent a number of hastily improvised fire ships among them. To save themselves the Spanish ships were obliged to cut their cables and make for the open sea. On the next day the final great encounter took place, known as the battle of Gravelines. It lasted the whole day, and extinguished all the remaining hopes of the Armada. The English again pursued their policy of long-range firing, resisting all attempts of the enemy to come to close quarters. They poured a murderous succession of broadsides into the Spanish ships, and by night few of these were in a condition to continue the fight.

On the following day Medina-Sidonia held a council of his commanders, and finally decided that the only hope for the fleet was to take advantage of the wind and escape by way of the North Sea and round the north of Scotland. Thus commenced a terrible voyage, and ship after ship was driven ashore and lost on the coasts of Scotland or Ireland.

In 1595 Drake obtained command of an expedition organised to raid Panama and the West Indies, and he set out with a fleet of 27 ships carrying 2,500 men. In contrast to the good luck that attended all his early expeditions, this voyage was unfortunate almost from the start. Drake found that he could no longer take the Spanish colonies by surprise; and although he captured several towns and cities it was to find that all treasure had been removed. To add to the misfortunes of the expedition sickness developed among the crews. Drake who hitherto had escaped now fell a victim to the fever, and after a few days of illness he died on 28th January, 1596, while his ships were anchored off Portobello, the scene of one of his earliest exploits against the Spaniards. His body was enclosed in a leaden coffin and was committed to the Atlantic Ocean.

How Wireless Waves Curve Round the Earth

The Heaviside Layer

ONE of the minor mysteries of wireless is that radiations sent out from a powerful station are readily received on the other side of the world, in spite of the fact that the Earth is round. When wireless waves were first discovered they were regarded, quite correctly, as being similar to light waves. Light does bend round corners, but only to a very limited extent, and generally speaking it may be regarded as travelling in straight lines. Wireless waves, on the other hand, appear to follow the curved surface of the Earth without difficulty. This was unexpected by many early experimenters, and it was prophesied that Marconi's efforts to use the waves for trans-Atlantic telegraphy would fail because the waves would radiate outward in straight lines like the rays of light from a lighthouse, instead of bending round the surface of the Earth to reach the receiving station. It was even stated definitely in certain quarters that good results could only be obtained if the stations in communication were within sight of each other, and it was in efforts to overcome the supposed difficulty created by the curvature of the Earth's surface that the familiar enormous aerials were first developed.

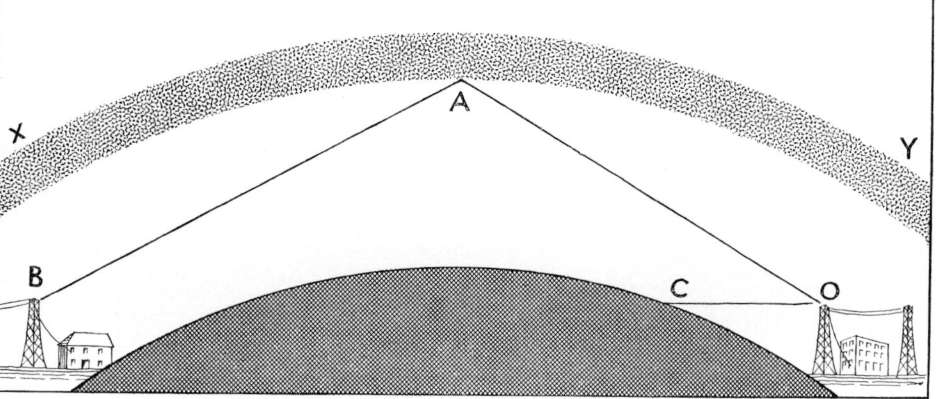

Diagram illustrating how wireless waves are reflected by the Heaviside Layer. The direct wave OC cannot reach B because of the curvature of the earth, but the sky wave OA is reflected downward to B.

The explanation that is now generally accepted of this peculiar behaviour of wireless waves is of special interest because it has brought to the notice of practically every user of wireless apparatus in the world the name of a pioneer whose work previously had remained in obscurity. This was Oliver Heaviside, the British scientist who suggested the existence in the atmosphere of what is now known as the Heaviside layer. This is a screen of electrified particles at a height ranging from 60 to 100 miles, which reflects downward the wireless waves that radiate outward from the Earth.

Oliver Heaviside (1850-1925).

Heaviside was born in London on 13th May, 1850. His father was an engraver who won considerable repute as a book illustrator, but it is interesting to note that he came of a family with scientific associations, for Sir Charles Wheatstone, a famous pioneer of telegraphy, was his uncle. Heaviside's interests as a young man were similar to those of Wheatstone, and he found employment with the Great Northern Telegraph Company at Newcastle-on-Tyne. Unfortunately he suffered from deafness, and eventually this became so serious that at the early age of 24 he was compelled to retire from active work. He went to live at Torquay, where he continued to work at various electrical problems connected with telegraphy and telephony.

It is impossible to give here a full account of the many important contributions that Heaviside made to electrical science, but it is no exaggeration to say that much of the efficiency of modern telegraph and telephone services is due to him. Many of the devices that enable several messages to be sent over one wire have been greatly improved by the adoption of his ideas, but perhaps his most interesting work was that which has enabled us to telephone with ease over long distances. He was the first to realise the importance of inductance in telephony, but his proposal to include loading coils in submarine cables in order to increase their self-inductance was ignored. Professor Pupin, an American scientist, independently made use of such coils with excellent results, and the practice is now universal.

Heaviside was not content with solving problems involved in ordinary telegraphy and telephony, for his work led him to deal with wireless, which was slowly being developed by Lodge, Marconi and others. It was then that he developed his theory of the Heaviside layer, the mysterious screen of electrified particles surrounding the Earth. Wireless waves cannot penetrate such a screen, and are in fact reflected by it much as light waves are reflected from the surface of a mirror. Waves travelling in a straight line that threatens to take them well away from the Earth are therefore intercepted by the layer and turned backward, to descend upon the Earth once more in positions where they can affect wireless receiving apparatus.

The existence of such a layer as that suggested by Heaviside affords the best explanation that so far has been produced for the fact that wireless waves are not lost in outer space, but circle the Earth in such a manner that they can be detected after travelling completely round it. The origin of the electrified particles of which it is composed is not known with certainty. A possible agent in their production is sunlight, which gives rise in our atmosphere to what are called "ions," that is, tiny, electrically-charged particles formed from the gases of which the atmosphere is composed. Sunlight at heights of 60 to 100 miles may be more effective in this respect, and this may account for the appearance of electrified particles in the position that the Heaviside layer is supposed to occupy, and in sufficient numbers to form a complete reflector.

An interesting alternative suggestion is that the ions of the layer come directly from the Sun, the centre of which is at so high a temperature that a proportion of the atoms contained in it are broken up, electrons or negatively-charged particles having been driven out of them. Many of these electrons are projected from the Sun with immense speed, and escape into outer space. Some of these may be caught up in the atmosphere of the Earth, and a proportion of them remaining suspended in it would form the reflecting layer.

Throughout his life in retirement in Devonshire, Heaviside continued to work at abstruse problems in electricity, and it is pleasing to know that his work eventually received recognition from the scientific world. He was elected a Fellow of the Royal Society in 1891, and in 1922 was awarded the Faraday Medal of the Institution of Electrical Engineers, being the first to be honoured in this manner. He died at Torquay on 4th February, 1925.

Russian Air Liner to Carry 36 Passengers

A giant new multi-engined air liner known as the A.N.T.14, has been built in Moscow. The machine is a five-engined high-wing monoplane to carry 36 passengers and is similar in external appearance to the Junkers G.38.

The wing of the machine has a span of 132 ft. 5 in. and is in three sections, the middle section being bolted to the top of the fuselage. The two outer sections taper in plan and thickness and are connected to the middle section at a slight dihedral angle. The whole of the wing is covered with corrugated duralumin.

The fuselage of the aeroplane is 86 ft. 11 in. in overall length and is almost rectangular in cross section. The two upper longerons are hollow metal tubes, but those at the bottom are metal sections, and are connected by means of a number of transverse frames and diagonals. The tail unit is of normal monoplane type and is braced to the fuselage and the fin by means of wires. The tail plane may be adjusted while the aeroplane is in flight. The aeroplane is provided with a split axle undercarriage, and the shock absorbers are carried on legs that run up into the wing.

The A.N.T.14 is equipped with five 480 h.p. "Jupiter IX" air-cooled radial engines. One of these is carried in the nose of the fuselage and the remaining four are mounted in nacelles carried in the leading edge of the wing. They give the machine a maximum speed at ground level of between 130 and 136 m.p.h., and the surprisingly low landing speed of 46.5 m.p.h. is claimed for it. The service ceiling is 4,000 m. or 13,120 ft. The machine weighs 23,450 lb. when empty and 38,150 lb. when fully loaded.

Woman's Altitude Record

A French airwoman, Mlle. Haryse Hilz, recently broke the world's altitude record for woman pilots by attaining a height of more than 10,000 metres, or 6.2 miles, in an aeroplane. The previous record was about 5½ miles, and was held by an American pilot, Miss Ruth Nichols, who flew a Lockheed "Vega."

New Fokker Machine for Dutch Air Line

A new Fokker aeroplane, known as the F.XVIII, has been adopted by the K.L.M., or Royal Dutch Air-lines, five machines of this type having been ordered for use on their service between Holland and the East Indies. It is a high wing monoplane of normal Fokker construction and is provided with three 440 h.p. Pratt and Whitney "Wasp" engines, which give it a maximum speed of 152 m.p.h., and cruising and landing speeds of 126 and 70 m.p.h. respectively. The machine is capable of carrying 12 passengers on short flights. When employed on the normal services of K.L.M. it will be provided with seats for only four passengers, however, and will then be able to accommodate a comparatively large amount of luggage and freight and will carry sufficient petrol to enable it to cruise for 930 miles without refuelling.

The F.XVIII weighs 9,587 lb. when empty, and when fully loaded has a weight of 16,640 lb. It can cruise comfortably with one engine out of action, when it has an absolute ceiling of 4,920 ft.

An artist's impression of a trans-Atlantic aeroplane of the future. It would be necessary for such machines to be fitted with powerful searchlights in order to carry out regular night flying.

Speeding Up Canadian Mail

During experimental air mail flights recently made in Canada, mails were exchanged between Ottawa and London in less than 4½ days, and in some cases the flights were several hours ahead of scheduled time. The C.P.R. liner "*Empress of Britain*" was the vessel concerned in the trials, which were carried on with both incoming and outgoing mail.

Letters from Great Britain to Canada were transferred from the liner to a minesweeper of the Royal Canadian Navy in Red Bay, in the Strait of Belle Isle. In this vessel they were carried to Bradore Bay, Quebec, and from this point were taken by seaplane and landplane to Montreal, a distance of about 910 miles. Mails for Ottawa, and also for New York and other American points to the south, were then forwarded by air, while those for points west of Ottawa were sent on by train. For outgoing mails this procedure was reversed, the "*Empress of Britain*" being overtaken in the Strait of Belle Isle.

An "Autogiro" with a 50 h.p. Motor

A new and revolutionary type of Autogiro is now being constructed. The machine will be a single-seater and is to be fitted with a small two-cylinder engine developing about 50 h.p. In flight, it will be controlled by tilting the rotor head, and this will make it possible for the lower stabilising wing at present fitted on "Autogiros" to be dispensed with. The rotor of the new machine may be folded, and as it will be only about 15 ft. in overall length, it may be accommodated in the space occupied by a motor car.

Further details of this interesting machine will be published when they are available.

* * * *

A new international record for speed over a distance of 2,000 km. (1,240 miles), has been set up by a French airman, M. Marcel Haegelen, who flew a Hanriot 41 monoplane over this distance at an average speed of 263.9 km. p.h., or 163.88 m.p.h.

A Mobile Mooring Mast for Airships

A huge airship hangar is now being constructed at Sunnyville, California, for the accommodation of United States Navy airships. The hangar is of similar shape to the one at Akron, Ohio, described on page 600 of our issue for August, 1930. It is 1,200 ft. in overall length and 300 ft. in width, and is provided with semi-circular rolling doors, each of which weighs 569 tons and moves on five 9-wheeled trucks.

The first mobile telescopic mooring mast ever constructed for aircraft will be used at Sunnyville. This will be carried on four trucks, about 64 ft. apart, arranged to travel along a special track. When in its lowest position the top of the steel mast will be 80 ft. above the level of the track, and it may be raised to any height up to 160 ft. in order to receive the nose of an approaching airship in its mooring cup. Mooring operations will be controlled either from a " crow's nest " or from a special operator's cabin below.

The mast will have a total weight of about 223 tons. The necessary power for its operation will be derived from two 125 k.w. electric generators driven by a petrol engine developing 565 h.p. These will supply current to four propulsion motors, each of 52 h.p., by means of which the trucks may be driven at a maximum speed of two miles per hour. A 100 h.p. motor is being installed for the purpose of raising and lowering the telescopic steel mast, and the mooring-line winch will be operated by a 130 h.p. motor. Efficient brakes are to be provided, and those fitted to the hoisting mechanism and the mooring winch will be electrical.

New Imperial Airways Service

A new desert air service between Baghdad and Galilee was inaugurated by Imperial Airways last month. The service, which is operated by an Avro Ten air liner, saves travellers the discomfort of a car journey of two days across the desert. The west-bound flight from Baghdad to Galilee is scheduled to occupy 5¼ hours, while the east-bound flight from Ramleh to Baghdad takes 7¾ hours.

New Napier Aero Engine

D. Napier & Sons Ltd., the constructors of the world-famous " Lion " engine, have now produced a new six-cylinder aero engine. The engine is known as type E.97 and is of the air-cooled type. The mounting is extremely clean and the engine has a remarkably low frontal area. It is suitable for use in fast single-engined machines seating three or four people, or for large multi-engined machines.

The upper illustration shows a triple-engined Ford passenger monoplane constructed entirely of metal. Below is a pilot dressed for high altitude work, during which intense cold is experienced.

One of the most unusual features of the engine is the lubrication system, the oil being transferred from one end of the engine to the other through a hollow camshaft. A special hand starting gear is provided.

The cylinders of the E.97 have a bore and stroke of 4½ in. and 5¼ in. respectively, while the compression ratio is 5.3 to 1. When dry the engine weighs 410 lb. It measures 4 ft. 10½ in. in overall length, and is 2 ft. 2 in. in width and 2 ft. 7½ in. in height. It is rated at 150 h.p. at 2,000 r.p.m. and the maximum power developed is 170 b.h.p. at 2,300 r.p.m.

German Airman's Third Atlantic Flight

Herr Wolfgang von Gronau, the well-known German airman, has made a third flight from Europe to America by way of Iceland and Greenland. His previous flights over this route were made in 1930 and 1931, and all were carried out in "Wal" flying boats, the machine employed this year being named the " *Greenland Whale.*"

On his most recent flight von Gronau left List, on the Island of Sylt, early on 22nd July, and as the calm conditions then prevailing made it difficult to take off, a Dornier " Super Wal " was taxied ahead of him in order to allow him to take advantage of its slipstream and of the waves it set up. The 1,120 miles between List and Seydisfiord, on the east coast of Iceland, were covered at an average speed of 112 m.p.h. The flight was continued next day and at 10.45 G.M.T. on 26th July, the " *Greenland Whale* " reached Cartwright, on the coast of Labrador. Great difficulty was experienced in alighting safely, owing to a dense fog that prevailed at the time, and von Gronau flew over Cartwright for 2¾ hours while waiting for the fog to clear. Eventually he made a safe landing under wireless guidance. The actual flying time from Iceland to Cartwright was 28 hours and von Gronau afterwards flew to Chicago by way of Montreal.

Small German Airship

An interesting semi-rigid airship, known as the Parseval-Naatz P.N. 30, recently has been produced in Germany. This is 151 ft. in length and has a diameter of 35 ft. 6 in., a height of 52 ft. 6 in., and a capacity of 91,830 cu. ft. It possesses accommodation for five passengers and is equipped with a Siemen Sh.14 seven-cylinder engine developing 115 h.p. This gives the airship a speed of 49.75 m.p.h., and a useful lift of more than 2,200 lb. The fuel carried gives a range of 620 miles.

The pressure of the gas inside the envelope is kept constant automatically and this vessel is claimed to be the smallest on which this arrangement is made.

Famous Air Line Companies

I.—Imperial Airways Limited

IMPERIAL Airways Ltd. was formed in 1924 by the union of the four British air lines then in existence. The new organisation provided services to six European countries, the total mileage of the routes covered being 1,760 miles. As the speed and convenience of air travel became more greatly appreciated the services were extended and to-day, eight years after the formation of the company, no fewer than 22 countries may be reached from Great Britain by means of its fleet of aeroplanes. There are daily services to the Continent over routes with a total length of more than 1,000 miles, while the Empire airways to India and Africa, over which weekly services are operated, have added 13,000 miles to the total distance covered, bringing the length of the air routes operated by the company to 14,000 miles. In addition, Imperial Airways machines are often called upon for what is known as special charter work, to distinguish it from the operation of timed services. Business men who wish to visit overseas countries, invalids who are unable to travel by train, and people who are in need of speedy means of travel in emergencies are carried on flights of this type.

The best known of the European services of Imperial Airways is that between London and Paris. Actually flights on this service are made from the aerodrome at Croydon to that at Le Bourget, passengers travelling between these air ports and the centres of the respective capitals by road. Three return flights are made daily on this service, except on Sundays, when there are only two; and the journey is made in luxurious air liners in which meals are provided. Another important service operated by the company is that between London, Brussels and Cologne. Flights on this route are made twice daily, with one on Sundays, and connections may be made by this service at Cologne with the network of German air lines that makes it possible for any German city or town of importance to be reached in a comparatively short time. In addition, services are maintained between London and Zurich by way of Paris and Basle.

The remaining regular services of Imperial Airways are of great importance, for they provide a speedy means of transport between widely separated parts of the Empire. At present there are two of these services in operation, one between London and Karachi, India, and the other between London and Capetown. The advantages of these are enjoyed by those who wish to travel to and from Egypt, Palestine, Kenya, Tanganyika Territory and Rhodesia, in addition to those whose destinations are India or South Africa. The services are well organised and carry mail and passengers with a regularity that is a striking illustration of the reliability of modern aircraft backed up by an efficient system of maintenance. The Indian service has been in operation since March, 1929, and that to Capetown was inaugurated in January, 1932. Great extensions undoubtedly will be made when necessary, and experimental flights across India and beyond have already been made in preparation for the establishment of an air service to Australia. It is hoped to bring this in operation when world trade conditions are more favourable, and then a weekly service will be provided by means of which this distant part of the Empire may be reached in 11 or 12 days.

Travellers on the two great Empire routes now in operation do not fly throughout in the same machine, different aircraft carrying out duties on separate sections. In addition, the comfort of passengers is a great consideration, and their journeys by air are interrupted in order to enable them to obtain rest. Thus, on the outward journey, they fly from Croydon to Le Bourget, and then proceed to Brindisi by train, sleeping accommodation being provided. At Brindisi they embark in a flying boat in which they are carried to Athens, where they spend the night. If they are going to India they are flown to the Sea of Galilee, and complete their journey to Karachi by way of Rutbah Wells, Baghdad, Basra, Jask and Gwadar, arriving at their destination six days after leaving Croydon. Passengers for Capetown and other places in Africa are flown from Athens to Mirabella, Crete, and from there across the Mediterranean

IMPERIAL AIRWAYS FLEET

Identification Letters	Names	Type Names	Routes
G-AAGX	Hannibal	Handley Page "Hannibal"	Cairo to Karachi Section of Indian Route.
G-AAUE	Hadrian		
G-AAUD	Hanno		
G-AAUC	Horsa		
G-AAXC	Heracles	Handley Page "Heracles"	London to Paris.
G-AAXD	Horatius		
G-AAXE	Hengist		
G-AAXF	Helena		
G-ABFA	Scipio	Short "Kent"	Mediterranean Section of Indian and African Routes.
G-ABFB	Sylvanus		
G-ABFC	Satyrus		
G-EBLF	City of Glasgow	Armstrong Whitworth "Argosy"	London to Paris, and Cairo to Khartoum section of African route.
G-EBOZ	City of Arundel		
G-AACI	City of Liverpool		
G-AACJ	City of Manchester		
G-AAEJ	City of Coventry.		
G-EBMM	City of Melbourne	Handley Page W.10	Special hire work.
G-EBMR	City of Pretoria		
G-EBMX	City of Delhi	De Havilland "Hercules"	African Route.
G-EBMY	City of Baghdad		
G-AAJH	City of Basra		
G-AARY	City of Karachi		
G-ABCP	City of Jodhpur		
G-ABMT	Not yet named		
G-EBVG	City of Alexandria	Short "Calcutta"	Mediterranean and Khartoum-Kisumu section of African Route.
G-EBVH	City of Stonehaven		
G-AASJ	City of Khartoum		
G-AATZ	City of Swanage		
G-AASP	Achilles	Avro X	London-Brussels-Cologne.
G-ABLU	Apollo		
G-AAGW	Not yet named	Westland "Wessex"	Special hire work.
G-EBBI	Prince Henry	Handley Page W.8b	Special hire work.

The photograph at the top of this page is a three-quarter front view of the first of the Armstrong Whitworth "Atalantas" to be constructed. For permission to publish this photograph and the upper one on the opposite page we are indebted to the courtesy of the Editor of "Flight." The complete list of Imperial Airways machines in the panel is given in response to repeated requests from readers. Eight "Atalantas" are shortly to be added to the fleet.

Sea to Alexandria and Cairo. When the African route was opened the journey from Cairo to Capetown was made in a variety of types of landplanes and flying boats, but these will be displaced by Armstrong Whitworth " Atalanta " machines, a photograph of one of which is reproduced on this page.

The introduction of " Atalantas " on the African section of the Capetown route will provide a typical instance of the care taken to employ machines that are specially adapted to the section of the route on which they are to be used. Many of the aerodromes established between Cairo and Capetown are at comparatively high altitudes, and the new aeroplane is specially designed for work under these conditions. It is equipped with four Armstrong Siddeley " Double Mongoose " engines that develop a total of 1,400 h.p. With any one engine stopped, the type is capable of maintaining a level course at any height below 7,000 ft., and of flying at a true air speed of at least 90 m.p.h. Actually, when the aeroplane is carrying full load and is cruising at an altitude of about 7,000 ft., the horse power needed to fly on four engines is less than two-thirds of the normal horse power developed by the engines at ground level. The aeroplane is designed to accommodate 17 passengers and their luggage, but from seven to nine will be carried on the African service in addition to a normal crew of three and a quantity of mail. We hope to publish an illustrated article describing this machine in an early issue of the *"M.M."*

An Armstrong Whitworth " Atalanta " in flight over Coventry. This machine is the first monoplane to be employed by Imperial Airways for operation over regular air lines.

The fleet of Imperial Airways has undergone interesting developments as the company has grown. The machines originally employed became too small to cope with the increasing traffic, and from time to time larger, more powerful and speedier machines have been introduced. For instance, when the twin-engined machines, such as the Handley Page W.8b and W.10, formerly employed between London and Paris, became inadequate, they were replaced by triple-engined aeroplanes of the Armstrong Whitworth " Argosy " type. The " Argosies " are equipped with three engines, developing 1,260 h.p., and this is an additional safeguard in cross-channel flying, for the machines are so designed that they can maintain height on any two engines if the third should fail, even when they are carrying a full load of passengers and mails.

Several " Argosies " are in regular operation, but larger and more powerful machines have now been introduced. These are the giant Handley Page biplanes of the " Hannibal " type.

The nose of a Handley Page " Hannibal " air liner. The cars underneath the wing and the fuselage give a good idea of the immense size of this machine. We are indebted to Imperial Airways Ltd., for this photograph.

The Handley Page machines were fully described on page 308 of the *"M.M."* for April 1931. They are equipped with four engines, and apparently the policy of Imperial Airways is to bring into use machines with this number of power units, for the Short " Kent " flying boats employed on the Mediterranean sections of the Empire air routes and the Armstrong Whitworth " Atalantas " also have four engines. Of the eight Handley Page " Hannibals " operated by Imperial Airways, four are employed on the service between London and Paris, and the remainder fly over the Asiatic portion of the route to Karachi, having been equipped specially in order to make them suitable for this purpose.

Passengers in modern air liners are provided with comfortable seats, and a journey by air is no longer an ordeal or even an adventure. In the past one of the greatest drawbacks was the noise from the engines, for even in cabin machines this made conversation between passengers almost impossible; but this difficulty has been overcome in the most recent machines of Imperial Airways. The cabins of these aircraft are provided with walls and roofs designed to damp out external noises and the machines themselves are designed to lessen the disturbances to passengers caused by their engines, with the result that the interior of the cabin in the most recent types of Imperial Airways liner is generally admitted to be as quiet as a compartment in an express train. The accommodation is more luxurious than that on a train.

An air line can only be operated in safety, particularly in bad weather, when advantage is taken of every means of informing pilots of their positions and of the weather conditions ahead of them. Elaborate weather forecasts are therefore prepared for the use of Imperial Airways pilots, and in addition all machines are equipped with wireless apparatus in order that communication may be maintained with Croydon, or with a wireless station in the vicinity of the aerodrome to which a pilot is flying. Special means are adopted to deal with bad weather conditions, and with fog, the greatest enemy of the airman. How flying is made safe in all weathers was fully described in the article that appeared on page 434 of the *"M.M."* for last June.

An elaborate testing and inspecting system has been built up at Croydon by the Engineering Department of Imperial Airways in order to ensure that machines in service are in perfect condition for flying. The engineers are arranged in shifts, so that a certain number are on duty day and night; and immediately an aeroplane lands it is handed over to a foreman and an inspector, who examine closely every part of the machine and test each engine separately. They make out reports, and if any defect is discovered mechanics are set to work upon it. Knowing that the safety of the people flying in the machine depends on the skill and care with which this work is carried out, both inspectors and mechanics do their duty very thoroughly, but in order to prevent any possible oversights a further inspection is made, and only on receipt of a final satisfactory report may a machine undertake another journey.

In addition to these precautions, all aeroplanes in service are inspected every morning before making a flight, and certificates of airworthiness for one day are issued, if they are found satisfactory. All machines are thoroughly overhauled after having flown a stated number of hours.

HOW THINGS ARE MADE:

Fireworks: Preparing for "The Fifth"

FIREWORK-MAKING is among the oldest of the world's industries. Long before Europe discovered the secret of gunpowder in the 13th century the Chinese had grown old in the art of pyrotechny, and for very many centuries now no great public celebration has been complete without its firework display. In the British Isles such spectacles have steadily increased in popularity, and now several large factories and some thousands of workpeople are engaged throughout the year working at high pressure to provide fireworks for large numbers of public displays and to satisfy the British boy's demand for "big bangs" on Guy Fawkes night.

It is an interesting fact that in spite of the rapid growth in the output of firework factories, the production methods have changed comparatively little. In very few of the processes involved is it possible to employ machinery. The product is a dangerous one, and, quite apart from the fact that better results are achieved by hand work, precaution against explosion dictates that the bulk of the work shall be done by hand. The very term "factory" is something of a misnomer, for actually a firework factory consists of a series of separate small workshops, often accommodating no more than two workers. The advantage of this arrangement in case of explosion is obvious, but it is remarkable how little actual danger really exists, for the most strict precautions are taken to guard against the possibility of sparks or fire.

Girls in the Standard Factory are seen here bundling and packing fireworks preparatory to despatch. This photograph and the lower one on the following page are reproduced by courtesy of Standard Fireworks Ltd., Huddersfield.

The workpeople are required always to wear special nail-less shoes, and visitors are provided with rubber overshoes. The workshop floors and benches are covered with linoleum fastened down with copper nails, the tools employed are of wood or soft metal, and the workshops are swept at least three times a day, for a tiny speck of grit might cause a serious accident. It is recorded that Messrs. Brock and Company, the famous Sutton firm of firework makers, were fined heavily on one occasion because a cobweb was discovered in one of their workshops! The cobweb itself was not dangerous, but it afforded evidence that the workshop had not been cleaned in the thorough manner laid down by law.

Two of the largest works in the Kingdom are those of Messrs. C. T. Brock & Company and Messrs. Standard Fireworks. The Brock factory at Sutton, Surrey, consists of between 200 and 300 buildings and, viewed from the air, has the appearance of a small town in one of the western American States. At the gates one notices a large cylinder not unlike a dustbin. This is the largest fireworks mortar ever constructed. It is 25 in. in diameter and can fire to a height of 800 ft. a shell weighing over 200 lb. which, on exploding, covers an area of 15 acres of sky! Actually this mortar is fired only on rare occasions.

The factory is divided into three main sections—the non-explosives area, the explosives area and the magazine area. In the non-explosives area are the sawmills, the blacksmiths' and fitters' shops, the paper cutting shop, stores for paper and chemicals, the buildings in which are rolled paper tubes or cases in which the firework composition is contained, timber stores, Christmas cracker-making plant, the canteen, and the set-piece-making shop.

The last-named building is where the famous Crystal Palace set-pieces are drawn out on a floor 160 ft. in length by 60 ft. in width. Near this building are stored in racks the frames on which are outlined the pictures that form the set-pieces—battleships, portraits of members of the Royal family, outlines of volcanoes, fountains, etc. There also is the woodwork of the mechanical fireworks, such as acrobats, boxers, fighting cats, racehorses, greyhounds, and the machinery of the huge wheels and various other devices that help to make up the wonderful display. Near by is the shed in which are stored the mortars from which the bombshells are fired, many of these being of considerable size, ranging up to 16 in. in diameter. Close at hand is the printing works, where posters and the coloured jackets for the 5th of November fireworks are printed.

An aerial view of the Brock factory at Sutton. The metal screens separating individual workshops are clearly shown. For this photograph and the upper one on the next page we are indebted to C. T. Brock & Company Ltd.

The explosives area is divided into two parts, and here the actual firework-making goes on. This part of the works is divided by a wide road into two sections, known as the "colour" side and the "black" side respectively. Workpeople on these two sides never mix, and no tool or implement used in one is ever taken to the other. On the colour side are made the coloured fire stars that contain potassium chlorate; on the other side the golden fountains and white fire stars in which the ingredients of gunpowder, potassium nitrate, sulphur and charcoal are used. It is to the presence of the charcoal which, in a finely powdered state is rather apt to spread itself, that the name " black " side is due. Potassium chlorate and sulphur if mixed are liable to go off at any time, and their use together in firework compositions is forbidden by law. It is with the object of preventing any chance of these two chemicals meeting that this definite division of the factory is made.

The work buildings in this area form two main rows connected by tram lines, on which run the trucks that take the finished work to the drying rooms and magazines. The tramway system has a total length of about six miles. The buildings themselves generally consist of two compartments, each of which has a door at each end, and from it all iron and steel is eliminated.

This illustration shows the operation of shaping crackers, commonly known as "rip-raps," at the Brock Factory.

Hanging on the wall in each compartment is a board setting out the operations for which that compartment is licensed, and the quantity of explosive material allowed in it. This quantity, and also the number of persons employed in a building, varies with the nature of the work, in some cases being as little as a few ounces of composition and only one individual. The magazines, 33 in number, are separated by considerable intervals, and occupy an area of many acres. They are surrounded by trees that would lessen the effect of an explosion in the very unlikely event of one taking place.

The Standard Fireworks factory situated high up on the moors near Huddersfield, not far from the Moorside Edge broadcasting station, is laid out on lines similar to the Brock factory, although it differs in many points of detail. Here also there is nothing spectacular about the manufacturing processes. In one long workshop there are some 50 girls deftly rolling cases for all manner of ingenious fireworks. Sheets of pasteboard lie on a table in front of each girl, who has a round stick in her hand. A flick of the wrist, a twist of the fingers, and a smear of glue, and a long roll of paper tube is ready and is quickly thrown into a basket. As soon as this is full it is taken away, and the tubes are sawn into lengths under rapidly whirling knife-blades. Next the tubes pass through a machine that twists and seals the butt-end, and so to another basket ready for the drying ovens before filling. That in brief is the making of the case. Squibs, crackers, sparklers, rip-raps and catherine wheels are all made in this manner.

Rolling the cases for fireworks in the Standard Factory at Huddersfield.

In the filling shops the operations differ very materially according to the kind of firework. Types of powder vary, and ingredients for bangs, for lighted balls and sparks are added each in its proper place.

The baskets of finished fireworks then pass into the counting and bundling room, where they are quickly seized by girls who, with remarkable accuracy, pick them up in loads of twelve and tie them into bundles. It is almost uncanny to watch the girls pick up twelve correctly every time, but with constant practice the hand accustoms itself to the feel of a dozen and automatically rejects eleven or thirteen as not correct.

In the course of our journey round the works we encounter a queer-looking barrow, somewhat similar to the restaurant wagons seen on railway station platforms, but in this case carrying countless rows of wires, stuck vertically in a wire tray and looking like huge wire hairbrushes. These wires are to be made into sparklers, those fascinating indoor fireworks that throw off bright white sparks and yet are perfectly safe because the sparks do not burn and the ends of the sparklers do not drop. The process of manufacture is simple but interesting. Each tray of wires is dipped into a solution that looks very like grey mud, so that one end of each wire is heavily coated, and the trays of coated wires are then finished by being placed in a hot oven for a certain period. When work is in full swing more than 20 miles of wire are used each day in the manufacture of sparklers.

The enormous quantities of fireworks consumed in a year can best be realised from a brief survey of some of the amounts of materials used in 12 months. The Standard factory alone consumes more than 100,000 lb. of gunpowder, 70,000 lb. of saltpetre, 250 tons of straw-board and paper for casings, and five tons of glue—and the bulk of the product goes up in smoke in the course of that glorious hour or two on Guy Fawkes night.

The use of fireworks for other purposes than amusement must not be overlooked. At sea they are employed in great variety to provide identification signals for vessels passing Lloyd's signal stations at night. Such signals consist of hand lights, Roman candles, rockets, or Coston lights, the last-named being small hand lights arranged to burn with either one colour or two or more colours in succession. A considerable number and variety of signals can be produced by making full use of the various combinations thus available. For example, the White Star burn a green light at bow and stern ; the Cunard Line, off the Irish coast, burn a blue light followed by two golden star rockets ; and the Ulster Steamship Company fire three vertical lights, yellow, blue and red, followed by two Roman candles together, each throwing two yellow, two blue and two red stars.

Light signals are used also to communicate between vessels of the fishing fleets, and with the carriers, and they are employed also to a great extent by the coastguard and at harbours and ports. Then there is the life-line-carrying rocket that has resulted in the saving of thousands of lives from wrecked vessels. The idea of a rocket of this nature was put forward in 1807 by a Cornishman named Trengouse, but it was not until 1855 that the line-carrying rocket, in a greatly improved form, came into general use. At first such rockets were used entirely for carrying a line from shore to ship, but more recently rocket apparatus has been developed to enable a wrecked ship to fire a line to the shore. Wrecks usually take place when the wind is blowing onshore, and therefore a rocket fired from a ship travels with the wind and has a much better chance of reaching its destination than one fired in the opposite direction.

Fireworks are used also to a great extent in the form of maroons to provide sound signals. Maroons giving warning of air raids became unpleasantly familiar in London during the Great War.

The use of fireworks on active service during the Great War was of much greater importance than is generally realised. There was, for instance, the smoke screen brought to perfection by Wing-Commander F. A. Brock, R.N.A.S., who was killed at Zeebrugge on 23rd April, 1918. Commander Brock also devised the anti-zeppelin bullet that proved such an effective check on the zeppelin raids, and the million candle power Dover flares used in hundreds every night by the anti-submarine patrol in the Straits of Dover.

"*Cheltenham Flyer's*" Record Speed

The Great Western Railway's "*Cheltenham Flyer*"—the world's fastest train—has again been accelerated and as foreshadowed in the "*M.M.*" for August, its new schedule requires a speed of over 70 m.p.h., start to stop. Commencing on Monday, 12th September, the running time for the 77¼ miles from Swindon to Paddington was reduced from 67 to 65 minutes, thus raising the average speed from 69.18 to 71.3 m.p.h.

The G.W.R. can proudly claim that this is the first time in the hundred years of the world's railway history that a train has been regularly scheduled at 70 m.p.h., or over. The cut of two minutes was made by deducting half a minute from the former running times allowed between Swindon and Steventon; Didcot and Reading; Reading and Slough; and Southall and Paddington respectively.

Apart from the occasions when special runs have been made and records achieved, the ordinary working of the "*Cheltenham Flyer*" from day to day during the past months has shown that the new accelerated schedule was well within the power of the "Castles." On Tuesday, 6th September, for instance, engine No. 5016, "*Montgomery Castle,*" one of the newest batch, in charge of Driver J. W. Street and Fireman F. W. Sherer, with a train of seven coaches weighing 230 tons, arrived at Paddington six minutes early, in spite of a long slack to 10 m.p.h. at Didcot and signal checks at Reading and Acton. Perhaps the most meritorious run ever made by this celebrated train was on Whit Tuesday, 17th May last, when with a heavy load of 11 crowded coaches, weighing fully 360 tons, the 77¼ miles were covered in 62 minutes, so that even with such an exceptional load, the present new schedule was improved upon by three minutes. This latter feat also stands to the credit of Street and Sherer with engine No. 5006 "*Tregenna Castle.*"

On Monday, 12th September, when the new timing came into force, Driver T. Lewis and Fireman W. White with engine No. 5016, "*Montgomery Castle,*" and a train of eight coaches weighing 265 tons made the run in 61 min. 8 sec. The average speed was almost 76 m.p.h.

An interesting view of one of the outside cylinders and motion of a G.W.R. 4-cylinder locomotive of the "Abbey" series. The characteristic form of the slide bars is plainly shewn, their outer ends being arranged to clear the connecting rods, which have solid-eye big ends with circular bushes.

Accelerations on British Railways

In the winter time-tables of the L.M.S.R., which came into force on 12th September, more than 1,000 passenger trains have been accelerated. Following on the improved services introduced in May and July, this means that during the present year the L.M.S.R. have accelerated a total of 3,101 passenger trains so as to cut running times by 10,084 minutes—representing a saving in travel time of 168 hours per day.

The latest accelerations cover a wide field, ranging from important business trains between London, Manchester, Liverpool and winter health resorts, to local services in the London and principal provincial areas, and many cross-country trains. Between London and Manchester there are now three trains—two up and one down—booked to make the journey in 3¼ hours. One of these has been named "*The Comet,*" and leaving Manchester at 5.40 p.m., it is timed to run the 133 miles from Stafford to Euston in 127 minutes at an average speed of 63.1 m.p.h. Another new booking at over a mile a minute is the run of the down "*Lancastrian*" (6.0 p.m. from Euston) which does the 177 miles from Euston to Wilmslow in 176 minutes, an average of 60.3 m.p.h.

On the Midland route between Manchester and London (St. Pancras) six expresses have been speeded-up, while 11 trains between Euston and Liverpool are altogether 114 minutes faster each day compared with a year ago.

The L.N.E.R. has also added to its accelerations in its winter services. There are now six expresses on this line running at average start-to-stop speeds of 60 m.p.h. or over, the fastest being the run from Grantham to King's Cross, 105½ miles in 100 minutes, giving an average of 63.3 m.p.h. On the East Coast main line the 8 a.m. from Newcastle and the 2.5 p.m. express from Edinburgh (which is provided with radio-gramophone equipment) now arrive at King's Cross 21 minutes and 10 minutes earlier than previously.

On the G.W.R., in addition to the brilliant run of the "*Cheltenham Flyer,*" there are 11 other trains performing start-to-stop journeys at speeds of 60 m.p.h. or more, and a further 46 at speeds of 55 m.p.h. and over.

The winter time-tables of the S.R. show numerous revisions. The popular "*Bournemouth Belle*" Pullman train, which ran daily during the summer, continues to run on Sundays only throughout the winter. A noteworthy improvement is the introduction of a 15-minute service of electric trains on the Dartford Loop Line in the non-business hours and on Sundays. This means that no less than 249 additional trains a week will be provided, for there will be 33 extra trains each week-day and 51 additional services on Sundays.

London "Underground" Developments

The great three years' programme of extensions and improvements which the London Underground Electric Railways are carrying out at a cost of £11,000,000, is now rapidly maturing and some of the most important works have already been completed. The first section of the Cockfosters extension of the Piccadilly Railway from Finsbury Park to Arnos Grove was opened for traffic on 19th September. Stations have been built at Manor House, Turnpike Lane, Wood Green, Bounds Green and Arnos Grove. The remainder of the new line will be opened next year.

The reconstructed station at Marble Arch has been completed and brought into use. It has been thoroughly modernised in a style similar to the station at Piccadilly Circus but on a smaller scale. The old lifts have been superseded by escalators which are speedy, yet quiet, in action.

Fast Runs by L.M.S.R. "Baby Scots"

An order for some additional standard 3-cylinder 4-4-0 compound express locomotives is now in hand at Derby Works and the first two of the new batch—Nos. 935 and 936—are already in service. They have both been noted at Birmingham recently, having worked there from Derby. Mr. Stanier has introduced several alterations in the details of these new engines as compared with the earlier ones of the class, and, like the latest tanks and 0-8-0 engines, they have round-headed rivets in some places where countersunk ones formerly were used.

Another 2-6-4 tank engine has been completed at Derby and is working in the Central Division. It is numbered 2383.

The latest "Baby Scots" (reconstructed "Claughtons") in service are Nos. 5949 and 6010. Nos. 6010 and 5974 are stationed at Camden shed; Nos. 5949, 5959, 5985 and 5987 are at Manchester (Longsight). The Longsight "Baby Scots" are sharing with "Royal Scots" the working of the fastest expresses between Manchester and London. No. 5959 was the first to be tried on the accelerated up "*Mancunian*" and with a load of 300 tons arrived at Euston one minute early, having run the 177 miles from Wilmslow in 171 minutes. The fastest run made as yet by the "*Mancunian*" was on 23rd August when, with "Royal Scot" engine No. 6134, "*Atlas*," and a train of 300 tons, Driver Cobb and Fireman Lapham, of Camden shed, reached Euston eight minutes early, having averaged 64.75 m.p.h. from Wilmslow. A check was experienced at Lichfield and from there to Euston the average speed was 69.75 m.p.h.

It is stated on good authority that when certain bridges have been strengthened, "Baby Scots" will be employed on the Derby, Birmingham and Bristol section of the Midland Division.

An order has been placed for five small 0-4-0 shunting engines. They will have saddle-tanks and a short wheel base to fit them for working in yards where there are sharp curves.

2-8-0 Goods Engines for L.N.E.R.

Four more of the standard 3-cylinder 2-8-0 standard freight locomotives have been turned out from the works at Doncaster and are numbered from 2958 to 2961. These complete the order for eight engines of this class, all of which are working heavy freight trains on the former G.E.R. section, chiefly between March (Whitemoor Marshalling Yard) and Stratford.

The Passing of the "Gladstones"

The S.R. 0-4-2 express locomotive No. 197 of the L.B.S.C.R. "Gladstone" class was withdrawn for scrapping at the end of August. It was built in 1888 and received the name "*Jonas Levy.*" It continued in active service right up to the end, putting in almost every day the full round of duties described in the "*M.M.*" for June last. Of the 36 engines which comprised this famous class, only one—No. 172—now remains at work. It is stationed at Brighton.

Our photograph, reproduced by courtesy of the Baltimore and Ohio Railroad, shews how the atmosphere of a sleeping car on that line is cooled before a night run. The motor vehicle houses a fan that draws in air across ice cakes and discharges it through a metal duct into the sleeping car, the warm air passing out through the overhead ventilators.

Shower Baths for Locomotives

A novel method of washing locomotives has been adopted by the Canadian National Railways. Instead of being washed by hand, the engines are passed through and under a hoop-like washing frame fitted with spray nozzles. As this is reached, the front wheels of the engine close an electrical circuit that turns on hot water sprays having a pressure of 140 pounds to the square inch. When the engine and tender have slowly passed through the frame the rear wheels break the circuit and the water flow ceases. A cleaning compound mixed with the spraying water dissolves oil and grease and leaves on the washed surface a film of wax which renovates the paintwork and discourages rust.

L.M.S.R. 4-6-0 locomotive No. 10451 of the Horwich 4-cylinder design. These engines were developed on the former Lancashire and Yorkshire Railway, and with the "Claughtons" formed the chief express locomotives in the Western Division of the L.M.S.R. before the introduction of the "Royal Scots."

G.W.R. Locomotive News

The new engines at present building at Swindon are all of standard tank types. Ten 0-6-0 tanks, numbered 5800-9, should be ready for service early this month and ten more of the same class will follow later. These engines will not be fitted with the automatic signalling apparatus or the gear for working auto trains. A start has been made on 20 2-6-2 tank engines similar in all respects to the "6100" class recently built. They will be numbered from 6130 to 6149 and the first will probably be in traffic by the end of this month.

Straight outside admission steam pipes, similar to those on engines of the "Hall" class, have been fitted to 12 2-cylinder 4-6-0 engines of the "2900" class, and two more 4-6-0 express locomotives of the "Star" class—No. 4038, "*Queen Berengaria,*" and No. 4048, "*Princess Victoria*"—have been fitted with outside steam pipes like those on No. 4002.

L.M.S. Royal Train

In readiness for the King's journey to Ballater and back in connection with his usual summer visit to Balmoral, the L.M.S.R. Royal train was recently repainted and thoroughly renovated. It is said that the L.M.S.R. authorities had proposed to repaint it in their standard deep-red colour but in deference to the King's own wish it was done again in the former L.N.W.R. colours, the upper panels being white, tinged with blue, and the lower a dark chocolate.

Electric Signalling on L.M.S.R.

A further stage of the automatic electric colour-light signalling which is being introduced by the L.M.S.R. between Camden and Watford, with a view to increasing and accelerating the electric train services on this section of the line, was brought into operation on 4th September, when the new system of signalling was extended from Willesden to Kilburn, leaving the sections from Hatch End to Watford and from Kilburn to Camden to be converted later in the year.

A Boon for Rail Travellers

As a result of the Pooling Scheme that has been adopted by the L.N.E.R. and L.M.S.R. passengers between any two points served by both companies can use their return tickets (except excursions) by any direct route. For example, passengers who have travelled from King's Cross to Edinburgh by "*The Flying Scotsman*" may return to Euston by "*The Royal Scot.*"

The Story of the Flexible Locomotive

I.—Solving the Curve Problem

THE history of the steam locomotive shows an almost continuous expansion in size and power, yet the appearance of a new locomotive larger than any of its predecessors has usually called forth opinions that development had reached its maximum. This was the case as long ago as 1851 when the Crampton locomotive "*Liverpool*," shown at the Great Exhibition of that year, was described as the "ultimatum of the narrow gauge." The term "narrow gauge" refers of course to the now standard gauge of 4 ft. 8½ in., as distinct from the "broad gauge" of 7 ft. 0¼ in. laid down by Brunel on the G.W.R. Since that time, however, as the strength of rails has increased and tracks have become better laid, it has been found possible for greater weights to be carried by the permanent way, and the size and weight of the locomotive have steadily increased.

The "South Carolina," an early attempt at an articulated locomotive. It was built in 1832 to the designs of Horatio Allen, a famous American locomotive pioneer. Photograph by courtesy of the Baltimore and Ohio Railroad.

British railways are now faced with the serious fact that the limits in height and width permitted by the standard loading gauge have now been reached. This is the penalty we have to pay for having pioneered in railway construction. In the early days of our railways no one could foresee the enormous development that would take place, and as a result bridges and tunnels were constructed on a scale that was in keeping with the small locomotives of the time. In many cases the difficulty has been overcome in recent years by opening out the early structures and by replacing old underbridges by new ones capable of carrying heavier loads. In order to attain any great increase in the possible width of locomotives, however, station platforms would have to be altered, and possibly the "six-foot way" between up and down tracks would have to be increased. The cost involved in such tremendous alterations makes their accomplishment out of the question. In America and on the Continent, where loading gauge dimensions are more liberal, considerably larger engines have been built than those we have in use in this country, although the track gauge is the same. Now, however, even American designers seem to be unable to move further in the matter of height and width, although they may proceed to the extent of some 3 ft. beyond our height limit of 13 ft. 6 in.

The only direction in which our locomotives can expand, therefore, is in length; but here a difficulty is immediately encountered in regard to curves. It would be impossible for a locomotive with as many as 10 or 12 coupled wheels to negotiate any but very easy curves, and as a matter of fact there are certain restrictions on even our six-coupled express locomotives. There are many sections of line in England that can only be worked by light tank engines with very short rigid wheelbases. Thus the S.R. still maintain three antique tank locomotives of a design dating from 1863 for use in North Cornwall. One of these pigmies has recently been overhauled and fitted with new cylinders at Eastleigh, so that their maintenance in service seems likely for some time to come. Their diminutive proportions render them suitable for service on the Wensford Branch, where much china clay traffic is dealt with. The curves and light construction of the line make a moderate weight and short wheelbase essential in the engines working over it.

In some cases, in order to work trains where curves are very sharp, and at the same time traffic is heavy, engineers have designed locomotives with many driving wheels, several pairs of which are without flanges. This plan of flangeless driving wheels is quite practicable, but it cannot be applied to more than a small proportion of wheels, otherwise the engines would become unsafe for running at high speeds. Then there are numerous

systems for giving a certain amount of lateral play to the wheels on curves. These are satisfactory to a certain extent, but there are obviously limits to the amount of play that can be tolerated, because of the oscillation set up at speed on a straight track.

Another method open to the locomotive designer is to employ the swivelling bogie principle. This has been utilised wherever expansion of locomotives has been absolutely necessary, and where at the same time the limits of the loading gauge have been reached. The application of the principle may be made on one or other of the systems of articulation that have been devised. Many articulated locomotives work in a similar manner to an ordinary bogie coach. The boiler may be looked upon as the coach body running on two bogies that are fitted with cylinders to make two separate locomotives or power units. As in the case of the bogies of coaches, these separate driving units are constructed so that they follow the curve of the rails. In this manner a locomotive twice the normal length can negotiate an ordinary curve without difficulty, and with perfect safety.

The upper illustration shows a double-boiler "Fairlie" locomotive of the Welsh Highland Railway. The driving wheels are mounted in steam-driven bogies, and allow the engine to take sharp curves easily. In the lower picture appears an American locomotive of the "Mallet" compound articulated type. The high-pressure cylinders drive the rear set of coupled wheels, and the leading set mounted in a pivoted truck are worked by the low-pressure cylinders.

There are many designs of articulated locomotives, the best known being the "Fairlie," the "Mallet," the "Kitson-Meyer" and the "Garratt." The "Fairlie" locomotive was designed and patented in 1864 by Mr. R. F. Fairlie, a British engineer, although a very early attempt at a similar design is shown by the "*South Carolina*" of 1832, for which the American, Horatio Allen, was responsible. The principle of the "Fairlie" is that of two boilers having one common fire-box. In other words, it is to all intents and purposes two completely separate engines back to back, with the fire-box between. The fire-box door is necessarily placed at one side where the fireman stands, and the driver controls the operation of the locomotive from the other.

In these respects, then, the "*South Carolina*" anticipated the "Fairlie," and was further remarkable for having two boiler barrels between each smoke-box and the common fire-box. There was thus a total of four barrels. Two cylinders, one at each end, were situated on the centre line of the engine, and both exhausted into tall chimneys at each end. Thus, although Fairlie was responsible for what was perhaps the first successful application of the plan, the "*South Carolina*" was certainly an early step in the same direction.

An example of a "Fairlie" locomotive in this country is shown in one of the accompanying photographs. This locomotive belongs to the Festiniog line of the Welsh Highland Railway. It will be seen that it has two sets of coupled wheels, and these swivel in a similar manner to those of a railway coach. The appearance of the engine strongly suggests that it is trying to travel in both directions at once! This is beyond its powers, but it can travel equally well in either direction and is therefore very convenient for single-track working. The boiler is much larger than could otherwise be possible, and the more even weight distribution resulting from the wheel movement enables the locomotive to operate on a lightly-laid track.

An interesting story is often told of an episode concerning a Mexican "Fairlie," which serves as a striking illustration of the exceptional ability of these engines to keep to the rails, however sharp the curves may be. The Orizaba Incline on the Mexican Railway is a long and difficult climb extending over 30 miles. One day a "Fairlie" locomotive was shunted into a siding after assisting a train to climb the bank. The enginemen dropped off in order to snatch a hasty meal, but owing to the brakes having been carelessly adjusted the engine commenced to move backward, but so silently as to be

A 2-6-0 : 0-6-2 locomotive of the " Kitson-Meyer " type. This resembles a large tank engine in which the driving units are pivoted so that they can partially rotate, their movement being similar to the bogies of an ordinary coach.

unnoticed by the crew. It was only when they heard something jolting over the points of the siding that they realised what had happened. Pursuit was out of the question, so a frantic message was flashed by telegraph to give a clear course to the runaway, although it was considered fairly certain that it would leap over the edge of a precipice at one or other of the difficult bends on the line and be smashed to pieces. One can imagine, therefore, the amazement of everybody concerned when it was found that the locomotive had come quietly to a standstill 30 miles farther down the Incline, without having received the slightest damage. The distance had been covered in well under half-an-hour, and the fact that the engine kept the rails is a striking tribute to the flexibility of the " Fairlie " arrangement.

The Festiniog engine, which is described as being of the 0–4–0 : 0–4–0 type, is practically an 0–8–0 broken in halves, but owing to the flexibility of the " Fairlie " design it can traverse curves that would be absolutely impossible for an engine of the ordinary 0–8–0 type. The disadvantage of such engines is that the driver and the fireman are separated by the common fire-box, and that in the event of the engine overturning they run considerable risk of being crushed. This difficulty is done away with if two independent boilers and fire-boxes are used, and this modification of the "Fairlie" design was effected in 1902 by the Vulcan Foundry. A further advantage of this change is that on steep gradients the variation in water level is not so great.

A " Mallet " locomotive of unusual design running on the Southern Pacific Railroad. It is run cab foremost, the tender being at the chimney end as the engine uses oil fuel, and the driver therefore has a very good look-out ahead, for there is no smoke or steam to obscure his view.

The use of separate boilers had been introduced in 1885 in some engines built by the then Rhode Island Locomotive Works. These were known as " Johnstone " locomotives after their originator. Although swivelling bogies were employed the cylinders, unlike those of a " Fairlie," were attached to the main frames, and the motion was thus necessarily complicated. As a result of this construction the steam did not have to pass through any articulated joints, but this advantage was outweighed by the inconvenience resulting from the complication of the valve gear. A further modification is seen in the single-boilered " Fairlie " engine, for although the double boiler was one of the features of the original design it was not an essential one, and Fairlie himself had built a locomotive having only one boiler. This development will be considered after the " Garratt " design, to which it is somewhat similar.

Another interesting type of articulated locomotive is the " Mallet," which takes its name from Anatole Mallet, whose locomotives on the Bayonne-Biarritz Railway were the first in which the principle was embodied successfully. Only one boiler is used, and this is carried on two driving units. The rear unit is an integral part of the locomotive, in the same way as the driving wheels of an ordinary 4–4–0 ; but the front unit is able to move laterally like a huge pony truck. Its centre of rotation is located between the centres of the cylinders in front of the rear driving wheels. Owing to its movement in this manner special arrangements are necessary to support the boiler on curves, and this is effected by a special bearing saddle or saddles, which may have spring gear, in order to keep the boiler central when the engine regains the straight track. The most important feature of any locomotive is a boiler with good steaming properties, and the great length of the " Mallet " allows plenty of room for the fitting of a boiler of ample capacity.

The " Mallet " has become extremely popular throughout Europe and the United States. It is a type of locomotive particularly well adapted to the tremendously heavy freight services that are involved by the use of high-capacity wagons in America. On one occasion, on the Virginian Railways, a coal train of 111 wagons having a total weight of 15,400 tons was worked by a " Mallet " locomotive of the 2–10–0 : 0–10–2 type. This vast train was hauled unassisted over a distance of 130 miles, and this fact shows the tremendous power that can be developed by such engines.

The " Mallet " system of articulated locomotive is the only one where the double expansion of steam, or compound working, has been successfully applied. The high-pressure pair of cylinders are located on the rear driving unit, and as this is rigidly attached to the boiler, steam at boiler pressure has no flexible joints to pass through that are likely to cause trouble. To this point a great deal of the success of compound working in " Mallet " designs is due. The low-pressure cylinders are attached to the leading pivoted driving unit, and as the steam passing through them is at a much lower pressure than boiler steam, no trouble is occasioned with the flexible joints through which it must pass.

On the Chesapeake and Ohio Railroad the existing 2–6–0 : 0–6–2 " Mallet " compounds had to be supplanted by something more powerful. The 2–8–0 : 0–8–2 engines that were built were provided with four cylinders, all taking steam at boiler pressure, since low-pressure cylinders of the diameter necessary for the required power output could not be accommodated owing to the restricted width of a certain tunnel in the Allegheny Mountains. These particular locomotives were built so as practically to fill the loading gauge. As a result of their performances a number of earlier 2–6–0 : 0–6–2 " Mallets " were converted to simple engines with four high-pressure cylinders.

Several attempts had been made to operate single-expansion " Mallets " in earlier times, but various difficulties were met with, such as trouble in the passage of high-pressure steam through flexible joints, and the fact that the boiler capacity was then hardly sufficient to fill four cylinders at once.

Continued on page 770)

Flexible Locomotives—*(Continued from page 764)*

Mallet himself always insisted that the step was not in accordance with the principles of the design, but modern improvements have overcome the early difficulties and made single-expansion "Mallets" a success.

"Mallet" locomotives are employed for all kinds of services on narrow gauge systems, while on standard gauge lines, particularly in America, they are used for banking and shunting duties in addition to the haulage of heavy freight and mineral trains. A disadvantage of the type is that owing to the front unit only moving on a curve, the boiler is displaced towards the outside of the curve. It is therefore a less satisfactory design in this respect than a locomotive that has two movable trucks.

The "Kitson-Meyer" locomotive is a very interesting design. The same general principles as in the "Fairlie" and the "Mallet" are employed and it is very similar in appearance to a huge tank engine, except that the tanks are placed rather far forward, leaving the firebox sides unobstructed. Kitson & Co. Ltd., of Leeds, introduced a number of modifications to the original Meyer engine, and as a result the name "Kitson-Meyer" has been applied to engines incorporating these characteristics. The cylinders are placed at the rear of each bogie, or at each end of the engine. The superstructures of engines of this pattern are carried on the steam-driven bogies. These bear the load on two pivots placed as nearly as possible to the centre of the coupled wheel-base, and thus their movement on curves approximates very closely to that of an ordinary bogie coach. Both bogies partially rotate and accommodate themselves to the rails. Engines of the original "Meyer" design have their cylinders facing each other at the inner ends of each bogie; and the superstructure is carried on the rear bogie by means of special bearings and brackets and on the front bogie by a spherical pivot so as to allow for the variations in level and curvature that are encountered on the road.

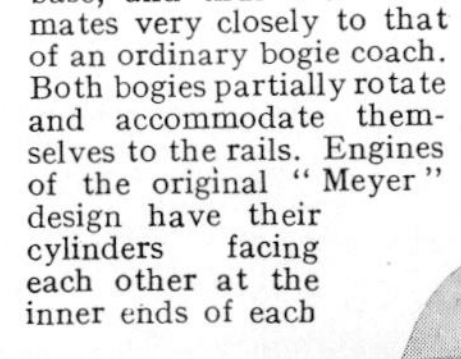

A baby elephant stands patiently while his weak leg is being strapped up to support it. He seems to know that the uncomfortable apparatus is for his own good.

The engine shown in the illustration on page 764 was built by Kitson & Co. Ltd., for service in South America on the 3 ft. gauge Colombian National Railway, which is noted for a continuous stretch of extremely severe gradients, the maximum being about 1 in 25. The engine may be regarded for all practical purposes as consisting of a pair of "Mogul" or 2-6-0 engine units supporting the boiler, tanks and bunker in the manner peculiar to the design. Although only a relatively small locomotive, the tractive effort at 85 per cent. of the boiler pressure is 40,000 lb., or very slightly below that of a G.W.R. "King," so that the possibilities of articulated designs in the matter of power are well brought out by this comparison.

A later development has been the 2-6-2 : 2-6-2 or "double Prairie" type, and a step further gives us the 2-8-0 : 0-8-2. Locomotives of the former pattern are in use on the extremely tortuous Kalka-Simla Railway in India, on a gauge of 2 ft. 6 in. Examples of the latter are found on the Great Southern Railway of Spain. As it was required that these should handle heavy mineral traffic over a line of somewhat light road bed, a design of adequate power was called for, yet without an excessive concentration of weight. It is noteworthy, therefore, that although the engines have an adhesion weight of over 90 tons, the average load on each axle is not more than 11 tons 7 cwt. The special merits of the articulated locomotive for such duties are obvious. There are many locomotives of the Kitson-Meyer type in use in Spain and South America.

IX.—By Frank Hornby

THIS month I commence my promised description of the Meccano Factory and the varied and interesting processes that are carried out in it. I am writing this particularly for readers who may be unable to visit the Factory, but at the same time I hope my account will come as a pleasant reminder to those who have already made a tour of the Factory with one of our special guides.

The plan reproduced on the next page, taken in conjunction with the little sketch reproduced in the heading above, will be helpful in making clear the layout of the Factory, which covers an area of nearly five acres, and gives employment to over 1,100 workers.

Perhaps the best way of explaining the work of the various departments of the Factory will be to describe the processes through which a new item added to the Meccano or Hornby Series must pass. First of all instructions are issued to our designers to prepare samples and estimates of manufacturing costs, and in due course these are presented to the Directors. They are considered in conjunction with the type and style of packing to be employed, and the quantity that may be expected to sell during the ensuing year. Finally, when a decision on these points is reached, orders are issued to the Works to manufacture, let us say, 50,000 of the new article.

Drawings of every part of the new product, schedules of the quantities of material required and of the operations involved and their sequence, are prepared. A set of blue prints from the drawings is sent through to the Tool Department for the designing and the making of the tools, with which the components of the new product will be manufactured. This work must be carried out within very fine limits and a high standard is rigidly maintained. The great popularity of Meccano and Hornby Trains is due in no small measure to the precision of the work of our Tool Department.

In its simplest form a press tool consists of a punch and a die, relative in shape, so that when a piece of metal is placed between them and pressure applied a desired form is produced. Typical simple tools of this type are those used for blanking metal shapes from sheets or coils of metal; piercing tools, the function of which is obvious, and forming tools that bend pieces of metal to desired shapes. A press tool can be carried into many stages of complication by the multiplication of the operations it is required to carry out at one stroke of the press. These are known as "compound" tools, and may actually carry out all the processes of blanking, piercing, and forming at one operation, and in addition assemble components at the same time. An instance of a simple set of tools may be cited in those required to emboss a design on metal, say the window framing of a passenger coach. The lower part of the tool, clamped to the bed-plate of the press, has the actual design cut into its surface in reverse. The top tool, fixed to the ram of the press, bears the design in relief, allowances being made in this relief work for the thickness of the metal to be pressed between the two parts of the tool.

The complicated mechanism of the jig-boring machine, referred to in our description of the Tool Department, is excellently revealed in this illustration.

The production of a set of tools is a long job. In the case of the tools for one of our better classes of train sets—a No. 2 Special, for instance—the task may involve several months' work with an ultimate cost running into thousands of pounds. Every individual operation in the production of a train set calls for a specially designed tool, and in this particular instance more than 300 press tools are required.

On receipt of the prints for the new product the tool designer proceeds to lay out the design for the tools. A requisition showing the dimensions and specification of all the material required to make the tools is sent to the Stores, where the required material is prepared. Preparing the steel for issue to the tool-maker may involve cutting perhaps 20 pieces of steel from bars to stated sizes. This is done by a circular cold saw that in three minutes will cut through a bar of mild steel 6 in. in width and 2 in. in thickness. It takes rather longer to cut through the higher grades of steel such as a carbon tool steel, or a chromium alloy steel. Each part of the tool is made from the steel particularly suited to the work it will be called upon to perform. For instance, the base plate of a tool is invariably made from mild steel or cast iron, whereas the die will be of cast or alloy steel.

The first operation after receiving the tool steel in the Tool Department is to machine or grind the pieces on all surfaces. From this point the job is put into the hands of a tool-maker who will be held responsible for the production of this particular tool. He proceeds to outline the shape of the tool on the steel and to do all the preparatory work in readiness for machining the metal to shape. All machine work on the tools is done on special machines, such as turning, jig-boring, grinding, slotting, etc. This machining has to be done with great accuracy, but the degree of precision required will vary according to the particular job. For certain parts of the tool a limit of one-thousandth part of an inch is near enough; for others it may be necessary to work to the extreme fineness of one ten-thousandth part of an inch!

The tool-maker now fits all the parts together, after which they are ready to be heat-treated to give the steel its maximum ability to resist the particular strains and stresses to which it will be subjected in operation. The heat treatment varies considerably, according to the grade of steel used in the tool and the result desired from the treatment. Carbon and alloy steel tools are hardened right through by raising them to a given degree of heat—780°C. for carbon steel, 1,000°C. for alloy steel—in either a gas, electric or salt bath furnace. Immediately the tools are brought from the furnace they are cooled rapidly by immersion in a water or oil bath. The tool is heated a second time to temper the steel to a given degree, the temperature employed in this operation being varied according to the degree of temper required. It is rare for any greater degree of temperature than 300°C. to be required in this process. The tempering process lowers the hardness of the steel to working requirements.

Mild steel cannot be hardened in this way, as the carbon content is too small; but the surface of the metal can be hardened if treated by a process known as "carbonisation." This process varies according to the size of the part and the depth of hardness required. Small parts are submerged in a bath furnace of cyanide with a working temperature of 1,000°C., and then quickly cooled in water. Large parts are packed in metal boxes with a carbonising mixture (bone and charcoal, etc.) and are raised to the required degree of heat in a furnace in which they remain for a time that will vary according to the depth of hardness required, six hours being a normal period to secure hardness to a depth of 1/16th of an inch. The cooling process, known as "quenching," is carried out by immersing the parts in water as in the case of small parts.

This illustration shows one of the larger presses described, a 70-ton double-crank power press, fitted with one of the latest safety devices to safeguard the operator's hands.

After hardening, all cutting parts of the tool are ground. The tool is completely re-assembled and is now ready for the necessary tests that must be carried out before the tools are passed to the Production Departments for use.

While the work of preparing the tools has been going on, the estimating staff have been busy ascertaining the quantities of materials required in the production of the order. These materials must be ordered from the makers and be in the Stores ready for issue to the Production Departments immediately the tools are completed. Another section orders the necessary packing materials and the cartons in which the articles are to be packed.

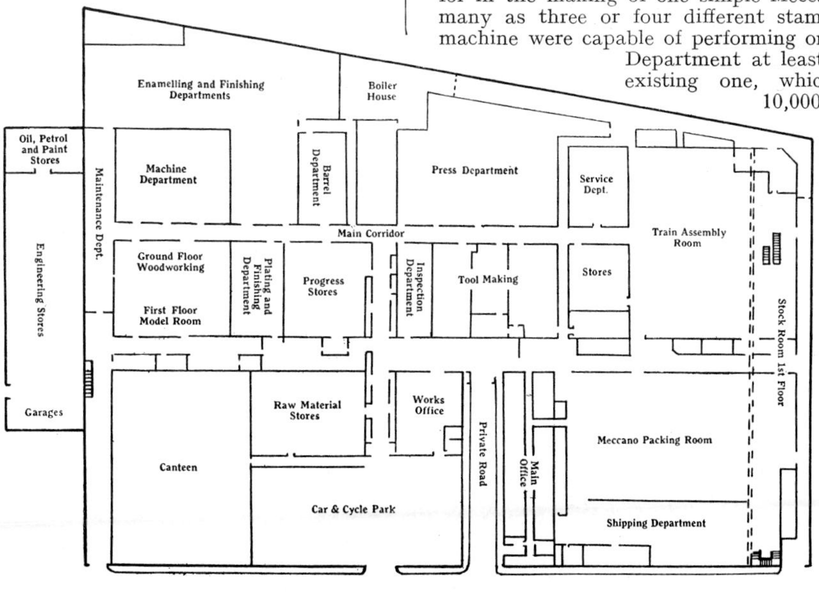

The Raw Material Stores provides the visitor with a vivid impression of the wide range of the activities of the Factory. From 200 to 300 tons of steel, brass and tinplate are maintained as a floating stock. The strip steel used for Meccano parts is stacked in coils weighing approximately ¾ cwt. each, and ranging in width from ½ in. upward, according to the part to be made from them. The ½ in. size is used for 12½ in. Meccano Strips, which are stamped from the strip longitudinally. The sizes from 5½ in. downward are blanked from wider strips, the width of the strip varying according to the length of the part to be stamped from it.

Perhaps the most interesting material is the tin-plate used for Hornby products. This is packed in boxes and varies in thickness or gauge according to the job for which it is intended, the heaviest sheets being those used for the boilers and framings of the No. 2 Special and No. 3 classes of locomotive. The greater part of the material is plain, the colouring and design being applied by spray-painting and transfers, processes that will be described in a later article.

When the tools are completed and the raw material is assembled, the processing passes into the hands of the Progress Department the work of which is to supervise the actual production. How involved this work is may be realised from the fact that there are 560 individual parts in a No. 2 Special Train Set. The production of all the parts required for any particular job must be kept running simultaneously so that they may reach the Progress Department Stores together in readiness for assembly. Any delay in regard to any one part would cause a serious hold-up of the whole product.

The first of the Production Departments is the Press Department, where there is a range of presses. Hand-operated presses carry out the lighter classes of work, while the heavier power-driven machines perform the heavier and more complicated work. An interesting feature is that each machine can be adapted to perform any stamping job within the limits of its capacity, by the insertion of the appropriate tools. This interchangeability is an essential feature, for in the making of one simple Meccano part there may be as many as three or four different stamping operations. If each machine were capable of performing only one operation, a Press Department at least 10 times the size of the existing one, which covers approximately 10,000 sq. ft., would be necessary. Not all the machines in the department are presses; other machines include a number of guillotines used for shearing tinplate sheets to required dimensions in readiness for blanking operations.

As a typical example of the working of the department we may take the making of a Flanged Plate. The blanking, piercing of the equidistant holes, and flanging, involves three operations in three power presses, working at a pressure of from 20 to 30 tons. In the first operation the plates are blanked from a coil of steel, the coil being placed on a coil holder, and its end fed into the machine. The top or blanking tool is shaped like the plate, with its flanges laid flat. This part of the tool is fixed to the ram of the press. The bottom portion or die of the tool is of hardened alloy steel, and has a correspondingly-shaped hole cut out, so that the two parts of the tool fit exactly one into the other. The bottom part of the tool is fixed to the bed-plate

This plan of the Meccano Factory will help readers to follow the progress of a Meccano part in the course of manufacture, as revealed in this and the succeeding articles. The plan is interesting to study in conjunction with the aerial view published in the March "M.M."

(Continued on page 818)

Life Story of Meccano—(*Cont. from page 773*)

of the press. The steel is fed into the machine automatically, the coil travelling at a speed sufficient to feed the exact amount of metal necessary to make one blank during the time in which the ram moves up and down. At each downward stroke the top tool cuts through the coil, blanking out a piece of metal the exact shape of the die.

The second operation is the piercing of the equidistant holes. In this case the press is inclined backward from the vertical and the blank from the first operation is fed into the chute of the tool, to fall by gravity against a location plate that holds it in position while the piercing operation is carried out. The upper portion of the tool used in this case contains a series of punches, and the die has a corresponding series of holes. Immediately above the die is what is known as the "stripping plate," also containing a series of holes through which the punches pass in their journey to the die. As the upper tool makes its downward blow it stamps out the holes, and on its upward stroke it draws the perforated plate clear of the location plate. The perforated plate is stripped from the punches by the stripping plate, and falls vertically into a chute and thence into a receptacle placed behind the machine.

The third operation is the bending of the sides, or flanging of the plates. The type of press and the feeding are precisely as in the second operation. The upper tool coincides in shape and size with the inside form of a finished Flanged Plate, the lower tool corresponds to the outside form of the plate.

The big press shown in the illustration on page 773 is one of the largest in the department and works at a pressure of 70 tons. Among typical operations performed by this machine are the bending of 24½-in. angle girders from flat girder strip; blanking the circular pieces of steel for Hornby turntables, and the combined forming, piercing and blanking of Meccano 3 in. pulley wheel sides in one operation.

A particularly interesting section of the department is the Hornby rail-making plant, which comprises guillotine, quadruple-action presses and rail curving machines. First of all standard sheets of tinplate 20 in. by 28 in. are cut into small sheets of a width equal to the length of the rail to be made. These sheets are passed through a rotary gang slitting guillotine and cut into small strips 19 at a time, which are fed into the rail-making presses at the rate of from 40 to 50 per minute. With a single blow the presses convert the strips of tin into lengths of rail, Vignole's section, after which they are carried away on a continuously-moving belt to the curving machines.

The curving is done on wheels of different diameters according to the radius required. The edge of the wheel is grooved to take one half of the Vignole's section of the rail. At the top of the wheel, and running in contact with it, is a series of small rollers lying alongside one another, each grooved to take the other half of the Vignole's section. The space in the grooving allows the rail to pass through as it travels with the wheel, and it is quickly bent to the curve required. The curved rails as they leave this machine are stacked in bundles in readiness for assembly to the sleepers.

Another interesting press, the Wright high-speed die-ing machine, is used particularly for blanking operations. The making of a 5½″ Strip is a typical job. With a double tool the machine can turn out 200,000 such Strips in a day of 8½ hours—a striking contrast to the output of 12,000 strips from a hand-fed normal speed power press. In operation, a coil of steel is fed into the machine by means of an automatic roll feed, so that the blanks are cut from the coil at even spacing without any waste of material. Before entering the tool the steel is oiled by passing over an oiled felt roller running in an oil bath. At each stroke the machine pierces two strips and blanks out two others.

The Wright machine is used in the production of a wide range of parts, among these being all sizes of strips from 5½ in. downward, spanners, washers and trunnions. Using a multiple tool, as many as 1,000,000 washers can be turned out in a day!

(*To be continued*)

New Torch for Scouts and Hikers

Scouts as well as hikers, will be interested in the new "Hike-lite," an Ediswan torch that projects a beam of light 300 feet. This all-British product, which can be used either as a hand torch or adapted as a reading lamp, incorporates a number of new features including a day-and-night all-point compass fixed at the top of the torch between the bulb and the bevelled plate glass lens. A hinged metal cover protects the lens from breakage, whilst the hinge pin also carries a metal loop for fastening the torch to the belt or fixing inside a car. Fitted inside the cover is a mirror for shaving or general use.

Other features are a focussing adjustment and a 3-way safety switch with "Off," "On" and "Intermittent" positions. Focussing is adjusted by a turning movement of the head. The depression of a stud enables the whole head of the torch case to be removed, thus making the interchangeability of the bulb an easy and simple matter. Each torch is fitted with a spare bulb, protected from breakage by a domed cover fitted inside the bottom cap.

The new torch can be obtained from all leading Stores, and from shops retailing electrical accessories or camping equipment.

Building Your Own Motor Cars!

The New Meccano Constructional Outfit

THE motor car is one of the most fascinating examples of modern mechanical development. The thrill of high-speed travel on road or track is rivalled only by the aeroplane, and the actual design and construction of a motor car provide an almost unlimited store of interest and education. Nowadays there are very few people who are not interested in some way in motor vehicles, and even those who do not actually own cars have a good idea of the principles on which they operate, and are able to pick out the best-known makes by noting their distinctive external features.

It is natural that cars should make a particularly strong appeal to Meccano enthusiasts, and their great popularity among model-builders is shown by the large numbers of cars that are submitted in every possible *"M.M."* building contest. Meccano is splendidly adapted for building the chassis of a model motor vehicle, and the Meccano Chassis, Super Model No. 1, is a good example of the accuracy with which the mechanical features can be reproduced. The chassis does not by any means form a complete vehicle, however, for the bodywork and external features play an important part in the general scheme. Standard Meccano parts have certain limitations when employed for this purpose in model car construction, and for that reason there have been produced the Meccano Motor Car Constructor Outfits. These Outfits enable strikingly realistic models of sports and speed cars to be built—each one a masterpiece of design and workmanship.

Fig. 1. A striking example of a light sports two-seater built with the Meccano Motor Car Constructor. The bodywork, wings, wheels and seat are finished in brilliant coloured enamel, while the radiator, lamps, bumper, brake lever, and other parts are chromium-plated.

In the Motor Car Constructor Outfits the interchangeability of standard Meccano parts has been retained, with the result that the builder can vary his designs according to his own ideas. The individuality of the models thus made possible is further increased by the introduction of three distinctive colour schemes for the bodywork of the models, so that the model motor builder may obtain an Outfit with which to build cars in the colours that attract him most.

In the first of these colour schemes the bodywork of the car is in green enamel, the mudguards and running boards are in cream enamel, and the seat is in bright red "crackle" lacquer that gives it a very leather-like appearance. The second colour combination has the bodywork of the car in brilliant red, the wings cream, and the seat section in blue; and in the third scheme the body is enamelled blue, the wings are cream, and the seat section has a red finish. To add to the smart effect of these colour schemes, the radiator, bumper bar, lamp rings and brake lever are all chromium-plated, and the realistic disc wheels and the honeycomb portions of the radiators are coloured red. The appearance of a Meccano car built in any of these colour schemes is extremely smart and the completed model is remarkably like the real thing!

We must now leave the external appearance of the cars to deal with some of the outstanding mechanical details. Ackermann-type steering gear is provided for the front wheels, with worm and nut actuating mechanism, and there is a strongly built clockwork motor drive for the rear wheels. The steering gear has been carefully designed to enable an extremely delicate adjustment of the front wheels to be made by rotating the steering wheel placed in the dash. The front wheels are mounted on stub axles pivoted to the sides of the chassis frame of the model. The stub axles are provided with extension arms connected together by means of a track rod, which in turn is coupled to a bell crank with a nut block attached to this crank. The end of the steering column is threaded so that it may work inside the threaded hole in the nut block, and thus there is obtained in the Meccano car a very close copy of the worm and nut gear that is used on many actual cars.

When the steering wheel is rotated the threaded end of the steering column draws the nut block up or down, and consequently the bell crank to which the nut block is attached is actuated. The bell crank carries a pin that engages with a slot in the centre portion of the track rod, and movement of this pin causes the track rod to be moved to one side or the other. As the track rod is coupled to the stub axles on which the front wheels are mounted, any movement of it will cause the road wheels to be swivelled, so that the model can be made to travel in either a right-hand or a left-hand direction. The accuracy with which this ingenious gear operates will be found particularly useful when it is required to set the model travelling on a curved course. By rotating the steering wheel it is possible to direct the car so that it will pass round various obstacles.

A specially designed clockwork power unit is provided for the Meccano car models, the clockwork mechanism being produced on similar lines to the famous mechanisms that have contributed so largely to the world-wide success of Hornby Trains. This motor, however, has been designed with special regard to the particular requirements of a model racing car, and it incorporates a spring that gives a remarkably powerful drive at high speed, together with an exceptionally long run. When fully wound the motor drives the car for a distance of 150 ft. at a scale speed of approximately 100 m.p.h.!

Another interesting mechanical feature is the brake mechanism. This is of the internal expanding type, and is controlled by means of a brake lever mounted on the outside of the body at the right-hand side of the dash. The mechanism of the brake is particularly ingenious, and it provides an effective braking action on the clockwork motor while the latter is being wound up, and when the car is required to be kept at rest on the ground.

The brake gear consists of a drum having a split rim and a special tapered cam that is pivotally connected to the brake

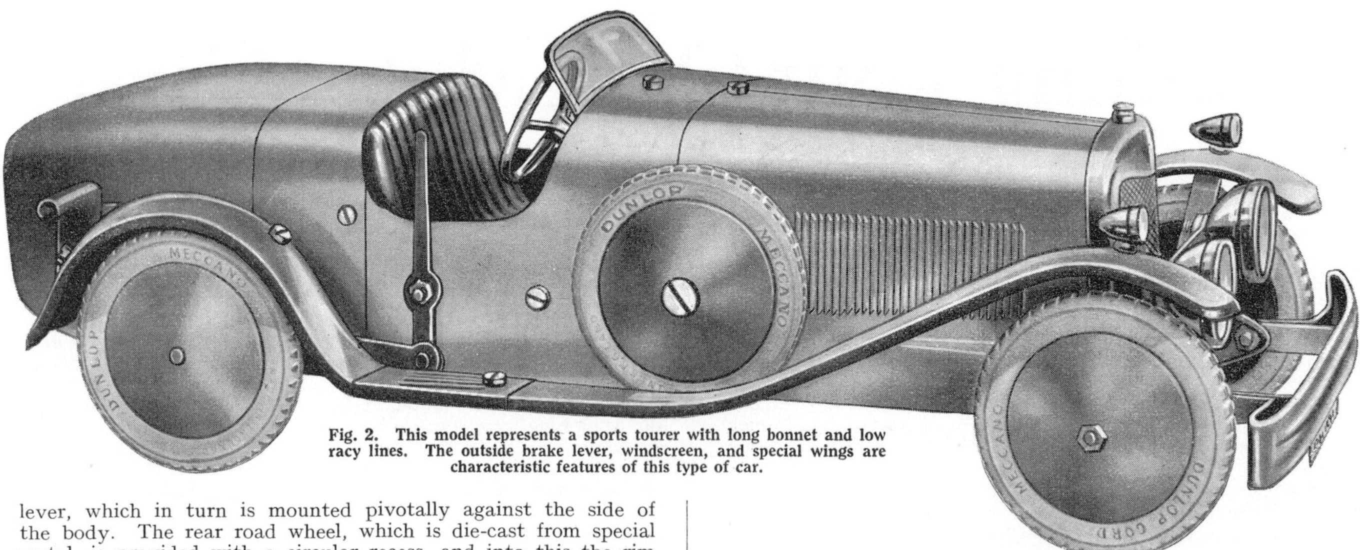

Fig. 2. This model represents a sports tourer with long bonnet and low racy lines. The outside brake lever, windscreen, and special wings are characteristic features of this type of car.

lever, which in turn is mounted pivotally against the side of the body. The rear road wheel, which is die-cast from special metal, is provided with a circular recess, and into this the rim of the brake drum fits. The tapered actuating cam is pushed into position between the split rim of the drum, and the control lever is arranged so that when in the forward position the brake is "off." To apply the brake the lever is drawn back, and the tapered cam then comes into action and forces the split rim of the brake drum outward. The rim then makes contact with the circular recess in the rear wheel and the friction results in a powerful braking action.

The addition of correct-type steering and braking mechanisms enables a series of interesting operations to be carried out when preparing the model "for the road." The brake lever is first of all drawn back so that the brake is applied fully. The clockwork motor is now wound up by means of the key provided, and the complete car is placed on the ground. If the car is desired to travel forward in a straight line, the steering wheel is rotated so that the front wheels are exactly in line with the rear pair; while movement of the wheel to either the right or the left will result in the car describing a curved path in its run. After the steering has been adjusted the brake lever is moved into the forward position, thus releasing the rear wheels, and the car will then move off gradually, gathering speed until it is "flat out"! The car will travel at speed for the full 150 ft. The best results as regards speed and length of run are obtained when the model is run on a concrete, tar macadam, or other surface that is both smooth and hard.

Turning once again to the external fittings and features of the cars, it will be noticed that two distinct types of radiators are included. These are interchangeable, so that either may be fitted to the model as required. The radiator fitted to the car shown in Fig. 1 is of graceful modern design. It has curved sides, and a "centre line," which is an outstanding feature in the design of actual modern radiators. The radiator incorporated in the car shown in Fig. 2, on the other hand, has parallel sides, and the general sturdy lines of the powerful British speed car that the model represents. Two types of rear body section are also supplied, one being of the rounded pattern as shown in Fig. 2, and the other of graceful streamline tapered type, Fig. 3. The wheelbase and overall length of the car can be altered as required. The car shown in Fig. 1 is a short wheelbase type, while the models illustrated in Figs. 2 and 3 have long wheelbases.

Another very interesting variation in the arrangement of the Constructor parts is in building a light six-cylinder speed machine. Modern racing cars are classified in accordance with the total cubic centimetre capacity of the cylinders of the engine. The "baby" M.G. Midget thus comes in the 750 c.c. class, which means that its engine has a total cylinder capacity of 750 cubic centimetres. Many light racing machines, however, have engines with capacities between 1,000 and 1,500 c.c.

Popular British cars in the "light racer" class are the Riley, Fraser-Nash and the Aston-Martin. Among the famous French cars of this type are the Amilcar, Salmson, and Buggatti, while numerous light racing cars are manufactured by Italian, German, and other Continental concerns.

It is possible to build a very realistic model of this kind with the Meccano Motor Car Constructor Outfit. Unfortunately it has not been possible to include an illustration of this model here, but it may be said that the model incorporates many of the features of a real light racing machine and is of the short wheelbase type.

Full constructional details for building each of the fine models mentioned in this article are contained in a new Instruction Manual included in each Motor Car Constructor Outfit. The constructional details are made clear by means of numerous illustrations, so that no difficulty should be experienced in reproducing any of the models described.

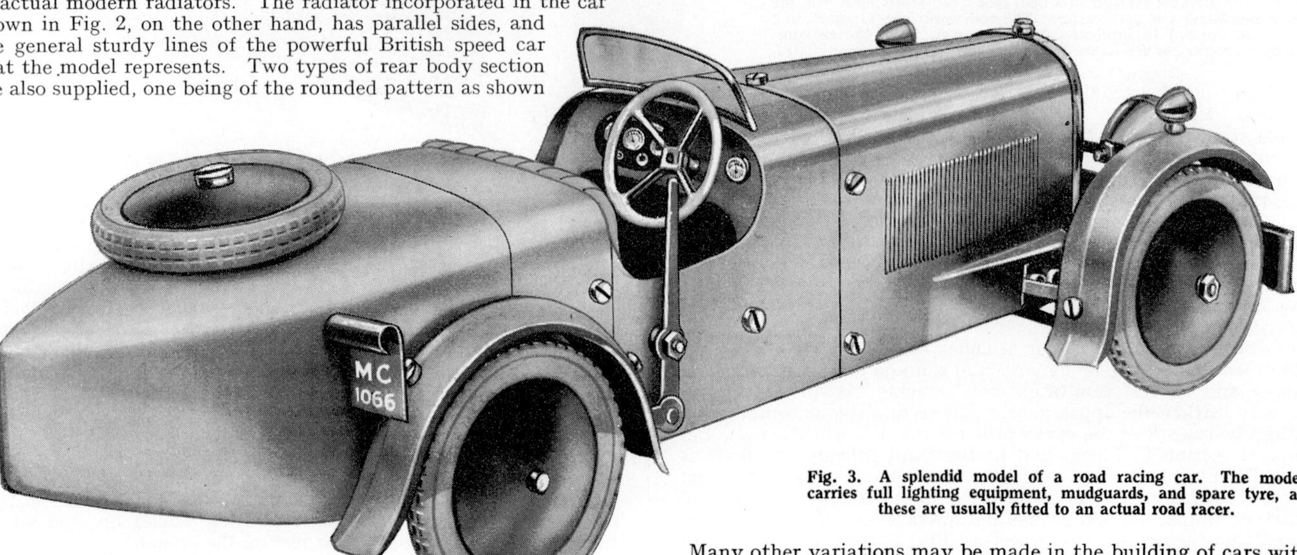

Fig. 3. A splendid model of a road racing car. The model carries full lighting equipment, mudguards, and spare tyre, as these are usually fitted to an actual road racer.

Many other variations may be made in the building of cars with the Outfit, and the model motor engineer may thus design cars to his individual ideas.

A New British Sports Car

A new British sports car capable of very high speeds has made its appearance. It is a supercharged $1\frac{1}{2}$-litre model designed by the Squire Manufacturing Co. Ltd., of Henley-on-Thames, and is not streamlined. It is built very low and is not intended primarily for racing or for maintaining high speeds in competition work, but as a touring car for the driver who likes to have plenty of power in reserve, and to be able to corner with speed and precision. In accordance with what is now almost standard practice for speed cars, a pre-selector gear box is provided to enable gear changes to be made with the minimum of fatigue so that full advantage can be taken of the gear provided, and the car also has a hydraulic braking system. The wheels are set wide apart to increase the stability when cornering at speed.

Speed Roads for Fast Motor Travel

In view of the high speeds of which modern cars are capable I often wonder how long it will be before we have roads devoted solely to their use. Special roads known as "autostradu," have been built for this purpose on the Continent. They are provided with perfect surfaces and on them there are long stretches without crossings, while curves are banked as on racing tracks in order that high speeds can be maintained without risk. The construction of roads of this kind would help to reduce the alarming number of road accidents that occur daily on our roads, and a charge made for their use would help to meet the cost of making them.

When motor roads are available, motorists will be able to take full advantage of the high speeds of which modern cars are capable, and those to whom speed does not appeal or who have no reason for travelling quickly will still be able to make use of ordinary roads. Even more speedy cars will be produced and it is interesting to see how modern design is approaching the problem of providing them. Streamlining of course is prominent in these endeavours and many remarkable cars in which attention is given to this have already made their appearance. One of the most notable was the car designed by Sir Dennison Burney, a further innovation in which was the removal of the engine to the rear, the driver and his passengers sitting well in front of the rear axle. This plan is favourable to the production of a car of the "tear drop" or "pear" shape that would give very efficient streamlining and this would be the more effective in that the front wheels could be completely covered in.

A British Production Streamlined Car

The Chrysler "Airflow," which was illustrated and described in our issue for May last, was the first car to make any really revolutionary change in external appearance for many years, and its appearance has been followed by that of others, including the Singer "Airstream," claimed to be the first British production car with a streamlined body. This car is similar in outline to the Chrysler machine, having a curved front and being rather wider than normal. In spite of its unusual form, it provides spacious accommodation for four passengers. It has fluid flywheel transmission and independent springing for all four wheels.

As might be expected, experiments in streamlining have led to the design of "freak" cars, and several remarkable examples were to be seen at the Paris Motor Show held in the first week of October. Some of the streamlined bodies on view there were built so low that there was very little room for windows, and these cars promise to be death traps in the event of accident. Others were remarkable for their immense tails. The worst offender was a long two-door saloon, the tail of which is seven ft. behind the back axle, and the tapering rear section of another car on view consisted of about 20 sq. ft. of steel panelling that has to be lifted every time the petrol tank requires to be filled.

The Paris Show illustrated the general tendency to instal pre-selector and semi-automatic gear boxes. The Citroën front wheel model was a great attraction, and it is very gratifying to read of the excellent impression made by such British cars as the Rolls-Royce, the Bentley sports saloon and coupé, the Humber "Pullman" and various open two-seaters made by the Hillman and M.G. companies.

An M.G. Magnette photographed while taking part in the Italian Mille Miglia "round the houses" race. Photograph by courtesy of the M.G. Car Co. Ltd.

Exhibits at the British Motor Show at Olympia showed the same general tendencies as those at the Paris Show, but there was no exaggerated streamlining. A brief note on the general trend of design as exhibited at the Show is given in the Editorial page.

The World's Speed King

Although in recent years Great Britain has lost some of her cherished speed records, Sir Malcolm Campbell still holds the land speed record of 272.46 m.p.h., achieved in runs over a measured mile on Daytona Beach, Florida, in his famous car *"Bluebird."* This car has a Rolls-Royce engine, and it is interesting to learn that Sir Malcolm owns several Rolls-Royce cars, with one of which he is shown in the upper illustration on the next page.

Sir Malcolm has undoubtedly had the longest racing experience of any living British driver. He first took up the sport with a motor cycle and rapidly graduated to motor cars. For many years he has taken part in races on the Brooklands track and elsewhere, but has won most renown by his numerous attacks on the land speed records, made in this country, South Africa and the United States. It is well known that one of his most cherished ambitions is to be the first man to exceed a speed of 300 m.p.h. in a motor car. If he does decide to attempt this feat, it is almost certain that he will do so in the *"Bluebird."*

This Year's Racing Successes

The feature of this year's motor racing season on the Continent has been the success of the Mercédès, the German car that was prominent in earlier years of racing but has not achieved many striking successes in recent years. The revival of this famous car was marked by success in the French Grand Prix, and since then it has won practically every big Continental prize. It is not new for a single make of car to assert its supremacy throughout a racing season. The Alfa-Romeo did this last year, and previously Bentley cars won the Le Mans 24-hour race four years in succession. A new British racing car has been developed in the "E.R.A.," and it is to be hoped that next year this will prove a serious competitor to the Continental makes. I hope to publish photographs and a full description of this interesting car in an early issue of the Magazine.

Sir Malcolm Campbell, the world's most famous and successful racing motorist, with one of his Rolls-Royce cars at Brooklands. Photograph by courtesy of Rolls-Royce Ltd.

An interesting racing car also has been produced by the Triumph Company and although they do not intend to enter into a racing campaign next season, it is possible that the car then may be used for racing purposes by private owners. At present it will be sold as an ultra-performance two-seater and every one put on the market will be guaranteed to have covered a flying mile at a speed of more than 100 m.p.h. The "Dolomite," as the car is known, has a 17.85 h.p. engine that has eight cylinders, and a Wilson pre-selective and self-changing gear box is fitted.

Thrills at Brooklands

There were some very interesting and thrilling incidents at Brooklands during the 500-mile race of the British Racing Drivers' Club. It rained practically throughout the night before the race, and also during the greater part of the event itself, and the cars flashing round the track sent up such streams of spray that they might easily have been mistaken for motor boats! Great interest was taken in the event because of the large number of entrants capable of really high speeds, for this made passing difficult and sometimes dangerous, since at Brooklands cars travelling at speeds of more than 100 m.p.h. have to use the top of the track, which limits the available width as far as they are concerned to not more than 20 ft. The poor visibility and treacherous surface added to the troubles of drivers.

Anxious moments for the passengers! Acrobatics during a side car race at a grass track meeting. This interesting photograph was taken by one of our readers, W. M. Hunter, of London.

For some time before the event the favourite was J. Cobb's Napier Railton which is able to maintain an average speed of 120 m.p.h. round the track. G. Eyston's Magnette and Dixon's Riley also have lapped Brooklands at about 120 m.p.h. Of these three famous race drivers the only one to secure a place was Dixon who, in spite of being badly stung by a wasp just before the start, won at a speed of 104.8 m.p.h. A. W. K. Von der Becke and E. McClure were second in another Riley at a speed of 101.65 m.p.h. and J. D. Benjafield and A. T. G. Gardner third in an M.G. Magnette. Out of 32 starters only seven finished the race.

The Shelsley Walsh Hill Climb

A hill climbing contest almost invariably provides great excitement for the spectators, who are thrilled by the roars of the exhausts of giant cars as they race up the steep gradients of the chosen hill and make spectacular turns at the sharp corners and tortuous bends usually included. The Shelsley Walsh Autumn meeting organised by the Midland Automobile Club is no exception, for the course is 1,000 yds. in length and is marked by numerous sharp bends and an "S" curve.

This year the stiff climb was made more difficult by rain, for the course was water-logged. The presence of the two-litre E.R.A. already mentioned was a great attraction. With Raymond Mays at the wheel this car made the fastest climb of the day, the time being 44 secs., the next best being the 44 1/5 secs. accomplished by Whitney Straight in a Maserati.

What might have been a serious accident occurred to W. E. Harker, who was accelerating up the hill and approaching the "S"-bend when his throttle jammed open and the car charged the bank at full speed. Fortunately the driver was not badly hurt.

The E.R.A. also did well at the Donnington meeting early in October. The two-litre model successful at Shelsley Walsh was not present, but a smaller model driven by Raymond Mays won the 100-mile race for the Nuffield Trophy, at an average speed of 61.5 m.p.h. R. J. G. Seaman in an M.G. Magnette entered by Whitney Straight, was second at a speed of 59.02 m.p.h. while the third place was gained by M. B. Evans, also in an M.G. Magnette, who completed the course at an average speed of 57.06 m.p.h. The fourth place was gained by Earl Howe in a Delage.

Thrills were not absent at Donnington. In one of the earlier events two drivers touched wheels when they were fighting for a corner at high speed. One of the cars spun round and, going backwards, went right through the fence on one side of the course, while the other overturned.

By P. A. Tent

Inventive Genius in Great Britain

In proportion to population Great Britain has more inventors than any other country in the world, and the varied character of their activities was revealed at the great Exhibition of Inventions held in October by the Institute of Patentees. When opening the Exhibition Lord Askwith, President of the Institute, remarked that inventive genius in this country has not been slow in spite of the depression, and pointed out that during the six months ending 30th June, no fewer than 19,403 applications were made for patents, an increase of about 1,000 in comparison with the previous six months. This is an encouraging contrast to the position in the United States, where the number of applications for patents in the past year was 3,000 less than in the preceding twelve months.

At previous Exhibitions Lord Askwith commented on the fact that the occupation of an inventor does not necessarily have any bearing on the products of his inventive genius. This year's exhibits have again demonstrated this, for they include a miniature greyhound racing track invented by a motor frame worker, an alarm clock produced by a medical specialist and a weather-proof deck chair contrived by a film actress.

Other inventions to be seen at the Exhibition include mechanical means of cleaning windows that are awkward to reach; a device for cutting off the top of a boiled egg that only penetrates the shell and does not break up the yolk; a piano that plays colours instead of music, producing more than 1,000 different shades in any variation desired and giving continually changing colour effects that are said to be as beautiful and attractive in their own way as great music; and a door for poultry houses or similar buildings that automatically closes at dusk and opens in the morning. These and many other novel devices show that our inventors are hard at work and display ingenuity and originality in their ideas. I hope later to be able to give further details of the more attractive inventions on view, and congratulate the Institute of Patentees on the success of this year's Exhibition and on the magnificent work it is doing in encouraging those engaged in invention.

A device for painting white lines on roads with the aid of "Orolo" creeper track. It was designed by M. Capiomont, a French engineer, and our photograph is reproduced by courtesy of H. C. Slingsby, Paris.

Novel Use for Creeper Track

Since their introduction, creeper tracks have been applied to many remarkable purposes, and the upper illustration on this page shows another simple application that has been invented by M. E. Capiomont, a French engineer. This is the "Securitus" apparatus in which the "Orolo" track units of Roadless Traction Limited are employed for painting white lines on roads. The necessary paint is delivered from a container to the creeper track and this makes good contact with the surface as the apparatus is wheeled along the road. The marks produced are as good an indication to motorists and other road users as a continuous white line would be, and can be laid down with little effort and with a great saving of time. Economy also is claimed in the quantity of paint required.

Egg Cleaning by Electricity

The second illustration on this page is an interesting reminder of the increasing extent to which machinery is now used in connection with agriculture, and of the widespread application of electricity. It shows an electric egg cleaner through which the eggs pass automatically to be brushed with hot water and finally dried. An electric motor drives the long brushes employed for cleaning the eggs and the temperature of the water in the cylindrical chamber through which these pass is raised to any desired degree by means of an electric immersion heater fitted with an independent switch. The eggs are fed in through an aperture at one end of the machine and are dry when they emerge on a wire tray at the opposite end. The machine is capable of dealing with 3,000 eggs per hour and these can be packed immediately they are delivered on the collecting tray, which is specially designed to facilitate their packing in boxes. The machine is simple to use and easily controlled, and occupies little space.

The "Summit" electric egg cleaner, in which 3,000 eggs can be washed and brushed in an hour. Photograph by courtesy of Cope and Cope Ltd., Reading.

A Motor Car Testing Laboratory on Wheels

The efficiency of modern motor vehicles depends very largely on the care that is taken to provide them with the lubricants and petrol best suited to them. Petrol companies carry out experiments to decide the grade of oil and the type of fuel that is best suited to any particular make of car, and the illustration on this page shows a device that has been introduced by the Associated Oil Company, California, to enable accurate road tests to be carried out quickly and easily.

The device is set up in the rear of the car under test, the instruments and tanks for oil and fuel being mounted on an iron stand that is bolted to the floorboards. Each of the six tanks holds one and a half gallons, and petrol from any tank can be fed to the carburetter of the engine directly, or through a glass measuring vessel that contains one tenth of a gallon and is used when the consumption of fuel is being tested. The distance travelled during a trial is registered by a speedometer that is graduated to show when a thousandth of a mile has been covered, and thus the mileage obtained with any fuel can be measured with extreme accuracy.

A motor car testing laboratory that can be installed in a few hours in any make of car in order to find the best grades of oil and petrol in various climatic conditions. We are indebted to the Associated Oil Company, California, for permission to reproduce this photograph.

A car fitted with the device is literally a laboratory on wheels. In practice it is run in various conditions, ranging from high altitudes in the Californian Mountains to the heat of Death Valley, and gauges measure the temperatures of important parts of the engine and chassis. The information obtained in this manner enables the company to recommend the grades of oil and petrol to be used by the motorist on the Pacific Coast, whatever conditions of climate he may encounter, or to provide him with suitable grades if these are not already available.

Ingenious Building Devices

Among the many interesting new things to be seen at the International Building Trades Exhibition held at Olympia during September, one that seemed to me to mark a great advance was the "Turnall" building slab, manufactured by Turners Asbestos Cement Company of Manchester. This is a new building material of asbestos cement and is intended for use in the construction of flat or low pitched roofs. Slates, tiles, corrugated iron and similar materials used for roofing purposes are coverings only, placed on a structure of beams or girders that give them the necessary support. The "Turnall" slab itself is capable of carrying part of the roof load, however, for it consists of top and bottom sheets with corrugations connecting them. Thus it is virtually a continuous Warren girder, as is seen in the accompanying illustration showing a roof being constructed from slabs of this kind, and is so strong that a single slab supported on boards 5 ft. 6 in. apart can sustain a weight of more than half a ton placed in its centre. It is made in one piece and its total thickness is 2 in., the standard length and width being 6 ft. and 2 ft. 6 in. respectively. Slabs of this size can readily be handled by two men, and their use reduces the number of roof supports required.

Laying asbestos cement roofing slabs that are built like girders. Photograph by courtesy of Turners Asbestos Cement Co., Manchester.

Another interesting new material exhibited by this company was asbestos reinforced aluminium foil. This consists of asbestos paper on each side of which a thin sheet of aluminium foil is inseparably attached by means of a bitumen adhesive. The bitumen makes the sheet proof against damp and vermin, but the greatest value of the device is in maintaining an even temperature in buildings in which it is used. As most of my readers know, a bright metallic surface does not absorb heat readily and also is a poor radiator. A wall in which sheets of this kind are incorporated therefore acts as a heat insulator, retaining internal heat in cold weather, and keeping out external heat when the temperature outside is high. It is intended to be fitted behind the internal linings of walls with an air gap on each side of it, the low heat conductivity of air then adding to its effectiveness.

Aluminium is used in this interesting heat insulator because it is easily rolled into the thin sheets required and does not tarnish, and tests have proved the high efficiency of the combination of this metal with asbestos.

Lamp in Policeman's Truncheon

An interesting invention by a sergeant of the Metropolitan Police is a truncheon that incorporates a lamp. The truncheon is of the standard type and at one end is bored out in order to accommodate a battery and lamp. There is a switch on the handle, where it can be manipulated easily, and a spare bulb is carried in the other end of the truncheon. The entire lamp can be dismantled and removed quickly on unscrewing the lens.

The invention is not intended to replace the standard lamp carried by policemen, but to supplement it, and it has the advantage that a constable entering a dark building can have his truncheon ready in one hand and can use it as a lamp while having the other hand free to open doors or for any other purpose.

The inventor of this truncheon has previously distinguished himself by the production of interesting devices of various kinds, including a sand sprinkler for lorries and motor cars, that helps to prevent skids in wet weather, and a combined front and rear light designed for use on bicycles.

Machines Used by Imperial Airways

Huge Air Liners combine Speed with Luxury

IN the early days of civil aviation the saving in time that could be made by means of an aeroplane was considered sufficient in itself to induce travellers to go by air. Little attention was paid to the comfort of passengers, and in cold weather it was often necessary for them to be wrapped up almost as much as if they were in the cockpit of an open machine. It was soon realised, however, that if the aeroplane were to become really popular it was necessary for air travel to be made as comfortable as any of the ordinary methods of surface transport. From that time steady progress towards comfort has been made, and in these days air liners are quite as pleasant to travel in as the first-class coaches of railway trains. The idea of comfort has been extended also to private flying, and practically all the light aeroplanes that are now produced are of the cabin type, or are provided with special covers that can be put over the cockpits to protect the occupants.

The most luxurious machines built in this country are undoubtedly those that have been designed for operation on the services of Imperial Airways. These types include the Armstrong Whitworth "Argosy" and "Atalanta," the Handley-Page "Heracles," and "Hannibal," and the Short "Scipio" and "Scylla"; and in this article we intend to give brief details of these machines, paying particular attention to the arrangements that have been made for the comfort of passengers.

An Armstrong Whitworth "Atalanta" of Imperial Airways in flight above the clouds. Our photograph is reproduced by courtesy of "The Aeroplane."

The oldest of the air liners used by Imperial Airways is the Armstrong Whitworth "Argosy," which has seen much service in all parts of the world. It is a biplane of the triple-engined type with a wing span of 90 ft. 4 in., and a length of 67 ft. It has a maximum speed of 110 m.p.h., and is capable of flying for a period of $5\frac{1}{2}$ hours at a cruising speed of 95 m.p.h. The standard "Argosy" carries 20 passengers, 10 seated on each side of a gangway that runs down the centre of the cabin; and although this machine was produced some years ago the passengers are accommodated very comfortably. The cabin is heated and lighted by electricity, and there is an efficient system of ventilation. The machine is used on the cross-Channel services of Imperial Airways, and for many years has been employed on the "Silver Wing" service.

The latest Armstrong Whitworth liner, the "Atalanta," has accommodation for only 17 passengers, but the appointments in the cabin are more luxurious than are those in the earlier type. A special feature is that every passenger is able to control the condition of the air in his immediate vicinity, fresh air being led from an orifice in the nose of the machine to outlets over each passenger's seat. The amount of air coming through these outlets can be regulated by the individual passenger, who is able also to arrange for it to be heated if he desires. The stale air is sucked away through a port at the rear of the cabin. The big glass windows of the cabin are arranged so that in the event of an accident they could easily be knocked out, and in addition there are two emergency exits.

The "Atalanta" is a high-wing monoplane with a wing span of 90 ft. and a length of 71 ft. 6 in. It is the first and only monoplane of such size to be used by Imperial Airways, and has four 340 h.p. Armstrong Siddeley "Serval" radial air-cooled engines. These give the machine a maximum speed of 156 m.p.h. and a cruising speed of 125 m.p.h., the normal range being 400 miles.

The latest version of the "Atalanta" provides seating accommodation for 20 passengers in addition to a full load of freight and mail. Four Armstrong Siddeley "Jaguar" engines, each developing 400 h.p., are substituted for the "Servals," and the machine has a maximum speed of 165 m.p.h. and is able to cruise for 400 miles at a speed of 135 m.p.h.

Imperial Airways possess six machines of the "Atalanta" type, which they use on the South Africa and India and Eastern services. Two other "Atalantas" are owned by Indian Trans-Continental Airways, an associated company of Imperial Airways.

The "Heracles" and "Hannibal" types, which are also comparatively new are the biggest aeroplanes used by Imperial Airways. The two types are identical in external appearance, being biplanes with four engines, two arranged on the lower wing and two on the upper. The "Heracles," of which there are three in existence, is used on Imperial Airways European services, while the "Hannibal" type, of which there are five, was built for the Africa and India services. The European type has accommodation for 38 passengers in two cabins, while that intended for service in the East carries only 24 passengers, owing to the fact that more room is necessary for comfort in tropical countries.

In the design of the "Heracles" and "Hannibal" types close attention has been paid to the provision of comfortable accommodation for passengers. The position of the fuselage is in itself evidence of the care and thought that has been expended in this direction, for it is situated below the planes in order to reduce engine noise in the cabin. Placing the cabin in this position also provides passengers with an uninterrupted view downward and outward, and alleviates the tendency to air-sickness of those who have not become accustomed to travelling by air. Another device that helps to reduce the noise in the saloons is the provision of a rapid metal cover that eliminates noise due to the flapping of fabric. The space between the cover and the interior decorations also is padded with sound-insulated material, and the floor is covered with carpet.

The saloons are normally warmed by hot air drawn from an engine exhaust muff, and in order to prevent the entrance of oily vapours with it the air supply is taken from a point in the leading edge of the upper plane. Before reaching the saloon it passes through a regulator in which cold air can be added in order to attain any desired temperature. The control for this is placed in the corridor between the saloon and the buffet.

The efficiency of the ventilation is also a feature of the machines. Fresh air taken from the outside of the centre slip-stream is led by pipes to the tubular members of the light luggage racks in the cabins, and diffused from these into the saloon through slots. When necessary this air can be warmed by introducing into it a part of the supply of hot air. A special regulating valve for this purpose is placed near the main hot air valve and local control is provided by means of valves fitted alongside the seats. An independent supply of fresh air is obtained from large adjustable intakes situated aft of the pilot's cabin and this is led through semi-circular ducts arranged in the roof of each one of the saloons.

Machines of the "Heracles" and "Hannibal" types weigh 13.4 tons when fully loaded and are capable of flying at a speed of 130 m.p.h. The upper plane of each type of machine has a span of 130 ft. and a chord of 16 ft. 6 in., and the span of the lower plane is 94 ft. and it has a chord of 11 ft. 6 in. The overall length is 86 ft. 6 in. and the height with tail down is 25 ft. The wheel track is 28 ft. 2 in. in width. The "Hannibals" make use of four Bristol "Jupiter" XF MB type engines, each of which develops 555 h.p., while machines of the "Heracles" type use "Jupiters" of the XI F type.

Various flying boats have been used by Imperial Airways from time to time, but the standard machine now is the Short "Scipio," originally known as the Short "Kent." This machine is a biplane, and s fitted with four engines carried in nacelles slung between the wings. It is 113 ft. in span and 78 ft. 5 in. in length, and when fully loaded it weighs 14.3 tons and has a speed of 135 m.p.h. It has been developed from the "Calcutta" but is considerably larger, the span of the upper wing of the "Calcutta" being approximately the same as that of the lower one of the "Scipio." A feature of the new machine is that the planing bottom of the hull is planked with stainless steel up to a little above the water line.

The flying boat has accommodation for 16 passengers, carried in a cabin fitted up as luxuriously as those of the landplane liners. It has large windows, sound insulation, good ventilation and lighting and heating, together with adequate provision of washing facilities. The general internal arrangements of the machine can be seen in the lower illustration on this page.

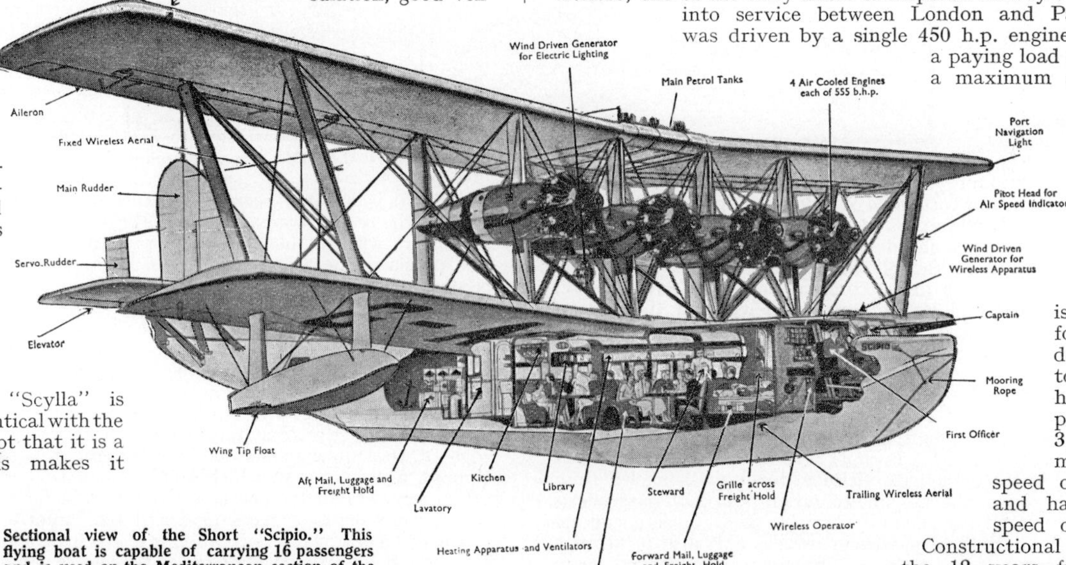

Sectional view of the Short "Scipio." This flying boat is capable of carrying 16 passengers and is used on the Mediterranean section of the Empire air services.

The Short "Scylla" is practically identical with the "Scipio," except that it is a landplane. This makes it lighter, and therefore it has accommodation for 39 passengers. An unusual feature of the layout of the new type is the large proportion of the fuselage space that is occupied by the cabins. In the extreme nose is the pilots' cockpit with accommodation for the Captain, First Officer and, on long journeys, the Wireless Operator. When the machine is serving on the London to Paris route, the Captain or First Officer operates the radio set. Immediately aft of the cockpit is the forward cabin, which has seating accommodation for 10 passengers. The seats are arranged facing each other, six on one side and four on the other, and there are large tables between the seats, with a gangway down the middle.

Aft of this cabin is a large compartment with a baggage hold on the starboard side. On the port side is the kitchen, which is provided with every facility for serving meals. The equipment includes ice chests, fruit racks, wine cases, sink, cupboards, and so on, and there is plenty of room for two stewards to prepare meals simultaneously.

This compartment is followed by the middle cabin, arranged in a similar manner to the forward one and seating 10 passengers, while the aft cabin seats 19 passengers. Access to all cabins is gained by a door on the port side, and there is a small lobby at the entrance that prevents undue crowding of passengers as they enter the aft saloon or pass from one cabin to another.

A sectional drawing of one of the two Short "Scylla" aeroplanes used on the cross-Channel services of Imperial Airways Ltd. The illustrations on this page are published by courtesy of Imperial Airways Ltd.

The windows in the cabins are exceptionally large and allow a clear view from every seat; and in dull weather extra lighting is provided by dome lights in the roof. There are electric lamps over each table, and above the windows are racks for light parcels. The cabins are 11 ft. 9 in. in width, and the first impression on entering any of them is of their spaciousness. They are all scientifically heated and ventilated, and each passenger can control the amount of hot and cold air passing round him.

The most recent British air liner to be produced is the four-engined De Havilland "Diana." This is not yet used by Imperial Airways Ltd. but has been produced for Qantas Empire Airways, an associated company, for use on the Malaya–Australia extension of the eastern Empire route, which is to be inaugurated next month.

It is interesting to compare this luxurious new liner with the D.H.18, one of the early liners of Imperial Airways. This was put into service between London and Paris in 1922, was driven by a single 450 h.p. engine, and carried a paying load of 1,100 lb. at a maximum speed of 115 m.p.h. and a cruising speed of 95 m.p.h. In contrast to this, the modern "Diana" type of machine is driven by four engines developing a total of 800 h.p., carries a pay load of 3,147 lb. at a maximum speed of 170 m.p.h. and has a cruising speed of 145 m.p.h.

Constructional progress in the 12 years from 1922 to 1934 is demonstrated by the fact that whereas the D.H.18, built to carry six passengers and a crew of two, weighed 7,200 lb., a machine of the "Diana" class, designed to carry 10 passengers and a crew of two, weighs no more than 6,350 lb. even when incorporating all the factors of structural security that are an essential factor of British air design. We hope to publish a fully illustrated article on this interesting machine in an early issue.

Six-Engined "Sentinel" Locomotives

Interesting Order for Columbia Railways

THREE locomotives that embody a number of exceptionally novel features and drastic departures from usual design, have been built recently at the Shrewsbury Works of Sentinel Waggon Works Ltd., to the order of the Société Nationale de Chemins de Fer en Colombie, South America. They are intended for heavy haulage work on a railway with steep gradients and curves of small radius, and, we understand, are to be the prototype of a range of similar locomotives on two, three and four axles.

In the particular locomotives about to be described a six-axle arrangement was adopted because the Colombian railways are built with light-gauge rails, so that axle loadings must be kept as low as possible; and also because the severe gradients require that the locomotives shall be able to exert a high tractive effort. There are no coupled wheels or visible cylinders and valve gear, and the chimney appears to rise from the very centre of the boiler.

One of the six-engined "Sentinel" locomotives built for the Société Nationale de Chemins de Fer en Colombie. Photographs on this and the opposite page by courtesy of Sentinel Waggon Works Ltd., Shrewsbury.

The main frame that carries the boiler, tanks, bunker, cab, etc., is mounted on two six-wheeled bogies by means of hemispherical pivot bearings and plain side bearings. The outer axles of the two bogies are mounted in Bissel type trucks, which have sufficient side movement, controlled by springs fitted to the trucks, to allow the locomotive to negotiate freely a curve of 87½ yards radius. Each axle is separately driven through gearing by a small totally enclosed compound expansion steam engine, mounted on the bogie. Separate flexible steam pipes with ball joints connect each engine with the main throttle valve, and allow for movements of the engine. Flexible joints are also provided in the exhaust pipes.

The boiler is of the "Woolnough" water-tube type and, compared with the ordinary smoke-tube locomotive boiler, is very short. In front of the boiler, at the leading end of the locomotive, there is space within the outer casing to accommodate a tank with a capacity of 960 gallons, and further forward still there is an air reservoir for the Westinghouse brakes, and the sanding gear equipment for the leading bogie.

Between the boiler and the tank, and to one side, there is a small platform on which a small turbo-generator is mounted to provide current for lighting purposes. A Weir feed pump, specially modified to suit the conditions, is situated in the right-hand corner of the back of the cab. Behind the cab there is a coal storage bunker with a capacity of 3 tons, and a second water tank holding 240 gallons, which is connected to the larger tank at the forward end of the locomotive by a balance pipe. The amount of water in the tanks is indicated by a gauge glass at the back of the cab. Behind the tank there is also another air reservoir for the Westinghouse equipment, and the sanding gear for the rear bogie. The Westinghouse air pump is mounted in a convenient position outside the tender on the left-hand side of the engine.

The "Woolnough" boiler has three drums, the two lower of which are disposed one on each side of the grate, and connected by banks of tubes, slightly curved and inclined at a steep angle, to a steam drum centrally placed above the grate. At a point about two-thirds along the length of the boiler a fire-brick wall 9 in. thick closes the space between the three drums and the banks of tubes, so that the products of combustion from the furnace are forced to travel outward through the tube banks. In the space between the tube banks and the boiler casing the superheater tubes are placed, and they are so situated that, while they can freely absorb heat from the gases, they also protect the boiler casing from the heat. From this space the gases, having circled around the ends of the fire-brick wall, travel back through the tube banks to the smoke-box, from which they are ejected up the chimney by the exhaust blast or the steam blower.

One of the engine cylinder blocks, with covers removed.

The air for the combustion of the fuel is drawn in through balanced louvres provided in a partition between the smoke-box and the front water tank, and passes outside the boiler casing, and within the external casing around the boiler, to the ashpan. This ensures that the boiler casing is kept cool and the combustion air preheated, so that heat that otherwise would be lost by radiation is put to good use. The balanced air louvres open proportionately to the amount of vacuum induced by the blast, and close automatically when steam is shut off.

The grates consist of two similar parts, each of which is mounted on a longitudinally arranged trunnion. Each half is operated independently from the footplate, and the arrangement allows the fire to be easily cleaned or dropped into the ashpan.

The six separate engines are of the double acting compound type with cylinders $4\frac{1}{4}$ in. and $7\frac{1}{4}$ in. dia. and a stroke of 6 in., driving a crankshaft that runs in roller bearings and carries at its centre a pinion. The pinion meshes with a gear wheel on the centre of the corresponding axle. Piston valves, which are operated by Stephenson link motion, control the steam cut-off and reversal. A valve consisting of a small piston is provided at each end of the cylinder. These valves are normally kept in position by a light spring, as the steam acts on both sides of the piston; but if condensed water is trapped in the cylinder it is forced upward as the main piston approaches the end of the cylinder, and the water escapes through a side passage to the steam chest or low-pressure receiver as the case may be.

Each engine is mounted horizontally in the bogie frame with its crank axle across the frame, and is supported at one end by the axle and at the other by a suspension link. This link is attached to the engine by a ball joint at a point slightly farther from the axle than the centre of gravity of the engine, and to the bogie frame above by a silent block rubber mounting. The result of this arrangement is that, while the engine is soundly supported, it is yet able to follow freely the movements of the axle. By far the greater part of the weight is carried by the link, and the remainder by the axle.

The Woolnough Boiler, opened to show arrangement of the tubes.

The whole of the motion gear and crankshaft assembly is enclosed in the crank-case, which is partly filled with oil; and therefore all the moving parts are thoroughly lubricated on the splash system. The crankshaft, to which the connecting rods and eccentrics are attached by roller bearings, is a built-up structure, and the pinion at its centre is cut and ground to form out of the solid, and forms part of a shaft to which two separate hardened and ground crankshaft pieces are keyed. Each of these pieces comprises a main bearing, crank pin, and eccentrics, and the two are identical. The pistons also are turned out of the solid, and the crossheads are of cast steel. The eccentrics are beautiful examples of high class workmanship, and are of very light and narrow section, in spite of the fact that they must be hardened and ground to take the rollers of the bearings.

The Stephenson link motion is operated by link gear from a screw-and-nut mechanism contained in a box mounted above the engine. Steam is brought to each engine from the main throttle valve through an individual pipe in which an isolating valve is placed in a position easily accessible from the track. By this means, if it should be undesirable to admit steam to any one of the engines, its isolating valve can be closed and the locomotive propelled by the remaining engines. In the unlikely event of the complete failure of an engine, it can be disconnected from its axle simply by unscrewing the large nuts on the crank-case end of the engine stanchions, so that the pinion on the engine crankshaft is taken out of mesh with the gear wheel on the axle. This operation requires only a few minutes.

As there are six separate engines under the driver's charge, it is necessary that they should be all controlled together so that the multiplicity of driving units shall not make his task too complicated. As far as most of the controls are concerned the matter is one of no great difficulty. Accurate setting in the works before the locomotive is sent away ensures equal cut-off for each of the engines. As already mentioned, the Stephenson links on the engines are operated by a screw-and-nut mechanism, and the six screws are all interconnected by rods with flexible joints and are carefully adjusted in the works to give the desired equal cut-off. In the case of the throttle valve, however, the matter is more difficult. If, for instance, this valve were arranged to admit steam to a main chest from which all six engines drew steam, the operation of the locomotive would be unsatisfactory, for if one axle slipped on the rails the engine driving it would take all the steam and starve the others. Each engine therefore is individually controlled. The throttle valve adopted is of the poppet type, and closes on to a conical seat beneath which there is a piston-like extension that covers six ports, each admitting steam to the pipe-line of one engine. The main valve lifts about one-eighth of an inch before its piston-like extension begins to uncover the ports, so that if one axle starts to slip a throttling action will take place in the port leading to the engine concerned, and the remaining engines will continue to draw steam at an adequate pressure for satisfactory running.

A semi-plan view of the interior of the cab.

As live steam is automatically admitted to each low-pressure cylinder for starting purposes, and this is at the high working pressure of 550 lb. per sq. in., arrangements had to be made to reduce the pressure to about 140 lb. before it is admitted, and this is effected by an ingenious charging, drain, and safety valve. Two ball valves can be lifted from their seats by rods that bear against plungers operated from the screw reversing gear controlling the Stephenson motion. As a preliminary at starting the link motion is put in mid gear and the plungers are forced outward, so that the rods lift the ball valves off their seats. With the brakes "on," the regulator is opened slightly, and steam enters at the bottom of the charging valve through a reducing valve. It then passes upward and through an external pipe back through one of the ball valves, which is held open by its rod, and by a branch that has a safety valve connection to the top of the low-pressure receiver. The steam returns to the charging valve by way of the other ball valve, and finally passes to exhaust, thus warming up the engine.

When it is desired to start the locomotive the Stephenson link motion is moved to the full forward or reverse positions. In these positions of the link motion only the lower of the two ball valves is held open, and then steam at high pressure (for *(Continued on page 901)*

Winter Train Services on British Railways

The winter train services now operating on British railways show some marked improvements as compared with those of last winter. Numerous accelerations have been made, and hundreds of the additional trains that were put on for the summer traffic have been retained. On the L.M.S.R. 158 trains have been accelerated, with a total saving of 10 hrs. 18 min. per day; while on the G.W.R. the train mileage has been increased by 2,079 daily over that covered by last winter's services.

Characteristic features of locomotive practice in Germany are illustrated by this large "Pacific" of the German State Railways. This was constructed by the famous firm of Fried. Krupp, A.G. of Essen, to whom we are indebted for this photograph.

Both the famous Anglo-Scottish expresses, *"The Royal Scot"* of the L.M.S.R. and *"The Flying Scotsman"* of the L.N.E.R., are now due at Euston and King's Cross, their respective London terminal stations, at 5.40 p.m., five minutes earlier than last winter. The non-stop run of 299¼ miles from Carlisle to London, made by *"The Royal Scot,"* is the longest in the world this winter. The L.N.E.R. *"Queen of Scots"* Pullman train has been accelerated to run non-stop the 47¼ miles from Glasgow to Edinburgh, the first portion of its run, in 55 min., a gain of three minutes.

Among the many quickened services on the G.W.R. the most noteworthy is the Channel Islands Boat express, which leaves Paddington at 10.15 p.m. instead of 9.25 p.m. as formerly, an acceleration of 40 minutes. The experimental streamlined railcar services between Birmingham and South Wales are being continued.

On the L.M.S.R. considerable improvements have been made in the Scottish train services and in those operated by the company in Northern Ireland. Main line trains between Belfast and Londonderry are timed to do the journey in from 25 min. to 35 min. less than last winter. The new *"North Atlantic Express,"* between Portrush and Belfast in both directions, is continuing to run through the winter.

The most outstanding improvement on the Southern Railway is the speeding up of the service to North Cornwall by the *"Atlantic Coast Express"* leaving Waterloo at 11 a.m., the arrival at Padstow being 32 min. earlier than previously.

New L.N.E.R. Locomotives

The newest "Pacific" locomotives turned out from Doncaster carry numbers and names as follows:—2502, *"Hyperion"*; 2503, *"Firdaussi"*; 2504, *"Sandwich"*; 2505, *"Cameronian"*; 2506, *"Salmon Trout"*; and 2507, *"Singapore."*

Of the new 2–6–0 locomotives of the K3 class on order from outside firms, Sir W. G. Armstrong Whitworth and Co. Ltd., have recently delivered Nos. 1302, 1304, 1306, 1308, 1310 and 1324, and Robert Stephenson and Co. Ltd., have delivered Nos. 1325 and 1332.

The further 20 passenger express engines of the 4–4–0 "Hunt" class that are on order have been allotted the following numbers and names:—230, *"The Brocklesby"*; 238, *"The Burton"*; 258, *"The Cattistock"*; 274, *"The Craven"*; 279, *"The Cotswold"*; 353, *"The Derwent"*; 357, *"The Fernie"*; 359, *"The Fitzwilliam"*; 361, *"The Garth"*; 362, *"The Goathland"*; 363, *"The Grafton"*; 364, *"The Grove"*; 365, *"The Morpeth"*; 366, *"The Oakley"*; 368, *"The Puckeridge"*; 370, *"The Rufford"*; 374, *"The Sinnington"*; 375, *"The South Durham"*; 376, *"The Staintondale"*; 377, *"The Tynedale."*

Since being stationed at Haymarket shed, Edinburgh, the new 2–8–2 express locomotive No. 2001, *"Cock o' the North,"* has been working the heaviest expresses between that city and Aberdeen and giving every satisfaction. Loads of 600 tons and over have been taken without assistance and time has easily been kept.

Southern Railway Build More "Schools"

The S.R. are building 10 more "Schools" class express locomotives at Eastleigh. There are already 30 locomotives of this class in regular use, and the success achieved by these has resulted in the decision to build more. The new engines, like their predecessors, will be named after famous public schools, and the numbers and names chosen are as follows:— 930, *"Radley"*; 931, *"Kings - Wimbledon"*; 932, *" Blundells "*; 933, *"Kings-Canterbury "*; 934, *"St. Lawrence"*; 935, *" Sevenoaks "*; 936, *"Cranleigh"*; 937, *"Epsom"*; 938, *"St. Olave's"*; 939, *"Leatherhead."*

"Schools" class engines have three cylinders, weigh 110 tons, and are the most powerful 4-coupled locomotives in the country.

For experimental purposes No. 862, *Lord Collingwood,"* a four-cylinder 4–6–0 express engine of the "Lord Nelson" class, has been fitted with a double chimney.

G.W.R. Locomotive News

New tank engines of the 0–4–2 type completed at Swindon recently are numbered 4835–9.

Several engines are now running with the newly-adopted G.W.R. monogram painted on the tender in place of the words "Great Western" that formerly appeared there.

Among the numerous engines of various old types to be condemned to the scrap heap within the past few months have been two of the inside-cylindered 2–6–0 "Moguls" of the 2600 class. Their numbers were 2602 and 2607.

Further 4–6–0 Locomotives for L.M.S.R.

Crewe works have completed further 4–6–0 engines of the improved "Baby Scot" class, and these are numbered 5618 to 5627.

The Vulcan Foundry have delivered about 20 of the new standard 4–6–0 mixed-traffic locomotives of the 5020 class. During the time they are being run in these new engines are usually stationed at Crewe, and a trip that is frequently taken is from Crewe to Derby and back. Contracts have been placed for the building of 150 more of these mixed-traffic engines so that with the 70 previously ordered, there will be 220 in service by the end of next year. Of those now ordered, 100 are to be built by Sir W. G. Armstrong Whitworth and Co. Ltd., and 50 by the Vulcan Foundry Ltd.

Two more "Claughtons," No. 5941 and No. 5943 "*Tennyson*," have been withdrawn for scrapping, together with two "Experiments" No. 5491, "*Prince George*" and No. 25525, "*Byzantium*."

Brighter Railway Stations

Experiments are being made on the L.M.S.R. with a view to making railway stations brighter and more attractive. Radlett Station has been repainted in gay colours—emerald green, pale blue and orange—and made brilliant with light at night. The interior also has been made more comfortable and inviting. If the experiment is judged successful it may be extended to many other stations, throughout the line.

A new standard colour-scheme also has been adopted by the L.M.S.R. for the nameboards on station platforms. These will consist in future of a board painted with a yellow ground, with the name and margins in black.

The "*Rocket*"

One of the most interesting exhibits in the Science Museum at South Kensington is the historic locomotive "*Rocket*," which was built in 1829 by George Stephenson for the Rainhill trials that preceded the opening of the Liverpool and Manchester Railway. Its present condition is somewhat dilapidated, however, and its form considerably altered from the original design. The authorities of the Museum have now ordered from Robert Stephenson and Co. Ltd., of Darlington, a full-sized replica of "*Rocket*" as it was built at first, similar to the model supplied by that firm a few years ago to Mr. Henry Ford for placing in his extensive Mechanical Museum at Detroit. The new model is to be constructed of materials corresponding to those used in the original "*Rocket*," which was built by the same famous firm.

S.R. Speed Up Engine Handling

A new mechanical coaling plant and a water softening plant have just been completed and brought into use at the S.R. locomotive depot at Stewarts Lane, Battersea. The coaling plant has a capacity of 150 tons, and trucks of coal are hoisted one at a time to the receiving bin at the top of the structure, rotated axially, and the coal tipped out en masse, after which the truck is returned to the rails below. Then, as the locomotives pass below, the tenders are filled from the mechanically operated chutes in one motion.

The driver of the L.N.E.R. "Pacific" locomotive in the background of this photograph is greatly interested in a discussion on the correct manner of lubricating the locomotive of a Hornby Pullman train. Photograph reproduced by courtesy of the Editor of the "L.N.E.R. Magazine."

World's Fastest Newspaper Train

The world's fastest newspaper train was introduced by the G.W.R. on 2nd October. It leaves Paddington for South Wales at 1.20 a.m. and, running non-stop to Newport, covers 133½ miles in 137 minutes, in spite of severe speed restrictions for four miles while passing through the Severn Tunnel. After Newport, where the train arrives at 3.37 a.m., it calls at Cardiff at 3.59 a.m. and principal stations to Swansea, where it is due at 5.44 a.m. The train is drawn by a locomotive of the "Castle" class, as used for the "*Cheltenham Flyer*," the world's fastest steam train.

This is the second night newspaper express to be speeded up by the G.W.R. in the last six months.

The famous "3-20 p.m. down Manchester" express of the G.C. Section of the L.N.E.R. leaving Marylebone terminus. The engine is No. 6165, "Valour," the War memorial engine of the G.C.R. Section.

When Guards had to Pacify Passengers

Extracts from old railway Rule Books make amusing reading. For example, we learn from one issued in 1848 that it was the duty of G.W.R. superintendents to make themselves well acquainted by frequent personal intercourse with the character and conduct of every man under their orders. The superintendent's duties also required him to see that the vehicles were properly cleaned and the glasses and handles made bright, and that "the buffers pressed against each other so that they receded about an inch." In addition he had to see that every passenger had a ticket, but where a passenger held a ticket for a station short of his destination his duty included seeing that the passenger alighted at the place to which he had paid his fare, unless "being a respectable party, he could satisfy the superintendent that he had no intention of paying an improper fare."

Smoking on any part of the company's premises or trains was prohibited, and idleness or neglect of duty punishable by a fine. In the case of detention or stoppage of trains, guards were instructed to explain the cause to the passengers and "endeavour to pacify those who may be annoyed."

Film Publicity on the L.M.S.R.

An enterprising piece of publicity work is being carried out by the L.M.S.R. in the exhibition of cinema films that have been prepared specially for showing the facilities for travel offered by that great line.

One of the films shows the passenger trains of the L.M.S.R., and some fine "shots" have been obtained of the principal expresses and, in particular, of "*The Royal Scot*," drawn by one of the latest 4–6–2 locomotives, and also of electric and steam-drawn suburban trains in the London area. Another film, entitled "*Ships of the Narrow Seas*," vividly portrays the L.M.S.R. Royal Mail route to Ireland.

These films are being exhibited first of all to the L.M.S.R. staff at various places throughout the system in order to make them better acquainted with the attractive services offered by the line. To accommodate the staff in charge of the cinema apparatus one of the old L.N.W.R. 42 ft. composite corridor coaches has been specially adapted. As now equipped it contains day, sleeping, and luggage compartments, and a work room where repairs can be carried out. It is probable that later the films will be given the wider publicity they well deserve, and there is sure to be keen general interest in the information they give so attractively.

Mixed Traffic Locomotives for L.M.S.R.

New Two-Cylinder 4-6-0 Design

THE requirements of the L.M.S.R. for a "general utility" engine have led to the production of a new design of 4–6–0 locomotive that embodies all the features that have become familiar since the appointment of Mr. W. A. Stanier as Chief Mechanical Engineer. The L.M.S.R. have thus joined the S.R. and G.W.R. in recognising the merits for general traffic purposes of the 4–6–0 engine with driving wheels of medium diameter. The S.R. have several classes of this type of engine, but the G.W.R. examples, which are very numerous, all belong to the "Hall" class.

The illustration on this page, reproduced by courtesy of the L.M.S.R., shows one of the new engines built by the Vulcan Foundry Ltd., of Newton-le-Willows, and the following description will be of interest to readers.

This class is unique in that it represents the first 4–6–0 design built since the formation of the L.M.S.R. group essentially for mixed traffic working, and its ready adaptability to either passenger or goods working is shown by its traffic classification "5P5F." Previous mixed traffic locomotives have all been of the 2–6–0 or "Mogul" wheel formation, the first 244 being after the Horwich design of Mr. G. Hughes. The subsequent 40, as described in the "*M.M.*" last March, represent the modification of this design according to the ideas of Mr. W. A. Stanier, who has impressed his stamp on L.M.S.R. locomotive practice, and whose successive designs for that company all bear a remarkable "family likeness."

Thus the new mixed traffic engines greatly resemble in outward appearance the new series of "5X" passenger engines with tapered boilers illustrated and described in the "*M.M.*" last May. But instead of the three-cylinder propulsion of these engines, two cylinders only are provided in the new design, these having the same moderate diameter, 18½ in., and long stroke, 28 in., as the Stanier "Moguls." The cylinders are placed outside, as the photograph shows, and have the valve chests above accommodating piston valves with a travel of 6½ in., Walschaerts valve gear providing the necessary movement.

The cylinders are slightly inclined and are connected to the driving wheels by rods of high tensile manganese molybdenum steel of fluted section; but the side rods coupling the wheels are of plain or rectangular section. The wheel centres are steel castings with the now usual triangular rim section as on previous engines of Mr. Stanier's design, and they have the balance weights built up of steel plates riveted to the spokes, the necessary adjustments for balance being made by the addition of lead between the plates.

The coupled wheel axle-boxes are steel castings with pressed-in brasses having suitable white metal crowns. Oil grooves are provided on both sides of the crown, and the oil pads can be examined by sliding out the underkeep while the axle-box is in position. Each box is fitted with a dust shield carried on the inside face. The crown of each box has an independent oil feed from a mechanical lubricator, with the standard back-pressure valves and flexible oil pipe connections.

The laminated bearing springs for the engine and tender are made of silico manganese steel, the plates being of a ribbed section, and the fixing in the buckle of the cotter type. The spring links are of the screwed adjustable pattern.

The standard type of four-wheeled bogie supports the front end of the engine, the weight being taken through side bolsters. Bogie side check spring gear is provided to ensure smooth riding.

The boiler is similar to that of the new "5X" three-cylinder passenger engines having a tapered barrel, Belpaire fire-box, moderate degree superheater, and top-feed apparatus. The last-named is accommodated under the dome-shaped cover on the boiler barrel. The regulator valve is incorporated in the superheater header in the smoke-box. The working pressure is 225 lb. to the square inch, which is relieved by two safety valves of the Ross "pop" pattern. The boiler plates are made of 2 per cent. nickel steel with a view to strength and lightness.

A steam manifold with a main shut-off valve is provided at the top of the fire-box door plate in the cab, and to this manifold are attached valves for the vacuum brake ejector and steam brake. The sight feed lubricator to the regulator, the pressure gauge, and the train heating apparatus are also supplied from valves on the manifold, as are the two injectors for feeding the boiler and the whistle, which is of the hooter type adopted for recent L.M.S.R. locomotives.

The cab fittings generally are of the company's standard type, the drive being arranged on the left-hand side. All controls can be conveniently handled. On each side of the cab there is a tip-up seat and two sliding windows with a small hinged window outside to act as a draught-preventer for the enginemen when looking out.

The coupled wheels and the tender wheels are acted upon by the steam brake operated by the driver's vacuum brake valve. A steam ejector is used to create the vacuum when the (*Continued on page 901*)

Dimensions of New L.M.S.R. Mixed Traffic Locomotives

Cylinders	
Diameter	**18½ in.**
Stroke	**28 in.**
Wheels	
Bogie	**3 ft. 3½ in.**
Driving	**6 ft. 0 in.**
Heating Surface	
Tubes	**1,460 sq. ft.**
Fire-box	**156 sq. ft.**
Superheater	**227.5 sq. ft.**
Grate Area	**27.8 sq. ft.**
Working Pressure	**225 lb. per sq. in.**
Tractive Effort at 85 per cent. working pressure	**25,455 lb.**
Adhesive Weight	**54 tons**
Weight of engine in working order	**72 tons**
Weight of tender in working order	**54 tons 2 cwt.**
Total weight of engine and tender in working order	**126 tons 2 cwt.**
Coal capacity	**9 tons**
Water capacity	**4,000 gallons**
Total length of engine and tender over buffers	**63 ft. 7¾ in.**

The Planning of a New Railway

From First Survey to Letting the Contracts

By R. D. Gauld, M.Eng., A.M. Inst. C.E.

THE methods to be adopted in planning a new railway depend very largely on the kind of country through which the railway is to run. At one extreme we have a highly developed, densely populated country like England, and at the other the kind of territory found in tropical Africa, or in the centre of Australia. In an undeveloped country traffic at first will be scarce, so that the line must be built as cheaply as possible; and, as there are few centres of population, it may have to be diverted considerably out of its direct course in order to get more traffic. The ideal railway is dead straight and absolutely level, although if the rare opportunity occurs of having the line downhill for loaded wagons, the uphill traffic being chiefly empties, this leads to economical working.

Packing the sleepers up to the correct level before ballasting. The rail is held up by the jacks shown in the illustration to facilitate operations. Photograph reproduced by courtesy of the S.R.

The Australian Trans-Continental line is straight and nearly level for 300 miles, because the object of it is to connect two fairly populous areas, across what is practically a desert. The embankments and cuttings, or earthworks as they are called, are very light, and there are no sharp curves. Railways in tropical Africa are usually planned to suit the lie of the ground in order to avoid heavy construction costs, and expenses are kept down by using a narrow gauge, and steep gradients and sharp curves if tunnelling or deep excavation is thereby avoided.

As our readers probably will be more interested in the problem as found in our own country, a few words must suffice to deal with railway planning in jungle, dense forest, and unmapped country. Generally, the task will be to design a railway to join two definite places. First of all there will be a reconnaissance or exploration survey of several possible routes, and this may be not only an engineering survey, but also an economic survey, to ascertain whether such things as minerals, cattle, and vegetation of commercial value, are likely to provide traffic for the line. The various routes will then be studied carefully, and on two or three of the most promising ones trial location surveys will be made, a higher degree of accuracy in measurement being required this time, and hence taking longer. From these surveys the final route will be chosen, and on it will be made a preliminary location survey that will form the foundation for the final location survey leading to the actual setting out of the line. The difficulties of the work will be due chiefly to such things as bad climate, poisonous insects, and shortage of water supplies.

A railway location survey showing the proposed course of the line, and the levels of the ground which it traverses.

Turning now to home conditions, let us suppose that the rising and thriving township of Menton-on-Sea has, by the efforts of its enterprising Town Council, so successfully advertised its wonderfully bracing air and its amazingly good beach that it has attracted crowds of visitors away from the bigger resorts of which they have become tired, and has persuaded many of them to take up residence. There is the great drawback, however, that the nearest point of the nearest railway, the Central, is about 16 miles away, and the nearest important station, Lanchester, is 20 miles distant. If only Menton could have the railway brought to it, its prosperity is assured.

Aided by the local Press, enthusiasm for the idea becomes general in the town, and the Council is petitioned to approach the Central Railway on the subject. A Railway Sub-committee of the Council is therefore formed, the Town Clerk writes to the General Manager of the Railway to ask for the favour of an interview, and in due course that gentleman receives the sub-committee.

The project so far can be discussed only in very general terms, but from statistical information supplied to him, as to the population of the town, its chief industries, and so on, the Manager thinks that further enquiry is justified. It is agreed that Lancheater will be the best place to make the junction if it is decided to build the branch, and it is arranged that the Menton authorities shall canvass the district between their town and Lanchester with a view to getting support for the railway. The Manager promises to consult his Directors, so that they may sanction the setting aside of a small committee of railway officers to explore the traffic possibilities of the district; and this being done, the Committee is set up and gets to work.

Traffic possibilities turn out to be distinctly good. There are three small country towns on what would be a fairly direct route, and they have no good road connection to anywhere of importance. A fair amount of dairy farming is carried on in the area, but is somewhat restricted by poor transport. Coal is known to exist at one or two places in the district, and the seams are at no great depth. The same seams are already being worked nearer the railway, and the building of the branch is certain to lead to sinking of new shafts.

The country is a comparatively easy one from the point of view of railway building, and it is assumed that the cost for a double line will not exceed £10,000 a mile. For 20 miles this is £200,000, and at 5 per cent. interest on the money the branch must make a profit of £10,000 a year to pay its way. A rough estimate of probable traffic shows that it probably will not do this for the first few years, but is likely to do so in eight or nine years. There is, of course, also the unknown factor of the traffic it will contribute to the rest of the line. So a report is submitted to the Directors by the Manager, recommending that a detailed scheme and estimate should be prepared. A little pressure has been put on the Menton Council who, in view of the advantages to be attained by the town, have agreed to demolish some derelict property and clear a site for the terminus, afterwards selling the site to the Railway for a nominal figure.

After discussion, the Directors agree that the expenditure is justified, and the Manager is authorised to proceed. He therefore instructs the Engineer to prepare a scheme for a railway from Lanchester to Menton, serving if possible certain named places between, and to co-operate closely with the traffic Department as to the stations, sidings, etc., required.

Forming a cutting by means of a steam navvy. The "spoil" is taken away over the temporary track in tip wagons and used to form embankments elsewhere. Photograph reproduced by courtesy of the G.W.R.

As heavy excursion trains at high speeds are expected to use the line, it is decided that the "ruling gradient," that is the steepest gradient that can occur repeatedly, shall be 1 in 176, representing a 30-ft. rise in one mile. This was used on the Great Central extension from Leicester to London. A short length as steep as 1 in 100 would be permitted if necessary, however, to save heavy expense. As the biggest engines will use the branch, the sharpest curve is to be of 20 chains radius, that is ¼ mile, a chain being 66 ft.

A set of what are called 6-inch Ordnance Sheets, or maps to a scale of 6 in. to a mile, published by the Ordnance Survey Department of the Government, are now obtained by the engineering staff, to cover the district in which the railway will lie. These sheets have on them the contours, or lines joining places of equal level, all levels being referred to what is called Ordnance Datum. A contour marked 50 is therefore at the same level whether the map shows a part of Perthshire or a part of Kent, and is 50 ft. above Ordnance Datum, called O.D.

Removing the sleepers of the temporary track to make way for the main line material. The track alongside is already laid, and the ballast has been tipped ready for spreading. Photograph reproduced by courtesy of the L.M.S.R.

By a process of trial and error, a centre line is now pencilled out on the sheets, starting from the junction point of the new railway, and using the contour lines, so that there will be as little cutting and embankment as possible, while at the same time the permissible gradient is not exceeded. This will give a series of straight lines at an angle to one another, and they must be joined by curves not sharper than the radius of 20 chains already decided as the minimum.

The sheets are now pasted together, being cut as required so that they form a roll about 18 in. wide. The line pencilled out is then walked over with the rolled map in hand, and a new line is laid down in pencil, as close to the old one as possible, but improving on it to suit the lie of the ground. An instrument called a hand level, together with a pole 5 ft. or 6 ft. long, is useful in helping to determine levels not actually given on the map. The new line is then drawn in carefully in the office with accurate curves and straight lines.

Levels are then taken along this line at definite places, such as where fences are crossed. As Parliamentary Regulations allow a deviation of 300 ft. in the country and 30 ft. in towns on either side of the centre line shown on the Parliamentary Plans, and a change of level up to 5 ft. in the country and 2 ft. in towns, it is necessary to make sure that within a 600-ft. wide strip the Ordnance sheets are correct up to date. There will usually be new buildings to be added.

The Company's legal staff now come on the scene, and reference, or give a number to, every field, enclosure, building, road or path inside this strip, with the names of the owner or lessee. The Parliamentary Plans are then prepared by tracing from the 6-inch maps, making sheets of a uniform size, each showing four miles of railway. A section is drawn under each plan with a vertical scale of 100 ft. to 1 inch. A firm of lithographic specialists are then given the tracings, which they redraw, and reproduce in a conventional style. After proofs are corrected, the Engineer sends a quantity of the plans to the Solicitor, who sends them to the various local authorities in whose areas the railway will lie.

The section of the railway is drawn with a base line whose level must be stated with regard to Ordnance Datum. The rail level is figured on at each change of gradient, and also distances in miles and furlongs. All public roads, railways and canals crossed, and how crossed, must be shown, with span and height of bridge, and necessary raising or lowering of roads. Heights and depths of embankments and cuttings, if over 5 ft., must be marked on. Public roads crossed on the level must have levels taken on them for 200 yds. on each side of the crossing, and enlarged sections of the crossing must be shown. If the road crosses by a bridge, a section is again required with the road gradients marked. Our proposed junction at Lanchester will involve a plan and section of the existing main line for 800 yds. on each side of the junction.

An estimate of the cost of the railway is now made by the Engineer in a form prescribed by the Ministry of Transport. It sets out the quantities and costs of such things as cuttings, embankments, culverts and drains, road making, permanent (*Cont. on page 901*)

KEMEX EXPERIMENTS IN TANNING AND DYEING

ONE of the most interesting branches of industrial chemistry is tanning, or the preparation of leather from hides and skins. The changes that take place during this process are very complicated and are brought about by steeping the hides in liquids containing tanning extracts manufactured from vegetable sources. One of the best known tanning materials is oak bark, which for centuries has been used extensively by tanners.

An interesting series of experiments that will help to explain the chemistry of tanning can be made with oak bark and similar substances. Old oak bark should not be used, the young bark from the inner side of the covering of the tree being the most suitable. A portion of this is shaved off and cut into small pieces, and a dessertspoonful of the fragments is placed in the wide-necked flask, which is half filled with water. The flask is placed on the universal stand, as shown in the lower illustration on the opposite page, with the lighted spirit lamp or bunsen burner beneath it. When the water boils the flame is turned low to keep the liquid steadily simmering, and the heating is continued for about five minutes. Alternatively a smaller quantity of oak bark can be boiled with half a test tube full of water, the tube being held in the test tube holder, or in a folded strip of paper, with its lower end just above a small flame, and shaken gently in order to prevent violent boiling.

After the contents of the flask have cooled and the fragments of bark have settled to the bottom, a little of the extract or liquid obtained is poured off into a test tube, which may be filled to a depth of about 1 in. A solution of Iron Alum is then prepared by shaking one measure of this chemical with half a test tube full of water, and on pouring a few drops of this into the extract a deep black precipitate is obtained immediately.

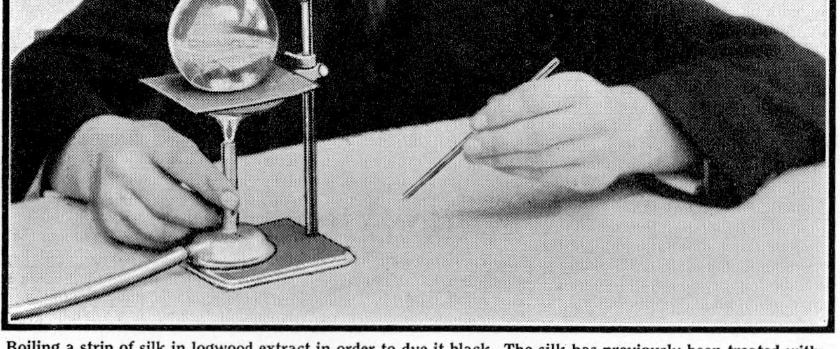
Boiling a strip of silk in logwood extract in order to dye it black. The silk has previously been treated with chemicals to enable the dye to be applied effectively.

In order to explain what has happened in the experiment we have just described, one measure of Tannic Acid is dissolved in half a test tube full of water and to half of this solution a few drops of the solution of Iron Alum already prepared are added. Again a black precipitate is obtained. This is iron tannate and is exactly similar in appearance to that already obtained. The oak bark extract in fact contains tannic acid, or tannin as it is sometimes called, and this chemical is responsible for the changes that occur in tanning. The name really denotes a group of very weakly acid chemicals that are found in oak bark, and also in galls, the curious hard lumps, often resembling nuts in appearance, that form on plants where the eggs of certain insects are deposited.

It is interesting to test other barks besides that of the oak in order to find which contain tannic acid and to form an idea as to the one that is most likely to be valuable to the tanner. In all cases the hard outside bark should be stripped off before testing. Tea leaves also contain tannin. In order to test for the chemical in this source, a few tea leaves are boiled vigorously with half a test tube full of water, or they are boiled for five minutes or even more in the wide-necked flask half filled with water. The clear liquid left after the tea leaves have settled is poured into a tube and tested by the addition of a few drops of Iron Alum solution. The production of a black precipitate shows the presence of tannic acid. It must not be supposed from this experiment that tea as ordinarily made contains a large proportion of tannin. Pouring boiling water over the tea leaves and straining away the liquid formed is less drastic than boiling them with water for some time and is less effective in extracting tannin.

The action of tanning agents is best seen from an experiment with the white of an egg. The chemical name for this is albumen, which is a complex organic chemical. About a quarter of a teaspoonful of the white of an egg is dissolved in half a test tube full of water and to this liquid is added the remaining portion of the Tannic Acid solution already prepared. A thick white precipitate immediately forms and this becomes hard and leathery when it is separated from the liquid by filtering and left to dry. A gelatine solution also gives a precipitate when treated with Tannic Acid.

Similar changes take place when hides are steeped in tanning liquids, for these contain albuminous substances, that is chemicals resembling albumen or containing it. Ham rind provides a convenient subject for an experiment that forms a nearer approach to actual tanning than that with albumen itself. A small piece is freed from fat and grease and is then soaked in a solution of Tannic Acid, prepared as already explained. The action of this chemical on the albuminous substances in the rind is slow and sufficient time must be given to allow it to penetrate. This may require several days, and from time to time the rind should be carefully lifted out and washed in order to follow the changes in its appearance. Eventually it will be found to be hard and leathery.

The vegetable kingdom is a great storehouse of chemicals of all kinds and certain plants and trees yield dyes or colouring matters. Wood, indigo and madder are good examples of vegetable dyes, and the colouring matter obtained from the wood of the logwood tree can be applied with good effect by the Kemex experimenter. This tree is a native of Mexico and Central America, from which countries it is exported in logs. The heartwood of the tree is the source of the dye, and is included in the range of Kemex chemicals in a convenient form for rapid extraction of the colouring matter. When it is boiled with water, a red liquid is obtained that can be used as an indicator, for with acids it becomes a striking yellow colour and it is turned blue by alkalies.

Logwood as a dye is chiefly useful for giving a good black on silk. It seems strange that so many different colours can be produced from this single material, but in all cases chemical changes are responsible, new compounds being made, or new forms of these.

produced, that show characteristic differences of colour.

In order to dye silk black it is necessary to make use of other materials in addition to the logwood, for the dye cannot be applied directly to the fabric with success. The chemicals used for this purpose are iron salts and tannic acid, in which the silk is first steeped. As we have already seen, a black precipitate of iron tannate is formed when solutions containing these two chemicals are mixed together. The iron tannate is capable of absorbing the logwood and because of its use in helping to fix the colour on the silk is described as a "mordant." This name comes from a Latin word meaning "to bite" and thus it expresses vividly the fact that its formation on the silk enables the colour to bite into the fabric and to remain firmly fixed on it.

A strip of silk about four inches long and an inch in width is convenient for an experimental effort to dye this material black. Two solutions are necessary for mordanting it. The first of these is made by dissolving six measures of Iron Alum in about three quarters of a test tube full of water and the second by dissolving an equal amount of Tannic Acid in the same quantity of liquid. When ready the two solutions are poured into basins in order to make them easily accessible. The strip of silk is steeped first in the Iron Alum solution. It is turned over in the liquid by means of the glass rod until every part of it has become thoroughly soaked, for the Iron Alum must be evenly distributed in order to obtain good results. About five minutes soaking will suffice and the strip is then stretched and hung up to dry.

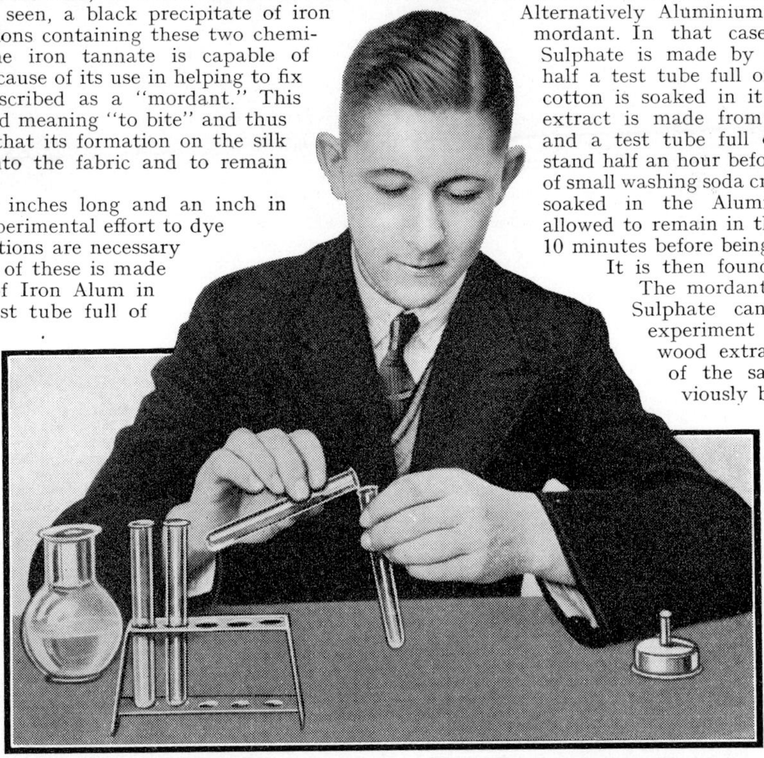

Tannic acid solution gives a white precipitate when added to albumen or the white of an egg.

Then follows a similar steeping in the Tannic Acid solution, when the black iron tannate is deposited on it, followed again by stretching and drying. In practice this process is repeated, the silk being soaked alternately in solutions of iron salts and of tannin, partly to ensure good mordanting and partly also to add weight to the silk. One soaking in each liquid probably will suffice in our experiment, but it is interesting to try the effect of giving more thorough immersions to a second piece of silk and to compare the results of the next process on the two samples.

For the final dyeing logwood extract is prepared by boiling about a quarter of the quantity of Logwood contained in the Outfit with sufficient water to half fill the wide-necked flask. The boiling is continued until a deep red colour is obtained and the liquid is then separated from the residue either by decanting it off or by filtering.

The wide-necked flask is then washed out and the logwood extract returned to it. The flask is placed on the universal stand with the lighted spirit lamp or bunsen burner under it, and the extract is heated to boiling point. The silk is then added and carefully stirred in the hot liquid. After boiling the strip of fabric in the solution in this manner for about 10 minutes, it is lifted out, dipped in cold water and wrung to expel as much liquid as possible. It is stretched and hung up to dry and will then be found to be dyed a good black colour. If the first trial is not very satisfactory, it can be repeated, varying the strengths of the solutions and the times allowed for steeping the silk in them.

Boiling chips of oak bark to extract tannin from them. The presence of tannin in the liquid is shown by adding Iron Alum solution to it, when a black precipitate is formed.

Experimenters should take care to wash their hands between operations with the different liquids in order to prevent them from becoming accidentally dyed. The glass rod used for stirring purposes also should be rinsed well under the tap before being placed in another liquid, and a further warning that will help to avoid breakages is that a glass rod is intended only for stirring purposes, and not for poking at materials placed in flasks or tubes.

A similar effect can be obtained by mordanting a piece of cotton with the same solutions and boiling it with logwood. Alternatively Aluminium Sulphate can be used as a mordant. In that case a solution of Aluminium Sulphate is made by dissolving four measures in half a test tube full of water and a small strip of cotton is soaked in it and then dried. A logwood extract is made from four measures of Logwood and a test tube full of water, and is allowed to stand half an hour before adding about six measures of small washing soda crystals. The cotton previously soaked in the Aluminium Sulphate solution is allowed to remain in the logwood extract for about 10 minutes before being taken out, rinsed and dried. It is then found to be dyed a good black.

The mordanting effect of the Aluminium Sulphate can be demonstrated in this experiment by placing in the logwood extract a second piece of cotton of the same size that has not previously been treated with this chemical. This piece of cotton also is dyed black, but the depth of colour is much less and the dye shows a tendency to be washed out on boiling with water.

A very interesting dyestuff that cannot be applied directly to textile materials and yet does not require a mordant is indigo, the well-known blue dye that formerly was obtained exclusively from a plant grown in the East but is now manufactured from coal tar products. Indigo is a very fast dye, that is one that cannot easily be washed out of the fabric after it has been applied, and it owes its fastness largely to the fact that the peculiar method of applying it fixes it firmly in the fibres themselves.

An interesting experiment with Congo Red will explain how the process of indigo dyeing is carried on. A pinch of this is dissolved in half a test tube full of water in order to give the liquid a pale pink colour. Six measures of Sodium Bisulphate are then dissolved in a quarter of a test tube full of water and the two solutions mixed, giving a blue liquid, for Congo Red of course is an indicator that changes colour when acidified. To the blue solution a few small fragments of Granulated Zinc are added. The metal is acted upon by the acid solution with the production of the gas hydrogen, which bubbles up through the liquid, and if the action is slow in starting it can be speeded up by gently warming.

Presently it will be found that the blue solution has become colourless. A piece of filter paper or blotting paper dipped into it and then waved in the air, or left in contact with the air for some time, gradually becomes coloured, however, and the solution itself regains its colour when it is left exposed to the air in the evaporating dish or a small saucer, or is shaken in a test tube so as to bring about intimate contact of the liquid with the air.

The explanation of these results is that the hydrogen acts upon the Congo Red to form a colourless substance. Similar changes take place when indigo is treated with agents that transform it into a substance called indigo white. In actual dyeing operations fabrics are steeped thoroughly in a vat in which indigo white has been prepared and when lifted out become blue because indigo is re-formed within their fibres by the action of the oxygen of the air.

GARAGING MECCANO MOTOR CARS

The accompanying illustration shows a realistic model garage and the two cars for which it has been built. The garage has been specially designed to accommodate one No. 1 model Motor Car and one No. 2 Car, and one corner is set apart as a store room for spares and equipment. This section is accessible from outside by a door, and the parts left over from the Outfits, after building the models, are kept in it. Inside the garage, places are provided for Spanners, Drifts, Winding Keys, Oil Cans, etc., so that they are immediately available when a car takes the road or requires adjustment. Fittings include electric lighting with concealed wiring and batteries.

Outside accessories can be seen in the illustration. A miniature tap is provided for a hose connection when "washing" the cars, this being situated behind the flag pole. Imitation flower beds and lawns are laid out on the table top, and a forcing frame, flower pots, garden seat and table enhance the life-like effect.

These particulars will give readers some idea of the fun that can be had with a model garage for their cars. In this way all adjustments and alterations can be carried out in a similar manner to actual practice, and if several cars are available much fun can be had by running a racing "stable." Every Motor Car enthusiast should have a garage for his cars, and the Meccano Garage is specially made to house a No. 1 or No. 2 Outfit Model or other Car of similar size. It is attractively finished in imitation rough-cast.

HEAVY DUTY BEARING

A bearing for carrying heavy loads can be made in the following manner. A Steel Ball is inserted in one end of a Socket Coupling and, at the same end, two ½" Reversed Angle Brackets are secured by ½" Bolts that are screwed into opposite tapped holes in the Coupling. Six Washers space each Reversed Angle Bracket from the Socket Coupling, and two Washers are placed between the head of each bolt and its Bracket. The Brackets are placed so that the two remaining lugs are over the Steel Ball and three Washers are placed between them before they are secured together. Two such units are required, one for each end of the shaft, and may be fitted in position on a Double Arm Crank bolted to the structure of the model.

The weight of the Rod is taken by the Steel Balls, but the Rod is held in position directly over the centres of the Balls by the Reversed Angle Brackets.

END THRUST BEARING

The device described above is also suitable for taking up the end thrust of a shaft. For such a purpose the exact spacing of the Reversed Angle Brackets is not necessary, and in fact, the ball can be retained in place by means of a single Angle Bracket secured to the Socket Coupling. The Rod would be journalled longitudinally in the Coupling, the remaining hole of which should be provided with a Collar to support the Rod. With this arrangement the end of the Rod bears against the Steel Ball and in this manner friction and wear are reduced to a minimum.

FAN WHEEL GOVERNOR

The length of run of a Clockwork Motor can be prolonged considerably by means of this speed-reducing device. A Bush Wheel is fitted with four Angle Brackets to which Dredger Buckets are secured by means of their clips. The four Buckets should each be fixed so that as the Wheel rotates, the open ends face the direction of rotation. The wheel thus formed is geared up from the Clockwork Motor to a ratio of 7 : 1 or greater as the circumstances require.

When the Dredger Buckets are rotated at speed a stage is reached when the resistance of the atmosphere on the Dredger Buckets prevents a further increase in speed. This form of governor gives a steady drive and is suitable for numerous different purposes. A similar type of governor is employed in clock striking mechanisms.

LARGE BOILERS

Models of steam engines sometimes require a larger boiler than Part No. 162, and in such cases one must be built up from separate parts.

A boiler of approximately 3½ in. diameter can be made in the following manner. Each end is formed from a circle of 2½" small radius Curved Strips that are secured around the rim of a Face Plate. Two 5½" Strips are overlapped one hole and bolted together, and are curved to fit round the outer rim of the Curved Strips to which they are secured by Angle Brackets.

Two ends are built up in this manner and may be connected together by Strips of suitable length. To complete the circle 20 Strips will be necessary, but it is not always necessary to fill in the entire boiler. An economy can be effected by leaving the underside open.

The realistic garage shown above was built by Mr. H. G. Ogden, Victoria, B.C., Canada, for his son Richard who, although only 5 years old, is a keen Meccano enthusiast. The garage accommodates the two cars shown in the illustration, and provision is made for tools and the additional parts left over from the Outfits.

SLIP CLUTCHES

In models fitted with automatic reversing gear that is required to operate for a long period, it often happens that the Gears do not mesh at precisely the same moment for each cycle of operations, and slight inaccuracy is likely to be increased to serious proportions after a period of operation.

Supposing for instance a model crane, to be used for demonstration purposes by a Meccano club, is fitted with an automatic reversing gear for the hoisting mechanism. The cord would be so arranged that when the load is lowered to its fullest extent there is no more cord on the winding drum which, as it continues to rotate, winds up the cord. After the load is hoisted there is a pause while the automatic reversing gear draws one Pinion out of engagement with its Contrate, and then when the second Pinion is engaged the load is lowered once again. If the Pinion disengages before the load is raised to its normal height, it will be clear that on the next wind the hook will be raised to the same extent higher than normal, and to prevent the possibilities of slight inaccuracy it is advisable to incorporate a slip clutch in the drive.

The slip clutch should consist of an ordinary friction clutch, such as is fitted to the Meccano Motor Chassis, and normally kept in engagement by means of a Compression Spring. One member of the clutch would be secured to the winding drum and the other would take up the drive from the reverse gear. The pressure exerted by the Spring would be so adjusted that under normal working, the clutch grips, but as soon as the winding drum is overloaded, as when the load reaches its maximum height, slip occurs. Thus the mechanism would be adjusted to give a slight overwind, which would be allowed for in the slip clutch, and the load would be hoisted to the same height each time.

There are numerous other applications for slip clutches, but they are especially adaptable for demonstration models that are required to operate for long periods without attention.

CARE AND MAINTENANCE OF CLOCKWORK MOTORS

We frequently receive requests for advice concerning the use of Meccano Clockwork Motors and how to prevent overwinding. There need be no fear of overwinding these Motors with any ordinary handling, but for the benefit of those boys who are naturally "heavy handed" the following method of winding will ensure that the spring is never wound too much. The Motor is allowed to run down completely and is then wound gently to its full extent and the number of turns of the key are counted. During the later stages more care should be exercised, and winding should of course cease as soon as it is felt that the key will not turn any more. Careful note should be made of the number of turns, and then in future when winding the Motor a slightly smaller number of turns should be made. Thus the spring will always be fully wound, but there will be a small margin to prevent the possibility of overwinding.

Clockwork Motors should be lubricated from time to time, and for the bearings Meccano Lubricating Oil should be used. This is of the correct consistency for the purpose and should be applied in small quantities. It is better to apply a little oil often, than much oil at infrequent intervals. The spring should receive periodical attention, and for this Meccano Graphite Grease should be used to ensure smooth running and prevent rust setting in.

The Motors should not be allowed to run down to their full extent before being put away after use. It is advisable to leave them with a few turns left in the spring. It is particularly important that the Clockwork Motors in the Nos. 1 and 2 Motor Car Outfits should not be allowed to run out completely. When running light these Motors run down very quickly, and if allowed to run completely out, damage may result to the spring.

SHORTER GRUB SCREWS.—There are two lengths of Grub Screws at present included in the Meccano system, namely 5/32" and 7/32"; but even the shorter size is sometimes found too long, especially in gear-box construction. When ½" Pinions are meshed with similar Pinions, or with 57-teeth Gears that slide out of engagement on the same side as the boss, the teeth must inevitably foul the Grub Screw in the Pinion. The only remedy for this has been to file down the Grub Screw until there is sufficient clearance for the Gear teeth.

Shorter Grub Screws that fit flush with the Pinion boss can be obtained from the Collars used in the No. 2 Motor Car Constructor Outfit. These Grub Screws will be found useful for other purposes, especially in gear-boxes, and your proposal that they should be included in the standard Meccano range will receive attention. (*Reply to J. Johnson, Reading.*)

PREPARING FOR HEAVY TRAFFIC

WHILE most miniature railway owners operate their trains more or less all the year round, it is certain that more attention is given to model railways during the winter months. In the summer, fine weather and outdoor attractions cause the running of trains to assume, for the time being, second place in the interests of their owners. In the case of portable miniature railways, therefore, that have to be put away when finished with, the various components may have been packed up some time when they are suddenly required to be prepared to take part in another model railway "season." Before the usually intensive traffic of the winter can be dealt with, however, it is invariably necessary to pay some attention to the condition of the equipment so that each item may do its part in the work of the system and so ensure its satisfactory and efficient operation.

It is a good plan to examine the different items thoroughly in order to determine how much attention or repair is necessary; and in this article we propose to give a few suggestions in regard to the best way in which this examination and overhauling should be carried out. These suggestions will be useful to those who already have some experience of Hornby Trains, and will be of interest also to those who are just commencing the hobby. There are many little points that can only be found by experience, and their discovery is made all the easier with the aid of a little practical advice.

The foundation of any railway is its track, and unless this is in sound condition the running of trains will never be smooth, and there may be constant danger of derailment. This applies as much to a gauge O track laid with Hornby Rails as to a full-size line, so before use the various rails, points and crossings should be carefully examined for any faults. Bent rails should be looked for, and if the damage in this respect is not serious, the rails will be fit for further use after the necessary straightening has been carried out. Bends along the length of the rail are usually only slight, and may be corrected with the fingers or by using a piece of wood to push the rail back into place. No hammering should be done, as this is certain to distort the rail.

The ends of rails are apt to get bent or pushed out of shape, either from continual connecting and disconnecting of the track, or as a result of careless handling. Pliers may be necessary to correct the damage, but they must be used with judgment. Usually it is the hollow rail head that suffers, and in this case it is useful to insert a spare rail connecting pin half in and half out of the rail, as usually fitted. There are usually some loose pins of this kind among the miscellaneous equipment belonging to any miniature railway. The pin thus inserted will assist in keeping the rail head true while the pliers are used to straighten the web or vertical portion of the rail below the head.

In preparing for the winter period of train running, accessories as well as the trains themselves should be examined to see that they are in proper order. Level Crossings, such as that shown in this illustration, may require a little attention to the gates.

Loose rail connecting pins should be tightened by pinching the rail head with pliers, taking care, however, not to deform the rail at all. Lost pins should be replaced, and new ones may be obtained at one penny per dozen. It is advisable also to check the gauge of the track by means of the rail gauge formed by the handle of the Hornby Locomotive winding key, or by means of the combined Rail Gauge, Screwdriver and Spanner. If the gauge portion of either of these is slid along between the rails, any tight places will be immediately revealed. The rails should be eased apart gently at such spots. Special care should be taken to detect any place where the gauge is tight on curves, as any tightness there will have the effect of increasing considerably the resistance to the trains passing round the curves. It may even result in derailments owing to the wheels being squeezed up out of the track.

Connecting plates should be applied between the sleepers at rail joints wherever possible. They are essential in order to prevent the joints from parting, and in addition to those supplied with Train Sets and boxes of rails, they may be obtained separately at 4d. a dozen.

Miniature figures and luggage are essential to the realism of a Hornby Railway system. Their paint may require touching up in the course of the overhaul of equipment suggested in this article.

Occasionally it is found that rails, especially curves in new condition, when joined up by the connecting plates have a springiness that results in the sleepers not settling down quite flat. To remedy this state of affairs, each rail should be twisted over with the hands towards the centre of the circle or oval. This twisting must be done gently, a little at a time, with each rail in turn, until finally they are persuaded to settle down properly. After this operation has been performed it will be well to check the gauge of the rails again.

In the examination of track components, points and crossings should not be neglected. The latter can hardly get out of order to any greater extent than ordinary rails, and the same remedies therefore may be applied. The moving parts of points, however, especially the switch blades, should be examined, as they may require a little bending one way or the other to ensure that they line up at each end with the fixed rails. Even if points are inclined to be stiff it is not advisable to oil their moving parts, as it may cause them to become excessively loose. Friction here is an advantage in keeping the switch rails set correctly.

Signal Cabins, as shown here, and other buildings should not be neglected. The business-like appearance of the layout will be quite spoiled if these are shabby or damaged, so they should be carefully treated.

When the track is in order the locomotives and rolling stock should be taken in hand. As a rule after a period of storage the running of both engines and stock is apt to be somewhat sluggish. The oil used for lubrication probably will have become thick, and a certain amount of dust will have settled on the oily surfaces. To obtain free running, therefore, it is necessary to remove the old oil and the dust. Paraffin is useful for this purpose, but petrol is better still, as it evaporates quickly and leaves a clean, dry surface. In the case of locomotive mechanisms it is better that these should be removed from the housings of their locomotives. This allows the mechanism to be given a thorough washing with paraffin or petrol, whereas if it is left in the housing an oil can containing the liquid will have to be employed to reach the various remote parts. It is advisable to carry out operations involving the use of paraffin or petrol out of doors.

When the mechanism is clean and dry, its moving parts should be lightly oiled with Meccano Oil, which is of just the right consistency for the moving parts of clockwork mechanisms. It is a good scheme also to apply Meccano Graphite Grease to the spring of the mechanism. In order to do this effectively it will probably be necessary to use a small paint brush to apply the grease. On no account should a thick oil be used for the mechanisms of Hornby Clockwork Locomotives. Such oils, instead of assisting the running of a mechanism, may actually have a retarding effect owing to their heavy nature.

A point to be watched when carrying out these operations is that all wheel treads should be cleaned of the dirt that becomes rolled into them after a period of running. This is frequently due to over-oiling of the locomotives or rolling stock, with the result that the oil finds its way on to the wheels and on to the track. Dust then adheres with the result that in time a peculiar form of "mud" is found on the wheels. To obtain smooth and easy running therefore the wheel treads must be wiped perfectly clean with a rag soaked in a small quantity of petrol.

In the case of tenders and rolling stock generally where the wheels are inside the frames, it is a good plan to remove the wheels entirely for cleaning (*Continued on page 901*)

An Ingenious Meccano Splint

Readers will be interested in another instance of the adaptability of Meccano, described by Mr. P. Maynard Heath, F.R.C.S., of Fleet, Hants, in "*The British Medical Journal*." On one occasion, having to improvise an aeroplane splint, Mr. Heath decided to make use of Meccano, and with the assistance of Mr. P. Rouquette he produced the very successful splint shown in the accompanying illustration.

The main portion of the splint consists of six 5½″ × 3½″ Flat Plates, two for the chest piece, two for the arm and three for the forearm. The chest and arm pieces are joined together by two 1″ × 1″ Angle Brackets, and their extremities are joined by two 12½″ Angle Girders that in turn are braced together by two crossed 5½″ Strips. A third 12½″ Angle Girder supports the extremity of the forearm plate. The 12½″ Angle Girders are attached to the Flat Plates by ½″ × ½″ Angle Girders and small wing nuts and bolts. The two chest girdles, seen at the left of the illustration, consist of two 12½″ Braced Girders, and are flexible so that they can be bent round the chest.

The splint is easily adaptable for either side of the body, and to a certain extent is adjustable in size by varying the attachments of the various parts. The angle between arm and forearm pieces can also be altered.

"Sentinel" Locos—*(Cont. from page 873)*

the throttle valve will be more fully opened) can find its way as before through the charging valve to the low pressure receiver. Since the upper ball valve is on its seating, however, the steam can go no further, and it is now that the reducing valve begins to function.

The steam pressure in the low-pressure receiver must not exceed 145 lb. per square inch, or the safety valve will lift and allow the steam to escape to exhaust. But the steam at its first entry to the charging valve may be at a pressure of 500-550 lb. per sq. in. This high pressure acts from beneath on the ball at the bottom of the reducing valve, and tends to lift it off its seat, together with the "piston" above. The area on which the steam above can act is much greater than that below, so that if the pressure beyond the valve exceeds a certain limit, actually about 140 lb. per sq. in., the "piston" is forced down and the ball valve is pushed on to its seating, preventing the admission of steam. Actually, of course, the valve maintains the ratio between the steam pressure on its two sides, so that if the pressure on the high-pressure side is less than 500-550 lb. per sq. in. the valve will close before the pressure on the other side reaches 140 lb. per sq. in.

When the locomotive is running normally with the cut-off at some earlier position, neither of the two rods is holding a bell valve off its seat, and consequently no steam finds its way via the charging valve to the low pressure receiver.

In many respects the cab arrangements are similar to those found in any ordinary locomotive, but one or two controls are differently placed. As will be seen from the accompanying illustration of the cab, there is a control pillar on each side. The lever working in a slot controls the throttle valve. Its first motion opens a pilot valve, which admits steam to the space below the main valve and puts it in balance. Behind the throttle lever and in a convenient position for the driver there is a handle controlling the reversing gear. A scale and pointer alongside the throttle lever indicates the direction of travel and the setting of the cut-off.

The flexible connecting-rods of the screw-and-nut mechanism for the Stephenson link motions have already been mentioned. These flexible shafts are linked under the footplate to a gear-box that is operated by chains from the handles on the control columns. Beside the control columns on each side there can be seen in the illustration the hand levers that control the Westinghouse brakes. The levers for the rocking grates, and the hand wheels for the soot blowers, can be seen on each side of the fire-door. The big valve on the top of the boiler is the main stop valve. The other valves control the admission of steam to the sanding gear, Westinghouse pump, injector, feed pump, etc.

The working parts of the engines are lubricated by splash from the oil in the crank-cases, while the roller bearing journals of the axles, being grease lubricated, need only very occasional attention. For cylinder lubrication a mechanical lubricator is provided. It is driven off the right intermediate wheel journal end of the trailing bogie, and forces oil under pressure into a six-feed distributor mounted in the cab.

These "Sentinel" locomotives have many interesting advantages. For instance, where several vehicles are in service and boiler inspection can be carried out on a routine basis, a complete boiler can be quickly removed from a locomotive and replaced by another. Similarly, when an engine requires overhauling it is a matter of little difficulty or expenditure of time to remove the engine and axle complete and substitute another. Further, the low axle weights, combined with the fact that the wheels and axles are in perfect running balance, reduce wear on the track, while the uniform torque gives a high factor of adhesion. The "Woolnough" boiler, it is claimed, is capable of raising steam in less than half the time that would be required for an ordinary locomotive boiler for the same power, and with a steam consumption by the compound engines of 13 lb. per B.H.P. hour it is believed that a 50 per cent. saving in fuel burned will be obtainable.

Junior Section—*(Continued from page 911)*

and at the same time to take the opportunity of clearing any dirt from the frames and bearings themselves. It is surprising what an amount of dirt can be picked up by the running gear of miniature rolling stock. Special attention should be paid to the journals or bearing portions of the axles as their oily condition tends to collect dirt.

After refitting the wheels of the various vehicles and attending to their lubrication, it will be as well to examine the couplings of the different items of rolling stock. Bent couplings should be straightened with pliers and it is essential to see that the couplings are able to swing freely on the pivots securing them to the vehicles to which they belong. The sharp curves of miniature railway systems require the couplings to move sideways when a train is passing round them. To avoid

An interesting aeroplane splint constructed in Meccano. For this illustration we are indebted to the courtesy of the Editor of "The British Medical Journal."

any trouble owing to undue friction, therefore, special attention should be paid to the couplings, not only the hooks but also their attendant links. In addition to being bent sideways, couplings may have become distorted in an upward or downward direction. Faults of this kind should be corrected, for to ensure that the couplings function properly under all conditions they must be in correct alignment. The straightening of couplings that are bent up or down is more difficult to carry out than in the case of those bent sideways, but using small pliers little trouble should be experienced.

Another Engineering Problem

The problem published on page 66 of the "*M.M.*" of January last attracted considerable attention, and we now give details of another similar problem. The piece of steel illustrated here measures 4″ × ½″ × 3/16″ and has in its centre a shallow slot shaped as shown. The slot does not penetrate right through the metal but only about halfway, and it measures approximately ½″ × ¼″ × ⅛″ deep. The slot was made by means of a flat file, and readers are invited to test their skill in finding the method in which the job was done. The correct solution will appear in a future issue of the "*M.M.*"

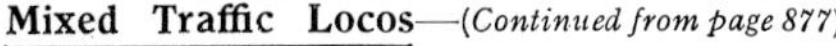

Mixed Traffic Locos—*(Continued from page 877)*

train is stationary, and a vacuum pump driven off the left-hand crosshead performs the same function while running.

Sanding apparatus of the mechanical trickle type delivers sand to the front of the leading coupled wheels and to the front and rear of the middle coupled wheels. In addition to this a de-sanding apparatus is embodied, which comes into use automatically, so that after the engine has used the sand, in the forward or reverse direction as the case may be, the rails are cleaned with hot water to prevent interference with the track circuits.

To obtain smooth riding the draw gear between engine and tender is designed with buffing spindles controlled by coiled springs. These spindles have specially designed heads that ride on an inclined plane provided on the rear engine buffer beam. The tenders fitted to these locomotives are of the new 4,000 gallon type carried on six wheels. The coal bunker, which has a capacity for nine tons of coal, has been carefully arranged so that as far as possible the coal will be self-trimming. A bunker door gives access to the coal space from the footplate, and there is ample tool box accommodation. The sides of the bunker, which are very high, are turned inward along their top edges; and this feature, in conjunction with the comparatively low rear end of the tender, gives the vehicle a remarkable and distinctive appearance.

(Continued at foot of next column

Planning a New Railway—*(Cont. from page 879)*

way and fencing, sidings, junctions, stations, land and buildings, and signalling.

The Company's secretary now assembles the various plans and documents and hands them to the Company's Parliamentary Agents, who deposit what will be called the Menton Railway Bill at the Houses of Parliament. The last date for this in any year is 30th November, if the Bill is to be considered in the next Session.

The Bill passes through Parliament in various stages, the chief being Committee, during which it will be closely scrutinised and, if there is any opposition to it, compromise on certain parts may be necessary. However, we will suppose that, except for small amendments, our Bill has survived, so that about June it receives the Royal Assent, and becomes the Menton Railway Act, 1934.

The Engineer now gets his instructions to make the working survey. For this, the 25-in. to the mile Ordnance Sheets, or simply 25-in. sheets as they are called, are obtained, and as these show individual buildings, slight deviations of the line to avoid property can be planned on them. Of course all changes must be made inside "the limits of deviation" as already explained. Extra levels and cross sections are taken at some places to enable improvements to be schemed. After the amended line has been drawn on the 25-in. sheets, they are made into a roll as with the 6-in., and this is taken out and the line pegged out from it. Wooden pegs, 2 in. square and about 18 in. long, are put in at every chain. Every tenth one has a marker peg driven alongside it on the slant. Beginnings and ends of curves are also specially marked.

With this as a base line, a careful survey is made, going a bit wider each side than the railway fence is estimated to be, and levels are taken and a section drawn, together with cross sections where the ground is rough. This enables the working plan and section to be produced. The plan shows radii of all curves, span, width, height and description of bridges, numbers of the drawings showing bridge details, level crossings, road and stream diversions, culverts, and so on. The section shows formation level, that is, top of embankment and bottom of cutting, not rail level. Fence lines, and the tops and bottoms of slopes, are also shown on the plan.

The gradient line on the section can be varied within the limits of deviation, 5 ft. country or 2 ft. town, and a great deal of experience is necessary in fixing this. Stations should if possible be on the level, but must not be on a steeper grade than 1 in 260. Two gradients should not meet to form a dip in the tunnel or cutting, as if they do, drainage will be difficult. One main principle is to equalise the cuttings and embankments if at all possible, because if there is too much excavation it will have to be tipped to waste on land bought for the purpose, and if too little to form the embankments it will have to be dug out of land specially bought for it. Allowance has to be made also for the nature of the material and the angles of the slopes of the cuttings and embankments.

All new works such as bridges and culverts will be described above the section, at the place where they occur, in red ink, all existing details such as roads being marked in black ink.

The detailed working drawings of the separate structures, such as stations and buildings, will then be prepared, and from these the Specifications and Bills of Quantities. The former may be described as the engineering conditions that have to be fulfilled, the latter being the statement of the calculated amounts of the various materials and workmanship in the structures. When these are ready the Engineer will be in a position to let contracts for the work. The number of contracts into which the work is divided is decided, and selected firms are asked to tender for the work. The tenders are delivered sealed to the Secretary of the Company on or before a specified date. They take the form of a priced Bill of Quantities, showing what the Contractor's charges will be for the various operations. The time he requires in which to do the work is usually also an important consideration. It is possible of course that the same firm may get more than one contract. Generally, but not always, the work goes to the lowest tender.

We have now seen something of the history of the planning of a railway, from the time when a few individuals have the idea that such a thing would be desirable, up to the day when some person of note performs the ceremony of cutting the first sod. Let us hope that the optimism of the promoters will meet with its reward!

On the left-hand side of the tender is a special recess conveniently arranged to accommodate all the necessary firing irons. The tender is fitted with a water scoop, and the handles for controlling this and the tender hand brake are arranged vertically, bevel wheels transferring the motion to their respective gears.

Of these locomotives, which are to be numbered from 5000 upward, Nos. 5000 to 5019 are being built at Crewe, and 100 each by the Vulcan Foundry Ltd. and Sir W. G. Armstrong Whitworth and Co. Ltd. The first 10 of the class to be delivered by the Vulcan Foundry Ltd., Nos. 5020 to 5029, have been sent to Perth and some are sharing in the work on the Highland Section of the L.M.S.R. in place of the Highland "Clans," most of which have been transferred for duties on the Oban line.

The Fastest Four-Engined Air Liner

For Australian Empire Air Mail Service

THE history of Imperial Airways shows that the increase in popularity of air transport has been directly influenced by the improvements that have been made in the comfort and accommodation for the passengers, and also in the reliability of the engines, and consequent increase in safety. The single-engined machines that were first used for passenger work in the early days quickly gave way to more roomy and safe types employing two engines, and these eventually were replaced by triple-engined machines. The latest aeroplanes that have been built for Imperial Airways, such as the Armstrong Whitworth "Atalanta," the Handley Page "Heracles" and the Short "Scipio" flying boat, are all of the four-engined type. In view of these facts it is only natural that a four-engined liner should have been selected to operate the section of the England-Australian air line between Singapore and Brisbane, which involves a 512-mile crossing of the shark-infested Timor Sea.

The machine that has been chosen for this work is a new de Havilland product that has been given the type-name "Diana," and the story of how it was selected is interesting. When the Australian Commonwealth Government decided to inaugurate the Singapore-Brisbane service, tenders were called for from companies willing to undertake its operation. The requirements provided that the machines to be used should have a cruising speed of not less than 95 m.p.h. for the first two years, and that after this they should be replaced by aeroplanes capable of cruising at speeds of at least 110 m.p.h. If a company intended to employ during the first two years machines capable of cruising at 110 m.p.h., however, they would be allowed to use the same type for the whole period of five years. The aeroplanes were also required to be of the multi-engined type, capable of flying level at an altitude of 2,000 ft. with one engine cut out, and with a cruising range of not less than 600 miles against a head wind of 30 m.p.h.

At the same time that the conditions of tender were published, the Managing Director of Queensland and Northern Territory Aerial Services Ltd., the well-known Australian air line company whose lines were described in our issue for May 1933, was in England negotiating with Imperial Airways Ltd. for collaboration between the two companies with a view to securing the tender. Qantas Empire Airways was eventually formed as a joint company, consisting of representatives of the English and Australian air line companies, and the directors began to look about for a suitable type of machine. The de Havilland Aircraft Co. Ltd. had been planning a new air liner for some time, and as they were able to state confidently that their machine would not only be capable

The upper photograph on this page, published by courtesy of "The Aeroplane," shows the first machine of the D.H. "Diana" class. The lower illustration shows the cockpit of a "Diana." This photograph, and the two on the opposite page, are published by courtesy of Imperial Airways Ltd.

of conforming to the Australian requirements but also of exceeding them by a fairly wide margin, one of these machines was ordered.

One of the most important conditions of the Australian Government was that any machine tendered for the service must have received a certificate of airworthiness dated not later than 31st January 1934. The contract for the D.H. machine was not placed until four months before this closing date, when only preliminary sketches had been prepared and every detail of the machine still had to be designed before manufacture could start. In addition, a new engine intended to be used in the machine still had to be perfected and put through the Air Ministry type test. The work of design and production was rushed through with great speed, however, and on 14th January the machine made its first flight. The certificate of airworthiness was eventually obtained on 30th January, one day before the final permissible date!

The nose and engines of "Delphinus," a liner of the "Diana" class owned by Imperial Airways. The shape of the nose differs from that of the one shown on the opposite page owing to alterations that have been made in the layout of the pilot's cabin.

The machine that has been rushed together in this manner is a biplane somewhat similar in general external appearance to the D.H. "Dragon." The pilot, for instance, is carried right in the nose of the fuselage, which is very blunt; while the upper and lower wings are both connected to the fuselage. The "Diana" differs from the "Dragon" in the fact that there are four engines instead of two, all four being carried in nacelles mounted in the leading edge of the lower wing; and also in that the wings are of extremely narrow chord. They are in fact probably narrower than those of any other big biplane built in this country.

When "Gipsy Six" engines are employed, the "Diana" has a top speed of more than 170 m.p.h. and cruises at 145 m.p.h. for a distance of 450 miles when carrying 10 passengers. The worst section of the journey on which the machine is to operate is the crossing of the Timor Sea, and it should be quite capable of this task, for with one engine stopped a height of 15,000 ft. can be maintained even when carrying full load.

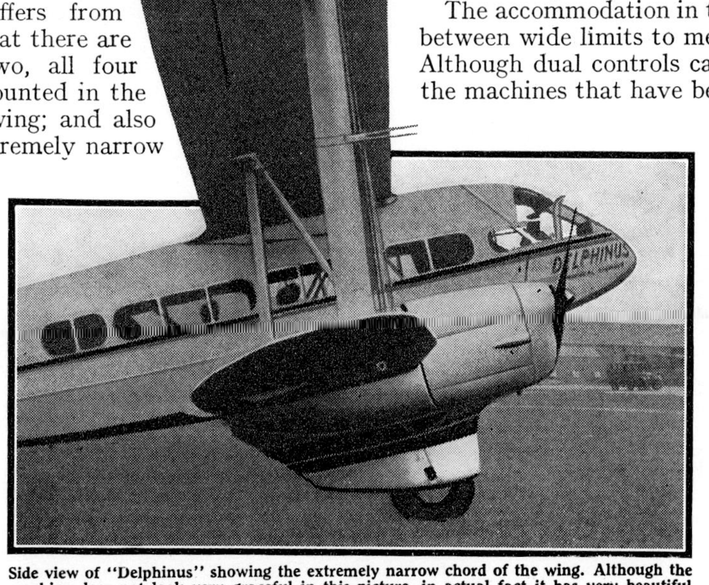

Side view of "Delphinus" showing the extremely narrow chord of the wing. Although the machine does not look very graceful in this picture, in actual fact it has very beautiful lines when seen in the air.

Even if two engines on the same side should stop, the machine could still remain in the air with the pilot in full control, and in fact it would be possible to turn against the running engines.

The "Diana" follows modern de Havilland practice in being built almost entirely of wood, and it is the first machine to be produced incorporating a new method of using plywood and spruce. This method has been evolved for the fuselage, which is 43 ft. 11 in. in length and consists primarily of a three-ply box. It differs from most fuselages by the fact that the plywood is inside the box, and the spruce longerons, struts and stringers are outside it. There is then a covering of fabric, and the space between it and the three-ply is filled with special sound-insulating material. The fabric is provided with Zip-fasteners near the control wires at the tail of the fuselage, so that they can easily be examined.

The wings are 44 ft. in span and are of normal construction, consisting of wooden spars and spruce ribs covered with plywood and fabric, although a tubular metal spar is used on the centre section as far as the inner engines. Ailerons are provided on both upper and lower planes, but only the lower ones are connected directly with the controls in the cockpit. They are joined to the upper ones by a streamlined steel tube, and thus when the bottom ones are moved those on top have to move in unison.

The accommodation in the "Diana" can be adapted between wide limits to meet individual requirements. Although dual controls can be arranged if necessary, the machines that have been built for Qantas Empire Airways are provided with only a single set. Behind the pilot is a seat and table for a navigator or radio operator, and the cabin comes next with, in a special long-distance luxury model, armchairs for eight passengers. Behind this is washing accommodation and a luggage hold. Other versions are available with 12 seats and accommodation for passengers' luggage or 14 seats and luggage; while there is also an air ferry model designed to carry 16 passengers.

The Railways of Switzerland

III.—Mountaineering by Rail

By "Observer"

AMONG the many triumphs achieved by Swiss engineers, perhaps the most astonishing are to be found in the wonderful mountain railways which, with daring enterprise, have been constructed, and are operating safely and efficiently, in places where it seemed utterly impossible that railways could be either built or worked. Some of these lines scale the face of seemingly inaccessible heights and attain to amazing altitudes. From Zermatt, the Gornergrat line climbs to over 10,000 ft. above sea-level; and even this is surpassed by the Jungfrau Railway, which achieves a height of more than 11,000 ft.

The Gornergrat station, 10,140 ft. above sea level. This and the other illustrations to this article are reproduced by courtesy of the Swiss Federal Railways.

Some of the mountain railways are of considerable length and traverse regions of marvellous beauty and engrossing interest. Among these may be mentioned the Bernina, Rhaetian and Furka-Oberalp Railways, and the line from Brigue via Visp to Zermatt. These are all metre gauge railways, with many formidable gradients, and worked in places on the rack-and-pinion system.

Other railways have been built for the specific purpose of ascending particular peaks and enabling visitors to reach famous view-points or engage in the sports that may be enjoyed on Alpine heights. Of such, the railways up the Rigi, Pilatus, Niesen and Rothorn are well-known examples. These mountain railways are of various gauges and are operated by different methods. Some are funicular, or cable, railways, while others have the rack-and-pinion system; and although many are worked by electric power, there are still some in which steam is the motive agent. Of purely rack-and-pinion lines there are 15 now in operation in Switzerland, and 13 other lines where rack working is employed only on the steepest sections, ordinary adhesion methods being used on the easier portions. There are also 52 "funiculars," including one that claims to be the steepest railway in the world. It is situated at Piotta, on the St. Gotthard route, and ascends to Piora, rising 2,145 ft. in $\frac{7}{8}$ mile, the maximum gradient being slightly steeper than one in $1\frac{1}{4}$!

Emerging from a tunnel on to the Wolfort Viaduct on the Pilatus rack railway. The steam coach shown is of special construction in view of the severe gradients.

Another extraordinary form of transport provided in the Alps is that of the wire-rope aerial suspension line. Of this type of railway there is at present only one actually operating in Switzerland. It runs from Gerschnialp up to Trübsee, near Engelberg. Formerly there was a line of this kind up the Wetterhorn at Grindelwald. The remains of it may still be seen, but damage caused by avalanches resulted in its being closed. In the French Alps, in the neighbourhood of Mont Blanc and Chamonix there are several of these suspension railways, one of which has a swing, without any intervening support, of 4,430 ft.

The first rack-rail mountain railway to be built in Europe was that up the Rigi, the massive ridge of mountains situated between the lakes of Lucerne, Zug and Lowerz. This was opened in 1871, and runs from Vitznau, at the base of the mountain, on the shores of Lake Lucerne, and pursues a winding course up the mountain side until the Kulm is reached at an altitude of 5,905 ft. The length of the line is 4.38 miles and its maximum gradient 1 in 5. Steam traction is employed, the locomotives being specially designed with a central cogwheel that works on a rack laid between the rails. The average speed is about 5 m.p.h. and the engine is located, as is customary on all extremely steep railways, at the lower end of the passenger coach. The views obtained both from the summit and during the journey are of great splendour. Another railway, using electric power, has more recently been constructed up the other side of the Rigi, starting from Arth-Goldau, an important junction, where connections are given with the St. Gotthard and other routes.

Probably the most popular of the Swiss mountain railways is the one up Mount Pilatus, which was finished in 1888. This is a shorter but much steeper line than the Rigi. It starts from Alpnachstad on the Lake of Lucerne, and in rather less than 3 miles climbs 5,344 ft. and attains to the Pilatus-Kulm station, 6,791 ft. above the level of the sea. The maximum gradient is 1 in 2, the average 1 in 3, and the easiest 1 in 5. There are several tunnels, and the permanent way is extraordinarily strong and solid. The rails are secured to huge granite blocks cemented in the mountain side, construction of this nature being necessary to provide against the tendency rails would have to slide down if laid at such an acute inclination on ordinary sleepers, especially when trains were ascending or descending. For the sure control of the train on its descent, and as a precaution in case of mishap, no less than four separate systems of braking are provided.

Owing to the abnormally steep gradients a specially-devised form of rack-rail is employed, having teeth, not on the upper edge as is usual, but on both of its sides, into which horizontal cogged wheels fitted to the locomotive engage.

Another remarkable mountain railway, that up the Jungfrau, near Interlaken, has the distinction of being the highest railway in Europe. It mounts to an altitude of 11,342 ft. and takes the wondering traveller well up towards the summit of that noble peak. This railway took 14 years to build, and lies for the greater part of its length in the interior of the mighty snow-clad Alps. One great advantage gained by thus tunnelling through the rock is that protection is thereby provided for the track against avalanches and landslides. The lower terminus of the Jungfrau line is at Kleine Schiedegg, 6,770 ft. above the sea, which can be reached by the railways that climb thither from both Lauterbrunnen and Grindelwald.

A striking view on the way to Jungfraujoch, giving a good idea of the remarkable scenery visible from the mountain railways of Switzerland.

The first stage, the 1¼ miles to Eiger Glacier station, is mostly in the open and comparatively easy, with a gradient of 1 in 8. Beyond that the line goes up for much of the way at an inclination of 1 in 4 through the tunnel that was cut out laboriously by means of electric drills in the hard limestone rock. The bore is 10 ft. wide and 14 ft. 3 in. high, and has a semi-circular roof. It is lighted throughout, and the trains, which are electrically propelled, take about 20 min. to pass through it. There are intermediate stations at Eigerwand and Eismeer, and these also are part of the tunnel, enlarged to form a hall in each case and to give all necessary accommodation. The upper terminus is at Jungfraujoch station, and this again is hewn out of the solid rock and has large plate-glass windows through which an enthralling panorama may be seen.

Among the longer journeys that can be made by mountain railways in Switzerland, one of the most pleasurable is to travel from Brigue through Visp to Zermatt, and then to go forward over the yet steeper line to the Gornergrat. Although the line from Brigue to Zermatt is laid to the metre gauge, the modern rolling stock is surprisingly spacious and comfortable. The first-class is up to the best "Pullman" standard and the second-class is quite luxurious. In both, the wood-work, metal-work and upholstery are exceedingly tasteful and attractive, and the large frameless windows make observation of the scenery delightfully easy. The third-class coaches are also excellent, but like most Swiss "thirds" have no cushions.

The Matterhorn Peak seen from the Gornergrat Railway. This photograph shows the pyramidal form of this remarkable mountain.

After leaving Brigue the line runs for 5½ miles along the bottom of the Rhone Valley, side by side with the standard-gauge lines of the Swiss Federal Railways; while on the hillside on the right the Lötschberg line can be seen steadily ascending. At Visp, the Zermatt line turns away to the left and enters upon the arduous ascent of the Visp and St. Nicholas valleys, which are famed for the rare magnificence of their scenery. For mile after mile the railway keeps close to the foaming torrent of the Visp, and at different stages of the journey an imposing succession of giant peaks may be seen, until at length, as the train curves round just before Zermatt is reached, the peerless pyramid of the Matterhorn breaks into view. The valley is particularly grand and impressive in the neighbourhood of Stalden where it forks, the left hand branch going up to the much-favoured resort of Saas Fee.

This Visp-Zermatt line is now operated by electric traction, separate locomotives being employed; but previously steam was used, and some traces of the former method still remain in the form of disused hydrants and other provision for steam locomotives. Of the 21¾ miles between Visp and Zermatt, 4⅝ have to be worked by rack-and-pinion, the steepest gradient being 1 in 8. On the sections worked by ordinary adhesion, the maximum rise is at 1 in 40. Altogether the line ascends from 2,140 ft. at Visp to 5,315 ft. above sea level at Zermatt. The speed on the rack sections ranges from 8½ to 12½ m.p.h., while on favourable stretches of the ordinary sections as much as 28 m.p.h. may be reached. The time taken for the 27¼ miles from Brigue to Zermatt, including stops, is 1 hr. 50 min.

From Zermatt, that incomparable Alpine mountaineering centre, the journey is continued in an electric narrow-gauge train, operated on the rack-and-pinion system, that climbs resolutely for six miles to the summit at the Gornergrat, 10,140 ft. above sea-level, the maximum gradient being 1 in 5 and the time taken 1¼ hr. Although this altitude is rather less than that attained by the Jungfrau line, yet for the Gornergrat railway it is claimed that it is the highest open-air railway in Europe, because except for a few short tunnels the line is in the open all the way.

Just above Zermatt the train passes over a fine viaduct thrown across the deep gorge of the Findelen, and proceeds through larch woods and grassy slopes, gay with a gorgeous profusion of Alpine flowers, to the first intermediate station at Riffelalp. In the higher stages beyond Riffelberg, after the tree line has been passed, vegetation becomes more and more scanty, until before the summit is reached, a region of perpetual snow and ice has been entered. At the summit one gazes spellbound on more than 50 glaciers and a seemingly countless array of mighty peaks.

A Minute I Shall Never Forget

By Commander Attilio Gatti

DURING my stay in the Lukanga country on my last expedition from Cape to Cairo I met a Dutch hunter who invited me to go with him on a buffalo hunt. I learned later, to my disgust, that this individual followed the unsavoury profession of slaughtering wild animals to sell their flesh to the natives in the mines. When I met him he seemed a pleasant-enough chap, however, and I accepted his invitation with alacrity.

We set out at once on foot followed by native gun-bearers, and after an hour's march came in view of a wide stretch of plain covered by reeds, which during the day was the resting place of a huge herd of some 500 buffaloes. A small river about thirty feet wide crossed the plain at this point, and my companion posted me on one bank behind an immense antheap.

"You stay there," he told me in quite a dictatorial tone, "and I'll go on the other side of the stream. In about ten minutes the herd will come out to drink."

I did not relish his air of command, but it was too late to protest, for he hurried away to cross the river, wading through the water, which came up to his shoulders.

A short halt for lunch, on our way to the Lukanga swamps.

Ten minutes, half an hour, passed without a single buffalo putting in an appearance, and without my being able to discover where the hunter had stationed himself. The longer I waited, the more distasteful it seemed to me to stay comfortably hidden until the animals came peacefully down to drink and then shoot them from ambush. So, finally, I stepped out from behind the antheap, handed my rifle to my boy, and started to walk toward the reeds, calmly filling my pipe with no sense of impending danger.

Then, suddenly, I heard a far thundering, and the ground trembled beneath my feet. The curtain of reeds parted violently, and in an instant the horizon seemed filled with hundreds of huge animals trotting in my direction.

"Rifle," I said, stretching out my hand and keeping my eyes fixed on the buffaloes.

"Hey, give me that rifle," I repeated. Hearing no answer of any kind I looked behind me. My boy was running away, had reached the edge of the stream and was about to cross it. I yelled at him. He hesitated for a moment, then threw the rifle on the ground and jumped into the water.

Bang! Bang! Bang! Three shots, one after another, sounded near me. A furious bellowing answered from the herd, and I saw a big bull fall to his knees. Two others jumped high in the air and then started at a quick gallop, followed by the whole grand mass of powerful brutes.

I started running toward my rifle, when two other shots came from the other side of the stream. And in that second I fell flat on the ground with a violent pain in my left foot. My first thought, of course, was that I had been hit by a bullet, but I found that I had stepped into a hole in the ground, spraining, or perhaps breaking the bone of my ankle.

I made a desperate effort to get up, but although the rifle and the river were less than thirty yards from me, and that oncoming sea of horns provided me with plenty of impetus, my foot refused to support me.

Bang! Bang! The shots meanwhile continued. Had he gone crazy, that Dutchman, or was he trying to save me? I managed to stand on my right foot and waved my arms in the air to show him where I was, meanwhile shouting at the top of my lungs in the hope of frightening the buffaloes, who were now about fifty feet from me.

Forty—thirty feet, and I saw the leaders lower their big crooked horns in a fine position to gore me. I shouted and waved my arms more than ever, but I must confess I closed my eyes, sure that it would soon all be over for me.

That was a minute I shall never forget!

Then I felt encompassed by noise, dust, movement, and an acrid odour. I opened my eyes, and nearly lost my equilibrium at the dizzy passage of heavy bodies that almost brushed me on either side. Others and others followed, but at the shouting and gesturing I continued instinctively to make, they snorted when they reached a point some ten or twelve feet from me, and swerving sharply to the left or right, swept past me.

At last the crazy charge was over, and a quick glance around showed me the big cloud of dust rolling on and several huge bodies stretched immobile on the ground. Sick at the sight of the poor animals butchered by that Dutchman, I hopped on my one good foot to the edge of the river.

Using my rifle as a cane I made all haste to cross before the buffaloes could circle around and return to the spot.

MECCANO MAGAZINE

Editorial Office:
Binns Road, Liverpool 13
England

Volume XX. No. 10
October, 1935

With the Editor

Brains Unlimited

I see that the old subject of brain versus brawn aroused the interest of the scientists who attended the meeting of the British Association at Norwich last month. Nowadays scientists know quite a lot about brains, even if they cannot explain exactly how these enable us to think and invent. Brains are extremely delicate mechanisms, and curiously enough it is this very delicacy that has enabled us to follow their development through the ages, because it has been necessary for Nature to protect them by enclosing them in a thick bony box or case. There are no fossilised brains in the ordinary sense of the word, but the boxes in which they were enclosed have been preserved in the case of many of the creatures of the past, and these boxes show us at least the size of their contents.

We may congratulate ourselves on having the best developed brains of all the creatures that have ruled the Earth. The tyrants of the reptile age grew to huge dimensions, but their brains did not increase in proportion. One of these monsters that weighed about 20 tons had a brain no larger than an egg, which gave it only about a quarter of an ounce of brain to every ton of body and limb. We are much better equipped, for on the average we have nearly half a hundredweight of brain per ton of body. Unfortunately, however, the possession of a large brain does not necessarily mean great ability, for weighty thoughts often arise in brains far below the average in size. A big head is an even less reliable guide!

This revival of interest in brains reminded me of a famous book, *"The First Men in the Moon,"* by Mr. H. G. Wells. In this the author describes the imaginary inhabitants of the Moon who are supposed to have reached a later stage of development than exists on Earth. Many of the Moon people indeed have developed to such a pitch that their brains have burst the bounds of a comparatively tiny box such as that in which our own brains are confined. Their heads have become wobbling jelly-like masses, so far exceeding their bodies in weight and size that the unfortunate owners are unable to walk and have to be carried about! They are in fact, merely gigantic thinking machines. The greatest of all the Moon people is the Grand Lunar himself, a creature with a dwarfed body and shrivelled limbs, but whose brain is a mighty engine that has to be sprayed by attendants in order to keep it cool! Let us hope that such a fate is not in store for the future inhabitants of our planet.

The G.W.R. "Centenary Special" near Badminton on its run from London to Bristol on 31st August last. The locomotive is No. 6000 "King George V." Photograph by W. Vaughan-Jenkins, Bath.

Are Speed Records Worth While?

The announcement that Sir Malcolm Campbell in *"Blue Bird"* raised the land speed record to 301.129 miles an hour on the Salt Flats at Salduro in the United States has again brought up the question of the value of record-breaking. Some people tell us that efforts to achieve such enormous speeds are sheer waste and have no practical value, for we shall never require to travel so fast in ordinary life. It is certainly interesting that Sir Malcolm's last two efforts to raise the record have come at a time when speeds in built-up areas are being restricted to 30 miles an hour, or only a tenth of his record speed; but that is only one side of the story. The perfection of the present-day motor car is due largely to the experience gained by automobile engineers in designing engines to attain the ever higher speeds demanded by Sir Malcolm and other record breakers, and by tyre manufacturers in making tyres capable of withstanding the enormous strains involved. If the automobile industry had never been called upon to provide anything faster than the ordinary touring car, it certainly would not have reached its present efficiency.

At any rate I am sure that all readers will join me in congratulating Sir Malcolm in achieving his great ambition to travel at the rate of five miles a minute.

Our "Footplate Trip" Articles

The articles by "A Railway Engineer" describing footplate trips on various well-known locomotives have been received with great enthusiasm, as I felt sure would be the case. There is something specially fascinating about a run on the footplate, and these articles provide a very realistic substitute for an opportunity that comes to few of us. Readers will be interested to know that further articles are in preparation; these will deal with locomotives of the S.R. and the G.W.R. and also with Irish locomotives.

A new feature this month is the account by Mr. O. S. Nock of a trip from Liverpool to Belfast in the motor ship *"Ulster Queen."* Mr. Nock will follow this with other articles dealing with cross-channel services, and with a trip along the West Coast of Scotland and among the islands of the Hebrides. I have often been asked for articles of this kind, and I shall be glad to know what readers think of the new series.

Giant Creeper Cranes at Work

Building the Arch of Sydney Harbour Bridge

THE opening to traffic of the Sydney Harbour Bridge, Australia, on 19th March, 1932, marked the completion of one of the greatest engineering feats of recent years. The mighty structure is the largest arch bridge in the world, and its building was followed with increasing interest, not only by the people of Sydney and the surrounding district, among them thousands who daily crossed Sydney Harbour by ferry steamer to and from their business in the city, but also by engineers and others in all parts of the world.

The most spectacular part of the work undoubtedly was the erection of the great arch that springs from huge granite abutment towers on each side of the harbour and crosses the water in a single span 1,650 ft. long. At its crown this arch has a clear height of 170 ft. above high water. It had to be built without interference with the shipping passing into or out of the harbour, and the builders of the bridge, Dorman Long and Co. Ltd., of Middlesbrough, therefore adopted a method similar to that employed when they erected the arch bridge across the River Tyne, described in the "*M.M.*" of March 1931. The shore ends of the arch were begun simultaneously, and the two sections of the structure were built out from both sides of the harbour with the aid of two immense cranes designed to creep along the arch itself as it was completed and to hoist into position the steelwork for the next section to be erected. These cranes are of the type described as "creeper" cranes and they were specially built for the work by The Wellman Smith Owen Engineering Corporation Ltd., of London and Darlaston. They were first erected at the maker's works, and after being thoroughly tested were dismantled and shipped to Sydney, where they were re-assembled on the approach spans of the bridge.

One of the 120-ton creeper cranes at work, erecting the southern half of the arch of the Sydney Harbour Bridge. This illustration and the upper one on the opposite page are reproduced by courtesy of The Wellman Smith Owen Engineering Corporation Ltd., London and Darlaston.

Each crane weighed 600 tons and was capable of lifting 120 tons at a radius of 54 ft., and the special safety gear with which it was provided increased the total weight to 633 tons. It was built up on a structural steel undercarriage 148 ft. wide that extended across the full width of the arch of the bridge and overhung the main trusses by 25 ft. The undercarriage consisted of a rectangular framework formed by two transverse girders and two side girders over the chords, and was mounted upon four bogies that travelled upon the two outer top main booms, or chords, of the arch. Each had four unflanged wheels running directly upon the flange plates of these chords. The front bogies were fitted with horizontal guide rollers that bore against the flange plates, and both front and rear bogies had safety clips to prevent any possibility of the structure tilting.

The gear for hauling the crane up the chords was mounted in the rear part of the undercarriage and consisted of a double drum winch driven by a 50 h.p. motor. The ropes from the drums passed through an 8 to 1 sheave gear to an anchor incorporated in plates attached to the chord in front of the crane, and the winch was provided with ratchet and clutch gear so that if required each drum could be operated independently while the other was kept stationary. The purpose of this was to enable the crane to be hauled centrally along the true line of the bridge.

The main hoist was operated by two 120 h.p. motors and could lift the maximum load of 120 tons at a speed of 12½ ft. per min., so that more than half-an-hour was required to raise a bridge member from the harbour to the upper parts of the arch. Derricking was effected by means of two 50 h.p. motors operating through spur and bevel reduction gearing, and the maximum load could be derricked throughout the full range in five minutes. Cross traverse gear was provided to enable the crane to be moved across the full width of the arch, and this was operated by a 50 h.p. motor geared to toothed wheels that engaged with a rack on the undercarriage. The speed of the traverse with a load of 120 tons was 30 ft. per min., and special switches automatically reduced this speed when the crane came within 10 ft. of either side of the undercarriage.

In addition to the main hoist each crane had a supplementary or "jigger" hoist that was operated from the main jib and could lift a load of 20 tons at a speed of 25 ft. per min. This could be used for light loads, but was chiefly employed in adjusting the angles of bridge members lifted by the main hoists, in order that they could be fitted exactly into their correct positions. Thus it worked in conjunction with the main hoist, and in spite of their great lifting capacity the two cranes were very delicate in action, and the positions of their loads could be controlled to a very small fraction of an inch.

The arch completed. The cranes then worked their way back to the shores, erecting the deck hangers and deck as they went, and this photograph shows the first deck hanger in position.

Other smaller cranes included in the equipment of the creeper were two $2\frac{1}{2}$-ton derrick cranes, each driven by a 10 h.p. motor, that were required for dealing with stores, riveting stages and other requirements. They were carried on a frame that was attached to the back of the traversing carriage and was adjustable, so that it could accommodate the two cranes to the varying slope of the upper chord of the arch. These two cranes could be swung completely round, and thus could be used to transfer material from the back of the creeper to the front. They also were used for placing workmen in position to bolt and rivet together the bridge members.

The crane system was completed by a 5-ton crane that travelled on a track 50 ft. in length laid along the front girder of the undercarriage. It was equipped with slewing gear that enabled it to command the whole breadth of the steel structure as far as the arch trusses, and was of great service as the principal means of access to the working positions on the arch, especially during the later stages of erection.

A closer view of one of the creeper cranes and its "assistants."

The creeper cranes were capable of advance up a slope of 20 deg. at the rate of 1 ft. per min. As each weighed 600 tons, any failure of the haulage gear might have had very serious results, and on the steep slope of the chords on which they travelled a slip of even one inch might have given the immense masses sufficient momentum to overcome any practicable resistance. Safety gear therefore was designed to come into action instantly and automatically if any failure of the haulage gear should occur.

In building the bridge, the construction of the southern half of the great arch was begun first and considerable progress was made in building the first panel on that side before the second creeper crane came into action on the northern half of the arch. When the respective first panels were completed the cranes advanced slowly under their own power over a temporary ramp on to the panels, which at the bottom were bolted to the main bearings of the bridge and at the top were secured by heavy steel cables firmly anchored in concrete. From their new positions the cranes erected the second panel of each half of the span, and afterwards advanced along the top chords of the structure. In this way they travelled forward panel by panel, in each new position building one panel of the arch in advance of themselves.

From the time when each half of the arch began to project well over the water until its construction was completed the steel members required were placed on barges, floated into position beneath the projecting end of the arch and lifted up to the working level by the main hoist of the creeper cranes. All crane movements were controlled by telephonic communication between the cabs of the cranes and the barges hundreds of feet below. The greatest quantity of steelwork lifted from the barges in one day was 598 tons.

Each half of the arch comprised 14 panels, and when these were completed, and the two sections were joined together, the cranes began to work their way back to their starting points, on the way erecting the hangers and other portions of the deck of the bridge and its supporting structure. The largest of the hangers is 193 ft. in length and weighs 38 tons. The railway and roadway stringers for the deck, which are connected to the hangers by pins 14 in. in diameter, were erected in one piece. The scheme of hanger erection adopted enabled rapid progress to be made, and within nine months of the closing of the arch the steelwork erection of the big main span was completed.

Throughout the arduous and exacting task of erecting the two halves of the arch, the deck hangers and deck itself, the cranes operated with the utmost precision.

We are indebted to the Wellman Smith Owen Engineering Co. Ltd. for the information contained in this article.

Footplate Runs on the L.N.E.R.

V.—The "Mikados"

By a Railway Engineer

TO say that the new 2–8–2 express engines *"Cock o' the North"* and *"Earl Marischal"* are setting up entirely new standards of performance on the Edinburgh-Aberdeen route is to put the case very mildly indeed. Their superiority even over the "Pacifics," is amazing. Southbound from Aberdeen, where "Atlantics" are limited to 340 tons and "Pacifics" to 420, the new engines are rostered to take 550 tons tare, which, with a well-filled train, would mean a gross load of nearly 600 tons behind the tender. At present *"Cock o' the North"* is stationed at Haymarket, and is making two return trips a day from Edinburgh to Dundee; while *"Earl Marischal"* working from Dundee shed, is making the run from there to Aberdeen and back twice daily.

"Earl Marischal" ready to start from Aberdeen in charge of the 10-20 a.m. express. This photograph shows very clearly the smoke-deflecting side sheets that have been fitted outside the original smoke-box casing plates of this locomotive.

My first experience of *"Earl Marischal"* was on the down *"Aberdonian."* The load was 482 tons tare and 515 tons gross, and with this heavy train a "Super-Pacific," rejoicing in the appetising name of *"Salmon Trout,"* had had somewhat of a struggle to keep time from Edinburgh. But when *"Earl Marischal"* took over at Dundee, matters were completely reversed. With a load that was only just equal to "Pacific" maximum in this direction, No. 2002 made light of the task. The engine returns to Dundee, however, on the heavy and popular 10.20 a.m. express. The Aberdeen-Penzance through carriage is conveyed on this train, and there is also a portion for King's Cross, which is due at 9.55 p.m.

In readiness for a trip on this train, I joined Driver Arbuthnot and Fireman Conning, a Dundee crew, in the locomotive yard at Aberdeen. Here, standing among Caledonian 4–4–0s, Midland Compounds and North British "Scotts," the vast size and unorthodox appearance of *"Earl Marischal"* seemed more pronounced than ever. The cab interior is almost identical with that of the "Super-Pacifics," and there is an excellent look-out ahead. Unlike *"Cock o' the North,"* this engine is fitted with additional smoke deflecting screens at the front end, but these do not interfere with the driver's view in the least.

This table shows in comparative form the performances of different engines over the 5.5 miles from Stonehaven up to Carmont Summit.

Engine	Load in Tons	Time of Ascent	Speed at Summit
Caledonian McIntosh Superheater 4-4-0 No. 14442	**250**	**10 min. 40 secs.**	**37¼ m.p.h.**
Midland Compound 4-4-0 No. 1143	**260**	**10 min. 30 secs.**	**36 m.p.h.**
North British 4-4-2 No. 9868 "Aberdonian" (now scrapped)	**300**	**11 min. 0 secs.**	**34 m.p.h.**
L.N.E.R. "Pacific" No. 2566 "Ladas"	**400**	**11 min. 40 secs.**	**31 m.p.h.**
"Earl Marischal"	**515**	**10 min. 43 secs.**	**36 m.p.h.**
North British 4-4-2 No. 9869 "Bonnie Dundee" piloted by "Scott" class 4-4-0 No. 9413 "Caleb Balderstone"	**565**	**11 min. 13 secs.**	**34½ m.p.h.**

We backed down to the station to find awaiting us a heavy train of 479 tons tare and 515 tons with passengers and luggage. The running about to be described compares in most interesting fashion with that of the North British "Atlantic" No. 9869 *"Bonnie Dundee,"* whose work, with a 355 ton load, I described in the June number of the *"M.M."* Reference to the gradient profile published in the same article will help readers to appreciate the wonderful hill-climbing of the "Mikado" type of engine.

Like the "Pacifics," the cut-off of these engines in full gear is 65 per cent., but this was used for only a very few yards at the start. On most engines drivers are usually reluctant to open up to full regulator immediately, in order to reduce the likelihood of slipping; and I have known it to be two miles from the start before the wide open position is reached. Driver Arbuthnot was using full regulator 50 yards from the start, however, and a mile out, cut-off was back to 25 per cent.

The climb out of Aberdeen was amazing. Two miles from the start we were doing 39 m.p.h., while on the steepest part of the rise where, with *"Bonnie Dundee,"* working on 53 per cent. cut-off and hauling 355 tons, speed fell to 30½ m.p.h., *"Earl Marischal"* sustained 36 with a load of 515 tons, on 25 per cent. cut-off! I could hardly hear the exhaust, and the smooth, buoyant riding of the engine strengthened the impression of effortless travel. Actually 2,000 horse power was being developed, and when the grade eased to 1 in 160 beyond Cove Bay, the pace rose from 36 to 42 m.p.h. in 1½ miles. Thus Portlethen summit, 7 miles out, was passed in the remarkable time of 13¾ minutes.

The easiest of easy running now followed. A cut-off of 18 per cent. with the regulator less than one-fifth open accelerated this big train to 61 m.p.h. at Muchalls; and Stonehaven, 16¼ miles, was reached in 23½ minutes, a gain of 1½ minutes on schedule.

The restart, up steeply-rising gradients, was magnificent. After 100 yards cut-off was back to 40 per cent., and in three-quarters of a mile to 32 per cent., yet speed rose steadily on the 1 in 90 ascent to 30 m.p.h. by the time Dunnottar Box was passed. Then the grade eases to 1 in 423, for ¾ mile, before the final 1½ miles at 1 in 102 to Carmont summit. On passing Dunnottar, cut-off was reduced to 25 per cent.; we accelerated rapidly to 39 on the easier stretch and breasted the summit at 36 m.p.h.

It is when direct comparison is made with the work of other engines, however, that the astounding ability of the "Mikados" is revealed. In the past few years I have had runs with quite a number of different types of engine over this route, and the ascents from Stonehaven provide some arresting figures. In the accompanying table are details of six southbound climbs, the time given in each case being that of passing Carmont summit from the dead start at Stonehaven, a distance of 5.5 miles. The fastest climb was made by a Midland Compound 4–4–0, but *"Earl Marischal"* practically equalled this, hauling very nearly double the load! Furthermore, all the other engines were being worked extremely hard. The N.B. 4–4–2 *"Aberdonian,"* for example, was being driven with the regulator three-quarters open and 53 per cent. cut-off, whereas *"Earl Marischal"* on 25 per cent. cut-off was taking things very quietly.

Now, 18 to 22 per cent. cut-off, and the regulator varying between one-fifth and one-half open, took us down the falling grades to Kinnaber Junction at an average speed of 61 m.p.h., the highest rate being 67 at Craigo viaduct. It is due to the fact that *"Earl Marischal"* has such a soft blast that, in addition to the streamlined front end, the extra smoke - deflecting screens had to be provided on each side of the smoke box. These are most effective, and at high speed the lightly drifting cloud of exhaust steam is given a most artistic-looking upward twirl and is thrown high and clear of the cab. We slacked carefully to 15 m.p.h. over Kinnaber Junction, and completed the $24\frac{1}{2}$ miles from Stonehaven into Montrose in exactly 32 minutes.

"Earl Marischal" in the locomotive yard at Aberdeen. Remarkable work is being done by this locomotive and by No. 2001 "Cock o' the North" between Edinburgh and Aberdeen, as is evident from the accompanying article.

Yet another splendid start was made up the steep bank out of Montrose. Working on 32 per cent. cut-off, we accelerated to 30 m.p.h. at Usan. On the trip described in the June *"M.M.," "Bonnie Dundee"* practically equalled this time, with a 355 ton load, but the 4-4-2 was working on 60 per cent. cut-off! *"Earl Marischal"* ran very easily down to Arbroath, arriving there in the excellent time of $20\frac{3}{4}$ minutes for the $13\frac{3}{4}$ miles. No higher speed than $63\frac{1}{2}$ m.p.h. was touched. On the final stage, along the dead level of the Angus coast, hardly any effort worth mentioning was required from the great engine, and Dundee was reached dead on time.

On another occasion I rode on the footplate of the *"Aberdonian"* right through from Aberdeen to Edinburgh. This time *"Earl Marischal"* was in charge of Driver Campbell, who was responsible for the run with *"Bonnie Dundee"* described in the June *"M.M.,"* but in this case assisted by Fireman Dorrard. With a load of 493 tons tare and 530 tons with passengers and luggage, the running was very similar to that made by Driver Arbuthnot on the 10.20 a.m. express. Driver Campbell used rather longer cut-offs with the regulator not fully open, and in consequence his uphill times were not quite so good. The downhill speeds were faster; 67 was touched at Muchalls, 70 at Craigo and 66 on the descent from Lunan Bay. On the last stage adverse signals unfortunately prevented a punctual arrival in Dundee, but the net time was well inside schedule.

At Dundee, No. 2001 *"Cock o' the North"* came on, in charge of Driver Shedden and Fireman Hardisty of Haymarket shed, Edinburgh. Since the introduction of the 2-8-2 engines, the departure of the *"Aberdonian"* has become quite a popular nightly event in Dundee. It provides the only opportunity of seeing these two giants together, and on this occasion a crowd quite forty strong gathered to see us off. On account of the rotary cam poppet valve gear, *"Cock o' the North"* differs considerably from *"Earl Marischal"* in the footplate arrangements. The reversing gear is operated by a vertical wheel, very similar in appearance to that used on modern Southern Railway engines such as the "King Arthurs" and the "Schools." On the right-hand side of the cab is a speed indicator of the Teloc type, which also records the mileage covered.

Part of the cab of "Earl Marischal." The driver is accommodated on the left-hand side, where the regulator handle, screw-reverse gear and vacuum brake valve are fitted in convenient positions.

An even more interesting comparison than in the case of *"Earl Marischal"* is provided between the work of the "Super-Pacific"—*"Windsor Lad,"* whose running on the same express I described in the July number of the *"M.M.,"* and that of the *"Cock o' the North"*; the 4-6-2 was hauling 440 tons and the "Mikado" 530. For 53 out of the $59\frac{1}{4}$ miles from Dundee to Edinburgh *"Cock o' the North"* was working on no more than 18 per cent. cut-off.

Getting away from Dundee up the steep ascent on to the Tay Bridge, Driver Shedden quickly linked up to 35 per cent., while from Esplanade station to the middle of the bridge we were cutting off at only 25 per cent. *"Windsor Lad"* needed 40 per cent., and yet, with 90 tons less load, took $\frac{1}{4}$ minute longer to pass Tay Bridge South Junction.

On my trip with *"Cock o' the North,"* we had left Dundee in the gathering dusk, and as we crossed the bridge a soft bluish haze hung over the Firth; the first lights were twinkling in Dundee and Tayport, making a delightful picture.

Once across the bridge *"Cock o' the North"* got going in great style. We passed St. Fort at 61 m.p.h., and then steam was shut off altogether, the valves were put into mid-gear, and we coasted for two miles at about 58 m.p.h. The slacks to 55 m.p.h. at Leuchars and Cupar were strictly observed, the 1 in 160 rise to Springfield was mounted at 48 m.p.h., and we were through Ladybank junction, 20 miles in $27\frac{1}{2}$ minutes, $1\frac{1}{2}$ minutes early at a reduced speed of 50 m.p.h.

Now we had a remarkable exhibition of *"Cock o' the North's"* hill-climbing ability, for the ascent of Falkland Road bank was made on 18 per cent. cut-off. From the Ladybank slowing we accelerated like lightning to 60 m.p.h. before Kingskettle, and then took the $3\frac{1}{2}$ mile climb at 1 in 100 at a minimum speed of $25\frac{1}{2}$ m.p.h.

On the descent to Thornton a very severe permanent way check was experienced, to 10 m.p.h., but nevertheless we passed that junction slightly before time, $40\frac{3}{4}$ minutes for the $28\frac{1}{2}$ miles from Dundee. Speed was reduced to 25 m.p.h. through the station, and then the driver opened out to 25 per cent. cut-off. On the 1 in 130 ascent that follows, speed had risen to 32 in half a mile, cut-off was brought back to 18 per cent., and we continued to accelerate up to the 1 in 155, passing Dysart summit at 34 m.p.h.

Then came an extraordinary display of the engine's "coasting" ability. On the descent through Kirkcaldy steam was shut off when speed had risen to 55 m.p.h., yet we continued to accelerate and attained 65 m.p.h. Even beyond Kirkcaldy, where the gradient flattens out to 1 in 660, speed was maintained at about a mile a minute, while the average speed over the 5.3 miles from Dysart to Kinghorn was 59.3 m.p.h.—entirely without steam!

We slacked heavily to 25 m.p.h. through Kinghorn and again to the same low speed at Burntisland; and then came a fine ascent to Dalgetty. *"Windsor Lad"* had been worked at 30 per cent. cut-off throughout here, but *"Cock o' the North"* was given only 18 per cent. as far as Aberdour, and opened out to 25 per cent. for the last mile. Yet No. 2001 made slightly faster running with speeds of 45 on the level mile out of Burntisland and $31\frac{1}{2}$ at Dalgetty.

After an easy descent to Inverkeithing, with speed not exceeding 50 m.p.h., the tremendous climb on to the Forth Bridge, 2 miles at 1 in 70, was tackled in great style. Passing Inverkeithing at 24 m.p.h., Shedden used 25 per cent. cut-off until within half a mile of the top; here he opened out to 35 per cent. and *"Cock o' the North"* entered the bridge at 19 m.p.h., again a faster climb than that of the "Pacific," despite much shorter cut-offs and a train 90 tons heavier. *"Cock o' the North"* has a much sharper beat than *"Earl Marischal,"* due largely to the somewhat explosive exhaust of the poppet valves, and going through North Queensferry tunnel and on the Forth Bridge we literally roared. In these conditions, crossing the bridge was a more enthralling experience than ever. Among the many lights on both sides of the Firth, I could just pick out the shipyard at Rosyth where the gallant Cunard liner *"Mauretania"* is being broken up.

And now came a thrilling final burst of speed into Edinburgh. On 18 per cent. cut-off, we accelerated with tremendous rapidity to 68 m.p.h. at Turnhouse, swung over Saughton Junction at 64, and so through Haymarket tunnel and into the heart of Edinburgh. We reached Waverley within 3 seconds of our schedule time, 84 minutes 57 seconds from Dundee. Allowing for the permanent way check near Thornton, our net time was 83½ minutes.

It is difficult to comment adequately on such magnificent locomotive performances as these. As far as weight pulling is concerned, the 2–8–2 engines have solved the difficult problem of the Aberdeen route for many years to come, for it is not possible to handle trains heavier than 530 tare tons at the stations.

My warmest thanks, and indeed those of every reader, are due to Mr. G. A. Musgrave, Locomotive Running Superintendent of the Scottish Area of the L.N.E.R., through whose kindness I was privileged to make these most interesting journeys.

A trial run with No. 2001 "Cock o' the North" in the early days of that engine. Its curious appearance at the front is accentuated by the fitting of an indicator shelter for the trial period.

These L.N.E.R. "Mikados" are of interest as being the first 8-coupled locomotives introduced in this country specially for the operation of express passenger trains. It is just 10 years since the first appearance of the type on the British standard gauge, also on the L.N.E.R. The two engines then built, Nos. 2393 and 2394, were intended to haul mineral trains of 100 loaded wagons. In speed trials between London and Grantham before the building of *"Cock o' the North"* and *"Earl Marischal,"* one of these mineral "Mikados" attained a speed of 65 m.p.h.!

The name "Mikado," originated from the fact that the first 2–8–2 locomotives were built in 1897 for Japan. They were for freight service on the Nippon Railway.

How Southern Stock reaches the "Tube"

By H. C. Raindle

FROM the Southern Railway terminus at Waterloo to the Bank Station in the City there runs a most useful section of the Southern Railway. This was originally the Waterloo and City Electric Railway, but it was amalgamated with the former L.S.W.R. in 1907. It was first opened in 1898, and thus was quite an early "tube" line, its tunnel dimensions and low-built rolling stock being of the restricted size usually adopted for deep-level railways.

In view of its "tube" character, and the number of passengers carried at busy hours, it is commonly referred to as the "drainpipe." Only one class of passengers is catered for, and a curious feature is that tickets are obtained on board the trains themselves.

Thousands of persons travel to the City over the line, but probably few of them ever give a thought to the manner in which the coaches they travel in have reached the "tube," as there appears to be no obvious physical connection at Waterloo. Actually the coaches reach their underground haunts by way of a hydraulic lift situated in the carriage sidings on the Windsor line side of the station, and so out of sight of passengers on the platform.

Waterloo and City rolling stock being hauled up to Waterloo from Eastleigh. The difference in size between "tube" vehicles and those of standard dimensions is very striking.

The rolling stock on this "branch" of the Southern Railway is constructed at the company's own works at Eastleigh. It is also maintained at that place, and on journeys before and after repairs the customary practice is for the coaches to be conveyed as a special train, on their own wheels, of course, between Eastleigh and Waterloo.

The coaches are not numerous, nor are their journeys to and from Eastleigh, so that they are rarely seen above ground. However, I was fortunate enough to obtain some time ago the accompanying photograph of three of these vehicles on their way up from Eastleigh. A close study of this reveals some interesting features in the design of the stock. As they are of "tube" dimensions, their restricted height in relation to the relatively low tender of the locomotive, and the trailing wagon, is very apparent. From the photograph it would seem that the coaches are painted in two colours, but actually they are finished in the standard green of the Southern Railway, the "two-colour" effect being due to the sun.

An unusual feature is that the interior of the stock is not upholstered but plain and rather heavy woodwork is found instead.

THE HEADLAMP CODE IN HORNBY RAILWAY WORKING

ONE of the many attractive features of a Hornby Locomotive is the provision of lamp brackets to accommodate the miniature Detachable Headlamps that are made specially for them. The possessor of a miniature locomotive naturally wishes to fit lamps on his engine and to be able to alter their positions in accordance with the practice he has observed on real railways. All Hornby Locomotives from the M3 Tank upwards therefore are provided with lamp brackets in the appropriate positions, and Detachable Headlamps are available for them and indeed are supplied as standard equipment with the larger models.

As most readers know, different classes of trains are indicated by various arrangements of the headlamps in accordance with the British Standard Headlamp Code. For this purpose three lamp brackets are fitted on the footplate above the buffer beam of the engine, so that one is in the middle, above the coupling hook, and the others are above the buffers. A single bracket also is placed centrally in front of the chimney, or below it, on the upper part of the smoke-box door. A similar set of brackets is provided in corresponding positions at the rear of the tender, or the bunker of a tank engine, to allow the necessary indications to be displayed when running backwards. The code employed is given in the H.R.C. Senior Booklet and the purpose of this article is to explain fully what each indication means and to show how to use the code in miniature railway working.

It will be realised that with the use of one or more lamps, in conjunction with the four brackets, a variety of indications can be given. Under the British Standard Headlamp Code, no more than two lamps are required at once. As keen Hornby Railway operators let us suppose we are about to run an express train. The headlamp indication for this involves the use of two lamps, one placed on each of the brackets above the buffers. This is not a difficult arrangement to remember and is one that most readers frequently employ. This indication also has two emergency uses. It is displayed by the locomotive on a breakdown train that is on its way to deal with a mishap. The same code is carried also by a light locomotive that is required to assist a train, the locomotive of which has been disabled in some way.

Several different headlamp indications are used for fast freight trains, according to the stock employed. In this photograph of a train of Hornby Biscuit and Luggage Vans the position of the headlamp on the G.W.R. "County of Bedford" at its head shows that the train is regarded as "brake-fitted" throughout.

A familiar indication is that carried by the locomotive of an ordinary stopping train. This requires the use of a single lamp displayed on the bracket below the chimney. In the case of engines travelling backwards the lamp is placed on the corresponding bracket on the tender or bunker. This indication is carried by any train to which the general term "ordinary passenger train" can be applied, whether it is a main line stopping train, a train in an intensive suburban service or an ordinary slow branch line train.

In addition to covering all "ordinary passenger trains," a single headlamp placed below the chimney also identifies a breakdown train that is not on its way to a mishap. It is carried by such a train when returning to its depot after such an occurrence, or when proceeding to the site of some engineering operation down the line, where the services of the crane are required.

Coming now to non-passenger trains, the indications become very varied, since there are more classes of trains to be provided for. In real practice a locomotive having one lamp below the chimney and one over the right-hand buffer might be hauling one of several different classes of train, but in each case the vehicles would be found to be fitted with continuous brakes throughout. Thus any train so fitted that is carrying perishables, such as meat, fruit, or fish, or livestock, would display this indication, which also applies to a train of empty coaches if this is proceeding for a reasonable distance, and is not merely being shunted or moved between a station and a siding. In addition, this comprehensive indication distinguishes mineral, goods and even ballast trains, that happen to be made up exclusively of brake-fitted vehicles.

A miniature L.M.S.R. express train passing over a level crossing. The headlamp code involves the use of two lamps for express trains, one lamp being mounted on each bracket above the buffers.

On a Hornby Railway the provision of brake-fitted vehicles of course must be left to the imagination, and the miniature railway owner therefore should classify his goods stock according to whether they are supposed to be brake-fitted or not. In general covered Vans can be considered as brake-fitted, but open Wagons, Timber, Lumber, Trolley and Tipping Wagons should be regarded as non-fitted. Milk Tanks also should rank as brake-fitted wagons, but ordinary Tank Wagons should not.

The next indication to be considered requires a lamp below the chimney and one on the buffer beam, but in this case the lower lamp is placed over the left-hand buffer. This disposition of the lamps is used on trains carrying perishables, on which only some of the vehicles are brake-fitted, and also on fast cattle or general goods trains that are partially fitted with brakes and travel at speeds above 25 m.p.h. The fitted vehicles in this case must be marshalled next to the engine, for otherwise their braking power would be useless. In the composition of trains of this kind on a Hornby Railway the distinction between the vehicles supposed to be brake-fitted and those that are not therefore should be observed carefully.

The locomotive of the approaching train in this photograph displays a single headlamp in front of the chimney, the indication for an ordinary passenger train. The tail lamp is prominent on the other train.

Trains of the same kind as those just described, and composed of similar stock, but running at speeds lower than 25 m.p.h., carry a lamp below the chimney and one on the central bracket over the buffer beam. This indication also is used for trains carrying ballast or engineering materials for work on the line that are running long distances without breaking bulk.

Light engines that are travelling any distance, either singly or coupled together, carry one lamp placed on the central bracket above the buffer beam. Sometimes, however, they display the indication of the train they are to work. This also applies to an engine with a goods brake van coupled to it when proceeding to colliery or dock sidings, for the purpose of collecting wagons to form a train to be taken to a concentration yard for marshalling.

A goods or mineral train taking its load through to its destination without any roadside work displays two lamps over the buffer beam, one in the central position and the other over the right-hand buffer. A similar train stopping at intermediate points carries a single lamp only, and this is placed over the right-hand buffer; and the ordinary local goods train carries exactly the opposite indication to this, namely a single lamp over the left-hand buffer.

As mentioned by *"Tommy Dodd"* last month, suitable tail lamps have recently been introduced into the Hornby Series. These can be fitted to the brackets provided on the latest types of No. 2 Coaches, No. 1 Coaches and Guard's Vans and the No. 1 Pullman Coaches as re-designed this season. In actual practice a train is not considered complete unless it is displaying a tail lamp, and if a train without a tail lamp were observed by a signalman, he would immediately advise the box in advance and also the box in the rear in order to have the matter investigated. The bell code used by signalmen provides for such a contingency, so that the necessary message can be transmitted in both directions without loss of time. On a Hornby Railway therefore it is important to see that wherever possible a train is "completed" by the addition of a miniature tail lamp.

From the signalling point of view light engines constitute "trains" in themselves and so carry tail lamps. This practice therefore should be followed in miniature. One of the engine lamps usually is employed for the purpose, and a movable slide having a red glass is incorporated in these lamps, so that they can be used as tail lamps, or for signalling in emergencies. A lamp with a red slide is also used when an engine is backing an empty train out from a station into the carriage sidings, which may be some distance away. The lamp is placed on the front of the engine which becomes temporarily, when backing, the tail of the train. Such features can be reproduced by using a Hornby Locomotive headlamp with a red-painted "bull" instead of the standard white one, and a lamp so treated should form part of the equipment of each engine on the line. The re-painting of the "bull" is easily carried out, and small features of this kind add greatly to the interest and realism of operations.

BEST WISHES FOR 1936 TO ALL MY READERS—THE EDITOR

MECCANO MAGAZINE

Editorial Office:
Binns Road, Liverpool 13
England

Vol. XXI. No. 1
January, 1936

With the Editor

Thanks to Readers

My first task this month is the pleasant one of thanking readers for their Christmas messages of greeting and good wishes for the New Year. These messages have come from all parts of the world and have been a source of great pleasure to me and to my staff. An interesting feature has been the large number of letters sent by Air Mail, showing that, as always, "*M.M.*" readers are thoroughly up to date.

In response to my invitation last month, large numbers of readers have already written to express their opinion of the "*M.M.*" and to make suggestions for improvements. Some of these suggestions are impracticable, but others are quite interesting, and I hope to refer to them next month.

British Railways During the Past Year

Great railway activity took place during the year. On the L.N.E.R. Britain's first streamlined train "*The Silver Jubilee*" commenced to run on the fastest schedule in the world over more than 200 miles, at 67.07 m.p.h. On a demonstration run the very high maximum of 112½ m.p.h. was recorded twice. It will be interesting to see whether the other groups will adopt streamlining. The G.W.R. made tentative experiments in this direction with two locomotives, but up to the present no developments seem to have resulted.

To commemorate the centenary of the G.W.R. a new express, "*The Bristolian,*" with up and down averages of 67.6 and 67.1 m.p.h., was inaugurated to improve the service from Bristol to London. Another advance which may have important results was the putting into service by the L.M.S.R. of the first turbine-driven locomotive to be constructed by a British railway company. This nameless No. 6202 has worked with success on most of the important trains. The longest through engine working in Britain, from London to Aberdeen and back, 1,079½ miles in 36 hours, has been inaugurated by the L.M.S.R.

Still further developments are to be expected in the future. In our "*Railway News*" pages this month are given details of the £30,000,000 scheme of reconstruction and improvement that is to be carried out during the next five years. This will have important results, and will make the railways more capable than ever of dealing with the increasing demands of the public for all classes of traffic. At the same time even greater safety will be ensured by the improved signalling arrangements and by the extension of track circuiting and automatic train control. As far as possible all plant, machinery and materials will be products of the United Kingdom, so that the scheme will help to reduce unemployment.

Steady Progress in Aviation

In aviation the year was one of steady progress, particularly in the development of commercial air services, and both in this country and on the Continent more passengers and air mail were carried than ever before. There was no great international event such as the MacRobertson Races of 1934 or the earlier Schneider Trophy Contests, but during the year some notable long-distance flights were accomplished, two of them by well-known airwomen. In January last Mrs. George Putnam, better known as Miss Amelia Earheart, flew across the Pacific Ocean, from Honolulu to Oakland, California, and covered the 2,408 miles in 18 hr. 15 min.; and during a recent flight from Lympne, Kent to Port Natal, Brazil, Miss Jean Batten crossed the South Atlantic Ocean, 1,700 miles, in the record time of 13 hr. 15 min. The latest record for a solo flight from this country to Australia was set up in September last by H. F. Broadbent, who covered the distance in 6 days 21 hr. 19 min.

Ascents into the stratosphere continued to attract airmen and scientists. In November last two officers of the United States Army Air Corps, using a helium-filled balloon, ascended to the record height of 74,000 ft., or nearly 14 miles. At the maximum height the temperature was intensely cold both inside and outside the gondola, and the sky had become black, probably due to the absence of dust in that part of the stratosphere.

There are many indications that 1936 will be a very eventful one in aviation. The new Zeppelin airship is to be launched shortly, and her first trans-Atlantic flight will be watched with much interest. Another important event will be experimental flights across the North Atlantic by British and American aircraft of new design and great power. These flights are a necessary preliminary to the introduction, not later than 1938, of regular trans-Atlantic air services.

Petrol from Coal

One of the most wonderful recent achievements of chemical engineering has been the production of petrol from coal on a commercial basis. This success follows eight years of extensive research at a cost of £1,000,000, for which the credit is mainly due to Imperial Chemical Industries Ltd. The opening of their new plant at Billingham on the Durham coalfield last year marked the start of a completely new British industry.

This plant is the first to make petrol on a commercial scale. It occupies about 40 acres among a collection of other chemical plant covering 800 acres, forming the second largest chemical works in the world.

A Great Viaduct Road

Historic Welsh Highway Reconstructed

ONE of the most striking modern feats of engineering was completed recently when a magnificent new viaduct road built on the fringe of the sea between Penmaenmawr and Llanfairfechan, North Wales, was opened to traffic. This stretch of highway, which forms part of the main Chester-Holyhead road, is cut from the side of Penmaenmawr Mountain, and although it is only 3,000 ft. in length its construction represents a remarkable achievement of engineering skill. At one point the road is carried 100 ft. above the sea on a beautiful viaduct 600 ft. in length, and at another point it passes through Penyclip headland by means of two tunnels. Tremendous difficulties had to be overcome in constructing the viaduct and tunnels, and the work, which has taken more than four years to complete, has cost about £66 per foot.

The road along the rocky coast of North Wales has for centuries provided one of the principal links between England and Wales, and the section that lies between Penmaenmawr and Llanfairfechan has always been a source of great difficulty to traffic. The history of the road goes back to the sixth century. In the time of Charles I it was the only passage available for the transport of mails to and from Ireland, and although in some places it was a mere track scarcely a yard in width it was designated the "Kinges Highway." This state of affairs was due probably to the fact that the road was in the charge of and maintained by an old hermit, whose only recompense for his labour was the charity of well-disposed passengers. In 1720 the then Lord Lieutenant of Ireland, the Duke of Ormond, made another road lower down the mountain side. This road does not appear to have been any better maintained than the earlier track, however, for travellers frequently fell down the precipitous sides and were killed. The famous Dr. Johnson, recording in his Diary a journey he made along the road, says: "I was much relieved when my journey past this point was over."

The road seems to have remained in this unsatisfactory condition for many years after that time, but with the gradual increase in traffic it became imperative to carry out considerable reconstruction in order to make the passage reasonably safe and free from obstruction at all times of the year. In 1811 therefore Thomas Telford, the famous bridge and road builder, was commissioned by the Government to improve and reconstruct the road round the Penyclip headland. This Telford undertook to do, and he built the fifth of the succession of roads of which traces still remain on the hillside.

A view of work in progress on the piers of the Penyclip viaduct. The telegraph poles in the top left corner of the illustration indicate the line of the old Chester-Holyhead road. For the illustrations to this article we are indebted to Howard Humphreys and Sons, London.

In 1846, when Robert Stephenson was engaged in the construction of the railway from Chester to Holyhead, the Penyclip headland again came into prominence, for a storm washed away a massive sea wall that was being built on the edge of the sea to enclose what is now called Viaduct Bay at the foot of Penyclip, across which the railway had to pass. As a result of this disaster the wall scheme was abandoned, and the railway was carried over the Bay on a viaduct supported on open arched piers. This viaduct was the forerunner of that which carries the L.M.S.R. main Chester-Holyhead line to-day.

Unfortunately for Telford's road, however, the sea washed between the piers of the viaduct, and in time did such considerable damage by undercutting the hillside that landslides occurred and the road collapsed on several occasions. Each time it was rebuilt higher and higher up the face of the mountain. In 1899 Sir Benjamin Baker, the English engineer who designed the special vessel that carried Cleopatra's Needle to London and who was actively concerned in the construction of the Forth Bridge and other big engineering works of his time, was asked to examine the road, and as a result of his report it was decided to build a sea wall at the foot of the hill and to erect other massive stone ramparts to protect the hillside.

The continual rebuilding of the road up the side of the mountain had gradually increased its gradient until eventually the limit of reasonable steepness was reached. In that state the old road remained until the magnificent new viaduct road was completed recently. It had a gradient of 1 in 11, and in places a width between its walls of only 14 ft. With the great increase in traffic during recent years these narrow sections caused considerable hindrance, and at times, the very heavy holiday traffic that uses the road during the summer was held up for considerable periods.

The Caernarvon County Council therefore decided to carry out an elaborate scheme of reconstruction in order to make the road capable of accommodating all kinds of modern traffic. With the assistance of the Government this scheme has now been successfully completed.

Workmen clearing the site for the viaduct foundations. The L.M.S.R. railway viaduct is shown on the left.

The new road begins at Gerizim Chapel on the Llanfairfechan side of Penyclip headland, and some idea of its principal features may be gained from the accompanying illustrations. The first section consists of a widening of the old road for a distance of about 450 ft. to a width of 27 ft. To enable this to be done a strong retaining wall had to be built as a support to hold the soft mountain rock in place and prevent landslides. At the end of the 450 ft. stretch of widened road the new road leaves the line of the old road, and for a distance of 500 ft. is supported by massive retaining walls both on the north or sea side and on the south. The wall on the sea side has in one place a height of 64 ft. from the foundation to the level of the coping, and it has a base width of 25 ft. This section forms the approach to what is probably the most interesting part of the whole scheme, a 600ft. viaduct, the construction of which may be gathered from the lower illustration on this page. The viaduct carries the road over an inlet in the coast, known as Viaduct Bay, and consists of seven 80 ft. spans, the deck being 70 ft. above the deck of the other and smaller viaduct that carries the main Chester-Holyhead line of the London, Midland and Scottish Railway. The railway viaduct can be seen in the illustration at the top of this page and the line of the old road that has now been abandoned is indicated by telegraph poles. Higher up the mountain traces of the earlier roads are still visible.

The viaduct during construction, showing steel plating in position.

The piers of the new road viaduct are 90 ft. in height from foundation to road level, and are built of concrete faced with blue-grey stone from the Penmaenmawr quarries. The arches also are made of reinforced concrete. The road itself is supported by a reinforced concrete deck and is surfaced with tar macadam and provided with kerbs of granite. At the eastern end of the viaduct the road is carried on reinforced-concrete beams, which on the sea side are supported by a stout wall, while on the land side they rest on the natural ground.

At the end of this section the road again passes on to the natural rock and is taken through a tunnel 115 ft. in length, in which it passes through Penyclip headland almost under the old road. The tunnel is followed by about 500 ft. of open road, which is cut from the mountain side and is protected from falling rock from the heights above by extensive facing work. This open section runs into a second tunnel, which is 180 ft. in length and passes directly under the old road at a sharp corner known locally as the "Clip," Each of the tunnels has an elliptical arch with a major axis of 34 ft.

The last section of the work is that which joins the new road to the old. At this point considerable difficulties were encountered, and a great retaining wall, 74 ft. in height from the foundation level to the coping, had to be built in order to fill in a very deep gulley. The ground behind the wall was then made up to road level and the junction with the old road was effected, the traffic being diverted on to the new road to enable this to be done.

In addition to the splendid new road at Penyclip another portion of the old Chester-Holyhead road at Penmaenbach $3\frac{1}{2}$ miles away has been modernised and made safe for all classes of traffic. This part of the scheme was completed at the end of 1933. At Penmaenbach the road originally ran round a blind bend on a wind-swept headland known as Giant's Thumb, and was frequently blocked by falls of rock from the steep mountain side. That road has now been replaced by a concrete lined tunnel that has a maximum headroom of 21 ft. and a minimum of 16 ft. at the kerb line. The excavations for this work necessitated the removal of 9,000 cubic yards of rock for the entrances and about 17,000 cubic yards in the tunnel itself. The tunnel is traversed by a 27 ft. carriageway and a 4 ft. 9 in. path with a guard verge on one side as in the tunnels at Penyclip.

Footplate Runs on Irish 2-6-0s

Remarkable Work by L.M.S. (N.C.C.) Engines

By a Railway Engineer

UNTIL comparatively recent times the Northern Counties Committee line of the L.M.S.R. had a very roundabout route to the north-west of Ireland. At Greenisland, six miles out of Belfast, all trains for the Londonderry line had to reverse direction, and as a consequence overall times of even the principal expresses were slow. In January 1934 a new loop line was opened, giving a direct line to the north and saving 2½ miles on the journey. Very shortly afterwards some remarkable accelerations took place, and the 65.2 miles from Belfast to Portrush was scheduled to be run in 80 minutes, inclusive of one stop, of two minutes' duration, at Ballymena.

L.M.S.R. (N.C.C.) 2-6-0 No. 96 "Silver Jubilee." The tablet exchange apparatus for single line working is a prominent feature on the side of the cab.

The new loop line includes a gradient of 1 in 76½, three miles long, that occurs in the middle of a bank 4¾ miles long on which the grade is nowhere easier than 1 in 102. To be good enough for this, under the heaviest loading conditions, some fine new locomotives of the 2–6–0 type were introduced. The coupled wheels are 6 ft. in diameter. The cylinders are 19 in. in diameter with a piston stroke of 26 in., and have piston valves operated by Walschaerts valve gear. The first four of the new type were put into traffic in July 1933, and since then four further engines have been added to the class.

By the kindness of Major Malcolm Speir, Manager and Secretary of the N.C.C., I have been privileged to make a number of footplate journeys on these engines, during which I witnessed feats of locomotive performance that to my knowledge are quite unique. The first run to be described was made on the up *"Portrush Flyer."* This express makes three intermediate stops and is allowed 90 minutes for the journey of 65.2 miles. The load was, for an engine of such moderate dimensions, the very heavy one of 10 corridor bogies, 298 tons tare and 315 tons with passengers and luggage. The engine was one of the newest of the class, No. 96 *"Silver Jubilee,"* and was manned by Driver McNally and Fireman Graham of Belfast shed.

The driver's lookout on one of the N.C.C. "Moguls," showing the good view ahead that is afforded.

The Irish gauge is 5 ft. 3 in. and the extra width over the English standard makes possible a very roomy cab and gives a splendid look-out past the straight-sided Belpaire fire-box. Like all N.C.C. engines, these 2–6–0s are equipped for left-hand drive, the reversing gear being of the screw type. The regulator has two ports rather similar to that of the Midland Compounds. It has this difference; the small port, usually referred to as the "first regulator," is used for light steaming, while the second or main regulator is used for ordinary fast running on the level or uphill.

Getting the "right away" dead on time, 7.15 p.m., Driver McNally almost immediately opened out to full regulator and set the cut-off at 40 per cent. Up the steep rise at 1 in 76–122 *"Silver Jubilee"* steadily gathered speed, cut-off was reduced by 2 and 3 per cent. to 30, and a mile and a half from the start we were doing 26 m.p.h. As we mounted on to the cliffs, there was a magnificent view seawards; from the entrance to Lough Foyle, the Inishowen peninsular stretched out into the Atlantic, and behind its rolling ridges could be seen the wilder peaks of the Donegal Highlands.

By now we were running into Portstewart our first stop, 2.7 miles of steep grades covered in exactly 8 minutes. From here there is a more favourable start; cut-off was quickly back to 20 per cent. and the *"Flyer"* was soon into its stride. The line ran southward now, the Londonderry line converged on our right, there was a sharp crash as the single-line tablets were exchanged, and we swept through Coleraine at 60 m.p.h. For half the distance from Portrush to Belfast the main line is single, but the passing loops are laid out so that expresses can go through at full speed. Locomotives are fitted with an automatic "catcher" for the tablet, which consists of a pair of steel jaws. The tablet, a leather pouch, is suspended on a standard at the lineside and as the engine passes is caught in the jaws. With the train going at 60 m.p.h., the tablet was often wedged so tightly that the driver or I had to help the fireman dislodge it. It is then set ready to be given up at the next station, but it is not swung out until the station is being approached.

By this time, we had passed Macfin and soon reached Ballymoney, our second stop, 11.6 miles from Portstewart in 16 minutes, dead on time. This station is the junction for the Ballycastle branch. In addition to its 5 ft. 3 in. gauge main lines, the N.C.C. have a considerable mileage of narrow gauge line, only 3 ft. gauge, of which the section from Ballymoney to Ballycastle forms part.

The restart from Ballymoney is severe. For 5½ miles the line rises at grades varying between 1 in 114 and 1 in 150, with some very short strips less steeply. We got away in great style and with cut-off varying between 35 and 40 per cent., kept up a steady 38 to 40 m.p.h. all the way up. Once over the top, cut-off was reduced to 15 per cent., and on faintly falling grades, we got up to 60 m.p.h. at Glarryford. This part of the line runs through very sparsely populated country, of isolated farms and extensive peat mosses; the gradients change constantly, though the general tendency is downhill, and there is much reverse curvature. Away to the east are the Antrim mountains. On this undulating stretch, Driver

McNally changed the cut-off to suit every rise and fall of the line; often the gear was notched up as early as 12 per cent., but full regulator was used throughout. We kept up a fine pace, speed rising to a maximum of 62 at Cullybackey, and reached Ballymena, our last stop, in 26¾ minutes from Ballymoney, 20 miles, again almost exactly to time. From here into Belfast, the line is double-tracked.

The restart is grand for speed exhibitions, for the line falls gradually to the low country round Antrim and passes quite close to the northern shores of that vast inland lake, Lough Neagh. This cannot actually be seen from the main line as it is surrounded by a belt of trees. To get the train on the move quickly, McNally used 40 per cent. cut-off at first, then back to 25, 20 and finally 15 per cent. *"Silver Jubilee"* got away in dashing style, and we were through Antrim 11.7 miles in 13¼ minutes at 69 m.p.h.

The remarkable ferro-concrete Greenisland Viaducts. These form part of a flying junction layout, and the new loop line to Londonderry and Portrush passes over the down Larne line. Photograph by courtesy of the L.M.S.R.

From here follow 10½ miles of continuous climbing to the summit of the line at Kingsbog Junction. The grades gradually steepen until the last four miles are at 1 in 180. This ascent was taken in splendid fashion, cut-off being advanced step by step until it was 30 per cent., for the final two miles. Here speed fell to a sustained 48 m.p.h., while the complete 10½ miles were run at an average rate of 53.7 m.p.h.

Now McNally changed over to the first regulator for the steep descent over the Greenisland loop. We approached the new line at 67 m.p.h., but the engine was carefully eased over Monkstown Junction to 50 m.p.h. In the meantime a wonderful panorama had opened out. Far below was Belfast Lough; the City with its shipyards and docks was spread out like a map, while across the water County Down appeared more brilliantly green than ever in the sunset light. We coasted smoothly over the graceful viaduct at Bleach Green, a remarkable structure of reinforced concrete, and joined the line from Larne harbour just before Whiteabbey. Over the loop line and right into Belfast, "Searchlight" signals are used.

A cab view, showing most of the important fittings, except the screw reverse gear. Well-lighted and commodious cabs are a feature of the N.C.C. "Moguls."

We touched 60 again at Whitehouse, and were now running along the shore of Belfast Lough. With Cave Hill towering above us on the right we were soon on the outskirts of the city and with a cautious run in, we stopped at York Road Station two minutes inside schedule, the 31 miles from Ballymena having been covered in 36 minutes, instead of the 38 booked. This was an excellent performance. The long periods at which the engine had been working at 15 per cent. cut-off, or less, made possible a very low coal consumption; to keep up full boiler pressure Fireman Graham never had to put on more than four shovelfuls at one firing and the average consumption on the journey was less than 30 lb. per mile.

In the reverse direction, I rode on the footplate of the 5.15 p.m. *"North Atlantic Express."* The load was one of only six coaches, making a total load, with passengers and luggage, of 190 tons behind the tender, the engine being the pioneer of the class, No. 90, *"Duke of Abercorn."* Another Belfast crew, Driver John Young and Fireman Fitzpatrick, were in charge.

Along the shore of Belfast Lough, we got away in great style, passing Whitehouse, 3.3 miles in a shade over 5 minutes, at 54 m.p.h. and then came the heavy ascent over the loop line. With full regulator and 40 per cent. cut-off, this bank, as steep as the southern ascent to Shap, was mounted at a sustained 36½ m.p.h. and we passed the summit at Ballyclare Junction, 8.2 miles from Belfast, in 12¼ minutes.

For the long descent to Antrim, cut-off was first of all shortened to 10 per cent.; then, as soon as we had attained 60 m.p.h., Young changed over to the first regulator. As we approached Templepatrick, as if this were not easy enough steaming, the engine was still further notched up, to 7 per cent. cut-off. The speed steadily rose, until approaching the foot of the incline near Muckamore, we were doing 71½ m.p.h. Even with a load of only 190 tons this was wonderful going with only 7 per cent. cut-off; it should be remembered too that only the first port of the regulator was being used.

At Antrim, the driver changed over to full regulator, and at Cookstown Junction in readiness for the gradually rising grades to Ballymena, cut-off was advanced to 10 per cent. Even this was easy working for uphill running, yet the 2 miles at 1 in 214 beyond Kellswater were mounted at a minimum speed of 52½ m.p.h. and we reached Ballymena, our only stop, in exactly the 35 minutes allowed.

Although such very early cut-offs were the general order of the day, Driver Young did not spare the engine when occasion demanded, and we fairly roared up the 1 in 100 rise out of Ballymena on full regulator and no less than 50 per cent. cut-off. As might be imagined, this produced an astonishing acceleration, speed rising to 43 m.p.h. in one mile from the start. A stretch of undulating line follows, the tendency of which is definitely "against the collar," but nevertheless cut-off was brought back to 10 per cent. We passed Cullybackey, 2.9 miles from the restart, in exactly 5 minutes, at 56½ m.p.h., and then approaching Glarryford, advantage was taken of a short length of falling grade to notch up to the amazing figure of 5 per cent. Never in the whole of my experience have I noted such a short cut-off. The regulator remained absolutely full open and speed mounted to 61 m.p.h. Down the steep bank to Ballymoney the first regulator only was used, but with this exception, and a brief spell at 10 per cent. after Coleraine, 5 per cent. with a full open regulator was used throughout from Glarryford to Portrush, and sufficed to maintain an average speed of 52 m.p.h. Thus the run from Belfast was completed in 78 minutes.

Motor Life-Boats Round British Coasts

The Splendid Fleet of the R.N.L.I.

THE modern life-boat fleet round the 5,000 miles of coast of Great Britain and Ireland began 31 years ago, when the first experiments were made with a motor life-boat by the Royal National Life-boat Institution. In that year, 1904, there was a life-boat fleet of 285 boats, two being steam boats, and 283 pulling and sailing boats. To-day the coastline of the British Isles is fully protected with a fleet of 170 life-boats, of which 124 are motor boats, and 45 pulling and sailing.

It is interesting to look back and see how the problem presented itself to the experimenters in the early days of the internal combustion engine. The engine must be water-tight but not air-tight. It must be as automatic as possible and very simple to control. It must not interfere with the rowing or sailing qualities of the life-boat, for she would depend on oars and sails if the engine were to fail; and it must not interfere with her self-righting qualities. It must be able to work smoothly with the boat standing on end or with a heavy list. At the same time, if the boat should heel over to capsizing point the engine must cut off automatically, or else, when the boat righted herself some seconds later, the engine would carry her away, leaving her crew in the water.

"The Three Sisters" life-boat at Coverack. A light type of motor life-boat 35 ft. 6 in. long, specially designed for stations where the boat has to be launched off a carriage over the open beach. The illustrations to this article are by courtesy of the Royal National Life-Boat Institution.

These were difficult problems, but they were solved. It is worth while to describe the ingenious way in which the last problem, that of cutting off the engine, was solved. There are two ways of cutting off the engine, one for engines with battery and coil ignition, and the other for those with magneto ignition. In both cases the object is to switch off the ignition when the boat lists to 60 degrees or 70 degrees, and prevent the circuit being operative for 25 to 30 seconds. In the first case the low-tension circuit is made by two terminals in a glass tube formed into an oval ring containing a small quantity of mercury. The two terminals are at the bottom of the ring, separated by a glass partition in the tube through which a small hole is punctured; and through this hole the circuit is completed in the mercury. When the boat reaches a list of 60 degrees or 70 degrees the mercury runs round the top of the ring and is all on one side of the partition, so that there is no circuit between the terminals. When the boat rights herself the mercury slowly trickles through the puncture in the partition until, at the end of about 25 seconds, the circuit is restored.

In the second case, with magneto ignition, the earthing wire is connected to terminals that normally do not form a circuit, but when the boat capsizes are connected together by the upsetting of a quantity of mercury, which thus short-circuits the magneto. This mercury flows away slowly when the boat rights herself, and so, after the necessary delay, the ignition circuit is restored.

The first experimental installation was a 12 h.p. two-cycle motor. The most powerful type to-day, the 60-ft. Barnett motor life-boat, is driven by two six-cylinder 80 h.p. engines, This, the largest type, can only be placed at stations where it can lie afloat.

The standard type, the Watson cabin, is 46 ft. 8 in. by 12 ft. 9 in. Her displacement in service conditions is 19¾ tons, and she has a mean draft of 3 ft. 8 in. She is divided into seven water-tight compartments, and is fitted with 142 air-cases and 10 relieving scuppers. She has a forward and an after cockpit, both fitted with shelters, with room in them for 12 people, and a cabin that will take 20 people, with sitting accommodation for 10. The cabin is fitted with an electric fan, which can be used to ventilate the hold as well as the cabin. In rough weather she can take 95 people on board.

She is built with a double skin of mahogany, keel of teak, ribs of Canadian rock-elm, and stem and stern posts of English oak. She is driven by two four-cylinder 40 h.p. engines. They are in a water-tight compartment, and each engine is itself water-tight, so that they would continue running even if the engine-room were flooded and the engines themselves entirely submerged, for the air-intakes are well above the water-line, even when the boat herself is water-logged. The exhausts are carried up a funnel amidships. Her maximum speed is 8¼ knots. As with all the Institution's motor life-boats, there is a great reserve of power, so that the maximum speed can be maintained even in very severe weather. This type carries 108 gallons of petrol, and the engines' consumption is 7½ gallons an hour at full speed, so that she can travel 116 miles at full speed without refuelling.

She carries a staysail and a trysail, which can be used either with the engine running or as an auxiliary power in the event of any failure on the part of the engines. She carries a crew of eight men, has a line-throwing gun, an electric searchlight, and a mechanical capstan, is lighted throughout with electricity, and has a fire-extinguishing plant, worked from the deck, which can throw jets of Pyrene fluid to all vital parts of the boat.

This type, like all the Institution's motor life-boats, uses petrol as fuel, but in 1933 a special light high-speed Diesel engine was built with which experiments were carried out in a reserve motor life-boat. As a result, a pair of 40 h.p. Diesel engines are being built. These are the first submersible Diesel engines to be designed and built in Great Britain. The great advantage of the Diesel is that the heavy oil that is used is not so inflammable as petrol, and the risk of fire is very much less; but the ordinary Diesel engines, with their low speed of revolution, have been too heavy for life-boats. During recent years Diesel engines have been so developed that it has been found possible greatly to increase the speed of the revolutions, and by so doing to reduce the weight of the engines to little more than the weight of petrol engines of the same horse-power. Until recently this light high-speed Diesel was not sufficiently reliable for the exacting conditions of the Life-boat Service, but the improvements made in it decided the Institution that the time had now come to see if it could be successfully adapted for life-boat work.

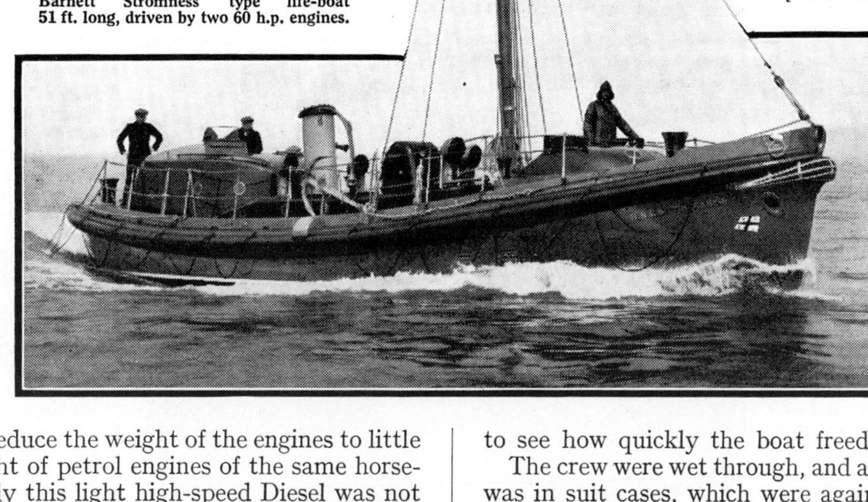

Barnett Stromness type life-boat 51 ft. long, driven by two 60 h.p. engines.

The motor life-boat described is one of five types that the Institution is now building, suitable to different parts of the coast. The heavier types must either lie afloat or be launched down a slipway—built usually of concrete. This means that their use is confined to stations where there is anchorage, or where there is sufficient depth of water inshore for it to be possible to launch down a slipway at any state of the tide. This has meant until recently that it was impossible to use motor power at a great many stations, because the heavier types of motor boat could not be launched. The most important developments of the last few years have been the design of two new types that can be launched without a slipway. One is the beach type, weighing 16¼ tons, which is launched on a semi-permanent slipway of rollers laid on the beach; the other is a still lighter type, weighing only 7 tons, that is launched off a carriage. At 19 stations there are motor caterpillar tractors for launching the light boats; and where there are not tractors they are launched by hand.

Recently one of these light boats, a self-righting boat, 35 ft. 6 in. by 9 ft. 3 in., with a 35 h.p. engine, went from the building yard at Cowes to her station at St. Ives, Cornwall. Rough weather was experienced during practically the whole of the passage, and on the second day's run, after rounding Portland Bill, she ran into a full westerly gale, which continued until she reached Brixham, just before midnight. There were rain squalls about every 20 minutes, and at these times, with the seas washing over the boat, the spray came over with such force that it was very difficult to keep the eyes open to steer a compass course. From midday till about 10 p.m. heavy green seas were frequently shipped, and everyone was surprised to see how quickly the boat freed herself of this water.

The crew were wet through, and all spare clothing, which was in suit cases, which were again inside double canvas bags and all covered by a large canvas sheet, was also wet. The total distance run was 236 miles. The boat was at sea 42 hours and 20 minutes, and the average speed for the trip was 5.6 knots. As the maximum speed in calm water on trials at Cowes was 7½ knots, this was a very good average for such weather, and shows the reserve of power that is possessed by all the motor life-boats.

Starboard side of CE6 type life-boat engine, developing 60 b.h.p. at 1,200 r.p.m. with reverse and reduction gear to 600 r.p.m.

A large number of these light motor life-boats have been built in the last few years, but the Institution is still not at the end of its experiments with light types. Two motor life-boats of a new and much lighter type are now being built. This type is 32 ft. long and weighs only 3½ tons, and will be driven by two 12 h.p. engines. One of the two boats will be fitted with Gill propellers, like other motor life-boats; the other will have a Hotchkiss internal cone propeller. Experiments will be carried out with these two boats before it is decided which of these methods of propulsion to adopt for the new light type.

James Watt, 1736-1819

The Father of the Modern Steam Engine

ONE useful feature about centenaries is that they enable us to refresh our knowledge of the great men concerned. Most people, if asked about James Watt, would probably say he was the inventor of the steam engine. This is quite wrong. Long before Watt turned his attention to steam, Savery and Newcomen had produced engines that came into practical use; and steam engines of a sort were invented by various people at a much earlier date. Watt's claim to fame lies in the fact that he took in hand the crude and wasteful steam engine of his day and turned it into an efficient source of power that was to revolutionise the modern industrial world.

James Watt was born on 19th January 1736 at Greenock, where his father carried on a large business as a carpenter and shipwright. During boyhood Watt was very delicate and he received most of his education from his parents at home. When not busy with his studies he spent many happy hours becoming proficient in the use of a set of carpenter's tools from his father's workshop, and in assisting in repairing nautical instruments. At 18 he was apprenticed to the trade of instrument maker, first with a Glasgow mechanic and later in London with a skilled maker of mathematical instruments. In London the working hours were very long, and after a few months Watt's health began to give way again and he therefore returned to Scotland.

Back in Glasgow he obtained an appointment as resident mathematical instrument maker to the University, and was provided with a workshop in the college buildings. The University had a model of a Newcomen steam engine, of the type then largely used for pumping water out of mines. This model did not work at all well, and Watt was asked to put it in order. He had little difficulty in doing this, but in the process he became greatly impressed with the deficiencies of the engine.

James Watt (1736-1819).

The Newcomen engine was invented in 1705 by Thomas Newcomen, a blacksmith and ironmonger, of Dartmouth, and was based partly upon an earlier invention by Thomas Savery, which was brought out in 1698. Savery's pumping engine, as it was called, was very imperfect, but it provided a starting point for various inventors interested in the possibilities of the steam engine. Of these, Newcomen appears to have been the most progressive. It is related that, having by some means become acquainted with Savery's engine, he built a model of it in his garden and in studying its operation quickly perceived its many faults. After long experiment and many failures Newcomen finally evolved his atmospheric pumping engine.

In this engine a pipe fitted with a stopcock led up from the top of the boiler to a vertical cylinder containing a close-fitting piston. The piston rod was connected by a chain to one end of a beam overhead, which functioned see-saw fashion upon a central axis. From the other end of the beam hung a long weight, the bottom of which was attached to a pump rod. Steam was generated in the boiler and passed upwards into the cylinder at a pressure slightly greater than that of the atmosphere, thereby raising the piston. As the piston end of the beam was thus lifted, the other end was correspondingly lowered and the pump rod depressed. This motion was aided and steadied by the balance weight.

The stopcock was then turned to shut off steam. Cold water was passed down a narrow pipe from a cistern above the cylinder, entering the latter at the bottom in the form of a jet, and this, condensing the steam, created a vacuum. The cylinder was open at the top and atmospheric pressure upon the piston immediately forced the latter down, thereby re-canting the beam to its original position and raising the pump rod. The descending piston forced out the injected water and condensed steam through an escape valve into a pipe leading down to an adjoining well. Steam was then re-admitted to the cylinder and the cycle of operations repeated.

It was clear to Watt that a tremendous wastage of steam took place in the Newcomen engine, and he determined to find some means of preventing this. His problem was to condense the steam without cooling the cylinder. For a time the solution evaded him, but eventually there came the brilliant idea of having a separate vessel in which to condense the steam. After doing its work the steam could then be passed from the cylinder into the independent chamber and there condensed by the injection of cold water. By this method the cold water would not be brought into contact with the cylinder at all, and the latter could be kept dry and hot during the brief period pending admittance of more steam.

Watt promptly set to work to put his idea to the test. A large brass syringe some ten inches in length and one inch and a third in diameter was borrowed and rigged up as a vertical cylinder. To prevent leakage of steam from this the exit of the piston rod was protected with leather packing. A hole was drilled down the stem of the piston and a valve fitted at the lower end, so that such steam as condensed on the first filling up of the cylinder could be drawn off independently of the condenser. From the roof of a small boiler a pipe led off and was connected to the top and bottom of the cylinder. A third pipe extended from the top of the cylinder to the new condenser, which had been roughly fashioned out of tinplate. Two pipes leading down from this chamber connected with the foot of a small air-pump, an innovation Watt installed to draw off the injected water and condensed steam, together with any air that gathered in the condenser. The two pipes and the lower portion of the air pump were accommodated in a large tank containing sufficient cold water to reach just above the base of the condenser chamber. This reservoir ensured the condenser and pipes being kept cold.

Steam was generated and admitted to the cylinder, the air thus displaced escaping by way of the piston valve. When the steam was considered to be in complete possession of the cylinder the steam cock was closed. The piston rod of the air pump was then pulled up, the air in the condenser chamber and the pipes being drawn after it, leaving a vacuum. Upon the condenser cock then being opened the steam rushed in from the cylinder to be immediately condensed. The pressure upon the cylinder piston being thus removed, the latter at once rose, lifting an 18 lb. weight suspended from its lower end. The condenser cock was then shut and steam re-admitted at the top of the cylinder, forcing the piston down again, after which the process was repeated.

In the Newcomen engine, in which the downward stroke of the piston was the working stroke, resulting in the lifting of the pump-rod, atmospheric pressure was used to effect this important motion. Watt had now performed this function successfully solely by steam pressure, and thus brought into being the first true steam engine.

It was at this time that Watt became acquainted with Dr. Roebuck, of Bo'ness, a medical man who had turned engineer, and in partnership with a man named Cadell had started the first ironworks in Scotland at Carron in 1760. Later Roebuck turned his attention to mining his own coal, but the Newcomen engines in his mines were unable to cope with the constant flooding of the workings. He therefore urged Watt to perfect his improved steam engine as quickly as possible. Watt was handicapped by lack of funds, and Roebuck, in return for a two-thirds interest in the invention, undertook to finance the experimental work and to pay for the patenting of the engine. Roebuck also put Watt in touch with Matthew Boulton, the founder of the famous Soho metal works at Birmingham. Boulton had built a model on lines of a Newcomen engine, and was experimenting with it. The two men took an immediate liking to each other, and Boulton ceased experimenting with his model until events should prove the success or otherwise of Watt's efforts.

An early Watt double-acting engine, erected at Soho in 1788.

In January 1769 Watt patented his steam engine, and a full size trial model was then erected in an outhouse behind Dr. Roebuck's residence. It took six months to build and included the largest cylinder Watt had so far used. This was made at Carron and was 18 in. in diameter and of 5 ft. stroke. When tried out the engine proved disappointing, however, leakages of steam and faulty construction of the cylinder being the chief troubles. Early in 1770 various modifications were made to the engine, but they failed to improve its performance, and in disgust Watt christened it "*Beelzebub!*"

In 1772 Roebuck became a bankrupt. He owed Boulton £1,200, and rather than take legal proceedings against his friend Boulton agreed to accept as payment the former's two-thirds share in the engine patent. "*Beelzebub*" was dismantled and sent to the Soho works, and later was re-erected with various important changes made in its construction. These changes brought about a great improvement, and when the engine was once more in working order it accomplished 2,000 strokes with 1 cwt. of coal. This performance was considered good enough to justify the manufacture of similar engines for sale, and before long the Soho works became the scene of great activity. Watt went to live at Birmingham, and thus commenced an active partnership with Boulton that continued for more than 25 years and brought them fame and prosperity.

This engine was single acting; that is to say, the steam pressure was on one side of the piston all the time, and worked as follows. The downstroke of the piston was effected by steam admitted to the cylinder from above by way of a valve that also admitted steam into the steam jacket cloaking the cylinder. During this stroke any steam remaining beneath the piston from a previous stroke was allowed to escape through a valve to a separate condenser. As the cylinder end of the engine beam was drawn down by the descending piston, the opposite end of the beam canted up proportionately, thereby lifting the pump rods and allowing the pumps to fill with water.

The top valve through which steam had been admitted and the bottom valve leading to the separate condenser then closed, and a second valve at the foot of the cylinder opened and admitted beneath the piston steam available from the earliest admission at the top. The excess steam entered and lifted the piston until there was an equal pressure above and below, when, the weight of the pump rods exceeding that of the neutralised piston, the engine beam recanted and the piston was quickly drawn up to the top of the cylinder, while at the other end of the beam the pump rods descended again and discharged the water pumped up. The valves then reversed and the cycle of operations was repeated.

The air and water forced into the condenser chamber at each downstroke of the piston were drawn thence by an air pump working from the same engine beam, and were ejected into a "hot well." Water was drawn from the hot well by a feed pump also actuated by the beam, and passed along a pipe back to the boiler.

Subsequently Watt made a great step forward by the production of his double-acting engine, in which the steam pushed first on one side of the piston and then on the other. The two earliest large engines of this kind were erected in the Albion flour mill, near Blackfriars Bridge, London in 1786, but were destroyed when the mill was burnt down in 1791. Finally he obtained still further efficiency by making use of the expansive power of the steam.

In 1800 Watt retired from business and went to live at Heathfield Hall. A large attic at the top of the house was fitted up as a workshop and became known as his Garret, and there he spent many happy days going over his old experiments in search of possible mistakes and in inventing new contrivances. When deeply engrossed upon some particular problem he would confine himself to his workshop for days at a time, even cooking his own meals on the attic stove rather than tear himself away from his hobby long enough to dine downstairs. The attic, with its contents much as Watt left them, is now in the Science Museum, South Kensington, London. Late in 1819 he was taken ill, and passed away peacefully on 19th August, at the age of 83. He was interred close to Boulton in a side aisle of Handsworth Church, where later a beautiful monument, carved by the famous sculptor Chantrey, was erected in his memory. Chantrey also executed the magnificent statue of Watt placed in Westminster Abbey.

Watt's house in Deltfield Lane, Glasgow.

Few pioneers in science and engineering have lived a life so remarkably full in years and achievement. Labouring for many years under the disability of almost constant ill-health, Watt nevertheless brought his steam engine to a state of efficiency that enabled it to usher in the age of modern mill machinery, to pave the way for the birth of steam locomotion, and to find employment for nearly 1,000,000 people. Many honours were conferred upon him during his lifetime by learned societies. He was also offered a baronetcy, but this he modestly declined.

An Interesting Fog Beacon

The illustration on this page shows a novel type of fog beacon that has been erected recently at Tilbury landing stage. The apparatus, which is known as a "Sinterae" fog beacon, makes use of two powerful electric lamps placed very close together and energised in rapid alternation, so that a vibrating beam of light is emitted. Compared with the steady light obtained from a single lamp of the same candlepower as one of the Sinterae flashing lamps, the power of the vibrating beam to penetrate a foggy atmosphere is considerably greater. When visibility is about 700 ft. the increased penetration of the vibratory beam over a steady light is not more than 50 ft.; but when the fog thickens and visibility falls to about 300 ft. the increased penetration of the vibratory light is approximately 200 ft.

The Moscow-Volga Canal

Earth nearly equal to the amount removed in making the Panama Canal is being dug out at express speed to make the Moscow-Volga Canal that is now under construction in Russia. Work on the canal was begun in 1932, and in three years the engineers have excavated as much material as was taken out during the 10 years in which the Suez Canal was being built. When the new waterway is completed, water from the Volga will raise the level of Moscow River, thus making it navigable for large boats, and will supply Moscow with millions of gallons of drinking water and generate electric power.

A New Holland-Amerika Liner

The Holland-Amerika Line is to be augmented by the addition of a luxurious 33,250 ton vessel that is to be built in Holland. The new ship will be named either *"Prinsendam"* or *"Nieuw Amsterdam,"* and will have a length of 750 ft. and a breadth of 88 ft. She will be equipped with propelling machinery of 34,000 s.h.p. and will have two funnels, one of which will be a dummy and will serve as a ventilator. There will be 10 decks, excluding boat, promenade and sun decks. Construction will commence shortly.

Moving a River

To move a river in order that an aerodrome may be built seems a fantastic task, yet such a scheme is to be carried out near Nice, France. The mouth of the River Var is to be completely diverted in order that an aerodrome can be built where its waters have flowed out to the sea for hundreds of years. The mouth of the river has been gradually silting up, and a delta has been forming beneath the surface of the water. Under the scheme that is now to be carried out the river bed is to be moved 200 yds. so as to leave as dry land the ground that at present forms the delta. On this land the aerodrome will be built.

The "Sinterae" Beacon at Tilbury landing stage, which is referred to on this page. Photograph by courtesy of Sinterae Ltd., London.

A Novel Use for Aero Engines

A novel method of preventing frost from damaging their orange groves has been adopted by a group of fruit growers in California. It is known that frost needs cold air in order to settle, and the aim of the fruit growers therefore is to keep the air in motion. The equipment used for the purpose consists of a 450-h.p. aeroplane engine fitted with an 8 ft. propeller, mounted on a tower 40 ft. in height, the platform of which revolves when the engine is running. The propeller blade creates a wind that circulates the cold air before it can settle close to the ground, and it has been found that one engine can keep an area of from 40 to 50 acres quite clear of frost.

Bridge News

The beautiful suspension bridge over the river Conway, North Wales, which was constructed in 1826 by Thomas Telford, has been condemned by the Ministry of Transport. The bridge is not in any immediate danger, but it is unsuitable to bear the enormous burden to which it has been subjected during recent years, for it only allows one-way traffic. It is therefore proposed to build another bridge that will provide for two lines of traffic, and to widen the main road through the town.

The Conway Bridge has a span between towers of 327 ft. and is supported by four chains on each side, each of the chains being composed of links 3½ in. by 1 in. and 9 ft. long. The chains lie vertically above one another, but are not connected.

Many new and interesting features are embodied in a lifting bridge recently completed across the canal at Glasgow. The bridge, the first of its kind in Britain, is balanced on trunnion bearings round which it revolves. These bearings are situated on the top of one of the abutments, and when the bridge opens the tail end, which is counterbalanced, drops into a pit situated below roadway level. The bridge was constructed by Sir William Arrol and Co. Ltd., who, in conjunction with a Continental firm of engineers, have been responsible for developing this type of bridge.

Rapid progress is being made in the construction of the cantilever bridge in the East Bay crossing of the San Francisco-Oakland Bridge in the United States. When completed this will be the longest cantilever bridge in the country, while its deck, which accommodates six lanes of vehicles on an upper level and three lanes of vehicles and two rapid transit tracks on a lower level, will give it a greater weight capacity than any cantilever in the United States. Only two existing cantilever bridges, the Quebec Bridge in Canada and the Forth Bridge in Scotland, exceed it in size.

A new road bridge that is being built across the Firth of Forth at Kincardine is now nearing completion. It is half a mile in length, with twelve 50 ft. spans and two central spans of 150 ft.

Pneumatic Cement Pumps at Boulder Dam

The lower illustration on this page shows a "Fluxo" cement pump that is being used in the construction of Boulder Dam across the Black Canyon of Colorado River, U.S.A., an account of which appeared in the February and March 1934 issues of the "*M.M.*" In building the Dam a total of about 4,000,000 cu. yds. of concrete will be required and about 755,360 tons of cement. The cement is brought to the site from different cement works and stored in eight circular silos. After blending, the material is delivered by a pneumatic conveyor to two concrete - mixing plants, one of which is about 100 ft. from the blending silos, while the other is on the Nevada bank of the river, and about a mile distant from the silos. The cement therefore has to be conveyed over a distance of some 5,600 ft., and it is for this purpose that the "Fluxo" pneumatic pumping plant illustrated on this page has been installed.

The apparatus makes use of a pair of cylindrical iron tanks with conical bottoms placed side by side. These are connected at the top by a horizontal trunk coupled by inclined branches and having a rectangular opening in the centre, into which the cement flows from a tank above. The trunk contains a rotating agitating device, and suitable gate valves feed the cement into each tank alternately. The tanks are filled by gravity and emptied under air pressure in a regularly alternating sequence, so that a steady flow of cement passes through the pipeline.

Sound Reproduction on Newsprint

A method of printing sound records on ordinary paper or newsprint was demonstrated in London recently. The records are made by wrapping a photographic film, measuring about 17 in. by 20 in., round a rotating cylinder. As the cylinder rotates, a narrow strip of the film is exposed to the light from a photo-electric cell, the illumination being controlled by the sounds transmitted to a microphone connected in the circuit through an amplifier. This beam of light is arranged to move along the axis of the cylinder, so that a series of lines of records of the sound variations are obtained on the film. The negative thus obtained is used to make a printer's block, and this block in turn is employed to obtain reproductions on separate sheets of paper, or on one or more pages of a newspaper.

To reproduce the sounds the paper record is wrapped round a similar cylinder in the receiving apparatus and is exposed to a narrow and highly-concentrated light beam from any convenient source. This light in turn is reflected from the record on to a photo-electric cell or cathode-ray oscillograph, the intensity of the reflection being controlled by the lines on the record that are exposed to the light as the beam traverses and the cylinder revolves. The variations in current thus obtained are then amplified and used to operate an ordinary loud speaker. It is claimed that there is no difficulty in obtaining good reproduction from an ordinary sheet of newsprint, provided that the surface of the cylinder is highly polished. Creases do not seriously affect the quality of the reproduction, and the records can also be printed on any paper, though their life is, of course, determined by the quality of the latter.

The geared-turbine depot ship "Woolwich." The vessel has a displacement of 10,600 tons and was built by the Fairfield Shipbuilding and Engineering Co. Ltd., Govan, Glasgow, to whom we are indebted for our illustration.

A "Fluxo" Pump used for pumping cement to the mixing machine at Boulder Dam, U.S.A. Photograph by courtesy of F. L. Smidth and Co. Ltd., London.

New Depot Ship for the British Navy

The Admiralty recently took delivery of H.M.S. "*Woolwich*," a new depot ship for destroyers, which is illustrated on this page. Although the vessel is not a fighting craft it possesses features of unusual interest. It was built by the Fairfield Shipbuilding and Engineering Company Ltd., of Govan, Glasgow, and has a length of 575 ft. and a displacement of 10,600 tons. The propelling machinery consists of 6,500 s.h.p. twin-screw single reduction geared turbines designed for a speed of 15 knots. Large workshops equipped with machine tools of the latest type are provided to deal quickly with every repair that is likely to be required in a flotilla fleet.

A "Radium Hen"

In spite of extreme care hospitals occasionally lose or mislay radium "seeds," the tiny gold needle-like radium containers that are inserted in the body in the treatment of cancer. In future when a seed is lost all a hospital needs to do is bring in the "Radium Hen," a new instrument that has been devised in the National Physical Laboratory, and which gets its name from the clucking sound it emits when placed near radium. The nearer it approaches the valuable element the more rapidly and excitedly it clucks. The apparatus consists of a neon glow-lamp enclosed in a light-tight chamber and supplied with a voltage just lower than that at which the discharge of the lamp normally commences. In the presence of radium radiations the discharge voltage of a neon lamp is rather lower than normal, so that the lamp glows more readily when near radium. The voltage to operate the lamp is supplied by a condenser charged through a suitable resistance by means of a dry battery, with the result that each time the lamp glows the exciting voltage falls and the glow is then extinguished. A pair of headphones in series with the lamp thus records each discharge as a quiet click. In use the glow lamp is mounted on a long handle suitable for exploring in any holes and corners where the needles are likely to be, and the presence of the radium is revealed by a rapid increase in the rate of clicking. Most needles or "seeds" get lost down sink pipes, and the apparatus is particularly useful in detecting the exact points in the pipes where the needles are lodged.

The Barmen-Elberfeld Overhead Railway

Advantages of a Suspended System

By Hans F. Kutschbach

THE development of towns that are situated fairly close to one another soon creates a demand for rapid and convenient transport facilities between them. The German towns of Vohwinkel, Elberfeld and Barmen are situated in the valley of the River Wupper to the east of the Rhine. The shape of this valley caused the development of these towns to take place along the course of the river, with the result that to-day the three form practically one town. In addition to this waterway they are connected by rail, by a street tramway system and, most interesting of all, by the well-known overhead Barmen-Elberfeld Railway.

During the last years of the 19th century the rapid growth of the three towns towards one another resulted in a great deal of street traffic congestion. With a view to relieving this an elevated electric railway providing rapid transit was proposed, and ultimately it was decided to adopt the system, then recently designed by an engineer named Eugen Langen, of a mono-rail suspended railway. This particular type was especially suited to the conditions to be met, for the only route available was above the river flowing through the three towns, and the numerous sharp curves at frequent intervals would have made the building of an ordinary surface railway a matter of great difficulty. Work was started in 1898 and the section of the line between Elberfeld and Vohwinkel was opened three years later. The completed system was finally opened in 1903 and is 8.3 miles long. Along the part of the line that follows the course of the river, the rails from which the cars are suspended form part of a triangulated framework, supported at intervals by "legs" that straddle the river banks. Elsewhere the framework is supported by "U"-shaped plate girder erections that remind one of giant croquet hoops.

The car bodies are suspended below the running rails. On their roofs are mounted two strong frames of special construction in which are arranged the running wheels and the electric motors for propelling the train. The power supply is direct current at a pressure of 600 volts, and the maximum speed is restricted to 25 m.p.h. Each car has its own motors, and trains are made up of two or three cars each. Special arrangements ensure that in the event of a derailment of the wheels the cars are prevented from falling from the track. No case of a car falling has ever occurred, and in the 30 years or so of the existence of the line only one fatal accident has been recorded. Even this instance was not due to any defects in construction or in maintenance, and in fact, ever since the opening, the working has been perfectly satisfactory and the frequency of the service afforded remarkable. The 20 stations are spaced at an average of 765 yards apart, and during rush hours the trains follow each other at intervals of less than two minutes.

A two-car train on the Barmen-Elberfeld Railway system over the River Wupper. The characteristic construction of the framework and the suspension arrangements are shown in this illustration.

The safety of operation, when the frequency of the service is borne in mind, is a striking feature of the system, and this, together with the punctual running and general trustworthiness of service, is no doubt largely accounted for by the soundness of the signalling system. In view of signalling developments during recent years on ordinary surface and underground railways it is interesting that train movements on the Barmen-Elberfeld line have always been controlled by automatic colour-light signals arranged on the "approach lighting" system. This means that the signal lights are illuminated only on the approach of a train within a certain distance of the signal, and that the lights go out when it has passed. Although various alterations have been made as a result of experience in operation, the main principles of the system are as embodied in the original apparatus.

The signalling sections extend from station to station. Entrance to a section is governed by a two-aspect starting signal with the usual red and green indications. There is in addition a special yellow light that can be illuminated, together with the red light, when permission has been obtained, by telephone from the station in advance, for a waiting train to proceed with caution into an obstructed section.

The station master at each station has under his care

the signalling apparatus, such as the operating relays, pilot lights and emergency switch gear for that section; and he has to take any special steps necessary for dealing with any emergency that may arise. He can keep a signal at danger independently of the automatic arrangements, if this should be necessary for any reason.

The automatic operation of the signals makes use of the 600-volt power current, and short lengths of special rail form contacts for the collector shoes on the cars. When one shoe on a car makes contact with one of these special lengths, the other is still on the live rail; and as the shoes are connected in parallel, current is then supplied to the signal circuit. Only the shoes on the first car of a train affect the clearing of a section; but if a train stops after only part of it has passed the contact rail, and then proceeds, or if one is backed on to a contact rail, there is no irregular clearing of the signal in the rear.

An interesting photograph showing the suspended Railway, the River, and the roadway alongside. The bridge that crosses them all carries a railway line of normal type.

In view of the success of this overhead railway it is surprising perhaps that similar systems have not been adopted more widely as the means of transport. Possibly the day of schemes of this kind has yet to come, when existing surface or underground systems are found incapable of dealing with more traffic. A great advantage of the overhead form of construction is that its framework is said to cost only half as much as a tramway, and of course it does not in any way obstruct the street or other surface traffic, but is carried along completely above it. A disadvantage that it shares with other railways of such a special nature is that the arrangement of points and crossings is a difficult matter.

How the line is suspended along the road. Bearers of plate construction replace the lattice form used elsewhere.

Special switch rails are used on the Barmen-Elberfeld Railway that have the effect of lifting the double flanged wheels of the cars clear of the main rail, and of diverting them as required, the main rail itself remaining unbroken. The operation of such switches is naturally somewhat slow and more complicated than that of corresponding main line equipment. In the latter case it is only necessary to move the switch rails a few inches, but on the suspended line a portion of the whole track has to be moved some feet in order to allow sufficient clearance for the cars and their suspending frames. The reversing of the trains at the terminal points is effected by running them round a loop line. A loop is also situated intermediately.

It may be that the experimental installation of the Railplane system at Milngavie near Glasgow shows a possible future development. This involves a trestle-like structure carrying overhead rail tracks from which are suspended cars whose bodywork is designed on the lines of airships. In addition to the running rail above each car there is a rigid guide rail to prevent any swaying of the car while in motion. The important point about this system is that it involves a non-adhesion drive. The propulsion of the car is effected by means of airscrews at the front and the rear, driven by electric motors that obtain their current from a live rail. The design of the bogies from which the cars are suspended is such as to check the tendency for the cars to rise in the air when in motion, to a greater extent than is required to relieve the weight on the laminated springs of the bogies. Two bogies of short wheelbase are used for each car, this two-point suspension being flexible enough to allow the trestle structure to follow largely the contours of the land.

Interesting details of the design are the measures adopted to promote rapid and silent running. Ball and roller-bearings are freely used, and combined with the shape of the cars they tend to reduce resistance to a minimum. For silence a patented steel wheel construction is adopted. A ring of rubber is placed between the wheel centre and the tyre, and it also acts as a shock absorber.

A full description of the Railplane system, together with illustrations, appeared in the August 1930 issue of the *"M.M."*

The Development of Smoke Deflectors

Interesting Experiments and Fittings

IN comparing ancient and modern locomotives, a point that strikes us very forcibly is the tremendous growth that has taken place in the size of the boiler. This has occurred of necessity, as heavier loads and higher speeds have required the development of greater power, and therefore increased steaming capacity. As a result of this growth of the boiler the chimney, which was the most prominent fitting of early engines, has so diminished in height as to be almost in danger of disappearing! In fact it appears to have done so completely when one is looking at a broadside view of *"No. 10000,"* the remarkable L.N.E.R. high-pressure 4-6-4 design. A steam locomotive without any visible chimney is almost unthinkable, however, and a head-on view of the same engine discloses the fact that the chimney is present after all. It is concealed, except at the front, by casing plates that are found as forward extensions to the boiler lagging, the chimney being placed between them on the sloping top of the smoke-box.

The ugly experimental smoke-deflecting apparatus formerly fitted to L.M.S.R. No. 6161 "King's Own" is shown in this illustration. The special arrangement of the smoke-box front and the plain chimney show up prominently. Photograph by R. A. Batty of Liverpool.

This unusual external front-end design is seen also in the 2–8–2 *"Cock o' The North."* The casing plates are intended to act as smoke deflectors, and they fulfil the same function as the separate side sheets fitted to engines of more familiar design, such as the L.M.S.R. "Royal Scots" or S.R. "Lord Nelsons." Readers may ask what is the actual purpose of smoke deflectors. It will be of interest, therefore, to consider the subject generally and some of the various experiments made in connection with it.

L.N.E.R. "No. 10000," showing how the chimney is situated between the extended side casing plates, which act as smoke deflectors.

In the moderate-pressure locomotive of normal 2-cylinder design, such as was standard for many years, the design of the valve gear is usually such that it is impossible to operate the engine in the same manner as those of modern design, with long-travel valves for short cut-off working. Thus most of the work in these older engines is performed with the valves cutting off fairly late and with a partly-closed regulator. The effect of this late cut-off is to give the exhaust steam a fairly high terminal pressure, with the result that it escapes from the blast-pipe with considerable violence. Such engines have little difficulty in lifting their exhaust steam and smoke well clear of the train.

During the period when engines of this type were generally employed more or less tall chimneys were in use. With the dwarfed boiler mountings common on the locomotives of to-day, however, and with modern methods of design and operation with early cut-offs, there is a tendency for the exhaust to hang about along the top of the locomotive boiler. This "blinds" the cab windows and thus impedes the driver's vision. This obscuring of the view is dangerous in that observation of the signals is made very difficult.

A solution to this problem developed in Germany about 10 or 12 years ago was the fitting of smoke-deflecting sheets alongside the smoke-box. These fittings have since been provided on numerous Continental locomotives, and have been adopted also in this country by the L.M.S.R. and the S.R. for certain classes of locomotives. On the S.R. various experiments were made before the decision to fit side sheets was reached. Engine No. 450, *"Sir Kay,"* was provided with a curious fitting to the rear of the chimney that was apparently intended to act on an air "scoop" and create an upward draught behind the chimney. Another engine, No. 755, *"The Red Knight,"* had what might be termed a modern short version of the louvred chimney of the "Jones" period on the Highland Railway. But apparently neither of these was found as satisfactory as the side sheets.

The necessity for efficient smoke deflection, in order to

ensure a clear view ahead for the driver, led to the fitting of side sheets to the L.M.S.R. "Royal Scots" and the large-boilered "Claughtons," and subsequently also to the "Baby Scots." As on the Southern Railway experiments were carried out with cowl arrangements behind the chimney of certain of the "Royal Scots," including No. 6100, *"Royal Scot"* itself.

Remarkable modifications were made experimentally to the front end appearance of No. 6161, *"King's Own."* The front top portion of the smoke-box appeared to have been sliced off at an angle and left flat. The standard chimney was removed, and a plain "stove-pipe" of forbidding appearance was mounted on the sloping surface of the modified smoke-box. In addition a "hood" or covering plate following the normal curve of the smoke-box was fitted in front of the chimney, over the flat sloping surface, in order to cause currents of air to deflect the exhaust steam and smoke well up out of the way. To assist in this the smoke-box door was made conical in the centre. The engine is now running with the standard deflectors.

A French State Railways 4-8-2 locomotive of notable design fitted with smoke deflectors at the side of the smoke-box. Photograph reproduced by courtesy of the French State Railways.

A similar scheme, but without the conical smoke-box door, was applied also to one of the L.N.E.R. "Super-Pacifics," No. 2747, *"Coronach,"* but this engine retained its original chimney. An additional modification is found on No. 2751, *"Humorist,"* shown in the lower illustration on this page. Here the chimney is flanked by two small side sheets so that the upper part of the smoke-box, which is flattened and sloping, resembles the arrangement found on *"No. 10000"* or *"Cock o' the North."*

An interesting view of an L.N.E.R. "Super-Pacific," No. 2751, "Humorist," fitted with a plain stove-pipe chimney on the sloping smoke-box. The chimney is flanked by small deflecting plates. Photograph by H. M. Madgwick of Worthing.

The ordinary "Pacific" locomotives with boilers pressed at 180 lb. per sq. in., appeared, in their early days particularly, to find little difficulty in getting their exhaust steam and smoke well out of the way. Since the provision of shorter chimneys for general service working, however, and the subsequent development of the "Super-Pacific" design, the problem of smoke deflection seems to have appeared. Owing to the short cut-off working made possible by the adoption of the higher pressure of 220 lb. per sq. in., and alterations to the valve motion, the exhaust is not lifted to any great extent under certain conditions. It is quite probable, however, that the tapered boiler fitted to these engines is of advantage in carrying away from the cab window, whatever steam tends to hang about the boiler top; and possibly this accounts for the absence of deflectors from the "Pacifics" as a class.

The G.W.R. alone appear to have no use for smoke-deflecting devices, yet strangely enough Swindon for the last 30 years has led the way in the matter of short cut-off working with steam at relatively high pressures. The use of tapered boilers, however, which on the G.W.R. are not of extremely large diameter at the smoke-box end, enables chimneys of reasonable heights to be provided. This, in conjunction with the probable effect of the tapered boiler in keeping the smoke away from the cab, may explain the continued absence of special smoke-deflecting fittings on G.W.R. engines. In this connection the free exhaust of Swindon products must not be forgotten. The "jumper" blast pipe used on G.W.R. engines enables the steam to escape as quickly as possible, and in conjunction with the other features mentioned assists in throwing the smoke and steam well up. It is significant, too, that since the adoption of these various G.W.R. features on the more recent standard locomotives of the L.M.S.R. the use of smoke-deflecting side sheets as fitted to the "Royal Scots" and "Baby Scots" has been abandoned.

In France recently, in addition to the provision of deflecting plates at the side of the smoke-box, the problem of securing a clear view for the driver has been approached in another manner. To keep the cab look-out windows clear of smoke, steam and cinders, a device known as the "Pottier deflector" has been developed. With this the look-out window is a plain unglazed opening, and the column of air that tends to enter this when the engine is in motion is opposed by another column acting in the reverse direction. This effect is obtained automatically as a result of aerodynamic screening by special deflecting plates. Other plates remove the whole of the air concerned, so that balanced air pressure is maintained inside and outside the cab window opening.

The apparatus is located in front of the cab spectacle plate, the cab roof being extended forward at this point, forming a "visor" or hood, as it were, for the deflecting plates themselves.

Coaling Large Steamships

Ancient and Modern Methods

COALING a ship is a necessary evil to which all hands object, because it means so much dirt, not only to the officers and crew, but also to the ship itself. A liner on a long cruise cannot carry sufficient coal to serve the full length of the voyage out and home, and must therefore call at a series of ports to take more fuel on board. Our cover, enlarged from part of a photograph sent to us by a reader, shows natives at work coaling the Orient liner R.M.S. "*Ormonde*" at Colombo, Ceylon. They load 6,000 tons of coal into the ship in $8\frac{1}{2}$ hrs., each native carrying half a hundredweight of coal in a basket on his shoulders. The baskets are emptied into chutes in the side of the ship, to the accompaniment of singing and a chanting of native songs. By the time coaling is finished everything is covered with coal-dust, and as this is always the case with this method of coaling by hand it is no wonder that the operation is regarded as being a most objectionable proceeding. In addition this method is laborious and slow.

33-Ton Hydraulic Coal Hoist at Newcastle-upon-Tyne. Photo courtesy of the Tyne Improvement Commission.

When steamships were small and required little coal these drawbacks were not serious, but as the size of steamships and the length of their voyages increased the coaling problem became more and more acute. By degrees various mechanical appliances were brought into use to speed up the operations. These have been improved and developed until to-day coaling by hand has been almost entirely abandoned and is now only economically possible at ports where ample and cheap native labour is available. The actual methods and plant employed in mechanical coaling vary in different ports according to local conditions and the number and size of the ships to be supplied. Naturally the most elaborate and most interesting machinery is to be found at the larger ports.

At Liverpool, for instance, the equipment available for shipping includes a whole fleet of floating coaling machines. These machines are of two types, one operated by a grab in conjunction with a belt conveyor, and the other by means of a bucket elevator and chute.

In the case of the former type the machine is moored alongside the vessel to be coaled and a barge laden with coal is brought alongside the machine. The grab then descends swiftly into the barge and its great steel jaws close upon a mouthful of coal weighing more than a ton. It is then drawn up and releases its coal upon a travelling belt conveyor that carries it across the deck of the ship and deposits it through the open hatchway of the coal bunker. The grab can coal a ship at the rate of more than 100 tons per hr.

In the case of the machines operated by bucket elevator and chute, the coal is carried on the machines themselves, some of which can accommodate 1,100 tons. It is made to fall in regulated quantities through a false bottom on to a travelling chain of buckets that hoist it to the top of the machine and discharge it down chutes extending over the decks into hatchways, or alternatively into the side ports of the ship's bunkers. These machines are capable of coaling a vessel at the rate of about 300 tons per hr.

An interesting coaling plant of much greater output is in use at Sandusky, Ohio, U.S.A. It is owned by the Pennsylvania Railroad. The plant is designed to handle 120-ton wagons fully loaded, but it has sufficient reserve capacity to deal with 150-ton wagons when necessary.

When the plant is in operation the loaded wagons are shunted to a point conveniently near, and pushed one at a time towards an inclined gangway that leads up to the "cradle" or platform of the hoist. At the foot of the incline each wagon passes over a pit, from which immediately appears a small contrivance known as the "barney-car." This consists of a mechanical arm attached to a small trolley running on a narrow-gauge track placed inside the track for the coal wagons, and it pushes each wagon up the incline to the cradle, where it is brought to rest ready for the next wagon.

The hoist carries the loaded wagon upward for a distance of about 30 ft., and then the tipping mechanism comes into operation and the wagon is slowly tilted on to its side. With a roar the 100 or more tons of coal are dumped into a great pan, from which the coal gravitates down a long tapering chute lowered into the hold of the ship. Before the noise of the descending coal has ceased, the tipping mechanism has righted the wagon and the hoist has returned it to the top of the incline. The wagon then descends a gangway to the "empties" siding.

A Novel Power Transmission Unit

The Autoflex Drive

ONE of the most important problems in any engineering workshop is that of transmitting the power of motors or engines to the machines it is desired to drive. Usually this is done by means of shafts, pulleys and belts, and before electricity came into general use it was customary to erect a line of shafting along the centre or sides of the workshop and drive it by means of one large prime mover such as a steam or gas engine. This method is still adopted by some engineering firms, but in the more modern shops the various machine tools are driven separately or in groups by means of electric motors. The largest type of machine tools are generally provided with a special motor, in many cases bolted down directly on to the machine bed, but the smaller machines usually are driven by means of belts from a motor fixed in a convenient place to drive a number of machines in a special group. By this means, groups or series of machine tools can be run independent of the remainder of the shop, and therefore, in the event of certain machines not being required, a saving of power can be effected.

An Autoflex Drive Unit arranged to drive a lathe. For the illustrations on this page we are indebted to Wearn's Autoflex Drives Ltd., London.

The power that a belt drive can transmit is determined largely by the natural grip between the materials of which the pulley and the belt are made, but no matter how good the pulley and belt are in this respect, they will not pull their load unless a certain minimum pressure exists between belt and pulley surface. This pressure can be maintained only by keeping a corresponding tension in the belt. Some means must, therefore, be provided for maintaining tension.

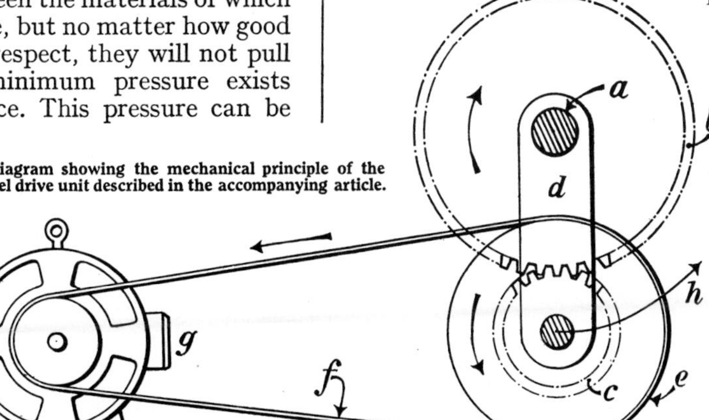

A diagram showing the mechanical principle of the novel drive unit described in the accompanying article.

Various means of providing proper tension in the belts have been devised, some of which have sought to decrease the amount and rapidity of belt stretch, to provide automatic means for taking up stretch and to increase the grip between belt and pulley so that less pressure is necessary.

The most satisfactory method however is to use some automatic means to maintain the desired belt tension, in spite of stretch, and on this page we illustrate a novel device that has been designed for this purpose. It is known as the Wearn's Autoflex Drive and is based on a very simple principle of mechanics. Whilst the drive possesses the properties of an automatic belt tensioning device and reduction gear, it also functions as an efficient shock absorber and safety measure.

The principle of the drive will be clear from an examination of the diagram at the foot of this page. The motor pulley drives through the medium of a single flat belt F on to the driven pulley E, and if the direction of rotation is as indicated by the arrow, the resistance to driving of the driven shaft A will tend to cause the pinion C to climb round the gear wheel B in the direction of arrow H, thus tightening the belt, which, of course, it is free to do, because it is mounted in the floating housing indicated by D.

The gear wheel B and the driven shaft A commence to rotate as soon as the torque due to the belt tension overcomes the torque created by the load, and thus any change in the load, no matter how small, is always accompanied by a corresponding change in the belt tension and a change in the position of pinion C around gear wheel B.

When a machine is fitted with the Wearn's Autoflex drive, any sudden increase in the load is automatically met by the provision of adequate belt tension, and in consequence, the belt is absolutely free from any tendency to slip, and this freedom from slip has been shown to be operative under the most exacting conditions arising from damp, oil or dust.

An Autoflex unit tested by the National Physical Laboratory showed a transmission efficiency of 95 per cent.

Empire Air Routes Exhibition

A most interesting exhibition organised by Imperial Airways is open at the Science Museum, South Kensington, London, S.W.7. It illustrates by means of striking models, charts, maps and photographs the development of air communication within the Empire. The exhibits include models of all types of aeroplane ever owned by the company, and of especial interest are the sectional models of new aircraft now being built for them.

Part of the Exhibition deals with the design of airports, and includes a large model of a modern airport and dioramas of three famous Empire ones. Fascinating working models show how wireless is used to control aircraft when they are flying in fog and above cloud, and the visitor by pressing a button can hear the voice of the pilot in the air calling for his position and the reply from wireless stations on the ground. Other attractive sections deal with the building of a flying boat, an aeroplane and aero engines. Models of a wind tunnel and a testing tank, that can be set working by the visitor, enable him to understand the important part they play in the design of aircraft.

The Exhibition shows more clearly than any written article the remarkable developments that have taken place in air transport during recent years, and this can be even better appreciated if the visitor first inspects the museum gallery where models of pioneer types of aircraft are permanently displayed. All *"M.M."* readers interested in aviation, who can manage to visit the Exhibition, will find that it well repays the time spent. It is open free daily until the end of this month, on Sundays from 2.30 to 6 p.m. and on weekdays from 10 a.m. to 6 p.m.

An illustrated handbook giving the history of aeroplanes and a detailed list of the Science Museum's exhibits of these machines has just been published. A review of it will appear in next month's *"M.M."*

Record Stratosphere Ascent

The most enthusiasm for ascents into the stratosphere is shown by the United States and Russia. The latest record ascent has been made from American territory by Capts. A. W. Stevens and O. A. Anderson, of the U.S. Army Corps. They ascended from Rapid City in the stratosphere balloon *"Explorer II,"* and soaring upward at an average speed of 600 ft. per min. they reached a height of 20,000 ft. in just over half-an-hour. As the balloon rose higher its rate of climb gradually decreased to about half the figure just given, and the greatest height reached was 74,000 ft. At that immense distance above the earth the temperature outside the gondola suspended beneath the balloon was –55 deg.

The descent took eight hours, and the balloon landed at White Lake, South Dakota, 240 miles from Rapid City. One of the most interesting things reported by the officers is that during the last stage of the ascent the sky appeared to them like a vast black awning.

A view from the hangar at Waalhaven Aerodrome. Photograph by courtesy of Royal Dutch Air Lines.

A Trans-Pacific Air Service

A regular air service across the Pacific Ocean will be established before the end of this year, as the result of an agreement between the New Zealand Government and Pan-American Airways. No details have been announced concerning the type or size of aircraft that will be employed or as to the frequency of the service.

New Record Flights

Several interesting record flights have been made during the past three months. Miss Jean Batten, in her Percival "Gull" flew from Lympne, Kent to Port Natal, Brazil in 61 hrs. The first stage of her flight was to Casablanca, a distance of 1,400 miles, and was accomplished non-stop. From there she flew to Dakar, on the coast of West Africa, where she took off for the 1,700 miles flight across the South Atlantic to Brazil. On this stage of her journey she set up a new record by crossing the ocean in 13 hr. 15 min. This was 3 hr. 25 min. less than the previous record, made by Senor Pombo in a B.A. "Eagle," in May 1935.

A Percival "Gull" was also used by H. F. Broadbent when he flew from Croydon to Port Darwin, Australia in the record time of 6 days 21 hr. 19 min. The previous record for this flight was made by Sir Charles Kingsford Smith in 1933 when he accomplished the journey in 7 days 4 hr. 47 min. Broadbent followed up his success by flying from Port Darwin to Sydney in 18 hr., and being the first man to cross Australia in one day.

The flight from Capetown to England has been accomplished in 6 days 8 hr. 27 min. by D. Llewellyn, the instructor at Hanworth, who was accompanied by Mrs. J. Wyndham, a well-known airwoman. They flew a Hendy "Heck" light aeroplane. The previous fastest time for this trip was 7 days 7 hr. 5 min., and was made by Mrs. Mollison in December 1932.

Air France Progress

Air France, in common with many other chief air transport companies, carried more traffic last summer than previously. The total number of passengers carried was 42,076, an increase of 9,748, and 780 tons of freight was conveyed by air, an increase of 69 tons. The quantity of air mail carried was also slightly greater than during previous summers.

Imperial Airways Notes

The twice weekly service between Croydon and Brindisi has been suspended indefinitely. It was operated with the Avro 652 low wing monoplanes purchased last year.

In addition to the new Short type flying boats mentioned last month the company have ordered a composite form of aircraft invented by Major R. H. Mayo and named after him. It is being built by Short Bros. (Rochester and Bedford) Ltd., and consists of a huge flying boat with a twin-float seaplane carried on the centre section of the wing. At the beginning of a flight the two machines will be locked together by special catches, and when they have risen to a sufficient height the catches will be released and the seaplane will fly off the flying boat and continue the journey alone, while the flying boat returns to its base.

The idea is that an aeroplane loaded too heavily to be able to take off unaided can be lifted into the air by a lightly loaded machine. It is claimed that the Mayo Composite Aircraft will enable a bigger payload to be carried for less engine power and at a lower cost than is possible with fully loaded aircraft ascending alone. Both the seaplane and the flying boat will have four engines, and when the two machines are locked together in flight the composite aircraft will resemble a huge eight-engined biplane with wings of unequal span.

Capt. W. Rogers, one of the company's pilots, recently completed 10,000 hrs. of cross-Channel flying, during the whole of which he has piloted passenger-carrying civil aircraft.

New Zealand Air Services

Important purchases of new aircraft for developing New Zealand internal air lines were mentioned in the October 1935 "*M.M.*" Union Airways hope to introduce a daily air mail service between Palmerston and Dunedin this month, and they will use one of their new D.H. 86s for the work.

Another company, Great Pacific Airways (N.Z.) Ltd., have ordered three Avro 652 monoplanes. It is expected that the machines will be delivered in time for the company to begin an air service between Auckland and Dunedin in June or July this year.

Larger South African Air Force

The South African Air Force is to be increased under a five-year scheme that will raise the total number of pilots and mechanics on the active list to 150 and 1,300 respectively. There will also be 1,000 pilots and 1,700 mechanics in the Reserve. Many of the new pilots will be trained at the Central Flying School, Pretoria and others will receive their instruction at the hands of new squadrons to be formed at Capetown, Natal and Bloemfontein. Light aeroplane clubs in South Africa may also train some of the pilots.

An unusual view of the B.A. "Eagle" 3-seater monoplane, showing the wings folded back. Photograph reproduced by courtesy of "The Aeroplane."

Improved Fokker FXXXVI

An improved version of the four-engined Fokker FXXXVI high wing monoplane has been designed by the Fokker Company. It is the same size as the FXXXVI which was described in the October 1934 "*M.M.*" but differs structurally, has a retractible undercarriage and is capable of carrying a greater load.

The pilot's cockpit in the Fokker F.XXII. Photograph by courtesy of the N.V. Nederlandsche Vliegtuigenfabriek.

New Russian Amphibian

Unfavourable weather conditions have made it impossible to maintain a regular air service between Moscow and Leningrad, and the railway continues to be the only reliable means of communication. The Experimental Institute of the U.S.S.R. hopes to remedy this state of affairs, however, with a large amphibian that has been designed by Grokhorski, the Russian inventor who is also Director of the Institute.

An experimental two-seater amphibian is to be built first, and if it is successful in operation a full size machine of the same design will be built. This will be able to carry 25 passengers and a crew of five, and it will have two engines powerful enough to give it a cruising speed of 125 m.p.h. The amphibian is to be of the monoplane type with a short and very deep wing, and with the engines projecting from the leading edge. Two long floats will be attached to the underside of the wing and it will be possible to use them either for landing on water or as skis for landing on ice. When required they can be replaced by an undercarriage provided with pneumatically-tyred wheels, so that the amphibian can travel across sands and fields. It is intended that it shall fly at high speed a few feet above the ground, and rise to a height of about 150 ft. when rivers, streams or other obstacles are approached.

Flashlight Aerial Photography

Aerial photography has been practised in the daytime for many years, and recently in America it was carried out at night with the aid of what are called "flashlight" bombs. At San Diago, California, an officer and a technical sergeant of the 23rd Photo Section, U.S. Army Air Corps., ascended late one evening to a height of 1,500 ft. in a Fairchild aeroplane equipped for aerial photography. They obtained an excellent photograph of the International California Pacific Exposition then being held at San Diago. The flashlight bombs used had a total candlepower of 500,000,000, and when in use lit up the scene below with great brilliance.

Gloster "Gladiators" for R.A.F.

New equipment for the R.A.F. includes Gloster "Gladiator" single-seater fighters, and some of these machines are being supplied to the recently re-formed No. 74 (Fighter) Squadron. This type of machine is a development of the Gloster "Gauntlet" in use by the R.A.F. and just added to the extensive equipment of the Danish Air Force. It is fitted with a Bristol "Mercury" Mk.IX engine rated at 615-715 h.p.

World's Largest Airship

New German Zeppelin Nearly Completed

By B. T. Denne

VERY soon, if all goes according to plan, Dr. Hugo Eckener hopes to launch his challenge to the airship critics of the world. This is the new giant Zeppelin, LZ.129, now nearing completion at Friedrichshafen, beside Lake Constance.

Dr. Eckener is a young man of modest, retiring disposition, difficult to get to know intimately, with no desire to show off his capabilities. Records of reliability and endurance achieved by ordinary aircraft do not greatly interest him, neither does he fear any very serious rivalry from the flying boat in trans-ocean air service. In accord with most advocates of lighter-than-air aircraft, he willingly gives the palm for speedy transit to aeroplanes, but he vigorously maintains that the airship, with its long range, great lifting capacity and suitability for night flying, comes into its own when oceans have to be crossed. This theory seems amply borne out in practice, as so far not even the largest flying boat has attempted to beat the *"Graf Zeppelin's"* record of 70 trans-Atlantic flights with passengers, freight and mail.

The corridor through the hull of the new Zeppelin, LZ.129. The illustrations to this article are by courtesy of the Deutsche Zeppelin Reederei.

For the past seven years Dr. Eckener has been experimenting with the *"Graf Zeppelin,"* which during that time has flown something like 702,120 miles and carried 16,940 passengers, 70,596 lb. of mail and 102,094 lb. of cargo without mishap to a single person or the loss of even a postal circular. Now all his thought is being turned to the vast new duralumin structure suspended in its hangar at Friedrichshafen, and in which, through Ludwig Duerr the designer, all the fruits of pioneer experience and the latest that science has to offer are being embodied.

Sectional drawing of the interior of the airship showing the arrangement of the passengers' quarters. In the foreground is the staircase leading to the lower deck.

The first thing that impresses a visitor to the hangar of the LZ.129 is the cathedral-like dimensions of the airship's skeleton, which towers 145 ft. and extends to a length of 812 ft. There are 15 main rings, the largest being 67 ft. in diameter, supporting the maze of braced girders, and 32 auxiliary ones form compartments for the 16 gasbags or balloonets. Much attention has been given to a new system of wire lacing for firmly holding the outer fabric, thus obviating the "billowing" effect often noticeable on the *"Graf Zeppelin."* Another improvement is the introduction of a new leak-proof material for the balloonets. This substance is of the gelatinoid formation, and is incomparably better than the very expensive gold-beaters'-skin, which was a source of continual trouble on the *"Graf Zeppelin"* and during each trip made it necessary for a member of the crew to spend his time going round smelling for escapes of hydrogen —an unpleasant occupation, considering the explosive nature of that gas.

The four engine gondolas of the LZ.129, each of which is as large as an aeroplane fuselage, are being suspended from the hull, and will house 16-cylinder Daimler Benz Diesel motors. Each motor develops 1,200 h.p. at full throttle, or 900 h.p. at half when the airship will be cruising at 80 m.p.h. The motors are the last word in workmanship and design. Their crude oil supply will be carried in the keel of the airship.

The list of ideas and inventions being incorporated in the LZ.129 is almost endless, and among the more important items are undoubtedly those concerning navigation and control. The instruments in the pilot house will include a large gyro-compass, with synchronising repeaters in other parts of the airship. A "whistling" altimeter that functions similarly to the sounding apparatus on a ship will enable the pilot to know his exact height above earth or ocean at night and in foggy weather. Other proposed innovations are a 5,500,000 c.p. searchlight so that the driftmeter can be used at night, and a curious apparatus, weighing two tons, by means of which a chemical called "Gel" (silicon dioxide) extracts pure water from the atmosphere. This water will be used in the kitchen, etc., and its availability will enable the quantity of water taken on board prior to each trip to be greatly reduced.

It is difficult for anybody who has not seen inside the *"Graf Zeppelin"* to appreciate the improvements made in space and in passenger accommodation on the LZ.129. In the older airship passengers and crew have to share the room afforded by a comparatively small gondola. There is only one saloon, doing duty as dining and recreation room combined. It has two doors at each end. The forward one leads to the small kitchen and the wireless room situated on either side of a narrow gangway, and beyond them are the chart room and the pilot house. The door aft of the saloon opens on to a similar passage, along the sides of which are 12 sleeping cabins, etc., and farther on are a store room and the crews' quarters within the hull.

Covering the huge skeleton of the airship with fabric.

On the LZ.129 all this has been changed, and there will be a feeling of spaciousness almost akin to that experienced on board a steamer. The pilot house, with the wireless room above, has been arranged to occupy a special gondola in the bow, and is quite separate from the passengers' part of the airship. This alteration will perhaps be most appreciated by members of the navigation staff, for on the *"Graf Zeppelin"* passengers have been known to trespass through to the "bridge" and amuse themselves by watching the officers at work, a trial the latter are said to have endured very patiently!

Behind the control gondola there will be a row of windows on each side of the hull to light two 45-ft. promenade sun decks. The upper (A) and lower (B) decks will be situated between the sun decks, as shown in the lower illustration on the previous page. Adjoining the starboard promenade on "A" deck there is to be a large dining room and entertainment hall and a combined writing room and library. Next amidships will be 25 sleeping cabins each containing two beds; which explains how accommodation has been provided for 50 passengers. In addition to being centrally heated, all cabins will have hot and cold running water, a wardrobe, table, service bell, etc., and of course the last row will be "outside" cabins, with windows abutting on to the port promenade. Coming down from above by way of a wide, very nautical staircase on to "B" deck, one will immediately be in the "works" of the airship, as here will be the kitchen with its electric stove and culinary equipment, the quarters of the 35 members of the crew, the chief steward's office, bathrooms, toilets, and a smoking room. This last might seem rather a daring introduction to an airship using chiefly hydrogen for buoyancy, but safety has been assured by an ingenious interlocking system of swing doors and special ventilation, effectually isolating the smoking room from the rest of the airship.

A view through the girder framework, showing the wire lacing, and one of the rings in course of construction on the ground.

Thus with typical thoroughness is being evolved a craft which Germany hopes will enable her to open up a new and unopposed trade route between Europe and North and South America. The historic *"Graf Zeppelin,"* with which Dr. Eckener made his name, is to be kept in commission, partly for reasons of national sentiment, but the years of pioneer adventure that it marks are now believed to be over. This is one of the reasons for the formation of the Luftschiff Zeppelin Reederei (Airship Traffic Company) who intend to exploit their new commercial venture to the full.

The *"Graf Zeppelin"* is much smaller than the LZ.129, her overall length being 772 ft., maximum diameter 100 ft. and maximum height 113 ft. Her propulsion machinery consists of five Maybach engines each carried in a separate gondola. Four of the gondolas are arranged in two pairs, staggered to avoid obstructing the slipstream, and the fifth one is placed centrally. The airship made her first flight on 28th September, 1928, and her first Atlantic crossing on 11th October the same year, when she flew to New York and back. During the past four years she has maintained a regular service between Germany and South America.

Airship development in this country ceased after the tragic loss of R.101 while on a flight to India on 5th October, 1930. The fateful journey was undertaken after the airship had been lengthened to provide room for an additional gasbag. When this alteration was completed the total capacity of the R.101 was 5,500,000 cu. ft. and her overall length was 800 ft. The R.100 was of slightly less capacity, being only 5,150,000 cu. ft. In the summer of 1930 she flew from Cardington to Montreal and back. She was broken up after the loss of the R.101.

L.M.S.R. Locomotive Work

The latest L.M.S.R. "Princess" class 4-6-2s are doing magnificent work on the turns of duty on the Liverpool services mentioned in the "*M.M.*" in November last. On a recent trip with the 6.5 p.m. "*Merseyside Express*," the newest of the class, No. 6212, "*Duchess of Kent*," had a load of 475 tons tare and 505 tons gross, and yet passed Rugby, 82.6 miles from Euston, in 81½ min. On the rise of 26.3 miles from Willesden to Tring speed averaged 60 m.p.h. throughout; the next 23 miles were covered at an average of 75 m.p.h., the maximum being 80½. In spite of the colliery slack at Polesworth and a bad signal check at Hademore crossing, Stafford, 133.6 miles, was passed in 134¾ min., and with a maximum of 81 m.p.h. down the Madeley bank the train was through Crewe, 158 miles, in 161 min. Fast running followed with a top speed of 75 m.p.h. near Weaver Junction, and Mossley Hill, 189.6 miles, was reached in 196 min., four minutes early; the net time being only 194 min. The net average speed was 58.8 m.p.h., a very notable figure, especially in view of the scrupulous care with which the various service slacks were observed. Copperwheat of Camden shed was the driver.

On the up "*Liverpool Flyer*," No. 6208, "*Princess Helena Victoria*," had the exceptional load of 438 tons tare and 470 tons gross, the train being packed. Starting brilliantly from Crewe, a speed of 51½ m.p.h. was sustained up the 1 in 177 of Madeley bank; and with a top speed of 80½ m.p.h. at Norton Bridge the train was through Stafford, 24½ miles, in 25½ min. Recovering very rapidly from the 40 m.p.h. slack there, speed was up to 74 at Rugeley and reached 80½ again at Hademore troughs. Thus Tamworth, 48 miles, was passed in 46¾ min. The Polesworth colliery slack followed, and then came another brilliant burst of speed. Nuneaton was passed at 70 m.p.h., the 1 in 320 rise to Bulkington was mounted at a sustained minimum of 64½ m.p.h., and with a long-sustained 75 beyond Brinklow, Rugby, 75.5 miles from Crewe, was passed in 71¼ min. The 46.2 miles from Milford to Rugby No. 7 Box had been covered at an average of 68.8 m.p.h.

At Weedon 80½ m.p.h. was touched for the third time, and after passing Roade, 98.2 miles in 91½ min., the engine was very slightly eased. Bletchley was passed nearly 3 min. early, however, but at Cheddington adverse signals brought the train practically to a stand. Up the 1 in 335 to Tring speed rose to 52½ m.p.h. in 4 miles—a remarkable feat; and with a swift descent towards London a punctual arrival was almost assured, despite the delay, but a final check outside Willesden made the total time 143¾ min. Net time was only 138 min. for the 152.6 miles, giving an average speed of 66.4 m.p.h. On the final descent speed averaged 75.7 over the 16.4 miles from Boxmoor to Wembley, the top speed being 79 m.p.h. We are indebted to Mr. O. S. Nock for these timings.

It is interesting to note that the speed restriction at Polesworth mentioned above, which is due to subsidence caused by mining operations, is to be eliminated by the purchase of the mineral rights of a section of one of the coal seams under the main line. The coal will be left undisturbed, and the removal of the restriction will allow trains to pass at 65–75 m.p.h. instead of slowing up as hitherto necessary. This will save about two minutes in running, and will be an important factor in punctual working and in possible future accelerations.

The down "Brisbane Express" at Hawkesbury River. The locomotive is a standard 4-6-0 of the New South Wales Government Railways. Photograph by R. B. McMillan, Victoria, Australia. (H.R.C. prize-winning entry.)

"The Yorkshire Pullman"

With the introduction of "*The Silver Jubilee*" Newcastle service last year, the former "*West Riding Pullman*" ceased to serve that city. Instead, Hull for the first time now enjoys Pullman facilities. Leeds, Bradford, and Harrogate are of course still served, and the name of the train is now appropriately "*The Yorkshire Pullman*." These revised workings terminated the connection of King's Cross enginemen with the Pullman trains, an association that has lasted ever since the service commenced in 1923. The drivers forming the "Pullman link" at King's Cross have enjoyed a wonderful reputation for punctual work, and the pages of the "*M.M.*" have frequently borne witness to the time - regaining feats of various members of this link. Leeds men now work the "*Queen of Scots*" trains, and "*The Yorkshire Pullman*" is worked by Doncaster men, as stops are made at that place on account of the Hull portion.

An interesting incident recently was the working of "*The Silver Jubilee*" on its up journey by a standard "Super-Pacific." Owing to a slight mishap a streamlined "Pacific" was not available, but No. 2503, "*Firdaussi*," brought the train into King's Cross one minute early, to the intense disappointment of those waiting in anticipation of seeing the streamlined "*Silver Link*" or "*Quicksilver*"!

A Locomotive Depot Removal

As part of the L.M.S.R. scheme for the modernisation of motive power depots on the system, the Western Division shed at Buxton has been provided with an improved track layout and with automatic coaling and ash plants. The locomotives and staff of the former Midland Division shed have been transferred to the Western Division shed.

The programme of improvements at various depots is proceeding, a recent step of importance being the installation of a new 70 ft. turntable of the articulated type at Camden.

The "*British Legion*"

The "Royal Scot" class locomotive No. 6170, that was mentioned in the *"M.M."* of last October as being fitted with a tapered boiler, has now been in traffic for some time. For the first few days of its existence it was nameless, but on 12th November, in the presence of a distinguished company at Euston Station, No. 6170 was officially named *"British Legion."* The late Earl Jellicoe performed the naming ceremony by breaking a bottle of champagne over the nameplate. This plate is not of the standard form, but is specially shaped and carries a replica of the lion's head surrounded by a ribbon carrying the words "British Legion" that is the emblem of that organisation. On this occasion the engine was manned by an ex-soldier driver and an ex-sailor fireman. The Union Jack, the White Ensign and the British Legion flag decorated the front of the locomotive.

The photograph on this page gives an excellent impression of the sturdy appearance of the engine. Apart from the provision of a tapered boiler it does not differ greatly in design from the other "Royal Scots," but the opportunity has been taken to incorporate various recent developments in design. As compared with the Stanier standard engines a dome is provided to act as a steam collector, and in addition it accommodates the regulator valve. Top-feed apparatus is retained, but in the form of a separate fitting on a manhole cover in front of the dome.

As the cylinder dimensions, driving wheel diameter and working pressure are unchanged, the tractive effort remains at 33,150 lb. A new feature is the provision of a continuous blow-down valve that allows a certain amount of water to escape from the boiler and assists in preventing the concentration of salts or mineral matter deposited by the evaporation of the water.

The cylinders are arranged as in the original "Royal Scots," but have been modified in order to provide a saddle to support the smokebox. This is set forward to some extent so that the outside steam pipes to the cylinders issue from it at an angle and slope backward, giving an impression of speediness to the engine when seen broadside-on. Except for minor alterations the motion is the same as for the original engines. The bogie is now arranged with side bolsters to transmit the load from the main frames.

A cab of the latest side-window type replaces that of the original "Royal Scot" design. Small glass windscreens are fitted on the outside of the cab between the two windows to protect the enginemen from draught when they are looking out. Steam sanding gear is fitted and grease-gun lubrication is applied to the brake gear and intermediate buffing gear, and also on the tender hand brake and water pick-up apparatus.

The tender is of the latest standard 4,000-gallon type carrying nine tons of coal. Its dimensions generally cause it to match the engine in a more satisfactory manner than do the older and smaller standard tenders fitted to the other "Royal Scots." The weight of the engine remains the same, 84 tons 18 cwt. in working order, but with the larger tender the combined weight becomes 139 tons 11 cwt. instead of 127 tons 12 cwt.

In the upper illustration is L.M.S.R. No. 6170 "British Legion" described on this page. Photograph by courtesy of the L.M.S.R. The lower photograph shows Ambleside station on the Furness Section of the L.M.S.R., with one of the large Furness "Baltic" tank locomotives at the platform. Photograph by Mr. J. Adams, Keighley.

Five-Year New Works Scheme

The recent announcement of the Government approval of a £30,000,000 scheme for railway development has no doubt been noticed by our readers. The programmes drawn up by each group are interesting in their variety and comprehensive nature. Work is to be begun as soon as possible and is expected to be completed within five years.

On the L.M.S.R. the long-debated electrification of the Wirral Section is to be effected, giving through working over the Mersey line into Liverpool. Euston Station is to be reconstructed, and other passenger and goods centres are to have improved facilities. Colour-light signalling is to be installed between Euston and Willesden and at other points of dense traffic. That the steam locomotive is expected to hold its own against competing forms of motive power in the future is shown by the construction of 369 new engines.

Main line electrification is a feature of the L.N.E.R. programme. This refers to the section between Manchester and Sheffield, which carries a heavy traffic in difficult country. Increased facilities for traffic operation, such as the provision of additional tracks, the doubling of single lines and the extension of colour-light signalling, are to be provided. Station and dock improvements are planned, and in addition to new locomotives and rolling stock the conversion of gas-lit vehicles to electric is to be accelerated. Track circuiting and automatic train control are to be extended.

The G.W.R. scheme similarly provides for the further extension of their automatic train control system, and other signalling, telephone and telegraph improvements. New lines are proposed, including a diversion between Dawlish and Newton Abbot and the doubling of single lines and improved facilities at various places. Diesel rail-cars will be provided for local branch services and a more extended use of heavier and powerful engines is to be made possible.

The S.R. electrification is to cover a still wider area, including the Portsmouth main line via Woking and Guildford. Extensions to the Central and Eastern Sections electrification systems also are proposed. A new line from Motspur Park to Leatherhead is to be constructed and various stations are to be rebuilt.

This plan will render the railways better able to deal with a more generally speedy and comfortable service.

A Famous Locomotive Class

The G.E.R. "Claud Hamiltons"

IN these days of locomotive standardisation the older types and classes of engines, with which we have been familiar for so many years, are disappearing more or less rapidly; in many cases they are being condemned as fast as their boilers and cylinders give out. In certain instances, however, it still appears possible to rebuild, or rather reconstruct, older locomotives in order to fit them for a further lease of life under modern conditions. A good example of this kind of renewal is found in the 4–4–0 locomotives of the "Claud Hamilton" class of the former Great Eastern Railway, now included in the L.N.E.R. group.

L.N.E.R. No. 8900 "Claud Hamilton" on a Southend train. This shows the locomotive with a Belpaire fire-box, before its recent reconstruction. This and the other illustrations to this article are by Real Photographs Co. of Liverpool.

The Great Eastern Railway served much of the East Anglian coast, and the increasing demands of the Cromer and other important main line traffic led to the introduction of the class in 1900. The first of them, from which the class gets its name, *"Claud Hamilton,"* then No. 1900, gained a gold medal at the Paris Exhibition of 1900. The *"Cromer Express"* had been steadily growing in weight since its introduction in 1897, and had been hauled successively by the 2–2–2 and 4–2–2 "single-wheelers" designed by Mr. J. Holden. The increasing weight, however, and the peculiar difficulties of the G.E.R. main line, made the coupled type of locomotive essential for the maintenance of the relatively fast schedule, and so the 4–4–0 engine with its larger boiler and adhesion weight, was adopted.

In appearance these locomotives were extremely ornamental, even for a period when great care was taken with the finish of locomotives and when engine-cleaning was almost a fine art. Possibly as a result of their designer's previous association with the Great Western Railway, the "Clauds," as they became known, had neat copper-capped chimneys. Brass caps were adopted later instead of copper. As was the case with many other British locomotives of that time, the edges of the driving wheel splashers were beaded with brass. The small raised splashers formed in the footplating for the accommodation of the coupling rods were very similar to the pattern used on many L.N.W.R. locomotives, and the openings in them, too, were provided with brass beading. The engines were finished in the blue livery of the Great Eastern Railway, with the elaborate lining out and the red-painted coupling rods that were popular years ago, and looked particularly handsome.

"Super-Claud" No. 8813 on a down express. This is a typical example of these engines with large boilers and extended smoke-boxes. The top-feed valves appear at the sides of the dome.

The increasing popularity of the *"Cromer Express"* led to the introduction, on 1st July, 1907, of new stock specially built for the service. The title of the train then became altered to *"Norfolk Coast Express."* The division of the train into portions for various destinations took place at North Walsham, to which point the 130 miles from Liverpool Street were run non-stop, at an average speed of 49.4 m.p.h., in 2 hours 38 minutes. As the chief express engines of that time, the "Claud Hamiltons" had to deal with this train, which was made up normally, including restaurant and kitchen cars, to 12 vehicles weighing altogether some 340 tons. Frequently at summer week-ends this load was increased, and the management of a load in the neighbourhood of 400 tons became a strenuous matter for a 51-ton 4–4–0 locomotive.

The "Claud Hamiltons" gained a special reputation in the working of these trains, and the remarkable running that was performed by them was stimulated considerably by the rivalry between the three locomotive depots that were jointly responsible for providing locomotive power for the train. These were Stratford, Norwich and Ipswich, and only picked locomotives with selected enginemen were assigned to this duty. The coal was of a special grade, and the trains ran only during the summer months, and thus mainly under favourable weather conditions. Even with these advantages the running conditions of the Great Eastern main line made the management of a locomotive of really moderate size, so heavily loaded, a task for "crack" enginemen only.

With fairly large driving wheels, 7 ft. in diameter, and of only 33 tons 7 cwt. adhesion, the acceleration by the "Claud Hamiltons" of such vast trains, not only at the start but after the numerous service slacks en route, most of them occurring awkwardly at the foot of inclines, is a source of wonder to us in these days of six-coupled engines with three and four cylinders. The boilers and cylinders were not of remarkable size, and superheaters were not experimented with until 1911, and then only on four engines. The steam-producing capacity of the "Claud Hamilton" boiler must have been extraordinary, and this, in conjunction with the conditions of maintenance and handling, probably furnishes an explanation of the amazing results.

By 1911 the class numbered 111, and it is remarkable that each lot of them, as they had been built, received earlier numbers than those preceding them. As a result, although the first engine *"Claud Hamilton"* was No. 1900, the 1911 batch were Nos. 1790–1799, the numbers of the class thus being consecutive, but in the reverse order of building dates.

As is frequently the case with a class of engines turned out over a period of years, different batches varied in details although the main features of the design remained the same. Those built from 1904 onward had fire-boxes of the Belpaire type, and boilers of these engines were pitched higher than those of the earlier ones with ordinary round-topped fire-boxes. Again, the leading sandboxes, which were situated above the footplate in front of the driving wheel splashers of the first engines, were on subsequent engines placed below.

There were numerous differences also in auxiliary equipment. Some engines had spark deflectors and special ash-ejecting blast pipes.

All of the class originally had power reversing gear. This and the tender water scoops were operated by compressed air. The Great Eastern was a "Westinghouse brake" line, so that the air compressor of the brake apparatus formed an obvious means of obtaining this auxiliary power.

"Claud Hamilton" class locomotive No. 8848, before the adoption of the L.N.E.R. colour scheme. This engine is representative of the class as superheated without increase in the size of the boilers.

Originally, Nos. 1860-1900 were oil fired on the Holden system, but the number so fitted was reduced to a mere handful after the system became no longer economical. Certain of the engines were again fitted for oil burning in 1921 and 1926, owing to coal strike difficulties, but the use of oil fuel has now been abandoned for some time and the fittings have been removed.

Apart from the experimental fitting of superheaters to four of the class in 1911, no further move was made in this direction until 1914. Since that time all of the class have been dealt with, retaining, until the more recent rebuilding of some of them, their ordinary slide valves. In addition since 1915 the fitting of Belpaire fire-boxes to the earlier locomotives has also taken place.

A further development was seen in 1923 when No. 1805 appeared fitted with a larger boiler than the original one. Its success apparently inspired the construction at Stratford in the same year of 10 further new "Super-Clauds," as they are called. These engines were turned out as L.N.E.R. products, and under the L.N.E.R. numbering scheme they are Nos. 8780-8789, thus conforming with the "numbering in reverse" followed for the rest of the class. In due course 29 more "Clauds" were provided with larger boilers, and so became "Super-Clauds," and an additional modification was the fitting of extended smoke-boxes. Extended smoke-boxes too were fitted to many of the engines with boilers of the original size.

The former "Clacton Pullman" express, now known as the "Eastern Belle," hauled by "Super-Claud" No. 8783. This photograph shows the appearance of the engines with large boilers and top-feed apparatus, but with the short smoke-box.

All these locomotives were at first painted the L.N.E.R. green standardised for passenger engines. More recently, however, the adoption of black for locomotives for secondary duties has affected the "Claud Hamiltons" as a class. Exceptions to this are Nos. 8900, 8783 and 8787, which still retain the L.N.E.R. green, in view of their reservation for any Royal Train duties between London and Wolferton, the station for Sandringham.

The association of Great Eastern engines with "Royal" duties, dates back to 1861 when the late King Edward VII, then Prince of Wales, acquired the Sandringham estate. From the diminutive 2-2-2 single-wheeler locomotive that was specially decorated for the Royal Wedding journey to Wolferton on 10th March 1863 of the then Prince and his bride, afterwards Queen Alexandra, to the engines now used, a succession of types have been employed that form in themselves an interesting chapter in the history of locomotive development. With the advent of the "Claud Hamiltons" these special duties passed to them in their turn. As a general rule two of these engines have been recognised as "Royal" engines, although the individual locomotives sharing the honour have varied at different periods. The present "Royal" engines have, therefore, a distinguished band of predecessors. No. 8900 *"Claud Hamilton"* itself, in addition to the special interest attaching to it, is also notable as having been selected as a representative locomotive for the Stockton and Darlington Centenary Celebrations in 1925.

Alterations carried out in recent years by the L.N.E.R. which do away with much of the characteristic appearance of the "Claud Hamiltons" have been the fitting of a plain cast-iron chimney and the removal of the "open work" of the coupling rod splashers. In some cases the chimney resembles the G.N. pattern and, with the now plain raised footplate, these alterations bring the engines more into line with L.N.E.R. standard practice.

The most drastic alteration in appearance, however, is seen in those engines, including the first of the class No. 8900, which have been completely reconstructed. In these, new frames have been provided, and new boilers having round-topped fire-boxes, an interesting reversion in this respect. The cab although still a double-windowed structure is of standard L.N.E.R. design. Some of these reconstructed engines are provided with new cylinders having piston valves with a long travel. Others retain the original cylinders and short-travel slide valves, also their power reverse gear. This, however, is removed from the piston-valve engines. All of them retain the power operation of the tender water scoops.

Whether the whole of the class will be dealt with in this way is uncertain. However this may be, the class has had an interesting history, and may be numbered among the various 4–4–0 engines, belonging to different British railways, that have consistently performed extremely good work, in spite of the theoretical limitations of their design.

Diesel Engines for the Iraq Pipeline

An Engineer's Journey to Mesopotamia

ON the point of departing from Haifa on the Mediterranean coast to reach the Mesopotamian oilfields by motor car through the desert, we left the Iraq Petroleum Company's administrative buildings certain that we should for a long time have to deny ourselves the ordinary comforts of civilisation. In our hands we held a small order form for our desert equipment, which we had to receive as the last preparation for our journey. On a fine December morning we packed the necessary provisions under the seats of our car. In order not to neglect any precautions, the engine and the tyres of our car were inspected once again.

Oil tanks at a pumping station, surrounded by safety trenches. The tanks have a capacity of about 11,000 tons each, and are fitted with floating covers. The illustrations to this article are by courtesy of Sulzer Bros. (London) Ltd.

Scarcely had we passed the last houses of Haifa and obtained a free view over the sea, when 16 gloomy gigantic steel erections came into sight on the side of the bay. These were the enormous oil tanks of the Iraq Petroleum Company, each with a capacity of 11,000 tons. We were not given much time to wonder at them, however; relentlessly our powerful eight-cylinder engine took us over the mountain chain of Nazareth, at an altitude of about 2,600 ft. In passing quickly through the little town there was not much to be noticed of its famous past.

After another hour we suddenly caught sight of the lake of Tiberias, lying about 700 ft. below us, and could also see the town of the same name. We drove along the lake at about 45 miles an hour, passing neat-looking settlements, and then entered the valley of the Jordan and approached the frontier of Transjordania. Even the venerable old Jordan has not quite escaped the influence of this century of technical progress; its waters are being dammed in order to provide energy for a modern hydro-electric power station.

Leaving the fertile banks of the Jordan behind, we moved towards the last chain of hills. Scarcely had we reached the top when we had before us over the bonnet of the engine a free view of the valley in front, a view of an unending yellowy-brown surface—the desert. Here for the first time we came into touch with the Iraq pipeline. Of the line itself there was certainly no longer much to be seen, since the pipes had already been welded together electrically and lay buried some 3 ft. below the surface. Only a small line of earth and stones, and a row of telegraph poles running parallel to it, indicated the track of the pipe line.

Raising a huge cloud of dust behind us, we now ran alongside the telegraph line. After having gone some distance east, we could see the cooling-water tanks of the pumping station "H5" standing on the horizon. Soon afterwards the gleaming tents of the settlement could be seen, and shortly after that an Arab, armed with a Turkish scimitar and rifle, opened the entrance in the barbed wire fence encircling the camp to let us enter.

Old oil still, as used by the natives in Iraq territory. The vapours are condensed in the vessel at the left.

Besides the single tents of the Europeans, there were several rows of tents for four persons, intended for erectors and passing guests. A little apart from these stood the lines of tents for the Arabs. In addition to its own power station, which serves to generate electric current, a small refrigerating plant was also installed in the camp for making the very necessary ice. If we looked upward over the tents for a change, we saw the two high masts for the antennae of the wireless station reaching up into the sky. Great attention has been paid to the health of the staff as well as to their personal safety. The doctor at each station has in his hospital a well-equipped dispensary and a clinic, and a motor car is available for transporting sick people.

We set out again on our journey in a north-easterly direction, and the tents and buildings of pumping station H-5 soon disappeared in the hot shimmering air of the desert. About half-way between H-4 and H-5 the desert began to get stony. We were approaching an extensive volcanic region that was formerly about 150 miles in circumference.

When it is remembered that the two pipelines were completed in one year, an approximate idea can be formed of the pace at which the work had to be carried out. The principal mechanical assistance in the work was given by the huge 40-ton lorries that had to be used for transporting the steel pipes from the railway stations at Baiji and Mafrak. After the pipes had been laid down ready in a line through the desert, the powerful trench-digging machines began their work, cutting a finished trench in the ground. A little behind them the pipes were hoisted up by small cranes fitted on caterpillar tractors; the ends of the pipes were held against each other while they were welded together by the erectors. The necessary electric current was generated on the spot in portable sets. When a certain length of pipe was ready welded, another "technical wonder" covered it with a layer of pitch and wound a kind of roofing paper over that. After the pipe thus prepared had been laid in the trench, a motor plough put the earth back into place and the work was finished.

There are no expansion joints provided in the whole length of the pipeline. The only precaution taken to prevent too great heat stresses consisted in the length of pipe welded and buried in one day not being welded with the previous length of pipe until the following morning. The pipe lying in the earth had consequently time to cool down during the night to the same temperature as the ground surrounding it.

The journey through the desert was for the greater part very monotonous. The only variety introduced now and then was the appearance of a troup of gazelles, a desert wolf, a sand hare or a fox. Also there was much to see in the desert that had no actual connection with reality; for example the mirages, which now and again showed a beautiful lake with islands on it, the whole picture suddenly disappearing as we approached it, leaving only dry ground in the place where water had been seen a moment before.

Searching for a leak in one of the pipes laid across the River Tigris. The pipe has been filled with compressed air, and the bubbles indicate the position of the defect.

While we were still occupied observing such phenomena, the fertile banks of the Euphrates were approaching. The river flows past pump station K-3 to the Persian Gulf in a deep cut in the desert, and an island beautifully situated in the middle of the river gives the district a very idyllic appearance. We had hardly crossed the river when the bare desert started again.

In contrast to the Euphrates, the banks of the Tigris are almost completely bare. They show clear traces of pitch and tar, however, from which it can be concluded that the oilfields are no longer far distant. We crossed the Tigris at Fatha on an aerial railway. The pipeline here is simply laid in the river, and describes a bend directed upstream.

About half way between K-1 and K-2 the desert began to change into a steppe, and about 10 miles before Kirkuk extensive corn fields with growing grain greeted us. This fresh vegetation does not remain long in the neighbourhood of Kirkuk. As soon as the actual summer begins, the temperature in the shade never falls below 115-122°F., and all vegetation consequently disappears.

We were quickly approaching the end of our journey. Already in the distance we could discern the derricks of the oilfields, and soon afterwards the town of Kirkuk, which lies partly perched on a flat rock and partly in a deep hollow. A little later we were standing in front of our future "home." We regarded with mixed feelings the half-round corrugated iron shed, protected against the heat of the sun with a thick layer of clay; but we were agreeably surprised to find inside three nicely furnished rooms, and also a bathroom and a small kitchen. A native oil refinery was smoking in front of our windows, just to remind us that we were not in a week-end cottage but right in the middle of the rather unromantic oilfields of Mesopotamia. The presence of petroleum has been known to the natives in Iraq for several centuries; already for ages it has been used for heating.

We strolled along the bed of a small stream, and at once noticed big spots of oil floating on the water; and when we examined the stream somewhat more closely we saw that many small bubbles were rising up, giving off a strong smell of poisonous natural gas. After having climbed higher up the rocky sides we came on the gas again on the hill top, but there it was burning, countless small flames issuing from holes in the ground. This natural gas is said to have been burning as long as anyone can remember, and is known to the natives under the name of "eternal fire." We went up the stream to the place where the floating spots of oil started, and soon found that they originated in an oil well trickling out of a rock, the black substance flowing into the bed of the stream. Close to this spot a well of sulphur water sprang from a cleft in the rock, and this health-giving water is used by the Arabs for bathing.

Here is also the district where the natives obtain their petroleum. First of all they dig a small hollow, in which a pool of oil has collected by the following day. This is baled out, filled into cans and transported to the refinery, where the petroleum is heated in a still and evaporated. The gases collect in a small dome, and are then cooled in a spiral tube that is fitted beside the still in a water-cooled cask. The vapours condense and appear at the end of the cooling coil as petroleum ready for use, and this is filled direct into tin cans. The oil cakes remaining in the stills are taken out when the distilling process is finished and used as fuel for the next lot of oil. The petroleum obtained in this manner is transported by passing caravans into all parts of the desert, where it is used for heating and cooking.

The Iraq Petroleum Company obtain their oil by means of the same methods, the only difference being that their wells are boreholes, some of which reach to a depth of 4,000 ft. beneath the ground level. At present the Company have 32 serviceable wells, each of which is capable of yielding 1,300–2,000 tons daily. The oil issues from the boreholes at a pressure of about 3,000 lb. to the sq. in., and passes through a de-gasing plant before it is pumped through the desert. In that plant the natural gases are extracted from the oil and then led away and burned. After the first purifying process, the petroleum flows into the oil tanks of the pumping station. If one of the tanks leaks, any flooding of the surrounding ground is prevented by a trench and wall of earth surrounding the tank. In order that an explosive mixture of petrol and air may not accumulate over the petroleum in the tanks, the roofs of the tanks are designed as floating double covers, which rise and fall with the level of the petroleum in the tanks.

Power station on the Iraq pipeline, equipped with six Sulzer 5-cylinder 4-cycle Diesel engines, each developing 500 b.h.p. at 300 rev. per min.

We at last approached the buildings in which the machinery of the station was installed, and on entering the workshop our attention was called to the excellent Diesel-electric fire-extinguishing plant. Leaving this building, the engine house, constructed entirely of steel, was facing us. Along the outside of one of the walls are six small steam boilers used in the winter months for raising heating steam from the exhaust gases of the Diesel engines.

In the lofty hall of the engine house we saw 6 Sulzer Diesel engines that transmit their power to direct-coupled reciprocating pumps working in an adjoining room, separated from the engine room by a gastight partition. In order that there may be no risk of igniting the petroleum gases, all the electric plant is located away from the engine house.

For this interesting description we are indebted to Sulzer Bros. (London) Ltd.

Books to Read

Here we review books of interest and of use to readers of the "M.M." We can supply copies of these books to readers who cannot obtain them through the usual channels. Order from Book Dept., Meccano Limited, Binns Road, Liverpool 13, adding 1/- for postage to the price. Postage on different books vary, but any balance remaining will be refunded.

"Motor Racing and Record Breaking"

By G. E. T. Eyston and B. Lyndon
(B. T. Batsford Ltd. 7/6 net)

As a book on motoring this breaks new ground by being devoted exclusively to racing and record breaking, and for this reason it will be welcomed by all motor enthusiasts. Captain Eyston's name needs no introduction to those who have watched the development of one of the most distinguished racing and record-breaking careers in the history of British motoring. With the aid of Mr. Barré Lyndon he has produced a book that not only contains a full account of the development of the sport from the very dawn of motoring, but also is packed with thrills.

What might be described as the world's first motor race of any importance started from Versailles on 11th June, 1895, and the course was to Bordeaux and back, a distance of 732 miles. The event was won by Emile Levassor in a 4 h.p. Panhard at an average speed of 14.9 m.p.h. One has only to contrast this with the speeds reached during the past year to realise the enormous progress that has been made by the automobile engineer. Motor racing is probably the most dangerous of all sports, and road racing is the most exacting of its many forms. The authors give us a vivid picture of what is involved in road racing, and the qualities demanded of the driver and all who are associated with him.

Track racing is entirely different in many respects, its special object being to develop machines in which everything is sacrificed to maximum speed. The driver's comfort is of minor importance, and effective brakes are often dispensed with, because normally they are not required until the end of the race, when there is usually plenty of room in which to stop the machine. The cars are more delicate than those built for the road, and a driver's greatest difficulty is to handle his machine with restraint. Only when the issue of a race becomes clear and he sees that victory may be gained by driving flat out dare he travel at full throttle, matching the chance of winning against the possibility of "blowing up" his engine. The chapter devoted to this topic gives a survey of track racing all over the world.

Pit work, that is the arrangements for fresh supplies of petrol, oil and water, for new tyres and the replacement of damaged or broken parts, is of enormous importance in long-distance races. We are given an excellent description of the extraordinarily efficient manner in which the necessary operations are carried out when a driver comes in to his pit. Another important part of the work of the pit is in signalling to a driver to inform him of his position in a race, and to let him know whether his speed is adequate or whether he must increase it if he is to win.

Midget cars immediately after the start in an outdoor race, Los Angeles. (From "Motor Racing and Record Breaking" reviewed on this page.)

Record breaking is still another quite distinct phase of motor speed work, having its own peculiar difficulties and dangers. The splendid achievements of Sir Henry Segrave, John Cobb and others are outlined, culminating in Sir Malcolm Campbell's achievement in September last of his great ambition to surpass 300 m.p.h.

Other sections of the book are devoted to round-the-houses races, hill climbing, racing in America and endurance racing. Then follow two chapters that will be of special interest to all motor enthusiasts, dealing respectively with the risks of racing and with present-day personalities among the most famous drivers.

The book is remarkably well illustrated by some 130 photographs gathered from all countries, and providing perhaps the best pictorial record ever brought together.

"How Wireless Came"

By John Langdon-Davies. (Routledge. 6/- net)

The aim of the author is not to help in the construction of a modern wireless circuit, but to describe the scientific history of wireless. He gives a full and clear account of the basic facts about electricity, which must be understood if a boy's wireless set is not to remain a mere box of tricks. By the time he has read the book, any boy will be able to understand diagrams of wireless circuits, and more important still, he will understand how science has gradually unravelled the secrets that made wireless practicable. To read this book is a delightful excursion into the realms of electrical application.

"Worlds In The Making"

By R. Barnard Way
(The Chatterbox Co. Ltd. 3/6 net)

This book is specially designed for those who, looking at the starlit sky on a clear night in winter, feel that they would very much like to know something about the stars—what they are made of, how far away they are, and how they came to be there. The great astronomers know a great deal about these things, but as a rule when they try to pass on their information they do so in a manner that is hard for us to understand. In *"Worlds In The Making"* the author has set down in the simplest possible language some of that tremendous story. The result is an absorbing narrative, which is greatly assisted by the author's own illustrations.

"Flying Dutchman"

By A. H. G. Fokker and B. Gould
(Routledge. 5/- net)

The interesting feature of this edition of *"Flying Dutchman"* is that the book has been re-written with all the technical terms put into simple language. In it Anthony Fokker, the famous inventor and airman, tells entertainingly the story of his life, from his very early days in Java, where his father was a wealthy coffee planter. To-day Fokker is a millionaire and head of an international aviation company that sells his machines throughout the world. Every boy who is interested in flying should read this book, for it relates the adventures of a very remarkable man and the great part he has played in the development of modern aircraft.

"Science: A New Outline"

By J. W. N. Sullivan. (Nelson. 5/- net)

Science to-day has so many branches and covers such a wide field that it is difficult for ordinary people to form a satisfactory idea of its progress as a whole. Mr. Sullivan's survey of modern science helps to overcome this difficulty, for it is a successful effort to give in concise form the scientific knowledge that intelligent people of all ages now require. It is graphically and attractively written, and every explanation, even of the most complicated topic, is clear and well reasoned. A special feature is that the use of mathematics is avoided throughout the book.

The first aeroplane produced by Anthony Fokker, at the start of a demonstration flight at Haarlem. (From "Flying Dutchman" reviewed on the previous page.)

The author begins his survey with the Earth, revealing what it is made of, how it is related to other bodies in space, and how it is supposed to have originated. This leads to a consideration of the matter of which the entire Universe is built up. The nature of the elements and the constitution of the atoms of which they are composed are explained, and a full account is given of the most recent developments in our ideas of the electron and other tiny constituents of the atoms themselves.

The author then turns from inanimate matter to the life that exists in the Earth. An amazing diversity of living forms have appeared during our planet's life-time, and their history is traced in outline from the simplest forms of bygone ages to the more familiar creatures of to-day. The emergence of man himself is dealt with in a separate section, and the fascinating story is brought to a close with a description of the astonishing manner in which Nature preserves equilibrium among the various forms of life.

"The Boy's Romance of Aviation"

By Capt. A. O. Pollard, V.C. (Harrap. 7/6 net)

In this comprehensive book Capt. Pollard, whose history of the Royal Air Force is a standard work, traces the progress of aviation from the earliest legends to the present day. He describes the failures and successes of the more famous of the pioneers of aviation, and shows the part each has played in the development of balloons, airships, aeroplanes and gliders. He goes on to deal with the influence of the Great War on aircraft, and with the post-war development of civil aviation. The chapter on Atlantic crossings by air recalls the thrills of the first non-stop flight across that ocean by Capt. Alcock and Lieut. Whitten Brown, of the R.A.F., on 14th June, 1919, in a Vickers "Vimy" bomber. Other notable flights across the Atlantic and to other parts of the world by aeroplane and airship are also described.

The author then turns to the actual construction and equipment of aircraft, and explains the rigging of an aeroplane. Special chapters deal with the tendencies of aero-engine design, the testing of aeroplanes for flight, and the purposes and operation of air navigation instruments.

The book is illustrated with nearly 50 excellent half-tone photographs and numerous line drawings, and has a good index.

"Useful Aspects of Geology"

By S. J. Shand, D.Sc.

(Thomas Murby and Co. 6/- net)

Professor Shand has the happy knack of describing even quite technical matters so simply and concisely that anyone can understand them. *"Useful Aspects of Geology,"* of which this is the second edition, was written mainly with the object of providing useful geological information for such people as landowners, prospectors, engineers, builders and farmers. It succeeds in this object, but at the same time it provides a remarkably interesting introduction to geology for the general reader. Theoretical matters are cut down to the minimum, and the information about different types of rocks and the changes that they undergo, and of the general geological structure of the Earth, leads up to practical information about the rocks as building materials. There are chapters on water finding and on oil, and a particularly interesting one on engineering problems, such as landslips, railway cuttings, reservoirs and underground works of all kinds. There are still many people in the world who ask: "What is the use of geology?" This volume provides a thoroughly satisfactory answer.

Pit signals to the driver, an important feature of any long-distance race. (See previous page.)

"Unsolved Problems of Science"

By A. W. Haslett

(Bell and Sons Ltd. 7/6 net)

One reads so much nowadays of the wonderful achievements of science that it is good sometimes to be reminded of the paths that still remain unexplored. Every new scientific discovery raises a new series of problems, and so the work of the scientist is never completed. This book may be described as an attempt at "stocktaking" in regard to the present extent of our knowledge. Commencing with an interesting chapter on the unending quest of science, the author passes on to review some of the great outstanding problems, such as the creation of the Universe, whether there is life on other worlds, and the strange risings and fallings of different parts of the Earth's crust. Then there are the so-called cosmic rays, many times more penetrating than the most powerful X-rays, that continually beat down on us from space, pass with ease through the thickest walls, slip through our bodies, and even reach to the bottom of the deepest lakes. In this connection an interesting account is given of the results of the wonderful flights into the stratosphere by Professor Piccard and others.

In subsequent chapters the author gives a fascinating account of the mysteries of the beginnings of civilisation, of Man as a machine, of Nature's building bricks, and of how the X-rays show weaknesses in materials that otherwise would be quite unknown to us. The final chapter deals with some of the interesting ways in which Nature still beats the scientist.

"The English Fairy Book"

By Ernest Rhys

"The Welsh Fairy Book"

By W. J. Thomas

"The Scottish Fairy Book"

By Elizabeth Grierson

"The Irish Fairy Book"

By A. P. Graves

(Philip Allan and Co. Ltd. 5/- net each)

The appeal of the fairy tale is universal, and year by year fresh collections of them are published. Most of these tales are of Continental origin, however, and therefore it is a pleasant change to come across four volumes devoted respectively to the fairy tales of England, Ireland, Scotland and Wales. The British Isles are rich in fairy tales and legends—far richer than most of us imagine; and in these books the best of them have been collected by authors who have done their work with keen enthusiasm as well as skill. Each volume has a coloured frontispiece and a number of interesting drawings.

Historic Beam Engines

Century-Old Veterans Still at Work

By J. R. Nichols

ONE hears, at intervals and with regret, of the demolition of some veteran steam engine which, after it has rendered faithful service for a century or so, is to be replaced by an up-to-date type of engine. Nevertheless there are still to be found, plodding along quite serenely, engines that were built in the pioneer days of steam engineering, and it is with some of these, and others recently scrapped or now out of use, that the present article will deal.

One of the oldest engines still at work is at the Broseley Tileries clay mine, where the shaft was sunk between 150 and 200 years ago, and it is thought that the engine was installed at that time. It is now used as a winding engine, operating a cage carrying 12-cwt. loads of clay from a shaft 318 ft. deep. It is believed that this engine was made by John Wilkinson, who had a foundry at Broseley, and in these days of high pressures it will doubtless surprise many readers to learn that its steam pressure at full load is only 4 lb. per sq. in. The only alteration that has been made throughout its years of active work has been the fitting of a new piston some five years ago. When the time comes for this veteran to be superseded it certainly will have more than earned its rest.

The 30 h.p. steam engine referred to in this article, installed at Messrs. Whitbread's brewery, Chiswell Street, London in 1785. It was designed by James Watt and erected under the superintendence of John Rennie. In 1887 the engine was removed to a museum in Sydney, Australia, where it stands as a monument to Watt's genius. Photograph reproduced by courtesy of Whitbread and Company Ltd.

At the silk-printing works of David Evans and Co. Ltd., Crayford, Kent, are two ancient steam engines, both well over 100 years old, and both in full commission to-day. These are used for pumping water and driving washing machines, and were undoubtedly pioneer steam prime-movers in the silk-printing industry. The smaller engine bears a brass plate engraved with the name "OVID TOPHAM, ENGINEER, LONDON," but has no date. The normal steam pressure used is 20 lb. per sq. in., and the leading dimensions are: bore of cylinder 12 in., piston stroke 23 in., flywheel 9 ft. 8 in. in diameter, speed 40 r.p.m. The writer is indebted to Mr. P. T. Stewart, Manager, for having the interesting photographs on the opposite page specially taken.

There are several extremely old engines at the Cornish tin mines. At Levant, for example, is one built at Harvey's Foundry at Hayle in 1827, which worked, first as a pumping engine and later as a winding engine, until the mine was closed in 1929.

At the mining village of Elsecar, near Sheffield, is an old beam engine pumping plant erected in 1787, which was in more or less continuous use until 1923. In 1928, owing to the electric pumping plants being out of commission on account of heavy rains, the old engine was restarted, and is still in working order. The design of this ancient engine, whose maker is unknown, follows closely on that shown in a book of 1796, entitled *"The Coal Viewer's and Engine Builder's Companion,"* by John Carr, and it is possible that he was the consulting engineer.

The cylinder of the Elsecar engine is 48 in. in diameter, and the stroke is 5 ft. The beam is made of cast iron in two sections, and is 24 ft. long by 4 ft. 4 in. deep, fitted with parallel motion at both ends. This beam was put in many years ago (by Grahams Foundry Co., of Elsecar, it is believed), replacing the original beam of wood, which was connected by chains to the piston rod and pump rod.

Actuation of the valves is by means of a plug-rod, which also works a 9-in. diameter pump for supplying the injection water. The present boilers are cylindrical, being 7 ft. diameter by 22 ft. long, and the working pressure is $1\frac{1}{2}$ lb. to $2\frac{1}{2}$ lb. per sq. in. A rod pivoted near the centre of the beam operates a plunger pump for supplying the feed-water. The water is lifted 129 ft. in a single lift, the bucket being 18 in. diameter; while the quantity delivered is 50 gallons per stroke, the engine making six strokes per minute. In 1928 the engine was indicated, and the mean effective pressure was then found to be 8 lb. per sq. in., with a water-horse-power of 11.4.

Hemp plaited spun yarn forms the packing for the piston, and is held in place by a junk ring. Any slight cylinder wear has been taken up by the packing, consequently it has never been necessary to re-bore the cylinder. This ancient engine was put under steam in 1931, on the occasion of the visit of members of the Newcomen Society, the object of this Society being to encourage and foster the study of the history of engineering. The Elsecar engine is a development of Newcomen's atmospheric engine, based on Smeaton's designs, and incorporating certain improvements made after Newcomen's death.

Thomas Newcomen was born in 1663 at Dartmouth, where he became an ironmonger and blacksmith. Briefly stated, his engines derived their power from the atmospheric pressure acting on the top of a piston, after the creation of a vacuum underneath it. The cylinder was provided with an outer casing or jacket, and after steam had been admitted to the cylinder the jacket was filled with cold water, thereby condensing the steam and lowering the pressure in the cylinder. The atmospheric pressure acting on the open top of the piston then forced it down, after which the water was drained off from the jacket and steam again admitted, the cycle of operations being repeated.

Old beam engine at Crayford. Photographs on this page by courtesy of David Evans and Co. Ltd.

Another old atmospheric pumping engine was at Westfield, near Rotherham, and it is believed that this was erected in 1823, probably by the firm of Walker, of Rotherham. This had a cylinder diameter of 4 ft. 6 in., with an average stroke of 5 ft. 9 in., and a maximum stroke of 7 ft. 6 in. The cast-iron beam was 25 ft. long, and 5 ft. 6 in. deep at the trunnions, with a weight of about 8 tons. The pit water was drawn in two lifts, the upper one of 37 yds. and the lower one of 22 yds., at 10 strokes per minute, lifting 48 gallons per stroke. After more than a century of work the engine was stopped in 1926, and scrapped in August, 1934.

Two other "old timers" recently scrapped were those at the Deptford Pumping Station of the Metropolitan Water Board. These were Boulton and Watt engines of 1812, and they worked until 1925. The order for the first engine was placed in 1810, and for the second in 1812, though most of the drawings are dated 1810. The original cylinders were 36 in. diameter by 8 ft. stroke, and drove four single-acting pumps. The horse-power was stated to be 55.2 nominal. The cast-iron beams were of an early type, probably made round about the time when it was considered preferable to use iron instead of wood. Cast-iron connecting rods were used, and the flywheel was secured to the square cast-iron crankshaft by light "wedges."

Another old beam engine at the Crayford Works.

Some interesting photographs appeared in *"Engineering"* (May 27th, 1932, pp. 618-9) when partial dismantling had taken place. It is interesting to note that a use has been found for some of the parts, since some of the parallel motion links have been erected as lamp standards at the Kempton Park pumping station.

Beam engines have played an important part in fen drainage work, superseding to a large extent the earlier windmills; now the old beam engines are being gradually replaced by Diesel pumping plant. The earlier beam engines drove scoop-wheels, which dip into the water, and it is owing to the subsidence of the land that certain of the scoop-wheels have had to be abandoned, as the level of a number of drains has become too low to allow sufficient dip on the ladles of the wheels.

At Southery there is a double-acting beam engine erected in 1842. This has a cylinder diameter of 42 in. and a stroke of 72 in., and runs at 24 revolutions per minute. It drives through 6 : 1 reduction gearing a 40 ft. diameter wheel, made in 1881, replacing the wheel installed with the engine. Another old beam engine, again double acting, belongs to the Mildenhall Fen Commission. This was made in 1844, and drives a scoop-wheel of 32 ft. diameter, which lifts the water from 5 to 12 ft.

One of the first engines to be constructed for a brewery by the old firm of Boulton and Watt, of Birmingham, was installed at Messrs. Whitbread's Brewery in Chiswell Street, London, in 1785. It was designed by Watt, its erection was superintended by Rennie, and the services of Smeaton were secured for designing six underground cisterns, the largest of which contained upwards of 3,600 barrels of beer! The engine remained at the brewery for over a century, being removed in 1887 to a museum in Sydney, Australia, where it stands as a monument to Watt's genius.

We should be glad to hear from readers who know of any other old engines of a similar type still in existence.—Editor.

An Interesting Moving Figure Clock

Ingenious Control System

By T. R. Robinson

IN the design of large public clocks there is nowadays a tendency to eliminate the ordinary dial system of showing the time, and to substitute large figure panels, with numerals indicating the hours and minutes. A typical clock of this kind is installed at Paddington Station, London, which was described in the "*M.M.*" for December, 1934.

A cleverly made form of public timekeeper that adapts a form of electric sign into a "moving figure" clock has recently been made to draw attention to the Seamen's Hospital, Greenwich. The visible part is shown in the upper illustration on this page, and consists of a panel divided into three sections. In these sections are arranged numbers of 15-watt electric lamps, and by switching on groups of these lamps Arabic numerals can be built up to give the hour and the minute. Each section of the panel has 35 lamps, and these are so placed that any desired numeral can be formed; while careful grouping of those lamps that will always be illuminated together has enabled the circuits between the sign and the controller, shown in our second picture, to be reduced to 19 for each numeral.

The "moving figure" Clock at the Seamen's Hospital, Greenwich.

Apart from the lamps and their wiring the sign is quite simple, and the really interesting part of the installation is the controller, which is a most ingenious piece of mechanism. Its time control is by a small synchronous-motor-driven clock, which is housed in the black casing to be seen in the bottom right-hand corner of the controller case. This clock is arranged to make a contact every complete minute, and this in turn actuates a mercury tube relay by means of a solenoid. The relay is located between the clock and the small motor that drives the contact drums of the controller. When the relay makes contact it starts up the small motor, and this then drives through a totally enclosed worm reduction gear to a disc that carries a small ball bearing mounted near its edge.

The mechanism that controls the moving figures.

This disc is arranged to make one complete rotation each time the motor is started up, and as this is completed, it breaks the motor circuit automatically by tripping the relay back to the off position. The motor then stops until the synchronous clock movement again starts it up.

The small ball bearing, which has been mentioned as mounted on the disc, therefore makes one turn per minute. As it rotates it comes into contact with a star-wheel mounted on the spindle of the first contact drum, and trips this one tooth, just in the same way that a counter is tripped. The star wheel has 10 teeth or divisions, and its contact drum is, of course, equally spaced out. As the wheel and drum are tripped round they alter the connections to the lamps in the right-hand section of the panel of the sign, causing the figures "0" to "9" to appear in order at minute intervals.

The star wheel of the drum also carries a short arm that has a second small ball bearing mounted at its end, and at each tenth minute this trips a second star-wheel, this time with six teeth, on the spindle of the second contact drum. The second drum has six sections, and these control the figures indicating the tens of minutes that appear in the central section of the sign.

The six-toothed star wheel carries still another arm, and this steps the final 12-toothed star wheel attached to the contact drum, which switches the lamps making up the hour indications in the left-hand section of the sign panel.

The whole action is really that of a metering counter, each star wheel advancing the next in order one space each time it completes one revolution.

The clock is a product of the Signs Construction Co. Ltd., London.

A Suction Dredger for East Africa

Shipped in Sections to Beira

Dock and harbour engineers have to be constantly on the alert to keep the waterways in their care free from sand and mud, for the prosperity of a port depends upon the number of ships that visit it, and this in turn depends upon the navigability of its approaches. In order to ensure a sufficient depth of water dredging vessels of various kinds are employed for the excavation of material from the bottoms of harbours and rivers. They are used also to a great extent for the purpose of straightening rivers and for land reclamation work.

The centrifugal pumping plant of the dredger "Manga" erected in the builders' workshops.

Dredgers may be described as machines for removing material from one place and depositing it elsewhere, the exact manner in which this is done depending on the nature of the material to be removed. Soft, sandy material will require an entirely different type of machine from that required for handling a hard rocky material.

Modern dredgers are operated either mechanically or hydraulically. The former type dredge up the spoil by means of buckets fixed to travelling chains, while the latter type suck up a mixture of soil and water, and deposit it either in hoppers provided in its hull or in separate barges moored alongside the dredger. The lower illustration on this page shows the dredger *"Manga,"* a suction dredger of this kind built by Fleming and Ferguson Ltd., Paisley, for use in land reclamation work at the port of Beira in Portugese East Africa. This vessel dredges the sand and mud from the harbour bottom and deposits it into separate barges. When the barges are full they are towed to the required place and the material is then pumped out and deposited on the land.

The upper illustration shows the two large centrifugal dredging pumps fitted in the *"Manga."* These are connected together in series, that is to say the discharge pipe of one pump is connected to the suction inlet of the other. The main suction inlet of the pumping plant is connected to a long flexible dredging pipe arranged so that it can be lowered into the water to the required depth, and the pumps are protected from damage that would be caused by the ingress of solid matter such as rock, etc., by gratings fitted over the outboard end. The outlet side of the pump plant is connected to pipes that lead over the side of the dredger and discharge into the hopper barges moored alongside.

As soil cannot be pumped without the admixture of water to transport it, the *"Manga"* is fitted also with a centrifugal diluting pump, which discharges sea water into the barges while the soil is being pumped out. The pumping plant is driven by means of steam engines of the totally-enclosed forced lubricated type.

The "Manga" undergoing tests at the maker's works before being shipped in separate sections to Beira. For our illustrations we are indebted to Fleming and Ferguson Ltd., Paisley.

An interesting feature in connection with the construction of the *"Manga"* is that after the vessel had been fully completed and tested in the builders' works she was dismantled and then shipped abroad on a large cargo vessel, in separate floatable sections. When the sections reached Beira they were lowered by the ship's derricks into the harbour and then bolted together. The machinery also was assembled in England, tested, and then taken to pieces and separately shipped to its destination.

Suction type dredgers are not common in England, but in the northern European ports vessels of this kind are constantly at work maintaining the navigability of rivers and estuaries.

HORNBY SERIES

HORNBY ROLLING S

Two No. 1 and one No. 2 Cuttings are illustrated above.

No. 1 CUTTING (END SECTION)
Base measurement: Length 7 11/16 in., width 6 in. Price, per pair 3/-

No. 2 CUTTING (CENTRE SECTION, STRAIGHT)
The addition of these Centre Sections enables a Hornby Railway Cutting to be extended to any length. They are intended to be used in conjunction with the End Sections (Cutting No. 1). Base measurement: Length 10¼ in., width 6 in. Price 2/-

No. 2 SIGNAL CABIN
Dimensions: Height 6½ in., width 3½ in., length 6½ in. Roof and back open to allow Lever Frame to be fitted inside if desired. Price 3/9

No. 2E SIGNAL CABIN
This Signal Cabin is suitably fitted for electric lighting. Otherwise it is the same as No. 2 Signal Cabin. Price 4/3

No. 2 SIGNAL GANTRY
"Home" or "Distant" Price 10/-

No. 2E SIGNAL GANTRY
"Home" or "Distant." Price 12/9

No. 2 Level Crossing

No. 2 LEVEL CROSSING
Measures 13½x10½ in., with two gauge O tracks in position. Price 5/6

No. E2 LEVEL CROSSING (Electrical). Similar to Level Crossing No. 2, but fitted with two electrical tracks. Price 7/6

No. E2E LEVEL CROSSING
Similar to No. E2 Level Crossing but suitably fitted for electric lighting. Price 9/-

No. 4 Tunnel

No. 4 TUNNEL (CURVED)
Base measurement: Length 20 in. Width 9½ in. For 2 ft. radius track only. Price 4/9

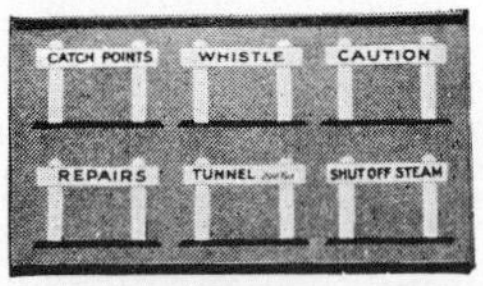

No. 8 RAILWAY ACCESSORIES
Notice Boards. Price 1/9

PLATELAYER'S HUT
Price 1/-

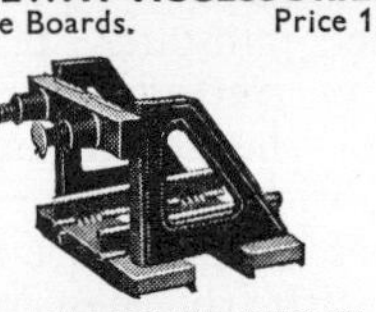

No. 1 BUFFER STOPS
(Spring type). Price 1/-

No. 1E BUFFER STOPS
as No. 1, but suitably fitted for electric lighting. Price 1/6

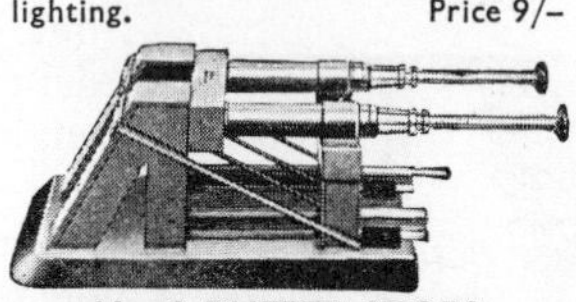

No. 2 BUFFER STOPS
(Hydraulic type). Price 5/6

No. 2E BUFFER STOPS
Similar to No. 2 Buffer Stops, but suitably fitted for electric lighting. Price 6/-

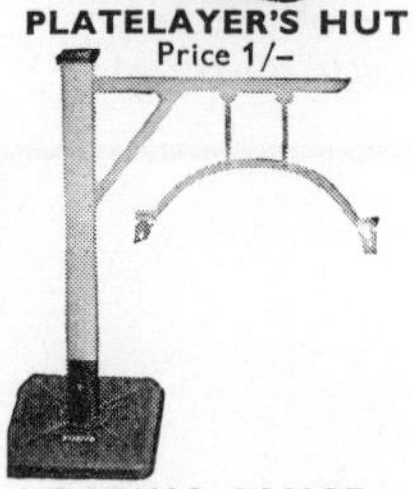

LOADING GAUGE
(Illustrated). Price 2/3

M LOADING GAUGE
Price 1/-

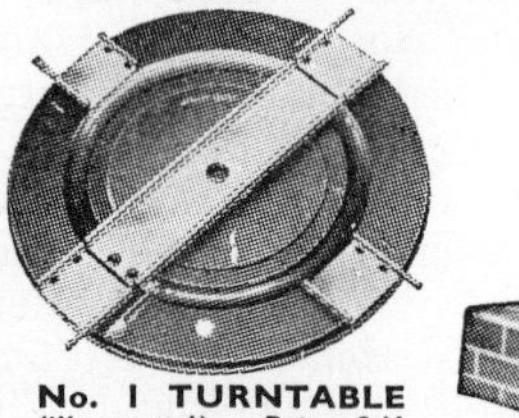

No. 1 TURNTABLE
(Illustrated). Price 2/6

No. 2 TURNTABLE
Price 3/9

No. E2 TURNTABLE (Electrical)
Similar to No. 2 Turntable, but fitted with electrical rails. Price 5/6

No. 1 GOODS PLATFORM
Length 13 in., height 6½ in., width 6 in. Price 7/6

PLATFORM CRANE
Fitted with a crank handle and ratchet mechanism. Price 3/11

No. 2 STATION
Built up with three detachable sections. Length 2 ft. 9 in., breadth 6 in., height 7 in. Price 8/-

KEEP ADDIN

A real railway system is constantly ex
ment are added: new tracks are laid: new s
and viaducts are constructed—every effo
Your Hornby Railway, too, can be ru
Coaches, Trucks, Wagons and Vans of th
Sheds that will gradually convert your pres
Remember, the more complete your

CRAWFORD'S BISCUIT VAN
Finished in red, with opening doors. Price 2/9

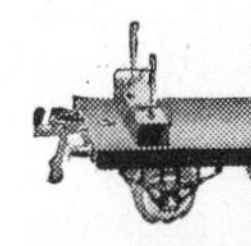

No. 1 LUMBER
Fitted with bol
stanchions.

***No. 1 CATTLE TRUCK**
Fitted with sliding doors. Price 2/9

BARREL WAGON
An interesting model of a t
wagon used on Conti
railways. Pri

FIBRE WAGON
This is an interesting model of a type of wagon used in France and other Continental countries. Price 1/3

No. 1 BANAN
An attractive mod
in yellow and red.

GUARD'S VAN
In colours to represent L.M.S.R., L.N.E.R., G.W.R. or S.R. Price 2/6

CEMENT WA
The door at th
opens. Finished i
Price 2/6

***COACH, No. 2 PASSENGER**
Suitable for 2 ft. radius rails only. First-third, or Brake-third. Price 7/6

COA

No. 1 SIDE TIPPING WAGON
"Robert Hudson Ltd., Leeds." Price 2/-

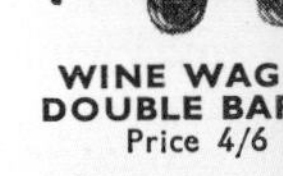

WINE WAG
DOUBLE BAR
Price 4/6

MO PETROL TANK WAGON "SHELL MEX"
Finished in cream with lettering in black. Price 1/-

MO SIDE TIPPING
Finished in bright yello
either side.

* In L.M.S.,

MECCANO LIMITED,

...CK & ACCESSORIES

HORNBY SERIES

...R RAILWAY

...loping. New rolling stock and new equip-
...ins and goods sheds are built: new tunnels
...er adequately for modern requirements.
...gressive manner. One by one you can add
...nd Stations, Signals, Bridges, and Engine
...ay into a really fine model Railway System.
... greater your fun and enjoyment.

TANK WAGON "CASTROL"
...lled green with letter-
...red. Price 2/-

***No. I LUGGAGE VAN**
With opening doors. Price 2/9

...N TANK WAGON "COLAS"
... blue. Price 3/6

***HOPPER WAGON**
Mechanically unloaded. Finished in green. Price 3/6

...W PLOUGH
...revolving plough.
Price 3/9

BRAKE VAN
Finished in brown, with opening doors. Obtainable in N.E. or S.R. lettering. Price 2/11

...LAT TRUCK
...able Drum. Price 1/6
...with Cable Drum ,, 1/9

***COACH No. I PASSENGER**
Price 2/6

...MAN COACH, No. 2 SPECIAL PULLMAN
Suitable for 2 ft. radius rails only. Price 13/-

GAS ...DER WAGON
... blue and red, let-
Price 1/11

***No. O WAGON, HORNBY**
Price 1/6

***No. I WAGON, HORNBY**
(Illustrated). Price 1/9

...CRANE TRUCK
...d in gold and blue.
...rane revolves on
... Price 2/11

MO ROTARY TIPPING WAGON
Finished in green. Container revolves and tips at any angle. Price 1/-

...S.R. lettering.

No. I LAMP STANDARD
(Single)
Price 3/3

No. 2 LAMP STANDARD
(Double, as illustrated). Price 3/9

No. 1A FOOTBRIDGE
Complete with Signals. Price 4/6

No. I FOOTBRIDGE. Without Signals. Price 2/11

No. I RAILWAY ACCESSORIES
Miniature Luggage and Truck. Price 1/-

No. 2 SIGNAL
"Home" or "Distant."
Price 2/-

No. 2E SIGNAL
Similar to No. 2 Signal, but suitably wired for electric lighting.
Price 2/9

No. 2 JUNCTION SIGNAL
"Home" or "Distant." Price 4/9

No. 2E JUNCTION SIGNAL
Similar to No. 2 Junction Signal, but suitably wired for electric lighting.
Price 6/-

No. I SIGNAL CABIN
Price 2/6

No. 2 RAILWAY ACCESSORIES
Milk Cans and Truck. Price 1/3

No. 3 RAILWAY ACCESSORIES
Platform Machines, etc. Price 1/6

No. 2 WATER TANK
Fitted with flexible tube and valve lever. Stands $8\frac{1}{2}$ in. high. Price 5/9

No. 2E WATER TANK
Similar to No. 2 Water Tank, but suitably fitted for electric lighting.
Price 6/6

No. 7 RAILWAY ACCESSORIES
Watchman's Hut, Brazier, Shovel and Poker. Price 10d.

No. 2 Engine Shed

No. 2 ENGINE SHED
This Shed will accommodate any Locomotive and Tender with an overall length not exceeding $17\frac{1}{2}$ in.
Price 22/6

No. E2E ENGINE SHED
Similar to No. 2 Engine Shed but suitably fitted for electric lighting. Provided with electrical track.
Price 23/-

VIADUCT Price 6/6 **VIADUCT (Electrical)** Price 7/6
VIADUCT Centre Section only ... ... ,, 4/-
VIADUCT (Electrical) Centre Section only ... ... ,, 4/6

M STATION SET (7 pieces) Price 3/-
The components of the M Station Set can be purchased separately as follows: M Signal Box. Price 4d.
M Signals. Price 4d. M Station. Price 1/-
M Telegraph Pole No. 1. Price 3d. M Wayside Station. Price 9d.

...ROAD, LIVERPOOL 13.

Flame Cutting and Profiling Machines

An Ingenious Electric Tracer

THE cutting of steel plate by means of an oxygen flame is one of the most interesting and important engineering processes developed during recent years. As compared with the older methods of cutting it is simple and results in a great saving of time, especially where intricate shapes have to be dealt with.

The accompanying illustration shows one of a series of oxygen cutting machines designed and produced by Hancock & Co. (Engineers) Ltd. This machine consists essentially of two tables coinciding exactly in plan. The upper table carries the design or template, and the lower one supports the plate or other work that is to be cut. By means of an arrangement known as an electric tracer, any outline traced on the upper table is followed exactly by the cutting flame moving over the plate on the lower table.

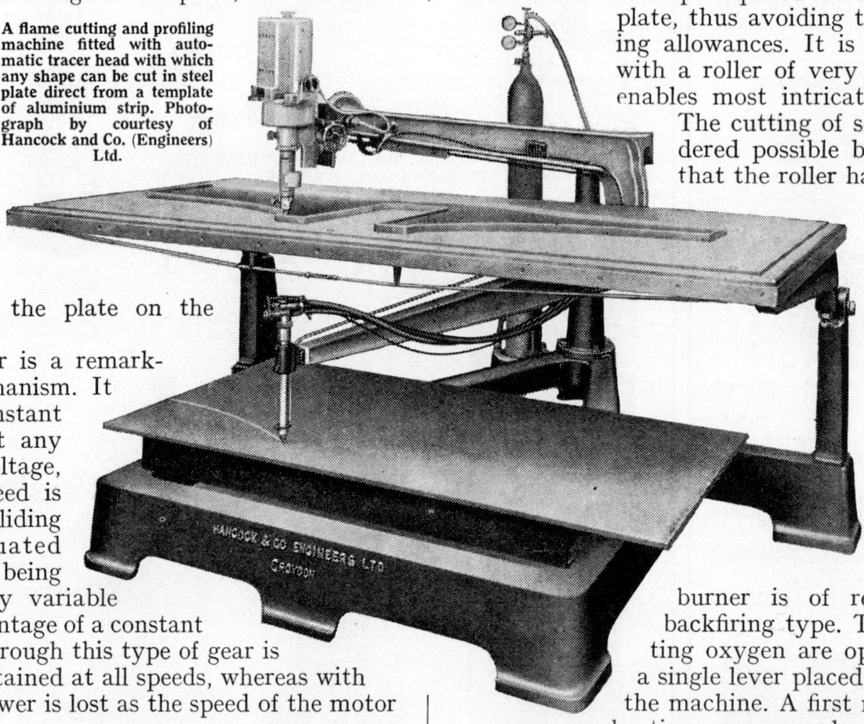

A flame cutting and profiling machine fitted with automatic tracer head with which any shape can be cut in steel plate direct from a template of aluminium strip. Photograph by courtesy of Hancock and Co. (Engineers) Ltd.

The electric tracer is a remarkably ingenious mechanism. It is fitted with a constant speed motor to suit any particular lighting voltage, and the cutting speed is set by means of a sliding pointer and graduated scale, the drive being through an infinitely variable gear. The great advantage of a constant speed motor drive through this type of gear is that full power is obtained at all speeds, whereas with resistance control power is lost as the speed of the motor is reduced.

The electric tracer head can be fitted with any one of three forms of drive. The first is guided by hand over the line of a drawing or blue print, enabling the operator to produce any required shape in the plate without the use of a template. The advantage of working direct from a drawing in this manner is very great, for there are many thousands of operations in which only one or two off are required, so that the making of a template would be a relatively expensive proceeding. The second form of drive is for automatic operation or repetition work. It consists of two rollers, differentially geared, which grip each side of a strip of aluminium that forms the template. The aluminium strip is either mounted in special chairs that are readily fixed in or removed from the table of the machine, or is screwed round the edge of a wooden template, thus forming a permanent template. This aluminium strip template is bent to the shape by hand, and it is estimated that 2,000 cuts can be made from it without renewal. The actual cost of this form of template is only twopence per foot length.

The third form of drive operates from a wooden template, which is usually cut with a Hobbies fret-saw. The method of operating is by means of a single serrated roller $\frac{1}{8}$ in. in diameter, which is held by hand against the edge of the wooden template. The roller is electrically driven, and passes along the edge of the template, guiding in turn the cutting burner below over the steel plate, and so producing the actual shape required. Several outstanding features are gained by this form of template. It is made from plywood, which is easily cut, and it is made to the exact size of the shape required to be produced in the steel plate, thus avoiding the necessity of making allowances. It is used in conjunction with a roller of very small diameter that enables most intricate shapes to be cut. The cutting of square corners is rendered possible by reason of the fact that the roller has the same diameter as the flame. No other drive incorporates such useful features. A further interesting point is that this single roller drive is provided also with a cone so that it will operate automatically by means of a channel template that forms a positive guide.

The cutting burner is of remote control non-backfiring type. The heating and cutting oxygen are operated by means of a single lever placed on the upper arm of the machine. A first movement opens the heating oxygen valve, and a second the cutting oxygen valve. The burner is usually supplied for use with oxy-coal-gas, the coal-gas being taken direct from the ordinary town gas supply.

The illustration shows how the burner is made to follow the movements of the tracer. It will be seen that the tracer and the burner are placed at the extremities of a U-shaped arm, hinged on links that in turn are hinged to a pillar. This combined hinging of the links and the U-shaped arm allows the tracer to be traversed anywhere over the surface of the table, and the burner follows its movements exactly. This type of machine is capable of cutting not only commercial mild steel and cast steel, but also most of the higher grades, such as those used in the making of dies. It will also cut manganese steel.

An important feature of the work produced by these machines is that it is sharp and clean at all edges of the cut. No cleaning is necessary, except where a machined surface is required.

For the information contained in this article we are indebted to Hancock & Co. (Engineers) Ltd., Croydon.

Making Marshland Fit for Farming

Ingenious Subsoil Lifting Machine

By Hans F. Kutschbach

AGRICULTURE has been practised since the late Stone Age, but more progress has been made during the last 200 years than in all the centuries preceding. If a farmer of the 17th century could visit a large modern farm he would be surprised by many things; but above all he would be amazed at the extraordinary extent to which machinery has been introduced to speed-up cultivation and lessen labour.

The subsoil lifting machine described on this page. The machine is the invention of two German engineers, and is used for preparing barren land for farming purposes.

Unless the soil is properly cared for it very soon loses its fertility, and especially is this the case with marshy land. In its early stages marshland is generally very fertile, but in a comparatively short space of time this fertility is lost owing to the fact that the nutritious substances that form plant food, sink and are absorbed into the subsoil, or earthy matter beneath the surface soil, where they collect to form a rich layer. Usually, however, this layer is too far down for the roots of crops to reach it.

With the object of overcoming this difficulty and effectively gaining access to this layer of highly fertile ground, two German engineers, Herr Max Jaeger and Dr. Rathjens, have devised the ingenious machine shown in the two illustrations on this page. This apparatus is said to be very effective in preparing barren marshy regions for farming purposes, and an important feature of the machine is that its use does not necessitate removal of the earth above the subsoil.

Essentially the machine consists of a long pipe that may be anything from 10 to 30 ft. in length, which is rotated by a motor and is supported between two driven creeper tracks. When the tracks are set in motion they carry the pipe forward, and as the pipe is mounted at an angle to the horizontal, this movement causes it to dig into the ground. The pipe is connected to the chassis of the machine through a universal coupling, and its lower end is provided with peculiarly shaped knives and intake openings. As the pipe rotates, the surrounding subsoil is loosened by the knives and falls through the intake slots into the interior of the pipe and on to a belt conveyer, which carries it to the top and deposits it on to a rapidly driven belt. This belt is fitted with vanes, and by its rapid action it scatters the rich subsoil right and left over the ground.

The subsoil lifter in action. A view of the front of the machine showing the distributor belt scattering rich subsoil.

With the aid of this machine heavy unproductive marshland can be turned into highly fertile soil suited for growing all kinds of crops; while sandy ground that is too light for agricultural purposes can be improved by lifting the marshy subsoil from below, distributing it over the surface, and then ploughing in the usual way.

Another application of the machine is in preparing the foundations for roads over boggy ground. Usually in work of this kind the marshy soil has to be removed and replaced by sand, a procedure that is not only expensive, but in the case of deep marshes, impracticable. The subsoil lifter is used to make a series of ditches, which are then filled with sand and act as drains.

These pages are reserved for articles from our readers. Contributions not exceeding 500 words in length are invited on any subject of general interest. These should be written neatly on one side of the paper only, and they may be accompanied by photographs or sketches for use as illustrations. Articles that are published will be paid for at our usual rates. Statements contained in articles submitted for these pages are accepted as being sent in good faith, but the Editor takes no responsibility for their accuracy.

The St. Lawrence River in Winter

When I lived in Montreal, Canada, my home was near the St. Lawrence River. This 2,000-mile river is navigable for half that distance by ships of up to 20,000 tons, but the Lachine Rapids above Montreal prevent them from proceeding higher.

At Montreal the St. Lawrence is almost two miles wide, but in spite of this it becomes blocked by ice about the end of November. Ice-breakers are used to keep the river open as long as possible, but these sturdy boats often get frozen in themselves. The strong current brings downstream newly-formed pieces of ice and these pile one upon the other, forming a very uneven surface. It is sometimes found possible to run traffic across the frozen river and a road is then marked out with small tree branches. A close watch is, of course, kept upon the ice for any sign of cracking. One winter many years ago, before the Victoria Bridge was built, an engineer operated a light railway across the ice, from Montreal to Longneuil on the opposite shore. It was very successful while the ice was frozen hard and deep, but when, after a spell of warmer weather, the ice gave way, the engine and track plunged into the water.

Ice-breaker cutting a channel through the frozen St. Lawrence River. Photograph by N. C. Meachem, Birmingham.

When spring comes the ice begins to break and then the ice-breakers get to work again to smash a channel through as speedily as they can. The first ocean liner to arrive at Montreal after the re-opening of the river is decorated with flags and streamers, and the Mayor of the city presents the captain with a gold-handled walking-stick as a souvenir of the occasion.

N. C. Meachem (Birmingham).

Climbing Mount Rheinwaldhorn

Last summer I had the interesting experience of climbing Mt. Rheinwaldhorn, in Switzerland. It is far from being one of the highest mountains in that country, but it is of special interest, chiefly because one of its several glaciers is the source of the River Hinterrhein that later becomes the Rhine.

Our party totalled eight climbers and two guides, and we started from the village of Hinterrhein about 3 p.m. The weather was rather sultry, but we made good progress. At 5 p.m. we halted for tea at a shepherd's one-roomed hut, which he had humorously named the "Grand Hotel." Further climbing followed, and we spent the night, or rather the first part of it, at the Zapport Club Hut. Our upward journey was resumed by lantern light at 3.30 a.m. About an hour later the darkness began to give way to daylight, and we had the thrill of seeing the sun rise, in a beautiful golden glow, above a distant peak.

Nearing the summit of Mt. Rheinwaldhorn, Switzerland. Photograph by W. S. Goodbody, Bristol.

By the time we stopped for breakfast we had climbed to a considerable height, and the air was very cold. We soon began to feel the warmth of the sun's rays, however, and our journey across the final stretch of snowfield was very pleasant. The snow gave firm foothold, and around us wonderful views gradually unfolded as we got higher. We reached the summit at 8.15 p.m., and signed our names in a little book that is kept under a boulder there.

From the summit of the Rheinwaldhorn there is a magnificent panorama of mountain scenery that extends from Monte Rosa, 70 miles to the west, to Piz Bernina, 50 miles to the east.

W. S. Goodbody (Bristol).

Ancient Britons' Cemetery

Dunstable has been the scene of many archæological discoveries. The upper photograph on this page shows students from the London University College and Hospital Anthropological Society carrying out excavations on a knoll at the top of Dunstable Downs. They had been closely examining the ground when one of the lady members of the party discovered a human skeleton at the foot of the knoll.

Students of Anthropology unearthing skeletons of ancient Britons, on Dunstable Downs. Photograph by A. M. Johnstone, Dunstable.

The students immediately concentrated their investigation upon that place, and on carefully removing a large area of turf they beheld many skeletons. It was evident from the various positions of the remains that some had been buried in separate graves, but others were huddled together in confusion. In one case there was a huge gash in the skull, possibly inflicted by a sword or an axe, and the arms of another were in a position that indicated they had been tied behind the back when the body was buried. An interesting relic of ancient superstition was seen in the fact that stones had been placed on the chests of some of the skeletons, presumably to keep down their ghosts!

Working with brushes and small pointed trowels, the students gradually cleared the chalky earth from the fragile bones until 40 skeletons lay exposed, whitening in the sunlight. It was found difficult to decide the exact period to which they belonged, but they were estimated to date from about 600 B.C.

When the students had numbered, photographed, sketched and thoroughly examined the remains they wrapped up some of the bones and packed them in crates for removal to London, for anthropological purposes.

A. M. JOHNSTONE (Dunstable).

Novel Braking System

At Balmain, a suburb of Sydney, the wharf of the ferry service to the city lies at the foot of a steep hill that reaches to the edge of Darling Harbour. An electric tramway from this busy point serves a large area of the western suburbs, and the trams easily climb the steep hill under their own power. Special precautions against accident are taken when they are descending it, and their wheel brakes are then supplemented by a device called a "donkey." This is a four-wheeled trolley, heavily weighted and fitted with large life-guards, and painted with silver and black stripes so as not to be a danger at night.

A novel braking device called a "donkey" attached to the front of a tramcar descending a steep hill at Balmain, near Sydney, Australia. Photograph by MacLeod Morgan, Cremorne.

The "donkey" stands on the track at the top of the hill, awaiting the arrival of trams from Balmain. When a tram arrives it halts with its buffer against the rear of the "donkey," and an arm projecting from this is connected to a cable running in a groove parallel with, and midway between, the two rails of the track. The cable passes over a pulley at the top of the hill, and its other end is attached to a counterweight that consists of a 15-ton trolley in a special tunnel under the road. As the "donkey" and tram descend the hill, the counterweight travels up the tunnel. When a tram ascends the hill, the "donkey" follows behind and halts at the summit in readiness to escort the next tram downhill. This system has been in use for many years and ensures safety at a very small maintenance cost in proportion to its usage—every 10 minutes in normal hours and every five minutes during the morning and evening rush periods.

MACLEOD MORGAN (Cremorne).

Some Famous Oak Trees

The many famous oak trees in Nottinghamshire include the Major Oak, the Seven Sisters, and the hollow oak tree that is said to have served as Robin Hood's larder. The most famous is the Major Oak, which stands in an open space about half-a-mile to the north of the village of Edwinstowe. It is probably 1,000 years old, and the massive proportions of its gnarled weather-beaten trunk make it a striking picture in winter, as then it is not hidden by a mass of foliage. The trunk is 30 ft. in circumference 5 ft. above ground, and its branches have a circumference of about 700 ft. The most remarkable thing about it is that it is quite hollow to a height of 15 ft., and there is standing room inside for a dozen persons. It is on record that seven persons have dined together in it.

In the same district, and near Welbeck Abbey, are the remnants of the Seven Sisters, an oak tree that once had seven trunks. They were from 80 ft. to 112 ft. in height, and the tallest was known as the "Duke's Walking Stick," the person referred to being the Duke of Portland.

F. CORNER (Bulwell).

The Lighter Side of Model-Building

Two Amusing Meccano Games

THIS month we make an interesting departure from the usual types of Meccano engineering subjects, and it is hoped that the following two examples will give model-builders some ideas for models of a similar nature. The first model to be described, a Bagatelle Table, is built with Outfit H; and the second, a Shooting Game, with Outfit G. The Meccano Steel Balls used with each model are not included in either of these Outfits but may be purchased separately.

The Bagatelle Table shown in Figs. 1 and 2 is similar to many found in amusement parks. Although the model is not entirely automatic it is extremely interesting, and will prove absorbing even to the oldest Meccano enthusiasts.

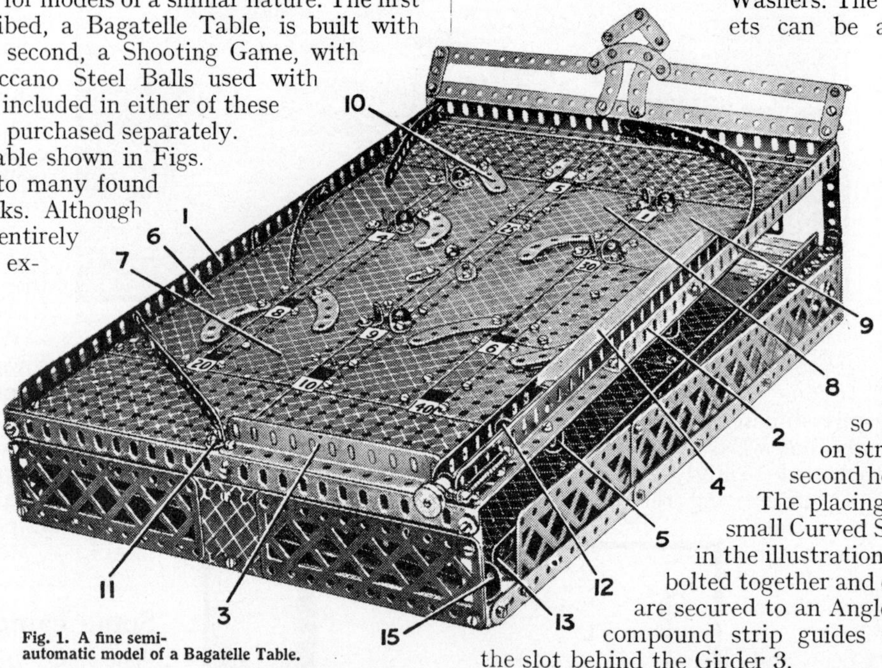

Commence the model by building a board as shown in Fig. 1. Each end of this consists of a $12\frac{1}{2}''$ Angle Girder and these are joined together by two side members 1 and 2. The member 1 consists of two $9\frac{1}{2}''$ Angle Girders overlapped one hole and the member 2 is formed from two $12\frac{1}{2}''$ Angle Girders arranged as shown in the illustration. A $5\frac{1}{2}''$ Angle Girder 3 is secured to the bottom of the board and a further $12\frac{1}{2}''$ Angle Girder 4 is bolted parallel to the side members as shown.

Fig. 1. A fine semi-automatic model of a Bagatelle Table.

A slot is formed immediately in front of the Girder 3 by bolting in place a $5\frac{1}{2}'' \times 2\frac{1}{2}''$ Flat Plate to one end of which is fitted a $5\frac{1}{2}'' \times 3\frac{1}{2}''$ Flat Plate. A $12\frac{1}{2}''$ Angle Girder 5 supports the inner ends of these Plates and also one end of three $12\frac{1}{2}'' \times 2\frac{1}{2}''$ Strip Plates 6, 7 and 8. Two $4\frac{1}{2}'' \times 2\frac{1}{2}''$ Flat Plates, overlapping two holes, are also supported at one end by the Girder 5. The Plates 6, 7 and 8, together with a $5\frac{1}{2}'' \times 2\frac{1}{2}''$ Strip Plate 9, are supported at their centres and ends by two more $12\frac{1}{2}''$ Angle Girders, portions of which can be seen in Fig. 1. The upper end of the board consists of two $5\frac{1}{2}'' \times 3\frac{1}{2}''$ Flat Plates and one $2\frac{1}{2}'' \times 2\frac{1}{2}''$ Strip Plate.

The positions of the 12 holes are shown in the photograph and the spaces between these are filled in by means of $5\frac{1}{2}'' \times 2\frac{1}{2}''$, $2\frac{1}{2}'' \times 1\frac{1}{2}''$ and $2\frac{1}{2}'' \times 2\frac{1}{2}''$ Flexible Plates. Small squares of paper are pasted below the holes and on these suitable scores are printed.

The two top holes on each side of the board are "backed" with pairs of $\frac{1}{2}'' \times \frac{1}{2}''$ Angle Brackets, the centre third hole down being similarly fitted. In the centre of the board two Flat Brackets are fitted and raised slightly by means of Washers. The angle of these Brackets can be arranged to suit individual ideas as also can the various Curved Strips and bolt heads. By altering these Strips, etc., certain holes can be made very difficult to enter and the scores raised accordingly.

A 2" Strip 10 is attached to one of the upper $5\frac{1}{2}'' \times 3\frac{1}{2}''$ Flat Plates and this is so arranged that a ball on striking it rolls into the second hole down in the centre. The placing of the $2\frac{1}{2}''$ large and small Curved Strips is shown clearly in the illustration. A $5\frac{1}{2}''$ and $2\frac{1}{2}''$ Strip, bolted together and overlapped two holes, are secured to an Angle Bracket 11 and this compound strip guides the Steel Balls into the slot behind the Girder 3.

The spring plunger for firing the Balls is built up in the following way. A $2\frac{1}{2}'' \times \frac{1}{2}''$ Double Angle Strip 12 is fitted between the side member 2 and Girder 4, and it carries a sliding Rod, on the inner end of which is locked a Collar. The outer end of the Rod carries a Collar and $\frac{1}{2}''$ fast Pulley, the Collar being fitted with a $\frac{3}{8}''$ Bolt carrying one end of a Spring. The opposite end of this Spring is bolted to the side member 2.

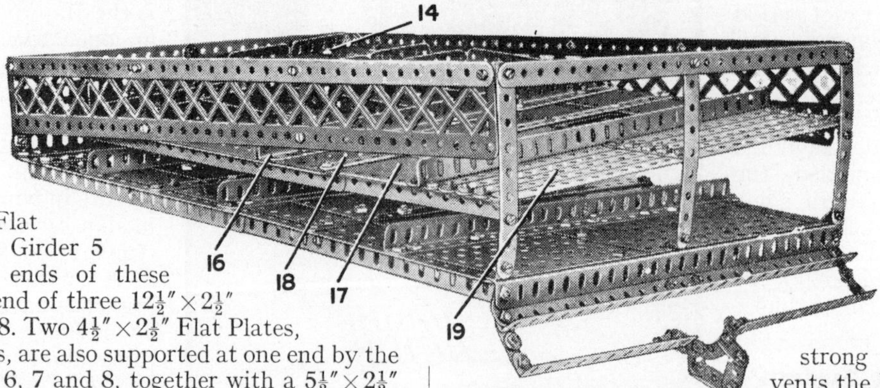

It is a good plan to line the inside of the channel, carrying the spring plunger, with strong paper, as this prevents the Balls from stopping before they reach the end of the channel.

Fig. 2. An underneath view of the Bagatelle Table showing the sloping return surface.

Below the board is fitted a sloping surface by means of which the Steel Balls are returned to the opening 13 ready for being used again. An underneath view of this sloping surface is shown in Fig. 2. Each side member consists of a $12\frac{1}{2}''$ and a $7\frac{1}{2}''$ Angle Girder. The Girders of the near side member in Fig. 2 are overlapped four holes, but those forming the other member are overlapped five holes. This extra overlap of one side member is necessary in order to form the opening 13.

The end of the sloping surface nearest the operating end of the model consists of five $3\frac{1}{2}'' \times 2\frac{1}{2}''$ Flanged Plates 14 secured edge to edge by a $12\frac{1}{2}''$ Angle Girder 15, Fig. 1. The other edges of these Plates are bolted to a $12\frac{1}{2}'' \times 2\frac{1}{2}''$ Strip Plate that is in turn secured to four $5\frac{1}{2}'' \times 2\frac{1}{2}''$ Flanged Plates and one $5\frac{1}{2}'' \times 3\frac{1}{2}''$ Flat Plate. The end flanges of these last mentioned Flanged Plates are secured to a $12\frac{1}{2}''$ Angle Girder 16, and the unoccupied flange of this is then fitted with five $5\frac{1}{2}'' \times 2\frac{1}{2}''$ Strip Plates 17. A $12\frac{1}{2}''$ Strip 18 prevents these Plates from buckling. The sloping surface is completed by the addition of a $12\frac{1}{2}''$ Angle Girder and five $12\frac{1}{2}''$ Strips 19.

The parts required to build the Bagatelle Table are: 6 of No. 1; 1 of No. 1b; 3 of No. 2; 3 of No. 2a; 5 of No. 5; 1 of No. 6; 6 of No. 6a; 14 of No. 8; 2 of No. 8a; 2 of No. 8b; 3 of No. 9; 2 of No. 10; 21 of No. 12; 2 of No. 12c; 1 of No. 15; 1 of No. 23a; 200 of No. 37; 5 of No. 37a; 24 of No. 38; 1 of No. 43; 1 of No. 48a; 4 of No. 52; 4 of No. 52a; 5 of No. 53; 2 of No. 53a; 2 of No. 59; 1 of No. 70; 5 of No. 90; 4 of No. 90a; 4 of No. 99; 2 of No. 100; 5 of No. 111c; 2 of No. 188; 1 of No. 189; 3 of No. 190; 2 of No. 191; 1 of No. 193; 6 of No. 195; 4 of No. 197.

The construction of the Meccano Shooting Game should prove easy if the instructions are followed carefully. Each side of the base is built up from two $12\frac{1}{2}''$ Angle Girders overlapping two holes. At one end the upturned flange of each compound girder carries a $5\frac{1}{2}'' \times 2\frac{1}{2}''$ Flanged Plate connected together top and bottom by means of $12\frac{1}{2}''$ Angle Girders 1 and 2, Fig. 3.

At the opposite end the sidemembers are secured together by a $12\frac{1}{2}''$ Angle Girder and at each end of this are fitted two $5\frac{1}{2}''$ Strips. One of these Strips is arranged to extend $\frac{1}{2}''$ above the other as shown. A $12\frac{1}{2}'' \times 2\frac{1}{2}''$ Strip Plate is now fitted to the firing end of the model together with two $5\frac{1}{2}''$ Strips 3 and two similar Strips 4 and 4a. The centre of the long Strip Plate supports a $2\frac{1}{2}'' \times \frac{1}{2}''$ Double Angle Strip 5, that will be used later for supporting the gun.

This structure of Strips and Strip Plates is strengthened by means of two bracing members, each of which consists of a $5\frac{1}{2}''$ and $3\frac{1}{2}''$ Strip. The sides of the shooting space are each filled in by means of two $12\frac{1}{2}''$ Braced Girders and one $5\frac{1}{2}'' \times 2\frac{1}{2}''$ Strip Plate. Two $12\frac{1}{2}''$ Strips bolted together and overlapping six holes are held in place above the Braced Girders and secured to them by Flat Brackets and a $3\frac{1}{2}''$ Strip 6.

A $12\frac{1}{2}''$ Strip is now bolted across the bottom of the rear flanges of the $5\frac{1}{2}'' \times 2\frac{1}{2}''$ Flanged Plates already mentioned and above this is fitted two $12\frac{1}{2}'' \times 2\frac{1}{2}''$ Strip Plates 7. A further similar Strip Plate is attached to the front flanges of the Flanged Plates together with two $12\frac{1}{2}''$ Strips 8 and 8a.

At the rear of the Angle Girder 2, three Obtuse Angle Brackets are fitted and these support two $5\frac{1}{2}'' \times 2\frac{1}{2}''$ Strip Plates 9. This compound Strip Plate, that forms a guard against Balls "fired" high, is suitably decorated with $2\frac{1}{2}''$ large and small radius Curved Strips as shown.

Two $1'' \times 1''$ Angle Brackets are now fitted to the inside of the Strip 8a, these being held in place by the Bolts 10. These Angle Brackets support an $11\frac{1}{2}''$ Rod on which are pivotally carried nine $2\frac{1}{2}''$ Strips, each of which is held in its appointed position by two Spring Clips. The upper end of each Strip carries a $\frac{1}{2}'' \times \frac{1}{2}''$ Angle Bracket in the slotted hole of which a bolt is accommodated carrying a Washer. A small piece of card, on which a cat or other animal is drawn, is clamped in place between the Angle Bracket and Washer.

Fig. 3. A thrilling Shooting Game built with Outfit G.

When a shot is fired and one of the "dummies" is knocked backwards, it is brought back into line at the end of a "shoot" by means of the Threaded Pin 11. This Threaded Pin is locked in the end hole of a long Strip that is held in position behind a $1\frac{1}{2}''$ Strip 12, as shown. The other end of the long Strip is pivotally attached by a bolt and Collars to a short Rod that is carried in the longitudinal bore of a Coupling 13. This Coupling is accommodated on the outer end of a long Rod formed from an $11\frac{1}{2}''$ and a $2''$ Rod. On this Rod two Cranks are carried, one of which is shown at 14. Each Crank carries a $\frac{1}{2}'' \times \frac{1}{2}''$ Angle Bracket at its upper end, and these two parts are joined together by means of two $5\frac{1}{2}''$ Strips 15.

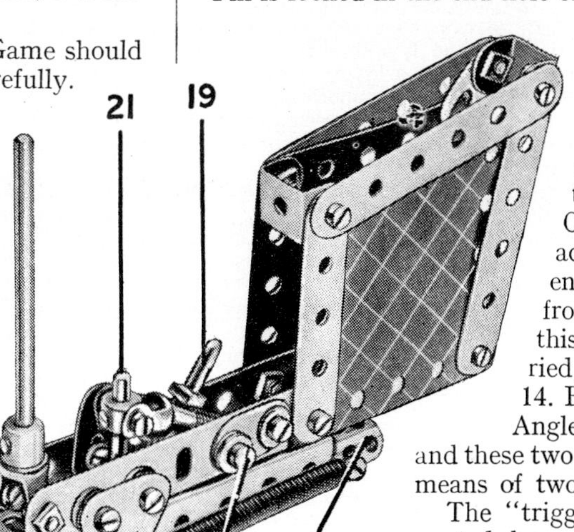

Fig. 4. The gun that is used for firing the steel balls in the Shooting Game. It is shown upside down to make the construction clear.

The "trigger" of the pistol is represented by a Threaded Pin 19 that is screwed into one of the tapped holes of a Swivel Bearing carrying the Rod 21. The Threaded Pin is screwed in tight against the shank of a Pivot Bolt that carries a Collar and four Washers. The Collar is pivotally connected to the gun by two $\frac{3}{8}''$ Bolts 20.

The parts required to build the Shooting Game are as follows: 9 of No. 1; 16 of No. 2; 3 of No. 3; 6 of No. 4; 11 of No. 5; 1 of No. 6a; 8 of No. 8; 4 of No. 9; 9 of No. 10; 2 of No. 11; 17 of No. 12; 2 of No. 12a; 3 of No. 12c; 2 of No. 13; 1 of No. 15b; 1 of No 16; 3 of No. 18a; 18 of No. 35; 156 of No. 37; 24 of No. 38; 1 of No. 43; 1 of No. 48; 1 of No. 48a; 2 of No. 52; 7 of No. 59; 2 of No. 62; 3 of No. 63; 1 of No. 77; 4 of No. 90; 3 of No. 90a; 4 of No. 99; 4 of No. 111c; 2 of No. 115; 1 of No. 116a; 1 of No 147b; 1 of No. 165; 2 of No. 190; 6 of No. 195; 4 of No 197

Fun with Meccano Dinky Toys

Making a Table-Top Layout

NOWADAYS everybody is talking about traffic problems, robots, Belisha beacons, and the like. These problems can be studied on the road, but it is much greater fun—and much safer!—to carry out operations on the table at home. With the wide range of vehicles of all kinds, petrol station and pumps, robots, traffic signs, etc., now available in the Meccano Dinky Toys series, street and road layouts of the most fascinating realism can be produced quickly and easily, and playing with them is fun of real interest. We know that many readers are already enthusiastic about such layouts, but for the benefit of those who have not yet tried a scheme of this kind we will describe the layout shown above.

The only materials required to make such a layout are a sheet of white or grey paper about 3 ft. square, some smooth cardboard about $\frac{1}{8}$ in. thick, and some grey and white water colour paint. The grey paper serves as a base for the layout, and on it the exact positions of the kerbs are drawn in in pencil. The areas of the layout that represent pavements, parks and buildings are then covered with a piece of cardboard cut to the necessary shape, a border $1\frac{1}{2}$ in. wide being left all round the cardboard to allow room for pavements.

A road layout for use with Meccano Dinky Toys. This will provide hours of fun and unlimited scope for experiment, and can be assembled easily by any boy or girl.

The pavements are made from strips of cardboard about $1\frac{1}{2}$ in. wide, painted grey and lined in with black ink to represent slabs. It is a good idea to cut the large pieces of cardboard enclosed by the pavements into triangles, squares and oblongs, as when this is done it is easy to re-arrange them quickly and so make up another and quite different layout when desired. In cutting the pieces, geometrical shapes should be adhered to as far as possible. Right-angled triangles, for example, can either be used separately, or two can be placed together to form an oblong; while three such pieces will make a trapezium-shaped area. One or two of the larger rectangular pieces should be divided diagonally with a curved cut, so that if the pieces are moved away from each other curved roads are obtained.

When the pavements have been arranged and the roads planned out, the vehicles, buildings and pedestrians are placed in position. In doing this care should be taken not to overcrowd the layout, for if too many models are included a great deal of the realism will be lost.

The layout on this page includes a Dinky Toy Petrol Station and two Garages. The pavement is omitted at several points round the Petrol Station in order to provide the necessary approaches to it and the Garages. The hoardings used to finish off the edges of the layout are simply pieces of cardboard with Miniature Posters gummed to them, and any number of these may be made as required. The road island seen in the rear is a circular piece of cardboard painted grey and provided with a centre post, on the top of which is a red warning signal. A match will serve excellently for the post, and the red head makes an admirable danger lamp!

Two different types of crossings are shown, one being a roundabout while the other is controlled by traffic lights. Pedestrian crossings are placed in judicious positions and the road studs for these are marked on the base paper with black ink.

At the robot-controlled crossing four two-face Dinky Toy Traffic Signals are used, two of these showing red and the other two green. In the illustration the signals are showing "green" to traffic proceeding along the main road past the front of the Petrol Station, and the Market Gardener's Van and the Daimler Car on the crossroad therefore are held up waiting for right of way.

At the roundabout the traffic is circuiting the island, and on the right-hand road a Dinky Toy Van, and the Sportsman's Coupé, that are visible behind the Filling Station, are seen waiting to allow the Businessman to cross the road via the pedestrian crossing, which is indicated by Beacons and dotted lines.

The vicinity of the garage is a particularly realistic portion of the layout. Here good use is made of a Breakdown Car, a Petrol Tank Wagon, and one or two figures from the Hornby Engineering Staff and Passenger Sets. Two men at the rear of the garage are busy repairing and cleaning cars, and the Breakdown Car is just towing in a broken-down Van, an operation that is watched with interest by a woman standing near. Further realism is added by the Man beckoning to a Newsboy, who is shown running towards him in answer to his call.

On the other side of the layout, in the main road, a group of three Businessmen are in earnest conversation, and a Woman and a Child are walking in the foreground. Two Dogs—which look as though they are just about to start an argument—are another feature of this section of the layout.

When the layout has been completed a great deal of fun can be obtained by arranging various traffic conditions. For example an accident can be staged. This might be caused by a motorist trying to beat the "lights" at the controlled crossing, or alternatively a pedestrian could be knocked over by a negligent motorist disregarding the Belisha Crossing. In either of these cases the Dinky Toy Ambulance could be introduced with good effect.

In making a layout on these lines success depends largely on the choice of a suitable scene. An actual busy crossing with which one is familiar is the best type to tackle first of all, but when some experience of the work has been gained added interest can be obtained by making up realistic road scenes to one's own ideas. To obtain the utmost realism, however, care should be taken to see that everything is in accordance with real life. For instance motor vehicles must not be shown on road crossings while the Traffic Robots are against them, and vehicles must also be placed behind the white lines at the crossings and on the correct side of the road.

ARCHITECTURAL MODELS

Model-builders seeking original applications for Meccano might well try building architectural models. The possibilities offered by these subjects are not fully realised, and although models of famous cathedrals and other structures of masonry have occasionally been illustrated in the "*M.M.*," it is clear that the majority of readers devote most of their energies to the building of mechanical models. The chief objection that is generally put forward against building models of architectural subjects is that once they are built there is no further pleasure to be had from them except as models of beauty and ornament.

It is not always so, however, as some models can be used in connection with Meccano Motor Cars, Aeroplanes or Dinky Toys, or with a Hornby railway, to provide realistic surroundings. For these purposes models of garages, aeroplane hangars, railway stations, and signal cabins immediately suggest themselves, and there are many others that will occur to readers. When the models are finished they may be photographed with appropriate accessories in position to represent scenes from real life. For the purpose of a photograph, only a section of a building need be built, sections of several structures being arranged in a similar manner to the scenery of a theatre, so that a limited number of parts can be used for obtaining imposing photographic effects.

The interest to be had from building architectural models quite counterbalances their lack of utility when completed. Original subjects for models are always interesting as they call for new ideas and new uses for parts. To reproduce a structure of masonry might at first seem to be quite a simple task, but if all the small details are to be brought out in the model it will be found that original ideas and a knowledge of how to use parts to the best advantage are necessary, if the best results are to be obtained. Many interesting hours can be spent building up reproductions of the world's most famous examples of architecture.

THE ARC DE TRIOMPHE

A particularly fine model of the Arc de Triomphe is shown on this page, and in it several Meccano parts have been applied to unusual purposes for incorporating as much detail work as possible in the model. The size of this model may cause readers to form the opinion that structures of this type can be built only with an extensive range of parts. Of course with a large Outfit many elaborate models can be built, but the subjects are not excluded from the possibilities of small Outfits, although the builders must naturally confine their activities to less ambitious models. As there is such a great range of subjects from which the constructor can choose a prototype for his model it is not difficult to find one that can be reproduced to advantage with a small Outfit. When comparatively few parts are available it is advisable to select structures that do not incorporate much small detail work.

Strip Plates and Flexible Plates prove their utility for models of masonry on account of the fairly large surfaces to be filled in, and as the Plates are perforated at the edges only, they produce a more solid appearance than do the perforated Flat Plates and Flanged Plates. The advantages of using these parts are evident from the illustration. They suggest smooth unbroken surfaces of stone that are not easily represented by other Plates or parts.

Architraves can be used for ornamental work, and such parts as Trunnions, Corner Brackets and Triangular Plates have their uses for special purposes. It will be noticed that a 2½" Triangular Plate is used to form the keystone of the arch illustrated, and Chimney Adaptors, Boiler Ends and Handrail Supports are used for ornamental work on the upper structure of the arch.

Different ornamental effects are produced according to the arrangement of the coloured parts. In the case of the Strip Plates and Flexible Plates, it is surprising how a different effect is obtained by turning the plain side outward instead of the striped side. The colour combinations on the model illustrated can readily be visualised.

ANCIENT AND MODERN

Many modern buildings have large flat surfaces and angular corners, the complete absence of curves being conspicuous. As the modern tendency is to make all corners right-angles, and the roofs flat, these subjects are excellent for reproducing in Meccano. The chief difficulty is to avoid making a model look too much like a square box, but the judicious use of coloured parts for window frames and doors will be found to make a wonderful difference to the appearance of a model.

An imposing model of the Arc de Triomphe showing how architectural subjects can be reproduced in Meccano.

The older styles of architecture are more varied and give the model-builder plenty of scope, although the models are not quite so simple to build. A little difficulty generally adds to the interest of model-building, however, by giving opportunities for original work. Parts can be applied to new uses, and there is always greater satisfaction to be derived from the completion of a model that has not been all "plain sailing" than of a simple one. It is often necessary to modify some of the decoration, or to omit it entirely from the model, if it cannot be reproduced with realism. On the Arc de Triomphe model the sculptural work on the side panels has not been represented owing to the difficulty of using Meccano parts to obtain anything like a true reproduction of the original.

IDEAS FOR FANCY DRESS

This heading might seem out of place on this page, but actually it has a definite Meccano interest for model builders who are now thinking out original schemes for fancy dresses. About this time of the year many readers are attending carnivals and parties where fancy dresses are popular, and most of them will be wondering how to attire themselves in an original manner. Here all difficulties are smoothed away for the Meccano enthusiast who takes his hobby seriously, for how better could he appear than as a Meccano Robot? His costume is sure to arouse interest, and will stand a very good chance of carrying off the chief prize for originality. Even if someone else hits upon the idea, which is unlikely, there are sure to be big differences between the costumes so that each will retain much of its originality. In the past many Meccano boys have tried out fancy dresses on these lines and have received prizes for their ingenuity.

There are various ways of making Meccano costumes. Some of them can be built up on a framework of Strips and Girders and worn like a suit of armour, but for obvious reasons Meccano is not used throughout for the construction. The framework can be filled in with cardboard or cloth, suitably coloured, and perhaps spotted to represent perforations. If legs and arms are to be encased in such a suit, ingenuity will be called for to devise satisfactory joints to allow a reasonable amount of movement.

Readers who can persuade their mothers or sisters to make garments for them can select cloth in Meccano colours and have it made up to represent Strips on the arms and legs, and Plates on the body. Small circular black patches can be sewn on to represent holes, and golden-yellow ones for the bolts. Model builders will be able to suggest different effects that can be achieved on similar lines.

Meccano parts are useful for many fancy costumes for adding finishing touches, and for accessories. They can be used for helmets and other head dress; and for swords, shields, fire-axes, etc., to properly equip the wearer.

LARGE CIRCULAR PLATE.—A circular plate for use with the Ring Frame to make a large flanged wheel could be used in some cases for locomotive driving wheels, but otherwise its applications would be very limited. In most cases where a large circular plate is required the Roller Race (No. 167a) can be used, and consequently there would be insufficient demand for a new part to warrant its manufacture. (*Reply to T. W. Pease, Lostwithiel.*)

SUBSTITUTE FOR SOCKET COUPLING.—The Socket Coupling provides a convenient way of joining together two wheel bosses, and is particularly useful for connecting Gears and Pinions in gear-box construction. This suggestion is that the Pinions should be drilled for inserting screws for attaching them to Gears. It is novel, but the objection to the arrangement is the small diameter of the Pinions. On the ½" Pinions there is not sufficient width between the teeth and the boss to allow for the insertion of a screw, and even on the ¾" Pinions the screw would have to be of smaller diameter than the standard bolts. It would also be necessary for all Gears to be similarly drilled for use with the Pinions. Although the idea is quite good, it is scarcely practicable for these reasons. (*Reply to A. R. Wright, Stamford, Northants.*)

A SYNCHRONOUS MASTER CLOCK

J. Thomas, Bristol, has succeeded in building the synchronous motor used in the clock described in the November, 1935, "M.M.," into the Master Clock featured in the September, 1935, Magazine. By doing this he claims to have made a clock that combines elegant appearance and absolute reliability.

To do this the pendulum movement from the Master Clock was removed and the motor then fitted in the position occupied previously by the impulse coils. A Worm on the armature shaft of the motor drives a 50-teeth Gear Wheel on a vertical shaft and this carries a Worm at its upper end. The Worm drives a 50-teeth Gear Wheel on a Rod journalled in the side plates of the clock. By fitting two further gear reductions of 3 : 1 and 2 : 1 a total reduction in speed of 15,000 : 1 between the motor and the minute hand is obtained. The minute hand therefore makes one revolution every hour.

In Search of New Models

Hints on Building Steamships

THERE is much fun to be had constructing ship models of all types, but many Meccano constructors seem to overlook these most interesting subjects for models. Once they try reproducing ships in model form they will realise that a most fascinating new field for constructional work has been opened to them, and will be eager to build different types. In a previous article in this series sailing ships were dealt with as subjects for attractive models, and readers who have built models of the old-timers, or of modern yachts, will now be keen to try ships of a different type.

On these pages some of the possibilities offered by steamships are investigated. Constructors taking a really keen interest in shipping will realise that under the heading of steamships enough model material will be found to provide interesting work for several years, but as the average model builder likes variation of his subjects we will deal here with only a few of the interesting types that can be built.

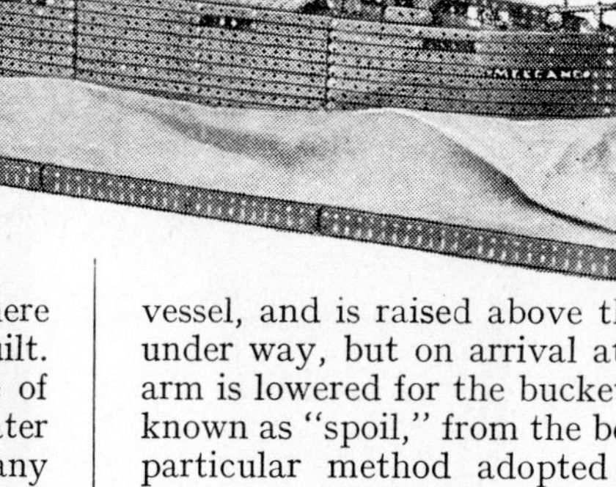

Fig. 1.
This Whaler pitches and rolls as though in a rough sea.

In the article on sailing ships mention was made of historic vessels as model subjects, and although a later period of history is covered by steamships there are many historic vessels that have particular interest, making them worth while building in Meccano. The interest in reproducing an old-time ship, or in fact any engineering structure of years ago, is largely due to the strangeness of the original compared with similar structures of the present day. The early steamships had paddles and sails and are in no way comparable with our present-day steamers. Boats intended for short distances were of even stranger appearance, particularly those built for experimental purposes.

The great increase in sea trading during the steamship era has been responsible for the development of numerous specialised types of vessel to meet the requirements of particular trades or for some definite service. Among the vessels for carrying special cargoes we find oil tankers forming quite a distinct class. The characteristic feature of these ships is their great length. The superstructure and bridge are placed at the stern and the engines also are mounted at the stern, below decks, so that the entire forward part of the vessel is devoted to the carrying of oil. Some cargo vessels, particularly those in service on inland waterways, are built on similar lines to oil tankers, but are provided with holds for cargo instead of the tanks. These ships can be reproduced quite easily in Meccano.

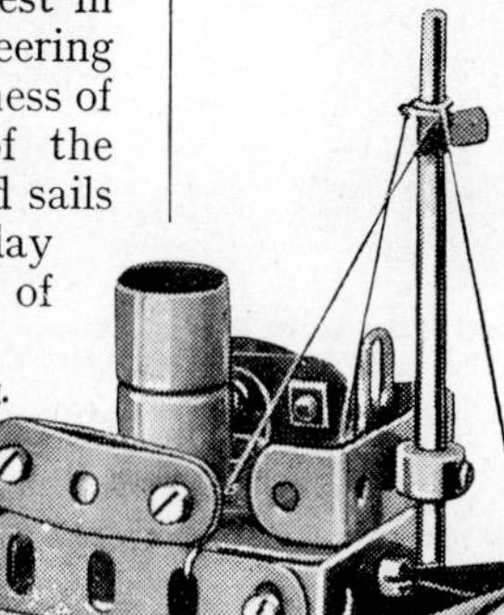

Fig. 2.
A diminutive Tug.

Before building the model the constructor should decide if it is to be a reproduction of only that part of the ship showing above the waterline, or if it is to represent the entire vessel. The four models shown on these pages are all waterline models, but where sufficient parts are available they may be built to represent the entire ship. A better effect is generally produced by a waterline model, for it is only the part of the ship showing above water that is usually seen, and a model of the entire hull looks rather unfamiliar.

It is a good plan to consider whether any means can be adopted to present to advantage the salient features of the vessel. An interesting way of showing off the working of a bucket dredger has been adopted in the model in Fig. 3. This model is mounted on suitable supports so that the bucket arm can be seen projecting from the bottom of the boat. The bucket arm operates in a slot in the centre of the vessel, and is raised above the keel when the dredger is under way, but on arrival at the place of operation the arm is lowered for the buckets to scoop up sand or mud, known as "spoil," from the bed of a river or harbour. The particular method adopted for displaying the model dredger shows the buckets operating, scooping up the spoil and depositing it at the top of a chute that conveys it over the side of the vessel to hopper barges alongside.

Another interesting way of mounting a model is shown in Fig. 1. The Whaler is fitted on a suitable baseboard with cloth or paper arranged to represent water. Dark blue or green material should be used, and this can be flecked with white to suggest broken waves and spray. The vessel is mounted at its centre on a pivot allowing universal movement so that the ship can be made to rock from side to side, and from stem to stern. In this way a most realistic pitching and rolling movement can be obtained, giving the ship the appearance of being in a rough sea; and if the coloured material representing the sea is attached to the sides of the ship, this also will move up and down with a motion like that of the waves.

At one end of the baseboard a Motor is mounted—an Electric Motor being most suitable for this purpose—and geared to give a very slow drive to a Crank. The Crank is connected by a pivoted Rod to one end of the ship, so that as the Crank rotates the ship rocks up and down and from side to side. The movement is best applied to fairly long models; and in the case of the ship shown the Motor can be mounted behind the model without being seen from the front. With small models it will be necessary to mount the ship on a raised baseboard to conceal the Motor beneath the board, a slot being cut to accommodate the connecting rod actuating the movement of the vessel.

Other ways of displaying model ships to show them up to advantage will occur to builders, and different methods will be adopted for different types of vessel. It is a good plan to construct several small tugs of proportionate size to a large model ship and to arrange them alongside, or connect them to towing hawsers. In this way the actual size of the real ship is suggested, as the comparison between the size of the ship and that of the tugs is immediately apparent.

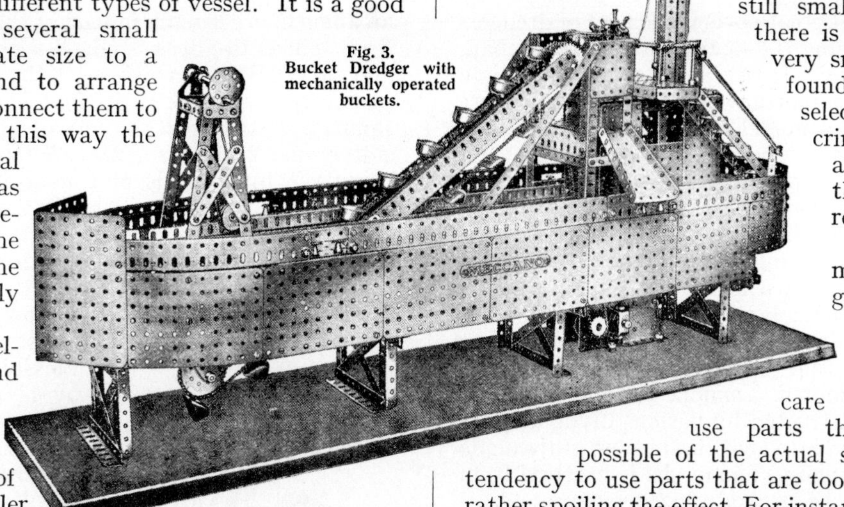

Fig. 3. Bucket Dredger with mechanically operated buckets.

When the model-builder sets out to find subject matter for steamship models he will be surprised at the great diversity of types. Among smaller passenger vessels there are the river ferries and lake steamers, with screw or paddle propulsion. Some of the American paddle steamers have many decks, giving them rather an unusual appearance, and making good subjects for model-builders who like to incorporate much detail work in their models.

The larger sea-going and ocean-going passenger vessels do not vary greatly in the essential points of their design, the most noticeable differences being in their size and the number of their decks and funnels. In building a model liner the constructor should seek out individual features and reproduce these with fidelity so that there can be no doubt concerning the actual vessel represented by the model.

Cargo vessels vary greatly in design according to the cargo they carry and to the conditions under which they operate. In addition to general cargo ships there are vessels designed to fulfil some special purpose, and these are probably the most interesting of all for the model-builder. Dredgers are included in this class, and in addition to the type illustrated there are suction dredgers—perhaps not so interesting as models—and grab dredgers. Bucket dredgers and grab dredgers provide interest not only as ship subjects but also as mechanical models.

Fig. 4. Passenger Liner.

The size of a model is obviously governed by the range of parts available for it, but even when large numbers of parts are available good fun can be had building small models. It is often the case that a small model built with a limited number of parts calls for more skill in the use of the parts than does a large model, if the most realistic results are to be obtained. The little tug in Fig. 2 is an example of the results that can be achieved with a small number of parts. In a small model such as this, correct proportions of the different parts must be sacrificed a little, but the tug proves that careful selection of parts can make it possible to build a very well proportioned model. The idea of simplicity can be carried even a stage further by building still smaller models in which there is less detail work. For very small models it will be found that parts must be selected with much discrimination if the models are to resemble the ships they are intended to represent.

Detail work on ship models of any size greatly influences their finished appearance. In reproducing small details, however, care should be taken to use parts that are as near as possible of the actual scale size. There is a tendency to use parts that are too large for the purpose, rather spoiling the effect. For instance, in making a model winch for mounting on the forecastle head, some constructors are tempted to make a model that actually works, when it would be far too large to be in keeping with the remainder of the ship. In such a case a dummy winch should be fitted and made to look like the actual mechanism.

On the Whaler and Dredger it will be noticed that bollards are mounted in appropriate positions, gaps being left in the sides of the vessels to expose them, as in actual practice. Buffers are used for the bollards. Ventilators fitted immediately in front of the funnel on the Whaler are made by mounting $\frac{3}{4}$" Flanged Wheels on Screwed Rods. Further small details are the port and starboard lamps mounted on the sides of the wheel-house. Each lamp consists of a Threaded Boss with a bolt screwed into the end to form the top of the lamp; and is secured to two $1'' \times \frac{1}{2}''$ Angle Brackets, one of which is attached to the wheel-house, the other being arranged beneath the Threaded Boss. On the small Tug a noticeable feature is the fender on the bows; used in actual practice to prevent the tugs from damaging the sides of a vessel with which they come in contact. A $\frac{5}{8}$" Rubber Ring is tied in position to represent the fender.

An important feature of any steamer is the funnel, and several ways of making funnels are shown on these pages. Strips are useful for the purpose, as they can be used for making a funnel of any diameter and height; and with Strips it is easy to form funnels of oval or round section. The Strips can be bolted to further Strips bent to form a circle or oval, or to Obtuse Angle Brackets. Two Chimney Adaptors are used for the funnel of the Tug.

Meccano Bucket Dredger

A Fascinating Meccano Model

A COMMON sight at great ports is the fleet of dredgers employed in keeping the docks and entrance channel navigable for shipping. Dredgers are not attractive in appearance, but their importance entitles them to more attention from Meccano model-builders than is usually given to them. The varied types of these vessels and their extensive mechanical equipment provide plenty of scope for enterprising model-builders, and miniature reproductions of suction, cutter-suction and bucket type dredgers are very interesting to construct.

The Meccano model shown in Figs. 1 and 2 is not a reproduction of any particular dredger, but it embodies all the main characteristics of a typical treble type dredger produced by the well-known crane makers, Priestman Brothers Limited, London. The hulls of these vessels are usually constructed by various Clyde dredger and hopper builders, and fitted with cranes and grabs made by the Priestman Company. The model is nearly 4 ft. in length and has a 9½ in. beam, and the three cranes with their grabs are operated automatically from a 6-volt or 20-volt Meccano Electric Motor.

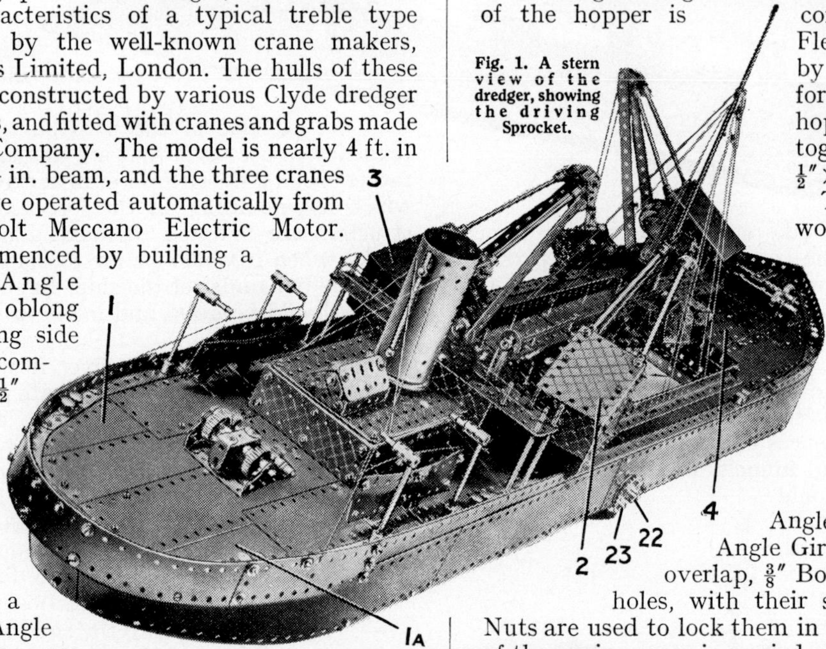

The hull is commenced by building a framework of Angle Girders to form an oblong 31″×9½″. Each long side of this frame is composed of an 18½″ and a 12½″ Angle Girder joined together end to end by means of a 7½″ Angle Girder. The two complete side members are connected together by a series of 9½″ Angle Girders, and these are braced by a number of 5½″ Strips. When the frame is complete it is fitted at each side with four 12½″×2½″ Strip Plates, as shown in Fig. 2. The front ends of these Plates are forced together to form the bow of the model, and secured to ½″×½″ Angle Brackets. Two 2½″ and two 2″ Strips are bolted to this part of the hull, as illustrated, to form the stem.

The upward sweep of the forward part of the ship is reproduced by two 12½″×2½″ Strip Plates, the top forward corners of these being bolted to the 2½″ Strips of the stem. A similar arrangement will be seen at the stern. The upper curve of this part of the model consists of three 5½″×1½″ Flexible Plates bolted to two 12½″ Strips curved to the correct shape, and 12½″ Strips are also used for strengthening the topsides of the bulwarks, both at the stern and at the bow.

The deck at bow and stern is fitted to several ½″×½″ Angle Brackets secured to the inside of the hull, but amidships it is attached to Angle Girders as shown in Fig. 1. The after deck is composed of 9½″×2½″ and 12½″×2½″ Strip Plates, and two 5½″×2½″ Strip Plates which are indicated at 1 and 1A, Fig. 1. These two Plates are set at an angle in order to fill in part of the curved portion of the deck. The entire deck is edged with a number of straight and curved Strips, which serve the dual purpose of hiding unsightly corners of Strip Plates and also filling in any small gaps existing at the ends of the Plates. Beneath each side crane, 2 and 3, a 2½″×2½″ Flat Plate is fitted, to carry the upper ends of the pivot and driving shafts.

The fore deck is built similarly to the deck just described, but a 4½″×2½″ Flat Plate 4 and a 5½″×2½″ Flat Plate 5 are fitted as shown. This deck is also secured to the hull by means of ½″×½″ Angle Brackets, and Strips are used along its edge. The narrow deck along each side of the hopper is constructed from 5½″×1½″ Flexible Plates, strengthened by 1½″ Strips. Angle Girders form coamings round the hopper, and they are secured together at the corners by ½″×½″ Angle Brackets.

Fig. 1. A stern view of the dredger, showing the driving Sprocket.

The engine room upper works and bridge are built next. An oblong of Angle Girders, 4½″×5½″, is first laid down on the after deck and two 5½″×1½″ and two 4½″×1½″ Flexible Plates are fastened to it. These are strengthened internally with 1½″ Strips and carry at their upper edges two 5½″ Angle Girders and two 4½″ Angle Girders. Where these Girders overlap, ⅜″ Bolts are passed through the holes, with their shanks pointing upwards. Nuts are used to lock them in position, and later the top of the engine room is carried on the four shanks and held in place by nuts. This engine room top consists of two 5½″×3½″ Flat Plates fastened by nuts, and it carries the funnel and skylight.

The base of the skylight consists of two 2½″×½″ Double Angle Strips and two 1½″ Strips. They are surmounted by two 2½″ Flat Girders set at an angle, the triangular gap at each end of these being filled in by means of two Flat Brackets secured to ½″×½″ Angle Brackets. The funnel is represented by a Boiler, minus Ends, the two edges of which are overlapped two holes. The escape steam pipe is fastened to the Boiler by two Handrail Supports, the lower Support of which secures a 1″×½″ Angle Bracket to the inside of the funnel. This is in turn bolted to a 2″ Pulley that is attached to a Wheel Flange by means of two ¾″ Bolts. These Bolts pass through the Wheel Flange and into the top of the engine room, where two nuts hold them in place. The method of bracing the funnel is shown in Fig. 1.

The bridge is supported on a structure built up of two 5½″×2½″ Flat Plates and two 2½″×1½″ Flexible Plates. The structure is secured to the deck by means of 4½″ and 1½″ Angle Girders and to the bridge by means of ½″×½″

Angle Brackets. The bridge consists of one 5½″×2½″ and two 3″×1½″ Flat Plates, round the edges of which are arranged a series of 1″ Threaded Rods. The Rods support lengths of copper wire, which represent handrails. The two end pairs of supports for the handrails are 4½″ Threaded Rods and these pass through the deck.

The arched structure across the hopper consists of two side members joined together by Double Brackets. Each side member is built up from a 5½″ Curved Strip, to the ends of which are bolted 5½″ Strips overlapping two holes. The centre of the 5½″ Curved Strip carries a Flat Trunnion that is attached to the side of the hopper by two 3″ Strips, held in place by ½″×½″ Angle Brackets. The purpose of the arch is to support four ½″ Pulleys, over each of which passes a length of chain. This chain can be purchased, in nickel or black finish, from this office price 3d. per yard. One end of each chain is secured to a Girder in the bottom of the model, and the other end is linked up by a length of cord to a windlass. Part of one of these windlasses is shown at 7, Fig. 3. In actual practice each chain is connected at its lower end to a big flap in the bottom of the boat, that is let down when a cargo of silt is being discharged.

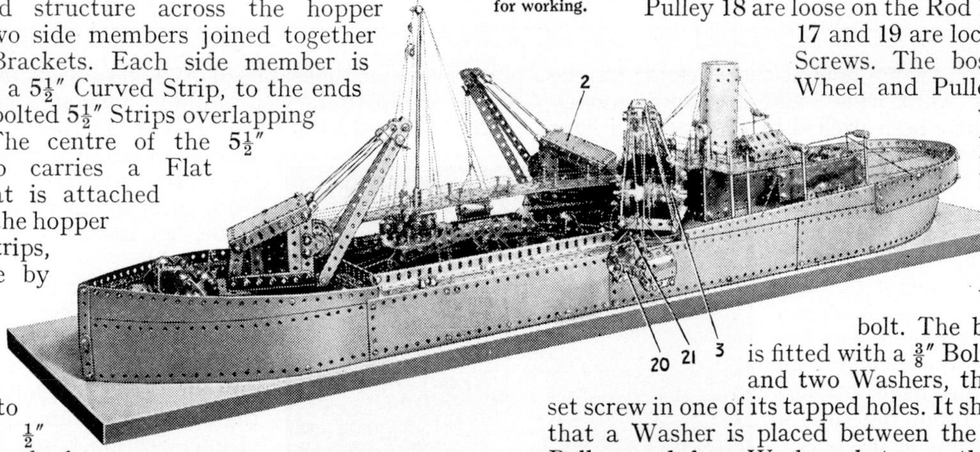

Fig. 2. The model mounted on a baseboard ready for working.

The forward crane is shown in Fig. 3, and a description of this will serve for cranes 2 and 3, which are identical with it in every respect. A 3½″×2½″ Flanged Plate, fitted at each side with a 3½″ Angle Girder, forms the crane platform. Each Angle Girder carries two 3″, two 2½″ and three 2″ Strips and they pass behind a second 3½″ Angle Girder at their upper ends. Where possible the Strips are bolted to this 3½″ Girder. The back of the crane consists of a 1½″×2½″ Flanged Plate 8. The roof is a 3½″×2½″ Strip Plate, but this is not fitted until the operating mechanism for the grab has been installed.

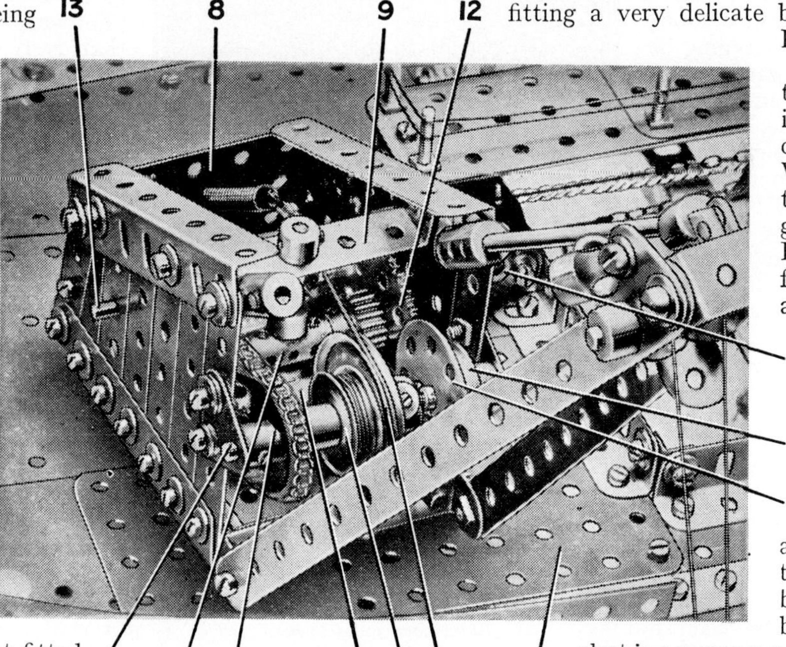

Fig. 3. A sectional view of one of the cranes in which the roof has been removed.

A 5″ Rod is passed through a hole in the base plate, 1½″ from the front edge, and it is journalled at its upper end in the 2½″×½″ Double Angle Strip 9. A 1½″ Contrate 10, a Coupling 11 and a Collar are mounted on the 5″ Rod, the Coupling being spaced away from the Contrate by three Washers. One end of the Coupling accommodates the inner end of a 1½″ Rod that carries a ½″ Pinion, meshing with the Contrate 10 and the 57-teeth Gear 12. The Gear 12 is in engagement with a second ½″ Pinion on the Rod 13, the other end of which is fitted with a 1½″ Sprocket Wheel. A length of Sprocket Chain couples up this Wheel with a 1″ Sprocket 14 that is locked on a Rod 15 journalled in 1″ Triangular Plates.

On the Rod 15 are mounted two ¾″ Flanged Wheels 16 and 17, the 1½″ Pulley 18 and the Bush Wheel 19. The Flanged Wheel 16 and 1½″ Pulley 18 are loose on the Rod 15, but the Wheels 17 and 19 are locked by their Grub Screws. The bosses of the Bush Wheel and Pulley are in contact with each other in the centre of the Rod, and one of the tapped holes in the boss of the Bush Wheel carries a bolt. The boss of the Pulley is fitted with a ⅜″ Bolt carrying a Collar and two Washers, the Collar having a set screw in one of its tapped holes. It should be noted here that a Washer is placed between the Bush Wheel and Pulley and four Washers between the Flanged Wheel 16 and Sprocket 14.

The Pivot Rod of the crane, already mentioned, is now passed through one of the holes in the deck of the dredger, and the lower end is locked in the boss of a Double Arm Crank. This Crank is bolted to one of the transverse 9½″ Girders of the hull. As the crane is rotated by hand, the Contrate 10 remains stationary and the Gears rotate. The mechanism is completed by fitting a very delicate band brake to the 1½″ Pulley 18 as shown.

The grab is connected to the hoisting barrel in the following way. A cord from the Flanged Wheel 17 is attached to the centre Rod of the grab, as shown at 20 in Fig. 2. A second cord from the Wheel 16 is attached by four short cords to the upper corners of the grab and secured in place underneath Washers. When the cords are correctly adjusted for length and the crane is turned, the grab will not only be raised and lowered but also opened and shut in a manner suggesting real dredging.

The crane is rotated from a ¾″ Pinion 21, Fig. 2, and the vertical shafts carrying the two Pinions for cranes 2 and 3 are connected together by a horizontal shaft and 1½″ and ½″ Bevels. A horizontal shaft is also connected to the vertical driving rod of the forward crane. Lengths of Sprocket Chain connect the two horizontal shafts to the Rod 22 carrying the driving Sprocket 23 for the model. This Sprocket is connected by Sprocket Chain, through a slip clutch, to a reversing gear similar to S.M. No. 63, and this in turn is linked up with a 6-volt or 20-volt Meccano Motor.

Prizes for Meccano Model-Builders!

For the Best-Built Models of Any Kind

MECCANO activities are now at their height, for the ranks of this world-wide band of happy model-builders have recently been swelled by thousands of boys and girls who received Meccano Outfits as Christmas presents and are now experiencing for the first time the joys of this greatest of all hobbies. Most of these newcomers to Meccanoland will no doubt be busy building the various models shown in the Instruction Manuals, but few of them will be content merely to copy models once they have obtained some experience. From the time a boy first uses Meccano, he has before him a constant encouragement to make slight changes in the construction of the various Manual models, and thus he is led on to build models from his own ideas.

There is nothing in the world to be compared with the joy and satisfaction of creating something new, and in order to ensure that every model-builder shall have ample opportunity to exercise his skill in designing his own models we are organising the competition announced on this page.

Every competitor has an equal chance in this competition, no matter what Outfit he may possess. All it is necessary to do is to think of a new model of any kind, no matter how simple, and then construct it as neatly as possible. Boys and girls of any age may compete and there are no fees to be paid.

Competitors may use any number of parts in constructing the models they wish to enter, but it is a mistake to think that the more complicated a model is, the better the chance it will have of winning a prize. Very often indeed the reverse is the case and a simple model that is well proportioned and displays sound constructional features secures a prize in preference to a model in the construction of which the chief aim has been to produce an intricate piece of mechanism without any regard either to proportion or correct principles.

In entering this contest competitors should try to be as original as possible in their choice of subjects, for in making the awards the judges will pay special attention to models showing initiative and which are not simply variations of models included in the Meccano Instruction Manuals.

This simple and neatly built model of a windmill pump was built by René Hosse, Antwerp, and is a good example of the kind of models that win prizes in Meccano competitions.

THE PRIZES

Cheques, Meccano and Hornby Goods

The prizes in Sections A and C are as follows:
1st Prize, Cheque for £3-3s.
2nd Prize, Cheque for £2-2s.
3rd. Prize, Meccano or Hornby Goods value £1-1s.
Six Prizes of Meccano or Hornby Goods value 10/6.
Six Prizes of Meccano or Hornby Goods value 5/-.

In Section B the prizes to be awarded are:
1st Prize, Cheque for £2-2s.
2nd Prize, Cheque for £1-1s.
3rd Prize, Meccano or Hornby Goods value 15/-.
Six Prizes of Meccano or Hornby Goods value 10/6.
Six Prizes of Meccano or Hornby Goods value 5/-.
A number of Certificates will also be awarded in each Section.

There are thousands of original subjects to choose from, but competitors who cannot think of a really unusual model should try to incorporate in their car, aeroplane, loco or other such model a new use for a Meccano part or a little detail work in order to make the finished model as realistic and interesting as possible.

Entries will be divided into three Sections as follows: Section A for competitors living in the British Isles and over 14 years of age. Section B for competitors living in the British Isles and under 14 years of age. Section C for readers of all ages living overseas. A fine range of prizes consisting of cheques and Meccano and Hornby goods will be awarded in each Section and full details of these appear in the panel on this page.

We wish to remind intending competitors that it is not necessary to send the actual model; a good photograph or a clear drawing is all that is required. Each competitor should take special care to see that his or her age, name and address appear on the back of each photograph or sheet of paper used, together with the letter A, B or C, indicating the Section in which the model is entered, and the name of the competition, i.e. "Winter" Model-Building Contest.

Photographs or drawings need not be the competitor's own work, but it is absolutely necessary that the model itself is his or her own unaided work.

Envelopes containing entries should be addressed to "Winter" Model-Building Contest, Meccano Ltd., Binns Road, Liverpool 13. It should be noted that drawings or photographs of prize-winning models become the property of Meccano Ltd., but unsuccessful entries will be returned to the senders if a stamped addressed envelope of suitable size is enclosed for that purpose.

Readers living in Great Britain and Ireland must forward their entries not later than 29th February, 1936. In order to give Overseas entrants plenty of time in which to build their models we have extended the closing date for Section C to 30th April, 1936.

The full lists of prize-winners will be published in the "*M.M.*" as soon after the closing dates as possible.

Model-Building Competition Results

By Frank Hornby

"September Contest" (Home Section)

In examining the entries in the "September" Contest I was particularly glad to find a large increase in the number of models submitted by boys under 14. Many of their models are really excellent pieces of work and quite equal to some of the models built by older boys entering in Section A.

The full lists of awards in the Home Sections of the Competition are as follows:

Section A (competitors over 14)

1st, Meccano or Hornby Goods value £3-3s.: F. Nunn, Colchester. 2nd, Goods value £2-2s.: R. Campbell, London, S.W.16. 3rd, Goods value £1-1s.: C. Williams, Manchester 11.

Goods value 10/6: R. Benson, Worsley, Nr. Manchester; W. Griffith and J. Rowe, Warlingham (joint award); T. Green, Stockport; A. Hope, Keswick; H. Lee, Ardrossan.

A neat model tramcar built by R. Benson of Worsley.

Goods value 5/-: W. Bowley, Derby; P. Bradley, Stanmore, Middlesex; G. Peek, Colchester; R. Walford, Newton Abbot; E. Whitehouse, Bristol 8.

Section B (competitors under 14)

1st, Meccano or Hornby Goods value £2-2s.: J. Cooley, Wisbech, Lincs. 2nd, Goods value £1-1s.: J. Driscoll, Perranwell, Cornwall. 3rd, Goods value 10/6: E. Jones, Newcastle Emlyn, Carmarthen.

Goods value 5/-: O. Arnold, Wolverhampton; M. Bryant, Skipton; F. Haynes, Wallasey; R. Johnson, Leigh-on-Sea; B. Mallinson, S. Ascot, Berks.; D. Middleton, Northampton; T. Smith, Exeter; R. Stevens, Bradford; J. Weir, Emsworth. Hampshire; H. Whitehouse, Bristol 8.

I am constantly advising competitors to find original subjects for their competition models, and I am glad to say that at least one competitor in this contest acted on my advice, and was awarded a First Prize for his efforts. The competitor concerned is F. E. R. Nunn, and his model is a representation of a studio camera crane such as is used in film studios for supporting the camera above the scene, to enable high angle pictures to be taken.

The model consists of a small travelling carriage on which is a pedestal carrying the jib and platform for the camera. The carriage is provided with 3″ Pulley Wheels fitted with Rubber Tyres and Ackermann steering gear, and the pedestal is made from two triangular frames of Strips, the apex of the frames forming the pivot for the jib. The jib is tubular in section and is 2½″ square at one end and tapers to 1½″ square at the other. It is pivoted a short distance from the wider end, which is loaded with weights to counterbalance the weight of the camera, operator and platform. The jib is moved up and down see-saw fashion by means of Screwed Rods rotated in Threaded Bosses fixed to the jib. The camera platform is in two pieces, the lower one pivoted to the end of the jib, while the second forms a turntable so that the camera can be turned round to face in any direction. A compensating Rod attached to the pedestal and the platform ensures that the platform remains horizontal no matter what position the jib is in. The model is quite simple in construction and owes its success mainly to its originality.

A large model of a universal type bucket excavator won Second Prize in Section A for R. O. Campbell. The model is sturdily constructed and will actually perform light work. One Meccano Electric Motor working through a special gear-box is used to drive the various mechanisms, including travelling, swivelling, raising and lowering of the bucket arms and the movement of the buckets themselves, each of the movements being independently controlled by a separate lever.

C. Williams submitted a fine model of an old galleon of the Elizabethan period. The model incorporates a large amount of detail and no trouble has been spared to make it a truthful representation of one of these interesting ships. I have compared the model with a photograph of an Elizabethan galleon and I am glad to say that there is very little that I can find to criticise.

The model tramcar illustrated on this page was built by R. Benson and won one of the smaller prizes in Section A. The main feature of the model is its simplicity, and this, coupled with neat construction, accounts for its success in this contest. The model is lacking in originality, however, and that is why it failed to win one of the principal prizes. The body is carried on a chassis consisting of two 12½″ Angle Girders fitted with bent 5½″ Strips at each end for bumpers. The model runs on Flanged Wheels that are secured on Rods journalled in Flat Trunnions. The curved ends of the car are made from Strip Plates, and the floor and the straight parts of the roof and sides are built up with Flat Plates. The stair treads are made with cord and the model is fitted with Lanterns from the Meccano Lighting Set. A finishing touch is provided by a destination board made from a 2½″ × ½″ Double Angle Strip held in place near the roof by 1″ × 1″ Angle Brackets.

Section B contains quite a number of interesting entries, chief of them being a model of the destroyer "*Viceroy*," which was built by J. E. Cooley, and won First Prize. The model is not an elaborate piece of work, but it is very neatly built and incorporates all the main features of the actual vessel. The hull is made from Strips, and Strips and Plates form the deck. The turret for the for'ard gun is a Bush Wheel, and the gun itself is a Rod held in a Sleeve Piece by two Collars and Chimney Adaptors. Just aft of this is the bridge, which is provided with another similar gun. A Plate fixed to the bridge and projecting under the barrel of the gun protects the crew of the latter from the fire of the gun above. The vessel has two funnels, the for'ard one being made from 5½″ Strips, and the other, which is rather shorter as in the actual destroyer, is a Boiler slightly compressed to make it oval in section. The ship is complete with anti-aircraft guns, torpedo-tubes and a searchlight, the last consisting of a Chimney Adaptor secured by means of a Hinge to a Wheel Flange. This in turn is bolted to a 2″ Pulley Wheel mounted on a vertical Rod. A length of Sprocket Chain makes an excellent ladder to enable the searchlight operators to reach the platform. Rubber Tyres held in place on the model by cord represent the Harley Floats or rafts.

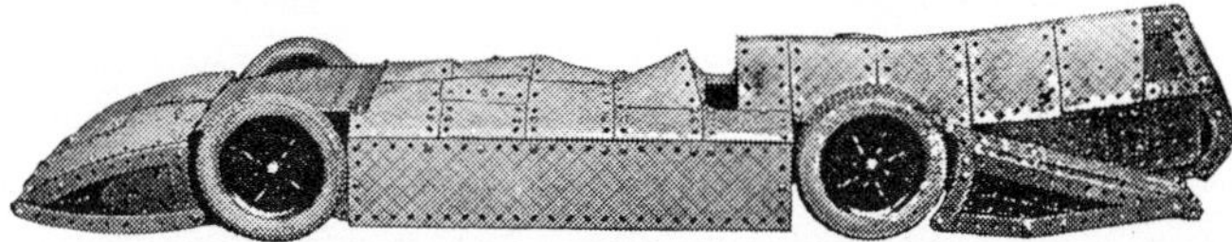

This model of Sir Malcolm Campbell's racing car "Bluebird" demonstrates the use of Meccano Flexible Plates. It was built by E. Jones, Newcastle Emlyn.

June "Lynx Eye" Competition (Overseas)

Section B

First Prize, Meccano or Hornby Goods value £2-2s.: K. Ho, Hong Kong. Second Prize, Goods value £1-1s.: C. Keekok, Singapore, S.S. Third Prize, Goods value 10/6: W. Kenny, Cloncurry, Australia.

Meccano or Hornby Goods value 2/6: R. Begg, Hamilton, Ontario; F. Mathers, Trochu, Alberta; H. Skelton, Ottawa, Ontario; P. Sevestre, Fecamp, France; R. Wragg, Rajputana, India; E. Meek, Wellington, New Zealand; L. Orsmond Muldersdrift, Transvaal; E. Fusslein, Zululand, S. Africa.

Dagenham M.C.—Recent model-building activities have included the construction of a locomotive and of a large crane. Talks and Games continue to be very popular. Club roll: 15. *Secretary:* J. Dobinson, 17, Freshwater Road, Dagenham.

St. Stephens (Saltash) M.C.—Two new Sections have been formed, one devoted to photography and the other to model-building in wood and cardboard. Electric light has been installed in the clubroom and is a great improvement. An electric motor operated off the mains supply is used for working the models. The invitation of the Plymouth M.C. to stage a display at their Exhibition was accepted. Model-building has been given a novel turn by the construction of a mechanised army. Several successful dances have been held. Club roll: 16. *Secretary:* A. Jackson, 5, Jubilee Cottages, St. Stephens-by-Saltash, Cornwall.

Hornsea M.C.—Recent lectures have dealt with many subjects, including "*Ancient Manuscripts*," "*Chemistry*" and "*The Peoples of Africa.*" The lectures for this session are equally varied, and range from "*Science and Gardening*" to "*The League of Nations.*" Club roll: 18. *Secretary:* P. Thom, 5, Alexandra Road, Hornsea.

Sid Vale (Sidmouth) M.C.—A Motor Lorry Contest attracted some very good models, many of which were of the latest types of vehicle. A display of models at a Sale of Work in connection with the Congregational Church won much praise from visitors. Another Model Illuminated Carnival Procession has been held in the schoolroom. It was headed by a tractor and included a well-made model of a Meccano Fire Brigade, built by H. Woodford. Many of the models were in the form of illuminated tableaux, and had striking lighting effects. A small charge for admission was made, and the club funds benefited by £1 7s. 6d. Club roll: 25. *Secretary:* L. R. J. Gliddon, Sheffield House, Sidmouth.

Plymouth M.C.—Several visits have been paid to the St. Stephens (Saltash) M.C., where some very happy evenings have been spent. Both Model-Building and Hornby Train operations continue to be very popular. A mock trial has been held and created so much merriment that the judge nearly lost his dignity! A vote after a debate on "*Electricity or Steam for Railway Motive Power?*" showed a large majority of the members present to be in favour of steam. The Woodwork Section, which was so successful last winter, has been re-opened, and the members are busy making models for the Hornby and other Sections of the club. The Annual Exhibition, held on 7th December, was opened by Sir William Munday and was a great success. The display included a working model railway, a complete fleet of miniature Plymouth tramcars, model steam engines and locomotives. Club roll: 69. *Secretary:* R. G. Symons, 47, Lisson Grove, Mutley, Plymouth.

Exeter M.C.—There is great activity in model-building, and nearly 30 models have been built in a month. A model Motor Olympia is being organised, and many different types of cars are being constructed for it. If it is a success other special shows, each devoted to some type of engineering model, will be held. A Dinky Toy Section is to be formed. Club roll: 36. *Secretary:* T. W. A. Smith, 98, Ladysmith Road, Exeter.

St. Columba's (Sunderland) M.C.—Meccano Nights continue to be the most popular feature of the club programme. They are attracting so many non-members, who come to get an idea of club life, that it is probable a waiting list will be compiled, and the applicants admitted in rotation. The club staged a fine Meccano and Hornby Train display at a recent Church Bazaar. The President has most generously presented the Hornby Section of the club with new rolling stock and equipment to the total value of £5. A Visitor's Night was the occasion for a most interesting lantern lecture on "*The Railways of Great Britain,*" and there was a record attendance of members, together with their parents and numerous friends. Club roll: 30. *Secretary:* R. Howe, Fulwell, Sunderland.

Wednesbury and District M.C.—This club is in need of new members to replace boys who have left Wednesbury. Any boy in the district who is interested in Meccano and would like to join the club will be cordially welcomed by the secretary at the address given at the end of this report. Club roll: 4. *Secretary:* A. L. Morgan, 17, Cobden Street, Falling's Heath, Wednesbury.

Whitgift School M.C.—Visits to places of interest are being continued during the winter session. Model-building is not being neglected, however, and members have been busy constructing a model breakdown crane. Club roll: 54. *Secretary:* J. A. Watson, 23, Addiscombe Avenue, Croydon.

Hutton School M.C.—A very interesting visit has been paid to Yeadon Airport. Model-building activities have been relieved by lectures and novel events such as an "Experience" evening, when each member present is asked to relate some strange experience of his own. A Meccano "Humanity" Night greatly exercised the ingenuity of model-builders, as it took the form of a competition for the most realistic robot. Club roll 12. *Secretary:* W. Holdsworth, 44, Victoria Road, Eccleshill, Bradford.

A happy group of members of the Fraserburgh M.C. The Rev. R. I. Mitchell, M.A., Leader, is in the centre of the front row, and next on his right is Master G. Smythe, secretary. The club was affiliated in October 1935. The older members meet in a room at Rathen West Manse, and the newly-formed Junior Section meets in the High Church Manse. Each clubroom is equipped with a library.

Sutton Valence Council School M.C.—In addition to the usual model-building meetings there have been several novel events, including a Firework Celebration, which was held on the appropriate day. A Detective Competition aroused great enthusiasm, and an Aeroplane Night did much to make all members "air-minded." Mention must also be made of a Treasure Hunt and of the jolly breaking-up party held at the end of last month. Club roll: 18. *Secretary:* James Chandler, "Herriard," Chart Sutton, Nr. Maidstone, Kent.

SOUTH AFRICA

Pioneer (Pietermaritzburg) M.C.—A model display by the members was included in an Exhibition held in the City Hall. The models were arranged in two classes and the Leader won the prize in the first class with his model of a Thornycroft motor vehicle. The prize in the second class was won by Sidney Coleman, with a model of an anti-aircraft gun. Several members correspond with Guild members in other countries. Club roll: 12. *Secretary:* A. H. Alley, 461, Burger Street, Pietermaritzburg, Natal.

Malvern M.C.—A most interesting visit has been paid to the offices of the "Star" newspaper, and members saw an afternoon edition of the paper being printed. They were shown all the processes, from the receipt of the huge reels of blank paper to the delivery by the printing presses of finished and folded copies of the newspaper. The members were given tea at the offices before leaving. The visit has been declared one of the best outings the club have had. An imposing display of models by members was shown at the "Star" Radio and Engineering Exhibition, held at the Selborne Hall. The display was the subject of many favourable comments by visitors and by the local Press. Club roll: 76. *Secretary:* B. H. Saunders, P.O. Box 8, Cleveland, Johannesburg.

AUSTRALIA

Melbourne M.C.—Model-building and Hornby Train Evenings are the chief features of the programme, and variety is introduced by occasional Reading Nights, when members bring back numbers of the "*M.M.*", books on model-building, etc. Interesting competitions are arranged to test the ability of members to carry out intricate railway operations correctly and quickly, and there is always great enthusiasm at these events. Club roll: 10. *Secretary:* Leonard Ison, 8, Hayes Street, Northcote, Melbourne, N.16.

NEW ZEALAND

Christchurch M.C.—Several new members have been enrolled. A lantern lecture on "*The Building of the Mersey Tunnel*" was much enjoyed. On a recent Model-building Evening a "Surprise Packet" competition was arranged. Each packet contained Meccano Parts, and the member to whom it was presented had to build a motor car or motor lorry, using every part contained in the package. The competition was a great success. Games Nights are always very popular, and like those devoted to competitions, always provoke a good deal of friendly rivalry between the members taking part. The club is open to boys over 10 years of age who have a Meccano or a Hornby Train Set, and new members will be welcomed. Club roll: 22. *Secretary:* L. W. Best, 28, Circuit Street, Strowan, Christchurch, N.Z.

CANADA

Rosemount (Regina) M.C.—The winter programme has included a short trip to Moose Jaw under the guidance of the Leader, and an interesting account of the outing appeared in a local newspaper. One of the most enjoyable events of the day was a pre-arranged visit to the Wireless Station CHAB, where the intricate apparatus by which the station programmes are broadcast was explained in a simple and interesting manner by an official. The club has recently moved to new quarters. Club roll: 16. *Secretary:* J. Watson, 974, Athol Street, Regina, Sask.

INDIA

Kognolkar (Nowgong) India.—Members are very enthusiastic and there are full attendances at all meetings. A club magazine is published regularly. Recent model-building has centred upon a Crane Exhibition, and some excellent models have been built for it. A visit to a local factory has been arranged. Club roll: 15. *Secretary:* R. M. Kognolker, Nowgong C.I., India.

EGYPT

Cairo M.C.—The club continues to progress satisfactorily, and meetings are held almost every night. The chief activity is Model-building, and members have recently concentrated their energies in constructing a large model monoplane. Club roll: 25. *Secretary:* Mohed Kamel Salem, 12, Bibars Street, Cairo, Egypt.

ITALY

Milan M.C.—The Draughts Competition proved so popular that a second one has been held. The President, Mr. C. Vigo, has left on military service. A Sports Section has been formed. Club roll: 14. *Secretary:* E. Vigo, Corso Genova 19, Milan.

New Year Greetings

This month I have the pleasure of wishing "A Very Happy New Year" to all members of the Guild and of Meccano Clubs. Many of them have already written to me to convey their good wishes for the coming year, and their accounts of the good times enjoyed during the Christmas season make delightful reading. In many clubs Christmas parties to which relatives and friends of the members were invited added to the general gaiety.

During the past year the Guild has continued to progress, both at home and abroad, and this is a striking testimony to the universal appeal that Meccano makes to boys. In addition to the many new recruits, there has been a gratifying increase in the number of clubs formed. I look forward to the time when these numerous new clubs have become thoroughly established and affiliated with the Guild. The older clubs have become stronger both in membership and in the club spirit, and their activities now cover a remarkably wide range of healthy pursuits. This fact is borne out by the excellent reports published in the "Club Notes" pages during last year. To-day Meccano clubs in all parts of the world are recognised institutions, and their Exhibitions and Concerts rank high among the social events of their districts.

Two Good Resolutions

This is the season for good resolutions. I should like every club member to resolve to do his utmost, not only to carry out the chief aims and objects of the Guild, but also to introduce his friends to the delights of membership. This would be a fine resolution to live up to, as it would mean that every member is helping somebody to get the best out of the world's greatest hobby, and at the same time "doing his bit" toward greatly strengthening the position held by the Guild.

Another good resolution that may be made by a Guild member is to write more regularly to the Secretary. The receipt of letters from friends in all parts of the world is a daily happy experience. The number of these letters seems astonishingly large until I compare it with the enormous membership of the Guild. This comparison brings home the solemn fact that in this respect I am not as fully in touch with my members as I desire to be, and I hope that during this year my mail bag will increase greatly in weight.

Meccano Club Secretaries

No. 35. E. H. Speers

E. H. Speers is secretary of the Boys' Institute (Wellington) M.C., which was affiliated in July 1931. An excellent programme is followed, and variety is provided by lectures, cinematograph exhibitions and excursions. An interesting club magazine is produced.

A New Film

Leaders of clubs possessing equipment for the exhibition of cinema films will be interested to hear that a 16 mm. silent film dealing with electric arc welding has been produced by Murex Welding Processes Ltd. It is divided into two parts, each comprising two reels of film. The first part deals with the various applications to which Murex electrodes are put, and includes "shots" taken at various works typical of the industries to which they belong and which use these electrodes. The second part of the film shows in detail the manufacture of Murex plant and electrodes at the company's works at Walthamstow, and the construction of motor generator sets at the Glasgow works of the Macfarlane Engineering Co. Ltd. A written commentary for use with the film is available.

A standard-size (35 mm.) talking film of the same scenes has also been made, and in this of course the commentary is recorded in the film. This is believed to be the first talking film relating to electrical arc welding to be made in the English language.

Either the talking or silent film version is available for hire to Meccano clubs able to show them, and application should be made by Leaders interested to the Publicity Department, Murex Welding Processes Ltd., Ferry Lane Works, Walthamstow, London, E.17. The film has already proved very popular, and the company ask that notice should be given as early as possible of the lecture date, so as to ensure that a copy of the film will be available in time.

Lantern lectures and the exhibition of cinematograph films provide very effective means of giving variety to club programmes, and I shall be glad to send to any Leader or secretary a list of lectures and films dealing with railway and industrial operations that have been prepared for the use of Meccano clubs. For the benefit of the officials of clubs in which lantern lectures and film displays have not so far been included in the programmes, I should like to point out that this list gives the names of firms and railway companies willing to loan films and lantern lectures for exhibition, and also explains the conditions attached to the loan.

Photographs of Clubs at Work

I have recently received some excellent photographs of club Leaders and club secretaries. In addition to these I am anxious to obtain some good photographs of club groups and of clubs actually at work, and I shall be very glad if Leaders will consider the possibility of having such photographs taken. There are of course difficulties in the way of obtaining successful photographs of interiors, especially by artificial light, but first-class results can be obtained with a little care and preparation. I feel sure that a series of photographs of this nature would be of interest to all members of Meccano Clubs.

Proposed Clubs

Attempts are being made to establish Meccano Clubs in the following places, and boys interested should communicate with the promoters whose names and addresses are given below:

Morden—M. Mullen, 24, Hillcross Avenue.
Rochdale—L. R. Wardley, 60, Canal Street, Castleton.
South Africa—R. H. Moodley, 10, Stirling Street, Capetown.
Thornton Heath—R. H. Smart, 14, Kensington Avenue.
Tralee—J. Wilson, Caherina, Tralee, I.F.S.
Upton—H. Davis, 49, School Street, Upton, Nr. Pontefract.
Ystrad Mynach—F. Davies, 8, The Square.

"LADY LUCK"

By Herbert S. Morton, Engineer

JIMMY got a job as fireman, and had a rough time. He told some of the boys about it.

"Was there a horseshoe on her?" they asked.

"I don't know," replied Jimmy. "What's that got to do with an engine steaming, anyway?"

"Why, everything," they told him, and laughed at his foolishness. "That's been your whole trouble."

Of course it sounded like boloney to Jimmy, but as he thought about it, there seemed to be some truth in it. Down town he saw a neat horseshoe tie pin, bought it and stuck it in his tie. Well, he thought, I'll try this do-funny out anyway, and see what happens.

Rusty the engineer was a man of gigantic stature, strong, and a hard hitter if ever there was one. He had a reputation for being hard-boiled too. No fireman would stay with him. Their explanation was that he trimmed his engine so hard that they could not keep a fire in her. Well, he had to, for he was on the most important mail train on the division. It was always heavy, and had a tight schedule. This same Rusty was no fool. He knew what an engine could do, and set out to do business. The roundhouse staff never left anything to chance on 231, his particular engine. It was in great shape, and had lots of speed. Rusty did not believe in luck. Plain horse-sense was more to his idea.

Photo: Courtesy] [*Canadian National Railways.*

A Canadian National mail train at speed.

A spring saddle bolt on Rusty's engine had broken, and it was booked to be replaced. Rusty went to see if it was done, and found a mechanic working on it. The man did not see him, and as Rusty watched, he saw the mechanic making an imitation one out of hard grease. The tool he used was a pen-knife. My, was Rusty mad? With curses enough to scare the devil he went for that mechanic. Threatened to break his neck, and then some. Then he chased the man clean out of the roundhouse. The next scene took place in the boss's office. He tore around, swore, threatened to report the matter to the M.M., and made the foreman go with him to see the work of art. Oh, yes, there was a new one in place when Rusty took her out next time.

Rusty's fireman had quit, and a spare man had to take his place. No one wanted the job, but it fell to Jimmy, his name being first on the list to go out. When he took the call he thought this would be his last trip. He had heard so much about Rusty and how tough he was. Knowing the train he ran, it looked like the end for him. However there was no good thinking about what might happen. He had to go. The tie pin got an extra shine before Jimmy put it in his tie. "If ever I needed Lady Luck it's on this trip," thought Jimmy.

Jimmy arrived at the roundhouse early, signed on, and went out to look the engine over. With extra care he looked over supplies. Most times he had to beg, borrow or steal something, but on Rusty's engine he found everything in place. Soon Rusty arrived.

"Hello, son. How's things this morning?" was his greeting. Then he saw the tie pin all shined up. "What's the horseshoe for? 'Luck?" he asked.

"Yes," replied Jimmy. "I'm new to this game, and sure need luck. 'Specially on this run."

Rusty asked his name. "You'll get on O.K. Jimmy," he said. "I guess no one has really showed you how to fire? Eh?"

"If you can show me I'll only be too glad to learn," answered Jimmy.

"When I've oiled up, I'll just do that, mate." Rusty told him. "See that the tender is full of water, and look at the sand."

Jimmy did as he was told, and soon Rusty was back on deck.

"What kind of a fire do you use?" he asked Jimmy.

"What kind?" queried the fireman. "No particular kind. I've tried every way I know, and always had bad luck."

"There ain't any such thing as bad luck in firing. Horse-sense is what you want. I'll show you a kind of fire that can't be beat. If you catch on, Jimmy, you'll have all the steam we want."

Jimmy was pleased. He watched Rusty line the fire. Up both sides, and under the door.

"There now, what do you think of that?" asked Rusty. "Don't forget, none in the front, the blast will draw all you want there. That's the horseshoe fire. Never mind what I do, you just keep on making a horseshoe in the firebox, and see what happens."

Time was up. They pulled out of the roundhouse, and backed on to No. 20. Right on time they were away. Rusty certainly knocked the can off her, and Jimmy felt sure he would fall down. He kept on feeding her the way Rusty had showed him, and for once had the pleasure of seeing the steam gauge stay up. As speed increased Rusty hooked her up, and Jimmy got the fire banked. She went back five pounds, so Jimmy got the poker and cleaned the fire. Up she went again, and opened the pops.

"That's the stuff, kid," shouted Rusty. Jimmy usually got a calling down for letting an engine pop, and was expecting his mate to let out a roar when she went up. Faster, and faster, they went. Speed increased until it seemed the limit was reached. 231 rolled, shimmied, jumped, shook, and Jimmy found it hard to stay on his feet. When he went to swing a scoop of coal into the firebox, the door would be somewhere else than where he expected it to be, and the coal would fall on deck. It was hard work, but with a difference. Jimmy had steam on the mail, something he couldn't get on a freight run.

Rusty asked cheerily, "How'r' you doing kid?"

"The best I can," said Jimmy.

"And it's all right," shouted Rusty. Jimmy had a quiet laugh. He thought of what the boys had told him about the horseshoe. He would have some fun with them.

Everything went well. What Rusty had told him was true. With the system of draughting locomotives in that day, they would steam with this kind of fire, and Jimmy became Rusty's regular mate. Twenty arrived on time, and the return trip on twenty-one, was O.K. The boys were curious when they saw Jimmy staying on with Rusty. Several had been out with him, and swore that sooner than go again they would quit.

"How did you make out?" they asked Jimmy.

"Fine," he replied.

"How'd you do it, Jimmy?" They were interested.

"With a horseshoe" he said, and laughed quietly.

Reprinted from The Canadian National Railways Magazine, by permission.

Commencing the Miniature Railway Hobby

Hints for Hornby Train Owners

MANY readers will recently have become for the first time the proud owners of Hornby Train Sets and will be busy finding out how fast their locomotives will run and what loads they will pull. It is the object of this article to give a few hints that may help them to obtain the greatest possible fun from their new hobby.

The first step is to lay the track. This is quickly and easily done by joining the rails together by inserting the projecting pins of each rail section into the corresponding rail heads of the next. The pins must be pushed fully home so as to bring the rails close together. Except for the rails intended for MO Trains, all Hornby Rails are provided with special connecting plates, the object of which is to grip the sleepers adjacent to the rail joints and prevent the rails from moving apart and causing derailments.

When new track is laid down for the first time it is sometimes found that the rails, especially the curves, do not settle down flat on the table or floor. This is due to the natural springiness, common to all kinds of tinplate track. To get over the trouble, each rail in turn should be twisted over gently with the fingers towards the centre of the circle.

An interesting view of a passing station. On this section of miniature railway the inner tracks are for fast trains, the platforms of the station being served by the outer loop lines.

After performing this operation it is advisable to test the track. For this purpose there is packed with each Hornby Electric Train Set a Combined Rail Gauge, Screwdriver and Spanner. On one side of the centre portion of this, between the screwdriver blade and the spanner jaws, is a projection that is shaped to form a rail gauge. This part is made to fit exactly between the rails, and if it is slid along the track any tight places will be quickly discovered. In Clockwork Train Sets the back of the handle of the Locomotive winding key is shaped to form a gauge and is used in the same manner. At any tight places on the track the rails should be eased gently apart.

When using a Hornby Electric Railway it is important to see that the connections from the power supply to the track are correctly made according to the instructions packed in the Sets. A fuse is included to prevent damage in the event of an accidental short circuit. It consists of a length of special wire that melts with the excessive current when a short circuit occurs. A small amount of the correct wire is included with each Terminal Connecting Plate or Combined Switch Rail, and further supplies can be obtained from any Meccano dealer. The correct kind of wire is stated in the instructions, and it is very important that this should be used.

Lubrication is a subject that is often neglected. The working parts of Hornby Locomotives and Rolling Stock cannot be expected to work correctly and keep on doing so if they are run dry. On the other hand, they do not work any better for being flooded with oil, which is an extreme that is liable to be reached when boys get an oil can in their hands! Any excess of oil should be avoided, for it invariably finds its way on to the track and gives rise to slipping. It also attracts dust and dirt. Meccano Oil is of just the right consistency for the general lubrication of Hornby Locomotives and Rolling Stock, and details of the points requiring attention are given on the instruction leaflets.

Each axle bearing of the rolling stock should have just a drop of oil, and the wheels should be spun round to see that they are free. It sometimes happens that, in course of packing, the wheel frames become pressed against the wheels and so tend to prevent their free rotation. The frames should then be bent gently outward so that the wheels have just sufficient play for easy running.

For springs Meccano Graphite Grease is specially recommended and is available in handy tubes. It can be squeezed from the nozzle of the tube on the parts that can easily be reached. For those parts that are difficult to get at, the grease can be applied by means of a small paint brush.

A Locomotive, or indeed any mechanism, is inclined to be stiff in running when new. With careful attention to lubrication, and with regular use, the capacity of a new engine will be found to improve steadily until it becomes "run in" and capable of the heaviest duties.

Although the working parts of Accessories should be lubricated, it is not advisable to oil the mechanism of Hornby Points. The switch rails may be stiff when new but soon become easy to operate. If they are oiled, however, they become too free and liable to move and so cause derailments.

ELECTRIC RAILWAY OPERATION

THE interest in Hornby electrically-operated miniature railway systems continues to increase rapidly. Not only are existing clockwork lines undergoing conversion, but new systems, electrically-worked from the beginning, are daily springing into existence. The degree of control available and the possibility of incorporating such refinements as illuminated accessories appeal strongly to those who aim at the utmost realism. Although in most cases miniature electrically operated lines represent steam systems of actual practice and "steam-outline" locomotives are used, there is a growing interest in completely electric systems or those on which the locomotives in use are of the true electric type. For this reason a few words in regard to the possibilities of such schemes will be of interest to our readers. Let us assume therefore that our line is to be operated solely by electric-type engines and that the 20-volt system has been adopted for the power supply. With regard to the layout and accessories, etc., such a line will not differ greatly from the usual style of system operated by steam-type locomotives. We will deal first with motive power and rolling stock.

In the Hornby range of 20-volt Locomotives there is an important electric-type express engine, the LE220, which is an ideal unit for fast and heavy traffic on a miniature "all-electric" system. It is fitted for automatic reversing and among its characteristic details there are two dummy current collectors of the pantagraph type on the roof. These can be raised or lowered as required according to the conditions that are supposed to exist on the line. Hornby Electric Railways operate on the third rail system; some real lines have locomotives arranged for both conductor rail and overhead current collection so that the presence of the pantagraph on a model adds to the completeness and interest of the locomotive. A Hornby Locomotive supposed to be operating on a overhead wire section should have the pantagraphs raised to their normal position. If however the conductor rail section is being negotiated the pantagraphs should be lowered until they settle down on the roof.

With the LE220 Locomotive we can operate long-distance express trains as is done on the Continent and in America; but our equipment will probably be English in type for the most part, so that our miniature railway must be considered as a glimpse of possible future practice in this country. Standard main line trains of Hornby Pullman Coaches can be assembled much after the style of the famous *"Brighton Belle"* of the Southern Railway, except for the use of a separate locomotive. If we have a leaning to Continental traffic of a special nature, the Riviera "Blue" Coaches could also be employed with advantage. International services of an interesting character could be represented by the inclusion of British-type Pullmans with the "Blue" vehicles of the International Sleeping Car Co. The wide interests of this concern are suggested by the title that appears on the Hornby "Blue" Coaches, *"Compagnie Internationale des Wagons-Lits et des Grands Express Europeens."* In addition, for those who plan their systems on broad lines there are the "Mitropa" Cars that represent the vehicles now so familiar on main line service in Germany.

A suburban train hauled by a Hornby LE120 Locomotive leaving a station. The use of the various Dinky Toys components adds considerably to the realism of the illustration.

The British-type Pullmans are intended for ordinary day use only, in that they do not represent vehicles with facilities for night travel. On the other hand the Riviera "Blue" Coaches are available in two types, either as sleeping cars or dining cars, and the same also applies to the "Mitropa" vehicles. The corresponding German titles on the "Mitropa" Coaches are "Speisewagen" for the dining car and "Schlafwagen" for the sleeping car. The French vehicles show the international character of the service on which they run by being lettered both in English and in French, *"Voiture-Restaurant"* for the dining car, or *"Voiture-Lits"* for sleeping car.

Although separate electric locomotives are used to a small extent in this country it is possible that their use will increase in future as electrification systems become more "long-distance" in character.

Another famous type that is represented in the Hornby Series is the Metropolitan electric locomotive of the London Passenger Transport Board. This is of special interest in that it is included in the realistic Hornby Metropolitan Train Sets, accompanied by appropriate Coaches of the compartment type that are used on the real trains running on the service from the country districts through to the City. The locomotive is finished in the familiar red-brown livery and has quite an imposing appearance. Like all the Hornby Electric Locomotives that represent actual electric prototypes, it has headlights that light up from the train-driving current.

A goods yard scene on a Hornby Railway operated entirely by electric-type locomotives. The LE120 Locomotive shown is suitable for local passenger or goods work as required.

The Metropolitan Coaches are of two kinds, one a first class vehicle and the other a composite brake-third with guard's and luggage compartments at one end. Each of them is fitted for electric lighting and has a switch for putting the lights on and off as required. The current supply is taken direct to the lamps in the coaches from the third rail by means of roller collectors mounted on the bogies. The complete train has a most effective appearance, especially if operated after dark. It can be used to deal with the through traffic that its prototype carries on layouts representing the Metropolitan section of the London Transport organisation, or it can be used for the suburban services of an electric layout where main line traffic is operated by steam-type engines.

An all-Pullman express passing a wayside station. The locomotive is the Hornby LE220, which is intended for the operation of long-distance express trains on electrically-operated layouts.

Interesting schemes of working requiring electric and steam type locomotives can be developed in miniature. In actual practice steam locomotives owned by the former Metropolitan Railway work the trains previously mentioned to Rickmansworth, where the change-over from steam to electric traction, and vice versa, takes place. Here the electric type engine represented by the Hornby model comes on and hauls the train over the remainder of the journey on the surface lines and then underground. In the opposite direction of course the process is reversed. This working in itself is a scheme worthy of development by owners of Hornby Electric Railways.

In addition, the close association of the Great Central Section of the L.N.E.R. with the Metropolitan surface lines suggests still further possibilities in the matter of the variety of stock that can be used at once on the same layout. The running of Hornby L.N.E.R. Locomotives, No. 2 Coaches on local trains and No. 2 Saloons on express trains, on the same track as the Metropolitan Train will thus give a good representation of actual practice. As a point of interest it may be mentioned that a Pullman car is run on certain through trains on the Metropolitan service, so that a Hornby Pullman Coach will not be out of place on a composite layout of the kind we have been considering.

On systems that do not represent any particular prototype the LE120 Locomotive can be used very appropriately. Smaller than the LE220, and without the automatic reversing mechanism of the latter, the LE120 is of useful design and of characteristic "electric" outlines. It is fitted with dummy pantagraph collectors so that the same conditions of operation as described for the LE220 Locomotive will have to be assumed. The character of the engine renders it suitable for short-distance traffic, and of course for freight service. When it is used with the Hornby No. 1 or No. 2 Coaches quite an effective-looking train is the result. In this country the true suburban traffic of electric railways is operated by trains of the motor-coach type, as for instance those of the Southern Railway. This type of unit is not yet represented in the Hornby Series, but some readers may be interested in the scheme that is employed by one or two enthusiasts. This involves the making up a train of No. 2 Coaches, with brake-third vehicles at each end, a Metropolitan or LE120 Locomotive placed in the centre of the train providing the motive power. The train then can be propelled in either direction as required, just as a real multiple-unit train, thus avoiding the "running round" of the engine at terminal points. This arrangement allows the rail layout at terminal stations to be simplified, as no cross-over roads are required for "running round" purposes.

The LE120 Locomotive is very well suited for goods work, and as it is comparatively short it does not occupy much space in the sidings. Goods traffic over the electrified lines in the Newcastle area of the L.N.E.R. is handled by electric locomotives, and the Metropolitan type also can sometimes be seen on goods duties.

HORNBY RAILWAY COMPANY

A REAL RAILWAY COMPANY WITH BOY DIRECTORS AND OFFICIALS

How to Become a Member of the Hornby Railway Company

Every boy who possesses a Hornby Train Set should join the H.R.C. and thus become entitled to wear the badge of membership, which is beautifully enamelled in colours and has as its central feature a tiny representation of a train. All that he has to do is to fill in the application form—a copy of which is enclosed in every Train Set, or may be obtained from the Secretary of the H.R.C., Liverpool—and to return this together with a remittance of 6d. (overseas 10d.) to pay for the badge. Immediately on receipt of the completed form the applicant is enrolled as a member of this great organisation, and a handsome certificate to that effect is forwarded to him along with his badge.

Members of the H.R.C. are entitled to many privileges. The chief aim of the Company is to enable its members to get as much fun as possible from their miniature railways. This can best be done by helping them to make their layouts and operations as realistic as possible, and competent railway experts on the staff at Headquarters therefore are continuously engaged in advising members how to make the best use of the material at their disposal.

Join a Local Branch

The greatest fun is obtained from Hornby Trains by joining one of the many local Branches that have been formed in various parts of this and other countries. These Branches are composed of Hornby Train owners who meet together in order to carry out railway operations on a more extensive scale than is possible for a single individual. Every member should join a Branch immediately, or if one does not exist in his neighbourhood, he should try to induce other enthusiasts to help him to found one.

The Hornby Railway Company is a world-wide fellowship of Hornby Train owners, and was formed to enable members to get as much fun as possible from their miniature railways. Its President is Mr. Frank Hornby, inventor of Meccano, and Managing Director of Meccano Limited.

Write for full details to the Secretary, Hornby Railway Company, Binns Road, Liverpool, 13.

New Lighting System for Hornby Accessories

By "Tommy Dodd"

FOR some years a feature of the Hornby Series has been provision for the electric lighting of suitable Accessories. When illuminated they add greatly to the realism and charm of a miniature railway system and their fascinating effect naturally renders them very popular with Hornby Train owners. This season an important alteration has been made in the actual details of the lighting system. Under the original scheme the current is led from the 3.5 volt circuit of the T20A or T6A Transformer to a Distribution Box, by means of special connecting leads with plug and socket fittings, and from the Distribution Box similar leads radiate to the Accessories. Accessories for use in this way are still available for the benefit of those who already have extensive installations.

The new system, which is known as the Single-Pole Lighting System, eliminates the Distribution Box and the somewhat cumbersome method of wiring necessary with it. Instead of twin leads with plugs and sockets being required for each individual connection, the new wiring scheme is much more simple and when installed looks far neater than the old one. The wires and fittings are quite unobtrusive and do not tend to fill up the often restricted space available within the area served by the line.

A busy "night" scene in the goods yard of a Hornby Railway. The illumination of the Goods Platform and the use of the Lamp Standards gives a realistic representation of actual practice.

We will examine a typical Accessory wired up for the new system, say for example a Signal No. 2E. We find that instead of the plug fittings previously used there are two terminals on the base. One of these has a red washer beneath it and is wired to the lamp holder mounted on the signal post. This is the "live" terminal. The other has no washer and is the "earthing" terminal. The principle of the single-pole scheme is that as the Accessories are all connected to a common earth, their live terminals can be connected one after another, up to the capacity of the Transformer lighting circuit, and without the necessity for any special fittings such as a Distribution Box. The common earth in this case is the track itself, special clips to fix to the sleepers providing a convenient means of connection. A leaflet of instructions is packed with each Accessory.

The actual installation of a lighting system should of course commence with the Transformer, of which the third pair of sockets serves the lighting circuit. With the Transformers are packed two plug fittings, a special Earthing Clip and, as usual, a Fuse Unit. There is also a coil of wire for the purpose of making the lighting connections. A piece of wire is cut from the coil of a sufficient length to reach from the Transformer to the track. This forms the earthing wire, and one end of it is secured to an Earthing Clip by means of the terminal provided on these fittings. The Clip is then attached to one of the sleepers of the track. The other end of the wire is fitted into one of the plugs and secured by the set screw. The Fuse Unit is now plugged into the lower of the two Transformer sockets serving the lighting circuit, and the plug we have connected to the earthing wire is inserted in the socket end of the Fuse Unit.

The first Accessory to be connected will be the one that is nearest to the Transformer and a second piece of wire should now be cut of sufficient length to reach from it to the Transformer. One end of this wire is secured to the second plug and this is plugged into the upper socket of the third pair on the Transformer. The other end of the wire is taken to the live terminal of the Accessory, the one that has the red washer, and the terminal nut is then screwed up tightly.

We must now provide for an earth connection to the Accessory. Each Accessory has packed with it an Earthing Clip. This is attached to a convenient sleeper on the track and a piece of wire is then cut to reach from it to the earthing terminal of the Accessory. As soon as the final connection is made the lamp of the Accessory will now light up, provided that the wiring has been correctly carried out.

The foregoing description relates to a single Accessory. Where there are others to be lit up also, it is a simple matter to make the remaining connections. The live terminal of the second Accessory is connected to the live terminal of the first and so on in succession with the remaining Accessories up to the number that can be illuminated by the Transformer. This varies from 14 in the case of the T20A, to 18 for the T6A. Each additional Accessory has its earthing terminal connected to an Earthing Clip attached to the track at a convenient point near the Accessory.

Join the Hornby Railway Company and become eligible for the competitions announced on this page.

H.R.C. COMPETITION PAGE

Join the Hornby Railway Company and become eligible for the competitions announced on this page.

A MISSING WORDS CONTEST

H.R.C. members continue to show keen interest in the railway problems that are set before them each month on this page. On looking through the records for last year we find that among the most popular contests are those that afford the competitor an opportunity for displaying his knowledge of railway operations and practice, together with general knowledge and keenness in observation. Among the most successful of these have been those involving word-building or word-finding problems of railway interest, and this month we announce another contest of this type.

In the centre of this page is a panel containing four short paragraphs dealing with platelayers and their duties in the maintenance of Britain's railways. Certain words have been omitted from these paragraphs, and the place of each one is represented by a series of four dots. It should be noted that the number of dots bears no relation to the number of letters in the missing words.

Competitors are required to find the missing words, and write them down on a sheet of paper in the order in which they would appear in the paragraphs. It is not necessary to copy out the whole of the paragraphs. All the missing words are quite simple and straightforward, and there is no "catch" or anything unusual in the manner in which they are used.

Can You Find the Missing Words?

The . . . . and the men under his charge, known as platelayers, perform duties every day which, if neglected, might result in . . . . to our fast expresses. They have to . . . . their allotted length of . . . ., which is usually about . . . . miles in length, and replace any missing . . . . and tighten up any loose . . . . .

In the . . . . when great variations in temperature are usual with . . . . days and . . . . nights, it is the custom to remove the . . . . a pair at a time, oil or . . . . them, and then replace them. This assists the . . . . and . . . . of the rails and helps to prevent the closing up of the . . . . spaces between the rails, an . . . . that may cause . . . . up of the track on a . . . day.

A good . . . . on the rails is absolutely essential for smooth running, and the . . . . spends a great deal of his time on his . . . . with his eyes at . . . . level, in which position even the smallest bumps and hollows in the . . . . are easily seen.

On the L.M.S.R. gangers are each supplied with a quantity of . . . . chippings, kept in a wooden bin at the side of the . . . . at a convenient place in the length under his control. The . . . ., when carefully packed under the . . . . by means of a . . . ., enable the rails to be raised to their normal . . . . in places where . . . . occur.

The competition will be divided into two Sections—Home and Overseas. Prizes consisting of any products manufactured by Meccano Ltd., to the value of 21/–, 15/–, 10/6 and 5/– respectively will be awarded to the four competitors in each Section who submit the most correct and complete lists. In the event of a tie for any prize, neatness or novelty of presentation will be taken into consideration.

When as many as possible of the missing words have been found the competitor's name, address and H.R.C. membership number should be written plainly in the top right-hand corner of the sheet. This should then be enclosed in an envelope marked *"H.R.C. January Missing Words Contest"* and addressed to Meccano Ltd., Binns Road, Liverpool 13. The closing date for Home entries is 31st January and for Overseas entries 31st March. Entries received after these dates cannot be entertained.

Railway Photographic Contest

Since announcing the last Photographic Contest we have decided to continue the series during the winter months. Therefore we again offer prizes this month for the best photograph of *"Any Railway Subject."* Members may submit photographs that have been taken during the summer season, or prints of typical winter scenes. Entrants may send as many prints as they desire, but no competitor can receive more than one prize in the one contest. On the back of each entry submitted must be given the sender's name, age, full address and his H.R.C. membership number.

It is important also to include a brief reference to the subject of the photograph, giving in addition the place where the exposure was made.

The contest will be divided as usual into two sections, Home and Overseas. Prizes of any product manufactured by Meccano Ltd., to the value of 21/–, 15/–, 10/6 and 5/– respectively, will be awarded to the senders of the best entries submitted in each section.

Envelopes containing entries must be marked *"H.R.C. January Photographic Contest"* in the top left-hand corner and posted to reach Headquarters at Meccano Ltd., Binns Road, Liverpool 13, on or before 31st January. The closing date for the Overseas Section is 31st March.

Voting Contest

The competitions put forward on this page last year were immensely popular, and the response by H.R.C. members suggested that all subjects were favourites. In order to help us to decide what particular type of contest is most popular we are announcing this month a Voting Competition on this point. It will be interesting to see how the comparative popularity of the different kinds of contests is shown by the votes accorded to them by competitors.

Every entrant is required to state:

(1) Which of the 12 main H.R.C. Contests of 1935 was his favourite.

(2) What he considers are the eight most popular of these Contests in order of their popularity.

Prizes of any product manufactured by Meccano Ltd., to the value of 21/–, 15/–, 10/6 and 5/– respectively will be awarded to the four competitors in each section, Home and Overseas, who forecast the final order of voting most accurately. A number of consolation prizes also will be awarded.

Envelopes containing entries should be marked *"H.R.C. January Voting Contest"* and posted to reach Headquarters at Meccano Ltd., Binns Road, Liverpool 13, on or before 31st January. Overseas closing date 31st March. Membership numbers must not be omitted from entries.

COMPETITION RESULTS

HOME

October "Missing Links Contest."—First: R. LUMLEY (20253), Plymouth. Second: E. BEVEN (35158), Sheffield. Third: G. H. GILL (36093), Chorlton-cum-Hardy. Fourth: G. SNOOK (30716), Plymouth. Consolation Prizes: R. SUTTON (34561), Wolverhampton; D. V. C. BENTLEY (24591), Loughborough; J. B. SHELDON (2311), Sutton Coldfield; C. E. WRAYFORD (6039), Moretonhampstead; K. E. MILBURN (26029), London, E.4; S. D. WILLIAMS (33832), Dartmouth.

October "Railway Photo Contest."—First: D. KELK (28579), Staplehurst, Kent. Second: E. C. MORGAN (10735), London, S.W.18. Third: V. L. BREEZE (2134), Lewes. Fourth: G. L. WILSON (2478), Wormit-on-Tay. Consolation Prizes: G. H. MAHY (26134), London, S.W.19; D. NEWTON (38775), London, N.21; H. WEST (99), Newport, Mon.; H. SUTTON (32476), Leeds 6; J. NORRIS (18622), Worcester; J. R. W. KIRKBY (5954), Belmont, Surrey.

October "Articles Suggestions Contest."—First: J. F. SHARPE (35752), Leeds 6. Second: D. T. WHITE (42549), Knebworth, Herts. Third: B. HARDIE (6792), Bristol 9. Fourth: R. W. GOODFELLOW (3593), Longbenton. Consolation Prizes: L. PARISH (18054), Coventry; J. L. MAKIN (30933), Preston; E. H. FREWIN (25098), Birmingham; J. B. SHELDON (2311), Sutton Coldfield.

OVERSEAS

July "Silhouettes Contest."—First: I. BROUGH (9112), Preston, Australia. Second: W. B. MOORE (20918), Toronto. Third: R. A. WRAGG (7913), Bandikui, India. Fourth: P. GALDES (14183), Malta. Consolation Prizes: D. E. YOCKNEY (39969), Auckland, New Zealand; W. JACK (8958), Ballarat East, Australia.

July "Railway Photo Contest."—First: M. CONLY (24290), Dunedin, New Zealand. Second: J. A. COATES (23863), St. Lambert, Canada. Third: H. GOODISON (42769), B.C., Canada. Fourth: K. F. CALDWELL (17284), S. Brisbane, Australia.

Branch News

PATRICROFT.—A new development has been the institution of a regular Social Evening each week. A Cup has been presented by an enthusiastic member, and it will be competed for monthly in indoor games. A Branch Library has been started, and the walls of the Branch Room have been decorated appropriately with railway posters. Discussions on railway topics have been held. Various improvements have been made, including the installation of electricity on the Branch track. A visit has been paid to the local engine sheds. It is hoped that a trip to the works of Nasmyth Wilson & Co. Ltd., will shortly be arranged. Secretary: A. Howarth, 42, Nelson Street, Patricroft, Nr. Manchester.

KIDDERMINSTER.—The Sixth Annual Exhibition has been a great success and the proceeds have been devoted to the installation of a new heating system in the Branch premises. Various developments have been taking place on the track, including the ballasting of a large portion. At each meeting from 40 to 50 boys can be employed on the line, and each is allotted specific duties. Practical tests are held from time to time and promotion is decided on the results. The bell code is used for signalling trains, and an unusual development has been the formation of an overhead goods yard, rendering one of the stations in effect a "low-level" one. A special campaign has been launched to increase the membership of the Branch. Regular visits are exchanged with neighbouring H.R.C. Branches and with Meccano Clubs. Secretary: E. Haines, "Yeoland," Stourport Road, Bewdley.

ST. THOMAS (EXETER).—A move has been made to a new Branch Room that is more central in situation than the former one. Before removal, however, train services were run at several meetings with great success. The track has been relaid in the new room, on a much longer table. The Branch continues to flourish, and visits are exchanged with the neighbouring Elmside (Exeter) Branch. The two Branches collaborated successfully in a "Meccano Motor Show" held last month, the proceeds being divided between the two Branches. Secretary: L. J. Robinson, 9, Union Street, St. Thomas, Exeter.

WARDEN HOUSE (UPPER DEAL).—Experimental running has been carried out with various layouts, and the advantages and disadvantages of different formations have been noted with a view to producing a perfect track. An exciting feature has been the holding of locomotive tests over layouts having several parallel tracks. The accommodation of the Branch Room is somewhat restricted, and arrangements are to be made for members to operate the layout in groups at different times. Secretary: H. M. Anderson, Warden House, Upper Deal.

NORTHAMPTON.—A Branch library has been instituted, and regular games nights are held. As a result of tests and some experimental working, timetable operation is now carried out regularly, and very few mishaps are experienced. It is proposed to elevate the Branch track to a raised foundation. One of the members gave the first part of an interesting talk on the *"Severn Tunnel,"* which was greatly enjoyed. Debates on various subjects, also an exhibition, are being arranged. Secretary: D. K. Adams, 8, Cedar Road, Northampton.

NEW SOUTHGATE.—Members have visited Paddington Station, and were allowed to observe all the more important features of working. Special interest was taken in the signalling arrangements, although entrance to the signal cabins was not permitted. Track meetings continue to be a success, and a new departure was made recently when an evening was devoted to the examining and testing of miniature steam locomotives. The Second Exhibition of the Branch is to be held this month, as announced at the foot of this page. Secretary: A. R. Wardle, 25, Limes Avenue, London, N.11.

FIRST SHEFFIELD.—Pressure of traffic has resulted in the permanent division of the fastest train on the Branch layout into two sections. These are respectively *"The Norseman Limited"* and *"The Northerner."* General rules for the conduct of Branch affairs have been formulated and a special set of rules now govern track operations. Constructional work on the part of members is encouraged and, in addition to the repainting of several locomotives in the special Branch livery, the building of coaches is to be undertaken. A visit has been paid to Retford to see *"The Silver Jubilee"* and *"The Yorkshire Pullman"* expresses. Secretary: W. B. Hutchinson, 35, Linden Avenue, Sheffield, 8.

KING'S ROAD SCHOOL.—Track layouts and operations have been given chief attention recently. Members of the Branch have been specially instructed in the care of locomotives and rolling stock, also in the laying down of different rail formations. Secretary: H. A. Argent, 15, Park Avenue, Chelmsford, Essex.

Members of the Sedbergh Preparatory School Branch, No. 289. President, Mr. A. L. Gladstone; Chairman, Mr. F. C. Bazett-Jones. This Branch was incorporated in May, 1935; special attention has been given to the development of the Branch layout, including the provision of lighting for Hornby Accessories.

EXHIBITION AT NEW SOUTHGATE, N.11.

An interesting exhibition organised by the New Southgate Branch of the Hornby Railway Company will be held on the 11th of this month at the Friends Meeting House, Waterfall Road, New Southgate. It will be opened from 3 p.m. to 7–30 p.m., and the charge for admission will be: Adults 3d. Children 2d.

Branches in Course of Formation

The following new Branches of the Hornby Railway Company are at present in process of formation, and any boys who are interested and desirous of linking up with this unique organisation should communicate with the promoters, whose names and addresses are given below.

ALTON—G. A. Eady, 5, Old Acre Road, Alton.

BIRMINGHAM—R. W. Hunt, 37, Weatheroak Road, Sparkhill.

DURHAM—R. Straughan, "Ancroft," Geoffrey Avenue, Neville's Cross.

SHIPLEY—Mr. R. T. Hopkinson, 14, Victoria Road, Saltaire.

Branches Recently Incorporated

294. SOUTHPORT—D. B. Moss, 141, Forest Road, Southport.

295. DUBLIN—Mr. S. B. Carse, 38 Oakley Road, Ranelagh, Dublin.

SETS (POSTAGE EXTRA)

10 Dutch Indies	2d.	5 Azores	2d.
20 „ „	4d.	10 „	5d.
30 „ „	8d.	15 „	8d.
10 Tunis	3d.	5 Sierra Leone	3d.
20 „	7d.	4 India Jubilee	6d.
30 „	1/–	4 Abyssinia	3d.
10 Ceylon	2d.	5 Persia	2d.
20 „	6d.	10 „	4d.
30 „	10d.	10 China	2d.
5 Syria	2d.	10 Japan	2d.
10 „	5d.	4 Borneo	3d.
15 „	8d.	5 Mozambique	2d.
5 Gold Coast	3d.	10 „	5d.
10 „ „	6d.	5 Colombia	2d.

J. RUSSELL

23, Shanklin Drive, Westcliff-on-Sea

NYASSA TRIANGLES! EGYPT AIR MAILS ! ! PICTORIALS ! ! ! 124 STAMPS 6d.

Including set of unused **Nyassa Triangles.** Set of **Egypt 1933 Air Mails** showing aeroplane flying over Pyramids. **15 Canada** including **Jubilee** and **Ottawa Conference** issues. Interesting **Brazil 1933 Airport Fund** stamp. **Roumania 1931 Aviation** stamps showing monoplane. Other stamps include unused air mails, surcharged issues and pictorials. All different. **Price 6d.** Other offers: **23** different **Jubilee** stamps, **2/–. 110** different **British Colonials** (Cat. value 15/–), **9d. (Postage 1½d. extra on all orders.)** Money and all postage will be returned if not satisfactory. We have numerous other offers at low prices. Hundreds of unsolicited testimonials have been received.

W. BENNETT
53, MARLBOROUGH ROAD, LONDON, E.8

QUEEN ASTRID Mourning Packet FREE!

Actually contains the beautiful portrait stamp issued to perpetuate the memory of Belgium's lovely Queen, whose tragic death shocked the world. Also a stamp depicting her husband, King Leopold, and the famous mourning stamp of King Albert. Nearly 60 different, including old Belgium, British Colonials and mint Russian stamps. Finally a large unused Colonial and the popular and unique Balloon stamp. All absolutely free. Just send 2d. postage requesting approvals, and new 1936 Catalogue. You get the best gifts and stamps from:

LISBURN & TOWNSEND LTD. (Dept. M.M.), Liverpool, 3

FREE WONDERFUL 1936 OFFER 25 NEW ISSUES AND NOVELTIES

Including **Andorra** (1935), fine new **Cayman Islands** (map of the Islands), obsolete Austria, China, Denmark, **Gwalior** Service, Hungary (Statesman Szechenyi), **new Kenya** (Kavirondo Cranes), **Roumania** (new portrait of King Carol), and many others. I will send this collection **absolutely free** to all stamp collectors sending 2d. postage (abroad 4d.).

G. P. KEEF, Willingdon, EASTBOURNE

No stamp collector should miss the opportunity of securing a free copy of **Whitfield King's Price List of Sets and Packets, 1936** Edition, just published. 156 pages absolutely up to date and contains, amongst other interesting features, an immense number of bargain offers at prices from a few pence. Make sure of your copy by sending a postcard now to:

WHITFIELD KING & CO., IPSWICH, SUFFOLK Established 1869

"DIAMONDS" ARE TRUMPS!

Thousands of "*M.M.*" readers have discovered this. **WHY NOT YOU?**

The **"DIAMOND" PACKET** contains approx. **1,000 UNSORTED STAMPS** from Convents abroad, and **MANY RARE STAMPS** have been found in it. 1 pkt., **1/6**; 3 pkts., **3/9**; 5 pkts., **6/–**. All post free inland. (Colonies 3d. per pkt. extra. Foreign, 6d.)

O. NERUSH (Dept. M.), 68, Turnpike Lane, Hornsey, LONDON, N.8

This marvellous packet is offered under cost as an advertisement, **45 different stamps each with a ship on it.** A regular armada. **GABOON**, a rare **FOOCHOW** (War Canoe), wonderful flotilla of caravels from**DENMARK**(completeset),**ITALY** (Naval Academy), **NEW CALEDONIA, IVORY COAST, COSTA RICA,** a fleet of **7 CHINESE** junks usually sold at 10d., **TRINIDAD & TOBAGO, MAURITIUS, SOUTH WEST AFRICA, NEWFOUNDLAND, U.S.A., B. GUIANA,** set of **S. AFRICA, GREECE, POLAND, INDO-CHINA,** etc. Price **4½**d., postage **1½**d. (abroad 3d. extra). Purchasers of this packet asking for approvals receive **FREE** set of **4 SPAIN** (Columbus, each with his ship on it). Senders of addresses of stamp collectors receive **FREE** set of **6 VENEZUELA** or **6 PERSIA, 100 BRITISH COLONIALS 1/–, 20 AIRPORT 6d., 6 TRIANGULARS 6d. VOLUMES OF B.O.P. CHEAP.**

H. C. WATKINS (M. Dept.), Granville Road, BARNET

FREE! 100 British Colonials

Don't miss this wonderful gift offer. Detailed list impossible. Send and see for yourself. To all genuine applicants for cheap attractive approvals, enclosing 1½d. post.
R. KIPPEN, 52, Cowley Road, Leytonstone, E.11.

100 DIFFERENT STAMPS FREE to applicants for ½d. approvals.—Cox, 21, Dennis Mansions, Westcliff.

SEND FOR FINE SELECTION, foreign or colonial stamps on approval, from ½d. Free packet to purchasers.—Sellick, Forde, Newton Abbot.

Common and Rare Stamps

Bargain Hunters' Approvals. Pick attractive space-fillers or rare items from ⅛ to ⅛ S. G. Cat. **You will come again!**
CAMPBELL, Halden Avenue, Teignmouth.

ONE THOUSAND STAMPS ON APPROVAL

From which you may select any 100 for 3/–.
This selection is not made up of the very commonest varieties, but contains stamps catalogued at 1/– each or more. (I do not sell less than 100.)
Special offer: 10 fine used PERAK, SELANGOR and SUNJEI UJONG, Cat. 5/6, for 1/–, post free.
H. HARDY, "Hoyland," Potter Heigham, Norfolk.

"BLUE MURDER" PACKET FREE!!

This interesting packet contains a number of stamps bringing to mind world-famous assassinations. The high value **ITALY** Ferrucci commem. (from which the packet takes its name), the complete set of **BOSNIA** (commemorative of the assassination of Archduke Ferdinand), **JUGO-SLAVIA** (King Alexander), **U.S.A.** (President Lincoln), **ITALY** (Julius Cæsar). Included also is a selection of mint stamps from **MOZAMBIQUE, SYRIA** (pictorial), **FINLAND, TURKEY** (surcharged), etc., and used British Colonials including a **SILVER JUBILEE.** The packet is free **only** to those who request approvals and send 2d. postage (abroad 1/–).
Hely. Hutchinson (M.5), Hurrock Wood, Kents Bank, Grange-over-Sands.

ALL BRITISH COLONIAL APPROVALS

Fine **BRITISH COLONIAL PICTORIAL SETS OF CAYMAN ISLANDS & GAMBIA FREE** to all Collectors sending 1½d. stamp and requesting **ALL BRITISH COLONIAL APPROVALS, BRITISH COLONIALS ONLY** on approval at bargain prices, including Jubilee issues, West Indians, East and West Africa, Cyprus, Gibraltar, Iraq, Samoa, and many other fine Colonials. (No stamps sent abroad.)
C. H. SHAW (Dept. M1), 95, CHRISTCHURCH AVENUE, KENTON, HARROW.

FREE!! "LOCO" SET AND ENGINEERING PACKET

Many different stamps, showing Aeroplanes, Engines, Pyramids, Palaces, Ruins, Castles, Ships, Steamers, Windjammers, Junks, Statues, Schools, Mosques and Churches from Brazil, Egypt, **Turkey, Morocco, Greece,** China, **U.S.A.** (Statue of Liberty), **Algeria,** Set of **3 Charkhari, Martinique, Caledonia, Niger, Tunis,** etc. **ALSO** a fine packet of **50 all different stamps. ALL ABSOLUTELY FREE.** Just enclose 2d. postage, **requesting Approvals.**
SHOWELL BROS., 42, Vanbrugh Hill, LONDON, S.E.3.

SPECIAL OFFERS

6 MONGOLIA (Cat. 3/4) ... ... **7d.**
3 GREAT BRITAIN, K.G., 2/6, 5/– & 10/– ... **1/6**
JUBILEES—(Few only), all different:
Mint and Used: 15 **1/3**; 25 **2/4**; 40 **4/9**
Mint ... 10 **1/–**; 20 **2/6**; 30 **4/6**
Mint Sets: Antigua, Barbados, Bermuda **2/6,** Ascension, Jamaica, Gibraltar **2/11**
NEW ISSUE APPROVALS—A SPECIALITY.
Cash with order. Post extra.
T. R. HUGHES, 7, WINCHESTER ROAD, N.W.3.

EVERY COLLECTOR NEEDS THIS ILLUSTRATED BOOK

Zoo in a Stamp Album—Ship Stamps—Watermarks—The Aerodrome—Single Country Collections—Olympic Games—Loose-Leaf Albums—Earthquake Stamps—Washing Day in the Stamp World—Three-cornered Market Place—British Empire Albums—Rare Stamps—Overprints and Surcharges—To Correspondents Abroad—Treasure Trove—Triangular Packets—Packets of British, French, Italian, Portuguese, Spanish and German Colonials—Building a Collection—West Indian Packets—Triangular Stamps—Philately Royal—Albums for Beginners—Penny Sets—English Men on Foreign Stamps—Emergency Papers—Shilling Sets—Advertising Stamps—Strip Pocket Books—Glossary—Stamp Tongs—Punctured Officials—etc., etc., etc. These are only a few Headings out of my **NEW SIXTY-PAGE BOOK,** which is **WELL ILLUSTRATED THROUGHOUT** and so full of the right sort of useful and interesting Philatelic information that **EVERY STAMP COLLECTOR MUST HAVE THIS BOOK,** FREE and POST FREE from

EDWARD SANDELL, 10, EVELYN GROVE, SOUTHALL, MIDDLESEX, ENGLAND.

For other stamp advertisements see pages 64 and xx

BRIDGES ON STAMPS

In our article last month we dealt with the interest to be derived from forming collections of stamps dealing with particular subjects, and we promised to deal in detail with one or two such subjects to illustrate the possibilities in greater detail.

Engineering topics naturally lie closest to the hearts of Meccano boy stamp collectors and we have chosen "Bridges" as a typical engineering subject, providing ample scope for forming a special collection.

There are altogether approximately 100 stamps illustrating bridges—none of them expensive—and with these it is possible to build up a fairly complete story of the development of the art of bridge building from the primitive suspension bridge, constructed of logs bound by ropes of fibre, used by native tribes to cross forest streams, up to giant modern engineering achievements such as the Sydney Harbour Bridge.

As we have commented, the stamp story will only be fairly complete. Obviously the great bulk of the stamps available are representative of modern types and there are no stamps at all to show the earliest forms, consisting of simple slabs of rock, or logs, rolled into position across narrow streams.

This type of bridge was the forerunner of the modern girder bridge, laid on stone piers, such as that spanning the Kizil Irmak in Asia Minor, shown on the Turkish postal dues issues of 1926. One of the largest bridges of this type spans the Hawkesbury River in New South Wales. This has seven spans, each approximately 416 ft. in length.

The pontoon bridge illustrated on the 5 lei value of Roumania's 1914 issue is another type of bridge that has been widely used since early times. The design shows a Roumanian force crossing the Danube in the course of their victorious campaign against Bulgaria. It will be seen that the bridge has been formed by anchoring boats in the river and laying planking across from boat to boat. The principle employed is a very old one, and there exist records of the passage of the army of Darius Hystapes, 600,000 strong, across the Bosphorus about 530 B.C. The pontoon bridge in that instance was 3,000 ft. in length! An even earlier instance is recorded by Homer, who tells of a pontoon bridge constructed in 800 B.C. by Cyrus, King of the Persians. In this instance stuffed skins were used as floats.

The 1 franc denomination of the French Somali Coast issue of 1915 illustrates a typical modern trestle bridge, a type used for short spans in country where difficulties of transporting other material make it impossible to construct more modern types of bridges. An abundant supply of big timber, a natural bridge-building material, being easily accessible, the popularity of the trestle bridge in Canada and the United States is readily understood. Indeed, the frequency with which such bridges are encountered makes them a feature of the North American Continent.

One of the most striking bridges on the North American Continent is the steel over-arch bridge spanning the River Niagara, 1,000 ft. below the famous Falls. This bridge is shown on the 5 cent. value of the U.S.A. 1901 issue, which we illustrated with our stamp article last month, commemorating the Pan-American Exhibition at Buffalo. The bridge crosses the gorge at a height of 190 ft. above water, and has a roadway 47 ft. in width and a total span of 1,240 ft. It is the third bridge to occupy this site, and was opened in August, 1893, to replace a suspension bridge that had stood for 40 years.

The most striking arch bridge in our collection, however, is the famous Sydney Harbour Bridge, to commemorate the opening of which Australia issued a special stamp in 1932. It took eight years to build, and its total cost was approximately £9,000,000. With a main span of 1,650 ft. and a clearance above high water of 172 ft., it is indeed the mightiest over-arch bridge in the world.

Another great Empire bridge that must be accorded a prominent place in the collection is the cantilever bridge crossing the St. Lawrence river at Quebec in Canada. Its main spans have a total length of 1,800ft., while the weight of the centre span is over 5,500 tons. This bridge was featured on Canada's 12 cent. stamp of 1928, one of the most popular pictorial stamps ever produced.

The appearance of rugged strength that this bridge gives hides an almost incredible story of disaster in its construction. In 1907, when construction was first nearing completion, the centre span tore loose as it was being hoisted into position and 100 steel workers were pitched into the river. In 1916, after modifications of the design had been carried out, another section failed, and it was not until September, 1917, that the centre span was safely bolted into position.

The $2 value of the U.S.A. trans-Mississippi Exhibition series of 1896, shows the St. Louis Bridge spanning the Mississippi. This bridge has a special claim to fame in that its construction marked what might be termed the commencement of the era of the steel bridge. Prior to 1867, the year in which the St. Louis Bridge was commenced, steel had been used in bridge building only to a very small extent. The total span of this bridge is 1,700 ft., and it has three main arches crossing the river, the centre one being 520 ft. in length and those on either side 502 ft.

Another interesting bridge is on the 5c. value of Uruguay's issue of 1930

(*Continued on page 63*)

WINTER SPORTS

STAMPS FROM GERMANY

Brand-new set issued for the Winter Olympic Games in the Bavarian Alps next month. Thrilling designs showing ski-ing, skating and bob-sleighing by members of the German National Team. Full set of 3 stamps, mint, **1/6**

THE NEW CHRISTMAS STAMPS

Fine new issues to double the interest and attractiveness of your album. Get them **now** at their cheapest prices.

Set No. 4489 BELGIUM. Beautiful portrait of the tragic Queen Astrid. Stamps in various colours with black mourning borders. 10c. to 2.45 francs. Complete, 7 unused, **1s. 8d.**

Set No. 4481 GERMANY. National Costume. Ten brilliant designs, 3 pf. to 40 pf. values. Complete set, 10 unused, **5s. 6d.**

Set No. 4500 LUXEMBURG. Charles IV, mediæval knight and Holy Roman Emperor—one of the most famous sons of the little Duchy of Luxemburg. 10c. to 1.75 francs. Complete, 6 unused, **2s.**

Set No. 4490 SWITZERLAND. Latest of the famous "Pro Juventute" sets, the best-known of the special Christmas series. 5c. to 30c. Complete, 4 unused, **1s. 8d.**

All prices are "postage extra."

WRITE FOR FULL LIST

of brilliant stamp bargains—sent FREE!

A NEW YEAR'S RESOLUTION **Buy GIBBONS' STAMP MONTHLY regularly each month during 1936. It makes you get a real kick out of collecting. Send 4d. for specimen number.**

THE MODEL SHOP LEADS AGAIN!

THE FIRST FLYING SCALE MODEL OF THE FAMOUS

POU-DU-CIEL (Flying Flea)

21" Span

A perfect miniature which flies beautifully.

Construction Set containing everything necessary to build a Model identical with the illustration.

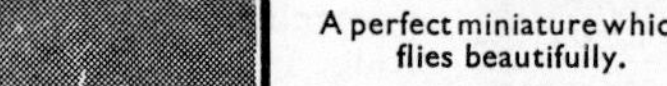

7/6 plus 6d. Carriage

Abroad, Postage 2/6 (dope not included).

ALL BRITISH "KEELBUILD" Construction Sets

Without question the finest kits on the market to-day. The revolutionary "KEELBUILD" system simplifies building, whilst the completed models are a joy to behold. What's more we guarantee them to fly—45 secs. is an average flight.

The kits contain absolutely everything necessary to build and include dope.

Mod. "HAWKER SUPER FURY" 22" Span
"ARROW ACTIVE" ... ... 24" Span
"PFALZ DXII" ... ... 22" Span
10/6 each plus 9d. carriage

LOCKHEED-VEGA ... ... 36" Span
30/- plus 1/- carriage
(Abroad 2/6 postage, dope not included)

New 12-page Catalogue, profusely illustrated, 2d. post free

1/6 HOMEBUILD 1/6 Construction Sets

SCALE FLYING MODELS

Puss Moth, Polish Fighter, S.E.5 Scout, Stinson Reliant, Fokker DVIII, Curtiss Goshawk, Monocoupe, Waco "C", Sparrow Hawk, Fairchild 24, Sopwith Camel, Boeing L.W., Fokker Triplane, Baby R.O.G., Boeing P.12.E.

12-in. to 15-in. Wing Span, **1/6** each, post free

Monocoupe, Waco Cabin, S.E.5 Scout, Boeing 247, Supermarine S.6, Curtiss Swift, Spad Chasseur, Sparrow Hawk, Texaco Sky Chief

16-in. to 22-in. Wing Span, **5/6** each, post free

Kits for SCALE AEROPLANES, GALLEONS and HISTORIC SHIPS, over 80 types **10d., 1/6, 2/9** and **10/6** per set, post free

THE MODEL SHOP
3, College Road, Barras Bridge, Newcastle-upon-Tyne

MODEL AIRCRAFT

All Warneford airplanes are scientifically designed with the necessary strength-weight ratio to withstand hard usage yet give a maximum performance.

"IMP" For long duration flights. Weight ratio is reduced to a minimum in this model to give the utmost duration of flight. Span 20⅝". Flying speed 1,098 ft. per min. Distance 800 ft. Ceiling 60 ft. **4/6** complete

"TERROR" A superb new fuselage model of a Fighter Aircraft with correct colours and markings. Span 18½". Flying speed 1,230 ft. per min. Distance 300 ft. Ceiling 30 ft. **5/6** complete

"DEMON" The monoplane with an exceptional performance. The best model for stunting—loops, rolls, banked turns, etc. Span 23". Flying speed 1,410 ft. per min. Distance 900 ft. Ceiling 80 ft. **7/6** complete

"SWIFT" For long distance flying and ease of control this machine is unbeatable. Span 26½". Flying speed 1,230 ft. per min. Distance 1,127 ft. Ceiling 80 ft. **10/6** complete

THE WARNEFORD "PARA-SHOOTER" (Patent No. 371,470).
Designed on new principles it is blown from a tube and makes a most realistic descent. Price 1/-

Other models **1/6** to **5 Gns.**
Sold by leading Stores, Toy Shops and Sports Dealers throughout the world.
Full illustrated Price List Post Free on application.

WARNEFORD FLYING AIRCRAFT, GREENWICH, LONDON, S.E.10

MECCANO

TWO-SEATER SPORTS CAR

A MOST REALISTIC MODEL

This splendid built-up model represents the modern sports two-seater, a type of car that combines speed and excellent road-holding qualities, and has become increasingly popular during recent years. Speed is suggested by the sweeping lines of the bodywork and mudguards, together with the sloping radiator and wind-screen.

The model faithfully resembles its prototype in all important respects. It is complete in itself, no constructional or assembly work being required. It steers from the wheel, and is fitted with a strong clockwork motor that gives a long and steady run.

Overall dimensions: Length, 8¼ in.; Width, 3¾ in.; Depth 2⅞ in.

Price **6/6**

The model is beautifully made and finished, and is available in three different colours—Red, Blue and Cream

Manufactured by
Meccano Ltd., Binns Rd., Liverpool 13

Stamp Gossip

and Notes on New Issues

Queen Astrid Mourning Stamp

The poignant feelings of the Belgian people at the tragic death of their beautiful young Queen Astrid, who, our readers will remember, was killed in a motoring accident in August last, are most strikingly symbolised in the beautiful special mourning stamp illustrated here.

The stamp is printed in black by the photogravure process, and is taken direct from a recent portrait of the Queen. It bears a premium of 5c. on its face value, 70c., this being devoted to anti-tuberculosis campaign funds.

Boulder Dam Commemorative

Among the many subjects that have been chosen for commemoration in the flow of special stamps from the U.S.A. in recent years, few have possessed the interest attaching to the Boulder or Hoover Dam in the Black Canyon on the Colorado River, shown on the U.S. 3c. stamp issued in September last to celebrate the opening of the dam by President Roosevelt.

The Boulder Dam must rank with the greatest of the world's engineering feats, and the quickest appreciation of its importance can be gained from the following facts of its size. At the base it is 650 ft. in thickness and at the top 45 ft. Its weight is estimated to be 6½ million tons and it will raise the level of the river backing up behind to a height of 590 ft. The impounded water will form a lake stretching back 113 miles from the dam and having a depth of 120 ft. outside the Black Canyon.

Jubilee Stamps

The demand for the Silver Jubilee stamps issued by the Crown Colonies, which remained on sale up to the end of last month, was so very heavy—in Singapore alone more than 1,600,000 of the 5 cent. Malayan issue were sold—that it was found necessary to make reprints of the whole series for 13 of the Colonies, and to make reprints of different values for another 23 Colonies.

All Jubilee stamps are obsolete now.

The 1935 Pro Juventute Issue

The annual Swiss *Pro Juventute* issue this year features portraits of typical girls from the Basel, Lucerne and Geneva cantons on the three low values, 5c., 10c. and 20c. respectively, and, in accordance with custom, the high value, 30c., is devoted to an eminent savant. This year Stefano Franscini (1796-1857) is chosen.

The 10c. and 20c. values are illustrated at the head of this page.

* * * *

A special stamp issue appeared last month to celebrate the Silver Jubilee of H.E.H. the Nizam of Hyderabad. The issue contains four stamps with designs as follows: 4pi., Unani Hospital; 8pi., Osmani General Hospital; 1a., University Building; 2a., Jubilee Hall.

* * * *

Poland's new 15 gr. stamp provides an attractive addition to the list of shipping stamps. It was issued to celebrate the commencement of the maiden voyage of the motor ship *"Pilsudski,"* of the Gdynia-America Shipping Company, operating between Poland and the United States.

The *"Pilsudski"* is one of two vessels ordered by the Company from the Monfalcone shipyards in Italy, but the second ship has been commandeered by the Italian Government for war service.

Whitfield King 1936 List

Every keen stamp collector should possess himself of a copy of Messrs. Whitfield King and Company's 1936 price list. Like the firm's annual catalogue this price list is growing rapidly in size, and the 1936 edition—the 67th annual list, by the way—contains over 150 pages, of which more than 130 are devoted to listing a remarkably complete range of long and short sets of interest to all collectors.

In addition to sets and packets of individual countries, Messrs. Whitfield King this year have introduced a range of new pictorial packets that will be of special interest to readers who are considering the compilation of a subject collection on the lines suggested in our stamp article last month.

Messrs. Whitfield King and Company, of Ipswich, tell us they will be glad to send a copy of this list, free of charge, to any *"M.M."* reader who applies for one.

Humour in Stamp Designs

The designer of New Zealand's Health Charity stamps is clearly a humorist. Only a year or two ago he perpetrated a stamp pun in using the slogan "Help Stamp out Tuberculosis" on an anti-tuberculosis fund issue. This year he shows us sunshine, the Key to Health, through a keyhole—and provides an unusually attractive design.

Incidentally, the portrait is an actual photograph taken on the beach at Paraparaumu.

Stamp Collecting—

(*Continued from page 61*)

marking the centenary of independence. This features a modern multi-span bridge across the Rio Negro. Uruguay is so proud of this bridge that when it was decided to issue this series of commemorative stamps, the Rio Negro bridge was an almost automatic choice for the first design.

The best example of communal pride in bridges comes from the Dominican Republic, where the completion of the building of a series of bridges was marked by three distinct issues of stamps, two in 1934 and one in 1935. Each of the 1934 issues contained three stamps, the first series featuring the San Rafael Suspension bridge, the largest in the West Indies. The ½c. value is illustrated here. The second series showed the Trujillo bridge, a trussed girder bridge across the Rio Yuna. The 1935 issue commemorated the opening of the Ramfis Suspension bridge across the Rio Higuamo.

In a short article such as this it is, of course, impossible to describe in detail all the bridges that appear on stamps, or indeed to mention more than a few of the stamps that are worthy of special attention, but readers who are desirous of forming a collection of bridge stamps, and who wish to secure more details, are invited to get in touch with the Editor, who will be happy to help them further.

We thank Stanley Gibbons Ltd. for their courtesy in loaning the stamps from which the illustrations for our stamp pages have been made.

THE JUBILEE PACKET

contains 100 different Superior stamps only (NO unused German); here are just a few of the fine stamps included: **SILVER JUBILEES** from **Jamaica, Canada,** King and Queen, **Ceylon,** 2 **Indian** and **Australia,** Anzac; also **NEW CEYLON** 2c. and 3c. pictorials; a large **Mozambique AIR MAIL;** ½d. and 1d. New Zealand **pictorials; EGYPTIAN AIR MAIL;** New **TANGANYIKA** unused; Br. **NYASALAND** ½d. and 1d. pictorials; **Scarce BR. GUIANA Centenary;** Belgium **Centenary;** Set of 5 **IRAQ,** pictorials and **King Ghazi,** etc.; China **Sun Yat Sen;** Swiss **Disarmament** and many other attractive stamps. Price 1/-, postage 1½d. Money refunded if dissatisfied. **THE PUKKA STAMP CO., 27, Normandy Avenue, BARNET.**

The "TRANSPORT" Packet

contains a wonderful assortment of 44 all different Foreign and Colonial stamps and includes the following which depict various means of transportation: **TUNIS** (Water Carrier), **JAMAICA** (Troopship), **MADAGASCAR** (Native Transport), **GREECE** (Steamer), **INDO-CHINA** (Boat), **MAURITANIA** (Crossing Desert), **TRANSVAAL** (Waggon), **BRAZIL** (Aeroplanes), **MIDDLE-CONGO** (Train), **SUDAN** (Camel), **FRANCE** (Horsewoman), **DUTCH INDIES** (Steam-boat), **AUSTRALIA** (Aeroplane), **GABOON** (Raft), **COLOMBIA** (Natives with Panniers), **SOUTH AFRICA** (Ship), **FRENCH GUIANA** (Native Carriers), **GERMANY** (Aeroplane), and **BELGIUM** (Train). Price **6d.** (abroad extra). All purchasers of this packet asking for approval sheets will be presented with **INDIA** Silver Jubilee Stamps.

BURDOCK & FLURY
4, MARLBOROUGH ROAD, LONDON, S.W.19

THE MYSTIC PACKET

1000 UNKNOWN UNUSUAL UNSORTED 1/3

Stamps on paper, etc., just as received from Convents, Missions, Bankers, etc. Guaranteed unpicked. Chance of a **FIND** in every lot. Send to-day for your treasure hunt to-morrow, **3** for **3/6, 6** for **6/6.** Abroad, **1/6** packet. **FREE!** 25 Br. Cols., including Jubilees, to approval Applicants, also **FREE EXCHANGE.** Send postage only. Overseas **3d.**

ASTLEY & CO.
(M25), Lowhill, WOLVERHAMPTON

333 STAMPS FOR 4½d.

GUARANTEED UNPICKED

As received from Convents, Missions, Bankers, etc., all over the world. Special offer to applicants for approval selections only. Postage 1½d.

EDWARD LORD
GRAFTON ROAD, KEIGHLEY

MOURNING STAMPS FREE

Get this fine collection of stamps issued in memory of famous Kings and Presidents, free. It includes **Belgium** (King Albert); **U.S.A.** (Pres. Harding); **Jugo Slavia** (the assassinated King Alexander), and **Germany** (Hindenburg). Sent absolutely free, to all genuine applicants asking for one of our famous "Grey" booklets of stamps on approval and enclosing 2d. postage. Price of this packet without approvals, 1/-. Just issued: The handsome **Belgium Queen Astrid** Mourning Stamps. Complete set of 8 unused, 1/9. Separate values, 10c.+5c., 1d.; 70c.+5c., 3d.
THE WINDSOR STAMP CO., 59, Lee Road, BLACKHEATH, S.E.3.

SENT BY AIR MAIL

Celebrated Richemont 6d. and 1/- packets sent on approval by Swiss Air Mail, as also sets and singles. Complete set Pro Juventute mint, 1935, 1/6. Latest Swiss pictorial set, used, 4d.

A. M. PHILLIPS
Richemont, St. Légier, sur Vevey, Switzerland.

FREE

MOZAMBIQUE CO., AIR MAIL, CEYLON (native tapping rubber), **KENYA-UGANDA-TANGANYIKA, ROUMANIA, MOROCCO AGENCIES,** and other interesting new issues, **all unused.** Send postcard for approvals, postage paid both ways. (None sent abroad.)

T. F. WILLIAMS
7, Islington Rd., Towcester, Northants.

FREE PACKET—500 STAMPS

This splendid New Year Gift is Free to all approval applicants—if you add 2d. for postage I will include 2 Fine Sets. (Abroad 6d. extra.)
CHAS. A. HILL, 51, MONINS ROAD, DOVER.

"R.C.M.P." Packet — FREE

This splendid packet contains the new **10 cent Canada** (Royal Canadian Mounted Policeman, as illustration), **New Ceylon** Pictorial (Native tapping rubber tree), Australia and Gold Coast Pictorials, New Zealand **1935, New Belgium** (train drawn by Diesel engine), France (Paris exhibition), Uganda Pictorial 1935 and 10 different Canada including the above and **Canada Jubilee** and the new 1935 issue.

All these new stamps free to genuine applicants for our Approval Sheets, who enclose 2d. for postage.

SHIRLEY STAMP CO., 19, SANDRINGHAM AVENUE, LONDON, S.W.20.

24 AIR STAMPS FREE

THIS FINE PACKET OF 24 ALL DIFFERENT AIR STAMPS FREE TO APPROVAL APPLICANTS ENCLOSING 3d. (in stamps) FOR POSTAGE AND PACKING.

A. B. LEWIS (Dept. C.22)
16, CRICKLEWOOD LANE, LONDON, N.W.2

"WORTH WHILE" 10 COLONIAL JUBILEES FREE

To approval applicants only. Everyone wants these elusive issues, and there are not enough to go round. I have managed to secure a good supply which I am circulating with my **"Worth While"** approval sheets. Send 3d. (Abroad 1/-) to cover postage, etc., ask to see some of these famous selections and you will make sure of having at least 10 of these beautiful **Used** stamps. Remember, **"Worth While"** sheets contain only worth while stamps, at prices which make them **Worth While.**
JOS. H. GAZE, DIDSBURY, MANCHESTER.

A FREE — FREE F

We are presenting this month the first packet of our new alphabetical series, the greatest gifts ever offered.

This month's packet contains stamps of countries from A to F and includes many beautiful pictorials. You cannot afford to miss this magnificent offer.

SEND A POST CARD TO-DAY FOR APPROVALS

THE UNIVERSITY STAMP CO., OXFORD

SENSATIONAL OFFER TO YOU

FREE QUEEN ASTRID MOURNING STAMP and **6 Large Italian Commemoratives, also 50** other varieties—send 1½d. postage for "Globe-trotter" Approval Selections—amazing value ¼d., ½d., 1d. upwards—and particulars of how you can have FREE Stamps every 14 days!! Write now—there's a stamp treat in store for you. **Special Offers** "GLOBE-TROTTER" Mystery Mixture—world-wide collected—Old and New Issues, Airmails, etc., 1,000 unsorted, unbeatable, 1/3. 25 Large Italian Commemorative Pictorials, 1/-. 10 Jubilee, 1/-. 50 Persia, 1/3. 100 British Colonials, 1/-. French Colonials, 25, 6d., 50, 1/-, 100, 1/9. 50 Airmails, 2/-.
GLOBE-TROTTER, 17, WINCHESTER ROAD, BIRCHFIELD, BIRMINGHAM.

APPROVALS

COLONIAL OR FOREIGN
From ½d. each, with discount.
REAL GOOD VALUE.

H. KEELEY
9, Market Buildings, Maidstone

COLONIAL JUBILEE STAMPS ARE NOW OBSOLETE

I have a few MINT Sets as follows:

Antigua ...	... 2/9	**Malta** ...	... 3/6
Basutoland	... 2/-	**Montserrat**	... 2/9
Cyprus ...	... 3/-	**Newfoundland**	... 3/3
Gibraltar	... 3/9	**S. Rhodesia**	... 2/6
Grenada ...	... 2/6	**Tangier** ...	... 1/-

Bargain Packets, 50 different British Colonials (containing stamps cat. up to 9d. each), **1/3.**
CASH WITH ORDER—**POSTAGE EXTRA.**
H. L. GOMM, 41, Upper Cranbrook Rd., Redland, Bristol 6.

I WANT 500

regular customers. Collectors who are so satisfied with the value offered in my selections that they will come to me for all their philatelic requirements. AND I have a scheme which will pay them to become **regular** customers. Send now for my **4-a-penny selections** and full particulars of the new scheme.

L. D. MAYNARD,
78, RICHMOND ST., SOUTHEND-ON-SEA.

Monster 500 Packet FREE!

This huge gift parcel contains 500 Unsorted FOREIGN and COLONIAL STAMPS, many scarce from **St. Pierre** and **Miquelon, Malay** (Tiger), **China, PORTUGAL,** GWALIOR, CHILI, BR. S. AFRICA, etc., etc. Just send 2d. stamp and request my EXTRA-LARGE-DISCOUNT APPROVAL SHEETS (Abroad 6d. P.O.).
E. EASTICK, 22, Bankside Road, BOURNEMOUTH.

10 MINT ABYSSINIA CAT. 4/4 FREE

Includes the following scarce stamps: 1917 ¼ guerche **(Throne of Solomon),** overprinted; Complete short set of 1919 Pictorial Issue, ⅛g. **(Antelope);** ¼g. **(Giraffes);** ½g. **(Spotted Leopard);** 1g. **(Ras Taffari** now **Haile Selassie, Emperor of Abyssinia);** 2g. **(ditto but different view);** 4g. **(ditto but different again);** 6g. **(St. George's Cathedral, Addis Ababa);** 8g. **(Rhinoceros;** 12g. **(Ostriches),** and 1928, 2m. **(Haile Selassie).** This fine packet will be sent free to all genuine applicants for approvals enclosing 2d. for postage. **M. HUMPHRIES, East Wittering Rd., East Wittering, Chichester, Sussex.**

FREE — NATIVE LIFE PACKET — FREE

This wonderful collection contains stamps from all corners of the globe, showing native life and industries, and contains: Madagascar (Bara chief), Mozambique (Native village), French Guiana (Carib archer), **obsolete** Martinique (Native beauty), Indo-China (Native ploughman), Sudan (Arab postman), and many other interesting designs. This splendid gift will be sent FREE to all genuine applicants for my popular approvals enclosing 1½d. postage (abroad 6d.).
MICHAEL HERBERT,
58, Larkswood Road, Chingford, London, E.4.

SILVER JUBILEE, mint, 25 British cols. and 25 Foreign free to approval applicants. Postage 2d. P. R. Lincoln, 60, High Road, Potters Bar.

STAMPS: 50 FREE to all selecting **1/-** worth or over from my approval sheets. Enclose **1½d.** for selection.—Burley, 21, Jardine Road, Aston Manor, Birmingham.

U.S. Boulder Dam, Mozambique Air, Ceylon and Australia Jubilee, Tanganyika (Pict.), Belgium Queen Astrid, Roumania (large), with Colonials, Pictorials, 4d. free with Selection, 6d. without. 6 Mongolia Pict. 6d. 23 Russia 5d.
J. R. MORRIS, 9, Audley Road, Folkestone, Kent.

FREE—50 STAMPS!!!

and perforation gauge.
Contains: Silver Jubilee Colonials and **NYASSA TRIANGULAR.** This fine packet is given free to all genuine applicants for my cheap approvals. Price list free.
D. T. CADOGAN,
61, South Main Street, Wexford, I.F.S.

"1,000 PACKET" 6d.

A WONDERFUL OFFER FOR
Postage 2½d. ex. Abroad 6d. ex.

The "1,000 Packet" contains 500 excellently assorted Stamps; **a complete Sheet of 100 Unused** (very useful for exchange purposes); a neat 12-page booklet for duplicates; 25 British Colonials usually sold at ½d. to 1d. each, including new issues; 375 Magic "Strip" mounts, very quick for mounting stamps, and list of stamp bargains. Free sets will be sent to those who send addresses of stamp-collecting friends. *Ask for Approvals.* 100 B. Colonials 1/-. 20 Air Post 6d. 10 Abyssinia 1/6. 10 Mozambique Triangulars (just out) 1/6. "B.O.P." and "Captain" monthly parts cheap.
H. C. WATKINS, M. DEPT., GRANVILLE ROAD, BARNET.

For other stamp advertisements see pages 60 and xx

Competition Corner

WHICH WERE THE MOST POPULAR COVERS IN 1935?

The Cover Voting Contest that we have held each year for several years past, to decide the order of popularity of the coloured covers of the previous year's issues, has retained a remarkable degree of popularity, and even before last December's issue was published we had received letters from readers expressing the hope that we would again feature this contest.

In the above illustration the splendid covers that appeared on the various issues of the "*M.M.*" during 1935 are reproduced in a reduced form in their order of publication—January to June in the upper row, and July to December in the lower. The reproductions are intended for reference purposes only. They convey nothing of the brilliancy of the colour of the originals, but new readers will find them of great assistance in forming their judgment. Those readers who possess copies of the 1935 issues, or are able to obtain them, should make a careful study of the originals before completing their entries.

Referring to each cover by its month of issue, each competitor is asked to state on a postcard:

A. The 1935 cover he likes best of all.

B. His idea of the order of popularity of the covers as decided by the massed votes of all the competitors.

This list must cover the whole year, every month being included. The name of the month must be given, and its number in the volume. Competitors need not place their own favourite cover at the head of list B, unless they believe that it will prove to be the popular choice of the remaining competitors. They should place it in the position in which they anticipate it will be placed by the massed votes.

The entrant's name and address must be added to the card, which should be addressed "Cover Voting Competition, Meccano Magazine, Binns Road, Liverpool 13." No competitor may submit more than one entry.

Cash prizes of 21/–, 15/–, 10/6 and 5/– respectively will be awarded to the four competitors whose lists most accurately forecast the final result. In the event of a tie for any of the prizes, preference will be given to the entry displaying the neatest or most novel presentation. Closing date, 31st January.

A separate set of prizes, to be awarded in precisely similar conditions, will be awarded in the Overseas Section which is reserved for readers living outside Great Britain, Northern Ireland, the Irish Free State and the Channel Islands. The Overseas closing date will be 30th April.

January Drawing Contest

Each month throughout this winter we are offering prizes for the best drawings or paintings submitted during the month. There are no restrictions as to subject or to size.

The entries each month will be divided into the usual two sections, A for readers aged 16 and over, B for those under 16, and cash prizes of 21/– and 10/6 will be awarded for the best entries in each section.

A separate set of prizes, to be awarded in similar conditions, will be reserved for competitors in the Overseas section.

Entries to the January competition must be addressed "January Drawing Contest, Meccano Magazine, Binns Road, Liverpool 13," and must arrive not later than 31st January. Overseas closing date, 30th April.

Unsuccessful entries will be returned if a stamped cover is sent for the purpose.

We give above the solution to the August Crossword Puzzle, the Overseas section now having closed.

COMPETITION RESULTS

HOME

November Sketchograms.—First Prizes: Section A, G. Burgess (London, N.12); Section B, G. D. Hay (Peterborough). Second Prizes: Section A, C. Weatherbed (Sheffield); Section B, K. Aston (Dorking). Consolation Prizes: F. H. Bailey (Luddington); H. G. Blake (London, S.E.20); G. A. Fox (Bournemouth); M. Tucker (Reigate).

Firework Story.—1. D. J. Chubb (Brighton); 2. W. G. Tweedale (Bury); 3. F. G. Oldfield (North Staffs.); 4. J. Finch (Hounslow).

November Drawing.—First Prizes: Section A, A. Symonds (Coventry); Section B, H. Shacklady (Bolton). Second Prizes: Section A, N. S. Griffiths (Gidea Park); Section B, J. Macken (Bromley).

OVERSEAS

August Crossword.—1. C. Keekok (Singapore); 2. R. Lewis (Masterton, N.Z.); 3. J. M. Demanuele (Valletta, Malta); 4. G. E. McKinnon (North Sydney, N.S.W.).

August Photo.—First Prizes: Section A, Miss N. Milne (Hawkes Bay, N.Z.); Section B, R. Sampson, (Sydney, N.S.W.). Second Prizes: Section A, C. J. Mallia (Cospicua, Malta); Section B, B. R. Masters (Paris). Special Prize: Section A, B. bin Silan (Perak, F.M.S.).

BOYS ! JOIN THE MECCANO GUILD

President:

MR. FRANK HORNBY

The Meccano Guild is an organisation for boys started at the request of boys and conducted as far as possible by boys. At its head—guiding and controlling, and taking a personal interest in it—is the President, Mr. Frank Hornby, inventor of Meccano and Managing Director of Meccano Limited, and it is ready to be of service to each individual member, and to help or give advice whenever requested. Membership of the Guild enables Meccano boys to get the best out of life.

The three great objects of the Guild are to make every boy's life brighter and happier; to foster clean-mindedness, truthfulness, ambition and initiative; and to encourage boys in the pursuit of their studies and hobbies, and especially in the development of their knowledge of mechanical and engineering principles. Every boy undertakes to promote these objects.

A Meccano boy who joins the Guild, becomes a member of a great brotherhood of world-wide extent, every member of which has promised to observe its great objects; wherever he happens to be, even in strange countries he will know that he has met a friend whenever he sees the little triangular badge. Thus the Guild brings together Meccano boys all over the world.

THE GUILD BADGE

Membership of the Guild is open to every boy possessing a Meccano Outfit or Hornby Train Set who satisfactorily fills in the application form. The only conditions are that members shall promise to observe the objects of the Guild and to wear their badges on all possible occasions.

The Meccano Guild badge is beautifully enamelled in blue and white. The ordinary form is made for wearing in the lapel of the coat, but brooch badges are issued to members who prefer to pin them in position, and applicants who wish to have this form of badge should indicate this when sending in their forms. In addition to the badge, each member receives a handsome Membership Certificate printed in orange and black.

HOW TO BECOME A MEMBER

In order to join the Guild all that is necessary is to fill up the form of application, and to forward it to the Secretary of the Meccano Guild, Binns Road, Liverpool 13, from whom an application form may be obtained if desired. A remittance to pay for the membership badge should be sent along with the completed form of application. The price of the badge is 7d. post free in the United Kingdom and 1/- post free overseas (25 cents Canada). The applicant is then duly enrolled as a member of the Guild and his badge of membership is sent to him. Each member has the personal interest of the President and is entitled to the friendly advice and assistance of the Secretary.

Boys living overseas should write to one of the Meccano agents at the following addresses: CANADA: Meccano Ltd., 187-189, Church St., Toronto. AUSTRALIA: Messrs. E. G. Page & Co., 52, Clarence Street, Sydney, N.S.W. NEW ZEALAND: Models Ltd., Third Floor, Paykel's Buildings, 9, Anzac Avenue (P.O. Box 129), Auckland, C.1. SOUTH AFRICA: Mr. A. E. Harris (P.O. Box 1199), 142, Market Street, Johannesburg.

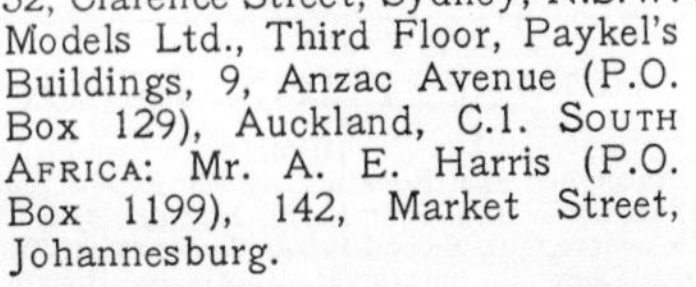

MECCANO CLUBS

Meccano Clubs are founded and established by enthusiastic Meccano boys under the guidance of the Guild Secretary at Headquarters. At the present time there are over 150 affiliated clubs in various towns and villages in this country and overseas, together with many others not yet affiliated. Each club has its Leader, Secretary, Treasurer and other Officials, all of whom, with the exception of the Leader, are boys.

Every Guild member should join a club if possible, for only in association with other Meccano boys is he able to obtain the greatest fun from his hobby. If the nearest club is too far away for him to join, or if he is unable to join it for any other reason, he should consider the possibility of forming a new club in his own district. A special booklet entitled "How to run a Meccano Club" is now ready, and will be sent to any reader (post free) on receipt of 2d. in stamps.

When a Meccano Club has been successfully launched and good progress is being made, affiliation with the Guild is granted. A beautiful club certificate, suitable for framing and hanging in the club-room, is presented, and the club becomes entitled to such privileges as the loan of interesting lectures and large models built at Headquarters.

THE CORRESPONDENCE CLUB

Members of the Guild are eligible to join the Correspondence Club, by which they are placed in communication with other Guild members in some other part of the country or abroad. To those boys who are interested in foreign languages the Correspondence Club presents a splendid opportunity of obtaining a correspondent in the particular country in the language of which they are interested. Stamp collectors also find the club of value. Full particulars and enrolment form will be sent on application to the Guild Headquarters.

THE SUN NEVER SETS ON THE MECCANO GUILD

ORDER OF MERIT

Traveller: "They threw me out of the side-door."
Sales Manager: "What did you say?"
Traveller: "I told them I came from a very important firm; so they took me inside again and threw me out of the main entrance."

* * * *

"Waiter, this menu is five days old."
"That does not matter, sir—we still have all the food."

* * * *

TWO INTO ONE WON'T GO

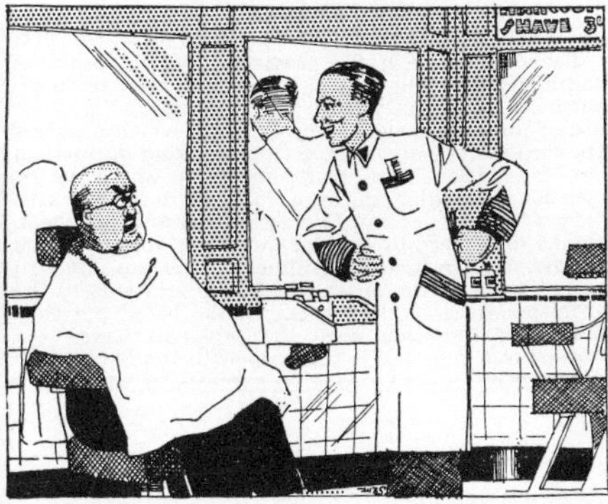

Fat Gent.: "What! Sixpence for a shave! Your sign says threepence."
Hairdresser: "Yes, threepence for one chin. You've got two!"

* * * *

Betty (at seaside): "Mummy, what would happen to me if I swallowed a crab?"
Mother: "Something dreadful, darling. It would probably kill you."
Betty: "Well, it hasn't."

* * * *

First Castaway: "Good heavens, cannibals!"
Second Castaway: "Now, now, don't get in a stew."

* * * *

Little Boy: "Mummy, if you show me which foot this shoe goes on I can guess the other."

* * * *

Two youths went to see a billiards match between well-known professionals. They watched one of the players pile up a huge break, and then one whispered to the other: "What do they call this game, Bert?"
"Why, billiards, of course," replied Bert.
"Well, what do they call the game we play at our club?"

* * * *

Sam: "Have any big men been born in this town?"
John: "Oh no, only babies."

* * * *

Pilot: "I suppose you have heard people say 'See Naples and die?'"
Passenger: "Yes, why do you ask?"
Pilot: "Well, we are over Naples now, and something's gone wrong with the engine."

* * * *

"Did you know the French drink their coffee out of bowls?"
"That's nothing; the Chinese drink their tea out-of-doors."

* * * *

The teacher had been trying to interest her class in the intriguing problem of Noah's hobby during the time of the flood.
"I think," she said, "that Noah must have spent his time fishing."
"No fear, Miss," broke in a young lad at the back, "he couldn't catch much with only two worms!"

* * * *

Prospective Lodger: "But you advertised this as a bed-sitting room."
Landlady: "That's right, sir."
Prospective Lodger: "Well I can see the bed, but where is the sitting room?"
Landlady: "On the bed, sir."

ALL THE SAME TO HER

New Lodger: "I am a journalist, and I use a nom-de-plume."
Landlady: "That's quite all right, sir, as long as it don't disturb me."

* * * *

Little Girl: "Did Santa Claus come down your chimney?"
Boy: "Well, Santa Claus didn't—we're economising this year—so father did it."

* * * *

Customer: "How much d'ye charge to press a pair of trousers?"
Dry Cleaner: "One shilling."
Customer: "All right, just press one leg for saxpense, and I'll have my photy taken side view."

* * * *

The tramp sidled up to the landlady of "The George and Dragon." "I haven't had a bite all day, mum," he said. "Can you spare a crust?"
"Certainly not," snapped the lady, and slammed the door in his face.
Another knock a few minutes later brought her back to the door. To her surprise it was the tramp again.
"What is it now?" she demanded.
"Please, mum, could I 'ave a few words with George?"

* * * *

Hunter: "Leaping towards me was a fierce lion."
Friend: "What did you do?"
Hunter: "Why, I beat it up."
Friend: "What! The lion?"
Hunter: "No, a tree."

* * * *

Mother (to naughty child): "Richard, you will try to be a good boy to-morrow, won't you?"
Richard: "Yes, mother. But please remind me in the morning."

* * * *

Two lads were gazing at a Zebra at the Zoo. "What a funny animal," said one. "What is it?"
"I don't know," replied the other. "A sports model donkey, I should think."

* * * *

"Now," said the teacher at the end of her talk on music, "What is harmonising, Percy?"
"The stuff you put on the top of cakes, miss."

* * * *

KING'S ENGLISH

The foreigner was trying hard to learn English. He struggled bravely when he came to "bough," "cough" and "though," but while passing a cinema one day he noticed on the board, "'Cavalcade,' pronounced success."
"Zis ees too much!" he groaned. "I geeve it up!"

* * * *

"Remember," said the employer, "that politeness costs nothing."
"I'm not so sure, sir," returned the youth. "Did you ever try putting 'Very respectfully yours,' at the end of a telegram?"

* * * *

Policeman: "What's the trouble, sonny?"
Small Boy: "Please, sir, have you seen a lady without a little boy who looks like me?"

QUITE CLEAR

Pat: "That was a foine sintiment Casey expressed at the dinner last noight."
Mike: "What was it?"
Pat: "He said that the swatest mimories in loife are the ricollections of things forgotten!"

* * * *

Old Gentleman: "I see that a man in London is run over every half hour."
Old Lady: "Poor fellow!"

* * * *

HE KNEW BETTER

Officer: "You can't stop here."
Motorist: "I can't, eh? Well, officer, maybe I shouldn't stop here, but you don't know this car as well as I do."

* * * *

Mr. Cork: "I planted some potatoes in my garden and what do you think came up?"
Mr. Stopper: "Potatoes?"
Mr. Cork: "No; fifteen pigs and ate them all."

* * * *

Gent.: "May I have some stationery?"
Clerk: "Are you a guest at this hotel?"
Gent.: "Certainly not; I pay two guineas a day."

* * * *

The popular actor was being interviewed.
"And what do you consider the highest praise you can get in the theatre?" he was asked.
"Applause from the gallery," he replied.

* * * *

Extracts from recent advertise:emnts:
"Mr. ——, Furrier, begs to announce that he will make up gowns, coats, etc., for customers out of their own skins."
"TO LET, Bed-sitting room for gent. 22 ft. long and 11 ft. wide."

* * * *

Pat: "Why wud ye always be usin' them safety matches?"
Mike: "Och, shure! In case the gas be lakin'."

* * * *

Overheard at a cinema as a picture of a famous racing craft was flashed on the screen in a pictorial item:
First Lady: "A yacht?"
Second Lady: "No, dear. Are you?"

* * * *

The mighty engines of the liner throbbed ceaselessly. The chief engineer wiped a perspiring forehead and scowled at the young man with the oil-can. "Look here," he growled, "you aren't helping me much with these engines, yet you said you knew something about the game."
"So I do," replied the other, "but on a smaller scale, you know."
"Well, what's your usual job?"
"Watch repairing!"

* * * *

"You might at least have kept up with the other jockeys," grumbled the owner of the last horse in the race.
"What, and leave the horse behind?" replied the jockey.

Diaries for 1936

The great popularity of the Charles Letts's "*School-Boy's Diary*" is easy to understand, as in addition to the usual diary portion it contains an excellent atlas and more than 50 pages of text covering a remarkable variety of subjects. There are helpful notes concerning professions and qualifying examinations, grammar and arithmetical tables, and a comprehensive list of sports records. The diary is published in cloth at 1/- and can also be obtained in leather cloth with pencil and maps at 1/6, and in leather with pencil, maps and pocket at 2/6.

The 1936 edition of "*Brown's Boy Scout Diary*" (Brown, Son and Ferguson Ltd., 1/- net) contains as usual much information of value to Boy Scouts, Rover Scouts, Wolf Cubs and Sea Scouts. The many articles deal with Scout law, proficiency badges, knots and their uses, Indian signs, camping hints, weather lore and many other interesting topics.

The "*Young Airman's Diary*" (Letts Quickref Diaries Ltd.) is certain to make a definite appeal to boys who are interested in Aviation. The literary pages of the diary are a store of information, and contain, in addition to lists of flying clubs and schools, types of aero engines and aircraft, internal air lines and notable flights, a short history of Imperial Airways and an interesting article on how an aeroplane is controlled. Other sections deal with air photography and air survey, distances from London by air, and explanations of aeronautical terms. The end papers have maps showing the situation of the principal aerodromes in the British Isles and the chief airports abroad. The diary is published at 1/-, 1/6 and 2/6.

Tables for Home Billiards

Few winter games are so attractive as billiards, and the small tables manufactured by E. J. Riley Ltd., make this fine game available for even the smallest rooms. The Riley home billiard tables are not toys. Every model is a perfect replica of a full-size table, including a slate bed, scientifically constructed cushions, durable covering and all necessary accessories. A specially interesting point of the Riley service is that all models can be obtained on seven days' free trial.

E. J. Riley Ltd., Deal Works, Accrington, or Department 3, 147, Aldersgate Street, London, E.C.1, will be glad to send an attractive art list of Riley Billiard Tables to any reader who writes to them mentioning the "*M.M.*"

"Goldtone" Bakelite Rear Lamp

Our cycling readers will be interested in the recently-introduced "Goldtone" battery rear lamp. The case of this lamp is entirely unaffected by rain, and will not rust or corrode: and owing to its high insulating properties the full life of the battery is assured. The switch and contact strips are strongly made of brass, and the sliding back enables a new battery to be inserted in a couple of minutes when necessary. The screw-on front gives access to the bulb. The light given is adequate for all purposes.

The price of the lamp, complete with bulb, battery and the necessary fittings, is 1/9. A descriptive leaflet will be sent free to any reader who writes for one, mentioning the "*M.M.*" to Ward and Goldstone Ltd., Pendleton, Manchester 6.

Safeguards for Night Riding

Bluemel Brothers Ltd., have just sent to us a copy of their new leaflet listing their several white "Safeguards" for cycle use. Readers who indulge in riding after dark would find this list of special interest, for it details a series of most efficient and reasonably-priced safeguards, several of which incorporate a prismatic reflector.

Bluemel Brothers Ltd., of Wolston, Nr. Coventry, will be glad to send a copy of this leaflet to any interested "*M.M.*" reader.

Fine Grain Development

The vogue of the miniature camera has brought in its train a problem for manufacturers of photographic materials—the production of a developer that will facilitate the making of large scale pictures from tiny negatives. Messrs. Burroughs Wellcome and Company have met the problem in characteristic manner. They have produced a "Fine Grain Developer" that has all the convenience and reliability of their other "Tabloid" brand developers and yet embodies all the qualities necessary to produce negatives fit for high-degree enlargement.

Every owner of a miniature camera, indeed, all who are interested in enlarging their own negatives, should secure a copy of Messrs. Burroughs Wellcome's latest pamphlet "Fine Grain Development." It deals with many interesting practical points in addition to demonstrating pictorially the excellent qualities of their "Fine Grain Developer."

Messrs. Burroughs Wellcome and Co., Snow Hill Buildings, London, E.C.1, will send a copy of the booklet free of charge to any "*M.M.*" reader who applies for one.

Answers to December Puzzles

No. 1. Houses to Letter (let or) For Sale.

No. 2. The answer is not 11 but none. Elephants cannot speak.

No. 3. Keyword: Exhaustion
1234567890

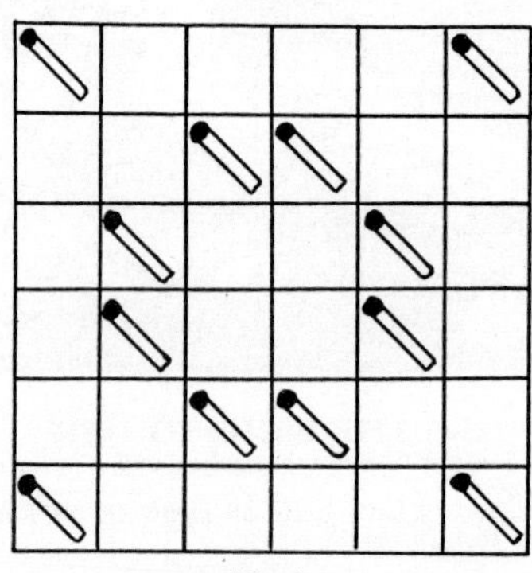

Fig. 1

No. 4. (1) Birds of a feather flock together.
(2) A rolling stone gathers no moss.

No. 5. Only three persons shared in the gift, related to each other as son, father, and grandfather. Each is therefore a son of somebody, while the two elder are fathers only.

No. 6. The window was diamond-shaped. By enlarging it to a square its area is exactly doubled. A window shaped as an isosceles or right-angled triangle will answer equally the conditions of the puzzle.

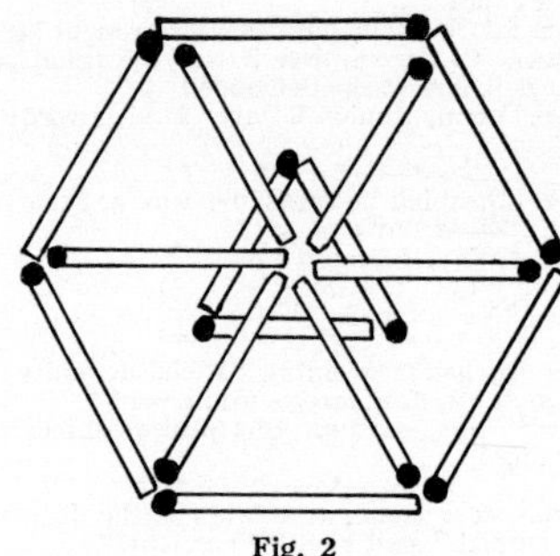

Fig. 2

No. 7. The matches are arranged as in Fig. 2.

No. 8. The paper should be cut and arranged as in Fig. 4.

No. 9. When the door is open.

No. 10. Wrong.

No. 11. Six weights: 1, 2, 4, 8, 16, and 32 lb. respectively.

No. 12. "What Am I?": Blockhead.

No. 13. Salmon, Mackerel, Oyster, Winkle, Plaice, Roach.

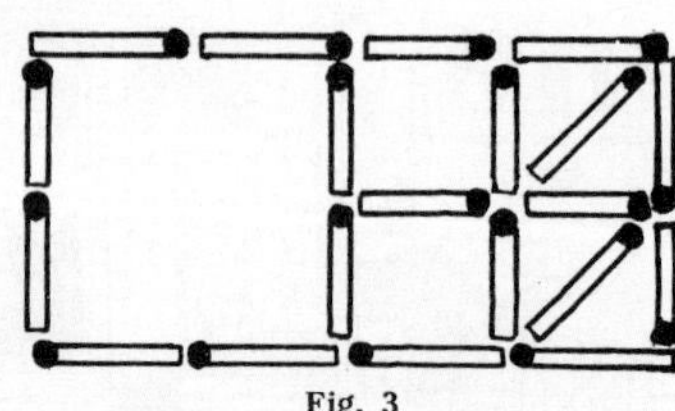

Fig. 3

No. 14. The coster originally had seven whole oranges. He gave four to the first keeper, two to the second keeper, and one to the third.

No. 15. The 12 matches should be rearranged as in Fig. 1.

No. 16. To rearrange the coins, place a finger on each of the second and fourth coins of the bottom row (heads), and with one movement withdraw them from the bottom row and move them round to a position immediately above the second and fourth coins in the top row (tails). Then, without stopping, but by firm pressure, the second and fourth rows are pushed down to allow the two heads to take up their positions in the top row. The effect of this is to push the second and fourth coins in each row into the row below.

Fig. 4

No. 17. The 20 matches are arranged as in Fig. 3. The two diagonal matches are removed to form six squares but no triangles.

No. 18. John Underwood, Andover, Hants.

No. 19. Sir, you will understand that in the year 1877 France was divided, laws were set aside, religion was upside down, and rebellion in every corner.

No. 20. Bill is still living with Jim Smith in this big city.

No. 21. Red Root Put Up To Order.

No. 22. The word is "Meccano."

"Cross-Sums"

By David Whitelaw. (Geoffrey Bles Ltd. 2/- net)

The popularity of the crossword puzzle continues undiminished. The original form has been retained, but made enormously more difficult in regard to clues. A new form has now been produced in which numbers are used instead of words, giving this kind of puzzle a new fascination, particularly for those who have no aversion to arithmetic as a form of entertainment. "*Cross-Sums*" contains 25 diagrams, and facing them, blanks to be used in working out the problems, which are arranged in increasing difficulty and are intended to be solved in the order given. The solutions to the problems are given at the end of the book, but they should be forgotten until the problems have been worked out. A pencil is provided with the book.

NEXT MONTH: "HOW A GREAT LINER IS LAUNCHED." PUBLISHING DATE: 29th FEBRUARY

MECCANO MAGAZINE

Editorial Office: Binns Road, Liverpool 13 England

Vol. XXI. No. 2 February, 1936

With the Editor

Readers' Suggestions

The extent to which readers have responded to my invitation to express their opinion of the "*M.M*" and to suggest means for its improvement is a gratifying sign of their interest in its progress. In view of the widespread circulation of the Magazine, it is perhaps scarcely surprising to find that in certain instances the suggestions made cancel each other out. For instance, some of my correspondents are in favour of reducing the space allotted to railway matters, yet from others come insistent demands for still more articles of this kind. Similar differences of opinions are expressed in regard to stamp collecting and other regular features. These differences of course are due to the variations in the interests of readers themselves, and illustrate how difficult it is for me to satisfy everybody.

What Readers Are Asking For

Coming now to the actual comments of readers, I find that very few wish me to leave out any of the well-established features that have made the "*M.M*" by far the most popular of all boys' magazines of its kind. The tendency is rather to ask for more, but unfortunately there are limits to the size of the Magazine if its price is not to be increased, which I am sure would not be popular!

Special interest is shown by a large proportion of readers in articles dealing with ships and motor cars, and footplate trips. I already have in hand some interesting shipping articles, including more sea trips by Mr. O. S. Nock similar in character to those that appeared in the October and December issues last year, and proved so remarkably popular. I hope also to resume and extend the road and track notes that in previous years have aroused enthusiasm. I mention this for the special benefit of some correspondents who have indignantly complained of the non-appearance of these notes in recent issues. As for accounts of footplate trips, "Railway Engineer" will deal with further interesting runs during the year.

Other interesting letters have suggested articles on such varied subjects as natural history, photography, British lighthouses, woodworking, county coats-of-arms and rifle shooting! I cannot promise to include contributions dealing with every topic proposed by readers, but as far as is practicable I shall try to meet their wishes where these seem to represent a general desire. I hope therefore that those of my readers who have not already written to tell me what they think of the "*M.M.*" will do so as soon as possible.

Tunnelling Triumphs

The news that a tunnel is to be driven under the Thames between Dartford, in Kent, and Purfleet, in Essex, is an interesting reminder of the comparative ease with which engineers to-day can overcome the difficulties that river estuaries present to communications. Whether a tunnel under one of these obstacles is to be driven through rock, clay or the soft mud in the bed of a river, the work can be carried out easily and safely, even when the bores are more than a mile in length and of such dimensions that the roadways in them can readily accommodate four lines of traffic.

Rock boring, such as was necessary in the case of the gigantic Mersey Tunnel, has been made easier by the introduction of electric and pneumatic boring tools, combined with the use of explosives to shatter large masses of rock into fragments. Tunnels of this kind are no longer bored by brute force, as was more or less the case when our earliest railways were constructed, and a wonderful gain in time and cost has followed the use of scientific methods.

Even more striking means of speeding up tunnelling and making greater enterprise possible have been invented for use in boring through river beds. The material in this case is soft and water percolates through it, threatening always to make its way into the workings. The modern engineer prevents this by the use of compressed air. The actual boring is carried out with the aid of the shield invented by Brunel and later improved by Greathead, and the pressure behind this is kept so high that the water is held at bay until the lining has been completed. This method in its turn introduced a second difficulty, for it was discovered that men working in compressed air were liable to a dangerous illness. Even for this a preventive has now been found in the air lock, in which normal pressure is gradually restored before the men leave the tunnel workings.

Penetrating Mountain Ranges

During recent years many wonderful tunnels have been driven under rivers and estuaries, notably under the Mersey in this country, and under the East and Hudson Rivers, New York, in the United States, and it is not difficult to realise that similar tunnels in other places would be a great advantage. For instance, it has been suggested that a tunnel should be constructed under the River Tyne. More tunnels also could be driven under great mountain ranges, and it is not surprising to learn that it is proposed to drive yet another tunnel under Mont Blanc.

Romance of Robinson Crusoe's Island

The Eventful History of Juan Fernandez

By Harold J. Shepstone, F.R.G.S.

THE news from South America that an enterprising hotel proprietor is about to erect a hostel on Robinson Crusoe's island, Juan Fernandez, and that a regular steamboat service is to be maintained between it and Valparaiso with the idea of attracting visitors to the island, calls attention to its romantic history. It was only recently that the bi-centenary of the death of Alexander Selkirk was celebrated. It was the stirring narrative that this Scottish sailor told of his lonely life on the island that led Defoe to write that masterpiece of adventure, "*Robinson Crusoe.*"

Juan Fernandez, which was discovered by a Spanish sailor of that name in 1563, lies some 450 miles off the coast of Chili, to which it now belongs. It is famous, of course, because of the self-imposed residence here of Alexander Selkirk, though he was by no means the first sailor, or even the last, to "crusoe"—if one may use such a term as defining solitary habitation—on the island. After Fernandez had reported his "find" to his government he settled down on the island, saying that he would end his days there. He certainly lived there for a time, but he soon grew weary of the lonely life, and it was not long before he abandoned his kingdom, leaving behind him as a gift to posterity a herd of goats and pigs.

Cumberland Bay, the only landing place on Juan Fernandez, Robinson Crusoe's Island.

When next the curtain lifts, the island appears as a shelter of the bold buccaneers. It lay conveniently near to the Spanish settlements, for on Spain the buccaneers made war with savage ferocity. Those were the heroic days of filibustering—the days of Lolonnois the cruel; Montbars the exterminator; Sir Henry Morgan, pirate and knight; Sharpe, and Dampier. They took their ships to the island to obtain water, and also to replenish them with fresh meat. For instance, after Sharpe's unsuccessful attempt to surprise La Serena, he and his men anchored off Juan Fernandez. He tells us that he found the shore so thickly covered with seals that he had to shoot a number of them before a landing could be effected. The goats had evidently multiplied, for his sailors signalised Christmas Day by shooting 60. As for pigs, besides those slaughtered for present needs, 100 were salted down. The waters were alive with fish, so that a sailor with a bare hook caught in an hour or two enough for all the crew. Occasionally, at their own free will, or by accident, men from these ships were left behind on the island. The majority only remained a few months, though there is the case of one, an Indian, staying on the island alone for three years. He was accidentally left behind from one of Dampier's ships.

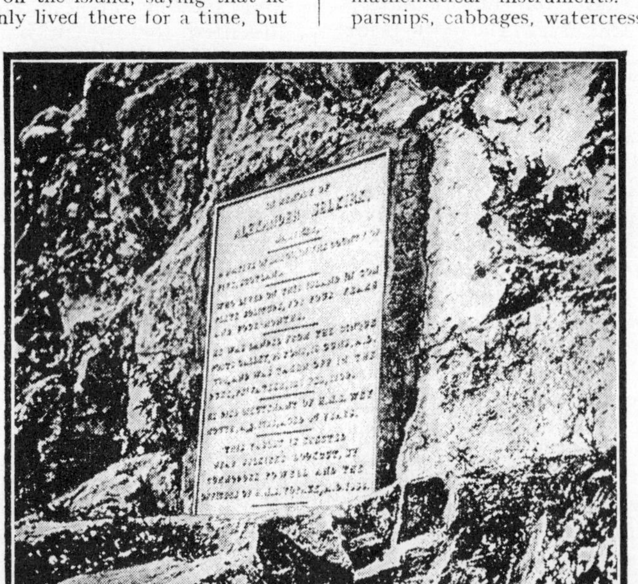

The tablet erected by officers of H.M.S. "Topaze" to Alexander Selkirk.

The real hero of Juan Fernandez, of course, is Alexander Selkirk, who was put ashore on the island in 1704. It was at his own request that he landed, for Selkirk had a grievance against his captain, and the two did not get on well together. Nevertheless, the self-marooned man's heart failed him when he saw the ship about to leave the bay, and he fell on his knees and begged his captain to take him on board again. But a deaf ear was turned to all his entreaties, and the vessel sailed away. It was lucky for him, too, that he was thus left behind, for the ship in which he came was captured by the Spaniards shortly afterwards.

Selkirk was by no means ill-provided for. He had a fair stock of clothes and boots, a tolerable amount of ammunition, a musket, a kettle, some pounds of tobacco, a Bible and other books, and a few mathematical instruments. He had vegetables, too, turnips, parsnips, cabbages, watercress, and parsley. Yet it took him eight months to reconcile himself in any degree to his lot, and when he did finally settle down he did not find life on his island kingdom so easy or so enjoyable as some writers have led us to believe.

Selkirk has told us that he found it extremely difficult at first to get any sleep owing to the multitudes of rats that swarmed over the island. They ate holes in his clothing and nibbled his toes whenever he laid down to rest. In the end he kept the vermin down by means of a band of tame cats. He grew by practice so fleet of foot as to keep his larder supplied with goat's flesh long after his ammunition failed.

The pimento tree, which flourishes on the island, supplied him not only with pepper, but also with candles and sweet-smelling firewood. He reared a large number of kids to ensure plenty of food in case illness interfered with his hunting, and indeed he was once laid up for almost a fortnight by tumbling over a precipice while pursuing a goat. He beguiled his idle moments by teaching his kids and cats tricks. Clothes he provided out of goat-skins; but he could not manage to make new shoes, so he had to go barefooted when his old ones were worn out.

During his long abode on the island he saw many ships pass, but of these only two put into shore. From them some Spaniards landed, who, perceiving Selkirk, gave chase. By this time, however, he had learned to run down a goat, and so had no difficulty in keeping his visitors at a safe distance. This was the only occasion on which the outer world invaded his solitude until the arrival of the ship in which he left Juan Fernandez for ever, after a stay of four years and four months.

Captain Rogers, who rescued Selkirk from his lonely kingdom, described him as "a man dressed in goats' skins, and wilder in appearance than the goats themselves." With him the glory of Juan Fernandez passed into fiction, and lives for ever in Defoe's pages. On his return to England, Selkirk met Defoe and told him of his adventures. They are supposed to have met at the Cock and Bottle Tavern in Bristol.

But Juan Fernandez had other castaways besides Selkirk and those already referred to. Defoe's hero had not left his little kingdom ten years before it was occupied by four deserters from an English ship, but they remained two months only. Again, in 1720, the "*Speedwell*" was wrecked off its shores, and her crew remained there some months, until they built a boat in which they departed, leaving behind them a colony of 11 white men, 13 blacks, and some Indians. These were supposed to have surrendered to, or been massacred by, the Spaniards, for two years later, when the island was again visited, no trace remained of them.

The cave on the island, in which Robinson Crusoe is believed to have lived for nearly 4½ years.

The only people who ever seem to have enjoyed their stay on the island were the members of Lord Anson's expedition in 1741. They had all been suffering terribly from scurvy, and the green food they found there afforded them welcome relief. Lord Anson stayed on the island for three months until his crews had thoroughly recruited. His chaplain has handed down to us an interesting description of the island as he found it at that time. There were plenty of goats and fish to be had in abundance; while radishes and turnips were growing wild in the sheltered valleys. Before they left, Anson planted a number of fruit stones, which soon added to the useful vegetation.

The first goat that was killed by Anson's men had its ears slit. It is well known that Selkirk, when he caught more goats than he wanted, sometimes marked their ears and let them go, and Anson's chaplain contends that this was one of the very goats that had passed through Selkirk's hands. He describes it as "an animal of a most venerable aspect, dignified, with an exceedingly majestic beard, and with many other symptoms of antiquity." Anson's chaplain was the first to apprise the world of a wonderful singing-bird, about as large as an English thrush, that is to be heard to this day on the island.

Look-out Point, where Crusoe watched for passing ships.

When Anson returned and wrote an account of his voyage he made many charming references to Juan Fernandez. As a result the Spanish Government became nervous, and fearing England meant to seize it they sent a military force to the island and officially occupied it. That was in 1750. A fort was erected and the place was used as a penal settlement. At that time the post of governor of the island was looked upon as one of the plums of the Spanish services.

But Spain did not occupy her possession long before the Chilians took it away from her and again turned the island into a penal settlement, and it was used as such for some twenty years during the early part of the last century. It has remained a possession of Chili ever since.

Since 1835 the Chilian Government have leased the island several times to private speculators. In 1868 it was let to Robert Wehrdan, a German engineer, who established a small but thriving colony there; and in the same year H.M.S. "*Topaze*" visited it and erected a tablet to the memory of Alexander Selkirk. In 1877 the island was let to an eccentric Swiss, who wished to taste the delights of seclusion. He took with him a small band of colonists who, from their manner of life, might have been styled the "Swiss Family Robinson," but they soon tired of the experience and came away.

Some 380 persons dwell on the island to-day, 180 of whom are under ten years of age. They are principally fishermen and whalers, and they reside in log bungalows around Cumberland Bay, many of which boast of beautiful gardens with cherry trees. Two schools, a small chapel, a cemetery, a post office, and the new wireless station are the only public buildings. The most noteworthy graves in the cemetery are those of two German sailors from the notorious cruiser "*Dresden*," the wreck of which lies in Cumberland Bay, where it was sunk in 1915 by the "*Glasgow*."

The island can be reached from Valparaiso in 25 hours by boat, and if a regular service is organised, as at present proposed, and suitable hotel accommodation provided, Robinson Crusoe's island will no doubt attract many visitors. Naturally what will appeal to all tourists are the places associated with Alexander Selkirk. There is the cave, or grotto, which he used as his house, around the walls of which are still to be seen a number of rusty nails and rude shelves and cupboards. Then there is Look-out Point, a lofty pinnacle, over 2,000 ft. above the level of the sea. Selkirk is said to have climbed this very peak every day during his first eight months' stay on the island in the hope of attracting the attention of a passing ship. At the foot of this hill is the tablet erected to his memory.

Although it appears barren from the sea, the island, which is some 12 miles in length and five miles across at its widest part, is well wooded and has many springs. The wild goats are still there, as well as a few wild horses, and many birds of beautiful plumage are to be seen in the woods.

There are trails over the mountains and through the woods. As one clambers over the hills one catches charming glimpses of sea and wooded valleys. When cruising steamers visit the island, as they occasionally do, their passengers invariably spend three or four hours ashore. Such visitors are always welcome. One of the school teachers acts as guide and conducts the party to places of interest. Then there is a chat with the oldest inhabitant and before leaving the island postcards are sent to friends which will bear the mark Juan Fernandez.

Belfast to Glasgow by L.M.S.R.

A Varied Journey by Train and Steamer

By a Railway Engineer

ONE could hardly imagine an inter-city journey that offers a greater variety either of scene, or of travel interest, than that from Belfast to Glasgow. First comes a dashing half-hour's run from Belfast to Larne by the N.C.C. boat "express"; then a sea passage of great charm; while it would be hard to find a route in the British Isles that makes more fluctuating demands on the locomotive than that covered in the Scottish portion of the journey, from Stranraer to Glasgow.

I made the trip by the 9.37 a.m. train from Belfast. This does not give quite such a fast overall time as the evening mail, which leaves at 6.25 p.m., but the running times are actually faster. This morning service is only operated during the summer months and reaches Glasgow at 3.16 p.m. The luxurious corridor stock of the *"North Atlantic Express"* is used, and as the latter only arrives from Portrush at 9.29 a.m., smart working is needed to get the boat train away at 9.37 a.m.

The 9.37 a.m. Belfast-Larne boat express approaching Larne Harbour. The locomotive is 4-4-0 No. 81, "Carrickfergus Castle," on which was made the footplate trip described in this article.

On this occasion, by the kindness of Major Malcolm Speir, Manager and Secretary of the L.M.S.R., N.C.C. Section, I rode down to Larne on the engine, and a more thrilling footplate trip I have never experienced. The engine was a superheated 4-4-0, No. 81, *"Carrickfergus Castle,"* which belongs to a class very similar to the L.M.S.R. standard Class 2P 4-4-0s but having 6 ft. diameter coupled wheels against 6 ft. 9 in. Our load was one of six coaches, 174 tons tare and 185 tons with passengers and luggage. The weather was rather doubtful at the start; a slight drizzle was falling and the rails were greasy in consequence.

The *"North Atlantic Express"* arrived on time almost to the second; No. 81 backed quickly down, and I joined Driver O'Neill and Fireman Kerr on the footplate. These engines have cabs which, though less commodious than those of the Moguls described last month, are considerably more roomy than most 4-4-0s on account of the wider gauge. The regulator is of the double port type as in the Moguls, but the reversing gear is operated by a notched lever. Although the booking of 30 minutes for a 24.3 mile run does not suggest anything very wonderful, this schedule actually involves some extremely smart locomotive work. The finish into Larne is made slowly on account of severe curves, while restrained running is needed also in the neighbourhood of Whitehead for the same reason.

Almost immediately, O'Neill opened on to the second regulator, using 42 per cent. cut-off; then, half-a-mile out, the gear was linked up one notch, to 32 per cent., and the regulator brought back slightly to about two-fifths open. In the meantime we were accelerating with tremendous rapidity along the shore of Belfast Lough, and were through Whitehouse, 3¼ miles, in 5½ minutes at 55 m.p.h. The regulator was now opened wider, and with the exhaust, already sharp, developing into a roaring tattoo, we tackled the rise to Greenisland. At Bleach Green Junction the Larne route diverges, and a moment later we dived under the graceful reinforced concrete viaduct carrying the main line, ourselves also on a high viaduct. The engine was going splendidly; except for a momentary drop to 49 as we passed Bleach Green, the speed was maintained at 51–52 m.p.h. all the way up the 1 in 136–157–97 rise to Greenisland, and we were through this junction, 6.7 miles, in 9½ minutes.

For 100 yards or so after we were over the top of the bank O'Neill let the engine accelerate rapidly without easing the regulator, but then he changed over to the first valve. Two-and-a-half minutes later we flew through Carrickfergus at 69 m.p.h., though speed was eased to 62 for the curves beyond. From this point the line is practically level all the way to Larne, such gradients as do occur being quite short. We were now once more running along the shores of the lough. Across the water were the rolling hills of County Down, terminating northward in Orlock Head and the Copeland Islands, while a brief backward glance towards Belfast showed the mellow ruined castle, after which our engine is named, standing in a commanding position right on the water's edge.

Once we were down on the level, harder going was needed than the first regulator, and on passing Downshire Park O'Neill opened out to three-fifths. The exhaust once again sharpened into a roar and we rocketed round the curves at an exhilarating 66 m.p.h., with high red cliffs on one side and the sea just below us on the right. The riding of *"Carrickfergus Castle"* on certain sections was decidedly reminiscent of that fiery L.N.E.R. "Atlantic" of whose exploits I wrote in the September *"M.M.,"* though in this case, owing to the wider gauge, the rolling died away much quicker.

The striking bluff of Black Head now came in sight, but a moment later the view seaward was cut off as we turned sharply inland and dived through Whitehead tunnel. A severe permanent way slack was in force just beyond this station, and we slowed carefully to 25 m.p.h.; but the moment we were over the affected length the engine was fairly opened out. Single line working begins at Whitehead, so that tablet exchanging at speed was now added to the thrill of the journey. We regained full speed very quickly and were soon flying alongside the upper reaches of Larne Lough at 65 m.p.h. The pace was eased a little round the curves at Magheramorne, but going once again on half regulator and 32 per cent. cut-off we reached a final maximum of 66 m.p.h. through Glynn.

By now a magnificent scene had opened out. Far across the water on the right were the jetties and station of Larne Harbour. The lough is very narrow at its entrance, but almost immediately broadens out into a spacious basin. The town of Larne lies well back from the sea beneath lofty hills, and the railway swings round in a wide curve in order to reach the Harbour station. We slowed down to 25 m.p.h. to take the sharp curve through the town station—a curve so severe that the tablets have to be exchanged by hand—and then, although a bare mile from journey's end, full steam was put on again. Accelerating rapidly, we were up to 43 m.p.h. before the final slowing down commenced, and then we stopped at the Harbour station within 3 seconds of time—29 min. 57 sec. from Belfast. Allowing for the check at Whitehead, the net time was only

28½ min., a very smart piece of work for a 4-4-0 locomotive.

* * * * *

Hustle did not cease with our arrival at Larne, for precisely eight minutes after the train stopped, the *"Princess Maud"* steamed out for Stranraer. This, far from being a special feat, is the regular schedule time, and is made possible by transferring all luggage and mails from train to steamer by means of a belt conveyor. The principle of this belt is the same as that of those used in modern mass-production factories. At Larne it is carried alongside the track on which the boat trains arrive, level with the luggage van floors, so that it is only necessary to place each package on the moving belt just outside. The belt is carried high above the landing stage and then on to a movable arm like the jib of a crane. When a ship is being loaded or unloaded this arm is lowered on to the deck, and at other times when the belt is not in use it is hoisted up out of the way. The efficiency and economy of this method are obvious.

The Larne line passing beneath the ferro-concrete viaduct carrying the Portrush line at Greenisland. The Larne line is itself carried on a similar structure immediately after passing underneath.

Since we left Belfast the weather had cleared beautifully, and for the rest of the day we were treated to the marvellous visibility that follows rain on the west coast. As we came out of the lough, and were swinging round East North-East, there was a magnificent view of the Antrim coast stretching away northward. Just to the north of Larne is a group of dangerous rocks known as the Maidens, one of which is crowned with a fine lighthouse. And now, across a sea sparkling in the sunshine, was spread out a panorama of rare beauty. To the north lay the southernmost islands of that romantic archipelago that fringes the west coast of Scotland; far away on the north-west horizon was Islay, while a little to the east were the mountains of Jura, vague dim-blue shapes riding out at sea. Nearer at hand was the Mull of Kintyre, while still further east, in the Firth of Clyde, lay Arran with its tremendous array of wild peaks. The Scottish mainland was as yet a long line of rolling hills, as it was impossible at this distance to pick out much detail. Looking southward as we got further out, the Copeland Islands and the entrance to Belfast Lough came into the picture and completed a circle of enchanting seascape.

The belt conveyor at Larne Harbour. Its employment in transferring luggage and mails between train and steamer enables connections to be effected with the minimum of delay.

We got away from Larne with such speed that there was no time to pay much attention to the stately ship in which we are now travelling. In outward appearance the *"Princess Maud"* and her sister ship *"Princess Margaret"* are quite distinctive among L.M.S.R. cross-channel ships, having only one funnel and a cruiser stern. In both these respects, and also in their general dimensions, they bear a striking resemblance to the latest Southern Railway ship on the Dover-Calais service, the *"Canterbury."* The latter vessel, however, uses oil fuel, whereas these two L.M.S.R. ships are coal fired.

Although the crossing takes only two hours, the *"Princess Maud"* and *"Princess Margaret"* are most luxuriously appointed. One of the most delightful saloons is an observation lounge just beneath the bridge. From this, even in wet weather, passengers can have an uninterrupted view of the sea ahead. At first sight it seems strange that both ships should have a large number of sleeping berths. The reason is that in the case of the 8 p.m. night service from St. Enoch, *"The Irishman,"* passengers go on board on arrival at Stranraer at 10.52 p.m. but the steamer does not sail till 6.5 a.m. the next morning, and Belfast is reached at the convenient hour of 8.58 a.m.

The general lay-out of the main turbines is rather similar to that of the *"St. Briac,"* which was described in the December number of the *"M.M."* Each turbine develops 2,700 h.p. while running at 3,000 r.p.m., the speed being 20 knots. Steam is supplied by four water-tube boilers of the usual Babcock and Wilcox type, each being fired by a mechanical stoker. Killochan coal is used; this is very small, no piece being bigger than a half-inch cube, and is fed into the furnaces through cylindrical rams, the speed of which can be regulated to meet every demand for steam. The working pressure is 225 lb. per sq. in.

Interesting though the engine rooms were, especially in the contrast they provided with the footplate of *"Carrickfergus Castle,"* I was not sorry to leave their hot steaminess for the bracing air on deck. Familiar Irish landmarks were becoming vague in the distance and the heather-clad hills of Galloway were drawing steadily nearer. A brilliant white lighthouse marked the entrance to Loch Ryan up which we sailed to Stranraer, but the most striking object was now the rocky islet of Ailsa Craig, which rears itself up so dramatically in the Firth of Clyde. It somewhat resembles the Bass Rock, off the Lothian coast, but has a much more pointed summit. The heather was in full bloom on the Galloway hills, and as we entered Loch Ryan the gradations of purple were indescribably lovely.

The sail up Loch Ryan is typical of many Scottish sea lochs. Along the shore is a belt of prosperous farming country and above that the hills gradually rise to their heathery summits. Here and there a small mountain burn enters the loch, and up its glen there is a vista of wilder, more lonely hills beyond. On this occasion the King's Cup Air Race was in progress, and as Portpatrick, not many miles from Stranraer, was one of the turning points, many of the competitors flew over us as we sailed up the loch. Most of them were too high to be recognised, but one monoplane passed very close flying extremely fast.

By now we were nearing Stranraer. Loch Ryan is very shallow at its head, and the railway is built on a narrow causeway that juts far out in the water. Even so, such big steamers as the *"Princess Maud,"* which has a gross tonnage of 2,800, approach the jetty at dead slow speed at low tide. The trains run right alongside the landing stages and, as at Larne, transhipment is carried out very smartly, though in this case there is no belt conveyor to assist. We berthed at 12.15 p.m.—two hours to the minute from Larne.

* * * * *

Two expresses run in connection with this steamer. At 12.25 p.m. a luncheon car express leaves for Dumfries and Carlisle. This carries a through coach for London, Euston, which is attached to the up "*Mid-day Scot*" at Carlisle. On the occasion of my trip this train conveyed a heavy load of nearly 300 tons, and was hauled by two Standard 4-4-0s of Class 2P. The Glasgow train, which leaves at 12.35 p.m., is known as "*The Fast Belfast*," and had a modest load of only four coaches, a total load of 140 tons; the engine was a Midland Compound, No. 914. These Glasgow-Stranraer boat trains were for many years known by the nickname of the "*Paddies*," before they were given official names. As far as Ayr, however, the route is terribly severe, and even with this light train some really hard locomotive work was needed.

For the first seven miles Glasgow trains follow the Carlisle route, and over this section we were delayed somewhat by the train in front. The line is single throughout, and some difficulty was experienced at one of the passing loops, where a goods train had to be crossed, owing to the length of the train. So we left Dunragit six minutes late, but from here onward did some excellent work. At Challoch Junction, where we diverge from the Carlisle route, the line is right on the shore of Luce Bay and the prospect southward is delightful. Beyond golden sands the coast stretches away to the Mull of Galloway, while far out in the Irish Sea is the Isle of Man.

The L.M.S.R. steamer "Princess Maud" engaged on the Larne and Stranraer service. With her sister ship "Princess Margaret" she shares the distinction among L.M.S.R. ships of having one funnel and a cruiser stern.

From Challoch Junction follow 14 miles of very severe ascent to Chirmorie summit, 690 ft. above sea level. During this climb the line winds over the western spurs of the Galloway Highlands, and beyond New Luce especially is wild in the extreme. The climbing was made more difficult on this trip as we were stopped at the latter station in order to cross a down express. Thus we had to restart up the stiffest part of the whole climb. For three miles beyond this point the line rises at 1 in 57; No. 914 was evidently opened well out, for we maintained the excellent speed of 27 m.p.h. There is a slight dip through Glenwhilly, which cannot be taken advantage of for speed recovery, however, as a slack is necessary to exchange tablets—as always on this route, by hand. But up the subsequent 1 in 94 to the summit we maintained a steady 41 m.p.h., the engine roaring heartily all the way.

Chirmorie summit is a very lonely spot. A vast expanse of wind-swept moorland, rugged outcrops of rocks, snow fences to protect the railway, and a distant view of the Merrick range away to the east, make up a very austere picture. Eight and a half miles of steep descent at 1 in 70 now follow, but on account of the curves we did not get above 61 m.p.h. In the meantime the wild hill-country gives place to rough upland pasture. Below Barrhill the speed rose to 65 m.p.h., but we were soon slowing down again to take the loop through Pinwherry. The luxuriant vegetation here, the profusion of flowers, and the rich green of the meadows is the very opposite of the bleak country we passed through barely ten minutes ago.

An interesting view in the engine room of the "Princess Maud," showing the main turbines. Each develops 2,700 h.p. at 3,000 r.p.m., the speed of the vessel being 20 knots.

Hard climbing follows, at 1 in 70, up the valley of the River Stinchar. Here No. 914 steadily maintained 30 m.p.h. and had accelerated to nearly 35 ere we entered the summit tunnel. We emerge on the hillside high above Girvan with a prospect that almost takes one's breath away. Far below is the Firth of Clyde, alive with shipping and shimmering in the brilliant light; Arran lies behind, its peaks intense blue. What rivets the attention, however, is Ailsa Craig, a huge cone-shaped rock, standing grape-blue in the sea, its appearance at the same time majestic and sombre, for there is no fringe of sand or beach to relieve the stark rockyness of its shores.

The descent into Girvan is precipitous, at 1 in 54, and speed was not allowed to exceed 50 m.p.h.; but still we completed the 31¾ miles from Dunragit in 53 minutes, instead of the 54 minutes booked, in spite of the stop at New Luce. The net time of 49 minutes showed a gain of five minutes to engine, no mean performance over a route of such difficulty.

From Girvan onward the line is double tracked. Throughout the next 22 miles, to Ayr, the railway is a veritable switchback. Generally speaking we maintained an average of 35 to 40 m.p.h. uphill and 60-65 down, while the 21.4 miles from Girvan to Ayr were run in 32 minutes, including a brief halt of half a minute at Maybole. Schedule is 35 minutes, and we thus regained a further 3 minutes, reaching Ayr practically on time.

The last stage into Glasgow is one of the busiest stretches of line in Scotland, and throughout its 41½ miles it is practically dead level. This train is allowed 55 minutes, inclusive of a stop at Paisley, and with so light a load as 140 tons, it is of course a very easy task for a Compound.

Leaving Ayr the line quickly approaches the Firth of Clyde. Across the water the Isle of Arran looked magnificent with a mass of piled-up cumulus cloud hanging over the highest peaks. In the immediate foreground sunshine made brilliant play on the waters of the Firth. We bowled along past a string of famous golfing resorts, Prestwick, Troon, and Barassie, but after Irvine the line bears away from the coast and runs through a considerable coalfield. Beyond this comes a stretch of beautiful lowland country, the gem of which is the narrow Loch Winnoch lying in a shallow trough of the hills.

Soon, however, signs of industrialism crowd on all sides, but beyond Elderslie the really big mountains lying to the north of the Clyde can now be seen, with Ben Lomond soaring to a height of 3,192 ft. Soon we drew up at Gilmour St. station, Paisley, the 33¾ miles from Ayr having taken 41 minutes, as booked.

Immediately after leaving Paisley there is a fine view towards the Clyde. The river lies in a trough and cannot be seen from the train, but its course can be traced by an almost continuous succession of shipyards with their towering electric cranes. One yard, and one yard only, however, is the cynosure of all eyes, that of John Brown and Co. Ltd. at Clydebank. Even at this distance the Cunard White Star giant, "*Queen Mary*," can be clearly seen, and at the time of my journey the first funnel was just in position.

Beyond this point the line runs through densely populated suburbs. From Shields Road inward, train movements are under the control of St. Enoch signal box; this is the largest all-electric signalling installation in Scotland. Three-aspect day colour-light signals are used, while all interlocking on the lever frame is carried out electrically without any mechanical locking.

Running very cautiously now we crossed the Clyde viaduct, getting a remarkable impression of Glasgow's river, and, passing the now disused St. Enoch engine shed, came slowly under the great arched roof of the terminus, dead on time, having run the 101 miles from Stranraer in 166 minutes.

Europe's Greatest Bascule Bridges

Two Fine Structures at Antwerp Docks

By Hans F. Kutschbach

DURING the last few years extensive improvements have been carried out at the docks and harbours of Antwerp, including the construction of two giant bascule bridges to enable street and railway traffic to pass through the dock area. One of the bridges, which were built by Demag, Duisburg, Germany, is illustrated on this page.

The bascule type of bridge was chosen because a structure of this kind takes up little room, and can be opened and closed quickly so that traffic is interrupted for only short intervals of time. Also a bascule bridge can be erected without obstructing traffic on the waterway during the process. The leaf or bascule of the bridge illustrated on this page is 131 ft. in length, carries double line railway track and two footpaths, and has a total width of 44 ft. It weighs alone 360 tons and is provided with a counterweight that is attached to a lever mounted in a triangular frame about 36 ft. above the roadway. This frame can be moved in such a manner that as the bridge is raised or lowered the counterweight sinks or raises simultaneously and counterbalances the weight of the leaf, thus reducing the power required from the operating motors. The counterweight is made of concrete and scrap and weighs about 685 tons.

One of the two giant bascule bridges at Antwerp docks. The leaf is 131 ft. in length and weighs 360 tons.

The driving power is provided by two motors, each of which is capable of opening and closing the bridge at half maximum speed, so that the drive can still continue to function if one of the motors should fail. The power of the motors varies automatically during the movement of the leaf, in accordance with increases or decreases in the resistance due to wind pressure, which varies from time to time.

The double lever of the counterweight being built on to the supporting frame in which the engine house is located.

Electric brakes are provided, so that if the speed of the bascule tends to exceed that of the motors its movement is checked. The opening and closing of the bridge normally occupies about one minute, and all the movements, including opening and closing of the traffic barriers at the approaches, are controlled from a cabin situated close to the bridge.

The power plant is accommodated in an engine house 19 ft. above the ground, and in addition to the motors there are two hand-operated windlasses for operating the bridge in case of emergency. With the hand drive eight men can raise or lower the bridge in about one hour, against a wind pressure of 5 lb. per sq. ft.

When the bascule is in its fully raised position it is held by two automatic interlocking hooks, and these must be released before it can be lowered. This task is performed automatically by means of powerful electro-magnets, which function when the main switch that controls the current to the driving motors is closed.

Shortly before the bascule reaches its fully lowered and raised positions the speed of the driving motors is automatically gradually reduced, and the motors are then brought to a stop by limit switches. In order to prevent the bascule from settling down too violently at the end of the lowering operation, liquid buffers are provided in the abutment.

Extensive safety devices are installed to ensure the smooth operation of the bascule, and the motors for the various drives are interlocked electrically with each other in such a way that they can be switched in only in the correct sequence. Signals at the approaches give warning to traffic as to whether the roadway is clear or not.

Marvels of Bird Migration

Striking Flights by our Spring Visitors

By Eric Hardy, F.Z.S.

MIGRATING birds mostly fly by night and rest and feed by day, and thus we seldom meet with big migration flocks in our rambles. At night, even in cities, a sudden thrush-like call from the darkness often can be overheard, however; this is the call of the leader of a migration flock keeping the birds together in the dark.

The millions of bird travellers that in spring enter Europe, chiefly from Africa and Asia Minor, use coastlines, river valleys and mountains as their guides, and as they are mostly long-sighted they can make out these forms at night from the great heights at which they often fly. Astronomers watching the skies at night through their telescopes sometimes see parties of migrating birds, those of duck and geese being as much as 1,000 ft. or more in altitude. On misty nights the birds fly lower, and turn towards bright lights, such as lighthouse lanterns or the glares of well lighted towns and cities, as if hypnotised or dazzled.

The great migration routes they follow from Africa to Europe are three in number. The first, serving Russia, Turkey, Roumania and Poland, that is Eastern Europe and a little of Central Europe, passes from the Nile Valley up the coast of Palestine and across Asia Minor and the Bosphorus. The second, probably the most crowded of the three, is followed by birds flying to Central Europe and by some of those travelling to Western Europe and the British Isles. It crosses the Mediterranean Sea round Malta to Italy and then passes over the Alps into Austria and Germany. The third stream of migrants, consisting of birds travelling to Western Europe, leaves Africa at Morocco and follows the coasts of Spain and France. On their way up the French coast some of these birds break off and travel overland, later crossing the English Channel to the Downs and the east coast of England. Others enter Cornwall, and the main stream of these migrants passes along the North Devon coast, where it breaks up, some of the birds going up the Severn valley to Wales and the Midlands, others across the Bristol Channel, along the coast of Pembrokeshire and over Cardigan Bay to North Wales, reaching the North of England and Lakeland by way of the Dee Estuary. A branch of this flight passes over the Irish Sea to the Isle of Man and thence to Scotland, and other birds reach Ireland directly from Land's End and there follow routes along the coast.

The map reproduced on this page shows the migration routes of the birds entering Great Britain. The large arrows marked A show how they arrive on our southern coasts and the smaller arrows indicate their subsequent courses to their summer quarters. It will be seen that the birds arrive earliest along our coasts. They work inland up the valleys, the most important routes in the British Isles being the courses of the Severn, the Thames, the Humber, the Dee, the Forth, the Tay, Solway Firth, the rivers entering Waterford Bay and the Shannon, which are numbered 1 to 9 on the accompanying map. Our spring migrants also arrive earlier in the west than in the east, the earliest making their appearance in Cornwall and Pembrokeshire and the latest district to receive visitors being north-east Scotland. The arrows at B show the routes followed by the birds that fly onward to nesting places farther north than the British Isles and by others that winter in this country and spend their summers nearer the Arctic Circle.

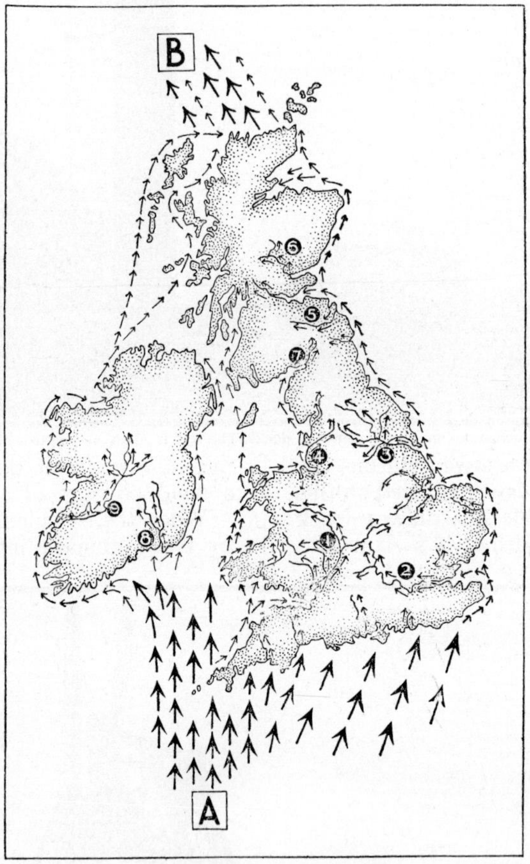

On this map the arrows show the spring migration routes of British bird visitors from the south. These routes follow the coast and the numbers indicate the principal river valleys along which birds make their way inland to their nesting places.

The general direction of migrating birds in spring of course is northward, but there is one part of our coast where the strange sight can be seen of spring migrants actually flying southward. This is on the Norfolk side of The Wash, and is due to their need for the coast as a guide. The birds following this route come up the Norfolk coast from the Thames Estuary, so far flying northward, but at Hunstanton the coast suddenly turns to the south and they follow it into the Wash, to turn eastward to Skegness and eventually northward again to the Humber.

All our migrant birds do not come from the same winter quarters each spring. Most of our summer visitors come from Africa, but Africa is a large continent. For years naturalists could not understand why certain birds, such as the wheatear, the chiffchaff warbler, the yellow wagtail, the ring-ouzel or white-breasted blackbird of the moors, and the wryneck, arrive much earlier than other migrants, and why the swift, turtle-dove and nightjar are so tardy in reaching our shores. The problem was solved by fixing numbered aluminium identity rings to the legs of captured birds, which were then released, later captures revealing their African haunts. It was then realised that the wheatear arrives in England earlier than most birds because it has the least distance to travel, for it winters in North Africa. The nightjar, swift and other birds arriving late, winter in Central and South Africa, and take a month or more to make their home flight. Similarly the terns or sea-swallows of our sand-dunes, which are not true swallows but swallow-tailed gulls, puzzled the naturalists of the last generation, for the big, yellow-billed Sandwich tern arrives on our coasts nearly a month earlier than the red-billed common tern. We now know the explanation, for it has been discovered that the Sandwich tern winters in West Africa, and the common tern in Natal and other parts of South Africa.

The arctic tern, which unlike the common tern has a dark tip to its coral red beak, is believed to be the world's greatest migrant, for it nests farther north, and winters farther south than any other tern. Its range includes the Arctic and Antarctic Circles, so that its migration route may cover 20,000 miles. In America, the golden plover covers over 2,000 miles, nesting in North America and wintering in Central America or the north of South America. No bird regularly crosses the Atlantic from east to west, though the kittiwake and other birds occasionally do, for the migration routes lie nearly from south to north.

Our British swallows are famous for the homing instinct they display in returning year after year to the same nest in a barn or stable. In trials with marked swallows in Germany, birds caught after migrating home, and released more than 100 miles away from their nesting place, always found their way back to their nests. This wonderful homing instinct is now known to be general among most of our migrants, however, and is not the monopoly of the swallow. It is chiefly a habit of the older birds, for young birds a year old tend to disperse over a wider area, which of course is Nature's way of avoiding overcrowding. In Cheshire, marked turtle-doves have been proved to return seven and twelve years in succession to the wood in which they were born, although they spend their winters in Central or Southern Africa. Willow-warblers, terns, nightingales and other species also return approximately to the area they occupied the previous year, a remarkable fact in view of the extensive journeys they make, and the vast amount of countryside their tiny eyes must see each year.

The size of a bird has nothing to do with the length of its migration journey. The heron is 3 ft. long and is the biggest common bird in our country, but it probably does not fly further than across the English Channel, or from Sussex to Northern Ireland, at the most, whereas many warblers only four or five inches long fly from Central Africa. The greatest flights usually are made by the terns, swallows and other birds with long narrow wings, and the shortest journeys by those with broad, rounded wings.

Terns, or sea-swallows. These birds haunt sand dunes on the seashore and are spring migrants from South Africa.

Birds closely related to one another differ greatly in regard to migration. Thus the partridge is a stay-at-home non-migrant, but the quail, another game-bird closely related to it, is a spring visitor from the African deserts. Similarly the water-rail remains all year with us, merely moving coastwise when winter frosts freeze up the lakes and brooks. On the other hand, its relative the land-rail, or corncrake, spends its winters in Africa. The corncrake is a meadow-bird of ventriloquial voice that is rarely if ever seen in flight in this country, for when it is followed it runs away through the grasses instead of taking wing. Yet when the urge to migrate comes, it can fly as far as other migrants, although it does not exercise its wings in summer. The swallow is a great contrast to the corncrake in this respect, for normally it flies 2,000 miles a week in its winnowings about after flies during its stay with us.

Most of our warblers come to us for the summer from Africa, but the Dartford warbler and the hedge-sparrow, which despite its name is a soft-billed warbler, not a true sparrow or finch, do not migrate at all. This is a matter of food, for the warblers, rails and other birds that must migrate for the winter to Africa need many more insects than our winters provide, and those that stay in Great Britain can feed on vegetable matter, such as fruits and seeds, as well as insects, and thus find sufficient food here in winter.

The need for food is one of the chief reasons for bird migration. Birds that cannot winter in Great Britain must migrate to warmer Africa, where insects are ever abundant. Why then do not the migrants stay in Africa and nest there, instead of coming north? The answer is that the average number of eggs in a nest is four or five. There may be as many as a dozen or more in the cases of titmice, ducks and partridges, and many birds have two, some three, broods in a year. All these broods mean hungry nestlings to be fed, and although Africa can produce a sufficient number of insects to feed its own birds and the winter visitors from Europe, it cannot feed also the offspring of all these birds. Some therefore must seek other quarters to avoid overcrowding, and the birds that are weakest or least vigorous in finding nesting places migrate when the north is becoming warmer and insects are becoming more numerous there.

A colony of gannets on a cliff. These birds spend their winters in Morocco or off Western Europe.

It is interesting to consider how birds know that it is time to migrate. Careful studies have shown there are two main indications of this. Changes in light and temperature provide one of these. On keeping migrant birds in an aviary during the migrating season, and using artificial lights and heating apparatus to bring the light and temperature back to those normal during the nesting season, a Canadian scientist found they had no inclination to migrate when released. Other birds caught during the resident season, and put in an aviary where the hours of light were shortened and the temperature lowered, migrated when released, though it was not the normal time for them to do so, and other birds remained undisturbed. The second important indication that it is time to migrate is the urge to nest. Sometimes birds that should be migrating make no effort to go north, and specimens of these birds have been found to be immature when examined by experts.

How fast do migrant birds travel? It is difficult to pace them by means of motor cars or aeroplanes, as can be done with birds at other seasons, but most of them then have flying speeds about 20 m.p.h. above their normal rate. For instance, the migrating swallow flies at speeds from 34 m.p.h. to 40 m.p.h., and sometimes touches 50 m.p.h. or more, although its normal speed after settling down in an area is from 23 m.p.h. to 28 m.p.h. Similarly, the speed of the lapwing plover when migrating is 37 m.p.h. to 50 m.p.h., but at other times is from 24 m.p.h. to 40 m.p.h. The migrating speed of the tern is 27-28 m.p.h., and the speeds of the sand-martin and the willow-warbler are 31 m.p.h. and 27 m.p.h. respectively. The golden plover achieves the much higher speed of 70 m.p.h., and other fairly high speeds include the 42-51 m.p.h. of the turtle-dove, the 32-38 of the wheatear and the 27-40 m.p.h. of the house-martin. The land rail or corncrake when migrating flies at 34 m.p.h., the stone-curlew or Norfolk plover at 25-30 m.p.h., the wagtail at 30 m.p.h., the cuckoo at 27 m.p.h., and the black-headed gull at 21-30 m.p.h.

From these figures of migration speeds it will be seen that birds do not fly as fast as many people assume. For instance, the idea that swallows rush through the air at 100 m.p.h. or even more appears to be a delusion due to the streamline effect of the swallow's body, which is built not for speed, but for rapid manœuvring on the wing. For comparison with the figures given above, it may be pointed out that the highest speed on record for the homing pigeon is 99.306 m.p.h. It is doubtful if any migrant exceeds 100 m.p.h. normally, but the swallow, the swift, the golden plover, the starling and others may sustain speeds of 50 m.p.h. or more for long periods, and swifts have circled with ease round aeroplanes travelling at not less than 100 m.p.h. Although most of the migrating birds fly in flocks, there are a few exceptions, like the cuckoo and corncrake. I have watched very carefully on the coast and around the lighthouses and have only met with odd cuckoos and odd corncrakes in both the spring and autumn migrations.

Modern Fire Fighting Machines

Two Centuries of Development

HISTORY is full of accounts of the devastation caused by fire to life and property. Villages, towns and cities in all parts of the world have suffered at some time or another from the destructive force of this disastrous element. We in this country have on many occasions witnessed terrific conflagrations, an outstanding instance that every reader will be aware of being the Great Fire of London in 1666. Another great fire occurred at Gateshead in 1854, when 50 persons lost their lives and over £1,000,000 damage was done. In recent years, however, there have been no fires of this magnitude, and this is due to the great improvements that have been made in the means employed for the prevention and extinction of fires.

The first modern steam motor fire engine. It was built by Merryweather and Sons Ltd., London, to whom we are indebted for our illustrations.

In fighting fires, water is the chief agent employed; and in towns where the supply of water is abundant, and where there is a constant and high pressure in the public mains, the task of the firemen is much simplified. In such cases it is generally only necessary to attach the fire-hose to the hydrants, and the pressure in the mains is sufficient, without the aid of any pumping engine, to throw a jet over the whole burning mass. All districts, however, are not so favourably situated, and for the equipment of an ordinary fire brigade completely equipped fire engines with powerful pumps are required.

The high speed motor fire engines of to-day, which are capable of throwing powerful jets of water to heights of hundreds of feet, and which are often equipped with great telescopic escape ladders, have been developed from the early manual operated pumping carts, and in this article we are describing some of the many interesting stages in their history.

A fine "Greenwich Salamander" fire engine supplied recently to the Borough of Colne. It is driven by a 65 b.h.p. petrol motor and carries an extending escape that reaches to a height of 35 ft.

Probably the most famous name connected with the development of fire engines is that of Merryweather and Sons Ltd., London, the well known firm of fire appliance manufacturers. The firm of Merryweather has been in existence for over two centuries. Their oldest ledgers date back to the year 1799, and the firm has in its possession at their Greenwich works some of the ancient appliances that were used in the Great Fire of London in 1666.

In 1792 a patent was granted to their predecessors for a fire engine pump. This pump may be said to be the forerunner of the manual pump as it stands to-day, for very few improvements have been found possible since that time. In 1829 John Braithwaite produced the first horse-drawn steam fire engine, but it was not until some 30 years later, when a Merryweather machine won the first prize against competing engines of other makes at the Crystal Palace, that these machines came into general use. This engine was subsequently purchased by the Admiralty and used for the protection of Devonport Dockyard. It remained in commission until 1905, and has now found its way back to the makers' works, where it will remain as a specimen of the earliest steam fire engine.

From the latter half of the last century onward progress in the construction of every description of fire appliance has been continuous and rapid. In 1899 a machine was built in which the steam engine that drove the pumps was also used to propel the vehicle along the ground, thus displacing horses. This engine was made for the municipality of Port Louis, Mauritius, and it was steered from the front by means of a handwheel. The engine drove the pumps direct, and a countershaft and gears were provided by means of which it could be disconnected from the fire pump and made to drive the two rear wheels through roller chains. The pumps delivered 300 gallons of water per minute, and could throw a single powerful jet to a height of 150 ft., or several jets to a somewhat lower height. Coal bunkers were provided on each side of the fire door, which was placed at the rear so that the fire could be regularly stoked while the engine was travelling to a fire.

This machine was capable of climbing an ascent of 1 in 10 at 10 m.p.h., while on more or less level roads a speed of between 20 and 30 m.p.h. was reached. It proved so successful that others of the same kind were built, but most of these were provided with oil fuel burners in place of coal fired furnaces.

With the introduction of the internal combustion engine Merryweathers turned their attention to the manufacture of petrol driven fire engines in place of the older horse drawn and steam propelled vehicles, and were the first British manufacturers to construct an engine of this type. In June 1903 a combination petrol motor chemical and fire escape was supplied to the Tottenham Fire Brigade. It was placed in service at Harringay, which incidentally, was to become the first all motor station in the world, and it was stated of this machine that for rapidity in starting, speed on the road, and efficiency in dealing with fires it was absolutely unparalleled by any other life saving appliance then in existence.

A modern Merryweather machine equipped with a "Hatfield" pump capable of delivering 400 gals. of water per minute, and a 50 ft. portable extending escape.

On April 30th 1904 a new type of engine, which was destined to revolutionise fire brigade practice, left the Merryweather Greenwich Works. This was the first motor "Hatfield" fire engine, which had been built for Baron A. de Rothschild for the protection of his French estates. This machine was fitted with the now well known "Hatfield" pump, which was originally introduced as an electrically-driven reciprocating pump for fire service at Hatfield House, the residence of the Marquess of Salisbury. The "Hatfield" pump was adapted to meet the requirements of fire engine service and the name was then given to the whole vehicle. The original "Hatfield" fire engine had a 30 h.p. petrol engine, a 300 gallon pump, chain drive to the road wheels and drive to the pump through a raw hide pinion and spur wheel. The engine had magneto ignition as well as an accumulator and coil.

At the latter end of 1904 the Finchley Fire Brigade took delivery of the first combination pump and first aid machine ever built. This motor also was fitted with a "Hatfield" type pump, with a capacity of 200 to 250 gallons per minute, and also a first aid cylinder which held 60 gallons. A 50 ft. sliding carriage fire escape completed the equipment.

Two years later a machine fitted with a centrifugal or turbine pump made its appearance. The pump was made of aluminium and was capable of delivering 600 gallons of water per minute, and in all essential features its design corresponded with the turbine motor fire engine of the present day.

A streamlined fire engine owned by the Lancaster Corporation. It has a 65 b.h.p. petrol engine, "Hatfield" pump and an extending ladder, which is carried in a trough in the roof of the body.

The first station of the London Fire Brigade to be equipped entirely with motor driven appliances was opened in 1906 and was supplied with three Merryweather automobiles, large numbers being subsequently ordered to replace the horse drawn machines previously in use.

For many years continental manufacturers had been making machines fitted with turntable escapes, but there was no demand in this country for such equipment. In 1908, however, Merryweathers built the first British machine of this kind for service in the Shanghai Fire Department. This machine was also the first one to be made in which the engine that propelled the vehicle was used also for raising and extending the ladders. There were four ladders that together extended to a total height of 80 ft. In the travelling position they rested horizontally on the carriage, but on reaching the scene of operations the power of the propelling motor was transferred to the escape machinery, and the raising and extending of the ladders to their full extent was effected in less than a minute. These operations were carried out entirely by one man through two levers arranged side by side in the rear of the machine.

Although few radical changes have been made in the design of fire engines during recent years, continual improvements have been made to the chassis and engine unit and also to the pumps and other equipment in order to render the machines as efficient as possible. The lower illustration on the opposite page shows an up-to-date machine that embodies all the most modern improvements. It is in service with the Colne Fire Brigade and has a four cylinder petrol engine that develops 65 b.h.p., and is fitted with steel disc type wheels and pneumatic tyres. The rear wheels have twin tyres, and four wheel brakes are provided. The main fire pump is a 400 gallon "Hatfield" pump, and a 30 gallon first aid tank also is provided and takes its supply from the main pump. The machine is fitted with a two section Merryweather extension ladder that will reach a height of 35 ft. The equipment includes a five lamp dynamo lighting set, electric starter, carillon bell, mechanical tyre pump and a towing bar fitted at the rear of the chassis.

One of the most interesting fire engines now in service in this country is the streamlined Merryweather machine owned by the Lancaster Corporation, and which is shown in one of the accompanying illustrations. The superstructure of this machine is of special streamline design, the body being of the covered-in-type and constructed with steel panels. Longitudinal seats on each side of the interior provide accommodation for six to eight men, and they are hinged to open upwards to allow access to the hose lockers. Access to the lockers can also be obtained by means of doors on the outside of the body. Narrow boxes are provided at the back of the locker seats to house standpipes, etc.

The fire pump, which is arranged outside the body behind the back partition, is a Merryweather patent "Hatfield" of rustless metal, and will deliver 275 gallons of water per minute at a pressure of 170 lb. per sq. in. A 40-gallon first aid tank connected to the main pump also is provided.

A first aid hydraulic hose reel is mounted on the rear locker inside the body, and the first-aid hose can be paid out through a porthole at each side, fitted with suitable rollers. The hose reel carries 120 ft. of hose, branch pipe and shut-off nozzle.

At the rear is a towing bar for towing a trailer pump when desired, and an aperture is provided in the back partition of the body to enable one of the firemen to operate the line controlling the brake of the trailer pump. Two towing hooks are also fitted at the front end of the chassis frame.

An extension ladder is carried in a trough in the roof of the body and is provided with suitable rollers and a locking device that can be operated from the front seat. Among the numerous fittings are an amber spotlight for use in fog, a powerful searchlight in a swivelling bracket complete with 150 ft. of cable and tripod for use off the machine, syren, four 7 ft. 6 in. lengths of rubber suction hose and one 10 ft. length of armoured section hose. The machine is painted vermilion, picked out in gold and fine-lined white.

ENGINEERING NEWS

Digging its Way to Work

The illustration on this page shows an unusual piece of excavator work that was carried out recently. A small ⅜ cub. yd. shovel excavator was delivered by Ruston-Bucyrus Ltd., of Lincoln, to Baylis Brickworks Ltd., Birmingham. On arrival at the brickworks the driver in charge of the machine found that there was no way down to the working face at the bottom of the quarry, where the machine was required. He therefore had to set to work to dig a zig-zag path down the 60-ft. sloping face, and this task he completed in three days. In the illustration the machine is shown about to run off the ramp on to the quarry bed.

A view of the quarry where the novel excavation referred to on this page was carried out. For this illustration we are indebted to Ruston-Bucyrus Ltd., Lincoln.

Maiden Voyage Record

On her maiden voyage the new P. and O. liner *"Strathmore,"* which was described in the *"Engineering News"* pages of the November, 1935, *"M.M.,"* set up a new record for the passage from Marseilles to Bombay, which was accomplished in exactly 10 days. The previous record for this run was held by the Italian motor liner *"Victoria"* with a time of approximately 11 days for a voyage of about 102 miles less from Genoa. The *"Strathmore"* steamed at an average of 20.07 knots, and the actual speed from Suez after clearing the canal was 20.56 knots. As the P. and O. Company had not planned a special attempt on the record, the fine performance of the *"Strathmore"* is particularly interesting.

£20,000,000 London Tunnel Plan

A great tunnel scheme, estimated to cost £20,000,000, has been prepared by the surveyor to the Commissioners of Crown Lands, as a solution to traffic congestion in central London. The plan provides for a main tunnel 100 ft. wide under the Thames from Charing Cross, together with a series of branch tunnels 60 ft. wide at various points on each side of the river. The greatest depth of the tunnel below the surface would be 100 ft. If the plan were adopted there would be also seven radial sub-circuses, from which would lead branch tunnels.

A New Three-Wheeled Tractor

A new three-wheeled tractor, of the type known as a "mechanical horse," which is designed to handle a 2-ton load on any type of two or four-wheel trailer, has been introduced by the Ford Motor Co., Dagenham. The new machine is known as the "Tug," and is equipped with the standard four-cylinder engine used in the Ford 8 h.p. models, and which develops 22 b.h.p. at 3,500 r.p.m. The chassis has an overall length of 10 ft., an overall width of 5 ft. 9 in., and a wheelbase of 7 ft. 4½ in. The turning circle is 16 ft., or 21 ft. with a standard trailer.

A special articulated trailer is built for the "Tug," and when this is used the driver can back the "Tug" up to the trailer and couple up without leaving his cab. It is necessary to leave the cab in order to operate the uncoupling lever, which also applies the brake on the trailer. In addition to this special two-wheel trailer, a light four-wheel trailer, equipped with a normal type of towing bar, is also available for use. With a platform body this trailer, which is capable of carrying 30 to 50 cwt. loads, weighs no more than 17 cwt.

New Cruiser for Australian Navy

H.M. Royal Australian Navy has recently been augmented by the addition of the new 7,000-ton cruiser *"Sydney,"* built by Swan, Hunter and Wigham Richardson Ltd. The *"Sydney"* is 530 ft. in length and has a beam of 56 ft. 8 in., and in general design and equipment she belongs to the modified "Leander" class. She has two quadruple torpedo tube mountings, eight 6 in. guns in twin mountings, four 4 in. guns, and several other guns of smaller calibre, and carries amidships a catapult for launching seaplanes. She is propelled by four screws driven by geared turbines that have a total output of 72,000 s.h.p., and steam is raised in oil-fired water-tube boilers. The turbines and the boilers were constructed by the Wallsend Slipway and Engineering Co. Ltd.

A Giant Electro-Magnet

A giant electro-magnet that weighs 37 tons and has a force of attraction of 60 tons between its poles has been constructed for the experimental laboratory of the University of Upsala, Sweden. The magnet housing, fully assembled, has an outside diameter of 5 ft. 7 in., an inside diameter of 5 ft., and a length of about 7 ft. Each pole block with cores and pole pieces weighs about 5 tons. The magnet is mounted in a roller frame, which allows it to be turned into a horizontal or a vertical position and also rotated about a vertical axis.

Proposed Severn Bridge

Monmouth County Council have decided to join with Gloucester County Council in seeking Parliamentary authority to construct a bridge over the River Severn at English Stones, together with the necessary approach roads on each side of the river. The line of the bridge would be nearly over the Severn Tunnel, and the cost of constructing it according to the engineers' preliminary estimates is £2,480,000.

Lorry-Mounted Crane for Persia

On this page is illustrated a mobile crane of a rather unusual type. It was made by R. H. Neal and Co. Ltd., of Ealing, for the Anglo-Iranian Oil Company, for work in Iran, and is capable of making a lift of two tons at a radius of 14 ft., or a lift of one ton at a maximum radius of 20 ft.

The crane is mounted on a lorry chassis of the standard Albion make, and is a standard 2-ton model, with slight modifications to meet the tropical conditions in which it has to work. It is supported on a reinforced superstructure, and is driven by a special power unit built up from a 24 h.p. engine, the drive from which is taken through a roller chain to the main shaft, and from there to the hoisting drum through machine-cut spur gearing. The engine is fitted with a large tropical radiator, and a Ferodo plate clutch for disengaging the engine when starting up or when the crane is not in use for short periods. Included in the hoisting mechanism is a load-sustaining safety device, which makes the crane foolproof in operation, and prevents any possibility of the load being accidentally dropped by an unskilled driver. Slewing, derricking and luffing of the jib are controlled by Ferodo reversing clutches, and the various motions are operated from a bank of levers, which can be seen in the front of the crane.

The underframe of the crane is fitted with screw jacks and special fittings for relieving the chassis of stresses when the crane is lifting across the frame.

A lorry-mounted crane designed specially for work in Iran. It is capable of handling a load of 2 tons, and was built by R. H. Neal and Co. Ltd., of Ealing, to whom we are indebted for the illustration.

New Engines for H.M.S. "*Renown*"

An order for the construction of new machinery for the battle-cruiser "*Renown*," which was laid down in 1914 at the Fairfield Yard, Govan, has been placed with Cammell Laird and Co. Ltd., of Birkenhead. The machinery at present fitted comprises a quadruple-screw arrangement of Brown-Curtis direct-drive turbines, supplied with steam from 42 Babcock and Wilcox oil-fired boilers. After the Falkland Islands engagement in the Great War it was decided to lengthen "*Renown*'s" hull by 100 ft., and this, together with the fact that since the war the vessel has been fitted with bulges, with considerable increases in her side armour, has reduced her speed and necessitated higher powered machinery. It is expected that reconditioning of the hull will be carried out in one of H.M. Royal Dockyards simultaneously with the provision of new engines.

Moving a Road with Air

Compressed air is being used by the New Jersey State Highway Department to move an eight mile strip of concrete highway sideways a distance of 12 ft. The task is effected simply by placing a length of hose in a narrow space alongside the strip of concrete to be moved. The hose is then inflated with air, and as the pressure rises the hose expands and pushes the concrete sideways. The place it is to occupy is previously graded and the concrete simply slides over the ground surface, no rollers or other device being employed.

The concrete is 9 in. thick and is in slabs that each weigh about 30 tons. From 12 to 14 of these slabs are moved at each operation.

A striking test of quality! A standard 36×8 Firestone motor car tube inflated to a diameter of 8 ft. Photograph by courtesy of the Firestone Tyre and Rubber Co. Ltd.

Car Components Made from Farm Produce

At the River-Rouge plant of the Ford Motor Co., machinery is being installed for making certain motor car parts from a plastic material produced from Soy beans. The machinery includes giant mixers, storage tanks, presses and moulds, and when the installation is complete it will cover about 86,000 sq. ft. of floor space and will be the largest factory in the world devoted to turning farm produce into industrial articles. It is estimated that the factory will have an output of 100,000 parts a day.

A Unique Highway

A splendid express highway that will provide for five traffic lanes, and will be the only one of its kind outside New York City, is being constructed in St. Louis, U.S.A. The new road forms part of a super-highway 38 miles in length, and not a single street intersection at grade level will be encountered within St. Louis itself, a feat that is to be accomplished by carrying the highway through subways at some points, and at other points over cross roads by means of overpasses. Where the road passes through subways wide sloping banks will be provided, and these will be grassed and laid out as flower beds.

Great American Bridge Scheme

Work is proceeding rapidly on the new Triborough Bridge scheme across the East River, New York, which when completed will form a new arterial highway for vehicular and pedestrian traffic between the boroughs of Queens, Manhattan, and the Bronx. The bridge will connect also with Randall's and Ward's Islands over which it passes. The complete scheme will consist of a suspension bridge over the East River, a vertical lift bridge over the Harlem River, through truss spans over the Bronx Kills and an adjacent railroad yard, together with a section of girder viaduct approaches, and altogether will have a total length of 3½ miles. The suspension bridge will have a main span of 1,380 ft. and end spans of 705 ft. The deck will be suspended 135 ft. over water level and will be supported by two wire cables each 20¾ in. in diameter.

* * * *

A small motor tug equipped with two 350 h.p. gas engines that operate on suction gas made from small coke, is in use on the River Rhine. The vessel is very economical in fuel costs, and its performance is stated to be satisfactory.

How Gears and Gear Units are Made

Transmitting Heavy Loads at High Speed

GEARS and gear units are used for the reduction and increase of speed almost wherever power is transmitted. The extent to which they are applied is illustrated by the products manufactured at the Park Works of David Brown and Sons (Hudd) Ltd., at Huddersfield, which range from small speedometer gears to monster mine winding and similar gears 30 ft. in diameter. A large proportion of these gears are absorbed by the automobile industry, and the "DBS" patent worm drive of this firm is applied to more than 100 makes of motor vehicles. In this connection it is interesting to note that the gear box gears for Sir Malcolm Campbell's "Bluebird," in which the world's land speed record of 301.377 m.p.h. was created, were of "David Brown" manufacture. These gears were eight in number and were made of high nickel chrome molybdenum case hardening steel. Their teeth were generated and ground on machines of high accuracy, and they provided forward speeds to transmit no less than 2,500 h.p.

The gears manufactured by David Brown and Sons (Hudd) Ltd. may be divided into four main sections. The first of these comprises general industrial gearing and includes a very large range of self-contained gears and geared motors of the helical, bevel and worm type for every class of speed reducing and increasing mechanism. Turbine reducing and increasing gears up to the largest sizes also come under this section as well as helical, worm and spiral bevel gears for the cement, paper, steel, rubber, mining, chemical and textile industries and for public utility work. In short, every piece of mechanism that can be rotated by means of toothed gearing comes within the scope of the firm's activities.

Heavy type single reduction gear unit for cogging mill at the works of Arthur Lee and Sons Ltd., Sheffield. The illustrations to this article are reproduced by courtesy of David Brown and Sons (Hudd) Ltd., Huddersfield.

Marine gearing forms the second section. In this the principal demand is for helical gearing up to the largest sizes manufactured for ships' propulsion, steering and reversing gears and worm, helical and bevel gears for auxiliary machinery and shipyard plant. Traction gearing is included in the third section. The firm manufactures gear box gears, complete change-speed units, steering gears and units, clutches and worm gear differential units, and the "David Brown" patent worm gear is applied to motor vehicles and also to trolley buses, oil and electric locomotives and railcars. Finally comes the machine tool section, including a variety of machines developed to ensure the highest accuracy in the finished product.

One of the most important advances in gear manufacture has been made possible by the advent of "generation." In this, the gear tooth profile is automatically generated by a straight-sided cutter, hob or grinding wheel, or by a disc cutter where the profile is accurately ground to true involute form. This process is particularly valuable in the case of double helical gears, in the making of which reciprocating cutters are now largely used. Plano-generating is the name given to this method.

On account of the heavy stresses imposed upon modern gear drives, it is essential that only the highest grade materials shall be employed and the service of an up-to-date metallurgical department is necessary for proper control. In the metallurgical department at the David Brown Works all bars and billets are checked by analysis and tests of their physical properties and, more important still, concealed weaknesses are searched for, since only by continual vigilance in the selection of all raw materials can the necessary high standard and uniformity of composition be maintained. Working in conjunction with this department is a physical laboratory where further tests are made on materials for impact, hardness, tensile strength, resistance to compression and transverse or bending stresses, while in a separate mechanical research laboratory vigorous tests are made for running efficiencies, temperature rises, coefficients of friction between oils and metals, noise production and other features of every type of gear and complete unit.

For mine winding and colliery drives, paper, rubber and steel rolling mills, sewage and drainage plants and other high duty applications helical gears now have a widespread use, and their superiority over straight-toothed spur gears is an established fact. In the case of the spur gear the load is suddenly applied along the top edge of the tooth and is released as suddenly when engagement ceases. On the other hand, with a helical gear, contact is made at one corner of the tooth face and the load traverses diagonally across the whole width of the face of the gear. In addition there are always more teeth in contact. The load therefore is more evenly distributed, and this contributes largely to quieter and smoother running, increased load capacity and long life.

Helical pinions usually are made of high carbon forged steel, and alloy steels such as carbon-chrome or nickel-chrome may be used in the case of exceptionally heavy loading. The material for the wheel may be a cast iron of high tensile strength, or cast steel, or it may be comprised of carbon steel forged rings shrunk on to cast iron centres, the material used depending on the duties to be performed and the conditions of working. Wheels up to 8 ft. diameter usually are made solid; above this size the boss may be split to relieve contraction stresses and fitted with turned steel hoops, shrunk on after the slots have been filled.

Double reduction turbine gears for the coal hydrogenation plant of Imperial Chemical Industries Ltd., at Billingham. Each gear weighs 50 tons and transmits 3,250 h.p.

Three methods are employed in the production of helical gears at David Browns, and the choice of the one to be used depends on the size of gear and the conditions in which it operates. The first method is known as plano-generating, in which the teeth are generated from the solid by means of profile-ground rack-type cutters operating from either side of the gear. Right and left hand helices are produced meeting at the centre of the face-width, thus affording maximum load carrying capacity. These gears are produced in sizes up to 15 ft. diameter by 2 ft. 6 in. face-width.

The illustration on the opposite page shows a 63.5 in. centres heavy type single reduction gear unit for cogging mill drive supplied to Arthur Lee and Sons Ltd., Sheffield. This gear is designed to transmit 1,500 h.p. normally, and a peak load of 8,000 h.p. when reducing from 600 r.p.m. to 80 r.p.m. The double helical gears employed were accurately generated by the plano-generating process and the unit was supplied complete with fly wheels to damp out fluctuations in the drive.

Form milling or end milling is the name given to the second method. This process is used chiefly for heavy gears of large pitch up to those with diameters of 19 ft. and face-width of 5 ft. that are suitable for such applications as mine winders and rolling mill plant. The right and left hand helices blend together at the centre, being milled from the solid by means of accurately ground cutters.

Triple helical gears with continuous teeth are produced in a similar manner. An example of this type is illustrated in the lower photograph on this page, which shows the wheel of a triple helical gear, 90 in. between centres, for electric winders supplied to Markham and Co. Ltd., of Chesterfield, for East Rand Proprietary Mines Ltd. Each set of these gears normally transmits 2,687 h.p., and a peak load of 5,579 h.p. when reducing from 200 r.p.m. to 31.5 r.p.m. of the winding drum. The wheels are of cast steel and were made in halves. They have 166 teeth and are 13 ft. in diameter and 34 in. in face-width. The pinions were forged solid with their shafts. They were made from forged steel and have 26 teeth, their overall length and diameter being 10 ft. 6½ in. and 26 in. respectively.

Triple helical gears for electric winders for East Rand Proprietary Mines Ltd. Each set transmits a peak load of 5,579 h.p.

The third gear cutting process used by David Brown is hobbing, the cutters employed being known as hobs. This usually is applied to wide faced gears of fine pitch, such as are embodied in high speed turbine gears of both land and marine types, but its use is not necessarily confined to this class of work. Special machines having accurate dividing and feed mechanisms are used, and the hob shields are ground after hardening in order to eliminate any errors due to distortion caused by the hardening process and also to ensure the preservation of exact tooth form during numerous re-sharpening operations. Gears up to 14 ft. in diameter and 7 ft. in face-width can be dealt with at Park Works.

The upper photograph shows double reduction turbine gears for the I.C.I. (Fertiliser and Synthetic Products) Ltd. coal hydrogenation plant at Billingham.

Some Facts about Railway Wheels

Types for Engines, Carriages and Wagons

By R. D. Gauld, M.Eng., A.M.Inst.C.E.

COMPARED with their humble origins about a hundred years ago, our railways are now colossal undertakings of the greatest complexity. They employ hundreds of thousands of people, receive and spend millions of pounds every year, and in addition to the line, rolling stock and stations, are owners of hotels, steamships, harbours and docks. The whole vast organisation has developed from the discovery that wheels running on rails were a great improvement on any transport system previously known, so that the wheel and the rail are the two primary devices on which the whole elaborate structure depends. Not only for this reason, however, but also because the wheel is itself a remarkable invention, it will be interesting to find out something about this very essential railway appliance.

A coach wheel of the Mansell type in which the centre between the boss and the rim is formed of hard wood blocks.

We are not here concerned with the kind of wheels used on luggage barrows, horse vans, and so on, although strictly speaking these also are railway wheels. We will confine our attention to the wheels that actually run on the rails, and which can be divided into the three main classes, engine, carriage and wagon wheels.

At one time engine wheels were made of cast iron, and at a later date of wrought iron; but nowadays practically all such wheels are made of cast steel. This refers to what is called the wheel centre, consisting of the hub, the spokes, and the rim. Outside the rim is the tyre, which takes the wear, and, by means of the flange, guides the wheel on the rail. The cast steel centre is toughened by an annealing process, and the hub or boss is bored to receive the axle, and also the crank pin if the wheel is a driving wheel. The boring is done in a lathe, and at the same setting the rim is turned to the correct size to receive the tyre.

The diameter of engine driving wheels varies considerably, according to the type of engine. For express passenger work we find such figures as 6 ft. 6 in. for the "Royal Scot" and L.M.S. Compounds; 6 ft. 8 in. for the L.N.E.R "Pacifics"; 6 ft. 7 in. for the "Lord Nelsons" and "King Arthurs" of the Southern; and 6 ft. 6 in. on the Great Western "Kings." In the days of the single-driver engines much bigger wheels were used, as for instance the 8 ft. drivers of the Great Northern engines. Goods and mixed traffic engines have smaller wheels, the 2–6–0 L.M.S.R. mixed traffic locomotives having a driving wheel diameter of 5 ft. 6 in. The wheels of tenders have diameters between 3 ft. and 4 ft. A very usual diameter for carriage wheels is 3 ft. 6 in., while for wagons 3 ft. 0 in. is a general figure. It may be mentioned here that the standard distance back to back of engine tyres in this country is 4 ft. $5\frac{5}{8}$ in. with tyres $5\frac{1}{2}$ in. wide, the corresponding dimensions for carriages and wagons being 4 ft. $5\frac{1}{2}$ in. and 5 in.

A modern pressed steel coach wheel. These are used almost exclusively for up-to-date coaching stock, although sleeping cars invariably retain the Mansell pattern of wheel, as it is less noisy.

Wheels are pressed on to their axles by hydraulic pressure, which is at the rate of about eight to 10 tons for each inch of diameter of the wheel seat, that is, the hole in the boss of the wheel. For a usual example, say a 5 in. seat, the boss is bored 1/100 of an inch less in diameter than the axle, and 40 tons or more would be needed to force the axle home.

You will have noticed the crescent-shaped weights in engine driving wheels, which even in one set of wheels have different sizes, and are fixed at different positions on the wheels, relative to the coupling rod. The object of these weights is to assist the internal balance of the engine, which without them would run very badly, and soon knock itself to pieces. On cast steel wheel centres the weights are sometimes solid, sometimes hollowed out to some extent to form pockets into which lead can be run, so as to get very exact results. Another design is that in which mild steel plates are riveted on to each side of the spokes, the spaces so formed being filled, or partly filled, with lead.

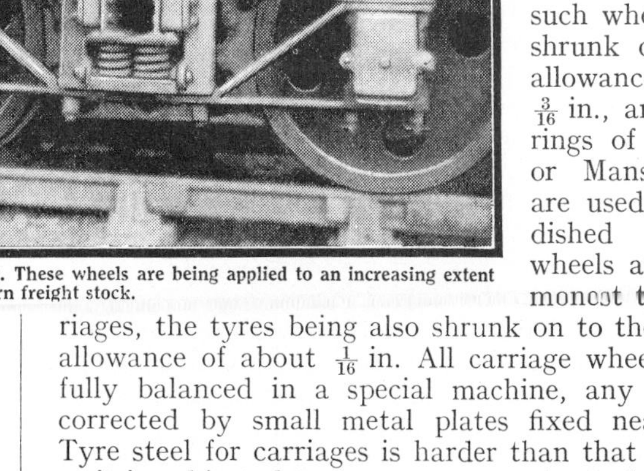

The ordinary spoked wagon wheel. This is commonly used on goods rolling stock, but is giving way to the modern steel disc wheel.

The tyres for locomotive wheels, both engine and tender, are made from a single piece of steel, rolled to the required size and shape in a special rolling mill, so that there is no join or weld in the tyre. When finished, it is bored out to a diameter slightly less than that to which the wheel centre has been turned. The difference, or shrinkage allowance as it is called, is usually 1/750 to 1/1000 of the diameter of the wheel centre. The tyre is heated in a furnace or over a ring of gas jets, until its temperature is about 250 degrees Fahrenheit. It is then placed flange upward in a shallow receptacle, usually of cast iron, and the wheel centre lowered into it. A fine spray of water is then played on to the tyre all round. But the grip of the tyre on the wheel centre so obtained is not considered sufficient for safety, and additional security is got in several ways. One method is to use $\frac{7}{8}$ in. or 1 in. studs spaced between each pair of spokes, and screwed through the edge of the wheel centre, entering the tyre about $1\frac{1}{4}$ in. to $1\frac{1}{2}$ in. Another very usual method is to use a retaining ring, which is a thin steel ring laid along the inside of the wheel, covering the joint between centre and tyre, and recessed into both, being riveted through the lip of the tyre by $\frac{5}{8}$ in. rivets.

A bogie bolster wagon running on steel disc wheels. These wheels are being applied to an increasing extent to modern freight stock.

New tyres are 3 in. thick, and after shrinking on to the centres are turned on the tread, with the correct angle of coning of 1 in 20. It is important that all driving wheels that are coupled together should be of exactly the same diameter, otherwise slipping will occur. The tyre tends to wear hollow, and is from time to time turned down in the lathe, until a minimum thickness of $1\frac{5}{8}$ in. is left after the last turning. It is scrapped when worn down to $1\frac{1}{2}$ in. but sometimes, for the largest driving wheels, less wear than this is allowed.

Some figures for the average life of engine tyres may be interesting. For driving wheels, 50,000 miles before returning is usual; 25,000 miles for leading bogie wheels, and 30,000 to 40,000 miles for tender wheels. It is worth noting that the 4–4–0 type of engine has been found the most economical in tyre wear. When several wheels are coupled together it is usual to make one or more pairs with slightly thinner flanges, to assist the passage round curves; and some 0–8–0 engines have a pair of wheels with blind flanges, that is flat rims, for the same reason.

Wheels for tenders are similar in design to driving wheels. Carriage and wagon wheels, however, show some interesting differences. At one time wooden centred wheels, known as the Mansell type, were much used for carriages. They introduced a difficulty for the signal engineer, because the wood was a sufficiently good insulator to prevent a carriage so equipped from operating the track circuits on the line. It was therefore necessary to bond the tyre to the steel boss of the wheel by a copper or metal strip, to carry the electric current. The tyres of such wheels are also shrunk on, with an allowance of about $\frac{3}{16}$ in., and retaining rings of the Gibson or Mansell pattern are used. Nowadays dished steel disc wheels are the commonest type for carriages, the tyres being also shrunk on to these, with an allowance of about $\frac{1}{16}$ in. All carriage wheels are carefully balanced in a special machine, any error being corrected by small metal plates fixed near the rim. Tyre steel for carriages is harder than that for wagons, as it is subjected to greater wear and tear by the power operated brakes. Carriage wheels are usually finished by varnishing, the tyres being painted white. A rough black lacquer or bituminous enamel is generally used for wagon wheels.

Long-Lived Express Locomotives

"Atlantics" of the L.N.E.R. (G.N. Section)

It is a remarkable fact that certain high-speed expresses are hauled by some of the oldest locomotives that are still in service in this country on main line duties. These veterans are the L.N.E.R. 4–4–2 "Atlantic" engines of former Great Northern design employed in the working of the famous Newcastle and Edinburgh Pullman trains on the portion of their journey between King's Cross and Leeds. Although the loads conveyed by these trains are limited to eight cars or some 330 tons, it must be remembered that by the fastest train between these points, the "*Queen of Scots*," an average speed of nearly 58 m.p.h. has to be maintained for almost 186 miles over a by no means easy road. At the time of the introduction of the class a load of 250 to 330 tons was held to be a heavy train. Indeed, the pre-War 2 p.m. up express from Leeds, which for many years made the longest run on the G.N.R., used to run from Wakefield to King's Cross at 56.4 m.p.h., but with a load averaging less than 200 tons.

The up "Queen of Scots" Pullman Express hauled by L.N.E.R. large-boilered "Atlantic" No. 4442, the "Royal Train" engine of the former G.N.R. The illustrations to this article are by courtesy of the L.N.E.R.

The G.N.R. "Atlantics" have had a long period on first-class duties. The type was introduced on the G.N.R. in view of the increasing weights of the chief expresses, with which the locomotives then existing were finding it difficult to deal. Bogie coaches were coming more into general use, and this, together with the introduction of corridor and restaurant stock, made necessary the development of greater power on the part of the locomotives.

After bringing out two classes of 4–4–0 locomotives, Ivatt decided to produce an engine of a different type. About this time 4–4–2 locomotives had been recently introduced, and were making a name for themselves on the Atlantic Coast Line in the United States; hence the use of the term "Atlantic" to distinguish the type. This "Atlantic" wheel arrangement was adopted for the new G.N.R. design. The 4–4–2 type allows of a material increase in boiler capacity over the 4–4–0, and this no doubt was an important factor in its selection. The new engine was of the true "Atlantic" type, having a very short coupled wheel-base, with the driving wheels in front of the fire-box, and with outside cylinders connected to the rear pair of driving wheels. In spite of the opportunity afforded by the presence of small trailing wheels to provide a wide fire-box, unrestricted by the frames or the driving wheels, the first, or small-boilered, series of G.N.R. "Atlantics" retained the narrow fire-box common to British locomotive practice.

Although notable engines at the time, the well-known "Klondykes," as they were called, their advent having coincided with the famous Alaskan "Gold Rush" in 1898, appear to us to-day to be of quite moderate dimensions. They were quite successful, however, so that it was subsequently decided to apply a much larger boiler to the same design of engine. This resulted in the appearance of the famous No. 251; but further small-boilered engines, the "252" series, were built at the same time, the idea being, apparently, that if the gigantic boiler, for those days, of No. 251 proved successful, the small-boilered engines would be converted to the new arrangement. But this transformation has never been carried out.

Apart from the size of the boiler barrel, measuring 5 ft. 6 in. in diameter, perhaps the most striking feature of No. 251 was the employment of a wide fire-box of the "Wootten" type spread out across the frames behind the driving wheels, as commonly used in American practice. The combination of this large boiler and firebox, with their remarkable capacity for the generation of steam, together with comparatively moderate-sized cylinders resulted in an engine that could scarcely be run "out of breath."

In spite of their remarkable capacity, however, the Ivatt "Atlantics" in their earlier days did not show up very well on fast and heavy duties. Although capable of continuous steaming for long stretches, and of rapid downhill running, they appeared to be deficient in tractive power for hill-climbing. As time went on, however, superheating was coming into vogue, and experiments were made with one of the small-boilered engines. As a result it was decided to incorporate superheaters and piston valves in the last 10 "Atlantics," Nos. 1452-1461, that came out from Doncaster in 1910.

The addition of superheating apparatus and the accompanying enlargement of the cylinders made a marked difference in the efficiency of the "Atlantics," and gradually its application was extended to small-boilered and large-boilered engines alike. By this time Mr. H. N. Gresley, the

present Chief Mechanical Engineer of the L.N.E.R. had taken the place of Mr. Ivatt, who had retired in 1911.

The years 1909 and 1910 were remarkable for the "locomotive exchanges" made between different pre-grouping companies, but the only one affecting the G.N.R. was the running of the L.N.W.R. 4–4–0 "Precursor" class engine, No. 412, "*Marquis,*" on certain trains out of King's Cross in 1909. In return, G.N.R. No. 1449, a large-boilered "Atlantic," went over to the L.N.W.R. and worked on the main line out of Euston. From all reports the G.N.R. engine appears to have done quite well during its temporary service on the L.N.W.R. The second item of interest was the appearance of No. 1442 of the same class at Shepherd's Bush at the White City Exhibition.

The first G.N.R. "Atlantic" No. 990, of the small-boilered series, and the first of the type in Great Britain. It is now named "Henry Oakley" and bears the L.N.E.R. number 3990.

The booster-fitted "Atlantic," now L.N.E.R. No. 4419 and formerly No. 1419. It was the first locomotive in Great Britain to be fitted with a booster, and is the only G.N.R. "Atlantic" with a side-window cab.

Ivatt was a keen experimenter and a four-cylinder variation of the original "Klondyke" design appeared in 1902 in the shape of No. 271. It was converted to the 2-cylinder arrangement in 1911, having been fitted with Walschaerts valve gear in 1904. It still remained unique when the outside cylinders were removed, for this left it as an inside-cylinder 4–4–2, the only example of the type on the line.

In the early years of this century the subject of compound locomotives was being given considerable attention. Ivatt built a large-boilered "Atlantic," No. 292, as a compound, the cylinders being four in number and disposed two inside and two outside the frames. Outside valve gear of the Walschaerts type was employed to operate the valves above the high-pressure cylinders. Another Doncaster compound was No. 1421. This engine, as well as No. 292, could be worked continuously as a simple or as a compound, as required by the work to be done, by the operation of a special change valve. No. 1421 was finally converted to the simple type in 1921. No. 292, however, finished its career as a compound.

It is interesting to note that a further experiment with 4-cylinder simple propulsion was made in 1915. Engine No. 279 was provided with four cylinders and outside Walschaerts gear. This conversion made No. 279 the most powerful express passenger locomotive then in the possession of the company.

During the War period, when train loads increased to gigantic proportions, the G.N.R. "Atlantics" performed some extraordinary work, even though the times of the principal expresses were greatly extended as compared with pre-War standards. With their relatively limited adhesion weight of only 36 tons and a tractive effort of 17,300 lb., the starting of heavy loads out of King's Cross sometimes proved difficult, and the climbing of the "Northern Heights" to Potter's Bar was necessarily slow. In view of this difficulty it is interesting that in 1923 a booster was fitted to the trailing axle of large-boilered "Atlantic" No. 1419. A booster is a small auxiliary steam engine that can be applied to a normally idle pair of wheels. Its power is transmitted by means of a movable pinion so that the booster can be cut in and cut out as required. Trials were carried out over heavy gradients with a train of 18 coaches, and the advantage of the booster was at once apparent. It was found that certain modifications were necessary, however, and the alterations that were undertaken resulted in the locomotive being capable of starting and re-starting a load of 535 tons on a gradient of 1 in 100.

With the multiplication of the Gresley "Pacific" design after grouping, however, it became possible to confine the "Atlantics" to more lightly-loaded fast trains, such as the "Harrogate Pullman" services and their developments.

Airspeed "Envoys" for South Africa

The South African Government have bought seven twin-engined Airspeed "Envoys" and they are to be delivered early this year. They will have 310 h.p. Armstrong Siddeley "Cheetah IX" engines, giving a top speed of 211 m.p.h., and their equipment will include Sperry blind-flying instruments. Three of the machines are for the South African Air Force, and each of these will have a Lewis gun mounted in a protected position on the top of the fuselage, and a Vickers gun for the pilot, and will carry a load of bombs. The other four machines will be used for commercial air transport, two being five-seaters and two six-seaters.

Zeppelin Progress

The new Zeppelin LZ.129 is expected to be ready for her first flight by the end of this month. During the spring and summer she will make several flights, one of which will take her across the North Atlantic to New Jersey; and in the autumn she will join the *"Graf Zeppelin"* in operating the regular air mail service to South America.

The *"Graf Zeppelin"* is now being overhauled in readiness for the resumption of this fortnightly service in the spring. She is still in good form, and this will be her eighth year of service on this important route. Her retirement from it is being considered, however, and the construction of a new airship, LZ.130, to replace her, will be begun at Friedrichshafen when the hangar has been vacated by the LZ.129. The Zeppelin works there are being extended so that the completion of LZ.129 and work on the third airship can be hastened.

French Record Flight

A prize of £2,000 offered by the French Air Ministry for the fastest flight from Paris to Madagascar has been won by M. Genin and M. Robert, the holders of the previous record. They used a Cauldron-Simoun monoplane fitted with a 180 h.p. Renault engine, and flew from Le Bourget, Paris, to Antananarivo, Madagascar, in 57 hr. 32 min., averaging 110 m.p.h. This was 27 hr. 47 min. less than their previous record time for the journey.

The First *"Miles Merlin"*

The first *"Miles Merlin"* monoplane, described and illustrated on page 90, was purchased by Capt. G. Birkett of Birkett Air Services. He co-operated in the designing of the aeroplane, and since taking delivery of it he has flown it a great deal abroad, chiefly between Jibuti, in Abyssinia, and Cairo, a distance of about 2,000 miles, in connection with Press work.

Capt. Birkett flew back to this country in December, and the *"Miles Merlin"* has since been fitted with wireless telegraph transmitting and receiving apparatus. This equipment will help to get over the language difficulty when the aeroplane is chartered for Press work in countries where English is not spoken. It will be necessary to carry a wireless operator in addition to the pilot, but the latter will be relieved of wireless duties.

Air-flow study at Farnborough. The automatic camera mounted on the tail of this Parnall monoplane is filming the movements of tufts of wool attached to the wing. Photograph by courtesy of "Flight."

D.L.H. South Atlantic Service

When the two depot ships *"Westfalen"* and *"Schwabenland"* had to be overhauled last autumn, the D.L.H. South Atlantic air mails were carried by the *"Graf Zeppelin"* until the ships resumed their stations. This disorganisation will be avoided in future, as a third depot ship has been ordered by the D.L.H. It will be used to replace the *"Westfalen"* and *"Schwabenland"* in turn when they next require overhauling.

The new vessel will have a speed of 15 knots, and is expected to be ready this summer.

Vacancies in the R.A.F.

The Air Ministry announce that there are 300 vacancies in the R.A.F. this month for Boy Entrants for training as wireless operators, armourers and photographers, and those accepted will be given 12 to 16 months' training in the particular trade to which they are allotted.

Boys between 15¾ and 17¼ years on the first of this month are eligible, provided they have attended a secondary, junior technical or central school up to the age of 15½, or have attained an equivalent educational standard. There is no entrance examination, but candidates must be nominated by a recognised authority and present themselves for interview. Boys still at school can obtain full particulars and application forms from their headmasters, and boys who have left school can obtain them from the local Ministry of Labour advisory committee for juvenile employment, or the local education authority, or from the Air Ministry (Boy Entrants Dept.), London, W.C.2.

Proposed North Atlantic Air Mail Service

The first survey flights in connection with the proposed air mail service between this country and Canada and the United States will be carried out between 15th March and 15th May this year. If all goes well a regular air mail service will be introduced in 1937. It will be operated by a northern route, and there will be landing stations at London, Northern Ireland, Newfoundland, Montreal, New York and Washington.

Two wireless floating beacons will be established to guide the aircraft. The British Government have undertaken to maintain one beacon, which will be anchored in the Atlantic at a point about 600 miles west of Ireland; and the U.S. Government will have the other one placed a similar distance east of Newfoundland. The mails from this country will be flown by Imperial Airways, and those from America and Canada will be brought here by Pan-American Airways.

It is understood that the two companies will share the preliminary expenses of the undertaking.

Air Service Extensions

Every week brings forecasts and announcements of new or extended air services to be introduced this spring.

A contract has been signed between the Portuguese Government and Crilly Airways Ltd., for the conveyance by air of mails between Lisbon and London, and the new service is to be in full operation by the first of this month. Passengers will also be carried. As British aeroplanes cannot be delivered in time, Fokker F.XIIs will be used, and they are expected to make the trip in 9½ hr. These three-engined cabin monoplanes cruise at 151 m.p.h., and have seating for two pilots and 16 passengers. A Lisbon-Oporto service may be started this year.

In Russia last year a freight service was operated between Moscow and Vladivostok, a distance of over 5,000 miles, and passengers were carried over part of the journey. This year a regular passenger service over the whole route will be introduced, and also two branch services linking up with it. Another important air service to begin this spring will operate between Moscow and Prague.

British Continental Airways' service to Amsterdam is to be extended to Copenhagen and Stockholm, by way of Hamburg and Malmo. The extended service will begin early in May, and new D.H.86 machines will be used.

High Speed Lockheed "Electras"

L.O.T., the chief Polish air transport company, have ordered four Lockheed "Electra" 10A monoplanes. These 12-seater twin engined aeroplanes have 400 h.p. Pratt and Whitney "Wasp-Junior" engines and can attain a top speed of 206 m.p.h. at 5,000 ft. When received from the makers they will be used on the company's internal air lines.

A more recent version of the Lockheed "Electra," called type 10E, is now being put into production, and three of them have been bought by Pan-American Airways for their services to Alaska, Mexico and Cuba. The "Electra" 10E has two Pratt and Whitney Wasp 83HI engines that give it a top speed of 215 m.p.h. and a cruising speed of 205 m.p.h., and make it the fastest cruising twin-engined aeroplane in the United States. It carries two pilots and 10 passengers, and 240 lb. of luggage or other freight. The undercarriage is retracted during a flight.

An Avro "652" monoplane viewed from the rear. The neat streamlining of this design is well brought out. Photograph by courtesy of A. V. Roe and Co. Ltd., Manchester.

Mass Parachuting in Russia

In Russia the military authorities attach great importance to ability to descend from aircraft by parachute. The necessary training is not yet compulsory in the Red Army, but according to General Voroshiloff, the Defence Commissar, so many of the men wish to be trained as parachutists that the demand greatly exceeds present facilities.

Some idea of the extent to which training has already been carried out is shown by the fact that at a demonstration during the autumn manœuvres last year 1,200 armed men landed by parachute at Kieff Aerodrome at the same time, and another 2,500 landed during the next 40 min. This mass descent of an army introduces a new factor into warfare on land.

Tata Air Lines Developments

The new coastal air mail service between Bombay and Trivandrum, the capital of the State of Travancore, mentioned in these pages last August, has now been in operation for just over three months. The southward flight is made on Tuesdays and takes just under nine hours, including two stops on the way. The return flight to Bombay is made on Fridays and in faster time, taking slightly less than seven hours, including two stops. Passengers are carried on these trips when the quantity of mail makes this possible.

The proposed coastal air service from Madras to Colombo still awaits the completion of the Colombo Airport.

One of the Fokker F.XXII 4-engined monoplanes belonging to the K.L.M. Photograph by courtesy of N.V. Nederlandsche Vliegtuigenfabriek.

New Aircraft for Imperial Airways

New equipment under construction for Imperial Airways includes 12 high-speed Armstrong Whitworth monoplanes, in addition to the 29 Short Empire flying boats mentioned in these pages last December. The monoplanes will be of the high wing type and will be driven by four Armstrong Siddeley "Tiger" engines each of 900 h.p. An advantage of high wing monoplanes for passenger work is that the occupants of the cabins have an unobstructed view from all the windows.

Each monoplane will seat 27 passengers by day, in three 9-passenger cabins situated one in front of the wing and two behind it and separated by doors. There will also be a freight and luggage compartment, a mail compartment and a kitchen. At night sleeping accommodation will be available for 20 passengers, four in the front cabin and eight in each of the two rear cabins. The bunks will be arranged in pairs, one above the other.

"The Star of India"

Under an agreement recently drawn up between Indian National Airways and the Government of India, the company will maintain and operate the Viceroy's Avro "642," *"The Star of India."* This machine was illustrated on page 341 of the *"M.M."* of June 1935.

Protecting Wooden Propellers

A new process patented in Germany is designed to preserve aeroplane propellers from changes due to atmospheric conditions. In this process, according to the aeronautical correspondent of the *"Daily Telegraph,"* the leading edge of each blade is reinforced with a narrow brass sheath soldered to a strip of gauze, and the propeller is then covered with a sheet of celluloid forced into the wood under pressure.

New Japanese Aircraft Carrier

A new Japanese aircraft carrier has been launched from the Kure Naval Dockyard. It is called *"Soryu,"* and is of 10,050 tons. It will have a speed of 30 knots, and will carry an armament of twelve 127 mm. guns, and will be the second largest Japanese aircraft carrier, the largest being the *"Akagi,"* of 26,900 tons. Other aircraft carriers are the *"Ruyjo,"* of 7,600 tons and the *"Hosho,"* 7,470 tons.

High-Speed Light Aeroplanes

Three New British Types

THIS month we describe three interesting new types of British light aeroplanes, the D.H. "*Hornet Moth,*" the B.A. "*Swallow*" and the "*Miles Merlin.*"

The "*Hornet Moth*" is the latest cabin light aeroplane produced by the de Havilland Aircraft Co. Ltd. It is the successor to the open cockpit biplanes known throughout the world under the general name of "Moth," and of which more than 4,000 have been sold. Many of these earlier types have been described and illustrated in the "*M.M.*" The new machine is the company's 87th design, and incorporates all the knowledge gained since the first "Moth" was produced in 1925. It was introduced at the King's Cup Air Race, 1934, when it was flown by Capt. G. de Havilland. A year was then devoted to improving the design, and during that time two more experimental machines were built and many hundreds of hours of tests were carried out, and every feature of the new type was tried and retried.

The B.A. "Swallow" in flight. This illustration and those on opposite page are reproduced by courtesy of "Flight."

It is a sturdy little biplane, ideal for civilian flying schools and also very suitable for the private owner. The enclosed cabin gives ample and comfortable side-by-side seating for two occupants. By reason of being under cover, the learner, seated beside the instructor, is relieved of the paraphernalia of helmet, goggles, flying clothing, speaking tubes, and other gear necessary in a tandem-seated open cockpit aircraft. Conversation is possible in a normal pitch of voice, and of course the instructor, with such excellent contact with his pupil, can demonstrate and explain the movement and action of the controls and instruments in the most effective manner. Dual control is provided by a central "stick" fitted with two branches fixed at angles to which one's hands rest naturally. A second set of engine controls can be fitted on the starboard side of the cabin.

The first "Miles Merlin" light transport monoplane. Photograph reproduced by courtesy of Phillips and Powis Aircraft Ltd., Woodley.

Both occupants of the cabin have an unrestricted outlook in all essential directions, and the view for landing could not be better. Sliding windows provide ample ventilation without creating annoying draughts. A large door on each side of the fuselage permits the easiest possible entrance and exit, and there is an emergency escape panel fitted in the transparent roof of the cabin. Beneath the seating in the cockpit is a space for keeping tools or other gear, and if necessary this space can be utilised for an extra petrol tank of 8½ gall. capacity.

The undercarriage is designed for rough ground and to withstand the harsh treatment to which a machine used for school work is subjected. When the machine is in flight the fairings of the undercarriage legs can be turned to present their broad side to the airstream and thus act as a powerful air brake. The tail unit is of the ordinary type, and the fore and aft trim of the elevators is controlled from the cockpit by the pilot.

Another important point in favour of the "*Hornet Moth*" as a training machine is that it is exceptionally easy to fly. Stability and control have been perfected in it to such an extent that a pilot can "cruise" indefinitely, execute all manœuvres and even land without touching the rudder bar, which need be used only for directional control when taking-off, and for ground manœuvrability. It is almost impossible to make the aeroplane spin, provided the rudder is not used; and this is very re-assuring to a pilot flying in all weathers. It means that when in cloud, fog, or rain all he has to do is to remove his feet from the rudder bar and control the machine entirely by movements of the stick. Provided he maintains sufficient altitude for the country over which he is passing, he should never get into trouble and he need never get the machine into a dangerous attitude.

The "*Hornet Moth*" has an overall length of 24 ft. 9½ in.,

and the wing span of 32 ft. 7½ in. is reduced to 9 ft. 6 in. when the wings are folded; the machine can then be housed easily in a garage little larger than most motor car lock-ups. The wings, fuselage and tail unit are of wood and covered with fabric. The engine is the standard 130 D.H. "Gipsy Major," and every part of it is easily accessible by reason of the low height of the engine "nose" and the quickly detachable cowling that forms the bonnet. This engine gives the aeroplane a top speed of 131 m.p.h., and a cruising speed of 111 m.p.h. at 1,000 ft. The rate of climb is 800 ft. per min. and the absolute ceiling, or greatest height to which the aeroplane can fly, is 17,800 ft. With a normal load of petrol the range is 376 miles. Extra fuel tanks can be fitted, and the fuel capacity is then 43½ gall. and the range 817 miles.

Another view of the B.A. "Swallow." The rather severe lines of this excellent two-seater are very noticeable.

The two other aeroplanes illustrated here are low wing monoplanes. The B.A. "*Swallow*" is a two-seater with open cockpits arranged one behind the other. There is no need for the occupants to wear goggles or special clothes on that account, however, as transparent curved screens in front protect them from bad weather. Dual control is fitted, of course. The forward part of the fuselage has double walls, and in the cockpits the inner wall is covered with plywood. A very clean design has been obtained by reducing external fittings to a minimum, and the straight lines of the machine give it a rather severe appearance.

The "*Swallow*" is produced by the British Aircraft Manufacturing Co. Ltd., and is an improved version of the British Klemm "*Swallow*" mentioned on page 13 of the "*M.M.*" of January 1935. The wings and fuselage are of wood covered with plywood, and the elevator and rudder are also of wood and covered with fabric. The wings are 42 ft. 8¼ in. in span, and taper in plan and elevation. They are arranged so that they can be folded back, in which condition the overall width is only 15 ft. 1 in., or little more than one-third of their span when spread. The undercarriage is an improved non-retractable type and the legs are fitted with specially designed shock absorbers.

The machine is very easy to fly, and it is perfectly safe in the hands of an amateur pilot; indeed, the makers claim that it is the safest in the world to fly. The stalling speed, that is the speed at which the aeroplane ceases to maintain its height, is well below 30 m.p.h. It is worth noting that the "*Swallow*" achieves this low stalling speed without the use of wing flaps and slots. The aeroplane can be fitted with either a 70/75 h.p. British Salmson engine or a 75/76 h.p. Pobjoy "Cataract II." With the more powerful engine installed it has a maximum speed of 112 m.p.h. and cruises at 98 m.p.h. The fuel tanks are in the wings, and the fuel gravitates from them to a service tank immediately behind the engine. The take-off run, with full load, is only 50 yd., and the rate of climb is 800 ft. per min. The absolute ceiling is 17,000 ft.

Apart from being a low wing and single-engined aeroplane, the "*Miles Merlin*" has little in common with the B.A. "*Swallow*." It is a development of the "*Miles Falcon*" described and illustrated in the "*M.M.*" of February 1935, and is produced by the same firm, Phillip and Powis Aircraft Ltd., of Reading aerodrome. It is the first 5-seater British commercial aeroplane designed to use a variable pitch propeller. The "*Merlin*" is produced as a private charter or feeder line aeroplane, and it can be used either as a mail carrier or as a comfortable miniature air liner. If required it can easily be converted into an aerial ambulance.

This view of a D.H. "Hornet Moth" in the air gives a good idea of the excellent outlook from the cockpit.

It is built of wood with plywood-covered wings and fuselage. The trailing edges of the wings are fitted with the Miles patent split flaps, which are operated hydraulically by a small pump in the cockpit and not only reduce the landing speed but make the approach and landing an easy matter. The cabin is 6 ft. 6 in. in length and averages 4 ft. in width, and is very similar to that of the "*Falcon*." The windscreen that forms the upper front of the cabin slopes forward like that of the older machine, and large side windows further help in making the cabin very light. The seats are arranged in two rows of two and three respectively, and behind the second row is a luggage locker large enough to take a stretcher when the aeroplane is used as an ambulance.

The "*Merlin*" has a 200 h.p. D.H. "Gipsy VI" engine, and attains a top speed of 155 m.p.h.

G.W.R. 1936 Programme

Quite apart from the works to be carried out under the Government loan scheme, announced in last month's *"M.M.,"* the G.W.R. have planned the largest programme of renewals and additions that has been undertaken by them for some years. The "Castle" class is to be increased by 25 new engines, and in addition to 10 engines of the "Hall" class, 100 new locomotives of a similar type for general traffic purposes will be built. Ninety tank locomotives are included in the programme, 10 of these being fitted for auto-train or "pull-and-push" working.

Further end-vestibuled rolling stock, as put into service last year for the *"Cornish Riviera Limited"* will give increased comfort on long distance services. Special vehicles for pleasure parties and coaches affording a modern cafeteria service will be built. A further 1,250 freight vehicles completely fitted with the vacuum brake will be added to G.W.R. stock. The company already operate the highest proportion of fully brake-fitted freight stock in the country.

Over 400 miles of track are to be completely or partly renewed, in addition to the usual maintenance of stations and other structures. Some 50 bridges are to be partly or wholly reconstructed.

The *"Bournemouth Belle"* Runs Daily

The popularity of the all-Pullman *"Bournemouth Belle"* service has increased to such an extent that the train will continue to run daily during the year between Waterloo, Southampton, and Bournemouth. Until recently, daily running has been confined to Summer holiday periods, the train running on Sundays only during the Winter.

This modern service was commenced in 1931, although Pullmans were included in the Bournemouth services of the former L.S.W.R. many years ago, but were discontinued even before the War. The present *"Bournemouth Belle,"* however, consists of first and third-class Pullmans, affording all the luxury and convenience of an up-to-date hotel.

S.R. "Schools" Class Performance

With the normal winter loads of about 300 tons, the "Schools" class 4-4-0 engines can usually be relied on to put up some sparkling performances on the 80-minute expresses between London and Folkestone. On a recent occasion No. 919, *"Harrow,"* ably driven by A. W. Ely of Ramsgate shed, reached Folkestone in exactly 77 min. in spite of signal checks through the London suburban area. On the steeply-rising length from New Cross, the 9.4 miles from Hither Green to Knockholt summit were run at an average of 47.3 m.p.h., and 1½ min. lost by signals had been regained as early as Sevenoaks.

Speed rose to 74 m.p.h. on the descent to Tonbridge, which was passed exactly on time in 38½ min. from Charing Cross, a distance of 29½ miles. Some fast running followed, with an average speed of 65.3 m.p.h. over the 34.4 miles from Paddock Wood to Shorncliffe. A speed of 72½ m.p.h. was reached on the dead level near Headcorn, and Westenhanger summit, after 8 miles rising almost continuously at 1 in 266, was "topped" at 58½ m.p.h. Folkestone was reached 3 min. early.

The net time was not more than 75½ min., giving a start-to-stop average of 55.6 m.p.h. over this difficult route. The exact load was 288 tons tare and 305 tons with passengers and luggage. This run was recorded by Mr. O. S. Nock.

* * * *

Colour-light signalling is to be installed at Newcastle Central Station. The new system will be similar to that at present in operation between York (Poppleton Junction) and Northallerton.

Southern 4-6-2 tank locomotive No. 517 at Feltham, where the class is used chiefly on goods workings to and from the marshalling yard. The Urie "stovepipe" chimney is still retained on these engines, but it is now without the capuchon or raised lip at the front. (H.R.C. prize-winning photograph.)

Speedy Irish Railcars

Some rapid schedules are being operated by two railcars in service on the N.C.C. section of the L.M.S.R. The most noteworthy of these consists of running the 31 miles from Belfast to Ballymena in 45 minutes, inclusive of four stops. After some smart running between stops, the journey concludes with a non-stop run from Dunadry to Belfast, 15.9 miles in 22 minutes. On a recent trip on the service, Railcar No. 1 kept time without difficulty in spite of a furious head wind and driving rain. This car is fitted with two 140 h.p. Leyland petrol engines driving through a hydraulic torque-converter. The smartest run in the initial stages was from Antrim to Muckamore, 1.9 miles in 3 minutes, in spite of one mile rising at 1 in 196 from the start; the maximum speed was 46 m.p.h. On the final length, speed was sustained at 47 m.p.h. up the 1 in 180 grade to Kingsbog Junction, and rose to a maximum of 57 m.p.h. afterwards. For a railcar designed for short-distance work, and without any special aids to fast running such as streamlining, this is an excellent performance. The rough day provided a severe test of the efficiency of the windscreen wipers, and very well they emerged too, while the riding of the car at high speed was most comfortable. This particular car is covering a daily mileage of 300, including four of these fast runs in each direction between Belfast and Ballymena.

We are indebted to Mr. O. S. Nock for these timings.

* * * *

In the caption for the lower illustration on page 23 of last month's issue reference was incorrectly made to "Ambleside" station. This should have been "Arnside," the error having arisen through a mistake in copying. It did *not* escape the notice of our lynx-eyed readers!

* * * *

The L.M.S.R. "Turbomotive" is working between Liverpool and Euston. Leaving Liverpool at 8.15 a.m. it returns on the down *"Merseyside Express."*

The upper illustration shows L.M.S.R. No. 2537, one of the new two-cylinder 2-6-4 tanks recently put into service. Photograph by courtesy of the L.M.S.R. The lower illustration (H.R.C. prize-winning photograph) shows a typical station scene at Bangor, North Wales, where a varied consignment of parcels is being dealt with.

L.M.S.R. Locomotive and Rolling Stock Developments

During 1936 the L.M.S.R. plan to add to their stock 133 locomotives, 111 locomotive boilers, 687 carriages and 9,485 wagons. In addition 900 containers are to be built, and three steamers; and 600 miles of permanent way are to be renewed. The locomotives will be built in the Company's shops, and 48 of them will be similar to the existing 3-cylinder 4-6-0 "Jubilee" class. New passenger tank locomotives of the 2-cylinder 2-6-4 type, as shown in the photograph above, will be constructed to the number of 70, also 15 2-8-0 heavy freight locomotives.

The passenger coaches will afford increased comfort, and the bulk of them will be of the modern vestibuled and corridor type. The freight wagons will range from the 12-ton standard open wagon to 30-ton bogie timber trucks. The new containers are to be designed to meet the requirements of particular industries, and will increase the Company's total stock to 7,528. The road transport programme provides for over 300 motor vehicles.

Contracts also have been placed to the value of £2,800,000 under the Government loan scheme for the construction of 369 steam locomotives and 270 passenger carriages. Sir W. G. Armstrong Whitworth and Co. Ltd., are to build 227 4-6-0 mixed traffic tender engines of class "5P.5F." The Vulcan Foundry Ltd., are to build 69 2-8-0 freight engines. The North British Locomotive Co. Ltd., have secured the contract for 73 2-6-4 suburban passenger tanks. All of these locomotives will be of the 2-cylinder type.

The construction of the passenger coaches has been allocated as follows: one hundred third-class vestibuled coaches are to be built each by the Metropolitan-Cammel Carriage and Wagon Co. Ltd., and by the Birmingham Railway Carriage and Wagon Co. Ltd.; fifty brake-thirds of similar construction are to be built by R. W. Pickering and Co. Ltd., and the Gloucester Railway Carriage and Wagon Co. Ltd., will be responsible for the construction of 20 new kitchen cars. Apart from the employment caused by the construction of these locomotives and rolling stock, the work will involve the use of some 40,000 tons of steel and 5,000 tons of non-ferrous metals, thus providing additional employment in the production of the raw and semi-manufactured materials required.

Euston Station to be Rebuilt

The most important of the schemes to be carried out by the London Midland and Scottish Railway under the Government loan arrangement is the rebuilding of Euston Station, including the hotel and offices. Many of the existing buildings were erected nearly a century ago to the designs of Hardwicke, and the reconstruction will involve a complete demolition of all buildings between the Station and Euston Road, and rebuilding within those limits.

Mr. Percy Thomas, the new President of the Royal Institute of British Architects, has been appointed as Consulting Architect, to co-operate with the Company's Architect, Mr. W. H. Hamlyn, F.R.I.B.A., and the Chief Civil Engineer, Mr. W. K. Wallace, in the preparation of plans and designs for the whole of the buildings embraced in the scheme. These include the railway station, hotel, and offices for the Company's staff.

The Procession to the Scrap Heap

With the passing of 1935 several classes of L.M.S.R. locomotives, well known and famous in their day, have become extinct as the result of the rapid progress of locomotive standardisation. The old 0-4-4 Kirtley well-tanks, so familiar on Midland lines in the London area, have now all gone. The class originated in 1869 and numbered 26 engines in all. The last survivor was No. 1219. Also obsolete now are the smallest of the 4-4-2 tanks of the L.T. and S. section, the last being No. 2073 built in 1884. So too have passed the L.N.W.R. 4-6-0 "Experiments," first built in 1905 chiefly for the Anglo-Scottish traffic. Again, the last two "Claughtons" with original small boilers, Nos. 5951 and 5984, have been withdrawn, and it is said that the large-boilered rebuilds are soon to follow. It is significant, too, that the superheated "Precursors" and "George the Fifths," hitherto unaffected by scrapping, have commenced to be reduced in numbers.

* * * *

The 14 new L.N.E.R. locomotives of the "Sandringham" class will bear names of the following famous football clubs: *"Huddersfield Town," "Derby County," "Sunderland," "Middlesbrough," "Sheffield Wednesday," "Arsenal," "Manchester City," "Leeds United," "Grimsby Town," "Doncaster Rovers," "Newcastle United," "Sheffield United," "Norwich City"* and *"Hull City."*

Strange Rivers and Waterfalls

A Cataract that Changes its Direction

By H. E. M. Kensit, M.E.I.C., M.A.I.E.E.

THERE is perhaps nothing in nature that shows more striking extremes in its characteristics and behaviour than water in its numerous forms. It appears as dew, rain, snow and ice; it is found in springs, rivers, lakes and oceans, where it may carry with it an endless variety of its impurities, some actively beneficial, others harmless, and a few poisonous; and its effects are equally as varied, ranging from its life-giving properties as a drink to the immense power of a great waterfall and the destructive force of a raging sea.

The Reversing Falls at the junction of the Saint John River with the harbour of Saint John, New Brunswick. Photograph by courtesy of the Department of Trade and Commerce, Canada.

Water is the most ceaselessly restless of the elements. It travels by land, sea and air, it can rise far into the heavens or penetrate deep into the bowels of the earth, and when free is always in a state of motion. Even in the stillest of lakes it does not rest, although we cannot see it move, for it is being ever drawn to the heights above, to fall again as rain. When held as ice in a glacier it may move only a few inches in a year or in many years, but as vapour in the skies it may travel at vast speeds. After falling as rain, or snow, it eventually reaches the rivers, in which it may travel thousands of miles on its way back to the sea. Each drop may go through amazing adventures before it reaches the ocean, for in its course it may render many services to man, supplying his home needs, irrigating his fields, or generating vast amounts of power for use in his industries. Its arrival in the sea does not necessarily end its career, for it may again be evaporated by the wind and the Sun to become part of the clouds and fall once more as rain. It is not surprising, then, that water can furnish us with many strange sights, including great rivers that pour up "ready-made" from the depths of the earth, others that disappear entirely into cracks or fissures in its surface, or flow backward, and cataracts that reverse their direction of fall or play other astonishing tricks.

A village in the precipitous cliffs of the Yellow River. The entrances to cave dwellings can be distinguished on the upper terrace. Photograph reproduced from "Wandering in North China," by Harry A. Franck, reproduced by courtesy of the Appleton-Century Co., New York.

Most rivers start in a very small way, countless trickles of water from melting snow or rain meeting together to form a little stream that in its course is swelled by others that have originated in a similar manner. Some rivers start full-grown, however; that is they emerge suddenly in large volume from the ground at the outlet of a subterranean river, from water-bearing strata or a natural artesian well. A few form navigable rivers, operate a power plant or drive a factory at their very source.

Perhaps the most famous of these precocious streams is the Fontaine de Vaucluse, 40 miles from Avignon in the south of France, which is the source of the River Sorgue. There a subterranean river issues from a hole 60 ft. deep and 28 ft. wide at the foot of a circular ring of limestone cliffs over 650 ft. high. An underground passage gives it access to the Sorgue, but at times the water surges up above the crater with great force and discharges overland into the river below. The nature of the country is such that most of the snow and rain over an area of nearly 650 sq. miles then percolates below the surface and reappears at this outlet, to give an average flow of 800 cu. ft. per sec. The volume of this underground stream is sufficient to supply the needs of a city of five million people.

Another example is Silver Spring, Florida, where a stream with an average flow of 580 cu. ft. issues from the limestone into a pond or basin with a surface area of more than an acre and a depth of 35 ft. The cold water of the spring flows in great volume in the midst of a sub-tropical forest, and the basins and caverns from which it comes can be seen through windows in the bottoms of boats on the pond. The water is so clear that fishes swimming below the boats seem to be suspended in mid-air, and sunlight reflected from bright objects in the water creates truly magical effects.

An aerial view of the Victoria Falls, Rhodesia, where the Zambesi River plunges into a narrow fissure 400 ft. in depth in practically level country. Photograph by courtesy of "The Aeroplane."

In contrast to the rivers that spring from the earth are others that dive deeply into it. There are good examples of these lost rivers in the plains of Idaho in the United States, a nearly flat area of almost 20,000 sq. m. with the rugged Saw-Toothed Mountains rising in the north to a height of 6,000 ft. above the surrounding country. A large part of this area is covered by immense beds of volcanic lava, and through the centre flows the Snake River in a deep canyon that in places is bounded by sheer cliffs of lava 700 ft. high, and is surpassed in grandeur only by the Grand Canyon of the Colorado.

The lava beds extend almost to the mountains, from which issues rivers of considerable size with such picturesque names as Big Lost River and Little Lost River. These disappear in the cellular and fissured lava and flow 50 miles or more underground before bursting through the precipitous lava walls of Snake River Canyon in great volume and at heights of 220 ft. and more above the level of the river. At the Thousand Springs there is a stretch of nearly half a mile in length from which numerous springs gush out between the permeable rock and the solid lava. The waters of these springs once fell in beautiful foaming falls up to 195 ft. in height, but now are collected in flumes and used to operate a hydro-electric power station.

The Trick Falls, Glacier Park, Montana, during the spring floods. In dry periods the water pours out through a natural tunnel near the bottom. Photograph by courtesy of the United States National Park Service.

Another river that for part of its course becomes lost is the Guadiana in Southern Spain. This stream rises in the Sierra Morena, to disappear about 30 miles from its source and proceed by a subterranean channel about three miles in length to its junction with the Zancara River. It is lost in a flat country, in the centre of what has been described as an immense prairie, and does not reappear on the surface of the earth until it has passed beneath the subterranean arch of what may be described as a great natural bridge.

The Hoang Ho, or Yellow River, in China, has the unenviable claim to distinction of being one of the world's greatest killers. It has changed its course 11 times in the last 2,500 years, and is subject to catastrophic floods at frequent intervals. It slaughtered more than a million people during a great outburst in 1897, and as recently as 1934 overflowed its banks to become 30 miles in width, covering farms and villages to a depth of 10 ft.

The Yellow River is about 2,700 miles in length. It rises in Tibet and winds across Northern China through the Yellow Valley to the Yellow Sea. It carries down immense quantities of yellow mud and this, together with the dust forming from it when it is deposited from the river, gives its hue to everything in its course. The water of the stream itself and of the sea into which it flows, roads, houses, fields and the clothes of the inhabitants of the valley all become yellow, and the former Emperors of China actually called themselves "Lords of the Yellow Earth." The river has carved its way through the immense deposits of sediment that it has produced.

Waterfalls may be no less mysterious or remarkable than rivers. For instance, the appearance of the Trick Falls on Two Medicine Creek, Glacier National Park, Montana, varies with the time of the year, and at the mouth of the St. John River, New Brunswick, Canada, there is a fall that actually reverses its direction every time the tide in the harbour rises and falls.

Here we review books of interes and of use to readers of the "M.M." We can supply copies of these books to readers who cannot obtain them through the usual channels. Order from Book Dept., Meccano Limited, Binns Road, Liverpool 13, adding 1/- for postage to the price. Postage on different books varies, but any balance remaining will be refunded.

"The Story of Telford"

By Sir ALEXANDER GIBB
Alexander Maclehose and Co. 16/- net)

It is surprising that we have had to wait so long for a really good account of the life of Telford. His period was the great age of engineering when civil engineers were playing an enormously important part in pushing forward civilisation. In canals, harbours, roads and bridges Telford exerted a world-wide influence on the civil engineering of his time, and as First President of the Institution of Civil Engineers he was a prominent figure in the birth and development of a great profession. The present book is of particular interest in being written by an eminent engineer whose great-grandfather was one of Telford's chief assistants.

Telford's life work was concerned almost entirely with the improvement of communications in one way or another. In all he constructed not far short of 2,000 bridges, large and small, and he planned, surveyed and constructed between 3,000 and 4,000 miles of roads. He lived to see the beginning of the railway era, but he took no part in its development.

He started life in a humble way in a small thatched cottage in Eskdale. His father died a few months after the boy was born, and the mother had barely sufficient means to keep herself and the child. It cannot be said, however, that this poverty in his childhood had any handicapping effect on Telford's career, and indeed in later life he often declared that in his opinion it was actually an advantage to be born poor. He received the usual excellent village education that was typical of Scotland at that time, and this proved a sufficient foundation for the vast technical knowledge he acquired steadily throughout his life.

In the course of his work as County Surveyor of Salop he built the first bridge to his own design, a three arch stone bridge across the Severn at Montford, some four miles from Shrewsbury. His next structure was the iron bridge at Buildwas, the second iron bridge built in Great Britain, and only a few miles away from Coalbrookdale, where was the first iron bridge in the country. The successful completion of these structures started him on his career and led to his selection as engineer of the Ellesmere Canal to join the Mersey, the Dee and the Severn. In connection with this scheme was the great aqueduct of Chirk that carried the canal over the valley of the Ceriog, and the Pont Cysylltau aqueduct, in which the canal water was carried in an iron trough. It was this latter work that Sir Walter Scott described as "the most impressive work of art he had ever seen."

Telford's extensive highland surveys and his construction of the Caledonian Canal occupied a considerable period of his life. His letters written during this period show something of the difficulties with which he had to contend, and the dogged determination with which he pushed aside all obstacles, human or otherwise! He took life very seriously and was not gifted with a superabundance of humour; but some of these letters from Scotland show that he was capable of seeing the funny side of things, even in difficult circumstances. He was fortunate at this time in having a remarkably efficient and trustworthy staff of assistants. They were men who held strong views in regard to their work and everything else. One of them had an extraordinary belief that the only safe cure for all ills was a plunge in cold water; and his son, describing his father's cure of one of the servant maids suffering from all the symptoms of incipient fever, says: "Last night we threw two buckets of sea water over her; to-day she is going about her work as usual!"

Thomas Telford.

Telford's Menai Suspension Bridge and his London-Holyhead road may be said to have been the means of introducing a new era in communication between England and Ireland. He was the first to apply engineering principles to road making, in which respect he differed from his contemporary Macadam who, while claiming to have entirely revolutionised the art of road work, disclaimed all title to the name of engineer. Macadam preferred a soft and yielding foundation to one that was rigid and inelastic, and for constructional purposes he relied upon angular pieces of stone that could be passed easily through a ring 2½ in. in diameter. Telford insisted on having a foundation of large stones, and in principle his roads differ little from present-day practice in road-making for the heaviest traffic. His methods had the great drawback that they were too costly, however, except for the most important mail routes. Macadam's roads were simpler and cheaper and could be constructed more rapidly, and therefore came into far more widespread use than those of Telford, but there was some degree of superficiality in his work.

It is interesting to note Telford's attitude to railways. He was by no means unsympathetic towards the new means of transport, but he seems to have doubted whether the great enthusiasm of its pioneers would be justified. He was actually approached by the promoters of the Liverpool and Manchester Railway to be the engineer for that line, and his refusal appears to have been based on a feeling that to take on this work would make him guilty of disloyalty to the canals and the canal proprietors who had so fully relied upon him. Even if he had lived it is doubtful whether he would have come into prominence as a railway engineer.

Telford died on 2nd September 1834, in his 78th year, and was buried in Westminster Abbey. In the following paragraph Sir Alexander Gibb sums up the great man's career: "So at last the long life ended —fortunate perhaps above all that it had been rounded off and completed in a way that few achieve. . . . There were no loose ends, as there had never been any in his lifetime; and that is remarkable when one considers the immense list of his works. He was fortunate, too, in that his reputation had been established for many years before he died, and indeed in the last twelve years he had no rival. With him an age of engineering ended. His influence on engineering has not ended and never can."

This is a book that should certainly be read by all who are interested in civil engineering. It is well illustrated by a series of excellent photographs.

"The Wonder Book of Tell Me Why"

(Ward, Lock and Co. Ltd. 5/- net)

The "Wonder Books" Series is now too well known to require recommendation. This new addition tells in picture and story of some of the most wonderful —and sometimes also the most familiar—things in the world. It covers a very wide range of topics, including astronomy, botany, geology, machinery and engineering, and zoology, and many general subjects that do not come under any of these classifications. The answers to the many puzzling questions are by well-known experts, and the book is illustrated with eight colour plates and nearly 300 excellent reproductions from photographs. This is an ideal gift book.

"Creative Woodwork"

By W. T. James and J. H. Dixon

(Pitman. 8/6 net)

This is a book for all who are interested in the art and craft of woodwork. It is intended primarily for teachers, and describes a scheme that is well adapted to encourage boys to develop originality and artistic sense as well as to instruct them in the use of tools and the mechanical side of woodwork. It is full of suggestions for designs of great value, and its wide range and the practical character that results from the long experience of its authors as teachers of handicrafts make it equally valuable to students and to those who make artistic woodwork their hobby.

In a book of this kind drawings and illustrations play a very important part, and those included in the present volume are excellent in type and of great practical value. In addition to a very large number of drawings in the text there are 39 plates, and special interest is attached to a group of these that illustrate antique and modern examples of artistic craftsmanship.

"Through the Weather House"

By R. A. Watson Watt

(Peter Davies. 7/6 net)

The weather is a subject of perpetual interest to all of us, and readers will welcome this story of modern weather forecasting, which is an amplification of a series of interesting talks broadcast by the author during 1934. Weather experts are concerned with the atmosphere, and the various strata of this, from the lowest layer, in which we live, to the stratosphere and the regions above it, constitute the floors of the "Weather House." How conditions in these layers affect our weather is explained in simple terms, and in doing so Mr. Watt reveals some of the mysteries of weather forecasting. He does not claim to teach his readers to become their own weather prophets, but shows how the evidence on which weather reports are based is collected and interpreted. The author's light and easy treatment of his subject is enjoyable, and his readers will obtain clear ideas of the causes of the various kinds of weather we experience. Excellent diagrams and delightful pictures of cloud effects add to the interest of the story.

Pelicans busily engaged in toilet operations. (From "The Wonder Book of Tell Me Why," reviewed on this page.)

"Boy Scout Tests and How To Pass Them"

(Brown, Son and Ferguson Ltd. 4/6 net)

The new edition of this handbook will be welcomed by all keen Scouts. It has been compiled by Imperial Headquarters, Boy Scouts Association, London, and Mr. R. E. Young, and gives full instructions for the Tenderfoot Test, the Second-Class Test and the First-Class Test. In addition there are chapters on 68 different badges, ranging from the Airman Badge to the World Friendship Badge. It is not intended that Scouts should attempt to qualify for a badge merely by reading the appropriate section, however. As indicated in the preface, this should be supplemented by further reading and by practical work under competent instructors, and when used in this manner the book will prove an excellent guide.

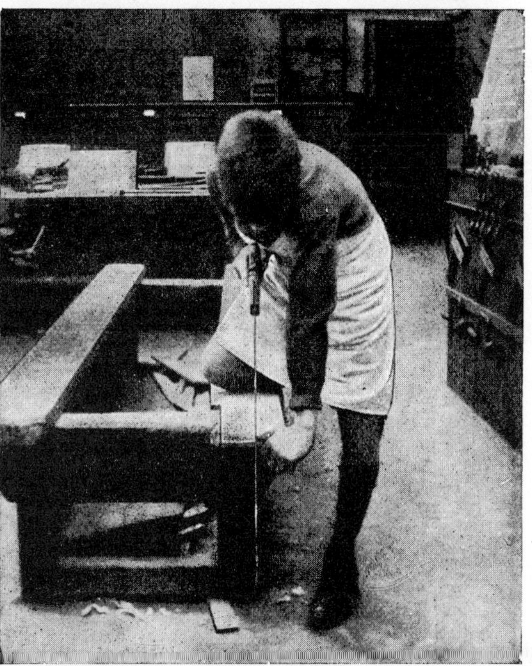

The correct way to use a ripping saw. (From "Creative Woodwork," reviewed on this page.)

"Through My Telescope"

By W. T. Hay. (Murray. 3/6 net)

The announcement in 1933 of the discovery by Mr. Will Hay of a remarkable white spot on Saturn revealed this famous comedian as a keen and enthusiastic astronomer who spends his leisure hours in his own observatory. His telescope is to him a familiar companion, with the aid of which he watches the skies carefully and seriously, and he has now placed his knowledge and experience at the disposal of others who are interested in the heavens but cannot make use of elaborate equipment.

"Through My Telescope" is an admirable introduction to astronomy, telling the story of the Sun, Moon and stars and showing how their features can be studied and their movements followed with the simplest of instruments, and to a certain extent with the naked eye. The book is well illustrated by means of seven plates and many well-chosen diagrams.

"Street Fair"

By Marjorie Fischer

(Geo. Routledge & Sons Ltd. 6/- net)

It is not easy to describe this book, because it is quite out of the ordinary. John and Anna, who are on a visit to Paris with their mother and aunt, are dragged round sightseeing from this place to that until they become utterly bored. One night they slip away and visit a wonderful street fair, and a few days later, by accident rather than design, they find themselves in the train journeying to the south of France, alone and with very little money. Not in the least daunted, they succeed in having heaps of fun and getting into and out of all kinds of scrapes. They find the remarkable mongrel pup Bou, who joins wholeheartedly in any mischief that is afoot, and finally, after a marvellous fortnight, they return to mother and aunt. This is a book that should not be missed.

"Flight"

By Agnes Rogers

(Harper and Brothers. 7/6 net)

"Flight" tells the story of aviation in pictures, each with its appropriate text. It contains more than 175 photographs dealing with every branch of modern aviation, from the achievements of pioneers such as the Wrights and Bleriot, and the outstanding flights of Lindbergh and other famous figures, to the wonders of modern mail and passenger traffic, survey work and exploration by air. All who are "air-minded" will enjoy this compact and vivid record of the conquest of the air.

"Futility"

By Lieut.-Col. A. W. Ryland

(Arthur A. Stockwell Ltd. 3/6 net)

This is a story of modern piracy, full of exciting adventure on the high seas. The manner in which the diabolical schemes of villainous wreckers are foiled is well described, but the book would have been more satisfactory if the author had refrained from occasional short "lectures," for these interfere with the action.

A Selection of HORNBY ELECTRIC TRAIN SETS (20-volt and 6-volt)

EM120 (20-volt) or EM16 (6-volt) GOODS TRAIN SET (non-reversing). Price 15/-

EM320 (20-volt) or EM36 (6-volt) TANK GOODS TRAIN SET (reversing). Price 24/-

HORNBY No. EO20 (20-volt) PASSENGER TRAIN SET (reversing). Price 30/-

HORNBY No. E220 (20-volt) MIXED GOODS TRAIN SET (automatic reversing). Price 47/6

HORNBY No. E320 (20-volt) RIVIERA "BLUE" TRAIN SET (automatic reversing). Price 67/6

PRODUCT of MECCANO LIMITED LIVERPOOL

HORNBY No. E320 (20-volt) PULLMAN TRAIN SET (automatic reversing). Price 72/6

A selection of HORNBY ELECTRIC LOCOMOTIVES (20-volt and 6-volt)

EM120 (20-volt) or EM16 (6-volt) LOCOMOTIVE (Non-reversing) ... Price 8/6

HORNBY No. EO20 (20-volt) LOCOMOTIVE (Reversing) ... Price 22/-

EM320 (20-volt) or EM36 (6-volt)TANKLOCOMOTIVE (Reversing) ... Price 16/6

HORNBY No. E120 LOCOMOTIVE (20-volt) (Reversing) ... Price 24/-

HORNBY No. E120 (20-volt) or E16 (6-volt) TANK LOCOMOTIVE (Reversing) ... Price 24/-

HORNBY No. E120 SPECIAL LOCOMOTIVE (20-volt) (Automatic reversing). Price 30/-

HORNBY No. E220 SPECIAL LOCOMOTIVE (Automatic reversing)...Price 37/6

ELECTRIC

Perfect

This is the dawn of t
Electric Trains reach
The locomotives a
appearance and fir
patented and excl
or reversing at a
lating their spee
bring your hous
down to the c
ensure smoot
Then ther
able Hornby
stood up t
speedy and
ted in ea
thing is
The
Rolling
patent
matic
wealt
sorie
of
Ho
no
S
H

HORNBY No. E320 LOCOMOTIVE (Automatic reversing) ... Price 35/-

MECCANO LIMITED,

and
EED
TRAINS
CKWORK
LMS
An illustration of a Hornby No. 2 Special et, hauled by a Hornby No. 2 Locomotive, the latter a true-model of the real L.M.S.R. Compound Locomotive.
ailways
and the new Hornby
lectrical perfection.
and beautiful in
m are fitted with
tarting, stopping
k, and for regu-
o Transformers
nating Current
r 6-volts, and
nning.
of incompar-
s, that have
years. A
nism is fit-
d every-
Hornby
d with
auto-
the
cces-
eart
a
em
E
A
A Selection of
HORNBY CLOCKWORK TRAIN SETS
MO PASSENGER TRAIN SET (non-reversing). Price 5/6
M1 PASSENGER TRAIN SET (reversing). Price 8/11
M3 TANK PASSENGER TRAIN SET (reversing). Price 13/9
HORNBY No. O GOODS TRAIN SET (reversing). Price 17/6
HORNBY No. 2 TANK PASSENGER TRAIN SET (reversing). Price 40/-
HORNBY No. 3C PULLMAN TRAIN SET (reversing). Price 62/6
PRODUCT of MECCANO LIMITED LIVERPOOL
A selection of
HORNBY
CLOCKWORK
LOCOMOTIVES
MO LOCOMOTIVE
(Non-reversing) ... Price 2/9
MI/2 LOCOMOTIVE
(Reversing) ... Price 4/6
M3 TANK LOCOMOTIVE
(Reversing) ... Price 7/6
No. O LOCOMOTIVE
(Reversing) ... Price 10/6
No. 2 SPECIAL TANK LOCOMOTIVE
(Reversing) ... ... Price 21/-
No. 1 SPECIAL LOCOMOTIVE
(Reversing). Price 17/6
No. 3C RIVIERA "BLUE" LOCOMOTIVE
(Reversing) ... ... Price 24/-
No. 1 LOCOMOTIVE
(Reversing) ... Price 12/6
ROAD, LIVERPOOL 13.

High-Level Bridge Across Little Belt

Novel Method of Construction

The Jutland approach spans of the Little Belt Bridge nearing completion. This illustration and the one on the opposite page are reproduced by courtesy of "The Railway Gazette."

ON the 14th May last King Christian X of Denmark officially opened the Little Belt Bridge, built across the strait after which the structure is named and connecting the peninsula of Jutland and the island of Funen. The bridge is the outcome of a decision in 1924 to replace the train ferry service across the strait by a more economical means of communication. The ferry had been operated since 1872, and in fair weather made the trip in about 15 min. At first a bridge wide enough to carry only the double track of the Danish State Railways was proposed, but as the volume of motor traffic using the ferry was increasing rapidly it was decided eventually that the bridge should also carry a roadway. In 1927 the construction of a combined railway and road bridge was sanctioned by the Danish Government, and in 1928 the work was entrusted to a Danish engineering company in co-operation with two German firms.

The bridge has a total length of 3,864 ft. 7½ in., of which 2,707 ft. is over the Little Belt at a height of 108 ft. above mean sea level, sufficient to enable the tallest masted steamers passing through the strait to clear the structure. This part of the bridge consists of five steel truss spans of unequal length and supported by four tall piers and two shore abutments. The southern approach is 452 ft. 1½ in. in length and includes three reinforced concrete arches, and the northern or Jutland approach, 703 ft. 6 in. in length, has five similar arches. The largest arch is 127 ft. in span and 86 ft. in height.

Map of Denmark, showing the situation of the bridge.

The construction and sinking of the caissons that form the foundation of the main piers was the most difficult part of the work. The Little Belt flows swiftly and there is 133 ft. of water in the deepest part of the channel. Preliminary borings showed that the bed of the strait is of clay to a great depth, and that for at least 15 ft. down it is impervious to water. These conditions were considered unsatisfactory for the employment of the usual type of caisson, in which the working chambers are filled with compressed air to keep the water out while the workmen excavate the earth beneath the caisson.

Novel methods were adopted to overcome these difficulties. The caissons were built on the Jutland shore, and were 147 ft. in length, 79 ft. in width and 50 to 60 ft. in depth. The outer wall of each of them consisted of two parallel sides joined by semi-circular ends, and was built of vertical reinforced concrete tubes of 3 ft. 11 in. internal diameter. The inner wall was of similar tubes ranged in pairs at regular intervals. The bed of the strait is very uneven, and on this account what were the tops of the tubes before the caisson was righted, but actually were the cutting edge, were shaped to correspond with the contour of the bed of the strait at the pier site. Another effect of building the caisson upside down was that the working chambers then occupied the upper part of the interior and the upper deck was at the bottom of the caisson! Thick concrete walls divided the intervening space into several compartments, for the reception of water ballast.

When the caisson was completed it was floated from the slipway, and was capsized by filling the wall tubes at one side with sand and flooding one of the interior compartments at that side with water. As it heeled over the ballast fell out of the tubes and the caisson floated right way up. It was brought to an even keel by admitting some of the water ballast to one of the compartments on the opposite side. It was then towed alongside a floating concreting plant, and the construction of the upper part was begun. As this work progressed the caisson became heavier and it was necessary to tow it into deeper water, and finally it was taken to the pier site where, owing to the specially-shaped cutting edge, it rested evenly upon the bed of the strait.

Preparations were made for sinking the caisson into the bed to the required depth. A temporary platform was erected across the top of the caisson to provide a base for two boring machines and two cranes with which to lower the rotary cutting tools down the tubes. The clay cut away by each tool was broken up by powerful jets of water pumped down the tube and was washed up the hollow shaft of the drill to the surface, where it was ejected. The tools slowly cut their way downward and as the cutting edge of the caisson bit deeper into the bed of the strait, that portion of the bed which was enclosed by the caisson walls rose higher in the working chambers. When it had been sunk in this way to a depth of 25 ft. boring was stopped, the tubes were filled with concrete and the arduous task of excavating the clay that filled the working chambers was begun. This operation was greatly simplified by the fact that as the clay was impervious to water the workmen engaged in removing it were able to work under ordinary atmospherical conditions, instead of in compressed air. This was an immense advantage, and resulted in a considerable saving in plant and time. The clay was broken up, loaded into buckets and hoisted to the top of the caisson and dumped overboard. The chambers were excavated to a depth of 14 ft. and were then filled with concrete.

The piers erected upon the caissons are not solid throughout, as this would have imposed an excessive burden upon the underlying clay, but they are of cellular construction with some of the cells filled with water. They are 240 ft. in height from foundation level. The abutment piers are of reinforced concrete, and that on the Jutland shore is built upon a foundation of piles also of this material. The corresponding pier on the other shore has an ordinary foundation 50 ft. below mean sea level.

One of the specially-built caissons being launched from the slipway.

The superstructure of the bridge was erected on the cantilever principle, the girder work being built outward from each main pier, and falsework attached to the underside of the superstructure was used in assembling the decking. The lofty approach spans are a graceful feature of the structure as a whole. Each consists of four parallel reinforced concrete arches, two wide ones that carry the double line of railway and two narrow ones that carry the road and footwalk respectively. The Jutland approach spans are shown in the upper illustration on the previous page.

The ferry superseded by the bridge was a link in the Copenhagen-Esbjerg route of the Danish State Railways, and crossed the strait at a point approximately four miles northward of the bridge. The diversion of the route to include the bridge involved the construction of new stations and bridges at Middelfart on the Island of Funen, and at Fredericia, in Jutland. The new line has shortened the distance by rail between the capital and Esbjerg.

The opening of the bridge on the 14th May was also the occasion for the introduction of new express Diesel train services on the Danish State Railways and the double event was celebrated by special illuminations, fireworks and torchlight processions. The bridge was opened to the public shortly after the Royal party had travelled across it in two of the new streamlined trains, and by midnight at least 40,000 cars and 200,000 people had crossed it. The shortened route and the speedy travel of the new trains has reduced the time of the journey from London to Copenhagen from about 39 hrs. to 32 hrs. and the time for the journey from Copenhagen to some of the other important cities in Jutland has been almost halved.

An Ancient Irish "Single-Wheeler"

THE restoration of a derailed locomotive to the track may be a difficult process, or it may be comparatively easy, according to the situation of the mishap and the facilities available for dealing with it. The engine in the accompanying photograph left the track as the result of the derailment of a coach, and was hurled down a steep embankment. It turned completely round and came to rest on its side. The situation of the derailment was awkward enough, but in addition to this it was impossible to use a breakdown crane to assist in the work of salvage. This was because the Waterford and Tramore Railway on which the engine was working, although forming a section of the Great Southern Railways of Ireland, has not any actual connection with the main system and its terminus at Waterford is more than a mile from any other line.

The old tank locomotive referred to in this article. In this photograph it is shown raised up after falling down an embankment, but before being returned to the main line.

In such circumstances the raising of the engine to an upright position had to be performed by the aid of jacks and timber packing. This much being accomplished the elevation of the engine to the top of the embankment was the next problem. This was solved by arranging a special sloping track parallel with the actual permanent way, and up the "ramp" so formed the engine was hauled by means of winches! Having reached the top it was transferred by means of jacks over to the running lines and then towed away.

This locomotive, originally No. 1 of the Waterford and Tramore Railway, was built as long ago as 1855, but apart from its great age—80 years—its interest lies in its single-wheeler design. It was in fact the last of that type to be seen in Ireland. Of the old fashioned well-tank type in which the water is carried in a tank below the footplate, it represents a small type of engine commonly used years ago for local and branch services. Frequently tender engines were rebuilt as tanks when their period of usefulness on the main line was over. In spite of the extreme liability of single-wheelers to be affected by weather conditions, No. 1 has chiefly been employed in the winter months, the heavier summer traffic being dealt by two coupled engines of the 0-4-2 tank types.

Apart from its quite isolated character the Waterford and Tramore Railway is peculiar in having no intermediate station on its 7¼ mile run. Its passenger vehicles are of very miscellaneous character, and include 4-wheelers and 6-wheelers, which are however not fitted with continuous brakes. A curious feature also is that as the platforms at both stations are on the same side of the line the carriage doors open on that side only!

These pages are reserved for articles from our readers. Contributions not exceeding 500 words in length are invited on any subject of general interest. These should be written neatly on one side of the paper only, and they may be accompanied by photographs or sketches for use as illustrations. Articles that are published will be paid for at our usual rates. Statements contained in articles submitted for these pages are accepted as being sent in good faith, but the Editor takes no responsibility for their accuracy.

Red Squirrels in Cheshire

For many years I have been interested in all kinds of wild life, but it has only been during the last 10 years that I have been able to study nature "in the raw." At present I live on the outskirts of the once enormous Delamere Forest, where there is now a large bird sanctuary on the shores of Oakmere, a picturesque stretch of water. This sanctuary has encouraged all kinds of wild animals and birds to frequent the district, for they seem to realise that in these parts man is their friend.

One of the red squirrels of Delamere Forest devouring nuts provided by a friend. The photograph by S. W. J. English, Delamere Forest.

About 18 months ago it was noticed that more red squirrels than usual were inhabiting the surrounding woodland, which consists mainly of pines. I began to leave Barcelona nuts and pieces of cake about for the tiny animals, which are very much smaller and prettier than their enemy, the grey squirrel. The nuts always disappeared soon after dawn, but it was a long time before I saw anything of the red squirrels. Gradually one of them lost his shyness, however, and appeared during the afternoon, and soon he would sit up and beg for more nuts. The next step was to make him eat from my hand, and I accomplished this in about six weeks. Afterwards progress was much more rapid, and soon he would climb up my leg and on to my shoulder. At first his nervous companions watched him enviously from the shelter of a tree, but in time they also lost their shyness. Now as many as eight are sometimes seen together in the open. Normally squirrels sleep throughout the winter, but in districts where people are in the habit of feeding them they appear all the year round, though their visits are fewer in winter than in summer. S. W. J. English (Delamere Forest).

Trevose Head Lighthouse

Trevose Head is a conspicuous promontory on the west coast of Cornwall, and is visible from places as far apart as Pendeen Watch, 39 miles away and just south of St. Ives, and Hartland Point, 40 miles away in North Devon. The lighthouse at the end of the promontory was erected to warn ships off the Quies, a dangerous reef of high rocks extending westward for about a mile. Visitors are not allowed into the lighthouse in misty weather, when the great fog horn is in operation. In such weather a double blast is sounded on the horn every minute, and can be heard 30 miles seaward. On the day I and a party of others visited the lighthouse the mist lifted soon after our arrival, and we were admitted.

I was greatly interested in the power house, where two 25 h.p. oil engines, working in shifts, drive compressors supplying air at 25 lb. per sq. in. to the fog horn. The lantern is 210 ft. above sea level, and its three lenses and the steel superstructure carrying them have a total weight of three tons, and float in mercury. The lenses are set at 60 degrees to each other, and make four revolutions a minute, giving a single brief flash every five seconds. The lantern is rotated by a centrifugally-governed weight mechanism that has to be rewound every 40 min. The 1,500 c.p. light from the paraffin-vapour incandescent burner passes through the red glass surrounding the lamp and is transformed by each lens into a beam of 1,000,000 c.p., that is visible to ships 23 miles away. Along the coast the light can be seen over proportionately longer distances, and when the air is clear it can be seen from the cliffs of Lundy Island, over 50 miles away. P. F. Woodman (Exeter).

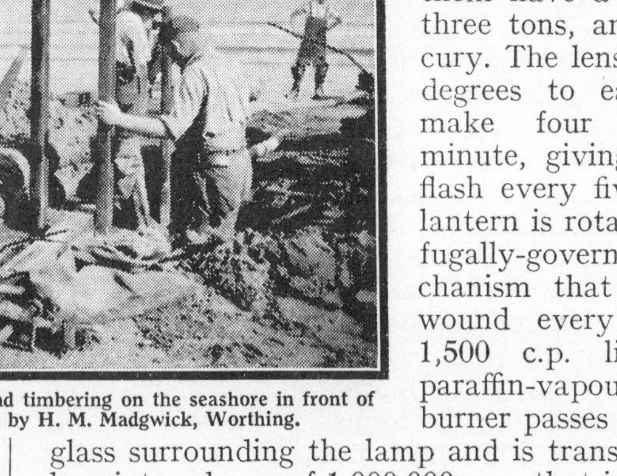

Fixing groynes formed of old rails and timbering on the seashore in front of Dawlish Station. Photograph by H. M. Madgwick, Worthing.

Thatched Walls

In this age, when durable walls can be erected quickly and cheaply, we do not usually think it necessary to protect the boundary walls of our gardens with thatch, slates or tiles. In earlier times, however, when labour was cheap, builders often considered it worth while to thatch farmyard and garden walls. Not only cob, but flint and stone walls also were thatched.

Some of these thatched walls can still be seen in various parts of the country, and the one shown in the upper photograph on this page is an old wall beside the main road at Dorchester. The thatched barn that rises beyond the wall makes the scene even more picturesque. A few examples of thatched walls may also be seen in Berkshire, but they are most plentiful in Wiltshire. Some thatched walls date back to Saxon times, and it is interesting to note that the word "thatch" itself is derived from the Saxon "theccan," which meant "to cover."

An old thatched wall beside the main road at Dorchester. Photograph by J. D. U. Ward, Chelsea.

In many cases walls that were thatched originally are now protected by tiles, slates, or with the more modern and unsightly material, corrugated iron.

J. D. U. Ward (Chelsea).

A Fire at Sea

Some time ago while on the voyage home from Australia I had the rare experience of seeing a fire at sea. We were crossing the Bay of Biscay, which had its famous unbroken swell at the time, when we came upon a ship on fire from stem to stern! Our liner cruised round the blazing ship for some time, searching for lifeboats and for persons in the sea. It was obvious that no living person could be aboard her, for she resembled a raging inferno. We had no information as to whether her crew and any passengers had abandoned her, or were lost, and eventually we stopped our engines and stood by.

Trevose Head Lighthouse, on the west coast of Cornwall. Photograph by P. F. Woodman, Exeter.

The experience was one of the most weird I have ever had. One minute our ship was lifted by the heavy swell, and we found ourselves gazing down upon the flaming mass, wallowing in the trough of the waves, and the next minute we in our turn were down in the abyss while the burning vessel glared beacon-like on the crest, seemingly ready to roll right down upon us.

The officers of our ship assured us that we were half a mile away from the fire, but we seemed to be much closer than that, and we could hear distinctly the roar and crackle of the flames. Our officers were almost as thrilled as ourselves by the sight, and told us that a man might go to sea for a lifetime and never encounter such a wonderful and dreadful spectacle.

No trace of the crew or lifeboats of the doomed ship was found, and when it became certain that there was no need for our assistance, we got under way again. Later a wireless message was received that her crew had been safely taken off by another ship two hours before we arrived on the scene. She was a Russian cargo boat laden with oil and timber. No wonder she blazed so furiously.

M. Atkinson (Edinburgh 10).

Novel Use for Old Rails

When railway track is renewed the old rails are not scrapped, but are used for various kinds of maintenance work on the railway, such as signal posts and supports for wire fencing. At Dawlish, where the station is on the shore, a novel use has been found for old rails, and the lower photograph on the opposite page shows workmen of the G.W.R. Engineer's Department using them for constructing groynes to protect the station from the buffetings of the sea. The rails are bedded in a concrete foundation, and when the concrete has set timbering is fixed horizontally between them.

H. M. Madgwick (Worthing).

A Visit to Hamburg

A few years ago I spent a very interesting fortnight in Hamburg. The first thing that impressed me about the city was the cleanliness of the buildings, due probably to the extensive use of gas instead of coal. To ensure public safety many of the roads have separate tracks for bicycles and pedestrians, and there is a special strip of sand for horse riders. Each policeman carries a sword and a revolver instead of a truncheon.

The chief of the many and varied means of transport in Hamburg is the "Hochbahn," or overhead railway. This name is hardly suitable, as in places the railway goes underground, and at others it runs on the surface. The coaches of the trains are similar to those of the London Underground Railways, and the system is worked by electricity. At the level crossings there are no swing gates as in England, but two long thick poles with chains hung from them that can be lowered to block the road. The poles are raised and lowered by means of winches at the sides of the road.

C. F. Midgley (Keighley).

Diesel Engines for Racing Cars

First Speed Records in New Class

THE Diesel internal combustion engine is becoming familiar to everybody, for since its introduction by Dr. Rudolph Diesel, its inventor, about 1895, it has been developed to such an extent that it is now capable of many applications. Engines of this type differ from those using petrol in the absence of sparking plugs and magnetos, for the heavy oil employed in them is ignited as a result of the high temperature developed in their cylinders by the compression of the air necessary for combustion.

The racing car, fitted with a Perkins "Wolf" Diesel engine, in which Mr. R. Munday created the first Three-Litre Diesel Class Records. The illustrations to this article are reproduced by courtesy of F. Perkins Ltd., Peterborough.

A Diesel engine possesses many advantages as compared with a petrol engine. One of these is the comparative simplicity due to the absence of electrical means of firing the charge. In addition, the oil used is comparatively cheap and is practically non-inflammable, a feature that makes the engine much safer than one using petrol, which has a low ignition temperature, and has made the development of Diesel engines for use in motor cars and aeroplanes very desirable.

When the Diesel engine was introduced, and during its earliest stages of development, it was much heavier than a petrol engine of corresponding power, but continual improvements in design have resulted in considerable reductions in weight. Means also have been discovered of making it efficient over a greater range of speeds than formerly. Formerly it was expected to be most suitable for running at comparatively low speeds, such as those required for the engines of certain types of ships. Diesel engines are now used for motor lorries and even for ordinary motor cars, however, where high crankshaft speeds and flexibility are necessary.

The Perkins "Wolf" Diesel engine installed in the racing car shown in the upper illustration on this page.

Perhaps the most striking evidence of the great adaptability of the modern Diesel engine is the success that has been achieved in creating high speed records with racing cars fitted with it. As recently as 1934, the Association of International Recognised Automobile Clubs decided to admit speed records made by Diesel-engined cars, and the first attempt to achieve high speeds with racing cars of this kind was made at Brooklands in October 1935 by Mr. R. Munday, the well known racing driver, whose Parry Thomas special chassis was fitted with an 18 h.p. "Wolf" engine for this purpose. This engine is designed and manufactured by F. Perkins Ltd., Peterborough, and is a standard Diesel engine for use in motor lorries. It was specially tuned in order to give a racing performance, but the only other alteration from the standard "Wolf" commercial engine was the lightening of its reciprocating parts.

The records were made in the three-litre Diesel class, and the highest speed reached during this pioneer effort was 94.70 m.p.h. in a run over a kilometre with a flying start. This record was made with the aid of a supercharger that increased the pressure to about 8 lbs. per sq. in. above that of the atmosphere. The test was made in the usual manner, the record speed being the average for two runs in opposite directions over the measured distance.

The supercharger was disconnected when the attempt was made to set up other records, and official timings over distances of 50 miles and 100 miles then gave speeds of 88.44 m.p.h. and 88.13 m.p.h. respectively. Over distances of 50 kilometres and 100 kilometres the corresponding figures were 88.11 m.p.h. and 88.13 m.p.h., and during the trials a distance of 88.25 miles was covered in an hour.

The official rating of the "Wolf" engine is 18 h.p., and as prepared for use in motor lorries it develops 45 b.h.p. The engine that was specially tuned and prepared for use in Mr. Munday's Parry Thomas special car developed 65 b.h.p. at a crankshaft speed of about 3,000 r.p.m.

A New Model Electric Roundabout

Dinky Toys Used with Meccano

THE fine model electric roundabout illustrated on this page has been designed specially to enable owners of Dinky Toy Motor Cars to use them in conjunction with their Meccano Outfits. The model is quite simple to build and is most realistic in motion, and as the cars are fitted with electric lights, it presents a really fascinating appearance.

The cars run on a circular track consisting of a circle of cardboard or tinplate 15¾ in. in diameter. From the centre of this a disc 7½ in. in diameter is cut, and the outer edge of the circle is strengthened by means of 2½″ Strips bolted in place as shown in the illustrations. It is very important to cut the track accurately to the diameter stated, otherwise difficulty will be experienced in fitting the Strips round the outer edge.

The construction of the frame on which the track is mounted is shown in the lower illustration, and neither this portion nor the body of the model should present any difficulty. The track is mounted on a framework of Angle Girders, which is constructed on four 5½″ Angle Girders and four 4½″ Angle Girders that radiate from a 4″ Circular Plate as shown. Two Angle Girders diametrically opposite, are provided with vertical 2½″ Angle Girders at their ends, and at a distance of 4½″ from these with 2″ Angle Girders. These pairs of Angle Girders are connected across their upper ends by 4½″ Angle Girders, on which the highest portions of the track rest. At its lowest points the track is bolted to 4½″ Angle Girders that are secured direct to the radial girders, and at its intermediate levels to 4½″ Angle Girders secured to the radial girders by 1½″ Angle Girders at the outside and Flat Brackets at the inside. Four Dinky Toy Two-seater and four Four-seater Sports Cars are connected together in a ring which is assembled as follows. The centre of the ring is a Bush Wheel to which are bolted eight Hinges, each Hinge carrying a Collar in which is secured a 3″ Rod. The Cars are secured to the ends of the 3″ Rods by means of a Flat Bracket, which is pushed between the chassis of each Car and underneath the seat. A 1″×½″ Angle Bracket is then bolted to the Flat Bracket, and to the Angle Bracket is fixed a Hinge that carries two ½″×½″ Angle Brackets.

The upper Angle Brackets form supports for the Pea Lamps that are used to decorate the model, and ⅜″ Bolts are pushed through the lower ones and are secured to the ends of the 3″ Rods by means of grub screws in the longitudinal holes of the Couplings 1. Each Coupling is fitted with a bolt and these are linked together by cord as shown. The Pea Lamps are pushed tight against the Angle Brackets, and the wires are held close to the 3″ Rods by insulating tape or gummed paper. One wire from each lamp is connected to the bolt that holds its Hinge in place. The remaining wires from the lamps are connected together and the method of incorporating them in the general circuit will be explained later.

The Cars are made to revolve by means of a 6″ and a 5″ Rod connected together by a Coupling. This compound rod is journalled at its lower end in a Bush Wheel that forms the centre of the base, and at its upper end in a Face Plate. The Rod carries a 1½″ Bevel Gear 2, a slip-ring and the radial Rods to which the Cars are connected. The slip-ring is a Wheel Flange 3 secured to but insulated by Insulating Bushes and Washers from a Bush Wheel. The bunch of wires from the Pea Lamps are electrically connected to the Wheel Flange, and for the sake of neatness all the other connections are covered by a Face Plate 4. In the illustration at the foot of this page the Face Plate is raised to reveal the construction of the revolving unit.

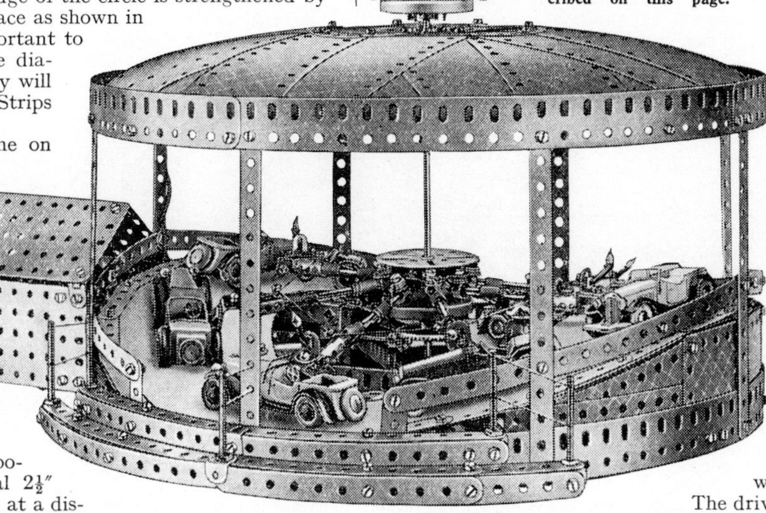

The Meccano Electric Roundabout that is described on this page.

The 1½″ Bevel Gear 2 meshes with a ½″ Bevel Gear 5, which is on the same Rod as the 57-teeth Gear Wheel 6. This Gear drives Rod 7 through two ½″ Pinions and a second 57-teeth Gear Wheel, and Rod 7 is provided with a 50-teeth Gear Wheel that meshes with a ¾″ Pinion on Rod 8. The drive is transmitted from Rod 8 to Rod 9 by means of a further 50-teeth Gear and a ¾″ Pinion. Rod 9 and the armature shaft of the E1 Electric Motor that drives the model carry ¾″ Sprockets, which are connected by Sprocket Chain.

Under the roof of the model are four 3.5 volt lamps, and the lighting circuit for these is as follows. The lamps are supported on 1½″×½″ Double Angle Strips, the 6 B.A. centre Screws of the Lamp Holders being carefully insulated from the Double Angle Strips. The four Screws are connected by a length of wire and one of them is connected also to an insulated Pendulum Connection that makes contact with the insulated Wheel Flange on top of the model. The outer cases of the four exterior Lamp Holders are in contact with the Wheel Flange, and the 6 B.A. Screws are electrically connected by contact with the rim of a 1″ fast Pulley Wheel. A wire is taken from the insulated Pendulum Connection down one of the vertical roof supports and to the insulated Terminal 10. Terminal 10 is also connected to the insulated Pendulum Connection 11 that makes contact with 3. The other Terminal, 12, which also is insulated, is connected by a short piece of wire to the insulated Terminal of the Motor. The third Terminal 13 is in electrical contact with the model.

The model Roundabout with the roof and part of the gear-box removed to show the interior arrangement.

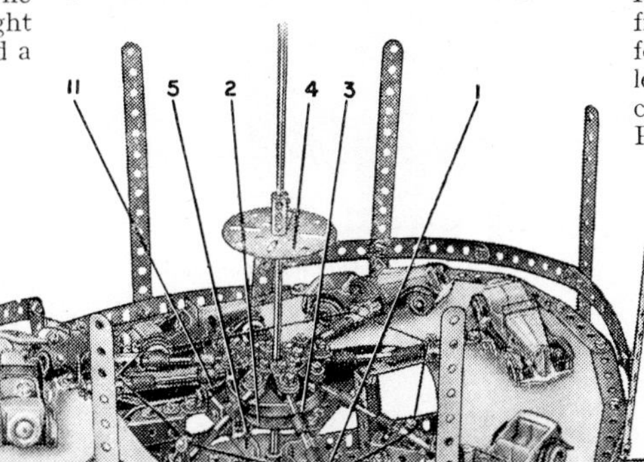

The upper 6-volt controlled socket of a T6A Transformer should be connected to Terminal 12, and Terminal 10 to the upper 3.5-volt socket. The lower 6-volt controlled socket should be connected to Terminal 13, and the lower sockets of the 6-volt uncontrolled and the 3.5-volt tappings should be joined by a piece of wire.

Meccano Suggestions Section

Edited by "Spanner"

(345)—Controlling Electrical Apparatus from a Distance (F. Jenkins, Birmingham)

To switch on a wireless receiver from a distant point would at first seem to be the simple procedure of connecting a switch in series with the set and accumulator. Where the control switch is near the set this method is quite satisfactory, but with long connecting wires to the switch there is a perceptible resistance offered to the electric current, causing a marked reduction in the efficiency of the receiver. To cut out the resistance the accumulator and switch must be near the set, and so it is necessary to employ a special device to work the switch. The device is operated from the distant point by a second switch in a separate circuit, so that the long connections affect only the device operating the main switch, and in no way influence the set.

One of the essentials of an operating device for remote control of a switch is that it should be positive in action. It must be equally satisfactory for switching the current on or off, and must offer no appreciable resistance to the current supplied to the set. These requirements are fulfilled in the device illustrated, which has been designed for controlling any electrical apparatus requiring low-voltage current, and is specially suitable for operating a radio receiver from a remote point. Two views of the mechanism are shown in Figs. 345 and 345a, and to show the electrical connections a wiring diagram appears on the opposite page (Fig. 345b). If carefully constructed and adjusted with correct clearances the controller will function with positive action.

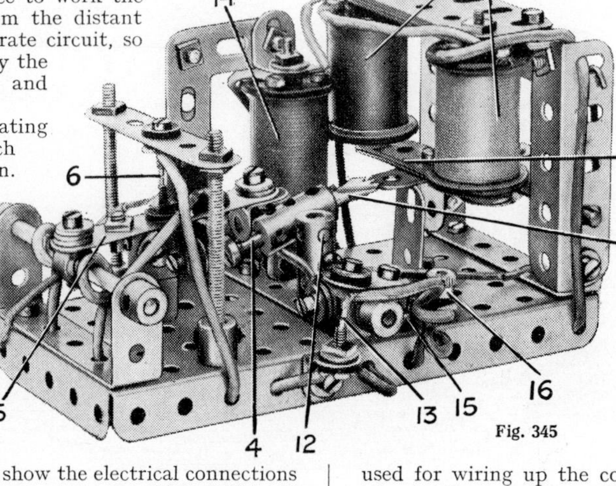

Fig. 345

Elektron parts are utilised in conjunction with Meccano parts for this model. The framework is built up on a $5\frac{1}{2}'' \times 2\frac{1}{2}''$ Flanged Plate, and two Magnet Coils 1, fitted with Cores, are fixed to four Flat Girders that are bolted to a $2\frac{1}{2}''$ Angle Girder secured to the tops of two vertical $2\frac{1}{2}''$ Girders. The latter are attached to a $2\frac{1}{2}'' \times \frac{1}{2}''$ Double Angle Strip at the base and carry Flat Brackets, the round holes of which coincide with elongated holes in the Girders to form journals for a $3\frac{1}{2}''$ Axle Rod. A Collar on this Rod has a $2''$ Strip secured rigidly to it, and two $2\frac{1}{2}''$ Strips placed together are bolted to this Strip to form the armature 2. The $2\frac{1}{2}''$ Strips are immediately below the poles of the Magnets 1, and the Rod carrying the armature is free to pivot in the vertical Girders. A $1'' \times \frac{1}{2}''$ Angle Bracket serves as a stop for the downward movement of the armature. The Coil 14 is mounted by means of its Core to an Angle Bracket on the end of a Bell Crank secured to a vertical $3''$ Strip. As will be seen from Fig. 345a, the Strip is reinforced by a Corner Bracket.

Across the centre of the Flanged Plate is a $2\frac{1}{2}'' \times \frac{1}{2}''$ Double Angle Strip supporting a $3\frac{1}{2}''$ Rod 9. Two Couplings are fixed near the centre of the Rod to carry a $1''$ Rod 12, on which another Coupling is free to pivot. This pivoted Coupling is provided with a Centre Fork 3 and a Pivot Bolt 4. At one end of the Rod 9 (see Fig. 345a) is a further Coupling carrying two Flat Brackets at 8, secured together and spaced from the Coupling by a Washer. Another Flat Bracket 11 is fixed rigidly at the other end of the Coupling and carries a Contact Screw that is insulated from the Flat Bracket by Insulating Bushes and Washers. Fig. 345 shows the arrangement of the Flat Bracket at the other end of the Rod 9. In this case the Bracket is attached to a Collar and carries an insulated Contact Screw.

A further Collar on the Rod 9 is provided with a bolt fitted with Washers for securing Spring Cord. The Spring Cord is attached by a Hook at one end of the base plate and is clamped between Washers on the bolt. The end of the cord is brought upward so that it bears beneath the underside of the Coupling on the Rod 12. By this arrangement the Rod 9 tends to rotate, keeping the contact points 10 closed, and the Pivot Bolt 4 tends to move upward so that it remains in contact with the Angle Bracket on the Strip 5.

This Strip is secured to a Collar on a $3\frac{1}{2}''$ Rod journalled in a $2\frac{1}{2}'' \times 1''$ Double Angle Strip, bolted across one end of the Plate. Two Contact Screws are insulated from the Strip as shown in Fig. 345a, and a length of Spring Cord, tending to pull the Strip downward, keeps the contacts 7 normally closed. The lower Contact Screw of the pair is attached to an Angle Bracket bolted to a $1'' \times \frac{1}{2}''$ Angle Bracket on the base Plate. Screwed Rods support a $2\frac{1}{2}''$ Strip carrying the upper contact 6 that is insulated from the Strip.

Flexible rubber-covered wire is used for wiring up the controller, and the method of connecting wire to the moving contacts should be noted. The wires to the insulated Contact Screws on the Strip 5 are each wound loosely once round the Rod carrying the Strip, and passed through holes in the base. By arranging the wires thus they do not interfere with the movement of the Strip 5, and are not likely to break on account of movement of the Strip. The wire to the upper contact 13 is coiled as shown in Fig. 345.

For electrical connections a careful study should be made of the diagram in Fig. 345b in conjunction with the two illustrations on this page. The Coils 1 are connected together in series, one of them being connected to the upper insulated Contact Screw 7. The other Coil is connected to one Terminal of the Coil 14 and also to the Terminal 16 on the base. The other wire of Coil 14 is led to the upper Contact Screw of the pair 6 and is extended for one of the connections to the set.

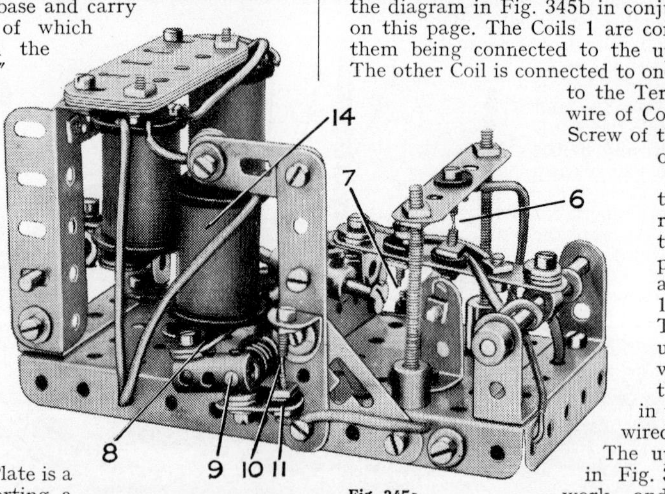

To simplify the wiring diagram the contacts 10 and 13 and their respective connections have been transposed; the connections to the points 10 in Fig. 345a being shown at 13 in the diagram, and those at 13 in Fig. 345 at 10 in the diagram. The operation of the device is unchanged by this alteration, which is only to avoid complicating the wiring diagram. Contacts 10 in the diagram (13 on the model) are wired in parallel with the contacts 6.

The upper contact of the pair 13 (10 in Fig. 345a) is earthed to the framework, and the lower one is wired to the lower Contact Screw of the pair 6, and to the Terminal 15 on the base. The lower contact 7 is earthed to the Plate.

Fig. 345a

One terminal of the accumulator is wired to the Terminal 15, and the second terminal of the accumulator is connected to the set and also to the push-button switch, the other wire from which is attached to the Terminal 16. Any length of wire can be used for the push button, but it is essential that both accumulator and control device are placed close to the set and connected up with short wires.

The mechanical operation of the controller will be understood from Fig. 345. When the Magnet Coils 1 are energised the armature 2 is raised. It lifts the Centre Fork 3 which overlaps at its tip only and consequently clears the end of the armature as it is raised. The Spring Cord returns the Centre Fork to its original position as soon as it is released. When the current is cut off from the Coils 1 the armature drops, this time striking the upper surface of the Centre Fork 3, the weight of the armature causing the Pivot Bolt 4 to raise the Strip 5 against the action of the Spring Cord, and thus to close the contacts 6 and open contacts 7.

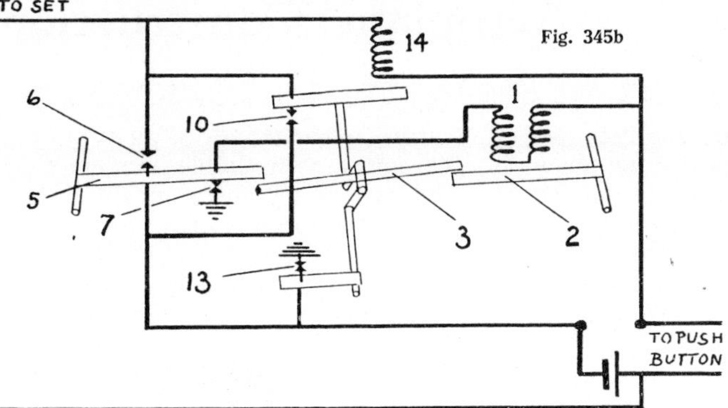

On passing current through Coil 14 the Flat Brackets 8 (Fig. 345a) are raised and the contacts 10 opened. The contacts 13 (Fig. 345) are closed. As the Rod 12 is moved away from the armature the Centre Fork 3 is released, thus allowing the contact arm 5 to drop. This movement raises the Centre Fork above the level of the armature again, and when the current is cut off from Coil 14 the device returns to its original setting.

By now referring to Fig. 345b the electrical operation of the device will be understood. As shown it is in the "off" position, and is ready to be energised for switching on the set. Contacts 6 and 10 are open, and contacts 7 and 13 are closed. When the push button is depressed the current flows through the Coils 1 and contacts 7 and 13 back to the accumulator. The armature 2 is raised, but the contacts are not altered until the push button is released and the armature allowed to drop on the arm 3. This action opens the contacts 7 and closes contacts 6, switching on the current for the set.

While the contacts 7 are open the Coils 1 are not in circuit with the push button. On again pressing the button the current flows to Coil 14 and through contacts 6. This Magnet Coil closes the points 10 and opens those at 13, and at the same time withdraws the arm 3 from beneath the armature 2. As soon as the arm 3 is released the switch arm 5 returns to its former position, but the current still flows to the set as the contacts 10 are closed. The Coils 1 remain out of circuit as contacts 13 are broken. On releasing the push button the contacts 10 open and 13 close, and the device is once again ready to be switched on the next time the button is pressed.

After the controller is completed minor adjustments will probably be necessary to secure efficiency. In particular the Centre Fork 3 must be carefully placed so that it swings clear of the armature 2 as the latter is raised, but projects sufficiently for the armature to catch it as it drops down again. Moving parts should be quite free, and the most suitable tension for the Spring Cord will be found by experiment.

It will be clear that this device, when used for wireless control, is suitable for battery-operated sets only and cannot be used with mains-operated receivers. It may be installed inside the wireless cabinet, and screwed down to the baseboard, so that it is kept free from dust and is not likely to be put out of order.

(346)—Simple Remote Control

(E. Thomas, Exeter)

The simple remote control device shown in Fig. 346 is not so reliable as the more elaborate one described on the opposite page, but it operates quite well, and those who do not wish to build the more complicated device will find this quite a good substitute.

Two Magnet Coils are attached by the Cores to a $2\frac{1}{2}'' \times 2\frac{1}{2}''$ Flat Plate. The Coils are wired in series and are connected to the insulated Terminals 6, which are wired to the push-button controller and the accumulator for energising the Coils.

The armature 1 is made up of three $4\frac{1}{2}''$ Strips and is provided with six $1\frac{1}{2}''$ Strips at the shorter end, the other end being fitted with a Pawl (without Boss) 2 that is pivotally mounted and held by a light wire spring. The Pawl engages between two Bush Wheels bolted together with their bosses outermost. Nuts and bolts are secured to one of the Wheels so that the nuts occur between the two, the second Wheel being held to the first by two additional nuts. Four Angle Brackets 3 are bolted to the first Bush Wheel to form a square. To prevent the Wheels from rotating too freely the wire 4 is arranged to press lightly on the nuts between them.

When the Magnets are energised the armature 1 is raised and the Pawl engages one of the nuts between the two Bush Wheels, which are thus rotated for 1/8th of a complete revolution. The Pendulum Connection 5 is so arranged that for

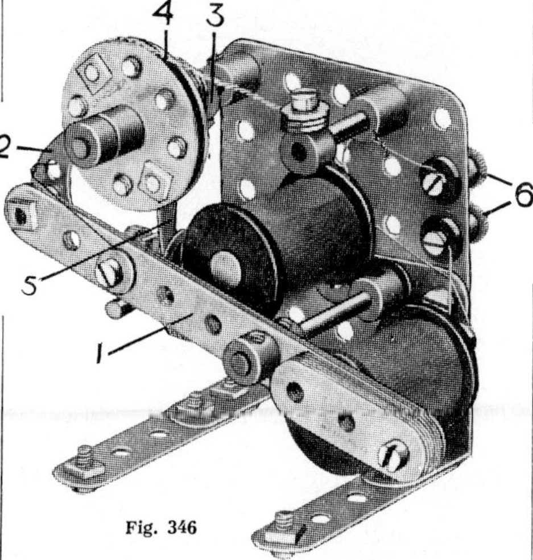

Fig. 346

alternate impulses of the armature it makes or breaks contact with one of the Angle Brackets 3.

Connections to the set are made from the Pendulum Connection and the frame.

Which are the Most Interesting Suggestions?

Readers' opinions on suggestions published in this section are a great help when new ideas are under consideration. Once again readers are asked to assist in the future selection of ideas by stating which of the suggestions published during the last year they consider the most interesting.

During 1935 twenty-five ideas appeared in the "Suggestions Section" (Nos. 320-344), and readers are asked to write down on a postcard the four that they consider the most interesting. The four suggestions should be placed in order of merit, and in writing them down it is only necessary to put the numbers under which they appeared. Below these the reader's full name and address should be given.

It is quite likely that readers living Overseas will show preference for different ideas from those preferred by Home readers, and in order to find out their true opinions, postcards received from Overseas will be treated entirely separately from those received from the British Isles. Every vote will be recorded according to its position on the list, and in this way the suggestions may be classified in their order of popularity.

In both sections senders of the lists most nearly corresponding to the final result of the voting will be presented with a cheque for £1-1s., and the next nearest to the general opinion of the voters will be awarded a cheque for 10/6. In addition the 12 runners-up in each section will receive consolation prizes.

The contributor whose suggestion is thus shown to be the most popular with Home or Overseas readers, or both, will receive a cheque for 10/6; and the other contributors whose ideas appear in the final results will be presented with consolation prizes.

Postcards should be addressed to "Spanner," "Meccano Magazine," Binns Road, Liverpool 13, and should be posted so that they are received before 31st March, except in the case of Overseas readers, whose postcards should be received not later than 30th April.

Cash Prizes for New Ideas

Cash prizes are awarded for all ideas published in the "Suggestions Section," except those appearing under "Miscellaneous Suggestions," and readers are invited to submit details of any new ideas that occur to them. Contributions should be original and should, if necessary, be illustrated with photographs or sketches.

Contributors are invited to send particulars of any ingenious mechanism that has not already been dealt with on these pages, and of new uses they find for Meccano parts. A mechanism need not be a complete model but perhaps part of a large model in which it serves some definite function. Practical uses for Meccano also will be considered for publication.

Model builders who are keen on inventing new mechanisms should consider which of their recent efforts are suitable for publication, and send details of the devices. Here is a good opportunity to earn some extra pocket money and at the same time to be of real help to other readers.

Ideas should be submitted to "Spanner," and some of those that cannot be dealt with fully will appear under "Miscellaneous Suggestions." Small prizes are awarded for these contributions.

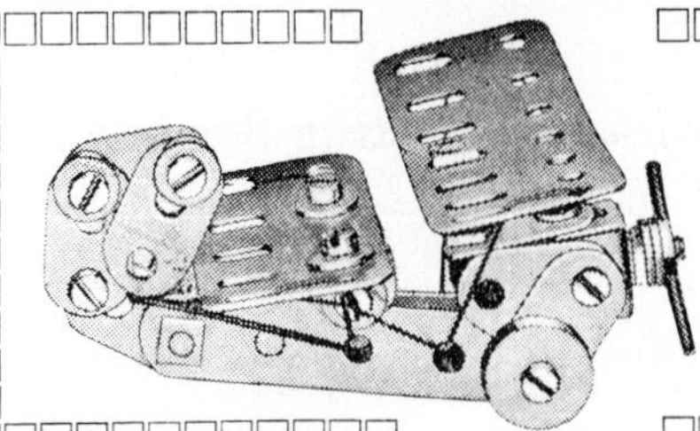

In Search of New Models

Aeroplane Construction

AEROPLANES offer a fine range of subjects for Meccano models. During recent years the tendency in design has been increasingly towards streamlining. To reproduce these streamlined forms in Meccano is not so difficult as the beginner might imagine, and after one or two attempts it will soon be found how best to obtain the curves that characterise most aeroplanes of modern design.

(Above) A simple reproduction of the "Flying Flea." (Below) Fig. 1. The D.H. "Dragon-Six" commercial biplane

The great diversity of aeroplane designs provides model-builders with a large and splendid range of subjects. First of all there are the two classes known respectively as biplanes and monoplanes. In the case of monoplanes, the wing may be fitted at the top or bottom of the fuselage, forming either a high wing or low wing machine; or the fuselage may be suspended from the wing, thus giving what is known as a parasol monoplane. Biplanes also show variations in design. In some cases the wings have a pronounced "stagger," that is the upper wing is mounted farther forward than the lower wing; and in others the spans of the two wings are unequal. Where the planes are unequal in span the lower wing usually is the shorter, and a machine in which the difference is large is known as a sesquiplane, the name simply meaning that it has one and a half planes.

There are also great differences between machines intended to be employed over land and those for use over water. Land planes have wheeled undercarriages, and in many cases these are retractable, that is they can be pulled up or otherwise moved into such a position that they offer no resistance during flight. On the other hand machines for use over water either have floats instead of wheels, or the fuselage is built in the form of the hull of a boat. Machines of the first kind are known as seaplanes, and those of the second kind as flying boats. Some machines can be used on both land or water. These amphibians, as they are called, have special mountings for the wheels in order that they can be raised clear of the floats or flying boat hull when alighting on water. Still other machines that are not amphibious can readily be adapted for use either as land planes or seaplanes by fitting the appropriate undercarriage.

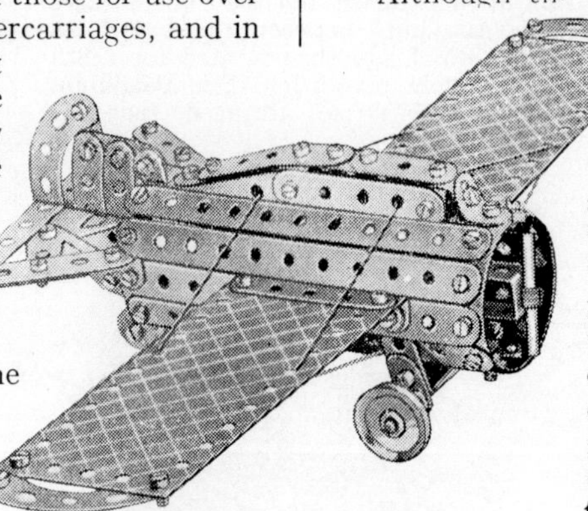

Fig. 2. The peculiar Stipa experimental monoplane.

It will be seen that the constructor who sets out to build aeroplane models has a great field before him, and the fact that the designs of different manufacturing firms for any one type vary greatly adds further to his range. How closely it is possible to reproduce the features of machines of all types and makes is shown in the many remarkable models that are submitted by competitors for entry in Meccano Model-building Contests. Five entirely new models are shown on this and the opposite page. No difficulty should be experienced in selecting further new subjects, for suitable prototypes can be found in any of the well-illustrated books on aircraft that are now published, and the pages of the "Meccano Magazine" also furnish illustrations and full details of machines of special interest and novelty.

The building of models of aeroplanes of unorthodox design is very attractive, for many of these can be built up in Meccano to make excellent models. An example of a very queer machine is shown in Fig. 2. This is of the Italian Stipa Monoplane, the fuselage of which actually forms a Venturi tube. The airscrew is placed at the front of the tube, inside which the engine is mounted, and the slipstream therefore is directed through the centre of the fuselage. Among the advantages claimed for this fuselage construction are increases in airscrew thrust and lifting effect. The Stipa Monoplane is an experimental two-seater, the two cockpits being arranged above the top of the fuselage.

Although the Fairey "Hendon" Bomber is not quite so unorthodox as the Stipa Monoplane, it is of unique design and is easily recognisable from almost any viewpoint. This machine is reproduced in the model shown in Fig. 3. It is a twin-engined low wing monoplane with streamlined fairings built beneath the wings for accommodating the landing wheels. The wheels are immediately beneath the engine nacelles. Twin rudders are a conspicuous feature, and the actual machine has three gunner's cockpits, one in the tail, one in the centre of the fuselage, and one at the nose. The pilot's cockpit is just in front of the wing.

Another long-range night bomber of unusual design is the Handley Page "Heyford," a twin-engined biplane of the raised fuselage type. The fuselage is not placed directly above the lower wing, as is usual in biplanes, but is suspended beneath the upper wing and the wheels are situated immediately beneath the lower wing and are not provided with any undercarriage struts of the usual type. Twin rudders are fitted.

The Cierva "Autogiro" is well known to readers, and those who have not already modelled this strange flying machine will find its construction particularly interesting. The absence of wings, and the revolving vanes mounted above the fuselage give the "Autogiro" a weird appearance when in flight. Another remarkable aeroplane is the Westland-Hill "Pterodactyl," a sesquiplane with a very short fuselage and a large upper wing that is swept back in the form of a wide V. There is no tail to the fuselage, the rudders being fitted at the tapered ends of the upper wings.

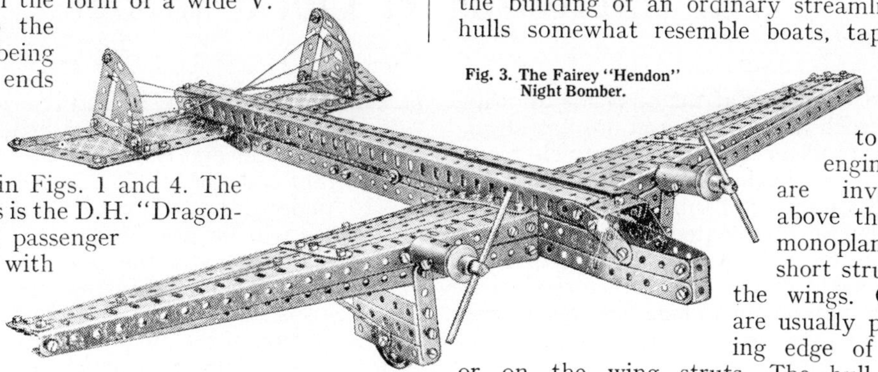

Fig. 3. The Fairey "Hendon" Night Bomber.

Models of two typical commercial machines are shown in Figs. 1 and 4. The first of these machines is the D.H. "Dragon-Six," a twin-engined passenger or freight carrier with seating accommodation and freight space that can be adapted to suit requirements. The shape of the fuselage is well reproduced in the model, and as in the actual machines of this type both upper and lower wings are attached direct to the fuselage.

The B.A. "Eagle" (Fig. 4) is a smaller machine of the cabin monoplane type, having accommodation for three. When in flight the undercarriage is drawn up to reduce the wind resistance, the wheels folding outwards to fit into receptacles beneath the wings. On fairly large models the retractable undercarriage can be made to work in a similar manner to those in actual practice, but it is not advisable to try to achieve this result on small models where there is insufficient space for the mechanism. When enough parts are available elaborate models can be built up, including all the refinements and necessary mechanism of the original machine. Movable ailerons, elevators and rudder can be made to operate from controls in the cockpit.

Racing machines give the constructor splendid opportunities for showing his skill and ingenuity. The D.H. "Comet" is an outstanding example of this class. It is a two-seater long-range monoplane of the cabin type with a very slender streamlined fuselage and twin engines mounted in front of the wing. The landing wheels are mounted beneath the engine nacelles, and when the monoplane is in flight they are drawn up into the nacelles, fairing caps fitting over the holes through which they pass. With careful selection of parts, the graceful lines of this machine can readily be reproduced, and Strips will be found most useful in the construction of a model of this famous machine.

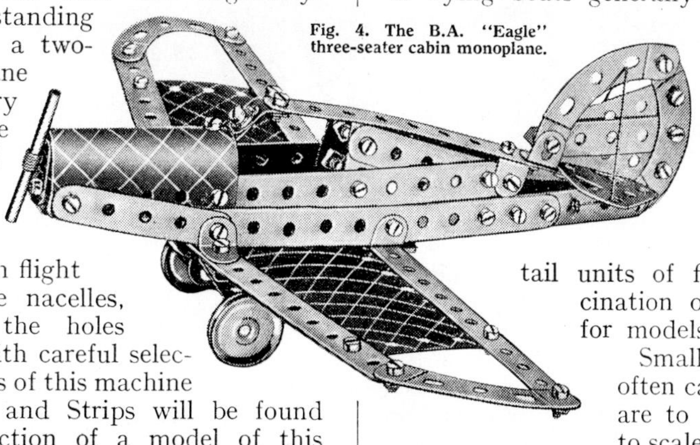

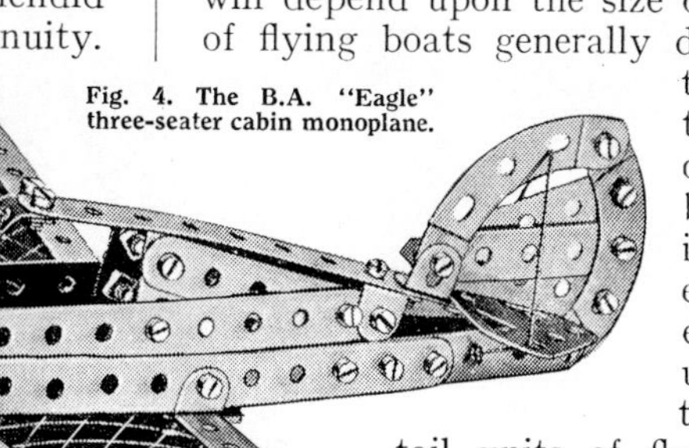

Fig. 4. The B.A. "Eagle" three-seater cabin monoplane.

A single-engined single-seater racing monoplane can be built on the lines of the Percival "Mew Gull." This is a small low wing cabin monoplane and has rather a short fuselage. The engine is totally enclosed, and streamlined fairings almost cover the wheels. The famous Supermarine S.6B that finally won the Schneider Trophy for Great Britain is a splendid example of a single-seater racing seaplane, and a particularly fine model of this is illustrated in the Instruction Manual for Outfits F to L. The model is a good example of the use of Strips for forming a streamlined fuselage, and a study of the method of construction adopted in this case will be very helpful to those who are building similar models.

Perhaps more skill is required for forming a flying boat hull from Meccano parts than is necessary in the building of an ordinary streamlined fuselage. The hulls somewhat resemble boats, tapering off towards the stern and sweeping upwards in a graceful curve to the tail unit. The engines of flying boats are invariably mounted above the fuselage and on monoplanes are fitted on short struts mounted above the wings. On biplanes they are usually placed at the leading edge of the upper wing or on the wing struts. The hull forms the cabin and is provided with a separate small cabin near the nose for the pilot. In the making of flying boat hulls Strips usually will be found most suitable for modelling the curves, but Strip Plates or Flexible Plates will prove useful for the sides. Features that must not be overlooked are the small floats placed beneath the wings to act as stabilisers. In most cases Strips will be found to be the most suitable parts for making the wing floats.

Most amphibian aircraft are flying boats fitted with landing gear that can be raised or lowered as required. The undercarriage is usually arranged to swing outwards so that the wheels are raised clear of the water, and sometimes the wheels fit into sockets beneath the wings when not in use. The mechanism for raising and lowering the wheels should if possible be reproduced in Meccano. As flying boat hulls are comparatively large it should not be difficult to arrange for this, but the constructor's opportunities in this direction of course will depend upon the size of the model. The tail units of flying boats generally differ considerably from the tail units of landplanes. The tailplane is often mounted on the rudder and braced by struts, and is usually in a direct line with the engines, so that the full effect of the slipstream is utilised. Other variations in the arrangement of the tail units of flying boats add to the fascination of these machines as subjects for models.

Small details on aeroplane models often call for careful attention if they are to be reproduced approximately to scale. The use of parts that are too large for the purpose makes the model look clumsy, rather spoiling its appearance, and it is frequently better to omit the details entirely than to make them too large. On three of the models illustrated Axle Rods are used for airscrews, and on the D.H. Dragon-Six $\frac{3}{8}''$ Bolts are used. The diminutive Flying Flea shown in the heading on the opposite page requires yet a neater air screw, Spring Cord being used in this case. Wing struts can be made from Spring Cord and in small models ordinary cord must be used for the struts as well as for bracing wires if these are fitted.

Quayside Unloader in Meccano

An Interesting H Outfit Model

THE loading and unloading at the quayside of coarse loose materials such as coal and iron ore has always presented a difficult problem. Until comparatively recent times it was carried out by hand, the usual unloading scheme being to fill a number of tubs in the hold of the ship and hoist them up to elevated wooden platforms on the quayside by means of the vessel's own derricks. As the volume of freight of this nature increased, some quicker and cheaper method of handling became urgently necessary. In 1880 a move in this direction was made by the invention in America of the Industrial Brownhoist tramway type of unloader, and it is from this early machine that present-day bridge cranes have been developed. Unlike modern machines of this type the early unloaders resembled short cable railways on which ran small self-emptying tubs. These tubs were filled by men stationed in the hold of the ship that was being unloaded, and when full were hoisted out and their contents discharged on to the ground between the two end columns of the unloader.

An interesting working model of an up-to-date Brownhoist bridge crane is shown in Fig. 1. Its prototype, which is stationed at the port of Rotterdam, Holland, is a little over 150 ft. in length and is fitted with a grab capable of lifting 10 tons at a time. The model is built to a scale of 1/3 in. to 1 ft., and its overall measurements are length 4 ft., and height 2 ft. 3 in. It is fitted with crane hooks in place of a grab, owing to lack of the necessary parts in the H Outfit with which it is designed to be built. A suitable grab could easily be constructed with a few extra parts, however. Further realism would be secured by mounting the model on $\frac{3}{4}$" Flanged Wheels and arranging it to run on rails built up from Angle Girders. These girders might be screwed down to a baseboard painted to represent a quayside.

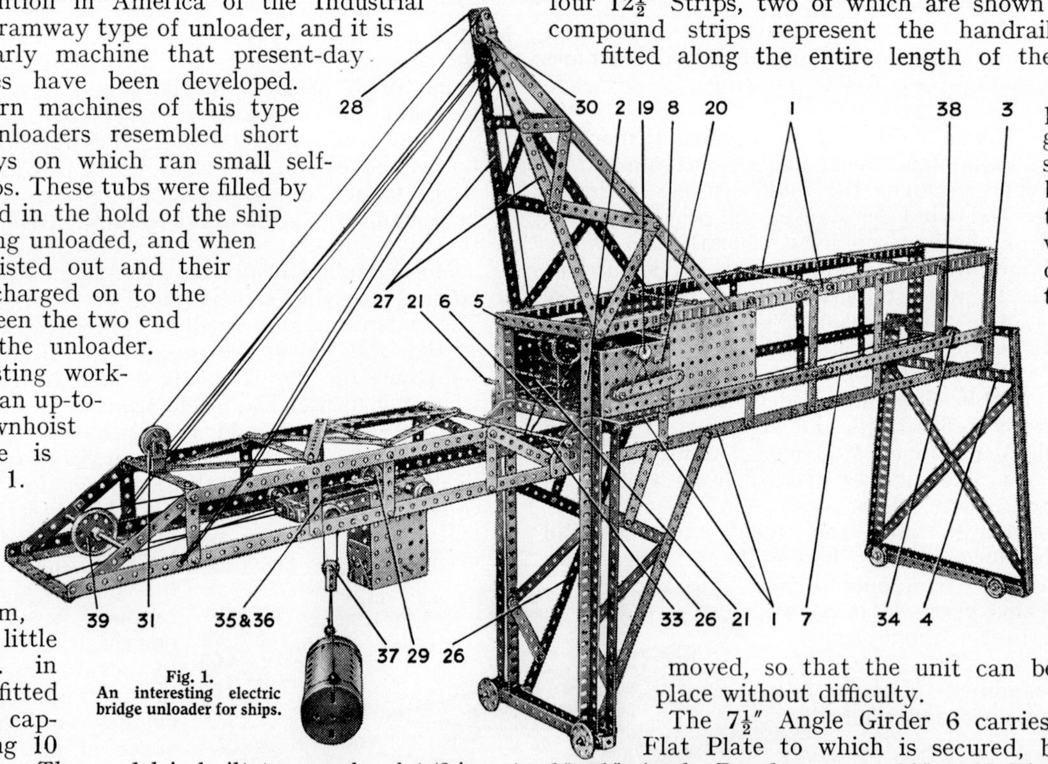

Fig. 1.
An interesting electric bridge unloader for ships.

The model is commenced by building up the four main girders 1, each of these being composed of two $12\frac{1}{2}$" Angle Girders connected together by means of two $2\frac{1}{2}$" Strips as shown in Fig. 1. When the four girders are complete they are secured together in pairs, each pair having two $5\frac{1}{2}$" Angle Girders 2 and 3, and five $5\frac{1}{2}$" Strips. The two pairs of long girders, when secured together in this manner, form the side members of the bridge section of the machine, and they are both connected together to form a long box girder by a series of Angle Girders and Strips.

At the rear end is fitted a $7\frac{1}{2}$" Angle Girder 4, and at the front end a $5\frac{1}{2}$" Strip 5 is used together with a second $7\frac{1}{2}$" Angle Girder 6. The Girder 6 forms part of the gear-box, as will be described later.

The top edges of the side members of the bridge are connected by four $4\frac{1}{2}$" Strips, one of which consists of two $2\frac{1}{2}$" Strips bolted together and overlapped one hole each. This section of the model is completed by the addition of four $12\frac{1}{2}$" Strips, two of which are shown at 7. These compound strips represent the handrails that are fitted along the entire length of the prototype.

At this point the gear-box should be built and fitted, as this will be more difficult when the remainder of the model is built. Before fitting the complete gear-box, however, the two $5\frac{1}{2}$" Strips 8 and 9 must be temporarily removed, so that the unit can be secured in place without difficulty.

The $7\frac{1}{2}$" Angle Girder 6 carries a $5\frac{1}{2}" \times 3\frac{1}{2}"$ Flat Plate to which is secured, by means of $\frac{1}{2}" \times \frac{1}{2}"$ Angle Brackets, two $3\frac{1}{2}" \times 2\frac{1}{2}"$ Flanged Plates. An E6 or E20b Electric Motor is also bolted in place as shown in Fig. 2. One of the $3\frac{1}{2}" \times 2\frac{1}{2}"$ Flanged Plates is fixed to the Motor side plate by means of a $2\frac{1}{2}" \times \frac{1}{2}"$ Double Angle Strip 10, and this part forms a bearing for one of the shafts in the gear-box.

A Worm on the armature shaft of the Electric Motor engages with a 57-teeth Gear 11 that is locked on a vertical 2" Rod journalled in the Double Angle Strip and one of the holes in the $5\frac{1}{2}" \times 3\frac{1}{2}"$ Flat Plate. The 2" Rod carries at its upper end a $1\frac{1}{2}$" Contrate that drives a sliding 4" Rod by means of a $\frac{1}{2}$" Pinion 12. Two Washers are placed on the Rod, between the $\frac{1}{2}$" Pinion and end plate, for spacing purposes.

Two Collars, one of which is shown at 13, are secured on the end of the sliding Rod, and these accommodate the shank of a bolt 14, between them. This bolt is carried in the centre of a $3\frac{1}{2}$" Strip, fitted with a Threaded Pin, forming the gear change lever.

The sliding Rod carries a second $\frac{1}{2}$" Pinion 15 and $\frac{3}{4}$"

Contrate 16, the Pinion being in engagement with a 57-teeth Gear when the gear lever is in its outer position. The 57-teeth Gear rotates a $1\frac{1}{2}''$ Pulley 17, the purpose of which will be described later. When the gear lever is at its inner position the $\frac{3}{4}''$ Contrate 16 engages with a second similar part mounted on the hoisting barrel 18. A length of cord is shown wound on this Rod in Fig. 2. The $\frac{1}{2}''$ Pulley 19 forms a brake drum, the arrangement of which is shown in Fig. 1. The $\frac{3}{8}''$ Bolt 20 forms a stop for the brake lever.

The Crank Handle 21, Figs. 1 and 2, carries the hoisting cord for raising and lowering the bridge extension. As will be seen from Fig. 1, the Crank Handle is journalled in one of the side Flanged Plates and one side plate of the Electric Motor. On the outside of the side Flanged Plate, the Crank Handle carries a 1″ fast Pulley 22, Fig. 3, and round this is passed a brake cord. The cord is secured at one end to the frame of the model and at the other end to one arm of a Boss Bell Crank 23. This Crank, which is mounted pivotally on a Pivot Bolt 24, carries on its horizontal arm a $3\frac{1}{2}''$ Strip fitted with the weight 25, a Coupling.

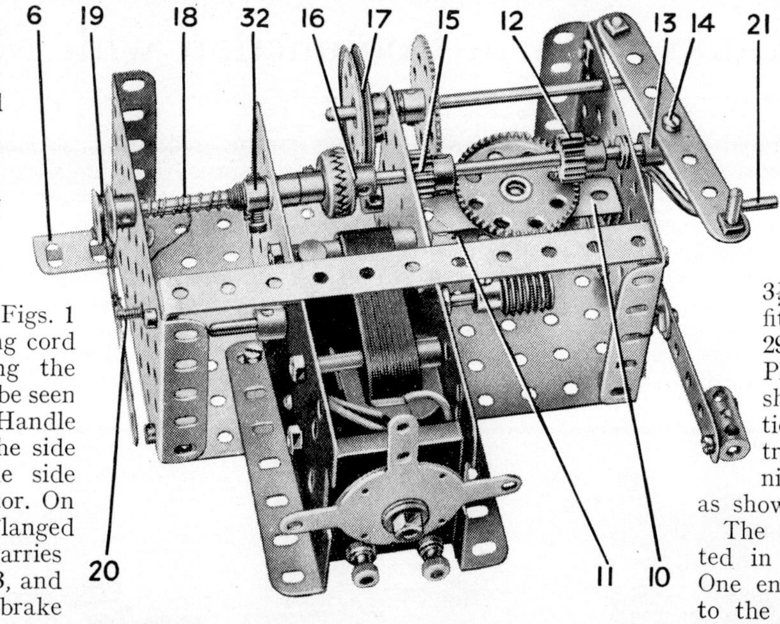

Fig. 2. The motor and gear-box, showing the hoisting drums and racking pulley.

The gear-box can now be fitted in position as shown in Fig. 1, and the construction of the model continued. The complete bridge and gear-box are elevated on four $12\frac{1}{2}''$ Angle Girders, the rear two being bolted, five holes from their upper ends, to the Girder 4. At the lower end the $12\frac{1}{2}''$ Angle Girders are joined together by means of two $9\frac{1}{2}''$ Angle Girders that are bolted together to form a channel section girder. This girder carries two $1\frac{1}{2}''$ Rods on which are secured two travelling wheels. For bracing members, 2″ and $12\frac{1}{2}''$ Strips are used as shown.

At the front end of the bridge the two $12\frac{1}{2}''$ Angle Girders are bolted to the end $5\frac{1}{2}''$ Angle Girders 2 and are overlapped four holes. The end of the Girder 6 is fitted with two $12\frac{1}{2}''$ Strips, and the lower ends of these, together with the ends of the $12\frac{1}{2}''$ Angle Girders, are secured together by means of two $7\frac{1}{2}''$ Strips. The next-to-end holes of these two Strips form bearings for the axles of the remaining pair of travelling wheels.

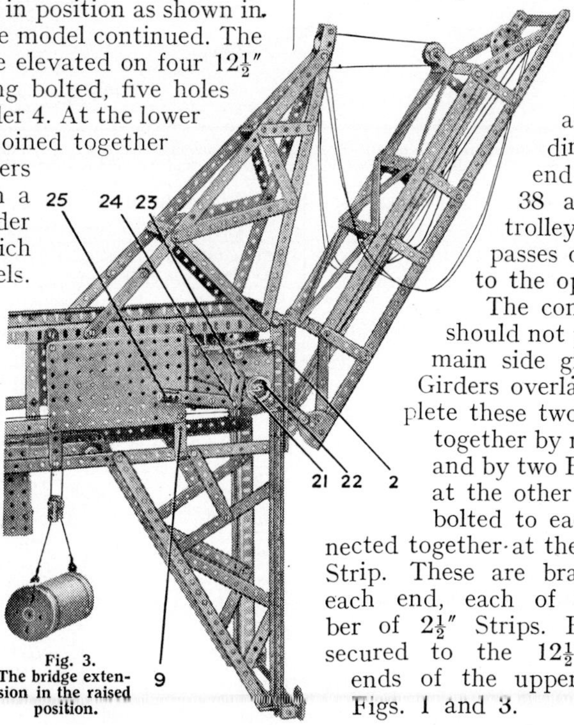

Fig. 3. The bridge extension in the raised position.

Two $12\frac{1}{2}''$ Strips 26 are now fitted to the lower set of girders 1, and these Strips are attached at their lower ends to $\frac{1}{2}''\times\frac{1}{2}''$ Angle Brackets bolted to the $7\frac{1}{2}''$ Strips of the front legs. These $12\frac{1}{2}''$ Strips are braced as shown in Figs. 1 and 3.

The structure surmounting the bridge can now be fitted. This consists of two $12\frac{1}{2}''$ Strips 27 connected together at their upper ends by a Double Bracket 28. The two rear members of the structure are each built up from a $12\frac{1}{2}''$ Strip and a $3\frac{1}{2}''$ Strip, each overlapping the other two holes. Bracing is fitted as shown.

The construction of the trolley for carrying the load, that runs along the bridge and bridge extension, can now be proceeded with. The frame is composed of two $5\frac{1}{2}''\times\frac{1}{2}''$ Double Angle Strips secured together at one end by two Flat Brackets. At the other end the Double Angle Strips carry two $3\frac{1}{2}''\times2\frac{1}{2}''$ Flanged Plates fitted with a $1\frac{1}{2}''$ Strip 29 and a $2\frac{1}{2}''\times1\frac{1}{2}''$ Flanged Plate at the bottom, not shown in the illustrations. At the bottom the trolley also carries a Trunnion and Flat Trunnion as shown.

The operating cords are fitted in the following manner. One end of a cord is secured to the Crank Handle 21, and from here it is taken over the Pulley 30, round the Pulley 31, and then secured to the top of the superstructure.

A second cord is secured to the Collar 32 and passed round the pivot Rod 33, round the Pulleys 34, 35, 36 and 37, and finally tied to the Strip at the end of the bridge extension. A third cord passes round the $1\frac{1}{2}''$ Pulley 17, and both ends pass in opposite directions round the Rod 33. One end is then taken round the Pulley 38 and secured to one end of the trolley. The other end of the cord passes over the Pulley 39 and is fastened to the opposite end of the trolley.

The construction of the bridge extension should not present any great difficulties. Each main side girder consists of two $12\frac{1}{2}''$ Angle Girders overlapping nine holes, and when complete these two compound girders are connected together by means of two $2\frac{1}{2}''$ Strips at one end, and by two Flat Trunnions carrying the Rod 33 at the other end. Four vertical $2\frac{1}{2}''$ Strips are bolted to each side girder and these are connected together at their upper ends by means of a $12\frac{1}{2}''$ Strip. These are braced by means of $4\frac{1}{2}''$ Strips at each end, each of which is composed of a number of $2\frac{1}{2}''$ Strips. Eight $\frac{1}{2}''\times\frac{1}{2}''$ Angle Brackets are secured to the $12\frac{1}{2}''$ Strips and these carry the ends of the upper bracing members as shown in Figs. 1 and 3.

List of parts required to build the model:

16 of No. 1; 2 of No. 1b; 25 of No. 2; 4 of No. 2a; 12 of No. 3; 2 of No. 4; 36 of No. 5; 2 of No. 6; 3 of No. 6a; 14 of No. 8; 4 of No. 8a; 2 of No. 8b; 4 of No. 9; 2 of No. 10; 3 of No. 11; 19 of No. 12; 1 of No. 12a; 5 of No. 15; 1 of No. 15b; 3 of No. 16; 2 of No. 16a; 5 of No. 17; 3 of No. 18a; 1 of No. 19s; 4 of No. 20b; 2 of No. 21; 4 of No. 22; 3 of No. 22a; 3 of No. 23; 1 of No. 23a; 2 of No. 24; 1 of No. 26; 2 of No. 27a; 1 of No. 28; 2 of No. 29; 1 of No. 32; 10 of No. 35; 200 of No. 37; 6 of No. 37a; 24 of No. 38; 1 of No. 43; 1 of No. 48a; 3 of No. 48d; 3 of No. 52a; 4 of No. 53; 2 of No. 57c; 18 of No. 59; 3 of No. 63; 1 of No. 73; 6 of No. 111c; 1 of No. 115; 1 of No. 126; 5 of No. 126a; 1 of No. 128; 1 of No. 147b; 1 of No. 162; 1 of No. 176; Electric Motor (not included in Outfit).

Novel Model-Building Competition

Using Dinky Toys in Conjunction with Meccano

On this page is illustrated a fine model of an arch bridge built up from Meccano parts. On the roadway several Dinky Toys are arranged to travel to and fro by means of a simple automatic mechanism. This model is a good example of the way in which Dinky Toys can be used to add the finishing touches to Meccano models, and a further example is shown in the fine roundabout illustrated on page 105. We believe that readers will have plenty of ideas for building other models of this kind, and therefore we announce a special competition in order to encourage them to put their ideas into practical form.

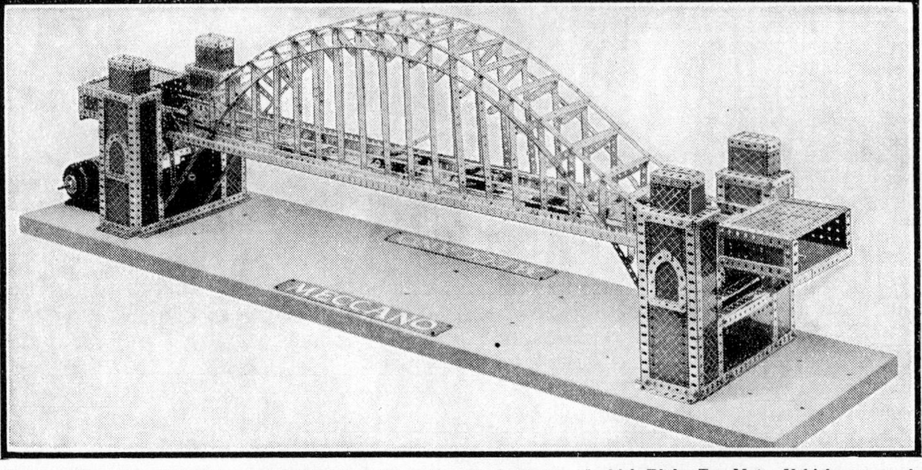

This fine Meccano arch bridge incorporates automatic mechanism by means of which Dinky Toy Motor Vehicles are made to travel to and fro along the roadway. A competition for novel models of this kind is announced on this page.

To enter this contest it is only necessary to build a model that incorporates standard Meccano parts and any of the Dinky Toys. Models may be of any kind whatever, and any quantity of Meccano parts and any kind and number of Dinky Toys may be used as desired.

The Dinky Toy Motor Vehicles, Aeroplanes, and Ships will be found especially useful in this respect. They can be used in a great variety of models, so that there should be no difficulty in selecting a suitable subject. It should be clearly understood, however, that models made entirely from Meccano, and which do not incorporate any of the Dinky Toys, are not eligible for this contest.

Models that can be set to work will stand the greatest chance of success, and these may be driven by any form of Meccano power unit such as an Electric or Clockwork Motor or a Steam Engine.

A little thought will supply plenty of ideas for models suitable for entry in this contest, and as the competition provides model-builders with a welcome change from ordinary Meccano model-building we look forward to receiving a large number of entries.

It must not be thought that because the models illustrated on this page and on page 105 are large and complicated that it is necessary to have a large Outfit and a big variety of Dinky Toys to compete successfully in this contest. This is not the case. It is possible to build quite simple models with which one or more Dinky Toys can be used, and such models will be given every consideration by the judges.

The contest is open to every owner of a Meccano Outfit. There are no entrance fees to be paid or forms to be filled in. Competitors may choose any type of model they like as the subject of their entry, and the more vivid the imaginative effort shown in designing models the better the chance of gaining a prize.

Actual models must not be sent. It is only necessary to submit either clear photographs or, if this is not possible, good drawings of models, together with a brief explanation of any structural or mechanical features that are not clear from the photos or drawings. Neither photographs nor drawings need be the competitor's own handiwork, but it is absolutely essential that the model itself is his own unaided work.

Entries will be divided into two sections: Section A, for readers of all ages living in the British Isles, and Section B, for readers of all ages living Overseas. Age will be taken into consideration when judging.

The competitor's name, address, and age must be written clearly on the back of each photograph or drawing sent in, together with the letter (A or B) indicating the Section for which the entry is eligible. Envelopes containing entries should be addressed "Meccano—Dinky Toy" Competition, Meccano Ltd., Binns Road, Liverpool 13. Photographs of prize-winning models become the property of Meccano Ltd., but unsuccessful entries will be returned to the senders provided that a stamped addressed envelope of the necessary size is enclosed with the entry.

31st March, 1936, is the last day on which entries can be received in the Home Section. Overseas readers must forward their entries so that they reach Liverpool not later than 30th May, 1936.

Competitors are advised to start work on their models immediately so as to have ample time to make any necessary alterations.

"Meccano—Dinky Toy" Competition

The Prizes

A complete and separate set of prizes as follows will be awarded in each of the Sections A and B.

First Prize, Meccano or Hornby Goods value £3-3s.

Second Prize, Meccano or Hornby Goods value £2-2s.

Third Prize, Meccano or Hornby Goods value £1-1s.

Five Prizes of Meccano or Hornby Goods value 10/6.

Five Prizes of Meccano or Hornby Goods value 5/-.

Certificates of Merit also will be awarded in each Section.

Model-Building Competition Results

By Frank Hornby

"Architectural" Contest (Overseas Section)

The full list of prizewinners in the Overseas Section of the "Architectural' Contest is as follows:

Three competitors obtained over 75 points and therefore share goods value £8 in proportion to the points gained: Miss Ana Rivarola, Buenos Aires, Argentine (87 points) £2/18/–; K. Orams, Christchurch, N.1, New Zealand (80 points) £2/13/–; J. Watson, Regina, Canada (75 points) £2/10/–.

The following competitors obtained between 65 and 74 points and receive proportionate shares of Meccano or Hornby goods value £4: P. Giese, Buenos Aires, S. America (72 points) 15/–; J. Capelli, Buenos Aires (69 points) 14/–; N. Soderberg, Falun, Sweden (69 points) 14/–; A. Casaretto, Buenos Aires (66 points) 13/6; A. Bacon, Deolali, India (66 points) 13/6; R. Begg, Hamilton, Canada (66 points) 13/6.

A pleasing feature of this contest is the success of Miss Ana Rivarola in winning the chief prize. I congratulate this young lady on her fine achievement and hope that she will continue to send in entries for these monthly contests. Her model is a particularly fine example of miniature architecture, and represents the facade of a Gothic church. The building includes three arched doorways surmounted by twin towers and spires. The doorways are each made from two Flat Plates converging at the top, and inside the triangle so formed are bolted curved Braced Girders. Much of the decorative work is done with 2½" Curved Strips and a Wheel Flange, and several Pulley Wheels of various sizes also are used. The towers on which the spires are built are provided with ornamental pointed windows, and above these is a balcony surrounded with Braced Girders to represent railings. The spires themselves are built on frameworks of Angle Girders, and the gaps are filled in with 2½"×2½" Flat Plates and Strips. The apex of each spire is fitted with a cross, which is made by bolting two 2½" Strips by their centre holes to a Collar mounted on a Rod that protrudes from the spires. Clocks represented by Bush Wheels provide additional decoration to the towers.

An interesting prize-winning model representing an Argentine railway station at night. It is the work of P. Giese, Buenos Aires.

K. J. Orams also sent a model of a church, the main portion of which is constructed on a frame of Angle Girders 18" long, 14" wide and 7½" high to the gutters. The walls and roof are covered in with Flat Plates and Flat Girders, gaps being left in the walls at intervals for windows, and Curved Strips and Strips are used for the window frames. As in the case of Miss Rivarola's model, the spires are built on a short tower, and this is placed centrally in the front of the model, its lower part forming the bell-ringer's room and the porch. A small room off the porch represents a vestry. The spire is built on a pyramid of Angle Girders, but as the entire structure is considerably smaller than Miss Rivarola's model only one 5½" Flat Girder is needed to fill in each side.

The other principal prizewinner, J. Watson, built a model of Parliament Buildings at Regina, Saskatchewan. The model is built on a considerably larger scale than either of the models already described, and is 12 ft. 6 in. long and 4 ft. high, but although so large it does not contain as much detail as I should like to see in a model of this kind, and also certain portions are built from non-Meccano parts. It is, however, a neat piece of work and a good reproduction of the actual building. In the actual building there are several ornamental pillars and for these cylinders of wood were used. The roof is made from corrugated cardboard, and the numerous windows are filled in with cellophane.

Six models submitted by P. Giese, N. Soderberg, J. Capelli, R. A. Begg, A. R. Bacon and A. A. Casaretto respectively, shared a prize of £4. P. Giese's model, which is illustrated on this page, represents the front of a modern railway station. In my opinion the best work has been done in the construction of the veranda over the entrance. The use of Dinky Toys adds a touch of realism to the model, which was greatly appreciated by the competition judges.

A ranch house forms the subject of J. Capelli's model, and it is evident that Capelli has a considerable knowledge of his subject. The front of the house is provided with a garden surrounded by low railings, which are represented by Braced Girders, and in the railings is a wicket gate, which actually moves on Hinges. Cardboard is used for the roof of the model, but this is the only non-Meccano part employed.

N. Soderberg's entry comprised two models representing a sports pavilion and a tower and aerial of the type used for transmitting television waves. The greater part of the sports pavilion is made from Strips, and Flat Plates are used for the walls. The television transmitting tower is constructed on four pillars, each made from two Angle Girders bolted together to form tubular girders. The upper part of the tower resembles the lantern house of a lighthouse in design, and is made from Flat and Triangular Plates. An aerial, represented by Meccano Cord, is supported on Rods that protrude radially from the top of the tower. Cord is also used throughout the model for bracing purposes.

R. A. Begg's model is an excellent example of a modern departmental store. The most conspicuous parts of it are a skyscraper structure at one end and a great arched main entrance. The model is quite simple in construction, however, and is built chiefly of Strips, and from the photographs it appears that it is intended to give a vague impression of the size and design of structures of this type rather than to show the details of their construction.

A. R. Bacon's model also is a very simple reproduction of the house in which John Bunyan was born. Although it is made entirely from Strips it is extremely neat, and the only portions that are not made from Meccano are the window frames.

The model sent by A. A. Casaretto is a church with twin bell towers, and as in the case of P. Giese's model, Dinky Toys are used to obtain a realistic effect.

Results of the August "Errors" Contest (Home Section)

First Prize, Meccano or Hornby Goods value £2/2/–: G. Sinclair, Canterbury. The Second and Third Prizes were combined and the total (£1/11/6) divided equally between R. Upton, London, E.4, and G. Dilworth, Stretford, each receiving Goods value 15/9.

Goods value 5/–: D. Brooks, Alveston, Nr. Bristol; J. Dobinson, Bromley; N. Chessells, Birmingham; P. Haddock, London, S.W.16; I. Kirkbride, Minehead.

Goods value 2/6: M. Capel, Oxford; J. Capon, Hadleigh; J. Geake, Manchester; D. Morris, Greenhithe; C. Trimmer, Gillingham.

"Holiday" Contest (Home and Overseas)

First Prize, Meccano or Hornby Goods value £1/1/–: A. Tarry, Harpenden. Second Prize, Goods value 15/–: G. Colwell, Gosport. Third Prize, Goods value 10/6: R. Myburgh, Claremont, S. Africa.

"Humorous Models" Competition (Home)

First Prize, Meccano or Hornby Goods value £1/1/–: T. Barron, Sollom Tarleton, Nr. Preston. Second Prize, Goods value 15/–: N. Wilsdon, Darlington. Third Prize, Goods value 10/6: R. Fautley, North Cheam, Surrey.

Enfield Grammar School M.C.—The club held its first Exhibition on the School Speech Day, and the display occupied two rooms. The chief models in the first room were a Meccanograph built and worked by a senior member and a model workshop loaned from Headquarters. The outstanding models in the second room were a reproduction of Watt's Beam Engine and of the Eiffel Tower. Part of the club's railway track was laid round the Tower. The first Games Night was very successful. A system of scoring was arranged, and at the end of the evening the Leader presented four prizes of Meccano products. Club roll: 32. *Secretary:* J. H. Pettifer, 31, Goat Lane, Forty Hill, Enfield.

Well Hall and District M.C.—A visit was paid to the Lightweight Cycle Show, in London, where members were very interested in the latest types of light bicycles. It is probable that a Cycling section will be formed this spring. Attendance at meetings continues to be good. Club roll: 8. *Secretary:* E. W. Quinton, 48, Beaconsfield Road, Mottingham, Kent.

Kendal M.C.—Several interesting visits were paid to the Lancaster H.R.C. Branch in connection with the recent Exhibition. Meetings continue to be held regularly although members are still without a clubroom. Plans are being made for a mock trial, debates, and a visit to Headquarters. Club roll: 10. *Leader:* Mr. L. Haslam, Middleton, Kirkby Lonsdale, Carnforth.

Bristol Grammar School M.C.—The club has been divided into Senior and Junior Sections, each having 20 boys. Model-building has been the chief activity, and a very successful Exhibition was held at the close of the last school term. Club roll: 40. *Secretary:* N. E. Ricketts, 10, Belgrave Road, Clifton, Bristol, 8.

Old Charlton M.C.—Some fine model motor cars and excavators have been constructed at recent meetings. Debates continue to be very popular, and have included one on the topical subject of whether pedestrians, cyclists or motorists have prior right to the road. A Stamp section has been formed, and a talk by the Leader on stamp collecting was listened to with interest. Arrangements are being made for visits to Croydon Airport, a local power station, and a local preserving factory. Members are busy rehearsing for a social to be held this month. Club roll: 22. *Secretary:* W. Jaques, 60, Gurdon Road, London, S.E.7.

Mallow M.C.—A talk on "*Gramophone versus Wireless*" was followed by a lively debate that ended in favour of wireless. A debate on "*Rail versus Road*" also proved very entertaining. A further visit has been paid to the local sugar beet factory, in connection with the elaborate model being constructed by members. Recent additions to this model include a fully-equipped garage, an automatic weighing machine, and extensive sidings. The model is lit by electricity, and will be the chief feature at the club's forthcoming Exhibition. A model of a local viaduct has also been constructed for the Exhibition. Club roll: 10. *Secretary:* D. Hickey, 42, Ballydaheen, Mallow, Co. Cork, I.F.S.

Islington M.C.—A very varied programme is being followed, and all meetings are well attended. Fretwork, games and talks are almost as popular as model-building. Recent talks have dealt with "*Life on an Arctic Trawler*," "*The Cinema Organ*," and "*The Testing of Aeroplanes in a Wind Tunnel*." Members have been busy getting ready for the club's first Exhibition. Club roll: 21. *Secretary:* S. Ryden, 54, Thornhill Road, Islington, London, N.1.

Todmordon Road Central School (Burnley) M.C.—The enthusiastic preparations for the Christmas Exhibition ensured its success. The models displayed included motor cars, aeroplanes and railways. Interesting lantern lectures have been held, one on "*America*" by Miss Yeadon, one of the school mistresses; another on "*The Railway Museum, York*," the slides being lent by the L.N.E.R. A club magazine entitled "*The Rota*" has been started, and the first issue was quickly sold out. A visit to the Rosegrove Engine Sheds has been arranged. Club roll: 31. *Secretary:* F. Smith, 80a, Master Street, Burnley, Lancs.

Middlesbrough M C—Owing to unforeseen circumstances the Leader, Mr. H. Richardson, has had to resign. The secretary is deputising until a new Leader can be found and he will be pleased to hear from any adult who would like to become the Leader of this club. Club roll: 40. *Secretary:* Mr. L. Shepherd, 29, High Street, North Ormesby, Middlesbrough.

Preparatory School (Sedbergh) M.C.—Most meetings are devoted to model-building, and a fine model of a Whaler has been constructed. It contains most of the features of an actual whaling ship, including the slipway in the stern, up which the captured whales are hauled to the deck. Other successful models have included an Overhead Railway and a Gantry Crane. The club is co-operating with the H.R.C. Branch at the school in preparing for an Exhibition in July, and members are very enthusiastic. Club roll: 11. *Leader:* M. B. Pearson, Preparatory School, Sedbergh, Yorks.

Members of the Islington M.C. Mr. V. Miller, Leader of the club, is on the left of the top row, and S. Ryden, secretary, is the seventh from the left on the same row. The club was affiliated in January 1935. Model-building and Fretwork are the most popular of its many activities.

Bridport Grammar School M.C.—The new lantern lecture "*A Trip Round the Post Office*," mentioned by the Guild Secretary in the November 1935 "*M.M.*" has been given by a local post office official, and was greatly enjoyed. The club library has been overhauled and extended, several new books being purchased out of club funds and others presented by members. Club roll: 28. *Secretary:* H. Dommett, West Allington, Bridport, Dorset.

St. Oswald's M.C.—This newly-affiliated club is making good progress, and has been divided into two sections, named "Nuts" and "Bolts" respectively. Members are enthusiastic model-builders, and some excellent models have been completed. A lecture on "*The Steam Engine*" by the Leader was much appreciated, and a lantern lecture on "*The Motor Car*" was also very interesting. The club football team continues to be successful. Club roll: 15. *Secretary:* R. H. Smart, 14, Kensington Avenue, Thornton Heath, Surrey.

Wheelwright Grammar School M.C.—This club was affiliated in November last, and three more members have since been enrolled. Model-building is the chief feature of the meetings, but occasional diversion is provided by evenings devoted to games or lantern lectures. At one meeting a mock trial was held and proved a very amusing affair. Club roll: 13. *Secretary:* D. G. Thackrah, 2, High Road, Northfields, Dewsbury, Yorks.

Sutton Valence Council School M.C.—Members are showing increasing skill and ingenuity in their model building, and a Super Model Competition held recently produced some fine work. An Inventors' Competition also proved very popular. The first winter session was concluded with a Christmas Celebration, and during tea the President, Mr. C. R. Boswell, visited the club. Afterward games were played and everybody had a great time. An interesting programme is being carried out this session. Club roll: 23. *Secretary:* J. Chandler, "Herriard," Chart Sutton, Nr. Maidstone, Kent.

St. Stephens (Saltash) M.C.—An invitation to exhibit models at the Plymouth M.C. Exhibition was accepted and an effective display was arranged. Prizes were given for the best models, and the first prize was awarded for a model of a traction engine. The club's own Exhibition was held later, in conjunction with the St. Stephens (Saltash) Branch of the H.R.C., and was very successful. The best models on view were the traction engine already referred to and a huge crane 4 ft. 6 in. in height which was worked by a stationary steam engine. A concert has been held, for which a stage complete with footlights was erected in the club room. Club roll: 16. *Secretary:* B. Braund, 9, Homer Park, Saltash, Cornwall.

EGYPT

Zagazig M.C.—This well organised club includes many different sections, and such matters as club management, the arranging of excursions and sports and the production of a club magazine are in the hands of special committees. The Leader would be pleased to receive copies of other club magazines as he feels sure they would be very helpful to him in showing what kind of articles to obtain for the Zagazig paper. The club hope to have an interesting display of models at a forthcoming Exhibition of Egyptian Industry, in Zagazig. Club roll: 20. *Leader:* Abdel Moneim Mangourie, 39,B, Gannabiet Sikka Hadid Street, Fagarig.

BRITISH WEST INDIES

Munro College M.C.—Many interesting lectures have been given, and the subjects dealt with have included "*The World's Most Dangerous Job*"; "*Byrd's Adventure to the South Pole*," and "*100 m.p.h. in the 'Flying Scotsman'*." A Fretwork section has been started, and the model railway layout has been reduced in size to make room for the new section. Bookbinding continues to be a popular hobby, and eight books have been completed. The "B" football team has suffered two defeats recently. Club roll: 26. *Secretary:* H. G. Maxwell, Munro College, Munro P.O., Jamaica, B.W.I.

NEW ZEALAND

Christchurch M.C.—The social on the club Birthday Night was so successful that another has been held, and there was again a good attendance of members, their parents and friends. Meccano and Hornby Competitions are arranged frequently as they are greatly enjoyed. The club has been visited by Mr. E. H. Spears, secretary of the Wellington Boys' Institute M.C. Club roll: 23. *Secretary:* L. W. Best, 28, Circuit Street, Strowan, Christchurch, New Zealand.

Clubs Not Yet Affiliated

Tudor M.C.—A Draughts Competition demanded much concentration on the part of those taking part. An extensive railway track has been laid and interesting railway operations carried out. It is proposed to stage a play, and as soon as one has been chosen rehearsals will be commenced. Club roll: 6. *Secretary:* D. Mathieson, 5, Kempton Avenue, Sunbury, Middlesex.

St. Michaels M.C.—Father Goddard, the assistant priest in the parish and Leader of the club, is allowing the members to meet in his study until a clubroom can be found. The club's equipment has been enriched by the generous gift of a Meccano Outfit by Mr. Rainforth, the local Meccano dealer, and the gift is much appreciated. Members are very enthusiastic, and it is hoped to obtain affiliation with the Guild at an early date. *Secretary:* H. Davis, 49, School Street, Upton, Nr. Pontefract.

Merit Medallion Awards in 1935

My list of the names of members of Meccano clubs at home and overseas who have been awarded special Merit Medallions during last year is published on this page. It is a representative list, and is striking evidence of the enthusiasm with which Meccano boys pursue their hobby and join in the Guild and club movements. A very pleasing feature is the record number of overseas members who have gained the award.

There are many clubs omitted that I would like to see mentioned in this list, and I cannot help feeling that their Leaders do not yet make sufficient use of Merit Medallions. I am not suggesting that the Meccano boy needs any artificial encouragement to do his best on behalf of the club to which he belongs, but it is only right that the enthusiasm and energy displayed should be recognised. The award of a Merit Medallion is a proof of such recognition, and is always greatly appreciated by the member concerned. I hope therefore that during this year the Leaders of clubs omitted or only briefly mentioned in the list on this page will take greater advantage of this practical means of rewarding good work. By doing so they will also make it possible for me to publish a list of record length in February 1937.

Two Merit Medallions are available for presentation each session in every club, and they are awarded on the recommendation of the Leader. No conditions are laid down in regard to the nature of the work by which they can be earned. They may be awarded for energetic recruiting, constructive ideas for improving the club programmes, conduct that sets a good example to more boisterous members, outstanding excellence in model-building, and in fact any activity that helps to increase the reputation of the Guild and of the club movement.

Merit Medallions Awarded in 1935

CHIPPENHAM—G. Dench. CLECKHEATON—K. Walker, D. Clay, J. Crowther, E. Nutter. CROYDON (Whitgift Middle School)—H. D. MacDonald. DAGENHAM—P. A. Bush, P. Tucker, J. Dobinson, F. Lyon, N. Snazel, R. Stokes. EDINBURGH (St. Giles' Cathedral)—I. M. Browne, D. C. Simpson, C. Baxter, W. Williamson. (28th Edinburgh)—N. Pratt, T. Meldrum. EXETER—C. Seamark, A. Fear, G. Turner, T. Smith, E. Shapland, J. Bell, W. Bradford, K. G. Sercombe. GLASGOW (Morison Memorial)—A. Gillies, A. Fraser, J. Glassford. HARROW (Claremont Avenue School)—G. Turton, A. Little. LONDON (Old Charlton)—H. Crosby, H. Cook. (Holborn Senior Boys' School)—L. Phillips, H. Sadler, F. Clark. MAIDSTONE (Sutton Valence)—B. Johnes, D. Price, D. Cleave. MALLOW—S. Lombard, D. Lehane. MIDDLESBROUGH—J. Byers, J. Jackson, G. Richardson, H. Wood. PLYMOUTH—S. Holloway, R. Symons, P. Liddicoat R. Tubb. SIDMOUTH (Sid Vale)—M. H. Mortimore. WEDNESBURY—A. L. Morgan, F. Danks.

OVERSEAS CLUB MEMBERS

AUSTRALIA (Thebarton Technical School)—M. Campbell, R. Brown. CANADA (Rosemount, Regina)—J. Watson, J. Favelle. EGYPT (Cairo)—M. F. Awad. FRANCE (Dunkerque)—J. Gamblin. (Villefranche)—J. Chambion. HOLLAND (Hilversum)—E. v. d. Vorst, F. Eisenberger, J. Noordra, J. Weinburg. ITALY (Milan)—G. de Corrado, L. Tagliabue, C. Ponzo, A. Viola. NEW ZEALAND (Ashburton)—T. Taylor, B. Furniss, E. Osborne, P. Kruse. (Christchurch)—J. Ancall, D. McKenzie. SOUTH AFRICA (Berea)—F. J. Metter, L. Michelow. (Malvern)—C. Curtis, B. Saunders, D. Stephen, B. Branch, C. Smyth. (Observatory)—D. Matthews, J. Liston. (Pioneer)—L. Alley, A. Henry. SWITZERLAND (Neuchatel)—R. Lanz, A. Garcin.

Correspondents Wanted

The Correspondence Club records show a long waiting list of boys in France and Egypt who desire to write to members in this country. In the majority of cases the correspondence is desired in English, and there is no need therefore for any Guild member who would like to write to members in those countries to hold back on account of language difficulties. For the benefit of newcomers I may point out that membership is open to all members of the Guild, and care is taken to bring together correspondents of similar tastes, who find great pleasure in the discussion of problems connected with the hobbies and other interests they have in common. Forms of application may be obtained from Headquarters, and I advise those who have not yet joined the club to consider doing so at once. I assure them that they will not regret having taken the opportunity of learning something of the interesting lives of Meccano boys whose homes are in other countries.

Running a Club Library

I have been pleased to note in recent club reports the increasing popularity of club libraries, and the adoption of this excellent idea by many clubs hitherto without their own supply of reading matter. Club libraries are very desirable, and it is not difficult to get together an attractive collection of books. The usual method of beginning is to invite each member to contribute a few books, and these gifts form the basis of the library. A small monthly subscription, or a charge of, say, 1d. per book loaned enables a fund to be built up with which books of engineering or general interests, in demand by the subscribers, can be purchased.

A library committee should be formed to fix the subscription rates and times of borrowing, to appoint a librarian and to decide on the books to be purchased. In this latter connection the "Books to Read" pages of the "*M.M.*" are a reliable guide to the latest books likely to interest club members. An excellent list of suitable books is also given on the inside back cover page of the booklet "How to Run a Meccano Club," a copy of which is, or should be, in the possession of every Leader.

An occasional Reading Night provides a pleasant diversion from model-building and games. A club library will be found very useful in the summer, as in this country at any rate it often happens that some outdoor excursion or other fixture has to be cancelled on account of rain. If the weather is very sultry the members are not likely to feel energetic enough for model-building or indoor sports, and the club library then provides a welcome source of restful recreation. Now is the time therefore to start building up a good library to meet just such an emergency.

Proposed Clubs

Attempts are being made to establish Meccano Clubs in the following places, and boys interested should communicate with the promoters whose names and addresses are given below:

EASINGTON VILLAGE—E. S. English, 3, Manor Cottages, Easington Village, Co. Durham.

INDIA—A. Singh, Bhagwan Bazar, Gowal Mandi, Lahore.

STAFFORD—Master D. J. Griffiths, 12, Call Avenue, Littleworth.

WALTON-ON-THAMES—M. Walsh, West Lodge, Burvale Hersham.

WEST CALDER—M. Anderson, 36, Breich Terrace.

* * * *

The Hutton M.C., formed among the pupils of Hutton Modern School, Eccleshill, Bradford, lapsed last year owing to the secretary, W. Holdsworth, and many of the members leaving the school. Mr. Holdsworth, who is now in business, is endeavouring to restart the club, which will not, however, be associated with the school. Any Guild member living in Bradford and district who would like to join the club, should write to him at 44, Victoria Road, Eccleshill, Bradford.

Lineside Effects in Miniature

The Development of a Realistic Railway

By L. T. A. Bern

THE railway described in this article was commenced about ten years ago in about the same way as the railways of most boys start; just a small locomotive, a few carriages, and a circular track of 1 ft. radius curves. Up to about eighteen months ago the track, now 2 ft. radius, which had been steadily increasing in size, was accommodated on the floor of a spare room. It had then reached such proportions that it was felt that a raised baseboard would be the next important improvement to be made, for a railway thus supported has great possibilities with regard to scenery and general realism, and of course has the very decided advantage of permanence and neatness. This was accomplished and the baseboard was constructed at a suitable height round the walls. The portions by the window and door were made removable for general convenience. Ample space is afforded underneath for spare parts, articles under construction, books, etc.

An interesting corner of the layout described on this page. This shows how the scenic background is made to fit in with the tunnel and other actual features in the foreground.

The track was now the first consideration, of course; and this was carefully laid for correct and practical working. Briefly it consists of a main oval, doubled at convenient points; two loop lines, carriage siding, engine siding with shed and works and goods yard. Then, after the placing of the stations in position came the scenic effects.

A start was made in one corner where the available space was greater than elsewhere, owing to the presence of a recess. It was decided that a tunnel, suitably constructed, would be the best means of disguising this awkward situation. One was constructed therefore by building first a light wooden framework, then moulding the external features in plaster of Paris. When quite dry this was suitably coloured. Steps were hewn from solid plaster, and a wooden handrail constructed and embedded in it to form a means of approach to the uplands over the tunnel. Here, to prevent cattle, and perhaps venturesome people, from wandering too near the edge with possibly serious results, a wire fence was erected a few scale feet in, and a stile constructed at the top of the steps. Most of this can be seen in the accompanying illustration, the stile being occupied at the moment the photograph was taken by a little girl, who seems greatly interested in the railway operations going on below. A background of hills was painted directly on to the wallpaper, and a roadway was included in the scheme of things to serve the little station just by.

Particular mention must be made of the aeroplane in the photograph, as it adds considerably to the realistic effect of the whole. This is one of the planes in regular service, and it is on its way to the landing ground, which actually is situated to the left of the tunnel and on the movable section directly in front of the window. Here the height of the background has had to be reduced considerably, and owing to the ground space being rather limited the major portion of the landing field has been painted on the background, including the hangar, marker, aeroplane and two of the windsocks. The control tower is built directly on to the scene, and is actually only about $\frac{1}{4}$ in. "deep."

Adjacent to the aerodrome is situated another corner section, but here no attempt has been made to hide the angle of the walls, as a small wayside garage serves the purpose quite effectively. This includes Petrol Pumps and Oil Bin, of the Dinky Toy Series which together with other items seem to bring the scene to life.

The outstanding items on this section of railway are the colour-light signals. These were home made and each fitted with red, yellow and green flashlamp bulbs, each bulb being wired to a control panel. These bulbs are lit by a large capacity 4-volt accumulator for correct working, and although all the old semaphore signals have not yet been supplanted, the work is going on apace. It is also intended to wire the telegraph poles to carry current to light the four stations.

A goods yard of convenient proportions adjoins, and forms a very busy little section indeed. It is equipped with a staff of handy little workers chosen again from the Dinky Toy Series, with plenty of home-made merchandise for them to handle. There is a crane for handling the heavier items in the goods yard. The usual large gates, giving access to the yard are shown, or at least the "yard" side of them is! Numerous road vans and wagons are employed for the prompt and easy conveyance of freight. On the opposite side of the room is the engine shed and works building. This structure was built over and around a mantle shelf, and successfully disguises any unsightliness it would have caused.

At first sight the coal trucks on the line present a rather heavy load for the locomotive; but, as frequently suggested in the "*M.M.*," the wagons have been provided with a false bottom of cardboard, coloured black, and covered with just a single layer of suitable pieces of washed coals.

Road-Rail Services for Hornby Railways

By "Tommy Dodd"

THE various miniature motor vehicles of the Meccano Dinky Toys Series have made possible the splendid fun of operating road services in conjunction with the trains running on Hornby railways. This month I am dealing with a recent introduction that is of special interest; that is the Mechanical Horses and Trailer Vans included in No. 33R of the Series of Meccano Dinky Toys. These realistic little vehicles are finished in the colours of the four British railway groups, and therefore whichever real group is followed as the prototype of the miniature railway, the appropriate road vehicles can be used.

Just as the real ones do, the Meccano Dinky Toy Mechanical Horses and Trailers form together an articulated unit, the front end of the Trailer being supported on, and coupled to, the tail of the power unit. This articulation renders the whole unit extremely flexible, and capable of manœuvring readily within close restrictions of space.

The whole idea in introducing into real practice the so-called "mechanical horse" was to produce a motor unit occupying no more space than the four-legged horse used for railway cartage work almost exclusively until recent years. And of course the mechanical horse on wheels had to be as easily persuaded this way or that as the real horse on legs. This was not an easy thing to attempt, as anyone will realise who has seen a carter getting his horse to back a van in a confined space between various obstructions. However, the problem was solved by the three-wheeled units, articulated with their trailers, that have become such familiar sights during the past few years.

Naturally the Meccano Dinky Toy reproductions—No. 33R—are very similar to the originals, both in details of construction and finish. The horse unit is a three-wheeler as in actual practice, and is fitted as usual with rubber tyres. The bonnet of the vehicle has the radiator represented in relief on the front, and there is also the registration number plate and a spotlight. At the sides of the bonnet are represented the usual louvred openings. Behind the cab the frame narrows, and on it between the rear wheels is mounted what we may term a coupling block. This has a slot pierced in it in the centre, into which the tongue of the tow-bar of the Trailer fits. The coupling block widens towards the rear, and its surface gradually slopes down rearwards. The reason for this construction will soon become apparent.

A feature of the real units is that special coupling gear is fitted, so that when the "horse" is backed on to the trailer the two become automatically coupled together. Similarly this operation can be reproduced with miniature ones if the Trailer Van is restrained from moving backwards, as it would be, for instance, when standing against a Goods Platform. The swivelling coupling and unit and dummy supporting wheels at the front of the van must be set straight, then if the Horse unit is backed up carefully, square with the Van, the coupling tongue on the latter will ride up the slot of the coupling block on the Horse and will settle in the slot. It is restrained from wandering by the raised edges of the coupling block, which guide it safely into the slot. Very young "drivers" of these vehicles may need a little practice before they are able to do this correctly each time, but the older boys will have no difficulty at all. The ability to couple Horse and Van in this manner adds greatly to the fun of operating them.

A busy scene at the Goods Platform on a jointly-operated Hornby railway. Mechanical Horses and Trailer Vans in L.M.S.R. and G.W.R. colours are shown backed up to the platform.

The Trailer Vans are attractive vehicles. All have the swivelling coupling and supporting unit at the front end, and the rear runs on the usual rubber-tyred wheels. Large opening doors are represented at the rear. The floor level at this end is conveniently low for loading and unloading purposes.

The L.M.S.R. units are finished in the familiar Midland red of that company, except that the upper part of the van body and the cab roof of the Horse are finished in black. The initials "L.M.S." decorate each component of the unit, and the words "Express Parcels Traffic" stand out boldly on the upper surface of the Van sides. Similar decoration schemes are used for the L.N.E.R. and S.R. units, with the L.N.E.R. dark blue and the familiar Southern green taking the place of the red of the L.M.S.R. vehicles. An interesting variation also is that the full title "Southern Railway" appears on the Trailer Vans of that company, and not merely the initials.

The G.W.R. units are finished in an extremely attractive manner. The standard brown and cream used for the company's coaching stock and road motors is employed, brown being used for the Horse and Van lower bodywork. The upper parts of the Horse cab and the Van body are cream. Each component of the unit carries the new G.W.R. monogram, and below this on the Van sides appear the words "Express Cartage Services."

PASSENGER TRAIN FORMATION

THE correct assembly of the trains on a miniature railway system adds considerably to the interest and effect of operations. Let us consider the various kinds of passenger trains that we can make up with Hornby railway components. Goods train formation is of course equally important, but it forms such a wide subject that it will be necessary to deal with it separately in a later issue. As the rolling stock contained in the Hornby Train Sets is naturally restricted to the barest requirements, mistakes can scarcely be made when the Train Set is first purchased and operated, unless a Guard's Van or composite vehicle is arranged elsewhere than at the tail of the train! It is when the Set is expanded into a more elaborate system that train formation becomes of special importance. The smaller passenger vehicles of the Hornby Series are quite suitable for their particular purpose, and where several of them are used together to form a complete train the assembly will be quite realistic.

The No. 1 Coaches are vehicles of greater possibilities. They can be used to form the express trains on smaller layouts, and they are also particularly useful for local and branch work on more elaborate systems. With them are associated the No. 1 Guard's Vans, which are similar in construction and finish, and enable complete passenger trains to be made up with the appropriate Guard's and luggage accommodation. In the case of suburban trains where return journeys are usually commenced very soon after the arrival of the train at a terminus, the make-up of the train should be such that it is capable of running correctly in either direction without any alteration in the formation. Thus, if sufficient equipment is available and the space afforded at the stations is sufficient, Guard's Vans should be placed at each end of suburban trains made up of No. 1 Coaches.

A long-distance train made up of Hornby No. 2 Saloon Coaches. As the load is a heavy one a pilot engine is backing down to assist the train engine that is already coupled up.

The new No. 2 Coaches are particularly suited for longer-distance suburban or "residential" services. Very realistic trains can be made up using the First-Third Coaches in the centre of the train, and with the Brake-Thirds placed appropriately at each end. On layouts where trains have to be restricted with respect to length a favourite scheme with some readers is to use

A short suburban train of No. 2 Coaches. Two Brake-Thirds are used together, as suggested in this article, so that Guard's and luggage accommodation are available at each end of the train without the train being of excessive length.

two of the composite vehicles together to form a train. This is an interesting arrangement, and certainly obtains the required results within the least possible space.

The Hornby No. 2 Saloon Coaches are particularly useful vehicles for the making up of main line expresses. They are of the favourite modern end-vestibuled type, and they can be correctly gangwayed together by means of the standard Corridor Connections. Details of this kind add considerably to the "long-distance" character of miniature trains, and give them quite an air of importance. In connection with these Coaches accessories that should not be overlooked are the Train Name Boards that are available. The roofs of the Saloon Coaches are not fitted as standard with holders for the Name Boards, but suitable Clips can be obtained that can easily be attached for the purpose. These Clips are available in two types, No. 2 for No. 2 Saloon and No. 2 Pullman Coaches, and No. 2S for the No. 2 Special Pullman Coaches.

An all-Pullman express on a Hornby railway. The No. 2 Special Pullmans closely follow in their details and finish the actual vehicles used on many famous expresses.

While dealing with Roof Clips it will be interesting to mention that the No. 2 Roof Clips are suitable also for use in connection with Metropolitan Coaches. These latter vehicles are used by many Hornby Railway owners for main line work, particularly by those whose layouts represent the L.N.E.R. Complete trains can be made up exclusively of Metropolitan vehicles, or they can be used in conjunction with the popular Saloon Coaches. They cannot, however, be gangwayed to the latter with Corridor Connections, as the Metropolitan Coaches are not adapted to the use of these fittings.

A main line train of No. 2 Coaches that includes a No. 2 Special Pullman in its composition. The provision of Pullman facilities in a train of ordinary stock is characteristic of S.R. practice.

The most luxurious coaches in the Hornby Series are the No. 2 Special Pullmans. These are available in two types—as ordinary Pullman Coaches and as Composite vehicles with guard's and luggage accommodation. They have end vestibules and straight sides, and as the window mouldings are neatly embossed the characteristic "squareness" of Pullman sides is reproduced. The vestibules are arranged with steps and opening doors, and communication with adjacent vehicles is possible by means of realistic corridor connections very similar to the actual Pullman gangways. Special bogies with equalised side frames and Mansell wheels ensure smooth running.

The distinctive pattern of roof with domed ends sloping down to the vestibules is copied, and neat miniature ventilators provide the finishing touch. The fascia or top rail of the coach above the windows is painted umber, as are the lower panels, the vestibules and the luggage ends, cream being used for the panels at window level only. A characteristic feature is the provision of names as in actual practice. The Pullman Coach is available named *"Loraine," "Zenobia"* or *"Grosvenor,"* and the Composite vehicle can be obtained named either *"Alberta," "Verona"* or *"Montana."* The grey shade of the roof was adopted on the recommendation of the Pullman Car Company, as representing the average condition of car roofs in service, though these are white when fresh from the shops. Automatic couplings and destination board brackets are further refinements.

The internal decorations and appointments of real Pullman cars are a notable feature, and of these the neat table lamps give a characteristic appearance when the car is seen from the outside. In the Hornby vehicles the transparent window strip imitation glass has representations of these lamps printed on it at intervals at the appropriate height to give a realistic effect.

These splendid vehicles offer great possibilities in the way of train formation. Famous all-Pullman expresses, such as *"The Golden Arrow," "The Queen of Scots,"* or *"The Yorkshire Pullman"* can be represented correctly on Hornby railways. Again there is the *"Bournemouth Belle,"* which now runs regularly throughout the year, thus showing the popularity of Pullman facilities. In addition to these trains there are the All-Pullman specials operated in connection with important race meetings such as the Grand National.

Join the Hornby Railway Company and become eligible for the competitions announced on this page.

H.R.C. COMPETITION PAGE

Join the Hornby Railway Company and become eligible for the competitions announced on this page.

CONCEALED STATIONS CONTEST

This month we give H.R.C. members an opportunity of putting their knowledge of station names to a practical test. In the panel in the centre of this page are 24 words made up from what appears to be a selection at random of letters from the alphabet. Each of these extraordinary-looking collection of letters when rearranged into correct order forms the name of a British railway station. There is no catch in any of the words; in spite of appearances, each will be found to be the name of a railway station on one of the four group companies' systems. Some of the stations are on main lines, others are less well known; but all are to be found without difficulty in "Bradshaw" which, if not available at home, may be seen at most local libraries or reading rooms.

Byancourn	**Gipnertsi**
Meowlcit	**Hamaxy**
Sidneseen	**Burflod**
Wagneyd	**Dosfenherd**
Tetwopckors	**Gerpswneeee**
Fontorwefo	**Goinslh**
Yothymlordm	**Lislagheas**
Fleksellu	**Bootleodwe**
Stoxtho	**Bentorsog**
Yekaloh	**Tywolhshor**
Ransau	**Fofnirddm**
Doryoef	**Urtascelloc**

When competitors have discovered all the correct stations, or as many of them as they can find, they must make a list of them in the order in which they appear in the panel. Alongside each station must be written the initials of the railway company on whose lines it lies. If any station belongs jointly to two companies, the initials of both companies also must be given.

Prizes consisting of any product manufactured by Meccano Ltd., to the value of 21/–, 15/–, 10/6 and 5/– respectively will be awarded to the senders of the entries containing the largest number of correct solutions. In the case of a tie for any prize, preference will be given to the entry that is neatest or presented in the most novel manner. In addition to the main prizes a number of consolation prizes will be awarded to the entries which, while below prizewinning standard, are at the same time praiseworthy efforts to tackle the contest.

Envelopes containing entries must be marked *"H.R.C. Concealed Stations Contest"* in the top left-hand corner and posted to reach Headquarters at Meccano Ltd., Binns Road, Liverpool 13, on or before 29th February. The closing date for competitors in the Overseas Section is 30th May.

Every entry submitted for this contest must be clearly marked with the sender's name, full address and H.R.C. membership number. In recent competitions several entries have been received from which either the name or the address of the competitor has been omitted.

Railway Photographic Contest

Last month we announced a winter series of Railway Photographic Contests in which competitors were invited to submit photographs of railway subjects that they took during the summer months, or snaps of typical winter scenes on the line. This month we announce the second contest of the series. There are no restrictions with regard to the railway subject chosen, and competitors may send as many prints as they desire, but no competitor can win more than one prize. The photographs submitted must have been taken by the competitors themselves, but the developing and printing may be the work of professionals.

On the back of each print submitted must be written the competitor's age, name and full address, and his H.R.C. membership number. In addition to these a short description of the scene of the picture must be given.

The contest will be divided as usual into two Sections, Home and Overseas, and prizes of any product manufactured by Meccano Ltd., to the value of 21/–, 15/–, 10/6 and 5/– respectively will be awarded to the senders of the four best entries submitted in each section. In the case of a tie for any prize, the prize money will be equally divided. In addition to the main prizes a number of consolation prizes will be awarded to those entries which, although they have not reached the standard required to qualify for one of the main awards, are nevertheless praiseworthy efforts and are deserving of some acknowledgment.

Envelopes containing entries must be marked *"H.R.C. February Photographic Contest"* in the top left-hand corner and posted to reach Headquarters at Meccano Ltd., Binns Road, Liverpool 13, on or before 29th February. The closing date for the Overseas Section is 30th May.

Competitors who desire their entries to be returned, if unsuccessful, should enclose an addressed envelope of suitable size, sufficiently stamped. It should be noted that prizewinning prints become the property of Meccano Ltd., and are not returnable.

Questions Contest No. 7

This month we announce the seventh Contest of this very popular series. To the senders of the four best sets of answers to the following 12 questions will be awarded any product manufactured by Meccano Ltd. to the value of 21/–, 15/–, 10/6 and 5/– respectively. In addition consolation prizes will be awarded.

Competitors should endeavour to write their answers on one sheet of paper only, on the back of which must be written the sender's age, name and full address, and his H.R.C. membership number.

Entrants in this contest who find themselves unable to answer all the questions should nevertheless send in their entries. In the event of more than one competitor sending an all-correct set of answers, the awards will be made to the competitors whose entries are submitted in the neatest or most novel manner. When answering these questions it is not necessary to go to any great detail and, provided that the conditions are satisfied, the shorter the answers are the better.

(1) Where is the L.M.S.R. Headquarters? (2) What is the average speed of the world's fastest newspaper train? (3) About how much coal do the four railway companies burn in a year? (4) What is the weight per yard of a standard main line rail? (5) How many sleepers are there to the mile? (6) At which station may locomotives of all four groups be observed? (7) Which is the fastest train in the world? (8) Which is the largest passenger station in Great Britain? (9) Where is most of the timber and banana traffic handled? (10) What is the standard rail length? (11) Which company first operated streamlined heavy-oil rail cars on express services? (12) Which is the largest and most powerful locomotive in Great Britain?

The Contest will be divided into two Sections, Home and Overseas. Envelopes containing entries must be marked *"H.R.C. February Questions Contest No. 7"* in the top left-hand corner and posted to reach Headquarters at Meccano Ltd., Binns Road, Liverpool 13, on or before 29th February. The closing date for the Overseas Section is 30th May.

COMPETITION RESULTS

HOME

December "Hidden Locomotives Contest." The very high standard of the entries submitted in this contest made it very difficult for the judges to decide upon the winners, but the final votes were cast in favour of the following competitors.—First: K. Costain (5108), Bolton, Lancs. Second: L. Parish (18054), Coventry. Third: C. E. Wrayford (6039), Moretonhampstead, Devon. Consolation Prizes: R. Lumley (20253), Plymouth; J. C. Button (10335), Crewe, Ches.; R. L. Martin (4283), Cheltenham, Glos.; R. G. Watson (24608), Small Heath, Birmingham 9; R. Barbary (5580), St. Ewe, Mevagissey, Cornwall; G. H. Gill (36093), Chorlton-cum-Hardy, Manchester.

December "My Favourite Locomotive Contest."—First: V. C. Kaile (17559), Mayford, Nr. Woking. Second: G. Jones (10143), Llanarth, Cards. Third: F. B. Astley (32874), Edenfield, Nr. Ramsbottom. Consolation Prize: V. R. Young (44359), Widnes, Lancs.

December "Shunting Puzzle." This contest produced many hundreds of entries, and the three following competitors sent in the first correct entries opened. They were awarded cash prizes of 5/– each.—D. Fear (18477), Taunton, Somerset; J. C. Button (10335), Crewe, Cheshire; G. Hepworth (18553), West Hartlepool, Co. Durham.

Branch News

WHITGIFT SCHOOL (CROYDON).—A track competition resulted in some excellent layouts being designed. The winning one was laid down at the next meeting and proved ideal for timetable working. During a very interesting tour of the works of the Quaisi Arc Welding Company members had the thrill of trying their hand at a welding job. In the company's own cinema theatre they watched films illustrating welding work. Secretary: J. A. Watson, 23, Addiscombe Avenue, Croydon.

ADDISCOMBE.—A Branch room has been obtained, and the Opening Night was made the occasion for a fine display of models built by the members. A lecture on the *"Railway Museum, York,"* was given by permission of the L.N.E.R. All the members were present and also many of their parents, and everybody greatly enjoyed the meeting. The Leader has given lectures on *"Famous Bridges"* and *"Railway Disasters."* The Branch library has started in flourishing style, 102 books being in stock. Secretary: G. Chandler, 62, Ashburton Avenue, Addiscombe, Croydon.

COTTESMORE.—The members now meet on Monday evenings instead of Wednesdays, and there is a full attendance at practically all meetings. Frequent changes of layout have done much to prevent track operations from becoming stale, and members have found that each new layout brings its own interesting problems of railway operation. Film shows run by the members and open to the rest of the school for a small admission charge are benefiting the Branch funds, and it is hoped to raise enough cash to purchase four new locomotives. Secretary: D. Woodburn, Cottesmore Central School, Lenton, Nottingham.

DAGENHAM.—A novel turn was given to a recent track meeting by running a Meccano locomotive built by one of the members. One meeting has been devoted to a discussion on *"How to improve the Branch Layout,"* and some very useful suggestions were put forward. Occasional Games, Reading or Model-building Evenings are popular. Secretary: P. Bush, 212, Church Elm Lane, Dagenham.

GLENGORSE (BATTLE).—Track meetings and film shows have been the chief items in the programme recently. A correspondence has been opened with the Elmside (Exeter) Branch, and the letters received from the latter are read with great interest. Secretary: K. J. Attwell, Glengorse, Telham Court, Battle, Sussex.

WIMBORNE GRAMMAR SCHOOL.—Several masters have joined the Branch and they are as enthusiastic as the younger members, and everybody is keenly interested in the track operations carried out. Meetings lasting half-an-hour are held during the school lunch hour on three days of the week for the benefit of members who are day or weekly pupils, and two meetings are held on Saturday evenings for those who are resident pupils. The Branch track is to be overhauled and relaid, and the opportunity will be taken to renew certain sections of it. Secretary: E. S. How, Wimborne Grammar School, Wimborne, Dorset.

Members of the St. Thomas (Exeter) Branch, No. 269. The chairman, Mr. W. A. Blake, is the second from the left on the back row, and the secretary, L. Robinson, is next on his left. This Branch was incorporated in June 1934, and has a steadily increasing membership. Visits are exchanged with the Elmside (Exeter) Branch.

ISLINGTON.—Members have been busy preparing for the Exhibition to be held this month at Unity Hall, Upper Street. An interesting diversion from ordinary railway operations has been provided by constructing model railway buildings with which to make the Branch layout more realistic. Recent talks have dealt with *"Life on an Arctic Trawler"*; *"The Cinema Organ,"* and *"The Testing of Aeroplanes."* Secretary: E. Muxlow, 7, Regents Park, London, N.W.1.

CHORLTON-CUM-HARDY.—Several new members have been enrolled and they are already quite expert in track operations. The Chairman has built a splendid terminal station, which has five platforms. The Branch track has been ballasted and miniature water troughs laid down. Other improvements include the construction of an L.M.S. locomotive depot, complete with carriage sidings. Secretary: G. H. Gill, 56, Highfield Road, Chorlton-cum-Hardy.

WATERLOO (DUBLIN).—A new layout has been made, representing the L.M.S.R. main line from London (Euston) to Crewe. Several new locomotives have been obtained, and the Branch equipment now totals 19 locomotives, 20 carriages and 30 wagons. Plans for improving the layout include the installing of colourlight signals between Euston and Willesden Junction. Secretary: S. B. Carse, 38, Oakfield Road, Ranelagh, Dublin, I.F.S.

ELMSIDE (EXETER).—In reviewing club activities during 1935 the secretary writes: "Our railway services have been a great improvement on previous years." Secretary: T. W. A. Smith, 98, Ladysmith Road, Exeter.

ITALY

MILAN.—In conjunction with the Milan M.C. the Branch members took part in a Table Tennis Tournament, which proved so popular that the event will be repeated. Visits have been paid to important engineering works in the district. Secretary: E. Vigo, Gorso Genova 19, Milan, Italy.

Branches in Course of Formation

The following new Branches of the Hornby Railway Company are at present in process of formation, and any boys who are interested and desirous of linking up with this unique organisation should communicate with the promoters, whose names and addresses are given below:

NOTTINGHAM—R. Ingham, 132, Mansfield Road.

SMETHWICK—R. M. Jones, 181, Rosefield Road.

INDIA—A. A. Khand, 170, Napier Road, Karachi-City.

Branches Recently Incorporated

296. FOREST SCHOOL—H. J. Pye, Forest School, Nr. Snaresbrook, London, E.17.
297. ST. STEPHENS (SALTASH)—R. Saunders, The Bungalow, St. Stephens.

SHIPS ON STAMPS

THE stamp collector who has the sea in his blood, a description that applies to most British boys, would find a congenial task in building up a collection of maritime stamps.

The field, or should we say ocean, is one of tremendously interesting possibilities and almost unlimited scope. So big is the scope, indeed, that after only a preliminary survey we realised that it was impossible to deal with the subject in one article. We found stamps picturing ancient native dugouts and mammoth ocean liners, oldtime caravels and modern men-of-war, lifeboats and whalers, docks, canals and harbours, wireless stations and lighthouses; and therefore in this article we must content ourselves with dealing with one section of the subject, the development of the mercantile vessel.

It is difficult to say when the possibilities of transport by river and sea were first realised. Possibly some prehistoric brave had his imagination stirred by the sight of a floating log. Travelling by log no doubt quickly became a fashionable game until the idea of digging out a seat was tried. The successive stages of development from "dug out" to the paddle-propelled canoe are short, but thus no doubt was born the science of navigation. A good specimen of a paddle-propelled canoe is to be seen on several of the values in the French Guiana 1929 series.

Later, although it is impossible to say when, sails were introduced. The illustration used for the design of the Egyptian Navigation Congress issue of 1926, based on a piece of ancient statuary found in the ruined temple of Deir-el-Bahari, depicting one of the earliest Egyptian galleys fitted with a crude mainsail on a central mast, suggests that sails were known long before the Flood. In this particular vessel the sail was merely an auxiliary, however, the principal form of propulsion being oars manipulated by a gang of slaves.

Less imposing among early sailing boats are the Maori war canoes illustrated on the Cook Islands issue of 1932, the Fijian pirogues illustrated in Fiji's 1891 issue, and the laquatois shown on various Papuan issues.

The best illustration of an early galley is that shown on the 1 Fr. denomination of the Tunis 1926 issue, illustrated here. This shows a typical Carthaginian galley engaged in the Mediterranean trade. It is fitted with a mainsail and a topsail, but again the principal form of propulsion is the oars. Many of the early Mediterranean galleys were of great size, and it is on record that the royal galley of the Emperor Caligua required the combined efforts of no less than 1,600 oarsmen to drive it through the water!

The Viking ships illustrated on the Danish issue of 1927 and on the U.S.A. Norse Centennial 5c. issue of 1925 are much later in date than the galleys just described, but nevertheless there is a remarkable resemblance between these vessels and the early Mediterranean craft, a point that will be noted on inspection of the Viking galleys shown on the higher values of Esthonia's 1919 issue.

The Viking ships were among the first ocean-going craft, and from these it is but a short stage to the tiny craft used by the early navigators, such as Columbus, Vasco da Gama, Jean Cabot and Sir Humphrey Gilbert. Columbus's flagship, the "*Santa Maria,*" is probably the most commonly depicted ship in our stamp collection. The best picture of it is on the Spanish 1930 Columbus commemorative issue, the 2c. value of which is illustrated here. Vasco da Gama's fleet of caravels is shown on various Portuguese issues; Jean Cabot's "*Matthew*" is shown on Newfoundland's 10c. commemorative issue of 1897; while the 1933 issue shows a view of Sir Humphrey Gilbert on the deck of the "*Squirrel.*" The "*Mayflower,*" in which the Pilgrim Fathers reached America, is shown on the U.S.A. 1920 issue.

In contrast with these tiny vessels, which virtually drifted about the world, it is interesting to show the Canadian ship "*Royal William,*" which is credited with having made the first transatlantic steamboat crossing in August, 1833. This is taken from the Canadian commemorative issue of 1933, celebrating the centenary of the "*Royal William's*" voyage.

Modern types of mercantile vessel are represented by the French liner "*Normandie,*" shown on a stamp issued by France in 1935 to commemorate the liner's maiden voyage; but a more interesting picture of modern steamships is to be found on the 1f.75c. stamp from Belgium's anti-tuberculosis charity issue of 1931, illustrated here. This shows Antwerp Harbour thronged with shipping. Quite a score of other liner pictures are available, principal among them being Poland's 1935 15gr. stamp showing the "*Pilsudski,*" a motor ship recently placed in service by the Gdynia-America Shipping Company; and a very unusual view of the two crack Italian liners, "*Rex*" and "*Conte di Savoia,*" on the 1L. value of the Italian issue commemorating the 10th anniversary of the commencement of the Fascist regime.

Ocean greyhounds provide spectacular subjects, but the most beautiful of all shipping stamps depicts nothing greater than a humble whaling ship shown on the 1½d. value of the Falkland Islands issue of 1933. We illustrate the stamp here, and we think our readers will agree that it is one of the most beautiful stamps ever printed, and deserving of a place in every collection.

The story of shipping stamps would not be complete without reference to the two extremes of modern vessels, tramp steamers and pleasure craft. The former are represented by the 30c. value of the St. Pierre and Miquelon issue of 1932; while one of the most famous yachts of all time, H.M. King George's racing yacht "*Britannia*" is to be found in Canada's Silver Jubilee issue.

"1,000 PACKET" 6d.

A WONDERFUL OFFER FOR

Postage 2½d. ex. Abroad 6d. ex.

The "1,000 Packet" contains 500 excellently assorted Stamps; **a complete Sheet of 100 Unused** (very useful for exchange purposes); a neat 12-page booklet for duplicates; 25 British Colonials usually sold at ½d. to 1d. each, including new issues; 375 Magic "Strip" mounts, very quick for mounting stamps, and list of stamp bargains. Free sets will be sent to those who send addresses of stamp-collecting friends. *Ask for Approvals.* 100 B. Colonials 1/-. 20 Air Post 6d. 10 Abyssinia 1/6. 10 Mozambique Triangulars (just out) 1/6. "B.O.P." and "Captain" monthly parts cheap.

H. C. WATKINS, M. DEPT., GRANVILLE ROAD, BARNET.

The "ENGINEERING" Packet

contains an excellent assortment of 44 all different Foreign and Colonial stamps and includes the following which show various engineering feats and masterpieces of ancient and modern times, **Newfoundland** (Ship), **San Marino** (Fortress), **Greece** (Bridge and Liner), **Indo-China** (Plough), **Niger Territory** (Native Wells), **Saar** (Mine), **Turkey** (Cruiser), (Fortress), (Trains), **Ireland** (Barrage), **St. Pierre and Miquelon** (Trawler), **Palestine** (Fortress), **Egypt** (Pyramid), (Sphinx), **Guadeloupe** (Sugar refinery). **Brazil** (Aeroplanes), **Belgium** (Train), **Middle Congo** (Bridge and Train). Price 6d. (abroad extra). All purchasers of this packet asking for approval sheets will be presented with **India** Silver Jubilee stamps.

BURDOCK & FLURY,
4, Marlborough Road, London, S.W.19.

THE MYSTIC PACKET

1000 UNKNOWN UNUSUAL UNSORTED 1/3

Stamps on paper, etc., just as received from Convents, Missions, Bankers, etc. Guaranteed unpicked. Chance of a **FIND** in every lot. Send to-day for your treasure hunt to-morrow, **3** for **3/6**, **6** for **6/6**. Abroad, 1/6 packet. **FREE!** 25 Br. Cols., including Jubilees, to approval Applicants, also **FREE EXCHANGE.** Send postage only. Overseas **3d.**

ASTLEY & CO.
(M25), Lowhill, WOLVERHAMPTON

— 1935 —

This fine free collection of 1935 Jubilee Year Stamps, containing Triangulars, Air Mails, Postage Dues, Jubilees, etc., is yours for the asking. Including **AUSTRALIAN** (Whitehall Cenotaph and Jubilee); **CEYLON** (Rubber Tree); **BELGIUM** (Queen Astrid and King Leopold); **GERMANY** (Return of Saar); **MOZAMBIQUE CO.** (Air Mail—Plane over Biera); **ANDORRA** (Recouverments); **ECUADOR** (Casa de Correos); **AUSTRIA** (Postage Due); **MANCHUKUO** (Liaoyang Pagoda); **TRINIDAD AND TOBAGO** (New Currency—First Boca); **POLAND** (Marshal Pilsudski Mourning); **NEW ZEALAND** (Pied Fantail); **CANADA**; **ROUMANIA** (Large Portrait); **TANNOU TOUVA** (Triangle—Map); and new pictorials of **KENYA**, etc., it is the finest gift offered. Absolutely free to all genuine applicants for a 'Grey' booklet of stamps on approval and enclosing 2d. If you do not want approvals, the price of this packet will be **2/6**. Our 1936 Price Lists of Packets or Albums and Accessories sent free on request. **SPECIAL OFFERS: 50 INDIAN STATES 1/3; 100 PORTUGUESE COLONIES 2/-.**

WINDSOR STAMP CO.
59, LEE ROAD, BLACKHEATH, S.E.3

4 DIFF. QUEEN ASTRID MOURNING STAMPS, 3d. —J. Sanders, 90, Newlands Avenue, Southampton.

Free to Approval Purchasers. "Sanctions" Packet and Stamp Outfit.—G. Kingsmill, New Barnet, Herts.

½d. APPROVALS. Good value. Please state requirements.—Winter, 89, Cobham Road, Seven Kings.

100 DIFFERENT STAMPS FREE to applicants for ½d. approvals.—Cox, 21, Dennis Mansions, Westcliff.

30 FREE STAMPS and stamp mounts to all applicants for my approvals.—D. L. Willis, 8, Francis Street, Wexford, I.F.S.

OBSOLETE "CRETE" FREE!

Set of 6 depicting King George of Hellenes and Crete enslaved. Request approvals enclosing 2d. for postage etc.

D. BRENCHLEY, 16, Gloucester Pl., Greenwich, S.E.10

MECCANO WRITING PADS

These Writing Pads are just the thing to use when writing to your friends or to the Editor.

They are supplied in two sizes, each consisting of 50 printed sheets of tinted bank paper with cover. Prices—Large, 1/- each (post free); Small, 6d. each (post free).

ENVELOPES

Special envelopes, attractively printed and matching the writing paper in colour, are also available. Price, per packet of 50, 8d. post free.

Meccano Ltd., Binns Road, Liverpool 13

"R.C.M.P." Packet — FREE

This splendid packet contains the new **10 cent Canada** (Royal Canadian Mounted Policeman, as illustration), **New Ceylon** Pictorial (Native tapping rubber tree), Australia and Gold Coast Pictorials, New Zealand **1935, New Belgium** (train drawn by Diesel engine), France (Paris exhibition), Uganda Pictorial 1935 and 10 different Canada including the above and **Canada Jubilee** and the new 1935 issue.

All these new stamps free to genuine applicants for our Approval Sheets. who enclose 2d. for postage.

SHIRLEY STAMP CO., 19, SANDRINGHAM AVENUE, LONDON, S.W.20.

FREE STAMP WALLET

(size 3½" × 5½") fitted with Perforation Gauge, etc., and containing

MINT 2/6 BRITISH COLONIAL

to approval applicants enclosing 3d. (in stamps) for postage and packing.

A. B. LEWIS (Dept. C23)
16, CRICKLEWOOD LANE, LONDON, N.W.2.

100 "WORTH WHILE" DIFFERENT 1/- Post Free

BRITISH COLONIALS INCLUDING JUBILEES. Covering Gold Coast Pictorials, ½d., 1d., 1½d., 2d.; Northern Rhodesia, Nigeria, ½d., 1d., 1½d., 2d., 3d.; Mauritius, 2c., 4c., 5c.; Iraq, ½, 1, 3 annas; N. Zealand, ½d., 1d., 1½d., 2d., 3d., 4d., 6d., 1/-; Newfoundland; Palestine; Fiji; Bahamas, etc., etc. Finest Packet **you** have ever had. **Money Back** if not satisfied. With **"Worth While"** Approval Sheets **only.**

JOS. H. GAZE, DIDSBURY, MANCHESTER.

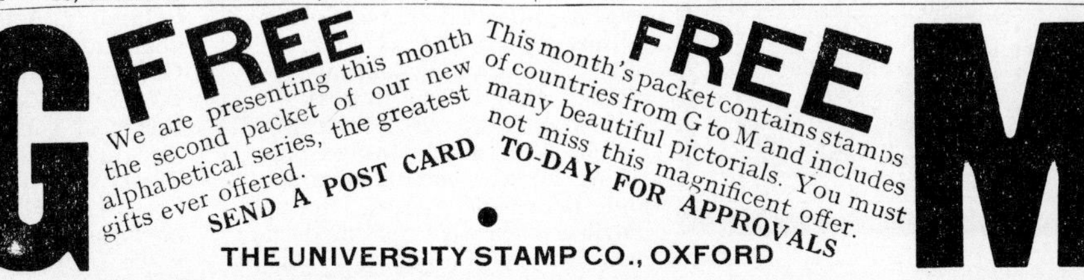

QUEEN ASTRID MOURNING PACKET FREE!

This huge gift parcel contains **507** UNSORTED FOREIGN STAMPS, including the large QUEEN ASTRID MOURNING STAMP, and others from FINLAND, CHARKHARI, CHILI, RUSSIA, CUBA, INDIA, etc., etc. Just send 2d. stamp and request my FAMOUS EXTRA-LARGE-DISCOUNT APPROVAL SHEETS (Abroad 6d. P.O.)

E. EASTICK, 22, BANKSIDE ROAD, BOURNEMOUTH.

JAMAICA JUBILEE PACKET FREE!

This **Wonderful** packet contains a Large **JAMAICA JUBILEE PICTORIAL**; a **Large PERSIAN AIR MAIL** overprinted **"Iran"**; French **Peace; SUDAN** Pictorial; **Nigeria; New Caledonia** mint Pictorial; **U.S.A. Bicentenary; OUBANGUICHARI** Pictorial and superb set of **8 INDIAN** including **New Issue. ALL FREE!** Just send 1½d. postage requesting our **High-Class** approvals containing **JUBILEE** stamps and latest **New Issue Pictorials**, etc. (Jubilee stamps bought).

THE PUKKA STAMP CO., 27, Normandy Ave., Barnet.

GLOBE-TROTTER'S OFFER TO YOU

FREE—10 Large Italian and Russian Commemorative Pictorials and **50 other splendid varieties**—magnificent stamps—the most sensational offer yet. Send 1½d. postage for "Globe-Trotter" approval selections—amazing value, ¼d., ½d., and 1d. upwards—and particulars of how **you can have FREE stamps every 14 days!!** Write Now—there's a stamp treat in store for you. **Special Offers. "Globe-Trotter" Mystery Mixture**—world-wide collected—old and new issues, pictorials, etc., **1,000 unsorted, unbeatable, 1/3.** 50 Persia, 1/5. 10 Jubilees, 1/-. 50 Airmails, 1/11. 50 Soviet Russia, many large pictorials, 1/5. 25–9d "Globe-Trotter" for sheer value—write now!

GLOBE-TROTTER, 17, WINCHESTER ROAD, BIRCHFIELD, BIRMINGHAM.

FREE! QUEEN ASTRID MOURNING STAMP AND OUTFIT

comprising mounts, perforation gauge, duplicate album, detector, and 50 stamps. All Free to approval applicants sending 2d. postage. Abroad, 6d.

WILKINSON
18, St. Peter's Road, Croydon

CHEAP APPROVALS

My beautiful Approval Selections are ideal for filling those vacant spaces. Pictorials, Colonials, and hard to get items. Selections from 4 a 1d. Free Gift Bi-coloured Persia all applicants.

A. V. TAPP,
108, CHESTERFIELD RD., BRISTOL

FREE 1936 SENSATION COLLECTION THE GREATEST GIFT OF ALL!

This grand packet includes **New and recent issues** of Kenya (**Unused pictorial**), Mozambique (Airplane), Canada (new portrait of His Majesty), Austria (Salzburg Peasant), New Zealand (**Pied Fantail Bird**), Germany (**Rare and beautiful Saar restoration issue**), and older issues from Italy, U.S.A., Belgium (King), Schleswig (**Unused Plebiscite issue**) and many other countries. To obtain this wonderful gift FREE, simply send **2d.** postage (abroad **6d.**) and request approvals.

MICHAEL HERBERT, 58, Larkswood Road, Chingford, London.

WHEN WRITING TO ADVERTISERS

Readers are urged to observe the following points when writing to advertisers:

1. **Mention the "M.M." and any special reference number quoted in the advertisement. This helps the advertisers to identify their offers and to give prompt attention.**
2. **See that the full amount of the price and any postage is included. It is unfair to expect advertisers to fulfil their undertakings promptly if short remittances are sent.**
3. **Give your full address.**
4. **Enquiries concerning advertisements or advertisers should be addressed to:**

THE ADVERTISEMENT MANAGER
MECCANO MAGAZINE, Binns Road, LIVERPOOL 13

SETS—ONE PENNY

Boys! Fill up those blank spaces from my new series of approvals. Sets 1d. to 3d. each. Send a p.c. for a selection now to:

CHAS. A. HILL, 51, MONINS ROAD, DOVER.

Splendid Selection of Stamps FREE

to applicants for bargain price Approvals. Post 2d. —Weston, 20, West Way, Finchley, London, N.3.

8 Roumania, King Carol, Large Heads ... 6d.
4 Egypt Military Stamps... ... ... 8d.
4 Tanna Touva, Zoological, 2 Triangles ... 3d
2 Queen Astrid, Belgium, Mourning ... ... 3d.
Post 1½d. extra. Selections from 4 a **1d.** (30 for **6d.**)

J. R. MORRIS, 9, Audley Road, Folkestone, Kent.

Stamp Gossip
and Notes on New Issues

A Complete Collection

In a stamp article recently we commented that most boy collectors set out with the idea of filling space quickly, in effect trying to collect all the stamps in the world.

The comment provokes the question, "What would a complete stamp collection cost?" An answer to this question was given in a recent issue of *Gibbons Stamp Monthly*, which said: "This question can never be accurately answered as many stamps listed in the big Gibbons Catalogue are absolutely unobtainable, but for those who like figures I may say that the prices given for used and unused stamps together in the big Gibbons Catalogue total something like three-quarters of a million pounds, about £300,000 of which is attributable to the British Empire section. In spite of the magnitude of the task, there are always at least two or three collectors in the world who are trying to build up complete collections of stamps on the basis of the lists given in the Gibbons Catalogue."

New Greek Air Mails

A set of striking mythological designs is employed for the new series of Greek air mail stamps, specimens of which we hope to reproduce next month. The stamps and designs are as follows: 1 dr., chariot of the Sun; 2 dr., Iris, the messenger of the gods; 5 dr., Daedalus and Icarus; 7 dr., Pallas Athenæ; 10 dr., Hermes; 25 dr., Ganamede and Jupiter; 30 dr., Celestrial chariot; 50 dr., Bellerophon and Pegasus; 100 dr., Phryxos and Helle on the flying ram of the Golden Fleece.

The Rarest Stamp

Bidding for the 1c. 1856 British Guiana stamp failed to reach the reserve price at the recent auction in London.

After starting at £3,500 the bids were carried by steps of £250 up to a figure of £7,500. The bidding stopped there, and the auctioneer declared that the stamp must be withdrawn from the sale as the offer was slightly below the reserve price fixed by Mrs. Arthur Hind, whose late husband bought the stamp at the Ferrari sales in 1922 at the then record price for a stamp of £7,350.

Following the withdrawal of the stamp, private negotiations were set on foot.

Air Mail by the Ton

The amazing growth of air mail operations is revealed in the 1934 statistics recently issued. These figures show that 251,000 tons of air mail matter were carried on the British lines, 279,000 tons by Canadian and 3½ million tons by U.S.A. lines, 216,000 tons by French, 759,000 tons by German and 200,000 tons by Dutch lines.

It will be some months before the 1935 figures are known, but it is certain that the British figures will show a tremendous increase as a result of the duplication of the services over the British Imperial trunk lines and the constantly increasing diversion of first-class mail matter to air mail carriage.

* * * *

In the philatelic press recently, in a comment on interesting postmarks, a correspondent drew attention to one postmark "Hell," this being from the post office of a little village in Norway.

One is carried quite to the other extreme by the discovery of a postmark "Equator, Kenya." This comes from Equator Station, a halt on the Kenya and Uganda Railway some 500 miles from Mombasa.

A New Dutch Air Stamp

The design of the recently issued Dutch air stamp, issued under a premium to aid the National Air Mail subsidy funds, shows an aerial map of Holland overshadowed by passing mail planes. The stamp, which bears a face value of 6c. and a premium of 4c., is to remain on sale throughout this year.

* * * *

The Mozambique Company has been busy with a minor flood of new issues in recent months. There have been a variety of commemorative issues in addition to a new air set.

Our readers probably will find the stamp illustrated here to be the most interesting. It commemorates the opening of a new railway bridge across the River Zambesi.

* * *

An important development in air mail history was opened up on 22nd November last by Pan-American Airways in the inauguration of the first trans-Pacific air service between San Francisco and Manila in the Philippine Islands, via Hawaii.

The service is to be extended to Canton in China in the near future, thus linking up Asia with America.

French West Indian Tercentenary

The French West Indian Colonies, Guadeloupe, Guiana, and Martinique, have each issued a series of commemorative stamps to mark the celebration of the tercentenary of the foundation of the French West Indies.

Each series contains six stamps and employs two designs, as follows: Guadeloupe, 40c., 50c. and 1f.50, Cardinal Richelieu at the foundation meeting of the French West India Company in Paris in 1635; 1f.75, 5fr. and 10fr., Victor Hugues and his corsairs. Hugues was a close friend of Robespierre, and was responsible for what is known as the Brigands War, an attempt to extend the French West Indian possessions. He captured Guadeloupe from the British and used it as his headquarters in a very determined effort to capture Grenada, Dominica and St. Lucia. He succeeded in taking the last-named island but later was compelled to abandon his prize.

Guiana: 40c., 50c. and 1f.50, showing the capture of Cayenne from the Dutch in 1676. The three higher values use a symbolical design.

Martinique: the three low values show a portrait of Pierre Belain d'Esnambuc, who was the first French coloniser of the West Indies. The higher values show a portrait of Victor Schoelcher, who abolished slavery in the Colonies.

A Stamp Essay Contest

Our advertisers, The Windsor Stamp Company, are offering prizes in a simple essay competition entitled "My Favourite Country for Stamp Collecting."

Essays may not exceed 300 words in length, and must be the unaided work of the competitor. Any "*M.M.*" reader may compete, but anyone who is not a customer of the firm will be required to pay an entrance fee of 6d.

Full details may be obtained direct from The Windsor Stamp Company, 59, Lee Road, Blackheath, London, S.E.3.

We thank Stanley Gibbons Ltd. for their courtesy in loaning the stamps from which the illustrations on this page have been made.

Competition Corner

FEBRUARY CROSSWORD PUZZLE

ACROSS

1. Departure
5. Preserve
9. Period
10. Spike
11. Rails
13. Property
16. Travelling Bag
18. Legislative Body
20. Harden
21. Evil
23. Summer Dish
24. Yield
25. Spill
27. Wounded
28. Pin
29. A Card Game
31. Limp
32. Tank
35. Bind
37. Colour
40. Useless
43. Filter
45. Sleeveless Cloak
47. Thong
49. Tree
50. Dislikes
51. Tenacity
53. Retaliate
54. Trader
55. Father
56. Number
57. Hill
58. Summits
59. Understood

DOWN

2. Retreat
3. Obliterate
4. Auction
6. Untidy
7. Stations
8. Battlegrounds
11. Hair
12. Baffle
14. Claw
15. Leader
16. Evil
17. Lick
19. Paradise
21. Pouch
22. Lair
25. Lukewarm
26. Bird
28. Kitchen Utensil
30. Cushion
33. Account
34. Carpenter's Tool
36. Before
37. Brim
38. Staff
39. Ease
41. Exploit
42. Rank
44. Everything
45. Provides
46. Forward
48. Cavities
50. Bird
52. Tear
53. Scold

Our series of crossword puzzles have enjoyed remarkable popularity, largely because they are set for our readers' amusement instead of for strenuous competitive effort. This month's puzzle will be found to follow the lines of the previous ones in that it provides a fair and interesting puzzle. The clues are all perfectly straightforward, and every word used can be found in Chambers' or any other standard dictionary. The rules that govern the solution of crossword puzzles are by now so well known that it is unnecessary to give any further explanation of the requirements of the competition.

Cash prizes of 21/–, 15/–, 10/6 and 5/– respectively will be awarded to the senders of the four neatest or most novelly-prepared correct solutions, in order of merit. The prizes will be duplicated for the Overseas section, which is open to all readers living outside Great Britain, Ireland, and the Channel Islands.

Entries should be addressed "February Crossword Puzzle, Meccano Magazine, Binns Road, Liverpool 13," and must be sent to reach this office not later than 29th February. Overseas closing date 30th May.

Competitors should not mutilate their magazines by cutting out the crossword illustration. Instead they should make a copy of the square on the same scale, or larger, and use that in submitting their entries for the contest. Readers who desire to have their entries returned, must enclose a stamped addressed envelope.

February Drawing Contest

Each month throughout this winter we are offering prizes for the best drawings or paintings submitted during the month. There are no restrictions as to subject or to size.

The entries each month will be divided into the usual two sections, A for readers aged 16 and over, B for those under 16, and cash prizes of 21/– and 10/6 will be awarded for the best entries in each section.

A separate set of prizes, to be awarded in similar conditions, will be reserved for competitors in the Overseas section.

Entries to the February competition must be addressed "February Drawing Contest, Meccano Magazine, Binns Road, Liverpool 13," and must arrive not later than 29th February. Overseas closing date, 30th May.

Unsuccessful entries will be returned if a stamped cover is sent for the purpose with the entry.

Competition Closing Dates

HOME

February Crossword Puzzle ...	29th February
February Drawing Contest ...	29th February

OVERSEAS

November Sketchograms Contest	29th February
True Firework Story	29th February
November Drawing Competition	29th February
Jig-Saw Advertisement Contest	31st March
Christmas Letter Contest ...	31st March
December Drawing Contest ...	31st March
Cover Voting Contest	30th April
January Drawing Contest ...	30th April
February Crossword Puzzle ...	30th May
February Drawing Contest ...	30th May

Watch the Closing Dates:

Competitors, both Home and Overseas, are particularly requested to make a careful note of the closing dates of the competitions.

In sending entries to competitions that are divided into age groups, competitors should take particular care to mark their ages clearly on the back of the entry. It is not sufficient merely to indicate the age group, as age allowances are given to ensure equality of opportunity for the younger competitors.

COMPETITION RESULTS

HOME

Jig-Saw Advertisement Contest.—1. S. J. Davis (Bristol); 2. R. P. and J. C. Walford (Newton Abbot); 3. W. K. Cocking (Redruth); 4. D. Morley Davies (Maesteg). Consolation Prizes: E. J. Boardman (Exeter); J. A. Pedler (London, N.14).

Christmas Letter Contest.—1. B. J. Powell (Misterton); 2. D. T. White (Knebworth); 3. E. P. W. Scott (Clapton, E.5); 4. E. N. Banner (Plumstead, S.E.18).

December Drawing Contest.—First Prizes: Section A, K. Dyson (Tadcaster); Section B, J. S. Taylor (Burnley). Second Prizes: Section A, J. C. Prendergast (Dublin); Section B, E. Buckman (Redhill).

OVERSEAS

September Photo Contest.—First Prizes: Section A, F. van Bulck (Brussels); Section B, F. H. A. Damant (Johannesburg). Second Prizes: Section A, A. A. Shawky (Giza); Section B, A. C. Das Gupta (Bengal). Special Prize: R. H. Warr (Cairo).

September Sketchograms Contest.—First Prizes: Section A, Nils Soderberg (Falun, Sweden); Section B, I. C. Dickison (Dunedin, N.Z.). Second Prizes: Section A, M. Stanley (Edmonton, Alta.); Section B, C. Cali (Malta).

Holiday Story Contest.—1. E. Azzopardi (Malta); 2. C. J. Mallia (Malta); 3. J. Gandy (Vancouver); 4. J. Robertson (Sydney, N.S.W.).

SAFETY FIRST

Squadron Leader: "And what would you do if a squadron of enemy 'planes were after you?"
Pilot: "Go into an air pocket and hide, sir."

* * * *

Customer: "But I don't want a cake of soap. I said stamps."
Village Shopkeeper: "Well, you'll 'ave to 'ave the soap too. Stamps be stuck to it."

* * * *

Stout Person: "Any use trying to borrow a fiver off you?"
Tight Person: "Ay, the exercise will do ye guid."

* * * *

Bob: "Yes, Dad, I'm quite a big gun at school."
Dad: "Well, then why don't I hear better reports?"

* * * *

Pavement Artist (to housewife): "Would you please keep your cat indoors, mum? Everytime I sketch a fish it comes along and licks it out."

* * * *

Teacher: "How many seasons are there?"
Tom (whose father keeps a shop): "Two."
Teacher: "What are they?"
Tom: "Slack and Busy."

* * * *

An Irishman was one day employed by an old lady in the country. At tea time she laid a small morsel of honey on his plate.
"Begorra, ma'am" said the labourer. "I see you keep a bee."

* * * *

A negro was charged in a country town with stealing. The magistrate, being doubtful if he understood the meaning of an oath, decided to examine him on the point.
"Rastus," he said, "you know what will happen to you if you tell a lie?"
"Yes, boss," replied Rastus, "me go down below—burn long time."
"Quite right," replied the magistrate. "And do you know what will happen if you tell the truth?"
"Yes, boss. I lose the case."

* * * *

Doctor: "What is your profession?"
Patient (pompously): "I'm a gentleman."
Doctor: "Well, you'll have to try something else; it doesn't agree with you."

* * * *

The baby pulled her brother's hair until he yelled. The mother soothed the boy. "Baby doesn't know how badly it hurts," she said, and left the room.
Presently frantic squeals came from the baby, and mother rushed in. "What is the matter with her?" she asked her son anxiously.
"Nothing," he replied. "Only now she knows."

* * * *

NASTY!

Indulgent Mother (to street trader): "How much are your balloons? My little boy would like to prick them with a pin."

LOST!

The absent-minded professor drove up to his garage, looked inside, returned to his car and drove to the nearest police station.
"Inspector," he gasped, "my garage is empty, my car's been stolen."

* * * *

He: "I'll have to scrap this razor, it won't cut anything."
She: "Why, Charles, you don't mean to say that your beard is tougher than the kitchen linoleum!"

* * * *

Black: "Has he changed much?"
Blue: "He thinks he has."
Black: "How's that?"
Blue: "He's always telling people what a fool he used to be."

* * * *

WARNING HIM

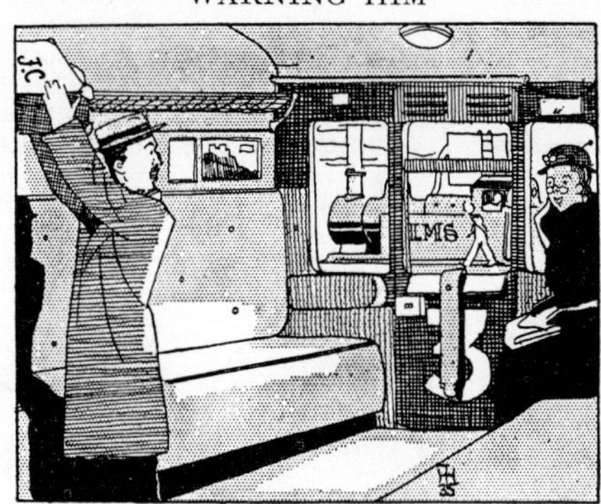

Nervous Lady (to fellow passenger who is politely placing her bag in the rack): "Thank you; I'll have it this end, please, over my seat. I always like to be near the communication cord, in case I'm shut in with a homicidal maniac."

* * * *

Annoyed at mistakes in his letters, the employer summoned his new typist.
"Don't you know the King's English?" he snapped.
"Of course I know he's English," she indignantly replied.

* * * *

Sergeant (addressing a dense recruit): "How many times must I tell you never to approach horses from the rear without speaking to them? One of these days, you know, you'll get kicked on the head, and then I shall have a lame horse on my hands!"

* * * *

Customer: "This hair restorer you sold me has made my hair fall out worse than ever."
Hair Specialist: "That's because you put on too much. You've made yours come right out instead of stopping half-way."

* * * *

The plumber was working and his new boy assistant was looking on. The latter was learning the trade, and this was his first day. After a while the boy said: "Do you charge for my time?"
"Certainly," came the reply.
"But I haven't done anything," said the boy.
The plumber had been inspecting the finished job with a lighted candle, which he handed to his helper. "If you must be so conscientious," he said, "blow that out!"

* * * *

A weary traveller had already moved along the crowded tramcar three times, and again he could hear the conductor calling: "Pass along the car, please." Two minutes later the conductor came for the fare.
"Fare," said the traveller, "why I'm walking it!"

* * * *

"I'm buying a lawn mower for my husband's birthday."
"A surprise?"
"Rather, he thinks I'm giving him an easy chair."

WELL RECOMMENDED

Foreman: "Do you think you are fit for really hard labour?"
Applicant: "Well, some of the best judges in the country have thought so."

* * * *

Mrs. Peach: "I'll take a pound of these sausages. Are they British?"
Butcher: "Yes, madam—the good old bulldog breed!"

* * * *

Student: "What is the date, please?"
Teacher: "Never mind the date; get on with the examination paper."
Student: "Well sir, I want to have something correct on it."

* * * *

Passenger (in an airplane for first time): "I understand that I must sit still, but what if I fall out?"
Pilot: "That's easy. Just grab anything you see and hold on."

* * * *

Mike had just returned from a visit to the United States, and was telling his friends all about it
"Did you meet with much hospitality in America?" he was asked.
"Sure," was the reply. "I was in hospital nearly all the time."

* * * *

Ted: "What's a quire of paper?"
Tim: "Choir of paper? Oh, it must be one of those music rolls for a player piano."

* * * *

Priest (addressing invalid): "I'm going to pray that you may forgive Casey for having thrown that brick at you."
O'Leary: "Maybe yer Riv'rence 'ud be saving toime if ye'd just wait till Oi get well, and thin pray for Casey."

* * * *

Neighbour: "Where's your brother Freddie?"
Boy: "He's in the house playing in a duet. I finished first."

* * * *

Mother (at circus): "Isn't he clever, darling? He's juggling with three pieces of sugar."
Modern Child: "Ask him to do it with three handfuls of granulated."

* * * *

Dentist: "How long has the tooth been troubling you?"
McDonald: "Twenty years."

* * * *

Professor: "I forgot my umbrella this morning."
Wife: "How did you remember that you had forgotten it?"
Professor: "Well, I missed it when I raised my hand to close it after the rain stopped."

* * * *

TACTLESS

Convict: "Yus, lady, I've done nearly twenty years."
Visitor: "Twenty wasted years! How it must make you wish to have your time over again!"

BOYS! JOIN THE MECCANO GUILD

President:

MR. FRANK HORNBY

The Meccano Guild is an organisation for boys started at the request of boys and conducted as far as possible by boys. At its head—guiding and controlling, and taking a personal interest in it—is the President, Mr. Frank Hornby, inventor of Meccano and Managing Director of Meccano Limited, and it is ready to be of service to each individual member, and to help or give advice whenever requested. Membership of the Guild enables Meccano boys to get the best out of life.

The three great objects of the Guild are to make every boy's life brighter and happier; to foster clean-mindedness, truthfulness, ambition and initiative; and to encourage boys in the pursuit of their studies and hobbies and especially in the development of their knowledge of mechanical and engineering principles. Every boy undertakes to promote these objects.

A Meccano boy who joins the Guild becomes a member of a great brotherhood of world-wide extent, every member of which has promised to observe its great objects; wherever he happens to be, even in strange countries he will know that he has met a friend whenever he sees the little triangular badge. Thus the Guild brings together Meccano boys all over the world.

THE GUILD BADGE

Membership of the Guild is open to every boy possessing a Meccano Outfit or Hornby Train Set who satisfactorily fills in the application form. The only conditions are that members shall promise to observe the objects of the Guild and to wear their badges on all possible occasions.

The Meccano Guild badge is beautifully enamelled in blue and white. The ordinary form is made for wearing in the lapel of the coat, but brooch badges are issued to members who prefer to pin them in position, and applicants who wish to have this form of badge should indicate this when sending in their forms. In addition to the badge, each member receives a handsome Membership Certificate printed in orange and black.

HOW TO BECOME A MEMBER

In order to join the Guild all that is necessary is to fill up the form of application, and to forward it to the Secretary of the Meccano Guild, Binns Road, Liverpool 13, from whom an application form may be obtained if desired. A remittance to pay for the membership badge should be sent along with the completed form of application. The price of the badge is 7d. post free in the United Kingdom and 1/- post free overseas (25 cents Canada). The applicant is then duly enrolled as a member of the Guild and his badge of membership is sent to him. Each member has the personal interest of the President and is entitled to the friendly advice and assistance of the Secretary.

Boys living overseas should write to one of the Meccano agents at the following addresses: CANADA: Meccano Ltd., 187-189, Church St., Toronto. AUSTRALIA: Messrs. E. G. Page & Co., 52, Clarence Street, Sydney, N.S.W. NEW ZEALAND: Models Ltd., Third Floor, Paykel's Buildings, 9, Anzac Avenue (P.O. Box 129), Auckland, C.1. SOUTH AFRICA: Mr. A. E. Harris (P.O. Box 1199), 142, Market Street, Johannesburg.

MECCANO CLUBS

Meccano Clubs are founded and established by enthusiastic Meccano boys under the guidance of the Guild Secretary at Headquarters. At the present time there are over 150 affiliated clubs in various towns and villages in this country and overseas, together with many others not yet affiliated. Each club has its Leader, Secretary, Treasurer and other Officials, all of whom, with the exception of the Leader, are boys.

Every Guild member should join a club if possible, for only in association with other Meccano boys is he able to obtain the greatest fun from his hobby. If the nearest club is too far away for him to join, or if he is unable to join it for any other reason, he should consider the possibility of forming a new club in his own district. A special booklet entitled "How to run a Meccano Club" is now ready, and will be sent to any reader (post free) on receipt of 2d. in stamps.

When a Meccano Club has been successfully launched and good progress is being made, affiliation with the Guild is granted. A beautiful club certificate, suitable for framing and hanging in the club-room, is presented, and the club becomes entitled to such privileges as the loan of interesting lectures and large models built at Headquarters.

THE CORRESPONDENCE CLUB

Members of the Guild are eligible to join the Correspondence Club, by which they are placed in communication with other Guild members in some other part of the country or abroad. To those boys who are interested in foreign languages the Correspondence Club presents a splendid opportunity of obtaining a correspondent in the particular country in the language of which they are interested. Stamp collectors also find the club of value. Full particulars and enrolment form will be sent on application to the Guild Headquarters.

THE SUN NEVER SETS ON THE MECCANO GUILD

MECCANO MAGAZINE

Editorial Office:
Binns Road, Liverpool 13
England

Vol. XXI. No. 3
March, 1936

With the Editor

The Passing of King George V

The death of his late Majesty King George V occurred too late for me to make reference to it in the February issue of the "*M.M.*" I cannot allow the event to pass by without comment, however, and I am sure that every reader of the "*M.M.*" at home and overseas will desire to join me in this expression of regret, belated though it necessarily is. The late King came nearer to the hearts of his people than any of his predecessors, and the loyalty and affection of his subjects continually increased during the 25 years of his reign.

King Edward VIII undoubtedly will maintain the splendid tradition created by his father. He has visited almost every part of the Empire and has come into intimate contact with people of all ranks and conditions of life. More than this, he has travelled in many European countries, in the United States, the Argentine and other lands, and everywhere has aroused the greatest enthusiasm by his fine personal qualities and his keen interest in everything he saw around him.

His late Majesty King George V. *Hoppé*

Britain's Great New Liner

We are all looking forward eagerly to the appearance in service of Britain's new giant liner, "*Queen Mary*." The great interest she has aroused is scarcely surprising in view of her size and our expectations of great achievements on the historic North Atlantic route. The capabilities of her engines and her speed will not be known until towards the end of the present month, when she will be taken down the Clyde for her official speed trials.

I am now making the necessary preparations to provide my readers with full information and interesting illustrations of this fine vessel.

Across the Atlantic by Air

By a strange coincidence, "*Queen Mary*" will make her maiden voyage at about the time when the new German airship will be completed. As my readers know from the article published on page 20 of the January issue, this vessel is intended for the service between Germany and South America that has been maintained regularly for the past four years by the "*Graf Zeppelin*" alone. Her builders are confident that the years of pioneer adventure in the airship world are now over, and that we are now on the eve of the establishment of regular trans-atlantic airship services.

This of course is an entirely new development, and further changes must be looked for when the plans now under consideration by Imperial Airways for aeroplane services between England and America take practical form. It seems to me that before many years have passed those who wish to cross the Atlantic will have the choice of travelling by sea or by air. It is difficult to forecast what the future will bring. Many difficulties have to be faced before regular air services will be available, and for a time at least the accommodation available in the flying boats and airships that will be used will be comparatively limited. The Martin flying boats designed for American trans-oceanic services carry 48 passengers. The new German airship will provide quarters for 50 passengers and 35 members of the crew, but the great Cunarder will carry over 4,000 people, including a crew of about 1,500. There is no doubt therefore that great ships such as the "*Queen Mary*" will find ample scope for the work for which they are designed, in spite of the greater speeds of which aircraft are capable.

Famous Bridges of the World

Steel Structures combine Strength and Beauty

THE bridge is perhaps the oldest of engineering structures, and probably the idea originated in a tree uprooted by the wind and drawn across a stream, or in a more or less regular series of boulders occurring naturally across the bed of a river. The great modern phase of bridge building, however, can be said to date back to the coming of cheap steel. Even in the construction of the simplest type of bridge, steel has points of superiority over masonry, but this superiority is most striking in the spanning of long distances at great heights and in the building of bridges in difficult situations.

Many of the most famous steel bridges combine strength and beauty of design to a remarkable degree. Perhaps the most beautiful of all types is the arch bridge, of which the largest and the most famous example is the Sydney Harbour Bridge, Australia. It took eight years to build and was opened on 19th March 1932, and is one of the greatest engineering feats of recent years. The bridge has an overall length of 3,770 ft. and its huge arch, springing from granite abutments on each side of the harbour, crosses the water in a single span 1,650 ft. long, and at its crown it has a clear height of 170 ft. above high water. The arch rests on four main bearings each weighing 296 tons and sustaining a load of 19,700 tons, and the thrilling story of its construction was told in the "*M.M.*" of October last. The four pylon towers, two at each end of the arch, are 285 ft. in height, and their erection involved the quarrying of 20,000 cu. yd. of granite, which was brought 100 miles by sea from Moruya on the south coast of New South Wales.

An impressive view of the George Washington Suspension Bridge, from the New York side of the Hudson River. At the right the main cables can be seen extending into the massive concrete anchorage. Photograph reproduced by courtesy of the Port of New York Authority.

The deck of the bridge carries a roadway 57 ft. in width, providing for six lines of the heaviest vehicular traffic, two lines of main electric railway on each side of the roadway, and two 10 ft.-wide footpaths on the outside of the permanent way, making a total width of 159 ft. 6 in.—the heaviest deck ever constructed.

In extreme contrast to the bold sweeping line of the Sydney Harbour Bridge is the severe horizontal line of the girder bridge across the Firth of Tay at Dundee. In spite of its severity it has a beauty of its own, as the accompanying illustration shows. The present Tay Bridge is actually the second to bear that name. The first one was a lattice girder bridge designed by Sir Thomas Bouch and built during the years 1870-6 at a cost of £350,000. It consisted of 85 spans, with a total length of 10,700 ft., and carried a single line of railway. During a gale on the night of 28th December 1879, 18 months after the bridge was opened, its 13 central spans, each 245 ft. long, were blown down while a mail train was crossing. The train was precipitated into the water 90 ft. below and 75 people perished.

The collapsed portion of the bridge was not rebuilt, but a new bridge of greater width and lower elevation was built about 60 ft. from the first one. Much of the material in the old bridge was utilised in this work. The present Tay Bridge is just over two miles long and carries a double railway track. Over most of the spans the lines are carried on the tops of the girders, but across the 13 centre spans they are laid between the main girders so as to allow a clearance of 79 ft. for the passage of ships under the bridge. It was opened for public use on 20th June 1887, the Jubilee anniversary of the accession of Queen Victoria.

It is an interesting fact that the disaster to the old Tay Bridge led to the erection of one of the most striking structures in the world, the cantilever bridge across the Firth of Forth. Originally it was planned to erect a suspension bridge designed by Sir Thomas Bouch. It was to have two spans of 1,600 ft. each, a clear headway of 150 ft., and towers 550 ft. above high water on the island of Inchgarvie and on the two shores. A start had been made on the foundation of the main pier on Inchgarvie island, but the appalling calamity to the Tay Bridge destroyed all confidence in Sir Thomas Bouch and work on the new bridge was stopped immediately. Various other means of crossing the Forth were then considered, and finally a bridge on the cantilever system was built. It was opened on the 8th March 1890 by King Edward VII, then Prince of Wales. The ceremony took place during a fierce gale, the sound of which, roaring through the steel framework, provided an object lesson in the enormous strength and stability of the giant structure, an imposing view of which forms the subject of our cover.

The Forth Bridge consists of two approach viaducts; three double cantilevers resting on two piers near the shore and on a central pier on the island; and two pairs of girders spanning the intervals between the ends of the central and side cantilevers over the channels. The South Approach viaduct has 10 spans of 168 ft. each and four arches of 66 ft. each, and the North Approach viaduct has five spans of 168 ft. and three arches of various sizes. The total length of the bridge, together with the approach viaducts, is about 8,296 ft., and the piers carry a total weight of 50,958 tons of steel.

This photograph of the famous Tay Bridge shows the severe lines of this lengthy structure. Photograph reproduced by courtesy of the L.N.E.R.

The cantilever portion of the bridge, including the two suspended spans, measures about 5,349 ft. 6 in. The three double cantilevers are symmetrical steel structures rising 361 ft. above high water level, that is, nearly as high as St. Paul's Cathedral. They are composed of a central portion over the piers from which two cantilever arms extend out on each side for a distance of 680 ft., tapering at their extremities, both horizontally and vertically.

The central parts consist of four vertical columns each resting upon a circular granite pier, and connected at the top and the bottom and braced together horizontally and vertically. The cantilever arms consist of two massive curved steel tubes at the bottom, in compression, and two flanged lattice steel ties at the top, in tension, braced together vertically and horizontally.

The ends of the cantilevers reaching out over the channels serve to support girders of 350 ft. span that complete the communication between the cantilevers over the channels, the whole thus forming a bridge with two clear openings of 1,710 ft. between the piers. Two lines of railway, with a footpath on each side, run through the cantilever arms.

The north cantilever of the Forth Bridge during construction. The cranes on the top of the cantilever give a good idea of the immense size of the bridge.

The Forth Bridge is of never-failing interest to the thousands who cross it by rail, but for complete appreciation of the bridge one should see it from a small boat.

For sheer gracefulness the suspension type of bridge has many claims to supremacy. Several notable suspension bridges have been built during the past 10 years, and each has had the distinction, for a time, of being the longest of its kind in the world. The record is held at present by the George Washington Bridge illustrated on the previous page. This fine structure crosses the Hudson River in a single span 3,500 ft. long, in the vicinity of Fort Washington Point on the New York side and Fort Lee on the New Jersey side. The situation is ideal for a bridge of this type, as on the New York side the land reaches a height of 200 ft. about 1,000 ft. from the shore, and on the New Jersey side it is 280 ft. high only 500 ft. inland.

The bridge was planned to have two decks, the upper deck to carry a roadway wide enough for eight lines of traffic, flanked by footwalks for passengers, and the lower deck to carry four electric railway tracks. As constructed, however, the bridge has only the upper deck, and the lower deck is to be added later.

The main span is suspended from four main cables that pass over towers at the ends of the span and are led down to, and secured in, massive anchorages. The towers carrying the main cables are 635 ft. high, above the river level, and differ from those of previous suspension bridges. At the New York end the bridge terminates about 100 ft. above the land, and the bridge approach was therefore built in the form of a long ramp 60 ft. wide. The construction of the New Jersey approach to the bridge presented an entirely different problem, for there the bridge terminates about 50 ft. below the top of the rocky cliffs. A deep cut at a fairly steep gradient was excavated to carry the approach roadway up to the surface.

The George Washington Bridge does not lack company, as there are close upon 60 bridges and viaducts within the bounds of the city of New York.

Recording and Predicting Tides

The Work of a Modern Observatory

By G. R. Rookledge

OBSERVATORIES may be divided roughly into two classes. In one class purely astronomical work is carried out, telescopes and other instruments being employed for studying the movements and composition of the Sun, Moon and stars. A famous observatory of this kind is that on Mount Wilson, California, where the largest telescope in the world is installed. This is a reflector with a mirror 100 in. in diameter, but even this giant instrument will be surpassed in a few years, when a new telescope will be erected there that incorporates the 200 in. glass disc the casting of which was described on page 512 of the *"M.M."* for September 1935.

Observatories of the second class are devoted to such purposes as exact time-keeping, and the improvement of navigation at sea. The Royal Observatory at Greenwich is largely concerned with work of this kind, and actually was founded by Charles II in 1675 for the purpose of making the seas safer by providing sailors with information about the positions of the stars that would enable them to find their way more easily.

Measurements of the rise and fall of the tides and the preparation of tide tables also are carried on in observatories of this kind, and near the port of Liverpool there is an observatory where predictions are made of the tides at the chief ports of the British Empire, with the exception of those in India. It is built on Bidston Hill, Birkenhead. This hill is about 200 ft. in height and commands a view of the estuary of the Mersey and Liverpool Bay, and in the great days of sailing ships was used as a station from which the arrivals of vessels off the port of Liverpool were signalled to their owners. The observatory now built on its summit was established in 1828 for the purpose of rating ships' chronometers, and was taken over in 1856 by the Mersey Docks and Harbour Board. To-day exact Greenwich time is broadcast from the Post Office Wireless Station at Rugby, and from other similar sources, so that the rating of chronometers is not now of so much importance, but other practical work of wide range and great value is carried on regularly in the observatory.

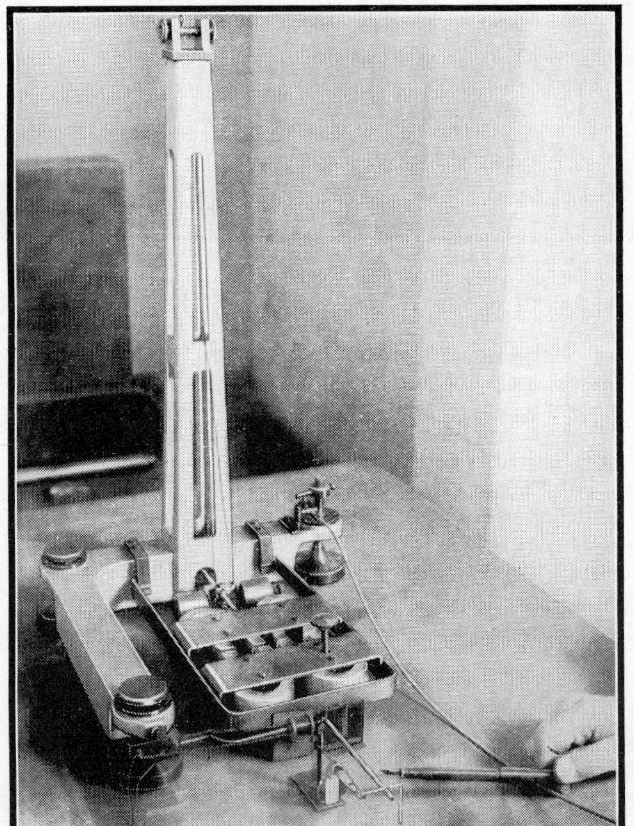

The seismograph at Liverpool Observatory, on which the occurrence of earthquakes is recorded. The instrument is so sensitive that in hot summer weather it can detect the bending of the rock strata on which it rests.

An unusually interesting task that falls to the staff of the Liverpool Observatory is that of controlling the time gun heard daily on Merseyside at one p.m. The gun itself is mounted on the river wall at Morpeth Dock, Birkenhead, and after the discharge the smoke can be seen hovering over the water of the Mersey alongside the dock. It is fired electrically from the Observatory, however, although this building is about three miles away. There a special clock with an average error of only half a second a day is carefully checked and corrected by means of time signals from Greenwich and the Eiffel Tower, and when its second hand reaches the position indicating one o'clock a circuit is automatically completed that instantaneously ignites a fuse in the gun and so fires its charge.

There is little risk of a misfire with this well-known time gun, for the circuit is tested every day at 12 noon, an hour before the time signal is to be given. Shortly before mid-day a dummy fuse is put in the gun and a switch on the side of the clock in the Observatory, three miles away, is closed so that the firing circuit is completed as the second hand reaches the hour. If all is in order an official at the dock signals back to that effect. The switch is then opened out again, the gun is loaded and a live fuse inserted. Immediately before one o'clock the switch is again closed and this time the gun is fired when the second hand indicates the hour.

The gun is loaded with 5 lb. of powder for each signal. After 100 discharges it is carefully examined and wax casts are taken of the bore in order to find if it is necessary to replace the gun.

The Liverpool Observatory also is one of the places from which we receive news of earthquakes, in whatever part of the world these may occur. The waves in the ground created by shocks of this kind travel rapidly through the Earth, and write their own messages on an instrument known as the seismograph, a long word that simply means earthquake writer. This of course must stand on a firm foundation, so that it is shaken as little as possible by accidental disturbances, and for this reason the Bidston instrument is placed in a basement, where it stands on the top of a masonry pillar built on the rocks underlying the hill. It also is carefully protected by means of covers, but these were removed before the photograph of the instrument on this page was taken in order to show the chief working parts.

The central feature of the seismograph, and the one that actually detects earthquakes, is a long light rod, known as the boom, and in the accompanying illustration this is pointed out by the fountain pen seen on the right. A heavy counterpoise is attached to the boom, which can be described as a horizontal pendulum suspended by means of two hinges in a similar manner to that in which an ordinary gate is hung. One of the hinges takes the form of a wire from the top of the rigid pillar of the seismograph to a suitable point along the boom. The other is an agate cup on the side of the pillar, in which a needle point on the end of the boom rests.

A rod suspended in this manner swings to one side when the ground beneath it is tilted, just as a gate automatically closes or opens if its upper hinge is not vertically above the lower one. The boom of the seismograph therefore swings first in one direction and then in the other with a vibratory motion when the rock on which it is supported is disturbed by an earthquake.

A seismograph of course must watch for earth movements day and night, and its records must be automatic and continuous. For this reason it is made to write its own record by attaching a light mirror to the free end of the boom and reflecting a beam of light from this to a sheet of sensitive paper. The beam of light comes from a box containing an electric lamp, the rays of which pass outward through a narrow slit to the mirror, which can be seen on the left of the boom in the illustration on this page. The sensitive paper on which the light reflected from it acts is wrapped round a drum that is housed in a second box, and is rotated slowly by clockwork at the rate of one revolution a day.

While the boom and its mirror remain at rest the photographic record consists of a series of parallel lines, for the drum is moved slowly to one side as it is rotated. Vibration due to an earthquake causes the beam of light to swing backward and forward across its normal path, however, and the distance to which the action of the light beam on the sensitive paper spreads on both sides of the central line shows whether the disturbance is serious or not.

The seismograph not only detects the occurrence of an earthquake, but records the time at which the indications are received and enables the distance of the centre of the movement to be calculated. For these purposes a shutter in front of the slit through which the beam of light leaves the lamp house is connected electrically with a clock in such a manner that it is closed automatically for five seconds in every minute, and for 20 seconds at the end of each hour. During these eclipses no record is made on the sensitive paper and the breaks thus produced provide a time scale for the instrument.

The vibrations due to an earthquake travel along two paths, one group of waves passing directly through the earth and the other following its surface. Since the two groups travel at equal speeds they do not reach the seismograph at the same time, but make separate records on the sensitive paper. The interval between the records is readily measured on the ingenious time scale of the instrument, and from this the distance they have travelled can be calculated. In this way it is possible to suggest where a serious disturbance has taken place before news of its occurrence arrives by ordinary channels.

The tides are the chief concern of Liverpool Observatory and our photograph shows one of the two wonderful Kelvin Tidal Predictors installed in it. Forecasts are made of tide times and heights at the chief ports in Great Britain and throughout the British Empire, with the exception of those in India.

The seismograph on Bidston Hill is so delicate that it can detect the tilting of the ground that follows the rise and fall of the tide in Liverpool Bay and in the Mersey Estuary. An even more delicate performance of which it is capable is the demonstration of the movements of the rock strata of Bidston Hill itself on a hot summer day. The layers of rock then bend as they expand and the instrument can be set to show when this happens.

The tides are the chief concern of the Liverpool Observatory, which is equipped with special instruments for studying them and for preparing the tables that give in advance the times of high and low water at the principal ports of the Empire, with the exception of those in India. One of the instruments registers the state of the tide in the Mersey continuously and thus enables its ebb and flow to be followed accurately. It was invented by Dr. A. T. Doodson, F.R.S., Associate Director of the Observatory, and is known as the Chadburn-Doodson Tide Recorder. Like the time gun mechanism, it is in two parts, the recording end at the Observatory being electrically connected with a mechanism at Morpeth Docks that registers the height of the water in the Mersey.

The Chadburn-Doodson Tide Recorder, which draws curves to show how the tide rises and falls in the Mersey estuary, three miles away. Electrical impulses transmit changes in the level of the water practically instantaneously.

At the dock a shaft has been sunk that has an outlet communicating with the tidal water of the estuary, and in it is a float that rises and falls with the tide. A wire from the float turns a pulley that is geared by means of a small differential and pawl mechanism to two sets of switches, one of which operates when the tide is rising, and the other when it is falling. Signals are thus transmitted along a Post Office telephone line to the recorder at the Observatory at the rate of 20 for each rise or fall of 1 ft. They are received by the instrument shown in the lower illustration on this page, in which they act on a step-by-step mechanism, similar to a ship's telegraph, that moves a pen up and down in accordance with the state of the tide, causing it to draw curves on sheets of squared paper wrapped round a rotating drum. The tidal changes for 14 days are recorded on one chart and the mechanism that controls the pen also rotates the pointer of a dial at the top of the instrument to show the height of the water at any moment.

Predictions of the times and heights of the tides at any port are based on calculations of the relative positions of the Sun, the Moon and the Earth, but other factors, such as the shape of the land around the port and the positions of the land masses in the area, also have to be allowed for. These factors, or "constants," vary from place to place and for each port are found by taking observations of the tides for a complete year. The calculations are very laborious, but fortunately it is unnecessary to carry them out in detail, for a wonderful machine invented by Lord Kelvin does the work easily and rapidly. There are only 12 tidal predictors in the world, and two of these are installed in the Observatory on Bidston Hill. They are valued at £2,000 each, but it is impossible to over-estimate their importance to navigators, who at any time may require to know with precision the state of the tide at a port in Great Britain or in some distant part of the Empire.

The upper illustration on this page shows one of the tidal predictors at Liverpool Observatory. To the ordinary visitor it presents a bewildering array of pulleys and dials, but it makes its complex calculations rapidly and efficiently. The constants for the port for which predictions are required are introduced by making adjustments to the geared dials at the base of the predictor and the rises and falls of the pulleys above are then combined to move a pen that traces a curve showing how the height of the water will vary from hour to hour.

Calculations of this kind can be made for years in advance, and the story of the tides during past centuries also can be read on the machine. An interesting example of this power to peer into the past was given recently when it was desired to confirm an account of the invasion of Jersey, in the Channel Islands, in 1781. It was said that the retreating army of invasion was cut off because its ships were left high and dry by the tide, and on appeal to the tidal predictor it was discovered that the tide in fact was low at the time of the incident. The machine works swiftly and with unerring accuracy both in securing such records of past tides and in making predictions.

How a Great Ship is Launched

A Triumph of Simple Mechanism

By B. S. Davies

MOST ships in the British Isles are launched stern first, and the slipway is constructed where a river or estuary is deep and fairly wide and clear of such obstructions as sandbanks. The slipway is built so that there is a gradual slope down to the edge of the water, and consists of a large clear piece of ground covered in concrete. A line of heavy wooden blocks, called keel-blocks, runs down the centre of the slipway, and on this the keel is laid. The keel forms the backbone of the ship, from which the hull is built up; and as the ship gradually takes form the keel-blocks take the whole weight of the ship. On each side of the line of keel-blocks, and running parallel to them, are the "ground-ways," which take the whole weight of the ship when she is being launched. These ground-ways, as their name implies, are secured rigidly to the ground in the slipway, and the distance between them is about one-third of the beam of the ship under construction. They are made of very strong pieces of timber, and look like huge wooden railway lines.

On top of the ground-ways are fitted the "sliding-ways." They are exactly similar to the ground-ways except that they are not fixed to the slipway, and they form the base of a framework called the "cradle," which is built up round the ship. The cradle takes the weight of the completed hull off the keel-blocks when the ship is ready for launching. In order to prevent the sliding-ways from slipping off the ground-ways a long piece of timber is bolted to the outer edge of each ground-way, so that it stands up and overlaps the edge of the sliding-way, rather like the flange of a train wheel. It also acts as a guide for the sliding-way when the launch takes place. The remainder of the cradle is built up on top of the sliding-ways.

It must be clearly understood that the cradle does not extend right under the ship, but is built up in two distinct parts, one for each side of the ship, that are exactly alike.

So far, then, we have the keel-blocks down the centre of the slipway with the ground-ways on each side, all of which are fixed rigidly to the ground. The sliding-ways rest on top of each ground-way and form the base of the cradle.

The "Empress of Britain" moving down the slipway when she was launched at Clydebank. Note the ground-ways and the keel blocks between them. The illustrations to this article are reproduced by courtesy of John Brown and Co. Ltd.

We will now follow the construction of the cradle in more detail, and in order to simplify this we will consider one side only. On top of the sliding-way, and extending along its whole length, a thick flat piece of timber is laid. This is called a "poppet-board," and it forms the base for large upright baulks of timber that are bolted together and placed at intervals on top of the poppet-board. These baulks are called "poppets," and are used near the bow and the stern of the ship. As they approach the midship portion of the ship they gradually diminish in height, until at the midship portion they are replaced by a large piece of timber cut to fit the swell of the ship's side. This is called the "stopping-up." The function of these various components will become evident later on.

Just above the tops of the poppets a steel plate is riveted to the ship's side so that it projects and the tops of the poppets fit neatly underneath it. Brackets on the upper side of this plate, which is called the "housing-plate," keep it rigid. The stopping-up is kept in position by means of another plate riveted to the ship and called the "housing-angle." Outside the poppets a long narrow plate of steel is secured to hold them rigidly in position and to prevent them from falling over. All this is duplicated on the other side of the ship.

The cradle, as these assembled components are called, is now a fairly slack fit, but it is all ready to take the weight of the ship. The means by which the weight is transferred from the keel-blocks to the ground-ways and the sliding-ways is very simple. All the builders have to do is to drive in a series of long tapered wedges between the poppet-board and the sliding-way. As the wedges are driven in, the poppet-board is forced up. It lifts in turn the poppets and the stopping-up, and these, bearing up under the housing-plate and housing-angle respectively, lift the ship. Thus the ship is lifted off the keel-blocks and rests in the cradle. It must be borne in mind that at this stage the ship is a mere shell having no machinery inside, so that comparatively speaking the weight to be lifted through this small distance is quite light.

Several days before the ship is to be launched the cradle is taken to pieces and the top surface of the ground-ways and the bottom surface of the sliding-ways are covered with a thick coating of special grease. The cradle is then re-assembled, but the wedges are not driven home. Large baulks of timber, called shores, are placed in various positions round the ship and the cradle to prevent the latter from sliding down the ground-ways now that their surfaces are greasy and slippery; and two specially constructed shores, 8 ft. or 9 ft. long, called "dog-shores," are put in certain positions to fulfil two very important functions. These are to lock the sliding-ways to the ground-ways when the ship rests in the cradle, and so prevent a premature launch when the other shores have been removed; and conversely, to unlock the sliding-ways from the ground-ways by some simple method when the time for the launch arrives.

Part of the cradle used at the launch of the "Empress of Britain," showing the poppets and housing-plate.

The method of fitting them is simple. Near the ends of the sliding-ways farthest from the water, and on their sides, are bolted large pieces of timber called "cleats." Similar pieces are fastened to the ground-ways, leaving a lateral space between them, and the two dog-shores are wedged in these spaces, one on each side of the cradle. Therefore any weight on the sliding-ways that tends to move towards the water causes the cleats thereon to push against the higher ends of the dog-shores which in turn push against the cleats on the ground-ways. The latter, being rigidly fixed to the ground, resist the pressure and keep everything in position. All that is required, therefore, is some simple arrangement whereby the upper ends of the two dog-shores are knocked down simultaneously in order to free the sliding-ways from the ground-ways. It is done by suspending two heavy weights, one on each side, over the upper ends of the dog-shores. The weights are supported by a piece of rope, one end of which is fastened to one of the weights, led through a pulley fixed to the housing-plate, and thence along the ship's side to the bow. From the bow it is led across the ornamental "launching block" and back along the opposite bow to the weight suspended above the dog-shore on the other side.

The stopping-up. This ship has four propellers, and the stopping-up has been carried well aft under the shaft housing tube of the inner port propeller shaft. The observer is standing at the stern and is looking towards the bow, port side.

The launching platform, from which the launching ceremony is carried out, is built round the bow of the ship, and the ornamental launching block is placed on this.

On the day of the launch the wedges are driven home between the poppet-boards and the sliding-ways so that the ship is lifted from the keel blocks and its weight taken by the cradle. Next all the shores are removed, except the dog-shores, which remain firmly wedged between the cleats on the sliding-ways and ground-ways. They are now the only means of preventing the ship in the cradle from sliding down to the sea.

A sharp knife is placed on the rope supporting the weights suspended above the dog-shores, where it lies on the launching block. The blade is given a sharp tap with a special hammer, thus severing the rope. The released weights drop on the dog-shores, knocking them from between the cleats on the sliding and ground-ways, and thereby unlocking them. The sliding-ways with the cradle and the ship glide down to the water over the ground-ways, gathering speed until, in a smother of foam, the ship takes the water. In order to check the way of the ship after her initial plunge, huge piles of chain cable are dumped alongside her on the slipway before launching, and the ends of the cables secured on board. Then as the ship moves down the slipway she drags the cables after her and the weight is sufficient to reduce her speed. As the vessel floats, the cradle falls away from her, and she is taken in charge by tugs.

Locomotive Development on French Railways

Some Results of Scientific Rebuilding

By a Railway Engineer

DURING the past few years some striking developments in locomotive design have taken place on the French railways. Continued use of the compound system of propulsion, and intensive research into almost every detail of the machine, have produced engines that can safely be described as the most efficient in the world. It is remarkable, too, that none of these is new; scientific rebuilding of comparatively old engines, whose usefulness was on the wane, has been carried out with conspicuous success, so much so that many recent feats of haulage that stand to their credit would have been thought utterly impossible, with steam, a few years ago.

Pride of place in this enterprising programme of rebuilding must undoubtedly be given to the Paris-Orleans Railway, and it is largely the results of this company's conversions that have inspired equally notable changes on the Est and the Etat Railways. The first rebuild on the Orleans line consisted of a very extensive alteration to one of that company's standard 6 ft. 3 in. 4-cylinder compound "Pacifics"; this has now been followed by a still more remarkable conversion of one of the similar engines with 6 ft. wheels into a 4–8–0. New cylinders have been fitted with poppet valves; great care has been taken to provide very large and direct passages for the steam; the boiler has been fitted with a greatly enlarged superheater, and a "Kylchap" blast pipe with a double chimney has been included.

A Nord 4-6-2 locomotive No. 3-1172. This is one of the remarkably successful rebuilt locomotives acquired from the Paris-Orleans Railway. Characteristic features include the double chimney and very large outside steam pipes.

One of these engines was recently put through a test of the most vigorous kind on the "Nord" railway between Calais and Paris, and achieved a performance that has never been equalled with steam. Normally speed is limited by law to 120 kilometres per hour, that is 74½ m.p.h.; but this strict rule was relaxed on the occasion of the test run, and with the exceedingly heavy load of 635 tons behind the tender, the engine ran the 102.9 miles from Calais to Amiens in the astonishing time of 85½ minutes! For some distance speed was sustained at 84 m.p.h. on the dead level. Restarting, the 80.8 miles from Amiens to La Chapelle depot, Paris, were run in 70½ minutes. On this last section the engine sustained 70 m.p.h. up the 1 in 200 bank to Survilliers, and fitly concluded an astounding performance with a maximum of 91 m.p.h. on the descent into Paris, where the gradient is 1 in 200.

During a recent visit to the French capital I was privileged to inspect a number of very interesting locomotives, including one of these remarkable Paris-Orleans rebuilds. The main line of the latter company is electrified as far as Orleans, but since electrification has taken place several of the steam locomotives have been transferred to the Nord, and although there is no steam locomotive depot of the Orleans line in Paris, I was able to inspect and photograph several of the company's former engines at the La Chapelle depot of the Nord.

In making a tour of the Parisian running sheds, let us first of all repair to Bercy, on the Paris, Lyons and Mediterranean Railway. The express services of this company are largely worked by "Pacifics," but about 10 years ago, in order to cope with increasing train loads, a colossal 4–8–2 "Mountain" type was introduced. One of these engines was standing in the yard, and it took a considerable time to appreciate fully its vast proportions. They are, of course, 4-cylinder compounds, but they differ in certain important respects from the usual French practice. The high-pressure cylinders, which are 20 in. diameter by 25½ in. stroke, are placed inside the frames, while the low-pressure, which have the enormous diameter of 28⅜ in., are outside. The outside cylinders drive the leading pair of coupled wheels and the inside drive the second pair. The front of the smokebox is cone-shaped, in a rather similar way to the partly streamlined engines put into service last year on the English G.W.R., but otherwise there is no attempt at streamlining. However, these engines have considerably fewer "gadgets" mounted externally than most French locomotives. One point that struck me forcibly was the very restricted space in the cab. Although from outside it appears to be fairly roomy, the fire-box actually projects some distance in, and there is no greater space than on an L.N.E.R. (G.N. section) "Atlantic." The fire-door is placed much higher than on English locomotives; this I found to be a feature common to most French engines, and would appear to make the fireman's task more strenuous.

One of the large 2-8-2 suburban tank locomotives of the Est system. The smoke deflectors, the chimney cover and the generally "lofty" appearance make these engines very different from British tanks.

Only two other types are stationed at Bercy, a mixed traffic 2–8–0 design, and a powerful 4–8–4 suburban tank. In France, by the way, wheel arrangements are classified by the number of axles instead of the number of wheels, so that a "Pacific" is a 2–3–1, an "Atlantic," a 2–2–1; French forms of the same class names are used, for example "Pacifique," "Atlantique" and "Montagne."

Next comes the Est, the Paris running sheds of which are situated at La Villette. Here again the premier engines of the company are of the "Mountain" type. The design differs in many respects from that of the P.L.M.; the high-pressure cylinders are outside and drive the second pair of coupled wheels, whereas the low pressure are inside and drive the leading pair. The high boiler pressure of 290 lb. per sq. in. is used, while several familiar English fittings are employed such as the Worthington feed water heater and a Davies and Metcalfe exhaust steam injector. The weight of the engine alone, in working order, is 117 tons.

An Etat locomotive No. 231-777 at Batignoles. This engine is fitted with a special clear-vision cab outlook device which is prominent in front of the cab.

Another outstanding Est type is a 4-cylinder compound 4–6–0. As originally built these were admirable engines in every way, but with increasing loads they had to be superseded on the heaviest duties. Inspired no doubt by the results obtained on the Paris-Orleans, several of these engines have recently been rebuilt extensively. The original low-pressure cylinders have been retained, but new high-pressure cylinders with piston valves having double admission and exhaust passages have been fitted. Various other changes have been made, such as the inclusion of a Worthington feed water heater and modified blast pipe, the net result of which has been simply to revolutionise the performance of the engine. One of them sustained a speed of 70 m.p.h. on the level with 600 tons behind the tender.

All these French compounds are arranged so that the cut-off in the high- and low-pressure cylinders can be adjusted independently. In this way they differ from the English Midland Compounds in which one reversing gear is used for both. The French arrangement calls for very skilful handling on the part of the driver, for unless the ratio of volumes between the high- and low-pressure cylinders is kept correct the engine is liable to become choked. As in the case of the P.L.M. engines, the cabs are not only cramped, but very exposed to the weather as compared with modern British practice. Scant attention seems to be given to the enginemens' comfort, while the fuel employed makes the conditions on the footplate still more unpleasant. Powdered coal in the form of briquettes is used; this is easy to handle as the lumps are of a uniform size, but it is extremely dusty, and a great number of French enginemen wear goggles to protect their eyes.

Several very fine 2–8–2 suburban tank engines were in the yard at La Villette. These are 3-cylinder simples of great power. The cylinders are 20 in. diameter by 26 in. stroke, and these, combined with small driving wheels only 4 ft. 8 in. diameter and a boiler pressure of 203 lb. per sq. in., produce the very high tractive effort of 48,070 lb. at 85 per cent. of the boiler pressure. The local trains out of Paris are, however, exceedingly heavy, loading up to 600 tons, and with these trains the 2–8–2 tanks often attain speeds of 60 m.p.h. From the illustration on page 136 it will be seen that they carry smoke deflecting plates at the front end and the characteristic hinged cover to the chimney.

From the east, we now move over to the west of the city to visit the Batignoles sheds of the Etat system. This company recently added a large number of "Mountain" type express engines to its stock, of identical design to those of the Est; but perhaps the most striking Etat development has been a very successful rebuilding of some of the standard "Pacifics." The general plan has been much the same as that carried out by the Paris-Orleans. In this case the original high-pressure cylinders with their piston valves have been retained, but the engines have been fitted with new low-pressure cylinders having poppet valves. The rebuilds have been found capable of hauling loads of 100 to 150 tons more than previously, without any increase in coal consumption.

One of these engines, No. 231–777, was especially interesting in being fitted with a clear-vision cab outlook, a most ingenious device that does away with the necessity of having glass screens. A series of curved plates are arranged in such a way that the airstream caused by the motion of the train is deflected across the driver's outlook so that no air, rain, or snow enters the cab. Trouble has always been experienced on locomotives with the glasses becoming obscured, but this form of aero-dynamic screening completely solves the problem, for the driver looks out through a perfectly clear opening. The upward current of air created also counteracts any tendency for the exhaust steam to beat down, although most modern French engines have deflecting screens alongside the smokebox. Although, to quote the shed foreman at Batignoles, "*Ce n'est pas beau!*", the device has proved a great boon, and it will be interesting to see whether it is tried in this country.

A giant P.L.M. "Mountain" locomotive. The conical smoke-box door is a notable feature, and recalls the use of these fittings on the P.L.M. locomotives of many years ago.

The Etat, like the Est, has a very heavy suburban traffic, and, in order to increase the accommodation in the trains, has put into service a large number of double-decker coaches. Practically all these trains are operated on the "push and pull" principle, whereby the engine is permanently coupled to one end of the train and in one direction of running is at the rear. This principle has been widely adopted in this country for light branch trains of two or three coaches, propelled by a 2–4–2 tank engine for example, but it is a thrilling sight indeed to see a Paris suburban train of 500 tons tearing along at 55 m.p.h. with a huge 2–8–2 tank engine bringing up the rear!

The Etat system serves Normandy and Brittany, and some very

fine locomotive work is put up on the boat expresses to Cherbourg, Havre and Dieppe. The Etat engines, like those of the Est, are painted black, relieved by a simple white lining. All the French railways use a rather sombre colour-scheme; the P.L.M. engines are painted olive-green of a rather more yellowish tinge than the English Southern Railway; the Paris-Orleans uses a slate grey, while the Nord locomotives are almost exactly the same colour as the London Brighton and South Coast in pre-grouping days, a deep sepia brown.

Last of all we come to the Nord, perhaps the most familiar of all foreign railways to English people. Appropriately enough, La Chapelle sheds were the most fascinating of all, for here were to be found engines of all ages, ranging from veteran De Glehn compound "Atlantics," to one of the very latest Paris-Orleans rebuilt "Pacifics," which had been recently acquired by the Nord.

An Est version of the "Mountain" type of locomotive. The chimney seems to be conspicuous by its absence owing to the smoke deflectors and other apparatus in the neighbourhood of the smoke-box.

Just as the foundations of modern British locomotive practice were laid when the Great Western 4-cylinder 4–6–0s of the "Star" class came out in 1907, so equally modern French practice has gradually developed from the amazingly successful 4-cylinder compound "Atlantics" of the Nord, built as long ago as 1900. Slender and graceful, the Nord "Atlantics" are surely the most handsome French locomotives ever built.

Altogether contrasting was a tremendous Paris-Orleans rebuilt "Pacific." The huge outside steam pipes and ingenious valve gear, combined with the numerous other appliances that have been added to increase efficiency, make these engines an awe-inspiring sight. On the Nord they are known by the class name of "*P.O. Transformation*"; certainly "transformation" most aptly describes the improvement in the performance of the engines that has been effected, though actually "*transformation*" is merely the technical French word for "rebuild."

The success of these Paris-Orleans experiments has already influenced locomotive practice far beyond the confines of France. The most notable examples that occur to mind are the L.N.E.R. "Mikados"; in the design of "*Cock o' the North*" and "*Earl Marischal.*" Mr. Gresley freely acknowledges his inspiration as having come from the Paris-Orleans, and French locomotive engineers in their turn have taken the keenest interest in the exploits of the L.N.E.R. engines, quite apart from the visit of No. 2001 to France.

One of the famous Nord "Atlantic" De Glehn compounds. The brilliant performance of these engines early this century aroused considerable interest, and a locomotive of similar type was built for the G.W.R.

Although the magnificent P.O. rebuilt engines have become the premier locomotives of the Nord, the "Super-Pacifics" of the latter company are capable of superb work and are easily the finest *new* French locomotives that have been put on the road in recent years. They represent the highest development of the De Glehn compounds and embody 30 years of hard experience and intensive research. The boiler pressure is 246 lb. per sq. in., and the total weight of the engine in working order is 99 tons. Externally they are of striking appearance. The chimney is wedge-shaped at the front, to assist in throwing the smoke clear; the fire-box is long and narrow, and once again the space on the footplate is rather cramped. One of the most noticeable points is their extraordinary silence when starting away, even when hauling loads of over 500 tons.

In returning to England I was treated to a really splendid example of French locomotive performance, on the 10.30 a.m. Boat express from Paris (Nord) to Boulogne. The load was a heavy one of 520 tons behind the tender, and included a through sleeping car from the Riviera. The engine was a Nord "Super-Pacific," No. 3-1284. The schedule is a fast one, for the 140.6 miles from Paris to Etaples have to be run in 142 minutes; but although for the last 60 miles of this section we encountered a very strong west wind off the sea, we reached Etaples exactly five minutes early.

The start from Paris is on falling grades, and getting away smartly we were through St. Denis, 3.8 miles, in 6 minutes, at 61 m.p.h. From here there is a continuous ascent of 14 miles, at 1 in 200, to Survilliers. The climb is made slightly easier by short level strips, but even so involves some hard work. On the bank speed fell off steadily at first, but on passing Villiers the exhaust sharpened into a roar, and in less than 3 miles, climbing at 1 in 200, we had accelerated to 62 m.p.h.! On the last three miles there was a very slight falling off, but even so we breasted the summit at 59 m.p.h.—a magnificent piece of work with 520 tons.

On the ensuing descent speed rose rapidly to the legal maximum of 74½ m.p.h. The driver then maintained this rate unvaryingly for mile after mile. All French express locomotives are fitted with speedometers, and this enables the engines to be run exactly at the speed limit, without the slightest excess. So, we were through Creil, 31.2 miles, in 31½ minutes, speed being carefully reduced to 53 m.p.h. for the junction.

Another long climb follows, though at rather easier grades, beginning at 1 in 415 and finishing with some lengthy stretches at 1 in 250. This 23 miles from Creil up to Gannes was covered at an average speed of 59 m.p.h., and the summit point, 54.2 miles from Paris, passed in 55¼ minutes. A long spell at 72 to 74 m.p.h. followed, on easy down grades, and Longeau, 78.2 miles, was passed in 75½ minutes. Then came the severe service slack to 20 m.p.h. through Amiens, this important centre being passed in 79 minutes for the 81.1 miles from Paris.

From here the line is almost dead level right on to Etaples, and maintaining a general average of 65 to 67 m.p.h. we passed Abbeville, 108.9 miles, in 106½ minutes, and reached Etaples in 137 minutes. In the short run thence to Boulogne some hard running is needed. As far as Dannes-Camiers, 4.6 miles out, the line rises at 1 in 350, and here we attained 53 m.p.h. Then 2½ miles at 1 in 133 follow up to Neufchatel, and this bank was mounted at the splendid minimum speed of 44½ m.p.h. We swept down the corresponding fall to Hesdigneul, touching 73½ m.p.h., and despite a bad signal check reached Boulogne (Ville), 16.9 miles, in 21¾ minutes—a very smart piece of work with a 520-ton train.

On restarting from the town station we crawled down a main thoroughfare, with the engine's high-pitched squeak of a whistle repeatedly sounding, and so into the Maritime station, where the Southern Railway steamer "*Biarritz*" was waiting to take us across to Folkestone. This splendid example of French locomotive performance made a very impressive finish to a visit of exceptional interest.

The L.M.S.R. "Jubilee" Class Locomotives

Names of Empire and Naval Interest

IT has been decided by the L.M.S.R. to provide names for all the locomotives of the three-cylinder 4–6–0 "Jubilee" class. This step no doubt will be very popular with railway enthusiasts, especially those whose favourite railway is the L.M.S.R. Two of the engines had already been named before the decision to deal with the class as a whole was made public. These were No. 5552, "*Silver Jubilee,*" the first one built, which was so named in connection with the Royal Silver Jubilee celebrations of last year; and No. 5665, "*Lord Rutherford of Nelson,*" specially named on the occasion of the recent opening of the new L.M.S.R. research laboratories at Derby by Lord Rutherford.

The engines yet to be constructed will be put into service complete with nameplates, but the names are being added as convenient to those of the class already running. This accounts for some of the engines being observed with names and others without, a feature that has puzzled some of our readers. The list on this page gives the names selected for the whole series of 179 engines, either built, under construction or proposed.

In their design as three-cylinder 4–6–0 locomotives the "Jubilee" class follow the very successful "Baby Scot" series Nos. 5500 to 5551. The parallel boiler of the latter engines however is replaced by the tapered form favoured by Mr. Stanier, the Chief Mechanical Engineer of the L.M.S.R. This carries a higher pressure—225 lb. per sq. in.—against the 200 lb. of the "Baby Scots." As the three cylinders are reduced in diameter to 17 in., from the 18 in. bore of the "Baby Scots," the difference in the respective tractive efforts is only slight. The figure for the "Jubilee" class is 26,610 lb., and for the "Baby Scots" 26,520 lb., at 85 per cent. of the working pressure in each case.

Names of L.M.S.R. "Jubilee" class Locomotives

No.	Name	No.	Name	No.	Name
5552	Silver Jubilee	5612	Jamaica	5672	Anson
3	Canada	3	Kenya	3	Keppel
4	Ontario	4	Leeward Islands	4	Duncan
5	Quebec	5	Malay States	5	Hardy
6	Nova Scotia	6	Malta	6	Codrington
7	New Brunswick	7	Mauritius	7	Beatty
8	Manitoba	8	New Hebrides	8	De Robeck
9	British Columbia	9	Nigeria	9	Armada
5560	Prince Edward Island	5620	North Borneo	5680	Camperdown
1	Saskatchewan	1	North Rhodesia	1	Aboukir
2	Alberta	2	Nyasaland	2	Trafalgar
3	Australia	3	Palestine	3	Hogue
4	New South Wales	4	St. Helena	4	Jutland
5	Victoria	5	Sarawak	5	Barfleur
6	Queensland	6	Seychelles	6	St. Vincent
7	South Australia	7	Sierra Leone	7	Neptune
8	Western Australia	8	Somaliland	8	Polyphemus
9	Tasmania	9	Straits Settlements	9	Ajax
5570	New Zealand	5630	Swaziland	5690	Leander
1	South Africa	1	Tanganyika	1	Orion
2	Irish Free State	2	Tonga	2	Cyclops
3	Newfoundland	3	Trans-Jordan	3	Agamemnon
4	India	4	Trinidad	4	Bellerophon
5	Madras	5	Tobago	5	Minotaur
6	Bombay	6	Uganda	6	Arethusa
7	Bengal	7	Windward Islands	7	Achilles
8	United Provinces	8	Zanzibar	8	Mars
9	Punjab	9	Raleigh	9	Galatea
5580	Burma	5640	Frobisher	5700	Britannia
1	Bihar and Orissa	1	Sandwich	1	Conqueror
2	Central Provinces	2	Boscawen	2	Colossus
3	Assam	3	Rodney	3	Thunderer
4	North West Frontier	4	Howe	4	Leviathan
5	Hyderabad	5	Collingwood	5	Seahorse
6	Mysore	6	Napier	6	Express
7	Baroda	7	Sturdee	7	Valiant
8	Kashmir	8	Wemyss	8	Resolution
9	Gwalior	9	Hawkins	9	Implacable
5590	Travancore	5650	Blake	5710	Irresistible
1	Udaipur	1	Shovell	1	Courageous
2	Indore	2	Hawke	2	Victory
3	Kolhapur	3	Barham	3	Renown
4	Bhopal	4	Hood	4	Revenge
5	Southern Rhodesia	5	Keith	5	Invincible
6	Bahamas	6	Cochrane	6	Swiftsure
7	Barbados	7	Tyrwhitt	7	Dauntless
8	Basutoland	8	Keyes	8	Dreadnought
9	Bechuanaland	9	Drake	9	Glorious
5600	Bermuda	5660	Rooke	5720	Indomitable
1	British Guiana	1	Vernon	1	Impregnable
2	British Honduras	2	Kempenfelt	2	Defence
3	Solomon Islands	3	Jervis	3	Fearless
4	Ceylon	4	Nelson	4	Warspite
5	Cyprus	5	Lord Rutherford of Nelson	5	Repulse
6	Falkland Islands	6	Cornwallis	6	Vindictive
7	Fiji	7	Jellicoe	7	Inflexible
8	Gibraltar	8	Madden	8	Defiance
9	Gilbert and Ellice Islands	9	Fisher	9	Furious
5610	Gold Coast	5670	Howard of Effingham	5730	Ocean
1	Hong Kong	1	Prince Rupert		

Externally the tapered boiler makes a considerable difference in appearance and the smoke-box of the "Jubilees" is of the circular type finished flush with the outside boiler sheeting. In the "Baby Scots" the smoke-box is horse-shoe shaped in section, and in accordance with the former Derby practice it is raised above the surface of the boiler. The boiler fittings are different in the new engines and include top-feed apparatus. The cab too is altered to the double-window kind and among minor details a Caledonian type hooter is fitted in place of the Derby whistle.

Differences are noticeable too between the tenders fitted to the respective classes. The "Baby Scots" have the older standard tender developed from Midland practice, holding 5 tons of coal and 3,500 gallons of water. The earlier "Jubilees" had a further development of this type, with higher sides which raise the coal capacity to 7 tons. The later engines have however been provided with the more imposing 9-ton, 4,000-gallon vehicles which are longer and wider and have their very high sides turned inwards at the top. One of these was also attached to No. 5552 "*Silver Jubilee*" at the time of its exhibition at Euston last year. It still retains this vehicle as, in view of the special finish of the engine and tender in black and chromium plate, no other tender would be suitable. It is reported that some of the "Jubilee" class are now to lose their 4,000 gallon tenders as these are to be fitted to the "Royal Scots." The "Jubilees" will receive in exchange the older standard 3,500 gallon tenders discarded by the latter engines.

The "Jubilees" have proved themselves speedy and efficient locomotives. Engines of the class are in use on practically all sections of the L.M.S.R. and undertake all but the heaviest duties.

Constructing World's Largest-Bore Tunnel

In connection with the San Francisco–Oakland Bay Bridge scheme, now being carried out in the United States, a huge tunnel is being constructed, which when completed will be the world's largest bore. The tunnel is being built through Yerba Buena Island, and without its concrete lining will be 76 ft. wide by 58 ft. high, and will accommodate two traffic decks, the upper one with six lanes for fast automobile traffic, and the lower with three lanes for heavy trucks and two tracks for interurban trains.

Some idea of the great size of the tunnel may be had from the fact that a four storey building could be pulled upright through it. When completed the tunnel will be continuously lined and will be 540 ft. in length, and the roof will be supported by 16-in. steel arched ribs embedded in concrete and placed 3 ft. apart.

A novel method of excavating the tunnel is being employed. Three bores were first drilled through the island, one at each lower side and one above and between them to form the crown. These were then blocked out into a horseshoe-shaped excavation, and this is now being concrete- and steel-lined from 3 ft. to 5 ft. thick before the core is dug out. About 250 ft. of the total length has now been lined, and a power shovel, which enters from one of the portals, is being used to remove the thousands of cubic yards of rock within the lining.

Australian Submarine Cable Completed

A new submarine cable has been laid across the Bass Straits between Australia and Tasmania. It connects the land lines of the Australian mainland with those of Tasmania, and completes the network of telephonic communication between all the States of the Commonwealth. The cable is 161 nautical miles in length, and will enable the simultaneous operation of at least five telephone circuits, a broadcast programme, and seven high-speed telegraph channels over a single insulated conductor. A full description of th cable will appear in the *"M.M."* in due course.

Largest Gear Rims Ever Forged in England

The illustration on this page shows a giant gear wheel rim 14 ft. 3 in. in diameter that was made recently at the Vickers Works of the English Steel Corporation. This is the first time in this country that a gear rim of such great size has been forged. The forging operation was carried out under a new 7,000-ton electro-hydraulic press recently installed at the works, which makes possible the forging of even larger rims of this type.

The largest gear wheel rim ever forged in this country, under the 7,000 ton press at the maker's works. Photograph by courtesy of the English Steel Corporation Ltd., Sheffield.

The portion of the ingot required for two rims, after being trepanned with a 24 in. hole, was expanded under the press to slightly over 10 ft. in diameter. It was then re-heated and forged to 14 ft. 3 in. diameter, the forging being subsequently heat treated and machined into two rims. The expert knowledge required for carrying out this operation will be appreciated when it is realised that the machining allowance is about 1 in. on all surfaces, and that as measurements have to be taken while the forging is hot, allowance has to be made for the contraction that takes place as the forging cools. In this case the forging was $1\frac{3}{4}$ in. larger on the internal diameter when finish forged than it was after cooling.

The gear wheel rims have been made for a single reduction geared turbine that is under construction for the Ellerman Line at the Birkenhead yard of Cammell Laird and Co. Ltd.

Shipbuilding News

The owners of the French liner *"Normandie,"* the Compagnie Générale Transatlantique, have recently put into commission on their Marseilles-Algiers service, the *"Ville D'Alger."* This vessel, which is of the twin screw type, is propelled by geared turbines of 20,000 h.p. and has an overall length of 484 ft. and a gross tonnage of 9,764. The vessel, which is larger than any previous ship operated in trans-Mediterranean service is equipped for carrying mails, passengers and cargo, and having a speed of 22/23 knots will be able to make the crossing in 20 hours. Among her outstanding features are elaborate fire prevention equipment and luxurious passenger accommodation.

A new motor-driven tanker, which will be capable of carrying 27 grades of oil at one time, is being built for the Anglo-American Oil Co. Ltd. The ship will have a deadweight tonnage of 10,200, and the tanks will hold about 2,500,000 gallons of oil.

A new icebreaking and buoyage vessel is to be built for the Swedish Government, and a novelty in its equipment will be a magnetic coupling between the engine and propeller shaft. The purpose of the coupling is to eliminate mechanical connection between the engine and propeller and so reduce the risk of damage in ice. By means of special control apparatus it will be possible to obtain any desired degree of slip in the coupling from zero up to full speed of the engine.

Harland and Wolff Ltd., Belfast, recently launched the *"Dunnottar Castle,"* a 15,000 ton passenger and cargo motorship for the Union-Castle Mail Steamship Co. Ltd. The vessel is 560 ft. in length, and will be used for service between Great Britain and South and East Africa.

Novel Automatic Rammer

The device shown in the lower illustration on this page is known as the "*Kangarammer*," and is used to great extent in road-making and light pile driving. It is made by C. H. Johnson and Sons Ltd., of Manchester, and, as its name implies, is a rammer. It is entirely self-contained and is fitted with a special type of internal combustion engine. The firing of the charge in the engine cylinder causes a piston to be forced downward against the pressure of a return spring, and the whole device is thereby made to "jump" upward about 18 in. Ramming is effected by the drop from this height and by the weight of the tool, which, depending on the size in use, is between 140 lb. and 230 lb. Pure benzole is carried in a tank at the base of the tool, and a simple but efficient carburetter is provided by wire metal sponges and steel spiral wire contained in the tank. The charge is fired by a sparking plug controlled by a press button, and each time this button is operated an explosion occurs, and the tool is "jumped." About 60 blows can be delivered per minute, and a 230 lb. machine can be operated for about eight hours with half a gallon of benzole. By adaptation of the base the machine can be made suitable for concrete breaking and similar purposes.

The Zuyder Zee to Become Dry Land

The Dutch Government have in hand a big scheme of reclamation which when completed will make the famous Zuyder Zee, the great semi-inland lake, dry land. The work of reclamation was started in 1920 and the first part of the scheme consisted in draining the north-western area and turning it into fertile land. This work was completed in 1931, and the Government have now decided to start on the north-eastern area, which covers about 117,500 acres. This work will take five years and will cost about £17,000,000, and when it is completed there will be land available for nearly 500,000 people. The entire reclaimed Zuyder Zee will provide sufficient land for 2,500,000 people, and when the work is finished the two islands of Urk and Schokland will become part of the mainland.

A New British Light Cruiser

Among the new naval vessels recently launched is the light cruiser H.M.S. "*Penelope*," which was built by Harland and Wolff Ltd., at Belfast. The vessel is 480 ft. in length and has a displacement of 5,200 tons, and will be propelled by 64,000 s.h.p. turbines, which will give her a speed of $32\frac{1}{4}$ knots. She will be equipped with six 6 in. guns, four 4 in. anti-aircraft guns, two three pounder guns, and a catapult for launching seaplanes.

Fine Plant for Steel Rolling Mill

The upper illustration on this page shows part of a large rolling mill plant erected on the electrical machine test bed at the Trafford Park Works of Metropolitan-Vickers Electrical Co. Ltd., Manchester. The plant has been made for the Briton Ferry Steel Company, and consists of two 2,900/9,000 h.p., 60/150 r.p.m. reversing motors, and a flywheel set comprising two 4,200 h.p. geared high pressure turbines, a $28\frac{1}{2}$ ton flywheel, two 2,400 k W., d.c. generators and two 1,000 k W., d.c. generators. It will drive large bar mills.

A four machine flywheel Generator Set that forms part of a rolling mill equipment for the Briton Ferry Steel Company. The plant is shown on the test bed at the Trafford Park Works, Manchester, of Metropolitan-Vickers Ltd., to whom we are indebted for the photograph.

A "Kangarammer" in action. A description of this ingenious device is given on this page. Photograph by courtesy of C. H. Johnson and Sons Ltd., Manchester.

A Fire-Testing Station

An interesting fire-testing station is now in service at Boreham Wood, Elstree. It consists of two separate buildings constructed of re-inforced concrete filled in with panels of "foamed-slag," a new form of concrete. One of the buildings is the fire-testing building proper, while the other is used for fire-fighting appliances and offices. In the fire-testing building there are three gas-fired furnaces for testing floors, walls, and columns. In the case of the floor furnace, the specimen to be tested is laid on top of a raised pit, and submitted to a load on top and heat underneath. Wall specimens are placed under a ram capable of exerting a pressure up to 500 tons, and a movable testing furnace is then wheeled against them, heat and pressure to the required degree thus being obtained. For testing columns two semi-circular banks of burners are used and water is applied to the specimens while still under load by means of hoses. A raised control room, from which the entire floor area is visible, contains the whole of the governing and recording mechanism for the building.

British Cars in Demand

As an indication of the growing popularity of British cars abroad, it is interesting to learn that during the month of December, 1935, M.G. Cars were shipped to no less than 11 different countries, including Java, Czecho-Slovakia, Germany and the United States of America.

Roads of Salt

Several experimental highways in the surfacing of which common rock salt was used have been constructed in the United States. The roadways are made of clay and gravel treated with a compound made of ordinary rock salt, and they survived the recent devastating floods in that area without appreciable effect. About 100 miles of these salt highways have been laid down in various parts of the country, and after several months' use carrying heavy traffic they have proved entirely satisfactory. The rock salt not only compacts the clay but also crystallises in the road surface and retards evaporation of moisture, thereby keeping the surface moist and firm and providing practically a non-skid road.

Record Lifting Magnet

A remarkable electro-magnet that is believed to be the largest lifting magnet ever constructed in this country was recently made at the works of the Igranic Electric Company. It measures 65 in. in diameter, weighs 4 tons 5 cwt., and is capable of lifting over six times its own weight.

An Improved "Eagle"

The B.A. "Eagle" illustrated on this and the opposite pages is an improved version of the British Klemm "Eagle" described in the "*M.M.*" of January 1935. It is a low wing cantilever monoplane with wings of 39 ft. 3 in. span, which taper in chord and thickness and are arranged so that they can be folded back, in which condition the overall width is only 14 ft. 10 in., or less than half their span when spread.

The retractable undercarriage of the "Eagle" is not arranged to be lifted up vertically as are most English undercarriages of this type, but, by turning a handle in the cockpit, is lifted up sideways until each wheel and leg is completely encased in a special receptacle provided in the wing. It can be raised in 10 seconds, and lowered even more speedily. The winding mechanism is inter-connected with the throttle control, and this ensures that the pilot cannot fully throttle back to land unless he has previously wound down the undercarriage.

The cabin is roomy and comfortable, with the pilot's seat placed centrally in the front part and a double seat for two passengers behind it. In the improved "Eagle" the doors are much higher than previously and meet over the centre of the cabin. When both are open there is therefore unrestricted access and exit on each side of the cabin, as shown in the illustration on this page.

A D.H. "Gipsy Major" engine is fitted, and gives a cruising speed of 130 m.p.h. The take-off run, with a full load, is 195 yd., and the rate of climb is 700 ft. per min.

The B.A. "Eagle" low wing monoplane. The doors meet over the centre of the cabin, and when both are open, as shown, there is unrestricted access and exit on each side of the cabin. This aeroplane is an improved version of the British Klemm "Eagle." This illustration and the upper one on the opposite page are reproduced by courtesy of "The Aeroplane."

New Japanese Air Service

The Japanese Air Transport Company have increased their air service between Hekuoka and Daihoku, Formosa, and three trips are now made each week. Until this increase only mails were carried, but the service is now available to passengers, who are conveyed in a Douglas D.C.2.

Record American Flight

A new record has been set up for the trans-continental flight from Los Angeles to Newark, New Jersey, by Howard Hughes, the well-known American airman. He flew a Northrop monoplane, and covered the 2,450 miles in 9 hr. 27 min. 10 sec., at an average speed of 260 m.p.h. The previous time was 11 hr. 34 min., and was accomplished in February 1935 by Leland S. Andrews and a crew of two, who flew in a Vultee V–IA monoplane from Burbank, California, to the Floyd Bennett Field, New York.

Hughes is also the holder of the world's speed record for landplanes, as in September last, using a Hughes special monoplane fitted with a Whitney "Wasp Junior" engine, he attained a speed of 352 m.p.h. This beat the previous record, set up a year previously by another American, James Wedell, in a Wedell-Williams monoplane, by 47.2 m.p.h.

A Chance for Inventors

One of the things an air pilot often would be glad to know, especially during the closing stages of flights over long distances or in bad weather, is the exact amount of fuel in the tank or tanks of his aeroplane. The problem of devising a means of indicating this information at all times, irrespective of whether the aeroplane is in flight or on the ground, probably has already been considered by inventors interested in aeronautical matters. If so, they will be spurred to greater endeavour by the German Air Ministry's recent offer of £10,000 for any invention that will solve the problem.

More 1935 Air Traffic Figures

Air traffic figures for 1935 continue to be published, and without exception show steady increases in both passenger and freight traffic.

K.L.M. report that last year they carried 100,196 passengers, an increase of 14,227 over the 1934 total; and that nearly 96,000 of the people were carried on the European services. The quantity of freight conveyed by air last year was nearly 315 tons greater than in 1934, and the total amount of mail similarly transported increased by 65 per cent. on their European services.

The aircraft of Highland Airways Ltd., last year carried 97,937 lb. of mail, which was 450 lb. more than in 1934; and 3,815 passengers were carried, as compared with 3,007 during the previous year. The Kirkwall - Aberdeen service is to be extended to the Shetland Islands this spring, the actual date depending upon the completion of wireless stations at Kirkwall and Shetland. The company's three D.H. "Dragons" have been fitted with wireless equipment in readiness for work on the extended route. The Kirkwall-Aberdeen service was operated last year from May until the end of October.

Beacon for Blackpool Tower

A well-known landmark on the Fylde coast, Lancashire, is the Blackpool Tower, 550 ft. in height. It contains a passenger lift by which visitors can ascend to a gallery almost at the top, from which a remarkable view is obtained on clear days. The Tower is soon to serve an additional and more serious purpose, as it is to be surmounted with a beacon that will be used to guide aircraft flying in fog.

Named U.A. Machines

The three D.H.86 aeroplanes of Union Airways Ltd., New Zealand, have been named "*Karoro*," "*Kotuku*" and "*Korimaka*" respectively. They are being used on the new daily service between Palmerston North and Dunedin.

D.H. Aircraft Progress

Some interesting facts showing the great popularity of de Havilland aircraft were revealed at the recent annual general meeting of the de Havilland Aircraft Co. Ltd. It was mentioned that the D.H.86 Express air liner is in use on the services of nine important air transport concerns, and that 16 more aeroplanes of this type are on order. The D.H.86 is a four-engined biplane, and a fleet of this type of aeroplane was supplied to Quantas-Empire Airways Ltd. in 1934 for the Singapore-Brisbane section of the England-Australia Empire air service. The D.H. "Dragon Rapide" is even more popular, and is being used by 28 commercial air companies. Many machines of both types have been sold to private owners.

The latest de Havilland civil aeroplane to be put into production is the "Dragon Fly," a twin-engined five-seater biplane with wings of unequal span. The upper wings are attached directly to the top of the fuselage and are provided with ailerons, and the lower wings are built out from the bottom of the fuselage and have split flaps along their trailing edge between the engine nacelles. The arrangement of the seating in the cabin is rather unusual. There are two seats side-by-side, a single seat immediately behind them, and to the rear of this a seat giving room for two people extends across the back of the cabin.

Work now in hand also includes the designing of a high-speed four-engined passenger monoplane that will be more than twice the size of the D.H.86. The construction of the first machine of this new type will begin immediately plans are ready, and it may be completed in time for trial flights next autumn.

This rear view of the B.A. "Eagle" shows the neat lines of the fuselage and the gracefully tapered wings.

New D.L.H. Depot Ship

Further details are now available about the new depot ship being built for the D.L.H. by the Hamaldt shipyard at Kiel. The ship will have a displacement of about 2,000 tons, and the propelling machinery will consist of two M.A.N. 1,000 h.p. Diesel engines. The special deck fittings will include a crane for hoisting flying boats on board and a catapult for shooting them off.

R.A.F. Firing Range at Chesil Bank

The announcement last year of the Air Ministry's intention to establish bombing and air-gunnery ranges at Chesil Bank brought forth many protests from the local fishermen, and also from ornithologists who declared that the swans near there would be seriously disturbed and even endangered by the bombing practices.

The Air Ministry have now decided that the bombing targets shall be placed a quarter of a mile farther seaward than had been planned, and that during the winter months the firing range shall be established farther west than at first proposed. It is anticipated that these measures will avoid any disturbance or danger to the swans. The fishermen also have been considered, and when they wish to pass to and from their fishing grounds while R.A.F. practices are going on, a request to the officer in charge will be sufficient to suspend operations until they are out of range.

An artist's impression of a trans-Atlantic aeroplane of the future. It would be necessary for such machines to be fitted with powerful searchlights in order to carry out regular night flying.

Autogiro for Danish Air Force

The Danish Government continue to favour British aircraft, and their latest purchase is a British-built autogiro. Two D.A.F. pilots were sent to this country for instruction in the flying of this type of aircraft, and on completion of their training they flew the purchased machine to Copenhagen.

Belgian Fairey Military Aeroplane

The Belgian works of the Fairey Aviation Co. Ltd., have produced a large military aeroplane, the design of which is based on the well-known Fairey "Fox" two-seater fighter produced at the English works of the company.

The new Belgian aeroplane is a low wing monoplane with an 860 h.p. supercharged engine, and can attain a top speed of 236 m.p.h. at 14,000 ft. It can climb to a height of 37,700 ft., and the cockpit can be warmed when the aeroplane is flying high. The Fairey "Monofox," as it is called, is adaptable for use either as a single-seater fighter or a two-seater reconnaissance-fighter or light bomber. When used as a single-seater fighter its armament consists of four machine guns, arranged one on each side of the nose and firing through the airscrews, and one in each of the upper wings. When used as a two-seater fighter it is provided with an additional gun, which is mounted in the observer's cockpit and can be fired in many directions. The machine carries wireless and is equipped for night flying and "blind" flying.

British Aerodrome Schemes

The development of civil aerodromes in this country is continuing steadily. The Leeds-Bradford municipal aerodrome at Yeadon is to be almost doubled in size, and is to have a control tower and beacons, Customs offices and a new hangar, so that it will be adequately equipped for use by both day and night air services. The Air Ministry are going to instal direction-finding apparatus and teleprinting instruments, and the aerodrome will then be able to receive regularly weather reports issued by Barton (Manchester) aerodrome, the chief wireless signalling station in the North. When the improvements are completed Yeadon will probably be used by Railway Air Services as a calling point in their proposed London-Glasgow service.

A municipal aerodrome is to be constructed at Luton, about two miles from the heart of the town. Keswick also has decided to have an aerodrome, but a site for it has not yet been obtained. Air Ministry officials recently visited the Newcastle aerodrome at Woolsington in connection with a proposed installation of direction-finding apparatus, at an estimated cost of £1,500.

Swansea is also to have a municipal airport, and an effort is to be made to get the landing ground ready for use by early summer.

Heston Airport

Growing Importance for Internal Air Routes

THE rapid growth of internal air services in this country during the past three years has hastened the provision of well-equipped aerodromes at the various termini. Aerodromes that a few years ago were merely the headquarters of civil flying clubs or training schools have become important points in an extensive network of air services.

The best example of this swift development is Heston Airport, in Middlesex. In 1928 the land now occupied by this airport was a market garden. A company called Airwork Ltd. was founded in that year to buy the site and to lay it out as an aerodrome, for a training school for civilian pilots. This work was completed in 1929 and the training school was established. The Household Brigade Flying Club also made use of the new aerodrome, and in addition it became the headquarters of the Heston Aero Club.

In 1933 regular internal air services were introduced in this country. One of the pioneer companies was Spartan Air Lines, and they adopted Heston as the London terminus for their services between London and the Isle of Wight. This was the beginning of Heston's history as an airport. Other newly-formed air transport companies were not long in realising the favourable situation of this airport and in adopting it as one of the termini of their services. By the end of 1934 it had become second to Croydon in importance as a Customs airport. During that year 3,700 aircraft and 12,307 persons cleared Customs at Heston, an increase of 182 per cent. on the figures for 1933.

Aerial view of Heston Airport. The large building in the foreground is the new Airwork central repair station. The illustrations to this article are reproduced by courtesy of Airwork Limited, Heston Airport, Hounslow.

Last year this development was continued and a new record set up in the amount of traffic dealt with, 17,903 passengers passing through the airport on the regular air services. These services included the London–Isle of Wight one already mentioned, and a similar one run by Portsmouth, Southsea and Isle of Wight Aviation, a service to Blackpool operated by United Airways Ltd. and a service to Jersey operated by Jersey Airways Ltd.

Heston owes its popularity as an airport to its accessibility, freedom from fog, and the ample provision made for expansion. In regard to accessibility, the airport is near the main traffic route to the West of England and is only 30 minutes' drive by car from Hyde Park Corner. From the pilot's point of view it is equally convenient, as the populated areas that are avoided by airmen whenever possible lie to the east, in which direction the airways are little frequented, for pilots flying to Holland and Germany usually prefer to make a detour across the North Sea. The principal internal air routes lie to the north, south and west of London, and Heston is ideally situated as a terminus for all traffic of this nature.

Its freedom from fog is due to the fact that the prevailing wind is south-west, and the smoke and the dust particles that are the main causes of the dreaded London fogs are blown to the north-east, in a direction away from Heston.

The "heart" of an airport is the control tower, from which aircraft are guided in their arrival and departure, and traffic congestion is reduced to a minimum. An elementary control system at Heston was introduced on 1st May, 1934. Under this system control is exercised from 10.30 a.m. until one hour after sunset, and is indicated by a yellow cube displayed on the wireless mast that surmounts the control tower. When the cube is in position the area enclosed between the hangars and a line of concrete blocks set in the ground about 50 yds. clear of the concrete "apron" is regarded as a neutral zone, and no aeroplanes are permitted to land within this area.

The continued growth of air traffic at Heston made it necessary last year to provide full airport control, and an enlarged control system involving wireless communication came into force on the 15th April 1935. This system was at first handled by Airwork Ltd., but on 11th November last it was taken over by the Air Ministry, and the control of London's two leading airports, Croydon and Heston, thus became centralised under one authority. Wireless communication and direction-finding facilities were also introduced at Heston last April when a new wireless station for ground-to-air telephone and telegraphy on a wavelength of 862 metres was put into service by the Air Ministry. The success of this improved control is shown by the fact that the movements of 94 aircraft have been directed by wireless from the station at the airport in one day.

Another important addition to these facilities for helping aircraft in bad weather is now being made by the installation of the Lorenz blind-landing system. It will be the first of its kind in this country, and is expected to make possible the safe approach and landing of suitably equipped machines when visibility is practically nil. A detailed description of the system would be extremely technical, but sufficient can be said here to give a general idea of the method of operation. The system makes use of ultra-short waves, and the main beacon transmits on a wavelength of nine metres. Vertical guidance is provided by a series of curves, each distinguished by a different strength of signal. By maintaining the indicator at a certain signal strength, the aircraft is guided down whichever of those curves provides the most suitable angle of approach. Directional guidance is provided by two zones, to the right and left of the approach path, distinguished by oral signals, either dots on the one side or dashes on the other. These zones overlap along the correct approach path, where the dots and dashes merge into a combined signal.

Passengers embarking in a D.H.86 Express air liner drawn up at one corner of the concrete "apron" that extends along the front of the hangars.

Night landings are frequently made at Heston, and the airport has therefore been equipped with powerful floodlights. There are three floodlights, each of 1,250,000 c.p., on the boundaries of the airport. They are operated from the control tower, and their direction is varied according to that of the wind, the light facing the incoming pilot being switched off to avoid dazzle. A number of boundary lights are also provided, of which the general arrangement consists of two 6.6-volt electric lamps, the upper one enclosed by an amber glass globe and the lower one illuminating a wide opal glass cylinder that extends to a height of 3 ft. above the ground. This illuminated cylinder shows the height of the boundary light and gives the pilot of an aeroplane an indication of perspective. The lights are operated on a distribution voltage of 230, which is stepped down to six volts by a separate transformer installed at the base of each light.

A busy scene inside the central repair station. The variety of aircraft being dealt with gives some idea of the interesting work carried out in this great building.

The aerial view of Heston airport on the previous page shows the general layout of the buildings. At what may be described as the "arrow head" is the control tower just referred to. Beneath it is the Terminal building, in the east wing of which are the Traffic and Customs offices. The building contains the clubhouse of the Heston Aero Club, a restaurant and a hotel, and private rooms are also provided for the Household Brigade and Old Etonian flying clubs. Plans are under consideration for the complete re-building of the structure to provide more room. The Airwork School of Flying is in a new western extension of the Terminal building. The flying equipment of this school consists of Avro "Cadet" and de Havilland "Moth" open-cockpit training machines.

In the south-east corner of the aerodrome is the Public Enclosure, arranged so that visitors can watch the flying in comfort and from an unobstructed viewpoint; and there is indoor accommodation in case of sudden showers.

East of the Airwork school are five aeroplane hangars, which have a total garaging space of 89,000 sq. ft. The hangar nearest the school is 100 ft. wide and 80 ft. long, and was the first all-concrete hangar to be built in this country; it has two storeys. Each of the next three hangars contain two rows of "lock-ups" for housing aeroplanes with folded wings, and the space between the two rows is large enough for aeroplanes with wings that cannot be folded. The fifth or end hangar accommodates aeroplanes of up to 90 ft. wing span. In front of the hangars is 58,000 sq. ft. of concrete "apron." Last year the equipment at Heston was increased by the construction of a new hangar 100 ft. in width and 200 ft. in length, to the north-west of the landing area.

The most outstanding building is the Airwork Central Repair Station. All overhaul and repair of aeroplanes is carried out there, and the engine workshops are equipped with the most modern plant and machinery. Complete aeroplanes can also be built on the premises.

Gravel Washing and Grading Plant

Crushing Rock for Making Concrete

By W. A. and T. A. Evershed

CONCRETE is now used to such an extent for road making, building and other purposes that we may almost be said to live in the Age of Concrete. Its base is Portland cement, which is manufactured by grinding clay and limestone or chalk with water, and calcining the mixture in huge rotary kilns at a temperature of about 2,800 deg. F. The product is ground to a fine powder and concrete is made by mixing this with sand and gravel or small stones of uniform size to which the name "aggregate" is given. The surfaces of these added materials are coated with cement, which also fills the spaces between them and sets to bind them firmly together.

A simple gravel washing and grading plant. Gravel and water enter the revolving drum on the right and the cylindrical screen on the left separates sand and gravel from flints and large stones

The material mixed with cement must be chosen very carefully if concrete of sufficient strength is to be produced, and for most purposes is specially treated before use. Its chief source is the gravel beds found in most parts of the country. Gravel consists of small pebbles of varying sizes that have been worn round and smooth by the action of water, and the deposits forming the beds were laid down in prehistoric times, some of them by the action of water melting from the glaciers of the Ice Age.

Typical gravel beds are to be found in East Anglia, and the material in these varies from a fine sand to large flints weighing several pounds each. When a deposit of gravel is being worked it is necessary to grade the product, that is to divide it into portions consisting of grains falling within certain definite limits of size, for each grade is specially adapted for the formation of a particular type of cement. It is equally important that the material should be thoroughly cleaned, for it may be contaminated with soil containing salts and chemicals that would interfere with the chemical changes taking place during the setting of the cement. Engineers and others using concrete specify carefully cleaned and graded material, and the plant at a gravel bed must be designed to give a product satisfying their requirements.

A bucket elevator feeding gravel into a washing and grading plant.

The usual plan adopted for these purposes is to wash the gravel thoroughly with water and then to pass it through sieves of different meshes. This of course is done mechanically, and the two illustrations on this page show a simple plant devised for this purpose. This is erected at a gravel pit in East Anglia, where the raw material excavated from distant working faces is brought by lorry to an elevator. The gravel is carried upward and delivered into a chute that leads it into a large revolving drum, shown in the upper illustration on this page. Water pumped up from the lowest point in the bed is admitted with it, and the gravel is well washed as it passes through the drum. Thorough cleansing is ensured by the use of internal ribs that lift the gravel and give it a push forward as they pass under it.

The separation of the washing water and the grading of the material follow immediately. The gravel and water enter a cylindrical screen or sieve that is fixed to the drum and rotates with it. At the end of the screen nearer the drum the holes are so small that only water and the finest sand can pass through them. The next two sections are perforated with larger holes and deliver fine gravel, consisting of particles up to about an inch in diameter, and a pile of this material can be seen in the left foreground of our illustration. The final section of the screen allows flints and larger stones up to about 2½ in. in diameter to fall out, and in our photograph these are seen being collected in a wheelbarrow ready for removal and stacking elsewhere. Larger stones and flints drop out of the open end of the screen.

The drum rests on four rollers, each about 9 in. in diameter, and is held in position by means of tracks formed by angle irons, riveted on it and encircling it, in which the rollers run. Great care is necessary in assembling a plant of this type in order to ensure that the axis of the drum is exactly horizontal and no strain is transferred to the angle guides. The rollers are set in pairs at opposite ends of the drum. One pair rotates idly, and the others are driven by means of bevel gearing and so cause the drum itself to rotate. The screen cylinder is bolted to the end of the drum and is supported on the cantilever principle, and a portable steam engine is employed as the source of power.

A travelling grab that loads gravel into waiting lorries. The washing and grading cylinders are seen on the right.

The sand, and other products of this plant serve various purposes. The finest washed sand is used exclusively for cement concrete, and the fine and coarse gravels are employed as aggregates for cement for paths and similar purposes. The small flints also can be utilised as aggregate in coarse concrete, and those that are too large for this purpose are in demand for banking up roads at corners, constructing foundations, and similar work.

In another type of plant employed in an East Anglian gravel works the drum and screen cylinder are slung on a form of chain that transmits the power needed to revolve them. At this pit a travelling grab is in use to load the grade of sand or gravel required into waiting lorries, and the two photographs on this page show this grab in action.

Loading a lorry with gravel that has been washed and graded in the plant shown in the upper illustration on this page.

Gravel pits are not the only source of the aggregates and sand required for concrete, and work in the quarries in the sides of the Malvern Hills illustrates another method of providing the necessary material. There granite is blasted away from the hillside, and when blasting is not in progress men can be seen clambering about high up the quarry face, prising loose rocks away until they crash down to the bottom of the quarry, bouncing from rock to rock as they fall and breaking into fragments under the terrific impacts. Some of the rocks dislodged weigh several tons each, and pieces from these that are too large to be handled are subsequently drilled and blasted to a convenient size.

The broken stone is loaded into deep wagons and conveyed to the crushers. These are of various types, but in practically all of them the rock fragments are literally squeezed between two jaws, with serrated faces made of specially hardened steel. One of the jaws is fixed and has a vertical face. The other is set at a small angle and swings alternately towards and away from the fixed one, gradually reducing the size of the stones as it works them downward and finally allowing them to drop out when they are of the correct size. The moving jaw is driven by an eccentric on a stiff shaft suitably geared to the power unit. Its range of movement is remarkably small, perhaps not more than half an inch, but is sufficient to enable it to do its work.

The stone is reduced to the size of road metal when it emerges from the jaws of the crushers and is then crushed further, this time to form a kind of gravel, known as gravel chips. The machines in which the second crushing is carried out are of various types. Spring loaded rollers are used in one of them, and stone that is ejected by the screen that sorts the product is automatically returned to the rollers; in another the stone passes through a cylinder, with specially hardened internal ribs, that revolves at high speed and hurls it about violently until it is crushed into fragments small enough to fall through the screen; but perhaps the most interesting consists of two steel tubes, one of which is set eccentrically within the other, the stone being relentlessly crushed between them as it reaches the sectors where the distance between them is decreased.

The plant used for providing sand for work on the Lloyd Dam, at Bhatgar, near Poona, India, was an interesting example of overseas practice in stone crushing and grading. When it was completed in 1928, this dam was the largest mass of artificial masonry in the world. It is 5,333 ft. in length, 190 ft. in height and at its base is 124 ft. in width, the total volume of masonry in it being 21½ million cu. ft.

The Lloyd Dam was built of stones specified to weigh not less than 40 lb. each, and these were laid by hand in lime mortar. It was necessary to start several quarries to furnish the stone in order to keep up the rate of progress required, and the quarry chips, consisting of pieces less than 40 lb. in weight, were used for crushing into sand, for the river sand was not clean enough and was not available in sufficient quantity. The crushers were of the type with fixed and movable jaws, and the small stones from them were carried to the top of a series of spring loaded roller mills that transformed them into sand. This passed along a revolving screen cylinder and rejected material was returned to the rolling mills.

A Streamlined Ferry Boat

Motor Vessel with Unusual Lines

THE world's first completely streamlined motor ferry made her initial appearance in July last year, when she was put into service on the almost landlocked waters of Puget Sound, Washington, on the Pacific Coast of the United States. This vessel is called the *"Kalakala,"* a name that in the language of the Chinook Indians, who formerly flourished in the north west, means *"Flying Bird,"* and is pronounced "Kah-lock-ah-lah." She is 276 ft. long, with a beam of nearly 60 ft., and has five covered decks. She has been built for service between Seattle and Bremerton, a distance of about 15 miles, and her speed of 18 knots enables her to complete each trip in 45 minutes. Her passenger carrying capacity is 2,000 and in addition she has accommodation for 110 motor cars.

The "Kalakala," the streamlined motor ferry boat in service between Seattle and Bremerton, Washington, U.S.A. Photograph reproduced by courtesy of the Puget Sound Navigation Co., Seattle.

The *"Kalakala"* presents a striking appearance as she slips through the water, for she is painted aluminium and this, in conjunction with her gracefully curved outlines, attracts instant attention. Her hull is made of steel throughout and is electrically welded. It is divided into 25 water-tight compartments, making the vessel practically unsinkable, and the streamlining is carried out as far as possible below the water as well as above, the waterline shape having been carefully worked out to reduce wave action to a minimum.

The wheelhouse on the top deck is built entirely of copper and the steering gear installed in it is hydro-electric in type and is very sensitive, giving great manœuvring power. Communication between the wheelhouse and the engine room is maintained by telephone and an automatic telegraph system also is installed for this purpose. This system is believed to be the first of its type to be incorporated in a vessel that plies on inland waters.

The main engine of the *"Kalakala"* is a Busch Sulzer Diesel unit of 3,000 h.p. working on the two-stroke cycle. It has 10 cylinders and is said to be the largest engine of its type installed in a vessel on ferry service. A second Diesel engine furnishes power for auxiliary service. This has six cylinders and works on the four-stroke principle, developing 600 h.p. It is directly connected to a 400 k.w. generator that supplies current through the vessel, but when in port shore lines may be connected in order that the necessary current supply may be received in this manner. Fresh water cooling is used for the engines, the temperature being carefully regulated and controlled, and a special boiler using waste heat from the engine is devoted to steam heating purposes. In very cold weather additional heat can be provided by a special booster boiler.

In addition to being virtually unsinkable, the *"Kalakala"* is practically fireproof. Special precautions have been taken to avoid disastrous fires that might start on the motor car deck, and any outbreak there can be extinguished in a few seconds by means of a deck spray system. Other safety devices include the provision on the main deck of lifeboats equipped with gear allowing them to be launched in a very short time; and there is a life-preserver in a special compartment in each of the upholstered chairs with which the saloons and lounges are furnished, in addition to life-preserver racks of the usual type fitted on all ships. The comfort as well as the safety of passengers has been carefully considered in planning the vessel and an air conditioning plant maintains a healthy atmosphere on all her decks.

The changes in outline due to streamlining have not led to any sacrifice of space in the *"Kalakala,"* and her five decks provide plenty of room for all purposes. The main deck is devoted to the storage of motor cars, which are parked in six lanes separated by raised walks of corrugated steel. The main passenger cabin is furnished with upholstered settees accommodating 700 people, and forward of these is an observation room. Other observation rooms are placed fore and aft on the upper deck, and all are provided with wide plate glass windows to allow passengers to obtain good views of the scenery of Puget Sound. A dining room that also gives its occupants an excellent outlook occupies part of the upper deck, and the passenger accommodation generally is furnished with luxury in all respects equivalent to that in an ocean liner.

As would be expected in a vessel with the modern appearance and equipment of the *"Kalakala,"* the interior furnishing and decoration of the vessel are of strikingly up-to-date type. The interiors of the cabins are of steel that has been given an attractive appearance by the use of lacquers of various colours sprayed on the metallic surfaces, and each room has its own colour scheme, with distinctive suitable draperies. An efficient form of indirect lighting is used throughout the vessel. The galley also shows the influence of modern ideas, for this is finished in the nickel-copper alloy known as Monel metal and cooking is carried on solely by electrical means.

The Bendix Servo Brake

Balanced Action Helps to Avoid Skidding

NO feature of a motor car is of greater importance than its braking system, and this must enable its driver to pull up smoothly and easily in a comparatively short distance without violent pressure on the brake pedal. There is little need to emphasise the danger of bad braking, especially for those who have experienced the alarming sensation of being in a car that has skidded violently to one side immediately the brakes have been applied, or even has turned completely round so that it is facing in the direction from which it came.

Skids of course are particularly prevalent on wet and slippery roads, but may be avoided even in these conditions. Brakes may be so designed that they exert their full power with the slightest pedal pressure, however, and in these circumstances they do not lock the wheels, as they may when applied by brute force in cases of emergency. An even more important cause of skidding is uneven braking, for if the action takes effect on one wheel before the others, there is a great tendency to pull the car out of its line of travel. For instance, this is the case when one of the back wheels is heavily braked before the other wheels are affected. The effect is exaggerated if the second rear wheel is still driving the car and skidding often is the result. Similarly a car tends to revolve round a front wheel if braking takes effect first on it, producing a front wheel skid.

An interesting modern braking system that requires comparatively little effort on the part of the driver, and affects all four wheels equally and at the same time, is illustrated on this page. It is the Bendix Balanced Servo Brake. The brake shoes of this mechanism are of the usual internal expanding type, but they are fixed only at the ends where the brake mechanism is applied, the floating ends being connected by an adjuster. Only one of the two brake shoes is brought immediately into contact with the brake drum when the brakes are applied. This shoe is known as the primary shoe. It is carried round slightly by the friction between its lining and the drum, and this movement is used to apply the second shoe. In ordinary brakes the power of this turning effect is completely wasted, but with the Bendix servo brake only about one third of the effort needed to apply the usual type of two-shoe brake is required.

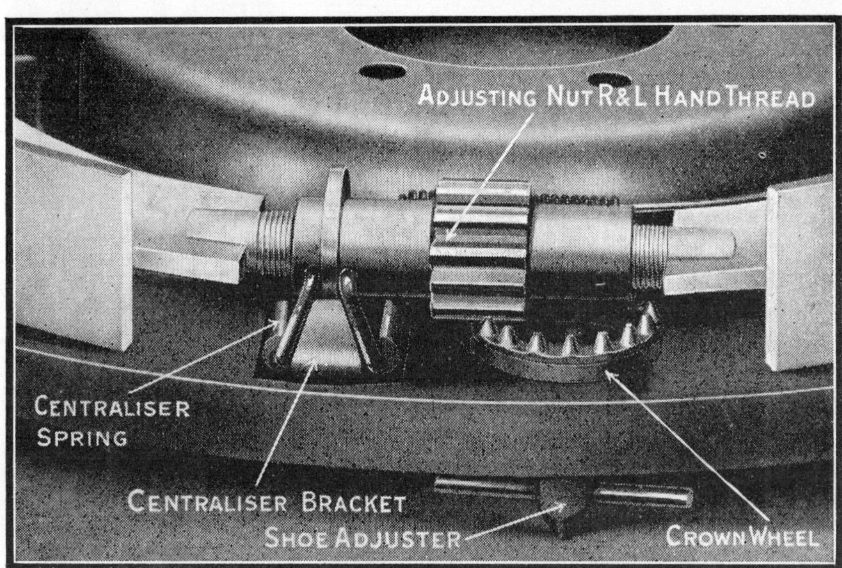

The adjusting mechanism of the Bendix Servo Brake. The illustrations to this article are reproduced by courtesy of Bendix Limited, Birmingham.

The lower illustration on this page shows what happens when the driver applies the Bendix brake. The plunger seen in the illustration is then pulled into its housing. This plunger is made of hardened steel and through its shank a hole is drilled to accommodate two hardened steel balls in contact with each other. They project from the plunger on each side and as they are carried down they press on the inclined faces of hardened steel tappets that are pushed apart and carry the movement to the primary shoe, and thence to the secondary shoe by the servo action already described. Springs return the brake shoes to their normal position when the brake is released.

All brakes require adjustment from time to time to keep their efficiency, and this is remarkably simple in the case of the Bendix servo brake. As shown in our upper illustration, the free ends of the brake shoes are connected by means of an adjusting nut, with right hand and left hand internal threads into which are screwed plungers with slotted upper ends fitting over the tongued ends of the brake shoe. The nut is rotated in order to bring the shoes nearer together or farther apart as required, and this is easily carried out by means of the shoe adjuster, which acts through a crown wheel and a gear on the adjusting nut. The crown wheel is fitted with an automatic ratchet device that retains the setting of the brake shoes. When adjustment is necessary the adjuster is turned in a clockwise direction until the shoes come into contact with the drum. It is then reversed through half a turn, an amount that is readily measured by turning until four clicks of the ratchet mechanism have been heard.

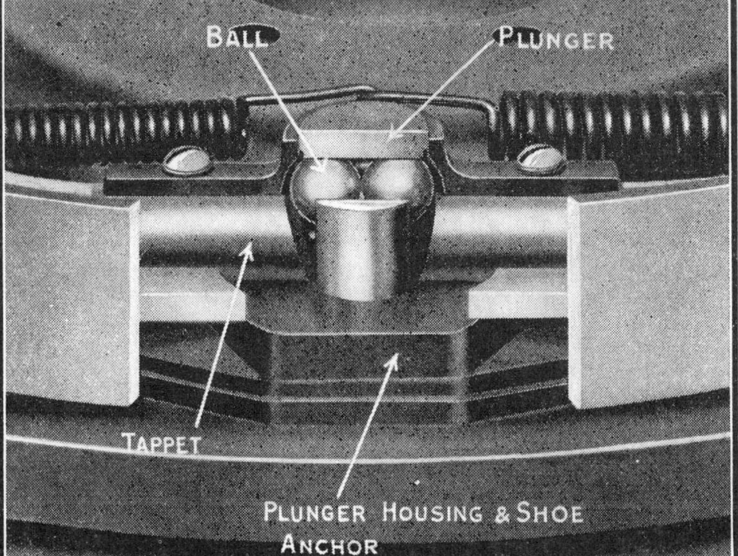

How the Bendix Servo Brake is applied. The shoes are expanded when the plunger is pulled into its housing.

The brake operating mechanism is provided with compensators between the front and rear brakes as well as between the two brakes on each axle. This ensures easy and even braking on all four wheels and it is possible to pull up, even in difficult circumstances, without skidding or changing direction, even when the linings of the brakes are unevenly worn or the shoes are in faulty adjustment. The foot pedal operates brakes on all four wheels, and the hand lever can be arranged to act on the rear brakes only, or on all four. For normal driving the foot brake is the one most in use, and with any arrangement the hand brake gives sufficient power to hold a car on any hill.

Railways and The Royal Funeral

The arrangements for the funeral of His late Majesty King George V depended to a great extent on railway services. In addition to the running of the Royal Funeral Train first from Sandringham up to London and then from London to Windsor, and the special trains for guests on the latter occasion, suitable arrangements had to be made for the numerous foreign royal personages and delegations arriving from the Continent.

Chief interest of course centred on the operation of the Royal Funeral Train. On 23rd January last this left Wolferton, the station for Sandringham, drawn by L.N.E.R. 4–6–0 locomotive No. 8520, manned by Driver Thurston and Fireman Tobell. At King's Lynn No. 2847, *"Helmingham Hall,"* a three-cylinder 4–6–0 of the "Sandringham" class, came on in charge of Driver Collis and Fireman Foister. The usual route by way of Ely, Cambridge and Hitchin to King's Cross was followed and L.N.E.R. stock was used. Nine coaches made up the train.

The same train was used on the G.W.R. from Paddington to Windsor on the day of the funeral, and on 25th January was transferred to that system via Canonbury and Acton. On Tuesday 28th January it left the G.W.R. depot at Old Oak Common for Paddington with the 4–6–0 locomotive No. 4082, *"Windsor Castle,"* attached at the rear. This was the engine that was driven by His late Majesty on the occasion of his visit to Swindon Works in 1924. On arrival outside Paddington, the engine heading the train having been detached, *"Windsor Castle"* propelled the train into No. 8 platform. In addition to this train, there were five specials, scheduled to leave before it, that conveyed the invited guests to Windsor. Mr. J. M. Craig informs us that these were drawn respectively by "Castle" class engines, *"Tregenna Castle," "Raglan Castle," "Dorchester Castle," "Goodrich Castle,"* and *"Llanstephan Castle"*; *"Morlais Castle"* was attached to a supplementary special that was not required, however. *"Windsor Castle,"* in charge of Driver Sparrow and Fireman Miles, was draped with the Royal Arms and carried the special Royal headlamps with crowns on top. When the train was re-assembled for the return journey, L.N.E.R. men were available to deal with the couplings. Only four specials in addition to the Royal Train were required for the journey to Paddington, the Royal Train departing after the first special. Several speed restrictions to 10 m.p.h. were enforced for the occasion and supplementary signalling instructions were issued.

In connection with the royal visitors and delegations from the Continent the S.R. provided 10 special trains, seven special steamers and 13 special coaches.

An L.M.S.R. local train hauled by the 0–6–0 Standard freight locomotive No. 4288. When required these engines do useful work on the slower passenger and excursion trains. (H.R.C. Prize-winning photograph.)

Names of New G.W.R. "Castles"

The names selected for the 25 locomotives of the "Castle" class that are to be built this year are as follows: *"Beverston Castle," "Bridgwater Castle," "Barbury Castle," "Compton Castle," "Cranbrook Castle," "Clifford Castle," "Denbigh Castle," "Devizes Castle," "Dryllwyn Castle," "Eastnor Castle," "Hatherop Castle," "Lamphey Castle," "Lydford Castle," "Ogmore Castle," "Picton Castle," "Penrice Castle," "Powis Castle," "Sarum Castle," "Sudeley Castle," "Tenby Castle," "Tretower Castle," "Thornbury Castle," "Wardour Castle," "Wilton Castle," "Upton Castle."*

Progress of S.R. Engineering Works

The Southern Railway are making good progress with a scheme that will greatly facilitate the handling of traffic on the Western section between Waterloo and Wimbledon. This scheme includes the re-arrangement of the existing track and the construction of a flying junction and an immense ferro-concrete bridge near Wimbledon. Extensive signalling alterations are involved and colour-light signals are being installed between Waterloo and Hampton Court Junction.

A new power-operated signal cabin is to be built at Waterloo, and this will undertake the duties at present performed by six other cabins. The increase and acceleration of train services as the result of electrification, and the necessity of providing for the future, have been the chief reasons for the preparation of this scheme, which will cost approximately £500,000 to complete. Ten years ago 1,046 trains were dealt with at Waterloo during a normal day of 24 hours; to-day 200 more have to be moved over the same layout of lines in the same time. This explains the urgent nature of the operations, which are expected to be completed at the end of next May.

Extensive station alterations, permanent way and signalling work are already in hand in preparation for the electrification of the lines between London and Portsmouth. It is planned to complete the work in three years.

"Right Away!"

From *"The Railway Gazette"* we extract the following:

"It is told of a certain Midland Railway guard, residing in a small town in the Midlands, that one night, while sleeping in a chair by the fire, he surprised his wife and family by suddenly jumping up, seizing the cat, who was asleep on the rug, bundling her into the oven, banging the door to, and then shouting "Any more for Nottingham?"—*"The Windsor Magazine"* of March 1897.'

Good Running on Anglo-Scottish Trains

We have received details of the following runs from Mr. O. S. Nock.

On the L.N.E.R. 5.45 p.m. express from King's Cross, "Pacific" No. 2561, *"Minoru,"* with Driver Sparshatt in charge had a load of 410 tons and started well, passing Potters Bar 12.7 miles in 18½ min. Adverse signals at Hatfield and Welwyn North cost fully 8¼ min. altogether, but from Hitchin to Fletton Junction the 43.1 miles were run at an average of 73.7 m.p.h., 82 m.p.h. being attained on four separate occasions. Peterborough, 76.4 miles, was passed in 81¾ min., and 60 m.p.h. was maintained throughout the ascent from Werrington Junction to Stoke Summit. Grantham, 105.5 miles, was reached in a net time of 104¾ min.

A Nord "Super-Pacific" locomotive showing the prominent smoke deflectors and the wedge-shaped chimney. A splendid run behind one of these engines is described on page 138 of this issue. Photograph by Mr. O. S. Nock.

Coming up on *"The Flying Scotsman,"* No. 2552, *"Sansovino,"* with Driver Payne, had a load of 520 tons. Even so an acceleration to 45 m.p.h. was recorded up the 1 in 200 ascent to Stoke, and the 18.6 miles from Corby to Werrington Junction were covered at an average speed of 80.6 m.p.h., the maximum being 86.5 m.p.h. Peterborough, 29.1 miles, was passed in 28 min. 55 sec., and an average of 63.3 m.p.h. was made over the 58.1 miles from Yaxley to Brookmans Park. Up the long 1 in 200 rise to Stevenage, speed did not fall below 51 m.p.h. Notable speeds were 74 at Huntingdon, 72 at Tempsford, and 78 at Hatfield. In spite of checks at Potters Bar and Hadley Wood the run finished brilliantly, a maximum of 75 m.p.h. at Wood Green bringing the train into King's Cross in 110½ min., thus improving on schedule by half a minute. The net time was 104 min. It is remarkable that on this run, apart from the start from Grantham and the recovery from the slack through Peterborough, no longer cut-off than 25 per cent. was employed, of course with the regulator full open.

S.R. 4-6-0 locomotive No. 2329, "Stephenson," formerly a 4-6-4 tank, under repair at Nine Elms. The second and third pairs of coupled wheels have been removed, the rear end of the engine being supported on jacks and timber packing. (H.R.C. Prize-winning photograph.)

On the L.M.S.R. No. 6119, *"Lancashire Fusilier,"* of the "Royal Scot" class, working through from Crewe to Perth on the 7.30 p.m. from Euston, had a gross load of 420 tons. In the latter stages of this long run a splendid start from Stirling produced an acceleration to 46 m.p.h., before the ascent to Dunblane. On the 1 in 75 grade the minimum was 27.5 m.p.h. The gradually rising length to Gleneagles was covered at 50–54 m.p.h., the 17.2 miles to that place taking 27 min. 13 sec. In a thrilling finish a maximum of 83.5 m.p.h. was recorded below Auchterarder and several miles through Strathearn were covered at 75–76 m.p.h. The 33 miles from Stirling into Perth were completed in 41¾ min., 13.8 miles from Gleneagles to Hilton Junction having been covered at an average of 74.2 m.p.h. Driver Garrett of Crewe was responsible for this fine performance.

Another Crewe engine No. 6118, *"Royal Welch Fusilier,"* made some fine running with a gross load of 380 tons on the 11.30 a.m. Sunday express from Glasgow to Euston. The 102.3 miles to Carlisle were covered non-stop in 123¼ min. Up the heavy ascent to Craigenhill Summit speed was maintained at 36 m.p.h. On the final pitch of the rise to Beattock Summit speed fell to 40½ m.p.h., but the 52.6 miles from Glasgow to that point were covered in 73½ min.—2½ min. under time. The average speed from the start had thus been 43 m.p.h. and the train had been lifted a clear 1,000 ft. On the descent 80½ m.p.h. was recorded before Beattock Station, and with 72.5 m.p.h. at Kirtlebridge and 73 m.p.h. at the Solway Firth Gretna was passed 7½ min. early, 93.7 miles in 112.5 min. Beyond Carlisle the locomotive work was spoilt by checks.

* * *

The "Royal Scot" locomotives are to be provided with larger tenders.

Recent G.W.R. Train Workings

Mr. J. M. Craig sends us the following observations:

During recent heavy rains in the South of England the *"Cornish Riviera Limited"* and similar trains were worked by "Castle" class engines instead of "Kings," and Weymouth trains had "Moguls" in place of "Halls." An interesting instance of these workings was on Saturday 11th January, when at 10.20 a.m. and 10.25 a.m. respectively two specials to Bristol for a Cup-tie enjoyed the services of "King" class engines; but the *"Cornish Riviera Limited"* had *"Shirburn Castle,"* and *"Kilgerran Castle"* took *"The "Cornishman."* *"Tintagel Castle"* and *"Llanstephan Castle"* were also seen on the *"Riviera"* train.

Owing to the closing of the Severn Tunnel on Sundays, passengers travelling by half-day excursion trains to Newport and Cardiff from London enjoy an extra bit of travel on the outward run, the train proceeding after Swindon via Gloucester. A stop is made at this latter station, but no passenger business is done. The return is made by the direct route as the Tunnel is opened again about 8 p.m. The difference in time for the two routes is exactly half-an-hour, and on 12th January *"Wigmore Castle"* kept time quite easily on the longer outward trip.

Streamlined Locomotives for the L.N.E.R.

A further 17 4-6-2 locomotives, generally similar to those of the "Silver Link" series already in service, are to be constructed by the L.N.E.R. Remarkable success has attended the working of the existing streamlined engines and it is understood that these new locomotives also will be streamlined. Streamlining has solved the problem of lifting the exhaust steam and smoke clear of the cab so that the driver's view is not obstructed; and the reduction of wind resistance effected by streamlining at speeds in excess of 60 m.p.h. has been found to result in improved coal consumption.

Four further 2-8-2 "Mikado" locomotives of the "Cock o' The North" pattern are under construction for service on the difficult Edinburgh and Aberdeen route.

Vehicles to be constructed under present orders include a number of restaurant and sleeping cars, together with 214 vestibuled coaches for first and third class passengers. In addition contracts have been placed for the construction of 160 of the passenger coaches to be built under the Government loan scheme.

How Railway Sleepers are Prepared

Wonders of the G.W.R. Depot at Hayes

THERE can be few less spectacular items of railway equipment than the ordinary wooden sleeper. Its very existence probably is overlooked by the majority of railway passengers; yet the soundness of each sleeper and its correct application in the track play an important part in preserving the reputation of British railways for safe and smooth travel. Wooden sleepers still represent typical British practice, although steel ones have been used experimentally to some extent by all four groups.

The importance of wooden sleepers may be judged from the fact that the G.W.R. have recently put into operation at Hayes, 11 miles from Paddington, a new depot for their handling and preparation; and this installation is designed to deal with half a million sleepers annually. Incidentally the G.W.R. relaying programme for the current 12 months calls for some 623,000 sleepers.

Wooden sleepers, which are 8 ft. 6 in. long, 10 in. wide and 5 in. thick, are usually of Baltic pine from Russia, Douglas fir from British Columbia, or Jarrah from Australia. The Baltic pine trees are about 14 in. in diameter, and when cut down they are hewn lengthways to produce a log roughly 10 in. square. These logs are cut off to length and thus form sleeper blocks and it is in this state that they arrive in this country. They are sawn in half lengthways, so that a Baltic pine sleeper has one sawn side and three hewn sides. Douglas fir or Jarrah sleepers are cut from much larger trees and are therefore sawn on all four sides.

Stacking sleepers for seasoning at the G.W.R. depot at Hayes by means of a 5-ton travelling crane. The illustrations to this article are by courtesy of the G.W.R.

Sleepers reaching the Hayes depot arrive in barge loads of about 1,100 on the Paddington Canal. They are unloaded by crane and placed in the seasoning and stacking yard, which is conveniently adjacent to the canal and can accommodate about 750,000 sleepers. The sleepers are so stacked that the air has access to all sides of them and they remain in the yard to dry or season for a period of about six months.

When required for use the sleepers are taken from the stacks on flat wagons and are unloaded by crane on to a staging outside the main depot building. Thence they pass inside along a roller conveyor which delivers them at a convenient point close to what is known as an "adzing and boring" machine. This machine makes them ready to receive the chairs, the adzing process being the formation of the seating or recess on the top of the sleeper for each chair. Each sleeper is thus given the same effective depth, so that a uniform length of chair bolt can be used. Adzing is carried out by a series of rapidly revolving knives or adzing drums under which the sleepers pass on an endless chain that conveys them through the machine. As the bases of the chairs are serrated, or formed with small projections, the knives of the adzing drums are profiled to produce a similar surface on the sleeper. Thus any tendency to movement sideways on the part of the chairs is restrained.

From the adzing knives the sleepers pass to the other side of the machine and there have drilled through them four holes for the chair bolt holes. A brush, also part of the machine, removes the shavings and borings. Six sleepers a minute can be dealt with by the adzing and boring machine, which also saws them to the standard length of 8 ft. 6 in. and automatically rejects any sleeper over $5\frac{1}{4}$ in. thick. Passing off the machine, which is situated in a bay at one end of the depot building, the sleepers are loaded on to trolleys running on narrow gauge rails to undergo one of the most interesting processes involved in their preparation for use.

To obtain as long a life as possible from the pine or fir sleepers, which are soft wood, they must be treated with a preservative. Creosote, a by-product of the manufacture of coal gas, is the medium used. This impregnation is carried out in two big cylinders which resemble boilers in appearance and are situated at one end of the depot. A stout door at each end of the cylinder, hung on a massive hinged frame, allows the sleepers to be run in on the trolleys and then out again when creosoting is over. The capacity of each cylinder is 600 sleepers or 10 trolley loads. The cylinders at Hayes are the largest in the country and are 90 ft. long and 6 ft. 9 in. in diameter.

When the sleepers are inside and the doors are shut, a vacuum is created inside the cylinder, and then creosote heated to 150 degrees Fahrenheit is drawn up from the service tanks below. Pressure pumping now commences, the maximum pressure being 200 lb. per square inch; but the figure worked to depends on the nature of the timber.

Baltic pine is rapidly impregnated and requires only an hour to an hour and a half for each sleeper to pick up about three gallons of creosote. A lower pressure is thus sufficient for such timber than for Douglas fir, which takes about four hours but does not absorb so much creosote. Jarrah hardwood sleepers are not treated, but are used "clean."

The men on the right of this photograph are hammering in the chair bolts. The sleepers then pass to the chairing machine at the far end of the conveyor, the chairs being slipped over the bolts and the nuts started on the way.

When the time is up, according to the type of timber, pumping ceases and the creosote is allowed to run off. Then a vacuum is created and maintained for about a quarter of an hour to dry the sleepers. The trolley loads are then hauled out at the opposite end of the cylinders from which they entered and remain to drain for a short time.

The sleepers now proceed down the building to the chairing plant. The chairing machine is situated at the side of the building, so that the sleepers are now unloaded in an outward direction from the tracks that pass down the centre of the depot. They are placed, several at a time, bottom side uppermost, on the bolting table where operators at each end of the sleeper insert the chair bolts, threading them through the ribbed washers that prevent the bolt heads working on the sleeper itself. The bolts are hammered home, and the sleepers, now turned right way up and with the bolt heads below, are skidded down on to a conveyor that leads them to the chairing machine. On their way there they have the chairs slipped over the bolts and the nuts are given a start on the bolt threads. The chairs are taken from a parallel conveyor that enters the building from the chair storage bank outside, and delivers them conveniently to hand for the men standing between the two conveyors.

End view of the creosoting cylinders, showing the massive nature of the doors and their hinges. The right-hand cylinder holds a charge of sleepers ready for creosoting.

Arriving at the chairing machine, each sleeper is stopped on the bed of the machine. An operator causes hydraulic rams to descend and engage the jaws of the chairs, setting them correctly to gauge and pressing the chairs on to the sleeper with a force of 10 tons on each ram. While they are thus secured four revolving spanners are operated through a friction drive which automatically slips when the nuts have been tightened sufficiently.

Now completed, the chaired sleepers pass off the machine on to a conveyor leading to a projecting wing of the building through which runs a siding. An elevator lifts them on to the sleeper trucks waiting there to receive them. As a rule the G.W.R. employ special "crocodile" sleeper wagons, each holding 160 sleepers. The sleepers which we have followed from the first stages of their preparation are now ready to be sent to wherever they may be required for new lines or for relaying.

The Hayes works cover an area of 19 acres. The machinery is electrically operated and the arrangement is such that the movement of the sleepers is progressive. Unnecessary man-handling is eliminated by the use of the conveyors and the other labour-saving devices. In addition to the creosoting service tanks inside there are storage cylinders outside with a total capacity of 65,000 gallons.

The average life of a creosoted sleeper is from 20 to 25 years. A Jarrah sleeper, although untreated, will last from 20 to 30 years, but these sleepers have the disadvantage that they induce harsher running than soft wood kinds, and the fastenings inserted in them are more liable to become rust-bound. The length of service obtained from a sleeper naturally varies with the situation and conditions. A damp spot such as in a cutting will shorten their service; but a dry stretch subject to breezes is more favourable to a longer life. Sleepers are not in first class tracks for the whole of their lives. After they have been removed from the main line they can usually be employed for a further period in sidings or in other places where traffic moves slowly

World's Largest Electrified Metal Mine

The distinction of being the world's largest electrified metal mine is claimed for one at Bingham, Utah, in the United States, in which copper ore is extracted. There actual mining operations are carried on by means of giant electrical shovels and the haulage system employs electrical locomotives and equipment of the most up-to-date type.

The mine is situated in a canyon, on both sides of which copper ore is found, and open cut working on a very large scale is practised, electric shovels cutting successive terraces in the face of the mountain as they remove first the overburden that covers the ore, and then the ore itself. The overburden is deposited in cars that are hauled away by the electric locomotives and dumped down another side of the mountain, while the ore itself is hauled to mills 17 miles away for treatment.

All the locomotives employed are specially designed for this service and are of very heavy construction, each being rated at 75 tons. A striking feature is that they can obtain power through an overhead conductor, side rails, or a trailing cable that is automatically unwound to the required length from a reel under the platform of the cab, and can be extended to allow working at a considerable distance from the supply point. In addition, the locomotives are suitable for operation by means of accumulators.

A section of the electric railway at the copper mines of the Utah Copper Company, Bingham, in the United States. Photograph by courtesy of the General Electric Company of New York.

An interesting feature of the mining town of Bingham is that it consists of one long street stretching along the floor of the canyon, the sides of which are too steep to allow side streets to be made. The town is believed to be the longest of its size in the world. The slopes above it are scarred by workings, and narrow shelves have been scooped out of them for the railways along which ore and overburden are transported

Electric Sparks in Threshing Machines

Electricity at times makes its appearance in unexpected places. An excellent instance of this is the electrification of a steam lorry running on rubber tyres. This can readily be caused by the emission of steam and products of combustion from the funnel, the friction electrifying both the escaping materials and the funnel in the same manner as an ebonite rod and a piece of flannel become oppositely electrified when rubbed together. The electrical charge on the funnel is retained by the lorry, the rubber tyres of which act as insulators, and instances have been known in which people on the ground touching the lorry have been surprised to receive electric shocks. The remedy is to hang a trailing chain from the lorry itself, when the electrical charge is continuously earthed.

Paper passing through printing machines or between the metal rollers of calendars also may become electrified by friction, and then is liable to curl up in a manner that is exasperating to those who wish to make use of it. Another strange place in which electricity may make its appearance is in a threshing machine, where it may be generated by the rubbing of the straw during its passage through the machine. In really dry weather sparking actually may take place, and several disastrous explosions due to this cause have occurred in the United States. In these cases the explosive medium was dust in the machine, which was ignited by the electric sparks, and the use of fans to remove the dust and of earth wires to dissipate the electric charges prevented further disasters of this kind.

Allowing Explosions to Escape

I scarcely think that the dangers of dust explosions are fully realised. Explosive mixtures are formed when finely divided particles of flour, starch, powdered milk and even chocolate are mixed with air, and an atmosphere in which dust from products of this kind is present in large proportion may explode when a match is struck, when an electric spark occurs, or even when an electric lamp breaks.

One way of preventing explosions of this kind is to keep down dust as far as possible, but this cannot always be done, and other means then must be adopted to cope with the danger. Flames must be carefully excluded from buildings in which dust explosives are possible. Care also should be taken to prevent the generation and accumulation of frictional electricity that may cause a spark, and it has even been suggested that special electric lamps with double bulbs should be used in order to prevent the flash from a broken lamp from igniting an explosive mixture.

An even more interesting method of avoiding damage from disasters of this kind is to allow dust explosions to escape from the plants in which they occur. If an explosion is confined within the walls of a building damage of enormous extent may follow the immense increase in pressure. This pressure can be released by fitting automatic or self-opening windows, and the power of an explosion may then be dissipated comparatively harmlessly. The value in practice of this remarkable method of dealing with explosions has been shown when dust has exploded in grain elevators and other grain-handling plants equipped with opening devices

How Man Loads the Earth's Crust

I wonder how many of my readers stop to consider how the building of large cities adds to the loads carried by certain areas of the Earth's surface, particularly in the United States, the home of the skyscraper and giant buildings. For instance, it has been calculated that the extra weight imposed per square mile on the Earth's skin by the buildings of New York and the cities immediately surrounding it amounts to no less than 45 million tons. Fortunately, the surface layer of the east coast of America is so strong that even the weight of New York and its neighbours does not trouble it greatly.

There is one place in the United States where Man's activities are expected to cause the Earth's surface to sink, however. This is in the course of the Colorado River, immediately above Boulder Dam, where an artificial lake that will be 115 miles long is now being formed. The weight of the water in this lake will be about 42,000 million tons, and on the average each square mile of the bed of the lake will be called upon to carry an additional weight of 190 million square tons. This immense load is expected to cause sinking to the extent of 2 ft. over a wide area.

Forging an ingot of platinum before rolling it into wire. Lengths of platinum rod can be seen on the left. The photographs on this page are by J. F. Stirling, Manchester.

A Really Precious Metal

Throughout the ages gold has always been regarded as the most precious of metals, and our respect for it has greatly increased since the withdrawal of gold coinage and the great rise in the value of the sovereign and of articles made of the metal. To-day gold has many rivals, however, and of course is far less precious than radium, the value of which is about £7,000 an ounce.

Another interesting precious metal is platinum. In the 18th century the bulk of the supply of this white metal came from South America, and its name is derived from the Spanish word "*platina*," which simply means "little silver." It was then regarded as practically worthless. Comparatively large quantities were thrown away in order to prevent its use in adulterating gold, and little more than 100 years ago, when the metal was discovered in Russia, swindlers in that country were alleged to have sold gold bricks that were really gilded platinum and were of much less value to their unsuspecting purchasers than the more familiar metal. To-day platinum is worth nearly £30 an ounce and is considerably scarcer than gold.

Platinum also is a rival to gold as a "noble" metal. This name marks the resistance offered by gold to the attack of acids and corrosive agents, and platinum is equally remarkable in this respect, the only liquid that can dissolve it being a mixture of hydrochloric and nitric acids to which the name of *aqua regia*, or royal water, is given because of its effect on these noble metals.

Casting an ingot of platinum. The molten metal is being poured from an electric furnace in which it is heated to a temperature of nearly 2,000°C.

Twice as Heavy as Lead

Most of our present supply of platinum comes from Russia, but in view of its scarcity and high price eager search is being made for it in all parts of the world. At present anyone who set out to corner the supply, and was successful in obtaining sufficient of the metal to melt down into a cube with an edge of 1 ft., would find that he possessed the greater part of platinum in existence, and he would be able to consider himself a millionaire. His cube would be a very unwieldy possession, however, for it would weigh more than a ton, the metal being one of the heaviest in existence and twice as dense as lead. A cube of coal of the same size would weigh only 40 lb.

No doubt many of my readers know that platinum is largely used in making laboratory apparatus, particularly for crucibles in which chemicals are raised to very high temperatures. It is particularly suitable for this purpose because it has the very high melting point of 1,755 deg. C. Another peculiarity is that it expands at about the same rate as glass. For this reason glass vacuum tubes through which platinum wires are passed to conduct electric currents to the gases inside them remain sealed when the temperature rises, because the metal expands sufficiently to fill up the hole as this increases in size. For purposes of this kind it can now often be replaced by an alloy of nickel and iron, however. This is called platinite, and of course is not so costly as the much rarer noble metal for which it is a substitute.

Record Shipment of Quicksilver

While dealing with this interesting metal, I am reminded of a recent record shipment of another comparatively rare and costly element of this kind. This is mercury, or quicksilver, the only metal that is liquid at ordinary temperatures. This metal has recently found a new use in the mercury turbine, in which its vapour plays the same part as does steam in an ordinary turbine engine. The only mercury turbine in the world is being erected in the United States and the 120 tons of mercury required for it reached New York in two instalments, each in 3,553 iron flasks containing 76 lb. of the metal. The total quantity is sufficient to fill 50 million ordinary thermometers, and its value is more than £70,000. The plant in which it is being installed will develop 20,000 Kw. and needless to say great care is being taken to condense the whole of the mercury vapour used in the turbine and to return it to the boiler in which it is evaporated.

Island that Disappears in Winter

Some time ago I mentioned a curious lake in Styria that disappears every summer, when hay and other crops are grown on its bed. There is an equally remarkable lake in Latvia, on which a large island appears every spring, only to vanish when winter approaches. Good use is made of the temporary island, for it yields excellent crops of hay, but even the people who work on it every summer declare that they have never yet witnessed its actual disappearance.

There is a natural explanation for the appearance and disappearance of this strange island. It is believed that a part of the marshy soil at the bottom of the lake has become detached and is lifted to the surface by the gases generated in it in spring, when the temperature is rising and the chemical action producing the gases is becoming more vigorous. The island loses its buoyancy and sinks, when the cold weather of late autumn stops the evolution of gases. The island is not lost, like the grass islands carried down by the River Amazon in the flood season, but reappears next year.

A High Speed Automatic Lathe

Mass Production of Small Turned Parts

IN modern engineering works operations are carried out with remarkable speed and precision, largely by means of automatic machines of various kinds. Great accuracy is necessary in these operations, irrespective of the size of the work, and it is particularly important to keep within fine limits in the production of small parts, such as the screws and other parts that are required for clockwork mechanisms, electric meters and instruments of all kinds, and for use in wireless receivers. The manufacture of such parts as these on a mass production scale demands the use of intricate automatic machinery capable of repeatedly performing various operations at high speed for long periods.

The small parts that have been specially mentioned and others of a similar kind are turned, that is they are produced by means of automatic lathes, and the Wickman 10 m.m. High Speed Precision Automatic Machine illustrated on this page provides a suitable means of manufacturing them with the required accuracy and speed. This lathe is a small one of British manufacture, designed by A. C. Wickman Ltd., Coventry, and made by Bryant Symons and Co., London. It is capable of dealing with a wide variety of work, and the cutting tools required for any operation can be fitted or changed with ease.

The Wickman Automatic Lathe is strongly built, and hardened chrome nickel steel is used for parts that are heavily stressed. All high speed shafts are mounted on ball bearings. The machine is 4 ft. in length and 4 ft. 2 in. in height, and weighs 15 cwt. It may be driven either from a countershaft or by means of a 1 h.p. electric motor running at a speed of 1,410 r.p.m. It takes steel bars up to 4 in. in length and 10 mm., or little more than one third of an inch, in diameter, but contains the mechanism for all the operations that can be carried out on larger lathes.

The machine can be used as a universal lathe controlled by hand, but also can be made entirely automatic in action, when one operator is able to attend to several machines. Push buttons for starting and stopping are placed in a convenient position on the front of the lathe when this is driven by motor, and in addition there is a limit switch that stops the machine when the bar on which work is being carried out is used up. This switch is very sensitive and is brought into action immediately the bar feeding arrangement comes into contact with it.

The headstock, or spindle head, of the lathe is of the sliding type, working on hardened ground surfaces, and for small movements, when the work being turned is up to $2\frac{3}{4}$ in. in length, its motion is controlled by a lever actuated by a plate cam. A separate bell cam is provided for use with longer work, up to the maximum of 4 in. The return movement is obtained by the use of a weight fastened to the headstock by means of a chain. Three spindle speeds are provided, these being 8,967 r.p.m., 6,676 r.p.m. and 4,520 r.p.m. respectively, and for each speed there are available no fewer than 117 changes in feed, or the rate at which the tool advances along the work.

Rear view of the 10 m.m. Wickman High Speed Precision Automatic Lathe with back cover removed to show the motor drive and the drive to the camshaft. Photograph by courtesy of A. C. Wickman Ltd., Coventry.

There are four tool slides, and a micrometer adjustment is provided to enable the tools to be set with great precision in readiness for carrying out operations. The high speeds employed and the robust and rigid construction of the machine allow the use of high speed cutting alloys, and as each part is finished it falls into a work catcher equipped with a device that separates it from the swarf or turnings.

The automatic movements of the tool slides, by which each tool is brought into correct position when required, are controlled by cams mounted on a camshaft. This shaft is driven from the main driving shaft of the machine in such a manner that the rate of feed may be varied within the wide limits already referred to, and the cams are so designed that they can easily be removed without disturbing the camshaft.

Lubrication of all moving parts, with the exception of the main spindle bearings, is by the "one shot" system, and some of the gears incorporated in the machine run in an oil bath. If no provision were made for cooling the work in progress, this would become over-heated during the high speed operations carried out on it, and a centrifugal pump therefore is incorporated to pour over it a stream of coolant, the liquid usually employed for this purpose being oil or an emulsion of oil and water.

An interesting safety device is incorporated in the camshaft mechanism of the lathe. This operates a limit switch that breaks the circuit immediately if the belt driving the spindle is broken.

The "Bristol" Axial Engine

A New Power Unit for Motor Buses

INTERNAL combustion engines have been designed in several forms, the one most familiar to readers being that usually adopted in the engines of motor cars, in which the cylinders are placed in line with their pistons and connecting rods acting on a long crankshaft. Most engines of this type have four or six cylinders, and the greatest number that can conveniently be arranged in this manner appears to be eight. When a larger number of cylinders becomes necessary, in order to give either increased power or greater flexibility, the V-shaped engine is adopted. In this two blocks of cylinders in line are placed at an angle to each other in order to allow of the use of a single common crankshaft, which is shorter than would be required if the same total number of cylinders were used in a single line. A noteworthy example of an engine of this type is that installed in the Rolls-Royce 40 h.p. car introduced in September, 1935, which has 12 cylinders in two blocks of six each.

The crankshaft of the "Bristol" Axial Engine. The crank pin is set at an angle of 22½ deg. Illustrations by courtesy of the Bristol Tramways and Carriage Co. Ltd., Bristol.

Many aeroplane engines are of one of the two types just mentioned. Another type that has been largely used for aircraft is the radial engine. In this the cylinders and crankshaft occupy roughly similar positions to the ribs and stick of an opened umbrella, but the cylinders are set exactly at right angles to the crankshaft, and in comparison with the stick of an umbrella the crankshaft itself is very short.

Engineers never rest in their endeavours to improve their products, and the internal combustion engine is no exception to this rule. Now a new type of engine that possesses many advantages has been developed by the Bristol Tramways and Carriage Co. Ltd. for use in their fleet of motor buses. It is called the "Bristol" Axial Engine, and an idea of its layout can best be obtained by imagining the cylinders of a radial engine closed over the crankshaft in the same manner as the ribs of an umbrella fold over the stick. In this position the cylinders lie in a circle round the crankshaft, and the resulting engine in its casing to some extent resembles an electric motor in appearance. As the lower illustration on this page shows, it is compact, occupying only two-thirds of the space of one of similar capacity with its cylinders in line, and there is an even larger proportional reduction in weight.

The "Bristol" Axial Engine, which has its cylinders parallel to the crankshaft.

The pistons of an axial engine move parallel to the crankshaft, and it seems remarkable that motion in this direction can be transformed into the necessary rotation. This is effected very simply by means of a star member, or "wobble plate," acting on a crank pin that slopes at an angle to the line of the main shaft, as illustrated in our upper photograph. The star member is attached to ball bearings on the ends of the crank pin, which it encloses like a sleeve; and its points project outward, each being attached to the outer end of the connecting rod of one of the cylinders. As the pistons move backward and forward along the cylinders they are at different stages of their cycles of movements, and when the piston in any one cylinder has completed its "downward" motion, that in the opposite cylinder is at the "top" of its stroke. The star member therefore executes a peculiar motion, from which its name of wobble plate is derived. It does not itself rotate, but its action causes the slanting crank pin to turn, carrying the crankshaft with it.

The arrangement of the cylinders in a circle round the crankshaft allows a simple and efficient rotary slide valve system to be used. There is a single port in the end of each cylinder, and the nine ports of the engine are set in segments that together form a circular path for a valve rotating over the heads of the cylinders. The valve has four pairs of inlet and exhaust ports, and these are placed alternately in communication with the single port of each cylinder. One great advantage of this arrangement is that the valve rotates comparatively slowly, its speed being geared down to one eighth of that of the engine itself. The rotary valve has been adopted for this engine not only because it forms a very efficient breathing system, but also because it is cheaper to produce and maintain than a system of poppet valves.

One of the greatest problems in the design of internal combustion engines is that of balancing the reciprocating motion of the pistons and connecting rods against the rotary motion of the crankshaft and other revolving parts. This is essential if undue vibration and wear are to be avoided. The "Bristol" Axial Engine can be balanced with comparative ease by fixing bob weights to the crankshaft at points opposite to the ends of the slanting crank pin. These weights can be seen in the upper illustration on this page, and as they rotate they set up centrifugal forces that tend to turn the engine in the opposite direction to that due to the movements of the pistons and connecting rods.

The capacity of the "Bristol" Axial Engine is seven litres, and it gives more power for a lower consumption of petrol than the "Bristol" engine of the same capacity with its cylinders in line. Other advantages claimed for the new engine are lower maintenance costs, owing to the simplicity of its design and the comparatively small number of its working parts; and high mechanical efficiency. High crankshaft speeds also can be employed because of the use of light reciprocating parts and a geared rotary valve.

HORNBY SERIES

HORNBY ROLLING

KEEP ADDIN

A real railway system is constantly expanding and developing. Ne signal cabins and goods sheds are built: new tunnels and viaducts ar Your Hornby Railway, too, can be run in the same progressive manner. O Signals, Bridges, and Engine Sheds that will gradually conve Remember, the more complete your

***COACH, No. 2 PASSENGER**
Suitable for 2 ft. radius rails only. First-third, or Brake-third. Price 7/6

MO SIDE TIPPING WAGON
Tips either side. Price 1/-

GAS CYLINDER WAGON
Finished in blue and red, lettered gold. Price 1/11

No. I CRANE TRUCK
Finished in gold and blue. The Crane revolves on its base. Price 2/11

WINE WAGON DOUBLE BARREL
Price 4/6

...o. I ...IPPING WAGON
Price 2/-

MO PULLMAN COACH
Price 9d.
MI PULLMAN COACH
(Illustrated). Price 1/-
No. O PULLMAN COACH
Price 1/3

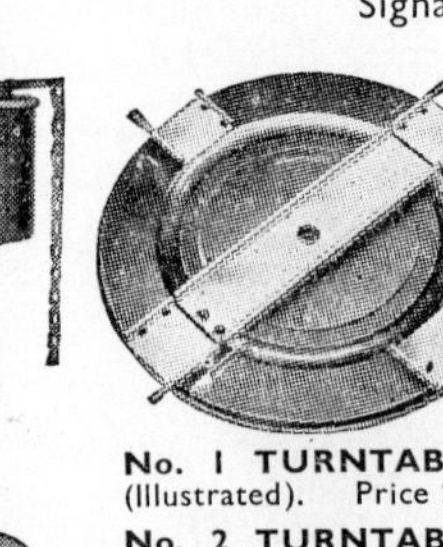

No. 2 WATER TANK
Fitted with flexible tube and valve lever. Stands $8\frac{1}{2}$ in. high. Price 5/9
No. 2E WATER TANK
Similar to No. 2 Water Tank, but suitably fitted for electric lighting. Price 6/6

No. I TURNTABLE
(Illustrated). Price 2/6
No. 2 TURNTABLE
Price 3/9
No. E2 TURNTABLE (Electrical)
Similar to No. 2 Turntable, but fitted with electrical rails. Price 5/6

ISLAND PLATFORM
Length $32\frac{1}{4}$ in., height $6\frac{3}{4}$ in., width 3 in. Price 5/6
The Ramps can be purchased separately. Price per pr. 1/9.

E ISLAND PLAT
This Platform is suitably wired for lighting. Otherwise it is the same as the Island Platform il above. P

No. I RAILWAY ACCESSORIES
Miniature Luggage and Truck. Price 1/-

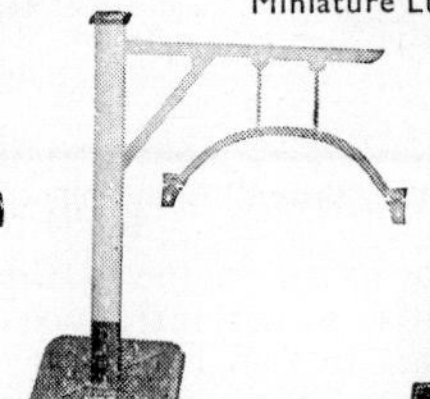

No. 2 BUFFER STOPS
(Hydraulic type). Price 5/6
No. 2E BUFFER STOPS
Similar to No. 2 Buffer Stops but suitably wired for electric lighting. Price 6/-

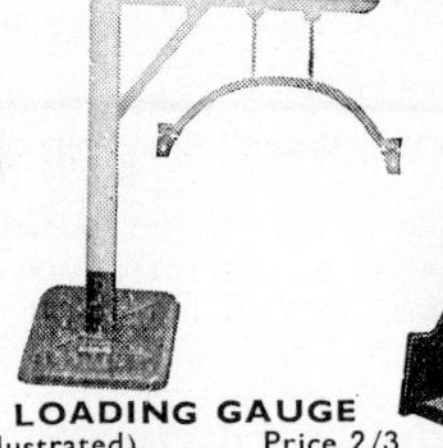

LOADING GAUGE
(Illustrated). Price 2/3
M LOADING GAUGE
Price 1/-

M Series FOOTBRIDGE
Price 1/3

No. 7 RA... ACCESS...
Watchman'... Brazier, Sh... Poker.

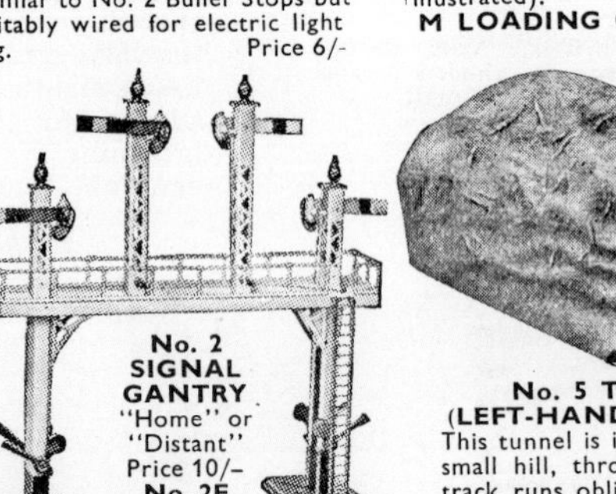

No. 2 SIGNAL GANTRY
"Home" or "Distant" Price 10/-
No. 2E SIGNAL GANTRY
"Home" or "Distant." Price 12/9

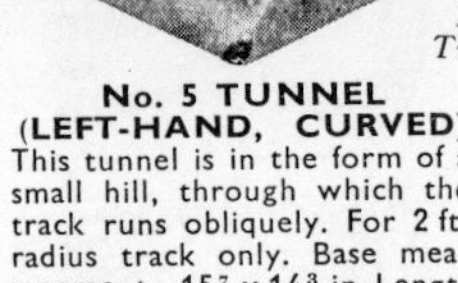

No. 5 Tunnel

No. 5 TUNNEL (LEFT-HAND, CURVED)
This tunnel is in the form of a small hill, through which the track runs obliquely. For 2 ft. radius track only. Base measurement—$15\frac{3}{4} \times 14\frac{3}{4}$ in. Length of track $14\frac{3}{4}$ in. Price 6/9

PLATELAYER'S HUT
Price 1/-

RAILWAY...
Platform M...

No. ...
Built up with three detachable sections. Le...

***No. I CATTLE TRUCK**
Fitted with sliding doors. Price 2/9

***No. I LUGGAGE VAN**
With opening doors. Price 2/9

FIBRE WAGON
This is an interesting model of a type of wagon used in France and other Continental countries. Price 1/3

BITUMEN TANK WAGON "COLAS"
Finished in blue. Price 3/6

No. I LUMBER WAGON
Fitted with bolsters and stanchions. Price 1/6

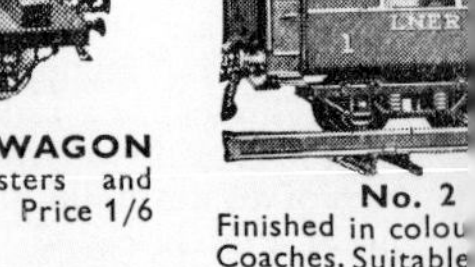

No. 2 ...
Finished in colou... Coaches. Suitable...

OIL TANK WAGON "CASTROL"
Enamelled green with lettering in red. Price 2/-

MO PETROL TANK WAGON "SHELL MEX"
Finished in cream with lettering in black. Price 1/-

No. 2 PULLMAN COACH
Suitable for 2 ft. radius rails only. Price 9/6

SNOW PLOUGH
With revolving plough. Price 3/9

TROLLEY WAG...
Suitable for 2 ft. radius rails o...

**Lettered L.M.S., N.E., G...*

MECCANO LIMITED,

...CK & ACCESSORIES

HORNBY SERIES

...R RAILWAY

...nd new equipment are added: new tracks are laid: new stations, ...very effort is made to cater adequately for modern requirements. ...n add Coaches, Trucks, Wagons and Vans of the latest types; and Stations ... Hornby Railway into a really fine model Railway System. ...the greater your fun and enjoyment.

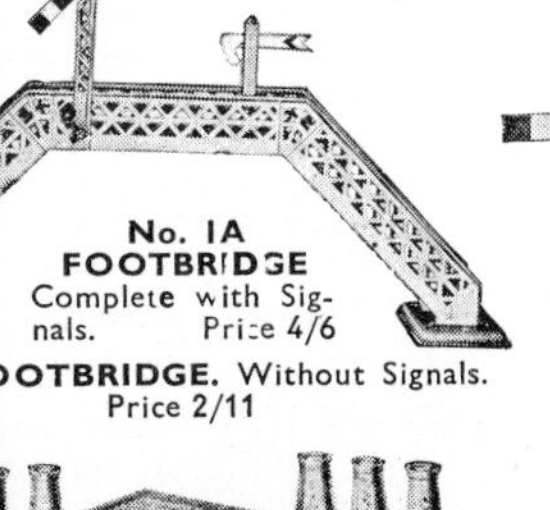

No. 1A FOOTBRIDGE Complete with Signals. Price 4/6

...OOTBRIDGE. Without Signals. Price 2/11

No. 2 ...AILWAY ACCESSORIES ...k Cans and Truck. Price 1/3

No. 1 JUNCTION SIGNAL "Home" or "Distant." Price 2/9

No. 1 SIGNAL CABIN Price 2/6

No. 1E LAMP STANDARD Electrical (Single) Price 2/11

LAMP STANDARD No. 2E Electrical (Double) Price 3/3

No. 1 LAMP STANDARD (Single) Price 3/3

No. 2 LAMP STANDARD (Double, as illustrated) Price 3/9

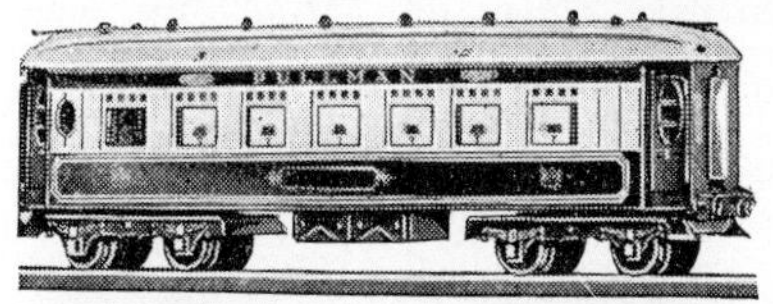

No. 2 SPECIAL PULLMAN COACH Suitable for 2 ft. radius rails only. Price 13/-

BARREL WAGON An interesting model. Price 2/6

CHOCOLATE VAN "CADBURY'S" Opening doors. Price 2/9

...CUTTING (Straight) ...ouble Cutting, mounted ... over which the railway ... be laid. Length 15⅝ in., ... in. Price 6/-

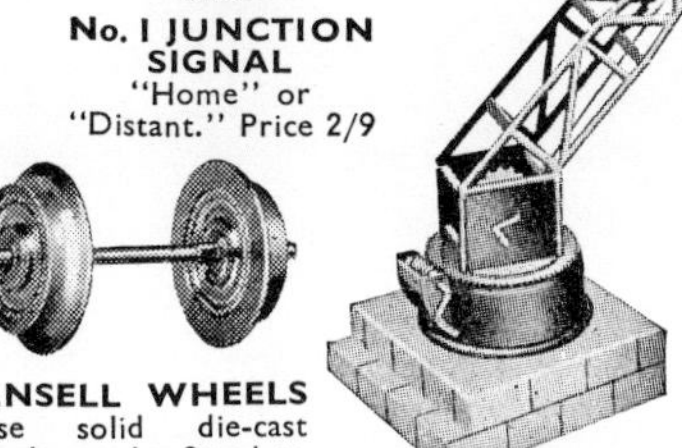

MANSELL WHEELS These solid die-cast Wheels can be fitted to Hornby Coaches, Vans, etc. Price per pair 3d.

PLATFORM CRANE Price 3/11

No. 1 BUFFER STOPS (Spring type). Price 1/-

No. 1E BUFFER STOPS as No. 1, but suitably fitted for electric lighting. Price 1/6

BRAKE VAN Lettered L.M.S. or G.W. Price 2/11

***FLAT TRUCK** Without Cable Drum. Price 1/6 Complete with Cable Drum. Price 1/9

STATION HOARDING Price 6d.

No. 4 Tunnel

No. 3 TUNNEL (Curved) Base measurement—Length 15 in., width 9½ in. Price 4/-

No. 4 TUNNEL (Curved) Base measurement—Length 20 in., Width 9½ in. For 2 ft. radius track only. Price 4/9

...h 6 in., height 7 in. Price 8/-

No. 1 GOODS PLATFORM Length 13 in., height 6⅜ in., width 6 in. Price 5/11

COAL WAGON Fitted with an embossed representation of coal. Price 2/3

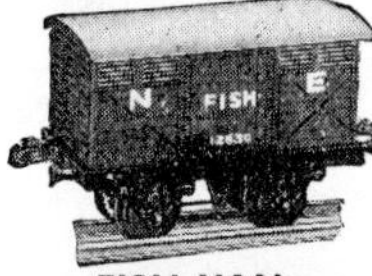

FISH VAN Lettered N.E. only. Price 1/9

MEAT VAN Lettered L.M.S. only Price 1/9

No. 1 ROTARY TIPPING WAGON Finished in blue and pale gold. Price 2/6

...H ...E.R. Saloon ... Price 3/6

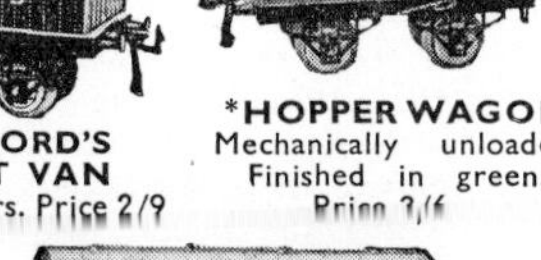

CRAWFORD'S BISCUIT VAN Opening doors. Price 2/9

***HOPPER WAGON** Mechanically unloaded. Finished in green. Price 3/6

No. 2 TIMBER WAGON Suitable for 2 ft. radius rails only. Price 2/6 Enamelled in green and red.

CEMENT WAGON The door at the top opens. Price 2/6

No. 1 BANANA VAN An attractive model, finished in yellow and red. Price 2/9

...OPEN WAGON "B" Price 2/-

***COACH No. 1 PASSENGER** Price 2/6

BREAKDOWN VAN AND CRANE Opening doors. Suitable for 2 ft. radius rails only. Price 5/11

WAGON, COVERED (FRENCH TYPE) Price 2/6

BRAKE VAN Finished in brown, with opening doors. Obtainable in N.E. or S.R. lettering. Price 2/11

Books to Read

Here we review books of interest and of use to readers of the "M.M." We can supply copies of these books to readers who cannot obtain them through the usual channels. Order from Book Dept., Meccano Limited, Binns Road, Liverpool 13, adding 1/- for postage to the price. Postage on different books varies, but any balance remaining will be refunded.

"L.M.S.R. Enginemen's M.I.C. Papers, 1935"

(L.M.S. Magazine. 4d., post free)

On page 374 of the *"M.M."* for June last year attention was drawn to a booklet, published by the *"L.M.S. Magazine,"* that consisted of reprints of special articles appearing in that journal during 1934 on subjects of practical interest to enginemen. We have now received a copy of a similar reprint containing articles of the same type that were published in the *"L.M.S. Magazine"* during 1935. Like its predecessor, this is intended to convey to railwaymen exact information on locomotive mechanisms, but also will be attractive to all readers of the *"M.M."* who are railway enthusiasts.

The most prominent feature of the booklet is an article on Diesel locomotives, contributed by D. C. Urie, L.M.S.R. Superintendent of Motive Power. This is in two parts, one explaining the general principles of internal combustion engines, and the other dealing more particularly with the Diesel engine and the transmission gear of Diesel locomotives.

Other topics dealt with include the latest form of L.M.S.R. Walschaerts valve gear, the new standard brake valve of the company, and the exhaust steam injector, the working of which is explained at length. Instructive diagrams help to make clear the operation of each of the appliances described, and as far as space allows notes are included on the course to be followed in the event of failure on the road.

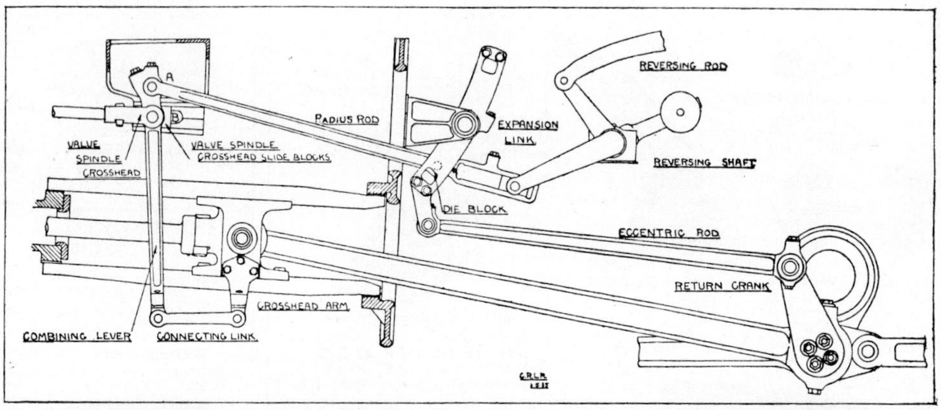

Diagram showing the Walschaerts valve gear employed on the most recent L.M.S.R. locomotives. (From "L.M.S.R. Enginemen's M.I.C. Papers, 1935," reviewed on this page.)

"Aeronautics"

By M. J. B. Davy, A.F.R.A.E.S.
(H.M. Stationery Office. 2/6 net)

This publication is intended to serve as an introduction to the study of the development of heavier-than-air craft, with special reference to that section of the National Aeronautical Collection at the Science Museum, London, which has been formed to illustrate this branch of science. The aim of the author has been to indicate the more important stages in the evolution of mechanical flight by providing a brief account of the early speculations and experimental work that led to the invention of the aeroplane and its subsequent development.

This historical survey is followed by a detailed catalogue of the heavier-than-air craft exhibits in the Science Museum. The book is illustrated with many excellent photographs of early and present types of aircraft, and is rounded off by a very useful index.

"The Revolution in Physics"

By Ernst Zimmer. (Faber and Faber. 12/6 net)

We have long been accustomed to the idea that everything is built up of atoms, and in recent years we have probed more deeply into this problem and discovered the electrons, protons and other particles from which the atom is built up. The most recent discoveries in this field can fairly be described as sensational, for they show that at times matter appears to consist of waves instead of the solid particles that we have previously imagined. The author of this account of modern physics therefore is justified in making use of its startling title.

The book is one of the best of its kind, and the explanations given in it of modern scientific ideas are remarkably clear and simple, as far as accounts of such complicated matters can be. It is not one for beginners in science, but rather for those who already have some knowledge of physics, to whom it will give clear ideas of recent advances, and will appeal to all who are attracted by the scientific world picture.

"Elementary Craftwork in Metal"

By Alfred J. Shirley
(B. T. Batsford Ltd. 5/- net)

The author's aim in preparing this book was to provide a basis on which teachers and students might work in the early stages of handcraft in metal. Its first two sections deal with design and with the chief materials and processes, and then follows a graded course of models, each illustrated by a full-page plate of drawings, and an appendix containing a miscellaneous collection of useful information. Apart from its main purpose the book will be of great interest and value to all who are interested in metalcraft.

"Science in Wonderland"

By Professor A. M. Low. (Lovat Dickson. 5/- net)

With this book Professor Low breaks new ground to a large extent in abandoning the usual popular descriptions of various scientific wonders, and instead taking the twins John and Betty into the heart of things by changing them into molecules, electric charges, sound waves, etc., and relating their physical and chemical adventures. The author writes interestingly, and generally speaking his experiment is a success. The book should make a definite appeal to the average boy or girl with scientific interests, and certainly should arouse their curiosity to seek further information on the various topics. The illustrations by Gilbert Dunlop are well suited to the text.

"The Book of Speed"

(B. T. Batsford Ltd 5/- net)

This volume was first published in 1934, and met with so great a demand that a further edition has now become necessary. The opportunity has been taken of bringing it up to date by the inclusion of an additional chapter, appropriately entitled *"The Pace in 1935,"* dealing with the records established in the past year, and of many new photographs illustrating the additional speed events described in it.

The successive chapters of the book describe great speed achievements in aeroplanes, airships, motor cars, motor cycles, steam ships, speed boats and railway trains, explaining how the records established have been raised as Man's mastery over his materials has increased. Thrilling accounts are given of famous speed events, such as the creation of the world's land speed record by Sir Malcolm Campbell, and the flight in which 400 m.p.h. was reached for the first time in history. These are contributed by the men who actually took part in them, and readers can appreciate the difficulties of their tasks and the sensations they experienced while engaged in efforts that have "caused the world to shrink, and increased the pace of life," as the effect of their work is described in the foreword to the book, which is written by Comdr. Stephen King-Hall.

One of the most attractive features of the book is its wealth of photogravure illustrations. There are 150 of these, many of them occupying a full page. All are reproductions of actual photographs and they cover every phase of the world of speed.

"Chemical Discovery and Invention in the 20th Century"

By Sir W. A. Tilden, F.R.S. (Routledge. 15/- net)

This remarkable book by the late Sir W. A. Tilden was first issued in 1917, and has now been revised by Mr S. Glasstone, who has brought each section thoroughly up to date. The book is a complete survey of chemical progress since the beginning of the present century. It is invaluable to students who wish to look ahead and see something of the more complicated regions of the chemical world into which they have entered, and also will provide fascinating reading for all readers of the "*M.M.*" who wish to know how chemists work and what they are doing.

The plan adopted by the author is distinctly original, for he begins with descriptions of famous modern laboratories and explains how the equipment provided is employed in chemical work of all kinds. This section in fact forms a complete guide to the activities of the chemist, in whatever branch of work he may be engaged, and enables the reader to picture the scene within the chemist's workshop.

An excellent account of modern discoveries and theories then follows. This deals with many subjects of absorbing interest, including the discovery of radium, the structure of the atoms and the architecture of molecules, and the properties of colloids. Modern applications of chemical discovery in daily life and industry are then dealt with, and to many readers it will be a revelation to find in how many places the chemist is in contact with his everyday activities. Particularly striking chapters deal with hormones and vitamins, those mysterious chemicals that are essential to bodily health, the development of the plastic industry that has given us insulating compounds that can readily be moulded to artistic shapes, and the production of plant food by electrical means from the nitrogen of the air.

Although chemical formulæ are used, as of course they must be in dealing with the more complicated substances, it is not necessary to have a deep knowledge of chemistry to be able to appreciate the contents of the book. Illustrations have been used freely, for in addition to portraits of 12 famous chemists closely associated with the developments dealt with, the book contains 131 drawings and plates, most of the latter being photographic reproductions of scenes in famous laboratories and in chemical works.

Arc furnaces at Notodden, Norway, that are employed in the manufacture of nitrates from the air. (From "Chemical Discovery and Invention," reviewed on this page.)

"Science in the Making"

By Gerald Heard. (Faber and Faber Ltd. 7/6 net)

The material of this book is made up largely of the talks on science that were broadcast some time ago by Mr. Heard. The author's idea is that whereas the specialist is steadily pushing forward science in its various branches, he has neither the time nor the inclination to bring his work before the general public in a form that they can understand. Still less is it the job of the specialist to link up his work with that of other investigators, in such a manner as to place before the public a picture of the advance of science as a whole. The author therefore concludes that this job is one for the layman—hence the present book.

Mr. Heard is in close touch with the scientific literature of the day, and he has set himself the task of passing on, as one layman to another, the most striking and interesting facts he has gleaned. The result is an exceedingly interesting account of recent scientific discoveries and tendencies, covering practically every branch of science in which the average man is likely to be interested. The book can be thoroughly recommended to all who wish to know what is going on in the scientific world without struggling through the complexities of scientific literature.

A volume of this size is a little forbidding without a single illustration, and the sections would have been easier to read if broken up into shorter paragraphs.

Natives agitating the contents of an indigo vat by beating the liquid with paddles in order to cause the dyestuff to separate from it. (See above.)

"Track Topics"

By W. G. Chapman. (Great Western Railway, Paddington Station, London, W.2. Price 1/-)

The shilling handbooks issued by the G.W.R. "For Boys Of All Ages" are well known and deservedly popular. The latest addition to the series, "Track Topics," is fully up to the standard set by its predecessors, and is accurately described by its sub-title: "A Book Of Railway Engineering." It is arranged as a series of talks, and in the first one we are given some idea of the extent and variety of the activities of the G.W.R. Engineering Department, which has to deal with a total of over 9,000 miles of track, 1,675 stations for passenger and goods traffic, 12,000 bridges, and a total tunnel length of 60 miles.

We are told much about Brunel, that giant among the early engineers, and his various G.W.R. achievements, culminating in his remarkable Royal Albert Bridge at Saltash, whereby he linked Devon with Cornwall. The components of the track of to-day are dealt with, including a description of their manufacture; and in addition to ordinary track, the various types of crossings in use are dealt with by diagram and description.

The maintenance work involved on the way and works generally leads up to a complete account of the Severn Tunnel, in view of its special position in regard to constructional difficulties and the elaborate plant necessary for keeping it in a fit condition. Viaducts and bridges come in for their share of attention, also the special means necessary for the safe carriage of exceptionl loads whose weight or bulk necessitate engineering restrictions on the route. Finally there is a general talk on railway buildings.

Altogether it is a most interesting and entertaining book, very well illustrated, that will be read and referred to time and again by "*M.M.*" readers generally and in particular by G.W.R. enthusiasts

"The World of Nature"

By H. C. Knapp-Fisher (Gollancz. 6/- net)

Mr. Knapp-Fisher has set out to explain the world of nature for readers who have had no special scientific training, and has written an attractive and accurate account of the forms and lives of the many creatures inhabiting it. He begins with a study of living things on the sea shore, and after dealing in a short section with what we know of the manner in which life is affected by its surroundings, he passes on to discuss the plant world, insect life and the creatures that can be summed up under the title "Fish, Flesh and Fowl." Thus he covers a very wide field, with satisfaction to his readers, who also will greatly appreciate the well executed line drawings in the book that provide illustrations of more than 500 forms of life.

Traffic Signals in Miniature

Automatic Control of Model Crossing

By S. B. Johnson and N. B. Fortune

AS schoolmasters in charge of classes of keen and enquiring boys, we are expected to know something about everything, and in particular are continually being asked how things work. With the growing use of automatic traffic control signals, it was only natural that we should be called upon to explain their operation, and we decided that this could best be done by making a demonstration model. Some of our enquirers were boys from 13 to 14 years of age, and with them we tackled the problem of designing and constructing such a model. No published instructions were available, but a highly successful scheme was evolved, working from first principles, and the constructional work gave ample scope for the skill and ingenuity of the wood worker, the metal worker, the electrician and the engineer.

A model of an automatically controlled traffic crossing, with a Meccano Motor Car Constructor model waiting for the signal to cross. The model was constructed by pupils of Lapage Street Modern School, Bradford, under the supervision of the authors of the accompanying article.

A sheet of plywood one yard square, strengthened with battens underneath it, provided the foundation for the model, and across it four substantial strips of wood were screwed to outline the crossing. The road surfaces are represented by pieces of plywood 1 ft. in width. These are made to slide in grooves in the cross-strips, and can be removed when desired to reveal the wiring, which is laid in the space, about 1 in. in depth, beneath them.

The rotating switch controlling the signals. This is driven by a Meccano E6 Electric Motor and current for the various circuits is picked up by copper brushes.

Making the signal standards provided a satisfying exercise for the ingenious constructors. They were turned in the workshop lathe from $1\frac{1}{4}$ in. square section oak, and orange lacquered wooden globes were added as a final embellishment. A section at the top of each of course was left rectangular in shape. Three holes $\frac{3}{4}$ in. in diameter and about $\frac{3}{8}$ in. in depth were bored in these sections, and three further holes $\frac{3}{4}$ in. in diameter were drilled at right angles to the first set to form the lamp chambers. Meccano $3\frac{1}{2}$-volt lamps were easily inserted in these chambers by a screwing action, so that the central contacts projected slightly outside.

A flat drill was next passed up the centre of each pylon from the base to break into the first lamp chamber, this work also being carried out on the lathe. The holes made in this manner house the wiring. As the model is intended for demonstration purposes, it is desirable that the leads to the lamps themselves should be visible. For this reason they were brought to the outside of the pylon through small holes, and run in grooves cut with a blunt mechanical gauge to their respective lamps, and soldered directly to the central contacts. The common return lead was looped across to make contact with the screw fittings when the lamps were inserted. Before wiring, the black and white strips were applied to the pylons with lacquer, the work on the curved surfaces being adroitly accomplished while each standard was rotated in the lathe.

Metal facings were next cut from sheet copper to cover the open sides of the lamp chambers, and holes were bored in them to correspond with those in the standards. Cowls of the same material were soldered on and painted. The next problem was to add the coloured media for the lamps. At first we thought of using coloured glass, but finally decided in favour of sheet gelatine. This is too transparent to be satisfactory by itself, and small squares of the material in appropriate colours therefore were glued on to strips of thin semi-opaque paper—jam covers actually were used—and these in turn were glued in position on the backs of the prepared metal facings. The result proved entirely satisfactory, the light being well diffused and sufficiently powerful.

There are 12 lamps in the four robots, and our first idea was to wire them in parallel and control them with a four-contact rotary switch. After many experiments this proposal was abandoned, for we realised that we could not reproduce the correct sequence of colours in this manner. As readers probably know, the full changing sequence is amber alone, red alone, red and amber together and green alone, amber alone again showing when the green light disappears. When amber is showing on one pair of diagonally opposite signals, the other pair must show amber and red. These changes cannot be accomplished with the circuit we had in mind originally, and in the end we decided to wire each pair of diagonally opposite signals in separate parallel circuits, both of which themselves were in parallel.

The model with the plywood representations of the road surface removed to show the wiring.

A distributor had then to be designed in order to supply each lamp with current at the correct moment and to maintain it for the required period. This took the form of a cylinder of wood on which we screwed seven curved brass strips to make contact with brushes leading current to the lamps. The strips were soldered together to make electrical contact, so that when current is applied to any one part of the strips it can be picked up again at any other part. The central strip passes right round the cylinder and provides the common pickup. On each side of it are the three strips required for each of the two circuits, and the lengths of these and their positions were so adjusted that contact was made with their respective brushes at the exact time required, and for the correct period, as the drum was slowly rotated. The brush leading current into the common pickup strip was placed on the opposite side of the drum to the two sets of three brushes by means of which current is led to the lamps.

An enlarged view of the top of one of the robots with a cover plate removed to show the lamp chambers.

The drum is driven by a Meccano E6 motor through simple gearing employing a Worm, Part No. 32, meshing with a 57-teeth Gear Wheel, Part No. 27A, that is carried on a $3\frac{1}{2}''$ Axle Rod suitably supported on two Angle Brackets, Part No. 12A, bolted to the motor casing. On the same shaft and between the Angle Brackets is another Worm that engages with a Pinion Wheel, Part No. 26, fitted to the end of a $6\frac{1}{2}$ in. Axle Rod that passes through the motor frame and forms the axis of the drum. The Axle Rods are positioned by Collars and the drum end of the $6\frac{1}{2}$ in. Axle Rod is supported by a Bracket. Bush Wheels screwed to the ends of the drum secured it to its axis. This construction is shown in the lower illustration on the opposite page.

Current is supplied through a mains transformer that had previously been built by one of the boys engaged in making the model. This transformer has two output circuits, one of 4 volts that is employed for lighting the lamps, and another of variable voltage that is adapted to drive the Meccano E6 Motor. A Meccano T6A Transformer would be ideal for use with the model. Accumulators also could be employed, and a clockwork motor would serve to drive the drum if an electric motor were not available.

The wiring is carried out in the coloured connecting medium employed by radio constructors, the insulation of the leads to the red, amber and green signal lamps being red, yellow and green in colour respectively. The return lead is common to the two parallel circuits and is in blue. The actual layout of the connecting wires is shown in the upper illustration on this page. The ends of all wires leading to the brushes were soldered in position. The brushes were made of copper strip hammered flat at the end and were carefully bent to the height necessary for correct timing.

An independent switch was incorporated in the lighting circuit, and we also found it advisable to insert a small resistance, for surges in the current provided by the transformer caused a tendency to burn out the lamps.

Pedestrian crossings with miniature beacons, white lines on the roadways, and pavements partly covered with coloured sandpaper to represent grass verges were added to the model. These are not essential, but they enhance the appearance and realism of the structure.

FROM OUR READERS

These pages are reserved for articles from our readers. Contributions not exceeding 500 words in length are invited on any subject of general interest. These should be written neatly on one side of the paper only, and they may be accompanied by photographs or sketches for use as illustrations. Articles that are published will be paid for at our usual rates. Statements contained in articles submitted for these pages are accepted as being sent in good faith, but the Editor takes no responsibility for their accuracy.

Animals on Our Rhodesian Ranch

Many boys have become acquainted with the wild beasts of other countries by seeing them at zoos. It is interesting to watch them through the bars of a cage or enclosure, but it is much more fascinating to observe them in their natural homes.

An antelope killed on a Rhodesian ranch. Photograph by R. Robertson, Enstone.

Out in Rhodesia, where I lived for some years on a farm with my parents, there were many wild animals, and on our walks we often saw antelope, the most common being duiker, koodoo and bushbuck. It is pretty to see two or three duiker playing together or grazing. If we wanted them to look up, a sharp whistle would attract them; but the smallest movement on our part caused them to bound quickly away. They are about two feet in height and very graceful. Their fawn coats tone in very well with their surroundings, especially in the dry season. It is a fine sight to see a herd of koodoo, with the white stripes on their grey bodies showing up in the sunlight. The bulls are distinguishable by their long spiral horns, sometimes measuring as much as 52 or 53 inches. Koodoo cows do not carry horns. The chief enemies of the antelope are lions, leopards, and wild dogs. We seldom saw any of these animals in the daytime, as they hunt their prey at night.

Wild pigs are common in all parts of Rhodesia, and are a trouble to any farmer who grows maize. They raid the crops at night, eating large quantities of cobs and trampling down the plants. Farmers are therefore obliged to employ natives armed with guns to guard the crops, and to shoot down as many wild pigs as they can. My father gave the natives thus employed a shilling for every pig they killed, and all the meat except the hams, which had to be brought to him.

We often saw monkeys, generally swinging from one branch to another among the trees. There were some rocky hills on the farm on which dwelt colonies of baboons, and their barking cries could be heard from a considerable distance. Often, at night, might be heard a baboon screaming because it was evidently being attacked by a leopard. Driving near these hills it was quite a common sight to see groups of baboons. As they heard the approach of the car, male baboons about the size of small men would hurry across the road, followed by mother baboons with babies hastily hoisted on their backs.

The rhinoceros is not often seen in civilised parts. My father shot one once on our farm, however, which was situated only 23 miles from the nearest town. We all went to see the great beast, and I noticed how small its eyes were in comparison to its great bulk, and how thick the skin.

R. Robertson (Enstone).

The Fairlie locomotive "Merddin Emrys," of the Festiniog Railway, North Wales. Photograph by P. V. Davies, Penmaenmawr.

The Festiniog Railway

The Festiniog Railway in North Wales has the distinction of being the pioneer of narrow gauge railways. It was constructed in 1836 for the conveyance of slate from the quarries at Blaenau Festiniog down to Portmadoc, 14 miles away, for export, and is only 1 ft. 11½ in. in gauge.

The average gradient is 1 in 92 and the steepest 1 in 68.

At first the loaded slate trains travelled down to Portmadoc by gravity and the empty trucks were hauled back to the quarry by horses. Steam engines of the ordinary rigid frame type, tried on the route in 1863, proved unsatisfactory, but in 1869 a Fairlie articulated double-boiler locomotive was acquired, and was a great success. It was called *"Little Wonder,"* and its excellent performance attracted the attention of railway engineers all over the world. In 1870 a Royal Commission visited the district to study the railway and particularly its locomotive, and they were accompanied by representatives of many foreign countries.

A fine view of New York's skyscrapers. Photograph by D. Rebbeck, Knock, Co. Down.

The Festiniog line now has three Fairlie engines, one of which, the *"Merddin Emrys,"* is illustrated on the opposite page. They are very powerful and accomplish the up journey in an hour. A few 0–4–0 tender engines are used for slate traffic and for passenger trains when no "Fairlie" is available. The company have built all their own locomotives and rolling stock at their works at Boston Lodge, near Portmadoc. The line is very popular with tourists, and 64,000 passengers were carried along it in 1934.

P. V. Davies (Penmaenmawr).

A Free Trip Across the Atlantic

Each summer several of the large shipping companies take undergraduates from British Universities as supernumerary engineers on their ships. They give them a free passage out and home again, plenty of practical experience, and all the comforts of a first-class passenger. I had the good fortune last summer to enjoy this privilege, and made a free trip to New York and Bermuda and back, through the courtesy of the Cunard White Star Line.

Being greatly interested in Diesel engines, I was delighted to be aboard the fine motor liner *"Britannic,"* when she sailed from King George V Dock, London, on 12th July last year. After making calls at Le Havre, Southampton and Cobh, we set out across the Atlantic, with 450 passengers. The voyage was uneventful, and there was rather too much fog for my liking. I was on the four to eight watch, and when not down in the engine room I had lots of fun playing tennis, quoits, etc., on deck.

We arrived in New York at 9 a.m. on 21st July, and as we were due to sail the next evening I had not long to explore this great city. I managed to do quite a lot in the time, however, and my adventures included an ascent to the top of the Empire State building, the tallest building in the world, and a visit to Radio City, where I had the thrill of broadcasting for 10 minutes as a visitor "from the other side."

We sailed from New York on 22nd July at 5.30 p.m. for a week's cruise to Bermuda, with 1,250 passengers. During the three days we were at Bermuda I saw a wonderful display of fish and live coral at the aquarium, viewed the coral reefs through glass - bottomed boats, travelled many miles on coral roads and on an interesting narrow gauge railway, and surf bathed from beautiful beaches.

I had two more days in New York before sailing for home on the 26th July, and during that time I saw the *"Normandie"* arrive. I saw her again at Le Havre when the *"Britannic"* called there on the homeward trip. My arrival back at London on 7th August ended a most interesting trip.

D. Rebbeck (Knock, Co. Down).

Guiana's Mighty Cataract

The Kaieteur Fall, British Guiana, which is five times as high as Niagara. Photograph by R. Weil, Capetown.

One of the most magnificent cataracts in the world occurs on the Potaro River in British Guiana. It is the mighty Kaieteur waterfall which, until the recent introduction of air services provided better travelling facilities to tourists, had been visited by very few people since its discovery just over 60 years ago. The first white person to see the Fall was a Mr. C. Barrington Brown, who came upon it in April 1870, while engaged in a geological survey.

The breadth of the Fall at the brink varies according to the season, and the maximum width attained is about 400 ft. The total drop is 822 ft., and 740 ft. of this is a sheer perpendicular plunge, the remaining 82 ft. being a sloping cataract. Kaieteur is thus five times higher than Niagara. It is produced by the swiftly flowing river leaping over an immense escarpment of sandstone and conglomerate into a deep gorge. In the flood season the magnificence of this vast curtain of seething water amid a tropical landscape of great beauty is beyond description.

The name "Kaieteur," sometimes spelt "Kaieteuk," is a Red Indian word meaning "Old Man"; and the Fall got its name from the Carib custom of getting rid of the "old men" by sending them down the Falls, to be battered to death in the maelstrom below.

R. Weil (Capetown).

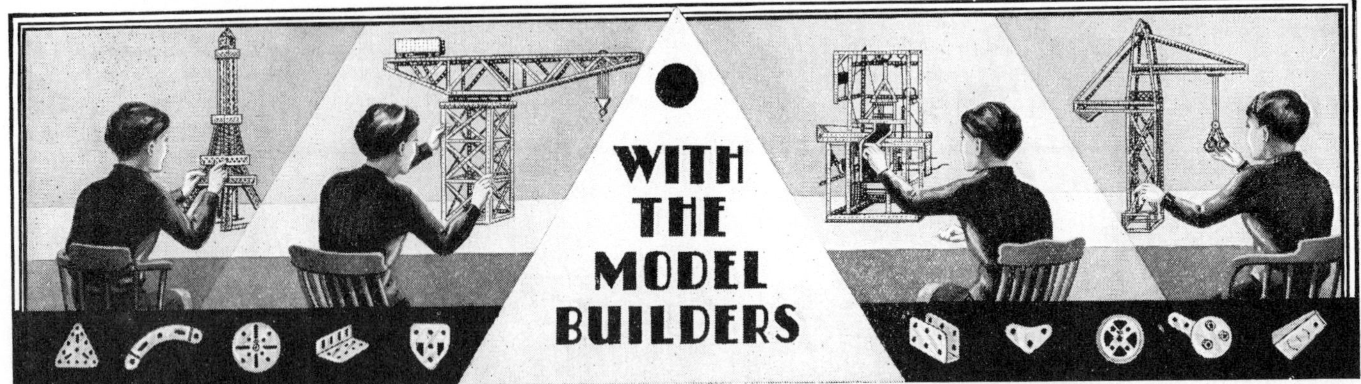

BRIDGE MODELS

On another page of this issue the model-building possibilities offered by bridges are dealt with, and here we illustrate an unusual view of a model of the new Sydney Harbour Bridge that is of special interest on account of the new use for Dinky Toys. This fine model closely reproduces the features of the massive arch spanning the harbour at Sydney, and the illustration shows how the Dinky Toy Cars are made to travel from end to end. The miniature vehicles are guided along the roadways between Strips at the outsides and a long Rod down the centre. Flat Girders are used for the roadways and are so arranged that a slot is formed in the centre of each. A small sheet of tin is cut to the size and shape required and inserted at each end of the bridge to extend the roadways.

A 2" Sprocket is fixed on a vertical Rod at each end of the bridge, and a continuous Chain running between them is arranged immediately beneath the slots in the roadway. A tensioning device is fitted to take up slack in the Chain by mounting the Rod of one of the Sprockets in a pivoted frame controlled by Springs. A short length of wire is attached beneath each Car near the front, and secured to the Sprocket Chain in such a manner that it does not interfere with the Chain passing round the Sprockets. The Rod of each Sprocket projects upwards above the level of the roadway and carries a Coupling, and the Rod that is in fixed bearings is driven from a Motor. As the Chain moves between the Sprockets the Cars are hauled along the bridge. On reaching the ends of the bridge they swing round the Couplings, Curved Strips being arranged to guide them into the roadways again. One of the Curved Strips can be seen on the left of the illustration.

The wires joining the Cars to the Chain should not be too long or the Cars will strike the Curved Strip at a wide angle and will not turn properly. In fixing them to the Chain the joints should be made neatly so as not to interfere with the smooth running of the Chain.

CURVED STRIPS

The present Meccano range of Curved Strips makes it possible to build many different curved structures, and among the several sizes available suitable parts will generally be found for almost any purpose. Occasionally, however, it is found that the Strips make curves slightly smaller or larger than those required for special purposes, and in cases where it is not possible to vary the construction slightly to accommodate existing Strips the model builder must devise substitutes. Very good curved strips can be made by bolting Flat Brackets together. By this means a strip of any length can be formed, it being possible to adjust the length within very fine limits owing to the play allowed in the slotted holes of the Strips. It is obvious that curved strips made up in this manner can be of large or small radius. In special cases they can be used for the rims of wheels. Flat Brackets can thus be resorted to for solving many small difficulties of construction, and it will be realised that their applications are not limited to the construction of regular curves as they can be used for forming almost any shape.

FUNNELS FOR SHIP MODELS

Funnels form one of the most conspicuous features of a model steamship or motor ship, a fact fully realised by shipbuilders who sometimes employ dummy funnels in order to improve the appearance of a vessel. Builders of small motor ships can greatly enhance the appearance by using the Meccano Ships' Funnels. These are available in two forms, No. 138, which is an upright cylindrical funnel, and Nos. 138a-z, which are of the raked type of oval cross section. The latter are available in correct colours representative of 26 different steamship companies.

Larger funnels can be made from Strips with which it is possible to make a number of different sizes and shapes to suit the vessel under construction. The best method of using these is to arrange them longitudinally and to join them together by Flat Brackets or Obtuse Angle Brackets. It will thus be apparent that by this means the tall slender funnels of the older steamships can be reproduced just as well as the modern fat and stubby funnels of motor vessels.

For large ships excellent funnels can be made from Boilers, and as these are made of fairly pliable metal they can be compressed to form funnels narrower than the standard diameter of the Boiler. The parts can be mounted at an angle, and if the ships are intended to represent those of particular steamship companies the Boilers can be enamelled in the correct colours. There are many model-builders who prefer not to enamel the Boilers as this rather spoils them for further use, and for these constructors there is the alternative of covering the parts with suitably coloured paper.

LARGE GEARS FOR ROLLER BEARINGS

Roller bearing units using Ring Frames or Hub Discs for races can be rotated through friction drive by using a rubber shod pulley that bears on the rim of one of the races. An extra large gear for providing a positive drive can be made by fixing Sprocket Chain round the rim of the roller race. The Chain should be a tight fit round the rim and can be held in place by short loops of wire. The wire should be passed through the holes on the inside of the race and a Washer may be inserted to prevent the loop pulling through. The ends of the loop are then passed through the Chain and bent over in a similar manner to that adopted for fixing the Dredger Bucket clips. The clips of Dredger Buckets can be used instead but the wire will generally be found more satisfactory.

Sprocket Wheels engage the Chain to drive the race. The race is thus converted into a large gear wheel and can be used in any model where an extra large gear is required. Sprocket Chain can be used in this manner for making up large gears of several different sizes, but the most suitable parts to use will be found to be Hub Discs and Ring Frames.

Dinky Toy Cars are hauled along the roadway on this model of the Sydney Harbour Bridge. One of them is shown turning at the end of the bridge.

ROLLER BEARING FOR SMALL OUTFITS

The usual method of supporting rotating structures in models built with small Outfits is to place one 3" Pulley over another to form a substitute for the more satisfactory roller bearing. There is considerable friction between the rims of the two Pulleys and much better results are obtained when a roller bearing or ball bearing unit is used. The objection to such a bearing is that of the number of parts required, but it is possible to make quite a useful roller bearing by using 3" Pulleys and ¾" Flanged Wheels. The Flanged Wheels are free to rotate on Rods carried in a Coupling. One Rod is passed through the centre transverse hole of the Coupling and two shorter Rods are fixed at right angles to the first in each end hole. The Flanged Wheels are retained in position by Collars or Spring Clips. A Threaded Pin screwed into one of the centre tapped holes in the Coupling is passed through the boss of one of the Pulleys, and another Threaded Pin can be used in the opposite tapped hole of the Coupling, or if two Threaded Pins are not available a long bolt can be used instead.

No difficulty occurs in arranging a drive for rotating the upper Pulley. It can be driven from a ½" or a 1" Pulley by a length of cord or a rubber band, and if Cord is used it will be found advisable to pass it twice round each Pulley to ensure a good grip.

MECCANO CAMS.—A number of readers have put forward suggestions for cams of various shapes to be introduced to the Meccano range. Cams can be applied to many purposes in model building, but the present range of parts is so adaptable that we have not yet encountered a case where standard parts cannot be used for making cams to reproduce the movement required. The functions of a small cam such as you propose are fulfilled by a Collar fitted with a 7/32" Grub Screw or with a bolt. The length of the projection above the Collar governs the lift of the cam and by fitting a longer or shorter bolt different lifts can be obtained. This would not be possible if a special part were introduced. The bolts do not give quite such a smooth movement as a properly designed cam but they are quite suitable for most purposes, and if a gentle lift is required for the tappet, the Kemex Stand Clamp (Part No. K31) can be used. This part is in the form of a large boss that is drilled eccentrically and fits snugly on a Meccano Collar or Coupling.

Larger cams can be built up to obtain almost any movement. Bush Wheels are usually the most useful parts for this purpose, and by bolting to them Flat Brackets, 1" Triangular Plates, Pawls without bosses, etc., a large variety of cams can be made. (*Reply to G. Meyer, Johannesburg.*)

SHIPS' VENTILATORS.—Ventilators add a note of realism to model ships and the proposal that these parts should be introduced to the Meccano range is quite interesting. It is, however, doubtful if the demand for them would justify their production as it is unlikely that they would be so popular as the Ships' Funnels. It is possible to make quite realistic representations of ventilators from existing Meccano parts such as Sleeve Pieces and Chimney Adaptors, or if very small ones are required Collars can be fitted on the ends of Screwed Rods. Most model builders obtain more satisfaction from building a model in which such items as these must be thought out and built up with standard parts, than they would if the essential parts were already made for them. (*Reply to H. M. Hodge, Plymouth.*)

WIDE-FACE GEARS.—Gears having face widths the same as the Pinions would have doubtful advantages in gear-box construction. Owing to their extra width they would necessitate greater sliding movement to disengage Pinions and would consequently make gear-boxes rather cumbersome. In certain cases wider Gears would be useful but these few instances would scarcely justify the cost of manufacture, and as this would be comparatively high the demand for the parts would be very limited. Two Gears can be butted together to give a double width face for use in special cases. (*Reply to W. H. Ward, Birmingham 15.*)

RATCHET SPANNER.—This is an interesting idea as no doubt such a tool would have certain advantages over the present type, but it is rarely that a case arises where a ratchet spanner seems really necessary. Owing to its special design the standard Spanner fulfils requirements for all ordinary model building, and we do not think that the restricted uses for a ratchet spanner would warrant its manufacture. (*Reply to S. Wilson, Southampton.*)

Motor Car Transmission Mechanism

A New Type of Differential Unit

SOME of the most interesting problems in connection with the construction of modern motor cars arise in designing the means of transmitting the power of the engine to the road wheels. A purely mechanical transmission usually is employed. This incorporates a clutch, gear-box, propeller shaft and a differential. Of these mechanisms the differential probably is the most ingenious and interesting. Its purpose is to divide the final drive and carry the power of the engine to each rear wheel independently. This is necessary, for when a car is steered to the right or left the outer road wheels travel over a greater distance than the inner ones and therefore turn faster. The use of a differential allows each of the driving wheels to rotate at its correct speed.

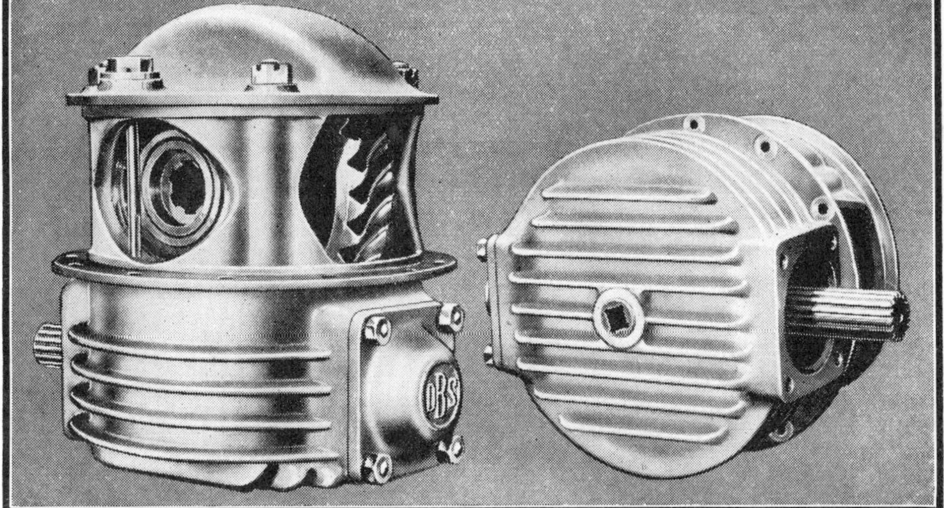

Two views of the Worm Gear Differential Unit described on this page. In that on the left the worm wheel can be seen in the upper half of the housing of the unit. Photograph by courtesy of David Brown and Sons (Hudd) Ltd., Huddersfield.

Several types of differential gear are in use, the most common being an arrangement of bevel pinions and wheels. The rear axle is in two sections, each shaft driving one of the road wheels at its outer end and carrying a small bevel wheel at its inner end. In mesh with these bevel wheels are others that form a link between them, and therefore between the two axle shafts. These connecting bevels are mounted on pins in a casing, called the differential cage, which encloses them and also carries the bevel crown wheel, if bevel drive from the propeller shaft to the rear axle is employed, or the worm wheel rim, in cars in which worm drive is used.

When the engine is started, the crown wheel or worm-wheel carries round the differential as a solid mass. The connecting bevels do not revolve, but simply link the shaft bevels together, so that an equal amount of power is transmitted to each road wheel. If one road wheel is now completely stopped, the connecting-bevel revolves and runs round the bevel on the stationary shaft, with the result that the other shaft bevel is driven at double speed.

When the one wheel is not completely stopped but merely slowed, the other road wheel automatically is speeded up in exactly the right proportion. This is exactly what happens when a car turns a corner and the inner road wheel is slowed by the resistance of the tyre on the road.

In recent years there has been a tendency in car design towards very low hung bodies, and this has necessitated specially designed differentials that "fit in" with the chassis requirements. The mechanism illustrated on this page is a typical example of this. It is a new type of differential unit made by David Brown and Sons (Hudd) Ltd., Huddersfield, and it has been developed to suit modern low hung car bodies without necessitating an interior tunnel to clear the propeller shaft.

The new gear makes use of worm gear and pinions, and is intended primarily for use as an underslung drive, but if necessary it may be inverted for overtype drives. The underslung arrangement permits a very low position for the propeller shaft and consequently a low centre of gravity and stability. The new unit is particularly useful for incorporation in pleasure cars, for low hung body work can then be combined with ample head room, while at the same time the ground clearance is ample for modern road conditions.

The gear housing forms a self - contained unit and includes all the bearing seatings of both worm and wheel, thus avoiding loose bearing caps, and providing great rigidity. The differential is of the four planet bevel type, and the pinions are carried on a star piece driven by the differential cage. The tooth form is of special shape designed to give maximum strength and durability, and carefully positioned oil grooves are provided to ensure efficient lubrication.

The worm wheel rim is fastened by high tensile steel bolts to flanges on the differential cage, in which are disposed the differential bevels on their cross piece, the whole forming a complete element, which is carried on two double purpose bearings in the housing. The worm is mounted at the rear end in two bearings, one of which takes the radial load, while the other carries the axial load only. The forward end of the worm shaft is carried on a single lip roller bearing.

The worm wheel is made from a special high tensile alloy, known as "Taurus" bronze, and the teeth are accurately cut and shaped to ensure that all wheels are interchangeable.

The aluminium housing is of light yet robust construction and is made in halves, which are held together by steel bolts. The bearing caps are cast in one piece with the top half, which is fitted with an accurately machined spigot that registers in a hole in the lower half, known as the axle banjo. This simplifies assembly of the unit and makes the differential unit and the axle banjo into what is virtually one complete axle unit.

In Search of New Models

Helpful Hints for Bridge Builders

BRIDGES are particularly good subjects for models, since Meccano parts are so well adapted for reproducing the girders, tie-rods and other members that make up these structures. The range of subjects available for models also is extensive, for there are many different types of bridge in use throughout the world and various materials have been employed in their construction. In this respect much depends on local conditions. In Canada, where wood is plentiful, many famous trestle bridges have been built of lumber hewn from forests in the vicinity. The trestle bridge is perhaps not so interesting as a subject for models as other types of bridge, but it can easily be reproduced with the aid of Meccano parts.

Fig. 1. The centre span of this Swing Bridge can be rotated by turning a handle.

The materials generally used in modern bridge building are stone and steel. The extensive use of stone is restricted to comparatively small structures, and these can be modelled very well by combining Plates and Girders. Strip Plates and Flexible Plates prove their worth in such models. Steel bridges make the best subjects for copying in model form, however. Among the best-known types are arch bridges, suspension bridges, and cantilever bridges. The arch bridge relies for its support upon massive arched girders that span the gulf to be bridged. The arches are placed one on each side of the bridge, the deck of which may be above or below the top of the arches. If the span is great it is more usual to suspend the deck from the arch girders by means of tension cables, and when the deck is above the arch all the members supporting it are in compression. In each case the arch girders are subjected to compression.

When a suspension bridge is being built, two towers, generally of masonry, are erected at each end and suspension chains are slung between them. The chains are extended downward beyond the towers and terminate in anchoring blocks. The deck of the bridge is then supported by tension members hanging from the chains, and the chains also are in tension.

Fig. 2. Bascule Bridge operated by a balanced beam.

On a bridge of the cantilever type the deck usually is supported at a level near the centre of the cantilevers. The structure below the deck is then subject to compression, as in an arch bridge, while the upper structure is in tension, as in a suspension bridge.

By considering the forces the different members of a bridge are called upon to withstand, a new interest is given to the building of the models. Members subjected to compressive forces should be represented in the model by Angle Girders, and if the loads are heavy, built-up girders of channel section—or of other suitable cross section—should be employed. In the case of curved girders that are in compression, as in an arch bridge, some substitute must be found for Angle Girders. In most cases Strips must be used, reinforced where necessary by further Strips or Curved Strips attached to Angle Brackets. The tension members of a bridge are more slender than the parts in compression, and Strips can be used to represent them. In some cases Cord is sufficient, but it may be found advisable to use string instead in order to preserve correct proportions.

These bridges give the model-builder good opportunities for using Meccano parts to advantage, and when completed they can be employed in a model railway system or can be used in conjunction with Dinky Toys. The interest of the models is greatly increased if they can be applied to purposes such as these. A novel way of using Dinky Toys on a model bridge is shown on the "*With the Model Builders*" page of this issue.

A great deal of pleasure is obtained from the construction of almost any type of bridge, but this is greatly increased when the structure can be set in motion in some manner when completed. Opening bridges are often employed for spanning waterways in cases where an ordinary bridge would leave insufficient head room for vessels to pass beneath. There are several methods of opening a bridge to allow the passage of ships. In some the main span is mounted on roller bearings so that it can be rotated through an angle of 90 deg. to take up a position parallel to the waterway. In another type the span is hinged at one end and the other end is raised until the moving span takes up the vertical position. A variation of this type occurs in the rolling lift bridges, which have large rolling sectors built on to the end of the lifting span. These bridges actually roll backward and upward at the same time. In some cases the moving span is raised vertically so that although still spanning the waterway vessels can pass beneath it.

There is another type that is used less frequently than the foregoing but has advantages peculiar to certain conditions. When a very long span is necessary it is obvious that the moving bridges of the kinds referred to are unsuitable, and if it is impossible to build a bridge with a continuous roadway, the transporter bridge is sometimes used to meet the requirements of the situation. This type of bridge has a main span supported high enough to avoid interference to shipping, and a trolley runs on rails beneath the bridge. Suspension cables attached to the trolley support a car at the level of the roadway below. By this means vehicles and passengers can be taken to and fro across the bridge without interfering with navigation.

Many of these models can be built up in Meccano, and if a Motor is available, made to operate under power. The fascination is not lost if a Motor is not at hand, for they can be operated quite well by means of a handwheel. Good examples of moving bridges are shown on these pages. Fig. 1 shows a simple model Swing Bridge in which the centre span is supported on a roller bearing. As the handle is turned the bridge rotates about its pivot, thus making way for water borne traffic.

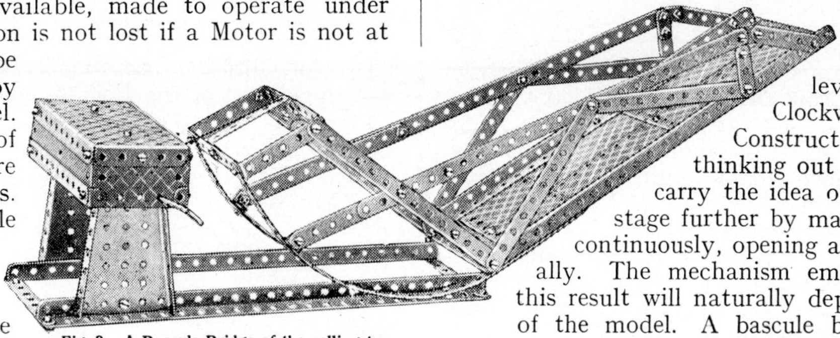

Fig. 3. A Bascule Bridge of the rolling type.

Fig. 2 shows a Lifting Bridge operated by a balanced beam. In this case a pivoted beam is connected at one end to the bridge, and at the other end carries a balance weight that helps to counterbalance the weight of the bridge, thus minimising the load on the Motor. With this arrangement a Motor of smaller power than would otherwise be necessary can be used.

An opening bridge of the rolling bascule type appears in Fig. 3, and its method of operation is apparent from the illustration. In actual practice the rolling sectors are generally provided with studs that fit into recesses on the rails carrying them. This is to prevent the sectors slipping on the rails, but on a Meccano model of such small size a similar method cannot be adopted. An ingenious arrangement has been employed to prevent the sectors slipping on the Strips supporting them. Cords are tied to each end of each sector and then to the opposite ends of the rails supporting them. On these bridges the balance weights are fitted at the rear of the rolling sectors.

Fig. 4. Vertical Lift Bridge with centre span in raised position.

A Vertical Lift Bridge is shown in Fig. 4. The centre span slides in vertical Girders and can be raised by means of four cords. A cord is secured at each corner of the span and they pass over Pulleys at the top of the towers, then passing down to the control cabin. A Worm drive operates the hoisting shaft, thus ensuring that the shaft cannot unwind owing to the weight of the bridge. Worm gearing is very useful in cases like this, as the driven shaft is automatically braked, without affecting the drive.

Much more fun is to be had from the models when they can be operated under their own motive power. Clockwork or Electric Motors can be used for driving them and should be geared to give a slow powerful drive. The movement of the actual bridges is invariably slow, so the models are true to type when driven slowly. A refinement that can be fitted to the models, adding to their interest in both construction and operation, is an automatic control to prevent overwinding. The device may consist of a stop that is tripped when the moving span reaches a certain position, thus stopping the Motor. Automatic control is simplified if an Electric Motor is used, but it is by no means impossible with a Clockwork Motor. In the former case electrical switches can be arranged to cut off the current for the Motor, or trip gear can be made to operate the Motor lever as in the case of a Clockwork Motor.

Constructors who delight in thinking out new mechanisms can carry the idea of automatic control a stage further by making the bridge work continuously, opening and closing automatically. The mechanism employed for achieving this result will naturally depend upon the design of the model. A bascule bridge or vertical lift bridge can be operated by an automatic reversing hoist as in S.M.18 (Standard Mechanisms Manual). Operation of a swing bridge could be controlled by a reversing gear or by a crank and lever movement. Other ideas for automatic continuous operation will occur to the model builder. Slow motion is desirable, and if possible there should be a pause when the span reaches the open and closed positions.

On a transporter bridge an automatic reversing gear can be fitted. In the Meccano super model (No. 21) a simple reversing gear of Contrate Wheel and Pinions is used and is controlled by trips at each end of the bridge. The trolley carrying the travelling car strikes one of the trips on reaching the end of its travel and a spring-controlled lever changes the direction of the drive. A pause is obtained by allowing the driving chain to pass freely through guides at each end of the trolley. A projection on the chain must travel from end to end of the trolley before setting it in motion.

In the majority of bridges stone plays an important part for foundations, abutments or supporting towers, according to the type of bridge. Bridges of short span sometimes consist of stout girders of I section supported on stone abutments, and even in long bridges of elaborate girder construction stone is generally used extensively for foundations, although these may not be exposed. Where stone is used to any great extent in the prototype of a model it should be reproduced by judicious use of Strip Plates or Flexible Plates, but in cases where it is applied to foundations only it is often more effective to use wood suitably painted to represent stone work. Wooden blocks cut to size and shape make excellent piers for supporting "mid-river" sections of a bridge.

A model bridge is set off to advantage when mounted on a baseboard that is made to represent part of the situation in which the bridge is used. Fig. 2 shows how this can be done with a lifting bridge. This model is supported on a wooden base painted to represent stone foundations, and a sheet of rippled glass represents the water of a canal.

Two New Meccano F Outfit Models

A Telescope and a Six-Wheeled Lorry

THE two new Meccano models dealt with in this article are a reflecting telescope and a six-wheeled lorry. These differ widely in type, but have attractive movements and illustrate interesting constructional methods. Both can be built with the parts included in Outfit F, with the exception that two 2″ Dunlop Tyres, Part No. 142A, also are required for the second model.

The Reflecting Telescope is similar to that installed at Melbourne Observatory, which has a mirror 48 in. in diameter. The mounting is of the equatorial type, in which the telescope itself is placed on one side of an axis, called the polar axis, that is set parallel to the imaginary line joining the Earth's north and south poles, and is capable of rotation about it. The weight of the telescope is balanced by that of a counterpoise and the instrument can be turned about a second axis so that it can be directed to any part of the heavens. No mirror is fitted to the model, but all the movements of the prototype are reproduced and the general appearance and operation of an instrument of this type is admirably illustrated.

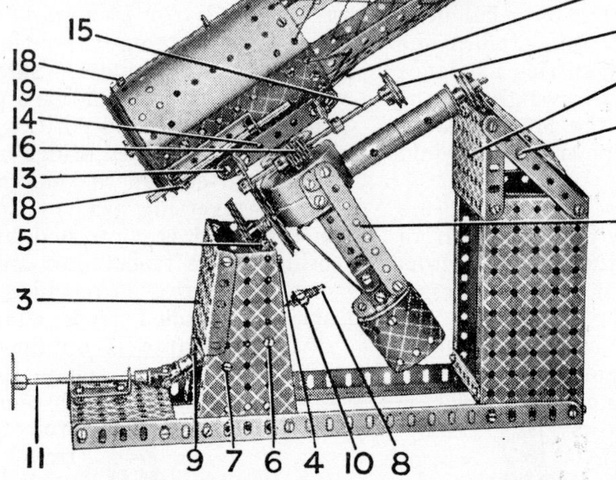

Fig. 1. A Meccano Reflecting Telescope that reproduces the movements of a real instrument.

The base of the model is first constructed. This consists of two 12½″ Angle Girders, laid parallel and secured together at one end by means of a 3½″×2½″ Flanged Plate. At their opposite ends the Girders are fitted with 3½″×2½″ Flanged Plates, which are joined by means of two 5½″×2½″ Strip Plates. The edge of one of these Strip Plates is shown in Fig. 1. A 3½″ Strip is bolted to the bottom of the visible flanges of the Flanged Plates, and to the top is secured a 3½″×2½″ Flanged Plate 1.

Two 3½″ Strips are bolted to the Plate 1 and to these are secured two ½″×½″ Angle Brackets. The securing bolt of one of these is indicated at 2, Fig. 1. Two 2½″×2½″ Flexible Plates overlapping three holes are now secured to the Angle Brackets between the 3½″ Strips, and to the lower edges of the Flexible Plates are clamped two similar Plates by means of a nut, bolt and Washer. The two last mentioned Plates overlap the 5½″×2½″ Strip Plates, already mentioned, for a distance of three holes and they are bent slightly in order to fill in the gap between the Strip and Flexible Plates. A bolt in the centre top hole of the 3½″×2½″ Flanged Plate 1 holds in place an Obtuse Angle Bracket that will later support the upper end of the Rod forming the polar axis.

Two 4½″ Sector Plates are now secured as shown to the base of the model, and to these is bolted a 3½″×2½″ Flanged Plate 3 and a 3½″ Strip 4. To the centre of the Strip 4 is attached an Obtuse Angle Bracket 5, the purpose of which is to support the lower end of the polar axis.

Two 3½″×½″ Double Angle Strips are held in place between the 4½″ Sector Plates by nuts and bolts, the two on one side being shown at 6 and 7. These Double Angle Strips form journals for the 3½″ Rod 8 that is prevented from sliding laterally in its bearings by means of a 1″ Pulley 9 and a Collar. A Collar 10 on the Rod 8 will be used later as a securing point for the cords by means of which the telescope is rocked, or turned about the polar axis.

The lower end of the Rod 8 carries a universal coupling that is constructed from a Small Fork Piece, a Swivel Bearing and two bolts. The free end of the universal coupling accommodates a 3½″ Rod 11, on the outer end of which is carried a Bush Wheel forming the operating handle. The Rod 8 must be made fairly difficult to rotate by gripping the 3½″×½″ Double Angle Strip forming its lower journal between the 1″ Pulley 9 and Collar. This expedient is necessary in order to keep the telescope at rest in any desired position. The 1½″×½″ Double Angle Strip, forming a journal for the Rod 11, is attached to the base by means of two ⅜″ Bolts. The Bolts are locked in the end holes of the Double Angle Strip by nuts, and two further nuts are used on each Bolt to secure them to the base.

Fig. 2. An underneath view of the Lorry shown in Fig. 4.

The telescope proper is next constructed. A Boiler without ends is opened out until it has a diameter of 3″, and the gap between its two edges is filled in with two 5½″×2½″ Flexible Plates. These Plates overlap one hole each and where they are joined a 5½″ Strip is secured in place. The end of this Strip is shown at 12, Fig. 1.

Two Double Brackets are now bolted to the 5½″ Strip and these carry two 3½″ Strips one of which is indicated at 13. This last mentioned Strip 13 forms a support for a 2½″×1″ Double Angle Strip 14 that carries at its extremities two Flat Brackets. These form bearings for the Rod 15 on which are locked a Worm 16 and 1" fast Pulley 17.

A $2\frac{1}{2}'' \times \frac{1}{2}''$ Double Angle Strip is now bolted to the telescope as shown, and this supports a 4" Rod held in place by Spring Clips that represent the "finder." In practice the "finder" is a small telescope parallel to the large one, and a star or other object to be examined is first picked up by it, the large telescope then automatically pointing in the desired direction.

The two Bolts 18 hold in place two $\frac{1}{2}'' \times \frac{1}{2}''$ Angle Brackets, in the unoccupied holes of which are locked two $\frac{3}{8}''$ Bolts. These Bolts are used for securing the 3" Pulley 19 in place when the model is completed.

In Fig. 3 the polar axis and balance weight are shown. The polar axis consists of two Rods, 2" and 5", inserted in the Coupling 20 and carried in the Boiler End 21. The Boiler End is prevented from sliding on the Rod by means of four Spring Clips as shown. A 2" Pulley 22 is locked on the 2" Rod and it is prevented from turning by the Bolt 23 that engages one of the holes in the Boiler End 24. This latter part is carried on a 5" Rod to which it is secured by a 57-teeth Gear and two $\frac{3}{8}''$ Bolts. The $\frac{1}{2}''$ loose Pulley 25 is used for spacing purposes.

Fig. 3. The polar axis and balance weight of the Meccano Reflecting Telescope.

Two Flat Brackets are now bolted to the Boiler End 21, from which each is spaced by a Washer. These carry in their slotted holes nuts and bolts that secure the upper Boiler End to the lower one in the manner shown in Fig. 1.

The Rod carrying the Boiler End 24 is now passed through the telescope in the manner shown in Fig. 1, a 1" fast Pulley pressing against the bottom inner surface of the telescope to hold the two units tightly together. The Worm 16 will now be found to mesh with the 57-teeth Gear secured to the Boiler End 24.

To complete the model the Rod forming the polar axis is journalled in the two Obtuse Brackets mentioned earlier, a second 2" Pulley being fitted. The rocking cords, which pass round the two 2" Pulleys in opposite directions and are secured thereto, are wound on the Rod 8, one being fitted clockwise and the other anti-clockwise. The two ends are secured to bolts in the Collar 10.

Fig. 4. A splendid Six-wheeled Lorry built with F Outfit.

The parts required to build the model Telescope are as follows: 6 of No. 1; 3 of No. 2; 6 of No. 3; 1 of No. 4; 1 of No. 6a; 2 of No. 8; 6 of No. 10; 2 of No. 11; 7 of No. 12; 3 of No. 12c; 2 of No. 15; 2 of No. 15a; 2 of No. 15b; 1 of No. 16; 1 of No. 17; 1 of No. 19b; 2 of No. 20a; 1 of No. 20b; 1 of No. 21; 2 of No. 22; 1 of No. 23; 1 of No. 24; 1 of No. 27a; 1 of No. 32; 6 of No. 35; 90 of No. 37; 10 of No. 37a; 13 of No. 38; 1 of No. 46; 1 of No. 48; 5 of No. 48a; 2 of No. 48b; 2 of No. 52; 3 of No. 53; 2 of No. 54; 4 of No. 59; 1 of No. 63; 2 of No. 111; 4 of No. 111c; 1 of No. 116a; 1 of No. 162; 2 of No. 163; 1 of No. 164; 1 of No. 165; 1 of No. 189; 4 of No. 190; 2 of No. 191; 2 of No. 195.

The second model is a miniature reproduction of a type of motor lorry that plays a very important part in modern road transport. Its construction is begun by building the main frames, each of which consists of two $12\frac{1}{2}''$ Angle Girders overlapping ten holes. They are connected together at the front by means of two $3\frac{1}{2}'' \times \frac{1}{2}''$ Double Angle Strips 1 and 2, and at the rear the Girders are secured to a $5\frac{1}{2}'' \times 2\frac{1}{2}''$ Flanged Plate 3 by Flat Brackets.

Two Double Brackets are now pivotally attached to the main frames by means of $\frac{3}{4}''$ Bolts 4. These Double Brackets carry the rear wheel springs, each of which is represented by one $3\frac{1}{2}''$ Strip and one $2\frac{1}{2}''$ Strip. The ends of the $3\frac{1}{2}''$ Strips are fitted with $\frac{1}{2}'' \times \frac{1}{2}''$ Angle Brackets that form journals for the 5" Rods forming the rear axles. One of these Rods supports one end of a No. 1 Clockwork Motor, the drive being taken to the 1" fast Pulley 5. The $1\frac{1}{2}''$ Pulley 6 is secured on a $1\frac{1}{2}''$ Rod carrying a $\frac{1}{2}''$ Pinion that meshes with the main gear of the Clockwork Motor as shown.

The rear end of the Clockwork Motor is supported by a $1\frac{1}{2}''$ Rod carrying a Collar at one end. This Rod passes through the upper set of holes of a pair of $1'' \times 1''$ Angle Brackets 7 and also through two suitable holes in the Motor side plates. This Rod is removed when winding the Motor.

The construction of the front springing and steering unit is carried out in the following manner. The $3\frac{1}{2}'' \times \frac{1}{2}''$ Double Angle Strip 1 carries two $\frac{1}{2}''$ Reversed Angle Brackets 8, the projecting flanges of which point towards the centre of the chassis and carry the springs.

The front axle 9 consists of two 3" Strips, overlapping three holes and bolted three holes from each end to the springs, as shown in Fig. 2. Each end hole of the front axle accommodates a $\frac{3}{8}''$ Bolt on which a $\frac{1}{2}'' \times \frac{1}{2}''$ Angle Bracket and the $1\frac{1}{2}''$ Strip 10 are secured by lock-nuts. Two Washers are carried for spacing purposes on each $\frac{3}{8}''$ Bolt.

The two $1\frac{1}{2}''$ Strips 10 are connected together by a tie-rod built up from two $2\frac{1}{2}''$ Strips overlapping two holes. A Threaded Pin 11 forms the connection between the $2\frac{1}{2}''$ Strips, and its shank passes through the end slotted hole of a Crank 12. This Crank is mounted on the $3\frac{1}{2}''$ Rod 13 representing the steering column. This Rod is journalled in the front axle and also in a compound strip bolted to the main frames. The compound strip is built up from two $2\frac{1}{2}''$ Strips overlapping three holes.

Each side of the cab is formed from a $2\frac{1}{2}'' \times 1\frac{1}{2}''$ Flexible Plate secured to the $5\frac{1}{2}'' \times 2\frac{1}{2}''$ Flanged Plate, forming the back of the cab, by a Flat Bracket. The mudguard is represented by a $2\frac{1}{2}''$ large radius Curved Strip that is attached to a $5\frac{1}{2}''$ Strip 14 by an Obtuse Angle Bracket. The $5\frac{1}{2}''$ Strip is secured to the main frame by two $2\frac{1}{2}'' \times \frac{1}{2}''$ Double Angle Strips, one of which is shown at 15. The inner turned up ends of these two parts project into the cab.

The parts required to build the model Six-Wheeled Motor Lorry are as follows: 6 of No. 1; 17 of No. 2; 6 of No. 3; 2 of No. 4; 9 of No. 5; 2 of No. 6a; 8 of No. 8; 7 of No. 10; 4 of No. 11; 13 of No. 12; 4 of No. 12a; 4 of No. 12c; 2 of No. 15; 1 of No. 16; 2 of No. 17; 1 of No. 18a; 2 of No. 20a; 2 of No. 20b; 1 of No. 21; 1 of No. 22; 1 of No. 24; 1 of No. 26; 118 of No. 37; 10 of No. 37a; 12 of No. 38; 6 of No. 48a; 2 of No. 48b; 1 of No. 51; 2 of No. 52; 4 of No. 59; 1 of No. 62; 4 of No. 90a; 2 of No. 111; 6 of No. 111c; 2 of No. 115; 1 of No. 116; 2 of No. 125; 1 of No. 186; 4 of No. 187; 2 of No. 188; 2 of No. 189; 4 of No. 190; 2 of No. 191; 1 of No. 193; 2 of No. 195; 2 of No. 197. Not included in Outfit: 2 of No. 142a and No. 1 Clockwork Motor.

Simple Models of Familiar Objects

An Ingenuity Contest

On this page is illustrated a simple and realistic model of an electric fan, an article with which every reader will be familiar. The outstanding feature of the model is its striking likeness to a real fan, and this is due to the skilful use that the builder has made of the few parts of which the model is constructed.

There are hundreds of other familiar objects that can be realistically represented with a few simple parts, and we think that model-builders will be interested in trying their skill in such work. We therefore announce a competition specially for entries of this type.

In entering the competition model-builders are asked to build models of any simple articles with which they are familiar. Models may represent objects used in the home, shops, or elsewhere, and competitors should not experience any difficulty in finding interesting subjects that require only a few parts for their construction.

Most readers will be familiar with the "Simplicity" Contests that have been organised in the past, and it should be understood that the present contest is not strictly a "Simplicity" Contest. Competitors may use as many parts as they wish in building their models for this contest, but models that incorporate unnecessary or non-Meccano parts will not win prizes. The quantity or nature of the parts used is left entirely to the competitor's discretion, and the aim should be to make the most realistic model possible using just as many parts as are necessary to that end.

Competitors may send in more than one model if they wish, and it is only necessary to submit either a photograph or a drawing. The actual model must not be sent. Each photograph or drawing should bear the competitor's full name, age and address, in capital letters.

The competition will be divided into two Sections: A, for competitors living in the British Isles, and B, for competitors living overseas. Age will be taken into consideration when judging the entries in order to give all competitors an equal chance of success.

The prizes to be awarded in each Section are as follows: First, Meccano Products value £3/3/-; Second, Products value £2/2/-; Third, Products value £1/1/-. There will also be five prizes of Products value 10/6 and five prizes of Products value 5/-.

It should be noted that photographs or drawings of prize winning models become the property of Meccano Ltd., but unsuccessful entries will be returned to competitors as soon as possible after the closing dates provided that a stamped addressed envelope is sent for that purpose.

This model electric fan is an example of the realistic work it is possible to do with only a few Meccano parts. It forms the basis of a competition announced on this page, and was built by M. Edmonds, Oundle.

Section A will remain open for entries until 30th April, 1936, and Section B, until 30th June, 1936. These dates ensure that readers living in any part of the world have ample time to prepare and send in their entries. Envelopes should be addressed to "Ingenuity" Contest, Meccano Ltd., Binns Road, Liverpool 13.

Correspondence relating to any subject not connected with the competition must not be enclosed in the same envelope as a competition entry.

Meccano "Mechanism" Contest

In this contest competitors are asked to solve a problem that might be met in certain specialised engineering practice, and prizes are offered for the best solutions submitted.

The accompanying diagram shows two pistons, A and B, that work in an enclosed cylinder. Piston A has a stroke of 3 in. The problem is to design in Meccano suitable coupling gear connecting the two pistons, so that each stroke of the piston rod connected to piston A will cause piston B to move through a distance of about 14 in. Both pistons must move simultaneously in opposite directions.

Competitors need build only the cylinder with its two pistons and the necessary coupling gear. A complete machine is not required.

Actual models must not be sent. It is only necessary to submit either a clear photograph or a good drawing, together with a detailed explanation of the mechanism. Neither photographs nor drawings need be the competitor's own handiwork, but it is absolutely essential that the mechanism itself is his or her own unaided work.

There will be one Section only, and readers living in any part of the world may enter. The competitor's age, name, and address must be written clearly on the back of each photograph or drawing sent in. Envelopes should be addressed to March "Mechanism" Contest, Meccano Ltd., Binns Road, Liverpool 13.

Prizes will be awarded to the senders of the best solutions as follows: First, Meccano Products value £2/2/-; Second, Products value £1/1/-; Third, Products value 10/6.

The closing date for all competitions will be 30th June, 1936, so that readers living in the most remote parts of the world will have ample time to prepare and send in their entries.

Meccano Model-Building Contest Results

By Frank Hornby

"Autumn" Competition (Home and Overseas)

A feature of recent contests has been the excellent work done by the younger competitors, and it is a surprising fact that in many cases the standard of work in the Section for boys and girls under 14 has been far higher than that in the Section for older competitors. While I am delighted to know that even the youngest enthusiasts are capable of building really good models and of finding original subjects, I should like to see some of the older competitors taking more interest and care in the finishing of their work.

Very often an otherwise good model is spoilt for the sake of a little time spent in applying those finishing touches that make all the difference. The present competition, I am glad to say, shows an improvement in this respect, but considering the great number of entries submitted, the proportion of really first-class models was not quite as high as it should have been.

The prizes were awarded to the competitors named in the following lists:

Section A (competitors over 14)

1st, Meccano Products value £3/3/–: R. Thorpe, Preston. 2nd, Products value £2/2/–: J. Smith, Leominster. 3rd, Products value £1/1/–: G. Sercombe, Exeter.

Products value 10/6: R. Byers, Barnsley; R. English, Parkstone, Dorset; S. Griffiths, Liverpool 15; C. Lynch, Clifton, Yorks.; D. Marston, New Ferry, Birkenhead; K. Pim, Exeter.

Section B (competitors under 14)

1st, Meccano Products value £2/2/–: E. Clements, Farnborough. 2nd, Products value £1/1/–: A. Aikman, Worthing. 3rd, Products value 10/6: T. Smith, Exeter.

Meccano Products value 5/–: J. Franks, Exeter; N. Fuller, Dagenham; P. Hands, Hillingdon; A. Horsfall, Edinburgh 10; J. Paterson, Roslin, Midlothian; P. Wickham, Leicester.

Skilful use of Strips has given a neat and realistic appearance to this model sideboard. It is the work of E. D. Clements, Farnborough, and won a First Prize in the "Autumn" Competition.

First Prize in Section A was awarded for a model that is a splendid tribute to its builder's powers of observation and attention to detail. It represents an elephant, with two impertinent-looking children on its back, being led by its keeper, and it was built by R. Thorpe. Each side of the elephant's body and head is made from Flat Plates, and its trunk, tusks, legs and tail are made from Strips and Curved Strips cleverly arranged and bolted together. The ears are Flat Trunnions. The figures of the keeper and children are made chiefly from Strips, Flat Brackets and Angle Brackets, and their heads from 1" fast Pulleys.

The model that won Second Prize owes its success to its originality of subject. It is a reproduction of a ruling machine, of the kind used for printing the lines and margins on bill heads, foolscap and notebooks. The inkers are a row of reservoir type pen nibs that are held in a special frame borne on springs, which make the nibs press firmly against the paper. The sheets of paper are fed beneath the nibs by two sets of multiple cords, and after printing they pass round a roller, the surface of which is covered with blotting paper. This soaks up the ink and prevents smudges.

T. Smith, Exeter, won a Third Prize with this small model motor break-down lorry.

Third Prize in this Section was won by G. Sercombe, with a fine model of a radio gramophone. The model has hinged doors, and a lid that opens and is fitted with automatic lidstays. A fancy fret design, of the kind with which gramophone cabinets are usually decorated, is reproduced with an arrangement of Braced Girders. The record turntable is made from a Hub Disc.

The two models illustrated on this page are successful entries from Section B and were built by E. Clements and T. Smith respectively. Clements' model won First Prize and is a reproduction of a sideboard that forms part of the furniture in the dining room at his house. The model is plain in construction and I like it because it does not incorporate any unnecessary parts. The pillars on each side of the mirror—which incidentally is represented by a sheet of polished tin-plate—are made from Strips bolted round further Strips bent into circles. Curved Strips are used at the bottoms of the pillars to represent ornamental beadings that are a feature of the actual sideboard.

The model has two cupboards and drawers, all of which can be opened, the former being mounted on Hinges and held closed by means of a movable catch. The drawers are made from Flat Plates and Strips, and the nuts and bolts are so arranged that the sides are left perfectly free from projections, which would prevent the drawer from sliding easily. The handles are made with pairs of Handrail Supports connected by 1½" Rods. The model is 2 ft. long, 1 ft. 10 in. high and 8 in. deep.

It was the simple construction and clean design of T. Smith's model breakdown lorry that attracted the judges' attention and earned it Third Prize. For the sake of compactness the chassis of the lorry is omitted, and the four rear wheels are attached to imitation leaf springs bolted directly to the rear platform of the lorry. The front wheels are not steerable but are mounted on a Rod that is journalled in bearings attached to two 3½" Angle Girders. These Angle Girders form the foundation for the bonnet and driving cab. The breakdown crane is built up from Strips and has a winding drum made from a Rod and 1" fast Pulleys.

A. Aikman did splendid work in building a model of a six-wheeled articulated lorry of the latest type, and if his subject had been more original he would no doubt have won First Prize. His workmanship is really remarkable for a model-builder of his age, and I hope he will continue to send in entries for these monthly competitions. The model he sent for the present contest is provided with a three speed and reverse gear box, clutch and differential gear, and the rear wheels are fitted with band brakes, which can be operated from the cab.

August "Errors" Contest (Overseas Section)

The following competitors were successful in winning the chief prizes in the "Errors" Contest announced in the August, 1935, issue of the "*M.M.*":

1st, Meccano Products value £2/2/–: P. Demanuele, Hamrun, Malta. 2nd, Products value £1/1/–: J. Rodriguez, Montreal. 3rd, Products value 10/6: W. Bladergroen, Amsterdam.

Meccano Products value 5/–: D. Parker, Brussels; Ontario, G. Russell, Marton, New Zealand; R. Wille, Capetown; J. Capelli, Buenos Aires; D. Murison, Buenos Aires.

Summer "Realism" Contest (Overseas Section)

The chief prizewinners in the Summer "Realism" Contest are as follows:

1st, Meccano Products value £3/3/–: C. Astrom, Morko, Sweden. 2nd, Products value £2/2/–: R. Myburgh, Capetown. 3rd, Products value £1/1/–: R. Hill, Toronto.

Exeter M.C.—Club statistics show that 200 models were built by the members last year, and that the average attendance at meetings was the highest since the club was affiliated in April 1925. The exhibits at a model Olympia Motor Show included racing cars, streamlined touring cars and several buses. Visitors to the show included motor engineers, and their compliments made the builders of the models blush with pride! Another attractive exhibit was a Meccano garage in which were 12 Dinky Toy motor vehicles. Club roll: 45. *Secretary:* T. W. A. Smith, 98, Ladysmith Road, Exeter.

Sid Vale (Sidmouth) M.C.—The first Winter Session closed with a Monster Competition, for which many models were built and the best of them illuminated. The event was a great success. The present Session opened with the annual New Year party, and everybody had a most enjoyable time. Club roll: 25. *Secretary:* L. R. J. Gliddon, Sheffield House, Sidmouth.

Stationers' School M.C.—This club has recently been revived and is now divided into General Engineering, Model Railway, and Electricity and Wireless sections respectively. The majority of the members belong to at least two of the sections, and this unity of interests, together with the general enthusiasm, has resulted in all meetings being well attended. At the second meeting a Lecture was given on "*The Progress of Engineering*" and later Lectures dealt with "*Scale-Model Coach Building*," "*Making Model Cars in Meccano*," "*Simple Circuits*" and "*Oil From Coal*." The Model Railway section is constructing a scale model O-gauge scenic railway for exhibition at the school's Open Evenings. A visit to the Stratford Locomotive Works has been arranged. Club roll: 15. *Secretary:* R. J. Post, 8, Bourne Road, Crouch End, London, N.8.

Fraserburgh M.C.—The committee now meet each week. A recruiting campaign in December last proved very fruitful and many junior members were enrolled. The juniors now hold their own meetings, and these are being very well attended. The club's first birthday was celebrated by a party and dance, at which refreshments were provided. The club funds are in a flourishing state, and therefore additions are to be made to the club's stock of Meccano. Club roll: 34. *Secretary:* W. J. Dawson, Phingask, Fraserburgh.

Wednesbury and District M.C.—An invitation from the Kidderminster Model Railway Club was accepted, and a very enjoyable time was spent with that organisation. Members obtained several new ideas that will help in running their own club more efficiently. An intensive recruiting campaign is being carried on, and it is hoped that it will result in a greatly increased membership. Club roll: 7. *Secretary:* A. L. Morgan, 17, Cobden Street, Fallings Heath, Wednesbury.

Hornsea M.C.—This club is divided into four sections called the Senior Scientists, Junior Scientists, Senior Engineers and Junior Engineers respectively. Several interesting Lectures and Cinema Evenings have been held, and the Junior Scientists' Section have held a series of Lectures each dealing with the history of a particular century. Another series has been concerned with Chemistry. Occasionally meetings of the Junior Engineers' section are devoted to Hornby train operations. Club roll: 13. *Secretary:* P. Thom, 5, Alexandra Road, Hornsea.

Old Charlton M.C.—A club Magazine has been started under the name of "*The Meccanic*," and it is hoped to publish it monthly. The first number contains contributions from several members of the club, and the Editorial staff are confident that every member will eventually discover himself to be a budding author! Club roll: 20. *Secretary:* W. Jaques, 60, Gurdon Road, London, S.E.17.

Bristol Grammar School M.C.—Model-building has been continued enthusiastically, and members took special pride in a fine model of a motor lorry which they built. An Exhibition was to have been held last Christmas but it was unavoidably postponed until the present session. Great preparations are being made to ensure it being an outstanding success. Club roll: 46. *Secretary:* N. E. Ricketts, 10, Belgrave Road, Clifton, Bristol 8.

Mallow M.C.—A second visit to the local sugar beet factory gave members the opportunity to obtain the further details of the plant they required to enable them to accurately complete their model of the factory. This model was displayed at the club's recent Exhibition, and was the subject of many compliments from visitors. Several new recruits were enrolled. At the close of the Exhibition the parents of members were entertained to tea in the club-room and afterwards witnessed a play entitled "*A Visit to Meccanoland*," which was presented by the members. An attractive programme is being carried out. Club roll: 16. *Secretary:* D. Hickey, 42, Ballydaheen, Mallow, Co. Cork, I.F.S.

Islington M.C.—At the first meeting of the present session an interesting lecture on "*Bridges*" was given by the Leader, and was listened to very attentively by the members. A topical talk about "*Frost and its Handiwork*" was given at a later meeting. New club officials have been elected, but they will be in office for only six months. This arrangement is considered to give all members a chance to attain office within a reasonable period. Model-building and Games evenings are held regularly. By way of further variation a club Tea Party has been held, and everybody had a great time. Club roll: 14. *Secretary:* K. V. Dines, 70, Thornhill Road, Barnsbury, London, N.1.

Members of the Tynecastle School (Edinburgh) M.C. This club was affiliated in February 1929, and its activities include model-building, Hornby train operations, and games. A Dramatic Section is responsible for the production of short plays at the club's Exhibitions.

Middlesbrough M.C.—Further reorganisation has taken place, and the club has again been divided into the original four sections called Rods, Bolts, Clips and Nuts respectively. An attractive Hornby Train Night enabled members to carry out many different railway operations on the club layout. Games maintain their popularity, and the favourites are Kim's Game, Draughts and Table Tennis. Club roll: 36. *Secretary:* L. Shepherd, 29, High Street, North Ormesby, Middlesbrough.

AUSTRALIA

Melbourne M.C.—Meetings have chiefly been devoted to Hornby train operations. The club electric control board has been rebuilt and the system extended, nearly all points and track sections now being electrically interlocked, so that all tracks are worked under single line conditions and the probability of collisions is thereby greatly reduced. A scheme of "master control" colour-light signals based on that used on the Victorian Government Railways has been introduced, and each member acting as a "driver" has to obey them. There is one master signal for each oval or section of track, and it is operated with a Hornby resistance controller. The club were pleased to receive a copy of "*The Sydney Meccanomag*," published by the Sydney M.C. Club roll: 12. *Secretary:* L. Ison, 8, Hayes Street, Northcote, N.16, Victoria, Australia

CANADA

Montreal Central Y.M.C.A. M.C.—Most of the recent meetings have been devoted to model-building and instructive talks and demonstrations in the use of Meccano Parts have been given. A large cupboard has been installed in the clubroom for the storage of members' Meccano and Hornby equipment. Plans have been made for visits to the works of the "*Montreal Daily Star*" and the Gillette Razor Blade Company. At the moment the club is without a secretary, as the former holder of this office has left Canada. A successor is to be appointed shortly. Club roll: 12. *Leader:* Mr. J. Rodriguez, 1900, Tupper Street, Apartment 4 Montreal, P.Q., Canada.

EGYPT

Cairo M.C.—Several new members have recently been enrolled. Model-building is being continued enthusiastically, and models completed recently have included a large monoplane, upon which members have been complimented by visitors to the club. A library has been started, and is already very popular. Club roll: 25. *Leader:* Mr. Mohamed F. Awad, 7, Atfet El Zawia Haret El Gameh, Cairo.

ITALY

Milan M.C.—The name of the Photo-Chemical-Electrical Section has been changed to Scientific Section, and that of the Cinema and Sports Section to Amusement Section. The second Ping-Pong Tournament was concluded recently. It proved immensely popular, and was an even greater success than the first one. The Programme Committee called a special meeting to consider future programmes, and a very useful discussion took place. Club roll: 14. *Secretary:* E. Vigo, Corso Genova 19 Milan.

NEW ZEALAND

Christchurch M.C.—Mr. R. A. Handisides, for so long Leader of the club, has been elected President, and Mr. J. Ancall appointed to succeed him as Leader. Most meetings are held out-of-doors at present, as it is summer in New Zealand. Cycle runs, picnics and games such as Cricket are the chief activities of the members. During a recent holiday the members went on a ramble round Lyttleton Harbour and in the course of their travels they were permitted to make a tour of the liner "*City of Tokio*," which was in port. The club has become acquainted with an invalid boy who is a keen Meccano enthusiast, and visits are being paid to him. On a recent visit by several members some large models built in the clubroom were taken, and the invalid enjoyed the surprise immensely. Club roll: 20. *Secretary:* L. W. Best, 28, Circuit Street, Strowan Christchurch.

SOUTH AFRICA

Pioneer M.C.—A fine display of models was arranged at the Maritzburg Amateur Horticultural Society's recent Exhibition in the City Hall, and attracted a great deal of attention. Club roll: 12. *Secretary:* A. H. Alley, 461, Burger Street, Pietermaritzburg.

Berea M.C.—Many enjoyable meetings have been held and the attendance has been very good. The Girls' Section has been disbanded, but the girls who still remain in the club continue to take a very keen interest in its activities. A dance has been held and the visitors included Mr. Sykes and several members of the Malvern M.C. The club co-operated with the Malvern M.C. in staging a splendid display at the Johannesburg "*Star*" Models and Hobbies Exhibition. The display took the form of a model of a Swiss mountain railway, and Hornby Riviera "Blue Trains" were operated over the track. Occasionally Games Evenings have been held, and two outdoor Tennis Tournaments have been played on a court kindly loaned by one of the members. An effort is being made this session to recruit more members. Club roll: 20. *Secretary:* L. Michelow, 74, Hillbrow Street, Berea, Johannesburg.

Planning Well Ahead

The second of the two winter sessions ends this month, and although it is so early in the year Leaders and officials of Meccano clubs are beginning to think of summer programmes. This is a very sound policy. A great deal of the falling-off in attendance of which some Leaders complain during the summer is due to failure to prepare a plan of campaign sufficiently far in advance. Although Meccano has so sure a hold on the affections of all Meccano boys, it takes second place during the bright days and long evenings of summer, when members naturally prefer to be out-of-doors. If they get the feeling that there is nothing very definite ahead they immediately lose interest, and this, of course, is fatal to the success of the club.

I therefore earnestly recommend those club Leaders and Secretaries who have not already done so to make arrangements for continuing their clubs during the summer months. It is not too soon to begin to form these plans, as practically all outdoor activities require a certain amount of preparation, and their success depends entirely on the efficiency with which this is carried out.

An interesting snapshot from New Zealand. Mr. W. C. Taylor (wearing cap), leader of the Ashburton M.C., and Mr. R. A. Handisides, President of the Christchurch M.C., enjoying a friendly chat, probably about the progress of their respective clubs.

Cycling and Rambling

The importance of early preparation is perhaps greatest in the case of clubs that intend to run a Cricket team, as nothing is more disheartening to a club than to find that it cannot obtain even a moderately full programme of fixtures, because application has been left until the beginning of the season. Cricket fixtures should be drawn up in good time, therefore, otherwise it will be found that local clubs are booked up and there will be little opportunity of securing a good fixture list.

If it is proposed to form a Cycling section, every effort should be made to get the members together and map out the programme for at least the first part of the season. It will be found that members will be much more enthusiastic when a definite programme has been arranged, as they will then know exactly what is going to take place. It may happen that some members are more keen on walking tours and do not wish to take part in Cricket or Cycling. In these cases walking expeditions may be arranged to take place once a week, when the surrounding country can be explored.

The Problem of the Small Club

It is a comparatively easy matter for a large club to plan out a comprehensive outdoor programme, because it has sufficient members to carry out a great variety of schemes. The position is much more difficult for small clubs, however. There are many clubs whose membership does not permit of the formation of a Cricket team or even of a Cycling section, and there is a danger that the Leaders of these clubs may come to the conclusion that it is not worth while to try to struggle on through the summer, and that the best plan is to close down until the first winter session arrives.

I admit that in a few cases local circumstances make it practically impossible to carry on during the summer, but as a general rule it is not only possible but preferable to have regular meetings throughout the long days, although perhaps at less frequent intervals than during the winter.

The Value of Interesting Club Reports

Club reports that reach me by the same mail sometimes present striking contrasts. The other morning, for instance, I received very different reports from two clubs that have been established a considerable time and have fairly large memberships.

The first report mentioned the more important of the models built by the members during the month, and included some interesting comments on a club Model-building Competition that had proved very popular. The names of the winners and the types of their models were also given. Lantern lectures are liked at this club, and the secretary gave me a list of those held since his previous report, and added a few details about them. Recent Games Nights were also considered worthy of mention, and I was very interested to read that during the month some new games had captured the members' enthusiasm, and that a few that had been very popular have been dropped for a while. This excellent report thus gave me both an adequate summary of the month's happenings and an insight into the members' reactions to them.

The second report was very brief, and merely told me that "during the month the club has made steady progress and the meetings have been well attended." I could not help feeling that the secretary of this club had missed his opportunity of giving his club a chance of well-merited publicity in the "Club Notes" page of the "*M.M.*" I was certainly disappointed, as from what I know of this club I am sure that its activities are fully as interesting and varied as those of the other club I have mentioned.

There is a moral in all this, of course, and I think it is a fairly obvious one. I hope, therefore, that those secretaries who have not been in the habit of sending me really interesting reports will try to do so in future, and thus help me to make the club's enterprise and activities known to all the Guild. There can be no better means of conveying to Meccano enthusiasts some idea of the enjoyment of club life than a description of recent activities which show that a club is really alive.

The Correspondence Club

Last month I referred to the many boys in France and Egypt who desire to write to members in this country. Several English boys have since applied for correspondents in those foreign countries, but the waiting list is still long, and I shall be glad to hear from other members who would like correspondents in France or Egypt.

Proposed Clubs

Attempts are being made to establish Meccano Clubs in the following places, and boys interested should communicate with the promoters whose names and addresses are given below:

Barnard Castle—S. W. Telfer, York House, The School.
Great Yarmouth—N. F. Gowther, 28, Hamilton Road.
Hastings—G. Hills, 21, Wellington Road.
New Galloway—G. Warnock, "Dalgowan," New Galloway.
Romford—L. Jones, 39, Rosedale Road.
South Africa—W. Ingle, 1, Queen Street, Malvern, Johannesburg.
Thornton Heath—J. E. Baker, 53, Westminster Avenue.

The Development of Realistic Layouts

Hints on Railwaylike Practice

NEARLY all miniature railway owners have a favourite real system. Some might find it difficult to say why one railway group appeals to them more than the others, but usually the favourite group is the one that serves their own district. All model railway enthusiasts are agreed on one point, however, and that is the desirability of reproducing as closely as possible the features of their favourite system on their own Hornby Railway layouts. In this article we give a few general hints on the development of layouts of this kind, for the special benefit of new readers.

As a rule it is best to adopt one's local railway as a prototype, for then traffic can be actually observed, and the favourite pastime of "watching the trains" turned to good account. If the traffic commonly handled is noted, also the rolling stock, then similar arrangements can be made in miniature. The range of rolling stock in the Hornby Series is such that little difficulty is experienced in representing almost any kind of train.

A realistic layout of the kind referred to in this article. This is operated by M. S. Tait, of Abercynon, Glamorgan, and reproduces the practice of the G.W.R.

Passenger trains are frequently given chief attention and, as pointed out in the article on pages 118 and 119 of the *"M.M."* last month, it is possible to make up most realistic passenger trains ranging from luxurious Pullmans down to the ordinary locals. Mixtures of passenger rolling stock from different groups should be avoided, unless the section or group concerned is one where joint and through working is extensively practised. If the layout is intended to be a joint concern from the outset, and always to be so operated, then of course it is necessary to provide the passenger vehicles of two or more Companies.

With freight stock however the situation is different. One frequently sees the wagons of all groups intermingled on the one train. But it should be remembered that any special types of wagons peculiar to one group that work through to another system are always returned to their owners as soon as possible. They are not despatched elsewhere, as are the ordinary vehicles whose working is shared by the different Companies.

In selecting the rolling stock for a system care should be taken that the right types of vehicles are chosen, according to the traffic to be dealt with. In mining districts for instance numbers of vehicles say for fruit or other special perishable traffic will not be common objects in the sidings. Open wagons will be required and if coal or minerals for shipment are to be dealt with the Hornby Hopper Wagon is a useful type to possess. Similarly in making up trains odd vehicles of special type such as a Milk Van or Milk Tank should not generally be included in an ordinary pick-up goods train. They should be conveyed in a fast freight service or, if convenient, by passenger train.

The layout of which part appears in the illustration on this page is one of many that we know of where the features of an actual system are carefully observed. This is operated by M. S. Tait of Abercynon, Glamorgan, and as might be expected it represents the G.W.R. Typical G.W.R. stock is therefore employed and for the haulage of the trains Hornby G.W.R. Locomotives are exclusively employed. Three of them appear in the photograph, a No. 3C *"Caerphilly Castle,"* a No. 2 Special *"County of Bedford"* and a No. 1 Special Tank, the last-named representing the numerous "Prairie" tanks of actual practice. The domeless boilers and characteristic appearance of these engines alone suggest the correct "Great Western" atmosphere.

As with the locomotives themselves so should the duties of the different engines be correctly arranged, as far as possible. Tender engines are necessarily used for main line work but a feature of modern locomotive operating is the use of them also on local work, in order to fill up time between more important turns. This is an advantage from the point of view of the Locomotive Running Superintendent of a miniature railway for it allows him to make the utmost use of a number of engines that appears comparatively small for the amount of work to be done.

Other features to watch are the practices of different Companies with regard to the use of two locomotives on one train. For instance on the G.C. and N.B. sections of the L.N.E.R. the assistant engine is attached to the train itself, not in front of the train engine. The latter therefore occupies the leading position; this custom ensures that the driver of the engine booked to work the train retains full control of affairs at the front end.

In the arrangement of accessories it is desirable to make the station layouts and such items as level crossings as much like the real thing as possible. Signals and signal cabins, cuttings and tunnels also play important parts.

The Mechanical Handling of Freight Traffic

Bale Stacking and Transporting Truck

THE use of mechanical equipment for the handling of freight at terminal and transfer points has been greatly extended by railways in recent years. In certain conditions where a particular type of traffic is heavy and more or less constant, special plant for its handling is necessary. A most interesting special appliance has recently been adopted by the L.M.S.R. This is known as a Bale Stacking Truck and two are in use at the goods depot at Frizinghall, near Bradford. This truck has been developed and manufactured by the firm of Wingrove and Rogers Ltd., of Liverpool. It is designed to grasp, elevate, and stack bales of wool or other items of freight of a similar nature. It can also pick a bale from a stack and convey it to a required spot, the whole of the operations being under the control of one man.

One of the Bale Stacking Trucks in use at Frizinghall, L.M.S.R., stacking bales of wool. Illustration by courtesy of Wingrove and Rogers Ltd. of Liverpool, the makers of the truck.

The miscellaneous nature of the freight dealt with by the L.M.S.R. at Frizinghall—a common characteristic of railway goods traffic—results in the bales there being of numerous shapes and as many different sizes. The stacking trucks however handle them all equally easily and are capable of dealing with bales up to five tiers high. At Frizinghall there is a roller conveyor for transporting bales in and out. A section of the conveyor is removable, as shown in the photograph on this page, in order to allow free movement on the part of the truck and the staff.

The vehicle consists essentially of a battery driven truck of the type commonly used for factory work, on which a framework and jib are mounted very much after the style of a crane. The chassis and jib of the truck are largely fabricated by electric arc welding. The jib can be elevated or lowered as required by means of a rope connected to the winding drum or winch. At the head of the jib are fitted special jaws for grasping the bales to be dealt with. These jaws are kept open by spring gear except when rope pressure is applied. On the latest trucks, such as those in use at Frizinghall, a special parallel motion device ensures that the jaws keep the bales level. It is of particular interest that the application of this motion was worked out experimentally by means of a model made of Meccano Parts, yet another instance of the use of Meccano in invention and industry.

Two electric motors are mounted on the truck chassis. One is for propelling purposes and is connected to the driving wheels by means of chains. The other motor is for hoisting and from this the drive to the winch is taken first through a worm reduction gear and then by means of a guarded spur gear. The winch gear has an automatic solenoid brake which will hold the load in any position when current is off.

Two controllers operate the motors, and there are three speeds of operation for the lifting gear and three speeds for travelling. When the jib reaches the limit of its travel an automatic switch comes into action and cuts off the power. The brakes fitted to the driving wheels are interconnected with the travelling controller and when the truck is not travelling they are always on. They are released by the depression of a foot pedal on the driving platform, which must be kept down all the time the truck is in motion. If the truck is stopped suddenly by means of the brake alone, the travelling controller handle must be brought back to the "off" position and the brake released before power can be applied to start the truck.

The speed of operation of the truck is striking. On an average it takes 2 sec. for a bale to be picked up and, without a pause in the motion, it can be lifted to the top tier of a stack in 8 sec. The travelling speed of the truck is 5 m.p.h. with a load, although the truck is not primarily intended for carrying purposes but is essentially for stacking. In certain warehouses the bales are hand-trucked to the pile and the stacking truck is then used solely for its designed purpose. On this work, stacking to three tiers high, 200 bales an hour can be dealt with.

The battery which provides the power supply for the motors consists of 16 lead cells of 161 ampère-hours capacity. It is contained in a steel box below the truck. The battery container itself is mounted on roller-bearing steel wheels and slides out sideways when it has to be removed for re-charging. A hand trolley is placed to receive it and the removal of one discharged battery and its replacement by a freshly-charged one can be carried out in 5 min. As a general rule 1,000 bales can be stacked before a further charging of the battery is necessary.

The whole truck with its hoisting gear can be turned within a circle of 8 ft. radius.

A JOINT RAILWAY SYSTEM

ON many occasions recently we have received requests from readers that we should deal with suggestions for joint railway working of an interesting character. We have therefore decided this month to consider the working of the Cheshire Lines Railway, the largest of all the British joint lines. This is familiar, at least by name, to many readers in the North of England, but perhaps not so well known elsewhere. The L.N.E.R. and the L.M.S.R. are the partners in this concern, which is managed by the Cheshire Lines Committee, two-thirds of whom are L.N.E.R. representatives and the remainder L.M.S.R. This proportion is explained by the fact that in pre-grouping days the Great Central, Great Northern and Midland Railways each had a one-third interest in the system, the two first-named companies being now part of the L.N.E.R.

An interesting scene on a jointly-operated Hornby layout. A fast freight train hauled by an L.N.E.R. locomotive is passing the sidings where an L.M.S.R. No. 2 Special Locomotive is about to "take water" from the Tank.

Although the system is known as the Cheshire Lines, its chief main line stretches from Manchester to Liverpool, the station in each city being called "Central." Connection is made intermediately with a line from Godley Junction on the L.N.E.R. (G.C. Section). Cheadle Heath is the point where connections are made with the L.M.S.R. (Midland Section), as we mentioned in April 1932 in the article "A Miniature Midland Section," which dealt with the operation on a Hornby layout of the Manchester services from St. Pancras. These trains are known familiarly as the "Twenty-fives" from the fact that they all depart from London at 25 minutes past a particular hour.

Although the Cheshire Lines has no engines of its own, it has its own rolling stock. The L.N.E.R. therefore provide the motive power for all joint trains and for those working through to the L.N.E.R. system. Through services to the Midland Section of the L.M.S.R. are handled by engines of that company. This adds to the interest and variety of the locomotives to be seen. The coaches in use vary from the oak brown vehicles of the Cheshire Lines to the familiar red of L.M.S.R. stock. On a Hornby layout the working on the same system of L.N.E.R. and L.M.S.R. locomotives will follow actual practice, and some really good fun is to be had in this way, especially when two or more Hornby Railway owners combine their stock to form a joint layout of this description and operate suitable services.

The chief expresses of the Cheshire Lines are those connecting Manchester and Liverpool. They were the first to provide an hourly service between the two cities, and their clockwork-like regularity has earned for them the nick-name of the "Punctual" service. For the make-up of these trains in miniature Hornby No. 2 Coaches in L.N.E.R. colours can be used very well, as their finish is similar to that of the Cheshire Lines stock. Alternatively those who possess Hornby Metropolitan Coaches can use these and, in addition, they can employ them to represent L.N.E.R. vehicles when required. L.N.E.R. locomotives are always used for these trains.

Very important too are the "North Country Continental" trains whose running was described in detail in the "*M.M.*" for February 1929. As far as the Cheshire Lines system is concerned these provide a through connection once each way daily between Liverpool and Parkeston Quay, Harwich. As these are corridor trains with restaurant facilities Hornby No. 2 Saloon Coaches will be best for representing them in miniature. For the kitchen portion of the Saloon Coach doing the duty as a restaurant car we can make use of a scheme previously suggested in these pages. If a strip of tracing paper is inserted between the celluloid "glass" and the sides of the vehicle, so that two windows at one end on both sides of the coach are covered, it will give the effect of the frosted finish frequently used on such windows in actual practice. To insert the paper it is necessary to remove the roof, but there is no difficulty in this as the roof is secured by four brass "ventilators." These can be unscrewed and later replaced without trouble.

Passenger and goods trains passing at a wayside station. The passenger train is a local of Hornby No. 2 Coaches, with a No. 2 Special Tank Locomotive; the goods engine is a Hornby No. O Locomotive.

For the through L.M.S.R. services between "Liverpool" and "Cheadle Heath," where they could connect either actually or in imagination with miniature "Twenty-fives," No. 2 Saloon Coaches in L.M.S.R. colours can be used. These represent end-vestibuled corridor stock with wide windows as now commonly used on L.M.S.R. main line trains. A Hornby No. 2 "Standard Compound," a typical Derby design, could be employed as representing the Midland engines employed.

Local and goods trains on the Cheshire Lines are handled by L.N.E.R. locomotives, chiefly of G.C. design, although standard L.N.E.R. types are employed to some extent. There is thus every reason for the employment in miniature of the standard types of Hornby Locomotives in L.N.E.R. colours. L.M.S.R freight engines also appear on through trains. The Cheshire Lines System is connected with the Liverpool Docks and thus deals with a heavy import and export traffic.

An L.M.S.R. express in miniature. The Hornby No. 2 Saloon Coaches that compose it represent in an appropriate manner the end-vestibule corridor stock of actual practice.

The greatest occasion in the year for special working on the Cheshire Lines is in connection with the Liverpool Spring Race Meeting, particularly on the day of the Grand National Steeplechase. The Cheshire Lines is then honoured by the visit of an all-Pullman Special from King's Cross that is always hauled by an L.N.E.R. "Pacific." This is the only occasion in the year when either this type of engine, or car, is seen in that part of the country. This working through is certainly deserving of reproduction on a miniature system for the Hornby Pullmans are very representative of the actual cars used. For the locomotive a No. 3 *"Flying Scotsman"* would be the obvious choice and the appearance of such a train will be very fine, especially if the coaches are provided with suitable name-boards bearing the words "Pullman Race Special." Suitable boards can be made at home from strips of card, the necessary lettering being put on with ink or paint as preferred.

In addition to this "Super-Special" other trains of ordinary stock are run in great numbers from practically all sections of the L.N.E.R., with a corresponding variety in the types of engines to be seen. A regular feature of this race traffic is the operation of a special train of horse-boxes which is run from Newmarket on the G.E. Section of the L.N.E.R. This running would be interesting in miniature although No. 1 Cattle Wagons would have to be used to make up the train, as the Hornby Series does not yet include horse-boxes. In this connection the Horses of the Series of Meccano Dinky Toys (Dinky Toy No. 2a) could be employed quite well in arranging realistic loading and unloading scenes with suitable figures in attendance.

Although the L.M.S.R. has its own station at Aintree, where the Meeting takes place, trains from the Midland Section are worked over the Cheshire Lines and use their station. All of them are heavy and as a rule a great deal of double-heading is seen in accordance with Midland tradition. Many of the engines are Compounds, so that in representing the working in miniature a gathering of Hornby No. 2 Special Locomotives would be interesting and realistic. Those readers who may have rebuilt such engines in the manner described in the *"M.M."* for February 1933, to represent the inside cylinder 4-4-0s of class "2P," can use these rebuilt engines also. Real class "2P" locomotives frequently appear as pilots to the Compounds and such a combination in miniature would look extremely interesting.

All these locomotives, both L.N.E.R. and L.M.S.R., are accommodated at the Cheshire Lines depot, at Walton-on-the-Hill, where a very busy afternoon's work is carried out on Grand National day. Coaling and watering is carried out there in readiness for the return journey.

Join the Hornby Railway Company and become eligible for the competitions announced on this page.

H.R.C. COMPETITION PAGE

Join the Hornby Railway Company and become eligible for the competitions announced on this page.

SIXTH LOCOMOTIVE NAME AND NUMBER CONTEST

This month we have pleasure in announcing our return to an old favourite among H.R.C. competitors, the well-known Name and Number Contest, in which competitors are invited to decipher jumbled locomotive names and numbers. Enthusiastic reception is always given to these contests, and we have no doubt that this month the response will be even greater because members will be keen to show us they are up to the minute and not lacking in their knowledge of locomotive names and numbers.

The accompanying panel contains the names and numbers of 40 locomotives, in which the letters and figures respectively have been jumbled up. Competitors are required to re-shuffle these into their correct positions, and to make a list of the names and numbers thus obtained. Solutions must be written out in the same order as they appear in the panel.

7016	Libtirgioshen	2854	Ftyvrooilcoilpe
4324	Cfunliblh	6169	Belolil
291	Wuheysrbsr	7445	Yixglonff
1585	Darhinsoairabs	2660	Joghiknn
791	Torhurptiesinp	293	Bardefild
5792	Gonabighours	4201	Tipvopliener
7265	Nersareiloe	1086	Thighforsandhelera
4869	Honrahlnocc	3205	Casklutes
9145	Lanhipcomal	927	Divelsrieresherv
1614	Ecolnaiand	5539	Lauphork
386	Yondorlder	1512	Niksliverg
8240	Sawinderstocl	2645	Scabnowe
5817	Throndeadgu	4439	Pillhandhil
2016	Narcyemuq	796	Saleandgavedirsois
5086	Thasnoatcelt	6170	Bearbanaled
5338	Yanterem	2569	Sanelugdogl
5287	Dnalrebmuhtron	2945	Hipnecenyrr
274	Lometac	6735	Dilrawnidswands
8342	Kingbrinoocheh	6048	Babyennathlylo
2426	Bestlanadahs	398	Staleovs

Many of the jumbled words appear to be a senseless collection of letters which would never resolve themselves into a locomotive name. This is not the case, however, for after juggling with the letters for a time the name of the locomotive will become apparent. In solving the contest readers should first decipher the name of the locomotive, and then its number can readily be found. For example, the letters of the first name on the list when correctly rearranged become *"British Legion,"* and when this name has been settled it is an easy matter to find the engine's number.

When a competitor has solved all the jumbled names and numbers, or at any rate as many of them as he is able to manage, he should make a neat list of them on a sheet of paper, together with his name, full address, and H.R.C. membership number.

The contest will be divided as usual into two Sections, Home and Overseas. Prizes of any products manufactured by Meccano Ltd., to the value of 21/-, 15/- and 10/6 respectively will be awarded to the three best entries submitted in each section. In the event of a tie for any prize, neatness will be taken into consideration when the judges make the final decision.

Envelopes containing entries should be marked in the top left-hand corner *"H.R.C. March Name and Number Contest No. 6,"* and posted to reach Headquarters at Meccano Ltd., Binns Road, Liverpool 13, not later than 31st March. Entries from competitors in the Overseas Section should be posted to arrive on or before 30th June.

Railway Photographic Contest

The wide range of subjects submitted in the winter series of photographic contests shows that many interesting photographs would have been lost to us if the photographic contests were abandoned during the winter months. One of the main reasons why these contests are so popular is that competitors are not tied down to any particular subject, and because they are permitted to send as many prints as they desire so long as they have a railway atmosphere.

Although a competitor may submit any number of prints he cannot win more than one prize in one contest. It is important that each print sent in should have on the back a description in a few words of the railway scene shown, the age, name and full address of the sender, and most important of all his H.R.C. membership number.

The Contest will be divided as usual into two sections, Home and Overseas, and prizes of any products manufactured by Meccano Ltd., to the value of 21/-, 15/- and 10/6 respectively will be awarded to the three winners in each section. In addition a number of consolation prizes will be awarded.

Envelopes containing entries must be marked *"H.R.C. March Photographic Contest"* in the top left-hand corner and posted to reach Headquarters at Meccano Ltd., Binns Road, Liverpool 13, on or before 31st March. The closing date for the Overseas Section is 30th June.

My Favourite Locomotive

To almost all railway enthusiasts there is usually one locomotive or class of locomotive which has a special attraction and is held in higher esteem than any other. The merit of such favourites is not necessarily their power or appearance, but sometimes results from personal association and familiarity with their work. We present therefore *"My Favourite Locomotive"* as the subject of this drawing contest.

Competitors may submit either pencil or coloured drawings as desired, but the judges will not necessarily award the prizes to the senders of sketches in colour.

To the three competitors in each Section, Home and Overseas, who submit the best drawings, prizes consisting of any products manufactured by Meccano Ltd. to the value of 21/-, 15/- and 10/6 respectively will be awarded. On the back of each entry must be clearly written the competitor's name, age, full address and most important of all his H.R.C. membership number. Unsuccessful entries will be returned if they are accompanied by a stamped addressed envelope of suitable size. Prizewinning entries become the property of Meccano Ltd., and are not returnable.

Entries should be marked *"H.R.C. March Drawing Contest"* and posted to reach Headquarters at Meccano Ltd., Binns Road, Liverpool 13, before 31st March. The closing date for competitors in the Overseas Section is 30th June.

COMPETITION RESULTS

HOME

January "Missing Words Contest."—First: D. H. Earle (41617), Wembley Park, Middx. Second: K. W. Ashberry (14344), Cambridge. Third: T. F. Fletcher (6057), Perry Barr, Birmingham 20. Fourth: C. Stevens (46092), Leyton, London, E.10. Consolation Prizes: K. Gandy (7571), Sheffield 8; H. Woolgar (29656), Shoreham-by-Sea, Sussex; R. Garner (43574), New England, Peterborough; R. Lumley (20253), Plymouth; T. Edwards (46484), Thetford, Norfolk; K. Scott (45479), Goswick, Northumberland.

January "Railway Photo Contest."—First: C. Spencer (44179), Sheffield 11. Second: E. C. Morgan (10735), Wandsworth Common, London, S.W.18. Third: J. C. Button (10335), Crewe, Ches. Fourth: D. Kelk (28579), Staplehurst, Kent. Consolation Prizes: D. S. Wakely (17486), Cheam, Surrey; D. J. Muirhead (41880), Hendon, London, N.W.4; F. G. H. Kennedy (25074), Tonge Moor, Bolton, Lancs.

January "Voting Contest."—First: T. W. Chatfield (9197), W. Worthing, Sussex. Second: B. O. Palmer (34301), Highcliffe, Hants. Third: D. Brooks (25150), Alveston, Nr. Bristol. Fourth: K. Paine (46145), Eltham, London, S.E.9.

OVERSEAS

September "Errors Contest."—First: J. Rodriguez (3647), Montreal, P.Q., Canada. Second: D. Murison (37642), Buenos Aires, South America. Third: D. Parker (38595), Brussels, Ontario, Canada. Fourth: J. Stanbridge (10236), Perth, W. Australia.

September "Railway Photo Contest."—First: G. E. Schulz (15425), Coromby, Victoria, Australia. Second: Marcus De Lima (34925), Poona, India. Third: G. Healy (43145), Prince Albert, Sask., Canada. Fourth: B. Forbes, Johannesburg, S. Africa.

October "Articles Suggestions Contest."—First: G. Healy (43145), Prince Albert, Sask., Canada. Second: G. Yule (34970), Melbourne, Australia. Third: J. A. Mallia (43679), Vittoriosa, Malta. Fourth: M. De Lima (34925), Poona, India.

October "Missing Links Contest."—First: H. C. Key (24764), Park Circus, Calcutta, India. Second: I. Brough (9112), Preston N.18, Victoria, Australia. Third: W. G. Hallack (17578), Capetown, South Africa. Fourth: R. A. Wragg (7913), Bandikui, Rajputana, India.

Branch News

St. Stephen's (Saltash).—Several meetings have been devoted to the renewal of the track. The double track sections are to be extended and it is hoped that eventually the whole layout will be provided with separate up and down lines. The Branch stock has been increased by the addition of two new locomotives. Visits have been paid to the Branch by members of the Plymouth M.C. and on one of these occasions a useful talk was given on the maintenance of Hornby railway material. Facilities for games are available and continue to be popular; table tennis matches have been arranged with the local Y.M.C.A. Secretary: B. Braund, 9, Homer Park, Saltash.

Claremont (Nottingham).—The first few meetings have been devoted to an examination of the rails and other material contributed by the members. After some experiments, a suitable layout has been devised and the train working has been greatly enjoyed by all. A station, engine shed and tunnel have been constructed by the Chairman. The Branch library has been commenced and a Branch Magazine is now produced regularly. It is hoped to pay a visit to the L.N.E.R. locomotive depot at Nottingham. Later on in the year, an Open Night will be held at which a play will be presented. Secretary: R. Ingham, 132, Mansfield Road, Nottingham.

Priory (High Wycombe).—Timetable arrangements have been overhauled, and better working has been secured as a result. An overhead branch line has been completed and a "pull and push" train works the service, operating in conjunction with the main line trains. Trials have been carried out with various locomotives hauling different loads. A feature of recent meetings has been the operation of the system with only the accessory lights in use. A visit has been paid to the Holywell Branch; two locomotives were taken, each acquitting itself well on "foreign" metals. Work on an outdoor track, already commenced some time ago, is expected to be resumed in a month or two. Secretary: J. T. Cosgrove, 54, Priory Road, High Wycombe.

Holywell.—Meetings have been resumed after a temporary suspension owing to various epidemics. Timetable operations have been conducted with success, and some additional locomotives have been put into service. Work is now in hand on an outdoor track in the Secretary's garden, but this is not expected to be completed until later in the year. Secretary: J. Spicer, 28, Holywell, Oxford.

Paignton.—A satisfactory layout has been arranged with a continuous main line and a terminal station. Some experimental train running has been carried out on this, but no definite running arrangements have yet been decided on. Rules for the conduct of the Branch generally, and for track meetings are being formulated. Secretary: H. M. Anderson, 22, Laura Grove, Paignton.

Members of the Umzinto H.R.C. Branch, Natal, South Africa. This Branch commenced operations in February, 1935, but is not yet an incorporated Branch. Regular meetings are held and the equipment brought by the members is combined to form a large layout.

Patricroft.—Considerable enthusiasm has been stimulated as a result of the institution of the Branch library and a games programme. It is hoped to include in the library copies of all the latest railway publications. Ordinary activities have continued as usual and additional locomotives and rolling stock have been put into service. New rails have been obtained and with these most of the existing layout has been relaid. Secretary: A. Howarth, Jnr., 42, Nelson Street, Patricroft, Manchester.

Forest Road Cabin (Southport).—Several meetings have been held and discussions have taken place on suggested track and working improvements. An experimental timetable has been devised and track operations have been carried out according to it. A new timetable giving more intensive working is in course of preparation. Secretary: D. R. Moss, 141, Forest Road, Southport.

Branches in Course of Formation

The following new Branches of the Hornby Railway Company are at present in process of formation, and any boys who are interested and desirous of linking up with this unique organisation should communicate with the promoters, whose names and addresses are given below:

Anglesey—I. Jones, Trefnan, Menai Bridge.

Barnsley—G. Atkin, P.O. Platts Common.

Blackrock—P. Doris, 74, Temple Road.

Cardiff—H. K. Lloyd, Milverton, St. John's Crescent, Whitchurch.

Glasgow—I. Stevenson, 4, Mariscat Road, Pollokshields, S.1.

Gourock—B. Higgins, Fairlight, Ashton.

Hounslow—B. Smith, 83, Clifford Road.

Hucknall—J. Hopkinson, 55, Long Hill Rise.

Liverpool—E. S. Green, 63, Sheil Road, Fairfield, 6.

Liverpool—H. A. Howard, 61, Springwood Avenue, Allerton, 19.

Liverpool—P. D. Weymont, 4, Eversley Street, Princes Avenue, 8.

London—D. Watkins, 22, Birkbeck Grove, Acton, W.3.

Monkstown—R. D. Pierce, 20, Monkstown Road, Co. Down.

Petts Wood—E. C. Smith, 144, Petts Wood Road.

Rayleigh—V. Cocks, "Valsior," Kings Road.

Stoke-on-Trent—H. Allen, 22, Wise Street, Longton, Stoke-on-Trent.

Teignmouth—J. Gibbings, The Beacon School.

Whyteleaf—S. Allen, 15, New Barn Lane, Whyteleaf, Surrey.

Coventry—P. Whitehouse, 9, Rochester Road, Earlsdon, Coventry.

Branches Recently Incorporated

298. Ravensbury (Morden)—A. M. Evans, 31, Arras Avenue, Morden.
299. Claremont (Nottingham)—R. D. Ingham, 132, Mansfield Road, Nottingham.
300. Fishponds (Bristol)—A. N. Ewing, 154, Thingwall Park, Fishponds, Bristol.
301. Rutherglen (Glasgow)—R. G. Langmuir, 11, Afton Street, Shawlands, Glasgow, S.1.

THE GREATEST ROYAL PHILATELIST

This portrait of King George V is possibly the best of all his stamp portraits. It is taken from the Falkland Islands centenary commemorative issue of 1933.

THE death of His Majesty King George V has taken one of the greatest philatelists of all time from the ranks of stamp collecting. There have been other Kings who have collected stamps but King George was outstanding among royal philatelists. His collection has been valued at various figures between £250,000 and £400,000, and it is the fact that King George's collection of British Colonial issues is the greatest and most nearly complete in the world. It is pleasing to know, therefore, that the collection is to be kept intact and, for the present at least, will remain in the care of its present curator, Sir Edward Bacon.

We dealt with King George's collection at moderate length in an article in our issue for May last, and in this short article we feel it would be appropriate to deal with his life and reign as shown in stamp designs. There is an enormous quantity of material available, of course, for until recent days almost every British Dominion and Colony used the King's head in its stamp designs as a matter of ordinary routine.

King George's first appearance in the stamp album was in 1897 when his portrait, as Duke of York, illustrated here, was used as the design for the 5c. value of a new issue for Newfoundland. This set was devoted to portraits of the Royal Family and included also Queen Victoria; King Edward VII and Queen Alexandra, then Prince and Princess of Wales; Queen Mary, then Duchess of York; and Prince Edward, now King Edward VIII, four generations of the Royal House.

King George as Duke of York. This portrait is from Newfoundland's Tercentenary commemorative of 1897.

King George in the uniform of an Admiral of the Fleet. This design was used for Southern Rhodesia's 1924 issue.

King George V and Queen Mary as Prince and Princess of Wales. These portraits are from Canada's Quebec Tercentenary issue of 1908.

King George mounted on his charger "Anzac." This design was used for the Australian Silver Jubilee commemorative issue.

Newfoundland has shown a penchant for using portraits of the Royal Family on its stamps and subsequent to the 1897 issue, portraits of King George, as Prince of Wales, appeared on the 1910 issue commemorative of the tercentenary of Newfoundland's colonisation; in 1911, to celebrate his coronation; in 1932, and, of course, in the 1935 Jubilee series.

The 1897 stamp had a special appeal to philatelists, however, in that just about the time of its issue, King George was president of the Royal Philatelic Society. His presidency was no mere matter of form, and his association with the Society was closely maintained throughout his reign. For many years past at the opening meeting of each year's session the members have had the privilege of inspecting a part of the King's collection. This 1897 issue is the only stamp available showing the King in civil attire.

Canada's Quebec Tercentenary issue of 1908 was the occasion of King George's second stamp portrait. In this, as our illustration shows, he was featured with Queen Mary as Prince and Princess of Wales on the ½c. value.

Two years later King George ascended the throne and by the end of 1912 the change-over from King Edward stamps to those bearing King George's portrait had been completed throughout the Empire, except in a small number of cases in which the change was not made until early in 1913.

King George in his robes as Emperor of India, as shown on each of India's New Delhi Inauguration commemoratives of 1931.

King George as Field-Marshal, as shown in New Zealand's 1926/35 issue.

This portrait of King George is from Newfoundland's 1935 issue.

King George and Queen Mary in their state robes. This stamp is from Canada's Silver Jubilee issue.

Thus there came portraits of the King in a variety of uniforms. There have been many striking pictures, of which the best, possibly, is that on the £1 value of the Falkland Islands centenary issue of 1933. In the space available here it is impossible to list them all, and instead we have chosen a representative selection for illustration here.

It is fitting that the greatest royal philatelist should have for his memorial among his stamp collection subjects a place on almost every page of their albums, but one could wish that British stamp issuing policy had permitted a freer use of commemorative issues during King George's reign. The Silver Jubilee alone, in a reign crowded with outstanding incidents, was marked by a special stamp issue.

Stamp collecting owes much to King George, and while in historical records our late King almost surely will be known as King George the Beloved, those who shared his enthusiasm for his hobby may be forgiven if by them he is proudly recalled as King George the Philatelist.

In his younger days King Edward too was interested in stamp collecting and on one occasion exhibited a portion of his collection. He was never an enthusiast, however, and the calls upon his time now will be too heavy to permit him to take more than a general interest in the hobby.

"1,000 PACKET" 6D.
A WONDERFUL OFFER FOR
Postage 2½d. ex. Abroad 6d. ex.

The "1,000 Packet" contains 500 excellently assorted Stamps; **a complete Sheet of 100 Unused** (very useful for exchange purposes); a neat 12-page booklet for duplicates; 25 British Colonials usually sold at ½d. to 1d. each, including new issues; 375 Magic "Strip" mounts, very quick for mounting stamps, and list of stamp bargains. Free sets will be sent to those who send addresses of stamp-collecting friends. *Ask for Approvals.* 100 B. Colonials 1/-. 20 Air Post 6d. 10 Abyssinia 1/6. 10 Mozambique Triangulars (just out) 1/6. "B.O.P." and "Captain" monthly parts cheap. **H. C. WATKINS, M, DEPT., GRANVILLE ROAD, BARNET.**

The "TRANSPORT" Packet

contains a wonderful assortment of 44 all different Foreign and Colonial stamps and includes the following which depict various means of transportation: **Tunis** (Water Carrier), **Mozambique** (Aeroplane), **Jamaica** (Troopship), **Madagascar** (Native Transport), **Greece** (Steamer), **Indo-China** (Boat), **Mauritania** (Crossing Desert), **Transvaal** (Waggon), **Brazil** (Aeroplane), **Middle Congo** (Train), **Sudan** (Camel), **Austria** (Horseman), **Dutch Indies** (Steamboat), **Australia** (Aeroplane), **Gaboon** (Raft), **Colombia** (Natives with Panniers), **South Africa** (Ship), **French Guiana** (Native Carriers), **Germany** (Aeroplane), and **Belgium** (Train). Price **6d.** (abroad extra). All purchasers of this packet asking for approval sheets will be presented with **India** Silver Jubilee Stamps.
Burdock & Flury, 4, Marlborough Rd., London, S.W. 19

TRIANGULAR PACKET

This rare and beautiful stamp was issued by Spain to commemorate the explorer Columbus, and shows his Flagship—Santa Maria. I am presenting it FREE, together with a collection of **10 other fine Spanish stamps** to all readers requesting approvals and enclosing 2d. postage (abroad 6d. P.O.). Send **to-day** for this extraordinary offer which can **never be repeated, as stocks are limited.**
MICHAEL HERBERT, 8, Woodstock Road, WALTHAMSTOW, LONDON.

STAMP BARGAINS

Colonial and Foreign from 1/3rd to 1/8th cat. being offered on approval. Everything from attractive "space fillers" at ½d. each to rare items at £1 each and over. No gifts but real bargains!
CAMPBELL, 1, HALDON AVE., TEIGNMOUTH.

JOIN THE "INVESTORS' STAMP CLUB"

Shares 6d. per month, plus 1½d. postage.
Show this to Dad. Jubilee Year was a good one for Investors. Every Shareholder receives 6d. worth stamps each month, principally new issues. March packet, for example, includes new pictorial Nigeria and eleven other Colonial pictorials. You will never get the same stamp twice. Money returned if not satisfied with value.
Dividend (minimum 4 per cent.) declared twice yearly and paid in cash or stamps.
Shares may be fully paid-up in advance—5/- per annum. **FIRST TWELVE** paid-up shareholders will be appointed **DIRECTORS** with valuable privileges.
Apply for full particulars to:
A. F. McQUARRIE, 83, Cliff Road, WALLASEY, Ches.

KING GEORGE V—Important Notice

THE STAMP OF TO-DAY IS THE RARITY OF TO-MORROW

Owing to the death of His Majesty King George V, all current British Colonials will shortly be obsolete. So now is your chance to obtain them before they become scarce.
I am therefore introducing EMPIRE MIXTURE guaranteed to contain only British Colonials, sent out exactly as received from Banks, Trading Stations and other Outposts of the Empire.
EMPIRE MIXTURE is the cheapest and best way to fill up the gaps in your British Colonial Collection, includes Silver Jubilees, Commemoratives, New Issues, Provisionals and heaps of other scarce stamps.
100 for **1/-**, 250 **2/-**, 500 **3/9**, 1,000 **7/3.** All post free (abroad 3d.).
As a special introductory offer I am giving to all purchasers of **3/9** or over a Queen Victoria Labuan stamp, cat. **5/-.**
Remit by Postal Order only.
K. HUMPHRIES, Dept. M., East Wittering Rd., East Wittering, Chichester, Sussex.

HISTORICAL PACKET FREE!

Contains 20 diff. Commemoratives, Centenary, War, Charity, Jubilee, Exhibition, etc., Stamps **Only.** Don't miss this opportunity. To all genuine applicants for cheap, attractive appros. enclosing 1½d. postage.
R. Kippen, 52, Cowley Road, Leytonstone, E.11.

ODDS & ENDS—ALL MINT

4 Basutoland Jubilee 2/3
4 Bechuanaland Jubilee 2/3
4 Cyprus Jubilee ... 3/3
4 Hong Kong Jubilee 2/-
4 Japan 1934 Red Cross 1/-
4 Newfoundland Jubilee ... 4/-
3 New Zealand Air Mails 1/2
9 Spain "Press Association" ... 1/6
4 Swaziland Jubilee 2/3

Cash with Order. Postage extra.
H. L. GOMM,
41, Upper Cranbrook Road, Redland, Bristol, 6.

FREE STAMP WALLET

(Size 3½ by 5½ inches) fitted with Perforation Gauge, etc., and containing **MINT SET OF BRITISH COLONIALS (1d.-1/-)** to approval applicants enclosing 3d. (in stamps) for postage and packing.
A. B. LEWIS, Dept. C.31,
16, Cricklewood Lane, LONDON, N.W.2.

N FREE ... FREE S

We are presenting this month the third packet of our new alphabetical series, the greatest gifts ever offered.
SEND A POST CARD

This month's packet contains stamps of countries from N to S and includes many beautiful pictorials. You must not miss this magnificent offer.
TO-DAY FOR APPROVALS

UNIVERSITY STAMP CO.
13, Walton Well Road, OXFORD

KING GEORGE V

Owing to the death of His Majesty, King George the Fifth, on January 20th, all the stamps of the Colonies and Dominions bearing his portrait will soon be obsolete. We are offering, free, a collection of stamps all of which show the Head of His late Majesty, including Australia, Canada, Ceylon, Fiji, Gold Coast, Gwalior, Hong Kong, Jamaica, Newfoundland, New Zealand, Straits Settlements, etc., to all applicants who send for a selection of stamps on approval and enclose 2d. In addition, we are giving the famous Newfoundland stamp showing the new King, Edward VIII, as Prince. Price of this packet without Approvals, 1/-. SPECIAL OFFERS of new sets: 3 Finland Red Cross, 1/1; 4 Holland Xmas Charity, 1/6; 6 Zanzibar 1936 (5c.-1/-), 3/-. Postage extra. Particulars of our big new Stamp Competition also sent free with Approvals.

WINDSOR STAMP CO.
(M.M. Dept.), 59, LEE ROAD, BLACKHEATH, S.E.3.

THE MYSTIC PACKET

1000 UNKNOWN UNUSUAL UNSORTED 1/3

Stamps on paper, etc., just as received from Convents, Missions, Bankers, etc. Guaranteed unpicked. Chance of a **FIND** in every lot. Send to-day for your treasure hunt to-morrow, **3** for **3/6, 6** for **6/6.** Abroad, **1/6** packet. **FREE!** 25 Br. Cols., including Jubilees, to approval Applicants, also **FREE EXCHANGE.** Send postage only. Overseas **3d.**
ASTLEY & CO.
(M25), Lowhill, WOLVERHAMPTON

GLOBE-TROTTER'S JUBILEE OFFER TO YOU

FREE.—AMAZING SILVER JUBILEE PACKET, including Silver Jubilee varieties, Air Mails, Large Italian and Russian Pictorial Commemoratives, New Issues, Colonials—60 Magnificent Stamps—the most sensational offer yet. Send 1½d. postage for "Globe-Trotter" approval selections—amazing value, ¼d., ½d., and 1d. upwards—and particulars of how **you can have FREE stamps every 14 days!!** Write Now—there's a stamp treat in store for you. **Special Offers.** "Globe-Trotter" Mystery Mixture—world-wide collected—old and new issues, pictorials, etc., 1,000 unsorted, unbeatable, 1/3. 10 Jubilees, 1/-, 50 Airmails, 1/11. 50 Soviet Russia, many large pictorials, 1/5, 25 9d. "Globe-Trotter" for sheer value.—**GLOBE-TROTTER, 17, Winchester Road, BIRCHFIELD, BIRMINGHAM.**

4 DIFF. QUEEN ASTRID MOURNING STAMPS, 3d. —J. Sanders, 90, Newlands Avenue, Southampton.

AERO-SHIP PACKET FREE!

This huge gift parcel contains **508** Unsorted Foreign Stamps, many scarce from **Mozambique** (Pictorial Air Mail), **Brazil** (Aeroplane), **New Caledonia** (Yacht), **Fr. Oceania** (Native Punt), **China** (Junk), **Br. S. Africa** (Frigate), etc., etc. Just send 2d. for postage and request my famous **Extra-Large-Discount Approval Sheets.** (Abroad 6d. P.O.)
E. EASTICK, 22, Bankside Road, BOURNEMOUTH.

FINE SURPRISE PACKET

Including beautiful Mint Set Columbus Ships given to all applicants for my Approvals enclosing 4d. postage.
If you are not on my Register—be sure to send and continue to receive more good things with further selections.
G. W. GREEN, 414, PADIHAM ROAD, BURNLEY.

CHEAP APPROVALS

My beautiful Approval Selections are ideal for filling those vacant spaces. Pictorials, Colonials, and hard to get items. Selections from 4 a 1d. Free Gift Bi-coloured Persia all applicants.
A. V. TAPP,
108, CHESTERFIELD RD., BRISTOL

100 "WORTH WHILE" 1/- Post Free

DIFFERENT BRITISH COLONIALS INCLUDING JUBILEES. Covering Gold Coast Pictorials, ½d., 1d., 1½d., 2d.; Northern Rhodesia, Nigeria, ½d., 1d., 1½d., 2d., 3d.; Mauritius, 2c., 4c., 5c.; Iraq, ¼, 1, 3 annas; N. Zealand, ½d., 1d., 1½d., 2d., 3d., 4d., 6d., 1/-; Newfoundland; Palestine; Fiji; Bahamas, etc., etc. Finest Packet **you** have ever had. **Money Back** if not satisfied. With **"Worth While"** Approval Sheets **only.**
JOS. H. GAZE, DIDSBURY, MANCHESTER.

BRITISH COLONIAL APPROVALS from ½d. Mint Papua Free.—Wilson, 48, Lambeth Rd., Middlesbrough.

Edward VIII Packet and Stamp Outfit free to Approval purchasers.—G. Kingsmill, New Barnet, Herts.

500 Stamp Mounts Free to ¼d., ½d. or 1d. Approval applicants.—Winter, 89, Cobham Road, Seven Kings.

FREE. 9 Nyassa Triangles to genuine approval applicants enclosing 3d. for postage.—J. Hayes, Meadfoot, Rosemary Hill Road, Sutton Coldfield.

ALL FOR 1/-

25 "ANIMAL" stamps illustrating Camels, Elephants, Giraffes, Monkeys, Tigers, etc. Also 1,000 Good Quality Stamp-Mounts. Postage 1½d.
D. Brenchley, 16, Gloucester Place, Greenwich, S.E.10.

14 Tannou Touva 1935, 9 Triangles, mint ... 2/3
4 Belgium Queen Astrid Mourning, mint ... 5d.
3 Belgium, Mail Coach Pictorial, mint ... ... 5d.
3 Belgium, Railways, Pictorial, mint ... ... 2½d.
Post 1½d. extra. Cheap Sets. Approval if desired.
J. R. MORRIS, 9, Audley Road, Folkestone, Kent.

THE JUBILEE PACKET

Contains 60 **Diff.** All Superior stamps (**NO** Unused German, etc.), including 7 **Large SILVER JUBILEE PICTORIALS** from **HONG KONG, KENYA, UGANDA, TANGANYIKA, JAMAICA, CEYLON, Australia, INDIA and CANADA (Princess Elizabeth)**; also a Beautiful **Queen Astrid** Commemorative illustrated in Jan. "M.M."; a **Large MOZAMBIQUE AIR MAIL pictorial; Set of NEW CEYLON pictorials; New TANGANYIKA; New CHILE AIR MAIL pictorial; NEWFOUNDLAND,** our new King; and **Pictorial NYASALAND,** etc., Price **1/-** only, post 1½d. extra. Satisfaction or Money refunded in full. Ask to see our Bargain approvals. **THE PUKKA STAMP Co., 27, Normandy Ave., BARNET.**

Stamp Gossip
and Notes on New Issues

Malayan Postal Union Issues

After 35 years of unification of their postage stamp issues, the four federated Malay States, Pahang, Perak, Negri Sembilan and Selangor, have re-adopted separate issues for their individual states. The four new issues have just appeared, each with one design only covering a full range of nine values from 1c. to 40c.

The designs for the Pahang and Perak issues both bear portraits of the respective Sultans. The Negri Sembilan design, illustrated here, embodies the emblem of the State, a shield bearing rice-stalks above a Star, the shield being surmounted by a Malayan dagger and sheath.

The Selangor design, also shown here, differs from the other three in that it shows the name of the State in native characters and only the word "Malaya" in English. The effect is rather misleading. The true reason for this departure is not officially stated, but it may be a gesture to the political importance of Selangor. The main feature of the design shows the mosque at the Sultan's palace at Klang.

Although each of the four States will maintain and sell only its own stamp issues in future, the stamps of one State will be usable in any of the other three. This facility will also apply to the new issue that is to be produced for the Straits Settlements.

The four States and the Straits Settlements will use a common series of postage due stamps, bearing the inscription "Malayan Postal Union."

Jubilee Issues

Readers who have a liking for figures will be interested to know that the total issue of Silver Jubilee stamps in Great Britain amounted to no less than 1,008,000,000! There were 353,400,000 at ½d., 150,400,000 at 1d., 490,000,000 at 1½d., and 14,200,000 at 2½d.

In a number of the general Colonial issues showing the view of Windsor Castle, as in the Straits Settlements 12c. stamp illustrated in our May issue, there is a variety that has come to be known as the "double flagstaff." A flaw in the printing plate produced a line suggesting another flagstaff to the left of the small central tower in the illustration. This variety has been very eagerly sought after, but Stanley Gibbons Ltd. do not intend to catalogue it.

King Edward VIII Issues

Several readers have written to enquire when they may expect the appearance of stamps bearing the effigy of our new King, Edward VIII. It is impossible for any statement on this matter to be made yet, but it is safe to say that, unless a royal mourning stamp in honour of King George is issued, there will be no further issues of Georgian stamps. Many months, of necessity, must pass before King Edward's portrait takes his father's place upon our stamps. It was almost 12 months after the date of his accession that King George's head was featured on British stamps generally, but Newfoundland and South Africa did produce a single stamp each in 1910.

Considerable work has to be done before the new stamps can be produced. Invitations must be issued to artists to submit designs for a complete new series, and these must be approved by the King himself. Designs having been chosen, the method of production must be decided upon, master dies engraved and printing plates prepared, all of which processes take considerable time. The same course must be followed for each of the Dominions and the Crown Colonies, so that it seems probable we shall have to wait until the closing months of the year before stamps of the new reign appear.

It is just possible that one or two of the Colonies may be able to feature an Edwardian stamp at an early date. Bermuda, for example, has a new pictorial series on order. Each of the stamps, we understand, was intended to include in its design a small medallion portrait of King George, and it may not be a matter of great difficulty to change the portrait to that of King Edward.

Swedish Postal Tercentenary

Those readers who are interested in the postal history of the world will welcome the postal tercentenary commemorative issue that has just appeared in Sweden. Sweden was the fourth country in Europe to have a Government Post Office, and the various developments in mail carrying services are featured in the series of 12 stamps which have designs as follows: 5 öre, Axle Oxenstierna; 10 öre, a mail runner; 15 öre, a mounted courier, 20 öre, mail-carrying sailing vessel; 25 öre, paddle steamer; 30 öre, a mail coach; 35 öre, Swedish Coat of Arms; 40 öre, a modern locomotive; 45 öre, A. W. Roos; 50 öre, mail 'bus; 60 öre, line; 100 öre, air mail 'plane.

New Greek Air Mails

As promised in our last issue, we reproduce this month specimens from the new Greek air mail series, brief descriptions of the mythological subjects of the designs of which appeared in our earlier note.

Our illustrations show the 1 dr. value featuring the Chariot of the Sun. The Greeks believed that daylight came when the Sun Chariot was driven across the sky by Helios, who is shown in the design controlling his fine steeds. The 5 dr. shows Daedalus fastening wings to his son, Icarus, preparatory to their attempt to escape by flying from the Island of Crete. The 30 dr. design shows Triptolemus and his flying dragon chariot. Triptolemus was not one of the Olympic gods, but he became the favourite of the goddess Demeter, who taught him the arts of farming. She gave him the chariot so that he might travel about the world teaching mortals the science of agriculture. Later he became King of Eleusis, and when he died was made a judge in Hades.

Austrian Heroes Series

The latest charity series from Austria is probably the finest that this country, renowned for its charity stamps, has ever issued. The designs introduce Austrian martial heroes, including several whose fame is world-wide. We illustrate the 12gr. value, which shows Prince Eugene of Savoy (1663/1736), the friend and ally of our own great Duke of Marlborough at the battles of Blenheim, Oudenarde and Malplaquet.

The remaining designs are as follows: 24gr., Field-Marshal Gideon Ernst Laudon (1717/1790), an Austrian of Scotch descent, whose greatest victory was against Frederick the Great at Kunersdorf in 1759; 30gr., The Archduke Karl (1771/1847). His greatest distinction was his brilliant campaign against the French army. In 1799 he was responsible for the defence of Vienna and ten years later he fought two battles with the mighty Napoleon, inflicting losses of upwards of 50,000 men; 40gr., Field-Marshal Josef Radetzky (1766/1858); 60gr., Vice-Admiral Wilhelm von Tegetthof (1827/1871); 64gr., Field-Marshal Franz Conrad von Hötzendorf, who was at the head of the Austro-Hungarian armies during the Great War.

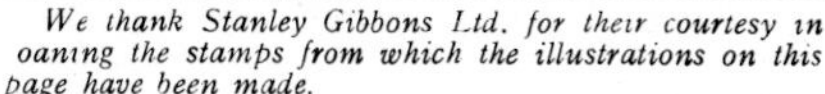

We thank Stanley Gibbons Ltd. for their courtesy in loaning the stamps from which the illustrations on this page have been made.

MECCANO LIMERICKS

No form of verse has attracted the humorist so readily as the limerick. The gay swing of its rhythm lends itself to fun making and as a result the limerick competitions we have featured on past occasions have always enjoyed great popularity.

This month we set our rhymester readers a new task—that of providing a suitable last line for a Meccano limerick, four lines of which are given here:—

Of Meccano a schoolboy once said,
As he dreamed of his birthday in bed,
It's undoubtedly clever
The best idea ever
* * * * *

No restrictions are imposed as to the form given to the last line. Readers may feature any one of Meccano's many merits to round off this excited young schoolboy's anticipatory joy. The line must rhyme with the first two lines, of course.

Cash prizes of 21/–, 15/–, 10/6 and 5/– respectively will be awarded to the senders of the four best entries in order of merit.

A selection of prize-winning prints from the Overseas Sections of the 1935 Photo Contests. The first of the 1936 competitions will be announced in our next issue. 1. "Spraying" (Miss N. Milne, Hawkes Bay, N.Z.). 2. "The Growing City" (B. B. Silan, Perak, F.M.S.). 3. "The Timber Hauler" (C. J. McCain, Sydney, N.S.W.). 4. "Old Jerusalem" (R. H. Warr, Cairo). 5. "Journey's End" (J. Credie, Capetown). 6. "Jubilee Spirits" (A. A. Olowu, Ibadan, Nigeria).

Some of our readers may feel that they can improve upon the specimen limerick we provide, and as an encouragement to them to try their hands we offer also cash prizes value 21/–, 15/–, 10/6 and 5/– respectively for the best complete limericks dealing with Meccano or any of its allied productions.

This competition is entirely separate from the "last line" contest, and competitors may submit entries and will be eligible to gain a prize in both.

Entries for both competitions may be sent in one envelope. They should be addressed to "Meccano Limericks, Meccano Magazine, Binns Road, Liverpool 13," and must reach this office not later than 31st March. Separate sheets of paper must be used for the separate competitions, of course.

Separate sets of prizes to the same amounts will be reserved for entries from Overseas readers. Overseas entries must arrive not later than 30th June.

March Drawing Competition

This month we are featuring the last of our 1935/36 series of Drawing Competitions, and those of our artist readers who have not yet taken part are urged to make use of this final opportunity of the season. No special subject is set, and the prizes are offered simply for the best drawings or paintings submitted during the month.

Entries will be divided into the usual two sections, A for readers aged 16 and over, B for those under 16, and cash prizes value 21/– and 10/6 respectively will be awarded to the best entries in each section.

A separate set of prizes, awarded in similar conditions, will be reserved for entries from Overseas readers, that is, those living outside Great Britain, Northern Ireland, the Irish Free State and the Channel Islands.

Entries to this month's competition must be addressed "March Drawing Contest, Meccano Magazine, Binns Road, Liverpool 13," and must arrive not later than 31st March. Overseas closing date, 30th June.

1936 Photo Contests

Amateur photographers among our readers will be pleased to know that we shall be commencing a new series of photographic competitions in our next issue.

The competitions, a separate one each month, will be featured throughout the Spring and Summer.

COMPETITION RESULTS

HOME

Cover Voting Contest.—1. J. F. Burrell (Bristol); Jt. 2 and 3. A. A. Warren (Norwich); A. J. Warren (Norwich); 4. C. P. Bruce (Larkhall).

January Drawing Contest.—First Prizes: Section A, A. Marsh (Coventry); Section B, A. Audsley (Cobham). Second Prizes: Section A, J. E. A. Burley (Birmingham); Section B, A. Briggs (Burnley). Special Prize: J. S. Taylor (Burnley). Consolation Prizes: G. Cooper (Jordans); P. Findlay (Leeds); B. C. Fountain (Hoddesdon); G. M. Gillespie (Peterborough); B. Kett (Upminster); K. A. Marshall (Weymouth).

OVERSEAS

October Doublets.—1. B. E. Harrison (Victoria, B.C.). 2. D. Tolkowsky (Palestine); 3. D. Murison (Buenos Aires); 4. E. K. Shorrock (Vancouver, B.C.).

October Drawing Contest.—First Prizes: Section A, W. Figgins (Wellington, N.Z.). Section B, G. F. Emmerson (Greymouth, N.Z.); Second Prizes: Section A, W. F. Bladergroen (Amsterdam); Section B C. A. Astrom (Morko).

FIRESIDE FUN

BY SPECIAL REQUEST

"Run away from my window at once."
"But it says 'Watch repairs' on your window, sir."

* * * *

The typist had addressed a letter to Newport, Mon., as Newport, Monday, and in due course the letter was returned by the Dead Letter Office. On being asked sarcastically by her chief whether she had ever heard of such a place as Newport, Monday, she replied: "No, but I thought it was all right, because there is such a place as Sheffield Wednesday."

* * * *

It was the oldest inhabitant's hundredth birthday, and the local paper sent a reporter to interview him.
"To what do you attribute your long life?" he was asked.
"To the fact that I was born so long ago," he replied.

* * * *

"Your watch may be good, but I dropped mine in the Thames a year ago and it's been running ever since."
"What, your watch?"
"No; the Thames."

* * * *

Peter: "Where are you going, mamma?"
Mother: "Father and I are going to a surprise party."
"Can't I go, too—and can't we take Mary along!"
"No, you weren't invited."
"Well, don't you think they'd be lots more surprised if you took us all?"

* * * *

The vicar of a country parish had succeeded in reconciling two old women who had been quarrelling for years, and he induced them to meet under the vicarage roof. In his drawing-room they shook hands. After an awkward silence one of them said: "Well, Mrs. Jones, I wish you all you wishes me."
"An' who's saying nasty things now?" snapped Mrs. Jones.

* * * *

Mother: "I put Bobby in the store-cupboard for being a naughty boy this afternoon, and he won't come out."
Father: "Of course, he won't; I've stored all the apples in there!"

* * * *

A visitor to the asylum had been asked by a patient to take a letter to the outside world, complaining that he was being unlawfully detained.
"You won't forget to deliver it to the mayor, will you?" emphasised the patient.
"No, I'll not forget."
As he turned to go, the visitor received a violent kick. "What's that for?" he demanded of the inmate.
"Just to remind you not to forget," he replied. "The last chap forgot."

* * * *

He was not used to taking meals in restaurants, but being in London he thought he would visit a famous old eating-house.
"Bill of fare, sir?" queried the waiter, as he sat down.
"Er—no, thanks," he replied. "I'll look at that after the meal."

HIS IDEA!

A negro was being examined for a driving licence. "And what," asked the examiner, "is the white line in the middle of the road for?"
"For bicycles," was the reply!

* * * *

Tom: "If you wanted to preserve a document for all time, how would you set about it?"
Bill: "I should leave it in a dentist's waiting-room."

* * * *

Teacher: "There's no difficulty in the world that cannot be overcome."
Pupil: "Have you ever tried squeezing tooth paste back into the tube?"

* * * *

A crowd had gathered at a fire. The policeman was moving them on, but one man objected. "Why should he stay," he said, pointing to a man in front, "while I have to move on?"
"Well," replied the policeman, "It's his fire."

* * * *

Examiner: "What is the distance between London and Glasgow?"
Candidate for the Police Force: "I don't know, but if that's going to be my beat, I'd rather not go on with the matter."

* * * *

"Is a ton of coal very much, papa?"
"That depends, my son, on whether you are shovelling or buying it."

* * * *

SERVICE!

"Could you please let me have a pint of petrol and half a pint of oil?"
"Yes, mum, and would yer like Bill to sneeze in yer tyres?"—*Courtesy "The Commercial Motor."*

* * * *

Jinks: "I suppose your landlord asks a lot for the rent of this place?"
Blinks: "A lot! He asks me for it nearly every day."

* * * *

"Shall I go to a mind-reader or a palm-reader?"
"A palm-reader; it's obvious that you've got a palm."

* * * *

A man received an indecipherable prescription from his doctor. After it had been made up for him by the chemist it was returned to him and he used it for two years as a pass on the railway, gained admission to dances, cinemas and theatres, while, in the evenings his daughters used to practise it on the piano.

* * * *

Teacher: "Now, Thomas, what are you doing—learning something?"
Thomas: "No, sir; I'm listening to you."

* * * *

"Tact," said the lecturer, "is essential to good entertaining. I once dined at a house where the hostess had no tact. Opposite me was a modest, quiet man. Suddenly he turned as red as a lobster on hearing his hostess say to her husband: 'How inattentive you are, Charlie! You must look after Mr. Brown better. He's helping himself to everything.' "

THE RIGHT SPIRIT!

Busy Man: "I am sorry that my engagements prevent my attending your charity concert, but I shall be with you in spirit."
Ticket Seller: "Splendid; and where would you like your spirit to sit? I have tickets here for a half-crown, five shillings and half-a-guinea."

* * * *

Yankee: "Yeah, I sure belong to New York."
Englishman: "Oh; now I understand. I thought New York belonged to you."

* * * *

Land Lubber: "Tell me your story, Ancient Mariner."
A.M.: "Well, once we were stranded—had to eat our belts and shoes to live."
L.L.: "No!!"
A.M.: "And then the boat turned turtle and we lived on that for six days."

* * * *

Angus (to Donald, who has bought a second-hand car): "Man, it'll be costing you a bit in petrol."
Donald: "Not so much. It's downhill to the town, and I can get a tow home most days."

* * * *

Patient: "Doctor, are you sure I have pneumonia? Sometimes doctors prescribe for pneumonia and patients die of something else."
Doctor: "When I prescribe for pneumonia you die of pneumonia."

* * * *

"You will notice," said the professor as he seized the handle of a piece of mechanism, "that this machine is turned by a crank." And he wondered why a ripple of laughter ran round the class.

* * * *

Black: "Have you ever wondered what you would do if you had Rothschild's income?"
Blue: "No; but I have often wondered what he would do if he had mine."

* * * *

Some street musicians, more noticeable for their vigour than their harmony, were taking a short rest before starting another tune. The trombonist turned to his mate. "What's the next tune?" he asked.
"The Blue Danube," was the reply.
" 'Blue Danube' be blowed," said the trombonist. "I just played that."

* * * *

Grocer: "Did that piece of boiled ham I sent along the other day do for the whole family?"
Mrs. Brown: "Almost, but they're getting better now."

* * * *

"Now, be sure and eat the skins when you have fruit. Force yourself to do it," the doctor advised.
"It's no good, doctor," the patient said when he came again. "I simply can't eat the skins. I managed banana skins, but pine-apples and coco nuts have me beaten."

* * * *

A BROAD HINT

Customer: "H'm; no tips, I see."
Waiter: "Yes, sir. Gives a gentleman a chance to show 'is independence, sir."

A Floating Pumping Station in Egypt

In countries where it is necessary to pump water from a river for irrigation purposes, trouble often arises from variations in level of the water and from the silting up of the channels along which it is led to the pumping station. Trouble of this kind was encountered in irrigating an estate, belonging to Prince Youssouf Kemal, on the banks of the Nile at Moeris, near Luxor, Egypt. Water for irrigation purposes formerly was supplied by a steam pumping plant. At the point where it is taken from the Nile extensive sandbanks are uncovered when the river is low and the bank is then 850 ft. from the edge of the water. The annual cost of dredging the canal that had to be cut to give access to the pump was £1,500.

The difficulties encountered in drawing water from the Nile for this estate have now been overcome by the use of a floating pumping station, which is moored in the river and rises and falls with the water. The new station is illustrated on this page. It is complete in itself, both the pump and the motor driving it being installed on the float. The pump is of the Sulzer centrifugal type and delivers 16,500 gallons per minute when running at 325 r.p.m. against a head of 33 ft. and absorbing 208 h.p. The water is delivered into a chute down which it flows into the irrigation system.

Floating pumping stations had already proved their value, particularly for hydro-electric power stations and for works in which provision is made for the storage of water in reservoirs for power purposes. In a remarkable plant of this kind installed on Lake Gosau, in upper Austria, by Sulzer Bros Ltd., five cylindrical floats, each about 20 ft. long and 7 ft. in diameter, and two others of the same diameter but with lengths of 46 ft. keep the entire station afloat. This station is equipped with two sets of Voith-Sulzer pumps, each delivering 26,400 gallons per minute against a head of water of 148 ft. when running at 960 r.p.m. One of the pumps requires 1,430 b.h.p. and the totally enclosed three-phase motor to which it is directly coupled is capable of developing 1,700 b.h.p. continuously.

Two similar floating power stations also were used for lowering the level of a lake in the Pyrenees that now serves as a reservoir for the pumping storage power station of the Societe Hydro-Electrique du Midi. These also were built by Sulzer Bros. Ltd. Each comprises four groups of Sulzer pumps delivering a total of 29,600 gallons of water per minute against a head of 49 ft. and requiring 544 b.h.p., and the electric motors driving the pumps of each group are capable of developing a total of 600 r.p.m. continuously. Each installation weighs about 55 tons and is supported on 12 floating cylinders.

A floating pumping station on the Nile. The centrifugal pump with which it is equipped delivers 16,500 gallons of water per minute. Photograph by courtesy of Sulzer Bros. (London) Ltd.

Electric Furnace in which White Mice can Live

We are so accustomed to think of a furnace as a centre of intense heat, close approach to which is painful if not impossible, that it is a little startling to hear of an electric furnace that melts metals with the greatest ease and yet into which one may thrust the bare hand without the slightest inconvenience or danger. This can be done with a high frequency induction furnace, which heats only electrical conductors, and white mice have actually lived in a furnace of this kind used by the General Electric Company of New York for experimental purposes.

An induction furnace may be likened to a special transformer in which the primary is a coil of copper conductor inside which is placed the mass of conducting material that is to be heated or melted. This material serves as the secondary of the transformer, and is rapidly heated to the melting point—and even higher if desired—because of the rapid changes or oscillations in the current induced in it. A gold ring on the finger of a hand thrust into the furnace would become hot immediately, although the hand would not be affected directly.

High frequency furnaces have been in laboratory and commercial use for years, but an application of special interest is in the manufacture of radio tubes. It might be thought that in order to obtain the necessary high vacuum within a tube it was merely necessary to remove all the gas by means of an efficient vacuum pump. In actual fact the operation is by no means simple, because metals and glass absorb large amounts of gas and water vapour that can only be driven out by heating. The metal parts used must be subjected to a higher temperature than the glass can withstand, and for this reason they are heated locally while the tube is being exhausted by placing it for a moment within a high frequency coil attached to a wooden handle. This forms a miniature induction furnace. The metal parts of the tube immediately become red hot, and the bubbles of gas and vapour are boiled out. The tube is then sealed from the pump with the knowledge that later heating of the tube by the passage of current through the filament will not cause any further release of gas.

Gibbons' Simplified Stamp Catalogue

One of the most interesting signs of the growth o interest in the stamp collecting hobby is the announcement by Stanley Gibbons Ltd. that they have found it necessary to produce a fourth edition of their Simplified Stamp Catalogue, although it is only five months since the third edition appeared.

The new edition is to be published on the 11th of this month and the information contained in it will be nearly five months in advance of that in any other current catalogue. It will include all the Empire issues of King George's reign, in addition to the latest values of the popular Silver Jubilee stamps, and in comparison with the third edition will list 556 more stamps and include 117 additional illustrations.

Those of our stamp collector readers who do not already possess a catalogue would find this a helpful addition to their stamp collecting equipment. Its price is 5/- and it may be obtained from any stamp dealer or direct from Stanley Gibbons Ltd., 391, Strand, London, W.C.2.

Ship Photographs

With the approach of spring and summer holidays, readers who live along our sea coasts, and particularly in our ports, will have increased opportunities of observing the movements of ships. Interest in shipping extends also to many readers who live inland, and practically all who share in it welcome opportunities of adding to their collections of photographs of liners and other vessels. A catalogue issued by our advertisers B. and A. Feilden, 12, Harlech Road, Blundellsands, Liverpool 23, gives lists of postcard photographs of liners and freighters of almost every British Line, and also of many of the foreign Lines.

The photographs themselves are of particularly fine quality, and those who are attracted by the hobby should write for this catalogue. Provided the "*M.M.*" is mentioned, B. and A. Feilden will send a specimen real photograph postcard and the catalogue for 3d. only.

Cycling Comfort

Cyclist readers of the "*M.M.*," particularly those with a passion for long-distance runs at high speed, will find special interest in the little booklet "*Cycling Comfort*" issued by Herbert Terry and Sons Ltd.

The principal feature of the booklet is an account of the attack on the English road racing records, made last year by the famous Australian team of riders, Hubert Opperman, familiarly known as "Oppy," Stuart and Milliken. The team was brought over from Australia specially for the attack by the B.S.A. Company, who also provided the machines, which were equipped with Terry Spring Seat Saddles.

The booklet can be obtained from Herbert Terry and Sons Ltd., Redditch, free of charge, if the "*M.M.*" is mentioned in the application.

Electrical Specialities

Our advertiser Mr. L. Wilkinson has just sent us a copy of the new "Wilco" electrical catalogue. Almost every conceivable electrical accessory, from insulated staples to mains motors, cycle lighting sets to vacuum cleaners, and shocking coils to voltmeters is included in the range of "Wilco" products, and illustrated in this useful and well-produced catalogue.

Mr. L. Wilkinson, 8, City Road, London, E.C.1, will send a copy of the catalogue, free of charge, to any applicant who refers to the "*M.M.*" when writing.

Leeds Model Railway Society

The Leeds Model Railway Society are endeavouring to extend their Junior Section, and invite Hornby Railway Company members of 14 yea s of age and more who live in Leeds and district to join this Society. Any H.R.C. member who is interested should write to Mr. H. Stonebridge, 12, Wakefield Road, Drighlington, Nr. Bradford.

* * * *

In reviewing Charles Letts' "Schoolboy's Diary" on page 68 of the January "*M M.*," we inadvertently gave the price of the leather edition with pencil, maps and pocket as 2/6. The correct price is 2/-.

MECCANO MAGAZINE

Editorial Office: Binns Road, Liverpool 13 England

Vol. XXI. No. 4 April, 1936

With the Editor

New "M.M." Features

Readers will be pleased to find that "*Road and Track*" again makes its appearance this month. This will be a regular feature throughout the summer, as in previous years, appearing alternately with "*Engineering News*."

I also have in preparation pages dealing with ships and shipping. In these details will be given of the building and launching of new ships, together with news of events of interest in connection with the sea generally. Thus the pages will cover the shipping world in the same manner as "*Railway News*" deals with matters of railway interest, and I am sure that they will please all readers of the Magazine.

Another attraction that I hope to include in forthcoming issues of the Magazine takes the form of articles describing trips by aeroplane. These will describe actual journeys in machines in service on British air lines. They will be similar to the accounts of footplate trips, by "A Railway Engineer," and of sea trips, by Mr. O. S. Nock, that have appeared in recent issues, and are certain to prove equally popular.

Are Record Flights Worth While?

The record-breaking effort of Flight Lieutenant T. Rose ended too late to allow reference to be made to it in the "*Air News*" pages of this month's issue, but it is not too late to congratulate the famous airman on his wonderful flight to South Africa and back again. It is astonishing to reflect that he reached Capetown, more than 7,000 miles away by the route he followed, in less than four days, and completed the return trip in little more than six days, in spite of being detained for a time in Tripoli because he had unfortunately omitted to obtain the necessary permits.

This is the third time that Flt. Lt. Rose has attempted to create records for the flight to South Africa and back, and his persistence in the face of misfortune has been amply rewarded. Those of my readers who heard him speak in the wireless programme on the day of his arrival in England no doubt will remember his suggestion that the game of record-breaking was scarcely worth the candle. It is true that it is no longer necessary to make daring but risky flights in order to show what aeroplanes can do, but I have no doubt that the call to record-breaking efforts, whatever the dangers involved, will continue to be irresistible.

The kind of flight to which I do very strongly object is that made by certain individuals whose chief desire is to achieve easy notoriety. These do little to make people air minded.

An Impression of the "Queen Mary"

A regular reader in Glasgow recently wrote to tell me about a visit he had been fortunate to make to the "*Queen Mary*" just before she left Clydebank for her trials. I am sure that readers are as interested in the great liner as I am, and give the following extracts from his letter.

"It was late in the evening when I reached the yard of John Brown and Co. Ltd., and I shall never forget the wonderful sight that presented itself when I turned the corner of a large building and suddenly saw the giant vessel gleaming in the glare of great floodlighting lamps.

"In the short time at my disposal I saw only a few of the things of interest in the '*Queen Mary*,' but I saw sufficient to convince me that she is the most marvellous vessel afloat. I realised for the first time her enormous size when I looked along the lengthy promenade deck, the circuit of which measures a quarter of a mile; and my impression of her spaciousness was increased when I mounted the navigating bridge and looked around me. I stood in one of the bridge houses, projecting 12 ft. over the side of the vessel at what seemed to me a stupendous height above the water.

"I could have stayed for a long time in the great wheel-house, where I was fascinated by the compasses, engine room telegraphs and speaking tubes, and by the steering gear, which is in duplicate in order to provide for all emergencies. One of the chief wonders of the '*Queen Mary*' is a gyro pilot that automatically will keep the vessel on her course with far greater accuracy than is possible with the best of helmsmen. Ahead of me I could see the foremast, with the crow's nest half way up. This is reached by means of a ladder running up the interior of the foremast, and even in their elevated position in it the men on the lookout will be warm and comfortable, for it has a roof and is provided with a glass windscreen and electric heaters.

"When I went below to explore the decks set aside for passenger accommodation, I was in danger of being lost. With her magnificent dining rooms and saloons, lounges, well-fitted cabins, recreation rooms, shops, libraries, swimming pools, and play rooms for children, '*Queen Mary*' is indeed a floating city. There is even a hospital, and I was not at all surprised to learn that enough electricity will be generated in the ship to meet the requirements of a town of the size of Birkenhead.

"I should very much have liked to inspect the great turbine engines of the '*Queen Mary*,' and the giant boilers that feed their gargantuan appetites for steam, but the engine rooms were closed."

Floating Cranes and their Work

Giant Strength Under Perfect Control

CRANES and their working are a perpetual source of interest, whatever their size or the purpose for which they are being used. Probably the most interesting member of the large family of cranes is the floating crane, for this usually is capable of dealing with immense loads of unusual character. To watch one at work is an experience that is seldom forgotten. Its freedom of movement adds to its fascination, for unlike the majority of land cranes, it can move to the scene of the work it is called upon to do, and it does so more slowly and more majestically than do cranes running on rails. Its only rival in this respect indeed is the blocksetting crane, the operations of which are more restricted in type.

The movements of a floating crane are leisurely, but they are none the less impressive in view of the immense size it usually possesses and the great loads it lifts. In spite of its immense power it is amazingly easy to handle and its electrical or mechanical controls are simple to operate and certain in action, for its capabilities are very carefully calculated when it is being designed.

The floating crane of the Harbour authorities at Le Havre picking up a heavy barge. Photograph by courtesy of Werf Gusto, Firma A. F. Smulders, Schiedam, Holland.

Floating cranes are supported on giant pontoons or hulls in which is accommodated the whole of the machinery for operating them in addition to that required for moving them through the water. They differ from land cranes in that they are not rigidly supported, for the position of the pontoon in the water varies with the movements of the jib and other moving parts, and of the load carried. In most cases the hull is so large that only a slight list follows the transference of weight accompanying these movements, but in others compensation is applied by pumping water ballast from one compartment to another in order to preserve a balance.

Floating cranes are not adapted for operations in rough weather. Their speed usually is up to 5 m.p.h., and often it is essential that they shall be attended by tugs to allow them to be manœuvred into position. They are used chiefly for special loading or unloading work, or for building or maintenance operations in connection with docks and harbour systems. An excellent example of the kind of service for which they are fitted is in installing boilers and engines in ships. The weights of the parts of these handled by a floating crane are very large, and these structures prove especially useful in lifting them from the dockside, to which they have been brought after erection, directly into the vessels themselves. Their use for this purpose saves both time and money, for otherwise it might be necessary to dismantle the boilers or engines, and to re-erect them in the ship, a tedious and wasteful method.

A floating crane of great interest that has accomplished many remarkable feats is shown on our cover this month. It is the *"Mammoth"* of the Mersey Docks and Harbour Board. This crane is fitted with triple expansion marine type engines that give it a speed of nearly 5 m.p.h. It is of the derricking jib type and is capable of handling loads up to 200 tons. It was built in Holland by Werf Gusto, Firma A. F. Smulders, and was towed from Schiedam to Liverpool without the jib being dismantled.

On one occasion the *"Mammoth"* transported across the Mersey part of a lock gate weighing 190 tons. This was the gate of the Alfred Dock, Birkenhead, which required strengthening and repairing and was removed to the Brunswick Dock, Liverpool, for this purpose. When the necessary work had been completed, half of the gate was transferred back to the Alfred Dock by the *"Mammoth,"* and the second half was afterwards taken across the river without difficulty. On each occasion the half gate was lifted from the dock wall and swung on to the deck of the floating crane, where it rested in an improvised cradle. Three tugs were then employed to take the *"Mammoth"* across the Mersey with its great load. Two of these were ahead of it and the third was astern.

Other noteworthy feats accomplished by the *"Mammoth"* have included the removal and replacement of bridges connecting the floating stages at New Brighton and Egremont with the piers giving access to them. These floating stages rise and fall with the tides and carry with them the outer ends of the bridges, the bearings of which are giant hinges that allow for the varying inclinations of the structures. In work of this kind the state of the tide has to be taken into consideration, and the bridge connection is made immediately the tide has risen to its full height, which of course is accurately known from the work of the tidal observatory of the Mersey Docks and Harbour Board on Bidston Hill, Birkenhead. Several years ago a bridge weighing 152 tons was placed in position at New Brighton Ferry, and more recently an existing bridge was removed for reconstruction and the rebuilt bridge, weighing 110 tons, was placed in position with the aid of the *"Mammoth."* The bridge installed at Egremont to connect the floating stage with the pier, also weighs about 110 tons.

A second 200-ton floating crane of similar design and appearance to the *"Mammoth"* was constructed by the same firm for the harbour authorities at Le Havre. This crane is capable of hoisting a load of 200 tons to a height of 160 ft. above the water line at a distance of 95 ft. from the centre line of the crane. Alternatively, a load of 150 tons can be hoisted at a distance of 130 ft. from the centre line.

There are two main hoisting blocks, each capable of handling a load of 100 tons, and the two are coupled together when the maximum load of 200 tons is to be lifted. The hoisting speed of these blocks is 4.5 ft. per minute. The winches are provided with strong electrical brakes that ensure safety in all operations, and the crane driver's cabin is situated under the jib in order to give him an uninterrupted view of his work. In spite of its great size, only three men are required for operating the crane, and a special switching system is incorporated in order to make the control as simple and safe as possible.

Steam is supplied by a boiler with a working pressure of 147 lb. per sq. in. This is situated in the pontoon, which also carries a triple expansion steam engine with surface condensers and the dynamos that supply the necessary current.

A more powerful floating crane, also built in Holland, was employed in the construction of harbour works in Spain. Blocks of stone or concrete of enormous size are necessary for breakwaters and jetties, which have to withstand the pounding action of the waves in stormy weather. These usually are placed in position by giant blocksetting cranes running on rails laid down for the purpose. This method could not be followed in the case of the Spanish harbour works referred to, and instead this powerful floating crane, known as the *"Hercule,"* was used. Blocks of concrete weighing 260 tons had to be placed in position. These were made on shore and carried by a travelling gantry to the water side, where the *"Hercule"* lifted them on to heavy pontoons that were towed to the site of operations. There the crane again lifted the block and placed it in position.

Side view of a floating crane used in building a Spanish harbour. The crane is shown lifting a test load of 300,000 kg., or about 300 tons. Photograph by courtesy of N. V. Intern, Scheepsbouwmij "de Maas."

The pontoon of this giant crane is of immense strength. It is 115 ft. 6 in. in length, 57 ft. 6 in. in breadth and 13 ft. 1½ in. in depth. An illustration of the crane lifting a load of 300,000 kg., or about 300 tons, is reproduced on this page. It will be noticed that the deck of the pontoon is not horizontal, its forward end being depressed owing to the distribution of the load supported. The deck of this floating crane in fact is never horizontal, whether the pontoon be loaded or light.

The increasing tonnage of modern vessels and the growth in size of the dock equipment necessary to deal with them have led to the construction of larger floating cranes. An interesting example of a modern giant floating crane was constructed in 1924 by Cowans, Sheldon and Co. Ltd., Carlisle, for a Japanese shipyard, and a second floating crane actually was employed in erecting it.

This giant crane is capable of lifting a load of 350 tons at a radius of 100 ft., or 300 tons at a radius of 121 ft., and of revolving through a complete circle with the load in position. The vertical distance through which these heavy loads can be raised is 140 ft. The main loads are lifted on two blocks, each of 175 tons capacity, and these may be used either together or independently as required. Auxiliary lifts of 50 tons also are provided. One of these gives a vertical lift of 200 ft., and the other is capable of traversing its load horizontally through a distance of 75 ft. The provision of these auxiliary lifts enables comparatively small loads to be lifted at high speed.

The 150-ton floating crane "London Mammoth" engaged on the shipment of railway coaches for South Africa. Photograph by courtesy of the Port of London Authority.

The jib is capable of derricking in from the maximum radius of 121 ft. to a minimum radius of 50 ft., and when in this position the height to the top of the crane is 240 ft. A roller path with a diameter of 50 ft. forms a mounting for the crane, which can be revolved with its load through a complete circle in either direction. The superstructure consists of a rectangular braced frame 66 ft. in height that supports the jib, which is raised and lowered by means of two steel screws 49 ft. in length and 14 in. in diameter, placed at the back of the crane and driven from the engines through a train of gearing. The lifting gears are fitted with specially designed hydraulic brakes to control the lowering of the loads.

The pontoon is 270 ft. in length and 90 ft. in width, with a draught of about 10 ft. It is so large that the provision of moving or water ballast is unnecessary. Behind the crane is a large deck area on which a load of about 700 tons can be carried. The propelling machinery, which is placed amidships, consists of twin screw compound engines supplied with steam from boilers working at a pressure of 150 lb. per sq. in. The hull is built of steel, and is divided by bulkheads into watertight compartments. Its deck equipment includes a steam windlass, capstans, steam and hand-steering gear, lifeboats and everything necessary for a sea-going vessel.

A great floating crane that works on inland waters was specially constructed a few years ago in Canada. It is capable of lifting a load of 500 tons, and its purpose is to remove the gates of the locks of the Welland Ship Canal when necessary, and to lower new gates into position. Some of these gates are of enormous size, those at the lower ends of some of the locks of this waterway consisting of two leaves, each weighing nearly 490 tons.

The pontoon of the floating crane is 90 ft. in length and has a width of 66 ft. In order to remove the leaf of a lock gate, it must be lifted vertically. The pontoon therefore has been designed with a blunt end that can be brought close up to the leaf to be hoisted. The frame used for lifting consists of two columns, suitably stayed and braced, at the blunt end of the pontoon. Across the top of the columns is a girder carrying eight sheaves, each 9 ft. 6 in. in diameter, over which pass the ropes supporting an equalising beam carrying a lifting pin that can be engaged with eyes on the gate. After passing over the pulleys at the top of the frame, the ropes are taken to a second set at the base, where their direction is changed to the horizontal to enable them to be connected to the lifting mechanism. Since the pontoon is comparatively short, ballast must be removed in order to keep it on an even keel during hoisting operations. Water is used for this purpose and the vessel is trimmed by pumping it as required into the forward or aft tanks.

The gate lifter is equipped with a boiler in which oil or coal may be burned. Steam is supplied at a pressure of 155 lb. per sq. in. to a vertical compound condensing steam engine that drives a 200 kw. 230v. generator. This generator supplies the power for the main gate hoist and also that required for the capstans, pumps, heaters and auxiliary derricks. The crane is towed from place to place as required by tugs, but otherwise is a self-contained unit. One reason for the use of a short pontoon of curiously stubby form is the necessity for negotiating the comparatively narrow waters of the canal and the entrances to the locks. In this respect the crane is unlike others of the same type, practically all of which are designed to operate in the spacious waters of harbours and estuaries.

Removing a Peal of Bells

Transport Difficulties in a Cathedral

By W. J. Aitken

MOST of us take church bells for granted. We listen with pleasure to their chimes, but few of us know that it is necessary to re-tune them at intervals because of the lowering of pitch that time and use bring with them. A single bell may be allowed to change its note to a considerable extent, but the bells forming part of a peal must be kept in tune. Fortunately their loss of pitch is gradual, and frequent re-tuning is not necessary. When the bells of St. Mary's Cathedral, Edinburgh, were taken down for treatment, therefore, I carefully watched their removal, for an opportunity of seeing how great bells are handled does not occur every day.

The peal of bells of St. Mary's Cathedral was installed in a belfry in the Central Spire, which is 275 ft. high and weighs 6,000 tons, its foundations being 60 ft. deep. The belfry itself is 100 ft. above the ground. The 10 bells forming the peal were cast by J. Taylor and Co., Loughborough, and each was given a name. The smallest is "*Humilitas*," which weighs 7 cwt. 31 lb., and the three next lightest are "*Fides*," "*Contentia*" and "*Patientia*," weighing 8 cwt. 56 lb., 8 cwt. 104 lb. and 9 cwt. 105 lb. respectively. Then follow "*Reverentia*," 11 cwt. 97 lb., and "*Pietas*," 15 cwt. 12 lb. Each of the remaining four bells weighs more than a ton. They are "*Spes*," 21 cwt. 35 lb., "*Pax*," 24 cwt., "*Grandium*," 29 cwt. 76 lb., and "*Caritas*," the giant of the peal, which weighs 2 tons 2 cwt. 77 lb. Thus the total weight of the peal is nearly 9 tons.

"Caritas," the largest of the bells of St. Mary's Cathedral, Edinburgh, being lowered on to rollers after it had been brought through the doorway. This bell weighs more than two tons.

After each bell had been detached from its mounting, it was lowered from the belfry into the Bellringers' Chamber below, and then passed through a trap-door in the floor, which is 5 ft. above the roof of the Cathedral itself. It was next passed through a hole in this roof and then lowered to the ground, a distance of 70 ft., by means of a hand winch, reaching the floor in the middle of the choir stalls, which are raised a little above the level of the main aisle to which the bells had then to be removed. It was necessary to traverse the aisle in order to reach the north door, through which they were to be taken out of the building

Two methods were used to move the bells, once they were on the aisle. The smaller and lighter ones were simply turned over on their sides and rolled on their rims to the door, a rail made out of wooden beams being used as a guide. The larger bells were lowered on to two rollers across which wooden beams were laid. The bell was then pushed forward, the rollers being replaced under the front of the beams as soon as they became free at the back. A little manœuvring was necessary at the junction of the main aisle and the passage leading to the north door.

Another difficulty then had to be overcome before the bells could be taken out of the Cathedral, for a few steps led from the doorway to the path outside. When dealing with the smaller bells it was possible to construct an incline of beams, down which they could be rolled slowly. The heavier bells could not be safely moved in this manner, and each of these in turn was brought out beyond the steps on projecting beams that were kept level with the floor of the main aisle. The bell was then lifted up by means of a pulley block fixed above it, as shown in the illustration on this page; the beams were removed, and the bell was lowered to rollers on which it was conveyed as near as possible to the gate at the end of the path, there to await the lorry on which it was to be taken away.

Nine of the 10 bells comprising the peal were brought out to the path in this manner, and then the task of loading them on the lorry commenced. As the bells had to be raised through a height of about 4 ft., a tripod was set up just outside the gate and a pulley block was suspended at its apex. The bells were then brought one by one to the edge of the pavement, and each in turn was pushed under the pulley and then raised while the lorry was backed in under it and between the legs of the tripod. The bell was then lowered as near to its assigned position as possible, but sometimes much pushing and pulling and repeated liftings and lowerings were necessary before the weight was distributed in the best possible manner.

The task of despatching the nine lighter bells occupied the working hours of a Saturday morning, and the largest bell was then left in the belfry. This was "*Caritas*," the tenor bell, which weighs considerably more than two tons, and its removal was undertaken on the following Monday. With great precautions it was lowered through the Bellringers' Chamber down to the choir stalls, and equally careful handling was required to get it safely to the main aisle. On account of its great weight this bell was extremely difficult to propel in the ordinary manner, and it was necessary to lever it along by means of a wooden beam.

Loading one of the bells on to a lorry for removal. Care had to be taken to distribute their weight evenly.

All went well until the junction of the main aisle and the passage leading to the North Door was reached, and there half an hour's patient work was necessary, for it was impossible to take the bell in a gentle curve round the corner because of the limited space available. The method eventually adopted was to run the bell to a point level with the middle of the passage leading to the door and then to turn it round, together with its supporting beams and rollers, until it could be moved in the required direction. For this purpose each of the two beams on which it rested was levered up in turn and the rollers were hammered round a few degrees. The levers were then moved to a position under the bell itself, and this was lifted while the beams supporting it again were placed at right angles to the rollers. This process had to be gone through several times before the bell at last was in a position to be rolled to the door.

A large block of wood, 12 in. wide and nearly 18 in. thick, was fastened to the bell, and this had now to be removed, for the doorway was too narrow to allow it to pass through. Its removal appeared to be a simple task, for it was secured only by four large nuts and bolts. It was soon realised that to unscrew the nuts was far from sufficient to release it, however, for two of the bolts had become firmly rusted to a metal plate that was sunk below the surface of the wood, and there was little hope of removing them by any ordinary means.

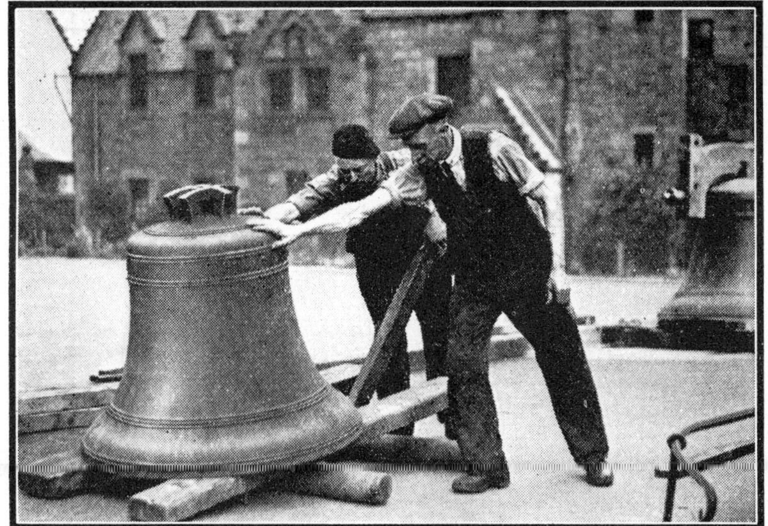

Moving a bell on beams and rollers. Each roller was replaced in front when it became free at the back.

After a short consultation, it was decided that the only way to separate the wood from the bell was to saw through the timber on each side of the bolts, and then to chip away the wood that remained, so that the troublesome bolts could be removed. After much hard work with the saws, only the wood to which the bolts were fastened remained, and on chipping that away, the bolts themselves were exposed to view and were then quickly cut through by means of a hacksaw.

In the meantime measurements were made of the width available between the large doors, as this was found to be inadequate for the passage of the bell while level, even when the heavy doors had been taken off their hinges and temporarily removed; and it was necessary to tilt the bell to one side. A block and tackle therefore was erected just inside the doorway. With this "*Caritas*" was raised about 2 ft., and beams and planks were piled at one side of the passage to provide the necessary tilted path on which the bell could be conveyed outside. When the track was ready, the rollers and beams on which the bell was to rest were put in position, and the bell was lowered on to them, levers being used to prevent it from slipping down the tilted track.

When the plans and preparations for the task had been checked over, two men took up their positions behind the bell, and slowly levered it forward, the others acting as guides. There was an anxious moment when the bell slipped a little sideways down the slope of its tilted track, but its movement was checked immediately, and it was soon levered back to its proper level. Apart from this everything went smoothly, and before long the bell was through the doorway and clear of the steps. The pulley tackle inside the church was then dismantled and reassembled outside the door, so that the bell could be raised to allow the tilting track to be dismantled and the rollers to be set level, when it was again lowered on to them.

The difficulties of handling this giant bell were now almost over. There was an awkward corner on the path leading to the roadway, but before long the bell was safely on the pavement, and like the others, it was hoisted on the lorry and was soon on the way to Loughborough to have its tune restored.

Diesel-Engined Car Records

Captain Eyston's recent success in establishing 12 records for a Diesel-engined car augments still further the already imposing list of land speed records held by this country. This famous racing motorist, with his co-driver Mr. A. Denly, at the Montlhery track near Paris completed a 24-hours' run at an average speed of 94.99 m.p.h. The car used was a four-seater streamline saloon fitted with a standard A.E.C. 6-cylinder Diesel engine, similar to those used in London omnibuses, and new records were set up also for 50, 500 and 3,000 kilometres, for 500 miles, and for 6, 12 and 24 hours. Rain and intense cold made conditions very difficult in the later stages of the attempt.

Captain G. E. T. Eyston's A.E.C. 6-cylinder Diesel-engined car, with which he recently set up new speed records at Montlhery. We are indebted to the Associated Equipment Co. Ltd., Southall, for this illustration and the one below.

It is pleasing to note that Captain Eyston has been awarded the Segrave Trophy, which was established in memory of Sir Henry Segrave, the great English motorist. The Trophy is awarded annually to a British subject who has upheld British prestige by actions requiring great courage and skill, and directed towards the development of land, sea or air transport. Previous holders of this trophy include Mrs. Mollison, Commander Kingsford-Smith, Mr. Waller and Squadron-Leader Hinkler. The only racing motorist who has previously received the honour is Sir Malcolm Campbell, to whom it was awarded in 1933.

Most of the land speed records are now held by Great Britain, and the keenness with which these are sought is shown by the fact that during last year no fewer than 222 successful attempts were made to set up new records. The most spectacular of these events of course was the fine performance of Sir Malcolm Campbell in attaining the amazing speed of 301.139 m.p.h. over a measured mile. During the last 10 years Sir Malcolm has successfully attacked the existing mile record no less than eight times, and has held it continuously since 1931. During the last five years he has broken his own record on four occasions.

A front view of Captain Eyston's Diesel-engined record-breaking car.

Rivals to "*Bluebird*"

Now there are rivals in the field. Sir Malcolm's record will be attacked in no uncertain manner this year by two famous British racing motorists, one driving a 5-ton giant car and the other a machine weighing only 30 cwt. The heavier car will be driven by John Cobb, and the small one by F. W. Dixon, and the attempts will be made on the Bonneville salt flats at Utah, between July and September next. Cobb is having a new car designed for him by Mr. Reid Railton, the designer of the present record holder's famous car "*Bluebird*," and it will have two Napier aero engines, probably developing a total of about 2,000 h.p. Dixon's car will be no heavier than an ordinary private saloon and not much bigger.

In view of the fact that German racing machines weighing only 15 cwt. and of 30 to 35 h.p. last year attained speeds of 200 miles an hour during ordinary road races, Dixon believes that it is possible to get from a car of twice the weight well over 300 m.p.h. on the perfect course provided by the salt beds of Utah. Sir Malcolm Campbell has recorded that during his record runs at Bonneville he seemed to be skimming through the air, for the surface does not drag so much as the sand of the course at Daytona he used formerly. His chief anxiety was in regard to pulling up, and he had to take the risk of braking when travelling at 250 m.p.h. Dixon's lighter car will be much easier to deal with in this respect.

Record Load for World's Largest Lorry

Turning for a moment from speed events, I think readers will be interested in a very different kind of record that was set up recently by the giant 14-wheeler Scammell Lorry owned by M.R.S. Ltd. and claimed to be the largest in the world. In the upper illustration on the opposite page this lorry is shown making its way through the streets of Sheffield carrying a huge ingot mould weighing 165 tons. This load was the heaviest the 14-wheeler has yet been called upon to handle.

Elaborate arrangements had to be made to ensure a safe passage when taking this giant ingot mould from the makers' works to the Vickers Works of the English Steel Corporation Ltd., a distance of just over a mile. The vehicle set out on its journey at 6 a.m., and travelled over icy roads with an escort of officials, and police in front and rear. The average speed was about 2 m.p.h. The passage through the gateway at the Vickers works required very skilful manipulation, particularly on the part of the rear steersman on the vehicle.

An exciting moment occurred when a right-angle turn and a slight lump of the road caused a momentary halt, during which smoke rose from the burning surface beneath the revolving driving wheels.

Highway Construction in Germany

The great scheme of road construction that is now in progress in Germany is going ahead so rapidly that nearly 2,000 miles of road will be ready for use this summer. Two great thoroughfares from north to south will then have been created and these will have two east to west connections, one in North Germany and the other in the south. The part of the scheme now in hand embraces some 4,375 miles of new roads that will link up the important economic centres of Germany. These roads will be built to a standard form of construction, with two separate carriageways, each 25 ft. in width, divided by a 16 ft. sward that will be planted with trees or bushes to shield drivers from the glare of the headlights of approaching vehicles. Intersections will be avoided by means of bridges and viaducts, and special turnings will be built to allow cars to leave or join the road without having to cut across the main highway.

The world's largest lorry transporting a huge ingot mould weighing 165 tons. Photograph by courtesy of M.R.S. Ltd.

Novelties at the Berlin Motor Show

Keen interest is being displayed in Germany in every branch of motoring, and this was evident at the great Berlin Motor Show, held in February. As usual the exhibits covered a very wide range, extending from small private cars to heavy transport vehicles produced for special purposes. The influence of Germany's wonderful new motor roads, already referred to, is reflected in the speeds for which the latest vehicles, both private and commercial, are designed. Many of these are capable of speeds in the neighbourhood of 70 m.p.h., and are fitted with engines of 150 to 300 b.h.p. It is particularly interesting to find that there were no fully streamlined designs, however, and only in the wings were there any of the sweeping curves that were so popular in body design a year ago.

The number of vehicles fitted with Diesel engines showed an increase over the number exhibited last year, and probably the most important exhibit in the show was the first private car with a heavy oil engine to be produced as a regular model by a well-known firm. This is of Daimler-Benz make and has a four-cylinder engine of 18 h.p.

A feature of the exhibition was the number of cars with engines so designed that they can by a slight alteration be made to operate on gas. One gas-operated machine on view was a municipal refuse collecting vehicle, and the gas is carried in six cylinders, arranged across the chassis, that hold sufficient gas for a run of about 40 miles. Other cars shown were equipped with gas producer plants, and one vehicle in this class is a 20-ton high speed lorry fitted with an engine of 110 h.p. running on gas supplied by an anthracite generator. For this vehicle it is claimed that even after standing idle for several days there is sufficient heat left in the generator for gas to be produced in a few minutes.

Other interesting exhibits included vehicles designed for railway and post office service. One of these, a complete mobile post office, is provided with counter, large extension tent with three demountable telephone booths, and a large electric clock. Another is equipped as a sorting office, with hundreds of pigeon-holes for the letters and a letter slot at the side. Both these vehicles are of Mercedes-Benz make.

In the accessories section were to be seen some tyres and tubes made from a synthetic rubber known as "Buma." The tyres had made severe journeys of over 6,000 miles and showed no appreciable signs of wear. This is the first time that tyres made from the new material have been included in the Berlin Show, although experiments in its manufacture have been in progress for the past 12 years.

Sir Malcolm Campbell, whose wonderful speed records are referred to on the opposite page.

The 1936 Monte Carlo Rally

This year's Monte Carlo Rally proved as popular as ever, and attracted drivers from all parts of the world. In this event competitors are given a choice of starting points in various parts of the Continent and the British Isles, and bad weather or poor roads, or a combination of both, often have made matters very difficult for those taking part. It is of interest to note that the route from Athens, which is about 2,500 miles and usually offers the most arduous conditions, this year proved comparatively easy, while the route from John O'Groat's, generally regarded as easy, provided the greatest difficulties owing to blizzards encountered in Scotland.

The main feature of the results was the success that attended Ford cars. Of 23 Fords entered, 16 managed to complete the course, and four of them were placed first, fourth, sixth and ninth, the general classification event being won by a Rumanian driver P. G. Cristea, driving a Ford V.8. The best performance by a British driver was made by Mr. D. Healey driving an eight-cylinder Triumph Dolomite.

In the coachwork and comfort competitions, held at the end of the Rally, British cars scored notable triumph. First prizes were won by Wolseley, Lagonda, Triumph and Rover cars, and the Grand Prix de Honneur, which is awarded only when a car of exceptional merit is exhibited, was won by a 25 h.p. Wolseley driven by H. E. Symons. The same car also won the comfort competition, a prize offered for the finest class car and a special award for the best finished engine. This car is the first following the difficult route from Athens to Monte Carlo that has won the comfort competition.

Start of the 1936 Motor Racing Season

Although several important motoring events have already taken place this year on the Continent, the real start of the 1936 racing season, so far as this country is concerned, comes with the British Empire Trophy Race, which is to be decided on 4th April. This event will be followed by the Land's End Trial, starting on 10th April, the B.A.R.C. Easter meeting on the 13th, the Junior Car Club International Trophy Race on 2nd May, and the Light Car Relay Race on 16th May.

On 28th May the new R.A.C. Isle of Man Race will be held. The new race replaces the Mannin Beg and the Mannin Moor Races hitherto run through the streets of Douglas. Entries will be confined to $1\frac{1}{2}$ litre type machines. The event will be run over a road circuit outside Douglas, and is likely to prove far more attractive to the general public than its predecessors.

A Non-Skid Tyre

A new type of motor tyre, which is claimed to possess the valuable quality of freedom from skidding on wet roads, has recently been put on the market.

Instead of the usual complex pattern on the tread the new tyre has a large number of thin flexible peripheral fins $\frac{3}{8}$ in. wide and 1/16 in. apart, and which stand $\frac{1}{4}$ in. high on the tyre. It is these fins that give the tyre its non-skid feature, for under the weight of a car they bend into a snaky pattern with the applied torque of the engine or in braking, and so give a squeegee effect on the roadway and provide better grip for driving or braking.

Moving pictures of cars fitted with these tyres show that they will stop a car dead-straight on a wet pavement at speeds at which cars with ordinary tyres would probably skid badly.

A Self-Contained Road-Breaker

Drill Driven by Two-Stroke Petrol Engine

A FAMILIAR sight in our streets is the breaking up of a roadway, whether of stone or concrete, or of its foundations by means of pneumatic drills, in which compressed air is used to drive down a piston that strikes a digging spike repeatedly, driving it home into the concrete. Usually several pneumatic drills are at work at once, each deriving its supply of compressed air through hose connected to a large compressor driven by a petrol engine.

The Warsop Road-Breaker in use. This tool is self-contained, the digging spike being operated by a two-stroke petrol engine. The illustrations on this page are by courtesy of George Cohen, Sons and Co. Ltd.

One of the drawbacks of the pneumatic drill is the size of the equipment and the difficulty of moving it about. This difficulty has now been overcome by the introduction of a road-breaker in which the use of compressed air as an intermediary is dispensed with, the petrol engine acting directly on the digging spike. The new drill is known as the Warsop Petrol-Driven Road-Breaker. It is entirely self-contained, and can easily be handled by one man.

The power unit of the Warsop Road-Breaker is practically a standard two-stroke motor cycle engine working in an inverted position. The working cylinder is extended downward to accommodate the moving hammer piston, the lower end of which slides in a counter-bored cylinder. The two pistons are opposed to each other and the explosion of the petrol mixture takes place between them. Thus they are driven apart, the engine piston moving upward and rotating the crank shaft, and the hammer piston moving downward to strike the head of the digging spike. The upper piston returns in accordance with the usual cycle of movements of a two-stroke engine, and the hammer piston is raised again by the pressure of gas admitted below it through a port that is uncovered by the engine piston during its upward stroke.

The fuel tank of the Warsop Road-Breaker is in the upper part of the tool, and holds 2½ pints of the mixture of petrol and oil used. The float chamber of the carburetter is concentric with the mixing chamber, a design that allows the machine to be inclined to an angle of 15 deg. to the horizontal without interference with effective operation, and the engine is started by means of a detachable handle that fits on one end of the crankshaft. Ignition is fixed and it is only necessary to operate the throttle while the tool is in operation. This is done simply, for the control is of the twist grip type and is incorporated in the handle, which is on top of the engine casing. A throttle stop is fitted so that the engine can be left to "tick over," or run slowly, when the tool is not actually at work.

The Warsop Road-Breaker weighs only 78 lb. and consumes about two gallons of petrol and oil mixture in an eight-hour day, or only about one-fifth of the amount that would be used in driving an air drill of similar working capacity. The speed can be regulated between 800 and 2,000 blows a minute, and from 1,500 to 1,800 blows in a minute constitutes an excellent working speed. There is less vibration with it than with a compressed air road breaker, largely because of the absence of mechanical connection between the hammer piston and the engine, and effective cooling is provided by fans on the ends of the crankshaft that draw air through the two.

A close-up view of the Warsop Road-Breaker at work.

A Warsop Rock Drill working on the same principle as the road breaker also has been introduced. This incorporates a simple mechanism for rotating the drill, and can be used satisfactorily for drilling holes to a depth of 3 ft., but as yet is not suitable for penetrating to greater depths. An interesting feature is that exhaust gases from the engine are employed to clear the hole of dust during drilling operations.

One of the greatest advantages of the Warsop Road-Breaker and Rock Drill is their portability. The scene of their operations can be changed more rapidly and easily than with pneumatic drills, for there are no hoses and other accessories to be moved, and the only interruption of active work that is necessary occurs when the petrol tank requires filling, an operation that takes comparatively little time. Rock drilling in open quarries can be carried out much more quickly with the new tool than with pneumatic drills, for the former can be moved at a moment's notice when a blast is about to take place.

Excavating Narrow Trenches

A Machine with 20 Digging Speeds

THERE is an ever increasing demand for the provision of gas and water mains, electric light cables and drainage systems, all of which must be laid underground. Most of the trenches required for this purpose are dug at the sides of main roads, and must be as narrow as possible, in order that traffic may not be disturbed unduly, while they are being excavated. They also must be deep, so that pipes or cables laid in them may be protected from mechanical shock due to the passage of heavy road vehicles. These limitations make it almost impossible to dig suitable trenches by manual labour. Excavators designed for this purpose therefore have been introduced, and in addition to digging clean trenches of the exact size required, these have the great advantage of increasing the rate at which the work is done.

The Allen-Parsons Super Duty trench excavator, Model 25, loading trucks with soil excavated from a trench 10 ft. deep. Illustrations by courtesy of John Allen and Sons (Oxford) Ltd.

The Allen-Parsons trench excavator illustrated on this page is an excellent example of a mechanism of this kind, and its digger buckets are capable of digging deep narrow trenches at remarkable speed as they are hauled along the endless chain carried by its boom. For ease in negotiating difficult surfaces, it is mounted on two creeper tracks, which can be started or stopped independently by means of friction clutches; and the entire machine can be swung round in a very small space by simply stopping one of the tracks.

The frame of the excavator is of massive construction and extends to its highest point. The power unit is a four-cylinder petrol engine of 36 h.p., and no difficulty is experienced in cutting through the most stubborn materials met with in trench excavation work. The gear-case is enclosed and is remarkably compact. In many respects it is the most interesting part of the machine, for it transmits the power for actual excavation, for moving the excavator at its work or along the roads, for driving the chain of digging buckets, for operating the conveyor that deposits the spoil, or excavated material, and for hoisting the boom as required. All the movements are under the control of the driver, who from his seat is able to reach the necessary levers without difficulty. The travelling speed of the machine is 1.66 m.p.h., and the 16 forward and four reverse digging speeds provided vary from 11 in. to 139 in. per min.

An unusual view of the excavator from the bottom of the trench it is digging.

One reason for providing many forward gears is to allow the machine to be speeded up or slowed down as the character of the material to be excavated varies. For instance, if this changes suddenly from comparatively loose dry earth to hard clay, the rate of digging and travelling can be immediately decreased. A safety clutch stops work when pipes or large stones are struck.

Rapid working in dry soil produces dust, but the casing prevents this from penetrating to the gears and bearings, which are thus protected from undue wear. The lower half of the case is filled with oil, which is sprayed continuously from the top of the case over the gears by means of a pump.

The digging boom can be extended, raised or lowered, and moved sideways into nearly every conceivable position relative to the machine. It is raised and lowered by means of cables operated by worm gear that automatically locks it in any desired position so that a trench of constant level is dug. The buckets are made from a special steel alloy. The cutting teeth mounted on them have an action like that of a milling machine and the excavated material is delivered in small pieces, a detail that makes its packing in the trench easier when the time comes for it to be returned.

Shallow surface cuts and trenches 10 ft. deep can be made with equal facility, and the width of these cuts can be varied from 1 ft. 3½ in. to 3 ft. 6 in. Changes in the width of the trench can be made by fitting larger or smaller buckets, but "side cutters" can be used when a wider trench is to be cut than the buckets actually in use allow. These side cutters are specially designed fittings that resemble the two halves of a bucket. They are joined together by a thick steel bar, and are attached to the endless chain in the spaces between the buckets. Material dislodged by them falls into the bottom of the trench and is then lifted out by the buckets in the usual manner. The speed of digging of course is considerably reduced when side cutters are in use.

The endless chain carrying the buckets is built up of fork-shaped links and self-locking cotter-pins, and the entire assembly fits together without bolts or rivets. It is therefore an easy matter to repair any damaged section in a very short time, and work of this kind can be carried out without delay at the excavating site, a feature of vital importance, especially in contract work.

The material raised by the buckets falls on a sloping metal shield, from which it slides down a conveyor belt, the frame of which can be moved across the machine so as to allow the spoil to be deposited on the more convenient side of the trench for the purpose. When the machine is in transit the conveyor is moved into a central position.

Refloating Sunken Ships

Marvels of Salvage at Scapa Flow

By W. A. Bagley

IN spite of modern invention, peril at sea is still considerable, and many wrecks occur every year. A ship may be fitted with all manner of safety devices, and be aided from the shore by lighthouses and radio beacons, but no ship-owner seeing his proud vessel steam away over the horizon can say with certainty that he will ever see her again. Storm and tempest may prove too much for the puny work of Man; a boiler may explode, or fire break out; or there may be a collision in the crowded approaches to a harbour, especially in foggy weather. An error of judgment on the part of those in command, or a defect in the compass or steering gear, may lead a vessel on to dangerous rocks, or cause it to collide with an iceberg. Indeed, our maritime history is literally strewn with great wrecks.

Some wrecks are never raised owing to the possible trouble and expense incurred being out of all proportion to the anticipated rewards. Most of them are dealt with, however, usually with one of three purposes in view. The first is to float and repair them, if possible, in order to restore them to their proper places on the high seas. The second is to prevent them from becoming obstructions to navigation. This is particularly important when a wreck occurs in the fairways or approaches to a harbour, or in a river. Its position is then marked with a wreck ship or a buoy, and sometimes it is blown up, a wasteful and summary method to which no further reference need be made. The third reason for dealing with a wreck is that the ship is worth a good deal as scrap metal, even with the price of scrap iron so low as it is at present. A sunken battleship might be worth thousands of pounds, and its gun-metal tubes alone are likely to be worth £100 each.

Before the days of lighthouses, it used to be a common occurrence for the callous inhabitants of certain coastal hamlets to show false lights, and deliberately cause a wreck in the hope of gaining valuable loot. Nowadays it is illegal to loot a wreck. The Board of Trade looks after wrecks cast up on the shores of Great Britain, and appoints Receivers to take charge of them, and many shipowners subscribe to various salvaging societies, who look after their interests.

A salvaged German battleship on the way to Rosyth. This vessel was raised upside down. The photographs illustrating this article are reproduced by courtesy of Cox and Danks Ltd.

Most of the plant for wreck raising is carried aboard a salvage steamer. This is a small but complicated vessel, and generally is made of wood, so that she can remain alongside a wreck in rough weather and withstand the buffetting of the seas. Her complement of gear and equipment is very extensive, so as to render her as nearly as possible independent of shore assistance.

As can well be imagined, her pumps, of which she carries a large variety, capable of throwing out thousands of tons of water an hour, are among her most important features. The latest electrical pumps are portable, and can be slung from derricks, which often are of the floating variety. They are submersible, and can easily be transferred to the wreck. Oil driven pumps also are extensively used, and their fuel can conveniently be carried in an ordinary ship's lifeboat. Steam pumps have certain advantages, and formerly were much used. They are often still retained to-day, as they are useful for pumping away such cargoes as sand, coal, grain, and even copper or iron ores. Their drawbacks are many, however. For example, time is taken to raise steam for them, and once started this has to be maintained, even when the pump is not actually at work. It is difficult to transfer them to a wreck, especially in bad weather, and the necessary coal takes up valuable space and has sometimes been washed away.

Oil-driven air compressors that can pump air for days together are included in the salvage vessel's equipment, as well as an oxy-acetylene plant, the fiery flame of which creates such intense heat that it can cut steel plates and girders under water. There are also drilling machines, hammers, high-pressure hydraulic rock boring apparatus, submarine photographic gear, searchlights worked from the ship's dynamo, a radio plant and many other features. The crew of officers, men, divers, artisans and others number about 80.

There are several ways of raising wrecks, and the method or combination of methods employed obviously depends upon such considerations as the position of the ship, the extent of damage, the rise and fall of the tide, and the state of the weather. The whole aim of salvaging is to restore the buoyancy of the ship and so refloat it. The simplest case is where the ship has been driven ashore by storm, and is being beaten up by the waves. In such cases the ship must be securely moored and lightened as much as possible by having the cargo jettisoned, the leaks patched up, and the water pumped out of her. If all goes well, the next high tide will carry her off.

Many wrecks occur in deep water, however, and the vessels usually are not visible from the surface. One method of salvage utilises the rise and fall of the tide when this is sufficiently marked. A pair of barges, or perhaps pontoons, of sufficient buoyancy are placed over the wreck, and wire cables as thick as a man's leg are fastened to the bollards of one barge and led under the wreck to the other barge, where they are again fastened. As many as six cables may be used, and when this part of the work is finished the wrecked vessel lies in a steel cradle. This is done at low water, so that the barges rise with the tide and lift up the ship. The amount of lift of course is the same as that of the rise of the tide. Sea water is sometimes let into the barges at low tide so as to sink them as low as possible when passing the cables under the wreck. This water is afterwards pumped out, and thus extra lift is secured.

After the ship has been lifted off the bottom it is towed into shallower water, the wires are wound up to suit the new draught, and the process is repeated until the wreck has been raised sufficiently.

This sounds simple enough in theory, but in actual practice it is often far from being so. A wreck often is found to be deeply embedded in sand, and holes have to be bored beneath it, or the cables have to be laid down in a position where the wreck can be towed over them.

If there is no rise and fall of the tide a different method is necessary. Two well-fendered pontoons are then used. A cable is passed under the wreck and one end is fastened to the first pontoon, which is hauled down to one side of the wreck by means of a winch on the second pontoon. The latter is then filled with water, and allowed to slide down the cable to the other side of the wreck, where it is fastened by means of a special grip operated from the surface. The water in the pontoons is then ejected, either by means of compressed air or by pumping. The wreck is thus buoyed up in exactly the same manner as a boy "swimming" with a pair of water-wings, and is raised to the surface.

When a wreck is lying upside down, compressed air is pumped into specially prepared compartments in it that are known as "air locks." This forces the water out through the lower openings, and pumping is continued until the volume of air thus trapped gives sufficient buoyancy to raise the wreck. The method is similar to that already described, but the air is held by the ship itself instead of the pontoons.

All hatchways, funnel openings, portholes, leaks, and other holes in the ship's structure of course must be sealed with a special cement or otherwise closed, in order to prevent the escape of the compressed air. The wreck also must be made strong enough to withstand the terrific pressure, and for this reason decks have to be strongly shored up and supported. It will be realised that this entails a considerable amount of arduous work by divers.

Raising one of the sunken battleships at Scapa Flow. On the left can be seen part of one of the pontoons, with the wheels over which passed the cables inserted under the wrecked vessels.

As the water is displaced, workmen enter the ship through a great iron shaft that is built up from the wreck, and stands out of the water like the top of a factory chimney. The shaft is fitted with a double air-tight trap door, so that the men can pass in and out of it without letting the compressed air escape. If such a calamity did occur, the water would surge in, and the men would be drowned like rats. Those engaged on work of this kind soon become accustomed to the atmosphere of compressed air, which acts like an invisible sheet of glass holding back the water.

The most famous of all salvaging exploits undoubtedly is the raising of the ships of the former German navy that were scuttled one bright midsummer morning in 1919 in Scapa Flow, the splendid natural harbour in the Orkney Islands. Without a single shot being fired, 72 ships, built at a cost of £40,000,000, went to the bottom as the sea cocks were removed. Their sinking was dramatic, but the struggle to raise them was even more thrilling. Most of the ships were raised between 1924 and 1931, and the *"Bayern,"* one of the remaining dreadnoughts, was brought to the surface early in 1934.

The beginning of the long task of salvaging the vessels came when Mr. E. F. Cox, of Cox and Danks Ltd., iron and steel merchants, shipbreakers and salvage contractors, walked into the Admiralty and boldly purchased the sunken battle cruisers and torpedo boats. Mr. Cox had previously bought two obsolete battleships for scrap, but this time the experts thought that he was attempting too much, and was throwing good money away. But he won through. It was a long job, in a bleak, lonely spot, almost out of touch with civilisation, that called for great moral courage as well as financial resources to the utmost. Mr. Cox spent more than £400,000 before his first ship was raised, and his wages bill was in the neighbourhood of £500 a week. In all he spent £450,000 to realise a profit of £10,000. Before he began, he had never salved a ship in his life. Now he is accounted one of the world's greatest experts on the subject.

The air locks used in salvage work are seen in this photograph.

Most of the processes used in raising the wrecks were similar to those already described, but Mr. Cox and his men converted salvaging into a fine art. For example, a quicker method was devised of fixing a cable under a ship, a process normally taking a day or two. The first cable carried a guide rope for the second, the second carried a guide for the third, and so on. A record was achieved by passing one cable under a vessel in 40 min., and as many as 10 were placed in position in two days. An old floating dock cut in two furnished the necessary pontoons, and cables costing hundreds of pounds were used.

The crowning triumph was the salvaging of the *"Hindenburg,"* a battle cruiser of 28,000 tons. No ship of her gigantic size had ever been raised before, and not until after three fruitless efforts had been made, and over £50,000 had been spent, was the feat successfully accomplished. She was lying the right way up, but started to overturn when lifting began. To prevent this, a huge block of concrete weighing 50 tons was placed against one side. Then she started canting over to the other side, and work again was held up until a second block was added, at considerable expense, to balance her.

Danger and serious accidents threatened on all sides. For example, on one occasion a giant chain, on which a small fortune had been spent, snapped and sent its links flying in all directions. No one was killed on duty, however, owing to the great care exercised; and during operations diversions of a lighter kind were provided by sportive whales and seal pups that disported themselves around the divers' air pipes.

The *"Bayern,"* which carried 24 heavy guns, was one of the largest of the dreadnoughts. She was 630 ft. long and 100 ft. wide, and had a displacement of 28,000 tons. She was lifted by Metal Industries Ltd., Rosyth, who bought the plant at Scapa Flow from Cox and Danks Ltd. after they had given up the job. The ship was at a depth of 120 ft., or 25 ft. deeper than the previous ships; but whereas some of the vessels previously raised had lists of 18 deg. to 23 deg., the *"Bayern"* was upside down, nearly level, and had a list of only 9 deg. Salving her therefore was a somewhat easier proposition, but the word "easier" must be used with caution, for the task indeed was a stern one.

The seven airlocks that had to be inserted in the vessel were each 100 ft. in length, and thus were longer than any previously constructed. Two principal requirements always had to be borne in mind. One was that the airlocks had to be so placed that the ship would rise in a balanced position. In addition, it was necessary to make sure that the pressure in the locks would be adapted to a sudden rise from the bottom, where the air pressure had to be maintained at 50 lb. per sq. in., to the surface, where only 10 lb. per sq. in. was possible. The locks had to be kept from bursting, and at the same time maintained in condition to support the ship.

It was a terribly arduous task for the divers, one of whom died; but engineering skill triumphed in the end, and the giant was afloat again, with 18 ft. of freeboard.

After their long immersion in the water, the raised ships presented a strange appearance. Searchlights, masts, and upper works generally were fantastically twisted, and marine growths of beautiful colouring and marking covered everything. Guns were festooned with long ribbons of seaweed, and shorter growths like grass grew everywhere. Spiny sea urchins, mussels, and baby oysters clung to the slimy plates, and offered a feast to the thousands of sea gulls that were attracted to the spot. Under a hot sun the growth soon decayed, however, giving rise to an intolerable stench.

The salvager is generally a hard-bitten practical man, who doubtless thinks chiefly of such matters as air pressure and the price of scrap iron. His divers raise treasure from the bed of the sea in the form of rusty iron plates, and not romantic "pieces of eight," and they display great pluck and endurance in carrying out their arduous work under water.

British Military Aircraft

Modern Bombers and Troop-Carriers

THE bombing aeroplane, or "bomber" as it is briefly called, may be compared with the long-range gun. It has an immensely greater range than the gun, however, and the bomb is discharged directly over the target, whereas the projectile from the gun covers the intervening miles after it has been discharged. Long-range bombing aeroplanes are very large, and are able to fly great distances without refuelling, and to maintain a high speed for long periods, an invaluable factor when they are pursued by enemy defence squadrons. When not employed on bombing expeditions some of them can be adapted to serve as troop-carriers, to transport freight and equipment, or to assist in evacuating besieged civilians. Such aeroplanes are called bomber transports.

The Bristol 130 Monoplane. It can be used as a Bomber or as a Troop-Carrier. This photograph and the upper one on the opposite page are reproduced by courtesy of the Bristol Aeroplane Co. Ltd., Filton.

The Bristol 130 aeroplane illustrated here is a typical example of the latest type of bomber transport. As a bomber it carries a crew of four and a heavy load of bombs, and when used for the transport of troops it carries a crew of three and 24 fully armed men. It has not yet been supplied to the R.A.F., and very few details are available. The illustrations show it to be a twin-engined high wing monoplane. The wing span is 96 ft., the length 67 ft. 9 in., and the height 16 ft. Hydraulically-operated flaps are fitted to the trailing edges of the wings. The two engines are Bristol "Pegasus III.M3s," mounted one on each side of the fuselage in nacelles faired into the wings. There are two guns in the aeroplane. One gun is in an enclosed turret in the nose, and fires through a vertical slit in the front of the turret. This slit can be closed by a patent fastener when the gun is not in use. The other gun is in an open position at the extreme stern of the fuselage.

This formidable-looking aeroplane is the Handley Page "Heyford" Express Bomber. A rotatory gun turret inside the fuselage can be lowered in the event of attack from below. Photograph reproduced by courtesy of "Flight."

Most of the squadrons of the R.A.F. and Auxiliary Air Force have day bombing aeroplanes, and these are of various types. No. 101 squadron, for instance, was until recently equipped with Boulton Paul "Sidestrand" day bombers, but these have been replaced by Boulton Paul "Overstrands." This twin-engined bomber is shown in the lower illustration on the next page. It is a development of the "Sidestrand," and in general design and layout the two machines are very similar. Many important improvements have been effected in the new type, however, including a general stiffening-up of the structure to enable the aeroplane to carry much greater loads and at the same time achieve an increased performance, better protection for the pilot and the two gunners, and provision for warming the cockpit.

The outstanding feature of the "Overstrand," however, is the totally enclosed turret provided for the forward gunner and built in the nose. A detailed description of the turret is not allowed, but it may be mentioned that it gives the gunner complete protection from the weather, and being mechanically rotated it enables him to work his gun much more easily and accurately than would be possible in an open cockpit. In the latter case the great air pressure on the exposed gun when the aeroplane is flying at a high speed makes it extremely difficult for the gunner to carry out the rapid readjustments of aim that are necessary to maintain accurate fire. The gun in the turret is so perfectly balanced that it can be directed upward or downward easily and swiftly. The turret serves also as a bomb-aiming position. The second or rear gunner occupies a cockpit just behind the wings, fitted with an improved

type of windscreen to protect him from the slipstream. In the event of the aeroplane being attacked from below he would be at a disadvantage, and there is therefore a gun specially mounted on the underside of the fuselage for use in warding off attack from below.

The "Overstrand" has a span of 72 ft., a length of 46 ft. 2 in., and a height of 15 ft. 9 in. Both upper and lower wings have ailerons, and the upper one has also Handley Page automatic slots. The undercarriage is of the divided type, one half being on each side of the fuselage and attached to the underside of the engine casings. The pilot's cockpit is between the gun turret and the wings and is totally enclosed, but it has a sliding roof. This cockpit and that of the rear gunner can be warmed by means of a new and efficient type of air heater fitted to the engine exhausts. This maintains a comfortable temperature in the cockpits however cold the outside air may be. Bristol "Pegasus II" supercharged engines are used, and they enable the aeroplane to attain a top speed of 153 m.p.h. at 6,500 ft. It can take off in 200 yd. and has a service ceiling of 22,500 ft.

The upper illustration is a front view of the Bristol 130 Bomber Transport. The lower one shows the Boulton Paul "Overstrand" Day Bomber. The mechanically-operated turret in the nose should be noted. This photograph is reproduced by courtesy of Boulton Paul Aircraft Ltd., Norwich.

Certain types of bombing aeroplanes are designed for use either by day or by night, and these are generally referred to as night bombers, to distinguish them from others intended for use only during the day. The night bombers in the R.A.F. carry a crew of at least five, and are of several types. One of the new squadrons formed under the present expansion scheme has been equipped with the latest type of Handley Page "Heyford" night bomber shown in the lower illustration on the previous page.

In both this and the earlier "Heyford" there are three cockpits. The first is a large one in the nose and is occupied by the navigator and a gunner who also acts as bomb-aimer. The second or pilot's cockpit is behind it, but far enough forward to be in front of the airscrews; and by its elevated position gives the pilot a good view in all directions. The third one, for the rear gunner, is behind the wings. There is also a screened and rotatory turret that is lowered through the underside of the fuselage when the aeroplane has to be defended from attack from below. In the event of such an attack the rear gunner may work the turret gun and the wireless operator give a hand by working the gun in the rear cockpit. Normally the wireless operator occupies a position within the fuselage, almost beneath the pilot's cockpit.

The "Heyford" illustrated differs in several important respects from the earlier version. The large cockpit occupied by the navigator and bomb-aimer has been altered to give a better outlook and more protection. The pilot's cockpit is now totally enclosed, and a new arrangement of the windscreen enables him to look out of the side windows and glance upward or downward without difficulty, no matter how fast the aeroplane may be flying. There is an automatic pilot installation, and an aerial camera can be fitted close to the wireless equipment. The rear gunner's cockpit has been modified, the top of the fuselage having been built up at the forward part and arranged so that the sides drop away by the gun position. By this arrangement the gunner is well screened and is helped to obtain accuracy of fire.

A heavy load of bombs of various sizes can be carried, and they are attached to racks in the thickened centre section of the lower wing. The bombs and racks are in a series of compartments each closed by a spring door. When the objective is reached the bombs are fused and fired by patent Handley Page gear.

The wings are of 75 ft. span and are made in three sections, and the centre section of the upper wing rests on the fuselage. They are of metal and are covered with fabric; both have ailerons, and the upper one has automatic slots. The fuselage is a long rectangular metal structure with a covering of aluminium sheeting. The undercarriage wheels are almost hidden by large fairings that extend upward and join the centre section of the lower wing. Rolls–Royce "Kestrel VI" engines are employed.

The Potez 54

The Potez 54 illustrated on this page is a twin-engined military aeroplane of the high wing monoplane type. It has a span of 72 ft. 6 in. and a length of 53 ft. 2 in. The wings are of metal covered with fabric, and each is built in two sections, which are attached to the fuselage and braced by struts and wires to the engine nacelles. The fuselage is of wood, but a metal bulkhead is incorporated behind the seat provided for the first pilot, and forms an anchorage for the front wing spars and bracing members. A monoplane type tail unit is fitted, and has an adjustable tail-plane. The undercarriage is in two separate units, and when the machine is in flight is retracted hydraulically by a rotary pump driven off the right-hand engine. At the end of a flight it is lowered by means of a hand pump.

The various cockpits are totally enclosed. The first one, in the nose, is occupied by a gunner, and below him sits the chief officer, adjacent to the bomb sights and releases. A large cockpit immediately in front of the wings accommodates two pilots seated one behind the other, and behind the wings is one occupied by a second gunner. This cockpit has guns both above and below the fuselage.

When used as a bomber the machine carries about 2,000 lb. of bombs. It is also adaptable for reconnaissance work, and is then equipped with photographic apparatus instead of bombs.

The standard engines fitted in the Potez 54 are 550 h.p. Hispano-Suizas and they give it a top speed of 192.5 m.p.h. at 13,120 ft. Alternatively Gnôme-Rhône 14Kdr or Lorraine "Petrel" engines can be installed, and in these cases the top speeds at the height already given are 208 m.p.h. and 192.5 m.p.h. respectively.

The Potez 54 twin-engined Fighter described on this page. Photograph by courtesy of Aéroplanes Henry Potez, Paris.

British Air Services to Scandinavia

There will be three regular British air services between this country and Scandinavia this summer, and two of them are already in operation. These are the services of British Continental Airways Ltd., and of British Airways Ltd. The last mentioned has attracted the most attention, as apart from the services of Imperial Airways, it is the first British air line to be granted a Government subsidy. British Airways Ltd. was formed early this year by the amalgamation of Hillman's Airways with the Spartan and United Air Lines.

The route of the new services is from Croydon to Amsterdam, Hamburg, Copenhagen and Malmö, a total distance of about 700 miles. It is being flown once daily in each direction, and the journey takes only about seven hrs., being one of the fastest in Europe. D.H.86s are used, but later they will be replaced by D.H.86A Express air liners.

Another development will be the extension of the services to Stockholm after the opening of an airport there on Sunday 23rd May next. The airport is just over four miles out of the town, and although not the largest in Europe it will certainly become the most important in Scandinavia. Paved runways 2,265 ft. long and 164 ft. wide have been laid down. The airport buildings include Customs Offices, a meteorological station and a wireless station. It is equipped with every modern facility for night flying, and the floodlighting and boundary lighting is very extensive. There are also special lights to indicate the situation of the runways.

Modernising the U.S. Air Force

Some big contracts are being placed by the U.S. War Department for new aircraft. Naturally very few details are available about the various types of aircraft concerned. One of the contracts, for 100 military aeroplanes and spare parts, has been given to the Northrop Corporation, of Inglewood, California. These aeroplanes will carry four machine guns, including a special machine gun in the rear cockpit, and 20 small bombs. Sufficient fuel will be carried for a flight, at cruising speed, lasting 8 hrs. They will have Pratt and Whitney engines of 750 h.p., and it is understood that these will give a top speed of 250 m.p.h.

New Heinkel Monoplane

A new high speed twin-engined monoplane has been produced by the Heinkel Company, in Germany. It is a development of their well-known He.70 monoplane, a type that has done good work on the Stuttgart-Seville section of the South Atlantic service operated by Deutsche Luft Hansa, and it is not surprising, therefore, that the D.L.H. are interested in the new product.

The machine is a low wing aeroplane with a span of 74 ft. 1 in., a length of 56 ft. 1 in. and a height of 12 ft. 6 in. Two 660 h.p. B.M.W. engines are fitted, and these give it a top speed of 214.37 m.p.h. and a cruising speed of 186.41 m.p.h. Both the undercarriage and the tail wheel are retracted when the aeroplane is in flight, and the legs of the undercarriage are then drawn up into recesses provided for them in the underside of the engine nacelles. There is a freight compartment in the nose of the fuselage and behind it is the pilot's cockpit. The passengers' cabin, to the rear of the cockpit, is arranged in two compartments and the front one is intended for use as a "smoker."

"Dragon Rapides" for Spain

The Spanish Air Force have taken delivery of three D.H. "Dragon Rapides" adapted for military use, and these are now in service in Spanish Morocco. The "Dragon Rapide" is a high wing monoplane with two D.H. "Gipsy Six" engines, each of 200 h.p., and cruises at 130 m.p.h. It climbs at the rate of 900 ft. per min. and carries sufficient fuel for a non-stop flight lasting 4½ hrs.

The military type of the "Dragon Rapide" is practically a "general purpose" aeroplane, as it can easily and quickly be made suitable for use as a small troop-carrier, a light-bomber or an ambulance, or adapted for reconnaissance duties. When equipped as an ambulance four stretchers are mounted in the cabin. It is armed with three machine guns, one being mounted in the pilot's cockpit and firing forward, another aft of the wings and firing backward, and the third placed so as to fire downward through the floor of the fuselage, where there is also provision for bomb dropping. The bombs carried each weigh 27 lb. and total 12.

Imperial Airways Notes

The steady growth of freight transport by air is shown by the fact that during a recent period of 12 months the air liners of Imperial Airways carried 1,778,726 lb. of urgent freight, a figure much greater than any recorded during a previous similar period. One of the most noticeable things about air transport at the present time is the increasing volume of freight that is being taken by air between London and the Continent and from England to destinations along the Empire routes.

The chief reason for this undoubtedly is the great saving in time that is achieved by this method of travel. Goods sent from London to Paris complete their journey in 3¾ hrs. by air route, as compared with 9 hrs. by surface transport, while to Cologne the 3½ hrs. by air contrasts with 12 hrs. by land and sea. On the Empire air services the time-savings are much more striking. Urgent freight consignments by air from London to Alexandria reach that city in 3 days, as compared with 9 days by surface transport, and from London to Karachi a freight transport surface time of 22 days can be reduced by air to 5 days. Capetown is now within 9 days of London by air freight dispatch, as compared with 18 days by surface routes, while to Brisbane, Australia, an air goods time of 12½ days compares with 42 days by land and sea.

Another reason is that goods despatched abroad by air obtain a more rapid Customs clearance than if sent by boat and rail. Fragile articles can be exported with the minimum of packing, and this partly accounts for the large consignments of wireless valves forwarded by air from London to points along the Continental air routes. The valves travel safely in ordinary cardboard containers instead of having to be packed in the special wooden crates necessary when transporting them by land and sea.

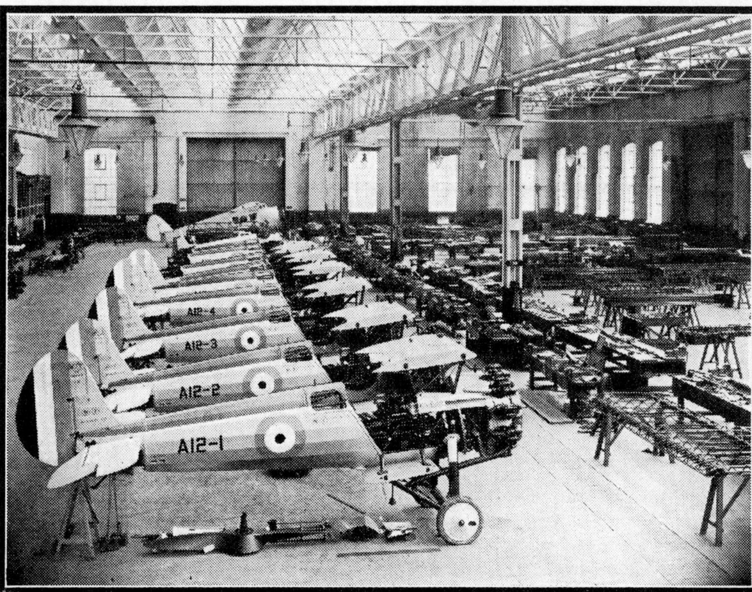

Bristol "Bulldogs" under construction in the works of the Bristol Aeroplane Co. Ltd., Filton, to whom we are indebted for the illustration.

More New Air Liners for Sabena

The Sabena Company, of Brussels, continue to increase their fleet of aircraft and to show a preference for the Savoia-Marchetti S.73. Recently four more of these machines have been ordered from the Savoia Company, of Milan, and when delivered they will be used on the Sabena service to Madagascar. This service is operated jointly with Air Afrique.

The S.73 is an 18-seater air liner, and has three 700 h.p. Piaggio "Stella IX.R.C." engines, which give it a cruising speed of 174 m.p.h. The passengers cabins are warmed by liquid heating, so that no fumes from the engine exhaust are drawn into them, and the required temperature is thermostatically maintained.

Mr. Ford's New Venture

The U.S. Department of Commerce has granted Mr. Henry Ford, the famous motor car manufacturer, an experimental licence for a new light aeroplane. The aeroplane is said to be fitted with a newly developed type of engine, and has dual control. Two passengers and 60 lb. of luggage can be carried.

The First Flight at Night

Now that regular night air services are in operation, it is interesting to recall that the first experimental night flight was made just over 25 years ago by Robert Grandseigne, a French airman who had recently helped to build the monoplane in which Bleriot accomplished the first flight across the English Channel. At 2.30 a.m. on 11th February 1911, Grandseigne took off from an aerodrome at Issy-les-Moulineaux. He flew to Paris and circled over the sleeping city for about an hour before returning to the aerodrome. The aeroplane he used was an early type of Caudron biplane.

* * * *

One of the Heinkel He.70 monoplanes operating the Seville-Stuttgart section of the D.L.H. mail service to South America recently achieved an average speed of 215 m.p.h.

The D.H. 86 "St. Catherine's Bay," on the sands at West Park, Jersey. It is one of the aeroplanes of Jersey Airways Ltd. Photograph by H. A. Breton.

Civil Aviation in the I.F.S. in 1935

In the Irish Free State privately-owned aeroplanes have to be registered with the Department of Industries and Commerce, and the number on the books of the Department at the end of last year was 29.

Kildonan Aerodrome at Finglas, formerly the headquarters of Everson Flying Services, was taken over early in the year by a new concern, Dublin Air Ferries Ltd., that began operations in March. The machines of this company were kept busy on private charter flights, and during the nine months to the end of the year they put in over 600 hrs. on this work.

King's Cup Air Race

The King's Cup Air Race is one of the most popular annual air events in this country. This year it will be held on 10th and 11th July, two months earlier than last year. It is again being organised by the Royal Aero Club.

The eliminating contest on the first day will consist of a flight over a set course totalling 1,240 miles; this is 287 miles longer than the course flown in 1935. The final, to be flown on the second day of the race, will again start and finish at Hatfield aerodrome, and will consist of several successive flights over a course about 50 miles in length.

There will be a change in the classification of the entrants, and in addition to the usual two classes for aeroplanes with engines of under and over 150 b.h.p., there is to be a third one for multi-engined aeroplanes, irrespective of the outputs of their power units.

Important Indian Air Race

The air race round India for the Viceroy's Challenge Trophy, in February last, was won by an Indian competitor, Lieut. Misri Chand, of the 14th Punjab Regiment. Flying a D.H. "Puss Moth," he covered the two-day course of 1,520 miles at an average speed of 116.5 m.p.h. Another Indian, Mr. C. V. Gadgil, of the Karachi Aero Club, was second, with a D.H. "Moth." There were 11 competitors, and nine of them completed the race. The finish was watched by Lord Willingdon, Viceroy of India, who afterward presented the trophy to the winner.

The race was organised by the Aero Club of India and Burma.

New R.A.F. Aerodrome at Singapore

At present there are three squadrons of the R.A.F. at Singapore, the headquarters of the Far East Command. The R.A.F. strength there is to be increased shortly, however, and a third aerodrome is being constructed to provide the necessary extra accommodation.

Guiding The Night Pilot

Marvels of Aerodrome Mechanism

By J. Carmichael Johns

"WINDING in . . . . winding in . . . ."

Nerves tighten in the control tower every time this message comes over the aerodrome's wireless. It means that outside, ten miles away in the darkness, a pilot is pulling up his trailing copper aerial. Soon he will be flying through the night unaided by any friendly voice in his earphones, for his wireless receiver is dumb without its aerial. Perhaps the control tower of the aerodrome he is heading for has been giving him quiet, concise instructions for the last hour. "Winging in . . . ." He sends out a final warning, and a second later the aerial is coiled up on its drum. The pilot glances from his instruments towards the airport; the responsibility of a safe landing now rests as much with the ground staff as it does with him.

The 1,250,000 c.p. "Chance" reflector floodlight on the roof of the traffic office at Heston Airport. The illustrations on this page and the lower one on the opposite page are by courtesy of Chance Brothers and Co. Ltd.

A mass of lights makes the aerodrome resemble a cluster of luminous jewels. Every light means something. The red ones mark obstructions such as office buildings, wireless masts, and hangars; the brilliant orange lamps that suddenly flash on mark the boundary of the landing ground. When the pilot sees them he knows that those on the ground are getting ready for him to come in. A giant "T" appears, apparently blazoned on the ground in white light. Actually it is a frame carrying electric light bulbs, and is mounted on a low mast. It indicates the direction of the wind. A pilot must land along the down stroke, pointing his machine towards the cross-head, as if the letter were an arrow. If the wind is blowing under four miles per hour, there is officially "no wind," and the "T" is set according to orders from the control tower. Before the pilot comes in the location beacon must be switched off, otherwise this lighthouse for airmen would dazzle him as it flashed out its welcoming beams.

"Chance" Mobile Floodlight-Beacon at Lympne. An advantage of this type of Beacon is that it can be hauled into the best position for guiding an aeroplane about to land.

Meanwhile, on the ground, loudspeakers announce in offices, hangars, and on the tarmac, that aircraft number "Y," pilot number "Z," ex-"Everytown," is about to arrive. This pilot, using a Morse lamp, has signalled the first and last letters of his registration number; now he is anxiously awaiting the control tower's O.K. If all is clear, his code message will be repeated by a green lamp, and his accustomed eye will quickly pick up the vital message. Sometimes, however, the signal is flashed back in red, and this means that he must not come down. Perhaps another machine is waiting to take off, or there may be half a dozen reasons why he must stay aloft. Should his petrol be running short, or any emergency make landing imperative, he sends an "S.O.S." by alternately switching on and off his navigation lights. Those on the ground know well what that means, and hastily do the best they can to clear the aerodrome.

When the pilot has received the O.K., he makes one more circle before coming in. His turns, like every manœuvre within three miles of the aerodrome, must be left-handed. This is a strict "Rule of the road" for airmen.

So sudden is the change below that one almost hears the floodlight switch being thrown. The orange-encircled landing ground leaps into pin-point relief as a million-candle-power lamp is focussed on it. Surely the pilot cannot sweep in out of blackness straight towards the eye of this giant searchlight? He will be blinded by the glare. But, as he starts to land, a grey shadow seems to project itself from the nose of his machine, and cleave a grey path in front of him, right across the landing ground. The pilot is protected from the light until he taxies to a standstill. Like all modern equipment, this landing flood was fitted with a shadow-bar, and by operating this in front of the lens, the effect just described can always be produced.

The pilot is now safely on the ground, so we can leave him and examine the system that made it all look so easy.

The ground floodlight, which we have just seen in action, is a wonderful piece of apparatus. It needs to be, for, next to the radio installation, it is the most important part of any aerodrome's night equipment. Somewhere on the control tower we shall find it mounted, a massive lantern-like structure fitted with a great semi-circular lens. If it is ultra-modern it may have a series of lenses. It floodlights every inch of the area where a machine may land, and throws the boundary fence into sharp relief. Light from the 10 kW lamp is concentrated into a wide fan, and projected almost parallel with the ground. No light is lost on the sky, for accurately set prisms in the top of the lens reflect the whole beam downward. This also intensifies the light to fifty times its original candle power.

The shadow-bar previously mentioned makes it possible to point the floodlight directly towards an in-coming machine without any risk of dazzling the pilot. Before this came into use, the lamp's position had to be changed so that it shone from behind the pilot as he landed. For this purpose it was usually mounted on a petrol - electric generator and towed by a tractor. Such types are often used to-day in certain circumstances.

A D.H.86 Express Air Liner floodlit by the landing lights of an airport.

Details of individual aerodromes differ of course according to a multitude of factors. We have been considering an average modern one. This difference in arrangements is particularly marked in connection with the type of location beacon employed. The object of a location beacon is to form a lighthouse for airmen, but its working must be adapted to suit local conditions. To take two extremes—the beacon at Heston is simply a powerful red neon light projector; that at Johannesburg aerodrome is a revolving lighthouse of nearly a million candle-power, which has been picked out by airmen 100 miles away. There is some very clever work in this Johannesburg beacon; for instance, if one of the many bulbs composing the lighting unit gives out, another is automatically fitted in its place. Some units are designed to act both as floodlight and location beacons, and these are particularly useful in emergencies, or on smaller aerodromes.

Most beacons have a definite frequency of flashes per minute, so that they are easily recognisable by pilots. Thus, apart from serving their own particular aerodromes, they form valuable landmarks for passing aircraft.

There is not space for anything but the briefest description of the control tower, the nerve centre of every aerodrome. One might call the officer in charge an aerial traffic policeman. His responsibilities become much heavier at night. He is in constant telephonic communication with the airport offices and ground staff, and—through the wireless operator—with all incoming machines. It is he who issues the orders giving or withholding permission for a pilot to come down. He sets the wind indicator "T," and sees to the operation of the shadow-bar. At a moment's notice, day or night, he can wireless a pilot the exact position of his machine in relation to the airport, or local landmarks; or he can tell him the weather conditions for any particular zone. Very often, if the airport is of any size, it has its own meteorological station.

The tower is usually surmounted by the location beacon and, apart from the controls just mentioned, contains switches that operate the main lighting systems. It occupies the most prominent position on the aerodrome, and commands an unobscured view of the sky.

Anything happening to this building, or its staff, would mean immediate disorganisation of the entire airport. Though such a situation is unlikely, modern airports are doing their best to be prepared for anything. Most of them are now equipped with complete emergency electric lighting, ground flares, and mobile floodlights mounted on tractors.

Now a word about the smaller, though equally important, obstruction indicators and boundary lights. The former are simply 60 candle-power lamps in scarlet shades. The latter are amber-covered and mounted 3 ft. above the ground on steel posts, and they enclose the area where it is perfectly safe for aircraft to land. There may be some distance between them and the boundary fence of the aerodrome, but the intervening ground is often not suitable for landing. It is a mistake to think that the orange lights mark out the actual shape of the aerodrome.

Many people do not realise that, weather conditions being favourable, it is not difficult for a night pilot to see where he is flying. Although detail is wiped out, every irregularity on the Earth's surface is thrown into relief, giving it the appearance of a contour map. The lights of towns are easy to pick out, while illuminated landmarks such as location beacons are visible at great distances. Indeed, some people prefer flying through a clear night to daytime flying. But that is night flying at its best; when there is fog or heavy clouds things are very different. A pilot then has only his instrument readings and instructions that have been given him by wireless to rely on.

Every commercial pilot must pass a stiff test of "flying under the hood"; that is keeping a machine on a fixed course, and an even keel, while the cockpit is covered over by opaque fabric. In such conditions a pilot's instrument board takes the place of his senses. Altimeter, compass, wind speed indicator, dials showing the machine's angle in relation to the ground—these and many more play a vital part. Obviously; yet many highly experienced pilots maintain that they rely on a mysterious sixth sense only acquired after many hours of blind flying.

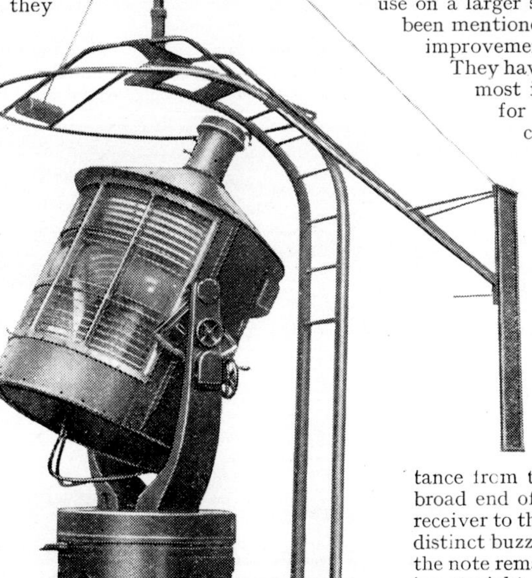
Another type of "Chance" Floodlight-Beacon. On the right is the shadow-bar, which is moved in front of the light when the Beacon is in use.

So far we have been dealing with night flying as it is done in Europe. The United States have tackled the problem far more thoroughly, probably because there are greater distances to be covered. Not only do they use on a larger scale all the apparatus that has been mentioned, but in addition they employ improvements almost unknown over here. They have a system that provides, on the most important air lines, "skyways" for airmen. Although the pilot cannot see them, they are as real and definite as a paved road, and will lead him to his destination just as surely. Radio-beacons make this possible. Imagine an automatic radio-transmitter placed at the head of a much-used air route. Continuously it sends out a wedge-shaped beam of wireless waves. In one dimension, up and down, the beam covers practically an unlimited range; across, however, it is first narrow—only 100 ft.—but broadens out to seven miles on 100 miles' distance from the transmitter. Flying into the broad end of the wedge, a pilot tunes in his receiver to the waves until he hears them as a distinct buzzing note in his earphones. While the note remains audible he knows he is heading straight along the beam; but if the note fades he knows he is off course, and alters his direction until the sounds strengthens.

Each beacon sends out notes of a different frequency, needing different tuning to pick up. Having learned the relation between these frequencies and his tuning dial readings, the pilot is able at once to name the point for which he is heading. Only lateral movement, not altitude, effects the reception of the buzzing note.

Between two radio beacons there is sometimes a silence zone, where no signals can be picked up. The pilot has then to carry on with his instruments and wireless instructions.

A Notable Marshalling Yard

Hump Shunting at Hessle (L.N.E.R.)

By a Railway Engineer

THE hump or gravity principle has been used for many years in railway marshalling yards, both as a means of reducing shunting engine mileage and also to make the sorting of goods trains easier generally. It is, however, only since the invention of the rail brake, or car retarder as it is called in America, that the great potentialities of the system for speeding up traffic have been fully realised. At Hessle, on the L.N.E.R. near Hull, there has recently been opened a remarkable example of a fully-mechanised yard, for dealing with all incoming freight trains. It lies to the north of the main line at a point about 3 miles west of the city and is used to sort all traffic for the various docks and goods stations in Hull, and also for destinations to the north-east, such as Hornsea, Withernsea and Bridlington.

Night operations at Hessle Marshalling Yard. A typical scene inside the control tower showing operators at the control panel and, in the left-hand corner, manipulating the rail brakes.

The tracks are laid out on what is known as the "balloon" system. Each train on arrival at Hessle is placed in one of the six reception sidings, and these tracks converge to a single line of rails that leads over the hump; the seventh track on the reception side is used only by light engines. The gradient on one side of the hump is as steep as 1 in 18. The entry to the reception sidings is under the control of Hessle Haven signal box, on the main line, but the hump yard inspector gives the signalman instructions as to which of the six reception sidings is to be used for each arriving train; this is done by means of an illuminated number indicator in the signal box operated by push buttons in the shunter's cabin at the top of the hump.

Each train is completely sorted out in one long continuous push. When it arrives in one of the reception sidings, a shunter walks along its length noting the destination of each wagon. It may happen that several trucks in succession are bound for the same place, but in any case the whole train is uncoupled into a series of sections, each of which is bound for a different destination. These sections are known technically as "cuts." A card giving a list of all the cuts, and their destinations, is then dispatched, by pneumatic tube, from a shunter's cabin at the top of the hump to the control tower, so that the operator can set the points to switch the cuts into their correct sidings.

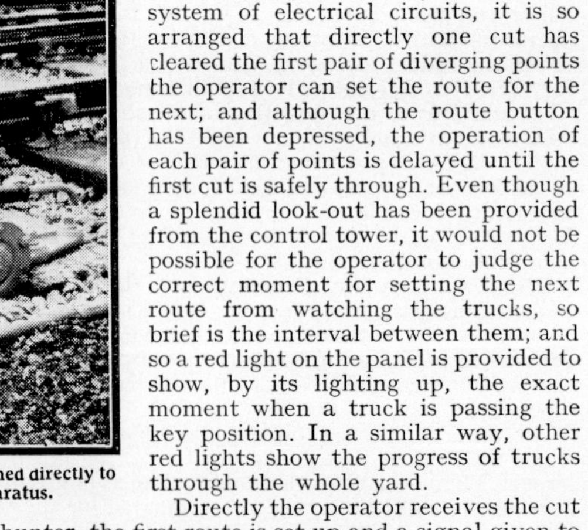

Points-operating mechanism, showing the air cylinder attached directly to the points, also the electro-pneumatic control apparatus.

In the meantime the humping engine has been attached at the rear and all is ready for the remarshalling of the train to begin. At Hessle, North Eastern 3-cylinder 4–8–0 tanks are used for this job. As will be seen when I come to describe the points operation, it is very important for the speed of humping to be correct, and to ensure this all the engines employed are fitted with precision speedometers. The rate varies between three and four miles per hour, and the actual speed required is communicated to the driver by means of a signal of special design, the aspects of which signify "Fast" and "Slow" speed respectively.

As each cut passes over the crest of the hump, it quickly gathers speed down the 1 in 18 grade and separates from the one following; and on reaching the first pair of diverging points it is travelling at nearly 20 m.p.h. At this speed, although there is an appreciable distance between successive cuts, there is a time interval of three seconds, at the very most, between the passage of the last truck of one cut and the first truck of the next; in this very short interval the points have to be moved.

Nothing short of automatic operation would meet such a case, and it is carried out in a most ingenious way. Near to the first diverging points is the control tower, a three-storey building in which the uppermost room houses the control panel. This is rather like a big sloping desk, on the top of which is laid out an exact replica of all the sidings. Instead of the usual type of lever in an interlocking frame, each pair of points has a thumb switch placed at its actual position on the map of the sidings; while tiny coloured lights on the tracks adjacent to the switch show how each pair of points is lying. For automatic working, each thumb switch is set in its mid-position, but the operator can move any individual pair of points by moving the switch either way. Before doing this, however, he has to operate a master switch that puts the automatic working out of use for the time being.

In the ordinary way, the points are worked automatically. Along the lower edge of the control panel is a row of 30 push buttons. The track over the hump forks out into 30 different sidings, and by depressing one of these buttons all the points on the route are set at once; there is no need for each individual thumb switch to be moved. The cuts follow each other so quickly down the hump that you cannot possibly wait for one truck to reach its final siding before setting the route for the next. By an elaborate system of electrical circuits, it is so arranged that directly one cut has cleared the first pair of diverging points the operator can set the route for the next; and although the route button has been depressed, the operation of each pair of points is delayed until the first cut is safely through. Even though a splendid look-out has been provided from the control tower, it would not be possible for the operator to judge the correct moment for setting the next route from watching the trucks, so brief is the interval between them; and so a red light on the panel is provided to show, by its lighting up, the exact moment when a truck is passing the key position. In a similar way, other red lights show the progress of trucks through the whole yard.

Directly the operator receives the cut card from the shunter, the first route is set up and a signal given to the driver to start humping. When the trucks start running down the 1 in 18 grade, all that the operator, with the destination card in front of him has to do, is to watch the red light at the key position, and set the next route as each truck passes. To help the operator, a special green light that indicates "Next Route Clear" lights up at the critical moment, and a buzzer sounds at the same time. In this way a train of 100 wagons is completely sorted out in about six minutes.

Humping at 3 m.p.h. means that the trucks are travelling fast after they have passed over the first diverging points, and it is now that the rail brakes come into the picture. Of the 30 sidings into which cuts can be sent, some may be almost full of trucks while others are nearly empty; and it is the function of the brakes to slow each cut down to the exact speed necessary to carry it to the end of the available space in the siding, and bring it gently into contact with the wagons already there. The brakes are placed just beyond the second pair of diverging points, where the tracks have spread out into four. They consist of 75 ft. beams on both sides of each running rail, which, when power is applied, move towards each other and grip the wheels of a wagon as it passes through. They are operated hydraulically, and the actual braking pressure can be varied through a wide range.

A view along one of the rail brakes. These are operated hydraulically, the brake beams embracing the wagon wheels as they pass along the rails.

All four brakes are under the control of one man and considerable skill is needed to get successful results; for the braking power required depends not only on the siding space, but also on the weight of the cut and the direction of the wind. A lightly-loaded wagon running into a high wind requires much less than a heavy one travelling with the wind. Care has to be taken also with loosely-packed loads; if heavy pressure were applied to a fast-running wagon, the retardation would be so sudden as to shoot a considerable part of the load right out of the wagon. In such a case the operator gives light braking at first, and increases the pressure as the truck passes through. Unlike his colleague at the point control panel, the brake operator depends very largely on a good look-out from the tower, and at night the yard is floodlighted.

Water pressure is maintained automatically at about 1,600 lb. per sq. in. by means of powerful pumps working in conjunction with a hydraulic accumulator. The latter rises to the full height of the control tower, and is accommodated at the back of the control room. The accumulator consists of a vertical cylinder in which the water pressure supports a piston carrying an enormous circular 40-ton weight. When the rail brakes are operated the water pressure is reduced and the weight falls a certain amount; then the pump automatically starts up, and by increasing the pressure in the vertical cylinder the weight is gradually raised until full pressure is restored. Then the pump automatically stops. Occasionally, when a succession of very short cuts is being humped, three, or even all four brakes are on at once; then, for a fraction of a second, the great 40-ton weight descends in a positively terrifying manner until it is checked by the increased pressure caused by its own fall. To prevent freezing up during cold weather, a small percentage of glycerine is added to the water.

A striking night photograph of the control tower. This shows the adjacent floodlighting unit that is used for "spotting" the progress of the wagons.

The control room has been superbly designed. On three sides windows extend from ceiling to floor, and the look-out is only interrupted by the slenderest of pillars. A large awning over the windows is provided by extending the flat roof of the tower.

It is the floor below the control room, however, that contains the heart of the whole system. At first sight it looks like a miniature telephone exchange, for in three steel cabinets hundreds of relays are housed. This resemblance to a telephone exchange is not merely one of outward appearance; each time a route is set up by pressing one of the buttons on the panel, the relays, electrically interconnected, perform a series of operations very similar to those that take place when a telephone line is called by dialling. Each button when depressed operates a particular group of relays, which through their contacts apply power to the necessary points mechanism. In addition to these tiny control relays there is another cabinet that houses the track indication relays. These are similar to the ones used for track circuiting in ordinary power signalling; highly sensitive instruments, they are used for detecting the presence of a truck in any part of the yard, and through their contacts the red lights on the panel upstairs are illuminated.

With such complexity of circuits, great care has to be taken to arrange the wiring so that each individual circuit can be quickly traced out. In the case of the heavier cables, small tags are attached bearing identification marks; but with the small telephone-type wires braiding of a great variety of colours is used, by which any particular circuit can be readily picked out. On the ground floor of the control tower are the air compressors for the points operation and the hydraulic pumps for keeping the rail brakes supplied.

Even though the points are operated automatically, the time available is so short that very quick throwing is necessary. Unlike tracks over which passenger trains are run, no facing points lock is required, and this helps to save time in operation. A powerful pneumatic cylinder is attached directly on to the points stretcher rod. The air supply to this cylinder is controlled by an electro-pneumatic valve that gives very rapid admission and exhaust of air. Also coupled to the points is an electric detector, which proves that the switches are fully home in either direction, and indicates this to the operator by a yellow light on the control panel. If, on account of a small stone or other obstruction, the switches failed to close by as little as one-eighth of an inch, no light would be shown on the panel, and traffic could not be put over the points. In actual practice the complete mechanism has proved to be the fastest points-operating machine ever built. When working the points individually by means of the thumb switches on the panel, the time taken is less than one second, during which interval a number of relays have operated, the points have thrown, and the detector, having proved everything correct in the new position, has lighted the appropriate yellow lamp on the panel! When working automatically the operation is even faster.

The whole yard is beautifully laid out. The track alignment has to be maintained very accurately in order to give the smoothest possible running for the wagons. Concrete edging is used to keep the ballast in place, grass verges line the embankments leading to the hump, and in the V-shaped spaces where the tracks diverge are grass plots. The control tower, in addition to being carefully designed from an operating standpoint, is a very pleasing example of modern architecture, and the general layout has an elegant appearance quite unlike that of an ordinary railway goods yard.

The control room is a fascinating place at all times, but especially at night. The floodlighting has been very carefully arranged, and from the moment the wagons pass over the hump each one can be seen picked out as though by a theatrical spot-light. The constantly changing red and yellow lights give the control desk a singularly beautiful appearance. A small point, but one that leaves a lasting impression, is the remarkable quietness of the working. Hardly a word is spoken between the operators in the control room; there is an occasional order given through the loudspeakers installed in the yard, but apart from that there is only the sharp grinding noise as each cut passes through the brakes. This alone is a welcome change from the incessant racket of an ordinary shunting yard. In a normal day 2,500 trucks are dealt with, but if necessary 3,000 or more could be got through.

The yard was brought into service early in December 1935, and less than a fortnight later it was subjected to a test of the most extreme kind imaginable. In the days immediately before Christmas, fog almost unparalleled in its severity hung over the whole country; but the yard dealt with the heavy Christmas traffic at practically normal speed. The visibility was absolutely nil at times, and although the progress of wagons could be followed on the point control panel, the brake operator had to judge his distance from the sounding of the "Next Route Clear" buzzer.

Importance of Refractories in Industry

Linings for Steel Furnaces

By G. H. Lohan

FEW people realise the great importance in modern life and industry of the products known as "refractories." The ordinary meaning of the word "refractory" is unruly or stubborn, and it has a special application to articles or materials that are difficult to melt, and are capable of withstanding the severe conditions that prevail where intense heat is employed.

Refractory materials are equally important in the manufacture of domestic fireplaces and in the construction of the largest furnaces employed in iron and steel making. Little is heard of them, and of the great part they play in the production of more imposing creations such as great ships and giant bridges, yet it can safely be said that we should still be in the Stone Age if we had not learned how to make good use of them.

A battery of high temperature round down-draught kilns capable of reaching a temperature of 1,600 deg. C. They are at the Worksop works of General Refractories Ltd., Sheffield.

Refractory materials are required to remain unchanged when everything with which they are in contact has been reduced to a molten mass, or completely burned away. They must retain their shapes when subjected to the pressure and "wash" of tons of boiling steel melted in the furnaces of which they form the linings, and must be resistant to the destructive effects of the hottest slags, gases and flames.

Comparatively few common materials would pass unscathed through such vigorous tests. Of those that are suitable, the best known and most widely used is fireclay, from which is manufactured the heat-resisting brick commonly known as the firebrick. Fireclay is used in making fireplaces for houses, and in various shapes is employed in building the furnaces in which metals are melted. It enters also into the construction of boilers of all kinds, power stations, gas works and coke oven plants, and indeed is used to line the kilns in which the firebricks themselves are made.

Fireclay is the product of a process of rock destruction that has extended over a period of millions of years. Ever since the Earth became cool, the rocks on its surface have been subject to the action of the Sun, rain, wind and ice, and have slowly been broken up to form the fine-grained mixture of minerals, usually plastic in character, that we call clay. The nature of this material of course depends on the character of the rocks from which it was formed. Some clays are more refractory than others, that is, the temperature at which they fuse is higher; and these are fireclays. A good fireclay is not usually very plastic, and a certain amount of clay that is more readily moulded often is mixed with it in order to enable bricks to be shaped more readily from it.

The method of extracting fireclay from the earth depends to a large extent on the nature of the deposit and its depth. In some cases it is mined underground, and in others it is worked in an open pit or quarry. It is then transported to the works, where usually it is stored in an open yard for a considerable time in order to become "weathered." No attempt is made to keep the wind and rain away from it, and weathering by these elements not only causes the breaking up of large lumps in the material, and makes this more plastic, but also removes oxides and sulphides of iron, thus improving the fireclay as a refractory material. If these impurities are present in the clay, they may cause serious damage both in the manufacture and use of the firebricks made from it.

When the clay has been weathered for a sufficiently long period, it is taken to the works and the manufacture of firebricks or other shapes begins. The raw material is first broken into small lumps in a crusher, after which it is conveyed to a pan mill to be ground. During the grinding process water and plastic clay are added, together with a certain proportion of calcined or burned fireclay, which is known to the brickmaker as "grog." This helps to strengthen the final product and to reduce the shrinkage that occurs during drying and burning. The proportion required varies with the nature of the clay used, and when a special type of brick is required both raw material and grog are carefully graded.

When the mixing is complete, the brick-batch, as the product is called, is taken to the making sheds, where the shapes are manufactured either by hand or by stamping in machine presses. The shapes are then carefully dried on floors heated by means of steam pipes beneath them, or by the use of waste heat from the kilns. They also may be dried in specially constructed ovens or tunnels. Drying is one of the most important stages in the manufacture of the bricks. Great care must be taken to maintain a steady and constant temperature throughout the process, so that the moisture present in the bricks may be driven off at a uniform rate. The finished product would be cracked if this moisture were turned into steam too rapidly while the bricks are in the drying stage.

Bricks and shapes that have been thoroughly dried are set in the kiln and fired, or "burned," to a temperature ranging from 1,200 deg. C. to 1,450 deg. C., according to the type of ware being fired and the class of work for which it is to be used. Various types of kiln are employed. The two most in favour are known as the round down-draught and up-draught kilns respectively. In the former the heat travels from the fire holes up to the crown or roof of the kiln. It then passes downward with a circular motion, heating the bricks as it passes through them, and finally makes its way through a hole in the floor to the flues leading to the "stack," or chimney. Up-draught kilns work in the reverse manner, the fire leaving through a hole in the roof.

Two pan mills used for grinding clay for refractories. In front of them is a pug mill, in which the raw material is made into clots so that it can be calcined more easily.

The object of burning the bricks is to melt certain of their constituents and thus to bind their particles together in one hard, solid mass. The temperature of the kilns must be raised very slowly until 900 deg. C. has been reached. The purpose of this is to drive out chemically combined moisture and carbonaceous matter. Heating can then be more rapid, and when the temperature has risen to that agreed on for firing, all air passages to the kiln are stopped up and heat is allowed to "soak" through the bricks. Soaking is costly, but it improves the products considerably, making them harder and more durable. After firing they must be cooled very carefully, for the too rapid lowering of temperature by any sudden rush of air might give rise to cracks and splinters.

During recent years the introduction of special steels has made it necessary to provide what can best be termed super-refractories, and in order to keep ahead of the demand manufacturers have continually to find new refractory materials and to devise methods for improving those already in use. Other materials that are now employed as refractories include silica, magnesia and chrome iron ore. Silica is found naturally in the forms of sandstone and quartz. It is highly refractory, and sandstone ground with a little lime or clay to bind it together is used in making silica bricks. Magnesia is made by calcining magnesite. Its melting point is 2,500 deg. C., but most magnesite bricks, as those made from it are called, contain a certain proportion of iron oxide and so have a refractory value equal to about 2,000 deg. Chrome iron ore contains both iron and chromium, as its name suggests, and together with alumina is the basis of "Diazite" bricks, which are now used in place of magnesite bricks in many British and continental steel works.

In the works of General Refractories Ltd. at Worksop are examples of the most modern plant for making super-refractories, including magnesite and "Diazite" bricks. The plant employed is unique, and before designing it the engineers of the company paid visits of inspection to refractory works in many parts of the world. It is so arranged that the material is not touched by hand throughout the process of manufacture.

The bricks are made up from constituents that have been carefully graded by means of vibratory screens, and are proportioned in each mixing to give the best results in the finished products. Tests are made continuously during the various stages of production to ensure that only super-refractories are produced.

The bricks are stamped out by a giant press that is illustrated on this page. It makes four bricks at a stroke and is capable of producing 750 bricks an hour. A pressure of 200 tons is exerted on each brick as it is made. From the press the bricks are run into tunnel driers, where the required temperature is maintained automatically by means of thermostats; and when dry they are burned in down-draught kilns of modern design. The temperature range employed is from 1,450 deg. C. to 1,600 deg. C.

The powerful press recently installed at Worksop, which exerts a pressure of 200 tons per brick, making four bricks per stroke at the rate of 750 bricks per hour.

It is interesting to note that the magnesite bricks when burned weigh up to 13½ lb. each, and each "Diazite" brick weighs up to 15½ lb. The company are now equipping works in other parts of the country with similar plant in order to meet the demands of British steel makers for bricks that will withstand the higher temperatures of their furnaces, and to render the necessity for relining these, involving temporary loss of output, less frequent.

Obviously high temperatures show a large increase in works fuel consumption. This has been overcome by the introduction of insulating bricks. These are used on the outside walls of furnaces and industrial heating plants. In addition to stopping heat losses, they enable furnaces to be raised to higher temperatures without additional fuel cost. With the kilns illustrated on the opposite page this saving amounted to over 35 per cent.

Digging for Gold in East Africa

Pioneer Work in Alluvial Deposits

By C. Maxwell Norman

A FEW years ago there were no gold diggers in the Lupa district of Tanganyika Territory, but now there are about 750. Some of them are doing very well, but most are only scratching out a bare existence. For the unsuccessful ones there is always the hope that any day they may strike a rich pocket of the precious metal and make a fortune, and to men with such a belief hardship means nothing and starvation is part of the game.

Gold was discovered in the Lupa District in 1923 in the gravel of the bed of the Lupa River. The region lies about 300 miles south-west of Dodoma, on the Central Railway, and is a hard country, verdant with tropical forest in the rains, but arid as the desert verges of the Dead Sea in the dry season. When the rains cease, the sun scorches every leaf and blade of grass to a sere yellow, the streams and rivers are dried up and the soil is baked to a hard red dust, so that a man might die of thirst if he did not take the precaution of establishing water bases for himself, or learn the whereabouts of the few water holes where wild creatures drink.

Panning in the Lupa river during the dry season, when the level of the water is low. Gravel for panning is being brought from diggings near by.

Quartz reefs carrying gold are scattered about the region and are mostly hidden by an overburden of soil. As the years have gone by, the outcrops of these reefs have been eroded, and rubble and gravel have been broken off and carried away by streams, so that now large areas of ground have a layer of gold-bearing gravel just below the surface. It is from this gravel, and from the sand in the dried-up river beds, that the digger wins his gold. Usually he recovers only the finest of tiny particles, but occasionally nuggets are found in rich pockets. Nuggets weighing an ounce are not infrequent, and several weighing as much as 50 oz. have been discovered. In 1927 a nugget weighing 120 oz. and containing 76 oz. of pure gold was unearthed, and two years later one digger obtained gold worth £1,000 in eight days' work. A man who is fortunate enough to make such a discovery may lose his money during months of unproductive work afterwards, however, and it is only the few who can be called successful.

The story of a gold rush in East Africa begins with the wanderings of a prospector, accompanied by a few native bearers. With him he carries a pan, an iron dish with sloping sides that is used for washing gravel in search of gold or other heavy minerals, making bread, carrying water or frying steaks from game animals he has shot. Whenever he comes to a likely place, such as the bed of a stream, he pans a little of the gravel to see if it contains any gold, for there is always the chance of finding the metal. It was in this way that the Lupa goldfield was discovered.

The rush itself follows if the prospector is successful. The news spreads when he turns up at some town with a pile of gold and sells it to the local bank. Gold news travels quickly, and soon men of all types are on the trail of fabulous riches "up country." Later come the traders, Indian transport riders, native storekeepers and Greek and Italian gold buyers. Government Inspectors, Police, and District Officials follow, native labour drifts into the area, small townships spring up, and soon the whole district possesses an ever-changing population, all following the fickle goddess Luck.

At a pinch, digging can be started with a capital as low as £5. The aspirant begins by going to the nearest Mines Office, where for 10/- he equips himself with a Prospecting Right that entitles him to hunt for minerals and to peg claims. He hires a few natives at 9/- a month and food, which costs as low as 5/- or 6/- a month per boy, and sets off. He may have a "hunch" where to go, or he may just wander up and down streams, or trek across country examining the soil and rubble beds on the watershed areas between the streams. Usually he starts out in the wet season and pans his way along, but some prospectors roam about during the dry season in order to locate likely places for work when the rains come and ample water is available.

There are two kinds of panning, wet and dry. Where there is water, the sand, rubble and gravel are loaded into the pan, which is held under water while lumps of clay are broken up with the fingers and the stones are removed and thrown away. Then the pan is given a shaking and a swirling motion to make the heavier particles sink to the bottom. Periodically the top is scraped off, and this process is continued until there is left only a small proportion of fine sand consisting usually of black heavy particles. Mixed with it is the fine gold-dust, the heaviest of all the grains in the pan. This remains until the last, and the whole of it can be recovered by a skilful panner. The prospectors themselves are often unskilled, however, and the panning usually is left to the natives, who allow much of the finer gold to escape.

Dry panning is a very tedious process. The soil and gravel are first laid out to become thoroughly dry, and all lumps are pounded with a stick or stone to break them up, and rubbed through the fingers. A pan is then loaded and the same shaking and swirling motion is applied as in wet panning. As the heavier minerals sink to the bottom, the pan is swirled in such a way as to allow the soil and gravel to spill out at the rim, a process that is helped by a little judicious scraping. Finally a heap the size of two clenched fists remains, and this is tossed up and down while the operator blows strenuously on it. Eventually nothing is left but the gold—if the metal is present.

The prospector who finds gold must next peg his claim, or anyone could come and take it. A claim is 300 ft. long and 100 ft. wide, and he measures this area out, and places beacons at the corners with boards or plates on them that state all the necessary particulars. Sometimes more than one claim is staked out. The discoverer then hurries in to the Mines Office to register his finds. Once that has been done, he has the sole right to work them.

Sluicing gravel from the banks of a stream. The gold is caught behind the riffles or cleats in the sluice box.

Now comes the serious part of the digging. The gold seeker hires more boys and supplies them with pans, picks and shovels. A camp is made by erecting a square hut built of raw poles cut in the bush, with sides and roof thatched with grass, and putting up a few similar round or square huts for his boys, and then he gets to "work." For the most part this consists in allowing the boys to pan all day long. They work from sunrise until about three or four o'clock in the afternoon, and then they bring up the gold they have retrieved. This is weighed and they are paid a bonus of anything up to 20 cents per pennyweight, or about 2½d. for one twentieth of an ounce.

The law prohibits natives from possessing or dealing in gold, and stipulates that the maximum bonus shall be 20 cents. This is done in order to prevent illicit dealing and theft, but there are always men who pretend to work a claim for the purpose of covering up the fact that they are buying stolen gold steadily, at rates much higher than the legal maximum. This gold of course really has been won by natives working for other diggers, and its buyers are tough customers and difficult to deal with.

Dry blowing for gold. The gravel is pounded in a pan, shaken and swirled round, and the lighter waste matter is blown away.

Periodically the digger makes a trip to the nearest "town" to sell his little store of gold to the local traders, who usually are licensed gold-buyers. He probably takes half the value of the metal in native foodstuffs and provisions for himself, and the other half he banks unless, as is frequently the case, he loses it in gambling.

Panning is not the only way of winning gold from alluvium. Different people have different methods, and much depends on how much capital a digger has. In the dry season a dry-blower may be used. This consists of a galvanised iron structure containing a crude fan that is rotated by means of a small petrol engine. The air current so produced is driven through a trough or hopper into which the broken-up gravel is slowly dropped. The heavy gold and "black sand" then drop down into a box below, while the lighter waste matter is blown away.

A wooden sluice box is used if water is available. The upper part of this is a launder or trough, sloping slightly towards one end, into which the broken-up gravel or "pay-dirt" is shovelled, or tipped from pans, while natives bail water from the stream and pour it over the top. As the gravel passes down the launder, the larger stones are picked off, and the remainder reaches a screen made of iron with holes punched in it. There it is again puddled up with the water, and the coarse light matter is removed by hand while the heavy particles pass through into the sluice box below. This also is a trough, but across it are placed riffles, or small cleats of wood, and the gold and black sand collect behind these obstructions. Periodically there is a clean-up, when the contents of the sluice are removed and the gold recovered by panning. Some miners use blanket to line the floor of the sluice box in order to give the gold something to stick to. Others put small amounts of quicksilver behind the riffles. The gold then dissolves in this metal to form an amalgam, from which it can easily be separated.

The life of an alluvial gold miner in Tanganyika Territory offers few attractions to the man who likes companionship. If he is diligent and sober-minded he goes out with his natives, teaching them and watching them at work. Most diggers prefer to leave everything to their boys, however, and are content to give them their daily rations of mealie meal and to check in the gold every evening. Food supplies are obtained by occasional journeys to the nearest trader, and meat by the use of the rifle. In the evenings there is little to do but to get to bed! It is scarcely surprising that many of those who endure such a lonely existence show a tendency to "go wild" when they return to civilisation, especially when their pockets bulge with money the local dealer has given them in exchange for their gold

L.N.E.R. Developments

The L.N.E.R. have placed an order with Robert Stephenson and Co. Ltd. for 11 locomotives of the 3-cylinder 4–6–0 type. These will be similar to the existing B17 engines of the "Sandringham" class. Beyer, Peacock and Co. Ltd. are to build 28 goods locomotives of the 0–6–0 "J39" class. Tenders with a water capacity of 3,800 gallons will be provided for 19 of them; the remainder will have 4,200 gallon tenders.

A modified form of streamlining has been applied to a five-coach articulated set that works on the 10.10 a.m. Leeds express from King's Cross. Rubber sheeting similar to that used on *"The Silver Jubilee"* train is applied between the coaches.

Thirty-five specially constructed wagons for the conveyance of containers have been ordered from the Birmingham Carriage and Wagon Co. Ltd. The supply of nearly 700 dynamos and over 12,000 standard cells for train lighting has been arranged with various manufacturers.

The now-famous L.N.E.R. *"Northern Belle"* cruising train is to run again during the coming summer. It will leave King's Cross at 9 p.m. on 29th May, 12th June, and 19th June for extended tours of the Highlands.

L.N.E.R. 4-6-0 locomotive No. 911, a three-cylinder engine of class "B16." An interesting run behind one of these engines is described on the next page. Photograph by Mr. O. S. Nock, Bushey.

More "Zephyrs" for the Burlington Route

Following the success of the *"Zephyr,"* the stainless steel streamlined American train described in the *"M.M."* for April 1935, and its successors, the Chicago, Burlington and Quincy Railroad have decided to introduce two twin-engined trains of a similar kind. These are for service between Chicago, Omaha and Denver, a route 1,039 miles long that is to be traversed at an average speed of 65 m.p.h., including stops. A power-baggage vehicle at each end and four sleeping cars will be included in the make-up of each 10-car train. It is hoped that these will be put into service during the coming summer.

The two four-car *"Twin Zephyrs"* are to be replaced on the run between Chicago and the Twin Cities, Minneapolis and St. Paul, by two new seven-car twin-engined units. These will be wider than the present trains and will have much more passenger accommodation.

The G.W.R. "A1 at Lloyds"

One of the G.W.R. "Star" class locomotives converted to a "Castle," formerly No. 4009, *"Shooting Star,"* has been renamed *"Lloyd's,"* in compliment to the famous insurance institution. It is appropriately numbered "A1."

The naming ceremony was performed at Paddington by Sir Robert Horne, Chairman of the G.W.R. Mr. Neville Dixey, Chairman of Lloyd's, and members of the Committee of Lloyd's were present, together with the General Manager and the principal officers of the G.W.R. The nameplate of the locomotive was surmounted by Lloyd's coat-of-arms and the official house flag was flown. An unusual feature was the display between the chimney and the cab of a flag signal in the international code, reading *"A1 at Lloyd's."*

Centenary of the First Railway in London

A special exhibition has been arranged at the Science Museum, South Kensington, to commemorate the opening 100 years ago of the London and Greenwich Railway. This was notable as the first railway in London. It was projected in 1832 and part of it, between Spa Road and Deptford, was opened in February 1836. A remarkable feature was that the line was carried throughout on a brick viaduct. It was hoped that the arches would be used as dwellings and warehouses, but as residences they were not successful. The extension to London Bridge was opened in December 1836, and the Greenwich end was completed in 1838. The line was leased to the old South Eastern Railway in 1845 and became merged in the Southern Railway in 1923.

The exhibition includes prints, books, pictures, medals and other relics loaned for the occasion by the S.R. and various private collectors. It will remain open until 30th April.

L.M.S.R. Locomotive News

At the time of writing the taper-boilered "Royal Scot" class locomotive No. 6170, *"British Legion,"* is working from Longsight on the Manchester and Euston service. On two successive days recently, trains headed by this engine regained time lost in the up direction. With 385 tons behind the locomotive, Driver Thomas and Fireman Walker made up 6 min. from Lichfield to Euston, the average speed being 68.4 m.p.h. for the 116¼ miles. The next day the same amount of time was made up by Driver Bowden and Fireman Shea between Nuneaton and Euston, the 97 miles being run at an average speed of 69.3 m.p.h., with 377 tons.

"Royal Scot" class locomotive No. 6126, formerly *"Sanspareil,"* is now named *"Royal Army Service Corps."* The naming ceremony was performed on 14th January last by Major-General W. K. Tarver, C.B., C.M.G., Colonel-Commandant of the R.A.S.C., in the presence of a gathering of officers of the regiment, and L.M.S.R. directors and officials.

Scrapping of G.N.R. "Atlantics"

Britain's earliest "Atlantic" locomotives, the small-boilered "990" series of the former G.N.R., are apparently doomed. Nos. 3982 and 3988 have already been withdrawn and the first of the class to be built, now No. 3990, also is condemned. This engine in its earliest form was illustrated on page 87 of the February issue of the *"M.M."* In view of its special interest as the first British "Atlantic" locomotive, its preservation by the L.N.E.R. in the Railway Museum at York would be welcomed by all interested in railways and locomotives. For many years the "990s" shared with their larger-boilered developments of the "251" series the heavy main line traffic out of King's Cross. With the introduction of the "Pacifics," however, they were displaced from this work, and since then have been principally employed on the Cambridge trains and other less arduous duties.

Brisk Work by L.N.E.R. Mixed Traffic Engine

Of the many notable locomotive types of the late North Eastern Railway, the large three-cylinder 4–6–0 mixed traffic engines formerly known as class "S3," but now L.N.E.R. "B16," are among the most distinctive. Although their driving wheels are only 5 ft. 8 in. diameter, they have a good turn of speed and are often employed on express passenger trains. No. 1374 of this type made an excellent run with the heavy 12 noon London express from Hull, hauling a load of 360 tons tare and 385 tons full. On account of adverse signals it took 8 min. 53 sec. to pass Hessle, 4.8 miles, but then the engine went ahead in fine style, working up to a sustained 64½ m.p.h. on the level at Broomfleet. Speed was eased to 45 over the junctions at Staddlethorpe and then a maximum of 59 m.p.h. was recorded before stopping at Goole, 23.7 miles in 31¼ min., or about 30 minutes net. Staddlethorpe, 17 miles from Hull, had been passed in 20½ min.

On restarting, Thorne, 7½ miles, was passed in 10½ min. at 58½ m.p.h., after which speed rose to a sustained 60 m.p.h. at Barnby Dun. Signals were "on" approaching Doncaster, but in spite of this the 17¼-mile run was completed in 23 min. or about 22 minutes net.

We are indebted to Mr. O. S. Nock for these timings.

S.R. Place a Record Order

The S.R. are losing no time in proceeding with arrangements for the electrification of the Portsmouth main line. Preliminary works already commenced were mentioned in these pages last month, and the company have now placed the biggest order ever known in this country for railway electrification equipment. This includes the supply and erection of electrical machinery for 27 rectifier sub-stations.

More Old Engines Withdrawn

With the scrapping of Nos. 3416 and 3417, only No. 3420 remains in service of the old G.N. 0-8-0 type. This was the only one of the class to be rebuilt with a large boiler. The G.E. "D13" 4-4-0s are disappearing rapidly. They were converted from 2-4-0s many years ago.

Brighter Colours on British Railways

Mr. H. M. Madgwick informs us that one of the Brighton main line six-car electric train sets, No. 2015, has been painted a bright emerald green shade that presents a striking appearance, especially in bright sunlight, as compared with ordinary S.R. green. From Ireland we learn that the five large 4–4–0 compound locomotives of the G.N.R. are being specially finished in blue, lined black and white, with bright red frames lined similarly. A coat-of-arms appears on the splashers below the nameplate, a welcome return to the use of such heraldic devices in these days, when the tendency is to give them up altogether.

In view of these experiments, and bearing in mind the special finish of the L.N.E.R. *"The Silver Jubilee"* train and its streamlined locomotives, it will be interesting to see whether brighter colours generally will come into use for railway stock. Already stations and other buildings are being dealt with in order to abolish the drab appearance that characterises many of them.

The illustration at the head of the page, reproduced by the courtesy of the Great Southern Railways of Ireland, shows a 4-4-0 locomotive of that line, as rebuilt and brought up to date. The locomotive seen in the lower photograph is one of those formerly employed on the S.R. narrow-gauge Lynton-Barnstaple line, and is now scrapped. Photograph by W. Vaughan-Jenkins, Bath.

Further L.M.S.R. Shed Improvements

Nineteen important L.M.S.R. motive power depots are to be reorganised and brought up to date this year. Improved track layouts to aid the rapid handling of engines will be provided, also mechanical coaling plant and other facilities. The depots include Bedford, Goole, Perth, Kingmoor, Mold Junction, Normanton, Stafford, Camden, Huddersfield, and various Lancashire sheds.

Electrifying the Wirral Railway

The Mersey Electric Railway was opened in 1886 as a steam-operated line and recently celebrated its jubilee. Almost at the same time the decision of the L.M.S.R. to electrify the lines of the old Wirral Railway between West Kirby, New Brighton and Birkenhead Park was announced. As the Mersey and the Wirral systems join at Birkenhead Park, the running of through trains from the Wirral termini over the Mersey system to Liverpool, and vice versa, is to be made possible. These services will be shared by the existing Mersey stock and new three-coach articulated sets that are to be provided by the L.M.S.R.

The Mersey Railway use a fourth rail for the return current, but the L.M.S.R. have decided on a running rail return system. The stock of both companies is to be fitted with change-over switches to allow for this. At present Mersey Railway vehicles have no heating apparatus, in view of their running in tunnels for most of their journeys, but this is now being fitted in order to make them suitable for use on through trains.

As a fitting celebration of their jubilee, the Mersey Railway have put into service several new trailer cars. These show a great improvement in comfort over the older vehicles and they are very handsome in appearance. The exteriors are finished with sheet steel panelling. With the introduction of these vehicles, six-car trains are being operated during the rush periods in place of the five-car units previously employed. Alterations at stations have been necessary to allow for this, especially at Liverpool (Central), where the tunnel and platform have been extended.

Luxury Stock for G.W.R. Main Lines

The end-vestibule system of construction that was a feature of the new *"Cornish Riviera Limited"* stock introduced last summer is to be applied to 124 new third-class coaches for use on all main line express services throughout the G.W.R. system. They will be of the side-corridor type with large windows affording an uninterrupted view on each side. The coaches will be built on steel underframes and finished externally with sheet steel panelling.

An Unusual Valve Gear Experiment

The "Walschaerts-Beames" Motion

The illustration shows the L.M.S.R. 4-6-0 locomotive formerly No. 5845 and now No. 25845, fitted with "Walschaerts-Beames" valve motion and temporarily named "Prince of Wales." Photograph by courtesy of the L.M.S.R.

FOR many years the use of inside cylinders in British locomotive practice was almost traditional, and the minimum of external working parts resulted in the invariable neatness of external appearance that characterised our engines for so long. Cylinders of the diameters necessary for the power output then required could be accommodated between the frames, and such designs were invariably steady in running. Another advantage, of special importance in the days before superheating, was that inside cylinders were protected from heat losses occasioned by condensation.

Even when outside cylinders were used, until the present century outside valve motions were rarely fitted, except on special designs. At the present time, the G.W.R. use inside valve gear exclusively for both two-cylinder and four-cylinder engines, and in this respect their practice differs from that of the other three groups.

An outside-cylinder locomotive with inside valve gear is quite usual, but the reverse practice sounds fantastic. There have actually been locomotives with inside cylinders and outside valve gear, however. These were seen on the Western Section of the L.M.S.R. This peculiar feature was not part of their original design. Each of the engines belonged to the "Prince of Wales" class of L.N.W.R. origin, and the modifications, which resulted in their "inside-out" appearance, took place since grouping.

The original L.N.W.R. "*Prince of Wales*" locomotive, No. 819, was turned out of Crewe Works in October 1911, and formed practically a superheated version of the 4–6–0 "Experiment" class then already in service. Larger cylinders with piston valves were fitted, in addition to the superheater, and the short smokebox of the "Experiment" engines became an extended one in the "Prince of Wales" class; apart from their names and numbers this external difference formed practically the only means of distinguishing one class from another. Locomotive work even in those days was a strenuous business, and the "Princes," as they became known, certainly did their share. They were so generally useful, apart from main line express work, that in addition to those built at Crewe 20 were constructed in 1915 by the North British Locomotive Company Ltd., and after the War a further 90 were built by the famous firm of Wm. Beardmore and Company Ltd. At the time of the formation of the L.M.S.R. group the number of "Princes," both Crewe-built and otherwise, was 245.

The moderate length of the engines, together with the short coupled wheelbase, rendered them useful for service on parts of the line where bigger engines could not be run owing to turning difficulties. A "Prince" and tender can be accommodated on a 50 ft. turntable, and is as convenient in this respect as a 4–4–0 engine of ordinary size, such as a "Standard Compound." As the cylinders are inside, the connecting rods necessarily drive on the leading axle. As a result of the "bunched up" design, therefore, a fairly angular position is assumed by the rods when they are on the top or bottom centres respectively. Joy's valve gear is used, as in so many other engines of L.N.W.R. design, and a characteristic of this motion is that part of its movement is derived from the connecting rod itself. The rod is drilled approximately midway along its length in order to accommodate the pin on which the "jack links" are pivoted. This is a source of weakness under heavy stresses, and appears to have contributed to several connecting rod breakages sustained by engines of the class.

As a result of these mishaps the problem presenting itself to Mr. H. P. M. Beames, in charge at Crewe at the time, was how to do away with Joy's valve gear and so eliminate the objectionable pin hole in the connecting rod; and yet operate satisfactorily the piston valves situated above the cylinders. The interesting expedient therefore was adopted of providing an adaptation of Walschaerts valve gear operated from the coupling rod pins in the leading driving wheels, the necessary connections to the inside spindles being made by rocking levers. With respect to the return crank and movement of the expansion link, the valve gear fitted was normal. In order to reproduce the reciprocating motion of the crosshead, which is relied on for an important part of the movement of Walschaerts gear, it was necessary to provide on each side what we may term a dummy connecting rod, working off the leading coupling rod pin and connected at its forward end to the bottom of what is normally the combination lever. In order to clear the whole of the motion satisfactorily and to render it easy of access for oiling and inspection, the footplating of the engines thus altered was raised for a portion of its length.

The plan appears to have met with a certain amount of success, but the number of engines so fitted has never been more than five. Four of these were conversions from the existing "Princes": No. 5632, "*Bret Harte*," the first to be altered; No. 5672, "*Condor*"; No. 5688, "*Tara*"; and the nameless No. 5762. The other, now No. 25845, was built new in 1924 by Wm. Beardmore and Co. Ltd., and was exhibited at the British Empire Exhibition at Wembley in that year.

Building a Railway Footbridge

Erection Operations Without a Crane

By R. D. Gauld, M.Eng., A.M.Inst.C.E.

THE building of such a light structure as a footbridge over the railway presents no great difficulty in handling and placing the material, but gives scope for some scheming to get the work done with the least possible interference with traffic. For a steel footbridge, the usual method of construction would be to put the middle portion of the bridge in position by means of a crane travelling on the rails. The supports and staircases could probably be erected without a crane. Reinforced concrete footbridges have been built similarly, the various portions being cast in moulds in a depot previously, and brought to the site and put in place just like steelwork.

The important feature about the job we are going to describe is that the footbridge was built without the use of a crane. This was possible only on account of the type of design adopted, and could not be used for most designs. The reasons will be explained later. There had previously been a timber footbridge in the same position, but in the course of years the timber had deteriorated considerably, and during a hot, dry summer the timber became very full of cracks. Finally, sparks from an engine set it on fire, and although this was noticed and stopped before it got a good hold, the bridge had to be closed in the interests of safety. As the railway company were obliged to provide a footbridge at this place, a design for a steel one was rapidly put in hand.

While the steelwork was being made, the new concrete foundations were accurately set out and put in to correct spacing and levels. The holding down bolts which would afterwards secure the bridge were cast in the concrete, but were set in tubes, so that they had a bit of freedom in case of any slight discrepancies in the measurements. The steelwork was prepared by one of the contracting firms who specialise in this work, and was loaded up by them, after being carefully inspected to see that it agreed with the drawings.

As the week-day traffic under the bridge is fairly heavy, it was decided that the job would have to be done on a Sunday. A date was then fixed, such that the steelwork would be certain to be ready, and also so that no other jobs in the same neighbourhood on the same day would interfere with the work. An insertion was then made in what is called the "*Fortnightly Notices*," which gives a list of all engineering works on, over, near, and under the line, for the information of drivers and others. Sometimes a speed restriction would be necessary, and if so, this would be described. For the present job this was not necessary, and the Notice simply stated that, between stipulated times, the work would be in hand, "between trains." This means that trains are not interfered with, but at the same time drivers are expected to keep a specially sharp look-out. Arrangements were also made to have look-out men available to give warning of approaching traffic, and if necessary to stop trains by means of detonators and flags, this, of course, being in emergency only. These look-out men are generally platelayers from the length of line concerned, as they best know the local conditions.

Every piece of steelwork for the bridge was given a distinguishing mark with white paint letters and figures before it left the works, the marks being recorded on a copy of the drawing of the structure. This ensured that all the pieces were correctly assembled at the site, so that the bridge fitted together just like a large-sized Meccano model.

Various stages in the building of a footbridge, from the erection of the stanchions to the completion of the span. This was performed without the aid of a crane, as described in this article.

The date and time being fixed, it only remained to arrange to get the material to the job. Luckily, on this occasion, an Engineer's ballast train was booked for the dumping of several wagons of ballast close by, so the two wagons containing the steelwork were sent out by the same train. It arrived at the site of the bridge at 7.55 a.m., and by 8.58 a.m. 12 men and a foreman had unloaded all the steelwork on to the side of the line, and the train went away.

The next step was to erect the columns, or stanchions, as they are called, carrying the lower landings of the staircases. There were four of these on each side, and as they were comparatively light, they were all in position by 9.45 a.m. The nuts of the holding down bolts were just sufficiently screwed down for safety, but not quite tight, in case a slight adjustment was required. The cross bracings for these stanchions were then bolted in place, after which the lower staircases were put in position. These were required to be fixed so as to give some anchorage to the job when the cantilevering started.

The top portions of the upper staircases on the down side of the line were tackled next. Each piece weighed about 6 cwt. and was lifted by means of a very light pole, well guyed to prevent movement, the lifts being made in suitable intervals between trains. Each side of the staircase was put up separately, then the bracings between them were placed. The up side staircases were similarly treated, the two sides being completed just before 3.0 p.m.

The top horizontal portion of the bridge had now to be fixed, and this was done bar by bar, two men standing on the cantilevered portions of the span, and lifting the pieces, which were quite light, by ropes. A little force was required to get the first bar in, as the unavoidable weight of the men on the cantilevered portions caused these to bend down slightly and so reduce the span. However, once the first bar was forced in, the remainder went easily.

The main holding down bolts were now screwed down tightly, the bases of the stanchions afterwards being cased in with concrete. By 4.20 p.m. all the essential portions of the steelwork to enable the bridge to stand safely on its own had been fixed, which completed the work for that Sunday.

On the following days, one or two additional bracings were fixed, also the timber stair treads and the timber deck of the top part of the bridge. The handrails were then put in position, and wire netting was fixed to the insides of the girders to close the large spaces between the parts of the girders. Steel smoke-plates were fastened under the bridge, above each set of rails, to take the blast from the engines and prevent it from damaging the steelwork. Renewing smoke-plates is a much cheaper job than repairing bridge steelwork that has been damaged by blast action.

It will be noticed that in this footbridge the staircases are each in two portions, the top portion on each side turning square to the bottom portion. This has the effect of greatly reducing the length of the top horizontal part, which may then be considered to be a span carried by two cantilevers. It is for this reason that it is possible to adopt the erection method described.

Here we review books of interest and of use to readers of the "M.M." We can supply copies of these books to readers who cannot obtain them through the usual channels. Order from Book Dept., Meccano Limited, Binns Road, Liverpool 13, adding 1/- for postage to the price. Postage on different books varies, but any balance remaining will be refunded.

"The Good New Days"

By Marjorie and C. H. B. Quennell
(Batsford. 6/- net)

The authors of this book are well known for their excellent stories of life in bygone England. In the present volume they deal with the life of to-day, and try to show us how we can progress towards the "Good New Days" that we hope are ahead of us.

They first turn their attention to modern farming, which presents strange contrasts with that of only a few generations ago. Then most of the work was done by hand, but to-day combine harvesters and other machines have transformed the industry, and the coming of the Grid promises to bring electricity within the reach of practically all farmers, even though they live in remote parts of the country. The growth of machinery in ordinary industry is no less remarkable. It has resulted in the introduction of the modern system of mass production. The authors rightly point out defects of the system, but its advantages are so obvious that there is little doubt it will extend, bringing with it greatly increased production, and improved prospects of better times for everybody.

A combine harvester at work, cutting and threshing corn in one operation. (From "The Good New Days," reviewed on this page.)

An interesting section deals with speed and power, and contrasts the slow and uncomfortable coach journeys of 100 years ago with the speedier and more comfortable ways of travel available to-day. The aeroplane of course is responsible for our greatest advances in this respect. It seems likely that even speedier communication will become possible in future, for pioneers are still at work setting up new records for long distance flights, the latest example being the trip to South Africa and back made by Flight Lieut. T. Rose, who on the outward journey reduced the record by more than half a day.

The book is written throughout in the usual easy and familiar style of the Quennells, and is amply illustrated by 101 excellent photographs.

"In Great Waters"

By Capt. S. G. S. McNeil

"Sea-Toll of Our Time"

By R. L. Hadfield
(Philip Allan and Co. Ltd. Each 2/6 net)

These books are included in the Nautilus Library, the volumes of which are devoted to the great literature that has grown up around the sea and those who devote their lives to it. *"In Great Waters"* describes the career of its author, who began as an apprentice in a sailing ship and had experience in vessels of various kinds before finally joining the Cunard Company, in which he rose to the rank of Captain. His life has been full of excitement, and at times danger, and he shows remarkable ability in telling stories of his experiences. A particularly attractive section of the book is taken up with the author's work during the War, when he was in command of mine sweepers during the Gallipoli operations. His stories of the *"Lusitania"* and the *"Mauretania"* also are fascinating, and it is interesting to learn his opinion that the *"Mauretania"* was not faster than the *"Lusitania."* Capt. McNeil had a great affection for the *"Mauretania,"* of which he was in command for many years; and he ends his book with an account of her narrow escape from collision when nearing Southampton on his last voyage, a catastrophe that was only averted by his own quick grasp of a dangerous situation.

"Sea-Toll of Our Time" tells the stories of 24 famous sea tragedies, beginning with the wreck of the P. and O. liner *"Aden,"* lost in 1897 on a reef off the island of Sokotra in a great storm, and ending with the sinking of the *"Vestris"* in the Atlantic Ocean in 1928. The remaining chapters deal with fire at sea, collision, stranding and other causes of great wrecks, and among them is a discussion of one of the greatest mysteries of the sea, the total disappearance of the *"Waratah"* after leaving Durban. Every story is thrilling, and the book will be read with eager interest as a record of heroism in difficult and dangerous circumstances, whether in a doomed vessel, in open boats after a catastrophe, or cast away on barren reefs or lonely islands.

"Workshop Practice"

By F. Johnston Taylor
(Technical Press Ltd. 16/- net)

The practical part of an engineering training can only be taught thoroughly in the workshop, but it is necessary to learn as much as possible of the principles on which it is based, and the purpose of the present volume is to supply this information to young engineers. Measurements, measuring machines and tools, and gauges and gauge systems are dealt with first, and are followed by sections on common workshop tools, bench work and the materials in which the engineer works. The rest of the book is devoted to detailed descriptions of lathes and their accessories, and of the many types of machine now so largely used in engineering workshops. Chapters on drop forging and stamping, and on welding complete this excellent book, which is copiously illustrated.

"Tool Making for the Craft Room"

By C. Howell. (Pitman. 2/-)

In the past beginners in handicrafts have spent much of their time making comparatively useless articles. Mr. Howell believes it is better to make some of the simple tools they need, and for their benefit gives working instructions and drawings, with descriptions of the materials used and the operations involved. A glossary is provided, and additional illustrations show actual tools made by the author's students.

"Junkers and World Aviation"

By Capt. F. A. Fischer v. Poturzyn

This book has been produced to describe and illustrate the work carried on by the well-known Junkers aircraft manufacturing firm. It is an enlarged version of its German original, translated into English by Mr. E. Morley, and we understand that it is being distributed in this country by W. H. Smith and Son Ltd., Strand House, Portugal Street, London, W.2.

In a sense the book may be described as the history of aviation in Germany, for it begins with the pioneer efforts of Hugo Junkers, the founder of the firm, who was at work on problems connected with flight in the early years of the century, and patented the all-wing aeroplane in 1910. This is followed by accounts of the developments that took place during the Great War, when metal construction was introduced, and the progress that was made immediately afterwards, in spite of difficulties imposed on German aviation by the restrictions then in force. Next comes a particularly interesting discussion of the growth of the Junkers system of construction up to the appearance of the Junkers G38, the nearest approach to the all-wing monoplane that has yet been produced. The section ends with a description of the growth of the network of air lines in Central Europe.

The manner in which Junkers aircraft and engines are built is next dealt with. The factories in which this work is carried out have been very carefully designed and laid out to facilitate production, and many tools and testing appliances have been developed in the works themselves in order to suit special requirements. Finally we are told something of the work that is being carried on in all parts of the world with the aid of Junkers machines.

A remarkable feature of the book is the very large number of photographic illustrations of Junkers machines, and of the factory operations by which they are produced. There are no fewer than 62 full-sized plates, many of them including several photographs, and all of very high standard. At the end of the book is a useful section giving photographs and dimensional details of Junkers aero engines and aeroplanes. All who are interested in the development of the aeroplane will find the book of absorbing interest as a record of a firm that has made great contributions to aviation.

A word must be added about the excellent manner in which the translation of the book has been effected. The English version is a faithful rendering of the German text, with correct equivalents for technical terms; and at the same time it has all the merits of a well-written original.

A Junkers Ju 52/3m monoplane. (From "Junkers and World Aviation," reviewed on this page.)

"Sea Scouting and Seamanship for Boys"

By W. Baden-Powell, K.C.
(Brown, Son and Ferguson Ltd. 2/- net)

In a foreword to this book, the Chief Scout informs us that it was written by his brother, under whom he began his own Scouting as a Sea Scout. The author was both a sailor and a boy at heart, and these qualities are reflected in his story of Sea Scouting, for he recognises the need for accurate knowledge of ships, boats and the sea, while remembering that the headquarters of the Sea Scouts can be made up into a jolly waterside camp.

The book is packed full of interesting and exciting information of all kinds. It begins with stories of sea scouting in olden times, and then follow descriptions of various types of ships and boats and directions for handling them in all circumstances. The treatment is very practical and thorough, and the lessons the author has to teach are driven home by means of stories drawn from his own experience. Swimming and rescue work, bends, knots, splices and tackles, and buoys and beacons are dealt with in the final chapters.

Although written for Sea Scouts, and admirably adapted to cover all their needs, the book will be of the greatest value to owners of small yachts and boats who are in need of a practical guide. It is well illustrated by drawings referring to features of importance in the text, and includes coloured plates of flags and buoys.

Junkers Ju 160 Express Air Liner in flight, with the undercarriage retracted. (See above).

"Rockets Through Space"

By P. E. Cleator
(George Allen and Unwin Ltd. 7/6 net)

Now that the use of aeroplanes has made the Earth appear so small to us, it is perhaps only natural that we should begin to look forward to the day when we can travel farther afield to the Moon, or even to Mars and more distant planets. How journeys in space may be accomplished is the subject of this exciting book, which is written by a pioneer in the consideration of the problems of space travel.

The necessary power for a journey through space can only be applied by means of rockets, which are the only power units capable of acting in empty space, and Mr. Cleator traces the development of the rocket from a mere firework into the rocket motor of to-day. This has not achieved any great results, and indeed its design is as yet the subject of pioneer experiments. The author tells the story of what has been done so far, and describes a theoretical rocket ship in which four people could be projected into space and brought back again. This would weigh 40,960 tons and cost £20,000,000.

The possible dangers of journeying through space are not overlooked by Mr. Cleator, who early takes occasion to remark that a safe return from an interplanetary voyage is highly desirable! He considers the risks of being frozen by the intense cold of outer space, of being roasted by the rays of the Sun, and of being shattered by collisions with meteorites, and in all cases shows very ably that the danger is either remote or can be avoided.

In spite of obvious difficulties, all of which are fairly stated, he is convinced that space travel one day will be possible, and if, as Professor A. M. Low suggests in his introduction, "it seems best to prepare ourselves for the delightful thought that interplanetary communication, or even travel, is not wildly impossible," no better way could be found than by reading his book. Photographs and diagrams of rocket motors that have already been constructed, and interesting drawings illustrating the chief features of the author's arguments.

"A Record of the Scientific Work of John Tyndall"

We have received from Mr. H. Young, M.R.I., 16, Causton Road, London, N.6, a copy of a record of the scientific work of John Tyndall, F.R.S., the famous physicist. This record, which should be of great value to students of science, librarians and secretaries of scientific societies and others, has been printed at the Chiswick Press for private circulation. Copies may be obtained from Mr. Young at the cost of 5/- each.

DINK

20

A FASCINATIN

One of the most fascinating of
charming miniatures are unique i
Recently many additions hav
range now available, including
will interest every boy and gi
Many of the Dinky Toy
touches to Hornby Railway
Signals, Road Signs, Motor
use in making up fascinatir
tions of British and fore
vessel the "*Queen Ma*
Navy, all of which c
model dockyards.
Unlimited fun
miniatures either
with some of th
exciting race ga
Every b
this delightfu
All the toys
ately, or
in compl
As
Hornby
list
the
Din

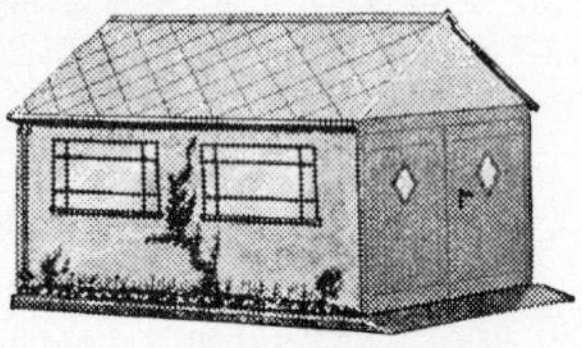

GARAGE
Dinky Toys No. 45
Fitted with opening double doors. Will accommodate any two Dinky Toy Motor Cars.
Price 1/6 each

25F 25B 25D 25C 25E 25A

COMMERCIAL MOTOR VEHICLES
Dinky Toys No. 25
Fitted with detachable rubber tyres and silver-plated radiators

No. 25a	Wagon	each	9d.
No. 25b	Covered Van	,,	9d.
No. 25c	Flat Truck	,,	9d.
No. 25d	Petrol Tank Wagon ...	,,	9d.
No. 25e	Tipping Wagon ...	,,	9d.
No. 25f	Market Gardener's Van	,,	9d.

Price of complete set 4/6

24E 24G 24F 24C 24D 24A 24H 24B

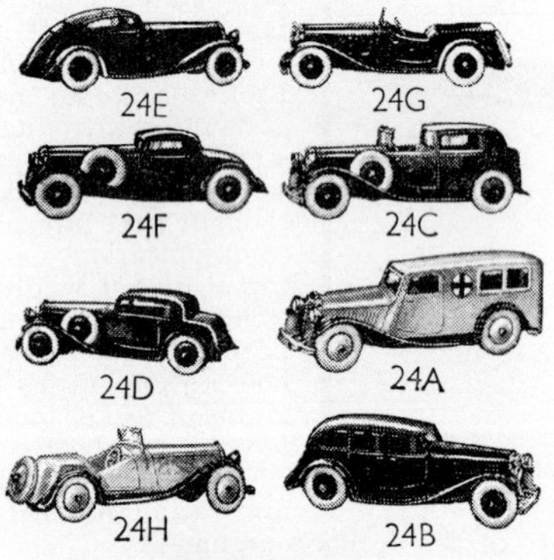

MOTOR CARS
Dinky Toys No. 24
Fitted with detachable rubber tyres and silver-plated radiators

No. 24a	Ambulance	each	9d.
No. 24b	Limousine	,,	9d.
No. 24c	Town Sedan	,,	9d.
No. 24d	Vogue Saloon	,,	9d.
No. 24e	Super Streamline Saloon	,,	9d.
No. 24f	Sportsman's Coupé ...	,,	9d.
No. 24g	Sports Tourer (4 seater)	,,	9d.
No. 24h	Sports Tourer (2 seater)	,,	9d.

Price of complete set 6/-

D.H. "COMET" AEROPLANE
Dinky Toys No. 60g
Scale model of plane used by C. W. A. Scott and T. C. Black in their Australian flight.
Price 6d. each

STREAMLINE SALOON
Dinky Toys No. 22h
Assorted colours. Fitted with rubber tyres.
Price 6d. each

TRAILER
Dinky Toys No. 25g
For use with Dinky Toys No. 25 (Commercial Motor Vehicles.) Fitted with rubber tyres.
Price 7d. each

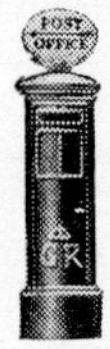

PILLAR LETTER BOX G.P.O.
Dinky Toys No. 12a
Price 3d. each

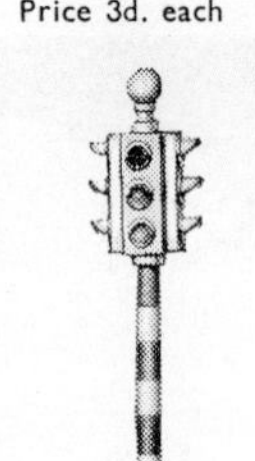

ROBOT TRAFFIC SIGNAL
Dinky Toys No. 47a
(Four-face)
Price 3d. each

ROBOT TRAFFIC SIGNAL
Dinky Toys No. 47b
(Three-face)
Price 3d. each

ROBOT TRAFFIC SIGNAL
Dinky Toys No. 47c
(Two-face)
Right-angle or Back-to-back.
Price 3d. each

R.A.C. HUT, MOTOR CYCLE PATROL AND GUIDES
Dinky Toys No. 43
This set is representative of the familiar personnel and road hut of the R.A.C. Each item is finished in correct colours.

No. 43a	R.A.C. Hut	each	6d.
No. 43b	R.A.C. Motor Cycle Patrol	,,	9d.
No. 43c	R.A.C. Guide directing traffic	,,	3d.
No. 43d	R.A.C. Guide at the salute ...	,,	3d.

Price of complete set 1/9

HALL'S DISTEMPER ADVERTISEMENT
Dinky Toys No. 13
This miniature of a well-known lineside advertisement is intended to be placed in the fields adjoining the railway track. Price 9d. each

STREAMLINE FIRE ENGINE
Dinky Toys No. 25h
Price 9d. each

G.W.R. RAIL CAR
Dinky Toys No. 26
Assorted colours. Price 4d. each

RACING CAR
Dinky Toys No. 23a
Assorted colours. Fitted with detachable rubber tyres. Price 4d. each

30A 30B 30C 30D 30F 30F

MOTOR VEHICLES
Dinky Toys No. 30
Fitted with rubber tyres and silver-plated radiator

No. 30a	Chrysler "Airflow" Saloon	each	9d.
No. 30b	Rolls-Royce Car	,,	9d.
No. 30c	Daimler Car	,,	9d.
No. 30d	Vauxhall Car	,,	9d.
No. 30e	Breakdown Car	,,	9d.
No. 30f	Ambulance (grey and red) ...	,,	9d.

Price of complete set 4/6

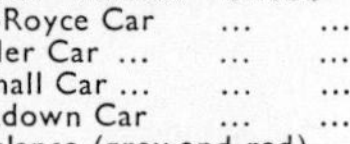

28A 28B 28C

28E 28N 28F

DELIVERY VANS
Dinky Toys No. 28/1

No. 28a	Golden Shred Van ...	each	6d.
No. 28b	Seccotine Van	,,	6d.
No. 28c	Manchester Guardian Van	,,	6d.
No. 28e	Firestone Tyres Van ...	,,	6d.
No. 28f	Palethorpe's Sausage Van	,,	6d.
No. 28n	Atco Lawn Mowers Van	,,	6d.

Price of complete set 3/-

TANK
Dinky Toys No. 22f
Price 9d. each

MOTOR TRUCK
Dinky Toys No. 22c
Assorted colours. Fitted with detachable rubber tyres. Price 6d. each

TRAM CAR
Dinky Toys No. 27
Assorted colours.
Price 3d. each

OF

60E 60D

Dinky Toys N
No. 60a Imp
No. 60b D.H
No. 60c Perc
No. 60d Low
No. 60e Gen
No. 60f Cier
Pr

No. 35a Salo
No. 35b Race
No. 35c "M.
Pr

MECCANO L

TOYS

s

TING HOBBY

:t of Dinky Toy collecting. These uring and perfection of finish. the series, and in the splendid nodels, there are items that

useful for adding finishing thers, such as the Traffic rol Pumps, are ideal for ere are also reproduc- ing Britain's wonder ships of the British realistic effect in

aying with these the floor, and Sports Cars ed. ould start y to-day d separ- btained

and ice of f

A.A. HUT, MOTOR CYCLE PATROL AND GUIDES
Dinky Toys No. 44
Collectors of Dinky Toys will find this new addition to the range of particular interest. Each item is finished in correct colours.

No. 44a	A.A. Hut	each 8d.
No. 44b	A.A. Motor Cycle Patrol ...	„ 9d.
No. 44c	A.A. Guide directing traffic	„ 3d.
No. 44d	A.A. Guide at the salute ...	„ 3d.

Price of complete set 1/11

CARAVAN TRAILER
Dinky Toys No. 30g
For use with the Saloon Cars in Dinky Toys Nos. 24 and 30
Price 6d. each

STREAMLINE TOURER
Dinky Toys No. 22g
Assorted colours. Fitted with rubber tyres.
Price 6d. each

PETROL STATION
Dinky Toys No. 48
Accurate reproduction of a filling station. Tastefully printed in appropriate colours.
Price 1/6 each

STREAMLINE BUS
Dinky Toys No. 29b
Price 6d. each

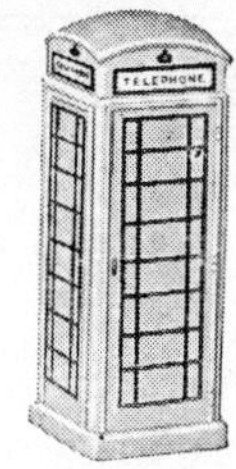

RAILWAY MECHANICAL HORSE AND TRAILER VAN
Dinky Toys No. 33R
Price complete, L.M.S.R., L.N.E.R., G.W.R. or S.R., 1/5

PRODUCT of MECCANO LIMITED LIVERPOOL

HOTCHKISS RACING CAR
Dinky Toys No. 23b
Assorted colours. Fitted with rubber tyres. Price 6d. each

TELEPHONE CALL BOX
Dinky Toys No. 12c
Price 4d. each

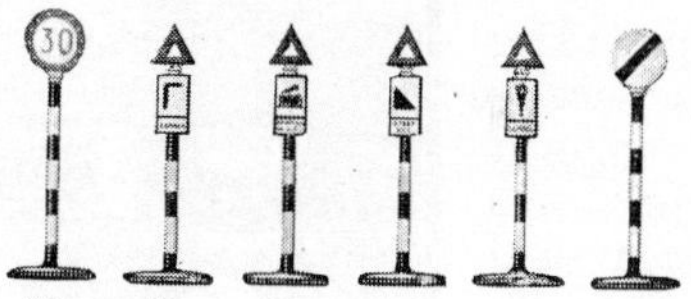

47e 47n 47s 47h 47g 47f
47r 47m 47k 47p 47t 47q 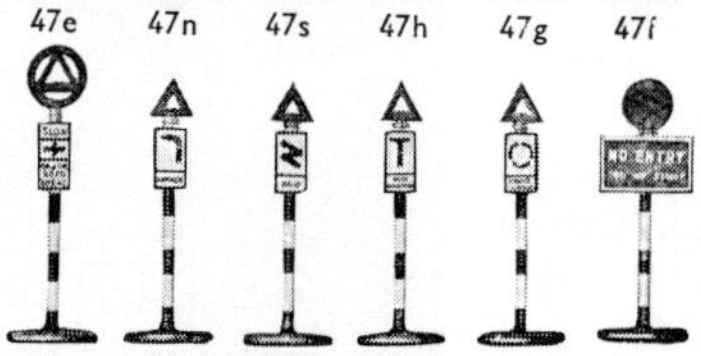

ROAD SIGNS
Dinky Toys No. 47

No. 47e	"30 Mile Limit" Sign ...	2 for 3d.
No. 47f	"De-restriction" Sign ...	„ 3d.
No. 47g	"School" Sign	„ 3d.
No. 47h	"Steep Hill" Sign ...	„ 3d.
No. 47k	"Bend" Sign	„ 3d.
No. 47m	Left-hand "Corner" Sign	„ 3d.
No. 47n	Right-hand "Corner" Sign	„ 3d.
No. 47p	"Road Junction" Sign ...	„ 3d.
No. 47q	"No Entry" Sign ...	„ 3d.
No. 47r	"Major Road Ahead" Sign	„ 3d.
No. 47s	"Crossing, No Gates" Sign	„ 3d.
No. 47t	"Round-About" Sign ...	„ 3d.

Price of complete set of twelve 1/6

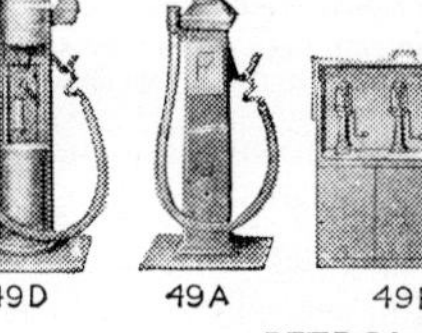
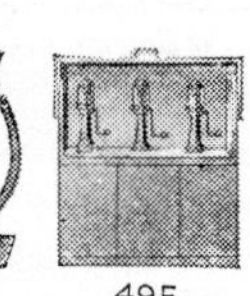
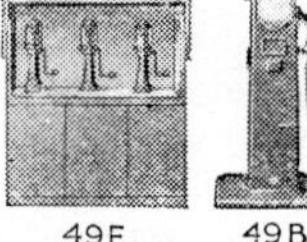

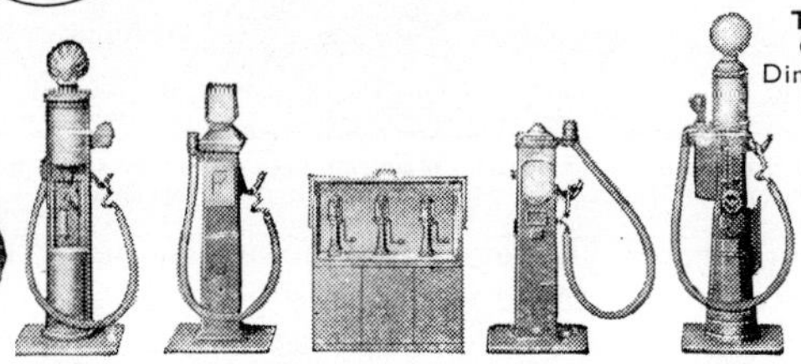

49D 49A 49E 49B 49C

PETROL PUMPS
Dinky Toys No. 49
Scale models fitted with rubber hose pipes. Finished in correct colours.

No. 49a	Bowser Pump	each 4d.
No. 49b	Wayne Pump	„ 4d.
No. 49c	Theo Pump	„ 4d.
No. 49d	Shell Pump	„ 4d.
No. 49e	Oil Bin (Pratts)	„ 3d.

Price of complete set 1/5

PILLAR LETTER BOX AIR MAIL
Dinky Toys No. 12b
Price 3d. each

ROYAL AIR MAIL SERVICE CAR
Dinky Toys No. 34
In correct colours. Fitted with rubber tyres.
Price 6d. each

60C

60B

OPLANES

... each 9d.
... „ 6d.
... „ 6d.
... „ 6d.
... „ 6d.
... „ 6d.

TRACTOR
Dinky Toys No. 22e
Price 9d. each

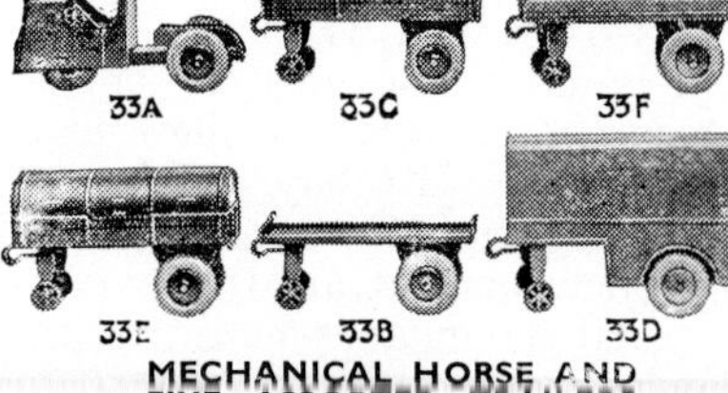

33A 33C 33F

33E 33B 33D

MECHANICAL HORSE AND FIVE ASSORTED TRAILERS
Dinky Toys No. 33
Fitted with rubber tyres

No. 33a	Mechanical Horse ...	each 6d.
No. 33b	Flat Truck	„ 6d.
No. 33c	Open Wagon	„ 6d.
No. 33d	Box Van	„ 8d.
No. 33e	Dust Wagon	„ 8d.
No. 33f	Petrol Tank	„ 8d.

Price of complete set 3/5

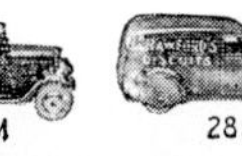

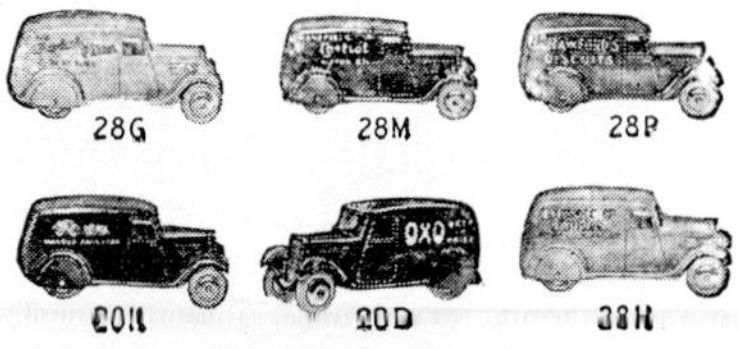

28G 28M 28P

28H 28D 28K

DELIVERY VANS
Dinky Toys No. 28/2

No. 28d	Oxo Van	each 6d.
No. 28g	Kodak Cameras' Van ...	„ 6d.
No. 28h	Dunlop Tyres Van ...	„ 6d.
No. 28k	Marsh and Baxter's Sausage Van	„ 6d.
No. 28m	Wakefield's Castrol Oil Van	„ 6d.
No. 28p	Crawford's Biscuit Van ...	„ 6d.

Price of complete set 3/-

BEACON
Dinky Toys No. 47d
(Realistic models of the Belisha Safety Beacons).
Price 1d. each

MOTOR BUS
Dinky Toys No. 29a
Assorted colours
Price 4d. each

.. each 3d.
.. „ 3d.
.. „ 3d.

VERPOOL 13

Road Construction Machinery

Building Highways for Speedy Traffic

THE coming of the motor car, and the ever-increasing speed and weight of modern motor vehicles, have brought about a revolution in our ideas of road requirements. As the density of traffic on our highways has increased, efforts have been made to cope with the new conditions by widening the existing roads, cutting off dangerous corners and straightening out curves. By-pass roads also have been constructed in order to avoid delays due to the difficulties of negotiating the crowded streets of busy towns and cities. Even these steps have proved insufficient and the construction of new roads has become urgently necessary.

Improvements also have been made in the material of which roads are constructed. The pounding effect of heavy lorries makes it necessary to provide a solid foundation, together with a surface that withstands the wear and tear of continual use, and does not break up, with the formation of pot-holes and cracks into which water can penetrate. Among the materials used for this purpose are tar macadam, asphalt and concrete.

Front view of a road tamping and finishing machine for making concrete roads of any strength or thickness. The illustrations to this article are reproduced by courtesy of Dingler'sche Maschinenfabrik A-G, Zweibrücken.

It will be realised that the construction of adequate roads is a serious problem for the engineer. He must not only consider their actual building, but also must pay attention to the shape of the surface. High crowns must be avoided as far as possible. Excessive slope towards the edges is no longer necessary, since water runs more easily off the prepared road surfaces of to-day than it did off the macadamised roads in use before the motor car became common. Banking also must be provided on the outer edge of curves in order to allow high average speeds to be employed with safety.

The growing use of concrete in making roads is an interesting development, and this material has been used in the construction of famous motor tracks, including that at Brooklands, and of roads for high speed motor traffic in European countries and also in the United States. The first step in making a concrete road is to mix the required proportions of Portland cement, gravel or broken stone, and sand with the necessary water. This is done in a machine and the resulting concrete is placed in position on the prepared foundation of the road and tamped firmly by means of hand rammers to force out the air between its particles. A wooden board placed on edge is then run over the concrete to smooth it down, and is worked about until the shape or profile is satisfactory.

Making concrete roads by this method is comparatively slow and laborious, and a machine that automatically tamps the concrete and gives it the correct profile has now been introduced. This is constructed by the Dingler'sche Maschinenfabrik A-G, Zweibrücken, a German engineering firm. It is available in several sizes to give road surfaces of various widths and can be adapted to the construction of tar macadam roads as well as those of concrete.

The machine is illustrated in the photographs reproduced with this article. It resembles a gantry crane that stretches from one side of the road to the other and travels along on wheels running on rails at the sides. It is driven by an internal combustion engine and its position can be regulated with the utmost accuracy. Concrete is fed into it continuously, and this is tamped and pounded into shape as the machine moves relentlessly forward, the prepared road foundation ahead of it, and behind it a smooth surfaced road that will be ready for traffic when the material has set. The machine was used in building the Avus motor track in Berlin, on which racing cars have been driven at speeds of 180 m.p.h. or more, and is finding employment in finishing the roads making up the great network of motor highways now under construction in Germany.

Tamping the concrete or other material as it is laid is the work of a battery of drop hammers beating vertically on its surface, or of a tamping beam. The hammers vary in weight according to the size of the machine and the purpose to which it is to be put. In one type, designed for making concrete roads of every thickness, they weigh from 120 lb. to 132 lb. In this case the hammers are 4 in. long and 10 in. wide. They fall through a distance that can be varied from $5\frac{1}{2}$ in. to 7 in. and make 70 strokes a minute.

Tamping beams are made of wood, and in some cases have steel or brass hoops screwed on them. Their effect can be increased by adding ballast plates to increase their weight. In certain machines they make as many as 330 strokes a minute, but in others this is reduced to 150 or even as low as 60 strokes per minute, the usual range of fall being 2 in. to $2\frac{3}{4}$ in. Whether drop hammers or tamping beams are used, the concrete is kneaded into the firmest possible mass, and voids in the aggregate are eliminated as far as possible.

As the concrete is poured out on to the road foundation it is spread about and given a preliminary shaping by a levelling beam in front of the tamping mechanism. This beam has an oscillating or to and fro movement across the road. Its stroke is about 4 in. and it makes about 220 movements a minute, pushing any excess of concrete in front of the machine as it beats the material to the desired level. A second levelling beam behind the tamper moves vertically, delivering about 600 blows a minute on the surface and making this more even than is possible by any other means.

The concrete road making machine at work. This view shows the back of the machine, with the rear levelling beam that gives the surface of the road its final shape. Beyond it are the concrete distributors.

The machine is so arranged that it can conveniently be operated from each side. It incorporates mechanism for driving it along the road in the direction in which it is desired to work. The speed of road making of course is governed by that at which concrete is fed into the machine, and with sufficient supplies of this material, a speed of about 6 ft. per minute is reached by the machine for making concrete roads of every thickness, to which reference already has been made. Other machines have different speeds. One concrete finisher for narrow roads suitable for cycling paths has a forward speed of 7 ft. 5 in. per min. and a backward run of 18 ft. 6½ in. per min., and has only one levelling beam.

All the four wheels on which a machine runs are directly driven in order to prevent vibration and twisting of the frame. Comparatively low power is required, and a 4 h.p. benzol motor is incorporated in the concrete finisher for narrow roads, while machines designed for heavier duties are fitted with benzol or crude oil engines of up to 15-16 h.p., according to their size and the speed at which they are required to work.

A stretch of concrete road prepared by a tamping and shaping machine. The rate at which these machines work is about 6 ft. per minute when ample supplies of road making material are available.

The machine can readily be built up or reduced in size to enable roads of various widths to be constructed, and the surfaces of highways of very great width, the whole of which cannot be covered by the machine in use, can be laid down in two or more strips. Rigid kerbs, tramway lines, steel joists or other temporary supports can be used to support the machine, and if a road requires banking at curves a device to enable the change of direction to be made can be fitted. Any camber or shape of road surface can be constructed by using levelling devices of suitable form, and the machine actually has been used to form the lining of the trough of a canal.

One great advantage of the machine is that the tamping and shaping forces are applied exactly at right angles to the unstable concrete. The result of this vertical compression is seen in the absence of corrugations on roads built by it. Irregularities of this kind are practically unavoidable when rollers are used in road making. Newly-laid surfacing material is plastic and unstable. At certain speeds a roller slides along it, and this, together with the vibration, gives rise to ripples or waves in the road. No such effects can occur with the new road making machine, but in order to ensure against them, and also to avoid joints that run straight across the road, and would affect the wheels at both ends of the axle of a fast running motor vehicle, the machine can be assembled along a line inclined at an angle of 25 deg. to the axis of the road. Actually a road built by the machine has few joints in its surface, for the work of laying down the material used is carried on continuously and without interruption.

Slight modifications are necessary when the machine is applied to the building of roads with bituminous surfaces, such as those of asphalt, tar or tarmac. The tamping and levelling beams are then moistened by sprays of water driven on to them by means of compressed air. The nozzles of the spraying device work under a pressure of 45 lb. per sq. in., and the water is broken up into minute droplets that thoroughly damp the necessary surfaces without using an excess of water. A special heating device is necessary in the case of asphalt, and acetylene burners in the tamping unit raise the temperature of the surfaces to from 150 deg. C. to 200 deg. C. in order to prevent the sticky mass from adhering to them.

An adequate supply of material must be provided for the road tamping and finishing machine, for it can only be used economically in large scale work in which there is no interruption to its steady progress along the line of a road. This has led to the introduction into service of a new concrete distributing car, the hopper of which swings out over the road bed and spreads the concrete over it.

These pages are reserved for articles from our readers. Contributions not exceeding 500 words in length are invited on any subject of general interest. These should be written neatly on one side of the paper only, and they may be accompanied by photographs or sketches for use as illustrations. Articles that are published will be paid for at our usual rates. Statements contained in articles submitted for these pages are accepted as being sent in good faith, but the Editor takes no responsibility for their accuracy.

Iraq's Greatest Barrage

A great barrage is now being constructed in Iraq at Kut, the scene of the famous siege during the Great War. It is being built across the Gharraf River, which flows into the Tigris, and I had the good fortune to be present at the laying of the foundation stone of the structure by the King of Iraq, when I obtained the accompanying photograph of the ceremony.

The laying of the foundation stone of the Kut Barrage by the King of Iraq, who is seen lifting mortar with a trowel. Photograph by J. G. Abbood, Baghdad.

The barrage has been built to supply water for irrigation purposes to great areas of land that have lain waste for many centuries, and also to minimise the danger of inundation when the Tigris is in flood. It will be nearly 2,000 ft. in length and 50 ft. in height, and 56 openings in it, each about 20 ft. in width, will be provided with sluice gates for regulating the flow of water. The work is being carried out by Iraqis working under the direction of British engineers, and is expected to be completed in 1938.

J. G. Abbood (Baghdad).

Ince Castle and its Cork Tree

Ince Castle is about four miles from Saltash, and although modernised and without its old moat and drawbridge, is still recognisable as a castle. A small arch at the entrance to its gardens bears the date 1657.

An outstanding feature of this interesting old castle is a cork tree in its gardens that is between 150 and 180 years old. There are very few cork trees in this country, and the climate of course does not permit the bark of the tree to be shaved off periodically, as is done with cork trees in Mediterranean countries.

Ince Castle was one of the last strongholds to surrender in the Civil Wars, when it was captured by a ruse. Ships approached it on the river that flows past it, and the soldiers defending it, fearing a bombardment, withdrew to where is now the castle lawn. A concealed land force then suddenly attacked the unguarded defences and forced an entrance.

J. Darton (Plymouth).

The Smallest House in Great Britain

There are many features of interest in the little old-world town of Conway, in North Wales, and probably the most curious is the tiny dwelling standing on the quay-side of the river. This is claimed to be the smallest house in Great Britain. It is only 5 ft. wide, and although its rooms are very small, they are furnished in the usual way. The door is of normal size.

On the opposite side of the river is a wooden landing stage, to which the river steamers are moored. These are driven by paddle wheels and in appearance reminded me of the *"Comet,"* the pioneer steamship built in 1812 by Henry Bell. At high tide the vessels are left high and dry at their berths.

This house at Conway is claimed to be the smallest in Great Britain. Photograph by J. Thomas, Glasgow.

The bridges across the River Conway are of special interest. The road is carried over the river by a suspension bridge built by Telford during the years 1822-1826. Before its erection travellers had either to be piloted across the shifting sands at low tide, or ferried across the swirling waters when the tide permitted. The up and down main lines of the L.M.S.R. span the river on two tubular bridges that resemble the Britannia Tubular Bridge in design, and another suspension bridge leads the town's water supply across the river. The 13th century castle, the town walls, and several fine old buildings of the Tudor period add to the attractions of this quaint Welsh town.

The presence of Conway Castle at one end of Telford's bridge influenced its design to a certain extent. An effort was made to reproduce the mediæval appearance and character of the Castle, but this was not very successful.

J. Thomas (Glasgow).

A Visit to Gibraltar

Gibraltar has been famous as a fortress for centuries and now is equally well known as a port of call for cruising liners. The great rock rises 1,400 ft. above sea level and is visible for many miles. Half a day usually is allowed for its inspection in the popular cruising itineraries, and although the time is short, the rock provides one of the finest shore excursions imaginable.

When a vessel arrives off Gibraltar, the passengers are taken ashore in steam launches, and a tour of the town can be made in a gharry, or horse cab. Several of these vehicles can be seen in the accompanying illustration. The drive to Europa Point, about three miles from the quay, is full of interest. This Point is the southern tip of the rock and from it one looks out southward across the straits to the African coast. Another interesting excursion, involving a walk of 1½ miles, takes the visitor past the Racecourse, and over the neutral ground connecting Gibraltar with the Spanish mainland, to the Andalusian town of La Linea, which is entered through the Spanish customs station.

A scene in Gibraltar, showing part of the rock and the gharries, or horse cabs, in which tours are made by visitors. Photograph by T. Brooks, Halifax.

Among the greatest attractions in Gibraltar are the galleries excavated within the rock on the west and north sides. These are hewn out of the rock itself and have a total length of more than two miles and are wide enough to allow the passage of a carriage. They formed part of the fortifications designed by military engineers during the 18th century, and the portholes, cut at intervals of 12 yds., were so constructed that men serving the guns in the galleries were safe from the shot of the enemy. The galleries are accessible only to British subjects, who must be provided with a permit before they are admitted. The tour of inspection is made in one direction only and no photographs can be taken on the way. Cameras must be handed in at the entrance, and a messenger takes them down to the exit to await the arrival there of the owners.

Gibraltar has often been attacked. The most memorable siege was that sustained for four years from 1779 to 1783, when the British garrison repelled the efforts by land and sea of combined French and Spanish forces.

T. BROOKS (Halifax).

The Run of the "*Deccan Queen*"

I obtained the accompanying photograph of the "*Deccan Queen*," one of India's fastest and most luxurious expresses, as it was approaching Lonavla station, on the Bhore Ghat. This train runs daily between Bombay and Poona, covering the distance of 119¼ miles in 2 hrs. 45 mins. The down train leaves Bombay at 5.15 p.m., and the up train leaves Poona at 7.40 a.m., both taking the same time to complete the run.

Two special rakes, or set trains, are utilised on this service, one of them being equipped with roller bearings and both being fitted with self-adjusting brakes. Each has a total tare weight of 278 tons and comprises eight coaches, including a restaurant car, made up in three articulated units of three, three and two coaches respectively. Both rakes are finished in royal blue, with gold lining and lettering, and the Great Indian Peninsula Railway coat of arms is carried on each coach.

The electric passenger locomotive shown at the head of the train in the photograph is one of 22 similar units supplied by Metropolitan Vickers Ltd. It has six motors, with a total output of 2,160 h.p., and is capable of a maximum speed of 85 m.p.h., but the greatest allowed is 65 m.p.h. In working order its weight is 102.45 tons, and its length is 53 ft. 6 in.

The "Deccan Queen" approaching Lonavla. This electrically hauled train of the Great Indian Peninsula Railway is one of the fastest expresses in India. Photograph by W. S. Eagle, Bombay.

The down "*Deccan Queen*" has a difficult task when it reaches the hills. Its first stop is made at Karjat, 62 miles from Poona, after a run of 70 mins., and there a halt of 4 mins. is made so that a banking engine may be attached. Gradients of between 1 in 50 and 1 in 37 are then encountered in the Bhore Ghat section, in which the train passes through 26 tunnels and climbs about 1,800 ft. to Lonavla, 236 ft. above sea level. This section is 17¼ miles in length and is traversed in 35 mins., the average speed being 30 m.p.h., but the next 36 miles are covered in 41 mins. without the aid of a banking engine. The up "*Deccan Queen*" of course requires no assistance between Lonavla and Karjat, for it descends the steep slopes of the Bhore Ghat. The service provided by these two fine trains is very popular with Bombay business men, especially at week-ends.

W. S. EAGLE (Bombay).

Two New Meccano E Outfit Models

A Cruising Yacht and a Pile Driver

THIS month we describe a Cruising Yacht and a Universal Pile Driver. The former is particularly handsome in appearance, and the latter is a good example of a realistic working model. Each can be built entirely from the parts included in E Outfit.

The first of the two models represents a popular form of yacht that really is a converted ship's boat. Many vessels of this kind can be seen at various places on our coasts during the summer. The changes necessary for the conversion usually are carried out by amateurs, and the vessels thus produced show wide variations. No standard prototype therefore is available for the model-builder, who is given considerable scope for the expression of his ideas of form and rig.

The model is Bermuda-rigged on each mast and has a small cockpit or well. Its construction is commenced by building up the keel from two 12½" Strips. These are held together by three bolts, two of which also hold together the parts of stands 1 and 2 respectively. These bolts are left slack and must not be tightened until the hull is completed. At the forward end two 2½" small radius Curved Strips are fitted, to the upper ends of which is secured a 2½" Strip 3. Two 2½" large radius Curved Strips are fitted at the after end, and these carry two 1½" Strips 4. Between the Strips 3 and 4 are fitted two curved side members, each of which consists of a 12½" and 5½" Strip over-lapping each other by two holes. These side members are curved so that the widest portion of the hull is at a point 5" from the stern. A ½"×½" Angle Bracket 5 preserves the shape at the stern.

Fig. 1. A typical small Cruising Yacht built with E Outfit.

The sides of the hull can now be filled in with Strip and Flexible Plates. At the bow two 2½"×2½" Flexible Plates are fitted on each side, and their lower edges are clamped between the Strips forming the keel and bow. The edges of the two Plates are clamped together by means of a nut and bolt and two washers 6. A 5½"×2½" Strip Plate is curved to the shape of the next section, shown in Fig. 2, and is secured in place at its lower edge by means of an Obtuse Angle Bracket. The bolts holding this Bracket are shown at 7. A 4½"×2½" Flexible Plate 8 is next clamped at one end by the bolt 9 to the Strip Plate mentioned earlier. At its other end this Plate is secured to a 2½"×1½" Flexible Plate 10, the corner and lower edge of which are clamped between the Curved Strips forming the stern. The construction is repeated on the port side of the model. The ends of the two bolts holding the 1½" Strips 4 together press against each other and the bridge so formed carries the rudder, a Flat Trunnion.

The construction of the cabin is commenced by fitting the 12½" Strips 11. These are secured at their after ends to 2½" small radius Curved Strips 12 that are bolted to the ½"×½" Angle Brackets 13. Two compound strips are built up, each of two 5½" Strips overlapping one hole, and on each side one of these is secured at one end to the Angle Bracket 13 and placed under Strips 11. In this position it is held by means of two Flat Brackets, and the holding bolts for these are indicated at 14 and 14a.

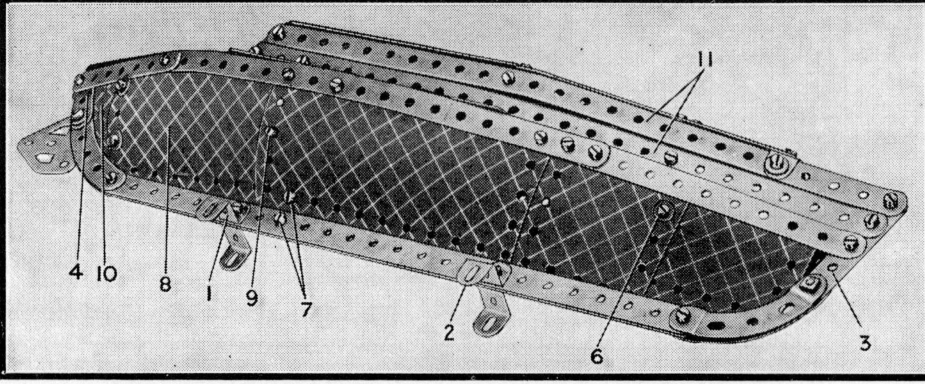

Fig. 2. The hull of the Cruising Yacht, showing how it is built up and its sides are filled in.

Two 2½"×½" Double Angle Strips are next curved slightly to the shape of the top of the cabin, as shown in Fig. 1, and bolted between its two sides. Across these are fitted five 5½" Strips. Three similar Strips are secured to the front Double Angle Strip and the middle one of these 15 overlaps the Strip 16 two holes. Two 3½" Strips 17 are also fitted at this point. Each of the side decks consists of one 2", one 3" and two 3½" Strips, all bolted to ½"×½" Angle Brackets on the hull.

The mizzen mast consists of two 4" Rods joined by a Coupling, and the boom 20 is secured to it by a Swivel Bearing. The main boom is held in place in the same manner. One of these Swivel Bearings is built up from a Small Fork Piece and Collar. The arrangement of the shrouds and halyards is shown in Fig. 1. The sails are cut from stiff white paper, the main and mizzen sails being laced to the masts and booms by continuous lengths of cord.

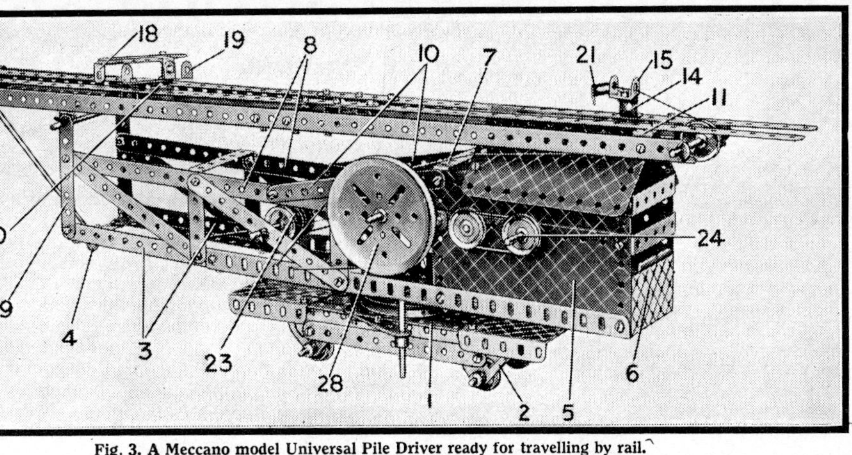

Fig. 3. A Meccano model Universal Pile Driver ready for travelling by rail.

The parts required to build the model Yacht are: 8 of No. 1; 14 of No. 2; 6 of No. 3; 2 of No. 4; 4 of No. 5; 2 of No. 6a; 6 of No. 10; 2 of No. 11; 3 of No. 12; 4 of No. 12c; 1 of No. 13; 2 of No. 15; 3 of No. 15a; 2 of No. 35; 77 of No. 37; 1 of No. 37a; 17 of No. 38; 2 of No. 48a; 1 of No. 59; 2 of No. 62; 1 of No. 63; 2 of No. 90; 4 of No. 90a; 4 of No. 111c; 1 of No. 116a; 4 of No. 125; 1 of No. 126a; 1 of No. 165; 1 of No. 176; 2 of No. 188; 4 of No. 190; 2 of No. 191; 2 of No. 195.

In constructing the second model, a Universal Pile Driver, the travelling base is first built. This consists of a 5½"×2½" Flanged Plate, to each end of which is bolted a 3½"×2½" Flanged Plate. The two latter Plates are connected by means of two 5½" Strips, one of which is shown at 1, Fig. 3. Two Flat Trunnions 2 are fitted to one end of the large Flanged Plate, at the other end of which two Trunnions are held in place by Flat Brackets. These Trunnions and Flat Trunnions are joined together by 5½" Strips and carry 3½" Rods on which the travelling wheels are gripped. Outriggers to prevent the machine from over-turning are fitted to the travelling base as shown.

The base of the superstructure is built up from two 12½" Angle Girders, each of which is extended by two 5½" Strips 3, overlapping one hole. Each pair of 5½" Strips is fitted with an Angle Bracket at its outer end and the two built up angle girders are connected by a 2½" Strip, fitted with a Double Bracket 4. This Double Bracket carries a Threaded Pin, arranged horizontally.

The revolving superstructure turns about a 3" Pulley that is secured to the 12½" Angle Girders by means of two ⅜" Bolts, each of which carries three Washers for spacing purposes. A 2" Rod, gripped in the boss of this Pulley, passes through the centre hole of the 5½"×2½" Flanged Plate of the travelling base, and is held in place by means of a Bush Wheel.

The slides for guiding the pile driving weight consists of four 12½" Strips, joined together in pairs by 2½". Strips. These compound strips are secured to the Double Angle Strips 11 and 12 at their upper and lower ends, and in the centre they are coupled to the frame by means of ½" Reversed Angle Brackets. Near the top a Reversed Angle Bracket 14 is bolted in place, and this forms a support for a Double Bracket 15.

The weight is built up from a 1½"×½" Double Angle Strip, at the bottom of which are bolted a Flat Bracket 16 and two ½"×½" Angle Brackets 17. The opposite end of the Double Angle Strip carries a 2½"×½" Double Angle Strip 18 and Double Bracket 19. A ½" loose Pulley 20 forms the guide and slides between the double compound strips already described. The Angle Bracket 21 engages with the Double Bracket 19 when the weight is being hoisted. When the weight is near the top, the bracket 15 causes these Brackets to slide apart, thus bringing about its release.

The Angle Bracket 21 is tied to a cord 22 that passes under one of the Pulleys 23, and is secured on the Crank Handle 24. The cord 25 for lowering the hammer frame also passes round one of the Pulleys 23, and is secured to a Crank Handle on which the 1" Pulley 26 is mounted. When lowering, the Driving Band 27 is used to connect the Pulley 26 and the Pulley on the Crank Handle 24, Fig. 3.

The duplicated cords for lifting the frame pass first round a Threaded Pin in the Double Bracket 4, and then round one of the Pulleys 23 before being secured to an Anchoring Spring on the Rod carrying the Pulley 28. The opposite end of the Rod carries a Coupling fitted with a ¾" Bolt for a handle, the Coupling being spaced away from the superstructure by a Double Bracket. Counter balance weights must be fitted inside the cab.

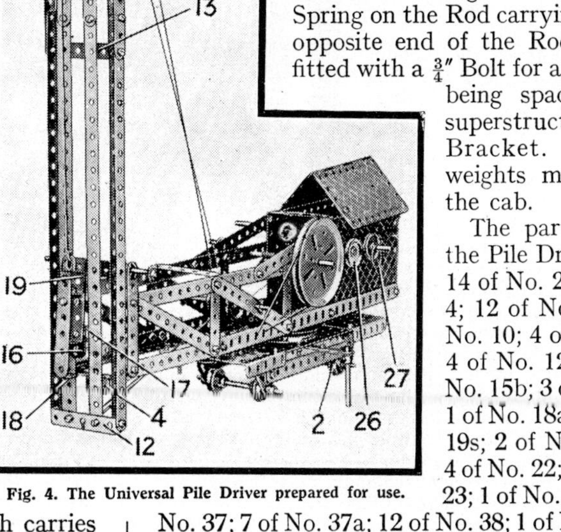

Fig. 4. The Universal Pile Driver prepared for use.

The parts required to build the Pile Driver are: 10 of No. 1; 14 of No. 2; 4 of No. 3; 2 of No. 4; 12 of No. 5; 4 of No. 8; 4 of No. 10; 4 of No. 11; 6 of No. 12; 4 of No. 12c; 1 of No. 15a; 2 of No. 15b; 3 of No. 16; 2 of No. 17; 1 of No. 18a; 1 of No. 19; 1 of No. 19s; 2 of No. 19b; 4 of No. 20b; 4 of No. 22; 2 of No. 22a; 1 of No. 23; 1 of No. 24; 14 of No. 35; 90 of No. 37; 7 of No. 37a; 12 of No. 38; 1 of No. 48; 8 of No. 48a; 1 of No. 51; 1 of No. 52; 2 of No. 53; 4 of No. 59; 2 of No. 62; 1 of No. 63; 1 of No. 111; 5 of No. 111c; 1 of No. 115; 3 of No. 125; 2 of No. 126; 2 of No. 126a; 1 of No. 176; 1 of No. 186; 2 of No. 189; 2 of No. 195; 1 of No. 198.

Meccano Suggestions Section

Edited by "Spanner"

(347)—Bendix Pinion for Self-Starter (E. Jones, Cardiff)

It is not very long since motor car engines had to be started by the laborious process of turning a crank handle, and some of the old cars required a great deal of manual effort in order to set the engine going. The practice of fitting self-starters to cars is now almost universal. The engine starts almost instantaneously at the touch of a button, and the driver of a present-day vehicle does not require the reserves of strength and patience once called for!

A small electric motor is generally employed for driving the engine until it fires and starts running under its own power. The usual practice is to arrange the motor so that a small pinion on the armature shaft can be brought into engagement with teeth cut in the flywheel of the engine. Reduction gear provides a powerful drive for turning the engine crankshaft, which is rotated at a comparatively slow speed. The starter motor therefore would be driven at very high speed when the engine comes to life, and would soon be ruined, if some automatic device were not fitted to disengage the driving pinion.

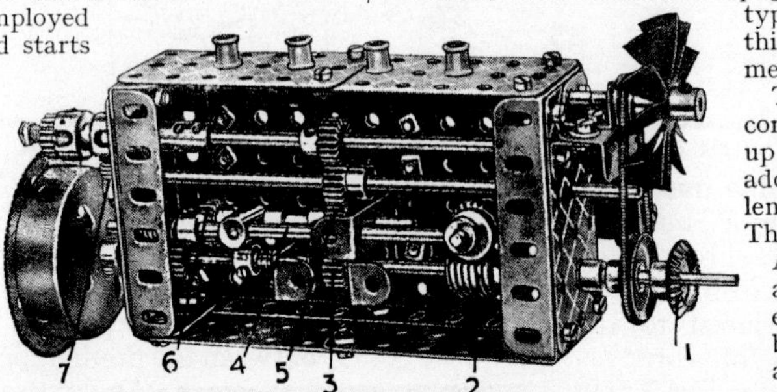

Fig. 347

The mechanism that is used for this purpose is known as the Bendix Pinion, and automatically uncouples the motor as soon as the Pinion is driven faster than the armature shaft. The principle of operation of the Bendix drive will be understood from the model illustrated in Fig. 347, in which the Bendix Pinion and the flywheel are driven alternately to show the automatic disengaging of the Pinion.

The Bevel Gear 1 is driven from a Clockwork or Electric Motor, and the Worm 2 and Pinion 3 are carried on the same Rod as the Bevel. The Worm drives a Pinion on a transverse Rod that carries a cam formed from the Kemex Universal Stand Clamp (Part No. K31). The end of the Rod 4 bears against the cam, the Rod being slidable in its bearings and fitted with a Compression Spring to keep it in constant engagement with the cam. A Coupling on this Rod controls the sliding movement of the Rod fitted with Pinions 5 and 6. The Pinion 5 is shown in engagement with another Pinion driving a further similar Pinion on the Rod of the Bendix Pinion. When the cam slides the Rod 4 to the left, the Pinion 5 is disengaged, and Pinion 6 is brought into mesh with a Pinion on the Rod of the flywheel.

A $2''$ Screwed Rod carries the Bendix Pinion and is attached to a $5''$ Rod by means of a Threaded Coupling. Locknuts are fixed on the end of the Screwed Rod to serve as a stop for the Pinion, which is fitted in a Socket Coupling. The other end of the Coupling carries a Threaded Boss, and a weight 7, consisting of a Collar and four Washers, is fixed to the Socket Coupling by a $\frac{1}{2}''$ Bolt.

This weight prevents the Pinion from rotating on its rod, and it will be clear that as the Screwed Rod is rotated in the Bendix Pinion unit it causes the Pinion to move into engagement with the $2\frac{1}{2}''$ Gear of the flywheel. This drives the flywheel, and in actual practice starts up the engine. The starting of the "engine" is achieved in the model when the Pinion 6 engages the Pinion on the flywheel shaft. When the flywheel spins round it causes the Bendix Pinion to rotate faster than the Screwed Rod carrying it, thus screwing it along the Rod until it disengages the gear. At this stage the Pinion 5 no longer drives the Shaft of the Bendix Pinion, which remains out of engagement until the flywheel stops after the withdrawal of Pinion 6. The drive is then once more transferred to the uppermost Rod.

In the illustration one of the side Plates is removed from the mechanism casing. When the Plate is in position the casing somewhat resembles a motor car engine, and a Fan is fitted and driven by Spring Cord from the driving shaft to improve the effect.

(348)—Automatic Reversing Gear (L. Keith, Edinburgh)

In constructing models of lifts, cranes, cable railways, etc., it is often desirable to incorporate a mechanism that will give a periodic reversal of the movement of the model. A drive that is reversed automatically is necessary also in many models demonstrating mechanical movements. A neat automatic gear change device is incorporated in the demonstration model of the Bendix Pinion, illustrated on this page, and in Fig. 348 is shown another type of automatic gear change, in this case for producing reversing movement.

The framework in this example consists of $7\frac{1}{2}''$ Angle Girders built up in the form of a square, with two additional Angle Girders of similar length inserted between opposite sides. The latter Girders support two $2\frac{1}{2}''$ Angle Girders bolted in the fifth and the eighth holes from the upper ends of the $7\frac{1}{2}''$ Girders. They are bolted beneath the longer Girders and the upper one has a Flat Trunnion bolted to it to serve as a bearing for a $4\frac{1}{2}''$ Rod. A $2\frac{1}{2}'' \times \frac{1}{2}''$ Double Angle Strip is placed parallel to the upper $2\frac{1}{2}''$ Angle Girder and directly above it, being fixed in position by a Flat Trunnion at each end.

A $2''$ Rod is journalled between the $2\frac{1}{2}''$ Angle Girder and the Double Angle Strip, and carries a $\frac{1}{2}''$ Pinion secured on the Rod between its two bearings. Above the Double Angle Strip is a $\frac{1}{4}''$ throw Eccentric, the purpose of which will be described later.

The $4\frac{1}{2}''$ Rod already mentioned is carried at one end in a Flat Trunnion and at the other end in a Trunnion bolted to the outer edge of the frame of the mechanism. It should be noted that at all points where a Rod is journalled in a hole, a Crank or Double Arm Crank is fitted to form a reinforced bearing. The $4\frac{1}{2}''$ Rod carries a Worm that is in constant engagement with the $\frac{1}{2}''$ Pinion on the Rod of the Eccentric. A $\frac{1}{2}''$ Pinion on the $4\frac{1}{2}''$ Rod engages with a $1\frac{1}{2}''$ Contrate Wheel on a Rod journalled in the second $2\frac{1}{2}''$ Angle Girder, and driven from the source of power, an Electric Motor or similar unit.

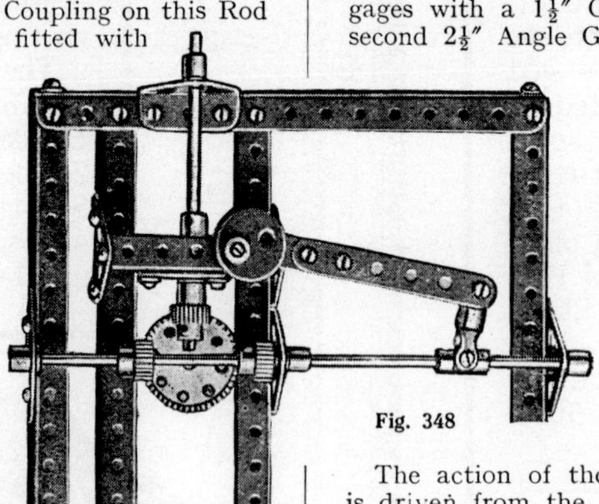

Fig. 348

Across the face of the Contrate Whee is another Rod so arranged that it is free to slide in bearings built up from Flat Trunnions and Cranks. This Rod is provided with two $\frac{1}{2}''$ Pinions that are brought alternately into engagement with the $1\frac{1}{2}''$ Contrate Wheel by means of the Eccentric, that is coupled to the Rod by a $3''$ Strip and Swivel Bearing. The Strip is connected rigidly to the Swivel Bearing by a Pivot Bolt and Collar, the "spider" of the Swivel Bearing being free on the Rod. It is prevented from moving laterally by means of two Collars.

The action of the model will now be seen. As the Contrate is driven from the Motor, it rotates one of the Pinions on the sliding shaft, and also slowly rotates the Eccentric through the third Pinion engaging with it, and through the Worm and Pinion. The Eccentric causes alternate Pinions on the sliding Rod to engage with the Contrate, thus reversing the direction of rotation of the Rod.

The positions of the Pinions on the Sliding Rod determine the period of rotation in each direction and the amount of dwell before reversal takes place. By varying these positions the driven Rod can be made to rotate for equal periods in each direction, or it can be caused to rotate for a very brief period in one direction and then to run in the reverse direction for a comparatively long period. The rotation also can be reversed instantly or after a pause.

It will be clear that if a Pinion of $\frac{1}{2}''$ face is substituted for one of the $\frac{1}{4}''$ face Pinions the period of rotation for one direction can be considerably increased. With this arrangement the reverse movement would have to be very brief unless a large Eccentric is used to give a longer throw.

(349)—Gearless Reduction Drive (L. C. Pudney, Gloucester)

Friction drives generally create a great deal of interest among Meccano enthusiasts. It is possible to obtain gear ratios that are variable within very fine limits by using friction gearing, and an unusual application of friction drive transmission is shown in Fig. 349. In this case it will be found that adjustments can be made to vary the ratio from about 25 : 1 to 150 : 1, or to even a greater extent.

The rod carrying the handwheel is the driving rod, the driven rod being fitted with the Sprocket. If a Motor is used for driving, the handwheel can be replaced by a suitable Gear. A Wheel Flange is carried on the driven shaft, and has a $1\frac{1}{2}''$ Strip bolted across its centre hole to keep the Rod central. This allows the wheel Flange to wobble about on the Rod, but it is prevented from rotating by a Threaded Pin carried in a Bush Wheel. On the inside of the Wheel Flange is a Collar fixed on the Rod to space the Flange away from the Flanged Plate serving as a bearing.

Fig. 349

A $\frac{1}{2}''$ loose Pulley is free to turn on a $\frac{3}{8}''$ Bolt fixed in a Coupling. The Coupling is attached as shown by a further Coupling to the driving Rod, and two more Couplings are arranged in a similar manner to maintain correct balance when the driving Rod is rotated. A Compression Spring on the driving Rod causes the $\frac{1}{2}''$ Pulley to bear against the Wheel Flange, pressing it into contact with the back Plate. In this way the Wheel Flange wobbles on its Rod as the $\frac{1}{2}''$ Pulley moves round the rim. The circular path made by the Wheel Flange on the back Plate is of smaller diameter than the Wheel Flange itself, and it is the difference in size of these two circles that governs the gear ratios.

By spacing the Wheel Flange farther from the back Plate, the diameter of the path followed by the rim of the Flange is decreased, resulting in a decrease in the gear ratio. Washers can be used for spacing purposes.

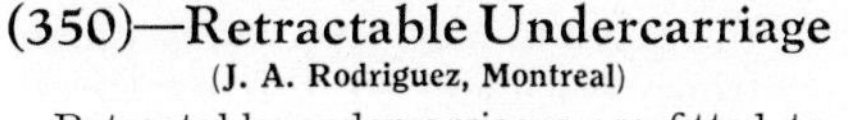

(350)—Retractable Undercarriage

(J. A. Rodriguez, Montreal)

Retractable undercarriages are fitted to many modern aeroplanes. The old style of undercarriage with exposed wheels offers considerable wind resistance, resulting in a decrease in the speed and efficiency of the aeroplane. The first step to minimise the drag of the undercarriage was to fit streamlined fairings over the wheels. This is still common practice, but there is an increasing tendency to design undercarriages that can be folded away out of the airstream. In some cases the undercarriage Vee struts are swung outwards so that the wheels fit neatly into recesses beneath the wings, and in others they are folded back into the engine nacelles, when the engines are fitted on the lower wings.

In the model illustrated (Fig. 350), the front legs 2 are pivoted on $\frac{1}{2}''$ bolts attached to Threaded Bosses that move along Screwed Rods 1. The rear legs 3 are pivoted to a $2\frac{1}{2}''\times\frac{1}{2}''$ Double Angle Strip by means of Pivot Bolts. The legs 2 are secured to the Axle Rod of the landing wheels, but the legs 3 are free of the Rod.

In the position shown the undercarriage is lowered ready for landing. The Screwed Rods 1 are geared together by two 57-teeth gears and a $\frac{1}{2}''$ Pinion, and cause the legs 2 to move towards the legs 3 thus raising the wheels to fit into the fuselage.

A similar mechanism can be applied to wheels that draw up into the engine nacelles, but side movement of the Vee struts must be prevented.

Fig. 350

(351)—Bell Striker or Clock Escapement (J. Tompkins, Birmingham)

The device shown in Fig. 351 was originally designed as a mechanism for striking the bell of an alarm clock, but it can be used also for a clock escapement. When used as a bell striker the Rod 2 can be provided with a Collar to serve as a hammer, or the Rod itself can be used as a striker according to requirements.

Two $1''\times\frac{1}{2}''$ Angle Brackets 3 are attached by Angle Brackets to the ends of a $2\frac{1}{2}''$ Curved Strip and engage $1\frac{1}{2}''$ Strips on a Face Plate. A Flat Trunnion and a Double Arm Crank are bolted to the Curved Strip, the Rod 1 being fixed in the boss of the Crank to serve as a pivot for the striker. When the Face Plate is rotated the $1\frac{1}{2}''$ Strips strike the Brackets 3 causing the striker 2 to oscilate to and fro. If the Face Plate is driven by a Motor the striker vibrates rapidly. The direction of rotation of the Face Plate must be anti-clockwise, and stops must be provided to limit the movement of the Rod 2.

If used as a clock escapement the device can be inverted and the Rod 2 and Flat Trunnion dispensed with. A suitable fork would then be suspended from the Rod 1 to engage the pendulum of the clock. This would be made from two 1″ Rods in a Coupling fitted to the lower end of a Rod suspended from the Rod 1, or the Coupling may be attached direct to the Rod 2 according to requirements.

Miscellaneous Suggestions

Under this heading "Spanner" replies to readers who submit interesting suggestions regarding new Meccano models or movements that he is unable to deal with more fully elsewhere. On occasion he offers comments and technical criticisms that, he trusts, will be accepted in the same spirit of mutual help in which they are advanced.

(M.188.) Autoflex Drive. Belt transmission in Meccano invariably presents the problem of how to avoid slip, just as in actual practice engineers are faced with the difficulty of reducing slip to a minimum. The device known as the Autoflex Drive illustrated in the January issue of the "*M.M.*" has inspired two readers (J. Gerrard, Hardhillock by Drummoak, Kincardineshire and R. McKears, Derby) to try this form of drive transmission for preventing belt slip in models.

The idea put forward by J. Gerrard is to fix two Face Plates together by 1″ Screwed Rods, carefully lining up the bosses and fitting them on the driven Rod. A 57-teeth gear is secured on the Rod between the two Face Plates, and a $\frac{1}{2}''$ Pinion meshing with the Gear is carried on a $1\frac{1}{2}''$ Rod journalled in the Face Plates. A Pulley on this Rod is driven by Cord from the power unit, and the tendency of the Pinion to ride round the Gear keeps the driving belt taut, automatically increasing the tension on the belt as the load increases.

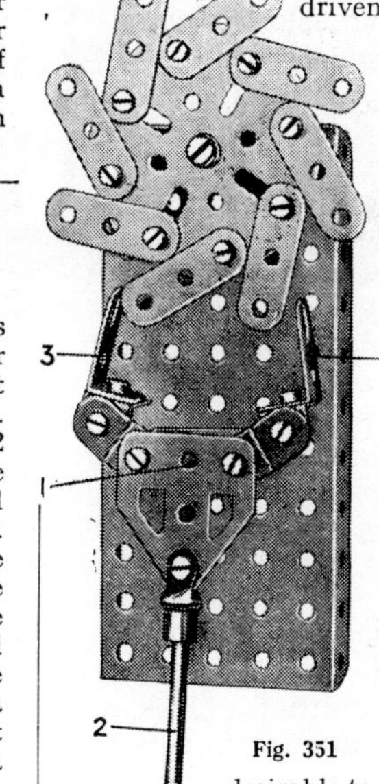
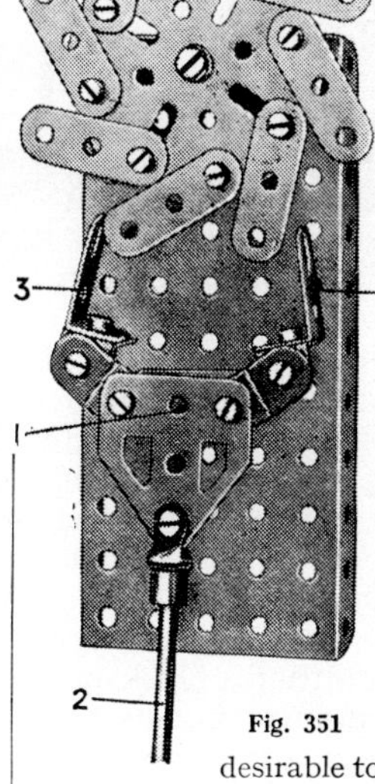

Fig. 351

An alternative arrangement proposed by the same contributor is to use a Coupling instead of two Face Plates, the two Rods being inserted in the end transverse holes. A $\frac{1}{2}''$ Pinion replaces the 52-teeth Gear.

(M.189.) Brake Control Lock. With a strap-and-lever brake it is often desirable to lock the brake lever in position to maintain a certain tension on the brake band, and thus to give a constant retarding effort on the brake drum. The necessity for locking a lever in position is not confined to brake mechanisms only, however, for it occurs in many instances in model-building, especially in gear-box construction. The control lever of a gear-box must be held in definite positions for the gears to remain in or out of engagement as required.

The proposal put forward by A. Coyne (Edwinstowe, Notts.) can be applied in most cases where it is desired to lock a lever in any position, and finer control is obtained with this device than in the case when a toothed quadrant is used for the lever. A sliding Rod is connected to the end of the lever which is then controlled by a push-pull movement, and bearings for the Rod are made from a Double Bent Strip attached to a Strip or to the framework of the model. A Spring Clip is fitted on the Rod between the Double Bent Strip and the frame, Washers preventing lateral movement of the Clip. As the Rod slides in its bearings it must also slide in the Spring Clip, which grips it firmly in any set position.

In Search of New Models

Building Miniature Workshops

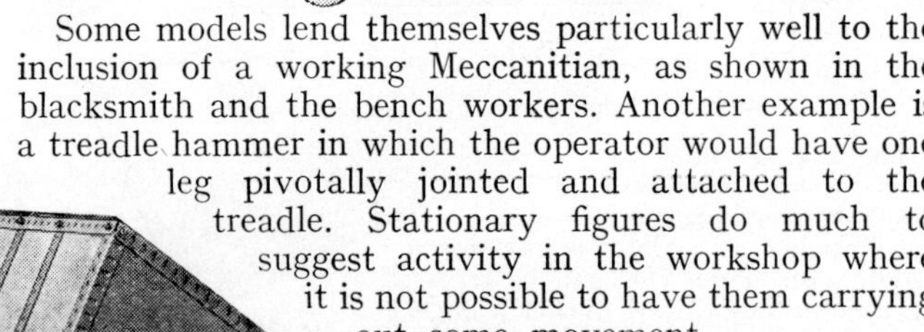

WORKSHOPS offer many possibilities for interesting models, and appeal just as much to the possessors of small Outfits as to those who have many parts at their disposal, for they may range from small models containing two or three machines to accurate reproductions of large fully-equipped shops. The model may be of a woodworking shop or an engineering workshop, the latter being the more interesting for a Meccano model. There are many different types of machine used in an engineering shop, and if they are reproduced on a fairly small scale, quite a large number can be incorporated in a model and driven from overhead shafting in a businesslike manner. To complete the model a roof can be provided as shown in Fig. 1.

The models shown on these pages will give an idea of the scope that is offered by these fascinating subjects. Complete workshops are shown in Figs. 1 and 2, and on close examination they will be found to differ in many respects. The first one is covered with a roof and comprises a dial press, a punching press, a drilling machine, a lathe and grinding wheels. The models are of fairly elaborate design, and are all driven from the overhead shafting carried in bearings beneath the roof. An Electric Motor provides the power for all the machines.

Fig. 1. A complete Workshop with power drive from shafting.

The lower model is of simpler construction, the machines being somewhat smaller and incorporating less detail. In this case there is a drilling machine, a lathe and a grinder, and in addition a blacksmith's forge and a work bench. The chief interest in this model lies in the small figures of engineers that are hard at work on their respective jobs. On the left one can be seen at a drilling machine, and in the centre is a lathe operator. Of the two figures behind the lathe one holds a part on the anvil while the other, the "smith," brings down his hammer with vigour. One of the bench workers is using a hack saw and the other a hammer, both of them being driven from the shafting.

Fig. 2. In this Workshop Meccanitians carry out different operations.

By adding figures such as these, a model of any workshop is made much more interesting and lifelike, for we have yet to see the workshop in which all the machines operate unattended. Small Meccanitians require only a few parts in their construction, short Strips being used for this purpose with a 1" loose Pulley for the head, the four holes in these Pulleys producing a strange likeness to a face. The models in Figs. 3 and 4 show figures built on these lines working at a drilling machine and lathe respectively. On these models there is no need for any movement to be made by the figures, the models only being driven.

Some models lend themselves particularly well to the inclusion of a working Meccanitian, as shown in the blacksmith and the bench workers. Another example is a treadle hammer in which the operator would have one leg pivotally jointed and attached to the treadle. Stationary figures do much to suggest activity in the workshop where it is not possible to have them carrying out some movement.

Equipment varies for engineering shops according to the work they carry out. A lathe and a drilling machine will be found in almost every workshop, however, and good examples of small models of these subjects are illustrated. Quite a simple lathe is illustrated in Fig. 4, the drive in this case being taken from a Pulley on the overhead shaft to a Cone Pulley on the lathe. Those who wish to build a more elaborate lathe might make one on the lines of that shown in Fig. 1. This is of the type known as a gap-bed lathe, the bed being deeper at the face plate end so that it can take work of larger diameter than can be accommodated over the bed proper. The model shown is provided with a Face Plate, and to make it more interesting a small part can be fixed in suitable clamps to represent the work being turned.

Planing machines often form part of the equipment of large engineering shops, and are easily made on a small scale in Meccano. If possible they should be provided with a quick-return motion for the work table in order to conform to actual practice, but on very small models it may be preferable to have a simple reciprocating movement imparted by a Bush Wheel and a connecting rod. This form of drive is used in the model Vertical Milling Machine illustrated (Fig. 5). The work table slides to and fro beneath the milling tool, and a small piece of wood has been cut to represent the work in this model. A coat of aluminium paint makes it look like bright steel that is being cut down by the tool.

Quite a large variety of model subjects suitable for including in a workshop are shown in the Meccano Manuals. Among this large range are examples for almost every Outfit, and, of course, the constructor need not build these exactly as shown, but can incorporate his own ideas and in many cases add a Meccanitian to provide a note of realism. The machines available for modelling include punching presses, band saws and saw benches

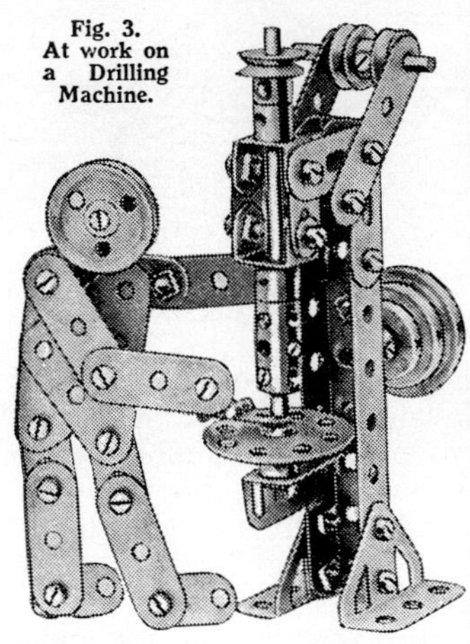

Fig. 3. At work on a Drilling Machine.

employing circular saws, mechanical hammers and stamping machines. A power hacksaw too is a useful machine tool, generally to be found in well-equipped shops.

In addition to the actual machines in the workshop a number of accessories will be required if it is to conform to actual practice. For instance, trucks are very necessary for moving parts about the shop, and an example of a small flat truck suitable for use in a model workshop is shown at the head of the opposite page. The small figure handling the truck adds to the effect. Larger trucks can be made, and in actual practice it is not uncommon for electric trucks to be used in workshops.

There is another type of truck that is generally to be found in engineering workshops. This is a truck used for handling heavy work so that it can be easily placed in position on the machines. The platform of the truck can be raised or lowered so that parts placed on it can be brought to the level of the machine and then transferred from the truck to the machine, or vice versa, with minimum difficulty. The Bale Lifter shown in the F-L Instruction Manual is of this type of truck.

Where the loads are too heavy for handling in this manner cranes are necessary, and these may range in size from small portable cranes, operated manually, to large gantries driven by electric motors. Where gantry cranes are employed in a building they are often arranged to run on rails high up above the machines. The usual procedure is to mount the rails against the walls along the sides of the building, and the gantry running on these rails is provided with another set of rails so that the crane trolley can move from side to side of the building. In this way the entire floor space can be covered by the crane. Such cranes as these are used only when particularly heavy loads are being handled.

Fig. 4. The Lathe Operator sets to work.

The drive to the different models is one of the most interesting parts of the construction of a workshop model. In real workshops the general practice is to mount electric motors in any convenient position for driving overhead shafts, and pulleys on these shafts are connected by belts to the machines. In most cases flat belts are used and two pulleys are arranged together, one being free and the other fixed. By sliding the belt from one pulley to the other a machine can be set in motion or stopped without interfering with other machines driven from the shafts.

The model-builder will desire his model to be complete in every detail and will arrange shafting for the machines. The many Pulleys in the Meccano range make it possible to drive several machines at different speeds from one shaft. If slip occurs with cord driving, Spring Cord can be used instead, and another alternative is to use Sprocket Wheels and Chain. Although chain is rarely used for driving the actual machines in this manner, it is very useful for models and suggests the wide belts used in actual practice. Whatever form of drive is used for the machine it is advisable to employ Sprocket Chain between the Motor and overhead shaft, and as a powerful drive is necessary if a number of models are connected to the one shaft a fairly large reduction ratio should be incorporated between the Motor driving shaft and the overhead shafting for the machines.

The arrangement of the overhead shafting must naturally be governed by the disposition of the machines in the model. In fixing these to the base board the position to be occupied by the driving shaft must be considered so that no difficulties arise later when this is mounted in position. Bearings for the overhead shaft can be suspended from the roof or can be carried on supports secured down to the base board. Shafting Standards (Nos. **177** and **178**) are specially designed for such use, and can be obtained in two different sizes.

In some cases machines are made as self-contained units with the motor incorporated in the machine. This practice is not easily carried out with small Meccano models owing to the size of the Motors, but the new *Magic* Motor is very suitable for incorporating in small models. The Motor is very compact and is intended primarily for use in models made with the small Outfits.

Another accessory that can be added to a model for making it more attractive is an electric lamp for illuminating the work table. The Meccano Lighting Set is available for this purpose, and the small lanterns can be used as inspection lamps as well as for mounting in suitable positions to illuminate the entire workshop. Another use for the Lighting Set occurs in the blacksmith's forge, in which red paper can be crumpled up and made to represent the fire. When a light is placed beneath it glows like a real fire.

Models made on such a small scale cannot be applied to any useful work, but a great deal of pleasure can be had from them when shaping operations are carried out on soft material such as wax. A piece of wax candle can be placed between centres on the lathe and turned like a table leg, or even made into a crankshaft. When fitted in a planing machine the wax can be shaved down to give a smooth flat surface. Fretwork drills or small twist drills can be used in a drilling machine, and a 5/32" drill fits accurately in a Coupling that serves admirably for a chuck. In this way miniature engineering parts can be made from wax as the real parts are produced on actual machines.

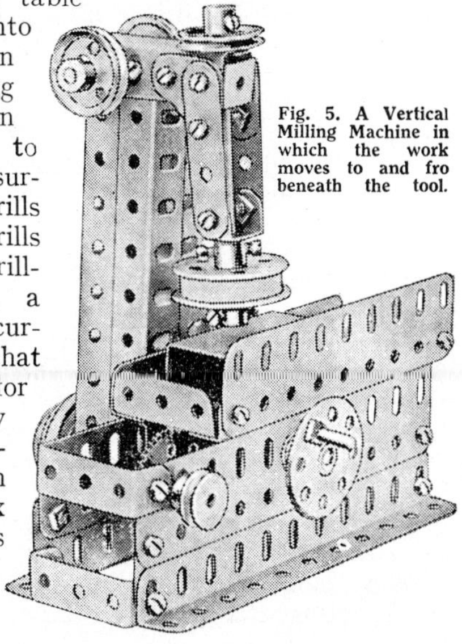

Fig. 5. A Vertical Milling Machine in which the work moves to and fro beneath the tool.

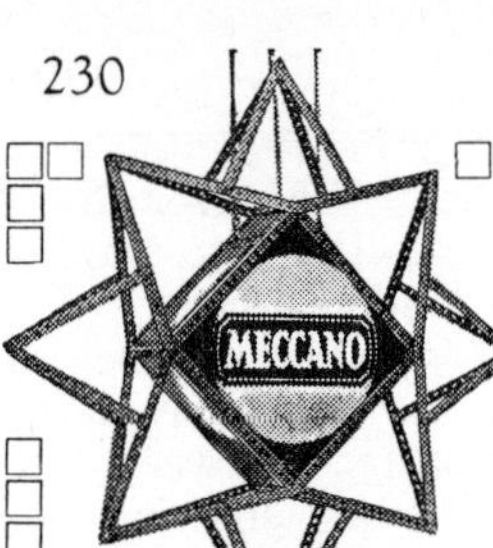

Models for Club Exhibition

Suggestions for Attractive Displays

EXHIBITIONS are important events on the calendars of all progressive Meccano Clubs. They are of great value as a means of adding to club funds, and of gaining favourable publicity that often results in the introduction of new members. A successful Exhibition increases the local prestige of a Club, but if it is to have the desired results it must be well organised, the co-operation of all members being called for to carry out the preliminary work necessary to ensure that it justifies its name. Visitors expect to see really interesting exhibits, and it is essential that they must not be disappointed.

Fig. 1. A fine model of the "Queen Mary."

The first consideration is to have a selection of attractive models to show the work done by the Club in this important branch of its activities. It is not essential that these should be large in order to achieve their purpose. Well-designed models of carefully chosen subjects built with medium-sized Outfits can be just as fascinating as large ones, and simple models made by the younger members are always appreciated on their merits. Visitors generally like to know the name and age of the builders, and this information should be neatly printed on a card attached to each model.

Working models generally have a stronger appeal than those in which there is no movement, but this does not mean that stationary models should be barred entirely. Such models can often be made more attractive by the introduction of electric lighting effects; in fact, the possibilities of illuminating any model should not be overlooked, as lights add brightness to a display.

Fig. 2. Three popular fairground attractions.

Two excellent designs for hanging lanterns appear at the head of this page. They are fitted with electric bulbs and "Meccano" transparencies, and it is a good idea to hang a lantern made on similar lines over the entrance to the exhibition. The transparencies for this should be appropriately lettered with the name of the club, and the word "Exhibition." By leaving the lanterns open underneath, as in the one shown on the right above, they can be used ef ec ively as lamp shades on the electric lights. The transparencies can be made on tracing linen or on a suitable grade of translucent paper.

Many models can be given an attractive appearance by inserting transparencies in suitable positions and placing lighted lamps behind them. A good example is shown in Fig. 4. Another refinement that could be effected with this model would be to place small bulbs on the rotating arms or on the Aeroplanes. To do this low-voltage bulbs must be used, and current for them should be picked up from a slip ring. A Meccano Transformer of course is the most convenient means of supplying the current for small bulbs.

A large model of the *"Queen Mary"* is shown in Fig. 1, and in this case lamps fitted inside the model add considerably to the beauty of its appearance. It is built approximately to scale, and many small details of the original are reproduced. In order to give an impression of the immense size of the *"Queen Mary"* two small tugs of scale size are placed alongside the model. Little details such as these help to make the models more fascinating. Other good ship models that could be used for exhibition purposes have recently appeared on the *New Models* pages of the *"M.M."*

An excellent plan for displaying model ships to advantage is to place them in a reproduction of a harbour or dock system. Docks can be made of wood and painted, and can then be provided with models of the usual machinery and equipment for the handling of cargoes. The principal items in such a layout are cranes, and small trucks and lorries can be added. Bridges may be incorporated and these should be of the opening type so as not to obstruct shipping. Such bridges may be made to work automatically for opening and closing continuously.

The Tower Bridge is shown in model form in Fig. 3. This could be used in a dock system for carrying a road over a busy waterway. An Electric Motor operates the bascules, raising and lowering them continuously. On models such as this, representing a definite prototype, the proportions of the original should be maintained, and as far as possible the models should be built to scale. The chief features should be reproduced, together with as much of the small detail work as the size will allow. Small models naturally offer less scope for the reproduction of the finer details than large models, and in these correct proportioning must be relied upon to identify the structure.

Dinky Toys can be used on the bridges to strike a note of realism. Alternatively the bridges may form part of a railway system, and clubs having a Hornby Railway section are able to combine Meccano and Hornby Train displays with excellent effect. Sidings may be laid on the dock system mentioned above, and there is a choice of a large range of bridge types for carrying the line over rivers and roads. Other ways for combining Meccano and Hornby Trains will readily suggest themselves. Models can be built of any of the engineering structures of a real railway, including wagon tippers, locomotive coaling plants, and cranes of many types. A steam shovel may be set in surroundings to represent excavation work and a train of wagons arranged to take away excavated material. Another model suitable for use with a railway is the Ship Coaler, which may be fed by coal wagons from the Railway System. The super model Travelling Bucket Dredger can be made to load up wagons, with loose material such as gravel, and in a miniature railway goods yard cranes for loading and unloading operations, motor lorries and small electric trucks can be included.

Fig. 3.
The famous Tower Bridge as an attractive model.

Amusing models are a welcome variation from the more serious engineering structures, and have the advantage that they generally require fewer parts. Some of the very simple models of this kind shown in the Manuals for small Outfits, especially the small figures that exhibit weird movements when carrying out different operations, never fail to cause laughter. Suitable models in the Manuals show Wrestlers, Acrobats, Gymnasts, and Horsemen in various attitudes. Animals as model subjects invariably attract attention owing to their unusual character, and as a rule their strange appearance has a humorous appeal.

A fascinating model of fairground attractions is shown in Fig. 2. On the left is a Roundabout, with horses and other peculiar animals and birds. Next to it is a representation of the thrilling form of amusement known as "The Whip," the cars being hauled along by a chain and swung rapidly round a wheel at each end of the platform. The model of the Ark on the right rocks from end to end, and as it does so strange animals poke their heads out of the windows. These are mounted on Springs and in some cases provided with a Spring for a neck so that they move about in a lifelike manner. One Electric Motor drives all three models by means of Sprocket Chain.

Many other fairground attractions make good subjects for models. They need not be elaborate to be effective as it is the movement of these subjects that makes them so fascinating. There are a number of varieties of roundabout, some having animals, others cars, and many having a combination of both. The animals can be made to jump up and down, and the cars to revolve. Cake Walks are well known and are easy to build. They may be provided with small figures, perhaps Dinky Toys, mounted on springs to give them movement when the model operates.

A section can be set apart for Aeroplanes built with the Aeroplane Constructor Outfits. These models can be used in conjunction with Meccano as in the example illustrated in Fig. 4, in which the Aeroplanes are shown suspended from universally jointed Rods. As the upper structure rotates, the models "fly" round in a large circle, swinging outward as the speed increases. The connections to the Aeroplanes must be made secure to prevent them from becoming detached and causing damage, and the speed should not be allowed to rise too high.

Models of this nature are often driven through Worm gearing, but if this form of drive is used a free wheel or friction clutch must be incorporated to prevent damage to the gearing when the Motor is stopped, for the inertia of the rotating structure causes it to over-run the motor when the latter is switched off.

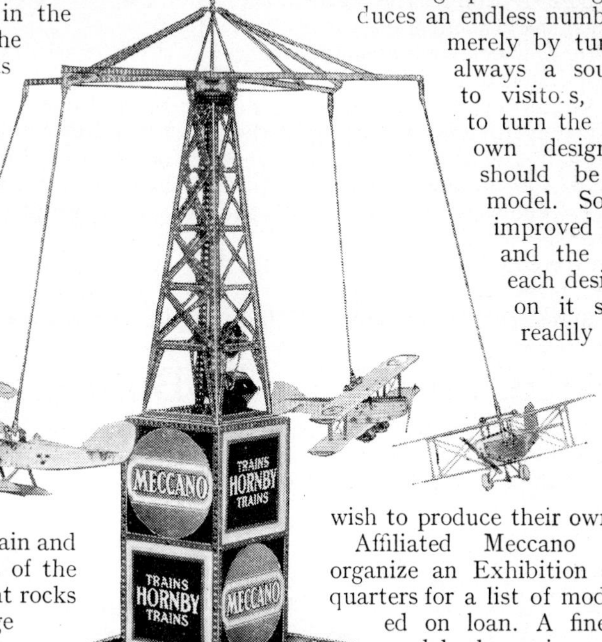

Fig. 4.
Revolving Aeroplanes on an illuminated base.

One of the most popular models at Exhibitions is the Meccanograph. This ingenious mechanism produces an endless number of attractive designs merely by turning a handle, and is always a source of great pleasure to visitors, who may be allowed to turn the handle and make their own designs. Specimen designs should be exhibited with the model. Some of them can be improved by artistic colouring and the formula for producing each design should be indicated on it so that a visitor can readily make any one he wishes. The Meccanograph can be a useful means of increasing funds by making a small charge, say one penny, to visitors who wish to produce their own design.

Affiliated Meccano Clubs proposing to organize an Exhibition should write to Headquarters for a list of models that can be obtained on loan. A fine selection of working models always is available and a revised list with attractive new models has just been prepared. The only expense incurred by a Club obtaining one of these models on loan is that of return carriage. Most of the models are supplied with a high-voltage motor for direct connection to the mains supply, but in certain cases 6-volt Motors can be installed when mains current is not available. The models can then be operated from an accumulator.

With the concentrated efforts of members, and this useful assistance from Headquarters, a successful Exhibition is assured.

Meccano Model-Building Competitions

A Clock Mechanism Problem

When a real engineer builds a machine he tries to obtain the results he desires with as few and as simple parts as possible, and this is often the greatest part of his problem, especially when even a single unnecessary part would greatly increase the cost of manufacturing the machine. It was with this object in mind that the peculiar clock mechanism shown on this page was designed. The interesting feature of this mechansm is that it enables the same speed ratio to be obtained with only two gears as is ordinarily obtained with four gears, and on account of its ingenious nature it has been selected to form the basis of one of this month's model-building competitions.

A range of fine prizes is offered for the most ingeniously designed reproduction, using only Meccano parts, of the mechanism. This consists of two gear wheels X and Y. The former has 12 teeth that are bent at right angles, in a similar manner to those of a Meccano Contrate Wheel, and the minute hand is attached to its shaft. Within it is a second gear wheel Y, which has 11 teeth and is mounted on an eccentric Z, which is pivoted on a shaft carrying also the hour hand. The two shafts of course are concentric, and one could be a tube or sleeve enclosing the other. The gear wheel Y is prevented from rotating by the rod W, which is attached to it, and at its lower end moves up and down in a slot in the framework carrying the entire mechanism. This framework is not shown in the diagram.

As the shaft on which the eccentric is pivoted rotates, the gear Y is not rotated, owing to the action of the rod W, but instead is lifted upward and then allowed to fall. As it does so its teeth are withdrawn from the spaces between the teeth of the gear X, and in each case engage with the next space. The gear X therefore is rotated, and with the tooth arrangement shown, its speed and that of its shaft carrying the minute hand is 12 times that of the first shaft.

X

Y

Z

W

The gear that forms the basis of the "Clock Mechanism" Competition.

In entering the contest it should be clearly understood that only two gears built up from Strips, Angle Brackets or other Meccano parts must be used in reproducing the mechanism. Any number of parts, however, may be used in making a suitable framework.

Competitors need only send either a good drawing or a photograph of the model; the actual model is not required. Competitors are advised to prepare a description of their mechanisms and enclose it with the photograph or drawing.

There will be one section only and competitors of all ages, living in any part of the world are eligible. Entries should be addressed to "Clock Mechanism" Contest, Meccano Ltd., Binns Road, Liverpool 13, and must be posted to reach Liverpool on or before 30th June, 1936. The prizes to be awarded for the most ingenious entries received are listed in the panel at the foot of this page.

Photographs or drawings of models that win prizes become the property of Meccano Ltd., but unsuccessful entries will be returned to the senders provided that a stamped addressed envelope of the necessary size is enclosed for that purpose.

"Small Outfits" Model-Building Competition

This competition provides readers who possess only small Outfits with a chance to win a prize of Meccano products and thereby increase their stock of parts. The contest is open to competitors of all ages living in any part of the world, and there are no fees to pay or forms to fill in. Competitors may choose whatever subject they like for their models, but the models must be built with an Outfit not larger than an F or one of the old No. 3 Outfits. Readers who possess larger Outfits than these may take part in the Contest provided that their models do not contain any parts not included in an F or No. 3 Outfit. Competitors may use Clockwork or Electric Motors to drive their models if necessary.

It is far more difficult to build a good model with a small Outfit than it is when one is allowed to use an unlimited number of parts, and competitors therefore should take care to choose a good subject and then reproduce it as neatly as possible. The fine prizes to be awarded for the most interesting models received are listed in the accompanying panel.

The Prizes

"Clock Mechanism" Contest

The prizes to be awarded in this Contest are as follows:

1st, Meccano Products value £3/3/-.
2nd, Meccano Products value £2/2/-.
3rd, Meccano Products value £1/1/-.
Five Prizes of Meccano Products value 10/6.
Five Prizes of Meccano Products value 5/-.

"Small Outfits" Contest

The prizes to be awarded in each section of this Competition are:

1st, Meccano Products value £2/2/-.
2nd, Meccano Products value £1/1/-.
3rd, Meccano Products value 10/6.
Ten Prizes of Products value 5/-.
Certificates of Merit will also be awarded in each section.

An example of the kind of models that will win prizes in this Contest is the fine miniature motor-cycle and sidecar illustrated on the opposite page. This model is built from an Outfit C with the addition of a Magic Motor, and it won a prize in direct competition with larger models.

It should be noted that it is not necessary to send the actual model. A photograph or a good drawing is suitable.

Entries will be divided into two sections: A for competitors living in the British Isles, and B for competitors living Overseas. Entries should be addressed to "Small Outfits" Contest, Meccano Ltd., Binns Road, Liverpool 13, and those for Section A must reach Liverpool before 30th May, 1936. Overseas closing date, 31st July, 1936.

Model-Building Contest Results

By Frank Hornby

Ingenious Work by Overseas Competitors

"Autumn" Competition (Overseas)

The awards in the Overseas Section of the "Autumn" Model-Building Competition are as follows:

1st, Meccano Products value £3/3/–: E. Aronsan, Hedmora, Sweden. 2nd, Products value £2/2/–: H. Stapleton, Wanganui, New Zealand. 3rd, Products value £1/1/–: D. Thomas, Victoria, B.C., Canada.

Products value 10/6: D. Graham, Edmonton, Alberta; W. Bladergroen, Amsterdam; F. Dressler, Breslau, Germany; V. Boned Gil, Barcelona; G. Bosch, Wyk-Maestricht, Holland.

Products value 5/–: E. Lipkin, Johannesburgh; T. Bates, Jamaica; J. Van Vollenhoven, Bussum, Holland; F. Ling, Halifax, N.S., Canada; D. McLeod, Natal, S. Africa.

Competitors in *"M.M."* competitions are constantly being advised to make their models as simple as possible, and to avoid using a lot of unnecessary parts, which only make a model complicated and detract from its appearance. The model that won First Prize in the "Autumn" Contest testifies to the soundness of this advice, for it owes its success almost entirely to its simple construction. The model, a motor-cycle and sidecar, is illustrated on this page. It is built with Outfit C and is driven by a Meccano Magic Motor, which forms the main part of the frame of the cycle. The drive is taken by means of a Rubber Driving Band to a 1" fast Pulley on the axle of the rear wheel, and the Motor thus drives the model along the ground in a realistic manner. The body of the sidecar is made from two Flanged Sector Plates and a $1\frac{1}{2}" \times 2\frac{1}{2}"$ Flanged Plate, and Flexible Plates are used for filling-in purposes. In my opinion the model, which was built by E. Aronsan, is a very fine piece of work for such a small Outfit and well deserves the prize it was awarded.

A large dragline is the subject of the model submitted by H. Stapleton, which was awarded Second Prize. The jib is sturdily built from Strips, and at its lower end rests on a ball race made from two 3" Pulley Wheels with Steel Balls interposed between them. The jib carries the operating cords to the end of which the drag-bucket is attached, and the power of the E1 Electric Motor that drives the model is distributed by means of a gear-box, which has controls for bringing the various movements of the machine into operation as required.

On page 106 of the February 1931 *"M.M."* is illustrated a locomotive fitted with a crane. This locomotive was chosen by D. Thomas as the subject for his entry in this Contest. I have compared the photograph that Thomas submitted with the *"M.M."* illustration, and apart from one or two minor points there is little to criticise adversely. In the model the driving wheels are eight 3" Pulleys coupled together by means of Strips, and to the cylinders by a Rod. The crane is made from Angle Girders and Plates and swivels on a ball race built up in a similar manner to that used in Stapleton's model dragline already mentioned, and is mounted on the tops of the water tanks of the locomotive.

Among the winners of Meccano Products value 10/6 I was attracted by a model seismograph by W. F. Bladergroen. This competitor has made several successful seismographs in the past and won a prize for a model of this kind in a previous contest. The present model is excellently constructed, and is so delicately adjusted that it is sufficiently sensitive to register the vibrations produced when a person walks across a room in which it is located.

A fine wool carding and condensing machine built by A. Ledent, Ruplemonde, Belgium.

This neat motor-cycle and sidecar built by E. Aronsan, won First Prize in the "Autumn" Contest.

"September" Competition (Overseas)

The prizes were awarded to the competitors named in the following list:

1st, Meccano Products value £3/3/–: A. Ledent, Ruplemonde, Belgium. 2nd, Products value £2/2/–: K. van Dommelen, Antwerp. 3rd, Products value £1/1/–: J. Wicht, Buenos Aires.

Goods value 10/6: J. Reade, New Zealand; R. Kett, Melbourne; E. Driver, Auckland; D. Uullicla, Calcutta; J. Ancell, Christchurch, New Zealand.

Goods value 5/–: R. Latimer, Rangoon; E. Azzopardi, Sliema, Malta; A. Butcher, Canterbury, New Zealand; J. Capelli, Buenos Aires; D. Murison, Buenos Aires.

The First Prize entry in this Contest is the model wool carding machine illustrated on this page. Machines of this kind are used in the wool industry for combing out the raw material and straightening the fibres, which are then condensed or twisted together to form rough thread. The model was built by A. Ledent and works as follows. The raw wool is fed into a box-like structure on the left-hand side of the model. From there it is taken up by fluted rollers and conveyed into the machine, where it is subjected to the combing action of a number of stiff wire brushes that revolve at high speed inside a large drum. From the drum the wool is fed between grooved rollers, which serve the purpose of separating and twisting the short fibres into the form of coarse thread, which is then collected on a spindle. Readers who are interested in textile machinery should refer to page 178 of the March 1935 *"M.M.,"* in which are described several other models of this kind.

A large model of a universal excavating machine won Second Prize for K. van Dommelen. The model found favour with the competition judges not because of its huge proportions or the amount of work attached to its construction, but because Dommelen has paid great attention to details and neat workmanship. The model reproduces a bucket type excavator, and runs on Hornby Rails. The upper structure is mounted on a Meccano Roller Bearing, and a truck loaded with ballast travels along it to balance the weight of the bucket arm as it is raised or lowered.

A model of the French liner *"Normandie,"* which incidentally is the first really good model of this ship that has yet been submitted for a model-building competition, was entered by J. Wicht and won Third Prize. Apart from generally neat construction there is little out of the ordinary in the model. The hull is 7 ft. in length, and the height of the model from water line to upper deck is 11 in.

Among the models that won the smaller prizes is a reproduction of H.M.S. *"Leith."* It was entered by E. Driver, and is built with only simple parts. If Driver had taken a little more care over the rigging and deck work of the model I feel sure he would have received one of the larger prizes.

The model sent by R. Kett is interesting, but it would have been more suitable for a "Realism" Contest. The photograph submitted shows a model steam-navvy at work in a sand pit, and the whole scene is remarkably realistic. The model is quite well built, but the good work done in the making of realistic surroundings did not count in an ordinary model-building contest.

Snape M.C.—The club continues to make good progress and the membership is steadily increasing. Mr. Reeve, the local schoolmaster, recently asked the club to provide a model for use in a school play. His request was complied with enthusiastically, and a model worthy of the occasion was constructed. Boxing, Table Tennis and other games are played occasionally as a diversion from model-building. During the winter a cup of cocoa was given to each member at the close of meetings, and this was much appreciated. Ambitious plans are being made with a view to making the club programme even more attractive. A Table Tennis Tournament is to be held. Club roll: 22. *Secretary:* W. Mayhew, "Sandpit Cottage," Snape, Saxmundham, Suffolk.

St. Stephens (Saltash) M.C.—Variety has been introduced into some of the Model-building Evenings by fixing a time limit for the construction of a particular type of model. It has been found that this not only makes model-building very exciting by speeding it up, but enables the latter part of the meetings to be spent in interesting games or discussions. At one meeting the outstanding model was a crane 3 ft. in length and operated by a Meccano No. 2 Motor. A large model of a bridge is being built with the club stock of Strips, Flat Plates and Angle Girders. The Model-building Section now possess a Tool Set, and they are busy making three cabinets for the storage of the club's Meccano and Hornby stock and other model-building materials. A miniature Goods Depot and a Terminus Station 7 ft. in length will be made when the cabinets are completed. Club roll: 16. *Secretary:* B. Braund, 9, Horner Park, Saltash.

Burnley Grammar School M.C.—Several exciting club Competitions have been held. In one of them the competitors were required to build original models in which every angle had to be a right-angle; and in another models had to be constructed with Wheels, Collars, Axle Rods and Couplings. On another occasion the competitors were given certain Meccano parts and asked to produce the best model they could in half an hour. The results of these contests have often been surprising, and have revealed remarkable ingenuity on the part of the model-builders concerned. An interesting visit has been paid to the factory of Morris and Wilkinson Ltd., Burnley, where the various processes by which "Beatall" metal ware are produced were shown and explained to the party. The tour lasted three hours, and was afterwards voted one of the best outings the club has had. Club roll: 22. *Secretary:* J. S. Keighley, Grammar School, Burnley.

Claremont Avenue School (Kenton) M.C.—Members have been busily engaged in printing posters and making drawings for the club Exhibition. Attractive Dinky Toy and Hornby layouts have been planned, and an effort is being made to devise many novel Meccano models for the occasion, so that the display will be a really outstanding one. Club roll: 14. *Secretary:* G. Furton, 5, Brookfield Crescent, Kenton.

Plymouth M.C.—A special service was held in memory of the late King, and the St. Stephens (Saltash) M.C. accepted an invitation to attend. A talk on the "*Flying Flea*" has been given by Mr. Dingle, the Leader of the St. Stephens club, and was much appreciated. The coxswain of the Plymouth life-boat, an express engine driver who has retired, and other interesting local people have consented to give talks in the near future. When the Meccano Section recently chose "Heath Robinson" railway models as a subject for model-building they not only created a novel change from ordinary models, but became involved in an amusing and very wordy controversy with the Hornby Section. The latter Section continue to provide excellent layouts and track operations, and their persistent clamour for more rails is gradually being satisfied. A Motor Car Section has been formed for the benefit of members who possess Meccano Motor Car Outfits, and is making rapid progress. A lantern lecture has been arranged. Club roll: 70. *Secretary:* R. G. Symons, 47, Lisson Grove, Mutley, Plymouth.

Dagenham M.C.—Mr. Baker, the President, attended the opening meeting last session and addressed the club. Outstanding models built at recent meetings have been a Traction Engine and a Big Wheel. Games and discussions are very popular. Arrangements are being made for a tea party. Club roll: 12. *Secretary:* J. Robinson, 17, Freshwater Road, Dagenham, Essex.

St. James' (Grimsby) M.C.—Members recently built a large model of a derricking crane. It had a four-movement remote controlled gear-box, and was operated by a steam engine. Great enjoyment was derived from working the crane, and many interesting operations were carried out before it was reluctantly dismantled. D. Allen has been busy repainting the club's old Meccano Parts, and future models will therefore look very attractive. Two new members have been enrolled and have added their Meccano Outfits to the club stock, which now contains a very large range of Parts. A visit has been paid to the Standard Ice and Cold Storage Company, Grimsby. The party was received by Mr. Yarworth who, as guide, made their tour of the factory most interesting and informative. Club roll: 6. *Secretary:* Alan N. Dixon, 65, Yarborough Road, Grimsby.

A group of officials of the Zagazig (Egypt) M.C., which was affiliated in October 1935. The President of the club is Mr. R. Mansour, who is seated on the left, and next to him is Mr. R. S. Yousif, Vice-President. The officials standing are (from left to right): Mr. A. M. Mangourie, Leader; Mr. A. Y. Auble, Secretary, and Mr. I. A. Ashmawy, Auditor.

Wheelwright Grammar School (Dewsbury) M.C.—A lantern lecture describing "*A Visit to Bournville Works*," the slides for which were kindly loaned by Cadbury Bros. Ltd., was greatly enjoyed. The models built for a recent club Exhibition were supplemented by some kindly loaned by Bickers Ltd., of Dewsbury. At this event a conjuring display was given by a member of the school, and proved very popular. A visit to Dewsbury Gasworks has been arranged. Club roll: 14. *Secretary:* D. G. Thackrah, 2, Highroyd, Northfields, Dewsbury, Yorks.

Well Hall and District M.C.—Cycling and Photographic Sections have been formed, and seem likely to be very popular. The establishing of a club library is under consideration, and each member has been invited to contribute a few books to form the basis of the library. A suggestion that a summer camp should be held this year has been received with enthusiasm. Club roll: 8. *Secretary:* E. Quinton, 48, Beaconsfield Road, Mottingham, Kent.

Gate House School (Ingatestone) M.C.—A successful Exhibition has been held in the club-room, and the models displayed included cranes, tractors and a jazz band. Short plays were given, and other attractions were a Waxwork Show and a Fretwork Display. The event was rounded off by an excellent supper. Saturday afternoon meetings have been devoted either to Model-building, Boxing bouts or short Walks. There have been more indoor meetings than usual owing to the wet weather frequently preventing outdoor sports. *Secretary:* E. Bull, Gate House School, Ingatestone.

St. Giles Cathedral (Edinburgh) M.C.—Speakers at the monthly services have included Mr. Ernest Brown, Minister of Labour, and Mr. Herbert Reid, the well-known author of stories for boys. Important additions have been made to the club's large stock of Meccano. A visit to the Scottish Motor Show at Glasgow was much enjoyed, and provided some useful ideas for future Model-building Evenings. Signal frames are being made for the club's Hornby layout. A recent Parent's Night was well attended, and 145 members, parents and friends were present. Club roll: 180. *Secretary:* D. Ashbrook, "Neantana," Corbiehill Road, Edinburgh 4.

Holy Trinity (Barnsbury) M.C.—Members are very busy preparing for an Exhibition, and every endeavour is being made to ensure that it shall surpass all previous events of its kind. A successful concert has been held. Club roll: 34. *Secretary:* H. C. Boys, 12, Stonefield Mansions, Cloudesley Square, Barnsbury, London.

Regent St. Central School (Heywood) M.C.—About 70 members took part in an excursion to Belle Vue Circus, which was greatly enjoyed. An interesting lecture on "*Iceland; its inhabitants and their habits*" has been given by one of the teachers at the school, and another teacher gave a most interesting lecture about "*Misericordes*," which are carvings under the seats in the choir stalls of old churches. Club roll: 150. *Secretary:* R. Nobbs, 6, Broadfield Street, Heywood.

Kendal M.C.—An excellent club-room has been obtained. The club has been re-organised and now looks forward to making good progress. A visit to Headquarters is being planned, and an interesting programme drawn up for the summer months. Club roll: 12. *Leader:* L. Haslam, Middleton, Kirkby Lonsdale, Carnforth.

S. Oswalds (Norbury) M.C.—Considerable time has been devoted to Model-building, and splendid models of bridges and motor cars have been completed. A lantern lecture describing "*Beautiful Manxland*," the material for which was kindly loaned by the Isle of Man Publicity Board, was greatly enjoyed. A club library is being organised. It has been decided to look out for a new club-room, as the present one is too extensive and leaves no club funds available for buying additional model-building materials or financing summer outings. The club football team has had a very successful season. Club roll: 15. *Secretary:* R. H. Smart, 14, Kensington Avenue, Thornton Heath.

Anderson Baptist M.C.—This club has resumed activities after having been suspended for several months owing to the serious illness of the Leader. It is hoped to hold regular weekly meetings, and to arrange an interesting summer programme. At present most meetings are devoted to model-building. Club roll: 15. *Secretary:* A. C. Kimber, 15, Regent Street, Reading.

Hornsea M.C.—A visit has been paid to the works of the East Hull Gas Company, where the party were very interested in the huge vertical retorts and the pumping and purifying plants. Finally they were taken into the engine house. The Engineers Sections of the club are to visit a local power station. Club roll: 14. *Secretary:* P. Thom, 5, Alexandra Road, Hornsea.

EGYPT

Zagazig M.C.—In a recent lecture the President reviewed the history of the club, and in another one the Leader dealt with the "*Object of Meccano Clubs.*" Recent outdoor events have included Rambles, Fishing expeditions and Excursions to scattered villages in the district. At one village special donkeys were provided to convey the party to the chief's house, where they were entertained. A moonlight trip on the Moise Canal was very much enjoyed. New Year celebrations included a tea party in the club-room. Club roll: 18. *Secretary:* Aube Yousif Auble, Gannabiet Sikka Hadid Avenue, Zagazig.

INDIA

Kognolkar M.C.—Competitions have added to the interest of Model-building Evenings, and have included a Meccano "Animals" Contest and one concerning Bridges. A local railway workshop has been visited. The Leader recently gave a lecture on "*Meccano and its Advantages.*" Club roll: 13. *Secretary:* R. M. Kognolker, Nowgong, C.I.

Planning a Summer Camp

When referring last month to the wisdom of making summer plans well in advance I mentioned particularly Cricket fixtures, Cycling runs and Rambles. Another item that calls for preparation many weeks ahead is the Summer Camp, if it is intended to organise one. The choosing of the site and the working out of the many details in connection with it require a surprising amount of time if the results are to be satisfactory. It is impossible to arrange a successful camp in a last-minute rush and, generally speaking, the more time taken for the preliminaries the better. If suitable arrangements are made beforehand the holiday will be a very happy one even if the weather is not too good. The majority of boys have their summer holidays about the same time, and if the Leader is able to fit in part of his holiday, there should be little difficulty about obtaining the necessary members for the camp.

I can assure Leaders who have not hitherto organised a Summer Camp that it is well worth considering. The general impression that a camping holiday is one beset with discomfort and difficulties that can be overcome only by the hardiest is far from correct. On the contrary, such a holiday, if well planned, is peaceful enjoyment. Of course the campers must be prepared to see the humorous side when things do not go quite as they should. If a friendly or too inquisitive cow treads on the eggs, for instance, it is foolish to get annoyed!

A camping holiday, given reasonably good weather, is ideal from the point of view of health and outdoor pleasure of the best type. Another great point in its favour is that it results in those taking part getting to know one another's real characters in a way that might take years under conditions of ordinary living. The experience of those Leaders who have taken their club members to camp, even if only for a short period, has been that the club has received a very great increase in strength and vitality. The close companionship of camp has broken down any barriers that previously may have existed between various sections of the club, and has produced a new spirit of enthusiasm that has resulted in marked progress in every branch of the club's work.

Meccano Club Presidents

No. 12. Mr. J. T. Favelle

Mr. J. T. Favelle is both President and Leader of the Rosemount (Regina) M.C. This progressive Canadian club was affiliated in August 1932, and has a splendid record of activity. It owes much of its success to the enthusiasm, generosity and careful guidance of Mr. Favelle.

Cricket Fixtures Wanted

Mr. R. H. Smart, the Secretary of St. Oswald's M.C., Thornton Heath, is organising a club Cricket Team, no members of which will be older than 15 years. He would like to hear from any other Secretary who is organising a Cricket Team this season, with a view to arranging fixtures. Secretaries interested should write to Mr. Smart at 14, Kensington Avenue, Thornton Heath, Surrey.

I am very pleased to print this invitation, and shall be delighted to perform the same service for any other Meccano club.

Revised List of Demonstration Models

The list of Demonstration Models available on loan to affiliated clubs has just been revised, and I shall be very pleased to send a copy to any club Leader who desires one. Models that have been in circulation for several years have been withdrawn, and their places taken by some splendid new ones chosen for the special interest of their movements. They include a Bascule Bridge, Waterwheel, Twin Beam Engine, new Motor Chassis, Motorcycle Engine, Pit Head Gear and a large Horizontal Engine. The new Motor Chassis is fitted with a 6-volt motor and requires a 6-volt accumulator. With the exception of this model, and the Meccanograph, which was featured in the old list, all the models normally are fitted with high-voltage motors using mains current, but in certain instances 6-volt motors can be fitted if desired to allow the use of accumulators.

No club Exhibition is complete without a Demonstration Model from Headquarters, and I hope that when planning Exhibitions Leaders will avail themselves of the privilege of borrowing any of the 15 models enumerated in this list.

Reports from Unaffiliated Clubs

The other day the secretary of a very young and unaffiliated club concluded a chatty letter to me by expressing a doubt as to whether I would be "interested in the doings of a club that is only in a small way." In replying, I assured him that his letter had given me much pleasure and that I shall look forward to hearing regularly of the activities of his club, and shall watch with interest its progress toward affiliation with the Guild.

I mention this little incident in case there are other secretaries of unaffiliated clubs who are under the impression that I am not sufficiently interested in the efforts of such clubs to warrant their sending me reports of their activities. I always follow the proceedings of these small clubs with the greatest interest, whether they are new ones striving to establish themselves firmly, or larger organisations needing only a Leader or a permanent club-room to enable them to qualify for affiliation. All interesting reports from the secretaries of unaffiliated clubs are used in the Guild pages of the "*M.M.*," and the publicity thus given often results in many new recruits for the clubs concerned.

Proposed Clubs

Attempts are being made to establish Meccano Clubs in the following places, and boys interested should communicate with the promoters whose names and addresses are given below:

BEDFORD—D. C. E. Gould, 35, Howard Avenue, Queen's Park.
HOLLAND—H. Ijzerhuis, Postbus 52, Zaandam.

Running Your Own Electric Railway

The Fascination of Remote Control

HORNBY miniature railways afford the owners of even the simplest layout many hours of splendid fun, but their fascination is greatest when the layout is electrically-operated. Perhaps the first advantage to strike the owner of a system that has been changed over from clockwork to electric is the fact that there is no winding up of the locomotives to perform. This may seem a small thing in itself, but when several engines are in use on a clockwork line the constant winding of them can become tedious. A point of importance too is that electrically-driven trains continue to run as long as the current is switched on. Thus they are not likely to end their journeys somewhat suddenly when nowhere near a station. This can happen on a clockwork system, unless the capabilities of the engines are well-known and their management is arranged accordingly.

The greatest advantages are realised in the degree of control that it is possible to exercise over the movements of electric locomotives. A much more realistic effect is obtained when the engine can be started or stopped, speeded up, slowed down or reversed as required, by the movement of a lineside switch than when the giant hand of the model railway operator is constantly thrust across the miniature "sky." Some hand-work of course is necessary, even on the most elaborate systems, but there is far less than is required when a clockwork layout is being operated.

Good fun with a Hornby Electric Railway! Two miniature railway operators busy running the train services on a well-arranged and attractive layout.

The maximum degree of control can be exercised over the larger 20-volt Hornby Electric Locomotives that have automatic reversing mechanism. As reversing is effected by switching off the current and switching it on again, complete control is possible by means of the speed regulator handle on the T20A and T20 Transformers. The speed regulator thus governs the starting, stopping, reversing, and speed control of the locomotive. This reduces the control apparatus to a minimum and is a great advantage in securing ease of operation. To make the reversing movement as rapid and smooth as possible the "off" and "maximum" positions of the speed regulator handle are adjacent to one another.

The knack of reversing is soon acquired, although beginners are apt to be a little awkward at first with the switching off and on again of the current. A point to notice is that if an automatic reversing engine is run into a station with its train and is stopped, it will start up in the reverse direction if the current is simply switched on again by the speed regulator. This is because the automatic reversing mechanism will have been actuated by the switching off and subsequent switching on of the current. In order to avoid this reversal the current should be switched off, as though to stop the train, and then on and off again rapidly before the train comes to rest. This causes the automatic reversing mechanism to operate twice so that no alteration in direction is effected on again switching on. The train therefore starts in a realistic manner in the correct direction.

In addition to the automatic reversing mechanism, these locomotives are fitted with a cut-out lever in the cab. When this is pushed in the automatic reversing gear is thrown out of action. If it is pushed in and pulled out again to its original position, the engine is reversed. Thus the lever provides a method of reversing by hand if required.

Where automatic reversing locomotives are employed the assembly of vehicles to form a tram can be carried out in a most realistic manner, for the movements of the engine to and fro are governed entirely by remote control. In conjunction with the use of the automatic couplings fitted to Hornby Rolling Stock, this enables the train to be made up without being touched by hand.

With the exception of the smallest electric engines that do not reverse and the EPM16 Special Tank Locomotive, the remaining Hornby Electric Locomotives, both 20-volt and 6-volt, have to be reversed by manipulation of a lever in the cab. Speed control however is still effected without touching the engine.

Of the 6-volt Hornby Electric Locomotives, the EPM16 Special Tank is exceptional in that it can be completely controlled from the lineside, both for speed and reversing. It requires special equipment, however, for it is reversed by reversing the direction of the current passing through the motor. The Reverse and Resistance Control Switch therefore is made for use with this Locomotive. This has separate levers for controlling the speed and the reversing movements. It must be used to control the locomotive, whether the Hornby Transformer-Rectifier or an accumulator is used as the source of power.

Circuit Breaker for Hornby Electric Trains

A New Device to Replace Fuses

By "Tommy Dodd"

THIS month I have to refer to a subject that is of special importance to all owners of Hornby Electric Railways, and to those who are contemplating the purchase of their first Electric Train Set. On electric railways of any kind, real or miniature, it is necessary to make some provision for cutting off the current in the event of a short circuit. Ever since the introduction of electricity into the Hornby Railway System a safety fuse has always been a feature of the Terminal Connecting Plate by means of which the power supply is led to the track.

The Hornby Circuit Breaker connected between a Transformer and the track. It will be noticed that it is inserted in the wire connected with the centre rail.

The fuse itself consists of a length of soft wire that is capable of carrying only a prescribed amount of current. When any mishap occurs, such as a derailment, that results in a short circuit between the centre rail and the running rails, the amount of current passing becomes excessive. This excessive current melts the fuse wire, so that the circuit between the power supply and the track is broken. The current is thus instantly cut off, preventing any damage that otherwise would be caused to the Transformer or accumulator. When the cause of the short circuit has been removed, a fresh piece of the correct fuse wire is fitted between the terminals of the Terminal Connecting Plate, and operations can then be resumed.

The renewal of the fuse wire is always rather a nuisance, and the situation is worse if the short circuit occurs when the supply of fuse wire has run out and the local shops are shut. All trouble of this kind is avoided by the use of the new Hornby Circuit Breaker. This device is incorporated in the circuit between the power supply and the Terminal Connecting Plate, as shown in the upper illustration on this page. In the event of a short circuit the Circuit Breaker "trips" and cuts off the current supply to the track. It also gives two positive indications of what has happened. There is a "click" from the mechanism when tripping occurs, and at the same time the red button on top of the casing of the Circuit Breaker rises.

The mechanism inside the Circuit Breaker casing consists essentially of an electro-magnet, a hinged armature and a flat contact spring. When conditions are normal the current flowing through the electro-magnet is not sufficient to attract the armature, and the latter remains in contact with the contact spring. The button rests on this spring near to the end that is normally in contact with the armature. When the current flowing becomes excessive, as the result of a short circuit, the armature is drawn towards the electro-magnet and releases the free end of the spring. This release breaks the circuit between the power supply and the track, and the action of the spring causes the button on the top of the casing to rise. The tripping of the mechanism causes the "click" already referred to. The Hornby Circuit Breaker thus reproduces in miniature the functions of the real circuit breakers that are a necessary feature of the distribution arrangements of any electric power system.

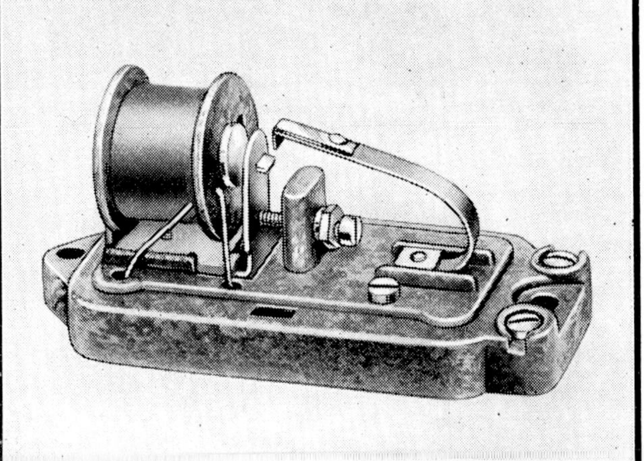

The mechanism of the Circuit Breaker, showing the electro-magnet, hinged armature and contact spring. The latter is shown in the "tripped" position.

It is most important that no attempt should be made to interfere with the adjustment of the Circuit Breaker mechanism. Each Circuit Breaker is sent out correctly set to "trip" at about two amperes. If the adjustment is altered in any way, even to a slight degree, the tripping mechanism may not come into operation to prevent the Transformer from possibly serious damage in the event of a short circuit occurring.

SPECIAL FREIGHT WORKING IN MINIATURE

A STRIKING feature of British railway practice during recent years has been the increasing provision of equipment for dealing with many kinds of special freight traffic. Not only has this involved the putting into service of appropriate rolling stock, but also terminal points have to be provided with the necessary facilities for handling the particular traffic. Hornby Railway owners are keen to include such services in their programme of operations in order to keep their systems up to date, and it is the purpose of this article to give a few ideas that can be developed more fully on individual systems.

The variety of goods wagons available in the Hornby Series makes it possible to assemble and operate practically any kind of freight train. Of the various specialised modern types perhaps the most attractive is the Milk Tank Wagon. The increasing use of these vehicles in actual practice for the rail carriage of milk in bulk is a development of recent years. The milk is worked up to London from the various producing centres in these tanks and the bottling and distribution is carried out from town depots. The real tanks are glass-lined and they are specially insulated so that their contents remain at an even temperature. They are instantly recognisable by their white colouring and in this and other details the Hornby Milk Tank Wagon is a close reproduction of the actual thing.

The lower photograph reproduced on the next page shows a train of these Tank Wagons hauled by a Hornby No. 2 Special G.W.R. Locomotive and gives a good idea of the realistic appearance of them. The real tanks are operated over all four railway groups so that all Hornby Railway owners can make correct use of the miniature vehicles on their own layouts.

In addition to milk specials there are many other fast trains of similar kinds that are run to convey farm produce and foodstuffs generally from the country districts to the towns and cities. In order to deliver their goods in time for the early morning markets the majority of such trains, except those travelling exceptionally long distances, make the best part of their journeys through the night. This is therefore a point to be noted by those Hornby Railway owners who make a practice of reproducing night conditions by operating their layouts with only the light from the Hornby electrically illuminated Accessories. The running of one or two freight flyers under such conditions will add to the fun and variety of operations.

Then there are numerous trains that carry fish, meat and fruit. For all of these appropriate vehicles are available in the Hornby Series and some very realistic trains can be assembled. The Fish Van is of special interest to L.N.E.R. miniature railway owners for it represents a type of vehicle used on that line for the specials from the fishing ports to the inland centres of population.

A fast freight train ready for departure from the goods depot. It is hauled by a passenger locomotive, a practice frequently followed for the lighter and fast trains on real railways.

The kind of meat traffic supposed to be carried affects the types of vehicles used. The popular Hornby Refrigerator Van represents the fully-insulated meat vans of actual practice that are fitted with refrigerating apparatus for carrying frozen meat imported from abroad. The white-painted exteriors of these vehicles, except for the S.R. ones, make them quite a striking sight when assembled into a complete train. The S.R. Refrigerator Van is equally distinctive in its way for it is painted the peculiar shade of pink that is preferred by the S.R. for such vehicles. The imported meat traffic from ports such as Plymouth, Liverpool, Southampton and elsewhere can thus be carried by rail in miniature.

For fresh meat traffic the ventilated Meat Van is the correct vehicle to use. This Hornby Van is based on L.M.S.R. practice and can be used in a realistic manner for the assembly in miniature of such trains as those run from Scotland direct to Broad Street, the L.M.S.R. City terminus, whence their loads are rapidly whisked away by road to Smithfield Market.

Another interesting L.M.S.R. Van is the No. O Banana Van. It represents the specially steam-heated and brake-fitted vans of real practice that are used in such numbers for the important banana traffic dealt with at Garston and

Avonmouth. The No. 1 Banana Van with its bright and attractive finish incorporating the familiar "*Fyffes*" label can be employed very well in conjunction with it, and will add to the variety of stock on a miniature banana special.

As a rule fast freight trains of this kind are hauled by engines specially designed for the work and classified generally as "mixed traffic" types. Quite frequently however express passenger locomotives are employed, if convenient. Modern types have sufficient reserve power to deal with the loads and the speed capacity of passenger engines is a decided advantage where timings are sharp. On a Hornby Railway therefore No. E120 Special or No. 1 Special Locomotives can be used as the regular engines, for they resemble fairly closely the mixed traffic types of actual practice. When necessary however or, if preferred, as a usual custom, express passenger locomotives of the E320 and E220 Special types can be employed on electrically operated layouts, or their clockwork-driven counterparts on other systems.

An interesting special train on a Hornby Railway. It is composed entirely of Flat Trucks, and is conveying a complete consignment of Caravan Trailers, Dinky Toys No. 30G.

For fast freight trains carrying general goods, which are run in large numbers nowadays, ordinary covered vans and open wagons are used to a considerable extent. The Luggage Van and Wagon of the Hornby Series can therefore be employed to good purpose for similar duties in miniature. A great favourite is the No. 2 Luggage Van, which is a bogie vehicle and therefore has a higher load capacity than the corresponding No. 1 Luggage Van, which is of the standard four-wheeled type. Very useful too is the Open Wagon "B." This is fitted with a raised longitudinal bar that can be made to support a Hornby Tarpaulin and thus protect from the "elements"—as in actual practice—any load that must be kept dry, but which does not require to be conveyed in a van. These Wagons are very popular on the G.W.R. and the S.R.

An express milk service in miniature. The Milk Tank Wagons of the Hornby Series that make up the train are very attractive and realistic vehicles.

A point that should not be overlooked is the operation of road motor services in connection with fast freight trains of the types we have been describing. The various lorries and vans included in the Series of Meccano Dinky Toys can be used very well for numerous miniature railway road services. In addition there are the Mechanical Horses and Box Van Trailers that are finished in the colours of the four group companies, as described by "Tommy Dodd" in the February "*M.M.*" Many boys operate quite extensive road services in connection with their miniature railway systems and this practice increases considerably the realism and interest of their layouts.

Another use for various vehicles of the Dinky Toys Series is as loads for Hornby Wagons or Vans, as appropriate. The No. 2 Luggage Van with its wide double doors is very suitable for motor car traffic and will accommodate two Dinky Toy Cars at once. It is more spectacular however to carry such loads on the Hornby Flat Truck and most boys prefer to use this vehicle for such work. Tractors, Cars, Wagons or Vans can be loaded on the Flat Truck and look most effective. A recent addition that can also be used is the Caravan Trailer, Dinky Toy No. 30G, an interesting and up-to-date vehicle. Such loads can be conveyed singly or they can also be made to represent a bulk consignment of motor or other vehicles being taken to an exhibition or show, or being conveyed for shipment abroad.

The marshalling of the vehicles composing a fast freight train is a matter of importance. The fast services of actual practice are only possible as a result of the fitting of much of the stock employed with automatic brakes and other equipment generally corresponding to that of passenger trains. Some of the freight trains are what are known as "fully fitted." They are "piped" or have continuous brake pipes connected throughout the train and must have brake apparatus provided on at least half of the vehicles. As all of them are piped, their position in the train whether they are brake-fitted or not, does not matter. The placing of several piped vehicles in between brake-fitted ones enables the braking power to be transmitted between the latter. "Partially fitted" trains are composed of some brake-fitted vehicles and the remainder ordinary stock; to make their brake power effective of course the fitted vehicles must be marshalled next to the engine.

In miniature therefore it is necessary to determine which wagons, or vans, shall be considered brake-fitted and which shall not. In general all vans can be imagined to be so fitted for their purposes necessarily make them suitable for fast freight work and, occasionally, for conveyance in passenger trains. Special types such as the Milk Tank Wagons also will rank as brake-fitted vehicles. Open wagons are not fitted as a rule, but there are exceptions such as the type represented by the Hornby Open Wagon "B." In assembling fast freight trains in miniature therefore it is necessary to bear in mind whether they are "fully fitted," or only "partially fitted"; and to take care that the correct vehicles are used, marshalled in the proper manner according to the type of train. If this is done the working of such trains becomes far more interesting.

Join the Hornby Railway Company and become eligible for the competitions announced on this page.

H.R.C. COMPETITION PAGE

Join the Hornby Railway Company and become eligible for the competitions announced on this page.

SIGNALLING CONTEST

In spite of the all-round accelerations of recent years, the high standard of efficiency and safety of travel on British railways has been fully maintained; in fact it is often stated, and with a good deal of truth, that the fastest trains are the safest. This satisfactory state of affairs is due largely to the efficiency of the signalling system. Signalling indeed plays such an important part in the organisation of every railway that no miniature layout can be considered at all complete without some system of signalling, however simple.

It is good fun to try one's hand at devising a system of signalling to suit the requirements of an imaginary station, and this month we give our readers a chance to exercise their ingenuity in this direction. The accompanying illustration shows a junction layout without signals; and competitors are required to submit their ideas for a complete signalling scheme.

It will be seen that a four-track section, with separate lines for fast and slow traffic, leads to the station in the down direction. After the station, however, the four tracks divide into two double track routes to A and B respectively. Double crossovers are arranged, so that down trains on the fast and slow lines can take route A or B as required. Further, up trains from A or B can reach the fast or slow lines when passing on to the four-track section. The traffic consists of express trains on the fast lines to A and to B, and corresponding up trains; and stopping trains on the slow lines to A and to B, and vice versa.

In planning the signals for this layout it is not necessary to make use of any special types; the single arm and junction patterns only are required. A total of 20 signals is necessary, of which eight are distants.

DOWN SLOW → UP SLOW ← DOWN FAST → UP FAST ← A B

The junction layout referred to on this page. Competitors are required to indicate the correct signals for the traffic that is dealt with.

To the competitors in each Section, Home and Overseas, who submit the most complete and correct signalling scheme consisting of any Meccano Product to the value of 21/–, 15/– and 10/6 respectively. In addition a number of consolation prizes will be awarded to the competitors whose entries are not quite up to prizewinning standard, but nevertheless are worthy efforts to tackle the contest.

Envelopes containing entries should be clearly marked *"H.R.C. April Signalling Contest"* in the top left-hand corner and posted to reach Headquarters, Meccano Limited, Binns Road, Liverpool 13, on or before 30th April. The closing date for competitors in the Overseas Section is 31st July. The name, full address and H.R.C. membership number of the competitor must be written on the back of his entry.

Railway Photographic Contest

Commencing with this issue, we shall announce each month until September a Railway Photographic Contest. Competitors are not restricted to any particular aspect of railway life, but may send prints of any subject so long as this has some connection with railway working. Readers should remember that a poor photograph of a really interesting character has as much chance as a good photograph of an ordinary subject. Although competitors may send as many photographs as they wish, no competitor may win more than one prize in one contest. The pick of the prizewinning entries will be filed for possible use in future issues of the *"M.M."*

The Contest will be divided as usual into two Sections, Home and Overseas, and in each will be awarded prizes of photographic material or any products manufactured by Meccano Ltd., to the value of 21/–, 15/–, and 10/6 respectively. In addition to the main prizes, a number of consolation prizes will be awarded. Envelopes containing entries must be clearly marked *"H.R.C. April Photographic Contest"* in the top left-hand corner and posted to reach Headquarters at Meccano Ltd., Binns Road, Liverpool 13, not later than 30th April. The latest date on which entries from Overseas competitors can be accepted is 31st July.

Competition Solutions

Shunting Puzzle—December 1935

The solution is as follows:

Run the Locomotive via D and branch B pushing the Van to A and leave it there. Return the Locomotive via B and D through E to F and shunt the Wagon on branch C towards the spur A and couple it to the Van which is already there. Pull the two vehicles back to branch C and leave the Van there and proceed with the Wagon to any point near E and leave it there. The Locomotive should then return via F to pick up the Van which was left on branch C. Run back with it via F and couple up with the Wagon at E. The locomotive then proceeds to pull the vehicles to F and then reverses to shunt the Wagon into the spur A via C. Leaving the Wagon at A the Locomotive and Van run via C, F, E, D, and B and draws the Wagon on to branch line B. After this has been carried out it is a simple matter to shunt the Van on to branch line C via D, E, and F. The Locomotive is then free to return to its original position E.

Owing to space restriction it is not possible to publish the solution to the *"Hidden Locomotives Contest"* announced last December, but readers specially requiring this should apply to Headquarters when it will be forwarded to them.

COMPETITION RESULTS

HOME

February "Concealed Stations Contest."—First: G. H. Hill (36093), Chorlton-cum-Hardy, Manchester. Second: H. Napper (47015), Blagdon Hill, Taunton, Som. Third: D. T. White (42549), Oakfields, Knebworth, Herts. Fourth: K. W. Jones (39968), Weedon, Northampton. Consolation Prizes: V. Cocks (42500), Rayleigh, Essex; J. M. I. Scott (29060), Kettering; L. Dudding (19120), Aldershot, Hants.; B. H. J. Harnden (33533), Upper Tooting Park, London, S.W.17.; R. Barbary (5580), St. Ewe, Mevagissey, Cornwall; K. Linsey (36783), Cambridge.

February "Railway Photo Contest."—First: H. S. G. Darke (4461), Hampstead Gardens Suburb, London, N.W.11. Second: C. Spencer (44179), Sheffield 11. Third: D. Fear (18477), Taunton, Som. Fourth: E. W. Oglethorpe (46851), Harrow, Middx. Consolation Prizes: E. C. Morgan (10735), Wandsworth Common, London, S.W.18; H. Sutton (32476), Leeds 6; J. R. Webb (25008), Maryport, Cumb.; L. E. Smith (9903), Pendleton, Salford 6.

February "Questions Contest No. 7."—First: W. Cross (34990), Northampton. Second: L. T. A. Bern (347), North End, Portsmouth. Third: C. S. Tricker (899), Mitcham, Surrey. Fourth: R. F. Embley (41047), St. Annes-on-Sea. Consolation Prizes: D. V. C. Bentley (24591), Loughborough, Leics.; L. Reason (32408), Bushey, Herts.; A. B. Stone (88), Nuneaton, War.; K. Greaves (39332), Oldham, Lancs.; W. Fleming (31024), Linthorpe, Middlesbrough.

OVERSEAS

December "Shunting Puzzle."—The entries submitted by the following competitors were the first correct ones to be opened and therefore, they have been awarded cash prizes of 5/– each. Warren A. René Toureau, Mauritius; G. S. Martin, Christchurch, C.I., New Zealand; and J. Hockey, Calgary, Alberta, Canada.

Branch News

ADDISCOMBE.—A lecture by one of the members on the railway system of the Isle of Man was greatly enjoyed. With the completion of the Branch track, several satisfactory running meetings have been held. The outlook is very favourable and further enthusiastic members have been recruited. A special feature of the programme recently has been the celebration of the second anniversary of the foundation of the Branch. Secretary: G. Chandler, 62, Ashburton Avenue, Addiscombe, Croydon.

FOREST SCHOOL (LONDON). — Regular meetings are held, but members may attend the Branch room each night. On various occasions timetable working of an experimental character has been carried out. Difficulties have arisen owing to the track being situated on the floor, but it is hoped to overcome this shortly by the provision of a raised baseboard. Sufficient locomotives and rolling stock are available for the working arrangements at present in force, and the track meetings held so far have been greatly enjoyed. Secretary: H. J. Pye, Forest School, Nr. Snaresbrook, London, E.17.

HOLYWELL (OXFORD).—The inclusion of an electrically-operated branch line has added greatly to the interest of recent track meetings. Although satisfactory services have been operated, the track itself is to have the attention of the Permanent Way Department of the Branch. Lantern Lectures have been given by the Secretary on the recently closed Brill branch line of the London Passenger Transport Board and on the Fairford branch of the G.W.R. The latest issue of the Branch magazine sold out rapidly. Although an increase in membership recently has to be reported the Branch is still open to receive further recruits. Secretary: J. Spicer, 28, Holywell, Oxford.

NEW SOUTHGATE.—A Lantern Lecture on *"London's Underground,"* using slides and information loaned by the London Passenger Transport Board, is considered to be the best that has been enjoyed so far. Shunting and signalling competitions have been the feature of meetings, but the most important event recently has been the Exhibition arranged by the Branch. In addition to the operation of the Branch track and a display of Hornby railway material and Meccano Exhibition Models, a free cinematograph show was a popular feature. The Exhibition was well reported locally and was a success financially. Various schemes for future Exhibitions have been discussed in the light of experience gained. Secretary: A. R. Wardle, 25, Limes Avenue, Southgate, London, N.11.

NORTHAMPTON.—Games nights continue to be popular and shunting competitions have been successfully introduced. A Talk on the *"Severn Tunnel"* and a Debate on the favourite subject *"Steam v. Electric Locomotives"* have been among events recently held. The Branch track has now been laid on a raised foundation and its opening was marked by special celebrations. Timetables have been worked out in a practical manner under the supervision of Mr. A. G. Buckingham, of the L.M.S.R., and the arrangements generally have been attended with success. The attendance continues to be very satisfactory. This is explained not only by the keenness of the members, but by the attractive programmes that are arranged. Secretary: D. K. Adams, 8, Cedar Road, Northampton.

ISLINGTON.—Subjects of recent Talks have included *"The Lure of the Footplate"* and timetable arrangements for the Branch track. A visit was paid to the Exhibition of the New Southgate H.R.C. Branch, which was greatly enjoyed. Definite duties have been allotted to the various members and the timetable arrangements discussed previously have been put into practice. It is felt that owing to the increasing membership it will be necessary to divide the Branch into two sections, Junior and Senior, and to provide additional track. Secretary: E. Muxlow, 7, Regent Park Road, Islington, London, N.W.1.

FIRST SHEFFIELD.—Special attention has been given recently to the Branch layout, and scenery is being prepared that will add considerably to its realistic effect. Special measures are necessary to deal with the heavy freight traffic on the line, and a branch line has been opened that is worked by an engine and coach on the "push and pull" system. Numerous new vehicles are under consideration both for passenger and goods traffic, and various experiments have been made with the locomotives belonging to the Branch. Secretary: W. B. Hutchinson, 35, Linden Avenue, Sheffield, 8.

FOLKESTONE. — Branch operations have commenced with members gaining experience at timetable working. Definite duties have been allotted to different members, whose efficiency is improving with practice. Meccano cranes have been constructed for loading operations and stations and tunnels are to be made. Secretary: G. Milton, 2, Rosemery Villas, Folkestone.

A scene at the sixth Exhibition held by the Kidderminster Branch, No. 157. The joint chairmen, Mr. Harris and Mr. Barker, are standing at the end of the layout. The Branch was incorporated in 1931 and the Exhibitions and Open Nights that are a regular feature of its programme are always well supported.

Branches in Course of Formation

The following new Branches of the Hornby Railway Company are at present in process of formation, and any boys who are interested and desirous of linking up with this unique organisation should communicate with the promoters, whose names and addresses are given below:

BECCLES—E. J. Hemmant, Village Farm, Gillingham, Beccles.

BOLTON—L. Monk, 30, Barcroft Road, off Bennets Lane.

LIVERPOOL—R. E. Jones, 3, Chalfont Road, Liverpool 18.

SOUTHAMPTON—C. Line, 4, Chichester Road, Bitterne.

WALLASEY—J. Brough, 10, Osborne Road, Wallasey.

Branches Recently Incorporated

302. FOLKESTONE—G. Milton, 2, Rosemery Villas, Saffrons Place, Folkestone.
303. SUTTON COLDFIELD—G. C. Low, 272, Boldmere Road, Erdington, Birmingham.

SETS (POSTAGE EXTRA)

3 Abyssinia ...	2d.	10 Tunis ...	3d.
3 Albania ...	2d.	4 Memel ...	3d.
5 Algeria ...	2d.	8 „ ...	7d.
5 Armenia ...	3d.	5 Silesia ...	2d.
10 Australia ...	2d.	10 „ ...	4d.
5 Barbados ...	2d.	10 Canada ...	2d.
5 Brit. Guiana	3d.	4 Cayman Is. ...	6d.
10 Bavaria ...	2d.	5 Cyprus ...	2d.
5 Bulgaria ...	2d.	10 „ ...	5d.
5 Bosnia ...	2d.	5 Deccan ...	2d.
5 Crete ...	2d.	10 Egypt ...	2d.
20 Czecho ...	2d.	5 Ecuador ...	2d.
10 Ceylon ...	2d.	20 France ...	2d.
10 China ...	2d.	20 French Col. ...	3d.

5 Gold Coast ... 3d.

J. RUSSELL
23, Shanklin Drive, Westcliff-on-Sea

KING EDWARD VIII PACKET FREE!

GOD SAVE THE KING. This packet includes a beautiful stamp of our new King wearing his Guards uniform, also his revered Father, the late King George, and the Queen Mother, also King Edward VII and Queen Victoria. 42 all different stamps you will be proud to own, including one depicting the ancient Royal Palace, Windsor Castle. Large Trinidad and Malay Tiger. Foreign issues include sets of Hungary, Spain, and Bohemia; and, finally, we are adding a very useful Duplicate Book and fine British stamp nearly 100 years old. Just send 2d. postage and request approvals.

LISBURN & TOWNSEND (Dept. M.M.), LIVERPOOL 3

FREE WONDERFUL 1936 OFFER 25 NEW ISSUES AND NOVELTIES

Including **Andorra** (1935), fine new **Cayman Islands** (map of the Islands), obsolete Austria, China, Denmark, **Gwalior** Service, Hungary (Statesman Szechenyi), **new Kenya** (Kavirondo Cranes), **Roumania** (new portrait of King Carol), and many others. I will send this collection **absolutely free** to all stamp collectors sending 2d. postage (abroad 4d.).

G. P. KEEF, Willingdon, EASTBOURNE

HIGH CLASS AIR MAIL and SHIP PACKET—FREE

Lithuania Air Mail Triangular stamp, **New Issue** Mozambique Air Mail, Siam Air Mail, also 15 Ships and Aeroplanes. No rubbish in this gift. Free to **genuine** approval applicants enclosing **2d.** for postage and packing.

SHOWELL BROS.,
42, Vanbrugh Hill, Blackheath, S.E.3.

THE "DIAMOND" PACKET IS THE ONLY PACKET

OF UNSORTED STAMPS ON THE MARKET with 15 years' reputation behind it. It contains approx. **1,000 UNSORTED STAMPS** from Convents abroad. **MANY RARE STAMPS** have been found in it. 1 pkt., 1/6; 3 pkts., 3/9; 5 pkts., 6/-. All post free inland. Colonies 3d. per pkt. extra. Foreign, 6d. extra.

Ask your stationer for the "Diamond" packet.

O. NERUSH (Dept. A), 68, TURNPIKE LANE, HORNSEY, LONDON, N.8

THE 'SHIP' PACKET

This marvellous packet is offered under cost as an advertisement, **45 different stamps each with a ship on it.** A regular armada. **GABOON**, a rare **FOOCHOW** (War Canoe), wonderful flotilla of caravels from **DENMARK** (complete set), **SENEGAL** (new pictorial), **NEW CALEDONIA, IVORY COAST, COSTA RICA**, a fleet of **7 CHINESE** junks usually sold at 10d., **TRINIDAD & TOBAGO, MAURITIUS, SOUTH WEST AFRICA, NEWFOUNDLAND, U.S.A., B. GUIANA**, set of **S. AFRICA, GREECE, POLAND, INDO-CHINA, F. OCEANIA**, etc. Price 4½d., postage 1½d. (abroad 3d. extra). Purchasers of this packet asking for approvals receive **FREE** set of **4 SPAIN** (Columbus, each with his ship on it). Senders of addresses of stamp collectors receive **FREE** set of **6 VENEZUELA** or **6 PERSIA, 100 BRITISH COLONIALS 1/-, 20 AIRPORT 6d., 6 TRIANGULARS 6d., 50 PERSIA 4/-, 2 ASTRID** (mourning stamps) **2½d., VOLUMES OF B.O.P. CHEAP.**

H. C. WATKINS (M. Dept.), Granville Road, BARNET

JUBILEE STAMPS
23 Different 2/-

A splendid pictorial packet containing used and unused items. Many of these stamps are already scarce.

Some other attractive offers:

***9 Abyssinia, 1919.** Large pictorials	**1/-**
***4 Egypt, 1933.** Air Mails, Plane over Pyramids	**6d.**
***1 Iceland Triangle, 1930.** Air Mail	**3d.**
3 Latvia Triangles, 1931-32. Air Mails	**6d.**
***5 Lithuania Triangles, 1932.** Air Mails, Map, etc.	**1/-**
9 Roumania, 1928-30. Schoolboy King issue ...	**4d.**

*Unused. **Postage 1½d. extra.**

Money and all postage will be returned if not satisfactory. Numerous other items are available at low prices. Hundreds of unsolicited testimonials have been received.

W. BENNETT,
53, MARLBOROUGH ROAD, LONDON, E.8.

FOOTBALL STAMP FREE!

Included in this free packet is the fine **ITALIAN** soccer stamp—have it in your collection and you won't mind who wins the Cup. The packet contains also another sports stamp, the I.F.S. hurley player; British, French and Portuguese Colonials; old **PERSIA**; mint Lebanon, Syria and Ukraine; **URUGUAY**; Scandinavians, etc. **FREE ONLY** to those requesting approvals and enclosing 2d. postage (abroad 1/-). The supply is strictly limited, so write at once.

HELY. HUTCHINSON
(M.8), HURROCK WOOD, KENTS BANK, GRANGE-OVER-SANDS.

SPECIAL OFFERS

JUBILEES—LAST OFFER at these prices.	
15 Colonial Jubilees—**USED**	**1/8**
6 **CANADA** Jubilee (Complete), used ...	**2/-**
MINT SETS—Bechuanaland, Swaziland, Hong Kong ... ... ea.	**2/-**
Nauru, Straits, and Ceylon **2/6** ea. Jamaica	**3/-**

WANTED TO BUY—USED COLONIAL JUBILEES—send your offers, quoting your lowest price.
100 PERSIA—all different **2/9**
Cash with order. Postage extra. **Note New Address**
T. R. Hughes, Ibis Cottage, Long Park, Amersham, Bucks.

THE FIRST STAMP Ever Issued

(British 1840 Penny Black) for P.O. 2/-! It is guaranteed genuine in every respect. Its companion stamp (1840, 2d. blue) for a further 5/- (cat. 15/-)! Other "Classics" which every Collector should have are the **Cape of Good Hope Triangulars;** we offer 1d. rose (cat. 40/-) for 12/6; 4d. blue (cat. 15/-) for 5/-; and 6d. pale lilac (cat. 40/-) at 12/6. Superb approvals of any country against approved English References or a deposit. **Full Lists Free.**

NORRIS & CO. (Dept. M), NORWOOD, LONDON, S.E.19

ALL BRITISH COLONIAL APPROVALS

Fine **BRITISH COLONIAL PICTORIAL SETS OF CAYMAN ISLANDS AND GAMBIA FREE** to all Collectors sending 1½d. stamp and requesting **ALL BRITISH COLONIAL APPROVALS, BRITISH COLONIALS ONLY** on approval at bargain prices, including Jubilee issues, West Indians, East and West Africa, Cyprus, Gibraltar, Iraq, Papua, Samoa, and many other fine Colonials. (No stamps sent abroad.) **C. H. SHAW (Dept. M.4), 95, CHRISTCHURCH AVENUE, KENTON, HARROW.**

ONE THOUSAND STAMPS ON APPROVAL

From which you may select any 100 for 3/-. This selection is not made up of the very commonest varieties, but contains stamps catalogued at 1/- each or more. (I do not sell less than 100.)

Special offer: BRITISH GUIANA 1899 PICTORIAL 2c. on 10c. and 2c. on 15c. MINT, cat. 2/6, post free 7½d.

H. HARDY, "Hoyland," Potter Heigham, Norfolk.

SPECIAL OFFER. 100 all different Persia, 3/-. 50 for 1/6. 500 Stamp Mounts Free to ½d. approval applicants.—Winter, 89, Cobham Road, Seven Kings.

Jubilees and mint British Colonials free. Request appro. Post. 1½d.—G. Kingsmill, New Barnet, Herts.

FREE—Stamps catalogued 2/- with approvals or packets of 100 different, 7½d.—Heath, 10, Aldridge Rise, New Malden.

FREE TRIANGULARS • JUBILEES • AIR MAILS FREE

We consider this to be the **finest Free Offer** we have yet made, as this unique collection includes: Switzerland (Dove of Peace), beautiful Costa Rica **Triangular** (Philatelic Exhibition), Canada **Jubilee** (King George and Queen Mary in State Robes), Chili (**Air Mail**) and a collection of British Colonials all showing his late Majesty (as Emperor of India, in Admiral's uniform, etc.) all of which will soon be obsolete. This wonderful packet will be given **FREE** to all who send 2d. postage (abroad 6d.) and request approvals. (Also details of further Free Gifts every time you buy from our sheets!!)

MICHAEL HERBERT (M.M.), 8, Woodstock Rd., Walthamstow, London

BARGAINS FOR COLLECTORS. Have you seen my Bargains? Large Colonial and Foreign stock selling from ⅛ to ⅛ Gibbons. All grades supplied from ½d. to £1 each and over. FINE ATTRACTIVE SELECTIONS.
B. MAY CAMPBELL, B.P.A., P.T.S.,
3, Haldon Avenue, Teignmouth, Devon.

ROYAL HOSPITAL, RICHMOND, SURREY, appeals to the readers of the Meccano Magazine to collect used postage stamps (British and Foreign) towards the new Extension Fund. These stamps should be sent to the Secretary-Superintendent.

4 DIFF. QUEEN ASTRID MOURNING STAMPS, 3d.—J. Sanders, 90, Newlands Avenue, Southampton.

22 GREECE, including Postage Due, free with approvals.—Edward Lord, Grafton Road, Keighley.

EVERY COLLECTOR NEEDS THIS ILLUSTRATED BOOK

Zoo in a Stamp Album—Ship Stamps—Watermarks—The Aerodrome—Single Country Collections—Olympic Games—Loose-Leaf Albums—Earthquake Stamps—Washing Day in the Stamp World—Three-cornered Market Place—British Empire Albums—Rare Stamps—Overprints and Surcharges—To Correspondents Abroad—Treasure Trove—Triangular Packets—Packets of British, French, Italian, Portuguese, Spanish and German Colonials—Building a Collection—West Indian Packets—Triangular Stamps—Philately Royal—Albums for Beginners—Penny Sets—English Men on Foreign Stamps—Emergency Papers—Shilling Sets—Advertising Stamps—Strip Pocket Books—Glossary—Stamp Tongs—Punctured Officials—etc., etc., etc. These are only a few Headings out of my **NEW SIXTY-PAGE BOOK,** which is **WELL ILLUSTRATED THROUGHOUT** and so full of the right sort of useful and interesting Philatelic information that **EVERY STAMP COLLECTOR MUST HAVE THIS BOOK,** FREE and POST FREE from

EDWARD SANDELL, 10, EVELYN GROVE, SOUTHALL, MIDDLESEX, ENGLAND.

SPORTS STAMPS

APRIL is probably the greatest month of the year for the devotee of field and track sports. It sees the wind-up of football and the opening of cricket, our two great national games, and each of its weeks brings some sporting event. It seems appropriate therefore to devote this month's article to stamps that deal with sports.

Almost every one of the popular sports has been featured on stamps at one time or another, largely to commemorate an Olympic Games series or to celebrate some great sporting achievement, as in Italy's issue of May, 1934, to commemorate the International Football Championship games held that year in Italy. This issue comprised five very striking designs, one of which is illustrated here; and in addition there were four air stamps. Similar sets were issued for use in Italian Post Offices abroad. Since Italy won this championship, beating Czecho-Slovakia in the final by two goals to one, the stamp issue has come to be regarded also as celebrating the Italian victory.

Football, as befits its place in public estimation, is the most commonly featured sport on stamps. In addition to the Italian series mentioned, the game was featured on the 2c. value of the Bulgarian issue of September, 1931, commemorating the Balkan Olympic Games at Sofia; the 2c. stamp of Colombia's series of January, 1935, in honour of the Third National Olympiad at Barranquila; the 3c. value of Holland's issue of March, 1928, celebrating the 9th Olympic Games at Amsterdam, and on the 2,000 Kr. value of Hungary's sports charity issue of 1925.

The first series of sports stamps ever issued came from Greece in 1906 to celebrate the Olympic Games held at Athens in that year. In many ways it is the most interesting issue also, for it confines itself to designs representative of the ancient Olympic contests, discus throwing, shown on the 1c. value, wrestling (30c.), and marathon running (1 dr.). There were nine designs in all, the others being of a symbolic or allegorical nature.

Discus throwing is the most commonly featured of the field events. It appears also on the 5c. value of the Belgian series commemorating the 11th Olympic Games at Brussels in 1920; the 4c. value of Colombia's 1935 Olympiad issue; each of the five stamps in Salvador's Central American Olympiad issue of 1935; and on the 5c. value of the U.S.A. series commemorating the 10th Olympic Games series at Los Angeles in 1932.

This U.S. series contained only two stamps, the other being a 3c. value, showing a sprinter on his mark; but a special 2c. stamp was issued in connection with the winter sports section of the 1932 Games, held at Lake Placid, N.Y., in February 1932. The ski-jumping design on this stamp is a splendid sports picture that merits inclusion in every collection of stamps illustrating sports.

Winter sports, unfortunately, are poorly represented among sporting designs. Indeed, apart from the U.S. stamp and the splendid new German and Austrian, to which reference is made in the Stamp Gossip page this month, we can call to mind only two designs, a ski-runner on the 200 Kr. of the Hungary's 1925 issue, and a skating scene on the 300 Kr. value of the same issue. The latter stamp is illustrated here.

Aquatic sports too are only meagrely represented, the best design being the diving picture on the 400 Kr. stamp of Hungary's 1925 issue, illustrated here. The 5c. of Bulgaria's 1931 issue also showed a diving picture, while a girl swimmer is shown on the 24c. of Colombia's 1935 issue. Sculling is best represented by the 1½c. of Holland's 1928 series.

Track events are comparatively well represented. In addition to the U.S. sprinter and the Greek marathon runners already mentioned, there are runners of different types shown on the 15c. stamp of the Belgian Olympic issue, Colombia's 7c. of 1935, showing a desperate finish right on the tape, and Holland's 10c. of 1928. Each of the five values of Cuba's 1935 Olympic Games series shows an exceptionally fine action picture of a hurdler. The 10c. of Colombia's 1935 series and the 2,500 Kr. of Hungary's 1925 issue also show hurdlers in action.

There is not space here to list all the sports stamps available, of course, but it is interesting briefly to survey the remaining designs. Among them almost every popular sport is shown, and many of the lesser known.

Thus we have chariot racing on the 15c. of Belgium's 1920 issue, gymnastics on the vaulting horse, fencing, and cycling on the 1c., 4c., and 10c. values respectively of Bulgaria's 1931 issue. Fencing is featured on the 2c. of Holland's 1925 issue and on the 500 Kr. of the Austrian sports issue also. Other items from Holland's series, additional to those already mentioned, are yachting (5c.), putting the weight (17½c.), horsemanship (15c.), and boxing (30c.).

The Phillippine Islands issue, commemorating the holding of the 10th Far Eastern Championship Games series at Manila in April, 1934, is particularly interesting for its three designs are representative of essentially modern games. They are baseball (2c.), lawn tennis (6c.) and basketball (16c.). The lawn tennis design is rather disappointing, but the other two are really fine action pictures.

The British Empire is disappointingly represented in our sports collection with only one stamp, the 2d., showing a hurley player, issued by the Irish Free State in July, 1934, to honour the Golden Jubilee of the Gaelic Athletic Association.

STANLEY GIBBONS' S·I·M·P·L·I·F·I·E·D STAMP CATALOGUE

Owing to the enormous demand for the third edition of our Simplified Stamp Catalogue, stocks have run out and we have had to print a new edition.

The new volume is the most up-to-date stamp catalogue in existence and includes all Empire stamps issued in King George's reign, all foreign issues to about mid-January, and Silver Jubilee prices up to time of going to press. Even if you have the Third Edition, you will want the fine, new, up-to-date Fourth Edition.

PRICE **5/-**

or post free, U.K. 5/6, abroad 6/2 from

SKYBIRDS

THE MOST MODERN OF ALL HOBBIES

Scale Model Aeroplane Construction

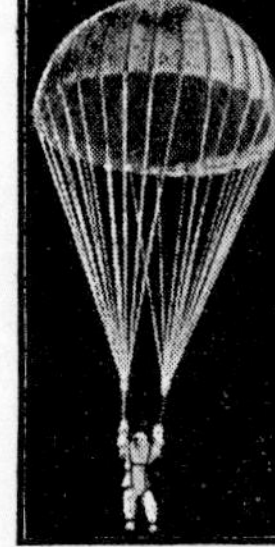

IRVIN AIRCHUTE
Complete with Lines and Parachutist, price 1/-

A Skybird model of the Heston "Phœnix"
Constructive set, 2/6. Assembled and Painted, 8/6

NEW! SKYBIRD JUNIOR
A complete cast model of the **PERCIVAL "MEW GULL"**
Price 1/- each

NEW CONSTRUCTIVE SET
B.A. "EAGLE"
Price 2/-

SKYLEAGUERS' RALLY—APRIL 17th, 2-30 p.m.
JEHANGIR HALL, IMPERIAL INSTITUTE, SOUTH KENSINGTON, LONDON

YOUR BADGES WILL ADMIT YOU!

Send stamps 7d., for the "Aero Modeller," the official organ of the SKYBIRD LEAGUE, to:

A. J. HOLLADAY & CO. LTD. (Desk B)
3, Aldermanbury Ave., London, E.C.2

GLOBE-TROTTER'S JUBILEE OFFER TO YOU

FREE.—AMAZING SILVER JUBILEE PACKET, including Silver Jubilee varieties, Air Mails, Large Italian and Russian Pictorial Commemoratives, New Issues, Colonials—60 Magnificent Stamps—the most sensational offer yet. Send 1½d. postage for "Globe-Trotter" approval selections—amazing value, ¼d., ½d., and 1d. upwards—and particulars of how **you can have FREE stamps every 14 days!!** Write Now—there's a stamp treat in store for you. Owing to immense popularity of the above offer and letters of appreciation, I am repeating same for one more month—don't miss it. **Special Offers.** "Globe-Trotter" Mystery Mixture—world-wide collected—old and new issues, pictorials, etc., 1,000 unsorted, unbeatable, 1/3.—**GLOBE-TROTTER, 17, Winchester Road, BIRCHFIELD, BIRMINGHAM.**

THE MYSTIC PACKET

1000 UNKNOWN UNUSUAL UNSORTED 1/3

Stamps on paper, etc., just as received from Convents, Missions, Bankers, etc. Guaranteed unpicked. Chance of a **FIND** in every lot. Send to-day for your treasure hunt to-morrow, **3** for **3/6, 6** for **6/6.** Abroad, **1/6** packet. **FREE!** 25 Br. Cols., including Jubilees, to approval Applicants, also **FREE EXCHANGE.** Send postage only. Overseas **3d.**

ASTLEY & CO.
(M25), Lowhill, WOLVERHAMPTON

T FREE — FREE Z

We are presenting this month the last packet of our alphabetical series, the greatest gifts ever offered. **SEND A POST CARD**

This month's packet contains stamps of countries from T to Z and includes many beautiful pictorials. You must not miss this magnificent offer. **TO-DAY FOR APPROVALS**

UNIVERSITY STAMP CO.
13, Walton Well Road, OXFORD

SAMOA EXPRESS

We are giving free to all genuine applicants for approvals, a complete set of the very rare **SAMOA** 'Express' stamps unused. Face value alone amounts to 9/9 and originals are catalogued at over £20 the set. This set is sent you absolutely free if you send for one of our famous 'Grey' booklets containing a selection of stamps on approval. Don't forget to include 2d. for post. Remember, our gift contains guaranteed genuine reprints from original plates. **Special Offers.** 5 Abyssinia, 6d.; 25 Colombia, 1/-; 5 Eritrea, 6d.; 5 Fiume, 4d.; 5 Iceland, 3d.; 5 Macao, 3d.; 5 Paraguay, 3d.; 5 Philippines, 3d.; 10 Vatican, 1/-. Postage extra.

WINDSOR STAMP CO.
(M.M.'Dept.), 59, LEE ROAD, BLACKHEATH, S.E.3.

100 DIFFERENT STAMPS FREE to applicants for ½d. Approvals.—Cox, 21, Dennis Mansions, Westcliff.

STAMPS BOUGHT, SOLD, EXCHANGED.—E. Burley, 21, Jardine Rd., Aston, Birmingham, Eng.

THE JUBILEE PACKET

Contains 60 **Diff.** Superior stamps (NO German) including 8 **Large JUBILEE Pictorials** from **CYPRUS;** Kenya; Uganda; Tanganyika; **JAMAICA;** India; **CANADA;** Ceylon and **GOLD COAST,** etc., also **LARGE U.S.A. AIR MAIL** Pictorial; **BELGIAN CONGO;** Mozambique Co.; **AIR MAIL & NEW TANGANYIKA** pictorial, etc. Price 1/- only, postage 1½d. extra. Satisfaction or money refunded in full.

THE PUKKA STAMP CO., 27, Normandy Ave., BARNET

MINT—NEW ISSUES

8 Nigeria Pictorials, ½d. to 1/- 3/6
9 St. Lucia Pictorials, ½d. to 1/- 3/9

These two issues will not have a long life
SO GET THEM NOW

4 Antigua Jubilee ... 3/3
8 Belgium "Queen Astrid"... ... 2/6
4 Cyprus Jubilee ... 3/3
4 Fiji Jubilee ... 3/3
4 S. Rhodesia Jubilee 2/6
6 St. Helena Centenary ... 2/6
9 Spain "Press" ... 1/6
4 Swaziland Jubilee... 2/3

CASH WITH ORDER—**POSTAGE EXTRA**
H. L. GOMM, 41, Upper Cranbrook Rd., Redland, Bristol, 6

100 diff. Stamps Free to approval applicants, good discount.—Gosling, 21, Powling Road, Ipswich.

The "NEW TRANSPORT" Packet

Contains a wonderful assortment of 44 foreign and colonial stamps including the following which depict various means of transportation, **Tunis** (water carrier), **Senegal** (bridge and boats), **Mauritania** (crossing desert), **Mid. Congo** (train and bridge), **Sth. Africa** (ship), **Germany** (aeroplane), **Austria** (horseman), **Indo China** (boat), **Mozambique** (aeroplane), **Gaboon** (raft), **Greece** (bridge and liner), **St. Pierre and M.** (trawler), **Fr. Guinea** (native carriers), **Dutch Indies** (Steamboat), **Madagascar** (native transport), **Brazil** (aeroplane), **Belgium** (train), **Roumania** (aeroplane), **Newfoundland** (steamship), **Fr. Morocco** (camels). Price **6d.** All purchasers asking for approvals will receive **Travancore** pictorials free.

BURDOCK & FLURY,
4, MARLBOROUGH ROAD, LONDON, S.W.19.

Philatelic Phascination

200,000 STAMPS, what a pity we have no time to sort them through! We have purchased a huge accumulation, formed, for goodness knows what purpose, by an elderly collector. The collection dates back to the early days of stamp collecting. Even in the very brief glance we have allowed ourselves, we have noticed many high catalogue, some rarely seen now-a-days. This is at a glance; we have no time at all to gauge the perforation, colour and other varieties which must abound.

There is nothing to equal the pleasure of sorting a large accumulation such as this, so, as we are denied the pleasure ourselves, we are making it over to our customers. We have weighed the mixture into bags and offer it just as it stands at **6d.** (there's a chance for you, boys and girls), **2/9, 5/3, 10/3** and **25/-** a bag, postage extra. There is both the chance of some pleasant finds (we ourselves have seen three stamps catalogued over £4, while turning the mixture over, also some penny blacks and early Colonial Imperfs.) and the certainty of some real Philatelic enjoyment.

We especially urge our own customers to take as big a bag as possible as we should not like them to miss it and there will be insufficient stock for repeat orders.

LIQUIFACTORS
43, RECTORY ROAD, LONDON, S.W.6. (ENG.)

Stamp Gossip

and Notes on New Issues

600 Acres on a Stamp!

The outstanding stamp in the new pictorial set that has been in course of gradual introduction by Ceylon is the 6c., illustrated here, showing an aerial view of Colombo Harbour, one of the largest artificial harbours in the world. The vast expanse of the port with its 600 acres of water is magnificently portrayed. It was intended that the 1 rupee stamp of this series should provide a companion picture with a view of Trincomates Harbour, but for "reasons of Imperial strategy" the idea was dropped.

Also we illustrate the 9c. value which shows a very charming view on a tea plantation. The production of tea is Ceylon's principal industry, the value of the exports totalling over eight million pounds sterling each year.

A Doughty General

Those of our readers, and they must be many, who have revelled in the works of the great French novelist Alexandre Dumas and his son, will be specially interested in the 10c. stamp from Haiti's new issue. This bears portraits of Alexandre Dumas, his father and his son. Dumas Père and Dumas Fils require no introduction, but Dumas Grandpère is of new interest, for his prowess with the sword was only less mighty than his descendants' power with their pens.

Thomas Alexandre Dumas was a mulatto, son of a French nobleman, a planter in the island of San Domingo. Early in life he quarrelled with his father and came to France, where he enlisted in the army. He rose rapidly from the ranks, and in 1793, at the age of 21, he was general in command of the Western Pyrenean army and popularly known as the "Black Devil."

Several good stories of his amazing strength are told. On one occasion his troops were attacking an Austrian palisade. They found some difficulty in scaling the obstacle, whereupon the impatient general dashed up, seized his men one by one by the seats of their breeches, and threw them over the palisade! The enemy fled in the face of this literal rain of foes!

General Dumas died in 1806 when his son, Alexandre, was only three years old.

Winter Sports Stamps

Readers who have been interested by our article on Sports Stamps this month will be specially attracted by the recent issues of Winter Sports stamps from Germany and Austria. A most interesting feature of the Austrian series is that the designs are taken from actual photographs, made by the famous Austrian sports photographer Lother Rübelt. The two specimens reproduced on this page show the happy results that have attended this idea.

The stamps were issued in connection with the competitions of the International Ski-ing Federation at Innsbruck on 21st and 22nd February last. There were four values, the 12, 24, and 35 gr., each showing a different view of the competition course, while the high value, 60 gr., shows a view of the Maria-Theresien Strasse at Innsbruck, with the Nord Kette, a famous mountain chain, in the background.

The German series, specimens from which we hope to reproduce next month, were issued to commemorate the 4th series of Olympic Winter Games held at Garmisch in connection with the 10th series of Olympic Games that will be staged at Berlin this summer. There were three designs as follows: 6 pf. skating; 12 pf. ski-jumping; 25 pf. bob-sleighing.

* * * *

St. Lucia has a rather interesting claim to stamp fame in that it is one of the few British Colonies that retained the same stamp design throughout the reign of the late King George V. The designs introduced at the time of King George's accession have remained in use, and only the Silver Jubilee issue of last year has intervened in that period.

Now a new pictorial issue has been introduced with designs as follows: ½d., 2d. and 4d., Port Castries; 1d., 2½d. and 6d., Columbus Square, Castries; 1½d. and 3d., Ventine Falls, Soufrière; 1/–, Fort Rodney, Pigeon Island; 2/6, Monument to the Inniskilling Regiment at Morné Fortune; 5/–, Government House, Morné Fortune; 10/–, the crest of the Colony.

Motoring Pioneers on Stamps

The opening of the International Motor Show at Berlin on 15th February last coincided with the celebration of the 50th anniversary of the introduction of the motor car. To mark the occasion Germany issued two commemorative stamps, 6rpf. and 12rpf. values, bearing portraits of two great motoring pioneers, Gottlieb Daimler and Carl Benz, respectively.

New Argentine Issue

Argentine has recently issued a complete new series with a range of designs typical of the country's many industrial and agricultural activities. The outstanding designs are the 15c. and the 1p., both of which are illustrated here.

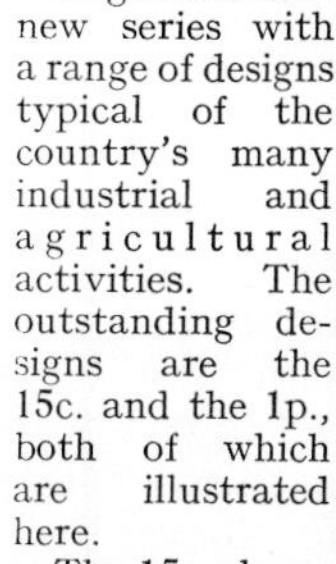

The 15c. shows the head of the famous bull "Faithful 20," property of a British rancher, for which the record price of 152,000 pesos (£8,400) was paid at the Buenos Aires cattle show in 1925. If his portrait may be used as a guide, "Faithful 20" is worth his price.

The 1p. stamp is remarkable for its insistence upon the Argentine title to the Falkland Islands. For very many years a quiet dispute concerning the rightful ownership of these islands has been dragging its weary way between the Argentine and British Governments, and it will be remembered that the Argentine refused to recognise the stamps issued by the Falklands in 1933 to celebrate the centenary of British administration, Letters bearing these stamps were surcharged on arrival in the Argentine. This gesture of defiance of British ownership, which derives from Spain's cession of the islands to Britain in 1769, threatens to bring the dispute to a head.

The remaining designs are as follows: 25c., ploughman; 30c., Patagonian ram; 40c., sugar-cane and factory; 50c., petroleum well; 2p., fruit products; 5p., Iguazu Falls. These cataracts are the largest falls in the world. More than 70 different cascades pour over them and the spray rises to a height of over 600 ft. The 10p. stamp shows a bunch of grapes, and the 20p. a cotton plant.

King Edward VIII Stamps

The preliminary steps towards the introduction of new coins and stamps bearing a representation of our new King are well advanced, and on 21st February a plaster cast of the King's head, prepared by the Royal Mint, was taken to Buckingham Palace for the King's inspection. Subject to His Majesty's approval the cast will be used in designing all the dies necessary in manufacturing King Edward VIII stamps.

We thank Stanley Gibbons Ltd. for their courtesy in loaning the stamps from which the illustrations on this page have been made.

Competition Corner

IF I WERE NOT MYSELF, WHOM WOULD I LIKE TO BE?

Every boy, no matter how contented he may be with his own lot, indulges at times in the really pleasant occupation of building "castles in the air." He dreams of the day when he may become a prominent figure in the business or profession of his choice, and inevitably his mind focusses itself upon some great man who has worked his way to the top and stands prominent among his fellows. With this idea in mind it occurred to us recently that it would be extremely interesting to know who are the men whom the vast army of "*M.M.*" readers regard as heroes in their own particular sphere of activity.

The only way of ascertaining this was to devise a voting contest, and for this purpose we give in the centre of this page a list of 10 famous men who may be regarded as outstanding and representative figures in their own walk of life. The object of the competition is to decide which of these men you would prefer to be if you were not yourself. We look forward to the result with interest, for it is certain that the combined voting will reveal many interesting facts bearing upon our readers' ambitions and the directions in which their future careers will run.

This charming study of a child's head gained First Prize in the Overseas section of the November Drawing Contest for V. L. M. Noguera, Buenos Aires, Argentine.

Aviation	Flt. Lt. T. Rose	Science	Lord Rutherford
Motoring	Capt. Eyston	Cricket	Don Bradman
Statesman	Anthony Eden	Rugby	Bert Gadney
Railways	H. N. Gresley	Industry	Lord Nuffield
Tennis	F. J. Perry	Music	Sir Thomas Beecham

The rules of the contest are very simple. Each competitor is required to set out on a post card each of two things:

(1) Which of the men named he would most like to be.

(2) His estimate of the order of popularity of these 10 men as it will be decided by the massed votes of all the competitors.

Competitors will understand, of course, that the person named in section No. 1 must not necessarily be placed at the head of the list in section No. 2.

No reader may submit more than one entry.

Cash prizes of 21/-, 15/-, 10/6 and 5/- respectively, will be awarded to the four competitors who give the most accurate forecasts of the final order of voting. In addition, there will be a number of consolation prizes. In the event of a tie for any of the prizes, preference will be given to the entry displaying the neatest or most novel presentation.

Entries should be addressed to "Vocation Vote, Meccano Magazine, Binns Road, Liverpool 13," and must reach this office not later than 30th April. A separate set of prizes will be reserved for entries from Overseas readers. Overseas entries must arrive not later than 31st July.

The 1936 Photo Contests

Throughout the coming spring and summer we shall offer prizes each month for the best and most interesting photographs submitted by readers. The photographs may be of any subject, and may be made with any make of camera, plate, film or paper. The only conditions will be that each photograph must bear the reader's name, age and address, and a title on its back. The exposure must have been made by the competitor, but the developing and printing may be professionally done.

Each month's competition will be divided into two groups, Home for those living in Great Britain, Ireland and the Channel Islands, and Overseas for those living outside those areas. Each group will be divided into two sections, A for those aged 16 and over, B for those under 16; and cash prizes of 21/- and 10/6, will be awarded in each section.

Entries sent this month must be addressed "April Photo Contest, Meccano Magazine, Binns Road, Liverpool 13," and must arrive not later than 30th April. Overseas readers should address as for the April Competition all entries that can reach us before the Overseas closing date for that Contest, 31st July.

Competition Closing Dates

HOME

Vocation Voting Contest ...	30th April
April Photo Contest ...	30th April

OVERSEAS

January Cover Voting Contest ...	30th April
January Drawing Contest ...	30th April
February Crossword Puzzle ...	30th May
February Drawing Contest...	30th May
Meccano Limericks ...	30th June
March Drawing Contest ...	30th June
Vocation Voting Contest ...	31st July
April Photo Contest ...	31st July

Watch the Closing Dates:

Competitors, both Home and Overseas, are particularly requested to make a careful note of the closing dates of the competitions.

COMPETITION RESULTS

HOME

February Crossword Puzzle.—1. H. McLachlan (Edinburgh); 2. B. Hardie (Bristol); 3. A. J. Anderson (Perth); 4. G. Burgess (London, N.12). Special Prize: E. H. Dalgleish (Nottingham).

February Drawing Contest.—First Prizes: Section A, D. H. Gibbs (Dundee); Section B, O. Collingwood (Redhill). Second Prizes: Section A, I. Macbryde (Paisley); Section B, J. T. Carr (Purley). Consolation Prizes: Section A, C. Williams (Manchester); Section B, B. Kett (Upminster).

OVERSEAS

November Drawing Contest.—First Prizes: Section A, V. L. M. Noguera (Buenos Aires); Section B, D. J. Johnson (Capetown). Second Prizes: Section A, D. E. Yockney (Auckland, N.Z.); Section B, G. F. Emmerson (Greymouth, N.Z.). Special Prize: Section A, S. D. Kurlawalla (Bombay).

True Firework Story.—1. R. Simpson (Sydney); 2. T. B. Johnson (Capetown); 3. B. N. Collie (Montreal); 4. W. J. E. Evans (Toronto).

November Sketchograms.—First Prizes: Section A, C. J. Mallia (Malta); Section B, G. F. Emmerson (Greymouth, N.Z.). Second Prizes: Section A, S. D. Kurlawalla (Bombay); N. Palmer (Wellington, N.Z.).

FUEL ECONOMY

Swimming Instructor: "That's better, Sir; you ain't swallerin' so much water—doing more to the gallon, so to speak."

* * * *

American: "Why, I can get across London streets with my eyes shut."
Englishman: "I once had a friend who boasted similarly."
American: "Well, and did he get across?"
Englishman: "Yes, sir! A marble one."

* * * *

"I have a brother who got himself into trouble by opening too many offices?"
"Did he over-expand?"
"No, the night watchman caught him."

* * * *

Teacher: "Next time you are late, you must bring an excuse."
Tommy: "Who from?"
Teacher: "Your father."
Tommy: "He's no good at excuses; mother finds him out every time."

* * * *

The new servant was clearing up when the distinguished writer entered his study. "You are not burning my papers?" he exclaimed, seeing the girl by the fire.
"It's all right, sir," replied the girl. "It's only some that's covered with writing. I've left the clean paper alone."

* * * *

Blimey, I'm fed up with this new foreman. 'E came to me this morning an' sez, 'ere you down in that 'ole, jump out! So out I pops. Jump in again, he says, so in I jumps. Out again, he says, and in, an' I does. So 'ere, I says, what's all this about? You just keep on jumpin' in an' out, he says, you bring more out on your boots than you do on your shovel.

* * * *

Tom had just returned from a visit to Germany.
"Did you have much trouble with your German in Berlin?" a friend asked.
"None whatever" he replied, "but the Germans did."

* * * *

Jack: "Our cat is bigger at night than in the day-time."
Tom: "How so?"
Jack: "Because it's let out at night and taken in in the morning."

* * * *

Visitor: "And what's your name, my good man?"
Prisoner: "9742."
Visitor: "Is that your real name?"
Prisoner: "Naw, dat's just me pen name."

* * * *

"Mother says she could have soled her boots with that steak!"
"Well, why didn't she?"
"She could not get the nails through!"

* * * *

Pat: "That was a foine sintiment Casey expressed at the dinner last noight."
Mike: "What was it?"
Pat: "He said that the swatest memories in loife are the ricollections of things forgotten."

A SLOW TRAIN

Ticket Collector: "Madam, your boy can't pass at half fare, he's too large."
Boy's Mother: "He may be too large now, but he was small enough when we started."

* * * *

Small boy: "What is a pedestrian, Daddy?"
Dad: "It's a man who has a wife, a daughter, two sons and a car."

* * * *

Friend (to artist): "I hear you are giving up your studio."
Artist: "Oh no, I'm not, whoever told you that?"
Friend: "Your landlord."

* * * *

American: "There are parts of America so fertile that if you drop an acorn into your garden at night, next morning up comes an oak tree."
Englishman: "Well, there's nothing remarkable about that. There are parts of England so fertile that if you casually drop a dead cat into your garden at night, next morning up comes a sanitary inspector."

* * * *

ASKING FOR TROUBLE

"P'r'aps yer shouldn't a painted yer letters on, Len, ain't they serspicious?"
Courtesy "*L.M.S. Magazine.*"

* * * *

Mother: "One helping of pudding is enough for a small boy."
Tommy: "Yet you say you want me to eat properly and you won't give me any chance to practise."

* * * *

Bob: "If Shapespeare were here to-day, he would be looked on as a remarkable man."
Bill: "Yes, he'd be more than 300 years old."

* * * *

"Willie," said the Sunday-school teacher, "you shouldn't talk like that to your playmate. Have you ever thought of heaping coals of fire on his head?"
"No, I haven't," said Willie, "but it's a great idea."

* * * *

Waiter: "Your coffee is special, sir; from South America."
Diner: "Oh, so that's where you've been, is it?"

A MATTER OF BUSINESS

Sam: "When're you going to pay me that £2 for pasturing your heifer? I've had her now for about ten weeks."
Bob: "Why, Sam, the critter ain't worth more'n £3."
Sam: "Well, s'posin' I keep her for what you owe me?"
Bob: "Not by a jugful. Tell you what I'll do. You keep her two weeks more an' you can have her."

* * * *

A visitor called at a doctor's house. "Is your father at home, dear?" she asked the doctor's small daughter.
"No, he's out giving an anæsthetic."
"That's a big word. What does it mean?"
"Three guineas," the child replied.

* * * *

Captain of cricket team (to new resident): "Will you join our cricket club, sir?"
New Resident: "Well, really, I'm afraid I know absolutely nothing about the game, I couldn't do anything except umpire."

* * * *

"Waiter! waiter! What is the meaning of this? There are two flies swimming about in my soup."
"Nonsense, sir. Why, they are both dead."

* * * *

A NEW ONE

Office Boy: "Please can I have the day off to-morrow to go to—"
Employer: "Grandmother to be buried, I suppose?"
Office Boy: "No, sir; married."

* * * *

Customer: "You're a young man to be left in charge of a chemist's shop. Have you a diploma?"
Assistant: "No, madam; but we have a preparation of our own that's just as good."

* * * *

Insurance Agent: "But you surely agree to taking out an insurance policy to cover your burial expenses?"
Wily Scot: "Na, na, mon; I micht be lost at sea."

* * * *

Mother: "I don't think the man upstairs likes Johnnie to play on his drum."
Father: "Why?"
Mother: "Well, this afternoon he gave Johnnie a knife and asked him if he knew what was inside the drum."

* * * *

"I'm not going to work at this place any more, Bill."
"Why?"
"Well, the boss passed a remark this morning that I didn't like."
"What was it?"
"He said, 'Jones, you won't be wanted here after this week.'"

* * * *

FORE AND AFT

A sailor was taking a short cut across a golf course, when a golf ball struck him on the back of the head.
"It wasn't my fault, I shouted 'Fore,'" spluttered the owner of the ball.
"Aye," replied the tar, "yer shouted 'Fore,' but the confounded thing struck me aft."

"Holiday Haunts"

(Great Western Railway. 6d.)

The holiday season is here again and we are all beginning to ask ourselves where we shall go. The 1936 edition of the G.W.R. Holiday Haunts Guide has been compiled to help us to answer this question, and in its 1,024 pages it deals with hundreds of inland and seaside holiday resorts in the area served by that company. The special attractions of these resorts are well described, and hundreds of fine photogravure illustrations not only add to the knowledge on which a decision will be based, but also make the volume highly attractive.

The book is divided into seven sections, each dealing with a definite holiday region. It includes excellent maps, and gives the addresses of no fewer than 8,300 hotels, boarding houses, private apartments and farmhouses. As a source of information to holiday makers it is complete and highly satisfactory, and all who are contemplating a holiday should not fail to consult it. Copies can be obtained at all G.W.R. station bookstalls and enquiry offices.

A working model of the S.R. cross-channel steamer "The Maid of Rutland," built by our reader H. Goodwin, of Birmingham. Photograph by courtesy of the "Bournville Works Magazine."

"Walking at Week-ends"

By S. P. B. Mais. (Southern Railway. Price 6d.)

The Southern Railway not only afford facilities for ramblers who wish to reach the interesting country in the wide area they cover, but also help them to make the most of their opportunities by publishing booklets describing suitable walks. This volume is the second written for this purpose by Mr. Mais and published by the S.R. The 14 rambles described in it cover districts in Kent, Sussex and Hampshire.

The book contains 128 pages. Each walk is clearly shown by means of a special map, and in addition there are many photographs of the country covered. The book is of a convenient size to fit the pocket, and has waterproof covers. It can be obtained at S.R. station bookstalls and enquiry offices.

The 1936 Model Railway Club Exhibition

The 1936 Exhibition of the Model Railway Club, to be held at the Central Hall, Westminster, during Easter week, will include a display of members' work, with working steam locomotives of all gauges up to 1½ in. scale. Free rides behind the larger locomotives will be given to visitors. Other exhibits will be a working Gauge O electric railway and a free cinematograph show.

The Exhibition will be opened at 2 p.m. on Tuesday, 14th April, and will continue until Saturday, 18th April, the hours of opening from Wednesday to Saturday being 11 a.m. It will remain open each night until 10 p.m., and the price of admission is 1/3, children under 12 years of age 6d. Refreshments will be available.

Gibbons' Simplified Stamp Catalogue

The extraordinary popularity of the stamp collecting hobby is displayed in striking manner by the appearance of the fourth edition of *Stanley Gibbons' Simplified Stamp Catalogue.* The third edition was published as recently as the end of October last, when supplies that were thought sufficient to last a year were printed. Actually the edition sold out within four months, and a new one has had to be prepared at short notice in order to meet a continuing demand.

The opportunity has been taken to include all recent issues of stamps of the British Empire and foreign countries. These additions have involved listing 500 new stamps and including 100 additional illustrations, and the catalogue now gives details of over 54,500 stamps, and contains 6,900 full-sized reproductions of them. Among the novelties now listed for the first time are the Queen Astrid mourning stamps, the new series from the Malayan Postal Union, and the fine Nigerian pictorials, in addition to the latest prices for the Jubilee issues.

The evidence given in the new edition of the amazing popularity of the Silver Jubilee stamps is perhaps its most striking feature. Many notable rises in price are shown. For example, the South West African set, quoted in the third edition at 4/-, is now priced at 25/-, and it may be added that since the catalogue went to press the price of this set has jumped to 40/-!

The catalogue is an ideal one for young collectors, and the information in it is more than four months in advance of that in any other catalogue. Copies can be obtained from any stamp dealer, price 5/-, or direct from Stanley Gibbons Ltd., 391, Strand, London, W.C.2, 5/6 post paid in the United Kingdom, 6/2 abroad.

Tents for Campers

Camping enthusiasts know that whatever part of their equipment may be the subject of economy, the tent itself must be sound. Readers who contemplate renewing this essential item, or buying a new tent in order to enjoy a camping holiday for the first time, will be interested in the new season's catalogue just issued by Nuttall and Company, Goodmayes, Ilford. This company specialise in tents fitted with wire cable edges and ridges, and it is claimed that these fittings ensure firm anchorage and a square "set" throughout the life of the tent.

An effective proof of the sturdiness of Nuttall and Company's tents products was given last September, when one of them erected in a field at Barkingside withstood the full force of a 90 m.p.h. gale without suffering the slightest damage.

A copy of the catalogue will be sent, free of charge, to any reader who applies to Nuttall and Company, Goodmayes, Ilford, and mentions the "*M.M.*"

Free Stamp List for "*M.M.*" Readers

The 1936 price list newly issued by our advertiser, Mr. Michael Herbert, is full of interest for stamp collecting readers. It gives details of a wide range of sets and packets, including many subject packets that provide good starting points for building up specialist subject collections such as we have recommended in our stamp pages recently.

Mr. Herbert, whose address is 8, Woodstock Road, Walthamstow, London, E.17, will be glad to send a copy of the list, post free, to any "*M.M.*" reader who applies for one.

MECCANO MAGAZINE

Editorial Office:
Binns Road, Liverpool 13
England

Vol. XXI. No. 5
May, 1936

With the Editor

A Duke who was a Coal Merchant

It is 200 years this month since the birth of the third Duke of Bridgewater, who is chiefly remembered by the canal built for him by James Brindley, the famous engineer. The charges made for transporting coal by road and river from the Duke's collieries at Worsley to Manchester and Liverpool were so heavy that he resolved to take it there on his own canal, and he called Brindley in to plan the necessary waterway. The idea of creating a new artificial river was sufficiently startling, for no canal for carrying merchandise then existed in England; but when Brindley proposed to take it across the River Irwell on a lofty bridge he was laughed at as a madman and his proposed aqueduct was sneeringly described as a castle in the air. It soon became a reality, however, and the novel spectacle then was seen of barges sailing over a bridge.

When Brindley built his aqueduct he did not anticipate that some day the Irwell beneath it would become part of a great ship canal between Manchester and the sea. His structure left insufficient headroom for traffic using the new canal, and a swing bridge therefore was constructed to carry the Bridgewater Canal over the waterway. This swing bridge was opened in 1893 and Brindley's "castle in the air" was then demolished.

The Duke's canal cost him about £220,000, and many times during its construction he was so short of money that he was compelled to send his agent round his tenants to collect any small sums that he could get. When the work was completed the Duke often watched the busy scene in his coalyard at Manchester, where people went with wagons, wheelbarrows, baskets and even aprons for supplies, and it is recorded that on one occasion he gave a customer a "lift up" with a sack of coal! The man was so astonished when he was informed who had helped him that he immediately dropped the sack, so that the Duke's well-meant effort was wasted.

Britain's wonder ship, the Cunard White Star liner "Queen Mary," which is described in the article on page 252. Our photograph shows the great vessel at Greenock, and is reproduced by courtesy of B. and A. Feilden, Liverpool.

Clock That Struck Thirteen

Visitors from all parts flocked to see Brindley's canal and the underground waterways beneath Worsley Hill along which barges penetrated to the workings of the Duke's coal mine. One of the curiosities they encountered at Worsley was a clock that struck 13 times at 1 p.m. The story is that the Duke's workmen excused themselves for late arrival in the afternoon by alleging that they did not always hear the single stroke that called them back at one o'clock. The Duke had noticed no delay in leaving off work at noon, when the clock struck 12 times, and devised this simple but remarkable scheme to ensure equal promptitude in returning.

Oil in Great Britain

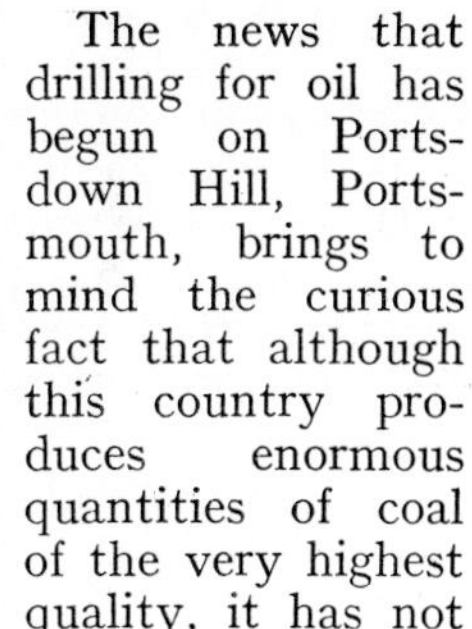

The news that drilling for oil has begun on Portsdown Hill, Portsmouth, brings to mind the curious fact that although this country produces enormous quantities of coal of the very highest quality, it has not so far yielded any of the rival fuel. Previous efforts have been made to find oil in Great Britain, but these were not commercially successful, and at present we are compelled to import our requirements. It is expected that we shall have to wait two years to learn if there is any prospect that the boring now in progress will tap a deeply buried reservoir of petroleum, but the outcome of the work will be awaited with keen interest. It seems difficult to believe that forests of derricks will ever make their appearance in this country.

One reason for the widespread use of oil is the ease with which it can be stored and handled. This has led to its use in ships, for instance, and many vessels that formerly burned coal in the furnaces of their boilers now burn oil. The "*Mauretania*," the most famous of all great ships, was converted from coal to oil in 1921, and those who read the article on coaling giant liners that appeared on page 16 of the January issue will be interested to learn that the Orient liner "*Ormonde*" underwent a similar change a few years ago.

Electro-Magnets in Industry

Handling Large Masses of Steel and Iron

OUR cover this month shows an overhead travelling crane lifting an iron casting by means of a circular electro-magnet. Steel or iron articles so lifted are literally hung underneath the magnet, and are held there in a tenacious grip by an invisible force until they are released by the movement of a switch. Cranes of this type work swiftly and easily, and their use illustrates one of the many important applications of the electro-magnet in industry.

An electro-magnet lifting iron turnings. The illustrations to this article are reproduced by courtesy of the Igranic Electric Co. Ltd.

The principle on which an electro-magnet works is simple. A rod of soft iron becomes a magnet when an electric current is passed through a coil surrounding it, and it loses its magnetism immediately the current is switched off. The design of electro-magnets used in industry for lifting is based on this. Coils are wound round soft iron cores, the attracting ends or poles of which are given the shapes and positions best suited for the purposes to which they are to be applied. The electro-magnet thus built up is suspended by means of a crane, and the leads from its coils are suitably connected to a source of current.

It is the ease with which electro-magnets can be controlled that makes them so valuable. They only act as magnets when current is passing through their coils, and therefore can readily be made to pick up or put down their loads exactly when required to do so. This cannot be done with permanent magnets, which cannot easily be made to part with the iron or steel they pick up; and electro-magnets have the further advantage over those of the permanent kind that they can be made much more powerful without difficulty by simply using larger windings, with more turns in them, and increasing the strength of the current.

Lifting ships' plates by means of electro-magnets.

Electro-magnets are used very largely for lifting heavy masses of iron and steel in foundries, factories and shipyards. Cranes of various types are installed to facilitate the handling of the metal. Those of the ordinary type involve such accessories as chains, ropes, and grappling hooks, but these are unnecessary when a crane is fitted with an electro-magnet. The operation of such a crane is very simple. The magnet is lowered until it is in contact with the load and the current is switched on. The crane then lifts the magnet, with its load adhering to it, and transports it to the new position desired. The magnet is then lowered to a safe position at rest, and the current is switched off, when the load is immediately released.

Different types of electro-magnets for lifting purposes have been designed in order to deal with the various tasks for which such devices are suitable. Handling billets, castings, pig iron and scrap is heavy work, and the circular magnet shown on our cover is an example of the more powerful magnets applied to purposes of this kind. The working surface on the underside of this magnet is heavily ribbed, so that it will have better gripping power on the irregular shapes with which it has to deal. Plates, bars and tubes are dealt with by means of rectangular magnets designed for lighter duty, and the lower illustration on this page shows magnets of this kind lifting ships' plates. The working surfaces of these magnets are flat, so that a good grip is readily obtained on smooth-faced metallic objects. Thin sheets or long thin bars are dealt with by mounting the magnets on spreader-bars, as shown in our illustration, in order to prevent them from drooping at their ends. If this were allowed, the contact with the magnetic pole might not be sufficient to ensure the safe transport of the load.

The upper photograph on this page shows a heap of turnings being lifted by means of an electro-magnet. In this case, and in those in which piles of scrap or small pieces of metal are involved, magnetic induction plays a part. Each piece of scrap metal in contact with the magnetic pole itself immediately becomes capable of attaching to itself a second piece, and this in turn is similarly converted into a small magnet. Thus an immense mass of turnings or scrap can readily be lifted, although the greater part of the mass is not actually in direct contact with the magnet.

Atmospheric conditions make no difference to the employment of a magnet, and electro-magnetic cranes are frequently employed in the open air. They can indeed be employed under water, and there they prove useful in salvaging operations.

A New 65-ton Trailer

Transporting Heavy Machinery by Road

SPEED in transport is an important factor in modern industry, and every effort continually is being made to reduce the time during which goods of all kinds are in transit by road and rail. Many special difficulties have to be overcome in dealing with problems that arise in this connection. One of these concerns the transport of bulky machinery, such as large engines, boilers and transformers. These often are too large to be carried intact by ordinary means, and often valuable time must be spent in dismantling a newly-built machine in order to reduce it to parts of convenient size for transport, and in re-assembling it on its arrival at its destination. The cost of the work involved in these operations also has to be taken into account.

Rear view of the Dyson 65-ton trailer, showing 10 of the 12 triple-tyred wheels, and the steering turntable over the front axle. The illustrations on this page are reproduced by courtesy of R. A. Dyson and Co.

One of the means adopted for reducing the time spent in the transport of exceptional loads of this kind is the provision of trailers specially designed to carry them. These trailers usually are of great size and are hauled by lorries or traction engines. They travel comparatively slowly and the time taken in carrying a machine by road naturally exceeds that required to despatch its separate parts, but a gain is apparent when the times required in the two cases to complete the installation are compared.

A giant boiler loaded on the 65-ton trailer.

An interesting trailer built by R. A. Dyson and Co. Ltd., Liverpool, for Charles D. Holmes and Co. Ltd., of Hull, is illustrated on this page. It was designed to carry engines and boilers, either fully erected or in large sections, from the works of Charles D. Holmes and Co. Ltd., to the docks, where they are hoisted directly into position in the vessels for which they are intended. It is 18 ft. in length and 10 ft. 6 in. in width and is carried on 12 triple-tyred wheels. The wheels are arranged in three rows of four, each row comprising two pairs of wheels carried on a short axle mounted on springs. This arrangement allows the wheels to adapt themselves to surface irregularities and road camber. The load therefore is always evenly distributed and the maximum weight per inch width of tyre is only 7 cwt.

An additional aid in spreading the load over the wheels, and thus of avoiding damage to the road surface, is a balance beam connecting the second and rear lines of axles. This is particularly useful when ascending or descending a hill, when it prevents one row of wheels from being overloaded.

Steering is effected by means of a turntable placed centrally over the front axles and connected to them. The second pair of axles are independently pivoted at their centres, and are connected by shafts to the turntable so that the wheels mounted on them follow in the tracks of those of the first row. Thus the vehicle turns easily and smoothly, and undue wear on the tyres is avoided. Smooth running is ensured by the use of Timken roller bearings in the wheel mountings and Ransome and Marles needle roller bearings on the compensating arrangement between the second and rear axles, and thus jerky action that may disturb the position of the load is prevented. Solid Dunlop rubber tyres are fitted to all the wheels, the triple tyres on the eight rear wheels being 20 in. by 26 in. by 6 in. in dimensions, and those on the four front wheels measuring 20 in. by 14 in. by 6 in.

The main chassis members of the unit consist of two 8 in. by 3 in. channels with plates 13½ in. in width and ½ in. in thickness riveted at the top and bottom, and the general design of the platform assists in the correct distribution. The trailer is so low that tall machinery can be carried under bridges where normally there would not be enough clearance.

"Queen Mary"

More Details of Britain's Greatest Liner

THE departure of the Cunard White Star liner *"Queen Mary"* from Clydebank provided a unique thrill for British people at home and throughout the Empire. Her passage down the Clyde was witnessed by thousands of spectators from all parts of Great Britain, who watched with breathless interest as she safely negotiated one by one the troublesome bends in the river. As she moved onward into more open water she passed the burned-out *"Atlantique"* waiting to be towed up the river to be broken up, and then occurred a moving little episode. *"Queen Mary,"* in all the glowing splendour of her youth, sent out a siren blast of recognition and sympathy; and received in reply a melancholy note from the French liner with whom fate had dealt so hardly.

The "Queen Mary," the stateliest vessel afloat, on the completion of her voyage down the Clyde. Photograph by courtesy of B. and A. Feilden, Blundellsands, Liverpool 23.

When *"Queen Mary"* reached her moorings at Greenock she continued to be a centre of attraction as she lay there brilliantly illuminated, with the waves rippling round her for the first time. Then came the southward voyage to Southampton, where again she was greeted by immense crowds as she was carefully manœuvred into the King George V graving dock, the largest in the world, for the final examination of the hull before the official trials.

The gross tonnage of the *"Queen Mary"* is 80,773, and she is 1,018 ft. in overall length and 1,004 ft. in length on the waterline. Her beam is 110 ft. From keel to masthead she measures 234 ft., and if she were placed in Trafalgar Square her foremast would tower 64 ft. above the highest point of the Nelson column. An interesting indication of her immense size is given by the fact that 70,000 gallons of paint were required to cover her exterior and interior surfaces. These have a total area of 50 acres, or roughly twice that of Waterloo Station.

The top of the first of the vessel's three giant funnels is 180 ft. above the keel and more than 70 ft. above the highest deck. Its greatest diameter is 36 ft. and its circumference 100 ft. The remaining funnels are equal in width, but slightly less in height, an arrangement that helps to keep the decks and ventilators of the vessel clear of smoke and fumes.

It is almost 96 years since the first Cunard liner made her appearance. This was the *"Britannia,"* which began her service in 1840. The *"Britannia"* was a large vessel for her time, but so great have been the advances in shipbuilding and engineering since her day, that the giant funnels of the latest addition to the Cunard fleet are wide enough to enable her hull to be passed through them!

Commodore Sir Edgar Britten, the first captain of the "Queen Mary," inspecting one of the vessel's 16-ton anchors. This illustration and those on the opposite page are reproduced by courtesy of Cunard White Star Limited.

When the *"Queen Mary"* was being planned, the utmost care was taken to ensure that she should be the most up-to-date and scientifically constructed vessel in the world. More than 7,000 experiments were made on models before her form was finally determined. Each model was tried in the experimental tank at Clydebank of John Brown and Co. Ltd., her builders. All the features of an Atlantic hurricane can be reproduced in miniature in this tank, and the models travelled a total distance of more than 1,000 miles up and down it during the trials, the result of which is a hull of a design to allow full use to be made of the ship's engines and to enable the sailing programme aimed at by her owners to be maintained in all weathers.

The hull structure of the *"Queen Mary"* comprises 12 decks, from the sun deck down to the lower decks, which are discontinuous in order to leave room for her extensive machinery. An unusual feature of its construction has been the use of special steel with the high tensile strength of 40 lb. per sq. in. in the superstructure. Altogether the total weight of metal in the hull and machinery is more than 50,000 tons, and the launching weight of the vessel, that is the weight of the hull alone, without machinery or equipment, was about 40,000 tons.

Steel plates ranging in length from 8 ft. to 30 ft. were riveted together in forming the hull. These plates and the girders employed in construction were hoisted into position by means of derricks erected in long lines along each side of the building berth, and as the vessel rose higher electric lifts were installed in order to carry the workmen to their tasks. Part of the riveting was carried out by hand, but a large proportion of the 10,000,000 rivets required were hammered in by means of hydraulic and pneumatic machines. If placed end to end these rivets would stretch a distance of more than 270 miles, or nearly from London to Newcastle.

One of the greatest feats accomplished during the building of the *"Queen Mary"* was the transport from Darlington to Clydebank of the stern frame, shaft brackets and rudder, which together weigh nearly 600 tons. The rudder itself weighs more than 140 tons. It is the largest ever constructed for any ship, and the task of hoisting it into position involved many days of intricate work. The anchors are of giant size and indeed are the largest ever installed in an ocean liner. Each weighs 16 tons and is of special design. The anchor cables,

wire hawsers and ropes used on the vessel have a total length of more than four miles, and special experiments were made in order to find the best position on the bows of the vessel for the hawse pipes, through which the anchor cables run.

Immense power is required to drive a great vessel through the water at high speed. The space devoted to machinery in the *"Queen Mary"* therefore is unusually large, and in length actually rivals some of the largest Atlantic liners. Four sets of Parsons single reduction gear turbines are installed. These are independent and act on four screw propellers. Each set consists of four turbines working in series and driving through pinions a large gear wheel connected to the line shafting. The casings of two of the turbines incorporate astern turbines, for use when reversing or manœuvring, that drive the outer propeller shafts. Altogether there are 257,000 turbine blades, varying in length from nearly 2 in. to more than 16 in., and every one of these was tested separately and fitted by hand.

Each of the four giant gear wheels is 14 ft. in diameter, and together they weigh nearly 320 tons. In spite of their colossal size, they have been constructed to very fine limits of workmanship. Each is cut to an accuracy of a thousandth of an inch, and the process of cutting each wheel occupied from two to three months. The gear cases weigh 200 tons and have been fitted to a limit of 1½ thousandths of an inch.

Steam for the four sets of turbines is supplied from 24 enormous boilers with a working pressure of 400 lb. per sq. in., occupying four rooms. The number of tubes in these boilers is nearly 160,000 and the main steam piping is more than 2,000 ft. in length. Three cylindrical boilers with a working pressure of 250 lb. per sq. in. also are installed. Steam for kitchen purposes is supplied by three double-ended boilers in a separate room, and these can be run independently of the main boilers, whether the vessel is at sea or standing in harbour. Oil fuel is used. This is stored in nearly 50 bunkers with a capacity of 6,300 tons, and nearly 3,000 ft. of piping lead from these to the furnace burners, of which there are nearly 200. There are six filling stations for oil fuelling and the bunkers can be refilled in eight hours.

The propellers of the *"Queen Mary"* are nearly 20 ft. in diameter and are the largest in the world. Altogether eight have been provided, leaving four spare ones for emergencies and replacements. They are of turbiston bronze and are four-bladed. The casting weight of each was 53 tons, and the molten metal was carried to the mould in huge ladles suspended from overhead travelling cranes that carried 20 tons. The casting took eight days to cool off, and after machining and polishing weighed 35 tons, or 10 tons more than the largest propellers previously manufactured. Each propeller was subjected to a very severe test in order to ensure perfect balance, and when on the balancing machine the slightest touch of the finger on the extreme edge of the blade was sufficient to cause it to revolve.

Electricity is used for practically all purposes in the new liner except that of actually propelling her, and she can fairly be described as the greatest electric power station afloat, for the seven 220-volt, 1,300-kW turbo-generators with which she is equipped have sufficient capacity to supply the full services of a town of nearly 150,000 people. Three of the sets provide current for deck machinery and hotel services. The four remaining turbo-generators supply power for driving auxiliary machinery in connection with the propelling plant and serve the lighting installation. One usually will be a spare, but all four can be run together. The two groups of generators are housed in separate rooms, and are designed to work independently. They can be interconnected, however, so that if one of them fails the other can supply a proportion of the current required for the services it maintains. Altogether 4,000 miles of cable are required to distribute the electrical energy generated.

From a navigational point of view the *"Queen Mary"* is wonderfully planned and every possible precaution is taken to ensure against mishap. The steering gear is duplicated so that if anything should go wrong with one set the other can be brought into use in a few seconds. A very small wheel is moved by the helmsman, and the power he exerts is increased stage by stage by gigantic hydraulic rams in order to move the 140-ton rudder easily and rapidly. The gyro pilot also is installed. When the course required has been set, this automatic steersman maintains it correctly, whatever the weather may be, and the steering is then more accurate than that of the most skilled of helmsmen.

The comfort of the officers on watch has been carefully studied. The wheelhouse is heated, and the front of the bridge itself is curved in such a manner that the air meeting it is deflected upward, to pass through a slot at the top of the bridge front and create a high pressure area in which the air is moving upward clear of the bridge. Anyone standing immediately behind the bridge front therefore is in an area of calm. Even in the exposed position in the crow's nest high up on the foremast, 130 ft. above the waterline, the men on watch will be well protected from the weather, for a glass screen is provided and electric heaters add to their comfort. The crow's nest is reached by climbing 110 iron steps inside the foremast, and telephonic means of communicating with the bridge are provided.

The *"Queen Mary"* is provided with 24 motor lifeboats, built of steel and 40 ft. in length, each of which can carry 145 people.

The photograph at the head of the page shows the "Queen Mary" at Greenock after her trip from the builder's yard at Clydebank. In the lower illustration, the huge sirens on the forward funnel of the vessel are seen. These can be heard at a distance of 10 miles.

On the Footplate of the Highland Mail

Fine Running Under Wintry Conditions

By a Railway Engineer

THERE is surely no more fascinating route in Britain than the Highland main line from Perth to Inverness. In the Pass of Druimuachdar it rises to 1,484 ft. above sea level—the highest altitude of main line railways in these islands—and at all times of the year train operation is fraught with considerable difficulty. It is indeed an eloquent testimony to the severity of the grades that the efficient Stanier 2-cylinder 4–6–0s are limited to a maximum tare load of 255 tons up the worst banks; on the Western Division these engines take up to 450 tons unpiloted, and I have timed one of them at 70 m.p.h. on the level with a gross load of 490 tons behind the tender.

I was privileged to ride from Perth to Inverness on the footplate of the 6.25 a.m. North Mail, and wintry weather with deep snow on the Grampians, combined with splendid locomotive work, made the trip one of the most enthralling runs I have ever experienced. This remarkable train carries, in addition to the postal section, sleeping car portions from both Euston and King's Cross, and a breakfast car; it is easily the heaviest train on the Highland and also considerably the fastest. On the day of my trip, an icy morning in mid-January, we had a load of no less than 15 bogie coaches, 455 tons tare and 490 tons with passengers and mails. Our train engine was No. 5086, a Stanier 4–6–0 in charge of Driver Nicholson and Fireman Wilson of Inverness; but with such a load piloting was absolutely essential, and we had in front a standard "Mogul" of the parallel-boiler type, No. 2805, with Driver Robertson of Perth at the regulator.

A heavy double-headed Highland express crossing the viaduct in the densely-wooded Pass of Killiecrankie. The engines are a standard L.M.S.R. 2-6-0 piloting a 4-6-0 of the Highland "River" class. Photograph reproduced by courtesy of Mr. H. C. Casserley.

Before 6 a.m. the Post Office sorters were at work. The vans equipped with the pick-up apparatus are mighty cold in such weather and the men were wearing overcoats and great mufflers under their yellow overalls. I was glad of the warmth in the cab of No. 5086. The footplate arrangements of these engines are almost identical with those of the "Princess Royal" class 4–6–2s, except in respect of the fire-doors. The "Princesses" have fireclay doors, which slide outward on rollers; whereas these 4–6–0s have an ordinary hinged door similar to that of the "Royal Scots." Mail traffic was so heavy that it was not until 6.42 a.m. that we got the "right-away," but then it was to make a brilliant start indeed.

The cab of a Highland 4-6-0 of the "Castle" class, showing the principal fittings. In the left-hand corner is the handle of the steam reversing gear.

As far as Stanley Junction we are on the route of *"The Granite City"* express, the running of which I described in the *"M.M."* for April 1935. Up continuously rising grades speed rose to 50½ m.p.h. at Luncarty, but then we slackened severely to take the sharp curve on to the Highland line at Stanley. The grade now steepened to 1 in 93, but with No. 5086 working on 30 per cent. cut-off and full regulator, we picked up from 15 to 27 m.p.h. in 1½ miles, and down the sharp fall to Murthly we quickly attained 55 m.p.h. We were through this station, 10¼ miles, in 15¾ minutes, and already 2¼ minutes of our late start had been regained.

From Stanley Junction to Blair Atholl the line is single, but at the passing loops tablets are exchanged at full speed. The apparatus is almost identical with that used in Ireland on the N.C.C. section of the L.M.S.R. which I described in the January 1936 number of the *"M.M.,"* when writing of the *"Portrush Flyer."* We were now launched on the 1 in 80 ascent to Kingswood Crossing; Nicholson advanced the cut-off to 40 per cent. and the beat developed into a tremendous roar. The pilot was a thrilling sight. The glare from her fire silhouetted the front of No. 5086, and in the darkness her exhaust was a vertical column, tinged dull red. We breasted the summit at the excellent rate of 34 m.p.h. and almost immediately the regulator was brought back to the "drifting" position, giving the merest breath of steam.

Soon we were bucketing down the 1 in 80 to Dunkeld at 55 m.p.h. Although it was now 7 o'clock, and there was a brilliant moon, it was pitch dark going through the woods and cuttings; all one could see ahead was the drifting steam from No. 2805 lighted by the fire, which looked like great tongues of flame. For a few moments it was inexpressibly weird. Then we swung through Dunkeld, 15½ miles from Perth, in 22¼ minutes, and were soon out in the open of the Tay Valley. For nearly 10 miles here the line is practically level and, with No. 5086 notched up to 20 per cent., speed rose to 62 m.p.h. By Dalguise 3¼ minutes had been regained, but then we had to make a special stop at Ballinluig, 23½ miles from Perth.

Climbing at 1 in 100, the two engines got their big train under way in good style, only to have to stop again at Pitlochry, five miles farther on and right in the middle of a 1 in 85 bank. The 28½ miles from Perth had taken 41¾ minutes, a very smart time, including as it did the stop at Ballinluig. Now in the beauty of a cloudless dawn we climbed into the Pass of Killiecrankie. In the narrowest part of the defile the railway crosses a tributary of the River Garry on a high viaduct, the hillsides are densely wooded, and high on the right there is a glimpse of Ben Vrackie. Once into the pass the line becomes level, and after we had exchanged tablets at Killiecrankie station speed rose to 46 m.p.h. before the stop at Blair Atholl. The 35¼ miles from Perth had taken 54½ minutes against a schedule of 53 minutes. This latter is for a

non-stop run; our engines, having to make intermediate stops at most difficult locations, had done well indeed to lose but 1½ minutes. The net time was only 47 minutes, a gain of six minutes on schedule.

Now there began the Druimuachdar tug-of-war. The first 4½ miles to Struan, although rising chiefly at 1 in 80, include some short level stretches, but beyond that station come a solid 11 miles almost entirely at 1 in 70. We got away in magnificent style, touching 41 m.p.h. at Struan; but then, with 40 per cent. cut-off and full regulator, speed settled down to a steady 26 m.p.h. up *"The Hill,"* as the enginemen call this bank. In the meantime the scenery was becoming majestic indeed. In the half-light before sunrise the Atholl hills deep in snow gleamed phantom-like against the pale blue sky; as we mounted, the cuttings became flecked with snow, above which the dead bracken rose golden brown.

Higher and higher we climbed up the western side of the broad strath, snow fences protecting the track at exposed places. Then, after rounding a shoulder of the great hills on our left, we turned into the narrowest and wildest part of Glen Garry. The snow lay deep here, the river was a raging torrent; but under a cloudless sky it made a picture of astonishing beauty. All the time the speed remained absolutely steady at 26 m.p.h. Despite this long "grind" on a fairly long cut-off No. 5086 was steaming very freely, in fact the needle seemed a fixture at 225 lb. per sq. in.

The upper illustration shows L.M.S.R. No. 14675, "Taymouth Castle," the first engine of the class to be built. In the lower photograph appears an up Inverness express near Daviot hauled by No. 14764, "Clan Munro," with No. 14691, "Brodie Castle," as pilot. The train includes portions for both Euston and King's Cross.

We were now approaching the dreaded Southern County March. Here the line crosses from Perthshire into Inverness-shire, and this desolate spot at the head of Glen Garry has been the scene of some terrible snow blocks. To-day all is fair—as yet—but both our engines were fitted with small snow ploughs in readiness for any emergency. Now the glen opened out on the left revealing Loch Garry, half frozen over, lying amid the gleaming white hills; we breasted the summit of the worst part of the bank, rapidly accelerated to 41 m.p.h. through Dalnaspidal, and so came into the Pass of Druimuachdar. We were among the giants of the Grampians. Every peak in sight was nearly 3,000 ft.; Ben a'Chaoruinn and the Boar of Badenoch towered on either side of the line, and a wild corrie on the left gave a glimpse of Brauch nan Iomairean and Ben Udlaman. It was an amazing sight to see range upon range of peaks all spotless white; but now heavy clouds were racing across the sky, and there was every sign of rough weather ahead. We took the last mile at 1 in 78 in our stride at a minimum of 39 m.p.h. and so crossed the highest railway summit in Britain, 17½ miles from Blair Atholl, in 36 minutes.

The regulator was quickly brought back to the drifting position, but cut-off was increased to 45 per cent. Had the engine been notched up to 15 or 20 per cent. we should doubtless have attained a very high speed down the steep descent into Strath Spey, but the curves make this out of the question. Using a long cut-off passes a large volume of low-pressure steam through the cylinders and gives a certain amount of cushioning action. The engine in consequence runs at a good steady speed without racing away and needing many brake applications. We worked up to 69 m.p.h., but as we neared Dalwhinnie the sky grew dark, bleak Loch Ericht away on the left was the colour of lead, and we were soon running in the teeth of a blizzard. The visibility was not more than a hundred yards at times, and speed was much reduced; ice packed up against the cab glasses, and the whole landscape was obscured in a flying welter of sleet and snow. Nevertheless we reached Kingussie, 36¼ miles from Blair Atholl, in 57¾ minutes, a further gain of 3¼ minutes on schedule.

Despite the storm we got away again in good style and then quite suddenly ran into clear weather. While the engines were working up to a very lively sprint, the pine forests of Rothiemurchus and the Cairngorm Mountains away to the right looked superb in the early morning sunshine. We touched 65 m.p.h. beyond Kincraig and completed the 11¾ miles from Kingussie to Aviemore in exactly a quarter of an hour—a still further gain of 2 minutes. At Aviemore, this spirited pair of engines came off, having regained no less than 11¼ minutes of lost time.

The load was now reduced to 401 tons tare and 430 tons gross, and our fresh engines were No. 5163, another Stanier 4–6–0, piloted by a Highland 4–6–0 of the "Castle" class built as long ago as 1902; this was No. 14682 *"Beaufort Castle."* I rode on the footplate of this veteran for the first part of the run, and a highly interesting experience it proved. The cab seemed very cramped after that of the spacious Stanier engine; a tarpaulin sheet was stretched from the roof to the tender to provide some additional protection, and it was an unusual thing in those days to look ahead over the top of the boiler through circular windows. The regulator is of the double-handle type, like that of a Great Northern "Atlantic," only much shorter; but the most interesting feature of these engines is the steam reversing gear. When the driver wishes to notch-up he operates a lever like a small regulator, steam is applied to the gear, and the pointer that indicates the cut-off slowly moves back on the scale. As soon as the desired position is reached steam is shut off. This arrangement enables quite fine adjustment of cut-off to be made.

Driver McLeod and Fireman Robertson of Aviemore shed were in charge, and after the first dozen yards or so cut-off was brought back to 40 per cent.; the regulator was gradually opened to five-eighths and we got away in fine style. *"Beaufort Castle"* quickly developed a full-throated roar that completely drowned the exhaust of the train engine. Climbing at 1 in 150 speed rose to 43 m.p.h., but three miles out the gradient steepens to 1 in 75; McLeod opened the regulator still wider, and we went up at 33½ m.p.h. Our 430-ton load would be divided roughly in the proportion of 180 tons to the "Castle" and 250 to the Stanier, so that this was first-class going on such a grade. Just before Carr Bridge there is a slight dip, but unfortunately we had to stop at the station in order to cross the 8.30 a.m. up express from Inverness, the 6¾ miles from Aviemore having been covered in 12 minutes start to stop.

In the ordinary way these two trains pass each other at Slochd summit while the mail is detaching its pilot, but as we were running late we were stopped at Carr Bridge rather than hold up the other train at the summit. This incident shows up clearly the difficulty of working a long single line, for unless both up and down trains are punctual and cross at their scheduled places, simply chaotic delays can occur. It is for this reason that the difficult section between Blair Atholl and Dalwhinnie, over Druimuachdar summit, is double-tracked throughout. We were lucky not to be held up more than five minutes on this occasion.

A Highland goods train approaching Blair Atholl. The engine is 4-6-0 No. 17920 of the "Jones Goods" class, one of which is shown on page 273 as now preserved and repainted in H.R. colours.

As a result we had to tackle the steepest part of the climb from a dead stop. For nearly 2½ miles from the start the line rises at 1 in 60, but the two engines climbed more brilliantly than ever. *"Beaufort Castle,"* still with 40 per cent. cut-off, was given absolutely full regulator, and I learnt afterwards that the Stanier engine was working on 45 per cent., also with full regulator. Between them, as might be imagined, they made a terrific noise. The performance of the "Castle" under such strenuous conditions was really most impressive. She rode very smoothly, without any of the side-to-side surging often experienced on old engines, and to the accompaniment of a steady, even, thunderous beat. Speed rose to 25½ m.p.h. on the 1 in 60, and as we swung round into the fastnesses of the Monadhliath Mountains and the grade eased slightly to 1 in 70, we quickly attained a full 30 m.p.h.

As we approached the Pass of Slochd Mhuic the wind caught us viciously, snow was driving again, and this time right through the cab; but speed was steadily maintained to the summit, 1,315 ft. above sea level. The 5½ miles from Carr Bridge had taken exactly 13 minutes start to stop—a very fine effort indeed. Here the pilot came off. Slochd is a desolate place even on the brightest of days, but with the wind screeching through the pass and sleet driving well-nigh level I was glad indeed to get into the shelter of the cab of No. 5163. This engine was manned by another Aviemore crew, Driver Munro and Fireman Malcolm.

L.M.S.R. 4-6-0 No. 5160 of class "5P5F" at Inverness. It has a small snow plough fitted, and the frozen snow on the buffers and buffer beam shows that it has encountered rough weather on the way.

In the remaining 22½ miles to Inverness the line descends 1,300 ft., but the very steepness of the gradients call for skilful enginemanship in order to maintain a good steady speed. Driver Munro worked No. 5163 in almost full forward gear, about 70 per cent. with the regulator closed practically the whole way. Descending at 1 in 60, we passed Tomatin, 3½ miles from the top, in 4¾ minutes, after a thrilling passage over the Findhorn viaduct at 63 m.p.h. This is a very graceful steel structure of nine spans that carries the line 140 ft. above the river; approaching from the south, its general lattice work was vividly silhouetted against the snowy hillside, producing a remarkably striking effect.

We covered the more undulating stretch of line between Tomatin and Daviot at a good 50–55 m.p.h. and then began the tremendous final descent, which is almost entirely at 1 in 60. From Daviot onward this section, which is the terror of up expresses, is double-tracked. Running once more in driving snow, we kept up a steady 60 m.p.h., crossing the great 29-arch viaduct across Strath Nairn, and so past Culloden Moor with its memories of the 1745 Jacobite rebellion. Far below, the Moray Firth could be seen vaguely through the snow, but soon we were approaching its shores; the line from Forres and Aberdeen joined at Millburn Junction and Inverness lay ahead. The 22 miles from Slochd to Millburn had been run in 25½ minutes.

Inverness is a unique station in that all the principal expresses are backed in. It is built in the form of a triangle, and in order to connect easily with trains for the far north, expresses from the south are run round the direct line to the north of the station and then backed into the northbound platforms. In our case there were connecting trains for Wick and Thurso, and Kyle of Lochalsh. We stopped at Rose St. Junction in 27¼ minutes from Slochd, and in another two minutes had backed into the platform. The 35 miles from Aviemore had taken 63 minutes, inclusive of the extra stop at Carr Bridge; the net time was 60½ minutes, while the running time was only 53¾ minutes. This was a further gain of 2½ minutes on schedule, so that altogether 13¾ minutes had been gained by the locomotives on the run from Perth. Although the two pilot engines had pulled their full weight, the principal honours rest, of course, with the Stanier 4-6-0s, both of which were loaded practically up to maximum.

The wintry weather was causing the operating officials at Inverness a good deal of anxiety, and one of the first questions we were asked on arrival was how things were "on top"—this referring to Slochd summit. On hearing what we had come through, the shed foreman remarked: "We shall have to get the snow ploughs out." At times such as this, there is no waiting for a block to occur before the ploughs are sent out. All the danger points are patrolled incessantly by light engines fitted with the small type of ploughs such as those that were carried by our engines on this trip. But such is Highland weather in the winter that even this precaution does not prevent drifts forming sometimes; a sudden change in the wind and a heavy squall may very quickly block the line. It is then that the monster ploughs are set to work. These are nothing more than enormous shovels on four wheels, and they are pushed by two or even three engines. With one of these implements snow lying two or three feet deep can easily be cleared, but in the Highlands a drift 10 or 12 feet deep may be formed in a single night. Forcing a way through this is one of the most thrilling and terrifying operations imaginable. The snow plough with its three engines retreats to a distance of about a mile, or even more; and then, the engines going absolutely "all out," charges full speed into the drift. Snow is hurled 30 or 40 feet into the air, and it often takes two or three "charges" to clear a bad drift.

Although a mere trifle compared with such conditions as these, No. 5163 on arrival at Inverness bore unmistakable evidence of the weather we had come through. The buffer beam and snow plough were coated with frozen snow, and the carriages had a distinctly Arctic appearance! Thus finished a journey that, for fine running and all-round interest, would take some beating.

Facts about British Railways

A Progressive Transport System

NATIONAL prosperity depends, as Francis Bacon truly stated, on the "easy conveyance of men and commodities from place to place"; in other words a thoroughly efficient transport system is a vital necessity to a country. British railways provide such a system for us, and we in Britain are fortunate that we have the best and safest railway system in the world at our command.

In an age of motor and air traffic people are apt to take railways for granted, until it is realised how necessary they are and what a huge concern the railway industry is. It represents the largest private undertaking in the land, with an invested capital of £1,092,517,000. The railways are Britain's best customers, for they purchase annually a tremendous amount of material, both finished and in the raw state. They are necessarily great employers of labour. The staffs of the four railway groups number 554,296, and railway requirements give employment indirectly to thousands of others.

Both collectively and individually British railways hold world's records in several respects. The fastest long-distance train in the world, over a journey of more than 200 miles non-stop, is the streamlined *"Silver Jubilee"* operated by the L.N.E.R. It averages 70.4 m.p.h. over the 232.26 miles between King's Cross and Darlington, as part of its journey from London to Newcastle-on-Tyne. The world's longest non-stop run is made by the L.N.E.R. in summer, *"The Flying Scotsman"* then making the 392.7 miles without a halt between King's Cross and Edinburgh; during the winter the record is held by the L.M.S.R. with the up run of *"The Royal Scot"* over the 299 miles from Carlisle to Euston, a service that is maintained all the year round. A world's record also is held by the S.R. in the extent of its suburban electric train service.

British railways collectively are the largest owners in the world of docks and of hotels. They are Britain's largest owners of motor vehicles and they are the largest household removers in the country. They have 6,754 passenger stations and between these there were made last year 1,155,457,000 journeys. The standard of safety on British railways is so high that the chance of the individual traveller meeting with a fatal accident is one in 89 million! In 1935 freight tonnage amounted to 261,241,000 and the total mileage of passenger and freight locomotives reached 560,983,000.

To carry the traffic there are 43,001 passenger coaches capable of seating 2,495,000 people at once; 17,464 brake, parcel and mail vans and similar vehicles and 7,236,000 railway-owned freight wagons. To haul them there are 20,165 steam locomotives. There are also 100 steam rail motors, 1,507 electric motor coaches, and 14 oil-engined units. There are 15,000 passenger motor vehicles in which the railway companies are interested, 8,333 railway-owned road motors for goods and parcels, 25,904 horse-drawn vehicles, and 13,247 horses. Railway steamers number 140 and they have a total gross tonnage of 182,573.

There is a total railway mileage expressed as single track and including sidings of 50,711, of which 1,544 are electrified. The smoothness of British railway travel is proverbial and is largely due to the excellence of the permanent way. To control the trains there are 10,435 signal cabins.

British railways realise that public requirements are constantly changing, so that it is necessary for their transport methods to show continual progress. Wider travel facilities are now available than ever before. It is possible even to obtain cards for stamps in order to save up by degrees for one's holiday journey. The service of meals on trains is an accepted feature of modern travel. Improved standards of design and comfort are constantly being introduced in new passenger rolling stock.

On the freight side British railways are now in the unique position of being able to supply all the numerous and varied services which traders require whether these are by rail, road, water or air. "Next morning" deliveries are a feature of the services afforded by the 600 express freight trains that run regularly between the important centres of population. Systems of registered transit are available whereby consignments of any size are delivered in accordance with a pre-arranged schedule. Special vehicles are in service for the conveyance of the numerous and varied loads that the railways, as common carriers, have to deal with. Terminal facilities have been greatly improved during the recent years and large sums have been spent on stations, sidings and docks. There are railway warehouses at all large centres where traders can rent space for the storage of their goods. In rural districts there is a completely organised system of motor lorry services operated from 1,750 railway stations, to link up outlying villages with local railway centres.

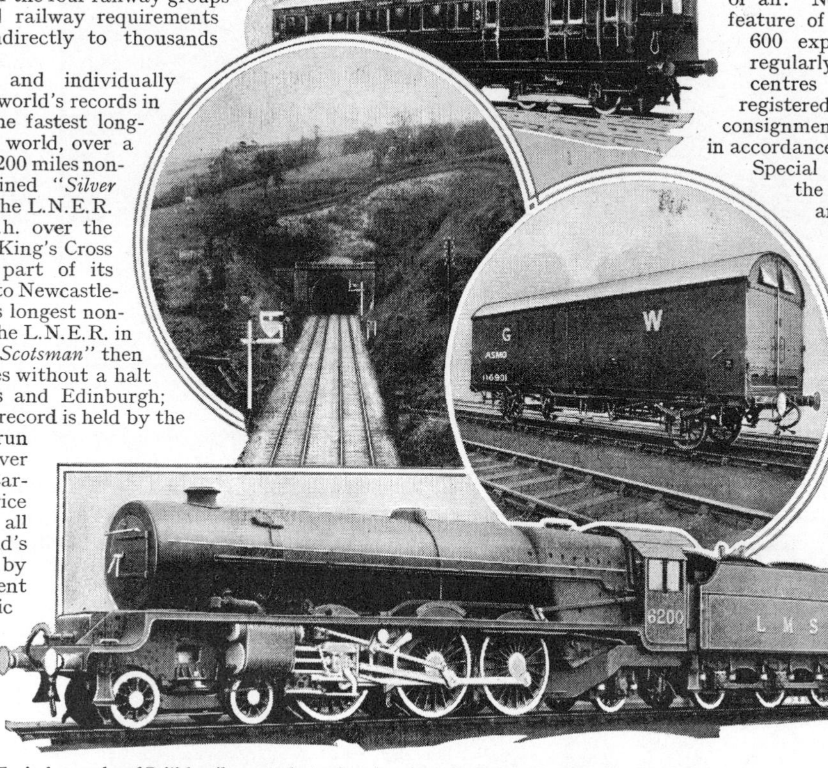

Typical examples of British railway stock, track and equipment. The top illustration shows an S.R. electric motor coach. Below it is seen the mouth of Cowburn Tunnel, L.M.S.R., and a G.W.R. motor car van. The locomotive illustrated is L.M.S.R. No. 6200 "The Princess Royal."

In order to take the fullest advantage of modern motive power considerable improvements have been, and are being, effected at locomotive depots. These include facilities for the rapid handling of engines, and the installation of mechanical coaling and ash disposal plants, larger turntables and water softening installations. Last year saw the introduction of the first streamlined locomotives in this country, also the first turbine-driven locomotive to be built in a British railway works.

Streamlined heavy-oil rail cars are in use on the G.W.R. Experiments are in progress with Diesel and Diesel-electric locomotives and there are 14 Diesel-engined rail cars in service.

Railway docks, harbours, and wharves are situated at 77 places. They include the world's largest graving dock, at Southampton, a port used by over 30 of the largest shipping companies in the world.

Air services are now operated by British railways in association with Imperial Airways Ltd. During 1935 there were 42 services in operation daily, and these covered more than 6,000 miles every week day during the summer months.

The interesting items mentioned in this article, and many others, are included in the booklet *"Facts About British Railways"* (1936), which is obtainable free on application from the British Railways Press Office, 35, Parliament Street, London, S.W.1.

"Now Let's Draw a Train!"

The Life Story of a Pencil

By J. F. Chambers

SOME of you will smile as you read the headline, and say to yourself: "Kid's stuff!"

But all of us had to learn to draw and to write when we were very young. It's a sort of craving, this wish to put our thoughts down. Even primitive men drew stories of adventures with wild animals, and you can see their crude drawings still, thousands of years old, on the walls of caves. They drew with bits of bone and flint, just as the Egyptian drew his "cuneiform" lettering with a stylus on clay bricks, which were afterwards baked hard. So next time you jot down something in pencil, remember that writing wasn't always so easy as you find it to be to-day!

Triple granite roller mills for grinding the mixture of graphite and clay used in making pencils. The photographs illustrating this article are reproduced by courtesy of F. Chambers and Co. Ltd.

Have you ever thought much about pencils? A mighty locomotive like the "*Silver Link*" begins "on the board," as the draughtsmen say—sketched "in pencil." Some of the cleverest drawings and the most thrilling stories and the most telling advertisements start as an idea dotted down "in pencil." A boy scrawls with one in his first year at school, and goes on using pencils all his life. So you can imagine that making pencils, which is my job, is pretty interesting.

People still call them "lead pencils," but the one the butcher's boy carries behind his ear, or the artist uses, is not made of "lead" at all. Originally the metal lead was used in crude pencils, but about 1564 a substance called "graphite" was discovered, in Cumberland, which was just right for making a mark with. Later, less than 100 years ago came the discovery that led to the birth of the pencil as we know it to-day. It was found that if graphite is ground up very fine, and mixed with a special clay, it can be "extruded," or squeezed out through a nozzle, just like squeezing toothpaste from a tube. It comes out as a thin stick or thread, and can be cut into lengths. Artificial silk threads are made in just the same way.

A machine that in one operation divides the slats containing the leads into six complete pencils and gives each of these the exact shape required.

Well, I think we're just about ready to start our tour of the Pencil Works at Stapleford near Nottingham.

You would be surprised at the tremendous number of different pencils we make. Besides the ordinary pencil in every quality and degree—from 6H, very hard, to 6B, very soft—there are copying ink pencils, cosmetic pencils for make-up purposes, coloured pencils for marking goods and parcels, and advertising pencils of every kind, with messages stamped on their sides.

As we enter the first department, you will see that the process is rather a dirty one, for men are grinding up the graphite. And you know how grubby your fingers can get from even one soft lead pencil! The powdered graphite is ground up by triple granite rollers, together with the washed clay, to a marvellous degree of fineness. This is done very carefully, for you know how annoying it is to "strike a bad patch" in the lead of a cheap pencil.

When the grinding process is complete, the graphite mixture has most of the moisture extracted, and is made into cylindrical cakes about 3 in. across and 6 in. high. These fit into the machines that extrude the lead. A ram squeezes out the mixture under enormous pressure, and the thin leads, or "slips" as they are called, come out of holes in a metal plate. Sometimes as many as 16 come out at once, and when they are the right length a girl dexterously snips them off and catches the slips on a grooved board.

At this stage the leads are still soft, and can very easily be broken in the fingers. So when dry they are taken away to be baked hard, and become the pencil-leads as we know them.

Thousands of carefully examined leads are packed into clay boxes or "seggars." A layer of powdered graphite is put on top to exclude the air, a clay lid is dropped on, and several boxes are then put in special ovens at a very high temperature. After baking, the slips are tested for strength, degree, and quality. In fact, at every stage of manufacture the inspection is very strict, so strict that only 2 per cent. of our pencils are rejected as faulty at the final inspection!

Stamping pencils with the name of the makers. The illustration shows the roll of metal foil that passes between the pencil and the stamping die.

While the slips are being made in one part of the factory, the wood for the pencils is being prepared in other departments.

We are very proud of our pencil-wood at Chambers'. It is Empire Cedar, grown in British East Africa. Although it is the ideal wood because of its uniform texture, even grain, softness for easy sharpening, and good colour, everyone used to say it was no good for pencils because it warped. We were not satisfied to leave it at that, and experimented again and again until we invented a secret way of seasoning the cedar wood so that it *won't* warp! I can't tell you how it's done—but the Government know it is a sound process, for all the pencils they buy are now "Empire Cedar"!

The wood comes to Stapleford from Africa in slats of suitable size, and after seasoning by our process the slats have circular grooves cut in one side, just half the diameter of a "slip." A clever little machine cuts perhaps six of these grooves at once, quick as lightning, and each groove is exact to a thousandth of an inch. The slats are next coated with glue on the grooved side, the slips are laid in, another slat is clapped on top, and then these are clamped together for the glue to set. Even the gluing is automatic.

Painting machine hopper for pencils, which are automatically coated with cellulose paint and dropped on a travelling belt to dry.

Next an ingenious shaping machine takes off the surplus wood, shaping the pencils round, hexagonal, oval or triangular. It is very fascinating to see a chunk of wood put in one end, and six pencils, almost complete, drop out at the other!

After shaping, the pencils are again examined, cut to the standard length of 7 in., and then put through painting or polishing machines. The pencils pass at the rate of 140 a minute through a tank containing cellulose paint, out through a rubber nozzle to take off the surplus paint, and on to a travelling belt. They arrive at the other end of the belt dry and ready to handle.

Naturally the ends become coated with paint too, so the next thing is to sandpaper the end clean, in yet another automatic machine. Some of our pencils have the butt end covered in an attractive contrasting colour paint, and there is an interesting fact here. If you put the paint on, leaving the end "square," you can chip it straight off with your finger. But if the end is slightly rounded, the paint stays put! So there is another machine rounding the ends!

We have not spoken of the busy, dexterous fingers of men and girls, tending all these complex machines, manipulating thousands of pencils a day with incredible swiftness—that must be seen to be believed!

So here is our pencil, with good lead, wood that cuts easily right down to the stub, a nice shape to handle, pleasantly coloured red or yellow or something else. But it isn't finished yet. Here is a clever little machine, working on the principle of a printing platen, which prints our firm's name, in gold perhaps, through a constantly moving roll of special gold paper, on the side of the pencil. And on the other side another arm stamps, for all to see, "EMPIRE CEDAR."

Some pencils come to you unsharpened, but here is a marvellous machine sharpening pencils as fast as you can count. And every point is just the right shape, so that you can write straight away—the wood smoothed off perfectly so as not to gather dust while awaiting a purchaser in the stationer's shop.

And so at last we get to the examining department, where eagle-eyed girls get a handful of pencils, lay them flat on the bench, roll them to see if they are true, study them for faulty painting or printing, swoop on a "dud" and throw it out. Other girls are bundling pencils. They never count them, but just pick up a dozen by touch! A dozen is picked up, once round, twice round with the twine, knot, break off the end—as quick as a conjuring trick.

So that's how a simple thing like your pencil is made—the tool that writes stories, builds bridges and helps to run this wonderful world to-day.

Dock Scheme for Shanghai

A new £500,000 wharf that is being built just outside the harbour area of Shanghai, when completed will give this great Chinese port one of the finest dock systems in the world. The wharf forms part of a scheme to provide an uninterrupted dock frontage of 2,500 ft., the first section of which will consist of two 590 ft. wharves, a small jetty for tenders and Customs launches, and an up-to-date Customs building with rest rooms and a café.

The wharves will be equipped with the best modern mechanical devices for facilitating the rapid loading and unloading of ships, including elevating trunks, stackers, mobile cranes and gravity roller conveyors.

New Cantilever Bridge for Australia

It is expected that construction will soon be commenced on a great bridge over Brisbane River, Australia, between Kangaroo Point and Bowen Terrace, in Brisbane. This bridge will be of the cantilever type. It will have a channel span of 924 ft., with a width of 60 ft. between the trusses, and will cross the river at a height of 100 ft. above high water level. It will be provided with a roadway 40 ft. in width and two 10 ft. footpaths, but provision is to be made for a 60 ft. roadway and two 10 ft. footways when needed.

The channel span of the bridge will consist of two cantilever arms each 308 ft. long, and a central suspended span also 308 ft. long. The shore anchor arms on each side of the main piers are each to be 269 ft. 6 in. long. The piers will be constructed of concrete, and the roadway is to be of reinforced concrete 6½ in. thick, with a surface of 1½ in. of sheet asphalt.

A Giant Globe

Preparations are now in hand for the World Exhibition to be held in Paris next year, and a notable exhibit will be a giant mechanical globe, 43 ft. in diameter, that will depict the Earth's continents and seas on a scale of one to 1,000,000. On this miniature world tiny ships operated by means of concealed electro-magnets will sail along the principal trade routes, and replicas of famous volcanoes will be set in action by pressing buttons. The globe will be surrounded by a platform for spectators and will revolve on its axis, illumination being provided by an artificial Sun and Moon.

Removing 70,000 Tons of Silt Daily

A great water-treatment plant that will be the largest of its kind in the world is to be installed on the Colorado River for the purpose of removing silt from the water pouring into the new All-American Canal from the Imperial Dam. It will be capable of removing 70,000 tons of silt a day, and is to be constructed near Yuma, Arizona, about 250 miles below the great Boulder Dam.

The 55-ton core of a 75,000 kVA Met-Vick Transformer that forms one of two similar units for the Fulham Power Station. Photograph by courtesy of Metropolitan-Vickers Electrical Co. Ltd., Manchester.

The plant will consist of six huge settling basins, 769 ft. long and 269 ft. wide, with a depth of 15 ft. These will be arranged in pairs and each pair will be fed from channels that in turn will receive their water from the headworks at the Imperial Dam. The rate of flow to the channels will be regulated by four huge roller gates, each 75 ft. long and 23 ft. high. The untreated water will flow evenly and slowly across the basins, and in its passage will deposit the greater part of the suspended solids on the bottoms of the basins. The deposited material will then be removed by 72 mechanically-operated clarifiers, each 125 ft. in diameter, that will continuously manœuvre the accumulating material to outlets in the bottoms of the basins from where it will be discharged and returned to the Colorado River below the dam. The clarifiers will be the largest ever installed.

A Novel Drilling Tool

A novel method has been adopted in order to bore a number of 5 ft. diameter holes for concrete foundation shafts at the Fort Peck Dam in the United States. The cutting tool consists of a split circular pan, 5 ft. in diameter, that is fitted with two sets of tungsten carbide cutting teeth. The pan is attached to the lower end of a 50 ft. pipe shaft, and is rotated by a 40 h.p. electric motor attached to the upper end of the shaft and provided with the necessary reduction gearing. The cutter is suspended from the boom of a crane, and in operation it is lowered to the surface of the ground before the motor is set in motion. When a foot or more depth has been drilled the motor is switched off and the cutter is lifted by the crane, the excavated spoil being brought up on the pan. When clear of the ground the pan is swung to one side for dumping. A depth of about 5 ft. per hour can be drilled with this apparatus.

Automatic Telephone Developments

The distance up to which subscribers on automatic telephone exchanges in this country can obtain their own connections simply by operating a dial on their instruments is gradually being extended. In the near future it will be possible to put through calls over distances up to 15 miles without the intervention of an operator.

Another interesting development that was announced recently concerns an automatic time signal to indicate that the period allowed for a telephone call is approaching its end. This signal, which will be something like the B.B.C. time signal, is to be introduced in most parts of the country, and will operate automatically 12 seconds before expiry of each three-minute period. The new signal will be more accurate in timing than the present "three minutes" warning given by the exchange operator, and the caller will not be distracted from his or her business, as sometimes happens when an operator suddenly intervenes during a conversation.

* * * *

A wonderful paper-making machine that weighs 2,000 tons and is nearly 500 ft. in length has been installed at Sittingbourne, Kent. It is capable of producing 2,500 miles of paper, 30 in. wide, a week, and is stated to be the largest in the world.

World's Largest Chain-Grate Stokers

The upper illustration on this page shows one of a set of eight travelling chain-grate boiler stokers that are the largest ever constructed. It was made by Babcock and Wilcox Ltd., for the Klip River electricity power house, South Africa, which is operated by the Victoria Falls and Transvaal Power Company Ltd.

The largest travelling chain-grate boiler stoker in the world. It is 33 ft. wide and 20 ft. long and is installed at the Klip River Power Station, South Africa. Photograph by courtesy of Babcock and Wilcox Ltd., London.

These stokers are 33 ft. wide and 20 ft. long, and have approximately 20 per cent. more grate area than the world's next largest, which are installed at the Philo power station, Ohio. They are to work in conjunction with Babcock and Wilcox water-tube boilers, and are of the forced draught type with closed front, but the fronts and ashpit can be opened and natural draught reverted to if desired.

The forced draught is supplied from a duct below the boiler and passes through the slack side of the chain grate, so that it picks up the waste heat in the chain links on its way to the fire. Beneath the working side of the grate are transverse sheet metal troughs fitted with adjustable dampers for the admission of the draught, and they enable the supply of air to the fire to be regulated as required. Towards the back end of the grate there is a series of clinker bars, which rest on the grate and guide the clinkers into a hopper.

The stoker is driven by an electric motor through two sets of gearing, each of which drives one half of the width of the grate. The motor runs at a speed of 1,000 r.p.m., and the gearing enables the grate to be operated at speeds ranging from about 14 ft. per hr. to 68 ft. per hr.

Tide Gauge for Chinese River

The lower illustration on this page shows an interesting tide gauge that is installed at the mouth of the Whangpoo River, China, for the purpose of warning pilots of the state of the tide and the depth of water.

The gauge bears a large dial, on which a moving finger indicates the height of the tide in relation to the minimum depth of water, while a small arrow points either vertically up or down to show whether the tide is on the flood or ebb.

An interesting tidal gauge that is installed at the mouth of the dangerous Whangpoo River, China, to inform pilots of the depth of water available for navigation at various states of the tide. Photograph by courtesy of The Renold and Coventry Chain Co. Ltd., Manchester.

A feature of the operating mechanism is the use that is made of steel chain drive. To a float working in a chamber under the gauge house, is connected a length of Renold steel chain that passes up through the structure and over a head wheel, and is attached to a counter-balance weight. The chain engages with special sprocket wheels, and these in turn are connected by supplementary chain drives to the other sprockets, on the shafts of which the indicating finger and the arrow are mounted.

An advantage of chain drive over other forms of transmission is that it combines freedom from slip, which is characteristic of toothed gears, with the flexibility of ropes and belts. These features give it a very high mechanical efficiency which has led to its use for driving machinery of all kinds ranging from bicycles to giant newspaper presses and talking picture apparatus.

Amateur Navvies Make a Canal

A Canal three miles in length is being excavated in Bengal by the voluntary labour of 20,000 men of all social ranks, rich, poor, Government officials and coolies working side by side. They have undertaken the task because the local government have no funds for the work, which has become necessary owing to the fact that a canal which used to drain away rainwater from a large area in Tippera district has gradually silted up, with the result that after the rainy season flood water remains, to become a breeding place for mosquitoes.

As the local authorities could not afford to re-make the canal an appeal was issued by the public for help, and men from all classes of society volunteered.

* * * *

A new bridge is to be built over the River Towy at Carmarthen to replace the present ancient structure. The bridge is a link in the Fishguard to London trunk road.

New Thames Tunnel

It is expected that work on the new Thames Tunnel, between Dartford, Kent and Purfleet, Essex, will be started this year. The work will take about four years to complete and will cost nearly £4,000,000. In addition, important arterial highways are to be constructed to link the tunnel with existing traffic routes. The tunnel probably will be built at a depth of 40 ft. below the river, and the only point along the route where engineering difficulties are likely to be encountered is on the north side of the Thames, where special precautions will have to be taken because of the nature of the formation.

Materials for a Great Dam

An idea of the vast amount and variety of material that goes to the making of a great dam may be had from the following details of orders issued by the contractors who are responsible for the erection of the Grand Coulee Dam now being built in the U.S.A. The materials purchased up to date range in size from pins to giant excavators, and include 121 miles of sheet steel piling weighing 12,600 tons, 30 steam hammers, 1,000,000 ft. of board timber, 4,500 tanks of oxygen and acetylene and 1½ miles of steam piping. The amount of calculation work involved on such a job is tremendous as is indicated by the fact that 10,000 pencils have been bought and used to date.

Finding Lost Pipelines

A new magnetic detector of great sensitivity has been produced in the United States for discovering the lost course of a gas or water pipe. The instrument is a surveying compass with an adjustable bar magnet, and fixed to the compass box and turning with it are two radial fins made of magnetic material, which serve as a magnetic aerial and effect a substantial increase in sensitivity.

When searching for a pipeline electric current from dry cells is sent through the pipe by making contact with its ends, an ammeter being included in the circuit. The detector is then set up at a point known to be on one side of the pipeline and the compass box is turned so that the fins are at right angles to the line. The bar magnet is then adjusted to give the necessary degree of sensitivity and to give the needle the same general bearing as the line. The detector is moved from place to place across the supposed line of the pipe and a graph curve is then plotted showing changes in current indicated by the ammeter as the detector is moved. The point directly below the peak in the curve indicates the position of the pipe.

The detector has been used successfully to locate pipes 7 ft. below the ground.

Le Bourget Airport

The Hub of many International Air Services

IN a comparatively few years Le Bourget has risen from an insignificant landing ground, with a few wooden huts and hangars, to be the chief airport of France. To-day it is the hub of numerous international air services, and aircraft leave there regularly for almost every European country. It is the headquarters of Air France, the principal French air transport company, who have their aircraft repair, inspection and testing shops there. Some idea of the importance to the airport of the traffic handled by this great company can be gained from the fact that on 8th June last year, when the Whitsuntide holiday traffic was at its height, 37 of the company's machines operated from Le Bourget and carried a total of 305 passengers.

The administrative buildings are grouped together on one side of the airport, and are set in grounds divided into well-kept gardens that at one point border on the landing ground and enable visitors to watch at close range the arrival and departure of the air liners. A feature of historical interest is an engraved stone set in the ground and commemorating the landing of Col. Lindbergh at Le Bourget on 21st May 1927, on the completion of his famous trans-Atlantic flight. The management building contains the administrative offices, of course, and also the Customs and Police offices and a restaurant. On the first floor is a buffet from the windows of which there is a fine view of the entire landing ground.

The offices of Air France at Le Bourget. The illustrations are reproduced by courtesy of Compagnie Air-France.

A large building immediately on the right of the airport entrance bears the name "Pavillon Paul-Bert," and part of the ground floor of it is occupied by a large waiting room for passengers. Adjoining this room are telephone booths and a telegraph office where passengers and their friends can despatch or receive messages by wireless. Much of the building is devoted to facilities for the exhaustive medical examination of pilots, navigators and mechanics, to determine their fitness or otherwise for their work. In the basement there is a compressed air chamber in which pilots are familiarised with the atmospheric conditions they will experience when flying at great heights, and are trained in the use of oxygen apparatus. The temperature of this chamber can be lowered to 50 deg. below zero.

Probably the most interesting room in the "Pavillon Paul-Bert" is a small one containing a table covered with wireless apparatus, a loudspeaker and a telephone. Towering above this gear is a large frame aerial in the middle of the table and reaching almost to the ceiling. On one wall is a large map of France on which the principal towns are indicated by graduated transparent circles. Thin cords each with a small ring at its free end are attached to the centre of the circles, and the rings are fastened to a sliding rod along the top of the map. The cords are used in determining the position of an aeroplane in flight, and when "plotted" each cord indicates the direction of a bearing. An approaching aeroplane, perhaps 200 miles from Le Bourget, on enquiring as to the best way to reach the airport, might be told by the operator in this room that "we make out your position to be 35 degrees. To get to Le Bourget proceed towards Cape..." (mentioning some geographical feature). Before these instructions are given the airports of, say, Dijon and Tours will have communicated their readings to Le Bourget at the request of the pilot. The cords are then plotted on the map according to these readings, and the point where the cords intersect shows the position of the aeroplane. So easily and quickly is all this carried out that the necessary information is communicated to the pilot of the machine within two minutes of receiving his enquiry.

A meteorological department is essential to any important airport, and that at Le Bourget occupies one of the main buildings. It is there that the pilots study carefully the weather forecasts before setting out on their flights. The department is also one of 12 French meteorological stations that regularly broadcast weather reports. The control building stands on the edge of the landing ground, and from one of its departments the arrival and departure of every aeroplane is notified to the control tower by a written message that is rolled up, placed in a cylinder and despatched through a pneumatic tube to the tower, where it is broadcast by wireless. The control tower then re-despatches the message by pneumatic tube to the wireless department in the same building. The operators in this room have the job of linking up the department with other important airports on the main air routes. These airports include Lyons, Strasbourg, Brussels, Croydon and Amsterdam.

Wireless masts and aerials within an airport would be a danger to aircraft taking-off or landing, and the Le Bourget transmitters are situated at La Morée, just outside the boundary of the airport. There are three of them, one operating on a short wavelength, the second on a medium one and the third on a long wavelength. The station is therefore well equipped to cope with the broadcasting requirements of the traffic and meteorological departments. There is another wireless station, at La Rosière, about ½-mile to the north of the La Morée station, and the operator there converses by wireless telephone with the pilots of aircraft in flight. His job is to ascertain their position, and if necessary to give them their bearings, and to communicate to them any weather advice and other useful information they require. In regard to aircraft bound for England this station keeps in touch with them as far as the French coast. They are then followed across the English Channel by the wireless station at Saint Inglevert, and on reaching the English coast they come within range of the wireless station at Croydon. Aircraft outward bound from Le Bourget to Germany are followed by the wireless stations of Cologne and Dortmund after they have passed out of range of La Rosière.

An aerial view of the airport. In the foreground are several of the large hangars. (Collection Air-France.)

The hangars at Le Bourget are vast reinforced concrete structures and are on the east and west sides of the landing ground.

The airport has, of course, prominent distinguishing signs that make clear its situation to approaching airmen, by day and by night. The most conspicuous sign during daylight is a large concrete circle, 164 ft. in diameter, in the middle of the landing ground. It is outlined by a white band nearly 16½ ft. in width, and has the name "Le Bourget" inscribed across it in an east-west direction, in letters 19 ft. 8 in. long.

Aircraft of Air France on the "tarmac" at Le Bourget. (Collection Air-France.)

At night the landing ground is illuminated by six powerful searchlights placed round the edge, and each has a flat beam of 180 degrees. The situation of the hangars is revealed at night by special red beacons, and the north boundary of the airport is indicated by red and white beacons placed at intervals of 164 ft. The wireless pylons are easily seen in the daytime, as they are painted with red and white alternate rings; and at night they are, with one exception, surmounted by clusters of red lamps. The exception is a pylon to the north-east of the landing ground, carrying a very brilliant searchlight of naval pattern which at night gives a flashing beam every three seconds. In clear weather this light is visible 50 miles away. A second pylon, 98½ ft. in height, is surmounted by a flashing beacon that shows a brilliant white light every 12 sec. and is sufficiently powerful to be seen 15 miles away. In addition to this extensive equipment there are two groups of permanent neon lights mounted on pylons at the north-east and north-west corners of the airport, and obstacles outside but close to the airport boundary, such as chimneys, tall houses, high tension cables, etc., are indicated by red flares.

Aircraft land in the direction of the wind, and at airports this direction is made known by pilots by a wind sock flown from the top of a mast or by some other device that indicates the direction very clearly. At Le Bourget it takes the form of a large letter "T" that is lit at night by white lamps fixed round its edges. Pilots are notified of the speed of the wind by means of a device adjoining the "T" and consisting of three illuminated bars each almost 10 ft. in length and arranged side by side. When none of the bars is lit the speed of the wind is less than 11.4 m.p.h.; when only one bar is lit the speed is between 11.4 m.p.h. and 22.8 m.p.h.; when two bars are lit it is between 22.8 m.p.h. and 34.2 m.p.h. and when all the bars are lit the wind speed is over 34.2 m.p.h.

The growing importance of Le Bourget and the rapidly increasing traffic have made larger accommodation for traffic and aircraft urgently necessary. New administrative and traffic buildings are to be built and the landing ground is to be practically doubled in size. The new administrative building will be built on the site of the present Customs and restaurant building. The ground floor will be in two parts, one containing the booking offices and waiting rooms, etc., and the other the Customs, baggage and freight departments. On the ground floor there will be the management offices, a restaurant and a large hall, and on the top floor there will be the airport traffic control services. It is estimated that the improvements will be completed by next summer.

We are indebted to the Fédération Aéronautique de France and to the Compagnie Air-France for the information contained in this article.

An Animal Engineer

There are many instances of intelligence and skill to the credit of creatures of all kinds, from the tiniest of insects to the elephant, the largest of present-day land animals, but those who are familiar with the beaver have no hesitation in describing it as the wisest and most energetic of all. The beaver may indeed be described as one of Nature's greatest engineers, for he provides himself with a secure home by building a dam across a river in order to keep the water at a permanent high level in the dry seasons. His purpose in doing this is to ensure that the door of his house is always under water, and so is closed to intruding land animals.

The skill with which the beaver carries out the work of making a dam and building a home is sufficient proof of his intelligence. He gnaws selected trees until they fall exactly where he wishes, and then he cuts them up into building lengths of about 5 ft. The dam itself may be 30 ft. to 40 ft. in length, 5 ft. or 6 ft. in height and 4 ft. in width, and the branches used in building it are interlaced with each other in an amazingly skilful manner. A straight dam is built if the stream flows gently, but this wonderful engineer builds a curved structure, with a pressure-resisting arch upstream, if the flow is more rapid.

The beaver's house also is constructed of branches, plastered together with mud, and the walls are very thick indeed. It forms a great dome, about 8 ft. across and 8 ft. in height, either in the middle of a stream or on its bank, and access to it can only be gained by means of a long passage, which may be 30 ft. in length, leading from the submerged entrance.

As would be expected of such a wise animal as the beaver, he lives in a community in which all share in the work and danger as well as the pleasure of life. When alarmed by the approach of an enemy, he gives warning by striking the surface of the water with his flat tail, and this is a signal for every beaver within hearing to dive for safety immediately.

The beaver to-day is found chiefly in Canada and the United States. At one time he was common in Europe, but he has almost disappeared on this side of the Atlantic, chiefly because he has been keenly hunted for the sake of his fur. This is perhaps fortunate, for a colony of hard-working beavers can cause disastrous floods and make large areas unfit for human beings to live in.

A magnificent view in the Valley of the Ten Peaks, Banff National Park, in the Canadian Rockies. In the foreground is Moraine Lake, behind which are some of the mountains that give the valley its name.

The Monarch of the Prairies

Another famous Canadian and North American creature with relations in Europe is the bison, which is usually but wrongly described as a buffalo, for the great hump on his shoulders and the long shaggy hair on the forepart of his body distinguish him from the true buffalo. Every reader must have revelled in the stories of the hairbreadth escapes of hardy adventures who braved him in his home on the American prairies. A well-grown bull may weigh little short of a ton, and one of this size must have presented a terrifying spectacle when charging with his head lowered, and his sharp curved horns ready for use.

It is difficult for us to imagine the American prairies as they were in the great days of the bison, when he was the monarch of the plains. It has been estimated that there were from 30,000,000 to 60,000,000 bison in North America when the New World was discovered. As late as 1870, when the country was being settled, there were still more than 5,000,000, and on one occasion a traveller in the West passed through a herd stretching continuously over 25 miles. Bison derailed trains and stopped boats on the rivers, but they could not live with the increasing population and the advance of the railways, and by 1880 they were practically exterminated.

Fortunately a few remained in the wild region near the Great Slave Lake in Canada, and two small herds in the United States also were preserved. The creature takes kindly to life in reservations, and to-day increasing herds are to be found in Buffalo Park, Wainwright, Alberta, Canada, in another reservation near the Great Slave Lake, and in the

Bison in the Banff National Park, Canada. These characteristic North American creatures are now to be found only in reservations.

Yellowstone Park in the United States.

It is two or three thousand years since the European bison was abundant, and now only a few herds remain in the Caucasus Mountains and in a reservation in Russia. These bison are smaller than those of America. When in their prime they lived in forests, and not on rolling prairies, and as a result the herds were smaller.

World's Largest Land Mammal

Even a bison weighing nearly a ton would look comparatively insignificant when placed alongside the baluchitherium, a gigantic creature three times as tall as a man, that flourished millions of years ago in Central Asia. The baluchitherium was the largest land mammal that ever lived, and he was twice as long as the elephant, the largest animal of this kind now living.

The beaver, Nature's greatest engineer, a rodent now scarce in Europe, but still abundant in North America. Our photograph was taken in one of Canada's National Parks, and shows the beaver's curious flat tail.

All that we have of this giant to-day is about 200 fossilised bones, laboriously collected during expeditions to the Gobi Desert, which was a paradise for animals when it stalked the Earth. After 10 years of patient work the bones have been sorted out and put together to reproduce a skeleton that shows it to have been nearly 18 ft. tall. Its shoulder would have towered above the head of the tallest of modern giraffes, and its weight must have been little short of nine tons. A baluchitherium would have been a costly animal to keep, for it must have required at least 500 lb. of vegetable food daily!

Secrets of the Deep Sea

Now that comparatively few places on land remain unexplored, the sea is the last place in the world to hold its mysteries. There is promise of revelations of its secrets in the continued use of Dr. Beebe's bathysphere, a steel ball in which that deep sea explorer was lowered to great depths, as explained in the "*Of General Interest*" pages of the "*M.M.*" for June 1935; but at present we receive only occasional news of the strange creatures that live far below the surface of the sea. For instance, a year or two ago a deep sea telegraph cable sunk to a depth of 4,500 ft. in the Bay of Bengal suddenly became "dead," and when it was hauled to the surface for examination a shark's tooth was found deeply embedded in it. The creature that had tried to make a meal of the copper strands of the cable, with disastrous results to itself, was not an ordinary shark, however, but an elfin or goblin shark, a curious fish with a mysterious blade-like projection on the top of its head.

Until the sudden appearance of this tooth there had been no suspicion that the elfin shark ever found its way into the Indian Ocean, for its home appears to be in the seas off the coast of Japan. A little more than 30 years ago its very existence as a living fish was unknown, but strange to say, almost as much was known about it then as now, for the fossilised teeth of elfin sharks that lived in the seas of 100 million years ago were familiar to scientists. It is curious that its appearance in the Indian Ocean should be revealed by the discovery of a tooth, since it was to the teeth of this creature that we owed our first knowledge of its existence.

There is another shark in Japanese waters that is fully as mysterious as the elfin shark. This is between 4 ft. and 5 ft. in length, and has a slender body that has suggested the sea serpent to many of those who have seen it. It is known as the frilled shark, because it has a series of frill-like projections round its neck. Like the elfin shark, it made a very dramatic appearance in regions remote from Japan, for a fine specimen actually was displayed on a marble slab in a fishmonger's shop in this country. Fortunately an expert who recognised the strange fish was among those who stopped to look at it. He wondered what this very rare shark was doing in England, so far away from its usual haunts, and on enquiry learned that it had been captured off the west coast of Ireland.

Cutting withies, or willow branches, near Burnham-on-Sea, Somerset. This work is carried out in February, and the branches being gathered are to be used in making hurdles. Photograph by Miss I. Marsh.

Both frilled and elfin sharks are in a sense relics of the past, for they represent a very primitive type of shark from which the formidable and voracious creatures that we know from stories and pictures have been developed.

Noises that we Cannot Hear

Noises that we cannot hear are by no means uncommon. A cat will respond to a sound that is too high-pitched for human ears, and other creatures behave in a similar manner.

Insects are sources of noises that are outside our own range of hearing. For instance, the cricket produces other notes than those we know so well when it rubs its hind legs against the rough surface of its fore wings. Although we cannot hear these notes directly, it has now been found possible to reproduce them in a lower pitch, and thus to give us some idea of their sound. For this purpose the waves are focussed on a quartz crystal cut in such a manner that it shows the peculiar property of producing feeble electric current in response to the pressure. The electric current is then amplified and fed to a loud speaker circuit, so that the original noises are brought within our range of hearing.

One very curious experiment carried out with this new apparatus has enabled the ticking of a watch to be heard at a distance of 30 ft., not by magnifying the sound so familiar to us, but by detecting higher notes that we cannot hear and translating them into others of lower pitch.

How the Value of Platinum has Changed

I have been able to obtain some further interesting details of the strange fluctuations in the price of platinum, to which reference was made on page 155 of the March "*M.M.*" During the War, and shortly afterwards, the price of this metal soared as high as £40 per ounce. The natural result was a search for substitutes, and this, with the increase in supplies from Canada, South Africa and South America, brought the price lower. The metal indeed is now much cheaper than was indicated in the March "*M.M.*" Its present value is about £7 per ounce, and thus it is actually of less value than pure gold, although its price was so high only a comparatively short time ago.

These details have been given me by Johnson Matthey and Co. Ltd., in whose works the photographs on page 155 of the March "*M.M.*" were taken. A platinum vessel weighing 322 oz. troy manufactured by that Company in 1809 cost £280. Its cost to-day would be £2,300 and during the War would have been £13,000.

Castles in the Holy Land

Engineering Triumphs of the Crusaders

By H. J. Shepstone, F.R.G.S.

ONE cannot travel through the Holy Land without being impressed with its relics of the Crusaders. These take the form of castles, forts, towers, churches and monasteries, and one encounters them not only in Palestine, but also in Transjordania and Syria. Great interest is now being shown in these historic remains of a picturesque and romantic age. Evidence of this is given by the restoration of a great castle built by Crusaders at Athlit, near Mount Carmel. This work is being carried out by the Antiquities Department of the Palestine Government, and across the Syrian border the French are repairing the Kalat-el-Husn, another mighty fortress of the same age near Homs.

The ancient walls of Tiberias, on the sea of Galilee. The walls were built by the Crusaders, and there were no buildings outside them 30 years ago, when our photograph was taken.

Up to the 11th century Christian pilgrims visited Jerusalem and the Holy Land without any serious vexation. Then came the Saracen invasion. Pilgrims were extortionately taxed, their persons and devotions insulted, and their lives imperilled. This led to the call for a crusade, the need for which was preached by Peter the Hermit, and for two centuries, from 1093 to 1291, armies from Western Europe invaded Syria and Palestine to wage holy war for the possession of Jerusalem.

Throughout the Crusades there breathed a spirit of romantic fervour that has never ceased to arouse admiration and wonder. The Crusaders were at once dreamers, worshippers and fighters. They believed in their mission, and their gallant deeds, particularly those of Richard I, the lion-hearted King of England, who led the third Crusade, never failed to grip the imagination. During the first Crusade, Jerusalem actually was taken and became the centre of a Christian Kingdom that lasted for some 80 years. Its fall led to renewed efforts, but eventually crusading zeal died away and Palestine remained in the hands of the Saracens.

One of the towers of the Kalat-el-Husn, a great fortified citadel built near Homs, Syria, during the Crusades.

The soldiers of the Cross certainly left their mark upon the sacred land of Palestine. Even the Church of the Holy Sepulchre itself may be said to represent Crusaders' work, for the south facade, and many parts of the sacred building, particularly the bell tower, was built by them during their occupation of Jerusalem. Both at Ramleh and Lydda, two important towns on the road from the Holy City to Jaffa, may be seen churches built by the Crusaders. The Church of St. John at Ramleh, built in the twelfth century, is said to be the finest example of a church of that period in existence. Ramleh was for a time the headquarters of King Richard.

Near Arsuf, just above the town of Jaffa, are the ruins of an old Crusaders' castle, interesting in that it was there that Richard defeated Saladin in battle, his greatest achievement in Palestine. Farther north at Athlit, a little to the south of Haifa and Mt. Carmel, are the remains of what was once a mighty Crusaders' stronghold. The ruins stand on a promontory jutting out into the sea, and all we have to-day are the remains of a great tower, magazines, church, huge banqueting hall, cisterns, and tombs. The *Castellum Peregrinorum*, or Castle of the Pilgrims, stood at Athlit. It was the principal seat of the Knights of the Temple, or Knights Templars, an order formed for the purpose of protecting travellers to Jerusalem from bandits that infested the route, and pilgrims visiting the Holy Land used to land there. The Antiquities Department of the Palestine Government have been excavating the site, and it is their intention to clear out the Bedouins who have taken up their abode among the ruins, and to make these more accessible to visitors. These relics of a heroic age are certainly worthy of preservation.

The principal attraction of Acre to-day is its Crusaders' castle. After the fall of the Holy City, Acre became the residence of the King of Jerusalem. It was there that Richard I landed during the third Crusade, and in the plains outside the city occurred many of his famous contests with Saladin, the chivalrous Saracen leader.

Tyre also can boast a reminder of the Crusades in the form of the remains of a fine old church. According to tradition this is the burial place of Frederick I, Emperor of Germany, called Barbarossa because of his red beard, who took part in the third Crusade but died before reaching the Holy Land. So far excavations have failed to locate his tomb, however. Going farther north, over the border of Syria, one finds Belfort Castle, standing alone on a great mound and forming a conspicuous landmark for miles. I recall discovering a little patch of snapdragon flowers on its walls. I was assured that the plant is not to be found elsewhere in Syria, and it is perhaps not a far-fetched inference that some Crusader's lady brought it from the garden of a distant French or English home.

The ruins of Belfort Castle, a stronghold of the Crusaders built on the summit of a mound in Syria.

Castle ruins are to be seen all the way up the coast to Antioch, the city where "the disciples were first called Christians." Antioch was the first city in Syria to yield to Crusaders, for it was taken by the armies of the first Crusade on their way to Palestine itself. No sooner had they captured the city than they were themselves besieged by a Moslem army from the east, and they were so worn by disease and starvation that it seemed impossible to hold out.

At the critical moment one of their number, a chaplain called Peter Bartholomew, had a vision of the Holy Lance. According to his story St. Andrew had revealed to him that this precious relic, the very spear that had pierced the Redeemer's side, had been hidden in the church of St. Peter. It was discovered there and its production filled the famished Crusading army with miraculous zeal. They rushed upon the besiegers, took them wholly by surprise, and routed them, capturing all their treasures and provisions.

Another part of the ruins of the Kalat-el-Husn. This Syrian castle was the greatest triumph of the military engineering of the Crusaders.

This occurrence, while saving Antioch, which remained under Crusader influence for 170 years, came near to defeating the whole enterprise, for from it developed a bitter quarrel between their leaders, Raymond of Toulouse, who supported the authenticity of the miracle, and Bohemond, who regarded it as a pious fraud.

The greatest of the Crusaders' castles, and the best preserved, is the Kalat-el-Husn, near Homs, which the Syrian Government intend to restore. It represents the supreme triumph of the Crusaders' engineering genius. It was a great fortified citadel perched upon a prominence, 1,000 ft. in height, that overlooked an extensive fertile plain. Within its walls were a palace with a great banqueting hall, church, monastery, barracks and armoury, and there the knights entertained each other and enjoyed a brilliant social life. The wonder of the castle is its great size and the massiveness of its walls, and indeed the western world has nothing to compare with it. It was protected by great towers with walls 30 ft. thick, a moat, and ramparts that were unscalable. As far as records show, no enemy ever succeeded in gaining entrance to it while it was in the possession of the Crusaders.

This superb relic of Crusader architecture is at present occupied by villagers, with their flocks of goats and cattle and horses. The great hall of the knights is half filled with rubbish, and the once grand chambers where lordly knights and their fair dames entertained guests listening to minstrels and jesters have been converted into houses. The peasants and their cattle are now to be turned out and the castle thoroughly restored. This should result in its becoming one of the show places in this land of sacred memories, and should do not a little to call attention to the formidable array of Crusader relics, picturesque reminders of a warlike and chivalrous age.

The Crusades not only introduced the western castle into the Holy Land, but also brought back from the East something of its architecture. They were responsible for the first great contact between the East and the West, and it was due to them, more than to all other causes, that there was such an immense increase of Eastern merchandise in Western markets, not only of relics from Jerusalem, but of Damascus ware and of Persian and even Indian produce. The direct influence of oriental architecture is to be seen in the models of the Dome of the Rock, the sublime edifice on the Temple Area at Jerusalem, that rose on at least three European sites during the Crusades; and in examples of Arabesque decoration brought home by Crusaders.

High Speed Patrol Boat for the Timor Sea

The lower illustrations on this page and the one opposite show a triple-engined high speed sea-going patrol and rescue launch recently built by the British Power Boat Co., Southampton, for the Australian Department of Defence. She was designed by Mr. Hubert Scott-Paine, the famous racing motor boat designer and pilot, who has spent almost a life-time in costly experimental work with craft of this kind. Her three Power-Meadows motors develop a total of 300 h.p. and give her a maximum speed of 27 knots, or 32 m.p.h. One of her most outstanding features is that she has a range of 950 miles at a cruising speed of 17–18 knots, or about 20 m.p.h., and could therefore travel from Land's End to John O' Groats by way of the Straits of Dover without stopping to refuel.

The control compartment of the new boat resembles the inside of a saloon car, for glass windows give an unobstructed view forward and to the sides, and an electrically driven revolving panel in the windscreen provides a clear view ahead when she is being driven through heavy seas or rain. She is extremely easy to handle. Her two rudders are operated by means of a steering wheel similar to that of a car, and only three small throttle-levers are required to give control of her motors. The design of these control levers is an adaptation of the system employed in aeroplanes, and they incorporate Power Bendix hydraulic gear, by means of which the motors are automatically put in and out of gear, and in and out of reverse.

The boat is for use in connection with the Empire Air Route scheme, and she will patrol the shark-infested Timor Sea, north-west of Australia, ready to dash to the rescue of aircraft that have been compelled to descend. She also will be required to aid ships in difficulties, to take part in the protection of pearl fisheries, and for general coastal duties. Marconi wireless receiving and transmitting equipment is installed to enable her officers to keep in constant touch with coastguard stations and aircraft in her area of operation. In her it will be possible to rescue and convey at high speed to land as many as 40 to 50 persons. A similar type of boat supplied by the British Power Boat Co. to the British Navy has a capacity of 100 men.

The "Duntroon," a motor vessel of 10,335 tons built for Australian coastal service. Photograph by courtesy of Swan, Hunter and Wigham Richardson Ltd.

A high speed patrol and rescue launch, for service on the Timor Sea, on her trials on Southampton Water. She was built by the British Power Boat Co., Southampton, to whom we are indebted for this illustration and the lower one on the opposite page.

British Cruiser and Destroyer Launches

Notable naval launches of the first few months of 1936 included that of H.M.S. "*Newcastle*," which took place in January at the yard of Vickers-Armstrong Ltd., Newcastle-on-Tyne. This vessel was the first of the "Southampton" class of cruiser to be launched, and she will be delivered in January 1937. She has a waterline length of 584 ft., a beam of 61 ft. 8 in., and a displacement of 9,000 tons. Her turbine machinery is of 96,000 s.h.p., and is designed for a speed of 32 knots. She will carry 6 in. guns in triple turrets, and her armament also will include eight 4-in. anti-aircraft guns, 22 smaller guns and eight torpedo tubes. She will carry two aircraft and will be fitted with a catapult to launch them.

A sister ship, H.M.S. "*Sheffield*," is under construction in the berth adjoining that vacated by the "*Newcastle*." The machinery for both vessels is being made at the Barrow-in-Furness works of Vickers-Armstrongs Ltd. H.M.S. "*Southampton*," the second vessel of this class, was launched from the Clydebank yard of John Brown and Co. Ltd., in March.

Two destroyers, H.M.S. "*Hero*" and H.M.S. "*Hereward*," also are being built at Newcastle by Vickers-Armstrongs Ltd. H.M.S. "*Hostile*," the first of the eight new torpedo-boat destroyers of the "*Hero*" class, was launched in January at Devonport, and H.M.S. "*Hunter*" was launched at Wallsend by Swan, Hunter and Wigham Richardson Ltd. in February. The vessels of this class have a displacement of 1,350 tons, and a designed speed of over 35 knots.

* * * *

Camper and Nicholson Ltd., of Southampton, are building a steel twin-screw motor yacht for Mr. T. O. M. Sopwith, the well-known yachtsman. This will be the largest of its kind yet built in the British Isles. It will have a length of 262 ft. 3 in., and a beam of 38 ft.

New South African Mail Vessel

The twin-screw motor vessel *"Stirling Castle,"* illustrated on this page, was built by Harland and Wolff Ltd., Belfast, for the South African service of the Union-Castle Mail Steamship Co. Ltd. She was launched on 15th August of last year and sailed from Southampton on her maiden voyage on 7th February.

The *"Stirling Castle"* has a gross tonnage of 25,550, an overall length of 725 ft., and a breadth of 82 ft. She has a curved, rounded stem and a cruiser stern, with two masts and one low streamlined funnel. Her hull is divided into watertight compartments by 11 bulkheads, and she has a continuous double bottom in which fresh water, water ballast and oil fuel are carried. Three hulls forward and four aft are available for ordinary cargo, and insulated cargo capacity of 330,000 cu. ft. is provided. This space will be devoted largely to the carriage of citrus fruits and similar South African products. She has accommodation for 297 first-class and 492 cabin passengers.

The Diesel engines of the vessel have a total output of 24,000 s.h.p., and give her a speed of about 21 knots. They are of the 10-cylinder, double-acting, two-stroke cycle type, employing airless injection of fuel, and are the highest powered ship's motor engines yet built in Great Britain. Five Diesel-driven generators, each with an output of 700 kw., provide electric power for auxiliary services.

The twin-screw motor vessel "Stirling Castle," built by Harland and Wolff Ltd., Belfast, to whom we are indebted for our illustration. This vessel has a gross tonnage of 25,550, and her two-stroke cycle Diesel engines develop 24,000 s.h.p.

American Liner Construction

The construction of a new liner of 33,000 gross tons for the United States Lines has been commenced at Newport News, Virginia, by the Newport News Shipbuilding and Dry Dock Company. The new vessel will replace the *"Leviathan,"* which was laid up last year. She will be of similar class to the *"Manhattan"* and the *"Washington,"* and will be operated in the service between New York and Europe. Her cost is estimated at £2,500,000.

There has been some discussion recently in New York as to the building in the United States of two 100,000-ton liners, that will be larger and faster than any ship hitherto either built or projected. The estimated cost is £20,000,000 and the two ships, if built, will be 1,250 ft. long and will be capable of a speed of 38 knots. The suggested design provides for telescoping funnels and a space 800 ft. in length and 140 ft. wide for the landing and taking off of aeroplanes.

Motor Ship for Australian Coastal Service

The upper illustration on the opposite page shows the *"Duntroon,"* a twin-screw passenger and motor ship owned by the Melbourne Steamship Co. Ltd., and employed in coastal service in Australia. She was built by Swan, Hunter and Wigham Richardson Ltd., and left the Tyne for Australian waters in August, 1935. She has the distinction of being the first passenger ship to be fitted with British built main machinery of double-acting, two-stroke cycle design, and it is interesting to note that she was the fifth motor vessel built in Great Britain since 1929 for the Australian coasting service.

The *"Duntroon"* is 472 ft. in length and 65 ft. in breadth, and has a gross tonnage of 10,335. Each of her two Diesel engines has six cylinders and together develop a total of about 7,200 s.h.p. Her contract speed is 16¾ knots, and during her trial she attained 19 knots.

Ample provision is made for the carrying of general cargoes, and in addition space is provided for refrigerated cargo, the total insulated capacity being about 14,500 cu. ft., and for the transport of livestock. A notable feature of the vessel is the sumptuous character of the passenger accommodation. The number of first-saloon passengers that can be carried is 266, and provision for 107 second-saloon passengers brings the total accommodation to 373.

Another view of the motor boat illustrated on the opposite page. The vessel's motors develop a total of 300 h.p. and she has attained a speed of 27 knots, equivalent to 32 m.p.h.

Motor Lifeboats of Novel Design

Two motor lifeboats, the first of a new type, have just been completed for the Royal National Lifeboat Institution. One of these boats has been named *"Royal Silver Jubilee, 1910-1935,"* and will be stationed at Wells, Norfolk, and the name given to the other, to be stationed at Ilfracombe, Devon, is *"Rosabella."*

The new boats are much lighter than any now in the lifeboat fleet, for each weighs about 3½ tons, while the weight of the lightest type of vessel previously employed is 6¾ tons. They are driven by two 10 h.p. engines of the latest design and will have a speed of about 6¾ knots. They are of very shallow draught and can therefore be used at stations where so far it has not been possible to provide motor boats owing to lack of depth of water.

The *"Royal Silver Jubilee"* is fitted with a Hotchkiss internal-cone propeller. In this device, which has never previously been used in a lifeboat, water drawn in at the apex of a rotating cone-shaped impeller rides up its surface, and is expelled with a greater velocity at its base. This method of propulsion is being used as an experiment in order to decide whether it will be adopted for other lifeboats of this new light type instead of a shrouded propeller.

A new motor lifeboat, named *"Sir Heath Harrison,"* commenced service at Port St. Mary, Isle of Man, early last month. She was built by J. Samuel White and Co. Ltd., of Cowes. The new vessel is 36 ft. 6 in. long and 9 ft. 6 in. wide, and has a draught of 2 ft. 1 in. She is of a type specially designed for stations where the lifeboat has to be launched off a carriage or the open beach. In service she weighs 6¾ tons, with the crew of seven and all gear on board.

The *"Sir Heath Harrison"* is built of mahogany and is divided into six watertight compartments with 115 air-cases. She can free herself in 12 seconds of a sea breaking on board. Sufficient petrol is carried to enable her to travel 100 miles at the maximum speed of 6 knots without refuelling, and the fore and mizzen masts are fitted to carry three sails as an auxiliary means of propulsion.

A fourth motor lifeboat, the *"Viscountess Wakefield,"* has been stationed at Hull. The boat is of the beach type and has a speed of 7¾ knots, with a range, at full speed and without refuelling, of 120 miles. Altogether there are now 128 motor and 40 sailing and pulling lifeboats in the active fleet of the R.N.L.I.

New "Mountain" Locomotives for South Africa

Heavy-Duty Mixed Traffic Engines

The illustration above shows one of the large 4–8–2 locomotives recently introduced for heavy passenger and freight service on the South African Railways. They are the largest locomotives of the "Mountain" type in South Africa. Our photograph is reproduced by courtesy of the makers, Robert Stephenson and Co. Ltd., Darlington.

IN the "*M.M.*" for December 1935 we gave details of a new class of 4–6–2 express passenger locomotives then recently introduced on the South African Railways. These engines, classed as "16E," show a great advance in size and power on previous "Pacifics" on these lines. Similar progress is shown by the 4–8–2 or "Mountain" type engines of class "15E" recently constructed by Robert Stephenson and Co. Ltd., Darlington, to the designs of Mr. A. G. Watson, Chief Mechanical Engineer of the South African Railways. These giants are intended for heavy passenger and freight trains and are the largest of the 4–8–2 type in South Africa. They resemble the "16E Pacifics" in their general design and outline. Both classes have poppet valves, and their boilers, except for the necessarily longer barrel of the 4–8–2s, are of the same design.

Each of the two cylinders of the new engines is cast in one piece with half the smoke-box saddle. These cylinders are interchangeable with those of the "16E" class, but in order to make them suitable for the new 4–8–2 "15E" class a cast iron liner or distance piece is fitted between the smoke-box itself and the top of the smoke-box saddle. The cylinders are so designed that the same pattern does for both sides of the engine; thus separate right-hand and left-hand patterns are not required. Steam distribution is effected by rotary camshaft poppet valve gear and many of the main details are interchangeable with similar parts used for the "16E" engines. The camshafts are arranged to admit steam at cut-offs ranging from 15 per cent. to 85 per cent. in full gear. In mid gear the valves are all held open. A by-pass position is provided in order to ensure free running when the engine is drifting.

The cylinders drive on the second pair of coupled wheels through connecting rods of heat-treated steel. These have been designed for lightness consistent with strength, and are of fluted section. The balance weights in the driving wheels are cast with cavities that can be filled with more lead if it should be found desirable to add to the present balancing weight of 20 per cent. of the reciprocating masses. Built-up crossheads are used. The bearings at the main crank pins and the coupling rod pins are fitted with floating bronze bushes. All these pins are hollow and are grease lubricated. Grease lubrication also is provided for the axleboxes.

The leading bogie, with wheels 2 ft. 6 in. in diameter supports a weight of 18 tons 19 cwt. The coupled wheels are 5 ft. in diameter, and the total weight sustained by them is 71 tons 12 cwt. A two-wheeled truck supports the rear end of the engine. The spring suspension is equalised throughout the coupled wheels and the equalisation is continued through to the truck. The main frames are each made in one piece from solid rolled slabs. They are reduced in thickness at the rear end to give clearance required for the side play of the trailing truck.

Steam is supplied from the boiler at a pressure of 210 lb. per sq. in. There is no dome, although the man-hole cover that is visible towards the rear end of the boiler barrel suggests a dome cover. Instead there is an internal steam collector of special design that terminates in a steam pipe connected to the header of the superheater. The boiler is fed by two injectors, placed under the footplate, that deliver the water through top-feed clackboxes on the front ring of the boiler barrel. One of these fittings and the necessary piping are clearly visible in the illustration.

There is a wide fire-box, the grate of which has an area of 62.5 sq. ft. It is fitted with steam-operated shaking gear and a dumping system that enables the fire to be dropped when required. The brick arch is carried by five arch tubes that add to the heating surface and aid in the circulation of the water. The fire-door is steam-operated, and a great part of the fire-box surface is fitted with flexible stays. The fittings include a soot blower that enables the tubes to be cleaned during the course of running.

The steam brake acting on the coupled wheels of the locomotive works in conjunction with the vacuum brake fitted to the tender. A special form of intermediate buffing gear fitted between the two vehicles is designed to minimise the wear of its components, and to promote smooth riding. Complete electric lighting equipment is provided, and the engines are fitted with speed indicators and recorders that are driven from the trailing wheels.

The coupled wheels of the new engines are larger than those of the older 4–8–2 locomotives of class "15CA," but as the boiler pressure is 10 lb. per sq. in. higher. there is little difference in the respective tractive efforts. Increased speeds with the same loads, or greater hauling capacity at the same speeds, therefore should be possible. It is notable that the generally increased capacity of the new engines has been obtained with a very small increase in their empty weight over that of the older class. The wide fire-box also is deep, and to secure this effect the height of the boiler centre is 9 ft. 2½ in. from rail level. This height is remarkable for an engine to run on track of 3 ft. 6 in. gauge, and exceeds that of many main line locomotives in this country.

The tender is similar to those already in service in the "16E" class, and has a capacity for 12 tons of coal and 6,000 gallons of water. It is supported on two four-wheeled bogies and weighs 66 tons 3 cwt. in working order. The total engine weight is 107 tons 14 cwt., so that the combined weight of the engine and tender in working order is 173 tons 17 cwt.

The appearance of these engines has practically coincided with the announcement that Mr. A. G. Watson, their able designer, is shortly to retire. During his term of office as Chief Mechanical Engineer of the South African Railways, the standard of efficiency of motive power and rolling stock has constantly risen, and extensive workshop and other improvements have been effected.

Rail Car with Pneumatic Tyres

Streamlined Vehicle for High-Speed Services

By H. F. Kutschbach

UNTIL comparatively recent years rail cars, driven chiefly by steam, conformed largely in their design and construction to the robust standards required of vehicles intended for general railway service. The altered requirements of modern times, and the continued development of the internal combustion engine, have resulted in the introduction of the lightweight high-speed rail car, which approximates in its construction to the standards observed in road motor coaches.

The impact of steel tyres on rail joints necessitates a heavier construction for a rail-borne vehicle than for a similar type for use on the roads, where advantage can be taken of the cushioning effects of rubber tyres. On this account many attempts have been made to adapt pneumatic tyres to railway vehicles, and particularly to rail cars. The area of contact of such a tyre is greater on the road than on the rail, however. In the former case this area can vary with the pressure on the tyre, but no such variation is possible with rubber tyres running on rails, and the load that can be imposed on them is restricted, especially on small-section rails. Several schemes therefore have been devised for employing rubber for the sake of its cushioning effect as part of composite wheels running on the usual steel flanged tyre.

The rail car described in this article leaving a station. The low construction of the car is of advantage for entraining passengers where there are no platforms, or only very low ones. Photographs by courtesy of the makers, Austro-Daimler Puchwerke A.G., Vienna.

An interesting method of making use of pneumatic tyres in conjunction with the usual steel-tyred wheels is applied in the streamlined rail car illustrated on this page, which has recently been put into service in Austria. The work of guiding this vehicle on the track is performed by wheels with steel tyres of the standard railway type, but the load is cushioned by pneumatic tyres that bear on internal cylindrical surfaces formed in the steel wheels. The latter are mounted on hollow axles, through which pass the axles on which the pneumatic-tyred wheels are fitted. These axles support the car body in the usual manner. Thus the running shocks sustained by the steel tyres of the track wheels are taken up by the pneumatic tyres and cannot be transmitted to the car itself, as there is no direct metallic contact. The load-carrying axles receive their motive power through the medium of bevel gears, and transmit the movement to the track wheels by means of the pneumatic tyres.

This system allows air-filled tyres of practically any size to be used, and therefore permits of increased carrying capacity. The load supported by each pneumatic tyre is not restricted by the small contact area on the rail head. Actually the conditions are much more favourable to cool running and long life than those in which pneumatic tyres are run normally on the road, for the cylindrical surface within the track wheels on which the tyres bear is very wide. It is found that the tyres keep cool during continuous high-speed runs of several hours' duration.

It is possible to continue running even with a flat tyre, and there need be no disorganisation of schedules from this cause. If a tyre becomes flat, perhaps because of a defective valve, then the carrying axle affected sinks a distance of about an inch within the hollow axle of the corresponding steel wheel. Only in these conditions is any proportion of the weight of the car carried on one of the axles of these wheels, and no weight is then imposed on the flat tyre, so that continued operation is possible without any danger.

With the adoption of pneumatic tyres for load-carrying duties it has been possible to employ lightweight construction in the chassis and body of the car, so that a low dead weight in relation to the number of passengers is realised. A streamlined outline has been adopted not only for its publicity value, but also on account of the higher maximum speeds made possible and the reduced running costs, as compared with the normal type of rail car. A low centre of gravity has been attained by placing the lattice girder forming the chassis with its lower beam passing under the axles and its upper beam just above them. In addition to the safety this low construction affords, it has the advantage of giving easier entrance from the ground or from low platforms. The lattice girder referred to is built up of pressings of high tensile strength, a form of construction that allows of sound design with the minimum of material, and a saving in weight also is realised by the use of welding in its fabrication.

Another view of the car, showing its streamlined form. A good outlook is ensured by the generous provision of windows.

The car is driven by a six-cylinder 80 h.p. engine of sturdy construction that is specially suitable for heavy duty. The grouping of the cylinders and other parts is so arranged as to permit of the easy removal of the pistons without undue dismantling of the engine. All engine parts that require regular overhauling, such as the water pump, camshaft, and the oil pump, are arranged to be demountable without disturbing adjacent units.

Hydraulic transmission is employed, with oil as the motive fluid, and the system is characterised by high efficiency, extremely gentle starting and excellent responsiveness generally. This has been achieved by the combination of a hydraulic coupling or clutch for direct drive and hydraulic reducing gear for acceleration and uphill work.

To save weight without reducing strength the car body is formed as a single unit with the chassis. The body pillars of steel sections are riveted to the side members of the chassis, the body framework generally being built up by welding and riveting.

New Aircraft for Air France

Air transport companies, like other forms of commercial enterprise, must modernise their equipment periodically to keep pace with developments. This year Air France are replacing many of their aircraft with faster and more up-to-date machines. The new equipment includes 20 Potez 62 twin-engined high wing monoplanes, and several of them have been delivered. Various services operated by the company will benefit, as six of the Potez 62s will be used on the London-Madrid route, seven on the Damascus-Hanoi portion of the Far East route, and several on the company's European air lines. The South American service of Air France is to have four of the aeroplanes, three of which will operate over the Natal-Buenos Aires stretch and one over the trans-Andean portion of the route.

The Potez 62 carries 14 passengers in a two-part cabin, six of them occupying the front portion and the remainder the rear one. It has a span of 73 ft. 7½ in. and its six fuel tanks are inside the wing. The two engines normally fitted are Gnôme-Rhône K 14s, which give it a top speed of just over 200 m.p.h., and 16 of the 20 Potez aeroplanes ordered by Air France will have this type of engine; the other four will have Hispano Suiza 12-XBRS-I engines. The engines are carried in nacelles slung beneath the wing.

Air France also have ordered six Caudron monoplanes, which will be used on their Africa service. These aeroplanes have two 220 h.p. Renault engines and cruise at 167 m.p.h. The passenger cabin seats six persons. Three triple-engined Fokker aeroplanes also have recently been acquired by the company.

Fine Flight by Supermarine "Scapa"

One of the Supermarine "Scapa" flying boats of No. 202 (Flying Boat) Squadron of the R.A.F., stationed at Malta, recently flew to Gibraltar, calling at Algiers on the way. The return flight was made non-stop, however, and the 1,000 miles were covered in 7½ hrs., an average of 133.3 miles per hour.

The Supermarine "Scapa" is a twin-engined biplane type flying boat with wings of unequal span. The wings, wing-tip floats, hull and tail unit are built of a specially treated aluminium-alloy, and the leading edge of each wing is covered with Alclad sheet, and the tail unit framework is covered with fabric. The upper wing is 75 ft. in span and the hull is 53 ft. in length. The gunner's cockpit in the nose has a hinged watertight door in the front that can be opened to enable bomb-sights to be taken. There are two other gunners' positions, both behind the wings. The pilot's cockpit is just in front of the wings, and immediately behind it are the navigator's, engineer's and wireless operator's compartments. No details of the performance of this flying boat are available.

Passengers entering a Savoia-Marchetti S.74 air liner. Photograph reproduced by courtesy of Agence Bruni.

First Atlantic Flight of "*Hindenburg*"

The new Zeppelin, christened "*Hindenburg*," has completed her first flight to South America. She left Friedrichshafen at 5.32 a.m. on 31st March, with Dr. Eckener in command, and with 50 passengers and a crew of 46 on board. No attempt was made to accomplish the Atlantic crossing in record time, and South America was reached by the 3rd of April. After flying down the coast of Brazil the "*Hindenburg*" landed at Rio de Janeiro at 9 o'clock next morning.

R.A.F. Vacancies

The Air Ministry announce that there will be 800 vacancies in the R.A.F. in August for boys for training as aircraft apprentices. Those accepted will be given three year's training by qualified technical instructors in the more highly skilled R.A.F. trades of fitter, fitter (armourer), wireless operator mechanic or instrument maker, before being appointed to a squadron. During training the general education of the apprentices will be continued under a staff of graduate teachers.

Applicants must be between 15 and 17 years on 1st August 1936, and must pass an entrance examination that will be held on 26th of this month in London and many provincial centres. The subjects set will be English, Mathematics, Science and General Knowledge. Boys who possess approved School Certificates with specified credits may be excused this examination. Full particulars can be obtained from the Inspector of Recruiting, Royal Air Force, Victoria House, Kingsway, London, W.C.2, and nominations for the examination must be received by Tuesday next, 5th May.

In September next there will be 200 vacancies for Boy Entrants for training as photographers, wireless operators and armourers. Boys between 15¾ years and 17¼ years on the 1st of that month will be eligible, provided they have attended a secondary or junior technical school or central school up to the age of 15½, or have attained an equivalent educational standard. There is no entrance examination and no previous experience is required. Full particulars can be obtained from the Inspector of Recruiting at the address already mentioned.

Blackburn "Sharks" for Portugal

The Portuguese Government have bought six Blackburn "Shark" torpedo spotter reconnaissance machines (seaplane version) for the Naval Air Service of that country. The "Shark" is fitted with an Armstrong Siddeley "Tiger VI.C" engine, and has a top speed of 152½ m.p.h.

Imperial Airways' Summer Services

The Continental services of Imperial Airways have been augmented to cope with the heavy summer traffic. There are now five flights in each direction every day on the London-Paris route, and four services daily to Cologne, three to Brussels and two to Switzerland. Fast aircraft bring Prague, Vienna, Budapest and Brindisi within a day's flying of London. The main European airway system now comprises about 30 companies operating over more than 60,000 miles of routes, and Imperial Airways' summer services, by establishing connections on the Continent with this great system, enable passengers from London to travel by air to about 200 European towns and cities. Connections also are established between the system of internal air services in this country and the main Continental and Empire routes. As an instance of this co-operation, passengers leaving Manchester by air at 10 a.m. can catch a connection at Croydon that enables them to reach Paris by 2.45 p.m., Brussels 15 min. later, and Cologne by 4 o'clock the same afternoon.

The summer service between London and Switzerland is being operated in co-operation with Swissair, as last year, but is an improvement upon previous schedules. Imperial Airways' machines now omit the call at Paris and fly non-stop to Basle, in 3¾ hrs., and Zurich is reached 40 min. later. Swissair make the trip from Zurich to Croydon in 3 hr. 50 min. On the Swiss aerodrome air-taxis are available that enable visitors to obtain splendid bird's eye views of the Alps in a flight lasting from ½ hr. to ¾ hr.

Many facilities are provided in combined week-end trips by air and land. Leaving London on Friday evening, the holiday-maker can fly to Germany, enjoy special steamer excursions up the Rhine, and be back in London by Sunday evening. Similar trips, in which air and land transport are combined, enable week-end parties to make air-and-rail excursions along the Belgian coast; and in an air holiday lasting about a week it is possible to make flights right round Europe, with ample time on the ground for incidental sight-seeing. There are also combined excursions, in which part of the journey is made by aeroplane and part by ocean liner. In this way one can fly across Africa, obtaining air views of forests, deserts, and wild life in its natural surroundings, and then return by sea in one of the liners leaving Capetown for England.

The American "Crusader"

The Ag-4 "Crusader" shown in the upper illustration on this page is an interesting departure from the usual type of cabin monoplane. The streamlined fuselage is so short that the tail unit is fitted to the rear ends of two long tapering "tail booms" that extend past the fuselage. The other ends of these tubular booms are just in front of the leading edge of the wing and are utilised as nacelles for the two 125 h.p. Menasco C4-S engines. The "Crusader" has a top speed of 233 m.p.h., and a cruising speed of 210 m.p.h. It is produced by the American Gyro Company, of Denver, California.

The wing is built up of steel spars and is covered with stressed aluminium-alloy sheeting, and the fuselage also is of metal and covered with a light alloy. The neat and compact cabin normally provides seating for a pilot and three passengers, but it can be arranged to accommodate five people. In addition to dual control, full night and cloud-flying equipment is installed. The "Crusader" has a span of 36 ft., a length of 21 ft. 8 in. and a height of 7 ft. 3 in.

The American "Crusader," a novel type of low wing monoplane in which the tail unit is mounted at the end of long, tubular booms. Photograph reproduced by courtesy of "Les Ailes," France.

Diesel-Engined Monoplane for Swissair

The latest addition to the extensive fleet owned by Swissair is a Junker Ju 86 high-speed monoplane, which is of special interest because it is fitted with two water-cooled Diesel engines. The engines are Junkers-Jumo 5s and give the monoplane a top speed of 195 m.p.h. The lower illustration on this page shows a Ju 86 in flight.

Junkers Ju 86 in flight. Photograph reproduced by courtesy of Junkers-Flugzeugwerk A.-G., Dessau.

Notable Air Events this Month

Empire Air Day was inaugurated last year by the Air League of the British Empire to give the public an opportunity of seeing for themselves what civil aerodromes are like, and of inspecting at close quarters the types of aircraft in use there. The co-operation of the R.A.F. extended this privilege to cover many R.A.F. stations, and the success of the joint project exceeded all expectations. This year Empire Air Day will be held on Saturday, 23rd May, and the R.A.F. will co-operate with the Air League in providing excellent facilities for the public to get into close touch with aviation. As last year many flying clubs will help by impromptu displays to make the day a very enjoyable one for visitors to aerodromes.

A week later the Isle of Man air races will provide another great attraction. There will be two races promoted by the Corporation of Douglas, and they will be open to both British and foreign pilots and aircraft. The first race will be flown on Saturday, 30th May, for prizes of £100, £70 and £30. The course mapped out is from Hanworth Aerodrome, Middlesex, to Ronaldsway Aerodrome, near Douglas, in the Isle of Man, with turning points on the way at Hooton, Blackpool, St. Bees Head and Maughold Head.

The second race will be flown on Monday, 1st June, and in this case there will be prizes of £50, £35, £25 and £10 respectively for the four best performances. The course consists of three successive circuits of the Island, the race beginning and ending at Ronaldsway. The turning points, other than the starting and finishing points, will be Douglas Bay, Maughold Head, Bride, Peel and Tynwald Hill.

New System of Naming Imperial Airways Fleet

Up to the present each class of aircraft in Imperial Airways' fleet has been known by the name of the first machine of that class to be put into service. With very few exceptions the aeroplanes in each class bear names beginning with the same initial letter, and that letter also is the initial of the makers of the aeroplanes concerned. The "Hannibals," for instance, were produced by Handley Page Ltd., the "Atalantas" by Armstrong Whitworth Aviation Ltd., and the "Scipios" by Short Bros. (Rochester and Bedford) Ltd.

This system is to be replaced by one in which the names of the makers of the aircraft will have no bearing upon the names chosen for each class, and what is described as "an alphabetical class sequence" is to be adopted. In this the initial letters A and B will be allocated to the existing fleet, with the exception of the 12 "Diana" class air liners, which will be known as "D" class. The letter "C" is to be reserved for the flying-boats now being built for Imperial Airways by the Short company, and the letter "E" for the land monoplanes under construction by Armstrong Whitworth.

The letter "M" has been allocated to the Mayo composite aircraft under construction at the Short factory.

Sand Rivers of the Zambesi Valley

Water Buried in the Beds of Streams

By Wilfrid Robertson

WHERE rivers are concerned, the usual order of things is that the farther one goes downstream the greater is the flow of water; but in the Zambesi Valley country, the wild and elephant-haunted territory in which I have wandered and hunted for many years, the reverse is the case. On the plateaux where they rise the water-courses start as rivers in the accepted sense, although their flow may be attenuated in the dry season. When they descend into the wide belt of low country bordering their destination, the Zambesi River, however, they alter completely in character, and except in the height of the rainy season there is no water in them to reflect the passing clouds or the torrid arc of sky.

Until one becomes used to them, there is something disconcerting about the Valley rivers. This is best realised on reaching one after a long and thirsty day's march, during which the guiding path leads through the close-growing mopani forest, with its hundreds of giant baobabs, and through belts of country covered with jessi-bush that only a rhinoceros can penetrate. Abruptly the mopani gives way to altogether different vegetation. Masses of dense foliage show in front, mighty timber clad in bright metallic green. Beyond the deep cool shade of the trees are reeds with stems 10 ft. high, whose feathery cream-coloured heads sway slowly in the breeze. The river bank appears. All the accessories of a river are there, among them the shady trees, cool reeds, and tall overhanging palms; but between the banks, instead of flowing water, is a level sheet of dazzling yellow-white sand. As if in mockery of the thirsty traveller, the heat flows pellucid just above the surface, in ironical imitation of the water that should be there.

In a deep gorge in the Zambesi Valley. It is only in rocky country such as this that the water of the rivers comes to the surface.

At the beginning of the world, when the tributary rivers cut their way down from the higher ground and gouged out their beds in the soft soil of the Valley on their way to the Zambesi, streams of water no doubt reflected the blue of the sky. During the passage of untold years the beds have slowly been filled with a deposit of coarse and well-washed sand, which hides the flow from sight and protects it from the evaporating power of the Sun.

Although the water cannot be seen, its presence is revealed by the deep-rooted trees and reeds. Slowly it filters onward, deep beneath the sand, appearing only when the river passes through rocky hills. There the deposit has had no chance to settle, and the stream becomes visible, running swiftly between the glistening water-polished masses of bed-rock, to vanish instantly when it again reaches level country.

There are villages on the banks of the river, and their inhabitants depend for their water supply during the long dry season on a deep hole scooped in the sand of the river bed. As the Sun sinks, the women of any one of these villages, each bearing on her head a large red earthenware pot, can be seen trudging in single file down the slope from the huts, to push through the reeds and congregate round the cavity in the sand. With the help of a large spoon-shaped calabash the water is laboriously baled out and poured into the pots. By the time all are filled the hole is dry, but an hour will see the bottom again covered with freshly filtered water. The women lift the jars on to their heads and turn away, leaving the children to cover the hole with branches to protect it from being fouled and trodden in by animals.

Wild creatures normally drink at places in the rocky country, where the water is forced to the surface. They are well aware of its existence beneath the sheets of sand, however, and where the overlay is thin they scrape it away with their feet. I have at times come on remarkably deep holes made by thirsty beasts, into which the water has percolated, thus saving my carriers the labour of digging at the end of a long day's march.

A considerable amount of the Valley country is covered with almost impenetrable bush, a close-knit tangle that can be traversed only along the age-old twisting tracks made by elephant and rhinoceros. None of these paths leads in one direction for more than a few yards, and their use is not unattended with danger to the human traveller. While he is hemmed in between the nearly solid walls of such a track, at a yard's range he may meet an elephant or a rhinoceros strolling in the opposite direction. Someone has to give way, and it won't be the animal that will oblige!

The straightest and best roads through the jungle-country therefore usually are along the sandy beds of the rivers. Loose ankle-deep sand is a particularly exasperating surface on which to travel. With each stride forward the foot slips half a step backward, doubling the labour and making marching a monotonous treadmill. Even when travelling light it is hard work, and the toil is considerable to anyone laden with a heavy express rifle, ammunition and water-bottle. The bare feet of the native bearers grip the surface better than do a white man's boots, but it is not long before even the natives begin to stagger and pant beneath their head-borne loads. To make matters worse, the Sun seems to concentrate upon the river beds. Heat beats down from above and is radiated upward from the dazzling surface, and the tree-clad banks of the river shut out any possible cooling breeze.

On the march along the sandy bed of a Rhodesian river. The water is below the bed and is reached by digging.

Under the midday Sun the watercourse appears to be flat and featureless, a glaring level of eye-searing sand. At the hour of dawn it is as revealing as an open book to those who can read it, however, for it speaks of the creatures that inhabit the district, of their numbers and their movements. As the Sun rises, its golden light catches the tops of the trees that line the river bank. Swiftly the rays descend, falling on the sheet of sand and turning its pale dun to dazzling whiteness. The slanting beams pick out each hollow and footmark, and impressions now show in bold relief that would be almost invisible at midday, when the Sun is directly overhead.

The great round marks of the feet of a herd of elephants stand out like gigantic enlargements of the perforations on a sheet of postage-stamps, each depression bordered by a half-moon of blue shadow on its eastern side and a clear-cut white line on the west. Crossing them is a series of V-shaped spoor, telling of the passage of a herd of sable antelope; and beside them are those of the small feet of a troop of impala. Lion, buffalo, zebra, all have left their footprints, and even the tiny three-toed marks of guinea fowl, francolin and other birds show beneath the overhanging trees, where the sand is damper. As the day advances the wind will blur the impressions; at dawn the marks of the feet of those that pass in the night stand out clear and sharp.

Every 12 or perhaps 20 miles along their sinuous course these rivers pass through belts of rocky country, winding about in deep gorges carved out by the flow of water for untold centuries. In one of these belts there is a ravine in which I have often had to camp in my journeyings. The stream runs strongly along its bottom, hemmed in by a thin line of dense jungle backed by vertical cliffs of rock from which hang festoons of maidenhair fern, and provides the only water that is accessible for miles around.

At night the spot was never a restful one, for with the coming of the dark the place became a veritable Zoo. Lions and elephants, buffalo and rhinoceros were among the visitors of many kinds. A ring of fires had to be kept burning at night, and a regular system of native sentries arranged. The flickering flames kept most of the callers from actually blundering into the camp; but it was disconcerting to be awakened suddenly by the heavy breathing or inquisitive snorting of some intruder standing in the darkness just beyond the circle of the light.

Trains that Arrive in Reverse

Although motor trains of the "push-and-pull" type perform half their journeys with the coaches leading, the arrival of a main line train at a station platform with the engine trailing sounds unusual. Yet this can be observed regularly at Limerick Junction in Ireland, and also at Inverness, as described on page 256 of this issue, and expresses from the southern extreme of the territory served by L.M.S.R. trains arrive at Templecombe in reverse, while those in the opposite direction depart from that station with their engines in the rear.

"The Pines Express," with its Liverpool and Manchester, Leeds and Bradford portions, makes part of its journey to and from Bournemouth over what was in pre-grouping days the Somerset and Dorset Joint Railway. This is now a jointly-owned L.M.S.R. and S.R. system. Its main line runs from the L.M.S.R. station at Bath to the S.R. system at Broadstone Junction, whence access is afforded to Bournemouth. The S.R. West of England main line is touched intermediately at Templecombe, for the L.M.S.R. trains make use of the S.R. station there. A steeply-rising spur connects the "Joint" line, which passes underneath the S.R. main line at right-angles with the station.

"Right away"-backwards! "The Pines Express" about to reverse out of the S.R. station at Templecombe. The headlamp indication is that authorised for expresses on the Somerset and Dorset line. Photograph by Mr. H. M. Madgwick, Worthing.

"The Pines Express," southbound, leaves the Joint line at Templecombe No. 2 Junction, and curving round to the right gains the platforms of Templecombe station. Its station business being discharged, there is no way for the train to regain its former route except by setting back out of the station over the spur that it has previously negotiated. For this reversing movement a shunting pilot engine is attached to what becomes, temporarily, the front of the train. Thus the heavy express, frequently double-headed in the Summer season, makes its departure from Templecombe with its own engines trailing. At No. 2 Junction the shunting pilot is detached and the train then proceeds on its way again.

The opposite process is necessary with the northbound train from Bournemouth. It reverses at No. 2 Junction and after the pilot has been attached in the rear it is shunted back up the incline into the station. The resumption of its journey is simple, for departure is made in the usual way with the train engine leading, the pilot engine being left at the station.

This train, and indeed all through services to and from the L.M.S.R. system proper, have to reverse at Bath, for the L.M.S.R. station there is a terminus. The engine of either a northbound or a southbound train runs in up to the buffer stops and is uncoupled. In the meantime a fresh engine is attached to the other end of the train and the next stage of the journey is commenced. When this reversing process, the adventures at Templecombe, and the heavy gradients and single-line working of the Somerset and Dorset route are borne in mind, it will be realised that good locomotive work is demanded, especially as no larger passenger engines than L.M.S.R. 4-4-0's of class "2P" are used.

"Lloyd's"

The G.W.R. "Castle" class locomotive, formerly No. 4009 "*Shooting Star,*" that we mentioned last month as having been renamed "*Lloyd's*" and numbered "A1," has since had its number changed to "*100 A1.*" This is more appropriate, as it brings the engine into line with the highest classification in Lloyd's Register of Shipping.

There has recently been scrapped at Swindon Works No. 3345, "*Smeaton,*" of the 4-4-0 "Bulldog" class. It was originally No. 3357 and was named "*Exeter.*" In March 1902 it was selected to haul the Royal Train from Newton Abbot to Plymouth where their Majesties King Edward VII and Queen Alexandra were to launch the battleship "*Queen*" at Devonport, after visiting Dartmouth to lay the foundation stone of the new Naval College for cadets. The name of the engine was then altered temporarily to "*Royal Sovereign.*" Such alterations were a favourite G.W.R. practice for special occasions and the engine used for the run from Paddington to Kingswear, and the return from Plymouth, was specially named "*Brittania.*" Its usual name was "*Baden Powell,*" but later in the same year it became "*Kitchener*" for another special occasion! It was one of the now obsolete 4-4-0 "Atbara" class.

The change of name of No. 3345 from "*Exeter*" to "*Smeaton*" recalls the removal from G.W.R. locomotives of place names that might be confused with those of stations on the system. It was found that travellers were sometimes misled by such names. Since its building in 1900 No. 3345 had run 1,170,839 miles.

New G.W.R. Rail Cars

Numerous additions have been made recently by the G.W.R. to the services operated by streamlined rail cars. New cars of the same general design as their predecessors are in use, but they have larger and lower observation windows giving increased visibility. Sliding doors replace the swing doors of the earlier cars. A total of 95 services is operated by streamlined rail cars on the G.W.R., and it is announced that further additions are shortly to be made.

The Portsmouth Electrification

Rapid progress is being made with the electrification of the S.R. main line to Portsmouth. When completed the through line will cover 74 route miles and will be one of the longest stretches of electrified track in the country. The electrical equipment in the 26 substations will be similar to that provided on the Brighton and Eastbourne routes. It will be automatically controlled from the control rooms that are being installed at Woking and Havant.

A Southern electric express train in Brighton station. The number "15" displayed in front shows that the train stops at intermediate stations, the names of these stations being given on the indicator at the side of the luggage compartment. (H.R.C. prize-winning photograph.)

Power for the operation of the new services outside the Western Section suburban area will be obtained from the substations of the Central Electricity Board at Woking and Portsmouth. The S.R. power house at Wimbledon is being extended to provide for the operation of the new services in the suburban area. The total length of high-tension cable to be laid is over 100 miles and there are about $10\frac{1}{2}$ miles of low-tension cable. More than 139,000 insulators and 150,000 copper bonds will have to be used to equip the track for electric working.

New rolling stock is being constructed for the operation of the services. This will include 48 four-coach units, 19 of which will be provided with a car that will include kitchen and dining accommodation for 3rd class passengers. Running in conjunction with it will be a 1st class coach including both compartments and saloon accommodation for diners.

Station alterations, further sidings and cleaning sheds, and additional repair facilities are being provided as part of the scheme.

Speeding by a "Sandringham"

Over the main line of the Great Central section of the L.N.E.R. the express that carries the Penzance-Aberdeen through coaches is timed at the same speeds as the crack expresses from Marylebone, and in consequence the fastest running of this lengthy through journey occurs on G.C. metals. On a recent occasion No. 2835 "*Milton*" of the "Sandringham" class made some fast running north of Leicester, with a gross load of 275 tons. A permanent way check to 35 m.p.h. was in force three miles from the start, but despite this No. 2835 was through Loughborough, 9.8 miles, in $12\frac{1}{2}$ min. at $80\frac{1}{2}$ m.p.h. After a minimum speed of 64 m.p.h. up the 3-mile rise at 1 in 176 to Barnston signal box, a second maximum of $80\frac{1}{2}$ m.p.h. was reached at Ruddington and the 23.4 miles from Leicester to Nottingham were completed in exactly the 25 min. booked.

Very hard work is needed on the next stage owing to heavy gradients and numerous slacks. A speed of 42 m.p.h. was sustained up the 1 in 130 bank past Annesley, and 73 m.p.h. was touched before Staveley; but the 38.2 miles from Nottingham to Sheffield took the full 48 min. scheduled. At Sheffield an ex-Great Northern "Atlantic" took charge.

We are indebted to Mr. O. S. Nock for these timings.

Increasing Use of Colour-Lights

Improved traffic working between Carlton Road Junction and Finchley Road will result from the replacement of the present semaphore signals by colour-lights. This section of the Midland main line out of St. Pancras carries a very heavy traffic. Main line trains to and from the North and suburban trains to Mill Hill, St. Albans, and other stations work over the line. It is situated entirely in cuttings or in tunnels, including the Belsize Tunnel, 1,822 yards long. Certain alterations are to be made in the placing of the new signals.

At Leeds (New) Station a new colour-light signalling installation is almost complete.

The renewal of signalling apparatus and the installation of colour-lights is to be effected during the year on L.N.E.R. lines in the neighbourhood of Newcastle-on-Tyne.

Locomotive Standardisation on the L.M.S.R.

Since the formation of the L.M.S.R. group in 1923 considerable progress has been made in locomotive standardisation. The locomotives belonging to the constituent companies totalled 10,316, and these were divided into 393 types. Progress has been such that at the end of 1935 the number of types had fallen to 185 and the total number of locomotives to 7,885. When the orders at present in hand are completed the number of types will fall to 150 and the total stock of engines will be 7,554.

With the replacement of obsolete types by new and more efficient motive power the double-heading of passenger trains was reduced by 20 per cent. for the twelve months of 1935, and an increased mileage of 5 per cent. per engine was realised. In spite of the more intensive use of locomotive power and the increasing demands on the engines generally, the capacity of modern L.M.S.R. locomotive stock is such that coal consumption figures continue to fall.

At the same time the reorganisation and modernising of motive power depots is making it possible to operate and maintain the locomotives on a more efficient basis. One result of this is to eliminate many of the separate sheds formerly maintained by the separate constituent companies at centres served by several of them. For instance, at Carlisle the former Midland depot at Durran Hill was closed early in the year and the 30 locomotives stationed there are now allocated at Kingmoor (C.R.) and Upperby (L.N.W.R.).

A 70 ft. turntable is to be installed at London Road, Manchester, for turning locomotives of the 4-6-2 "Princess Royal" class.

L.M.S.R. Locomotive News

Locomotive No. 6145 of the "Royal Scot" class, formerly "*Condor*," is now named "*The Duke of Wellington's Regiment* (*West Riding*)." The remaining locomotives of the class that have not so far been named after regiments are to be brought into line with the rest of the class in this respect. The new names are allocated as follows: No. 6128, "*The Lovat Scouts*"; No. 6131, "*The Royal Warwickshire Regiment*"; No. 6132, "*The King's Regiment* (*Liverpool*)"; No. 6133, "*The Green Howards*"; No. 6134, "*The Cheshire Regiment*"; No. 6135, "*The East Lancashire Regiment*"; No. 6136, "*The Border Regiment*"; No. 6137, "*The Prince of Wales's Volunteers* (*South Lancashire*)"; No. 6139, "*The Welch Regiment*"; No. 6140, "*The King's Royal Rifle Corps*"; No. 6141, "*The North Staffordshire Regiment*"; No. 6142, "*The York and Lancaster Regiment*"; No. 6146, "*The Rifle Brigade*"; No. 6149, "*The Middlesex Regiment.*" The names of historic locomotives previously borne by these engines are to be transferred to certain of the unnamed engines of the "Baby Scot" class.

The upper illustration shows the old Highland and Caledonian locomotives, preserved by the L.M.S.R. at St. Rollox, Glasgow, as repainted in their original colours. Photograph by courtesy of the L.M.S.R. The lower illustration, from a photograph taken by A. G. Hughes, Wallasey, shows G.W.R. and L.M.S.R. trains running alongside at Chester.

Two of the "5P5F" 4-6-0 mixed traffic locomotives Nos. 5157 and 5158 are to be named respectively "*Glasgow Highlander*," and "*Glasgow Yeomanry.*"

Among the locomotives recently withdrawn for scrapping are several of the 4-6-2 tanks of the former L.N.W.R. Many of the "George the Fifth" class have been withdrawn, including the pioneer engine No. 5320. This was built in 1910, so that its period of service has almost coincided with the reign of His late Majesty, after whom the engine was named.

"The Orcadian"

Yet another named train has been introduced by the L.M.S.R. Commencing this month, the Thurso portion of the 6.30 p.m. from Inverness and the corresponding portion leaving Thurso at 3.40 p.m. will be named "*The Orcadian.*"

Doncaster Station to be Rebuilt

The L.N.E.R. announce that Doncaster station, which is a very important junction and traffic exchange point is to be rebuilt. Additional up and down main lines are to be provided between the north end of the station and Marshgate Junction, where the West Riding and Hull lines leave the main line of the East Coast Route. This will eliminate the "bottle-neck" character of the present layout between these points, where at present only two main lines are available to carry the whole of the traffic to and from the North. An additional up line will be laid through the station, the present up platform being converted into an island. The down platform is to be lengthened to accommodate the longest trains calling at Doncaster. Colour-light signals are to be installed in the station area.

The new arrangements will allow of the simultaneous departure of trains for York or Hull, and Leeds. Similarly arrivals from York, Hull or Leeds will be possible at the same time.

Accelerated Anglo-Scottish Services

From Monday, 4th May, the principal Anglo-Scottish services by both West and East Coast Routes will be accelerated. The greatest individual acceleration will be that of the L.M.S.R. "*Midday Scot,*" which will leave Euston at 2.0 p.m. instead of 1.30 p.m., thus reverting to the departure time familiar for many years for this service until War-time decelerations caused its abandonment. Glasgow and Edinburgh will be reached, as now, at 9.35 p.m. and 9.55 p.m. respectively.

The service now provided to the Furness line and the Lake District by "*The Midday Scot*" will be afforded by a separate new train leaving Euston at 1.30 p.m. and giving earlier arrivals than at present. "*The Royal Scot*" is to reach Glasgow and Edinburgh 10 min. earlier, and its rival "*The Flying Scotsman*" will be 5 min. faster than now to Edinburgh and Aberdeen. The "*Queen of Scots Pullman*" will be accelerated by 10 min. in each direction.

The 11 a.m. on week-days, and the 4 p.m. on Sundays, from Inverness to King's Cross will each be 5 min. faster and various additional services are to be provided.

HORNBY

AHOY THERE, BOYS!......

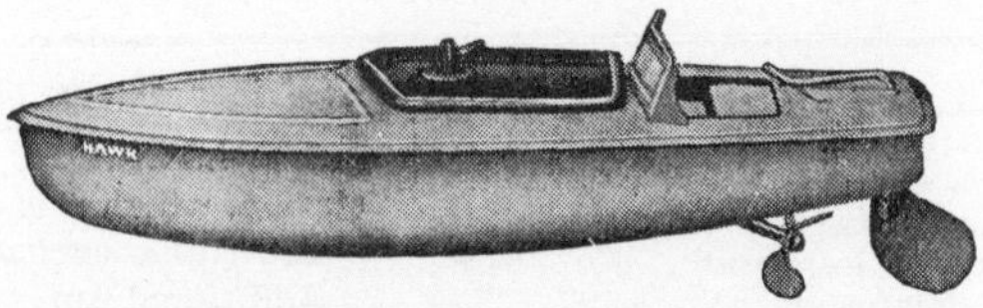

HORNBY SPEED BOAT No. 1. "HAWK." Price **2/11**
Travels over 100 ft. on one winding. Choice of three colour schemes. Dimensions: Length 9¼ in. Beam 3 in.

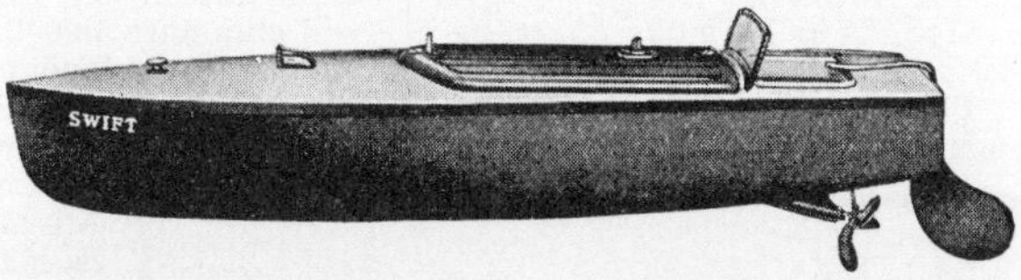

HORNBY SPEED BOAT No. 2. "SWIFT." Price **7/6**
Travels over 300 ft. on one winding. Choice of three colour schemes. Dimensions: Length 12½ in. Beam 3 in.

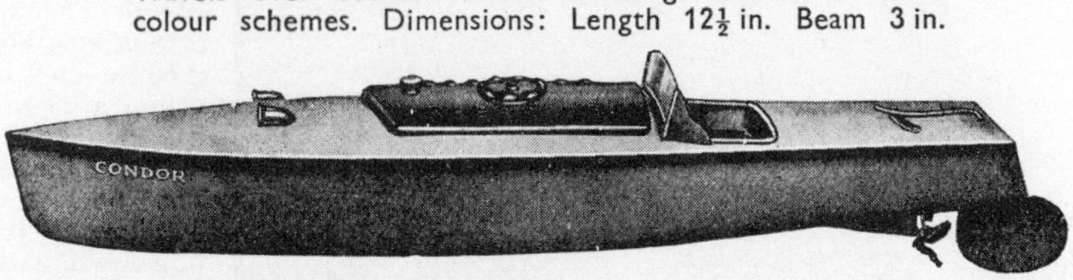

HORNBY SPEED BOAT No. 3. "CONDOR." Price **12/6**
Travels over 500 ft. on one winding. Choice of three colour schemes Dimensions: Length 16½ in. Beam 3½ in.

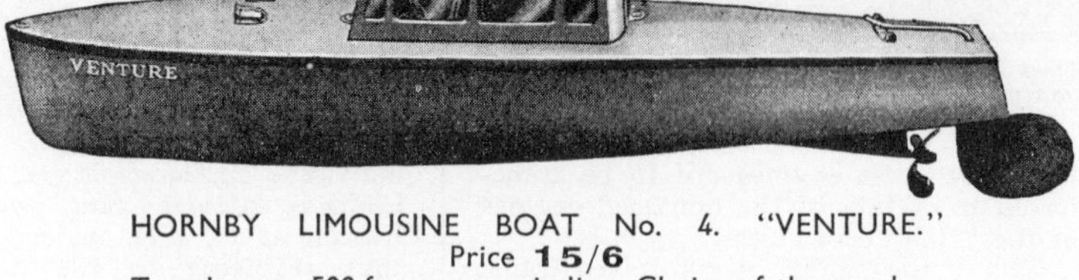

HORNBY LIMOUSINE BOAT No. 4. "VENTURE." Price **15/6**
Travels over 500 ft. on one winding. Choice of three colour schemes. Dimensions: Length 16½ in. Beam 3½ in.

HORNBY CABIN CRUISER No. 5. "VIKING." Price **16/6**
Travels over 500 ft. on one winding. Choice of three colour schemes. Dimensions: Length 16½ in. Beam 3½ in.

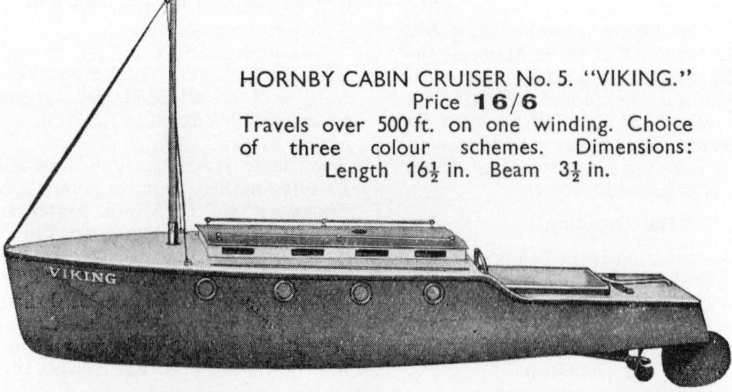

This is

Enjoy the Thr

One of the few outdoor hob preparation, either alone or wit is within the reach of almost eve hobbies, and it provides hours o

Hornby Speed Boats and Ra performance, graceful lines and b splendid boats. They introduce a will be proud to possess one of t

Nothing like the Hornby S before in model boat constructic

HORNBY SPEED BOATS

When other boats are slowing up, the Hornby Speed Boats are still going strong. The special design of the propeller and the unique methods employed in the construction of the hull give each model exceptional speed and length of run. Every line and every feature of the Hornby Speed Boats emphasises their excellent qualities, speed and reliability.

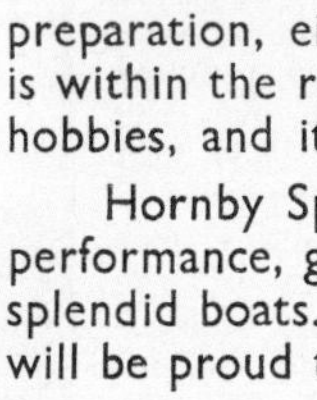

PENNANTS

Pennants for Hornby Speed Boats Nos. 3 and 4 may be purchased separately. Price **2d.** each.

Your deal range of Ho Once you h will not be your own.

Each mod combination tive appear

MECCANO LTD. -

SPEED BOATS

rnby Speed Boat time

Speed Boat Racing!

be carried on at any time without special
odel motor boating. This splendid hobby
s one of the least expensive of all summer
ls.

the best that can be bought. Exceptional
re the outstanding characteristics of these
of excellence in British toys and every boy

d Hornby Racing Boats has been known

HORNBY RACING BOATS

Hornby Racing Boats are superb! Compare these swift, powerful models with real racing craft. You will see they have the same design, the same slim, smooth lines.

The series of Hornby Racing Boats is composed of three exceptionally fine models, each of which is extremely "quick off the mark," maintaining a high rate of speed throughout the whole length of its run.

sed to show you the
ats and Racing Boats.
wonderful boats you
il you have one of

in a pleasing colour
n exceedingly attrac-

Join the Hornby Speed Boat Club
You may do so by purchasing the special badge (illustrated above) from your dealer, or direct from Meccano Ltd., Binns Rd., Liverpool 13. Price 6d.

ed by
ROAD - LIVERPOOL 13

HORNBY RACING BOAT No. 1. "RACER I." Price **4/6**
Travels over 120 ft. at high speed on one winding. Finished in Cream and Green. Dimensions: Length 8½ in. Beam 2⅜ in.

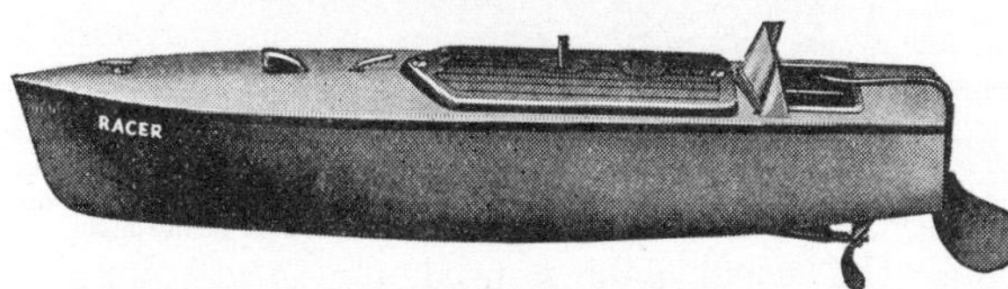

HORNBY RACING BOAT No. 2. "RACER II." Price **8/6**
Travels over 200 ft. at high speed on one winding. Finished in Blue and Cream. Dimensions: Length 12½ in. Beam 3 in.

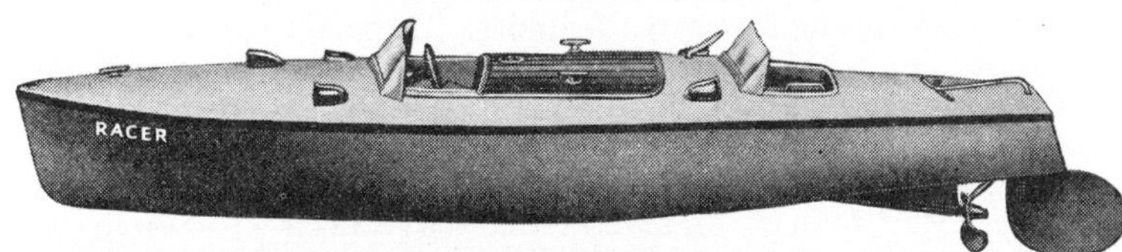

HORNBY RACING BOAT No. 3. "RACER III." Price **14/6**
Travels over 300 ft. at high speed on one winding. Finished in Red and Cream. Dimensions: Length 16½ in. Beam 3½ in.

HORNBY WATER TOY (DUCK). Price **2/6**
Travels over 100 ft. on one winding. Finished in appropriate colours. Dimensions: Length 9¼ in. Beam 3 in.

Miniature Railways That Carry Real Passengers

Garden Systems at Home and Overseas

By W. J. Bassett-Lowke, M.I.Loco.E.

ONE of the greatest attractions of the miniature railway hobby is the wide variety of the interests that it includes. Layout design, train operation, scenic effects, signalling and so on are all branches of the main subject that can be given special attention individually, or combined satisfactorily, on an indoor line. For such railways clockwork or electricity is invariably the motive power. Outdoor railways, that is lines designed and constructed to be permanent and to withstand the weather, have a special appeal and on such systems a steam-driven locomotive gives the utmost realism. The outdoor line is specially attractive in that real cuttings and embankments can be formed, and such engineering features as tunnels and bridges may be really necessary and not provided only for effect.

The thrill of a steam-driven locomotive only reaches its height when the model sets out to pull its owner, and this is now possible with engines running on so small a gauge as 2½ in. It is easier on the 3½ in. gauge, and as we progress through the usual gauges used for garden railways essentially designed for passenger carrying, 7¼ in. and 9½ in., to 15 in. gauge, we arrive at locomotives that are far from toys. They are powerful engines one-quarter full size, weighing three tons or more. These are capable of speeds up to 35 miles an hour, and of hauling loads of 20 tons behind them.

A 7¼ in. gauge "Royal Scot" locomotive on the "Charnwood Model Railway" in Pennsylvania operated by Mr. C. Norvin Rinek. The photographs to this article are reproduced by courtesy of Bassett-Lowke Ltd., Northampton, the makers of the engines illustrated.

The gauges that are most popular and useful to the private model railway owner are the 7¼ in. and 9½ in., and it is interesting to hear of several that have been recently constructed, two on estates in England, one in the United States and one in India. The first of these is owned by Mr. J. R. Jeffress of Kenton Grange, near Harrow, Middlesex. Mr. Jeffress has always been a railway enthusiast and has one of the most comprehensive and complete gauge "O" railways in the country, but lately he has taken up the hobby of garden railways. Like many persons with leisure and a mechanical bent, he has not only designed and supervised the construction of his own layout, but he also builds most of his 7¼ in. gauge models in the workshops on his estate.

His first locomotive is an L.M.S.R. *"George the Fifth"* locomotive built from early designs of Mr. Henry Greenly from castings supplied by Bassett-Lowke Ltd., of Northampton. This engine has a simple handsome outline, and the use of inside cylinders means that there is no outside gear to foul obstructions in the garden. In addition the comparatively short wheelbase of the locomotive allows it to negotiate sharp curves. There is also a 4–6–2 type locomotive of American design built in his own workshop, and a 4–6–0 L.N.E.R. locomotive. This last engine was originally built by Bassett-Lowke Ltd. in pre-War days as G.C.R. No. 1097 *"Immingham,"* and it still does good work at Kenton Grange.

A model of the L.N.E.R. express locomotive No. 4472 *"Flying Scotsman"* that was built in Mr. Jeffress' own workshop has recently been put into service; and the latest addition that is now nearing completion will be a model of the L.M.S.R. *"Royal Scot."* The track on this railway is continuous and possesses two stations. There are tunnels and sheds, and the rolling stock consists of bogie open wagons and one covered vehicle.

Going north, we come to Harness Grove near Worksop, the residence of Captain C. F. Ward Jones, where a splendid 9½ in. gauge railway is now being constructed by the owner for his son. When visiting this line the first railway building we approach is the engine shed. This is a very practical and modern building, from which the track emerges at a level of about four feet from the ground. The raising of the rail level enables the locomotive to be cleaned and attended to conveniently. The shed contains an electric blower for raising steam, and a bench with all necessary tools for the handling and maintenance of the locomotive. Oil containers are handy for drawing supplies and there are various other stores. Outside the shed is a bridge with two arches carried out in synthetic brickwork. The water tower nearby is mounted on four concrete pillars.

The line was laid by the owner, to a gauge of 9½ in., with flat-bottomed Vignoles rail, and is already half a mile long. From the shed it traverses an embankment and soon reaches the main railway station. This is a building of excellent design and inside is arranged an ingenious little refreshment room provided with tables, where one can obtain chocolates and refreshments.

Leaving the station the line crosses a small brook by an underbridge. It then traverses a picturesque woodland coppice for about 400 yds., passing a wayside station there, and returning by a loop to the main line again. There are two crossover roads, one at each end of the station. The radius of the curves is 80 ft.

The locomotive is an L.N.E.R. 4-4-2 "Atlantic" of G.N. design built by Bassett-Lowke Ltd. It has cylinders with a diameter of $2\frac{3}{4}$ in. and a piston stroke of 4 in., and the bronze valves are operated by Stephenson link motion. The boiler is fitted with copper tubes and has a correct Wootten firebox with a wide grate. The cab fittings include two injectors, pressure gauge, two water gauges, blower, whistle, and forced lubrication system. The locomotive is fitted with the steam brake and there are hand brakes on the tender. The owner has built his own rolling stock, which consists of several very realistic open wagons. These are very comfortable to ride in.

"Oiling up." The youthful engine driver in this photograph is busily attending to the $9\frac{1}{4}$ in. gauge L.N.E.R. 4-4-2 on the railway of Captain C. F. Ward Jones at Harness Grove, nr. Worksop.

Next there is the "Charnwood Model Railway" laid out by an American enthusiast in Pennsylvania. The line is laid out in circular form 800 ft. in circumference, with a spur to the engine shed. The curves are rather sharp, of 35 ft. radius and 40 ft. radius, and at one point the grade rises at 1 in 30.

The first locomotive made for this track was a "*King George V*" by Bassett-Lowke Ltd. As readers know, Canadians and Americans were greatly interested in the visit of "*The Royal Scot*" train to America. They went in their tens of thousands to view the "little English train" at the Century of Progress Exhibition at Chicago in 1933, and on the American tour of the train they crowded and flocked to the stations and level crossings to catch a glimpse of it. Among these admirers of "*The Royal Scot*" was Mr. C. Norvin Rinek, already a model enthusiast, and he so liked the lines of the English engine that he could not rest until he had an exact working scale model for his $7\frac{1}{4}$ in. gauge garden railway.

Another view of the L.N.E.R. 4-4-2 with the driver on board. This photograph shows the realistic lines of the engine and the substantial character of the permanent way.

So the second engine on this system is the L.M.S.R. 4-6-0 No. 6100 "*Royal Scot,*" again made by Bassett-Lowke Ltd. It incorporates a number of features to make it possible for an engine of this size to negotiate the 35 ft. radius curve. The engine is fitted with a mechanically-driven oiler, dumping grate, automatic pet cocks and snifting valves. It will negotiate the curves at almost full throttle. The Charnwood Model Railway is entirely English in character, and it is interesting to know that English engines, even if in miniature, are running in America to day.

Another overseas line on which a British type engine is operated is the "Indian Midland Railway" at Jhansi, that was described in the July 1935 "*M.M.*" This system is owned and was laid out by Mr. R. Horsfield, E.D., A. M. I. Mech. E., M.I.Loco.E., of the Great Indian Peninsular Railway. As might be expected, all the work is carried out with great thoroughness, even to the provision of interlocking and special signal and telephone instruments for train working between the two main stations. At the terminus is a ground frame signal cabin, a booking office with platform and journey tickets; and even train destination and timetable boards are provided.

The practice of this line is an interesting combination of British and Indian features. Thus the engine is a close reproduction of the 4-4-0 Standard Compound class of the L.M.S.R., the actual prototype belonging to the "1100" series so well known on L.M.S.R. main lines. This was constructed by Bassett-Lowke Ltd., at Northampton, and works at a pressure of 100lb. per sq. in. It is complete with steam-brakes, an injector working between pressures of 40 and 95 lb. and a feed pump. Steam and water gauges are of course provided. A boiler blow-down cock and cylinder drain cocks are fitted. The cylinders are lubricated by a hand-forced system. Oil cups for slide bars, bogie and leading coupled wheel boxes are employed, while a forced feed attends to the valves and trailing coupled wheel boxes.

The rolling stock includes four-wheeled wagons with L.M.S.R., G.W.R., and L.N.E.R. lettering. These are fitted with buffers, and screw couplings. The goods brake van, however, conforms to Indian Railway standard design and is similarly equipped.

The locomotive shed is equipped with an examining pit, and is complete with a repair bench, vice, the necessary tools, and an oil and waste store. Immediately outside the shed, which conforms to the "round house" type, there is a turntable serving the various tracks radiating from it. One track for a length of 9 feet is raised up from the ground. It thus allows for storm water flow and also forms an outdoor inspection "pit" for the purpose of cleaning the fire and for the very necessary examinations of the locomotive. Steam invariably is raised while the engine is on the pit.

These pages are reserved for articles from our readers. Contributions not exceeding 500 words in length are invited on any subject of general interest. These should be written neatly on one side of the paper only, and they may be accompanied by photographs or sketches for use as illustrations. Articles that are published will be paid for at our usual rates. Statements contained in articles submitted for these pages are accepted as being sent in good faith, but the Editor takes no responsibility for their accuracy.

Scenes on the Finnish Railways

There are now in Finland nearly 3,000 miles of railway, mostly state-owned, and a line has recently been extended northward to the Arctic Circle. The track, which is of 5 ft. gauge, is single throughout most of the north of Finland, and is laid down without chairs. At most of the local stations there are passing loops and the points are frequently hand-operated. Except near the bigger junctions, the system of signalling is not elaborate. Distant signals are not employed to any great extent on the local lines, but each station has its home semaphore.

A wood-burning 4-6-0 locomotive in Finland. The wide-topped funnel arrests sparks that might cause forest fires. Photograph by E. G. Lock, Kingston Hill, Surrey.

The locomotives, many of which are of American or German origin, are painted black. Some burn wood, a fuel in which Finland abounds; and others burn coal, most of which has to be imported. Locomotives of the 4–6–0 wheel arrangement, with driving wheels 5 ft. in diameter, are the most general type, and are used all over the country for mixed traffic. A wood-burner is shown in the accompanying photograph. The wide-topped funnel acts as a spark catcher to prevent the possibility of forest fires. This is a necessary precaution, since most of the Finnish lines run through forested country. In the south, coal-burning 4–6–0s with 6 ft. driving wheels are usually employed on the passenger trains, and large tank engines are used for some of the suburban traffic around Helsingfors.

The passenger rolling stock varies a good deal. The 1st-class coaches, sleepers and dining cars have eight wheels and are comfortably upholstered, but many of the 3rd-class coaches are old four-wheelers, and their plain wooden seats are somewhat hard for long journeys. The passenger stock is painted plum colour and bears the word "Suomi" on the sides, Suomi being the national name of the country we call Finland.

Freight trains are not very numerous, for many local trains run with mixed passenger and goods stock. In the vicinity of the ports goods trains play a more important part, however, especially in the great Finnish timber trade.

Expresses, on which a small extra charge is made, and fast and local or slow trains are run. The slow trains stop at all stations, but the halts are of very short duration, except those made to allow passengers to get refreshments. The best trains, hauled by coal-burning 4–6–0s, run between Helsingfors, the capital, and the seaport towns of Åbo and Vipuri, and on these routes the overall times average between 45 m.p.h. and 50 m.p.h. Long non-stop runs are not possible owing to the small tenders used and the absence of water troughs. E. G. Lock (Kingston Hill).

Painting the Menai Bridge

The lower photograph on this page shows the immense steel chains that support the Menai Bridge, the graceful structure that connects the mainland of Wales with Anglesey. It was taken at a point where the chains enter the ground at the Anglesey end, and shows the scaffolding erected for painting purposes. The tiny figure of a workman busily painting can be distinguished between the chains in the centre near the top of the tower. It was interesting to watch the men at work on the bridge, for they were slung over the side of the structure in travelling cradles. I was told that a silica-graphite paint is now used because it is thought to stand up to weather conditions more satisfactorily than the lead paints previously employed.

The steel chains of the Menai Bridge, the world's first great suspension bridge. Photograph by G. W. R. Heller, Gerrard's Cross.

The bridge is one of the most famous of the works of Thomas Telford, the great engineer who was punningly named the "*Colossus of Roads*" by his friend the poet Southey, because of his extensive road-building activities.

G. W. R. Heller (Gerrard's Cross).

A Uganda Chieftain at Home

While travelling recently through Uganda, I was asked by a friend if I would like to visit the native king of the district and I eagerly accepted his offer. Uganda is governed by a system of indirect rule, the native chiefs maintaining their own systems of administration under supervision by the British officials. This particular king or "mugapi," as he is called, has been on the throne since 1901, when Uganda first became a British Protectorate.

A note was sent to the palace, which was a medium-sized stone house of rather tumble-down appearance, to say that two "wazungu" would like an audience. While we awaited the reply we were shown the royal drums, which vie in importance with the king himself. They are only beaten on special occasions, and are kept in an outhouse and covered with rugs to keep them warm! A guard is on duty day and night, and a fire is kept continually burning in front of them. Sacrifices of milk and meat are offered from time to time.

The iron bridge across the Severn at Coalbrookdale, Shropshire. This was opened for traffic in 1779 and was the first cast iron bridge ever built. Photograph by E. H. Coles, London, W.11.

We were now told that the mugapi was ready to receive us and were ushered into a small room furnished in a dingy Victorian style, with decorations that evidently had been brought from England on the king's accession in 1901. The mugapi was sitting in an upright armchair at one end of the room with a soap-box as a footstool! Above his head were framed photographs of King George and Queen Mary, and above them again was a white card with "Welcome" printed on it. Like the majority of his race, the chieftain was finely built. He must have stood well over seven feet high and was broad in proportion. He was simply clothed in a kanzu, the ordinary native dress, which is a sort of nightshirt reaching to the ground.

A typical herdsman of Uganda with his cattle. Photograph by B. A. Soltau, Kenya.

We sat in chairs facing the throne and conducted our conversation by means of interpreters, although the mugapi seemed to understand a good deal of what we said in English. We found him rather difficult to talk to, for his knowledge of the outside world was limited. We discussed the five cars that he possesses, and he told us something of the customs and laws of his people, and their contentment under British rule. While we were talking his orchestra formed up outside and began to play weird native music that seemed to please him. We rose and took our leave after shaking hands with the mugapi and exchanging small gifts with him; and so ended one of the most interesting experiences of my life in East Africa.

B. A. Soltau (Kenya).

The World's First Iron Bridge

England can claim to have the first iron bridge ever built. This crosses the Severn at Coalbrookdale. It was opened for traffic in 1779, and is yet in active service.

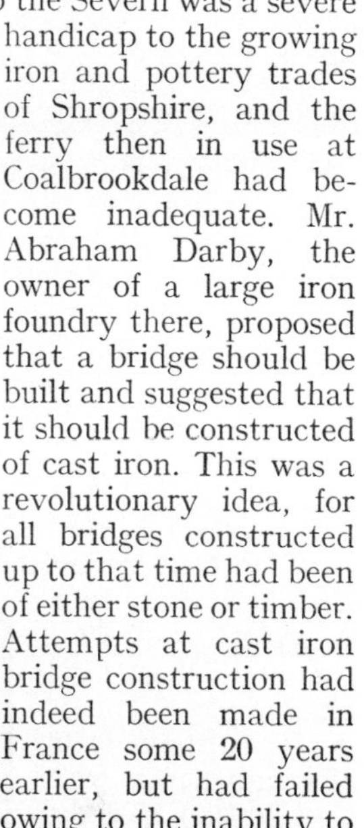

A little more than 150 years ago the Severn was a severe handicap to the growing iron and pottery trades of Shropshire, and the ferry then in use at Coalbrookdale had become inadequate. Mr. Abraham Darby, the owner of a large iron foundry there, proposed that a bridge should be built and suggested that it should be constructed of cast iron. This was a revolutionary idea, for all bridges constructed up to that time had been of either stone or timber. Attempts at cast iron bridge construction had indeed been made in France some 20 years earlier, but had failed owing to the inability to make large castings. Darby considered that this difficulty could be overcome, and so the project was begun and was carried out with success.

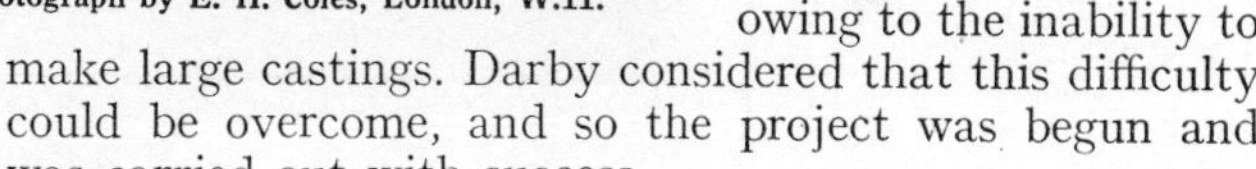

As can be seen from the upper photograph on this page, the bridge is almost semi-circular in outline. It has a span of 100 ft. and rises 45 ft. above abutments. The five ribs of the structure, each 140 ft. in length, were cast in two pieces. This was an amazing achievement in view of the lack of experience at that time of work of this description, and its accomplishment adds to the interest of this pioneer structure. E. H. Coles (London, W.11).

Thrills on the Eiffel Tower

On the day that my French friend and I went up the Eiffel Tower, there was a terrific gale blowing, with driving sleet and fog, and on glancing upward from the foot of the structure, we discovered that the top was completely hidden in mist. The liftman told us that we were the only visitors that morning. He was rather dubious about letting us go up, but we managed to persuade him to take us.

As the lift went higher the wind grew stronger, and when we stepped out on to the balcony, my first thought was that the top part of the Tower was going to snap off suddenly, for it was actually swaying from side to side. The wind threatened to blow us off the platform, and the rain lashed blindingly in our faces. I held fast on to the rail and shut my eyes, which were smarting and running with water, and then it seemed as though I were on the bridge of a Channel steamer in a storm! When I opened my eyes, I could see nothing for the mist and fog that enveloped us, and soon stumbled back into the lift. C. Lewis (Stoke-on-Trent).

A Fascinating Fun Fair Model

Roundabout with Dinky Toy Horses

ALTHOUGH many modern sources of amusement and entertainment are now available, the old-fashioned fun fair has not been pushed completely into the background, as the popularity of pleasure grounds at popular seaside resorts shows. Almost everyone has experienced the fascination and thrill of joy riding on the roundabouts that are such prominent features of fun fairs, and among these the hobby-horses are still favourites, in spite of competition from similar devices equipped with motor cars or flying boats.

It is good fun to build a working model of a roundabout with Meccano parts, and this is a much more simple task than at first appears. A typical example is the model illustrated on this page. This is made entirely from Meccano parts, with the addition of Dinky Toy Horses; it incorporates neat and interesting mechanisms, is easy to build, and will provide great amusement for its constructors.

The base of the model is a Geared Roller Race, but model-builders who do not possess this part can substitute a frame of Angle Girders, or a base made of Flat Plates. Four $3\frac{1}{2}'' \times \frac{1}{2}''$ Double Angle Strips are first of all secured in place, as shown in the lower illustration on the opposite page, two washers being used on each holding-down bolt to raise them slightly above the base. Each Double Angle Strip carries a $4\frac{1}{2}''$ Rod, at one end of which is a $\frac{1}{2}''$ Pinion and at the other a $\frac{1}{2}''$ fast Pulley. The Pinion is spaced from the Double Angle Strip by a washer and the Pulley by two washers. A Bush Wheel with its boss uppermost is bolted in the centre of the base. Two pairs of $2\frac{1}{2}''$ Angle Girders are bolted to the base so that they are parallel to one pair of diametrically opposed Double Angle Strips. These form supports for $3'' \times 1\frac{1}{2}''$ Flat Plates on which the Electric Motor is mounted, as shown in the detailed illustration of this section of the model.

A $2\frac{1}{2}''$ Rod journalled in the lower centre hole of the Motor side plates carries on the outside a 50-teeth Gear Wheel, which is spaced from the Motor side plate by a Collar, and on the same Rod, but between the side plates, are a $\frac{3}{4}''$ Pinion, a Coupling and a Collar. A $1\frac{1}{2}''$ Rod is journalled in the Bush Wheel already mentioned and in the longitudinal bore of the Coupling, and carries two $1\frac{1}{2}''$ Contrates 1 and 2. The Contrate 1 is in mesh with the $\frac{3}{4}''$ Pinion on Rod 15, and Contrate 2 makes contact with the four $\frac{1}{2}''$ Pinions mounted on the base plate. The drive is taken from the 50-teeth Gear Wheel on Rod 15 to 12 by means of a $\frac{3}{4}''$ Pinion. On Rod 12 there is also a 57-teeth Gear Wheel, and this engages a $\frac{1}{2}''$ Pinion on Rod 14, which carries also a second 57-teeth Gear Wheel. A $\frac{3}{4}''$ Pinion on the Armature Shaft of the Motor drives this Gear Wheel by means of a 50-teeth Gear Wheel and a $\frac{1}{2}''$ Pinion on Rod 13. Clearance for the various Gears and Pinions is given by washers and Collars.

The imitation organ in the centre of the machine forms the container for the gear-box. It consists of one $3\frac{1}{2}'' \times 2\frac{1}{2}''$ Flanged Plate and four $2\frac{1}{2}'' \times 1\frac{1}{2}''$ Flexible Plates bolted to the flanges of an E6 Electric Motor, the Flexible Plates being strengthened by means of $3\frac{1}{2}''$ Strips. The organ pipes are two 3", two 2" and one $1\frac{1}{2}''$ Rod. These are pushed through the lower flange of the $3\frac{1}{2}'' \times 2\frac{1}{2}''$ Flanged Plate and held in position by means of Collars.

This fine model Roundabout is easy to build, and its construction is detailed in the accompanying article.

The driving mechanism is enclosed in a cylinder made by bolting $9\frac{1}{2}'' \times 2\frac{1}{2}''$ and $12\frac{1}{2}'' \times 2\frac{1}{2}''$ Strip Plates to the rims of a Circular Girder and a Hub Disc, a space $4\frac{1}{2}''$ wide being left to accommodate the organ. The Hub Disc is used at the top and in its centre is placed boss downward, a $1\frac{1}{2}''$ Contrate, which is spaced from the Hub Disc by Collars on the shanks of the four $\frac{1}{2}''$ securing bolts. A 5" Rod is secured in the boss of the Contrate, and around it is placed a $3\frac{1}{2}''$ Gear Ring that is held in position by four 6BA Screws and is insulated from the Hub Disc by Insulating Bushes and Washers. Four Flat Brackets are bolted to the bottom of the cylinder, and bolts pushed through these are screwed into the Threaded Bosses 4.

For the base of the rotating structure a ring of tin-plate or cardboard having an external diameter of $15\frac{3}{4}''$ and an internal diameter of $7\frac{1}{2}''$ is used. Readers who constructed the model Roundabout described on page 105 of the February *"M.M."* will be interested to know that the circular track of tin-plate or cardboard used in that model can be used equally well in the Hobby-Horse. A Ring Frame is bolted to the inner rim of the base, and twelve $\frac{1}{2}'' \times \frac{1}{2}''$ Reversed Angle Brackets are bolted at regular intervals around the outer rim. Eight Rod Sockets also are secured to the outer rim. Curved $12\frac{1}{2}''$ Strips are fixed to the centre holes of the Reversed Angle Brackets, either by bolting direct or, where the holes do not coincide, by clamping with Flat Brackets; and a similar method is used to fix a Ring of $5\frac{1}{2}''$ Curved Strips to the free ends of the Reversed Angle Brackets, the object of this being to form a step around the base of the machine. When this part is completed it can be placed over the gear box so that the Ring Frame rests in the grooves of the four Pulleys 6.

The roof of the model is shown in detail in the upper illustration on this page. The centre is a 4" Circular Plate, to which are bolted eight $7\frac{1}{2}''$ Strips radially disposed and curved to the required shape, with a Bush Wheel in the centre. To the ends of the Strips is bolted a circle of Flat Girders, connection being made by means of Angle Brackets. Alternate $7\frac{1}{2}''$ Strips are provided with $2\frac{1}{2}'' \times 1''$ Double Angle Strips 11, which form bearings for four 5" Rods. A special E1 Motor combined pinion and pulley 10 is fitted to the inner end of each Rod, and these are spaced from the Double Angle Strips by two washers. The Rods are prevented from sliding inward by Collars and at their outer ends each carry a Coupling 8. A lock-nutted Pivot Bolt in each Coupling carries a small Fork Piece 7, which is free to rotate and is fitted with a $6\frac{1}{2}''$ Rod. A $\frac{1}{2}'' \times \frac{1}{2}''$ Reversed Angle Bracket is bolted to the end of each radial Strip, and to this is secured a Threaded Coupling, and a compound rod consisting of a 3" and a $2\frac{1}{2}''$ Rod is held in each Coupling.

The roof of the model, showing the lighting system and the operating mechanism for the jumping Horses.

The model is provided with 16 Horses (Dinky Toys No. 2A). Eight of these are fixed rigidly in position but the other eight are fitted with operating mechanism that causes them to move up and down as the structure rotates.

In order to mount each Horse, a washer is first of all pushed on to a $\frac{3}{4}''$ Bolt and clamped tightly in place by a nut. A second washer and nut are then screwed loosely on to the bolt, which slides into place between the fore legs of one of the Horses. The first nut fits between the Horse's legs, which are then clamped securely between the two washers by tightening the outer nut.

Each of the 16 Horses is similarly dealt with, care being taken not to damage the legs in the process. The Horses of each pair are connected by $1\frac{1}{2}''$ Strips, in the end holes of which the $\frac{3}{4}''$ Bolts are lock-nutted, and the centre holes of the $1\frac{1}{2}''$ Strips are used to attach each unit to Collars on the Rods in the Fork Pieces 7. Eight equally-spaced holes should be made in the tinplate or cardboard ring, four of which form bearings for the sliding Rods, while the others enable the stationary Horses to be fixed in place. The holes for the moving Rods of the jumping Horses should be reinforced by $1\frac{1}{2}''$ Strips.

When the roof is in position the eight vertical Rods are pushed into the Rod Sockets of the circular platform, and the sliding Rods also are placed in their respective bearings. The lengths of the eight vertical Rods are then adjusted so that the Ring Frame rests evenly on the four Pulleys 6, and the special Pinions 10 engage with the $1\frac{1}{2}''$ Contrate on top of the gear-box casing. A Compression Spring and a Collar hold the revolving structure in position, the former making allowance for any inequalities in the moving parts. The stationary Horses are held in place on Rods journalled at the top in the radial Strips of the roof and at the bottom in Couplings secured to the tinplate ring by Angle Brackets.

The Electric Motor and the gear-box. These form a neat and compact unit.

One of the most attractive features of the model is the electric lighting system with which it is equipped. Details of this and the position of the Lamps can be seen in the illustration of the roof of the model reproduced on this page.

The Lamp Holders are held in place by Angle Brackets, and their insulated Screws are connected together, and also to the insulated Pendulum Connection 9, by a length of wire. The outsides of the Lamp Holders make contact with the Flat Girders.

PARTS REQUIRED:

6 of No. 1a; 8 of No. 1b; 2 of No. 3; 1 of No. 4; 12 of No. 6a; 4 of No. 9d; 22 of No. 10; 1 of No. 11; 20 of No. 12; 8 of No. 14; 5 of No. 15; 4 of No. 15a; 11 of No. 16a; 11 of No. 16b; 2 of No. 17; 2 of No. 18a; 4 of No. 23a; 2 of No. 24; 3 of No. 25; 6 of No. 26; 2 of No. 27; 2 of No. 27a; 3 of No. 28; 260 of No. 37; 150 of No. 38; 4 of No. 46; 4 of No. 48b; 1 of No. 53; 26 of No. 59; 17 of No. 63; 8 of No. 63c; 4 of No. 64; 4 of No. 73; 11 of No. 89; 1 of No. 103a; 4 of No. 103b; 16 of No. 111; 4 of No. 111c; 4 of No. 116a; 1 of No. 118; 1 of No. 120b; 20 of No. 125; 8 of No. 133a; 1 of No. 143; 1 of No. 146a; 4 of No. 147b; 1 of No. 167; 1 of No. 167b; 1 of No. 172; 8 of No. 179; 1 of No. 180; 13 of No. 182; 8 of No. 183; 8 of No. 184b; 28 of No. 188; 16 of No. 192; 2 of No. 196; 2 of No. 197; 5 of No. 1561; 13 of No. 1575; 14 of No. 1583; 1 E6 Electric Motor; 4 E1 Electric Motor Pinions; 1 Meccano Pennant; 16 Dinky Toys No. 2a; 1 piece of tin-plate or cardboard $16'' \times 16''$.

In Search of New Models

Suggestions for Engine Builders

RECIPROCATING engines undoubtedly are favourite subjects for Meccano model-building. This is scarcely surprising, for the steam, gas, petrol and oil engines included among them can readily be reproduced with splendid effect, and the construction of models of this kind gives scope for ingenuity in devising means of representing a great variety of mechanical movements. In spite of the large number of reproductions of such engines that have already been built, the subject is by no means exhausted, and will continue to provide opportunities for the exercise of model-building skill.

Fig. 1. Strip and Flexible Plates have been used effectively in this model oil engine.

It is impossible to cover the whole ground of the representation of reciprocating engines in Meccano in a single article, for the subject is so vast. Steam engines of course were the first to be developed. The beam engine of the 18th century is a good subject for handsome models, and one of the best of the many Meccano representations of engines of this type that have been constructed is fully described in the F-L Meccano Manual. It is an accurate reproduction of Watt's beam engine that can be constructed with Meccano Outfit K, and incorporates three of the famous engineer's best known inventions. These are the separate condenser, the centrifugal governor, and the sun and planet gear that Watt used for a time instead of the crank, the simple means of changing reciprocating motion into circular motion that is now universally employed. The crank had many advantages, but it had been patented by a rival, and Watt refused to employ it until the patent had expired.

Fig. 2. A compact type of steam engine that in this article is suggested as a good subject for model-building.

Steam engines have undergone wonderful developments since Watt's time. Engines suitable for all purposes, and for every conceivable position in ships and on land, have been designed, and the variety of types forms an almost endless source of inspiration to model-builders. The reproduction of different kinds of marine steam engine alone would provide occupation for a long time. This attractive model-building subject was dealt with fully in a series of articles that appeared in the "*M.M.*" from March 1934 to August 1934, and described the construction of models of 16 different forms of marine engine. The simplest example was a scale reproduction of the tiny engine of the "*Comet,*" the famous pioneer steamship built in 1812 by Henry Bell for service on the Clyde; and the most complicated was a model, also to scale, of the engine room of a turbine steamship. These articles will suggest other attractive subjects to model-builders who are particularly interested in ships' engines.

Among the many different types of steam engines designed for general purposes is the over-type unit, an interesting self-contained stationary power plant in which the cylinder and valve-gear are carried above the boiler. An example that can be built with Outfit F is shown in Fig. 2. Its construction is typical of most Meccano models of this type, Strips and Flexible Plates playing an important part in the building-up of the boiler, fire-box and cylinder.

The crank shaft of this model closely follows a design published in the "*Suggestion Section*" of the "*M.M.*" The two Collars used in the construction of each web are connected together by a grub screw. This grub screw is first screwed half into one Collar, and the second Collar is then passed on to the remaining half. The crank pin, a 1" Rod, carries a Large Fork Piece forming the big end. The simple method of building the governor fitted to this model also is worthy of note.

Towards the end of last century, while engineers were striving to increase the efficiency of the steam engine, a few experimenters were endeavouring to burn fuel in the cylinder of an engine instead of the fire-box of a boiler. Their work has given us the modern internal combustion engine, using gas, petrol or oil. Gas engines were the earliest to be developed, and these were so efficient and free from trouble that they began to replace steam engines in mills and pumping stations, and came into use for many purposes.

Modern gas engines form excellent subjects for Meccano models, built with both large and small outfits. A single cylinder unit of this type closely resembles a steam engine in general design, but the valve gear usually is more complicated. Fig. 3 illustrates a model, built with F Outfit, that represents a typical single-cylinder gas engine. The most pronounced feature is the massive flywheel. This is essential in a single-cylinder engine of this type, for the power of the explosion of the mixture of gas and air is effective during only one of the four strokes of the cycle employed, that is once during two revolutions of the crankshaft. The momentum of the flywheel helps to give steady movement throughout the cycle. In the model a realistic flywheel is built up of a series of carefully bent $5\frac{1}{2}''$ Strips that overlap each other two holes. The two coincident circles of Strips, shown in the photograph, are secured together by means of four Flat Brackets.

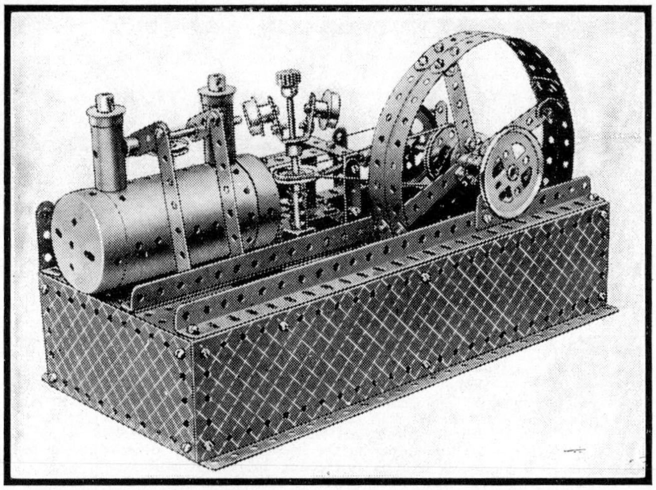

Fig. 3. This modern single-cylinder gas engine can be built with F Outfit.

Complicated fittings have been reproduced in the model in the simplest possible manner. It is always a mistake to overburden a small model with a wealth of details, for these tend to hide the characteristic features of the subject. This is very important from the point of view of appearance, for the general effect of a well-built model can be completely ruined by endeavouring to introduce too many fittings, especially when these cannot be well proportioned. The valve-gear of the model under discussion consists merely of two Cranks, mounted on a Rod, and two $3\frac{1}{2}''$ Strips secured to the ends of the Cranks. The governor also is simple, but is very effective.

A vast field has been made available to the model-builder by the rapid growth of the modern heavy oil engine. The model shown in Fig. 1, the prototype of which is a Petter "S" type, two-stroke cycle engine, is an excellent example. The original is a popular light engine of about 12 h.p. and its simple design makes it a very suitable subject for even quite small models. In reproducing it good use is made of Strip and Flexible Plates, especially in the construction of the "hot bulb" that in practice heats the heavy oil fuel before it is admitted into the cylinder. The large twin flywheels form another notable feature.

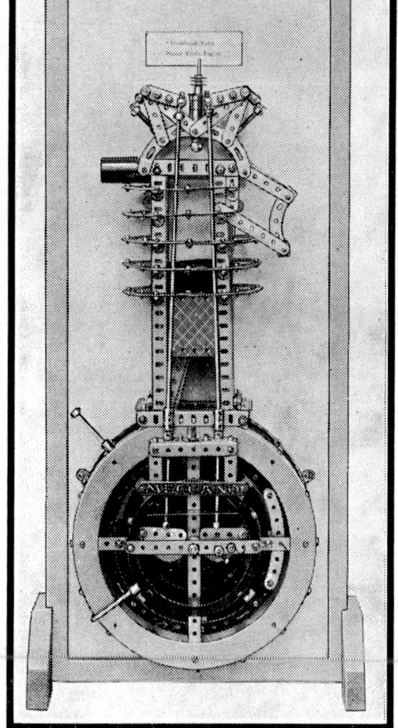

Fig. 4. A fine demonstration model of a four-stroke motor cycle engine.

A Meccano model engine that attracts much attention is shown in Fig. 4. This is a demonstration model of a single-cylinder petrol engine of a type used in hundreds of motor cycles and small boats, and every detail of operation is shown clearly and faithfully. Similar methods of construction can be applied to all classes of reciprocating engines, and excellent examples of multi-cylinder engines, including a fine four-cylinder demonstration model petrol engine for use in schools and engineering classes, have been built from time to time.

As will be seen from Fig. 4 the framework construction of models of this nature is as simple as possible, the mechanism only being reproduced fully. Circular Girders or Ring Frames are used to form an excellent crank case, and a square structure of Angle Girders is all that is necessary for the cylinder. Cooling fins represented by Curved Strips can be fitted if desired.

The exhaust pipe is reproduced by a framework of Strips, but the inlet is cleverly represented by a Funnel. This latter part can be used with equal success in small model oil engines to represent the cylinders. Ingenious use of Meccano parts also is seen in the construction of the sparking plug, in which Small Discs from a Meccano "X" Outfit have been used to form the cooling fins. The lower end of this plug is fitted with a 4.5 volt bulb that flashes at the beginning of each firing stroke to represent the explosion of the fuel mixture. This bulb is operated from a contact on one of the cam shafts and forms an interesting addition to the model. Strip Plates and $3''$ Pulleys are used in the construction of the piston.

Valve-gears and governing appliances are interesting subjects for reproduction in Meccano, and the various movements involved can readily be built and provide opportunities for the exercise of a little ingenuity. Models of governors have been described from time to time in the Magazine.

The valve gears of Walschaerts, Joy and Stephenson often are reproduced in model locomotives and marine engines. There are others of which models are seldom made, however, among them the valve-gears and link motions invented by Hackworth, Allan, Bremme and Gooch, all of which have their instructive value and can be well recommended for their general interest. A little time spent in "hunting" for interesting mechanisms of this kind in books dealing with engines, many of which can be consulted in a reference or lending library, is never wasted, and should lead to some really good and novel ideas for model-building.

Interest can be added to model engines by making them work, with pistons moving backward and forward and crankshafts turning. This can be accomplished by using Meccano Elektron Magnet Coils and Cores to represent the cylinders and pistons. Models of this kind will be described in subsequent issues of the *"M.M."*

KEEPING CHECK OF MECCANO PARTS

One of the many problems that confront the owner of a large selection of Meccano parts is that of keeping a check on the material available for model-building. If the stock of each part is known before the construction of a model is commenced, there is little likelihood of the builder having to postpone work owing to lack of parts. Commencing a suitable filing or tabulating system necessitates a certain amount of work, but time and trouble spent on it is more than repaid.

There are various methods that may be employed to keep a check on a collection of parts. In one of the simplest and best, the names of all the Meccano parts are written down in correct order, together with their list numbers, on the left side of the required number of sheets of foolscap paper, or of the pages of a small note book. The lists of parts to be found in Meccano Manuals and catalogues give the complete range. The rest of the space available is ruled off with vertical lines placed ½" apart.

It is then necessary to take stock and enter the numbers of each part in the appropriate space in the first column. The number of any part in stock can be found immediately from this list, which is kept continually up-to-date by inserting revised totals in the following columns when new parts are acquired. The stock can be checked periodically, and the date on which this is done should be placed at the head of the column giving the result.

SPLIT WASHERS

The need is often felt for some means of preventing nuts and bolts from working loose, especially in models, such as high speed engines, motor chassis and automatic machines, that are subject to considerable vibration and are liable to work loose when running for long periods. It is therefore advisable to fit some locking arrangement to the bolts used in all reciprocating and oscillating parts.

The usual method of locking in practice is by a split washer, as this causes a constant pressure between the thread of the bolt and that of the nut. There is no part of this kind in the Meccano system, but ordinary Washers, Part No. 38, can readily be cut and bent to form very efficient split or spring Washers. The rim of each Meccano Washer must be cut completely through at one point with the wire cutting edges of an ordinary pair of pliers. The two ends so formed are twisted about 1/32" apart. When the split Washer is held tightly underneath a bolt head, this gap is closed and a slight pressure is applied to the bolt.

Another easily made type of split washer can be formed from two complete turns cut from a Compression Spring, the washer so formed being similar in appearance to a key ring. In practice, washers of this type are used only where it is necessary to apply slight pressure to a bolt or where a shaft is to be allowed a little side movement. When used for the latter purpose, the washer is held between the main bearing and a collar fixed on the shaft.

AN UNUSUAL SPROCKET DRIVE

The Meccano model fair ground "Dodgem" illustrated on this page, is fitted with an unusual Sprocket Chain drive. Each of the eight cars in the model is connected by a piece of strong but flexible steel wire about 6½" long to a length of Sprocket Chain, hidden in the roof of the model, that runs in a horizontal plane and passes round a number of Sprocket Wheels of different sizes secured at various points. One Sprocket Wheel is driven by a concealed Electric Motor, and a second Sprocket is mounted on the end of a spring loaded arm to act as a jockey sprocket and take up any stretching of the Chain.

The fine steel wire is looped through the chain so that it does not catch on the Sprocket Wheels. As the chain rotates, the cars are caused to move in an irregular path, thereby creating an effect exactly similar to that of the actual machine.

A similar mechanism is used in model marine displays. The chain is then submerged to a depth of a few inches, and the model ships are secured to it by thin, rustless steel wire. The chain is hidden by adding colouring to the water. No doubt other applications of this interesting movement will be apparent to model-builders.

CORD AND BELTS

The usual method of transmitting a drive in the smaller Meccano models is by means of Cord passing round pulleys. In the larger models the Cord is replaced by Spring Cord, which provides a far more efficient and positive type of drive. Occasionally a lighter or heavier drive is required than can be transmitted by standard Meccano Cord, and in these instances some other material must be used.

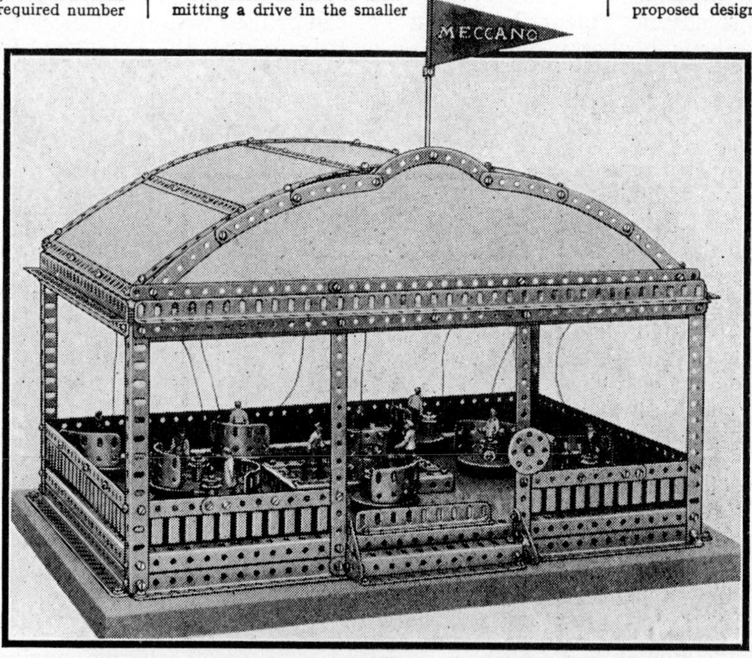

A Meccano "Dodgem" model, in which the cars follow erratic paths, and collide with or dodge each other, as unexpectedly and humorously as do those of its well known prototype.

For light drives, where friction must be cut down to a minimum, cotton or silk can be employed. An example of the use of cotton for transmitting a very light drive occurred recently in a model governor. It was necessary to rotate a 1" fast Pulley on a vertical Threaded Rod from a ½" Pulley carried on a horizontal Rod. The ½" Pulley was turned by a light friction clutch and only cotton was sufficiently pliable to transmit the drive.

For heavier drives Meccano Rubber Bands are extremely reliable, but are not really suitable if it is desired to reproduce wide belting. Dressmaker's tape and strips of canvas may be used with good effect in such circumstances. The two ends of the miniature belts can be sewn together, or linked by means of wire clips.

For really powerful drives, where Meccano Cord is not sufficiently strong or is liable to slip, it is a good plan to use bootmaker's twine. This is a special waxed thread of great strength and, although no thicker than Meccano Cord, it is capable of transmitting remarkable power without any trace of "slip." It can be purchased in lengths from almost any boot repairer for a few pence.

This material was used in a large Meccano Model Pithead Gear that was specially built for demonstration purposes at a recent engineering exhibition. In this case it was necessary to drive a hoisting drum, of 12" diameter from a reversing mechanism concealed below the base board of the model. Sprocket Chain was not desirable for mechanical reasons, and Meccano Cord had not sufficient strength to stand weeks of continuous running. The bootmaker's twine served the purpose admirably.

CREEPER TRACKS

Many suggestions have been submitted during the past year in connection with creeper track suitable for Meccano model tractors, tanks, cranes, etc. The proposed designs vary from simply moulded rubber belts to more complicated stamped-out metal squares, usually interlocked with each other or bolted to lengths of Sprocket Chain. These suggestions are now being carefully considered.

At present it is possible to build efficient creeper tracks with standard Meccano parts. Continuous lengths of Sprocket Chain passing round a number of Sprocket Wheels have a realistic appearance. Rubber Bands also may be employed with good effect when passed separately round pulleys or in the form of a solid track round Flanged Wheels.

A neat form of endless track that is particularly suitable for small models can be constructed from Hinges. The required number of Hinges are secured rigidly together by nuts and bolts, the bolt heads being inward, and the complete belt is passed round Flanged Wheels at each end. To enable the bolt heads to get a grip, the driving Flanged Wheel should be fitted with two or three small Meccano Rubber Bands. Alternatively, a thin strip of strong paper may be passed round the wheel and held in position by glue.

TAPERED FUSELAGE FRONT.—When building models with Meccano Aeroplane Constructor Outfits, it is only possible to represent aeroplanes having comparatively flat noses, a construction that gives a fore-shortened appearance to models. To overcome this the introduction of a special part has been suggested. This new part would be cast, and would be similar in shape to the forward end of many British interceptor fighters, the best known of which is probably the Hawker "Fury." This part would certainly add a touch of realism to the aeroplane models, and the idea will be kept in mind for further attention. (*Reply to A. Wolsterholme, Blackpool.*)

REMOTE CONTROL APPARATUS

Many readers no doubt have examined or built the double-acting relay described in the Suggestion Section of the "*M.M.*" for February last. This is accurate and reliable, but appears to have one fault that has been discovered by V. N. Spencer, Bristol. When the relay is in the "off" position there is a low-tension leak through the coils. This point appears to have been overlooked by its builder F. Jenkins, Birmingham, but, as V. Spencer points out, it can be readily overcome by adding an extra contact or a fourth magnet.

The fourth magnet would operate a contact that must be incorporated in the wiring to the set. It is simpler to add an extra contact to the arm 5 however, and this can be used to operate the set. The contact and set would then be isolated from the relay and no leakage could possibly occur. With this latter arrangement, great care must be taken to see that both Silver Tipped Contact Screws on the arm 5 are in contact together.

Building a Model Theatre

A Fascinating Subject for Animated Models

By "Spanner"

WHEN seated comfortably among the audience in a theatre I have often marvelled at the brief time taken to effect a complete transformation of the stage, and have wondered how all the effects are produced. An opportunity for finding out what happens behind the scenes came to me unexpectedly, and in a manner that could not have been more pleasing. The manager of a large theatre had the excellent idea that Meccano could be used for building a model of the stage to show to the public its essentials, so that they could see for themselves how things worked. He wanted the stage to be copied exactly, with all the moving scenes and usual properties, and thought that a few performing figures would add to the interest of the model, which he required to be working continuously when exhibited.

At first this seemed rather an ambitious scheme, but on thinking it over I realised that here was a subject that could be treated in many different ways, and one that called for sufficient ingenuity and careful thinking to make it truly fascinating. I visualised dancers, acrobats and comedians doing their turns; scenes changing and curtains moving; and at length my brain became almost bewildered by ideas for the complicated gear trains that were to achieve all this.

My first step was to visit the theatre while a performance was in progress. I was conducted through fire-proof doors to the back of the stage and was surprised at its great size in proportion to the part seen by the audience. Limelights were mounted on pedestals in the wings, and other powerful lamps were fixed on long batons suspended above the stage. Down each side of the proscenium front was a row of several dozen lamps shaded from the audience but glaring fiercely on to the stage. The footlights also contributed their share of brilliancy, and in addition three limelights situated in the auditorium were brought into use when the occasion demanded. All this illumination showed that much scope exists for arranging lighting effects in a model.

Many ingenious movements are incorporated in this working model Theatre.

The back of the stage and wings were in comparative darkness, and above my head I noticed a number of small lamps glowing red and green before a platform built out from the wall. There was the huge switchboard from which the electrician controlled the lighting effects. What each switch was for I did not learn, as the electrician was far too busy operating them to answer the many questions I would have liked to ask.

I was then led up a vertical ladder on to a platform high above the stage, to find myself almost surrounded by rows of ropes, pulleys and cleats. I stood beside the painted canvases that make up the scenes and hang vertically from pulleys some 40 ft. to 50 ft. above the stage, and in one corner of the platform was a powerful winch for raising and lowering the fire-proof safety curtain, with hydraulic cylinders to control its movement.

On leaving the theatre I considered all the possibilities that were opened up for a new model. So many ideas seemed to occur that it was difficult to decide which to apply and which to reject. It became clear that as the performers in the model would be small, and could not be reproduced in detail, they must necessarily be identified by their actions. The movements must be operated automatically and timed to occur at the right moment if the model is to work continuously without attention. This timing of the different movements promised to prove the greatest difficulty.

The general construction was fairly straightforward. To obtain correct proportions another visit was made to the theatre, and with a surveyor's tape and a note book rough sketches were made of the principal parts of the structure, with the chief measurements indicated to form a guide when building the model. A front view of the completed model is shown on this page. Finished in the new colours of blue and gold it looks very attractive indeed, and when the stage is provided with painted scenes and lit up it is most realistic.

The 16 figures shown on the stage represent dancers. They are arranged in four rows of four each, two rows being on each side of the stage. Each figure vigorously kicks one leg forward, those in the front rows operating together first and those in the back rows then following their example, the movement going on continuously. After a while the side curtains, made of black velvet, close to the centre of the stage, and a comedian walks across in front of them, making a comic figure as he glides across the stage, his legs moving and his crooked walking stick of Spring Cord shaking. The black curtains again part to reveal the dancers, and their action continues as the safety curtain is lowered.

Two figures represent the men who turn the handles of the winch for lowering the curtain, and in the illustration these can be seen on the elevated platform to the left of the stage. When the safety curtain reaches the stage level, there is a brief pause, during which the side curtains close, and it is then hoisted up again. After the comedian crosses the stage the side curtains part and the cycle is repeated.

At the back of the stage of the actual theatre there are two massive columns of masonry for supporting the upper platform and part of the theatre roof. These are reproduced in the model and one of them serves to accommodate the gearing for the operating mechanism. There are three automatic reversing gears, driven by an Electric Motor, and these control the raising and lowering of the safety curtain, the parting and closing of the side curtains, and the movement to and fro of the comedian. The reversing gears are carefully adjusted so that the three operations are carried out at the correct time in relation to each other, and slip clutches are incorporated to allow for overdrive.

Dancers like those used in this model could be incorporated in any model theatre as they are of simple construction and require only few parts. They are made as small as Meccano parts will allow without loss of correct proportions, each of the figures shown being made of a 2" Strip for the body and a $1\frac{1}{2}$" Strip for one leg. These Strips are joined together by a $\frac{3}{8}$" Bolt serving as a pivot for the Crank that forms the other leg. A $\frac{1}{2}$" Pulley is used for the head, and Flat Brackets fixed to Angle Brackets serve as arms. Further Flat Brackets represent feet. The Crank is used instead of another $1\frac{1}{2}$" Strip so that a Set Screw can be locked in its boss for attaching the operating cord.

A short piece of cord is tied between the Set Screw and the loop in the upper end of a wire that passes through a small hole drilled in the stage. Cord is used on account of its flexibility, but it is necessary to use wire for passing through the hole in the plywood stage. The kicking movement is obtained by attaching the operating wires for each row of figures to a Rod beneath the stage. At each end of the Rod is an Eye Piece sliding on vertical Strips, and cams built up of Collars and bolts raise and lower the Rod.

To produce the walking movement of the comedian the legs are extended so that they pass through a long slot cut in the stage, and are operated by an Eccentric driven by Rack and Pinion.

Testing Steels for Hardness

A Novel Use for the Diamond

By W. E. Glover

THE modern engineer makes great use of special steels and alloys, and it is necessary that he should have exact knowledge of their characteristics in order that he may employ them to the greatest advantage. One of the most important properties of a metal with which he is concerned is its hardness, upon which its behaviour in service largely depends. Until a short time ago the chief method of ascertaining hardness was by means of what is called a Brinell test, in which a hardened steel ball is pressed into the specimen to be tested. The size of the impression is then measured and compared with a fixed scale showing how standard materials of different grades of hardness would respond to the same pressure. Naturally there are limitations to the use of this method. For example, if the ball is pressed into a steel that is nearly as hard as itself, the result cannot be accurate, for the ball also is affected and made to lose its shape.

A machine introduced by Thomas Firth and John Brown Ltd., Sheffield, has now made possible far more accurate measurement of hardness. It is known as the "Firth Hardometer," and is illustrated on this page. The principle on which it works is similar to that of the Brinell test, for it includes a hardened ball indenter, but in addition it is fitted with a diamond that also can be pressed into test pieces in exactly the same manner.

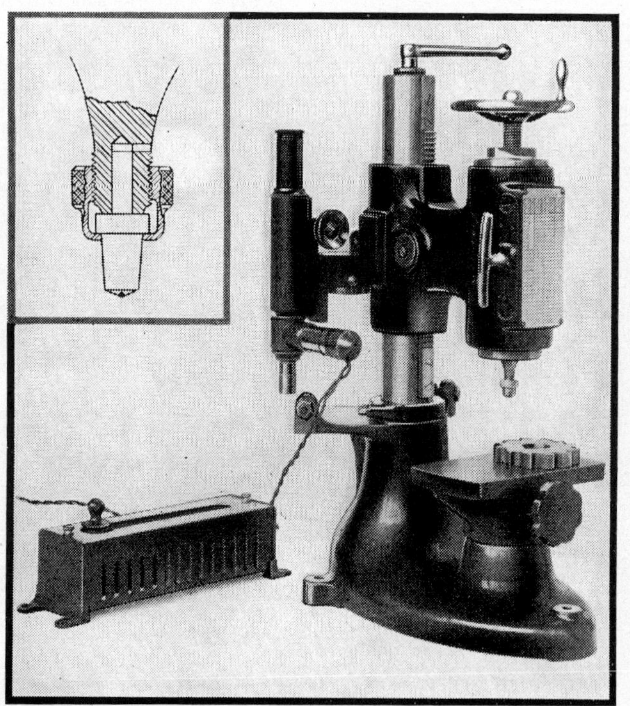

The Firth Hardometer, in which the hardness of metals is measured by pressing a diamond into test pieces. In the upper left hand corner is a sectional drawing, on a larger scale, of the diamond holder. Photograph by courtesy of Thomas Firth and John Brown Ltd., Sheffield.

The diamond used in the Firth hardometer is carefully selected, cut and polished. It has the standard angle of 136 deg. between opposite faces, and is set in a special holder. Unlike the balls used for the Brinell test, it does not vary in quality to any appreciable extent and gives consistent results. The machine therefore has opened up a new field for accurate work, and can be used to test specimens of any hardness up to that of the highest speed tool steel

The article to be tested first has to be prepared, for most metals bear a skin of material that is either harder or softer than the internal bulk. This skin is filed or ground off, and the new surface is then polished with a very fine emery in order to remove scratches and to provide a good measuring surface. The article is then supported on the anvil, as shown in the accompanying illustration, and the diamond is moved downward into contact with it by means of a hand wheel. Approximately a complete turn is then made, and finally the movement is automatically arrested when the exact load required for the test has been applied. This load is applied to the test piece through a spring.

The size of the impression produced must then be measured. For this purpose the head of the machine is swung round on its axis until the microscope, seen on the left of our illustration, is immediately above the mark made by the diamond. This carries a horizontal side tube in which is placed a lamp to illuminate the test piece, the light being reflected on to the specimen by means of a strip of glass placed in the body of the microscope, and at an angle of 45 deg. to its axis. The magnification varies between 80 and 210, according to the type of the machine.

The microscope is fitted with a micrometer scale to enable the size of the impression to be read directly. This is a satisfactory and accurate method of measuring, but has certain disadvantages when many measurements have to be made. One of these is the eye strain that frequently occurs when work is practically continuous. This difficulty has been overcome by fitting over the eye piece of the microscope an ingenious device that projects an enlarged image of the impression to be measured on to a slotted ground glass screen. This screen is in the front vertical face of the head and is marked with scales for purposes of measurement. A sharp image free from distortion is obtained and the necessary readings can be carried out easily and rapidly.

For soft metals and those of medium hardness the ball indenter is satisfactory, but for harder metals the diamond indenter gives better results. A certain minimum thickness is necessary in the materials to be tested. This depends on the load, the choice of indenter and the hardness of each specimen. Generally it is best to have a minimum thickness of seven times the depth of the impression when a ball indenter is used, and of 10½ times when a diamond indenter is employed.

A metal or alloy tested by means of a ball indenter is given a Brinell number, that is a number indicating its relative position on a hardness scale. A standard ball 10 m.m. in diameter is used and the number is decided by dividing the pressure on the ball, measured in kilograms, by the area of the indentation, in square millimeters. The same method is used in expressing the hardness of a metal tested by means of the diamond indenter, and this gives a second scale of what are called diamond hardness numbers.

The "*Royal Scot*" Reproduced in Meccano

A Fine Exhibition Model

ON this page we illustrate a fine model of the famous L.M.S.R. locomotive "*Royal Scot,*" built recently for exhibition purposes. The model is made entirely from Meccano parts, and readers who are familiar with the actual locomotive will appreciate the wealth of detail work it incorporates. In the red, blue and gold colours of the Meccano system, the model presents a fascinating appearance, and by manipulation of a lever in the cab it can be set working in a most realistic fashion.

For demonstration purposes the model is mounted on a stand, and in order that the mechanism may be set in motion without the model itself moving, the locomotive is raised from the rails by means of a strong framework of Angle Girders. The operating power is provided by an electric motor, which drives the wheels through Sprocket Chains and at the same time causes the valve gear to operate. The interior of the cab is illuminated by an electric lamp.

The driving wheels are made from Ring Frames, with flanges formed by circles of 4″ Curved Strips, and are interconnected by built-up connecting rods, each made from six 12½″ Strips, which are mounted on short Rods secured to the wheels by Double Arm Cranks. Serviceable balance weights for the drivers are provided by a number of 4″ Curved Strips.

One of the most remarkable features of the model is its graceful lines, which have been made possible by judicious use of the newer Meccano parts. An example of this is to be found in the cylinder block, which is made from Strip Plates. Inside a casing of these are fastened two 3″ Pulleys and a Boiler, the former representing the ends of the cylinder and the latter the valve chest. The crosshead is built up from two channel section girders made from 1½″ Angle Girders, and bolted to a Coupling and a Strip Coupling. Each of the channel girders is fitted with two Threaded Pins, and these carry Eye Pieces that slide on guide bars made from two parallel Strips. The Strip Coupling is connected to the centre pair of driving wheels by means of a connecting rod.

Strip Plates are used also to a large extent in the construction of the boiler, cab, and fire-box. In the case of the boiler the Strip Plates are bolted to Ring Frames, and it will be noticed that by this method of construction a remarkably neat appearance has been obtained. The smoke-box door is provided by a Circular Strip and a 6″ Circular Plate, and four Handrail Supports are secured to the latter to carry a Rod that represents the front handrail. The chimney is made from three Wheel Flanges, on top of which is a 3″ Pulley and then a fourth Wheel Flange, all these being held in place on a Screwed Rod passed through their centres.

The upper illustration shows a splendid model of L.M.S.R. No. 6100, "Royal Scot." The cab of this model is seen in our lower illustration.

The lower illustration on this page shows the interior arrangement of the cab. All the fittings and handwheels are copied as closely as possible from those in the cab of the actual "*Royal Scot,*" and it will be noticed that the new Meccano Steering Wheel plays an important part in giving the model an appearance of reality. Those used are mounted on Threaded Pins.

The electric motor that drives the model is controlled from the regulator seen in the centre of the control panel. The regulator quadrant is a Rack Segment and this holds a short Rod that carries a Hexagonal Coupling; a Crank Handle and a 1″ Rod form the hand lever and pointer respectively. The regulator operates by actuating the tumbler of an ordinary house lighting switch, which is fixed inside the fire-box and connected in the electric circuit of the driving motor. A realistic pressure gauge is made from a ½″ fast Pulley connected to two Handrail Supports by a bent Flexible Coupling Unit.

Novel Meccano Competitions Open to All

Prizes for "M.M." Readers

Novel Short Story Contest

Here is a fascinating Competition in which every reader of the *"M.M."* can participate as it is not necessary to possess a Meccano Outfit to be eligible for the Contest and there is no model-building to do. A range of fine prizes is offered and boys and girls of any age and living in any part of the world are invited to take part. All that competitors are asked to do is to take a pencil and a sheet of paper and write a short story incorporating the names of as many Meccano parts as possible or terms used in connection with Meccano model-building. The following short story is given as an example: "Pawl was playing with a Ball near a Motor Tyre store, when the Boss, who was a Crank by nature, Loomed up in front of him. 'Hook it, or I'll Collar you,' growled the old Buffer. Just then a Dog Clutched the Ball and tried to Bolt with it. Pawl wheeled round to Grab the dog, but only pinioned the Boss, who tore himself out of Pawl's Clutch and stepped on a Curved Strip of banana skin. He fell, waving his arms like Windmill Sails. 'You Worm!' he shouted, but this ended the Ball Race, for the startled dog coupled itself to his leg, and tore a Circular Strip from his trousers."

Study of the Meccano price list will reveal dozens of parts, the names of which can easily be incorporated in short stories of this kind, and it is great fun to weave a story round them. Stories must not be less than 50 or more than 150 words in length and it should be the competitor's aim to make his entry as humorous as possible. The more amusing a story is, the better will be its chance of winning a prize.

The prizes will be awarded for the story that is the most humorous and which contains the greatest number of part names and model-building terms.

Competitors may send in as many different stories as they wish provided that each story does not contain more than 100 words. No competitor, however, will be awarded more than one prize.

There will be one Section only and the prizes to be awarded are as follows: 1st, Meccano products value £2/2/–; 2nd, Products value £1/1/–; 3rd, Products value 10/6. There will be also ten prizes of Products value 5/–.

Entries should be written on one side of the paper only, and on the reverse side must appear the competitor's name, age and address.

Envelopes containing entries must be addressed to Meccano "Short Story" Competition, Meccano Ltd., Binns Road, Liverpool 13, and must be posted in time to reach Liverpool before 31st July, 1936.

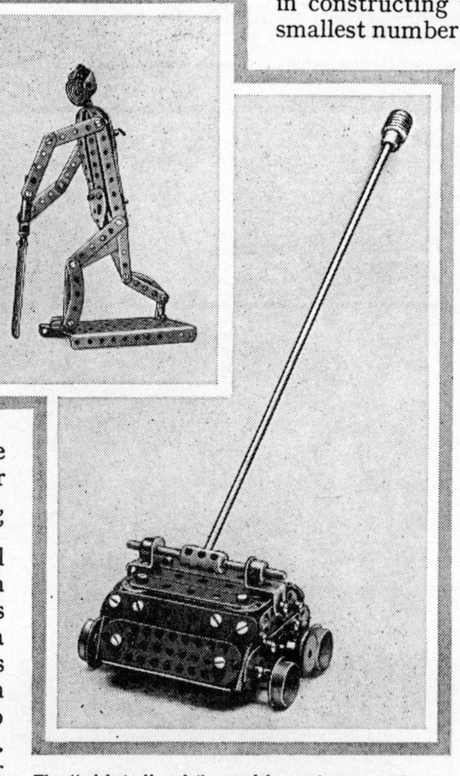

The "cricketer" and the model carpet sweeper shown here are good examples of the kind of models that are eligible for the "Simplicity" Competition.

Simplicity Model-Building Contest

In this Competition we are offering prizes to Meccano model-builders who succeed in constructing the most ingenious and realistic models with the smallest possible number of parts.

Competitors must not imagine that in entering this contest they are restricted to any specified number of parts. Any number or variety of parts may be used, but the prizes will be awarded to those who succeed in constructing the most ingenious models with the smallest number of parts without sacrificing a realistic appearance. This Contest is not for owners of small Outfits only, however, as in the construction of simple models and mechanisms it is possible to employ many Meccano accessories, such as Cranks, Gear Wheels and Couplings, that are not to be found in the smaller Outfits. Competitors may select any kind of subject for their models.

When the model is completed a good photograph or a drawing of it should be obtained. It is far better to send a clear drawing if the photographs are indistinct, or too small to enable the essential features of the model to be seen. Photographs or drawings need not be the competitor's own work, but the model itself must be entirely the result of his or her own unaided efforts.

More than one model may be entered in the Competition, but all entries from any single competitor must be sent under the same cover. No single competitor can win more than one prize; if two or more models are submitted they will be considered jointly.

Entries will be divided into two Sections: Section A, for competitors of all ages living in Great Britain; Section B, for competitors of all ages living Overseas.

The following prizes will be awarded in each Section for the most interesting models built with the smallest number of parts: 1st, Meccano Products value £3/3/–; 2nd, Products value £2/2/–; 3rd, Products value £1/1/–. There will be also five prizes of Products value 10/6, and five prizes of Products value 5/–.

No entry forms are needed, but each competitor must take special care to see that his or her name, address and age appear on the back of each sheet of paper or photograph submitted. Envelopes containing entries should be addressed "Simplicity" Contest, Meccano Ltd., Binns Road, Liverpool 13.

Closing dates: Section A, 30th May, 1936; Section B, 31st July, 1936.

Model-Building Competition Results

By Frank Hornby

"Winter" Contest (Home Section)

The results in Section A of the "Winter" Model-Building Competition are as follows:

1st Prize, Cheque for £3/3/-: F. Higgs, Leicester. 2nd, Cheque for £2/2/-: G. Clarke, Coton, Cambs. 3rd, Meccano Products value £1/1/-: C. Edyvane, Westhoughton.

Products value 10/6: D. Cashmore and J. Harley-Mason, Ruislip; J. Matthews, Fillongley, Nr. Coventry; R. Walford, Newton Abbot; D. Middleton, Northampton; L. Tucker, Reigate; F. Hilten, Cowes, I.O.W.

Products value 5/-: J. Sheldon, Smethwick; D. Brooks, Alveston, Nr. Bristol; J. Maskell, Leigh; T. Pearson, Burnley; R. Emdon, Plymouth; J. Cooley, Wisbech.

F. Higgs secured First Prize with a working model of a 6-ton mobile crane, operated by a high-voltage electric motor of the type used in Meccano demonstration models. The motor drives a special gear-box by means of which the power can be directed to any of the movements of the model. An ingenious mechanism also is fitted for releasing the brakes on the hoisting and luffing drums when the various movements are engaged. As the motor has an ample power output, the crane is able to lift considerable loads, and for this reason every part of the crane itself and of the chassis had to be sturdily built. Besides operating the crane the electric motor also drives the road wheels, and propels the model along the ground at a good speed.

This model is entitled "The Village Choir" and won First Prize in the "Meccanitian" Contest for G. Hudson, Doncaster.

The model illustrated at the foot of this page won Second Prize. It is a reproduction of a reaper-binder that cuts wheat, oats or barley, and binds it into sheaves. It was built by G. Clarke, and performs all the operations of the actual machine, a fact that testifies to the mechanical knowledge and model-building skill of its builder.

A console organ is the subject of the model submitted by C. R. Edyvane, who was awarded Third Prize. The organ is simply constructed and is only 5 in. high and 5½ in. long. With the exception of the keyboard or manuals, which consist of white cardboard marked with ink, it is made entirely from Meccano parts.

Among the winners of Products value 10/6 is a splendid model of a modern gas cooking range. The new Strip Plates play an important part in the construction of this model, which owes its neat appearance to their use. Ordinary Meccano Plates also are used, and the gas pipes are represented by Crank Handles and Rods, which are so skilfully arranged that it has not been necessary to bend any of them. The realistic appearance of the model is largely due to the use of Springs and Pawls to form burners and taps respectively and the skilful manner in which they are incorporated in the structure. The model was built by D. Middleton.

A good model of a reaper and binder built by G. Clarke, Coton, Cambs., that was awarded Second Prize in the "Winter" Contest.

A model of a full-rigged ship was sent by L. Tucker. The hull is made from Braced Girders, and the superstructure from Flat Girders and Plates. Rods are used for the mast and yards, and Meccano Cord for the standing and running rigging. If a little more care had been taken to secure a neat appearance, this model probably would have won a more valuable prize.

F. R. Hilten's model is a rather unusual type of bridge. It has no fixed piers, but floats entirely on the water, and is in the form of a rectangular pontoon on which are provided living quarters for the attendants, and compartments for the driving machinery. Along the centre of the pontoon is an aisle for the traffic, and at each end is a moving leaf that can be raised or lowered by means of cords. The model is about 45 in. long and 15 in. wide.

A deep sea diving suit provided T. Pearson with the idea for his model. It consists of four 2 in. Dunlop Tyres, above which are two Boiler Ends provided with a Chimney Adaptor to represent the window. On top of the upper Boiler End is a Pulley Wheel fitted with a Socket Coupling, and to this is attached a length of Sprocket Chain. Articulated arms are provided by means of Swivel Bearings and Worms, and the hands are made from End Bearings, the arms being secured to the model with the aid of ¾ in. Flanged Wheels. The legs are Sleeve Pieces pushed into ¾ in. Flanged Wheels, and are attached to the body of the suit by Rods that pass through the bosses of the Flanged Wheels and are provided at their lower ends with Couplings to form the feet. The ear pieces are Collars held on Bolts, and the air valve is a ½" Pulley.

"Meccanitian" Contest (Home Section)

The prizewinners in the Home Section of this Contest are as follows:

1st Prize, value £3/3/-: G. Hudson, Doncaster. 2nd Prize, £2/2/-: B. Plucknett, Devizes. 3rd Prize, value £1/1/-: J. Robinson, Dunton Bassett.

Meccano Products value 10/-: F. Saunders, Folkestone; K. Mardle, Carshalton-on-the-Hill; S. Wotherspoon, Liverpool; B. Wilde, Cuxton, Nr. Rochester; P. Wickham, Countesthorpe, Leicester.

Products value 5/-: J. Belasco, Edgware; J. Kennett, Richmond; J. Gerrard, Hardhillock by Drumoak, Kincardineshire; L. Slater, Portsmouth; G. Aspinall, Huddersfield.

"The Village Choir" is the title of the entry that won First Prize and is illustrated on this page. It was sent by G. Hudson, and is an interesting effort. Axle Rods are used to represent the organ pipes, and bolts with their heads enamelled white form the organ "stops." The figures of the choir are made up from Strips, and careful use of these has enabled the builder to obtain quite an amusing and realistic effect.

A tableau of five figures representing a group of carol singers was submitted by B. Plucknett and won Second Prize. This entry owes its success mainly to the care taken in arranging the figures in lifelike attitudes.

Third Prize was awarded to J. Robinson for a group of figures representing winter sports in the Alps, and composed of a man on skis, another skating and a third riding on a toboggan. The artistic manner in which the figures are arranged undoubtedly contributed to its success in this contest.

November "Outfits" Model-Building Contest

Section A (Competitors over 12)

1st Prize, Meccano Products value £2/2/-: A. Cole, Salisbury. 2nd, Products value £1/1/-: E. J. Stubley, Grantham. 3rd, Products value 15/-: J. Maguire, Belfast.

Section B (Competitors under 12)

1st Prize, Meccano Products value £2/2/-: T. Dewsnape, Devizes. 2nd, Products value £1/1/-: D. H. Tomkinson, Wells Green, Nr. Crewe. 3rd, Products value 15/-: J. Capel, Chipping Norton.

Section C (Overseas competitors of all ages)

1st Prize, Meccano Products value £2/2/-: Julian Tuteur, Toronto. 2nd, Products value £1/1/-: D. McLeod, Natal, S. Africa. 3rd, Products value 15/-: G. Hulley, Nantes, France.

Wednesbury and District M.C.—The club has been re-organised, and local schoolmasters are giving their support to it and advising their boys to join. Interesting reports in the local press of the club's activities also are helping to attract new members. Three meetings are held each week, and are well attended. The club-room has been equipped with benches suitable for Meccano model building and Fretwork, and electric light has been installed. Meccano Outfits and Clockwork Motors have been generously given by Mr. N. C. Till and Mr. J. Eccles. A Lantern Lecture on "*British Railway Engines*" was much appreciated. Club roll: 25. *Secretary:* A. L. Morgan, 17, Cobden Street, Fallings Heath, Wednesbury.

Pennthorpe School M.C.—There has been considerable model-building activity, some members working individually and others joining in the construction of a large motor chassis, each part of which was built by a separate group. The motor chassis was completed in time for the Exhibition at the end of the school term. The Headmaster of the School has given an interesting lecture on "*The Building of Railway Engines.*" Club roll: 25. *Secretary:* J. G. Slater, Pennthorpe School, Mead Road, Chislehurst, Kent.

Sutton Valence Council School M.C.—A recent model-building meeting was devoted to a Household Competition, in which those taking part had to build models of useful things for the home. The novelty of the Contest made it very popular, and the models constructed revealed ingenious uses of Meccano parts. A model Battleship Competition is to be held, and two prizes have been kindly given for this by Miss Agnew, Vice-President. Miss Agnew also has presented a picture of R.M.S. "*Queen Mary,*" and this now hangs above the Guild Certificate. Club roll: 23. *Secretary:* J. Chandler, "Herriard," Chart Sutton, Maidstone, Kent.

Burnley Grammar School M.C.—A novel Model-building Competition required competitors to build original models small enough to fit into a match-box. This gave rise to hard thinking, but those taking part rose to the occasion nobly. At another meeting members built in Meccano a complete model railway layout. Club roll: 22. *Secretary:* J. S. Keighley, Meccano Club, The Grammar School, Burnley.

Islington M.C.—The club's first Exhibition was a great success, and the splendid display of models was highly praised by the many visitors and in the local press. Recently talks have included one on "*The Lure of the Footplate,*" by Mr. V. Miller, Leader, and "*The Magic of the Circus Ring*" by the Assistant Leader. A visit was paid to an Exhibition arranged by the New Southgate H.R.C. Branch. Club roll: 14. *Secretary:* K. Dines, 70, Thornhill Road, London, N.1.

Sid Vale M.C.—The second Winter Session was notable for the large number of excellent models built. Frequent Model-building Competitions accounted largely for this, and the many different subjects gave plenty of variety to the programme. A Searchlight Contest produced several outstanding models, and was followed by a searchlight display that greatly interested all present. Many models of shop window electric signs advertising Meccano, Hornby Trains or Dinky Toys, were entered in an Electric Sign Competition. At a meeting given over to Hornby train operations, Mr. Foyle, President, gave the members a shunting test and set them several interesting railway problems, the working out of which on the club layout proved very fascinating. An illuminated Carnival attracted many visitors. Club roll: 20. *Secretary:* L. R. J. Gliddon, Sheffield House, Sidmouth.

St. Oswald's (Norbury) M.C.—Model building has been the chief activity. A Leader is urgently required, and the secretary would be glad to hear of any gentleman in the district who is interested in the club and would take over this office. Club roll: 15. *Secretary:* R. H. Smart, 14, Kensington Avenue, Thornton Heath.

Old Charlton M.C.—A Model building Competition in which Bridges had to be built from a limited number of parts was greatly enjoyed. Debates maintain their popularity, and a new departure in this line was a three-cornered Debate. In this the motion that "*Pedestrians have the prior right to the road*" was vigorously opposed by cyclists and motorists, and after a very interesting verbal tussle it was lost, the motorists gaining a majority of one vote. Another Debate that provided an entertaining evening was on the question "*Should white mice be kept as pets?*" This started rather tamely, but interest increased, especially when it was suggested that if white mice were allowed to live their natural lives in freedom, mankind should live in trees! It was finally decided by a very small majority that white mice should not be kept as pets. The club Magazine, "*Meccanic,*" is proving increasingly popular, and it is hoped that soon every member will contribute regularly to it. Club roll: 20. *Secretary:* W. Jaques, 60, Gurdon Road, London, S.E.7.

Hornsea M.C.—This club has now held more than 400 meetings, and the varied programmes provided continue to hold the interest of the members. The chief features are games evenings, Cinema Shows, and Lectures on many different topics, and occasional Hornby Train meetings. Club roll: 12. *Secretary:* P. Thom, 5, Alexandra Road, Hornsea.

Plymouth M.C.—In a few months' time the club will attain its 10th birthday, and the committee are trying to decide the most suitable way of celebrating the occasion. There will be a further celebration during the first Winter session. Mr. W. J. Ellis, Leader, has given interesting talks to the Hornby section on "*Making Inexpensive Accessories from Newspaper Pulp*" and "*How to Make a Lineside Model Tin or Coal Mine,*" and has lectured to the whole club on "*Fourteen Years Watching Railways.*" Following this Mr. H. Shapcote, M.A., President, who has been a railway enthusiast 70 years, gave a very interesting talk on "*The Earliest G.W.R. Engines.*" At one meeting the motion "*This house is of the opinion that an Air Force is of more use to this Country than a Navy*" was defeated by the narrow majority of two votes, after a most entertaining debate. S. Holloway recently brought to the club-room his beautifully made model of a Tram Shed, complete with Dinky Toy Tram Cars skilfully repainted in local colours. Club roll: 69. *Secretary:* R. G. Symons, 47, Lisson Grove, Mutley, Plymouth.

Whitgift School M.C.—The club has been busy planning and building models for an Exhibition. One member has declared his intention of constructing a model road, and as all efforts to find out how he is going to do it have failed, his progress will be watched with great interest! Club roll: 53. *Secretary:* J. A. Watson, 23, Addiscombe Avenue, E. Croydon.

St. Stephens (Saltash) M.C.—Models recently built by the members have included bridges, aeroplanes, ships and motor cars. The time allowed for the construction of each type of model was two hours, and this has been found sufficient to enable some excellent models to be produced. At the Aeroplane model-building meeting a low wing monoplane was considered the best produced, and an oil tanker was the best of the model ships. The last hour of each meeting is spent in games. The Woodwork section have completed the cabinets in which to store the club stock of Meccano Parts, etc., and are now at work on a 7 ft. model of Plymouth (Millbay) Terminus. Two members of Plymouth M.C. attended one meeting as guests. A large Exhibition is to be held this Spring. Club roll: 17. *Secretary:* B. Braund, 9, Homer Park, Saltash.

Senior members of the Ashburton and Christchurch Meccano clubs "snapped" during a recent joint outing when enjoying a rest on the breakwater at Timaru, New Zealand. The two Ashburton members are on the left of the photograph. The three Christchurch members include Mr. J. Ancall, Leader, who is standing in the front.

Mallow M.C.—The sugar beet factory model mentioned in previous reports of this club has been dismantled, and there is at present a lull in Model-building activities. A shunter employed at the factory recently visited the club and gave an interesting talk on his duties, demonstrating them by means of Hornby Trains. A Stamp section has been formed, and an introductory talk on the hobby has been given by Mr. W. J. Roche, Leader. Club roll: 12. *Secretary:* D. Hickey, 42, Ballydaheen, Mallow.

Claremont Avenue School M.C.—An interesting diversion has been the making of Jig-Saw Puzzles. Most meetings are concluded with a brief period of games. Model-building continues to be very popular, and a new member recently completed fine models of a lathe and a motor chassis. Many different types of models have been built in preparation for an interesting club Exhibition. Club roll: 13. *Secretary:* G. Turton, 5, Brookfield Crescent, Kenton.

CANADA

Montreal Central Y.M.C.A. M.C.—Model-building is the main feature of the meetings, and each week shows an improvement in the skill of those taking part. Several of the models recently built have incorporated a Meccano Steam Engine, a "Magic" Clockwork Motor, or a No. 2 Clockwork Motor. Arrangements have been made for visits to local factories, a picnic on Mount Royal, and a Lantern Lecture dealing with "*The Great War.*" Club roll: 9. *Leader:* Mr. J. Rodrigues, 1900, Tuppet Street, Apartment 4, Montreal, P.Q., Canada.

Strathcona M.C.—Talks are very popular, and subjects discussed have included "*Cranes*" and "*Bridges.*" Efforts are being made to increase the membership. Club roll: 6. *Leader:* Mr. M. Stanley, 9715, 83 Avenue, Alberta.

EGYPT

Cairo M.C.—Several new members have been enrolled. A fine display of models was staged by the club at the recent Agricultural Exhibition at Cairo, and proved a great attraction to the many hundreds of visitors. The Exhibition was open from 7 a.m. until 7 p.m. *Leader:* Mr. Mohamed F. Awad, 7, Atfet El Zamia Haret El Gameh, Cairo.

NEW ZEALAND

Ashburton M.C.—A very successful Parents' Evening marked the end of the financial year of the club, and the large attendance included many members of the Christchurch M.C. and their friends. There was a splendid display of models, and prizes were awarded for the best exhibits. An excellent concert was presented chiefly by members of the club and Merit Medallions and other awards won during the year were then presented. The evening concluded with supper and games. A large Hornby layout was provided for the amusement of children present who were too young to take part in the games. The senior members, accompanied by parents and by several visitors from the Christchurch M.C., recently made an excursion to Hakatere Beach. Club roll: 31. *Secretary:* Miss C. E. Furniss, 176, Burnett Street, Ashburton, New Zealand.

SOUTH AFRICA

Berea M.C.—Meetings are well attended and members take part keenly in the various club activities. Recent outdoor events have included an exciting paper chase. Visits to several factories in the district are being arranged. Club roll: 20. *Secretary:* L. Michelow, 74, Hillbrow Street, Berea, Johannesburg.

Visits to Places of Interest

During the Summer sessions most Meccano clubs take every opportunity of paying visits to places in which their members are interested, such as gas works, electric power stations, engineering works, factories, docks, fire stations, and tramway and bus head-quarters. In many clubs outings of this kind have become a regular feature of the Summer programme that is greatly appreciated by members, and the Leaders of new clubs should spare no effort to follow this example.

Generally there is little difficulty in making the necessary arrangements, for the officials of the undertakings concerned usually are glad to welcome a well-organised and well-behaved party of Meccano boys. It is very necessary to treat such visits seriously, and to make courteous application by letter two or three weeks beforehand. The number of members who will form the party should be mentioned, and the day and time on which it would be most convenient to come should be stated, although this of course is subject to modification if required. An assurance should also be given that the whole party, down to the youngest member, will be "on their best behaviour." Visits of this kind are a very great privilege, and the members taking part should bear in mind that any mishap or unpleasant incident may spoil the chance of other would-be visitors.

At the conclusion of the visit the Leader should thank the guide, and another point that should never be forgotten is the necessity for writing later to the officials concerned in appreciation of their courtesy.

Providing Funds for Outings

The number of visits to places of interest that can be made is generally limited by financial considerations. It is obvious that the cost of the outings cannot be met by club funds, as although the cost per member is small, the total amount in the case of a fairly large party is considerable. On the other hand individual members often find, on the date of the visit, that they cannot participate because they are unable to pay their share of the expenses. There are usually a few generous and more prosperous members who will offer to subsidise the unfortunate ones, but such action, however well-meant, is not a fair and satisfactory solution of the problem.

A little forethought and systematic preparation will ensure that all who wish to do so shall take part in the outings. One way in which this is achieved in many clubs is by running a savings bank purely for the purpose of accumulating funds to finance outings. Each member pays in at regular intervals a small sum, it may be only a copper or two, and this money, gradually increasing, soon becomes sufficient to meet the expenses of the various visits decided upon. When the time for a particular visit arrives, each member is able, if he so wishes, to draw from the bank sufficient money to pay his share of the cost of the outing, and in this manner quite a number of visits may be carried out without any difficulty on the ground of cost.

Meccano Club Secretaries

No. 36. M. F. M. Awad

M. F. M. Awad is secretary of the Cairo M.C. This Egyptian club was affiliated in January 1935, and its steady progress has been largely due to his enthusiasm and energy. Meetings are held almost every night, and are frequently attended by interested visitors.

Recent Successful Exhibitions

Reports of successful club Exhibitions, held either independently or in connection with some local bazaar or fixture during the winter sessions of 1935-36, have reached me from many quarters. It is evident that the value of a good Exhibition as a means of attracting new members and of making known the worth-while character of the Meccano hobby is being increasingly recognised by Leaders. In the early days of the Guild movement many Leaders were of the opinion that the organisation of an Exhibition was beyond the powers of all but the strongest clubs, but displays of high quality are now arranged by practically all clubs, and invariably arouse great interest.

One reason for the fascination exercised by these Exhibitions is that they are no longer haphazard arrays of models of all types and sizes, arranged on tables without regard to order or suitability. The models displayed still reflect the individual taste of members, but follow a definite plan, and every member does his best to ensure that the scheme adopted is effectively worked out. The most successful Exhibitions appear to have been those that included a well planned Hornby layout, on which fascinating operations were carried out. This is natural, for just as a successful shop-keeper takes care that his windows are arranged so as to attract and hold the attention of passers-by, so must a club display be provided with some feature that immediately draws attention, and thus leads visitors to examine carefully the more serious items that they would otherwise be liable to miss.

Several of the Exhibitions held by Meccano clubs during last session were commented upon very favourably in the local press. For instance, the joint Exhibition given by the Islington M.C. and H.R.C. Branch was reported as showing "the amazing variety of the boys' interests. Not only had they constructed ingenious Meccano models of buses, lorries and travelling cranes, but with infinite patience had constructed a complete aerodrome, perfect in every detail, and a model railway with excellent working trains and beautifully constructed stations."

South African Clubs' Fine Display

Occasionally an opportunity arises for clubs to participate in important exhibitions organised by outside bodies. Last Winter the Malvern and Berea clubs, of South Africa, staged a very fine Meccano and Hornby display at the Modern Radio and Engineering Exhibition organised by *"The Star,"* a Johannesburg newspaper, and held in the Town Hall of that city.

"The Star" commented that "the clubs' exhibit exercises enormous fascination for the thousands of children who flock daily to the Town Hall. Rarely is there a moment when the room is not filled by crowds of young enthusiasts watching the little train dodging in and out of tunnels, or the gas works model hauling up its trucks. The making of these models took nearly three months."

A Realistic Layout in Canada

Notes on Some Recent Improvements

CONSTANT developments are in progress on real railways to enable traffic to be handled more easily. Stations are rebuilt, new signalling installations are brought into use, new lines are put down, and junction and yard layouts are improved. In miniature also improvements and additions are always possible, and this is one of the greatest charms of the model railway hobby. We frequently receive from readers, both at home and abroad, details of the latest developments on their systems, and such information is always interesting, particularly when it is accompanied by a photograph showing the most recent state of affairs on their miniature railways.

It will be remembered that in July 1935 we published details of an interesting L.M.S.R. system in Victoria, B.C., operated by Mr. H. G. Ogden and his son. Since that time extensive additions have been made to the equipment, and the system generally has been developed to a greater pitch of realism and efficiency than before. A double line of rails is now provided throughout the main line circuit, with the result that express traffic has been increased, and this can be handled more easily than the former services. At the same time a branch line within the main circuit has been laid down, and this serves the country station of "Millbank." Actually the branch is a continuous loop for convenience in operating, and at times forms a useful alternative for heavy traffic on the main line.

Part of the extension of the layout of Mr. H. G. Ogden of Victoria, B.C., as described on this page. This photograph shows the turntable, store building and part of the new sidings, and the scene is effectively completed by the painted background.

At one corner of the system the baseboard has been extended to make room for sidings for coaching stock and for an additional engine shed. A new turntable forms the means of access to the shed, saving space by making points unnecessary. The construction and installation of the turntable was an interesting process, as the table is of the deck type and revolves in a proper pit. The pit was arranged by cutting a circular hole in the baseboard and fitting below it a sub-base to support the table and to form the bottom of the pit. The turntable itself is of wood and revolves on a steel spindle that turns in a metal centre-bearing. Its ends are supported on small wheels that bear on the pit bottom and give very smooth working. Light railings finish off the sides of the table and there are push-bars for the use of the enginemen turning the table. The edge of the pit is provided with radiating battens, as in actual practice, to afford a foothold for the men. The turntable is 15 in. long and will accommodate a large 4–4–0 locomotive and tender together.

Among further improvements is the provision of a coaling plant near the original engine shed. This is of simple construction, but it can be operated in a satisfactory and realistic manner. There is a raised stage underneath which the "loco coal" wagons stand. On the stage is mounted a revolving derrick that lowers a tub or skip to the wagons. When filled the skip is hoisted, the derrick revolves through a quarter of a circle, and the skip is then lowered and emptied into a chute that is placed at a convenient height to discharge into the tender or bunker of a locomotive standing alongside the stage.

Scenic effects also have received attention. The improvement that has resulted from the addition of an attractive background is brought out in a striking manner if the illustration on this page is compared with those that accompanied the original description in the "*M.M.*" for July 1935. To provide some variation in the lineside features, and to fill up a corner in an effective manner, a tunnel has been introduced on the main line near to the points where the branch line diverges. Its use there helps the impression of the complete separation of the branch from the main line as the latter disappears into the black bore of the tunnel. The latter is driven through a "ridge" that leads up to the "higher country" featured on the scenic background. The tunnel fabric was constructed in the manner frequently advised in these pages, brown paper well soaked in paste being laid over a previously prepared wooden framework of irregular shape. The "covering" of the tunnel is painted to harmonise with the scenic background and the bore is finished at each end with appropriate tunnel mouths. Minor but effective details are the boards at each end that give details of the length of the tunnel.

Additions have been made to the stock in the shape of Hornby No. 2 Coaches in L.M.S.R. colours. Two first-thirds and a brake-third make up an effective local train, and they are hauled as a rule by the No. 1 Special or No. 2 Special Tank Locomotives that were already in service. As the main station is named "Carlisle" it was decided to introduce representative L.N.E.R. stock also. Therefore a No. 2 Special Tender Locomotive of that company is now in use. This is "*The Bramham Moor*" of the latest "Hunt" class, which is very appropriate in view of the inclusion in the countryside of miniature hunt figures.

Smoke Deflectors for Hornby Locomotives

By "Tommy Dodd"

THIS month I have to deal with some interesting fittings that have recently become standard for those Locomotives of the Hornby Series on which their use is appropriate. These fittings are the smoke-deflecting side sheets that are provided at the front end of the Nord Riviera "Blue," L.M.S.R. "*Royal Scot*," and S.R. "*Lord Nelson*" Locomotives of the E320, E36 and No. 3C types. These up-to-date additions increase considerably the realistic effect of these engines and improve their massive appearance, as the accompanying illustration shows. Although the purpose of the real deflectors is the same in each case, there are some interesting differences in their design on the Nord, L.M.S.R. and S.R. systems; and these differences are reproduced as far as possible in the dummy deflectors fitted to the Hornby Locomotives.

The most striking are the deflectors fitted to the Riviera "Blue" engine. These follow the characteristic outline of the real fittings of the Nord "Super-Pacifics," and look very imposing, especially when the engine with its plain "stove-pipe" chimney is viewed head-on. The lower portion of each deflector is set out at an angle from the locomotive so that each side sheet overhangs the edge of the footplating. Then a slight bend brings the centre portion of the deflector upright; and above this the upper edge of each sheet is abruptly turned inward. The leading edge of this turned-in portion is cut away at an angle and this cutting-away continues partly down the vertical surface of each deflector. The two deflectors, one on each side of the smoke-box, thus have something of the appearance of a deep "scoop" in the centre of which is the smoke-box and chimney.

This illustration shows Hornby Locomotives fitted with smoke deflectors as described on this page. On the left is the S.R. "Lord Nelson," in the centre is the Nord Riviera "Blue" Locomotive, and on the right is the L.M.S.R. "Royal Scot."

The deflectors fitted to the English type engines are less elaborate in their style. Those on the "*Royal Scot*" model extend from the footplating vertically upward to a point approximately level with the upper hinge bar on the smoke-box door. There they turn fairly sharply inward. The forward edge of the turned-in part is rounded off, and helps to give the deflectors a better appearance than they would have if the vertical and horizontal edge had continued to a plain square corner at the front end.

The deflectors fitted to the S.R. "*Lord Nelson*" are even less elaborate. They extend vertically upward to the limit of their height, and the front top edge is well rounded off to a greater curve than that of the "*Royal Scot*" fittings. In their simplicity of type and outline they follow the deflectors fitted to the real "Nelson" engines, which are different from those in-sloping "blinkers," as the enginemen often call them, that are fitted to the "King Arthurs."

Although they differ in their actual shape, the deflectors fitted to these three Hornby Locomotives are alike in that each type has embossed edges. This feature adds to their strength in the same manner as the beading applied to the real ones. The embossing also improves considerably the appearance of the deflectors, making them look more "finished." All three types are alike in the manner of their fitting to the engine. The bottom edges of the deflectors have lugs that fit into slots provided in the footplating. In addition, to secure them in the correct position each deflector sheet has a small angle bracket formed at the rear edge, and through a hole in this bracket the handrail alongside the boiler passes. This attachment to the handrail resembles closely the method used in actual practice to stay the upper parts of the side sheets securely to the engine.

Readers may wonder what is the purpose of these fittings on real locomotives, and why they have only come into use during the last 10 years or so. They have become necessary as the result of the progress of locomotive design and the increased efficiency of the latest types. With modern locomotives capable of running on very short cut-offs, the exhaust pressure is low and there is a tendency for the steam from the chimney to drift along the boiler top and obscure the driver's look-out. The trouble is accentuated by the very low boiler mountings that are necessary on account of the large size of present-day locomotive boilers. The purpose of the deflectors is to cause an upward current of air in the neighbourhood of the chimney, and thus lift the exhaust steam and smoke well above the cab.

Some deflectors of the side sheet kind were first developed in Germany and are in fairly common use on the Continent. In this country the S.R. employ them for practically all their modern locomotives. They are employed on the L.M.S.R. only to a small extent; all the taper-boilered locomotives are without them. On the L.N.E.R. their use is confined to one or two locomotives and on the G.W.R. they are not in use at all. The tapered boiler in common use on the engines of that line, and on the latest L.M.S.R. engines, would seem to be of assistance in securing satisfactory deflection of the exhaust. The reduction of the boiler diameter at the front end enables a chimney of reasonable length to be mounted on the smoke-box, and this also helps to throw the exhaust well up, away from the driver's line of vision.

STATIONS AND THEIR EQUIPMENT

EVEN on the smallest Hornby Railway one station at least is a necessity; and on large systems several stations will be required so that the line may provide for the needs of the districts that it serves. A layout that has no station remains a mere desert track, for there is no place where the trains can deal with their passengers! The various Stations and Platforms in the Hornby range, and the station and halt of the M Series, enable miniature railway owners to provide their lines with stations in a satisfactory manner. But a mere Station on its own has a dull and lifeless appearance, quite unlike the busy aspect of the real thing. In this article therefore we shall consider the equipment of stations in such a way that they appear life-like and realistic.

Our first step should be to people the Station with railwaymen, and then with passengers. Otherwise there would be nobody to attend to the trains that arrive and nobody to use them! An appearance of bustle and activity is soon given by the addition of some of the Dinky Toy figures. Boys usually commence with one or other of the boxed sets; then as traffic develops and the business grows additions become necessary. Frequently more of one type of figure than another is required and it is a great convenience to be able to buy the individual items separately as they are wanted, rather than to have to obtain further complete sets. A flock of the Stationmasters for instance as contained in Dinky Toys Set No. 1 would be difficult to find work for; but the energetic Porter with bags, Dinky Toy No. 1E, and the ordinary Porter, Dinky Toy No. 1F, are always useful. The last-mentioned figure can be used for numerous purposes. This also applies to the Ticket Collector, Dinky Toy No. 1C, who, if he has his nippers removed, can be made to look as if he is handling milk cans or luggage and doing various other jobs, such as opening or closing carriage doors. A number of Engine Drivers, Dinky Toys No. 1D, will be necessary in and around the Engine Shed, but one can appear whenever a locomotive stands at the Station for any length of time. He can then be engaged in looking round his engine, as he has a big oil feeder in his hand. The Guard, Dinky Toy No. 1B, is a useful man also. In addition to his designed purpose he can be employed in other ways, especially if his flag is removed. He can then be used as an inspector, and with his hands raised he will appear as if urging the porters to attend to some job. Other uses for these figures will no doubt suggest themselves to ingenious Hornby Railway owners.

Part of the realistic miniature railway system operated by Mr. H. G. Ogden, Victoria, B.C. Special attention is devoted to details as is shown by the miniature figures, luggage, and other items on the station platform in the foreground.

The Passengers can be used in any number and variety, not only on the actual Station platforms, but also in the "streets" nearby and anywhere else along the lineside where their use is appropriate, such as at Footbridges and Level Crossings. In using these figures care should be taken to place them so that they look as "natural" as possible. A party of Hikers, Dinky Toys Nos. 3C and 3D, is quite reasonable; but the other figures should be well mixed.

The Train and Hotel Staff of Set No. 5 are specially suitable for use at the more important stations. "Hotel porters meet all trains" is a familiar announcement and it can be actually accomplished on a Hornby Railway with the aid of several of the figure No. 5C, which takes the form of a porter in striking livery and carrying a passenger's luggage. The white jackets of the train attendants show their calling. There are packed in each Set No. 5 two Pullman Car Waiters, Dinky Toys No. 5B, under the supervision of the Pullman Car Conductor, Dinky Toy No. 5A. They look well on the platform before the departure of a train if placed near the vestibule doors of the Pullman Cars. They will then appear to be assisting passengers to entrain, answering their questions and generally attending to their wants. Some boys make their Train Staff actually travel in the trains, securing them to the floors of Pullman Coaches by means of Seccotine or other adhesive. They look quite realistic thus when seen through the windows of a passing train.

We must not forget the Engineering Staff of Set No. 4.

These can be used very well at different points on the railway property, singly or in gangs.

With the Staff generally at work and with the Passengers presenting themselves in satisfactory numbers we must turn our attention to the various accessories that add to the characteristic appearance of station premises. There are the popular accessories that are available in Railway Accessories Sets Nos. 1, 2 and 3. These include pieces of luggage and a suitable porter's barrow in Set No. 1. Then there are the Milk Cans, whose clatter when empty, or their deeper rumble when full, is still a characteristic "railway noise." A four-wheeled trolley is provided for moving the cans and it is useful also for ordinary luggage. Set No. 3 includes two platform seats and there are two "penny-in-the-slot" machines. One is the familiar platform ticket machine and the other represents the nameplate-stamping machine of the type so popular with boys. The other item, a realistic pillar-box, is suitable for use on large stations or in the streets or roads in the neighbourhood of the line. A further Set of Railway Accessories—No. 9—contains some useful pieces. These are station nameboards which can be used very effectively.

A new item in the Dinky Toys range is the Telephone Call Box, Dinky Toy No. 12C. One or two of these look very realistic if placed on the station platform or other convenient part of the railway premises.

With these we practically complete the actual equipment of the station. Even so a glance round will reveal a strange bareness on the buildings generally and on the fencing. Then we realise what is lacking; we have on exhibition none of the familiar posters and other announcements that are such a feature of stations and other premises in real practice. Fortunately we can soon remedy this by the use of the Miniature Posters of the Hornby Series. These reproduce most faithfully the national advertisements with which we are all familiar, that greet us from almost every hoarding and space where the enterprising billposter can place them. The Miniature Posters are available in two varieties known respectively as Series 1 and Series 2, and as they are printed in the colours of the originals their effect is very striking. To enable them to be attached readily to walls, etc., they have gummed backs.

As the direct attachment of the Posters to paled fencing, footbridges and other items of this kind would not be convenient or very effective, there are special Poster Boards that are made in two sizes. These are flat metal plates that have two hooked lugs formed on the top edge and this makes possible the attachment of the Boards to Paled Fencing, the lugs being hooked over the top bar of the fence. In addition of course they are easily removable, which is a great advantage. The Poster Boards are obtainable separately, and a sample of the smaller size is enclosed in each packet of Posters.

An interesting view of the road approach to the Station on a Hornby Railway. The effective treatment of the surroundings is most important if the best results are to be obtained from the use of Stations.

In addition to these Boards there is also the Station Hoarding that is specially adapted for poster display and for the attachment for any announcement regarding train services, excursions and special trips that the miniature railway company are operating. It is suitable for use on Station platforms, in the fields along the line and on the road-side. In addition to their use for posters and bills generally they can be used very satisfactorily as timetable boards. The timetable displayed can be cut out of a small pocket railway guide and attached to the hoarding with Seccotine.

Although a miniature Station is necessarily to be considered chiefly from the railway point of view, its arrangement in relation to its surroundings are not to be neglected. Thus as far as possible a reasonable means of approach for the passengers should be provided, although when space is restricted surrounding details may have to be supplied by a scenic background only. If space permits of it there is great scope for the realistic arrangement of the Station approach and its details.

Paled Fencing and Station Hoardings decorated with Miniature Posters are again very effective here. The standard Dinky Toys motor vehicles of all kinds can appear on the "roads," and an up-to-date feature will be the formation of a car parking space by the Station for the convenience of passengers and others. The establishment of a Petrol Station, Dinky Toy No. 48, with its battery of Petrol Pumps outside, Dinky Toys No. 49, will add to the general air of realism.

A busy scene at a terminal station. Standard Passenger Platforms are used and the various Dinky Toys and Railway Accessories components give quite a realistic air to the scene.

Then the road services of the railway company that are operated from the Station must not be forgotten. For these the Mechanical Horse and Trailer Van, Dinky Toy No. 33R, is specially suitable.

To regulate the road traffic the various Robots, Traffic Signals, Dinky Toys No. 47A, 47B, 47C can be made good use of in appropriate places, also the familiar Beacon No. 47D and the numerous Road Signs of Set No. 47. At important points the R.A.C. or A.A. Huts of Sets Nos. 43 and 44 can be placed with the appropriate Guides near by.

Join the Hornby Railway Company and become eligible for the competitions announced on this page.

H.R.C. COMPETITION PAGE

Join the Hornby Railway Company and become eligible for the competitions announced on this page.

LOCOMOTIVE SHADOWS CONTEST

This month we are introducing a new contest that will be of exceptional interest to readers, for it provides them with a novel opportunity of making use of their knowledge of locomotives and their wheel arrangements. The accompanying illustration shows 25 locomotive shadows. Competitors are required to discover the identity of each one, and to state its class, its wheel arrangement and the railway company owning it. The shadows are not all of British locomotives, and among them are those of well-known locomotives of overseas countries, including Australia, Palestine, America, Germany, France, New Zealand and India.

When a competitor has identified all the locomotives, or as many of them as possible, he should make a neat list of them on a sheet of paper, together with the details in the order asked for above. The competitor's name, full address and H.R.C. membership number must be written on the back of his entry.

The Contest will be divided as usual into two Sections, Home and Overseas. Prizes of any products manufactured by Meccano Ltd., to the value of 21/-, 15/- and 10/6 respectively will be awarded to the three best entries submitted in each Section. In the event of a tie for any prize, neatness will be taken into consideration when the judges make their final decision. In addition a number of consolation prizes will be awarded to those members whose entries are not among the winners of the major prizes, but nevertheless deserve some reward.

Envelopes containing entries must be marked *"H.R.C. May Locomotive Shadows Contest"* in the top left-hand corner, and posted to reach Headquarters at Meccano Ltd., Binns Road, Liverpool 13, on or before 30th May. Overseas competitors must post their entries in time for arrival at Headquarters not later than 31st August. Entries received after the published closing dates cannot be accepted.

Railway Photographic Contest

Last month we announced the first of the summer series of Photographic Contests, in which competitors were invited to submit photographs of any railway scene. This month we give details of the second contest of this series. As in previous contests, there are no restrictions, except that the actual exposure must have been made by the competitor himself; the developing and printing may be the work of a professional. Competitors may send as many different prints as they desire, but no competitor can win more than one prize in one contest. It is important that every print submitted should have on the back the name of the competitor, his full address and his H.R.C. membership number. A short description of the scene of the photograph must also be given. As mentioned in last month's issue, the best of the prize-winning entries will be filed for possible use in future issues of the *"M.M."*

The Contest will be divided as usual into two Sections, Home and Overseas, and prizes of any products manufactured by Meccano Ltd., or photographic material if desired, to the value of 21/-, 15/- and 10/6 respectively will be awarded to the senders of the three best entries submitted in each Section. In addition a number of consolation prizes will be awarded. In the case of a tie for any prize, this will be equally divided among the successful competitors. Envelopes containing entries must be marked *"H.R.C. May Railway Photographic Contest"* in the top left-hand corner, and posted to reach Headquarters at Meccano Ltd., Binns Road, Liverpool 13, on or before 30th May. The Overseas closing date is 31st August.

Competition Solutions

"January Missing Words Contest"

This contest did not cause a great deal of trouble to competitors, and as soon as the key word "ganger" was discovered, there was little difficulty in filling up the gaps.

The missing words in the order in which they should be inserted, are as follows: Ganger, disaster, patrol, track, two, keys, fishbolts, springtime, hot, cold, fishplates, tar, expansion, contraction, expansion, occurrence, buckling, hot, surface, ganger, knees, rail, track, granite, track, chippings, sleepers, shovel, level, hollows.

"January Voting Contest"

The voting in this contest bears out our statement that all H.R.C. competitions are favourites, for all received good support and in some cases only two or three votes separated subjects in the list. The result was as follows: (1) "Missing Links"; (2) "Photograph Voting"; (3) "Locomotive Peculiarities"; (4) "Locomotive Silhouettes"; (5) "A Nightmare Goods"; (6) "Spot the Errors"; (7) "Jumbled Names" and (8) "Famous Trains."

COMPETITION RESULTS

HOME

March "6th Locomotive Name and Number Contest."—First: D. V. C. Bentley (24591), Loughborough. Second: G. H. Gill (36093), Chorlton-cum-Hardy. Third: E. W. Oglethorpe (46851), Harrow.

March "Railway Photo Contest."—First: C. Spencer (44179), Sheffield 11. Second: H. S. Darke (4461), London, N.W.11. Third: V. Lane (35556), Dublin.

March "Drawing Contest."—First: A. Marsh (20196), Coventry. Second: E. F. Whipp (45828), Plymouth. Third: R. W. Goodfellow (3593), Longbenton.

OVERSEAS

January "Missing Words Contest."—First: D. Murison (37642), Buenos Aires. Second: W. A. Carpinter (42509), New Zealand. Third: M. Van Olst (16062), S. Africa. Fourth: R. Pearson (29199), Australia. Consolation Prizes: I. Brough (9112), Australia; O. M. Mangourie (38666), Egypt; V. East (21196), West Australia.

January "Railway Photo Contest."—First: R. Pearson (29199), Australia. Second: G. Healy (43145), Canada. Third: J. Jasper (42664), Australia.

January "Voting Contest."—First: D. Parker (38595), Canada. Second: J. C. Carter (46374), South Africa. Third: P. Sevestre (43525), France. Fourth: A. McIntyre (30925), Canada. Consolation Prizes: A. G. Fellows (29952), New Zealand; W. A. Carpinter (42509), New Zealand.

Branch News

Spring Grove Central School.—Interesting developments have occurred in the operation of the Branch layout. Correct single line working on the staff system has been successfully tried. Various members take it in turn to supervise the train working and some have assisted the Chairman in the construction of a large model crane. Quite heavy weights can be picked up by electro-magnetic means. Secretary: S. Cordrey, 211, Hounslow Road, Hanworth, Middx.

Rutherglen (Glasgow).—The track baseboard has been rebuilt and after trying out various layouts, members planned a new permanent track. Double track is installed throughout and the system is complete with marshalling yards, engine sheds and carriage sidings. With the members becoming more experienced the standard of train working has improved and the mishaps experienced in the earliest stages are now very rare. A Branch library has been formed and a regular games night, and cycling and walking sections, are proposed. It is interesting that the Branch room overlooks the Glasgow-London main line of the L.M.S.R., so that it is an excellent point for the observation of real practice. Visits are to be made to the L.M.S.R. Motive Power Depot at Polmadie and to the Queen's Park Works of the North British Locomotive Company Ltd. Secretary: R. G. Langmuir, 11, Afton Street, Shawlands, Glasgow, S.1.

St. Thomas (Exeter).—The Branch is now well settled in the new quarters; on the Branch layout electricity is replacing clockwork as the motive power. The conversion of the rails from clockwork to electric has been carried out at special meetings held four times weekly. This has ensured the rapid conversion of the whole system. The attendance of members continues to be very satisfactory. In addition to the future work involved in the conversion of the layout, a Branch library is to be established. Secretary: L. G. Robinson, 9, Union Street, St. Thomas, Exeter.

Addiscombe.—A permanent track is now available, but further extensions are proposed. The rapid laying of fresh track will be ensured by the special organisation of the members for this purpose. The layout represents the G.W.R. system and, when it is completed, a service of trains will be operated that will reproduce all the chief features of the important G.W.R. services. The Branch has recently celebrated its second anniversary and its affairs generally are satisfactory. Secretary: G. Chandler, 62, Ashburton Road, Croydon, Surrey.

Islington.—After careful preparation the first exhibition held by the Branch was very successful. Various new members have joined as a result and, with increasing membership, the Branch is to be divided into Senior and Junior Sections. The track already in commission has been reserved for the use of the Juniors and the Senior members are now busily engaged in laying a line for their own use. A talk on the various famous clocks in the world proved very interesting, and particular enthusiasm greeted the exhibition of films showing the visit of *"The Royal Scot"* to America, and its subsequent tour in this country. Future arrangements will include games and other film programmes are anticipated. Secretary: E. Muxlow, 7, Regents Park Road, Islington, London, N.W.1.

Some of the members of the Northampton H.R.C. Branch No. 284 on a visit to the local goods yard. Chairman: Mr. G. L. D. Hodges; Secretary: D. K. Adams. This Branch was incorporated in 1935 and maintains an attractive and interesting programme, track meetings, lectures and discussions being varied with visits to places of railway interest.

Waterloo (Dublin). Train services on the Branch layout suffered a sudden temporary stoppage recently when the electricity supply failed. Trains already in motion were delayed and subsequent services were operated correspondingly late. With the adoption of a new timetable further motive power has become necessary and four new locomotives are to be obtained during 1936. An attractive feature is that all trains and station buildings are electrically illuminated. Secretary: S. B. Carse, 38, Oakley Road, Ranelagh, Dublin.

Elmside (Exeter).—Consistently good attendance at meetings has resulted in a great deal of traffic pressure on the Branch layout. In order to ease matters a two-minute service of trains has been introduced and, after certain difficulties in the early stages, timetable workings are now carried out in a prompt and efficient manner. Recently a locomotive failure unfortunately occurred at an exceedingly busy period, but the position has since been eased by the addition of two locomotives belonging to one of the Directors. Minor alterations are made for convenience in standard running arrangements. Train mileage continues to increase so that it is probable that the traffic figures for 1936 will considerably exceed those for last year. During 1935 a total of 940 trains was run. Of these 144 were expresses, 744 were excursions, locals and goods trains, and the remainder were specials. Altogether they covered over 80 actual miles. Secretary: T. W. A. Smith, 98, Ladysmith Road, Exeter.

ITALY

Milan.—The decision to institute a Meccano Model-building Section has been greatly approved. It is intended that the Meccano and Hornby train section shall work closely together and some interesting and realistic arrangements are expected to result. The programmes for 1936 are to be even more varied and interesting than before. At a general meeting of the Branch earlier in the year, the officials for the year were elected. Secretary: E. Vigo, Corso Genova 19, Milan, Italy.

Branches in Course of Formation

The following new Branches of the Hornby Railway Company are at present in process of formation, and any boys who are interested and desirous of linking up with this unique organisation should communicate with the promoters, whose names and addresses are given below:

Blaby—G. Thompson, Tre-vue, Welford Road, Blaby, Nr. Leicester.

Birmingham—E. T. Merriman, 20, Dyas Avenue, Walsall Road, Great Barr, Birmingham.

Bolton—L. Monk, 30, Barcroft Road, Smithills, Bolton.

Dublin—S. Smartt, 11, Villa Bank, Royal Canal, Phibsborough, Dublin.

Hastings—G. Hills, Mornington House, 21, Wellington Road, Hastings.

Heston—L. W. Jones, 26, Archard Avenue, Heston, Middlesex.

Kendal—B. Bland, 75, Highgate, Kendal.

Knutsford—A. Johnson, Cleabarrow, Plumbley, Knutsford, Cheshire.

Liverpool—J. B. Brough, The Torrs, Score Lane, Broad Green, Liverpool 16.

Newton Abbot—H. Dent, "Burwood," 17, Keyberry Road, Newton Abbot, Devon.

Nottingham—W. Lovelady, 7, Taunton Road, West Bridgford, Nottingham.

For other stamp advertisements see pages 304 and XVIII.

MAP STAMPS

THE stamp collector who is seeking a summer task that will provide him with enjoyable occupation on rainy days would find just the thing he seeks in the preparation of a collection of map stamps. A complete collection would comprise less than 50 stamps, every one of them possessing an interesting history, and not one of the stamps would be an expensive purchase. We illustrate on this page a few suitable specimens, and the stories attached to these will be more than sufficient to show the fascination of a complete collection.

In the *"Stamp Gossip"* notes in our last issue we reproduced the 1 peso stamp from the recent Argentine issue, and as this stamp illustrates the point that we wish to make, we are reproducing it again this month in company with the Falkland Islands 3d. stamp of 1933. The latter shows a map of the islands, which are the subject of dispute between the Argentine and British Governments. The Falkland Islands stamp was issued to commemorate the centenary of British administration. The Argentine stamp, however, insists that the islands are Argentine property, and it will be observed that the special colour used to pick out Argentina on the map is applied also to the Falklands.

The British Minister in Buenos Aires has been instructed to inform the Argentine Government of Britain's disapproval of this stamp, but it is unlikely that this disapproval will be followed by a refusal to recognise the stamp and a surcharge on all letters bearing it, which was the course taken by Argentina in dealing with the Falkland Islands stamp.

Not all disputes in which postage stamps have been used as propaganda have been amicably settled, and at the foot of the page we show Paraguay's $1.50 stamp of 1932, a stamp that might be described as a gesture of defiance. The south-western areas of the Gran Chaco are Argentine territory. The northern districts were divided almost equally between Bolivia and Paraguay by a treaty concluded in 1895, but unfortunately the boundary was not clearly defined and in time it became a matter of keen dispute between the two countries. In 1927, Paraguay brought the issue to a head by issuing a new series of stamps that included a map design in which the whole of the disputed territory was prominently labelled *Chaco Paraguayo.* Bolivia immediately retaliated by issuing a map stamp that labelled the territory *Chaco Boliviano.* The stamp war was followed by clashes between the frontier guards of the two countries and quickly a war broke out that cost both countries many men and much money before peace was finally achieved.

War almost broke out on the Island of Haiti over a similar incident. This island consists of two republics, Haiti and Dominica. In 1900 Dominica issued a map stamp on which the boundary between the two republics was so wrongly defined as to leave Haiti with only a very insignificant strip of territory. Patriotic citizens of Haiti banded themselves together and prepared to resist this "invasion." Fortunately Dominica's mistake was perfectly innocent and the responsible artist having publicly admitted his error, peace was restored before any serious clash of arms occurred.

Turning to disputes of a lighter nature, the newly issued Costa Rica 4c. stamp shown here is of special interest. The map is of Treasure Island or, to give it its official name, Cocos Island. This stamp is intended to proclaim Costa Rica's ownership of the Island, but the action is more precautionary than inspired. Costa Rican rights over the island have been generally acknowledged for many years, and dozens of treasure hunting expeditions have taken out licenses from that country permitting them to seek the pirates' hoards that are commonly supposed still to lie buried there. No important success has ever been recorded, but no doubt the lure will persist so long as this tiny island remains above the waters of the Pacific.

In 1897 a British Admiral and a party of bluejackets landed on the island and calmly started blowing it to pieces, presumably in the hope that the upheavals would uncover one or another of the hidden treasures! A prompt protest was made by Costa Rica, and the British Government's response was to place Cocos Island out of bounds for the Navy.

The majority of map stamps celebrate peaceful happenings, however, and the 1931 Newfoundland Atlantic map stamp, illustrated here, is one of the most interesting of all records of early trans-Atlantic flights. The stamp shows the routes taken on the early trans-Atlantic flights, including those of Hawker, Alcock, and Lindbergh. Newfoundland has issued two other map stamps at various times, but their interest is of a purely general and geographical nature.

Map stamps often are used to record the progress of development, as in the Canadian Confederation Jubilee issue of 1927 shown here. The stamp illustrates the growth of the Dominion from the early days of the original union of New Brunswick, Nova Scotia, Ontario and Quebec, formed in 1867 and represented by the heavily-shaded portion, to the vast territory that is the settled Canada of to-day.

There is not space here to touch upon more than a few of the map stamps that detail interesting historical tales, but any reader who desires to follow up this fascinating subject can obtain a full list of the suitable stamps from the Editor of the *"M.M."*

BOND'S

The 'Endeavour' Yacht.

Will sail in any weather.

These new Yachts are the latest thing for fast racing work. All of the hulls are hand made in best yellow pine. The two largest Yachts are fitted with Braine type automatic steering. Painted Pale Blue. Cabin Skylight extra.

Prices:

17 in. Yacht with automatic rudder ...	11/-
21 in. Yacht with automatic rudder ...	17/6
27 in. Yacht with Braine type steering ...	37/6
36 in. Yacht with Braine type steering ...	69/-

Carriage extra.

SAILCLOTH.

This Super Sailcloth is made from the finest **Union Silk** and is very light, extra strong. **2/3** yard, 42 in. wide. Plus Postage.

Send for Bond's 1936 Catalogue, it has 180 pages filled with all types of Locomotives, Boats, Aeroplanes, Tools and Materials. Price **6d.** post free.

BOND'S O'EUSTON ROAD LTD.,
254, EUSTON ROAD, LONDON, N.W.I.

'Phone: Museum 7137. Est. 1887.

French Agents: Messrs. J. Fournereau, 60, Rue Alphonse-Pallu, Le Vesinet (S-&-O.)

S. Africa Agents: Messrs. J. Alcock & Co., 69, Mooi Street, Johannesburg.

If you want to get on in the world you must look clean and smart. Untidy hair will destroy the whole effect of smart clothes. Always put Anzora on your hair every morning—then you will be sure of neat, tidy hair all day long. Anzora has been the supreme, Gold Medal hair fixative for generations and still stands supreme. Anzora suits every head—Anzora Cream for greasy scalps, Anzora Viola for dry scalps. In 9d., 1/3 and 2/3 bottles. Anzora Brilliantine for those who prefer glossiness. In 1/- bottles.

From all chemists, hairdressers and stores.

MASTERS THE HAIR

ANZORA PERFUMERY CO. LTD., London, N.W.6

20 French Colonials Mint Given Free

to all approval applicants enclosing 2d. postage. For your needs in Stamp Collecting—try me. For service, you should be on my register. Are you?

G. W. GREEN
414, Padiham Road, Burnley, Lancs.

AIR MAILS

Beautiful Air Mail Stamps sent direct to you from country of origin on special covers. Also **first day** covers of **NEW COLONIAL KING EDWARD VIII** stamps as issued. Write, enclosing 1½d. stamp for reply, to

A. F. McQUARRIE, 83, Cliff Road, Wallasey.

Jubilee, New Ceylon, used Colonials free! Request appros. Post 1½d.—G. Kingsmill, New Barnet, Herts.

TRIANGULAR PACKET FREE!

We have managed to obtain a further **limited supply** of the rare and beautiful **triangular** issued by Spain in memory of the explorer Columbus and depicting his Flagship Santa Maria. We will give this wonderful stamp together with 10 different Spain, to all readers requesting approvals and including 2d. postage. (Abroad 6d.) Price of the gift without Approvals is 8d.

MICHAEL HERBERT (M.M.),
8, WOODSTOCK ROAD, WALTHAMSTOW, LONDON.

BOOKS of British Colonials or Foreign or mixed Stamps sent on approval. Select what you desire at the rate of 2/- for 50 or 3/6 for 100 Stamps. These books contain stamps catalogued at prices up to half a crown each, or more.—P. Illingworth, Tranmere Park, Guiseley, near Leeds.

!! BONUS SCHEME !!

All customers enrolled. Do you want rarities, sets or cheap packets? Write to me. Have you got these stamps?

Obsolete mint set Mozambique Triangles 2/-; 200 Spacefillers 8d.; 20 Latin-American 6d.; 25 Airmails 1/-; 50 Victoria British Colonials 1/6; 6 1935 Persia Airpost 1/6. Thousands of stamps in stock.

Approvals and Monthly Bulletin on request.

F. J. LORD, 13, PRINCES ROAD, STAMFORD.

UGANDA & R.C.M.P. PACKET

This packet contains the best of our two previous packets, with some additional good stamps. **New Uganda** (illustrated), **10c. Canada 1935** (Royal Canadian Mounted Policeman), New Belgium (Train drawn by Diesel engine), **New Zealand 1935** (Kiwi bird), **Long set of 13 different Italy** (Foundation of Rome), Hungary (prisoners of war), China (Sun Yat Sen), U.S.A. (Olympic Games), **Ceylon 1935** (native tapping rubber tree), Siam (double head), **Australia Jubilee,** and **ten different Canada** including the above and **Canada Jubilee. All these new stamps for 4½d. only** to genuine applicants for our approval sheets. (Without approvals, 9d.)

SHIRLEY STAMP CO., 19, SANDRINGHAM AVENUE, LONDON, S.W.20.

NEWFOUNDLAND JUBILEE PACKET

Here is an opportunity to have a fine collection of stamps from the oldest **BRITISH COLONY.** This grand packet contains a **RARE SILVER JUBILEE,** portraits of Queen Victoria, **KING GEORGE V;** also Map of the Island, Statue, View of Trinity, etc., etc. This wonderful **FREE** packet is offered to all genuine collectors sending 2d. postage, etc. (6d. abroad), and asking for approvals.

S. CAMPBELL, 71, MANOR ROAD, TANKERTON, KENT.

100 diff. Stamps Free to approval applicants, good discount.—Gosling, 21, Powling Road, Ipswich.

100 Diff. Stamps Free to appro. applicants. Liberal dis.—Cuthbert, Newsham Lane, Broughton, Preston.

ANOTHER GLOBE-TROTTER TRIUMPH!

AMAZING FREE SILVER JUBILEE PACKET OFFERED FOR ONE MORE MONTH. Silver Jubilee varieties, Beautiful Airmails, Pictorial Commemoratives, New Issues, Colonials—60 magnificent stamps. The most sensational offer yet. Send 1½d. postage for "Globe-Trotter" approval selections—amazing value, ¼d., ½d. and 1d. upwards—and particulars of how **you can have FREE stamps every 14 days!!** Write Now—there's a stamp treat in store for you. Owing to immense popularity of the above offer and letters of appreciation, I am repeating same for one more month—don't miss it. **Special Offers.** "Globe-Trotter" Mystery Mixture, 1,000 unsorted, unbeatable, 1/6.

GLOBE-TROTTER, 17, WINCHESTER ROAD, BIRCHFIELD, BIRMINGHAM.

GREAT EASTERN OFFER

We have just completed a huge purchase of stamps from the Near East, for the special benefit of "M.M." readers. Magnificent large **Pictorials** and **Airmails** of **Lebanon, Egypt, Syria, Alaouites, Latakia, Iraq,** and **Trans-Jordan,** with high values to 4 piastres are special features. This mixture is being supplied in generous packets. **FREE and POST FREE,** for one month only, to applicants requesting approvals from

UNIVERSITY STAMP CO., 13, WALTON WELL ROAD, OXFORD

For other stamp advertisements see pages 302 and XVIII.

Stamp Gossip

and Notes on New Issues

Nigerian Pictorials

Among the last of the British Colonial King George pictorial issues, the recent Nigerian set is certain to take a high place, by reason of the beauty and the interest of the designs, which are as follows:—½d. (illustrated), a cargo steamer loading at the Apapa wharf, Lagos, 1d., native picking cocoa pods. Nigeria's cocoa exports are one of the Colony's greatest sources of revenue. 1½d., a tin dredger at work. Tin is another of the country's principal exports. 2d., tree felling. 3d., a fishing village. 4d. (illustrated), an up-to-date cotton ginnery. Cotton spinning is not yet one of the country's big industries but it is rapidly growing, because the climate is suitable both for the growing of the cotton plant and the spinning of the cotton itself. 6d., a Habe minaret at Katsina. The Habes are an advanced native race. 1/–, native cattle belonging to the Fulani tribe. 2/6, the Victoria-Buea motor road. 5/–, a native girl and a palm. Palm oil is another of the Colony's principal products. 10/–, the railway bridge across the river Niger at Jebba. This bridge carries the line from Lagos to Kano, the present terminus of Imperial Airways' Nigerian service. £1, native canoe on the Niger.

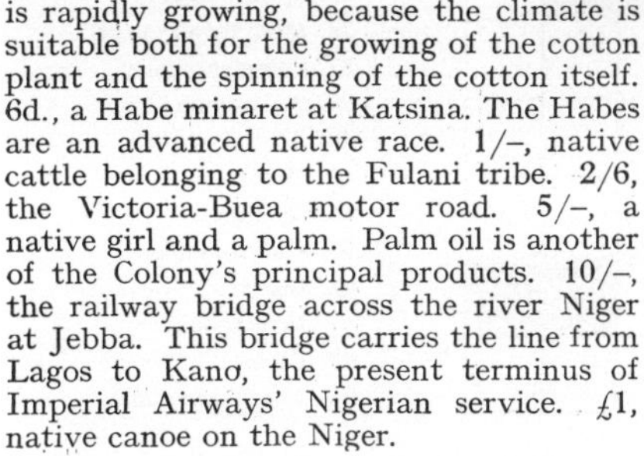

The Malayan Postal Union Issues

In our "Stamp Gossip" notes in the March "*M.M.*," in dealing with the newly issued stamps of the Malayan Postal Union, we drew particular attention to the Selangor stamp, in the design of which the name of the state is shown in native characters, as distinct from the remaining issues, in which the name appears in English. We understand from *Gibbons' Stamp Monthly* that the reason for the name appearing in other than English characters is that H.H. the Sultan preferred the use of Jawi characters (these are the script commonly used in Malaya), and that the design as approved was better balanced than it would have been if the wording had been in English.

The design is reproduced in our March "Stamp Gossip" page, and readers will be interested to know that the name "Selangor" is represented by the characters in the panel at the foot of the stamp, while the panel on the right of the stamp gives the word "Postage" and that on the left the words "and Revenue."

We hope to show other of the new Malayan stamps in an early issue.

New German Issues

There have been many issues of commemorative air stamps, but very few have possessed the interest attaching to the recent German Lufthansa commemorative, illustrated on this page. This stamp commemorates a really important air event, the foundation of the famous German air line, the Deutsche Luft Hansa, ten years ago.

The words Luft Hansa mean Air Union, and Luft Hansa on its formation in 1926 took over the complete network of air services then existing in Germany. Gradually it extended its operations into Russia, Scandinavia, Italy, England, and into Asia as far as Persia. More recently, a line has been thrown over to South America via Spain and North Africa, to link up with the German Condor Syndicate's operations in Brazil. Luft Hansa has been always in the forefront of progress technically, and its Junkers Ju. 52 machine is considered to be the finest air transport machine in the world. Its Heinkel 60 type is the fastest mail carrier.

The machine illustrated on the commemorative stamp is a Heinkel H.E. 70, a specially interesting addition to the list of aeroplane stamp designs because it is the first picture of a machine fitted with a retractable undercarriage.

Also we take the opportunity to show the portraits of Gottlieb Daimler and Karl Benz, the two famous motoring pioneers whose portraits were used on the German stamps issued to commemorate the 50th anniversary of the introduction of the motor car.

Gottlieb Daimler had worked in the factory of Otto, the famous pioneer of gas engines, and in 1884 he designed and brought out a light compact engine in which petrol was used as a fuel. He fitted this engine to a bicycle in the following year, and later to a motor car.

Karl Benz was the first to apply the petrol motor to light and practical road vehicles. His first car was produced in 1885. It had three wheels and an engine rated at ¾ h.p., and was capable of the then exceptional speed of 6½ m.p.h.!

Dr. Nansen Commemorative

One of the most interesting personalities of recent times was Dr. Findtjof Nansen, zoologist, scientist, explorer, diplomat, whose work at Geneva for refugees from distressed countries has recently been commemorated by charity stamp issues in Norway and France.

Dr. Nansen will best be remembered for his attempt to reach the North Pole in 1893-6. Though unsuccessful in achieving his objective, he penetrated farther north than any previous explorer. In 1906 he turned from exploration to diplomacy, becoming, in fact, the first Norwegian Minister to England after Norway's severance from Sweden in October, 1905. At the conclusion of the Great War Dr. Nansen took up the organisation of refugee relief work in Russia, and in 1923 he was awarded the Nobel Peace Prize. He died in 1930.

As our illustration shows, the design of the Norwegian stamp is a simple portrait of the great man whose work it honours. There were four stamps in this series with values and premiums ranging from 10 öre to 30 öre.

The French issue consisted of one stamp, 75c. value, bearing a premium of 50c., with an allegorical design representing progress and brotherhood.

New Zealand Anzac Commemorative

Although we are not yet able to reproduce a specimen of the stamp, we have had the pleasure of seeing an advance illustration of the New Zealand Anzac Commemorative, that was due to be issued at the end of last month. It is the most striking military stamp design that we have ever seen.

The stamp is issued to commemorate the 21st anniversary of the landing of the Australian and New Zealand Army Corps on the Gallipoli Peninsula during the campaign against the Turks, and shows a soldier of this famous Corps, in full kit, climbing over a heap of sandbags. In the background is shown one of the Gallipoli beaches and the precipitous slopes of the Peninsula.

We thank Stanley Gibbons Ltd. for their courtesy in loaning the stamps from which the illustrations on this page have been made.

Competition Corner

MAY CROSSWORD PUZZLE

CLUES ACROSS

1. Retaliates
6. Refrains
10. Animal
11. Starting point
12. Consumed
13. Extended
15. Lukewarm
18. Species of cattle
19. Heavenly body
20. Female horse
21. By
22. Meadow
24. Attribute
28. Respect
30. Re-iterate
32. Boredom
33. Plan
34. Glum
36. Portions
39. Perch
42. Respectful address
44. Grass
46. Platform
47. Beak
48. Tainted
50. Sullen
51. Precious stone
52. Fish
53. Before
54. Attack
55. Cloth.

CLUES DOWN

2. Spill
3. Frank
4. Colour
5. Sharpens
6. Eliminate
7. Posed
8. Part
9. Part of flower
13. Headgear
14. Steel-edged tool
16. Wrath
17. Traded
23. Insecurity
24. Set right
25. Subsides
26. Shapes
27. Scanty
29. Prosecute
31. Animal
33. Springs nimbly
35. More than prompt
37. Commencement
38. Swallow up
40. Abroad
41. Hinders
42. Nymph
43. Unfavourable
45. Insect
47. Incinerate
49. Bird
50. Expanse of water

The "*M.M.*" series of crossword puzzles have enjoyed exceptional popularity, principally, no doubt, because they are set for amusement rather than strenuous competitive effort.

This month's puzzle will be found to follow the lines of the previous ones in that it is fair and interesting. The clues are all perfectly straightforward, and every word used can be found in Chambers' or any other standard dictionary. The rules that govern the solution of crossword puzzles are so well known that it is unnecessary to give any further explanation of the requirements of the competition.

Cash prizes of 21/–, 15/–, 10/6 and 5/– respectively will be awarded in order of merit to the senders of the four correct solutions that are neatest or most novel in presentation. The prizes will be duplicated for the Overseas section, which is open to all readers living outside Great Britain, Ireland, and the Channel Islands.

Entries should be addressed "May Crossword Puzzle, Meccano Magazine, Binns Road, Liverpool 13," and must be sent to reach this office not later than 30th May. Overseas closing date, 31st August.

Competitors need not mutilate their magazines by cutting out the crossword illustration. Instead they may make a copy of the square on the same scale, or larger, and use that in submitting their entries for the contest. Readers who desire to have their entries returned, must enclose a stamped addressed envelope.

May Photo Contest

As we announced in our April issue, each month throughout the spring and summer we shall offer prizes for the best and most interesting photographs submitted.

Each month's competition will be divided into two groups, Home and Overseas, and these two groups will be divided into two sections, A for those aged 16 and over, B for those under 16. Cash prizes of 21/- and 10/6 will be awarded in each section.

The photographs may be of any subject and may be made with any make of camera, film or paper. Each photograph must bear the reader's name, age and address, and a title on its back.

Entries sent this month must be addressed "May Photo Contest, Meccano Magazine, Binns Road, Liverpool 13," and must arrive not later than 30th May. The Overseas closing date will be 31st August.

Competition Closing Dates

HOME

May Crossword Puzzle	30th May
May Photo Contest	30th May

OVERSEAS

February Crossword Puzzle ...	30th May
February Drawing Contest ...	30th May
Meccano Limericks	30th June
March Drawing Contest ...	30th June
Vocation Voting Contest ...	31st July
April Photo Contest	31st July
May Crossword Puzzle	31st August
May Photo Contest	31st August

Watch the Closing Dates:

Competitors, both Home and Overseas, are particularly requested to make a careful note of the closing dates of the competitions.

In sending entries to competitions that are divided into age groups, competitors should take particular care to mark their ages clearly on the back of the entry. It is not sufficient merely to indicate the age group, as age allowances are given to ensure equality of opportunity for the younger competitors.

COMPETITION RESULTS

HOME

Meccano Limericks.—Last Line Section.—1. B. Hardie (Bristol). 2. H. V. Stopes-Roe (Dorking). 3. P. Coley (Birmingham). 4. R. Jamieson (Liverpool). Consolation Prizes: S. C. Procter (Carshalton); J. Allen (Birmingham). **New Limerick Section.**—1. W. Whitaker (Hornsea). 2. K. Watts-Jones (Chatham). 3. P. B. Whitehouse (Birmingham). 4. E. Raymond Andrew (Wellingborough).

March Drawing Contest.—First Prizes: Section A, D. V. Gibbs (Dundee); Section B, J. S. Taylor (Burnley). Second Prizes: Section A, E. Whitaker (Leeds); Section B, K. Clark (New Chiswick). Consolation Prizes: J. G. Hall (Cottingham); D. A. Lambert (Ilford); R. Lawton (Gt. Crosby, Liverpool); E. H. Whalley (Redcar).

OVERSEAS

March Drawing Contest.—First Prizes: Section A, W. Figgins (Wellington, N.Z.). Section B, M. Conly (Dunedin, N.Z.); Second Prizes: Section A, M. Azees Ahmed (Mysore). Section B, W. Thomson (Maylands). Consolation Prize: S. Eriksson (Taranaki, N.Z.).

Christmas Essay Contest.—1. G. Caband (Vaud). 2. W. A. Carpinter (Christchurch, N.Z.). 3. D. Murison (Buenos Aires). 4. G. Cali (St. Julians).

Advertisement Jig-Saw Contest.—1. R. Allen (Toronto). 2. H. Dressler (Breslau). 3. J. R. Hurst (Buenos Aires). 4. S. A. Kock (Heldinia).

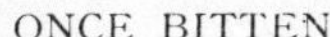

ONCE BITTEN

Lady: "You would stand more chance of getting a job if you would wash and shave, and make yourself presentable."
Tramp: "Yes, lady. I found that out years ago."

* * * *

Teacher: "Tom, what is a cannibal?"
Tom: "Don't know, mum."
Teacher: "Well, if you ate your father and mother for dinner, what would you be?"
Tom: "An orphan, mum."

* * * *

Blinks: "Jones is the most successful salesman I know."
Jinks: "How so?"
Blinks: "Well, yesterday he sold Mrs. Jones two dozen stair rods."
Jinks: "There's nothing very successful in that surely."
Blinks: "I didn't think so until I knew she lived in a bungalow."

* * * *

The new farm hand was ploughing, and the farmer told him to keep his eyes fixed on some prominent object at a distance that would act as a guide.
Coming back later on, the farmer was amazed to find that the plough had been travelling all over the field.
"What on earth are you doing?" he roared.
"I did just what you told me, sir. I worked straight for that cow in the next field, but the darned thing wouldn't stand still."

* * * *

Scotland Yard circulated a strip of six photographs of a man who was wanted. Shortly afterwards a telegram from the head of a small country police force reached the Yard.
"Have found four of the wanted men," it ran. "Hope to get other two soon."

* * * *

The teacher had been telling his class about different coins of the realm. Suddenly he pulled from his pocket a two-shilling piece, and slapped it on the desk.
"What's that?" he asked.
"Heads, sir," said a boy in the front row immediately.

* * * *

First Tramp: "You're looking downcast, Tim. What's the matter?"
Second Tramp: "I've found a recipe for home-made cake, and I haven't got a home."

* * * *

Policeman (after a collision): "You saw this lady driving towards you. Why didn't you give her the road?"
Motorist: "I was going to, as soon as I could discover which half she wanted."

* * * *

"Old Barnes is going to retire from business for good now."
"Yes, but I've heard him say that before."
"The judge has said so now."

* * * *

Betty: "You don't look like an old lady any more, now you've had your hair bobbed."
Granny: "Don't I, darling?"
Betty: "No; you look more like an old man."

THE TOUGHER THE BETTER

Diner: "Do you serve crabs here?"
Waiter: "We serve anyone; sit down."

* * * *

Scotsman: "Mon, I'm in awful trouble."
Friend: "How's that?"
Scotsman: "My girl's jilted me."
Friend: "Oh, hard lines, old man."
Scotsman: "Ye havna heard the worst: I'd just bought a tandem."

* * * *

"Has Roberts sold anything since he took up novel writing as a career?"
"Oh, yes; his business, his house and his car."

* * * *

Madge (aged four) caught sight of some Brussels sprouts in a greengrocer's shop one day.
"Oh, mummy," she exclaimed, "look at those dear little dollies' cabbages."

* * * *

Foreman: "My man, you ought to take a pleasure in coming to work."
Workman: "Lumme, guv'nor, you'll be makin' me pay entertainment tax next."

* * * *

He had taken up motoring late in life and was describing his experiences to a friend.
"I'm sure you went through a good deal when you were first learning to drive," said the latter.
"M'yes; I certainly went through a couple of hedges, a fence, and at least one garage door."

* * * *

ABSENT-MINDED

Bill's house had just been papered for the first time, and he asked his friend to have a look at it, as he had done the work himself.
"It's all right," said his friend, "but what are those lumps under the paper?"
"Good gracious," exclaimed Bill, "I forgot to take down the pictures."

* * * *

Freddy: "See that man leaving the field, auntie? Well, he has been sent off for a foul."
Auntie: "Well, one fowl won't go far between 22 men."

* * * *

"Dinah," said the mistress of the house, "What do you do with those grapefruit skins you take away with you?"
"I carries 'em home, ma'am," confessed the negro maid. "I'se think they make my dustbin look stylish."

* * * *

The foreman looked the applicant for work up and down. "Are you a mechanic?" he asked.
"No sorr," was the answer. "Oi'm a Macassey."

* * * *

"I say, guard," asked a fussy old gentleman, poking his head out of the train, "Is this my station?"
"No sir," replied the guard. "It belongs to the Railway Company."

* * * *

Teacher: "Tell me what you know about ants."
Small Boy: "There are two kinds of ants, insects and lady uncles."

HARD LUCK

Convict: "Say, boss, don't you get papers to read in this place?"
Warder: "No, Spike, but I've bad news for you. Your ticket in the Christmas sweep won a world cruise."

* * * *

Lady (to little boy crying): "What is the matter, sonny?"
Boy: "It was the man in the shop. He's going to send the police after me."
Lady: "But that shop is an undertaker's. What did you want in there?"
Boy: "Empty Boxes."

* * * *

The teacher gave each boy three buttons: one stood for liberty, one for life, and one for happiness. Next day she thought she would test their memory.
"George," she said, "where are the three buttons, and what do they stand for?"
"Here's life and liberty," said George, taking two buttons out of his pocket. "Happiness is sewn on to my best trousers."

* * * *

"Why are you carrying that umbrella over your head?" asked an inquisitive old man of a small boy. "It isn't raining and the sun isn't shining."
"I know all about that," said the little boy, "but when it rains Dad takes it out with him, and when the sun shines Ma sits under it in the garden. This is the only chance I get to use it."

* * * *

Summer Boarder: "What a beautiful view that is."
Farmer: "Maybe. But if you had to plough that view, harrow it, cultivate it, hoe it, fence it and pay taxes on it, it would look quite ordnery."

* * * *

"Want a job, do you?" said the grocer. "Well, I'll take you on. What's your name?"
"Simpson, sir."
"All right. Go and unload the chests of tea from the van over there and carry them up to the storeroom over the shop; and while you are up there, bring down three barrels of butter."
"Excuse me, sir, I said Simpson, not Sampson."

* * * *

First Burglar: "If I can pick this lock, we can lay our hands on £50,000."
Second Burglar: "Is that so? Well, go carefully with my sixpenny penknife."

* * * *

Ex-convict: "Could you help a poor man who has just left prison?"
Old Lady: "You should be ashamed to own it."
Ex-convict: "I didn't own it, mum—I was only a lodger."

* * * *

A BARGAIN

A Scotsman new to London, sat on a chair in Hyde Park. "I'm no understandin' what ye're wantin', mon," he told the collector.
"Twopence for the chair, sir," was the reply.
At that the Scotsman rose and examined the chair closely. "It's no so dear, mon," he said. "I'm thinkin' I'll hae twa."

A Famous West Highland Steamer

The Passing of the "Columba"

By J. H. Sutherland

CRUISES down the Clyde and in the West Highlands have been enjoyed by many thousands of people, who have learned to know well the vessels serving that wonderful holiday land. The most famous of all the ships engaged in this service undoubtedly was the paddle steamer "*Columba*," which began her career in 1878, and many people all over the world will scarcely be able to credit the news that she will cruise no more. So intimately associated has this famous paddle-steamer been with the Firth of Clyde, that Scotland's holiday waterway will veritably appear incomplete without her.

In many respects the "*Columba*" has been a remarkable craft; indeed, the most outstanding of her time. Actually she was built in consequence of another company intruding into the West Highland steamer traffic which had long been regarded as the preserve of David Hutcheson and Co., her owners, and the predecessors of David MacBrayne Ltd. She cost approximately £29,000 and was launched on 11th April, 1878, at Thomson's yard at Clydebank, now carried on by John Brown and Co., the builders of the "*Queen Mary*." Though the manufacture of steel was then at an experimental stage, it was decided to construct the new boat of this material, and the policy proved to be eminently successful.

In due course the powerful paddles of the "*Columba*" began to churn a snowy wake over the route she was to follow for 57 years. Her length of 301 ft. greatly exceeded that of any other Clyde steamer, even in the post-war days of larger craft fitted with turbine engines. Her speed of 21 knots created a sensation and stamped her as the fastest boat to ply on the Clyde estuary, but in recent years she became slower and her rate of progress then would approximate more nearly to 18 knots. With two well-set-up funnels, painted bright red with black tops, she presented an imposing appearance and, as might be expected, met with public approval from the outset.

The "Columba" at speed in Rothesay Bay. This famous West Highland steamer was launched in 1878, and continued in service until last summer.

At the time of her appearance the "*Columba*" possessed all the latest improvements, including steam steering gear, telegraphs between bridge and engine-room, and steam warping-sheaves. The post-office on board was by no means her least remarkable novelty, for it was the first institution of its kind on a pleasure boat. In addition, the deck saloons were extended to the full width of the steamer, an innovation that provided a sumptuous and spacious retreat when climatic conditions were unfavourable. She was licensed to carry 2,000 passengers, and could boast of catering arrangements on a comprehensive scale—an important matter in the diversion of pleasure sailing, which is a great creator of appetites.

The vessel was fitted with twin-cylinder oscillating engines that were cranked to a shaft carrying enormous paddle wheels, the original wooden floats of which were later replaced by steel ones. The only other mechanical alteration effected took place in 1900, when two large "haystack" boilers working at a pressure of 50 lb. per sq. in. were installed instead of those of the "Navy" type formerly used, and on only one occasion did the "*Columba*" undergo any exterior transformation. This occurred in 1929, when an experimental shade of grey was applied to the hull. But so unsatisfactory was the effect, and so greatly incensed were those who knew her, that the old colour was restored in little more than a week.

The paddle boxes, with the fan-shaped vents common to all MacBrayne craft, were rendered particularly handsome because of their carved gilt-work. The bows also could boast of elegant scrolls that indicated the artistic sense of those who fashioned steamers in bygone times. These can be seen in our illustration.

For many years the "*Columba*" held greater prestige during August and September than any other paddler. At the beginning of the shooting season her decks were crowded with people following the West Highland route to their Scottish residences and lodges, and one can imagine the volume of traffic and amount of luggage transported in this annual rush to the north.

Although she was more than half a century old, the active life of the "*Columba*" did not exceed 20 years, for she was purely a summer excursion boat and for the greater part of her existence occupied moorings in the sheltered harbour of Bowling, where she was a familiar object as she floated tranquilly at the base of Old Kilpatrick's green, rolling hills, accumulating a coating of grime from the endless succession of passing ships and from the adjacent railway. Yet out she would come every June, spick and span as only a proud crew could make her, and capable of holding her own against all comers during her four months' service. In 1929 her winter quarters were changed to Greenock.

At a distance the "*Columba*" was reminiscent of the "*Iona*" and the "*Chevalier*," older steamers belonging to the same company, for she had a similar design of fiddle-bow, and the same square stern and three-quarter length promenade deck. In truth, this type of rounded bow was already old-fashioned when the "*Columba*" took shape, but probably it was perpetuated in the newer boat as being a more harmonious factor than a straight stem.

For several decades the hour of 7.11 a.m. was synonymous with the departure of the "*Columba*" from Bridge Wharf, Glasgow. Thence she splashed her way down-river to Greenock, Gourock, Dunoon, Rothesay, Tarbert and finally Ardrishaig, accomplishing well over 150 miles on the round trip. At Greenock and Gourock she connected with trains from Glasgow, to suit those people who found the earlier start from Bridge Wharf to be inconvenient, and at Dunoon her decks were supplemented by many more passengers, including those borne thither by the L.N.E.R. steamer from Craigendoran. By the time Rothesay had been tapped in turn, there were sometimes incredible crowds to be seen aboard during the height of the season.

The writer retains a vivid recollection of the early part of the century, when the "*Columba*" gave evidence of her propensity for racing in matches against the "*Lord of the Isles*," the equally well-known paddle steamer of a rival company. Both vessels were timed to leave Rothesay quay at the same hour, and away they went, with black plumes belching from their funnels, separated by little more than a dozen yards and following a course barely 100 yards from low-water mark. For over a mile their progress invariably afforded much excitement to interested spectators, but the "*Columba*" inevitably would take the lead towards the silver'd fairway between the distant hills. This daily scamper continued for several seasons.

This well-known steamer will no longer kick up her heels in the glorious rush from the "tail o' the bank" at Greenock; never again will she go spanking through the Kyles of Bute; no more will her wash provide a thrill to the occupants of innumerable rowing boats, and the folks who were wont to view her return to Bridge Wharf will await her in vain.

The writer recently paid his last respects to this old "flier." She lay moored in a corner of Greenock Harbour awaiting the highest bidder—a pathetic-looking object to anyone who knew her in her prime, yet in her misfortune bearing an air of dignity.

NEXT MONTH: "STORY OF THE TRAMCAR." PUBLISHING DATE: 1st JULY

MECCANO MAGAZINE

Editorial Office: Binns Road, Liverpool 13 England

Vol. XXI. No. 6 June, 1936

With the Editor

An Absent-minded Professor

On 10th June it will be 100 years since the death of Andre Marié Ampère, one of the great pioneers of electricity. Ampère's name of course is familiar to every boy who has interested himself in electricity, for whenever we speak of a current as being of so many amperes we are paying tribute to the man and his work.

Throughout his career Ampère was so wrapped up in his studies and experiments that he knew little of what was going on around him. This is shown by the well-known incident that occurred at a meeting of the French Academy, at which he read a paper. On returning to his seat he found that a stranger had taken possession of it, and tried to compel the intruder to leave, completely oblivious of the fact that this was the Emperor Napoleon! The Emperor was greatly amused, and invited the scientist to dinner next day; but by that time Ampère had returned to his research and had completely forgotten both the Emperor and his invitation!

What are the mysterious-looking objects seen in this photograph? A prize of 10/6 is offered for the most complete solution to this puzzle received by 20th June. Solutions should be written on postcards only and addressed "June Editorial Competition," Meccano Magazine, Binns Road, Liverpool 13.

The *"Hindenburg's"* Record Flights

The record flights of the *"Hindenburg"* across the North Atlantic Ocean have raised once more the question of the value of airships. The great German airship made her first westward voyage in 68 hrs. 38 min. and returned in the remarkably short time of 48 hrs. 18 min., in each case with over 50 passengers and a considerable quantity of mails and cargo. Throughout the two flights the vessel travelled smoothly and easily, and the passengers seemed to have been greatly impressed by the absence of noise, and the comfortable and restful character of their crossing. In this respect the airship has a great advantage over the aeroplane, which is noisier and less roomy, although of course it is speedier.

The success of the *"Hindenburg"* may lead to a revival of interest in vessels of this kind in other parts of the world. Airship construction was stopped in this country and in the United States after the disasters to *"R101"* and the two American airships *"Akron"* and *"Macon,"* and only in Germany was the belief in the value of these great vessels retained. The achievements of the *"Hindenburg,"* and of the *"Graf Zeppelin"* before her, have completely justified this confidence; and if the new vessel maintains as regular and steady a service as her predecessor did on the South American service, we in this country may have to change our views. A new airship building programme already is being considered in the United States.

A Great Airwoman

Two months ago I made reference to the record-breaking flight to South Africa and back of Flight Lieutenant T. Rose, who made the outward and inward trips in a total time of about 10 days. As if this were not sufficiently astonishing, new records have now been created by Mrs. Mollison, who covered the 6,700 miles to Capetown in a little more than three days, and accomplished the return journey in less than five days, thus reducing the total time by more than two days.

This wonderful achievement is a tribute to Mrs. Mollison's skill and endurance, and to her great ability as a navigator. She had to cross the Sahara Desert, a flight of 2,000 miles, at night and flying blind; and at a later stage of the flight it cannot have been easy to find the aerodromes, some of which were hidden in the depths of the equatorial forest. She made no mistake, however. Her flight must be ranked as one of the most daring and successful ever achieved, and her welcome on again reaching this country was well deserved.

Carrying the Irish Mail

Holyhead to Dun Laoghaire by R.M.S. "*Cambria*"

By O. S. Nock, B.Sc., D.I.C.

THE history of the conveyance of the Irish Mail is one of the greatest romances of transportation. One of the earliest of a remarkable series of engineering works designed to lessen the journey between London and Dublin was the Holyhead Road constructed by Telford. When the coaches gave place to the railway, Robert Stephenson built the world-famous tubular bridge over the Menai Strait, a fitting counterpart to Telford's beautiful suspension bridge little over a mile away. Then the very first water troughs in the world were laid down near Bangor in 1861 to enable the Irish Mail to make longer non-stop runs. Now that these wonders have become almost a commonplace, the service is distinguished by some of the fastest cross-channel ships in the world, and certainly the fastest coal-burning vessels.

These splendid ships, the "*Cambria*," "*Hibernia*" and "*Scotia*," were built specially for the London and North Western Railway's Irish service. For the last hundred years the mails have always been landed at Kingstown, a fine harbour on the south side of Dublin Bay about seven miles from the Capital. Until 1860 the mails were carried by an Admiralty steam packet, but in that year the contract for their conveyance was awarded to the City of Dublin Steam Packet Company, who maintained the service till 1920, when it was taken over by the L.N.W.R. It was after the creation of the Irish Free State that Kingstown became known once again by its ancient title of Dun Laoghaire.

R.M.S. "Cambria" in the departure berth at Holyhead. This vessel and the others on the same service are capable of a speed of 25 knots.

The inner harbour at Holyhead is V-shaped. Approaching the station, the up and down railway tracks divide, one going to the left and the other to the right of the V; they then run right alongside the steamer berths. In the arrival berth was the "*Hibernia*," which had come in just before noon with the east-bound day mail. Our ship was the "*Cambria*," and from her decks the graceful lines of the sister vessel on the opposite berth were seen to great advantage. These are big ships; their gross tonnage is 3,470, the turbines develop no less than 16,000 h.p., and like all other L.M.S. cross-channel ships their boilers are fired with coal.

Loading the mails at Holyhead. "The Irish Mail" express is seen on the right of this photograph.

Holyhead Harbour is a long narrow channel in which it would be a slow and difficult business to turn ships of such size as the "*Cambria*"; and so, like the L.M.S. steamers on the Heysham-Belfast route, these vessels are fitted with bow rudders so that they can navigate stern first quickly; speed is always a first consideration with the Irish Mail. They are fitted with a second bridge, abaft of the funnels, from which the ship is driven when going astern, and here, a few minutes before sailing time, I joined Captain Turner.

On the stroke of 2.30 p.m. the gangways were let down, and then, by means of a rope stretched across to the opposite berth, the stern was slowly swung out from the quayside. Then, "Let go!"; the rope falls into the water with a resounding smack, and at the same moment "Half speed astern" is signalled to the engine room. A very slight quiver goes through the ship as the turbines start—the after bridge is right over the engine room—and we are under way. The harbour lies under the shelter of Holyhead Mountain and the narrow waterway leads north at first, but as we reach the outer harbour our course veers north-east for a while. Just at the turn there is an awkwardly placed sandbank, but apart from this Holyhead is an excellent harbour to enter or leave, with deep water on all tides.

We passed the old Admiralty pier from which the mail boats used to sail prior to 1880, and so came out into the wide natural harbour that lies between Holy Island and the mainland of Anglesey. As soon as we were well clear of the jetty the Captain changed right over to full speed ahead. Of course the turbines were not immediately reversed, the steam pressure has gradually to be reduced to zero, and then as gradually increased again on the forward turbines. In the meantime the ship was being swung round on to her true course, "West by North a half North"; this was to take us, with only the slightest changes, right across the Irish Sea.

As we changed over from steaming astern to ahead, two black balls that had been hoisted on the after mast were run down. With all these ships fitted with bow rudders some signal is needed to tell other craft that when steaming astern they are not merely manœuvering, but that for the time being their stern is their bow. In daylight the two black balls are hoisted, but at night a more elaborate signal is needed. In the ordinary way all ships carry two white mast-head lights, that on the forward mast being some 15 ft. lower than that on the rear mast, so that a ship on either beam can tell at once in which direction the vessel is steaming. At the same time a green light is carried on one side of the bridge and a red on the other to give the same message to oncoming ships. The "*Cambria*" and her sister vessels carry two distinct sets of navigation lights, one for ahead and one for astern; when direction is changed one set is extinguished and the other lighted.

By now, steaming at 23 knots, we were passing the end of the Holyhead breakwater; this is nearly 8,000 ft. long and shelters the entire haven. Southward, Holyhead Mountain towered up behind the sheer precipices of the North Stack rocks, and farther away was an even more dramatic piece of cliff scenery, the South Stack. This rocky islet, black and forbidding even on the fairest day, is crowned by a fine lighthouse; a small suspension connects the Stack with the mainland and adds not a little to the wild beauty of the scene. Away to the north the Skerries lighthouse gleamed white in the sunshine; the sea was an intense blue, and far away to the south-east loomed the giants of Snowdonia. Although it was brilliantly clear on the sea a distinct haze hung over the land, and the mountains appeared as a vague bluish-grey cloud; here and there a whitish gleam told of snow lying deep in the crevices. As we came out into the open sea the tide was running strongly in the race under the North Stack and for a few minutes the *"Cambria"* was pitching slightly, but as Holyhead Mountain receded into the haze the sea became extremely placid, shimmering in the brilliant sunshine.

In the wheelhouse of R.M.S. "Cambria." "Full speed ahead" is the order, as is very necessary if time is to be kept.

* * * * *

Half way down the vertical ladder leading into the engine room there is a very striking view of the whole layout. Just below are the main turbines, one driving each of the propeller shafts; the rotors of the turbines run at about 2,500 r.p.m. and they are geared down so as to give a propeller shaft speed of about 250 r.p m. These ships are capable of the remarkable speed of 25 knots, though 22 to 23 knots is sufficient to keep schedule time, which is always adhered to very strictly. Beyond the turbines, still looking from our stance on the ladder, is the control platform, and all its gauges, clocks and dials are mounted from the wall, or bulkhead as it is called in a ship, that divides the engine room from the stoke-hold.

Coming now to the control platform itself, among the many gauges is a counter that records the number of revolutions of the propeller shafts; it is by means of this instrument that the speed of the ship is regulated. The engineers know the exact number of revolutions that the shafts make during the complete crossing, and they calculate beforehand what the total revolutions should be at 10-minute intervals during the voyage, at 3.0 p.m., 3.10 p.m., 3.20 p.m. and so on. By checking the reading on the counter at these times they can tell very accurately whether they are ahead of or behind time, and can regulate the speed of the turbines accordingly. The working pressure of the boilers is 200 lb. per sq. in., but to maintain 22 knots only about 175 lb. per sq. in. is necessary. While I was on the control platform the Second Engineer checked the speed; the revolution counter showed that we were approximately 1½ minutes ahead of time, and so the very slightest reduction was made in the steam pressure in order to slow the ship down just a trifle.

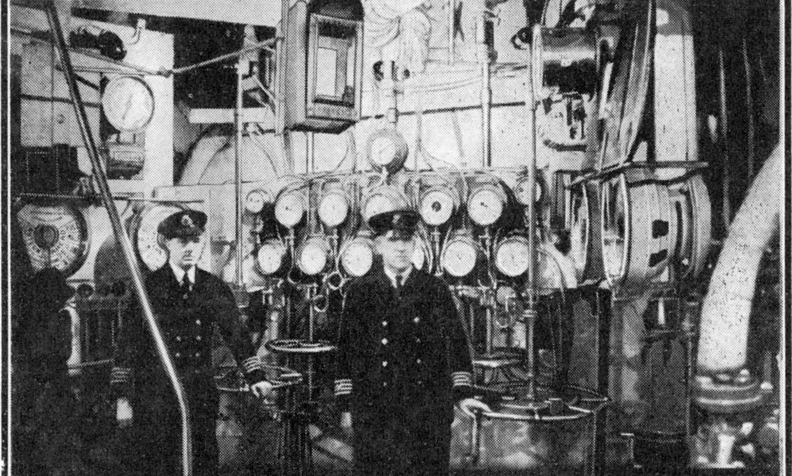

The control platform in the engine room. From here the engineer regulates the speed of the ship, according to the orders received from the bridge by means of the engine room telegraph.

There are nine boilers of the standard Babcock and Wilcox water-tube type, though of these only eight are used normally. All these boilers are hand fired, there being one stoker to each boiler. In crossing from Holyhead to Dun Laoghaire they burn between 20 and 23 tons, according to the weather; this means that each stoker fires a little under a ton per hour, which is about the same as on a modern express locomotive. Forced draught is used, and the upward current of air through the stokehold when going full speed is tremendous.

* * * * *

I came up on to the bridge again when we were just over half way across; the coast of Anglesey was just a vague line, but as yet there was no sign of Ireland. A bank of grey cloud hung on the western horizon, above which some thundery cumulus looked like a vast fantastic mountain range. The Chief Officer pointed out a topsail schooner far away on the starboard bow. Now, right ahead of us, the clouds were lifting to show a small arc of brighter sky on the horizon, and right in the centre of this patch was the Kish lightship, our first contact with Ireland. This beacon is anchored at the entrance to Dublin Bay; there are no rocks or shallows anywhere near, but it forms a useful point to steer towards. We were still steaming in brilliantly fine weather, but rainstorms were chasing each other northward along the Irish coast, and in the wake of one of these squalls came a first glimpse of land. A slanting grey mass was moving slowly across towards the Kish and in the brightening sky to the south there appeared, little by little, the outline of Bray Head and of the Wicklow Hills behind. There was a wistful and exquisite beauty about the way in which these mountains gradually took shape out of the mist. On the north side of the bay the Hill of Howth loomed out of the haze. In the earliest days of the service the Irish Mail was landed at Howth; to this little harbour came the old Sailing Packet in the times when it took four days to get from London to Dublin. The first steam packet also landed the mails at Howth. Just to the north of the promontory called the Nose of Howth was "Ireland's Eye," a rocky islet, and far to the north I could just pick out the profile of Lambay Island.

By the time we passed the Kish the coast stretching away to the south was being steadily revealed in all its beauty. The south side of the Bay has a fairly low coastline, but many miles to the rear is the long, high undulating ridge of the Dublin Hills, their crests still barely distinguishable from the grey of the clouds. Soon we were abreast of Dalkey; the spires of Dun Laoghaire rose against the sunset sky, and right ahead of us lay Dublin under a pall of smoke.

Like Holyhead, Dun Laoghaire is a real deep water harbour, and we maintained full speed almost up to the lighthouse. Right in the centre, running out from the shore, is the railway pier. We edged quietly up to the right-hand side of the jetty; we were alongside at 5.24 p.m., and in 2 hours 55 minutes almost to the second the gangways were run across.

There is a great tradition behind the carrying of the Irish Mail, and Captain Turner told me that if the mail steamers are only a minute late or early, Somebody wants to know why!

High Speed on the L.N.E.R. (G.C. Section)

Feats of Veteran "Atlantics"

By a Railway Engineer

IT is a rather remarkable fact that nearly all British locomotives of the 1900–1910 decade still employed on first-class express duty are of the 4–4–2 type. Some recent exploits of the sturdy North British "Atlantics," and of their amazing counterparts on the Great Northern section of the L.N.E.R., were described in the "*M.M.*" in June and September last year respectively, but on the Great Central section of the same railway "Atlantics" built as long ago as 1903 are daily putting up work of equally fine quality.

An up Bradford express near Rickmansworth. The locomotive is L.N.E.R. No. 6088, one of the "Atlantics" of the former Great Central Railway.

The Great Central main line to London was not opened until 1899. At every important town the new railway was in fierce competition with well-established routes and from the outset was compelled to run a very high-speed service in order to attract custom. The zenith of the company's speed achievement was reached in 1905 when the famous "*Sheffield Special*" was booked to cover the 164¾ miles from Marylebone to Sheffield non-stop in 170 minutes.

In the early days of the London Extension loads were very light and 4–4–0 locomotives could manage the fastest trains successfully; but in 1903, to be ready for heavier traffic, Mr. J. G. Robinson brought out the first of his famous "Atlantics." Technically they were simple and straightforward, and outwardly one of the most handsome locomotive designs ever put on the road. At the time of their construction they were much in advance of the times, and it is indeed a tribute to the farsightedness of their designer that they can be relied on for such important work under the strenuous conditions of to-day.

L.N.E.R. (G.C.) "Atlantic" No. 5363. This is the engine that made the remarkable run described in this article.

In 1906 Mr. Robinson made a trial of compounding, and built four "Atlantics" as three-cylinder compounds arranged on the well-known "Smith" system. These engines were most successful, and all four are running as compounds to-day; as far as my own experience goes their performances are indistinguishable from those of the simple engines. Another interesting experimental "Atlantic" was No. 1090, now L.N.E.R. No. 6090. This engine ran for some time as a three-cylinder simple. In pre-War days the Great Central and Great Northern ran a joint service between King's Cross and Manchester on which Great Central engines worked the trains as far south as Grantham. No. 1090, in its three-cylinder days, was often employed on this duty, and made some very fast running over the Great Northern main line between Grantham and Retford; at this latter junction the trains branched off, and reached Sheffield by way of Worksop.

It was in applying the principle of superheating to the simple "Atlantics" in 1911 that Mr. Robinson designed the superheater that bears his name and is now used all over the world. The addition of superheaters greatly improved the work of the engines, and nearly every one of the type, both compound and simple, has been so equipped.

In 1913 the celebrated "Director" class 4–4–0s came out, but the "Atlantics" were only partially superseded on the best expresses, and since that date, although very big 4–6–0s such as the two-cylinder "Sir Sam Fay" class, and the still more powerful four-cylinder "Lord Faringdons," have been in regular service on the Great Central main line, the old 4–4–2s have still retained their place in first class duty. Oddly enough the "Atlantics" have established a reputation for being better hill climbers than the much larger 4–6–0s!

To-day Mr. Gresley's big three-cylinder 4–6–0s of the "Sandringham" class are at work on the Great Central section, but at the time of writing none of them have been stationed at Leicester; in consequence one of the hardest, if not the hardest, turn on the whole system, the 6.20 p.m. out of Marylebone, is invariably "Atlantic"-hauled. Owing to the crowded state of the Metropolitan Joint line via Aylesbury at this time in the evening, this express takes the longer route over the Great Western and Great Central Joint line, via High Wycombe. Until the beginning of this year, the 107.6 miles to Leicester were booked to be run non-stop in 114 minutes, an average speed of 56.4 m.p.h.; slip coaches were carried for both Finmere and Woodford, and the minimum load out of Marylebone was one of 290 tons.

This tonnage did not by any means represent the limit of "Atlantic" ability, and I have observed No. 6090, now a two-cylinder simple, to keep time with a load of 340 tons. Only on one occasion, just before August Bank Holiday, when the train was made up to no less than 370 tons, have I known a pilot engine used. It seems a far cry now to the old days of the "*Sheffield Special*" when the maximum load was about 170 tons!

At the beginning of this year the two slip coaches were withdrawn, and the train was booked to stop at Finmere and Woodford. The time allowed to Leicester is now 119 minutes, including half a minute at each stop; with a minimum load of 250 tons this schedule represents quite the hardest task ever set to Great Central engines. In the third week that the new timing was in force I travelled down to Leicester and was treated to a really magnificent performance. The load was one of seven coaches, 241 tons tare and 260 tons with passengers and luggage; at the head of the train was "Atlantic" No. 5363, a two-cylinder simple built in 1906, in charge of Driver Newall and Fireman Lees, who are attached to the Leicester shed.

The cabs of these engines are much more spacious than those of most of their contemporaries. They are driven from the right-hand side, and the reversing gear is of the screw type. A double-port regulator is used, working on the same principle as that of the Midland Compounds. When the handle is in any position up to "half over" on the quadrant, steam is admitted through the small valve, or "first regulator" as it is usually called; beyond half way the main regulator is brought into operation. In contrast with the Great Northern "Atlantics," these engines have a long narrow Belpaire firebox, a distinctive feature of which is a fire-door placed unusually high above the footplate level. This of course makes for a cool cab, but, as in the case of the French locomotives that I described in the "*M.M.*" for March, does not ease the fireman's task. The G.C. "Atlantics" are most economical engines, however, and even on such strenuous turns as the 6.20 p.m. burn only about 45 lb. per mile, a satisfactory figure in the circumstances.

"Atlantic" No. 5264 on a down express. This engine has the tapered chimney provided after grouping in place of the wider curving pattern originally fitted. Photograph reproduced by courtesy of the L.N.E.R.

It was an ideal evening for fast running, calm and fine, and a severe permanent way slack in the early stages gave the driver an opportunity for some really exceptional work in making up the time thus lost. Getting away in fine style, the reversing gear was quickly brought back to a position half way between full and mid-gear, giving a cut-off of 40 per cent., and the regulator gradually opened to the full. Through Hampstead tunnels, climbing at 1 in 196–100, speed rose to 35 m.p.h. but fell back to 32 m.p.h. on the 1 in 95 to Brondesbury summit, where the North London line of the L.M.S.R. is crossed. Down the sharp descent to Neasden speed was not allowed to exceed 56 m.p.h., and immediately beyond the junction, where the Aylesbury route diverges, we encountered the permanent way slack, right down to 20 m.p.h. for nearly a mile. Recovering speed steadily up grades averaging 1 in 200, we passed South Harrow summit at 43 m.p.h. and a moment or so later were easing up to take the burrowing junction at Northolt that marks the beginning of the Great Western and Great Central Joint Line.

On account of the Neasden check, the 11½ miles to Northolt Junction had taken 19¾ minutes, 2¾ minutes over schedule; but now Driver Newall set about recovering the lost time with a vengeance. This is the route followed by the Great Western two-hour Birmingham expresses, and indeed it seemed as though the L.N.E.R. crew had pitted themselves against their G.W.R. rivals, so electrifying was our progress. In four miles of faintly rising line speed rose to 62 m.p.h., but then there begins the first stage of the ascent over the Chiltern Hills. As we approached Denham the driver opened out to full regulator but the cut-off remained unchanged at 40 per cent., in fact throughout from Marylebone to Leicester there was scarcely any variation from this figure either when working with the main or the first regulator. Meanwhile the engine was climbing splendidly. At Gerrards Cross after three miles of 1 in 175 grade we were doing 55 m.p.h.; beyond this station the rise continues at 1 in 254 and here No. 5363 accelerated rapidly to 60 m.p.h. before passing the summit near Beaconsfield. At this point she was developing nearly 1,500 horse power—a wonderful figure for so moderate-sized an engine.

A footplate view of "Atlantic" No. 5363, showing Driver Newall on the right and Fireman Lees on the left of the cab.

Readers who have travelled on the Great Central route cannot have failed to notice periods in every run when an intense rain of cinders falls on the carriage roofs, and probably will have attributed it to fire-throwing of a most extravagant kind. Actually it is the ejection of accumulated ash in the smoke-box. With any locomotive a good deal of ash collects around the blast-pipe during a run, and I have seen engines arrive at their destination with a great heap piled high above the nozzle. By means of this ingenious ejector on these G.C. engines the ash can be blown out periodically during the run, and the smoke-box kept not only clean but, what is more important on turns such as these, cool. On this run Driver Newall put the ejector on for the first time just after passing Gerrards Cross.

Changing over to the first regulator on passing Beaconsfield, we began the dip to the valley of the River Wye in dashing style with a maximum speed of 73 m.p.h. at Tylers Green, but unfortunately this break in the climb cannot be taken full advantage of owing to the permanent speed restriction to 35 m.p.h. through High Wycombe. On passing this station, however, we had run the 16 miles from Northolt Junction in 17 minutes, and already one minute of lost time was regained. Speed was picked up splendidly on the steep rise that follows, and by Saunderton summit we were steadily maintaining 48 m.p.h. up the 1 in 164 gradient. Far from there being any suspicion of shortage of steam after this hard work, No. 5363 approached the top "blowing off."

Now the regulator was brought back to the first port, and for the first mile-and-a-half of descent the acceleration was positively uncanny. We stormed through Princes Risborough at 73, and four miles farther on attained the terrific maximum, for an engine of this age, of 88 m.p.h. Over the last four miles of the Joint Line speed lay entirely between 75 and 82 m.p.h. on a stretch which, although undulating is no more than level on the average. The 34 miles of the Joint Line, from Northolt to Ashendon Junction had been covered at an average of exactly 60 m.p.h., inclusive of the slack through High Wycombe and the climb over the Chilterns! Passing Ashendon at 78 m.p.h. we kept up a tremendous pace, and even after a mile rising at 1 in 175 were still doing 68 m.p.h. when we rejoined the Aylesbury route at Grendon Junction. The 51¼ miles from Marylebone had been covered in 59 minutes, while over the last 15.3 miles we had averaged 75.2 m.p.h.

Just before Grendon, Driver Newall had reverted to the main regulator; we romped over the sharp ups and downs past Calvert at 65–70 m.p.h., and after three miles of continuous climbing at 1 in 176 had not fallen below 61 m.p.h. when steam was shut off for our first stop, at Finmere. The 59 miles had been run in 66¾ minutes; the whole of the loss caused by the Neasden slack had been wiped out and we were three-quarters of a minute early—a brilliant effort indeed. The net time was a little under 64 minutes.

The next section is a very difficult one. A timing of 16½ minutes start to stop for a run of 14.6 miles would need good going on the dead level, but between Finmere and Woodford there are nine miles rising it 1 in 176! Starting on this grade we were up to 38 m.p.h. in 1½ miles; then comes a dip for 1¾ miles at the same inclination. Accelerating like lightning we got up to 63 m.p.h. before tackling the 5½ miles of Helmdon bank where speed fell to a sustained 54 m.p.h. Onward to Culworth the line still has a rising tendency, though not so steep; but with almost full regulator we reached 67 m.p.h., and a minute later, after a short length of down grade, swept over Culworth Junction at 76½ m.p.h. But even with this magnificent running we failed to keep time, although the loss was only 41 seconds.

The last 34 miles from Woodford into Leicester are scheduled in 34 minutes. A stop of half a minute's duration is all that is allowed at both Finmere and Woodford, and slight overtime in each case made us three quarters of a minute late on leaving Woodford. But Driver Newall got some more brilliant work than ever out of No. 5363, made the final run in 32½ minutes, and brought us into Leicester nearly a minute early. Starting once again up a gradient of 1 in 176, we passed Charwelton, 2½ miles out, at 46 m.p.h., and then approaching the south portal of Catesby Tunnel Newall went over to the first regulator. From this point there is an unbroken descent of 7 miles at 1 in 176; acceleration was a little slow at first, but once into the "seventies" we simply romped away and touched 82 m.p.h. at Braunston. Keeping up 74-75 m.p.h. along the level beyond, we had not fallen below 64 up the sharp rise to Rugby, and then simply flew across the long viaduct over the L.M.S.R. main line at 73 m.p.h.

The "Ports to Ports" express from Newcastle-on-Tyne to Cardiff passing over Charwelton water troughs. The engine is Great Central "Atlantic" No. 5360.

Now came the ascent of Lutterworth bank, which consists of 5½ miles at 1 in 176, a dip of 2 miles at the same grade, and then a final 2½ miles again at 1 in 176 to the summit. After nearly two hours of such tremendously hard running some slight flagging in the engine's effort might have been anticipated here, but not a bit of it! Throughout the run Fireman Lees had kept the needle almost stationary at full boiler pressure, and we commenced this last climb with the engine blowing off. Without giving the speed a chance to fall, the regulator was pushed hard over immediately we came on to the grade, with the result that we took the first stage of the ascent at a minimum speed of 56 m.p.h., touched 67 on the dip through Lutterworth station, and went over the summit at 61 m.p.h.

The finish into Leicester was breath-taking. Once we were well over the crest of the bank, the regulator was brought back to the second port and speed rose to a well-sustained 87 m.p.h. at Whetstone. For several miles beyond, on a descent no steeper than 1 in 400-650, we kept up a steady 84-85 m.p.h., and within a mile of the stop we were still doing 80! The 8.2 miles from Ashby to Leicester South Goods Junction were covered in 2 seconds under 6 minutes, an average speed of 82.5 m.p.h., while for 27 miles of this thrilling last lap the average was 71.3 m.p.h. So the 34 miles from Woodford to Leicester were run in 32½ minutes.

On the complete run from Marylebone Driver Newall had made a net gain of 5 minutes on these difficult timings, and this was equivalent to a non-stop run over the 107½ miles in 108½ minutes. In response to my congratulations the driver remarked that No. 5363 was "the strongest engine he had ever driven"; certainly he put its strength to some purpose! As he further explained, they have acquired such perfect familiarity with the type that they can coax the very utmost out of them when occasion demands; such feats as this were quite unheard of in the so-called hey-day of the class, when for instance the "*Sheffield Special*" was made up of five or six coaches weighing 180 to 215 tons.

This performance was in the nature of a "swan song," however, at any rate as far as the Great Central "Atlantics" are concerned, for since the above was written they have been replaced at Leicester by some of the new "Sandringham" class 4-6-0s of the "Football Club" series. The "Atlantics" should still have a considerable lease of life, and a particularly interesting development is the transference of No. 6083 to Cambridge shed to work on the very fast buffet car expresses between there and King's Cross. In the meantime the redoubtable Leicester drivers have very quickly taken the measure of their new steeds. During the Easter holidays, Driver Newall on No. 2849, "*Sheffield United*" worked the 6.20 p.m. from Marylebone to time with a load of over 400 tons behind the tender—a fitting counterpart to his "Atlantic" run.

Railway Electrification Developments

Some interesting railway electrification schemes are in progress or are shortly to commence. The Portsmouth electrification of the S.R., now well in hand, has already been referred to in the "*M.M.*"

In the Wirral Peninsula, Cheshire, preliminary work is being done on the L.M.S.R. Wirral line. It is anticipated that this programme will be completed for Easter of next year. This will allow of the through running of trains between the Wirral line and Liverpool, in conjunction with the Mersey Railway. For these through services 19 all-steel electric set trains have been ordered by the L.M.S.R. Each train will consist of a third-class motor car with two motor bogies, a first-third trailer car and a third-class driving trailer. The cars will be of the centre-gangway type, with two wide doors on each side that will be air-operated under the control of the guard. This feature will ensure the rapid loading and unloading of the trains and the reduction of the time occupied at stations to a minimum. With a view to saving weight the contour of the coaches will be reduced from the size of normal L.M.S.R. main line stock, and the vehicles will resemble somewhat those in use on the London underground lines.

One of the Mersey Railway trains. These will be used in conjunction with new L.M.S.R. stock on through services, when the Wirral line electrification is completed.

The L.N.E.R. electrification of the Tyneside lines is to be extended from Newcastle to South Shields. The Tyneside lines were originally electrified in 1904 and were among the first surface lines to be converted from steam to electric working. The position of the conductor rail then differed somewhat from that now adopted as the national standard, and as the first move in the extension the opportunity has been taken quite recently to convert the Tyneside lines to this standard. Altogether some 80 miles of steel conductor rails had to be taken up and replaced Insulators also had to be moved and the various track cables altered. The alterations to the cars were carried out at Gosforth car sheds.

Giant Tanker for Iranian Oilfields

Ingenious Drive for Precipitous Mountain Roads

THE illustrations on this page show a 15-tonner Straussler oil tanker of striking design that has been built for use in Iran. The vehicle is intended to carry petrol in bulk from the oil-fields of the Anglo-Iranian Oil Co. Ltd., in the Persian Gulf for distribution in Teheran, a route of over 400 miles, and in covering which it is necessary to traverse numerous hairpin bends and very bad road surfaces, some of which are snow covered in winter, and a mountain pass 8,000 ft. above sea level. The vehicle has been specially designed to cope with these difficult conditions, and every effort has been made to ensure good road-holding and stability by maintaining a low centre of gravity combined with four-wheel front drive. The necessity for the latter will be appreciated when it is known that the mountain road in many places runs along the edge of precipices many hundreds of feet in height, where the smallest degree of skidding or swaying might easily lead to disaster.

Front view of a 15-tonner Straussler oil tanker specially designed for work in the Iranian oilfields. It is driven by a 150 b.h.p. petrol engine and has a speed of 38 m.p.h. For our illustrations we are indebted to Straussler Mechanization Ltd., London.

The vehicle was built by Straussler Mechanization Ltd., of London, and to ensure that it was reliable for operation over such a dangerous route a trial was arranged over 2,000 miles of difficult mountain roads in the Austrian Tyrol and the Alps, a test from which it emerged successfully.

Some idea of the size of this fine machine, which is capable of a speed of 38 m.p.h. may be had from the following figures. The chassis alone weighs 7½ tons, whilst the oil tank loaded weighs 15½ tons. The weight of the complete vehicle unladen is 12 tons. The overall length is 25 ft. 10 in. and the width 9 ft., and the top of the tank is 9 ft. above ground level.

The chassis is fitted with a Straussler eight-cylindered V-type engine, which has a bore of 98 mm., and a stroke of 120 mm. and develops 150 b.h.p. at 2,800 r.p.m. The power is transmitted through a clutch and six-speed syncromesh gear-box to a short propeller shaft inside the gear-box. At each end of this shaft is a spiral bevel drive and differential, and from each of these run universally-jointed shafts to the four front bogie wheels, the shafts being enclosed in tubular arms hinged to the frame. The gear-box is provided with six levers, one for each gear, the connection between the levers and the box being by push-and-pull cables in flexible conduits.

Each wheel of the Straussler oil tanker is independently mounted on hinged axle arms, and the drive is transmitted to the four wheels of the front bogie by means of universally-jointed shafts.

The engine has overhead valves, which are operated by twin camshafts, and is fitted with highly efficient lubricating arrangements for supplying cool oil to all necessary points. In this connection it is interesting to note that the two centre cooling elements of the radiator form part of the circulating system for the oil, and are used for cooling the lubricant. The engine is fed with petrol from a 200-gallon compartment in the main oil tank, the fuel being pumped to the carburetters by two Tecalemit pumps.

Probably the most notable feature of the vehicle is the fact that each of the eight wheels, which are arranged as two four-wheel bogies is independently mounted, and that the drive is by the four wheels of the front bogie. The frame on which the wheels are mounted resembles a backbone and runs practically the full length of the chassis, being composed of two deep channel section girders set back-to-back, about 1 ft. 7 in. apart. These are strongly braced with cast steel cross-members, and to the outer sides are attached brackets for the tank cradles, rear springs and wheel arms, and at the front there is a structure for the engine and cab.

In line with the rear-bogie cross-member, which is of box formation, there is a pair of brackets, which carry on pivots, the central mountings of a pair of inverted semi-elliptic springs, longitudinally arranged. The ends of the springs rest upon the rear-bogie wheel arms and provision is made for universal movement at the point of attachment.

The forward suspension system also comprises duplicated transverse underslung springs, a pair being used for the two leading wheels and a pair for the two second wheels. This suspension system permits a wheel articulation of over 18 in., and ensures that the minimum of vibration caused by rough ground is transmitted to the frame.

Each of the stub axles is provided with its own steering box, all the steering boxes being operated by a system of shafts and bevels from the steering column. As a result of this arrangement the vehicle can turn in a 60-ft. circle and can be steered with great precision and ease in all circumstances.

To provide for all emergencies the chassis is provided with two entirely independent braking systems. At the two ends of the propeller-shaft tube are contracting-band-type brakes, which are applied by means of a lever in the cab. The second system is operated by a pedal, which applies brakes on all the road wheels through a Westinghouse compressed air apparatus and fluid transmission.

Some Mountain Railways of Switzerland

The Engineer's Triumph over Nature

IN the earliest days of railways, before the hill climbing capacity of the steam locomotive had been proved, engineers generally proposed routes that would give them as level lines as possible. If an unduly steep incline, according to the standard of those days, could not be avoided at a certain point stationary engines and cable haulage were freely suggested. The latter method was indeed used to a certain extent, and it persisted even until 1908 on the 1 in 41/46 Cowlairs incline on the main line out of Glasgow of the former North British Railway. Not only was the ability of the locomotive to surmount inclines considered doubtful, but difficulty had been anticipated even in securing sufficient adhesion between a smooth wheel and a smooth rail to ensure the haulage of loads on the level. This accounted for Blenkinsop's adoption in 1812 of a rack rail and toothed wheels on the steam-operated line at Middleton Colliery near Leeds.

How amazed some of the early experimenters would be if they could see the incline railways now operated in different countries, and particularly those in Switzerland! In that wonderful country the skill of the engineer has enjoyed many triumphs, but the most amazing are probably those achieved in connection with the mountain railways. These rise to dizzy heights at almost impossible gradients yet they are worked with safety and efficiency. In addition to various local lines, which are notably steep in places, there are many railways specially built for the benefit of visitors to the "playground of Europe." It is interesting that on some of these rack-and-pinion systems are in use, a development, in a sense, of the early Blenkinsop arrangement. Electricity supplies the motive power for many of these lines, but steam is still in use also.

The first rack mountain railway in Europe was the Rigi line starting from Vitznau on the shores of Lake Lucerne. This was under construction from 1869 to 1871. It is steam-operated and has a length of 4.38 miles and a maximum gradient of 1 in 5. The rack is arranged centrally between the running rails, and this rack is traversed by a cog-wheel mounted beneath the locomotive and driven from the engine cylinders. As will be seen from the upper photograph reproduced on the opposite page the steepness of the gradients is such that the locomotives are built "on the slope" so that the boiler will be maintained in a horizontal position when on gradients. This form of construction gives the engines a very curious appearance when they are seen on the level. For ascending the incline the engine pushes the passenger vehicle, and in descending runs before it, a practice that is customary on mountain railways of this kind. The average speed of the train is about 5 m.p.h.

Remarkable views are obtained during the journey on this line, and from the summit. A curious illusion however that is borne on travellers making the journey for the first time is that, as the result of the inclination of the line and the special construction of the stock to allow for this, all objects observed from the train appear to be leaning at a dangerous angle! This is particularly marked on the downward trip.

A remarkable view on the electrically-operated Jungfrau mountain railway. This ascends to the highest railway station in Europe, 11,342 ft. above sea level.

After the establishment of the Vitznau-Rigi Railway numerous other mountain railway systems were constructed, one after the other. Of these the Arth-Rigi Railway up the other side of the mountain commenced in 1874. It is this railway, now electrically operated, that forms the subject of the cover illustration to this issue of the "*M.M.*" The starting point of this railway, Arth-Goldau, is a junction where important connections are made.

A remarkable system is that laid from Alpnachstad up Mount Pilatus. The maximum gradient of this is 1 in 2 and it climbs to a height of 6,791 ft. above sea level. Its construction was begun in 1886 and it was completed in 400 working days. Italian workmen, who built the road, frequently worked while suspended at the end of ropes. Even now the railway is carried at points on the narrowest of ledges, with little room to spare for the men engaged in permanent way maintenance. The permanent way is of very robust construction and the rails are secured to granite blocks cemented into the mountain side. The adoption of a special form of rack rail alone made possible the building of the line. The rack is double and is laid with its toothed projections horizontal. Thus the cogwheels on the trains are arranged horizontally also. A special design of steam-coach vehicle is employed on this railway, and in view of the extreme steepness of the gradients the boiler of the locomotive portion is arranged transversely across the vehicle, in order to secure a constant water level.

The mountain ascended by this line derives its name

from the legend that the uneasy spirit of Pontius Pilate was condemned to haunt its peaks. As he was believed to cause thunderstorms when disturbed, ascent of the mountain was forbidden by the Government of Lucerne in the 16th century!

The highest railway in Europe is that up the Jungfrau, which reaches an altitude of 11,342 ft. It commences at the Little Scheidegg, itself 6,770 ft. high, and climbs to the Eiger Glacier station, a distance of 1¼ miles chiefly in the open. For much of the rest of the way the line is in tunnel, which of course protects the line from avalanches. The difficulties of construction were considerable as may be imagined. After the route had been determined, dumps of supplies had to be set on convenient mountain ledges. In order to ensure the progress of the work throughout the year, special attention had to be given to the stores established at Eiger Glacier, which formed the base of operations for the work proceeding beyond that point, owing to the fact that communication between it and the lower points was rendered impossible by snow falls.

One of the steam locomotives of the Vitznau-Rigi rack railway. This is specially constructed, in order to keep the boiler horizontal and the cab vertical on the extremely steep gradients.

There are stations at Eigerwand and Eismeer, which also are part of the tunnel. At Eismeer giant "windows" are cut in one wall to afford a view. The upper terminus at Jungfraujoch is cut in solid rock and is the highest railway station in Europe. It is specially constructed to resist possible avalanches. This line is electrically operated, and numerous safety devices are in use. Automatic electric brakes are provided, but if the power current were to fail, current generated by the train running back would operate them.

A former steam-worked line, but now electrically operated, is that from Visp to Zermatt, a distance of 21¾ miles. This is interesting in that it is electrically operated with separate locomotives, and it forms a combined rack and adhesion system. Thus parts of the line are worked in the ordinary way by adhesion alone, and the maximum gradient here is 1 in 40. On the steepest sections, that are rack-operated, the maximum gradient is 1 in 8. Special attention has been given on this line to lightening the rolling stock. Welding is used extensively instead of riveting, and aluminium is employed wherever suitable.

The Matterhorn Peak and part of the Gornergrat Railway. This is an electric narrow gauge line operated on the rack system.

From Zermatt runs the Gornergrat Railway. This is an electric narrow gauge line worked on the rack system. Leaving Zermatt it crosses a notable cantilever structure over the Findelenbach gorge, and climbs to a height of 10,140 ft. above sea level, with a maximum gradient of 1 in 5. Except for a few short tunnels the line is in the open all the way, and it is claimed to be the highest open-air railway in Europe. This is a motor-coach line, each coach being of 250 h.p. Three-phase current at a pressure of 700 volts is used and is generated in a hydro-electric power station.

Although a mountain railway, the Rhaetian Railway has no rack-operated sections. It is, however, a steeply-graded system for an adhesion line and is electrically operated, although originally opened in 1889 from Landquart to Klosters for steam operation. Other sections were added from time to time until the whole scheme was completed in 1913. The high cost of operation by steam, owing to the fact that all coal had to be imported, had in the meantime brought about the decision to adopt electricity for the last section from Bevers to Schuls. The scarcity and high price of fuel during the War brought about the final electrification. First the steeper portions were tackled and then the various sections remaining were dealt with simultaneously. By 1922 the whole system had been converted to electric working.

A line, which in conjunction with the Visp-Zermatt and the Rhaetian Railways forms part of the route of the *"Glacier Express,"* that runs from St. Moritz to Zermatt, is the Furka-Oberalp Railway. This is a steam line operated partly by rack and partly by adhesion. The steepest gradient on the rack section is in the neighbourhood of 1 in 10. The rack is double, consisting of two toothed members laid side by side between the running rails. Superheated tank locomotives of the 2–6–0 type are used. On the adhesion sections of the line the engine is propelled by the outside cylinders driving on to the cranks of the ordinary driving wheels, and it then operates as a simple expansion engine. On the rack sections, however, compound or double-expansion working commences, for the rack pinions between the frames are connected to inside low-pressure cylinders.

Spirally-constructed inclines were freely adopted in setting out the line, and the Furka Tunnel, 2,138 yds. long, is at an altitude of 7,120 ft., and is approached each way by stretches of rack-operated line over which low speed is the rule.

The Story of the Banana

A Romance of Modern Business

MANY fascinating stories can be told about our everyday foods, and one of the most interesting of these concerns the banana. The use of this fruit as a food for man is older than written history, and it has journeyed far and in its travels has been linked up with many thrilling adventures.

The earliest home of the banana is believed to have been the moist tropical regions of Southern Asia. We know that in 327 B.C. the armies of Alexander the Great found it flourishing in India and no doubt it was growing there centuries before he conquered that country. Because of an old tradition that the sages of India reposed in the shade of the plant and refreshed themselves with its fruit, the banana was called Musa Sapientum, or fruit of the wise men.

The people of these ancient times found bananas so necessary that, when they went to make new homes in other lands, they carried dried roots along to be planted again. It is believed that in this manner the plant was taken from its original home to the eastern coast of Africa. From there it was probably carried westward across to the Guinea coast by the early Arabs, who were great traders. This journey across the Dark Continent no doubt took many, many years. When daring Portuguese explorers discovered the Guinea coast in 1482, they brought the plant and its African name "banana" to the Canary Islands, where they had established colonies.

Transporting bananas by light railway from the plantation to railhead for despatch to the port of shipment. For the illustrations to this article we are indebted to Elders and Fyffes Limited.

The next great step in the world journey of the banana was from these islands, off the coast of Africa, across the Atlantic to the New World. The Reverend Father Tomas de Berlanga, a Spanish priest, went as a missionary to the Island of Santo Domingo in 1516, a few years after the famous voyages of discovery by Columbus, and carried with him some banana roots from the Canary Islands. Other missionaries to the New World followed his example and planted bananas in order that there should be no lack of food. The result was that in course of time the plant spread from Santo Domingo to the other islands of the Caribbean Sea and to the tropical mainland. Thus the banana had to go more than half way round the world to reach Jamaica and Central America, where it is now most widely cultivated.

Bunches of bananas being loaded at railhead, where the light railways on the plantation converge.

After bananas came into general use in the Tropics it was many years before they were found in the markets of the Temperate Zone. The reason was that sailing ships were too slow and unreliable; specially constructed steamships were needed to bring this delicate, perishable fruit to the peoples of Europe.

Bananas were practically unknown in this country 40 years ago, except as a rare tropical luxury. How different to-day, when people in every part of the British Isles are able to secure at reasonable prices a regular supply of this delicious fruit the whole year round.

It is in Jamaica and in the low coastal regions of Central America that the tropical jungle, swarming with chattering monkeys and brilliantly coloured parrots, has given way to the greatest banana farms in the world. For 300 years after Columbus came these sunny lands of Central America were the seat of the great Spanish Empire in the New World and they are rich in stories of Spanish conquerors and of buccaneers. What a world of history centres around Panama, for instance. There, centuries ago, caravans toiled wearily through the dense tropical jungle laden with gold bound for Spain. Drake and other famous Elizabethans raided the Spanish possessions in the New World and later Henry Morgan, a brave but cruel pirate, led more than 1,000 men to the sack of the city of Panama.

Interesting as are the stories of adventures that happened long ago in the lands around the Caribbean Sea, to-day's happenings are quite as wonderful. Within the memory of living man the banana trade has developed from small beginnings into a great industry. It has been an important factor in the promotion of health and sanitation in these tropical countries, and has been responsible for the creation of railroads, steamships, air and radio communications. In fact, the history of the banana industry can be described with truth as one of the great romances of modern business.

Jamaica, one of Britain's oldest colonies, is only about half the size of Wales. It is so well cultivated, however, that it stands second in banana production, and in 1935 more than 20 million bunches, or close upon 2,500,000,000 bananas, were shipped from the island, most of them to England.

The banana plant grows in an unusual way. When fully grown and ready to bear fruit, it is from 15 ft. to 30 ft. high and measures from 9 in. to 16 in. in diameter at its base. It is therefore very often called a tree. It is not a tree, however, because there is no wood in it, for the trunk, or main stem, is composed of thick leaves wrapped tightly together in overlapping layers. The plant develops rapidly and the new leaf sheaths growing at the centre of the stalk push the older ones outward and so enlarge the trunk.

Each plant bears only a single bunch of bananas. After the fruit is harvested, the "tree" is cut down, when it quickly decays and enriches the soil. Several plants grow from the same mother root, or "mat," so that development of the bunches continues in steady rotation. The average annual banana production per acre is from 300 to 450 bunches, according to soil, climate, and the methods that are employed in the cultivation of the plant.

An astonishing variety of activities is necessary to establish banana production on a large scale. The first essential is that the jungle must be conquered. In creating a new plantation, the land has to be carefully chosen. It must be suitable for draining and fit for cultivation, and must be so located that the fruit to be produced can be conveyed by rail to a convenient port. There also must be a supply of labour on hand so that sufficient workers can be engaged. The site selected is surveyed and cleared of underbush, any heavy timber being left standing usually until after the planting. Drainage ditches are dug to carry off the water resulting from heavy rains, buildings are erected to shelter the workers and to house their supplies, and a hospital is built for the care of the sick. Railways are constructed to connect with the ports, and light, narrow railroads, called tramways are laid to link up the different parts of the plantation with the main line. Telephone lines are strung and a wharf is built. Much of this work must be done, or at least definitely planned, before the next step of planting is started.

At the port o. shipment the bananas are carried aboard by means of a conveyor belt system, as shown in this illustration.

When everything is ready, the cleared land is marked out so that the plants may be arranged in rows. Holes are dug about a foot deep and 14 ft. apart, and in each of them is put a piece of banana root, weighing three to four pounds. These "bits" are obtained by digging up roots of fully grown plants on other farms, and cutting them into proper sizes. Each "bit" that is planted must have one or more sprouts, or "eyes" like the eyes of a potato. Bananas can be planted in any month, which means that fruit is maturing constantly throughout the plantations.

Three or four weeks after the planting the first leaf appears above the ground and in the month that follows numerous shoots spring up from each of the "bits." The weak shoots are cut away and only the stronger allowed to grow whilst some "bits" of course fail to grow at all. When this is the case, the vacant spots in the plantation are filled by setting out young plants, called "sword-suckers," brought from the neighbouring farms, this practice being known as "supplying." In a large measure the progress of the plantation depends on the success attending the original planting.

Discharging the cargo of a banana ship. Conveyors are used and the bunches are transferred directly from the ship to waiting trucks.

Before the young plants appear above the ground, the large trees are felled and it will readily be imagined that at this stage the plantation resembles a heavy forest devastated and laid flat in a confused mass, rather than a banana farm in the making. To the uninitiated it might appear that the felling of the trees on the newly-planted ground would destroy the young plants, but this is not the case, as the latter grow up around the fallen logs, which rot away in a few years. As the enormous quantity of felled forest growth decays, it covers the ground like a mulch and actually creates the most favourable conditions for the growth of the banana plant.

The banana tree blossoms nine or ten months after planting. The stem that is to bear the bunch grows up through the centre of the stalk and comes out at its top. Then it bends over and down, the flower bud at its end looking like a big ear of corn in its husk. It is not long before these husks drop off, and the young bunch can then be seen with all its tiny bananas pointing downward. As they grow, their points gradually turn outward and upward, and remain in that position until the bananas are fully developed.

The first bunch is ready for harvesting from 13 to 15 months after the planting. It is made up of clusters called "hands," each with from 10 to 20 bananas or "fingers." A bunch normally carries six to nine hands, and its weight varies between 30 lb. and 65 lb. Sometimes a bunch is produced with as many as 20 hands, or more than 300 separate bananas, but this is rare.

Life on the plantation consists of much more than just planting and harvesting bananas, for there is a continual round of work to be done throughout the year. Weeds and other tropical growth quickly spring up and it is necessary to give the farm its first "cleaning" three months after planting. This process, which is an expensive one, is repeated about every three months so that weeds may not choke out the young banana plants.

Apart from such problems as the cleaning and keeping up of the plantations, there are plenty of everyday tasks to be done. For instance, the thousands of cattle, horses and mules on the various farms have to be fed and cared for. Buildings, roads and bridges have to be kept in repair and schools erected for the children of the plantation workers. Stores must be kept well supplied with a wide range of articles to meet the everyday needs of people who live in the tropics; and the big drainage ditches must always be kept in order so as to prevent heavy rainstorms from washing away roads and bridges, or damaging the tramways and the railways.

There may be a long spell of dry weather during which bananas will suffer from lack of moisture. Again a high wind, such as that experienced in Jamaica in September 1935, may blow down millions of plants heavy with fruit ready for harvesting. When disasters like these occur, months of work may be needed to put the plantations in working order once again.

Even when the fruit is to be eaten in the tropics, it is not allowed to ripen on the plant. If it does, it is likely to burst open, attract insects, and acquire rather an unpleasant taste. The finest flavour is developed only when the fruit is cut green from the plant and ripened afterwards; bananas therefore are harvested in a green condition. Great care is necessary in choosing the proper grade of fruit to be cut, for if too thin the bananas are not mature, whilst if too full they are liable to bruise before reaching the English market.

The "cutting gang" begins work at daylight on the day of a steamer's arrival in port. Each unit consists of a cutter, a backer and a mule man. A cutter, using a knife on the end of a long pole, cuts the plant a few feet below the bunch. As the plant bends, he steadies it with his pole so that the bunch may swing down easily and come to rest on the shoulder of the backer, who is waiting to receive it. Then the cutter with a long sword-like knife called a machette chops the bunch from the stalk and the backer carries it to the nearest road or tramway, where it is loaded either on to a pack mule or on to one of the little tramcars that run to almost every part of the plantation. The fruit then is carried to the main railroad, where the bunches are transferred to waiting trucks under the watchful eyes of the inspectors, who reject any that are imperfect.

Banana farming calls for a lot of intricate work, but the greatest problem of the industry perhaps is the need for getting the fruit quickly from the plantations across 5,000 miles of ocean to the ripening rooms of the wholesale fruit merchants at various centres throughout the British Isles.

When a wireless message is received at a tropical loading port such as Kingston, Jamaica, stating that a certain ship will be ready to take 100,000 bunches of bananas on a particular day, the men in charge know which farms are ready to supply the fruit. All the cutting orders are given well in advance, and the foreman of each farm knows just how many bunches he is expected to contribute to that particular cargo. As bananas are so perishable it is important to have the fruit available at the tropical port immediately the ship is ready to load.

Upon reaching the wharf, the banana train is moved into position alongside the steamer and a gang of labourers transfer the fruit expeditiously to the loading machines or conveyors, which consist of an endless chain of canvas pockets. They carry the bunches one by one over the side of the ship and into the holds below, where experienced workers carefully stow them. All this is performed under the closest inspection and any damaged bananas are not allowed to be shipped. A cargo of 100,000 bunches can be put aboard in about 18 hrs.

Cutting up bunches of bananas into "hands" and packing these into boxes for delivery to retail shops.

Bunches of bananas are not packed for shipment; they travel exactly as they are harvested in the tropics. The holds of all banana-carrying steamers are divided into several "decks," each partitioned into a number of compartments or "bins" of convenient size in which the fruit is stacked. These bins, which are constructed of wooden bars, similar to the "old farm gate," keep the bunches from shifting and becoming bruised in transit, and so ensure that the fruit will reach Great Britain in good condition.

At an early stage of the investigation into the transport of bananas across this 5,000 mile stretch of ocean, it was found that if the holds of the banana ships could be kept from getting too hot or too cold, and if they could be supplied with plenty of fresh air, the fruit could be carried in good condition at all times of the year. In the early days ventilators kept fresh air flowing through the holds of the ship, but modern vessels engaged in the trade have wonderful machinery, specially planned, to take care of their cargoes. Great refrigerating machines cool the holds before the fruit is loaded, and all the time during the voyage home they keep the air around the bananas at exactly the right temperature. Big fans keep cooled, fresh air circulating all the time around the fruit, and every few hours, day and night throughout the voyage, visits are paid to the holds of the ship to see that both air and temperature are as they should be. The refrigerating machines have to be very powerful, as bananas are not only fairly warm when loaded but actually give out heat during the voyage.

A banana train of 40 trucks leaving a junction on the way to the port from which the fruit is shipped.

It will be seen that the departure of a steamer for this country is by no means a signal for relaxed attention in the care of the fruit, which must be landed on this side in the same green condition as when it was harvested. Immediately upon the arrival of the steamer at the home port the quays are cleared and railway trucks are marshalled, for more than 500 specially constructed banana vans are needed to transport a full cargo by rail. Within a few minutes the fruit is being discharged from electrically-operated elevators to conveyors, and so into the trucks at the rate of no less than 8,000 bunches per hour; and fast trains leave with these banana vans for all towns in Great Britain. Upon arrival at the warehouses of the wholesale fruiterers the bananas are hung in specially constructed ripening rooms that reproduce tropical conditions exactly. The fruit is carefully ripened for five to six days, cut up into "hands," labelled with the familiar "Blue Label" and distributed to the retail shop. At every stage of their journey from the tropics to the table care is exercised to see that the bananas reach the consumer perfect in condition and mellow in flavour.

Bananas are sealed by nature in a glove-like, germ-proof skin that keeps out all dust and dirt. This makes them one of the safest, freshest and cleanest foods to eat. Like other fresh fruits, bananas should be eaten when they are fully ripe. When they are green, they contain a large percentage of starch, like an uncooked potato. During the process of ripening the starch is changed into fruit sugar, or natural glucose, which can be assimilated by the most delicate digestion. The extraordinary value to health of glucose, and the remarkable rapidity—only a matter of seconds—with which it supplies the human system with energy, are nowadays fully appreciated.

The impression still lingering in some minds that the banana is an indigestible fruit is quite fallacious. Although it is true that the banana, just like the apple, the pear, or the melon, is indigestible in its unripe form, when it is allowed to ripen, it is not only very digestible, but one of the most quickly and easily digested of all fruits. Indeed, a ripe banana, mashed and sieved, is one of the first solid foods nowadays given to infants by many doctors.

It is well to remember that yellow bananas with green tips are not yet ripe. The skin turns to a bright yellow in ripening, and all the green fades away, even from the tips. In another day or two brown spots appear on the golden-yellow peel and the pulp becomes softer and more mellow. At this stage, bananas are fully ripe. The fruit is then sugary sweet and the flavour is at its best. In this state they are fully digested in $1\frac{3}{4}$ hrs. as compared with $2\frac{1}{4}$ hrs. for apples, $2\frac{3}{4}$ hrs. for oranges, $3\frac{1}{2}$ hrs. for boiled potatoes, and $3\frac{3}{4}$ hrs. for plums.

The banana is one of the fruits that ripen after plucking, so that it is by no means necessary that bananas shall be fully ripe when they are purchased in the shops. They need only be kept in the home for a day or two for all trace of green to disappear from the skin, and thus indicate that the fruit inside is ripe and perfectly digestible.

Many people prefer to let the banana ripen still further until the outer skin begins to turn brown. In this condition the flavour of the pulp inside has developed to its highest delicacy and greater digestibility. It is wrong to put bananas not yet ripe into a cool place—a mistake that many people make—because a cold atmosphere keeps them from ripening properly and impairs their fine, natural flavour.

A Spanish friar travelling in the West Indies soon after the discovery of those islands hazarded the guess that the banana plant was the tree of life. In one way his suggestion was a good one. The banana is richer in proteins, or tissue-forming foods, in fat and in carbohydrates, which produce heat and muscle energy, than either the apple or the orange, and in addition to glucose and other beneficial constituents it contains the vitamins and mineral salts needed to protect our health and to build strong bones and teeth. It is therefore a protective food, and a ripe banana, which contains a large proportion of carbohydrates, and a glass of milk, rich in proteins, together make an ideally balanced ration. Bananas for the most part are just peeled and eaten in the simplest way, and that is why they are liked and used so much for picnics and on motor or train trips.

We are indebted to Elders and Fyffes Ltd. for the information given in this article.

HOLIDAYS AND THE CAMERA

AT this time of the year cameras of all kinds, new and old, make their appearance in surprising numbers. It is almost certain that more photographs are taken between June and September than during the remaining eight months of the year put together. This is the great holiday period, and no holiday is really complete without a camera. The range of possibilities within reach of even a novice with the cheapest form of camera is almost unlimited. The owner of a camera is able to bring home at the end of a holiday a record that is not only permanent, but actually grows in interest as time goes on. Without such a photographic record the memories of even the most enjoyable and interesting holiday become dimmer and dimmer, and finally fade away.

Those who possess cameras that have been laid by for some time should make sure that these are in good working order before they take them away on a holiday. Nothing is more irritating and disappointing to the amateur than to take a series of holiday snapshots and then find, when it is too late, that they are all spoiled because the camera was not light-tight, or the shutter was not working properly. The best plan is to expose a film and have it developed and printed. Then any defect in the camera is easily seen, and can be quickly remedied.

Cameras and photographic materials of all kinds are now so reliable and simple to use that no one should have any difficulty in securing a good series of holiday records. The failures that occur are almost always due to attempting impossibilities. The most important point to remember is that successful snapshots require a reasonably good light. It is little use to attempt them late in the evening, or during the day when the sky is overcast with dark clouds. The best advice that can be given to a beginner is to spend 1/6 on the "Wellcome" Photographic Handbook. This contains an exposure calculator that makes it the simplest possible matter to ascertain quickly whether the conditions at any moment are suitable for snapshots. In addition to the calculator the handbook is full of useful and interesting advice on almost every branch of photography, both indoors and outdoors.

Another thing that the beginner in photography must always bear in mind is that close-up photographs of rapidly moving objects cannot be taken with the average cheap camera. The fastest shutter speed of such a camera is generally about 1/25 or 1/30 of a second, and this is far too slow for any rapid movement at close quarters. Fairly good snapshots of objects moving at only a moderate speed may be secured with such shutters if the photographer stands well away from the object. Of course the resulting pictures will be very small, but they should be sufficiently sharp to allow of considerable enlargement.

A fine photograph of a dog family. This illustrates how it is possible, by careful arrangement of lighting, to suggest the actual texture of the animals' coats. For this photograph and the one below we are indebted to the courtesy of Ilford Ltd.

Many cheap cameras are of what is known as the "fixed focus" type; that is to say they are not provided with any means of focussing objects at different distances. Such cameras are perfectly successful for general views of any kind, but they cannot be used for near subjects such as head-and-shoulder portraits. This difficulty is overcome by placing in front of the lens what is known as a "portrait attachment," which automatically brings into sharp focus objects that are only three or four feet away from the camera. Such attachments, which consist of a lens mounted so that it can be slipped over the regular lens, may be obtained cheaply for most small cameras.

The majority of cheap cameras are provided with a "view finder" to show the extent of the picture that will appear on the film. This finder usually consists of a tiny lens that throws on to a mirror a miniature reproduction of the view. This type of finder is not absolutely accurate, and if a certain object that it is desired to include in the photograph is seen to come close up to the edge of the finder image, it is not safe to assume that this will appear as it is wanted on the film. In such a case it is best to move slightly further away, so as to bring the object more into the centre of the finder image and thus allow for a margin of error. The camera should be held so that the eye looks directly down on to the finder mirror.

Yachting scenes provide splendid material for snapshots.

In making the exposure the camera must be held quite steady. To the average person it is practically impossible to do this for more than about 1/15 of a second; and if a longer exposure is necessary the camera must be placed on a tripod, or on a convenient wall, fence or other solid support. Another important point is to press the shutter release gently and steadily in order to avoid jerking the camera at the moment of exposure.

Air Liners at Croydon

Visitors to Croydon Airport always find much to interest them, and one of the most fascinating sights is the departure of a large Imperial Airways or foreign air liner employed on one of the many regular air services. The photographs on this page were taken by an *"M.M."* reader, F. H. Done, of Northwich, during a recent visit to Croydon. They illustrate successive stages in the departure of *"Horatius,"* one of Imperial Airways aircraft working on the company's European services.

Before each flight an Imperial Airways air liner is completely overhauled, the engines are tuned up and the petrol tanks refilled. An industrious little tractor then tows the aeroplane tail first from its position outside the hangars back to the embarking area. The towing of an air liner with such a large wing span as the *Horatius"* has to be done slowly. Leaving *"Horatius"* standing in front of the airport booking offices, the tractor hurries away to attend to some other machine. The forward part of the great air liner is high above the ground, and a gangway is therefore fixed in position to give access to the cockpit. The passengers enter the long, luxuriously furnished cabin through a doorway in the rear portion of the fuselage and close to the ground; and at the same time the mails are loaded into one of the freight compartments.

Shortly afterwards the assistant pilot ascends the gangway to the cockpit, and starts the engines so that they will be already "warmed up" when the moment comes to take off. As the scheduled time for departure draws near the crew stand by the machine. Periodically the pilot glances at his watch, and eventually he climbs the gangway, the other members of the crew follow, the cockpit door is closed and the ground staff wheel away the gangway. The "right away" signal is given by an airport officer, and with a roar the engines spring into life, the wings vibrating under the strain. A last hand wave to the ground staff, the ensign is drawn in and the air liner moves slowly forward. Wheeling round to the right so as to be facing the wind it taxies across the landing ground with rapidly increasing speed, and after a take-off run that seems amazingly short for such a huge machine, it rises into the air and soon disappears from view in the direction of France.

Good Service by Bristol "Bulldogs"

The 12 Bristol "Bulldog" single-seater fighters bought by the Esthonian Government in 1931 are still in service, and although each has made more than 1,000 landings, the only repairs of any consequence that have been necessary were to two machines that were damaged through bad landings. One of them had to be fitted with a new tail-end to the fuselage, and the other with a new airscrew and axle.

Operating conditions in Esthonia are difficult, for there are many wide stretches of comparatively wild country in which a forced landing would be both unpleasant and dangerous. The climatic conditions are also severe, and the snow-bound country in winter makes it necessary to fit skis to the undercarriages of the "Bulldogs."

The departure of Imperial Airways' air liner "Horatius" from Croydon. The photographs (from top to bottom) show respectively, a general view of the air liner; the crew going aboard; the "Right Away" signal being given, and "Horatius" moving off.

Speeding up U.S. Air Freight Traffic

Pan-American Airways and about 20 other air line organisations in America have joined forces in a unified air express system which has made possible important accelerations in the transport of urgent freight. These air interests have also arranged with certain ground service organisations for an express door-to-door pick-up and delivery service, and as a result the movement of loads between cities and aerodromes has been greatly speeded up. The new system provides an improved air express service to more than 200 cities in the United States and Canada.

More "Singapore IIIs" for R.A.F.

The aircraft equipment of No. 205 (Flying Boat) Squadron, stationed at Singapore, is to be increased by the addition of two more Short "Singapore III" flying boats. This Squadron was supplied with four of this type of aircraft last year.

Summer Internal Air Services

The steady development of internal air services in Great Britain is reflected in the additional services and extensions to existing ones that are being put into operation this summer. Railway Air Services, for instance, are operating 62 regular air services, with a total route mileage of just over 1,000,000. Last year 42 daily services were operated by this company, the route mileage then amounting to about 600,000.

In addition to their Royal Mail service between London, Birmingham, Liverpool, Stoke-on-Trent, Belfast and Glasgow, and a service between Belfast and the Isle of Man, R.A.S. are running an afternoon service from Manchester and Liverpool to Belfast, serving Northern Ireland, which is also linked by air with Glasgow by two services daily. Possibilities of a further Scottish air service, to link Glasgow with Perth and Inverness, are being investigated.

The North to South service starts from Barton Airport, Manchester, and terminates at Brighton Airport, as last year. The aeroplanes call at Liverpool, Birmingham, Bristol, Southampton and Ryde, Isle of Wight, on the way. There are two flights daily in each direction, one in the morning and the other in the afternoon, and the total time for the full journey, including stops, is 2 hr. 35 min. Ryde is the terminus of services from Cowes, Portsmouth, Gatwick and Brighton. In the other direction Gatwick is used as the London terminus airport of the Isle of Wight services, being connected with Victoria station by fast Southern electric train services.

Highland Airways are operating their

Aberdeen-Kirkwall air service again this summer, and by the time these notes appear in print they will probably have extended it to Shetland. The opening of this further section only awaits the completion of the wireless station at Sumburgh, Shetland. The extended service will be flown on Mondays, Wednesdays and Fridays until the end of this month, the flights terminating at Kirkwall on other days. A daily service over the whole route will be flown during July and August, the peak months of the summer air traffic.

One of the Fokker F.XXIIs owned by Royal Dutch Airlines, more familiarly known as the K.L.M. It is a four-engined machine with seating for 22 passengers. Photograph by courtesy of N. V. Nederlandsche Vliegtuigenfabriek, Amsterdam.

"Finishing" School for Imperial Airways Pilots

The giant flying boats and monoplanes now being built for the Empire services of Imperial Airways will, when in operation, be flying night and day. Not only will crews have to be provided for these machines, but the men who handle them will require to be both skilled pilots and experienced in navigation and wireless. It will also be necessary for them to be qualified in such matters as ground engineering and the maintenance and overhaul of the aircraft.

Imperial Airways have therefore started a "finishing" school close to the Croydon Airport. This school is being attended by 70 men who are already qualified pilots and hold official licences as commercial airmen, and have spent long periods in the air. The pilots leave their classrooms at various stages of their tuition and carry out practical experiments in wireless in special test rooms. They also go over to the big repair sheds at the airport, so as to learn at first-hand of airway engineering in its everyday aspects. Another interesting branch of the tuition made necessary by the big expansion scheme lies in training landplane pilots to handle big flying boats. This is being done at Hamble, near Southampton, where triple-engined "Calcutta" flying boats are being used for instruction purposes.

It probably takes a pilot 12 to 15 months to pass through all the various classes of the finishing school. Then, when he has absorbed all this specialised instruction, he is not only an expert in flying and controlling modern air liners, but he has gained a grasp of navigation that includes meteorology, wireless, and airway engineering that will prove invaluable to him in his routine work on the Imperial air routes.

D.H. "Dragon Rapides" for Abroad

The high standard of de Havilland aircraft continues to be appreciated abroad. The Imperial Iranian War Ministry recently ordered three D.H. "Dragon Rapides," each seating five passengers, for use on several internal air lines one termini of which will be Teheran; and Aeroput, the Yugoslavian air transport company, have ordered a similar machine, the cabin of which will be arranged to seat eight passengers. The Adelaide Steamship Company have acquired two "Dragon Rapides" of the eight-seater type, and they will be employed by the subsidiary company, Adelaide Airways, on internal air services.

More D.H. "Dragon Rapides" are also to be employed on British internal air services this summer, and six machines of this type have been bought by Railway Air Services, who have also purchased two D.H. 86A Express Air Liners. When the new aeroplanes are in service they will bring the company's fleet up to a total of 18 machines.

The cockpit of a Douglas D.C.2 "Transport" Monoplane, showing the dual control equipment, including the two pairs of foot pedals for operating the rudder bar. Photo. by A. J. Kouyoumjian, Baghdad.

Soviet Air Force Progress

The number of military air pilots trained in Russia last year was 3,500, and a further 8,000 will be trained during 1936. The great importance attached by the military authorities to gliding is shown by the fact that by the end of last year 52,000 men had learned to glide. At one recent demonstration five gliders were towed by a military aeroplane to a height of 10,300 ft. and were then cast off. They landed safely at an aerodrome where, very appropriately, a glider rally was being held.

Reports of the present strength of the Soviet Air Force are conflicting. Apparently the total number of military aircraft in service is just over 3,000, of which about 1,000 are observation aeroplanes, 1,000 are pursuit aeroplanes, 700 are bombing aircraft and the remainder are fighters of various types.

The Growth of Empire Air Services

In 1932 the route mileage of the Imperial air routes was only 8,320. To-day the mileage of the air routes operated by Imperial Airways and its associated companies totals approximately 26,000, and when all the new Empire services are in operation this figure will be increased to just over 40,000. At the present time the aircraft of Imperial Airways are flying an average of 17,000 miles a day.

Hard-Working Aero Engine Pistons

Strange as it may appear, it is nevertheless a fact that during a flight from Brisbane to Singapore the pistons in the four engines of a Qantas Empire Airways D.H.86 air liner travel a considerably greater distance than the 4,361 miles that separate those two cities!

Readers who are mathematically inclined can easily verify this statement, from the following details. The stroke of the piston is 5.512 in. During each revolution the piston moves once up and once down the cylinder, a total distance of 11.024 in. The four engines each have six cylinders, and the normal revolutions in flight are 1,900 per min. During one minute of flight the 24 pistons therefore travel a total distance of 502,694.4 in., or, to simplify the solution, a distance of 41,891.2 ft. The average flying time for Qantas air liners between Brisbane and Singapore is 33 hr., or 1,980 min. By multiplying 41,891.2 by 1,980 we arrive at 82,944,180 ft., which is the distance travelled by the pistons of the four engines of a Qantas air liner flying from Brisbane to Singapore. In other words, the pistons travel 15,709 miles 352 yd., while the air liner travels 4,361 miles.

New Junkers Machines for South Africa

The South African Railways and Harbours Board have ordered three 10-seater high-speed air liners from the Junkers Company, of Germany. The aeroplanes will have a cruising speed of 215 m.p.h. at 6,100 ft. and when fully loaded will have a range of 655 miles. They will be used by South African Airways, a branch of S.A.R.H., on internal air routes.

The Eyes of the Navy

How a Modern Aircraft Carrier Operates

By B. S. Davies

AIRCRAFT used by the Navy can be classed under three main headings, namely, reconnaissance machines, fighters and torpedo-bombers. Whatever duty the machines themselves are designed to carry out, however, the operations in the carrier for flying off and alighting, or "landing on" are the same. The important point to remember is that with very few exceptions, all the aircraft used in carriers are land machines, that is to say, they are fitted with wheels, not floats. The flying deck of a carrier therefore is nothing more than a miniature aerodrome.

An airman's view of the aircraft carrier. The vessel shown is H.M.S. "Furious," which has specially fitted internal funnels to take smoke clear of the landing deck.

Compared with aerodromes ashore, the space in which machines have to land is very small indeed, and for this reason all the aircraft are designed to have a slow landing speed. Conversely, when flying off, they must be able to take off quickly and easily. Furthermore, all Fleet Air Arm pilots undergo special "deck-landing" training, for it must be remembered that they have to land on the deck of a ship that is moving through the water.

What then, is required of the carrier?

To start with, she must be able to steam at high speeds and maintain them for a considerable period; next, she must be capable of accommodating a large number of machines and have workshops for dealing with any type of repair; finally, she must have sufficient stowage for large quantities of petrol. Above all, we must not forget that she is a warship, and therefore must be armed with guns of suitable calibre.

A machine taking off from the deck of an aircraft carrier.

All the large aircraft carriers in use in the Navy, with one exception, are built with the bridge, funnels, mast and other parts of the superstructure on the starboard side, well clear of the flying deck. Immediately below the flying deck is an enormous hangar, and below that again is another hangar.

Machines are stowed with their wings folded back along the fuselage, and are transported from the hangars to the flying deck by means of huge lifts, situated at the ends of the hangars. These lifts are nothing more than large flat platforms made of steel, and are capable of accommodating one machine at a time with wings spread. Square holes of the exact size and shape of the lifts are cut in the upper hangar deck and flying deck, so that when flying is in progress, the lifts are left up and become one with the flying deck itself. At the fore end of the flying deck is a huge perforated steel wind screen. This is actually hinged to the deck, and is raised and lowered by machinery. It is used to protect machines on the flying deck when a high wind is blowing, or when the ship is steaming at high speeds. Round the edge of the flying deck, large steel meshed nets project to a distance of about 8 ft. as a precaution against machines over-running the deck and plunging overboard.

The upper illustration on this page shows H.M.S. *"Furious"* from the air. This vessel was designed to present an entirely unobstructed deck to the pilot. Special arrangements therefore had to be made to carry off the smoke and exhaust gases from the boilers, since the ship is driven by steam turbines and oil-fired boilers. These consisted of fitting internal fore and aft funnels, situated on each side below the flying deck, and the exhaust fumes from the boilers escape through the two large openings in the after end of the flying deck.

This is quite a satisfactory method for normal cruising, but when flying operations take place, it is essential not only that pilots shall have a clear view of the deck as they approach, but that the stability of the machines shall in no way be upset when flying at comparatively low speeds by passing through a mixture of smoke, hot gases and air prior to landing on. In order to overcome this, the passage of the exhaust gases is deflected, and instead of escaping through the openings in the flying deck, they are forced down and out of two other openings just below, in the ship's side. One of these can be seen in the photograph; the other of course is on the opposite side of the ship.

The bridge is situated at the fore end and on the starboard side of the flying deck, so that a machine has an entirely open but limited space on which to land.

This does not mean that the carrier with orthodox funnels and masts presents an obstructed deck. The contrary is the case, and many pilots prefer to land on this type of carrier rather than on the other, as the high superstructure helps them to judge height and distance as they overtake the carrier and descend to the flying deck.

Before a machine flies off or lands on, the carrier is turned into the wind, and it is the duty of the officer on watch to give the necessary orders to the helmsman to keep her dead into the wind. A very simple device is fitted to assist him. Right forward in the bows of the ship, a white line is painted on the deck in the exact fore and aft line of the ship. In front of it is a small steam jet, and as long as the feather of steam issuing from it blows along the white line, the ship is dead in the wind.

Having turned her into the wind, the next important point is to have the ship moving at the correct speed, whether a machine is going to fly off or land on. So let us see what happens from the time a machine leaves the hangar, flies off, lands on, and finally returns to the hangar again.

As soon as the pilot gets his orders, he climbs into his machine and starts up his engine for warming through. The lift is lowered and the machine wheeled on to it; the lift then ascends to the flying deck, during which time the machine's wings are spread. Meanwhile, up on the flying deck, the wind screen has been raised in order to protect the machine as she appears. When the lift reaches the level of the flying deck, it is locked in place, and the machine is pushed into a convenient position for flying off. This position depends on the strength of the wind, for if the wind is light the machine may require a long run; on the other hand, if the wind is strong, a short run will suffice. Let us assume that there is a steady breeze of 30 m.p.h., and that this particular aircraft has a flying speed of 70 m.p.h.

Alighting on deck. The members of the flight deck party are rushing out to seize the machine as she comes to a standstill.

The pilot now runs his engine up to see that everything is in order, while a party of men, known as the flight deck party, hold the machine. If satisfied, he closes his throttle and awaits the signal to fly off from the officer in charge of the flying deck.

Meanwhile, in response to orders from the bridge, the speed of the ship is increased, until she is travelling fast enough against the wind to enable the aircraft to take off without difficulty. Let us assume that a speed of 20 knots is sufficient.

The wind screen is now lowered, and immediately a wind of about 50 m.p.h. sweeps along the flying deck, for the speed of the wind made by the ship steaming at 20 knots is added to the 30 m.p.h. of the steady breeze.

The speed of this "resultant" wind is registered by an anemometer on the bridge, and by glancing at the dial the senior officer in charge of flying operations can see what the wind speed is at any moment. It is he who informs the Captain of the ship when the ship is moving at the correct speed. As soon as this is attained the Captain indicates to the officer in charge of the flying deck that the machine may fly off. This officer then signals to the pilot, and the men who have been standing by the machine move away as the pilot opens his throttle and the machine rushes along the deck. After a comparatively short run the machine reaches her flying speed and rises, and when she is safely in the air the speed of the carrier is reduced and her former course resumed.

The same procedure is gone through when the aircraft lands on again. The carrier is first turned into the wind and speed is increased until a wind with the necessary speed sweeps along the flying deck. Then a signal is displayed to indicate to the pilot that he may land on. Immediately he circles round and approaches from well astern, getting lower and lower until the machine skims over the after end of the flying deck, losing height and speed. As soon as the wheels touch the deck, she quickly loses speed and comes to a standstill, whereupon the wind screen is raised and the flight deck party rush out and seize her. Without delay, she is wheeled on to the lift, which disappears from sight as it descends to the hangar.

So much for the actual operation of flying off and landing on. When flying takes place, however, the air personnel are not the only members of the ship's company who are affected. In the engine and boiler rooms, everybody is on the alert, especially if the wind is fitful, for in such conditions the ship might be called upon for sudden high increases of speed. Calls of this description require prompt action in the boiler rooms; additional oil-sprayers must instantly be turned on so that more steam can be generated for the turbines. On the other hand, a machine might have an accident that necessitates the carrier stopping at once. Such orders demand high skill and prompt action, for the men below are dealing with engines and boilers developing something like 90,000 h.p.

Elsewhere in the ship, organised activity is manifest; men are standing by boats in case of accidents to machines; cranes, with which every carrier is equipped, are got ready for instant use; the medical staff with first aid equipment stand by. In fact, there is not a single department in the vast organisation of the ship that is not affected in some way or other.

When flying operations on a large scale are in progress, many machines are flown off. In these circumstances, all the machines required are ranged on the flying deck in the order of flying off. Then, as soon as flying commences, they follow one another in quick succession. As each machine leaves the carrier, the time is noted, for should a machine fail to return within a given period, a far-reaching organisation is put into force to carry out a search.

When the time arrives to land on a large number of machines, then the real efficiency of the pilots and ship's staff becomes evident. One after the other, the aircraft land on in quick succession and vanish from sight as they descend by lift to the hangars, for only one machine can be dealt with at a time. But it is surprising with what speed all this is accomplished, and typical of the skill of this highly efficient branch of the Navy.

H.M.S. "Eagle," an aircraft carrier in which the funnels, masts and superstructure are erected on the starboard side in order to leave a clear landing space for aircraft.

The number of men on board an aircraft carrier varies, but the normal crew of the *"Eagle"* is 750 naval officers and men, in addition to 250 officers and men of the Fleet Air Arm. Great care has to be taken of the aeroplanes used, and each machine has at least two men whose sole duty is to look after it. For instance, a single seater aeroplane is in charge of two R.A.F. airmen, a fitter and a rigger; and a machine fitted with wireless also has a Telegraphist Air Gunner, who is a naval rating and accompanies the pilot and the observer on their flights, in addition to being responsible for keeping the wireless apparatus in repair. A handling crew always deals with the same squadron and usually consists of about 10 naval ratings.

Speedy Work with *"The Irish Mail"*

Now that the principal Scottish expresses are hauled by "Princess Royal" class 4–6–2s, the hardest daily task undertaken by the "Royal Scots" is the working of *"The Irish Mail"* between Euston and Holyhead. On a recent journey with this train, No. 6120, *"Royal Inniskilling Fusilier,"* ably handled by Driver H. Jones of Holyhead, made some splendid running with a gross load of 460 tons. The 65.1 miles from Watford to Rugby were covered at an average speed of exactly 60 m.p.h. start to stop, the 48.6 miles from Tring to Hillmorton being run at 67 m.p.h., with a maximum of 78 m.p.h. Continuing from Rugby, Stafford, 51 miles, was passed in the remarkable time of 50½ min. and Crewe, 75.5 miles, was reached 5 min. early in 78 min. from Rugby. With a reduced load of 390 tons the 21.1 miles to Chester were run in 24½ min. a top speed of 69 m.p.h. being reached at Beeston Castle.

For the last stage of the journey the load was made up to as much as 514 tons tare and 540 tons full. By dint of magnificent locomotive work, the 84.6 miles from Chester to Holyhead were covered in 94¾ min.—1¼ min. under schedule—despite three permanent way slowings. The fastest running was made across Anglesey where speed rose to 73 m.p.h. at Bodorgan; in all, 15½ min. were gained on schedule on this remarkable trip.

Another very fast run was that made recently by one of Mr. Stanier's remarkably versatile 4-6-0 engines of class "5P5F" on the 4.40 p.m. up Sunday Scottish express from Crewe to Euston. No. 5028 was the engine, hauling a gross load of 380 tons. After a fine climb to Whitmore, speed rose to no less than 79½ m.p.h. on the descent to Stafford on a gradient as slight as 1 in 650, but on account of signal checks the 24½ miles from Crewe to Stafford took 35½ min.

After passing Rugeley there came some magnificent running, with an average of 66 m.p.h. from Lichfield to Rugby and maximum speeds of 75 m.p.h. at both Hademore troughs and Brinklow. Thus Rugby was passed in a net time of 74½ min. from Crewe, 75½ miles, that is in only 1½ min. more than the schedule of the up *"Liverpool Flyer,"* and with a mixed traffic engine!

After further good work south of Rugby, Euston was reached in a net time of 159½ min. for the 158.1 miles from Crewe, a gain of 10½ min. on schedule. On this last stage the highest speeds were 75 at Weedon, 76½ at Kings Langley, and 74 at North Wembley. Alcock, of Crewe shed, was the driver. These runs were recorded by Mr. O. S. Nock.

An interesting example of joint operation. An Oxford to York through train composed of G.W.R. stock and operated by an L.N.E.R. (G.C. section) 4-4-2 locomotive is shown in our photograph, which was taken at East Leake, and is reproduced by courtesy of the L.N.E.R.

G.W.R. Streamlined Parcels Rail Car

A new streamlined rail car specially built for parcels service has been brought into use by the G.W.R. This operates between London and local stations to Reading and Oxford. The car is similar in design to the streamlined passenger rail cars already in service, but instead of the windows of these cars it has three glass-panelled doors on each side to facilitate rapid loading and unloading. A series of racks is provided inside for the accommodation of parcels. The car is driven by two heavy-oil engines of 130 h.p. each, and is capable of speeds of 70 to 75 m.p.h. With the introduction of this rapid means of parcels conveyance it is hoped to avoid the delays that are sometimes suffered by ordinary passenger trains at stations where parcels traffic is dealt with.

"Right-Away," by Rail and Sea

Mr. Hugh Morgan, who has recently retired from the position of L.M.S.R. Station Master and Goods Agent at Holyhead after over 40 years' service, is one of the few railway officials who has ordered the departure of steamers as well as trains. For more than 23 years, Mr. Morgan has seen the "right-away" given to the Irish Mail trains and also to the Royal Mail steamers sailing from Holyhead. During the War, he was Night Station Master at Holyhead, and in this period nearly 3,000,000 troops passed through the port on their way to and from Ireland. At times of crisis, Mr. Morgan's name on the labels of reserved compartments or in the reserving of steamer accommodation afforded a valuable "alias" to prominent political or military personages whose travels were intended to be kept secret. In recognition of his services at Holyhead during the War he was awarded the diploma of the Lords Commissioners of the Admiralty.

A native of Liverpool, Mr. Morgan hails from a seafaring family and as a boy was employed with two Liverpool shipping firms. In 1895, however, he entered the railway service as a porter at Alexandra Docks, Liverpool, and rose through successive grades to the position from which he has now retired.

Clothing the L.M.S.R. Staff

To clothe its employees, the L.M.S.R. use 750 miles of British-manufactured cloth which, if stretched in a single line, would extend further than from London to Wick. The requirements are of a varied character, and include garments for station and yard staff, enginemen, permanent way men, guards, signalmen, messengers, carters, police, hotel and restaurant car staff and the crews of steamers. The height of the tallest man in the service of the Company is 6 ft. 8 in., and that of the smallest 4 ft. 3 in. Engine drivers possess the finest physique, with an average chest measurement of 50 in., but honours for height are carried off by the passenger guards.

G.W.R. Record Summer Service

The G.W.R. have introduced numerous additional expresses for earlier holiday-makers in May and June and the daily daylight service to the Channel Islands will operate from 8th June with a connecting boat train that will leave Paddington at 8.30 a.m. The full Summer Service will operate from 6th July to 27th September.

The number of trains to be run daily will be 6,540, covering a daily mileage of 126,790. Both these figures are G.W.R. records.

Streamlined rail cars will be operating over a further 2,104 miles daily as compared with last summer, and there will be expresses covering 1,667 miles daily at 60 m.p.h. or over. The services between London, Birmingham, and North Wales and Cambrian Coast resorts will be generally improved. Through trains between Birmingham, Hereford and Cardiff will be speeded up. On Saturdays, when the bulk of holiday traffic passes, the main and cross-country expresses will be greatly increased. In some cases, the ordinary weekday services will be nearly doubled. Expresses will be rearranged and run via alternative routes in order to maintain a steady flow of traffic to the West Country and South Coast resorts.

The *"Cornish Riviera Limited,"* on Saturdays, will become a group of three trains leaving Paddington respectively at 10.25 a.m. for Plymouth, Truro and Falmouth; at 10.30 a.m. for Helston, St. Ives and Penzance; and at 10.35 a.m. for Plymouth and the principal Cornish stations. The up *"Riviera"* will be two trains, one leaving Penzance at 10.0 a.m. and carrying passengers from St. Ives and Falmouth; and the other leaving St. Erth at 10.20 a.m. and carrying passengers from Helston, Par and Plymouth. Sunday editions of the *"Cornish Riviera Limited"* and the *"Torbay Express"* will also be run at the same times from Paddington as on weekdays, and the evening services are to be improved.

An Irish "Steam Cab"

A veteran combined locomotive and coach of considerable interest that is still in service on the Great Southern Railways of Ireland is shown in the upper photograph on this page. It is described as a "steam cab," and the locomotive portion is numbered 92.

The unit was one of several of this kind introduced in 1880 for branch line service. The possibility of mixed train working and the consequent necessity for performing shunting operations at wayside stations no doubt accounted for the adoption of six-coupled wheels. The work became too heavy for these combined units and they were withdrawn, with the exception of No. 92. This has been used for many years for the conveyance of officials between the works at Inchicore and Kingsbridge Station, Dublin, where the offices of the Company are situated.

The upper illustration, reproduced by courtesy of the Great Southern Railways of Ireland, shows the curious 0-6-4 "steam cab," or combined locomotive and coach referred to on this page. In the lower photograph is a powerful 4-8-4 narrow gauge tank locomotive built for service in Morocco. Photograph reproduced by courtesy of Henschel and Sohn A.G., of Cassel.

"The Merseyside Express" Accelerated

Since 4th May *"The Merseyside Express"* from Liverpool to Euston has been accelerated by 10 minutes, the journey now taking 3 hrs. 20 min. The 189.7 miles from Mossley Hill, near Liverpool, where a stop is invariably made, are timed to be covered in 189 min. This involves an average speed of 60.2 m.p.h.

On the first day of the accelerated schedule 4-6-2 locomotive No. 6210 *"Princess Patricia,"* with a fourteen-coach train, reached Euston four minutes early. The enginemen were Driver T. Lyon and Fireman W. H. Harris.

G.N.R. (Ireland) Dining Car Experiments

Experiments are in progress on the G.N.R. of Ireland with two types of cooking equipment on the Dublin-Belfast restaurant services. One car is fitted for gas cooking and another with a special anthracite-fired cooker. On the gas-equipped car four steel cylinders are carried, lying across the car below the underframe. These are removable and are charged daily to a pressure of 3,000 lb. per sq. in. at the Belfast gasworks. Non-corrosive steel piping arranged outside the car conveys the gas to a two-stage governor that reduces the pressure of the gas before it passes to the cooking apparatus.

The anthracite cooker in the other car is stated to be the first of its kind used on a railway in the British Isles. Only one firing of the cooker is required for a return trip between Belfast and Dublin.

Specials for Pigeon Traffic

During the pigeon racing season numerous special trains are operated by the L.M.S.R. to convey homing pigeons to the point where they are released for their flights. It is estimated that by September some two million pigeons will have been carried by the L.M.S.R. during this season, necessitating the use of 1,804 vans, in addition to luggage brake vans.

In order to assist the railway staff in the working of this traffic a special 72-page booklet is issued.

Better Protection for Fragile Goods

An interesting experiment has recently been completed by the G.W.R. with the object of reducing damage in transit to eggs, soft fruit, and other fragile goods that are liable to injury, however carefully they are handled. The interior of a van is fitted with a series of partitions that can be adjusted to hold the stacked goods firmly in position, no matter how small the load in the vehicle may be. The experiment has lasted a year, and it has proved so successful that a further 100 vehicles are being adapted.

Electric Welding Machinery

Making Metal Joints at High Speed

WE are all familiar with the blacksmith's forge in which the ends of a broken hoop can be heated and hammered together or welded. For this process the fire is raked out clean and free from clinkers and dross, and its temperature raised by blowing air through it by means of bellows. The hoop ends are left in the fire until they are white hot, and the ends are then gently hammered together until they are united. Finally the welded iron is allowed to cool down to its solid state.

In order to understand what happens when a weld of this kind takes place it is necessary to know the changes that occur in a metal when it is heated. Ordinary butter will serve as an illustration of these changes. When this is very cold it is solid and too hard to spread. On heating it becomes a liquid, but there is an intermediate state in which it is plastic and then it can easily be worked. If we wish to mix two masses of butter together, this cannot be done while they are frozen. It is easy when they are soft and plastic, however, and the constituents of the mixture formed by pressing them together will not separate, even when it is frozen again.

Many metals become plastic when they are heated. They cannot then be worked as easily as butter, but can readily be welded by hammering or applying pressure to squeeze together the pieces that are to be joined. The necessary force must be applied while the metal is still hot enough to be plastic. For example, pure iron remains solid up to a temperature of 1,130 deg. C., when it becomes plastic, and its melting point is about 1,500 deg. C. Iron and steel, and their alloys, therefore can be welded at some temperature between 1,130 deg. C. and 1,500 deg. C. The exact temperature that is most suitable depends upon the composition of the metal or alloy, for the presence of impurities alters the range of temperature through which it remains in a plastic condition.

At the blacksmith's shop heat is lost when the pieces of metal are taken out of the fire and more material than is really necessary must be heated in order to provide a reserve to check the rate of cooling. The ends to be welded therefore are usually made white hot for a length of say two or more inches. On the other hand, great care also must be taken not to overheat the metal, or burn it. When this happens with say iron or steel, the metal is oxidised and forms flakes of scaly material. This is not plastic, and its condition somewhat resembles that of butter that has been mixed with flour. Such a mixture cannot be pressed readily into a single mass, and similarly the scale formed when iron is overheated cannot be welded.

Ingenious machines are now available for welding operations of many kinds. In these the heat is localised at the position of the weld, so that the parts made white hot are comparatively small in extent. The temperature also is carefully controlled to reduce damage due to oxidation and the resulting weld therefore is stronger than that made by the cruder operations of the blacksmith.

The modern welding machine is electrical in operation. In it the parts to be welded are placed together and a very heavy current is passed through them and across the join. The electrical resistance at the point of contact is high compared with that of the rest of the circuit. The temperature there consequently rises rapidly, and when welding temperature is reached mechanical pressure is applied to squeeze the two pieces of metal together to form a sound weld.

A large butt welding machine welding blades for cutting out leather in a boot factory. The illustrations to this article are reproduced by courtesy of British Insulated Cables Ltd., Prescot, the makers of the machines shown in them.

This process is known as electric resistance welding. Alternating current similar to that used for ordinary electric lighting is employed, but the best results are obtained by employing a low voltage. A transformer therefore is used to change the mains supply voltage to that required by the welding machine.

In some cases the ends of two pieces of metal to be united are simply brought into direct contact, or butted together, to form what is known as a "butt weld." One form of machine in which this is done usually consists of a table supporting two sliding grips or rests that hold the electrodes, through which current is led in, and the work to be welded. The transformer is housed under the table and the necessary instruments to guide the operation are mounted in some convenient position. When the work is set up in the machine, turning a hand wheel slides the rests towards one another and the ends to be welded are brought into contact. The current is switched on and when the correct temperature has been reached the rests are brought slightly nearer together to squeeze the weld.

The power required for completing the weld usually is much greater than can be applied by hand. For instance, a total pressure of 50 tons may be necessary when welding together sections of pipes up to 18 in. in diameter and with a cross sectional area of 30 sq. in. Hydraulic power therefore is used to give the final squeeze.

The surface of a joint made by butt welding is slightly swollen owing to the heavy pressure that has been applied to the metal while it is still plastic. The increase in size is very slight, and in the case of a steel bar 1 in. in diameter is not much more in thickness than a wedding ring. The unwanted metal can easily be ground away from the outside, and its removal does not affect the strength of the weld.

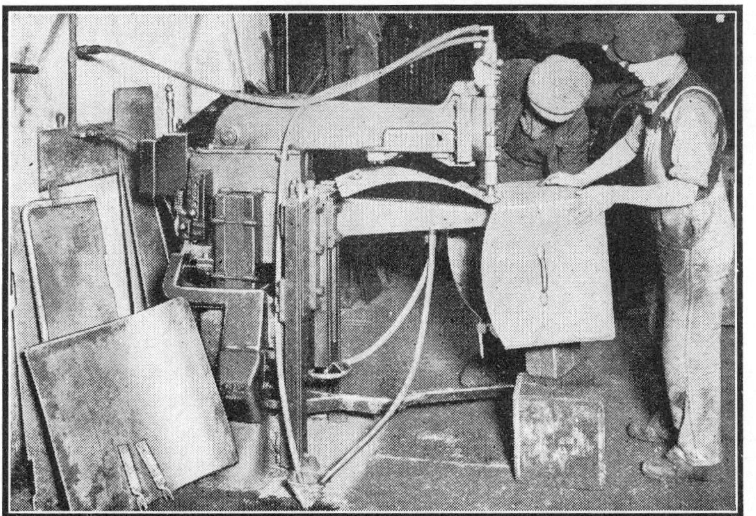

Welding the hinged lid on to a sheet steel tool box by means of a large spot welder.

Butt welding machines have been made to deal with wires less than 1/16 in. in diameter, but much larger machines also are in regular use. Some of these weld together metallic surfaces up to 40 sq. in. in area, and one machine employed in the production of sheet metal bodies for motor cars makes welds of this type 90 in. in width.

Sometimes pieces of metal can best be united with an overlap. If the joint need not be watertight, it may be sufficient to weld the parts to be joined in spots, each of which then takes the place of a bolt or screw. Spot welding, as this method is called, can be applied to materials of various thicknesses, from a few thousandths of an inch, as in the case of small wireless parts, up to half-an-inch. An interesting feature is that the welds made must occupy the same area as the bolt-holes they displace.

Two or more sheets to be joined together in a spot welding machine are placed between two copper tips, or electrodes, that are brought together by means of a hand lever or pedal, or in certain cases by power-driven mechanism. The necessary pressure is applied to the electrodes through a spring and current is automatically switched on when this is compressed to a certain extent. The spring is further compressed when the correct welding temperature is reached, and this completes the weld and automatically switches off the current.

A "continuous spot" welder seam welding spare-wheel supports in a motor car works

The machine can be so arranged that it is impossible for the operator to overheat the metals to be joined, or to stop the action before they are hot enough. This automatic action depends on the fact that the resistance at the point of contact falls as the metals become united. An increase in the strength of the current across the weld follows, and when this reaches a pre-determined value the electric circuit is broken automatically. This ingenious form of control is particularly valuable when thick material is being welded, for the temperature and appearance of the outer surfaces of the metal then are useless as guides to the conditions at the point where the welding is being carried out.

Spot welders usually are brought into operation by pressing a pedal down. They can be designed to make one weld each time the pedal is depressed, but if required they work continuously while it is down. In the latter case they work at high speed and may make up to several hundred welds an hour.

It is interesting to note that spot welding machines manufactured by British Insulated Cables Ltd. are used in the Meccano Factory for many purposes, including the welding of transformer casings and joining rudder brackets to the Hornby Speed Boats.

Sometimes it is insufficient to fasten two overlapping sheets of metal together by means of a few welded spots. In these cases the welding can be made in a continuous series of spots. Metal sheets to be united in this manner are passed between two rotating copper discs that act as electrodes, leading in the electric current. These act as rollers, pressing the sheets between them as they are welded in order to form a continuous joint. Such welds can be made in materials of thicknesses up to 3/16 in., and the disc electrodes employed are driven at a constant rate. It is necessary that the welding surfaces of the sheets should be clean. For this reason grinding, pickling, or sand-blasting is essential before seam welding, as this process is called, is carried out.

The main features of the welding process are its simplicity and economy. For instance, the longitudinal seams of five-gallon paint drums made of mild steel sheets .022 in. in thickness are welded at a cost of one-third of a penny per drum. The price includes grinding the edges before welding, labour and electrical energy for welding, and the cost of maintaining and replacing the electrodes.

A particularly interesting example of the value of welding is provided by the manufacture of tools for work on heavy lathes. The steel used for the cutting edges of these tools is expensive, and it would be wasteful to make an entire tool of it, for the greater part of the metal then would not serve the special purpose for which it has been produced. For this reason the body of the tool is made of less costly metal and cutting edges of the more expensive tool steel are simply welded on their ends

High Definition Television

Pictures Formed by Invisible Electron Beam

By W. T. Lowe and E. Phillips

WE are on the threshold of interesting developments in television, for work is now proceeding on the installation of two television systems in the Alexandra Palace, North London, from which regular services will shortly be transmitted by the British Broadcasting Company. These systems are a great advance on the one used in previous television broadcasts of the B.B.C. That system was mechanical in character and gave a picture that was built up of only 30 lines. Reception with a greater number of lines, and therefore with better definition, can be obtained mechanically, but only electrical apparatus will be used for the high definition television, with 240 or 405 lines a picture, that is to be broadcast from the new station.

The central feature of the new system is a special form of what is known as the cathode ray tube. This is a glass tube that has been exhausted to provide a vacuum, and contains two plates or wires, known as electrodes, that are connected by wires passing through the glass to the positive and negative terminals of a source of electricity. The electrode charged negatively is called the cathode and is the source of a stream of electrons, or particles of negative electricity, to which the name of cathode ray has been given. The production of electrons is stimulated by heating the cathode by current from a battery. The second electrode is known as the anode and as it is positively charged to 500 v. or more, it attracts the electrons, which pass at high speed across the space in the tube to strike its opposite end. If this end is covered with a fine layer of certain chemical compounds the impact produces a glowing green spot. A coating of this kind is known as a fluorescent screen. The materials usually employed in making it are compounds of zinc, calcium or cadmium, and special mixtures giving a white glow can now be used.

A transmitter for the television of cinematograph films. The pictures on the films are scanned by the Farnsworth Electron Camera referred to in the accompanying article.

The electrons forming the cathode rays travel with incredibly high speed, and are so light that they are easily diverted from their paths by making use of electrical attractions. The stream therefore offers an excellent means of changing variations in electric current into corresponding variations of light, and thus of presenting to the eye moving pictures of very high definition. It also can be used for television transmission, for it enables light rays to be translated into electric currents.

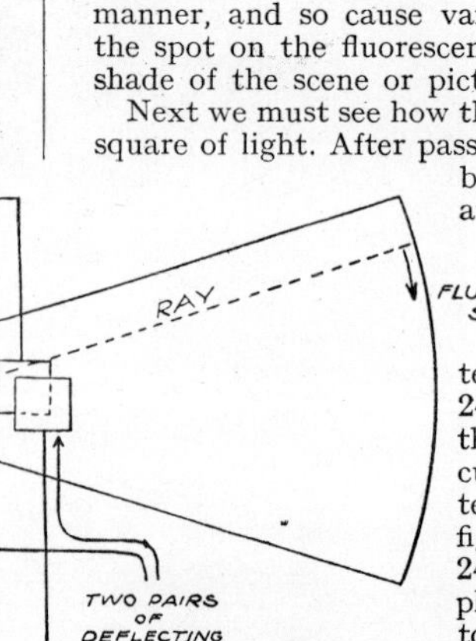

The cathode ray tube of a television receiver. The picture appears on the fluorescent screen on the base of the tube.

Let us now see how the cathode ray tube is adapted for use in a television receiver. The shape given to a tube employed for this purpose is that of a conical flask, the cathode being placed in the neck and the fluorescent screen on the broad base. Immediately in front of the cathode is a metal plate with a small aperture at its centre. This plate is the anode and is charged positively to attract the negative electrons at high speed.

Some of the electrons pass through the aperture and these form a pencil or beam that strikes the fluorescent screen. Similar electric charges repel each other. The particles of this beam are themselves negatively charged and therefore have a tendency to spread out to form a diverging ray. In order to prevent this, and to concentrate the beam so that as many electrons as possible pass through the aperture in the anode, the part of the tube between the latter and the cathode is surrounded by a metal cylinder, named the Wehnelt cylinder after its inventor. This is given a negative charge by means of a battery and its repulsive effect causes the electrons passing through it to bunch together in the centre of the tube, and to concentrate upon a small area or "spot" of the fluorescent screen on its base.

The Wehnelt cylinder also provides a means of controlling the number of electrons passing through the opening in the anode. If its negative charge is great the beam is bunched tightly, and when the charge is reduced the beam is spread out so that fewer electrons pass through the aperture. If the varying currents in the aerial of a television receiver therefore are suitably amplified and allowed to vary the charge on the Wehnelt cylinder of the cathode ray tube, the effectiveness of the electron stream will change in a corresponding manner, and so cause variations in the intensity of the glow of the spot on the fluorescent screen. In other words, the light and shade of the scene or picture being televised is reproduced.

Next we must see how the modulated beam is made to build up a square of light. After passing through the aperture, it is projected between two pairs of plates that are fixed at right angles to one another in the neck of the tube. One of the two plates of each pair is connected to the anode.

If it is desired to receive television pictures, each made up of 240 lines, at the rate of 25 a second, the other plate of one pair is fed with current from a local source that is interrupted 6,000 times a second, this figure being obtained by multiplying 240 by 25. At the same time the second plate of the other pair, at right angles to the first, is supplied with current interrupted 25 times a second. The purpose of this is to cause the beam to sweep backward and forward across the tube and also to move up and down. In this manner it builds up a square of light on the fluorescent screen at the rate of 25 times a second. As the beam is being modulated at the same time, a complete series of pictures is presented to the observer.

The necessary movements of the beam are brought about by an electrical device known as the time base. This consists essentially of an electrical condenser with an adjustable resistance, a battery and a glow discharge valve or a pentode. The deflecting plate in the cathode ray tube is in parallel with the condenser and discharge valve, and the battery is applied to the terminal of the condenser so as to charge it. When a certain voltage is reached the resistance of the lamp breaks down and the condenser is discharged through it.

The charge and discharge produces the following effect. As the condenser is being charged, a continually increasing voltage is impressed upon the corresponding deflecting plate, which attracts the beam towards it. At the proper voltage the lamp resistance breaks down and the condenser is discharged. The deflecting plate then loses its attractive power and the beam returns to its normal position near the second plate of the pair, which is permanently charged positively because of its connection with the anode. The condenser then again becomes charged, the beam is drawn towards the first plate and once more returns to its normal position when the discharge takes place.

Experimental work in progress in the Baird laboratories in connection with the latest developments in television reception. Photograph by courtesy of Baird Television Ltd.

This series of movements continues as long as the time base is in operation, and the movement of the electron beam that it brings about is too swift for the eye to follow. As the beam is pulled towards the deflecting plate of one pair and released it traces an up and down line the requisite number of times in a second. Another time base, with a slower rate of charge and discharge, acts upon the other pair of plates, pulling the beam from side to side 25 times in a second. In this manner the glowing spot on the fluorescent screen is made to cover the entire picture area, and it does this so quickly that the first impression has not been lost by the eye when the last one appears, so that the entire square appears to be illuminated. The pictures so built up are seen as a continuous record, as are those on a cinema screen, since they follow each other at the high rate of 25 a second.

This explanation deals with the simplest form of cathode ray tube and its operation in television receivers in which the picture is reproduced by varying the concentration of the electron beam. This plan has some disadvantages, however, and Manfred von Ardenne, a German scientist who has devoted much study to television problems, has invented a system in which the speed at which the beam travels across the fluorescent screen is varied instead. This is caused to move slowly where brightness is required and more quickly where a less brilliant result is to be produced.

The cathode ray tube has now been adapted for use in the transmission of television, its work in this being to transform variations in light received from a scene or picture to be televised into corresponding variations in electric current. These electric variations are then used to modulate the wireless waves on which the transmission is broadcast.

A Lorenz-von Ardenne television receiver exhibited at the German Radio Exhibition in 1935. The picture is 7½ in. by 8¾ in. in size. Photograph by courtesy of "Wireless and Television Review."

The first apparatus of this kind was invented by Dr. Vladimir Zworykin, an American scientist. It is called an Iconoscope, and in this country is used by Marconi-E.M.I. Ltd., one of the two companies providing television plant at the Alexandra Palace Station. The beam of electrons is produced by heating the cathode and is deflected by means of time bases in the usual manner, but it falls upon a plate set at an angle at the end of the tube and scans that instead of the base of the tube. The plate consists of a sheet of silver over the surface of which are scattered about 3,000,000 tiny globules of caesium, a soft metal that liberates electrons when stimulated by light. Behind the silver plate is first a sheet of mica, which acts as an insulator, and then a copper plate from which a wire leads to the amplifying system. This arrangement constitutes about 3,000,000 tiny electric condensers.

The picture to be televised is focussed on the silver sheet by means of a lens. Each globule of caesium then releases electrons, and the condenser of which it forms part therefore becomes charged. The greater the intensity or amount of light falling upon a globule of the metal, the greater its charge, and thus a sort of electric image of the scene focussed upon the silver sheet is produced. This is scanned by the electron beam, which travels methodically over the silver sheet, touching each globule of caesium in turn, and as it does so discharging the condenser of which it forms part. The discharge current flows through the copper plate at the back and thence to the amplifiers, and its variations in strength represent the variations in the intensity of the light falling upon the tiny areas of the screen to build up the picture focussed upon it.

A somewhat similar apparatus giving greater output is the Electron Camera invented by Philo T. Farnsworth, also in America. This has been developed in Great Britain by the Baird Television Development Co. Ltd., and its improved form, known as the Farnsworth Multiplier, will be used in the broadcasting service from Alexandra Palace that is to be operated by this company.

In the Electron Camera the scene to be transmitted is focussed on a plate, the surface of which is coated with material that emits electrons when light falls upon it. This plate is at one end of a vacuum tube and is negatively charged. At the other end of the tube is the anode, a smaller plate in which there is a minute opening. Electrons shot out by the cathode travel at high speed towards the anode, and electro-magnetic coils give the beam a scanning motion, so that electrons from each part of the image in turn pass through the opening and strike a collector connected to the amplifiers.

The programmes to be broadcast from Alexandra Palace are to be shared between the Baird Television Development Co. Ltd., and Marconi-E.M.I. Ltd., the two companies to which reference already has been made. The systems have different rates of scanning and give pictures of different sizes. In the Baird system scanning is at the rate of 240 lines for each picture and there are 25 pictures a second, while the sides of the picture will be in the proportion of four to three. The scanning is in strict sequence, that is each line follows the preceding one and there are 6,000 lines a second. In the Marconi-E.M.I. system there are also 25 pictures a second, but these are made up of 405 lines, and the ratio of their sides is five to four. Another difference between the two systems is that Marconi-E.M.I. scanning is interlaced, that is the picture is scanned first by 202½ lines and then by another series of 202½ lines that run in between those of the first series. It is claimed that this method eliminates flickering and in consequence gives a steady picture. As there are 25 pictures a second, the number of lines in the same period in the Marconi-E.M.I. system is no less than 10,125.

Miniature Automatic Telephone Exchanges

What must surely be the loneliest telephone exchange in Great Britain is illustrated on this page. It is at Ballachulish, in the heart of the Scottish Highlands, and is one of the new Rural Automatic Exchanges now being introduced by the General Post Office.

The telephone is as valuable in the country as in cities and in towns, and in emergencies the need for it may be even more pressing in a widely scattered area than in a place that is densely populated. Calls during the night hours are so infrequent in some villages and country areas that they do not justify the expense of keeping an operator on duty at the small exchange. The coming of the Rural Automatic Exchanges has solved the problem of providing a full service at all times, however, and many villages are now being equipped with them.

The building contains a set of line switches, selectors and other necessary equipment, and local subscribers can communicate with each other at any time by simply dialling the respective numbers. If a number outside the local exchange is required, connection with the nearest main exchange where operators are constantly on duty can be made by dialling "O." The mechanism used is of the standard Post Office type. Its maintenance calls only for the attention of a mechanic at intervals, and it works well, although often exposed to great changes of temperature in the small and isolated buildings in which it is installed. A public telephone kiosk usually is located outside the exchange, or at some convenient point, so that the benefits of the system are extended to all who live in the area.

The rural automatic exchange at Ballachulish in Argyllshire. Photograph by courtesy of the General Post Office.

Where Holidays may be Fine Days

It almost seems as if the best way to ensure a reasonably fine day in Rochdale, Lancashire, is to make that day a holiday. This suggestion is based on the fact that the average rainfall in that town is less on Sunday than on any other day of the week. In any case, this seems to be an interesting example of how weather can be modified to a slight extent, for it is probable that the volumes of hot gases rising from the factory chimneys of Rochdale on working days give the uplift required to raise clouds to higher and colder regions of the atmosphere, where their moisture is condensed into rain.

Another curiosity of our weather is the fact that there are certain times of the year at which rain has never fallen in London while records have been kept regularly. According to these records there has been no rain for 50 years in the mornings of 9th and 16th May and of 16th March, or in the evenings of 18th May and 3rd October. This of course is no guarantee that these periods will be fine in future years; but it is encouraging to learn that although there are periods of this kind that have always been fine, there are no corresponding ones that have always been wet.

A Halo without a Wearer

The halos that the best of us wear as the marks of our virtues are invisible, and halos in general are only seen in pictures and stained glass windows. There is at least one instance in which a halo could be seen plainly while its wearer was invisible or unknown, however, but in this case it surrounded a fragment of a chemical element instead of encircling a human brow.

This halo was found about 14 years ago in a piece of mica from Sweden. It has been known for many years that many specimens of mica contain small specks in which the colour has been lost. These marks show as concentric rings or halos when the mica is cut through them. They are due to the presence of minute amounts of radio-active elements, which act as guns of various calibres shooting out tiny particles to different distances. The range of each projectile, that is the radius of the halo it forms, enables the element producing it to be tracked down, but for years this halo defied all the efforts of scientific detectives to trace it to its source. Then it was discovered that it was due to a tiny fragment of a rare element known to them as samarium.

One reason for the failure to recognise the halo as that of samarium was that the element had not previously been suspected to be radio-active. Now we know that it does break up spontaneously, but it does so very slowly indeed, and a piece of the element would take more than a million million years to lose half its weight. It is impossible to measure its life directly by experiment, of course. The mica in which its halo was discovered is a laboratory in which this measurement has been in progress for ages, however, for the range of the projectiles the element shoots out is an indication of its durability.

Game Animals in Northern Rhodesia

Northern Rhodesia appears to be comparatively well-stocked with game animals, although the number of these in South Africa as a whole is diminishing. A rough estimate gives 300 giraffes, 1,500 rhinoceroses and 3,000 hippopotamuses among the rarer creatures, and 12,000 elephants, 50,000 zebras, and 60,000 buffalos among those that are more numerous. The total animal population is believed to be about one million, and this, equally distributed, would average about four individuals to the square mile, or approximately the density of the human population. The elephants and buffalos have trebled in number during the past 30 years.

A Modern Radiographic Department

The upper illustration on this page shows a scene of a kind that may be familiar to some of my readers. It is a reproduction of a photograph of the X-Ray room of the new Radiographic Department of Ilford Ltd., at Tavistock Square, London, W.C.1, which was opened as recently as December 1935, and is thoroughly up-to-date in its equipment. In addition to the X-ray room itself the Department includes thoroughly up-to-date dark rooms for development of X-ray photographs, a studio for clinical photography, and lecture and exhibition rooms.

The X-ray room of the Ilford Radiographic Department, London, the equipment of which is described on this page. Photograph by courtesy of Ilford Limited.

On the right of the illustration is a special wall unit for X-ray examination of the teeth. The patient undergoing this sits in comfort in the dental chair, and the small X-ray tube at the end of the hinged and jointed arm fixed to the wall can then be rotated round his head into various positions to enable radiographs, or X-ray photographs, of individual teeth to be obtained.

The couch in the centre of the room is suitable for all work in the horizontal position. Its top can be turned to several angles and the photographs required can be obtained with the aid of the X-ray tube shown above it, or of an additional one placed underneath. In addition there are screening stands of various kinds, where the patient stands or sits between the X-ray tube and a fluorescent screen that glows when the rays fall upon it. On their way to the screen the rays pass through the heart or lungs of the patient or any other part of his body that requires examination, and the resulting picture or image on the screen can be studied closely.

One of the stands employed for vertical work is specially devoted to X-ray photography. It is fitted with an electrically-driven film holder so that stereoscopic films can be taken with great rapidity.

High voltages must be applied to current X-ray tubes, and the necessary supply is obtained from a transformer and valve rectifier in a separate room. The current is conveyed round the X-ray room by means of aluminium rails placed high up on the walls, where there is no danger of accidental contact with them. Shock-proof cables connect the rails with the X-ray tubes, all of which also are of the shock-proof type. The control table, seen on the left of the central couch, can be moved about the room to bring it near the point at which work is being carried out. It is fitted with a time switch that allows photographic exposures down to 1/50th of a second to be given.

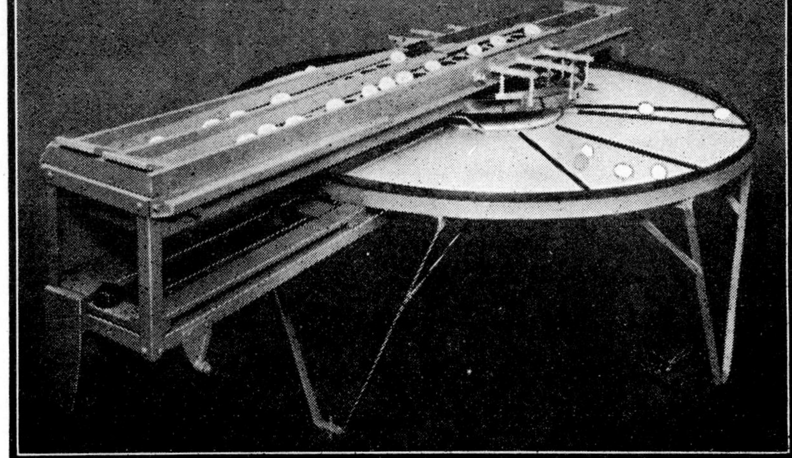

A machine that automatically grades and counts eggs at the rate of 7,500 an hour. Photograph by courtesy of Bingham Appliances Ltd.

Grading and Counting 7,500 Eggs an Hour

We all know how very disappointing an undersized boiled egg can be, and appreciate the greater sense of comfort derived from the appearance on the table of one that from its bulk promises to be double yolked. The extent to which eggs vary in size is astonishing. Feeding and the living conditions of hens generally no doubt influence the size of their eggs, but the breed of the birds has something to do with it. White Leghorns lay white eggs that may be as much as $2\frac{3}{4}$ oz. in weight, while Rhode Island eggs are brown in colour and usually weigh less than 2 oz. Imported Egyptian eggs frequently weigh less than 1 oz.

The price of an egg depends largely on its size, which also determines the use to which it is put. For this reason it is necessary that eggs should be graded, or sorted into batches of different sizes or weights, before they are marketed, and the accompanying illustration shows a machine that is capable of doing this at the rate of 7,500 eggs an hour. The central feature of the machine is a rotating unit that automatically weighs the eggs as they are fed on to it by an endless conveyor belt, and delivers them to different sections or compartments of a table. Each weighing unit is balanced and adjusted to give a standard of accuracy within 1/32 oz., and the eggs are graded into four, five or six sections, or even more if desired, the weight of every egg in each section falling between definite limits. The machine is driven by an electric motor and if necessary it can be fitted with a counting mechanism that automatically records the number of eggs delivered to each compartment.

An Invisible Door

A year or so ago a window without glass was invented for use in the cabs of locomotives. The driver of an engine fitted with it simply looks out through a round opening in the front of the cab, and he can do so in perfect comfort because baffle plates set up currents of air that deflect wind, snow or rain.

Now the window without glass has been succeeded by a doorway without a door. Strictly speaking there is a door in this case, but it is

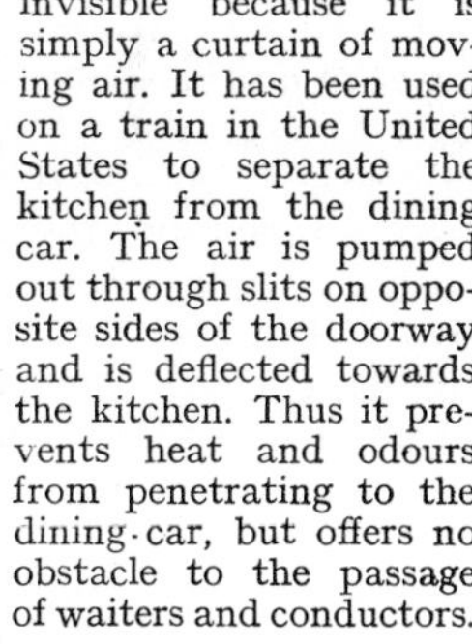

invisible because it is simply a curtain of moving air. It has been used on a train in the United States to separate the kitchen from the dining car. The air is pumped out through slits on opposite sides of the doorway and is deflected towards the kitchen. Thus it prevents heat and odours from penetrating to the dining-car, but offers no obstacle to the passage of waiters and conductors.

A Shock for the Fish

The description of these invisible barriers is a reminder that work on one of an electrical character is being carried out in this country. The object of the experiments is to electrify the greater part of a channel through which fish pass, in order to give them mild shocks that will divert them towards nets in which they can be caught.

It seems as if the problems involved in doing this have already been solved in America. There an engineer who wished to prevent fish from entering irrigating ditches suspended two sets of electrodes, consisting of cables or chains, in the water and passed a current between them. The result was a shock to the fish, and this was sufficient to deter them from further attempts to pass the barrier. There seems to be many possibilities in this remarkable scheme.

De Havilland Aircraft

The "Dragonfly" and the D.H.86A

Although slightly more monoplanes than biplanes have been produced in this country during recent years, the demand for biplanes is still considerable, as for many purposes it is almost essential that an aeroplane be fitted with two wings. A Service aeroplane, for instance, must not only be fast but also capable of carrying a good load at both high and low altitudes, and be able to withstand great stresses and strains while in the air. The larger total wing area of a biplane, although it involves a slight decrease in speed, gives the aeroplane both greater stability and carrying capacity. For these reasons most of the aircraft used in the R.A.F. and other Air Forces are biplanes. In commercial aviation the extensive development of internal air lines has been due largely to the production of special types of aeroplanes in which low horse power, low initial cost and economical maintenance are combined with high performance and high payload; and the majority of these types have been biplanes.

The numerous types of de Havilland civil and military biplanes produced have ranged on the military side from two-seater training machines to bombers, and on the commercial side from the lightest sports type to large air liners. The D.H.2, 4, 5, 6, 9 and 9A military types played parts of outstanding importance during the War and afterward, with the R.A.F. Early de Havilland successes in the commercial field were the D.H.34 and D.H.50 air liners, and later came the D.H.53, a light sports aeroplane with an engine of only 15 h.p.

A forward view of the D.H. "Dragonfly" in flight. The slender nose, sharply tapered wings, and streamlined undercarriage and engine nacelles are very noticeable. The illustrations to this article are reproduced by courtesy of "The Aeroplane."

In 1925 the company introduced the now famous D.H. "Moth," a two-seater open cockpit biplane fitted with a 100 h.p. "Gipsy I" engine. The high efficiency of this aeroplane led to its adoption by the Royal Air Force and many Air Forces abroad, and it has also been used extensively by flying clubs and private owners in all parts of the world, no less than 4,000 "Moths" being sold during the 10 years this type was in production. In that period various types were developed from the "Moth," and the latter was withdrawn last year, when the "Hornet Moth" cabin biplane was introduced. This aeroplane was described in the *"M.M."* of February last.

In 1933 two very successful new D.H. types, the "Dragon" and the "Express Air Liner," made their appearance. The "Dragon" was a six-seater passenger or freight-carrying aeroplane fitted with two 130 h.p. "Gipsy Major" engines. It was an immediate success by reason of its high payload capacity and high speed in relation to its low horse power. An improved "Dragon" called the "Dragon Rapide" was produced shortly afterwards. The "Express Air Liner" was specially designed to comply with the requirements of the Australian Government in connection with the Singapore-Brisbane section of the Empire air route, and a detailed description of this fine aeroplane was given in the December 1934 *"M.M."*

The latest de Havilland products are the "Dragonfly," a smaller version of the "Dragon Rapide" and the company's 90th design, and the D.H.86A, an improved version of the "Express Air Liner."

The "Dragonfly" is a twin-engined unequal-span biplane, the upper wing being 43 ft. in span and the lower one 38 ft. 6 in. It is a five-seater aeroplane, as experience has proved that this amount of accommodation is the most suitable for the privately-owned family aeroplane and for the air taxi, two purposes for which the "Dragonfly" is ideal. The arrangement of the seating is two in front, a single seat immediately behind them and opposite the cabin door, and a seat that extends right across the back of the cabin and provides room for two persons. There can be no comfort without spaciousness, and the cabin is 10 ft. in length from rudder bars to rear, 5 ft. in height and more than 4 ft. in width; each passenger therefore has 40 cu. ft. of space. Either cool air from individual adjustable ventilators, or warm air from engine exhaust muffs can be admitted at will. The windows are of a light and non-splinterable composition and extend the full length of the cabin; they are crystal-clear and provide the perfect view that adds so much to the attraction of air travel.

A new system of soundproofing is used that excludes noise throughout the range of audible frequencies, resulting in a cabin in which a party can cruise all day without suffering from noise-fatigue at the end of it, and enjoy normal conversation at any time. Preliminary tests of the system proved so satisfactory that it will be adopted in all future de Havilland aircraft. A shelf for light articles is situated above the back seat, and behind the cabin is a luggage locker that is reached by an outside door on the starboard side of the fuselage.

The two front seats in the cabin are spaced apart so as to be easily accessible. When there is only one pilot he occupies the left seat, and the central control column therefore has a fixed branch to the left, this branch being surmounted by the usual segmented wheel by which the pilot works the column. When there are two pilots to share the flying, a "stick" with a triangular handle is plugged in as a right-hand branch of the control column, for the second man. Throttle and altitude controls are on the left, and two rudder bars are provided. A convenient lever operates the "Comet" type split flaps fitted to the trailing edge of the centre section of the upper wing. Ailerons are also fitted to this wing. The wheel brake lever is of a new type and protrudes from the dashboard. It applies the brakes together, and when left partly on brings them under differential control by the rudder bars for steering on the ground.

The D.H.86A Express Air Liner, developed from the D.H.86 type used by Qantas Empire Airways Ltd., on the Singapore-Brisbane section of the England-Australia air service.

The fabric-covered fuselage of the "Dragonfly" is modelled upon that of the famous D.H. "Comet." The fin of the tail unit is an integral part of the fuselage and is covered with plywood, but the other tail surfaces are fabric-covered, with all controls partly inside the structure.

The undercarriage is of the divided type and has Dunlop low-pressure wheels fitted with powerful brakes. Each undercarriage leg is situated beneath an engine of the aeroplane, and both leg and engine are covered by a deep, streamlined fairing that merges into the underside of the lower wing. The upper portion of the fairing forms the engine nacelle, of course, and is hinged on the top centre line so that either side can be lifted up like the bonnet of a motor car, for attention and servicing.

Another view of the "Dragonfly" in the air. This machine is the 90th de Havilland design.

The two engines of the "Dragonfly" are 130 h.p. D.H. "Gipsy Majors," a type that has proved its high qualities in many notable flights, including 10 across the Atlantic, and in hundreds of thousands of hours of commercial operation. The engines are mounted, in rubber blocks, to quickly detachable welded steel-tube bearers at each end of the centre section of the lower wing. This system makes for great strength and economy of weight. Each engine has a $3\frac{1}{2}$-gallon oil tank in the fairing behind it, and a 30-gallon tank adjacent to it in the wing. These four tanks constitute the standard supply and give the machine a range of 625 miles, which is more than sufficient for normal use. It occasionally happens that a greater range is required, and an additional 25-gallon tank can be installed under the rear seat in the cabin for use when maximum payload is not carried. With this additional tank in use the range of the machine is increased to about 885 miles.

The D.H.86A Express Air Liner is a much bigger aeroplane than the "Dragonfly," as it is intended for use on long-distance commercial air services. It is, as stated earlier, a development of the type that has been in service during the past 18 months on the Singapore-Brisbane route operated by Qantas-Empire Airways Ltd., and it is also employed on Continental services of Imperial Airways and on several internal air routes in Great Britain.

The overall length of the D.H.86A is 46 ft. $1\frac{1}{4}$ in. and the height is 13 ft. The wings are 64 ft. 6 in. in span, and are of normal construction, consisting of wooden spars and spruce ribs covered with plywood and fabric although a tubular metal spar is used on the centre section as far as the inner engines. Ailerons are provided on both upper and lower wings, but only the lower ones are connected directly with the controls in the cockpit. They are joined to the upper ones by a streamlined steel tube, and thus when the bottom ones are moved those on the top have to move in unison.

The fuselage consists primarily of a three-ply box, but it differs from most fuselages by having the plywood inside the box, and the spruced longerons, struts and stringers outside it. There is then a covering of fabric, and the space between it and the three-ply is filled with special sound-insulating material. The pilot is accommodated in the nose of the fuselage, in a cockpit provided with a non-splintering glass windscreen and open side panels. The cockpit is separated from the cabin by a bulkhead in which is a door giving communication between the two compartments. Various arrangements of the passenger accommodation are available. They range from a long-distance luxury model with armchairs for nine passengers and a folding seat for a tenth one, to a "joy-riding" model designed to carry 16.

The four engines of the D.H.86A are carried in nacelles mounted in the leading edge of the lower wing. The two legs of the undercarriage are immediately beneath the inner engines and their coverings are one with the engine nacelles, as in the case of the "Dragonfly." The machine is available with either standard "Gipsy Six" engines and ordinary airscrews, or with the new Series II "Gipsy Six" engines and de Havilland controllable-pitch airscrews.

Books to Read

"Canoeing for Beginners"

By A. R. Ellis
(Brown, Son and Ferguson Ltd. 1/- net)

Canoeing is described by Mr. Ellis as a thrilling and adventurous recreation, and he offers his account of its essentials as the key to one of the finest and healthiest sports in the world. Although the book is small enough to be slipped into the canoeist's pocket it covers the entire subject, from acquiring a canoe to touring Great Britain in it. The sport is not costly. A canoe can either be made or bought, and the author gives useful advice on the various types available, paying special attention to the lightweight folding canoes that are steadily becoming popular.

Having acquired a canoe, the next thing is to learn how to use it, and here again the author is eminently practical. He is emphatic that a knowledge of swimming is essential, not because canoes are difficult to manage or liable to be overset easily, but because an attractive part of the sport includes the negotiation of such obstacles as weirs and rapids. This topic occupies the next chapter, which is packed full of valuable hints on canoe management in rough or broken waters. Suggestions for river and canoe trips follow, and the booklet ends with a brief but adequate account of rights and restrictions on the waterways of Great Britain.

"Modern Alchemy"

By Dorothy Fisk. (Faber and Faber. 6/-)

One of the greatest marvels of modern science is the achievement of the dream that for centuries was pursued by the alchemist—that of turning base metals such as lead and tin into silver or gold. As our knowledge of chemistry advanced, the possibility of transmutation was laughed away. In recent years we have discovered that after all the alchemists were right in one sense, for certain elements can be changed into others, and a few, such as radium, actually change themselves. Only very minute quantities of certain elements have been transformed, however, and we have not discovered how to make gold.

In this well-written book Miss Fisk covers the entire subject from the strange and mysterious methods of the alchemists to the discovery of radio-activity and the latest laboratory transmutations. The book is thoroughly up to date, and the story ends with the astonishing feat, accomplished by Professor Fermi, an Italian scientist, of building up an entirely new element that so far as we know has no counterpart in any form in Nature. Useful diagrams in the text help the reader to visualise the astonishing changes dealt with.

"Speed on Salt"

By G. Eyston and W. F. Bradley
(B. T. Batsford. 5/- net)

It is only recently that the Bonneville Salt Flats have been heard of in Great Britain as a result of the magnificent achievements of Sir Malcolm Campbell, George Eyston and others in the Autumn of 1935. Even now they are but a name and the history and the nature of the great American Salt Desert are little known to Europeans.

Synchronised paddling. From "Canoeing for Beginners," reviewed on this page.

In a foreword Sir Malcolm Campbell refers to these vast Salt Flats as "the only spot on the face of the earth where one can be assured of a straightaway run on a dead flat surface under conditions which will allow of speeds of 300 m.p.h. and upwards being achieved with comparative safety." He expresses the opinion that the Salt Flats "will be the future testing-ground of those inevitable developments in racing engines on whose results we shall base the practical everyday lessons which will govern the motor car, and to a certain extent the aeroplane of the future."

The book describes the early days of the Salt Flats, the journeys of the pioneers who risked their lives in attempts to cross this waterless waste, the gruelling experiences of the "Forty-niners" in their rush for gold, and the tragedy of expeditions lost for months without food. The authors give vivid descriptions of the speed record attempts made by Ab Jenkins, of Sir Malcolm Campbell's run of over 300 m.p.h., and the achievements of their own team, while George Eyston has contributed a thrilling account of his own personal experiences at the wheel when capturing the world's 24-hr. record. The detailed description of their exciting task is prefaced by an amusing account of their journey to the Salt Flats and the life in the little village which became their headquarters.

The large illustrations, many of which have not been published before, add greatly to the interest of this fascinating book, and show every phase of the speed records.

"Electricity for Boys"

By Ellison Hawks
(Ivor Nicholson and Watson. 7/6 net)

In spite of the fact that electricity is now used on an enormous scale for lighting and heating and for the production of power, it remains a mysterious force in the operations of which boys of all ages are so greatly interested that they cannot help wishing to know more about it and its wonders. The ordinary school book on electricity scarcely satisfies their needs, but these are admirably met in *"Electricity for Boys,"* which deals faithfully with the story of electricity, and also shows how it is used for locomotion, telegraphy and telephony, wireless, television and the production of X-rays.

Stress is laid on the practical side of electricity. Every boy enjoys doing and making things for himself, and ample directions are given for making simple apparatus from homely materials and Meccano parts with which successful experiments can readily be carried out. The electrical devices dealt with in this manner include motors and dynamos, electric bells and alarms, telegraph and telephone instruments, and wireless receivers, all of which work in a very satisfactory manner.

The book is written with the care and knowledge of boys' requirements that we have learned to expect from the author, and provides a store of absorbingly interesting reading as well as scope for the best kind of experimental work. It is copiously illustrated by means of 31 plates covering every phase of the applications of electricity, together with 214 drawings and figures in the text that show how electrical apparatus works, or simplify the task of the reader in following the instructions given for experimental work.

"Railway Modelling in Miniature"

By Edward Beal

(Percival Marshall and Co. Ltd. 3/6 net)

This interesting publication is described on the title page as "a practical handbook on the planning, building and operation of miniature railways, with special reference to 'OO' and 'HO' gauges"; and it certainly lives up to the purpose expressed in this description. Reference to the "OO" and "HO" gauges may puzzle readers who are not aware that these are the terms used to distinguish models of two different scales that run on the same gauge of lines—⅝ in., or exactly half that of Hornby Gauge "O" Rails. But the book can be read with profit, and many of the hints obtained in it can be applied, by owners of gauge "O" and larger layouts. Mr. Beal is himself a miniature railway owner and many of the photographs of his line give convincing proof of the soundness of his advice. In addition to these and other photographs there are innumerable sketches and drawings that illustrate clearly the various points that are dealt with.

A lifting bridge on a OO-Gauge layout. From "Railway Modelling in Miniature," reviewed on this page.

"Sands, Clays and Minerals"

(Vol. II. No. 4. 3/6)

Edited by A. L. Curtis

The current issue of this unique and interesting journal is larger than any of its predecessors and fully maintains the interest of previous numbers. As usual, it contains a wealth of original contributions by experts in the subjects dealt with. Some of these are highly technical, but there are many that will attract the ordinary reader of the "*M.M.*" with scientific leanings.

Among the articles of general interest may be noted one on the extraction of radium from the ores found in the far north of Canada and its preparation for medical and surgical use in hospitals; and an informative contribution on modern rotary drilling in oilfields. An attractive account is given of the use in industry of black diamonds and of stones that because of their colour or other flaws are of no value as gems. Other articles deal with gold mining in Southern Rhodesia, East Africa and the Gold Coast, and with the minerals used for colouring glass and enamels. Original photographs are freely used to illustrate these and other contributions that help to make a very attractive issue.

A large proportion of the contributions to this issue are concerned with the extraction and treatment of minerals found in various parts of the British Empire. In this connection the Editor makes a strong appeal for better use of the Empire's mineral resources, and points out that their development would lead to increased activity in shipping, shipbuilding, coal mining and other industries. An interesting summary of recent production of the various minerals found in the Empire goes far towards justifying his appeal.

"Living Dangerously"

(George Allen and Unwin. 7/6 net)

This book contains 37 stories told by some of the world's greatest adventurers, who have recorded for their readers experiences of dangerous living in various parts of the world on land or sea, or in the air. All are true stories originally broadcast from the B.B.C. Empire station at Daventry, and now collected in book form by Mr. Cecil Madden.

Each story is complete in itself, and the writers include men who have chosen difficult and dangerous careers, among them explorers, deep sea divers, news photographers, and those who have climbed mountains, sailed the sea in small boats, and indulged in various hobbies and pursuits. These have led them into hazardous and exciting situations, and their readers share in the thrills of the adventures.

Mr. George Eyston, the famous racing driver. From "Speed on Salt," reviewed on the opposite page.

"1001 Questions Answered About Your Aquarium"

By I. N. Mellen and R. J. Lanier (Harrap. 10/6 net)

There must be few readers of the "*M.M.*" who have not kept fish in a small home aquarium. Many of these no doubt have longed to go further with this increasingly popular hobby, especially since the introduction of the heated tank, in which the brilliantly coloured fish that normally live in tropical waters can be kept with success. They will find ample information on their hobby in this book, as will more experienced owners of aquaria. It deals not only with indoor tanks, whether for fresh or salt water, but also with garden ponds; and a useful chapter is included on the keeping of amphibians and reptiles, including baby alligators.

Considering the valuable material contained in this book, it is regrettable that it takes the irritating form of question and answer. One had thought that this method of bookmaking had vanished for ever. It inevitably results in a large proportion of questions and answers that are not of the slightest interest to anybody, and makes it difficult to find the exact subject on which one seeks information. A further drawback for British readers is that the book deals specifically with aquatic conditions in America.

The book is attractively illustrated by a large number of photographs and drawings of interesting fish and other inhabitants of aquaria, and includes three coloured plates of beautiful fish for the tropical tank.

"The Ancient Bridges of Wales and Western England"

(Architectural Press. 6/6 net)

Of all engineering works bridges seem to have the most persistent fascination, and this applies not only to the immense steel structures of the modern builder, but also to the more modest but delightful stone bridges of the past. The author of this book has made a complete survey of the ancient bridges of England and Wales. He has already described the results of his work in various parts of England in previous volumes, and now takes up the story of the ancient bridges of the west, from the Mersey down to the Severn and its tributary the Avon. This area of course includes Wales and in it there are many bridges of outstanding interest that in the course of time may almost be said to have become part of the wonderful scenery to be found there.

It is impossible in a short note to indicate even a few of the more attractive or important of the structures dealt with, but two that are outstanding are the ancient Dee Bridge at Chester, and Monnow Bridge at Monmouth, the only bridge in the country that still has a fortified tower or gateway on it. The stories of the many and varied bridges described are well illustrated by means of 90 excellent photographs.

This is Hornby Sp

HORNBY SPEED BOATS

Enjoy the Thrills of Spe

One of the few outdoor hobbies that can be carried on at any ti
friends, is model motor boating. This splendid hobby is within the r
expensive of all summer hobbies, and it provides hours of fun and th

Hornby Speed Boats and Racing Boats are the best that can b
lines and beautiful finish are the outstanding characteristics of these sp
of excellence in British toys and every boy will be proud to possess

HORNBY S

There are five splendid models
attractive colours. Each one follows
of a famous speed boat prototype.

Each model is built with the same precisic
Trains. Ask your dealer to show you the fu
they are!

Join the Hornby Speed Boat Club

If you own a Hornby Boat you should join the Hornby Speed Boat Club. You can do this by purchasing a special badge (illustrated above) from any Meccano dealer, or direct from Meccano Ltd., price 6d.

Pennants

Pennants for Hornby Speed Boats Nos. 3 and 4 may be purchased separately. They add the final touch of realism to these boats. Price **2d.** each.

Accessories

The Hornby Speed Boat and Racing Boat Clockwork Motors and Propellers with Shafts can be obtained separately by boys who prefer to build their own boats.

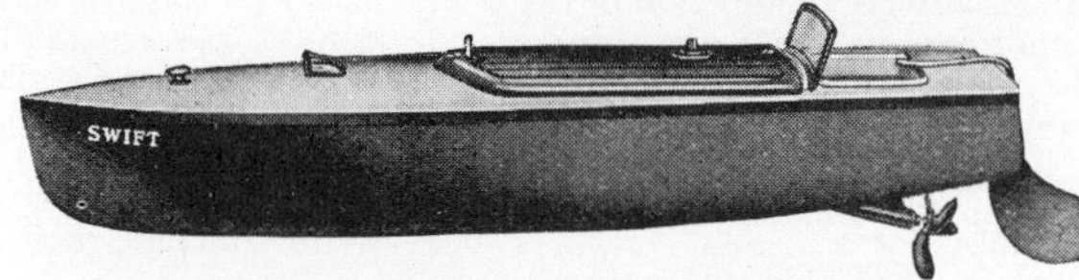

HORNBY SPEED BOAT No. 1. "HAWK." Pri
Travels over 100 ft. on one winding. Choice of th
schemes. Dimensions: Length 9¼ in. Beam

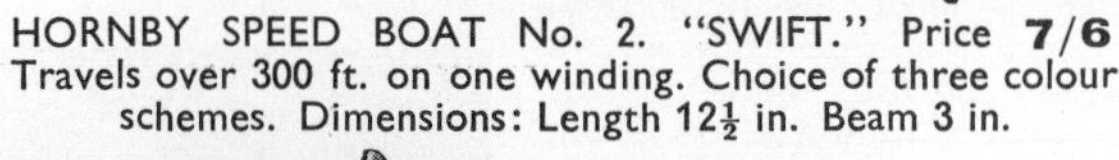

HORNBY SPEED BOAT No. 2. "SWIFT." Price **7/6**
Travels over 300 ft. on one winding. Choice of three colour schemes. Dimensions: Length 12½ in. Beam 3 in.

HORNBY SPEED BOAT No. 3. "CONDOR." Price **12/6**
Travels over 500 ft. on one winding. Choice of three colour schemes. Dimensions: Length 16½ in. Beam 3½ in.

HO
Trav

HORNBY LIMOUSINE BOAT No. 4. "VENTURE." Price **15/6**
Travels over 500 ft. on one winding. Choice of three colour schemes. Dimensions: Length 16½ in. Beam 3½ in.

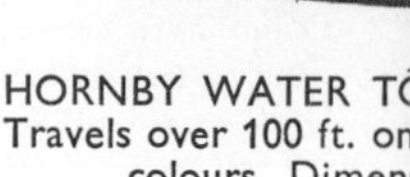

HORNBY WATER TC
Travels over 100 ft. on
colours. Dimens

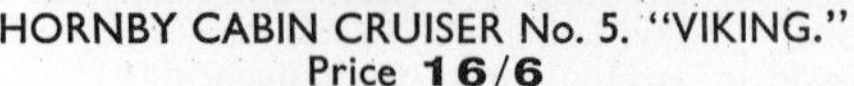

HORNBY CABIN CRUISER No. 5. "VIKING." Price **16/6**
Travels over 500 ft. on one winding. Choice of three colour schemes. Dimensions: Length 16½ in. Beam 3½ in.

Your dealer will be pleased
the range of Hornby Speed Bo
Boats. Once you have seen th
boats you will not be satisfied
one of your own.

Each model is available in a p
combination that gives it a
attractive appearance.

MECCANO LTD. . . . BINNS

d Boat time

ıt Racing!

ˌpecial preparation, either alone or with
ɛt every boy, for it is one of the least

ҳceptional performance, graceful
They introduce a new standard

ATS

ɔ choose, beautifully finished in
sign and general characteristics

ıship as the famous Hornby
: for yourself how perfect

HORNBY RACING BOATS

Hornby Racing Boats are superb! Compare these swift, powerful models with real racing craft. You will see they have the same design, the same slim, smooth lines.

The series of Hornby Racing Boats is composed of three exceptionally fine models. Each boat is extremely "quick off the mark," maintaining a high rate of speed throughout the whole length of its run.

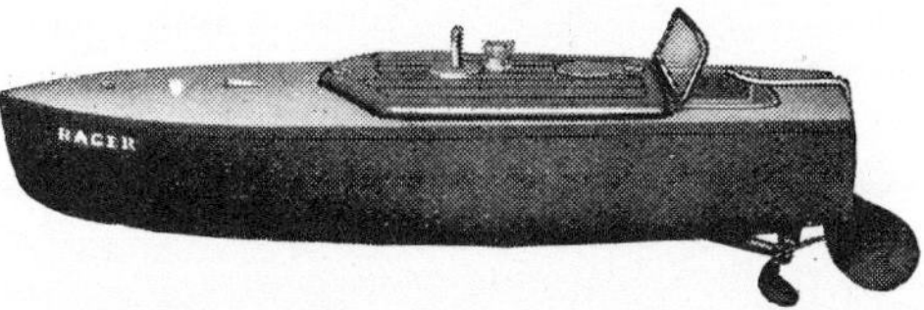

HORNBY RACING BOAT No. 1. "RACER I." Price **4/6**
Travels over 120 ft. at high speed on one winding. Finished in Cream and Green. Dimensions: Length $8\frac{1}{2}$ in. Beam $2\frac{3}{8}$ in.

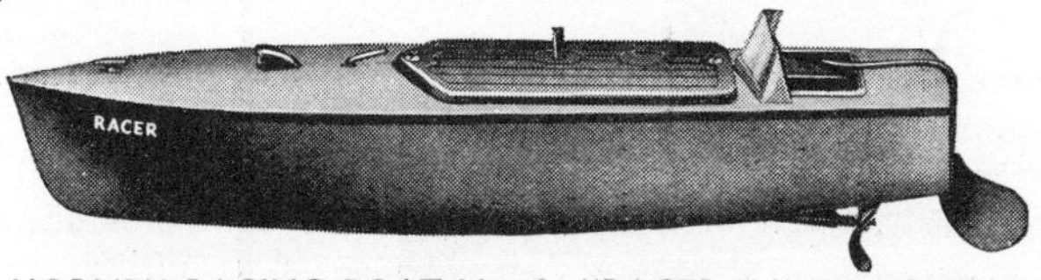

HORNBY RACING BOAT No. 2. "RACER II." Price **8/6**
Travels over 200 ft. at high speed on one winding. Finished in Blue and Cream. Dimensions: Length $12\frac{1}{2}$ in. Beam 3 in.

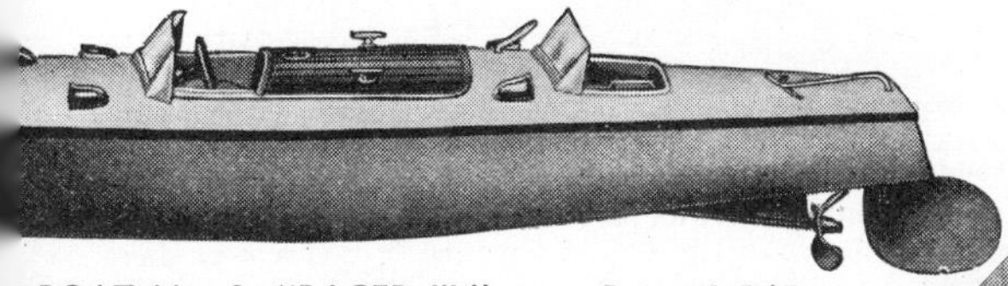

BOAT No. 3. "RACER III." Price **14/6**
at high speed on one winding. Finished in Red and
Dimensions: Length $16\frac{1}{2}$ in. Beam $3\frac{1}{2}$ in.

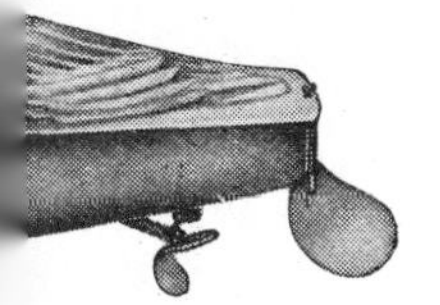

Price **2/6**
inished in appropriate
in. Beam 3 in.

. . . **LIVERPOOL 13**

The New Austin Seven Racer

The remarkable new miniature racing car designed and built by the Austin Motor Co. Ltd. is illustrated on this page. It is known as the O.H.V. Austin Special Racer, and probably will take part in all the leading racing events of the season.

The new machine is the first Austin Seven to have an engine with overhead valves. The weight of the car is little more than two-thirds that of the standard Austin Seven saloon, but its 744 c.c. engine develops nine times as much power as that of the road car.

The new Austin Seven O.H.V. Racing Car, which is described on this page. The machine is expected to figure prominently in this season's racing events. For the illustrations on this page we are indebted to The Austin Motor Co. Ltd.

The Austin Seven made its first appearance as a racing car in 1923 and in that year won first place in the 750 c.c. class in the Italian Grand Prix at Monza. By 1924 it had captured 22 International Class H records at Brooklands and Montlhery, and in the following years it achieved many victories in road events, including the 500 Mile Race at Brooklands in 1929, the Ulster T.T. in 1930 and the International Trophy at Brooklands in 1933. It has a splendid record and the new racer should fully maintain the reputation made by its predecessor.

The engine of the new car is supercharged and separate camshafts operate the inlet and exhaust valves. The drive is transmitted through a clutch of the single dry-plate type and a four-speed gear box with remote manual control. The oiling system of a racing engine is of the greatest importance, for continuous running at high speed makes great demands on the power unit. Three separate oil pumps are used in the new Austin Seven. One delivers oil to the forward end of the crankshaft, the big ends and the roller races at the end of the crankshaft. The second delivers oil at lower pressure to the hollow camshafts and the overhead gear, and the third picks up oil as it drains to the bottom of the crankcase and delivers it to the tank, thus keeping the crankcase dry.

The compact arrangement of the controls is a feature of the Austin O.H.V. racing machine.

Thrills and Collisions at Monte Carlo

Continental racing events usually are packed full of thrills and this year's race through the streets of Monte Carlo for the Monaco Grand Prix was one of the most exciting events that have been witnessed for some time. This "round-the-houses" race is the principal event of its kind in the world. This year it was preceded by a race for 1,500 c.c. cars, in which the British team of E.R.A. cars scored a remarkable success by securing first, second and third places. The driver of the winning car was the Siamese Prince who races under the name of B. Bira. His average speed was 52.99 m.p.h.

There were 17 entries in the Grand Prix itself, but one of them, an Alfa Romeo, had gone barely a dozen yards when an oil pipe broke, and a broad stream of oil was left behind on the road. This accident proved most unfortunate for the Mercedes entrants following close behind. One of these machines, driven by the famous driver Chiron, ran straight into the stream of oil, skidded and crashed. It was followed by another big Mercedes that failed to avoid the wrecked car and also came to grief, and other cars turned right round and only narrowly escaped disaster.

Altogether it was a bad day for the Mercedes machines, for shortly afterwards one of the two cars of this make remaining in the race skidded into the wall almost alongside the wrecked car of Chiron! Only one Mercedes was then left in the race. This was a big silver-coloured car driven by Caracciola, and as though to make up for the misfortune that had befallen his colleagues, this driver succeeded in staving off all his rivals, winning the race with an average speed of 51.69 m.p.h. after a thrilling duel with an Auto-Union machine driven by Varzi, who obtained second place. Another Auto-Union, driven by Rosemeyer, skidded and crashed through the barricades.

Excitement in the "Pits"

Now that the big events of the motor racing season are approaching, "pit" staffs are in for a busy and exciting time, for strategy and tactics play an important part in long-distance racing From the start to the finish of a race the members of the pit staffs have really strenuous times. In addition to their work in refuelling the machines in their teams, changing wheels and carrying out any minor repairs or adjustments necessary during the race, they have to keep records of the laps accomplished by each competing car, and the order in which they pass the pits. This information enables charts to be plotted that show at a glance exactly how the drivers of their teams stand in the race at any particular moment.

A scene at the "pits" on the Ards Circuit, Belfast, just before the finish of the R.A.C. Tourist Trophy Race las' year. The race was won by a Riley driven by F. W. Dixon, whose pit is No. 10. The illustrations on this page are reproduced by courtesy of "The Riley Record."

If one of the machines of any team is leading by a big margin, the driver may be given a signal from his pit directing him to slow down a little and so save his car from unnecessary strain and the possibility of trouble. In other circumstances a driver may be spurred on to greater efforts by means of flag signals telling him to drive his machine all out in order to keep ahead of a threatening rival, or to overtake the leader if at all possible. An example of a signal of this kind is given in the upper illustration on this page, which shows the pits on the Ards Circuit, Belfast, during last year's R.A.C. Tourist Trophy Race. The pit numbered 7, on the left, is that of E. R. Hall and a board with the sign "No. 10" is ready to be shown to him as he flashes past to tell him that No. 10 in the race, F. W. Dixon's Riley, is the only car ahead of him and to urge him to try to catch the leader, who eventually became the winner.

The scene in a pit during a race is a thrilling one. The noise is tremendous as competitors who have made calls for refuelling or repairs race their engines at top speed in getting away again. Other cars come in with a screech of brakes and squealing tyres, some with their radiators boiling, others perhaps with their engines mis-firing on some of their cylinders. Wheels and tyres are changed, minor adjustments are made, and tanks are refilled. Precise instructions and careful drill enable this to be done with amazing speed, and a double-wheel change and refuelling have often been completed in just over 30 seconds. All the while stop watches click and chart keepers work feverishly, cars streak past with a noise like thunder, and the signalman stands by with his flags, ready to give his driver any warning that may be necessary as he flashes by.

A pit staff at work changing the tyres of one of the Rileys entered by F. W. Dixon in the 500 miles race of the British Racing Drivers' Club at Brooklands in September 1935. The car was handled by Cyril Paul, seen on the left, and C. Brackenbury, who is sitting on the tail.

Motoring Under the Alps

If plans that the Swiss Federal Railway Authorities are now considering are carried out it will soon be possible to motor under the Alps between Switzerland and Italy through the Simplon Railway Tunnel. This tunnel consists of separate bores for up and down traffic and the scheme concerns the conversion of one of the bores into a motor road If it is adopted it will be necessary to instal a complicated ventilating system to dispel the fumes of the petrol used by cars, and to construct "sidings" in the walls of the tunnel into which cars that break down during the passage can be towed out of the way of the main traffic stream

The Simplon Tunnel links Switzerland and Italy and was built in 1906 It is over 12 miles in length and is the longest of the tunnels through the Alps.

This Month's Motor Races

Some of the chief events of the motoring season will be decided during June and so far as this country is concerned one of the most interesting is the Shelsley Walsh Hill Climb on the 6th of the month The hill chosen for the climb has a gradient of 1 in 6, sharp corners, and tricky bends, and the event never fails to provide spectators with plenty of thrills

This year's climb will be made particularly attractive by the presence of Hans Stuck, the famous German driver who is entering a new fast Auto-Union machine that has been specially fitted out for hill-climbing work. This year also the timing will be carried out electrically The timing instrument will be set in operation automatically when the starting signal is given, and it will be stopped when the front wheels of a car operate a contact on the finishing line.

The chief events on the Continent will be the Le Mans 24-hour Endurance Race, to be run on 13th and 14th June, and the French Grand Prix, the most famous of all Grand Prix events, on the 28th of the month. There is nothing really comparable with the Le Mans Race from a spectacular point of view, for the circuit over which it is run is wide and fast and permits very high average speeds to be attained The track consists of specially maintained main roads running through woods, and is 8.38 miles in length. The event is limited to 60 entries, and Britain will be strongly represented by Austin, M.G., Singer, Ford, Talbot and Frazer Nash cars. Last year the race was won by J. Hindmarsh and L. Fontes, driving a Lagonda, who covered 1,867.3 miles in the allotted time, at an average speed of 77.8 m.p.h.

The course over which the French Grand Prix will be run at Montlhery on 28th June is a combination of track and road circuit made up of 1½ miles of artificially banked track, on which very high speeds have been attained, and a road section 7½ miles in length with long straight stretches of which are perfectly straight. The record speed for the track section of the circuit is 147.79 m.p.h and that for the road portion 91.35 m.p.h.

This year the race is to be confined to sports cars that are not fitted with superchargers. In the past supercharged Italian and German entries have swept the board. Cars from England, America, Germany and Italy are making a formidable challenge and it will be interesting to see whether France can regain her national pride by winning the event.

Hack-Saw Blades in the Making

Interesting Processes at a Sheffield Works

IN articles that have appeared in past issues of the "*M.M.*" we have described processes entailed in the manufacture of various familiar commodities. This month we continue the series with a description of the many interesting operations involved in the making of engineers' hack-saw blades at the Sheffield steel works of James Neill and Company (Sheffield) Ltd., who are one of the largest firms of blade makers in this country. The original works was established about half-a-century ago for the manufacture of crucible steel, of which composite steel was the chief product. This material has a very hard face with a soft backing, and is widely used for making certain types of press tools, machine knives and cutters. These works also produce safety razor blades, permanent magnets and hack-saw frames. In this article, however, we are dealing only with the manufacture of hack-saw blades, and as these are made from crucible steel, a full description of their production must commence with the processes entailed in making this material. The material is melted in clay crucibles, the manufacture of which is one of the few surviving handicrafts in the engineering industry. In making the crucibles the operator uses his bare feet, and walks backward and forward on a bed of clay in a series of uniform movements, as shown in the lower illustration on the opposite page. Readers may think this process very slow, but actually it gives results unobtainable by any other means and its purpose is to expel any air contained in the clay.

When sufficiently mixed by treading, the clay is kneaded by hand for a short time, quantities of material sufficient for the making of a single crucible being dealt with separately. The kneaded mass is then put in the mould of a press, and a plunger is forced into it pressing the clay into the shape of a crucible. The formed crucible is then lifted out of the mould and a top taper is given to it by means of a hollow cone, which is pressed down on the material by hand. The crucibles are then stored on shelves for a preliminary drying, and great care is taken to keep the rate of drying approximately constant by controlling the temperature of the room by means of sliding louvres. The drying operation is completed in the steel foundry itself, the crucibles being first stored in racks above the furnaces and finally on the tops of the furnaces themselves. The crucible lids are similarly dried.

The furnaces are heated by producer gas, and the charge for the crucibles is prepared under the control of the works laboratory. Valuable constituents of the material, such as tungsten and chromium, are stored in a strong room, and are sent to the foundry in sealed packets, which are placed intact in the crucible. A charge takes about $3\frac{1}{2}$ hours to melt, the correct temperature for "teeming" or pouring being ascertained by means of an optical pyrometer. The ingot moulds are of cast iron made in halves, which are clamped together, and the ingots are of rectangular cross-section and for making hack-saw blades weigh about 120 lb. each. After teeming the ingots are allowed to cool very slowly and are then marked for identification.

The guillotine and tooth milling section at the works of James Neill and Co. (Sheffield) Ltd., Sheffield, to whom we are indebted for this illustration and the lower one on the opposite page.

The works laboratory now again takes charge. The numbered ingots in the warehouse are drilled at each end, and the combined drillings are then analysed. As the particular characteristics of the material depends on the amount of carbon it contains the results of the analysis are carefully recorded and classified, and the ingots are rigidly graded according to their carbon content.

The ingots are then passed on to the rolling mills and rolled into sheets about 20 in. wide by from 59 in. to 66 in. long, and in various thicknesses from 13 W.G. to 23 W.G. The grading of the ingots according to their carbon content is preserved through the rolling operation, so that sheets of one thickness only are made from ingots of the same carbon content. When the sheets are returned to the blade factory, classification by thickness automatically provides classification by carbon content, and by this means it is possible to ensure that the resultant blades, when subjected to the correct heat treatment for the particular carbon content, are of uniform hardness.

The sheets are then cut by guillotine shears into pieces known as "moulders," the width of which corresponds with the length of blade required, plus an allowance for subsequent rounding of the ends. The "moulders" are then passed through guillotines endwise and sheared into strips a little wider than the finished blade. The next operation is that of milling the teeth, and for this purpose the strips are firmly clamped into a solid mass containing about three gross of 23 W.G. strips, on the table of a milling machine of the type shown in the upper illustration in the opposite page.

The work table is mounted on inclined ways on the saddle so that the height of the surface of the block of blades may be adjusted relative to the cutters. The cutters are of what is known as the gang type, that is, each individual cutter is set with its teeth slightly behind those of the adjacent one, the resultant cutting edge being of helical form.

The setting of the teeth to ensure that each tooth has sufficient clearance to do its own share of the work is done on automatic machines made by the firm, the feeding of the blade being arranged to synchronise with the form of the setting rollers, so as to prevent "splitting" of the teeth in the process. The machines allow of any variation in thickness and width.

A view in the tooth setting and hack-saw blade finishing section of the machine shop at the works of James Neill and Co. Ltd., showing on the right part of the tooth cutting plant. For this illustration we are indebted to the courtesy of "Machinery."

After setting, the strips pass through heavy power presses, one stroke of which performs three operations simultaneously, i.e., the rounding of both ends, the punching of a hole at each end, and branding with the word "Eclipse," the trade name under which these blades are marketed.

The blades are now ready for heat treatment, and the exact nature of this depends upon the type of blade required. There are four different types. The all-hard blade is, as its name implies, hardened throughout its depth. Blades of this kind are usually preferred by skilled operators on account of their rigidity, but for hard work by less experienced persons, or when the work cannot be rigidly held, flexible blades are the more suitable, as they are unbreakable in use. The all-hard blades are heated in a gas-fired furnace to a temperature of about 800 deg. C, the temperature being automatically controlled by a thermostatic device. At the end of the period of treatment an electric bell signals to operators at each end of the furnace that a new batch is to be inserted and the heated one withdrawn. An adjustable time-switch enables the period of treatment to be set to suit the size of blade concerned.

A scene in the crucible department showing workmen treading beds of clay with their bare feet.

On removal from the furnace the blades are quenched in a bath of pure sperm oil, and are then removed to centrifugal separators, which remove the oil and leave the blades so dry that the scale may be shaken off by hand. The blades are then ready for tempering.

Flexible blades are hardened only in the vicinity of the teeth, and naturally undergo a different heat-treatment process. The temperature of the teeth and immediate vicinity is raised to about 800 deg. C, and the blades are then quenched in an oil well, thus effecting the hardening of the toothed edge only. The back of the blade is then left soft.

A third type of blade has teeth on both edges, and here again the hardening is confined to the toothed edges, the centre of the blade being left soft. This blade is used for small-diameter cutting, and tubes in which the blade does not pass wholly through the material cut. Both the flexible and double-edge blades are cleaned in the manner already referred to. All three types are, after cleaning, tempered by insertion in a large gas-fired furnace which is raised to the desired temperature. This furnace is provided with means for maintaining the temperature in a uniformly distributed manner. When the desired temperature has been reached the gas supply is cut off, and the furnace and the blades inside are allowed to cool without infiltration of air.

The final process consists of softening the ends of the blades in the region of the tension-holes by means of which they are fixed in the saw frame. This is done by placing them on an endless belt, by which they are carried over a series of gas jets.

During the process of manufacture the blades are inspected and tested in various ways. After setting, for example, a careful check is made to see that the amount of set is correct. The blade is inserted in a gauge having three slots, the first of which checks the thickness of the back of the blade, in the second slot the set teeth must not enter, and in the third slot the teeth must enter. This ensures that the set of the teeth is between limits of the width of the second and third slots. A number of blades selected daily at random are examined on a hardness-testing machine. In the warehouse, before bundling the blades, a final examination takes place, and they are then oiled by being passed through rollers covered with oil-soaked material, bundled into dozens and packed.

As a final check of the quality blades taken from each day's production are submitted to actual cutting tests.

FROM OUR READERS

These pages are reserved for articles from our readers. Contributions not exceeding 500 words in length are invited on any subject of general interest. These should be written neatly on one side of the paper only, and they may be accompanied by photographs or sketches for use as illustrations. Articles that are published will be paid for at our usual rates. Statements contained in articles submitted for these pages are accepted as being sent in good faith, but the Editor takes no responsibility for their accuracy.

A Pioneer Motor Car

I saw the old car shown in the photograph on this page at a garage near Worcester. I strolled over to have a look at it and the garage proprietor told me some of its history. It was built at Malvern and put on the road in 1889. Several types of power unit were tried out in it. The first was a steam engine, and afterwards it was made to run on ordinary coal gas, benzoline, and finally petrol. It had no rubber tyres, no springs and no upholstery, and at first the driver had to hire a man to walk in front waving a red flag. Its speed then was about 4 m.p.h., but later, when this restriction was removed, it achieved the much higher speed of 12 m.p.h.

The pioneer motor car described on this page. It was driven successively by steam, coal gas, benzoline and petrol. Photograph by R. Green, Birmingham.

The "joys" of motoring in this ancient car must have been very few, for its occupants rode on it and not in it, and had no protection from the weather. The steering wheel stands straight up, and the driver had to crouch forward over it in an attitude very different from that of the driver of to-day. The radiator resembles a huge gridiron, and the whole appearance of the vehicle is so strange that it is difficult to think of the motor car of to-day as its direct descendant.

R. GREEN (Birmingham).

A Trip to the Faröe Islands

Recently I visited the Faröe Islands fishing grounds in a trawler. We left St. Andrew's Dock, Hull, and steamed down the Humber, waving a greeting to the crew of the Bull Lightship as we passed on our way to the sea. After rounding Spurn Head, with its lonely lighthouse, we turned northward and by evening had picked up the flashing light of the lighthouse on Flamborough Head to the north of Bridlington Bay.

Our course followed the east coast of Great Britain and twice on our way northward we were out of sight of land, once when cutting straight across the Firth of Forth, and the second time when crossing Moray Firth. Then we entered the Pentland Firth, and in this narrow strait, through which the Atlantic tide races furiously, we found ourselves in very choppy water. Off Dunnet Head we headed straight for the Faröes, on our way passing the rocky Skerries with their warning light.

Early one morning I was thrilled to see rushing through the grey dawn the low dark form of a swift cruiser. I was told that this was a Danish fisheries protection vessel, employed to prevent illegal fishing within the three mile limit. This limit does not follow each curve of the coastline, as I had hitherto supposed. Instead two points at a convenient distance apart are selected, and an imaginary line is drawn to connect them. The limit then is a parallel line three miles out at sea.

A Hull trawler on the way to the Faröe fishing grounds. Photograph by J. W. Casson, Hull.

I was fortunate to see the Faröe Islands themselves, for these are often enveloped in fog. My greatest thrill came one day when I was on the bridge and the sky darkened, the wind began to blow hard, and the waves rose higher and higher. Lightning played vividly across the dark expanse of sea and cloud, and soon the waves began to sweep right over the bridge itself. I held on grimly, as the vessel dived into the troughs between the waves and then rose to mount the crests, on which she seemed to pause for a moment before plunging downward again with a shiver. For three hours no one could get to the bridge or leave it owing to the violence of the seas breaking over the trawler.

As we passed Dunnet Head again on our homeward voyage the skipper mounted the roof of the bridge and flagged a message to the lighthouse keepers. The news he gave was to be forwarded to the owners of the trawler by telephone. J. W. CASSON (Hull).

A Quaint Chinese Custom

The Chinese are noted for their devotion to their ancestors, and the custom known as the Cheng Beng Festival, or the Feast of Tombs, is still observed by Chinese all over the world.

Once a year, on the 13th day of the Third Moon, corresponding to the English month of April, the Chinese visit the graves of their ancestors, and offerings of a large roasted pig, two or three small pots of boiled rice, the staple food of the East, tea, cakes and fruits are placed on stone tablets in front of the graves for the dead to feast upon.

Offerings on the altar before a Chinese grave, over which can be seen the silver paper money referred to in the accompanying article. Photograph by Lim Kean Chuan, Penang.

When the dead have had their fill, which is decided by the toss of two coins, small square pieces of paper are burnt to serve as money for the dead in the next world. Other pieces of silver paper of the same shape are then scattered over the grave to conclude the ceremony.

The accompanying photograph shows a Chinese grave with the offerings upon the altar, and the pieces of paper-money scattered all over the grave also can be seen. LIM KEAN CHUAN (Penang).

Cruising in the Baltic Sea

During the summer of last year I enjoyed a fortnight's cruise to the northern capitals of Europe. I was one of a party of about 700 schoolboys and our home during the trip was the "*Neuralia.*" We left Tilbury on a baking hot day but met a refreshing breeze as we steamed down the Thames Estuary towards the open sea. Late in the afternoon of the third day we arrived at Arendal, a picturesque Norwegian town at the end of a small fjord surrounded by frowning coniferous trees. We landed amid the curious stares of the greater part of the populace, but fog in the North Sea had made us late and we only stayed two hours before steaming southward through the Kattegat to Copenhagen. There a civic reception awaited us, and when the formalities had been completed we proceeded on a motor coach tour of this delightful city. I was impressed by the number of cyclists in its streets; in Copenhagen even the business man goes to the office on his machine.

"Shooting the Sun" during a cruise in the Baltic Sea. Illustration by courtesy of the Secondary Schools Travel Trust.

Two days afterwards found us approaching Stockholm by a long island-studded inlet of the Atlantic Sea. Stockholm is a beautiful city with a wonderful new Town Hall and many fine shopping centres, where we had no difficulty in making purchases, as English is freely spoken.

After a happy stay of two days in Stockholm, we passed on to Helsinki, the capital of Finland, which is known as the "White City of the North" because it is built of white granite and is free from smoke. Drizzling rain that fell all the time we were there did not damp our spirits as we went ashore by tender, and in the evening we had tea in the Municipal Gardens as the guests of the authorities.

Next day we left Helsinki for the long trip to Kiel, and spent two lazy days playing deck games or splashing in the small swimming bath. When we awoke on the third morning, the "*Neuralia*" was anchored in Kiel Harbour, with battleships, submarines and Herr Hitler's state yacht forming a background to the scene. On going ashore we were greeted in a very friendly manner.

Next day we passed through the canal into the North Sea and on our way home passed the "*Bremen,*" travelling at great speed and throwing up a wash that tossed even our 9,000-ton ship about. The following day we spent in gathering our scattered belongings, and in the evening we enjoyed a deck concert and sing-song. As the white cliffs of England appeared through the dusk a strange hush fell upon us, to be broken by thunderous cheers for Old England.

C. SHAW (Millwall).

The Wild Cattle of Chillingham

I was never really afraid of bulls before I saw the wild cattle of Chillingham in Northumberland, but I was frightened even of the calves of that herd! The cattle are white, shaggy animals of great ferocity that have roamed the Cheviots for 700 years, but now are confined to a hill on Lord Tankerville's estate at Chillingham. They are ruled by a King Bull, who in the Spring has to struggle hard to retain his supremacy, for all the bulls then fight each other until one emerges as the conqueror. Those who are beaten slink away into the hills and are not allowed near the herd again.

When I went to see these creatures the keeper told me that not long before he had been chased by them and forced to climb a tree until they went away. Visitors are not allowed to approach nearer than 50 yards from them, but can look at the herd through field glasses. C. CLARKE (Berwick-on-Tweed).

Meccano Suggestions Section

Edited by "Spanner"

(352)—Electrically Operated Radial Engine

(M. Andrews, Salford)

Some time ago we described a four-cylinder car engine operated by solenoids and also a small single-cylinder engine driven in the same way. In each of these models the solenoids were built up from Bobbins, part No. 181, wound with thin copper wire. Owing to the interest that these models created we think that the engine illustrated on this page will be of interest to many Meccano model builders. This new model represents a five-cylinder radial, air-cooled engine, and it is built up from Elektron Magnet Coils and Cores. Considering the somewhat unorthodox method of operation, the model is surprisingly powerful and efficient, and is quite suitable for incorporating in a model aeroplane of suitable scale size. It works at a speed of about 200 r.p.m., but it is advisable to run it at about 120 r.p.m. This will be found to be quite fast enough for ordinary use.

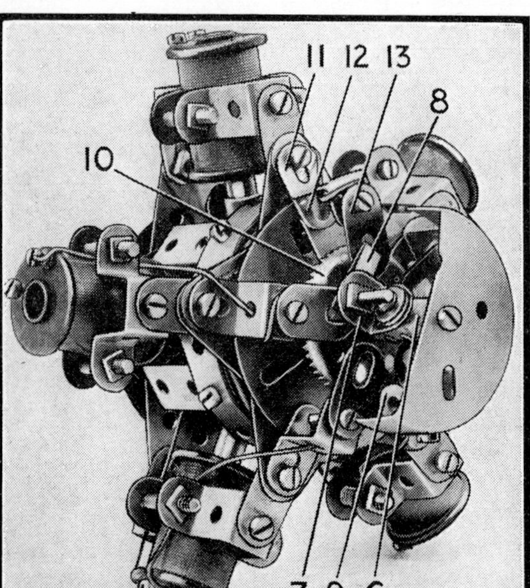

Fig. 352.

The building of the engine is commenced by bending a 7½" and a 2" Strip into a circle 3. To these Strips are secured five 1½"×½" Double Angle Strips, and these carry at their free ends a series of 1½" Strips. The 1½" Strips are arranged in the form of five triangles, the apex of each pointing outward. At each apex two Flat Brackets are bolted in place. The opposite ends of the 1½"×½" Double Angle Strips carry a similar arrangement of 1½" Strips and Flat Brackets, but in addition ½" Reversed Angle Brackets 11 are fitted.

The Flat Brackets 12 and the corresponding Flat Brackets at the other side of the engine serve to clamp in place two Face Plates both of which are shown in Fig. 352. The Face Plate, only partly shown in this illustration, should not be fitted until the crankshaft and connecting-rods are put into position.

The Magnet Coils should now be fitted, and this part of the construction is carried out in the following way. Each of the Flat Brackets secured to the top of each pair of 1½" Strips forms a support for a Double Bent Strip, and each pair of these latter parts are clamped together by ¾" Bolts. The Magnet Coils are held between the Double Bent Strips and are clamped in place by the ¾" Bolts. A Core is now inserted in each Magnet Coil and on the threaded portion of this is clamped a Collar by means of a grub-screw. As a further security the 6 B.A. Nut, supplied with the Core is screwed on to the threaded shank and tightened against the Collar. The unoccupied threaded hole of the Collar carries a Bolt on which is pivotally mounted a 1½" Strip.

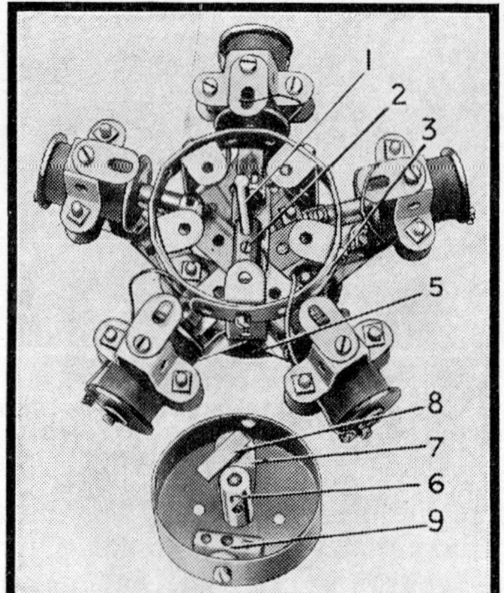

Fig. 352a.

The free ends of the five 1½" Strips, when they are all fitted in position, are carried on a 1" Screwed Rod that is fitted at each end into the centre tapped hole of a Coupling. Two grub-screws, one of which is shown at 2, Fig. 352a, are screwed in tightly to hold the 1" Rod in position. These two Couplings and the 1" Threaded Rod together form the crankshaft and this complete unit is supported on two short rods, one of which is shown at 1. The inner ends of these rods are secured in the plain holes at one end of each Coupling, and they are journalled in the bosses of the Face Plates already mentioned. Two Washers are carried on the 1" Threaded Rod on each side of the 1½" Strips and they serve to keep these Strips from rubbing against the Couplings. Two more Washers are used on the short rod opposite to 1, in order to give sufficient clearance between the Face Plate, shown fitted in Fig. 352a, and the crankshaft. A Collar is fitted on the outer portion of this Rod and bears lightly against the boss of this last-mentioned Face Plate.

Great care must now be taken in lining up all the 1½" Strips forming the connecting rods and also the Cores forming the piston rods. When this has been accomplished to the builder's satisfaction the Face Plate, not shown in the lower illustration, is fitted, and this forms the bearing for the Rod 1. This Face Plate is clamped in place by the Flat Brackets 12 in the manner already described. The Rod 1 also carries a 1½" Contrate Wheel 10 that forms a small flywheel.

The ½" Reversed Angle Brackets 11 each carry a Flat Bracket 13, and this is secured in place by a 6 B.A. Bolt and Nut and also an Insulating Bush and Washer. These Flat Brackets form the segments of a stationary commutator, and the brush is caused to rotate with the crankshaft and make contact with these. The brush is formed by bending a Pendulum Connection 8 as shown in the lower illustration, and securing it by a 6 B.A. Bolt and Nut to an Angle Bracket 7. This latter part is bolted to a Threaded Coupling 6, and three Washers are used for spacing purposes.

The Threaded Coupling is locked on the outer end of the Rod 1 by a grub-screw, and it must be so arranged that the brush 8 makes contact with each Flat Bracket 13 at exactly the right moment. Thus when one Core is ready to enter its respective Magnet Coil, the brush should make contact with the Flat Bracket opposite that Coil. The outer end of the Coupling 6 is threaded and it accommodates a Bolt that is used to clamp in place a Boiler End. In Fig. 352 this Boiler End is shown cut away in order to make the internal construction clear. At a point on the Boiler End opposite to the webs of the crankshaft a Coupling 9 is fitted and this forms a counterbalance weight.

It is a simple matter to connect the Magnet Coils. Each inside terminal of the coils is connected to opposite Flat Brackets 13, the remaining terminals all being connected together and linked up with an insulated Terminal on the frame of the model. A second main terminal is now fitted and this must be "earthed" to the frame. It will now be seen that the current flows through the frame of the model along the brush 8 and in turn through each Magnet Coil.

(353)—Aeroplane Modifications

(A. Hope, Manchester)

Last month, on the "With the Model Builders" page, a suggestion for a pointed nose piece to be used in conjunction with No. O Aeroplane Constructor Sets, was described. This idea has apparently interested many builders of Aeroplane Models and we have received a variety of suggestions in connection with these. Among the many letters received was one from Mr. A. Hope, Manchester 12, who brought to our notice some modifications that he has recently carried out in connection with No. O Aeroplane Constructor models.

Although in some cases new parts have been added to models and slight alterations made to existing parts, his work is nevertheless worthy of highest merit. His model Hawker "Osprey" Seaplane Fighter is very realistic. The Interplane Struts and Wing Struts have been slightly altered and the lower wing foreshortened. These rather drastic alterations are more than justified by the final appearance.

(354)—Balance and Lever Movement (A. Munja, Calcutta)

The upper illustration on this page shows a mechanism that is probably reproduced in Meccano for the first time. It is a demonstration model of a watch or spring-driven clock lever movement, and its construction is a triumph of accurate Meccano Model Building. All the parts used in this model are Meccano, except for a length of thin brass strip used for the "hair spring." The mechanism works at a much slower speed than an actual lever movement owing to the size of the balance wheel, but its beat is quite regular, and can be used to drive an actual clock.

Fig. 354.

The complete mechanism is shown mounted in a frame of very simple construction and no driving unit is shown fitted. Any of the Meccano Clockwork Motors are suitable for driving this mechanism for a short period, but the best method is to employ an Electric Motor driving through an epicyclic gear.

The balance wheel is built up from two Circular Strips across which is bolted a $7\frac{1}{2}''$ Strip. This carries at its centre a Double Arm Crank, the boss of which accommodates a 1″ Rod. To each end of this Rod is secured a Coupling in the outer ends of which are gripped 1″ Threaded Rods, pointed at their ends. The bearings, indicated at 6, can be formed from Grease Cups, but in this model they are specially made from bolts having a small conical depression in their ends. This depression is made with the aid of an $\frac{1}{8}''$ diameter twist drill. These bearings must be adjusted very carefully so that the balance wheel swings as freely as possible.

The hair spring is made from a strip of brass 4 secured at its inner end to one of the Couplings carried on the balance wheel pivot. This connection is made by a bolt and two Washers. The other end of the spring is clamped in the slot of a Strip Coupling mounted on a Threaded Pin shown at 5. The spring is an 18″ length of springy brass, $\frac{3}{8}''$ wide, and .010″ in thickness. The length of this spring must be so adjusted that when the balance wheel is in equilibrium the Threaded Pin 7 is immediately below the pivot of the balance wheel.

The Threaded Pin 7 engages with the "crutch" that is mounted on one end of the lever 3, formed from a $4\frac{1}{2}''$ Strip. The crutch is built up from two $2\frac{1}{2}''$ large radius Curved Strips, overlapping the Strip 3 two holes, and also two 3″ Strips. As will be seen, the Curved Strips sweep outward towards the 3″ Strips. The lever 3 is pivotally mounted on a Rod near one end, and at its lower extremity it carries a 2″ Strip and a Flat Bracket. These two parts are used in preference to a $2\frac{1}{2}''$ Strip for purposes of adjustment. The pallets 2 are each built up by $\frac{1}{2}''$ Angle Brackets as shown, and they must be arranged to correspond exactly with those in the photograph. The construction of the escapement wheel is shown in the illustration.

(355)—Lightning Arrestor (J. McIntyre, Invergordon)

Meccano has once again been found of use for practical purposes. Fig. 355 illustrates a neat safety switch for a wireless, designed by J. McIntyre, of Invergordon. No doubt many Meccano boys will put the model to good purpose.

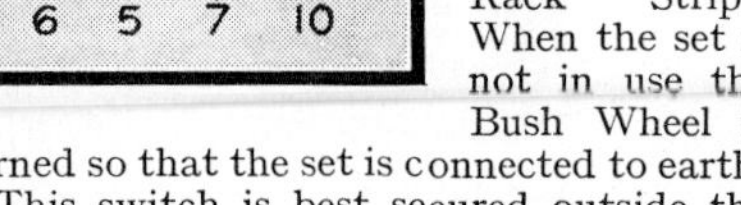
Fig. 355.

As will be seen it consists essentially of two $3\frac{1}{2}''$ Rack Strips 3 and 4 mounted on a small base-board by means of Double Brackets. One of the Double Brackets carrying the Rack Strip 3 is connected by a length of heavy gauge copper wire to an Obtuse Angle Bracket 5. A second Obtuse Angle Bracket is similarly placed on the opposite side of the base and is connected to Rack Strip 4. The wire 1 connects the Rack Strip 4 to the aerial and the wire 2 forms the earth wire. The connection from the set is made by the wire 10 to a crank 6 that carries in its boss a 2″ Rod 9. This forms the support for a Socket Coupling 8 and Crank 7 and the upper end of the Socket Coupling carries a Bush Wheel as shown.

With the Bush Wheel in the position shown in Fig. 355, the Crank 7 is in contact with the Obtuse Angle Bracket 5 and the set is earthed. When the Bush Wheel is turned to make contact with the second Obtuse Angle Bracket the set is connected to the aerial, and if this should happen to be struck by lightning, the charge leaks away to earth across the gaps between the teeth of the Rack Strips. When the set is not in use the Bush Wheel is turned so that the set is connected to earth.

This switch is best secured outside the house in such a position that the vertical aerial and earth wires can be brought close together without bending them to any great extent. This precaution adds considerably to the safety of the wireless set. The wire 10 is used to connect the switch arm 7 with the aerial terminal of the set. The earth terminal of the set must be connected in the ordinary way to "earth."

Results of Suggestion Voting Contest

This year's Suggestion Voting has again proved the popularity of gear-boxes. Electric Motors this year are also in the foreground, and much to the surprise of the judges the Counting Machine, Suggestion No. 324, received many votes. This is of course a very complicated mechanism, and one which normally would only appeal to few model-builders. The method of voting adopted was similar to that employed on previous occasions. The first four most popular models were selected by means of a system of points and the winners of the contest was found by a similar means.

The results for Home and Overseas Sections were very similar, first place being taken in both cases by the Four-speed and Reverse Gear-Box (No. 332), by a wide margin. The Counting Machine (No. 324) took second place in the Home Section, and fourth place in the Overseas Section. The third position Home and second position Overseas have been occupied by a model Synchronous Motor (No. 320), which has proved popular on other occasions. Another gear-box fills the fourth place in the Home Section and third place in the Overseas Section, this being the Three-speed and Reverse Gear-Box (No. 336).

No competitor submitted an entirely correct solution, and the system of points, to which reference has already been made, was resorted to. A maximum number of points was allotted for each suggestion placed in correct position on the competitor's list, and a reduced number of points according to the extent of the misplacement.

Home Section

The first and second prizes of cheques for £1/1/- and 10/6 respectively and other money prizes have been awarded to the following competitors. The winner J. Franklin Anderson, Hillhead, Glasgow, is to receive a cheque for £1/1/-. The second prize of 10/6 goes to B. Hardie, Bristol. Prizes of 2/6 have been sent to: L. Martin, Cheltenham; J. C. Thompson, Sutton-in-Craven, Yorks.; J. Staunton, Felixstowe; E. Wrayford, Moretonhampstead, Devon; W. Thomas, Swansea; E. Haffield, Dublin; G. Hope, Liverpool; J. Phillips, Liverpool; T. W. Green, Mapperley, Notts.; B. Dagnall, Sidcup, Kent; A. Dick, Brighton; V. Harding, Dagenham.

Overseas Section

The first prize of £1/1/- has been won by C. J. McCain, Sydney, Australia; and the second prize of 10/6 goes to Paul Cevestre, Fecamp, France. Each of the following 12 competitors receives a prize of 2/6: R. Burbery, Christchurch, N. Zealand; J. M. Brown, Cambridge, N. Zealand; F. van Bulck, Brussels; G. Sadler, Alberta, Canada; D. Murison, Buenos Aires; E. Azzopardi, Sliema, Malta; C. Keekok, Singapore; B. Walsh, Nelson, N. Zealand; J. Walker, Leichhardt, N. S. Wales; F. J. Abbott, Wellington, N.Z.; A. Carpinter, Christchurch, N.Z.; Pablo Giese, Buenos Aires.

(M170) Sprocket Wheels. The present system of Meccano Sprocket Wheels appears to have found some disfavour in the eyes of W. Bradshaw, Sheffield. In his recent letter he suggests that the present sprockets, except 18 and 36 teeth Wheels, should be replaced by wheels having 12, 24, 30, 42 and 48 teeth. With these, nineteen different ratios would be obtainable. The idea would be rather costly, however, and it is unlikely that we shall be able to carry out his suggestions for some time.

In Search of New Models

Windmills and Water-mills

WINDMILLS and water-mills are interesting structures in themselves and the construction of miniatures of them gives splendid opportunities for effective and realistic structural work, and also for the introduction of simple but interesting mechanisms. Thus they are useful subjects both for the Meccano enthusiast with a small Outfit and for the more experienced model-builder with larger resources. Windmills of course are more common in Holland than in this country, and there form a prominent feature of the landscape. It is therefore not surprising that many models of this kind have originated in Holland, and Fig. 2 on this page is an excellent example of one of these.

Fig. 1. Two Meccano model mills set in simple but effective scenery.

In this country many windmills are still preserved, although few are kept in working order. Model-builders who wish to reproduce their chief features may have seen some of the windmills yet remaining in existence, or may be able to obtain the details they require from photographs that have appeared in periodicals or in books on windmills. They vary in an interesting manner. In some cases they were built as towers and their four revolving sails or sweeps, as the miller calls them, were mounted on a revolving cap so that they could be turned to make the best use of the prevailing wind. The movements of the caps were controlled by fantails behind the sweeps that automatically turned them to the most favourable position. In other cases the entire windmill was mounted on a post and could be turned round for the same purpose. In the latter case a long beam that was either horizontal or sloped downward was used to turn the mill, and at its outer end was mounted on a wheel to ease the labours of the miller.

Mills driven by water are still used, especially in the hillier and more remote parts of the country, It is not perhaps easy to find examples of them, as in many cases they are at some distance from roads. A little exploration often reveals a really old fashioned water-mill still working, however. A few rough sketches or a photograph then will give the model-builder all the information he requires for constructing a really interesting model.

Fig. 2. A fine E Outfit Model of a typical Dutch Windmill.

Where possible what is known as the overshot type of wheel is employed in a water-mill. In this the floats fitted round the circumference of the wheel are arranged to form receptacles for the water, which pours into them from the mill dam as they reach the top of their circular course. In this case the water acts partly by impulse and partly by weight, and after doing its work is allowed to run into a trench or sluice underneath the wheel. Where the height does not allow a wheel of this kind to be used the undershot type is employed. In this the water is delivered to the floats at their lowest point and acts entirely by momentum.

Yet another type of windmill that the model-builder should bear in mind is the modern one, with several small vanes mounted on a high tower, usually a steel structure. Windmills of this kind are used largely for pumping water, either from wells or in drainage work. The fan is kept pointing into the wind by a specially designed fin, and it is used to drive the pump.

A model of this type of windmill is shown in Fig. 5. Others can be built in considerable variety, and very small Outfit models of this kind can be made to look extremely attractive. The main framework can be represented by four long Strips or Angle Girders, and bracing need have a no more substantial appearance than that supplied by cord. Strips can be used to advantage as cross members, however, as shown in Fig. 5. The fan is often built up from a Bush Wheel carrying radially disposed Strips twisted slightly to represent blades. The vane or fin for keeping the fan facing the wind is best represented by a Flanged Sector Plate, but in smaller models Flat Trunnions are often made use of.

The rotary movement of the shaft carrying the fan is converted into reciprocatory motion by means of a Crank or an Eccentric. In the model illustrated it is accomplished by a $\frac{1}{4}''$ throw Eccentric, to the strap extension of which is connected a long rod that is coupled at its lower end to the crosshead of the pump, which in turn is secured to the piston. For demonstration purposes models of this type usually are driven by Electric Motors, but many Meccano enthusiasts make them do real work by securing them in an elevated position out of doors. By careful adjustment these models can be made to work almost as efficiently as those used in actual practice.

The older type of windmill can be reproduced in Meccano with excellent results. The appearance of age and solidity is the necessary thing to embody in these models, and this is suggested in the model shown in Fig. 2, which makes good use of many new Meccano Parts, and is built with the new E Outfit. The main structure consists of four Angle Girders surmounted by

Fig. 3. A well-known and popular demonstration model of a Windmill.

four $2\frac{1}{2}''$ Curved Strips. To these are secured the upper portion of the mill that carries a horizontal rod on which the sails are secured. Strip Plates are used to fill in the body of the mill, and $4\frac{1}{2}''$ Flanged Sector Plates form the roof. The sails are built up from $12\frac{1}{2}''$ and $5\frac{1}{2}''$ Strips, and the effect of canvas or wood laths is captured by the use of lengths of Meccano Cord. A Road Wheel is used to represent the boss or centre of the sails. The small rotary fan arranged at right angles to the sail is built up in a similar manner to the fan of the windmill pump shown in Fig. 5, but Strips are used instead of Propeller Blades.

The small windmill shown in Fig. 1 is constructed in an entirely different manner. It is smaller in every way, and the sails are intended only as representations of the original and not as reproductions to scale. The body of the model is very strongly constructed of Flat Plates and Flat Girders on a framework of Angle Girders. Windows are reproduced by pairs of cross strips and the roof is built up from two $4\frac{1}{2}'' \times 2\frac{1}{2}''$ Flat Plates. The small vane at the rear is represented by a $2\frac{1}{2}''$ Gear Wheel. The building of the windmill seen in Fig. 3 is carried out in a similar manner, but this model is representative of the type in which the mill turns round. A tripod carries a large post that passes up inside the windmill to about half its height, and forms a very substantial pivot for the complete model.

Fig. 4. In this model a water wheel is used for driving a mortar mixer and stone crusher.

In the construction of mills operated by water wheels the model-builder is confronted with problems and ideas of an entirely different nature. The main feature of course is the wheel and this should receive first consideration. In the two models shown in Figs. 1 and 4, the wheel is of the undershot type, the rims in each case being Circular Strips. These are secured by eight short Strips to Face Plates representing the boss, and are connected by floats formed from a series of Flat Girders held in place by $\frac{1}{2}'' \times \frac{1}{2}''$ Angle Brackets. The wheel shown in Fig. 4 has floats consisting of $2\frac{1}{2}'' \times 2\frac{1}{2}''$ Flat Plates secured by Double Angle Strips.

The first of the two models is largely constructed with Braced Girders. The building, set on one side of the wheel, consists of four long Angle Girders and two Braced Girders of similar length. A small hoisting drum, set in the bottom of this building and fitted with an automatic reversing mechanism, raises and lowers an imitation sack of wheat that is to be seen plainly in the model. This additional movement greatly enhances its appearance when working, and also adds considerably to its interest. Similar movements can readily be fitted to any model windmill.

A simple but very effective setting has been arranged for the two models illustrated in Fig. 1. This consists of a board of suitable size on which the windmill and water-wheel are mounted. The board is painted green and round its edges are mounted pieces of imitation hedge. The effect created in this manner is well worth the trouble involved.

Water-wheels are put to comparatively modern uses such as mortar mixing and stone breaking, and this form of power plant makes an excellent subject for reproduction. The model water-wheel shown in Fig. 4 has two auxiliary machines coupled to it. One of these is a mortar mixer and the other a stone crusher. Both machines are very simply constructed and are driven from a motor concealed in the main building that also drives the waterwheel. Finish is given to the model by the addition of handrails and a small bridge. The bridge of course is represented as spanning the stream and consists of a $5\frac{1}{2}'' \times 2\frac{1}{2}''$ Flat Plate. Side chains are built up from $1''$ Threaded Rods and loops of Sprocket Chain are added to this. The attractiveness of the model may be increased by the use of a sheet of green rippled glass to represent a stream.

Interest can be added to Meccano models of windmills and water-mills by omitting a section of the walls and fitting model grinding machinery inside. This machinery need only be of a simple character, and it is a good plan to drive it by a Meccano motor. In a windmill the sails also may be coupled up to the power unit, and similarly the wheel of a water-mill may be connected to the motor. The impression is then given that the sails or the water-wheel are driving the inner machinery, especially if the motor can be concealed. Small working figures, of which much has been written recently in the "Meccano Magazine," also can be added, and they can be so arranged that they appear to operate the various grinding and threshing machines.

If possible lights should be placed inside a model fitted with machinery and moving figures. The following plan then will be found very effective. The lights are placed behind the figures and machines, and the open space in the walls of the mill is covered with good quality tracing paper. The shadows of the moving figures then are thrown on to the screen of tracing paper, with a very picturesque effect.

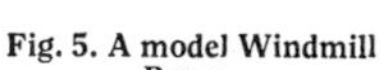
Fig. 5. A model Windmill Pump.

The fitting of Motors into these models is a matter that can be left largely to individual requirements. There are one or two points that should not be overlooked, however, the first of these being the speed of the sails or wheel. For the purpose of realism these should rotate slowly and evenly, and this is of particular importance in windmill models. An exception to this rule is the model Windmill Pump shown in Fig. 5, and similar models, the vanes of which should rotate at a higher rate of speed than those of the older types of windmills.

An Infinitely Variable Speed Controller

Adaptable to Machinery of all kinds

IN many branches of engineering it is necessary to use mechanisms for changing the speeds of rotating parts. For example, speed variations are essential on most machine tools in order to cut different kinds of metal at the most efficient speed. In the case of lathes it is usual to increase the speed of the revolving work as its diameter decreases so as to maintain a surface speed that is suitable for the particular metal being machined.

A Crofts Variable-speed Gear with independent constant slow speed drive for "setting-up" purposes.

Many different kinds of mechanism have been devised for the purpose of changing the speeds of rotating parts. Some of these are intended either for reducing or increasing the speed by a fixed amount, the mechanism being designed for one speed ratio only, while others enable a range of several speeds to be obtained. Included in the latter class of speed changing mechanisms is also a number of interesting devices by means of which a machine may be driven at any speed desired between a fixed minimum and a fixed maximum. A mechanism of this type, which is adaptable for use in connection with machinery of all kinds, is illustrated on this page. It is made by Crofts (Engineers) Ltd., Bradford, and one of its many applications is as a regulator for the mechanical stokers of steam power plants, where it controls the speed of the stokers automatically as the demand for steam fluctuates. The mechanism is also widely used in connection with textile machines and machine tools generally.

An electrically controlled infinitely variable-speed gear that will give any output speed between 20 and 180 r.p.m. For the photographs on this page we are indebted to Crofts (Engineers) Ltd., Bradford.

The mechanism is known as Crofts Infinitely Variable-speed Gear and consists essentially of special split expanding and contracting driving and driven pulleys that form wedge section grooves, the diameter of which can be varied infinitely between maximum and minimum limits.

Each pulley is formed from two cone-faced discs that are slideable on a shaft, and can be brought together or drawn apart as desired. The pulleys are connected by a special type flexible belt, to which are secured taper blocks or lags. These blocks are shaped at their ends to suit the angle of the inner or driving faces of the cones, and they move upward or downward on the cones as the halves of the pulley are brought together or drawn apart. The mechanism is so arranged that as the belt tread of one pulley increases in diameter the belt tread of the other pulley automatically decreases in diameter a corresponding amount.

If one of the pulleys is driven at a constant speed then by operating its cones the second pulley is enabled to run at any desired speed according to the diameter of the belt treads formed by each pair of cones. The diameter of the cones must be varied whilst the mechanism is in motion, and an infinite variation of speeds within limits determined by the size of the cones can be obtained immediately.

Movement of the cones on their shafts can be controlled either mechanically or electrically, and if desired the control can be entirely automatic in action. An advantage of electric control is that it enables a machine to be operated from any desired position, and several machines so equipped can be synchronised in action so that in any manufacturing process involving the working of two or more machines their speeds can be regulated to meet varying requirements at different stages of production.

A Crofts standard design Variable-speed Gear fitted for electric automatic control is shown in the lower illustration on this page. The Gear is operated by a motor that drives a constant speed shaft at 360 r.p.m. The variable speed shaft is coupled to a worm reduction gear through a friction clutch, which enables the driven machine to be stopped at will without stopping the driving motor. A reduction gear of 9 to 1 ratio reduces the final operating speed to a minimum of 20 r.p.m. with a maximum of 80 r.p.m., and any intermediate speed between these limits can be obtained.

The drive illustrated was specially designed for use with a machine that it was essential should always restart from rest at the minimum speed. To effect this the clutch lever on disengagement controls a reversible motor, ensuring that the variable-speed shaft returns to lowest speed.

The upper illustration shows a Crofts Variable-speed Gear for use where a constant independent slow speed was required for "inching" or setting-up purposes during preparatory work. A constant speed geared motor is coupled to the rotor shaft of the main Variable-speed Gear motor by an automatic ratchet coupling, and the main motor is in turn coupled to a worm reduction unit of 24 : 1 ratio.

During setting-up work, the geared motor drives the machine at 6 r.p.m., speeds being reduced in two stages (1) geared motor 1,500 to 148 r.p.m., (2) worm reduction gear 148 to 6 r.p.m. For production the main motor is switched on, and this on acceleration operates the ratchet coupling and disconnects the geared motor. An electric relay then cuts off the current to the geared motor. When the main motor is switched off, the ratchet coupling resets itself for the next cycle of operations.

The Carryall Scraper

Excavating and Levelling at High Speeds

EXCAVATING is an important part of the work of the modern civil engineer, for in nearly all his tasks, such as the making of roads, railways and canals and the construction of dams, it is necessary to dig out enormous quantities of material and to deposit this in some other place, either to fill up a hole or depression of some kind, to make an embankment, or merely to get rid of it. How to move earth and rock in these circumstances of course is an old problem, for engineering work of many kinds was carried out very early in the story of civilisation. Armies of men wielding crude picks and shovels, and provided with baskets for carrying purposes, were then employed. In time their primitive appliances gave way to better tools, and eventually to machines, and many ingenious and powerful excavators, such as giant steam or electric shovels and huge draglines, are now available. Many machines of this kind have been described in the *"M.M."*

The Le Tourneau Carryall Scraper, a speedy and powerful excavator that is described in the accompanying article. For our illustrations we are indebted to the courtesy of Tractor Traders Ltd., London.

On this page we illustrate a remarkable excavator known as the "Carryall Scraper." This digs out the material to be excavated, loads itself and automatically dumps its contents at any required point, and all these operations are carried out at very high speed. It consists of a large bowl mounted on six wheels fitted with big, low-pressure pneumatic tyres. When in action it is towed by means of a separate tractor power unit. The cutting edge is in front, and the depth to which it penetrates can be regulated instantly and accurately from the driver's seat. As the machine moves along, it scoops up the material in which it is working and this literally "boils up" from the cutting edge into the centre of the bowl, for a full load is scraped up in from half a minute to a minute and a half, the time depending on the power and speed of the tractor and on the condition of the soil excavated.

A Carryall Scraper at work levelling the site for the Promenade extensions at New Brighton. The machine is hauled by a petrol-engined tractor fitted with creeper tracks.

Part of the spoil falls into an apron that is fitted to the front of the bowl, and the rest against an unloading gate at the rear of the machine. As soon as the bowl has been filled, the cutting edge is raised clear of the ground and the machine is hauled away to the dumping ground. There its load is discharged even more speedily than it was taken up. The front apron is raised high to clear the material, which then is pushed off the front of the bowl by simply pulling forward the unloading gate at the rear.

The scraper is readily operated by one man, who manipulates levers controlling cables passing over a double drum on the power unit mounted on the tractor. One control lever raises and lowers the front apron and pulls forward the rear gate, and the latter is returned by means of heavy steel springs as soon as the lever is released.

The machine is made in three sizes, with capacities of 6, 8 and 12 cu. yd. respectively. It is designed to work in sand, light and heavy soils and even in rain-soaked sticky clay, and is very strongly built of special alloy steels in order to enable it to stand up to hard wear in rough conditions. Electric arc welding construction is used in making it, and there are no separate castings or rivets to break or work loose.

The Carryall Scraper finds useful application in making cuttings and embankments, and in grading or levelling land for highways, airports or constructional work such as the building of reservoirs. It also can be used in pits and mines, and indeed for almost any work in which material has to be moved quickly.

Summer Meccano Competitions

Prizes for Model Merchant Ships

This month we announce a competition for all kinds of model merchant ships. Models of warships, and naval vessels generally, are not eligible. The competition is open to every owner of a Meccano Outfit no matter what his or her age may be, and there are no entry fees. There is no reason therefore, why every model-builder should not avail himself of this chance to win a prize.

Merchant ships provide plenty of scope for model-builders as there are so many different kinds of vessels to choose from, including passenger liners, cargo ships, oil tankers, dredgers and steam tugs. Readers who do not have much opportunity of inspecting actual ships at close quarters will be able to find plenty of illustrations of various types of merchant ships in past issues of the "*M.M.*" or in the illustrated papers.

A fine model of a full-rigged ship built by Henry Lee of Ardrossen. It is a good example of the kind of models that will win prizes in the "Merchant Ship" Competition.

Models should be built as closely as possible to scale, but unless the model is a large one it is wise not to include much detail. A small model will look better if it is simply constructed, particular attention being given to obtaining a realistic outline for the hull and the superstructure.

Every model submitted must be built by the competitor without assistance from anyone.

When the model is completed and the competitor is satisfied that nothing further can be done to improve it, the next thing is to prepare an illustration of it. This may be either a photograph or a drawing, but it is best to send a photograph if possible. It should be clearly understood that the actual model must not be submitted, and those competitors who do not possess a camera, and cannot obtain a professional photograph, should set to work to make a neat drawing.

There will be one Section only, and in order to give competitors living abroad plenty of time to send in their entries the competition will remain open until 31st August, 1936. The age of each competitor will be taken into consideration in judging the entries.

The prizes to be awarded are as follows: First: Meccano Products value £5/5/–; Second, Products value £3/3/–; Third, Products value £1/10/–. There will be also five consolation awards of Products value 10/–. We hope that every reader will send in an entry and endeavour to win the valuable First Prize.

Entries should be addressed to "Ship Model-Building Contest," Meccano Ltd., Binns Road, Liverpool 13, and each photograph or drawing must bear the competitor's name, age and full address.

If the model contains any special features that are not shown in the photographs or drawings it is advisable to write a short description that will make everything quite clear and send this with the entry.

Photographs or drawings of unsuccessful models will be returned to the sender only when a stamped addressed envelope is enclosed for that purpose. It should be noted, however, that photographs or drawings of prize-winning models become the property of Meccano Ltd., and will not be returned.

Special Summer Voting Competition

At the foot of this page is a list of 18 Meccano Parts taken from the Meccano range. Readers are asked to choose from this list (A) the part that they think is the most useful in model-building; and (B) the six parts that they think will receive the most votes when the "A" votes of all competitors are added together. Competitors should then write the names of the parts, and the Meccano catalogue numbers on a post-card, which must also bear their name and address.

Postcards should be addressed "Meccano Voting Contest," Meccano Ltd., Binns Road, Liverpool 13, and must be posted in time to reach Liverpool before 31st August, 1936, which is the closing date for all entries.

Prizes will be awarded to readers who succeed in correctly forecasting the six parts that will obtain the highest votes, or if no correct entry is received, to those whose entries are most nearly correct. The prizes are as follows: First, Meccano Products value £2/2/–; Second, Products value £1/1/–; Third, Products value 10/6. A number of consolation prizes will also be awarded.

Most Useful Parts "Voting Contest"

Select your Parts from this List

12c.	Obtuse Angle Bracket	109.	Face Plate
28.	1½ in. Contrate Wheel	125.	Reversed Angle Bracket
30c.	1½ in. Bevel Gear	127.	Simple Bell Crank
44.	Cranked Bent Strip	136.	Handrail Support
52a.	Flat Plate, 5½ in. × 3½ in.	137.	Wheel Flange
77.	1 in. Triangular Plate	140.	Universal Coupling
94.	Sprocket Chain	147b.	Pivot Bolt
106.	Wood Roller	172.	Pendulum Connection
108.	Architrave	198.	Hinged Flat Plate

Model-Building Competition Results

By Frank Hornby

"Meccanitian" Contest (Overseas Section)

The "Meccanitian" Contest was announced in the December, 1935, issue of the "*M.M.*," and judging from the large number of interesting entries received in each Section model-builders enjoy taking part in competitions of this kind. The prizes in the Overseas Section were awarded to the competitors named in the following list:

First Prize, £3/3/-: J. Willems, Antwerp, Belgium. 2nd, £2/2/-: G. Corleo, St. Julians, Malta. 3rd, £1/1/-: J. Nie, Shanghai, China.

Meccano Products value 10/-: K. J. Orams, Blenheim, New Zealand; M. Orde, Chateau d'Oex, Switzerland; J. Thomas, Bombay, India; H. Owens, Melbourne, Australia; G. Phillips, Capetown, South Africa.

First Prize was awarded for an entry consisting of two models, the better of which is illustrated on this page. This represents a group of jazz musicians and their instruments, and is complete in every detail. Effective use has been made of Channel Segments, Strips of various lengths, and a Circular Strip, to form the decorations at the rear of the platform. Unfortunately, Willems has mutilated a considerable quantity of parts, but as the subject is one that is extremely difficult to reproduce with standard parts this lapse from good Meccano practice may be overlooked. It will be noticed that several ingenious uses have been found for many of the parts used in the group.

A dance band in a unique setting that won First Prize in the "Meccanitian" Competition for J. Willems of Antwerp.

The second model submitted by this competitor represents a billiards match. The top of the table is a rectangular piece of cardboard 8½ in. wide and 12 in. long. The cushions are formed from channel section girders each made from two Angle Girders bolted together, spaces being left for the pockets. The table is strengthened underneath with a strong base constructed from Strips and Angle Girders, and is supported on stout legs made from Couplings.

Each of the four figures comprising the group are constructed similarly to those shown in the illustration on this page, and each holds a cue, which is made from a Rod and is attached to the Meccanitian's right-hand by means of an End Bearing. The billiards balls are Steel Balls similar to those used in the standard Meccano Ball Race. Behind the table is a cue stand made from a Rod provided at its lower end with a 2 in. Pulley for a base and at the top with a Bush Wheel. The cues rest on the 2 in. Pulley, and are passed through the holes in the Bush Wheel to prevent them from falling. The top of the stand is decorated with a Handrail Coupling and a ½" fast Pulley.

A scene in a film studio during the "shooting" of a picture won Second Prize for G. Corleo. The camera used in the scene is a good piece of work considering the simple parts from which it is made. It is mounted on a trolley consisting of a 3½ in. × 2½ in. Flanged Plate provided with four 1 in. fast Pulleys for travelling wheels. On the Flanged Plate is a tripod made from three Rods, and this supports two Flat Trunnions and two Triple-Throw Eccentrics. The former represent the body of the camera and the Eccentrics represent the film spool. The lens is a Buffer held in place by an Angle Bracket and the view-finder is a Collar.

The "operator" is made from Strips, with a 1 in. loose Pulley for his head, and he is shown looking through the view-finder. The group includes also a spot-light, which is mounted on a base plate similar to that used in the case of the camera. The tower on which the light is mounted consists of a tube made from four 5½ in. Angle Girders, and the light itself is composed of two 5½ in. × 1½ in. Flexible Plates secured round the rim of a 3 in. Pulley. Spring Cord makes admirable electrical feed cables.

A more simple model constructed by J. Nie was successful in winning Third Prize. In this model there are three Meccanitians who are shown in various attitudes and together represent competitors in an archery contest. One of the Meccanitians is supposed to be shooting an arrow at a target. The second is looking down an arrow, presumably to make sure that it is perfectly straight, and his bow rests in the crook of his left arm. The third and last figure in the group is the score keeper, who has a 1 in. Rod for a pencil.

Two of the winners of Products value 10/- failed to win larger prizes owing to the fact that they are too complicated. One of these built by K. J. Orams is a representation of a school class of seven pupils who are shown sitting in four dual desks. One of the pupils, apparently more intelligent than the others, has his hand in the air. The teacher has a severe expression on his face, which incidently is represented by a Triple-Throw Eccentric, and in one hand he is holding a stick and in the other a sheet of paper from which he is reading the lesson.

The other entry was built by M. Orde and represents a cricket match. There is little to be said about the construction of the various figures as this is carried out on quite ordinary lines. It is the expert manner in which they are arranged that attracted the attention of the competition judges.

The other three prizes of 10/- were awarded for groups representing a football match, a procession and a gang of road-menders at work, which were submitted by J. Thomas, G. Phillips and H. Owens, respectively.

A prize of products value 5/- was won by D. McLeod, who sent a simple scene of a washerwoman at work. A "cat," made from two Double Brackets and a ½ in. loose Pulley, is curled up on the clean washing, and the woman in making an effort to drive it away, apparently has placed her foot upon the soap and slipped over! At first glance at the photographs submitted, I thought the model represented a gymnast in action!

R. Kett sent a working model of a blacksmith's shop. The subject is not original, but it is the ingenious way in which it is reproduced that attracted the judges, and earned for the model a prize value 5/-. This competitor's work is distinctly promising and I hope to receive further models from him.

"The Year's Best Model" Voting Competition

The six most popular models illustrated in the "*M.M.*" during 1935 as decided by the massed votes of competitors in this Contest are as follows: (1) C.N.R. Locomotive, built by H. G. Shorten, Regina, Canada (September "*M.M.*"); (2) Floating Seadrome, built by M. de Wilde, Antwerp (November "*M.M.*"); (3) R.M.S. "*Queen Mary*," built by P. Giese, Buenos Aires (July "*M.M.*"); (4) Traction Engine, built by C. Ingleby, Westgate-on-Sea (February "*M.M.*"); (5) Buckingham Palace, built by A. Fear, Exeter (November "*M.M.*"); (6) Barendrecht Lift Bridge, built by M. de Wilde, Antwerp (February "*M.M.*").

No competitor succeeded in placing the chosen models in the order shown above, and therefore the prizes were awarded to the competitors whose entries were nearest correct. The list of awards is as follows: 1st Prize, £1/1/-: R. M. Jeffery, Goudhurst, Kent. 2nd, 15/-: W. B. Hudson, Weymouth. 3rd, 10/-: J. Gambina, Sliema, Malta.

Todmorden Road Central School (Burnley) M.C.—A lecture on "*A Holiday in Belgium*" was given by Miss Bullock, one of the mistresses at the school, who has travelled a great deal. It was chiefly of architectural interest. Another lecture that was greatly enjoyed was given by the Leader on the topical subject of "*The Future is in the Air*." Considerable model-building has been carried out. It is proposed to construct a Hornby layout based upon one illustrated in the "*M.M.*" Club roll: 31. *Joint Secretaries:* L. Hinton, 4, Thirlmere Avenue, Burnley, and M. Dawe, 31, Butland Avenue, Burnley.

Well Hall and District M.C.—Stamp Collecting was discussed at one meeting, and further developments are probable. The Cycling Section has resumed its activities, and some interesting runs have been arranged. Club roll: 10. *Secretary:* E. W. Quinton, 48, Beaconsfield Road, Mollingham, Kent.

Holy Trinity (Barnsbury) M.C.—The second Winter session opened well, the first night being devoted to the Annual Social. The club then continued to work through an 11-week programme, in which Meccano and Section work alternated. At the conclusion of one meeting a cinema show was given by the Leader of a neighbouring Meccano club. The annual Concert on 12th March was attended by over 150 people, and the boys who took part performed very well. An outing to Chingford has been greatly enjoyed. Members are now looking forward to a successful Exhibition, which it is hoped to hold next November. Club roll: 28. *Secretary:* Mr. H. C. Boys, 12, Stonefield Mansions, Cloudesley Square, Barnsbury, London, N.1.

Bexleyheath Boys' Central School M.C.—Interesting model-building meetings have been held. On one occasion the Leader brought along a large blue print of part of a steamer, and members greatly enjoyed studying it. The preparation of a railway layout for the club's Open Day has been discussed. Club roll: 33. *Secretary:* D. Hicks, 4, St. Audley Avenue, Long Lane, Bexleyheath, Kent.

Old Charlton M.C.—Debates continue to be very popular, and one of the most interesting held recently was on the subject "*Should Airships be built?*" The opposer declared that aeroplanes were greatly superior and safer, and therefore there was no need for airships. He finally won by a large majority, only two members, the proposer and his seconder, voting in favour of airships. A debate on "*Steam versus Electricity on the Railways*" has been arranged, and also a talk on "*Motor Cycle Engines*." Model-building activities have been concentrated on preparation for the fifth Annual Exhibition. Models completed for the event include an automatic ship coaler built from a small Outfit, but nevertheless very effective in operation; vertical lift bridge; twin-cylinder horizontal engine; an excellent modified version of the "Meccano Boxers" demonstration model, and a good show of aeroplanes built from Aeroplane Constructor Outfits. Club roll: 20. *Secretary:* Mr. W. Jaques, 60, Gurdon Road, London, E.C.7.

Bristol Grammar School M.C.—The recent illness of several of the members has slowed down model-building work. Outstanding models built have included a quayside crane based on those at Bristol docks, and a block-setting crane. At one meeting a large track was laid down on the platform in the lower hall of the school, and many fascinating railway operations were carried out. Club roll: 40. *Secretary:* N. E. Ricketts, 10, Belgrave Road, Clifton, Bristol.

Fraserburgh M.C.—Model-building was temporarily suspended while new tables were built to enable members to construct their models under better conditions than hitherto. Cycling and Model Aeroplane sections have been formed. The Cycling section has its own committee, and plans are being made for a 10-days' tour of Scotland during the summer holidays. Three of the members have large light tents, and it is hoped that full advantage will be taken of this valuable equipment. The Model Aeroplane section has six members, and interesting flights have been achieved when weather conditions have been favourable. The club stock of Meccano Parts has been increased, and the equipment of the Junior section has been enriched by the addition of a complete Hornby "Flying Scotsman" Train Set. Club roll: 28. *Secretary:* W. J. Dawson, Phingask, Fraserburgh.

Wheelwright Grammar School M.C.—Model-building has been the chief occupation recently, and members are becoming very proficient in constructing Meccano models. A film show and a visit to the gas works have been arranged. Club roll: 14. *Secretary:* D. G. Thackrah, 2, Highroyd, Northfields, Dewsbury, Yorks.

Exeter M.C.—Cycling is very popular, and some enjoyable runs have taken place. One of the most appreciated features of the second Winter session was the Leader's practice of reading an exciting adventure story during the Monday evening meetings. A total of 52 models were built during that session, as compared with 35 during the corresponding period last year. They covered a remarkable variety of subjects, and in addition to the usual output of bridges, cranes, ships and motor cars, many models of a novel character were produced, including gondolas, buoys, caravans, horse and milk float with driver, a statue of Sir Francis Drake, a drinking fountain and a model of Will Hay with one of his pupils. Club roll: 60. *Secretary:* K. G. Sercombe, 18, Normandy Road, Heavitree, Exeter.

The "bottle" orchestra formed among the members of the Thebarton Junior Technical School M.C., Torrensville, South Australia, by Mr. E. S. H. Gibson, the Leader. The members' "instruments" are ranged in front of the group. This club was affiliated with the Meccano Guild in December 1928, and has made excellent progress.

Hornsea M.C.—This club recently celebrated its sixth birthday. Interesting lectures have dealt with aeroplanes, wireless, mathematics, "*The Wiltshire Downs*" and "*How We are Governed*." The Engineers' section have visited the L.N.E.R. hydraulic generating station, Hornsea. The party divided into two groups, one making a tour of the station under the guidance of the Hydraulic Engineer, and the other being escorted by the Electrician. This was followed by a tour of the workshop, and the visit concluded with a ride on the overhead electric crane across the building. Club roll: 14. *Secretary:* P. Thom, 5, Alexandra Road, Hornsea.

Islington M.C.—An interesting and varied programme has been followed, and has included talks, model-building, Chemistry experiments, and readings from the "*M.M.*" The latter part of most meetings is spent in playing games. A film show has been given by the Leader. Club roll: 17. *Secretary:* K. V. Dines, 70, Thornhill Road, Barnsbury, London, N.1.

Mallow M.C.—Members have been chiefly occupied in extensive preparations for the celebration of the club's birthday. The two former Leaders have been invited to attend the event. Substantial additions have been made to the club library. The subject of a recent Lecture Night was "*The Story of Our Ships*," and was much enjoyed. Club roll: 16. *Secretary:* M. D. Hickey, 42, Ballydaheen, Mallow, Co. Cork, I.F.S.

AUSTRALIA

Sydney M.C.—Model-building and Hornby Railway operations have chiefly occupied the attention of the members. Further additions to the club layout have been made, to represent a branch line to Carinnys. The branch is 56 ft. in length. An interesting lecture on "*Tasmanian Railways*" has been given by the secretary, who recently returned from a six months' visit to Tasmania. Some excellent outings have been planned, and these include an excursion to Toronto arranged in conjunction with the Railway Touring club. Another excursion planned jointly with that club is to Austinmer on the south coast, and it is anticipated that a 10-coach train will be required to convey the party. It is proposed to name the special train "*The Meccano Club Express*," and to have the name displayed on the locomotive and coaches. Club roll: 50. *Secretary:* T. Watson, Box 1749JJ., P.O., Sydney.

SOUTH AFRICA

Malvern M.C.—The membership of both the boys' and girls' sections of the club continues to increase. Very interesting models have been built, including racing cars, horse and cart, motor bus, double drop hammer, electric radio gramophone and an electric combination lock. Outdoor activities have included swimming and cricket. At a recent business meeting, the matters under discussion were concluded in good time and the remainder of the evening was given over to items by members. Those members who failed to contribute an item to the impromptu programme were fined threepence, and as there were several shy ones the club funds benefited appreciably! The evening was a great success, and resulted in many requests for more entertainments of this kind, as it is evident there are some talented members in the club. Club roll: 85. *Secretary:* B. Saunders, P.O. Box 8, Cleveland, Johannesburg.

EGYPT

Zagazig M.C.—A new clubroom has been obtained, which is more centrally situated than the previous one. A tea party attended by members and many of their relatives and friends was greatly enjoyed, and a feature of the event was a comic play by some of the members. A Correspondence section has been formed to establish correspondence with boys in all parts of the world. Visits have been paid to places of interest in Cairo, and on one occasion the Cairo M.C. was visited and a very happy evening was spent there. The models displayed by the club at the Exhibition of Egyptian Industry in February last included a large passenger liner, bucket dredger and model steam engines, and all were greatly admired by the many visitors. The club co-operated with the Cairo M.C. in this display. At a recent Visitors' meeting an interesting lantern lecture on "*The life of Henry Bessemer*" was much enjoyed. Club roll: 20. *Secretary:* A. Y. Ayoub, Sharia El Sikka, El-Hadid, Zagazig.

NEW ZEALAND

Christchurch M.C.—The club roll has been revised, and the names of members who have not attended during the past club year have been struck off the roll. The membership therefore now consists entirely of boys who are really keen Meccano enthusiasts, and this fact augers well for the future success of the club. Occasional Games Evenings are very popular, and always produce a great deal of fun. Preparations are well in hand for the club Birthday Evening, when the parents and friends of members will be invited to attend and join in the celebration. Club roll: 22. *Secretary:* L. W. Best, 28, Circuit Street, Strowan, Christchurch.

Unaffiliated Club

AUSTRALIA

Maylands (West Australia) M.C.—A Concert in which most of the members will take part is being organised to raise funds. A visit has been paid to the Australian Glass Manufacturers Ltd., East Perth, where a most interesting tour of the works was made under the guidance of officials of the company. Club roll: 17. *Secretary:* M. Thomson, 13, Kennedy Street, Maylands, Perth, West Australia.

Enjoying Outdoor Activities

Outdoor activities are now in full swing with practically all Meccano clubs, and the reports I have already received indicate that this is going to be a more successful summer than any previous one, regarded from the Guild point of view. With a few exceptions, due to unusual circumstances, all clubs are making definite arrangements to carry on club life throughout the summer. There are many signs that the old practice of allowing clubs to practically die out during the summer has gone. Most Leaders now realise that this involves the members missing a great deal of splendid outdoor fun, and also makes it very difficult to bring the club together again for the first Winter session.

Summer Camping Grounds

In my April notes I dealt with the subject of summer camps. I would like to supplement my remarks there by drawing the attention of Leaders to the recently-issued 1936 edition of the Great Western Railway Company's booklet *"Camping and Rambling Holidays."* This booklet gives a list of camping sites throughout the area served by this railway. In the case of each site the name and address of the owner or tenant is given, together with sufficient information to enable a club Leader to decide whether this particular place would be suitable or not. The amount of land available is given, the nature of the surrounding country is indicated, and in addition, an important point that is easily overlooked—the whereabouts of the nearest drinking-water supply. The booklet may be obtained on application to the Superintendent of the Line at Paddington Station, London, W.2, or to any G.W.R. London or provincial office.

The country served by the G.W.R. is varied in character. The sites mentioned in the booklet include both inland and seaside camp positions, and there is a wide choice open to those who wish to obtain this healthy and interesting form of holiday. Similar information may be obtained from the other British railway companies by officials of those clubs whose headquarters are in the parts of the country that they serve, and I advise Leaders who are interested to make immediate enquiries. Many important concessions are made by the companies in regard to fares for camping parties, and full particulars of these concessions can be obtained from the local railway station.

Master K. G. Sercombe, who recently served for a short period as Secretary of the Exeter Meccano Club. This club is now in its 12th year, and is one of the most successful affiliated with the Meccano Guild.

Organising Interesting Rambles

It is hardly to be expected that all the members of a club will be keen on cycling or playing cricket, and it is up to Leaders to arrange some other form of outdoor activity for those who do not wish to take part in these pastimes. In many clubs the solution to this problem has been satisfactorily solved by arranging walking expeditions, generally once a week, to various places of interest in the neighbourhood. Boys do not care for rambles just for the sake of walking, however, and some object must be provided in order to arouse interest; the walks must therefore be planned with this object in view.

The best plan is for the Leader to borrow from a local library one or two books dealing with the district. By studying these, together with a large scale map, he will soon acquire a really surprising amount of interesting knowledge, which he can impart to the members during the rambles in a chatty manner that will succeed in holding their attention. A happy result of rambles thoughtfully prepared in this way is that the eyes of the boys are invariably opened to things of great interest which they had never considered seriously because they were too familiar and were close at hand. It is not unusual for one or more members of a party to remark during a ramble that they have passed a particular place scores of times but have never known before that there was anything interesting about it.

If the Leader has any knowledge of botany, birds, geology, etc., his task is all the easier, but even if he has no particular leaning toward those subjects he can, by a little study, acquaint himself with them sufficiently to be able to make the rambles enjoyable to all taking part.

Australian Club's "Bottle" Orchestra

Most people know that if the neck of an empty bottle is held against the lower lip and air is forced across the opening a note is produced. With a little practice it is possible to produce the note any time it is required. These two simple facts inspired Mr. Gibson, the Leader of the Thebarton Junior Technical School M.C., Torrensville, South Australia, to organise a "bottle" orchestra among the members of the club. The idea was taken up enthusiastically and a large orchestra was soon formed, as is borne out by the photograph of its members and the bottles they use, which is shown on the opposite page. This novel orchestra was employed to illustrate points made in broadcast talks to schools by Mr. Gibson through the Australian national wireless stations 5C.L. and 5C.K.

The manner in which the desired musical effect is obtained is quite simple. If water is added to the empty bottle the note obtained is raised in pitch, and therefore by taking bottles of different sizes and adding water to each of them a set of notes corresponding to a musical scale can easily be obtained. If each bottle is given to a boy to hold and blow with the correct timing, quite effective music can be produced. The Leader, or any other senior member of the club who is musical, can easily arrange the music for the players. If the club lacks any suitable member for this task it is a good plan to number the bottles from 1 to 8 and to write the music in numbers.

During the first practice of the Thebarton "bottle" orchestra only single notes were played, but later, when the members had become more proficient, four-part harmony was produced. It is often possible to give two or three bottles to the same boy; his music being written in different colours to correspond with these various bottles, so that he can employ the correct bottle for each note. By this means the number of players can be substantially reduced and the management of the orchestra considerably improved.

Proposed Clubs

Attempts are being made to establish Meccano Clubs in the following places, and boys interested should communicate with the promoters whose names and addresses are given below:

CARLUKE—J. W. S. Scott, "Westfield," Carluke, N.B.

KIRKBY LONSDALE—N. Forsyth, 57, Main Street.

NEATH—T. M. Sullivan, "Wenvoe," Eastbourne Terrace, Penrhieutyn.

WELLINGBOROUGH—P. Henson, 24, Croyland Road.

A Visit to the "Sunshine Lines"

How an Outdoor Miniature Railway was Laid

By "Rosco"

WITH the approach of the summer many Hornby Railway systems are put away, or at least are somewhat deserted, while their owners seek pleasure and health out of doors. Even since the time when I commenced the miniature railway hobby I have wished to be able to continue my train operations and to enjoy the summer at the same time. To make this possible it was eventually decided to construct an outdoor line in the garden. Even the smallest of gardens is larger than many a room and the beauty of the summer flowers need not be disturbed by the presence of a shining miniature railway track running in a business-like manner amongst them. Rather will the garden have an added interest; and the railway will be much more like the real thing than is possible indoors, by reason of its more natural surroundings.

A Hornby No. 3 "Flying Scotsman" Locomotive emerging from the tunnel on the "Sunshine Lines." This photograph shows how the baseboard is arranged on posts, with large stones packed beneath it.

It was necessary, of course, to lay the track on a foundation of boards arranged above the level of the ground so that the amount of stooping involved in handling the engines and stock would be reduced. Actually, as can be seen by the accompanying illustration of the Hornby *"Flying Scotsman"* emerging from the tunnel, the line now described is about sixteen inches above the level of the lawn from which the photograph was taken, and about eight inches below the level of the flower bed along which it runs. Gradients are not really a desirable feature and unless the ground traversed is dead flat very much better running is obtained by making frequent use of the spirit level when fixing the boards, thus keeping them as level as possible. This may necessitate embankments, cuttings, bridges or tunnels, and these greatly improve the line, giving it an appearance of realism that is quite unobtainable in a room.

A picturesque scene on the outdoor railway described on this page, showing a train passing through a rock cutting.

A simple method of securing the boards was adopted, that of driving into the soil short posts of a few inches long, nailing the boards to their tops at ground level. Where the line was required to be a foot or more above ground level longer posts were used. It is well worth while to make the boards as rigid as possible for then the laying of the track on them is much simpler. Needless to say as the posts and boards were intended to remain out in all weathers, they were given a good coat of wood preservative. To prevent the boards from warping they are nowhere less than three-quarters of an inch thick; and a width of from five to seven inches is found suitable for a single track.

The next step was to lay the permanent way. This is made up of steel rail fixed in chairs on wooden sleepers, and the whole is secured by means of fine nails or screws through the sleepers into the baseboard. The layout consists of a continuous single track in the form of an oval and the complete circuit measures about 36 yards. The Hornby No. 2 Special Tank accomplishes this distance comfortably with a load of six or seven wagons. The No. 3C *"Flying Scotsman"* takes three bogie coaches round equally well, both of these being good performances for a clockwork mechanism.

Starting from the station the train gets up speed along a stretch of straight track. Immediately before entering a yard-long tunnel the track swings a little to the right and back again. Another three yards or so of straight and a wide curve ensues; then higher ground is encountered as a cutting is entered. From this a straight stretch of about four yards precedes another sweeping bend, in a second cutting through literally "towering" rocks. The line emerges onto the straight again and continues so for a distance of about ten yards. At the end of this is a further curve and then come three points giving access to the goods sidings and the engine shed. With the last curve, crossing a miniature ravine about eighteen inches deep by a plate girder bridge, the starting point is once more brought into view.

The station and the engine shed are home-made and like the baseboard and track are permanent fixtures.

Using the Two-Train Transformers

By "Tommy Dodd"

In the December 1935 "*M.M.*" were mentioned the two special Meccano Transformers that are now available for the operation of two trains at once. These are known as Type T22M for 20-volt railways, and Type T26M for 6-volt railways. This month I propose to deal with the method of using these Transformers and to show the increased possibilities that their use affords to the owner of a Hornby Electric Railway system.

It is a simple matter to instal either of these Transformers on a miniature railway layout. They do not incorporate any control gear nor have they any provision for electric lighting. They have therefore only one pair of terminals, so that no difficulty should be experienced in arranging the connections from the Transformer to the track according to the instructions packed with each Transformer. When the two trains are on the same track the connections from the Transformer are the same as if a single locomotive is being operated from a T20M or T6M Transformer. Under these circumstances, as there is only one Resistance Controller in use, the two locomotives will start and stop together and they will also run at the same relative speeds, according to their type and the load behind each of them.

A section of a Hornby electric double track railway with two trains passing one another. This is a typical example of a layout requiring a two-train Transformer of the type referred to on this page.

Possibly the Hornby railway owner will not require to run the two trains as separate units. He may perhaps wish to have two engines on one train, either as a novelty or as a matter of operating convenience. The two locomotives coupled together in this way, as the train engine and the pilot engine of a double-headed train, will work in complete harmony with one another.

So far we have assumed the use of only one track; but undoubtedly the greatest fun is enjoyed when there are two separate tracks, each with its own Controller. With a layout arranged in this way traffic can be operated in exactly the same manner as on the up and down main lines of real railways. Two trains can then be run quite independently of one another so long as the two tracks are quite separate and are not joined by means of any rail connections, such as Crossover Points. These would immediately provide an electrical connection between the two circuits and render ineffective any efforts at separate control. When Crossover Points are required it is necessary to arrange an insulating gap in the third rail of that portion of track connecting the up and the down line. Crossover Points arranged thus can be obtained to special order at the ordinary prices. With separate control for the trains one of them can run slowly and stop at intermediate stations while the other speeds on its way as a main line express, and so on.

Connections from the Transformer to the two Controllers and the track are arranged as shown in the lower illustration on this page. Each track has a Terminal Connecting Plate and to the fuse terminal on each of these is brought a lead from a Resistance Controller. The two Controllers are wired to one terminal of the Transformer. The other Transformer terminal is wired to the remaining terminal on either Terminal Connecting Plate.

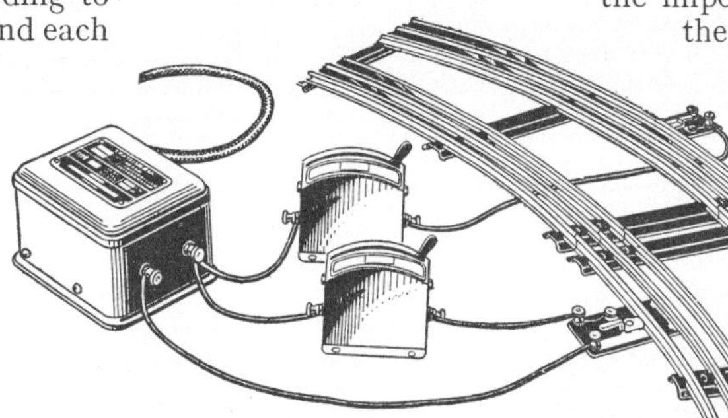

This illustration shows the method of connecting a T22M or T26M Transformer to Hornby Electric Double Track, when two trains are to be operated, one on each track.

All owners of Hornby Electric Railways are aware of the importance of the safety fuse incorporated on the Terminal Connecting Plates TCP20 and TCP6, and of the necessity of using only the correct gauge of fuse wire. On a 20-volt or 6-volt system with two trains running at the same time on the same track, the fuse should consist of No. 41 S.W.G. Tinned Copper Wire. When the two trains are on two separate tracks each of these tracks becomes a separate circuit, 20-volt or 6-volt as the case may be, each with a fuse on its own Terminal Connecting Plate. Each fuse on a 20-volt railway arranged in this way should consist of No. 32 S.W.G. Lead Wire. For a similar 6-volt railway No. 24 S.W.G. Lead Wire is correct.

The renewal of the fuse wire each time a short circuit occurs is apt to prove troublesome. This can be avoided when two trains are being run on two separate tracks by the use of two Hornby Automatic Circuit Breakers, one connected between each Resistance Controller and its respective track. The Circuit Breaker is not suitable for use where both trains are on one track.

SOME ELECTRIC RAILWAY SCHEMES

CONSIDERABLE attention is being given at the present time to railway electrification schemes and it is possible that in the near future we shall see some extensive developments. For this reason, and in view also of the increasing popularity of Hornby electric railways, it will be interesting to readers if we consider in this article the operation of miniature electric services.

It is chiefly on suburban work that electric trains have been employed in this country, although we must not forget the Brighton and Eastbourne electrification of the S.R., now complete, and the Portsmouth scheme now in progress; there is also the proposed electrification of the L.N.E.R. Sheffield to Manchester main line. The mileage of electrified track in this country is still comparatively small, but there is a considerable variety in the systems and equipment in use. It is not possible to represent them all by means of the components of the Hornby Series, but by variations in stock and in train make-up some interesting schemes can be developed.

An interesting scene on a Hornby joint Metropolitan and L.N.E.R. system. The Metropolitan train, including a Pullman Coach, is about to enter the tunnel, from which the L.N.E.R. train is emerging.

The oldest electric members of the Hornby Series are the familiar Metropolitan components, and good use can be made of them in the operation of a suburban service in miniature. The formerly independent Metropolitan Railway is now part of the London Transport organisation, and the term Metropolitan Line is used to distinguish this particular section of the system. Unlike other British suburban electrification systems, the Metropolitan Line uses separate electric locomotives for the haulage of some of its trains. These are the fast business services connecting the country districts with the City, which are composed of ordinary coaches and are steam-hauled over a part of their journeys. Thus separate electric locomotives are necessary to work these trains over the electrified length of their journeys up and down. These engines are used to a certain extent in freight services also.

The Hornby representative of this interesting type of locomotive can thus be employed on passenger or on goods trains as necessary. This Locomotive follows the characteristic outline of the real engines and it incorporates a great deal of realistic detail. The Hornby Metropolitan Coaches are of the normal compartment type, and each Metropolitan Set contains one first-class and one brake-third vehicle. Those included in the Electric Set are fitted for electric lighting, and this feature, in conjunction with the headlights of the Locomotive, gives the whole train an interesting and realistic appearance. The complete train forms a smart unit for suburban services, and additional interest will be given to operations if the change-over from the electric type to the steam type locomotive, and vice versa, is carried out regularly at a suitable station on the line.

A feature that is of special interest is the incorporation of a Pullman car in certain of the through Metropolitan trains. The reproduction of this practice in miniature will add considerably to the fascination of Metropolitan train operation. The inclusion of a Hornby No. 2, or No. 2 Special Pullman Coach in the make-up of a Metropolitan train gives an air of distinction to the service selected.

In addition to these electric trains requiring the use of separate electric locomotives, numerous electric trains of the motor-coach or multiple-unit type are operated on the Metropolitan Line. Compartment stock is used more particularly for those trains working into London over the surface electrified lines. Hornby Metropolitan Coaches are exactly what is required for these trains. Centre-gangway stock also is found, but the true home for these vehicles is in the London underground area. For such vehicles the nearest Hornby substitute is found in L.N.E.R. Saloon Coaches, which resemble Metropolitan stock in their colouring, and are of course of the end-vestibule centre-corridor type. The problem that remains is that of motive power, as electric motor-coach vehicles are not yet included in the Hornby Series.

Certain readers have therefore hit on the scheme of including in the centre of a formation of coaches of suitable type a Metropolitan electric locomotive. Actually the presence of the electric engine in the centre is not particularly noticeable, especially if brake-third coaches form the leading and trailing vehicles. These incorporate guard's and luggage accommodation at one end that can be taken to represent the driving and the motor compartments respectively of real stock.

The Hornby E36 Metropolitan Locomotive hauling a passenger train composed of appropriate compartment stock. This illustration gives a good idea of the realistic design of the Hornby Metropolitan components.

Similar arrangements as suggested for the Metropolitan can be adopted for the representation in miniature of the multiple-unit trains of other electrified lines. The stock employed will of course be varied according to the company and route represented. The well-known suburban services of the S.R. for instance could be run with Hornby No. 2 Coaches in S.R. colours and an LE120, or LE220, Locomotive in the centre of the train.

Again, L.M.S.R. No. 2 Coaches and an LE120 or LE220 Locomotive could be used to reproduce the trains running on the electric services of that Company. Some of the L.M.S.R. electric trains in the London suburban area, and those on the Liverpool and Southport line, are of the centre-corridor type with end doors. For the stock composing these, as for the Metropolitan trains of this kind, the nearest vehicle in the Hornby Series is the No. 2 Saloon Coach, but this time we shall require it in L.M.S.R. colours. For the Liverpool and Ormskirk trains, compartment stock as in the London area is chiefly used.

Freight operation by means of a Hornby Metropolitan engine. The prototype of this Locomotive is one of the few designs of electric locomotives operating on the railways of Great Britain.

Another of Liverpool's electric railways is the Mersey system linking both sides of the river of that name by means of the first tunnel beneath it. It has come prominently into notice recently in connection with the scheme for the electrification of the Wirral line of the L.M.S.R. Connection is made between the Mersey Railway and the old Wirral system at Birkenhead Park, so that L.M.S.R. steam-type trains can be run in miniature in conjunction with an electric service representing the Mersey trains. The latest Mersey coaches are not unlike Hornby No. 2 Saloons in general appearance, and they are painted in a similar shade of red to the L.M.S.R. vehicles. Multiple-unit trains are used, and a miniature Mersey system should certainly include some "underground" sections.

Similarly we could operate trains representing the Manchester and Altrincham joint electric services of the L.M.S.R. and L.N.E.R. Overhead wire equipment is used so that the pantographs on the LE120 and LE220 Locomotives will not be out of place. In view of their joint character these trains are finished in a manner very similar to that of S.R. stock. In miniature therefore S.R. vehicles could be used, without appearing noticeably inaccurate.

A great advantage of the multiple-unit type of formation is its handiness for working in and out of terminal stations. Frequently in miniature there is not a great deal of space to spare in terminals, so that the "running-round" facilities that are required by separate locomotives often cannot be provided. Thus unless another locomotive is available to draw the train out of the terminus, a considerable amount of manœuvring may be necessary to get the arriving engine on to the other end of the train ready for departure. The motor-coach type of train thus scores with its ability to run either way at will. With an LE220 Locomotive providing the motive power, as suggested for trains of this kind, the automatic reversing properties of this engine avoid any necessity for handling the train either in its arrival or departure at a terminus. Thus the miniature "multiple-unit" train can come in and go out as smoothly and with as little fuss as do the real ones. There is in fact one movement less involved in miniature, as the "motorman" does not have to walk from one end of the train to the other!

In addition to the representation of such services as are now operated electrically the electrification schemes at present in progress or in course of preparation suggest the anticipation of future working. The L.M.S.R. and Mersey Wirral scheme has already been mentioned. The L.N.E.R. main line from Sheffield to Manchester, when electrified, will employ separate locomotives for passenger and freight traffic. Overhead equipment is to be used, so that the LE120 and LE220 types with their dummy pantograph gear will be suitable units for a Hornby Electric Railway laid down on these lines. No doubt too in course of time the use of electric locomotives for freight traffic, over lines already electrified, will be greatly increased.

Join the Hornby Railway Company and become eligible for the competitions announced on this page.

H.R.C. COMPETITION PAGE

Join the Hornby Railway Company and become eligible for the competitions announced on this page.

"A DREAM JOURNEY!"

In the programmes of most H.R.C. Branches talks on railway and other subjects form a popular part of the regular programme. There is little doubt that the members who give such talks spare no efforts to make their information as complete and as interesting as possible. A little while ago we heard from the hard-working Secretary of a certain Branch who had made a journey on a well-known express and carefully noted as much as he could in order to describe the run at the next Branch meeting. His enthusiasm for the subject was such that one night he dreamt that he had given a talk, but it was all hopelessly mixed up! In a letter to Headquarters he described the actual journey, also the dream-journey, and it was interesting to see how they varied from one another.

We decided that this dream journey would make a good subject for an Errors Contest of the kind so popular with readers, and therefore reproduce the story exactly as told by our correspondent.

The train in which the dream-journey described on this page was made. The engine is a G.W.R. two-cylinder 4-6-0 No. 2937 "Clevedon Court," of the "Saint" class.

"On the day I went to Seaton I hurried to Waterloo to catch the "*Cornishman*," getting aboard the last coach of the train that formed the slip portion to be detached at Taunton The vehicles composing the train were the usual articulated stock, looking decidedly smart in their aluminium finish, and the engine was one of the 4-6-2 "Football Club" series No. 6130, "*Liverpool.*" The first part of the journey passed rapidly and uneventfully, as the automatic signals helped us to keep up a good speed in spite of the prevailing fog. I decided to 'explore' the train by means of the corridor running throughout and in the next coach came across the guard, who was preparing to detach the slip portion as we were nearing Westbury. I noticed carefully how he did it, pulling a lever in his van to release the slip coupling and gradually the detached coach eased away from us.

"Continuing through the train I entered the Pullman buffet car, where I dined, and afterwards was fortunate to be able to look into the Travelling Post Office van at the head of the train. Returning to my compartment I found that we were approaching Stephenson's tubular bridge over the Tamar. I noted the industrial character of the district. We passed several heavy coal trains coming up from South Wales, the freights of many of them no doubt being destined for the factories in the neighbourhood through which we were passing. Towards the end of the run the average speed maintained was not so high as previously, owing to the mountainous nature of the country there passed through.

"Finally we drew up at Queen Street station, Exeter, which is jointly owned by the L.N.E.R. I stayed on the platform for some little time watching hump shunting being carried out in the mechanised yard, which is opposite the station and which is fully equipped with modern rail brakes. Eventually I reached my destination by means of the connecting road service and thus ended a most interesting day."

Readers will see that here is a splendid opportunity for discovering mistakes. Some of the errors are well hidden and liable to pass unnoticed, so that the account should be read very carefully. When each competitor is satisfied that every mistake has been discovered, he should make out a neat copy of his list and forward it to Headquarters at Meccano Ltd., Binns Road, Liverpool 13, in an envelope marked "*H.R.C. Dream Journey*" in the top left hand corner. The competitor's name and address and H.R.C. number must be marked on each entry.

The competition will be divided as usual into two sections, Home and Overseas. In each of these the sender whose list contains the largest number of errors will be offered a choice of any products manufactured by Meccano Ltd., to the value of 21/-. To the two entries that are judged next in order of merit will be awarded similar prizes to the value of 15/- and 10/6 respectively. A number of consolation prizes will be awarded. The closing dates are 30th June for Home competitors, and 30th September for those competing in the Overseas Section.

Railway Photographic Contest

This month we announce the third of the series of Railway Photographic Contests commenced in April. There are no restrictions with regard to the subject chosen, but the actual exposure must have been made by the competitor.

Prizes of Hornby Train or Meccano goods to the value of 21/-, 15/- and 10/6 respectively will be awarded in each Section, Home and Overseas. Envelopes containing entries should be marked "*H.R.C. June Photographic Contest,*" and posted to reach Meccano Ltd., Binns Road, Liverpool 13, before 30th June. Overseas closing date, 30th September.

February "Concealed Stations" Contest Solution

Canonbury (L.M.S.R.), Wilmcote (G.W.R.), Essendine (L.N.E.R.), Deganwy (L.M.S.R.), Petrockstowe (S.R.), Woofferton (G.W.R.), Mytholmroyd (L.M.S.R.), Ulleskelf (L.N.E.R.), Oxshott (S.R.), Hoylake (L.M.S.R.), Sarnau (G.W.R.), Yeoford (S.R.), Presteign (G.W.R.), Yaxham (L.N.E.R.), Bulford (S.R.), Hednesford (L.M.S.R.), Preesgweene (G.W.R.), Sholing (S.R.), Galashiels (L.N.E.R.), Leebotwood (L.M.S.R.), Gosberton (L.N.E.R.), Holsworthy (S.R.), Minffordd (G.W.R.), Cullercoats (L.N.E.R.).

COMPETITION RESULTS

HOME

April "Signalling Contest."—First: J. R. Sleightholme (17091), York. Second: K. E. Milburn (26029), Chingford, London, E.4. Third: D. S. Dunsmore (33072), Sutton, Surrey. Consolation Prizes: W. Pollard (45922), Datchet, Nr. Slough, Bucks.; B. Gerrard (22476), Thornton Heath, Surrey; J. F. Cockshutt (14178) Streatham Park, London, S.W.16; R. Harvey (38560), Mundesley, Norfolk; C. W. Atkin (13233), West Kirby, Cheshire; J. C. Button (10335), Crewe, Cheshire; R. B. Williams (35085), Pelaw, Co. Durham; R. S. Dench (28187), Hall Green, Birmingham, 11; J. L. Stevenson (22346), Edinburgh 11.

April "Railway Photo Contest."—First: V. L. Breeze (2134), Kingston, Lewes, Sussex. Second: C. Spencer (44179), Sheffield 11. Third: F. Lowrey (47672), Harrogate, Yorks. Consolation Prizes: D. F. Forbes (14092), Leith, Edinburgh 6; E. C. Morgan (10735), Wandsworth Common, London S.W.18.

Branch News

New Southgate.—Various competitions were a popular feature at recent meetings, members having to guess the names of different stations from clues read out to them. A visit was paid to the Exhibition of the Model Railway Club at Central Hall, Westminster, and was greatly enjoyed, as the members gained many new ideas for improving the Branch layout. Secretary: A. R. Wardle, 25, Limes Avenue, New Southgate, London, N.11.

Waterloo (Dublin).—Several successful track meetings have been held at which timetable operations have proceeded normally. A special feature was made of holiday traffic working for the period of Easter. Certain trains were cancelled, but additional expresses were brought into use temporarily. These workings included special engine movements and both formed the subject of a "Special Notice" circulated among members. It has since been decided to renumber all the locomotives belonging to the Branch after various engines of the G.S.R. of Ireland. The number plates are to be obtained from the automatic nameplate machines that are found on railway stations. Secretary: S. B. Carse, 38, Oakley Road, Ranelagh, Dublin.

Chorlton-cum-Hardy.—An interesting visit was paid recently to the Manchester Central Fire Station. This visit was followed by a tea and a very successful Social. At track meetings timetable working has proved to be very popular, and good running was made on the first trip of a new express known as *"The Norseman."* It is intended to make timetable operations a standard feature and definite programmes are worked to at each regular Branch meeting. It is proposed to hold a small Exhibition in the near future. Secretary: G. H. Gill, 54, Highfield Road, Chorlton-cum-Hardy, Nr. Manchester.

St. Stephen's (Saltash).—Work has been in progress on a new track and satisfactory tests have been carried out over those sections so far completed. In order to give variety to the programme, the first meeting every other month is to be devoted to games. A Table Tennis league is run among Branch members and matches with other organisations are occasionally arranged. A visit has been paid to the Branch by members of the Plymouth Meccano Club, and a combined cycle run and ramble has been one of the most successful recent Branch events. Secretary: B. Braund, 9, Homer Park, Saltash.

Folkestone.—Shunting operations and goods working generally have been features of recent meetings. Some notable fast freight services are now operated regularly. The real Folkestone services from London are the prototypes on which the passenger operations on the Branch layout are modelled. It has been decided to include a miniature Folkestone Harbour in the layout and work has been started. A model steamer to stand at the quayside is now complete. New signals have been installed on the system and the Branch room itself has been repainted. Special arrangements were made for the Easter holiday traffic and these were successfully worked in an interesting manner. Secretary: F. E. Saunders, 79 Dover Road, Folkestone.

Some members of the Addiscombe H.R.C. Branch No. 280. Chairman, Mr. C. Chandler. Secretary, G. Chandler. This Branch was incorporated in 1934 and has progressed rapidly. A permanent track is available for train operations and a Branch Library also is maintained.

Claremont (Nottingham).—At a recent track meeting tests were made of the comparative speeds and hauling powers of the various locomotives. The practice of slipping coaches at various wayside stations has been adopted with success and is a popular feature. Members visited and greatly enjoyed an L.N.E.R. Exhibition of locomotives and rolling stock at Nottingham, and were keenly interested in the various aspects of railway working that were explained to them. Secretary: R. Ingham, 132, Mansfield Road, Nottingham.

Northampton.—The programme of this Branch continues to show a pleasing variety, which probably accounts in large part for the satisfactory attendances at meetings. Several Games Nights have been held. A shunting competition and timetable working have proved attractive. On the first anniversary of the foundation of the Branch, the first timetable ever arranged for Branch use was worked through, and comparison between this and present operating arrangements was of great interest. A series of lantern lectures is being arranged. Secretary: D. K. Adams, 8, Cedar Road, Northampton.

Elmside (Exeter).—Recent track meetings have shown a considerable improvement in train working, as new members have become used to Branch operating methods. A section for members interested in radio has been commenced. No special future arrangements have been planned, and the normal programme will be continued. Secretary: T. W. A. Smith, 98, Ladysmith Road, Exeter.

Islington.—An interesting talk has been given on the *"Post Office Tube Railway."* Two Lantern Lectures were particularly well enjoyed, one dealing with *"The Railway Museum"* (L.N.E.R.) and the other with *"Britain's Largest Railway"* (L.M.S.R.). Train working according to timetable has proceeded in the usual manner and attention has also been given to fretwork, games and other activities. Secretary: S. Gardner, 3, Tiverton House, Pleasant Place, Canonbury, London, N.

Rutherglen (Glasgow).—An interesting operation recently has been the taking down of the track and the overhaul of the baseboard. Considerable attention also has been given to repairs required by various locomotives, with which tests for speed and hauling power were then carried out. A new track is being laid down different in design from the former one, and train working arrangements for it are under discussion. Various competitions and a regular programme of games are being arranged for the near future. Secretary: R. G. Langmuir, 11, Afton Street, Shawlands, Glasgow, S.1.

AUSTRALIA

Sydney.—Various developments on the Branch layout have been taking place, and a new line 56 ft. long has been opened. It is single throughout, but has two passing loops at intermediate stations. An interesting talk was given at a recent meeting by Mr. T. Watson on *"The Railways of Tasmania."* Various excursions in conjunction with the local Railway Touring Club have been held, including visits to Kiama, Toronto and to Austinmer on the South coast. The Austinmer trip was particularly enjoyed and involved the special naming of the excursion train "The Meccano Club Express." This train will be used for future Branch excursions. Secretary: T. Watson Box 1749JJ, G.P.O., Sydney, Australia.

Branches Recently Incorporated

304. Glenpaston (Stamford Hill)—V. L. Passer, 5, Moundfield Road, Clapton Common, London, N.16.
305. St. Andrew's (Montpelier)—K. W. J. Bartlett, 33, Bath Buildings, Montpelier, Bristol, 6.

Reclaiming Oil from Waste Metal

Centrifugal Separators

THE power absorbed in driving a machine is indirectly converted into heat through friction. In machines employing cutting tools, both the tools and the materials dealt with become hot, and if the rise in temperature is not checked the former lose their edges too quickly and the latter depreciate in quality and value. These disadvantages are avoided by using a coolant, or cooling liquid, that also is of value in giving a smooth and finished surface to the work and lubricating the cutting edge.

There are several liquids that can be employed to prevent a rise in temperature during machining operations, and oil is one of the most popular of these for certain classes of work. For the purpose of mass production, parts machined at high speed are literally bathed in oil, and the turnings and swarf are washed away into a sump. The oil is allowed to drain into a reservoir below the machine, but much of it is held in surface tension with the metal, the amount retained depending on the extent of surface exposed. The waste material formed in these operations consists of pieces of very small dimensions, and its surface area is so great that it takes up a surprisingly large quantity of oil.

Automatic machinery must be kept working at full output, and requires lubricants of high quality for its cutting tools. The oil used is costly, and large quantities of it are required, especially in works where batteries of high-speed tools are kept continually at work. It is essential therefore that some means of recovering it from waste metal should be adopted, and it also is necessary to separate it from machined parts, especially if these are of brass or other non-ferrous metal, or are to be plated, varnished or lacquered.

A centrifugal oil separator with a charge of turnings in the rotating pan. Recovered oil is flowing from the outer casing. Photograph by courtesy of Manlove, Alliott and Co. Ltd., Nottingham.

Much of the oil used in work of this kind can be recovered from the work turned out, and also from cuttings, turnings and swarf, by ordinary drainage. Special methods must be employed in order to obtain the whole of the oil these retain, however, and centrifugal separators have been introduced for this purpose. A typical separator, designed and manufactured by Manlove, Alliott and Co. Ltd., Nottingham, is illustrated on this page. In it the material to be treated is whirled round at high speed, when centrifugal action causes the oil to fly outward into a collector of suitable form.

Inside the outer casing of the separator is a revolving pan consisting of a dished steel plate and having sloping sides. It is supported by a vertical driving shaft that extends upwards through it. The pan is charged with the oily material, but is not quite filled, because centrifugal force is greatest where the speed is highest, that is near the side of the pan, and the portion of the charge near the centre does not come under its influence to the same extent. The rotation of the charge tends to move the pieces of which it consists outward to the region where the effect is greatest.

A few clean rags usually are laid on top of the metal parts before the cover is screwed on the pan. These act only as filters to prevent fine swarf from leaving the pan when the machine is in motion. If different small parts are to be treated, and the number of each of these is insufficient to warrant the use of the machine for each kind separately, they are made up into separate bundles wrapped in clean rags. The separator then deals with them as effectively as if they were loose. Small parts, such as screws, bolts and nuts also can be dealt with in this separator.

When the cover plate has been screwed on the machine is set in motion, revolving at a speed of about 1,600 r.p.m. Under the influence of the centrifugal force developed, the oil is flung outward and expelled through the very narrow space between the knurled edges of the bucket and its cover, and is collected inside the outer casing and allowed to drain away to a collector.

The machine can be provided with counter gear to enable it to be driven by a belt through a shaft, as shown in our illustration, or fitted with an electric motor. Very little power is required to drive it, and that need only be applied while getting up speed, after which the revolving pan can be allowed to free-wheel. The separator is brought to rest by means of a hand brake.

The machine is speedy and very effective. A trial with 15 lb. 13 oz. of turnings produced 1 lb. 10 oz. of recovered oil. In another test, a charge of 23 lb. 10 oz. of oily turnings and screwings taken directly from machines yielded 1 lb. 1 oz. of oil, and one of the same weight taken from a heap of waste material that had been standing for several days, during which oil drained from it, produced 12 oz. of oil.

In many cases it is found most convenient to instal several small machines in different parts of a workshop rather than a single large machine. Centrifugal machines of greater capacity are used in special cases, however. For example, separators in the works of the Hoffman Manufacturing Co. Ltd., Chelmsford, recover from 500 gals. to 1,000 gals. of oil per day from about nine tons of material.

A NEW DOUBLETS CONTEST

The Doublets puzzles that we have set for our readers from time to time have proved consistently popular, and as it is now a considerable time since the last such contest, we are giving a fascinating new series this month.

For the benefit of new readers it must be explained that a Doublet consists of two given words, each containing the same number of letters. The puzzle requires one word to be changed to the other by placing connecting words between. The connecting words are known as links, and each link must differ from the preceding one by the alteration of only one letter. The test is to make the change in the smallest number of links.

To make the idea clear we give the following examples:

Store CORN in BARN
CORN - born - BARN
Face WIND from WEST
WIND - wend - went - WEST

In making the links only English words appearing in a standard dictionary may be used. Proper nouns, names of persons, places, etc., are not permitted. It is important to remember that the first solution arrived at is not necessarily the shortest. Competitors should go over their solutions carefully in search of short cuts that will eliminate overlapping links. Close study often reveals links that may be removed to improve the solution.

The Doublets to be solved in this competition are as follows:

Fill TANK with FUEL
Secure BOAT with ROPE
Hook FISH from POND
Make PLUG of WOOD
Go SLOW down HILL
Cut ROSES from TREES
Change NOTES to COINS
Dye GREY to BLUE
Change GEARS with LEVER
Release BIRD from CAGE
Sail BOAT on LAKE
Level SOIL with RAKE

This beautiful view of Rievaulx Abbey, Yorkshire, secured First Prize in the April Photo Contest (A Section) for Eric H. Coles, Notting Hill Gate, London, W.11.

In judging the entries, the 12 doublets will be considered as one contest, and cash prizes of 21/-, 15/-, 10/6 and 5/- respectively will be awarded to the senders of the four solutions showing the lowest total of links used throughout. In the event of a tie for any of the prizes, preference will be given to the entry having the neatest or most novel arrangement.

It will be observed that the combination of the 12 doublets for judging purposes will ensure that a brilliant solution of one doublet will carry its full weight by offsetting to some extent failure to secure the shortest chain in another.

Entries should be addressed to "Doublets, Meccano Magazine, Binns Road, Liverpool 13" and sent to reach this office not later than 30th June. There will be a duplicate set of prizes reserved for entries from Overseas readers, whose entries must reach us not later than 30th September.

Entries must be written on one side of the paper only, and each sheet of paper used must bear the competitor's name and address. The total number of links used must be noted on the first sheet.

June Photo Contest

As we announced in our April issue, each month throughout the spring and summer we shall offer prizes for the best and most interesting photographs submitted.

Each month's competition will be divided into two groups, Home and Overseas, and these two groups will be divided into two sections, A for those aged 16 and over, B for those under 16. Cash prizes of 21/- and 10/6 will be awarded in each section.

The photographs may be of any subject and may be made with any make of camera, film or paper. Each photograph must bear the reader's name, age and address, and a title on its back.

Entries sent this month must be addressed "June Photo Contest, Meccano Magazine, Binns Road, Liverpool 13," and must arrive not later than 30th June. The Overseas closing date will be 30th September.

Competition Closing Dates

HOME		
June Doublets Contest	...	30th June
June Photo Contest	...	30th June
OVERSEAS		
Meccano Limericks	...	30th June
March Drawing Contest	...	30th June
Vocation Voting Contest	...	31st July
April Photo Contest	...	31st July
May Crossword Puzzle	...	31st August
May Photo Contest	...	31st August
June Doublets Contest	...	30th September
June Photo Contest	...	30th September

Watch the Closing Dates

COMPETITION RESULTS

HOME

April Photo Contest.—First Prizes: Section A, E. H. Coles (London, W.11); Section B, A. Large (Alloa). Second Prizes: Section A, S. Coleman (Sheffield); Section B, T. W. W. Jones (Brampton). Consolation Prize: R. Dace-Brown (London, S.W.2).

Vocation Voting Contest.—1. C. Weatherbed (Sheffield 9); 2. S. C. Stephenson (Croft, Nr. Leicester); 3. M. M. Reader (Birmingham 16); 4. H. Fairbairn (London N.15). Consolation Prizes: C. E. Wrayford (Moretonhampstead); F. Fendley (Parkstone); D. Gillies (Glasgow S.1); E. Gurney (Watford); T. Allen (Hull).

OVERSEAS

Cover Voting Contest.—1. J. C. Carter (Capetown). 2. N. Lefcoe (Quebec); 3. L. Chapman (Christchurch, N.Z.); 4. J. J. N. Carter (Capetown).

January Drawing Contest.—First Prizes: Section A. W. Jones (St. James); Section B, J. van Dalsen (Pretoria). Second Prizes: Section A, Carlo Cali Corleo (St. Julians, Malta); S. Adelagun (Ibadan, Nigeria).

SUMMER STAMP COLLECTING

MANY boys at this season of the year, when the long hours of daylight make it possible to get out into the open in the evening, are tempted to tuck their albums and stamp mounts away into a drawer and forget about them until winter comes again. We confess to a little sympathy with their object. Sunshine is given to us to be enjoyed and no active person desires to be indoors when he can be out and about in the open.

To abandon the stamp collection altogether during summer is really a very serious mistake, however. Stamp collecting is now an all-the-year-round hobby. Postal authorities cannot hold up the demands of their routine business merely because stamp collectors in Britain find other attractions than stamps in summertime. The flood of new issues goes on unabated throughout every month. The stamps reproduced here illustrate this point, for they are chosen from new issues that appeared last summer. The collector therefore simply has to maintain contact with the hobby if he wishes to be up-to-date. The object of our article this month is to show how to maintain that contact without unduly intruding upon hours that can be equally enjoyed in more strenuous pursuits.

It is a simple matter to keep in touch with the new issues. It can be done in two ways. The first is by subscribing to a stamp magazine such as *Gibbons Stamp Monthly*, which includes every month a special supplement giving details of all new issues up to the time of going to press. The second is by subscribing to a new issue service. The usual arrangements for such a service provide for packets containing all new issues, or only certain types, such as Air Mails or British Colonials, up to a specified limit of face value, to be sent to the subscriber each month. The subscriber retains only those stamps he desires and returns the remainder. Usually the dealer running the service requires a preliminary cash deposit and a guarantee that stamps to a certain amount—a low figure usually—will be retained.

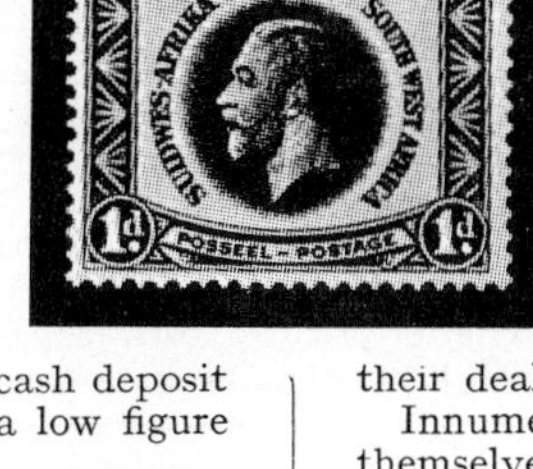

The time involved in looking over the new issues and deciding upon those to be purchased will not cut seriously into the time that might be devoted to games. One word of warning to the cricketing stamp collector, however. It is better to devote separate evenings to looking over stamps and oiling cricket bats. Linseed oil and mint stamps do not go well together!

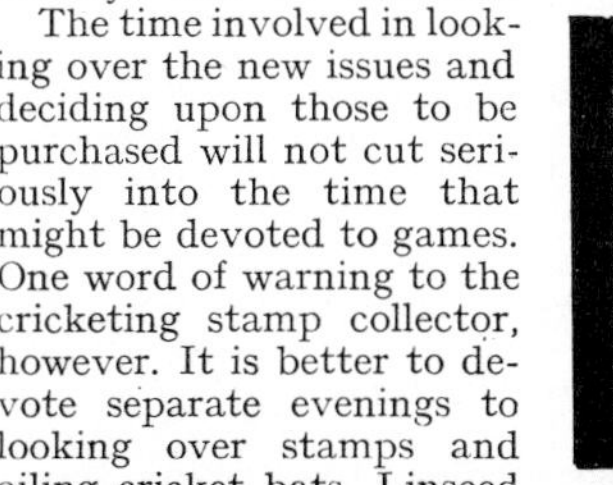

There are many little jobs around the collection that can be carried out in convenient stages and these tasks are just the thing for filling in odd moments in summer, when an engagement is cancelled at the last moment, for example.

Last summer we planned the layout of a new album, arranging the pages by ruling in the stamp positions lightly in pencil and indicating similarly the panels in which the writing-up was to be placed. We always like to draw in the lettered headings for the leaves of our albums, and the rough outlining of these, to serve as guides for the final work, was another congenial job that was spread over a series of odd half-hours. Later on, in the early autumn, the actual lettering in ink was done so that when the winter settled in, the whole of the album was ready waiting for the stamps themselves to be transferred from their old fixed-leaf printed album.

Many of our readers who are contemplating changing the method of their collecting next winter from a general all-countries arrangement to specialised subject collections, such as we have advocated in the "*M.M.*" from time to time, would find the summer's odd moments amply filled by planning on the lines we have indicated. Provision can be made then not just for the stamps already possessed but also for those that will need to be acquired to complete the story.

Those inevitable rainy afternoons and evenings that make games impossible are just the occasions for mounting up new issues that have accumulated, or, if the rain is not too heavy, for getting into town and visiting the stamp shops with the object of acquiring wanted stamps. Summertime is haymaking time indeed for collectors who make a habit of visiting their dealers.

Innumerable opportunities of improving the collection present themselves. Stamp dealers cannot close down their premises for a few months because some of their customers have forsaken them temporarily. Instead they must provide special inducements that will encourage collectors to buy during the summer. These special inducements take the form of lower prices and special bargain offers. The summer collector gets the benefit of those offers.

Incidentally, because business is proceeding at less than normal pressure, dealers have more time to devote to individual customers and in most cases are able and willing to discuss their stamp problems and give advice.

We have indicated sufficient possibilities in this article to show to our readers the advantages of maintaining contact with their stamps during the summer. The fact that bargains are to be picked up is really the least of these, and in our view the greatest dividend that any collector should look for from his stamp investments is in the form of life-long interests and enjoyment. A collection that is constantly cared for month in month out throughout the year will provide a steadily growing fund of pleasure. We urge all our readers to care for their collections this summer. The advantages will be obvious next winter.

"Meccano Parts and How to Use Them"

Every keen Meccano enthusiast wishes to carry out his model-building operations in accordance with correct engineering principles. In order to do this he must know the special functions of each of the parts that comprise the Meccano System, and to assist him in acquiring this knowledge there is published a manual entitled "*Meccano Parts and How to Use Them.*" In this manual all the parts in the system are listed and classified, and the uses of each individual part are described in detail. The descriptions are assisted by half-tone illustrations and sectional diagrams showing the parts actually in use in Meccano structures and mechanisms.

Ideal for the Model-Builder

An important section of the book is devoted to the various forms of Meccano motive power, and gives much useful information regarding the use of the Meccano Electric and Clockwork Motors. This manual forms an ideal constructor's guide and book of reference, and should be in the possession of every Meccano boy.

"*Meccano Parts and How to Use Them*" may be obtained, price 6d., from any Meccano dealer, or direct from Meccano Ltd., Binns Road, Liverpool 13, price 7d. post free.

Binding the "M.M."

There are two methods of binding the "*M.M.*" to preserve back copies from the mutilation that inevitably will be theirs should they be handled for any lengthy period without protection. First there is the spring-back binder system, that permits the copies to be inserted or removed from the binding case at will. This is intended primarily as a temporary arrangement for the protection of copies during the currency of their volume.

Handsome spring-back cases specially prepared for the "*M.M.*", with the name blocked in gold letters on the front cover, can be obtained from Meccano Limited, Binns Road, Liverpool 13, price 2/6 and 3/6 for sizes large enough to hold 6 and 12 copies of current issues respectively.

Permanent binding cases for back numbers of the Magazine can be supplied by Messrs. O. H. Bateman and Co., 23, Hanover Street, Liverpool. These cases are supplied in two sizes (1) for six copies, price 3/3 and (2) for twelve copies, price 4/9, post free in each case. The binding cases are supplied in what is known as "Quarter Basil, full cloth"—that is to say three-quarters of the sides are dark crimson cloth and the back and a quarter of the sides are dark crimson leather as shown above. The case is tastefully embossed in gold with the name "Meccano Magazine," and on the back is the name and volume number.

Binding Six or Twelve Copies

These binding cases are supplied so that readers may have their Magazines bound locally, but where desired, the firm mentioned above will bind Meccano Magazines at a charge of 5/9 for six issues or 7/6 for twelve issues, including the cost of the binding and also return carriage. The covers of the Magazines may be included or omitted as required, but in the absence of any instructions to the contrary they will be included.

Whilst the binding of the twelve Magazines is quite satisfactory, they form a rather bulky volume and for that reason arrangements have been made to bind six months' Magazines where so desired, as explained above. Back numbers for any volume can be bound and the case will be embossed with the volume number.

Readers desiring to have their Magazines bound need only make a strong parcel of them, include a note of their name and address together with the necessary remittance, and send the parcel direct to Messrs. O. H. Bateman and Co., carriage paid.

Stamp Gossip

and Notes on New Issues

Egyptian Army Post Issues

The Egyptian post office have placed on sale a special Army Post stamp, illustrated here, for the use of the British Forces in Egypt. The stamp shows a portrait of the late King Fuad and is inscribed "Army Post." The issue has been on sale since 1st March.

This issue is to replace the special seals issued by the Navy, Army and Air Force Institute by arrangement with the postal authorities and thus there disappears one of the most interesting stamp issues of recent years

The N.A.A.F.I seals were introduced in November, 1932 to enable British Forces in Egypt and their families to send ordinary letters to the British Isles, including the Irish Free State, at a reduced price. They were not available to prepay postage to any other parts of the world, and it was a strict requirement of the scheme that the correspondence must be posted in a regimental post-box Letters posted in ordinary Egyptian post-boxes, although bearing the letter seal, were surcharged, and thus there arose the curious situation that actually the postmark, and not the label, was the authorisation for carriage at the reduced rate. Indeed, in certain quarters this fact is the basis of a refusal to recognise the seals as postage stamps.

The new Army post stamp will be covered by precisely the same regulations for use, but its official issue by a postal authority gives it an unchallengable status.

The Late King Fuad

There is an old saying that misfortunes rarely come singly, and philatelists the world over must have thought of this old saw when they learnt of the death of His Majesty King Fuad of Egypt, who vied with our own late King George for premier place among royal philatelists.

King Fuad's interest in stamps commenced in his boyhood days and his personal collection, housed in 36 volumes, ranged over a very wide field of interest. In recent years, however, the late King had specialised, principally in the stamps of his own country and his Egyptian collections are without equal.

His Majesty The King

Our stamp collecting readers throughout the world will be pleased to learn that His Majesty King Edward VIII has been graciously pleased to grant his Patronage to the Royal Philatelic Society.

Thus the royal connection with stamp collecting maintained so closely by the late King George will be preserved.

Chilian Pictorials

The 400th anniversary of the discovery and conquest of Chile by Spain, represented by Diego de Almagro, in 1536 has been commemorated by the issue of a long set of 12 pictorial commemoratives featuring the agricultural and industrial features of the country.

The stamps range from 5 centavos up to 10 pesos in value, with designs as follows: 5c., the Atacama desert, one of the important locations of the Chilian nitrate industry. 10c., an oyster fishing fleet off Chiloe. 20c., Ocoa Palm trees, a variety of coconut that produces a fruit no bigger than a walnut; the sap of this tree provides a pleasant syrup. 25c., sheep farming. 30c., copper mines in Chile, which is one of the world's largest producers of copper. 40c., Araucanian Palms; this tree produces the piñon nut, which is somewhat like a brazil in appearance and a chestnut in taste. 50c., a view of the coal port of Lota. 1 peso, the wharves at Valparaiso, 1 p. 20, All Saints Lake, with the Volcano Puntiagudo in the background. 2 p., a portrait of Diego. 5 p., a group of cattle. 10 p., a mechanical shovel at work in the nitrate fields.

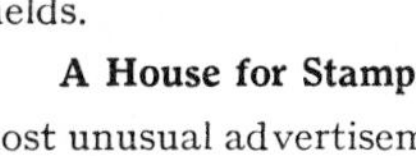

A House for Stamps

The most unusual advertisement we have ever seen in a philatelic newspaper appeared recently in *"Stamp Collecting,"* in which Mr. Robson Lowe, the London stamp dealer, offered a modern house on Wimbledon Common in exchange for a stamp collection on behalf of one of his clients. To avoid any misunderstanding, let us hasten to add that the cash value of the collection would need to be in the neighbourhood of £2,000 before it would be of interest to the collector responsible for the advertisement.

Ampère Commemorative

The 100th anniversary of the death of the French scientist Andre Ampère was celebrated by France on 27th February last by the issue of a 75c. commemorative stamp bearing a portrait of the scientist.

Ampère was born in Lyons in 1775 and very early in his career showed promise of great brilliance. After holding teaching posts at Bourg and Lyons from 1801–5, he was appointed Professor of Analysis at the Polytechnic School, Paris, in 1809, and became Professor of Physics at the College de France in 1824. His fame rests particularly on his researches in electro-dynamics and his demonstration of the relations between magnetism and electricity. Ampère's pioneer work in electrical science was recognised by the adoption of his name to signify the unit of electrical current strength.

Also in February, France issued a new air mail series of six stamps ranging in value from 85c. to 3 F. 50. Each stamp uses the design illustrated here, showing an aeroplane flying over Paris. Those of our readers who know Paris will be interested in seeking to identify many of the famous landmarks that can be picked out in the stamp design, such as the Eiffel Tower, L'Arc de Triomphe, the Church of the Sacred Heart at Montmartre, and Notre Dame Cathedral

L.Z. 129

The new German Zeppelin *"Hindenburg"* will shortly be as famous on stamps as its illustrious predecessor *"Graf Zeppelin."* The special stamp illustrated on this page was issued in March to celebrate the giant airship's flight across the North Atlantic early last month. The design depicts the airship in flight across the Atlantic, and at the head of the stamp is the inscription "With L.Z. 129 to North America."

* * * * *

In our next issue we hope to illustrate specimens from Germany's Olympic Games issue that was placed on sale on 9th May. The set contains eight excellent sporting designs.

We thank Stanley Gibbons Ltd. for their courtesy in loaning the stamps from which the illustrations on this page have been made.

FIRESIDE FUN

TRAVELLING LIGHT

Two negros were talking about the possibilities of a war. Sambo said: "I'm going to join the Cavalry." "Not me," said Rastus, "When de retreat am sounded, I don't want to be hampered by no hoss."

* * * *

Well-meaning Old Lady: "Are you going to Mrs. Smith's funeral, sir?"

Doctor: "No, I very seldom go to any of my patients' funerals."

Old Lady: "No, I suppose you might be doing nothin' else, sir, if you was to."

* * * *

Specialist: "Could you pay for an operation if I thought one was necessary?"

Patient: "Would you find one necessary if I could not pay for it?"

* * * *

Teacher: "Tommy, give me a definition of the word 'luck'."

Tommy: "A man was murdered in the street for his money. But he had left all his money at his office. That was luck."

* * * *

Magistrate: "What have you to say to this charge of begging?"

Tramp: "Well, it was not my fault, sir; I just held my hand out to see if it was raining and the gentleman dropped a coin in it."

* * * *

During a history lesson the teacher pointed out to the class that a surname often indicated the trade of the ancestors of those who bore the name. He gave the simple examples of Smith, Taylor, Baker and others.

Then he questioned one of the boys: "What were your ancestors, Webb?"

"Must have been spiders, sir!"

* * * *

The Irish foreman found one of his men asleep. "Slape on, ye idle spalpeen," he said. "So long as ye slape, ye've got a job; but as soon as ye wake up ye're out of wurrk!"

* * * *

The ferryman was asked by a timid lady in his boat whether any persons were ever lost.

"Oh, no," said he, "we always find 'em the next day."

* * * *

Mother: "Eat up your spinach, Molly. It puts strong, white teeth into your mouth."

Molly: "Then why don't you give some to grandpa, mummy?"

* * * *

Diner: "I want some chicken, and the younger it is the better."

Waiter: "How about an egg, sir?"

* * * *

Maisie: "Do you think those cookery classes accomplish anything?"

Polly: "Sure I do. I haven't seen a tramp around the place since they started."

* * * *

THRIFTY!

Bandit: "Your money or your life."

Traveller: "Take my life; I'm saving my money for my old age."

NOT GUILTY

An old negro in a Missouri town was applying for registration papers.

"What is your name?" asked the official.

"George Washington," was the reply.

"Well George, are you the man who cut down the cherry tree?" asked the other.

"No sir, I ain't de man. I ain't done no work for nigh onto a year."

* * * *

MISUNDERSTOOD

Chatty Traveller (of short stature): "I'm a little stiff from hiking."

Short-tempered Grocer: "I don't care where you come from. Let me have a look at your samples."

* * * *

A man entered a country post office. "Have you a parcel for Mr. Jones?" he asked.

"Ay," said the postmaster, "but how do I know you to be him?"

The man produced a photograph of himself. "Have a look at that," he said. "It's me, isn't it?"

"My, so it be," said the postmaster, handing over the parcel without another word.

* * * *

Little Betty (annexing the largest slice of cake): "Well, I s'pose it's no use being ladies first if you can't take the biggest piece."

* * * *

Father: "I don't want Jack to see his present until his birthday."

Mother: "I'll put it in the bathroom, he'll never think of looking there."

* * * *

First Clerk: "Have you and your boss ever had any difference of opinion."

Second Clerk: "Yes, but he doesn't know it."

* * * *

An American visitor to England was standing on a platform of a station when the *"Royal Scot"* rushed through.

"Do you call that an express?" he asked a porter.

"Bless your life, no!" replied the porter. "That's Bill doin' a bit o' shunting; he'll be back in a minute."

* * * *

Angler: "Yes, the fish was too small to bother with, so I got two men to throw it back."

* * * *

Teacher: "As we walk outdoors on a cold winter's morning and look about us, what do we see on every hand?"

Pupil: "Gloves."

* * * *

Having read that rare stamps fetch high prices from philatelists, a man in the South of England is treasuring one that has come into his possession. It is a 1½d. stamp on a postcard bearing the postmark "Aberdeen."

* * * *

Pessimist: "Cheerful? How can I be cheerful when every bone in my body aches?"

Optimist: "Well, you might at least be thankful that you are not a herring."

* * * *

As little Frank was out walking with his mother they passed a lady wearing a veil.

"Oh," exclaimed Frank, "why have they put wire netting round the poor lady's face?"

ALL SQUARE

Jones: "I'm awfully sorry my fowl got into your garden, and made a mess of it."

Smith: "That's all right, my dog has killed your fowl."

Jones: "Don't apologise, because my car has just killed your dog."

* * * *

Visitor: "Who is the responsible man in this firm?"

Office Boy: "I don't know who the responsible party is, but I get all the blame."

* * * *

An Englishman lost in a mist on a Scottish moor met a native and said: "I am lost."

The native replied: "Is there any reward for findin' on ye?"

Englishman: "No."

Native: "Then ye're still lost."

* * * *

A motorist was accused of exceeding the speed limit. The magistrate, calling for evidence, asked a country constable at what speed the defendant was travelling.

"Well, indeed sir, I do not know. He was going so fast I did not see him till he was out of sight!" said the constable.

* * * *

An old lady and her small niece were at a cricket match when it started to rain, and the players ran for shelter.

Little girl: "Fancy a little shower like that stopping the game."

Auntie: "Well, my dear, you see only three of them are wearing mudguards."

* * * *

Teacher: "Who can tell me what the former ruler of Russia was called?"

Class (in unison): "Tsar."

Teacher: "Correct; and what was his wife called?"

Class: "Tsarina."

Teacher: "What were the Tsar's children called?"

There was a pause and then a timid voice in the rear piped up "Tsardines."

* * * *

Football Club Manager: "I've found the very player we want. Eye like a hawk, body like a bullock, speed of a racehorse, kick like a mule."

Director: "It's a centre forward we want, not a farmyard."

* * * *

Mother (sternly): "You mustn't be conceited, Betty. You are always looking in the mirror."

Betty: "I'm not conceited, mummy. I don't think I'm half as good looking as I really am."

* * * *

Porter: "Anything else now, Ma'am?"

Old Lady: "Yes, you might run to the other end of the train. I want to test the communication cord."

* * * *

Jones: "Won't you have something more to eat, Mr. Smith?"

Smith: "Well—thank you—just a mouthful."

Jones: "James, fill Mr. Smith's plate."

* * * *

HIGHLY HONOURED

"Your dog's a friendly little fellow. He keeps sniffing at me and wagging his tail," said the guest.

"Oh, I expect that's because you've got his plate," said the small boy of the family.

NEXT MONTH: "TEST FLYING GIANT AIR LINERS." PUBLISHING DATE: 1st AUGUST

MECCANO MAGAZINE

Editorial Office:
Binns Road, Liverpool 13
England

Volume XXI. No. 7
July, 1936

With the Editor

Something to Think About

One of the most interesting features of my correspondence is the large number of letters I receive from readers asking me to solve some problem that is puzzling them. I am always glad to receive these queries and to do my best to answer them satisfactorily. I confess that some of the problems make me put on my thinking cap. They deal with almost every subject under the Sun, and show how keen *"M.M."* readers are to acquire all kinds of useful and definite knowledge.

Many of these enquiries deal with various forms of mechanism for perpetual motion, the hoary old impossibility that has worried inventors of all Ages and still attracts eager enquirers. Some of the perpetual motion schemes are so ingenious that it takes a good deal of careful examination to find the flaw that makes their working impossible. Before long I hope to publish an article dealing with some of the more interesting perpetual motion devices, past and present. Other readers are concerned with such matters as the speed of a wasp flying across a compartment in a rapidly-moving train; others want to know if the guard of an express train could shoot the engine driver if the speed of the bullet from his gun were the same as that of the train. I have been asked also if it would be possible to travel from England to America in a balloon by simply rising straight up in the air and descending several hours later when the world has turned round and America is directly underneath! Then of course there is the old problem as to what would happen if an irresistible force encountered an immovable object!

A New Feature

Many of the problems submitted to me are of general interest, and I intend to deal with a selection of them in a new *"M.M."* feature under the heading *"Something to Think About."* The first article in this series appears on page 402 of this issue, and deals with an imaginary journey through a shaft driven through the centre of the Earth from England to Australia. The reader who first wrote to me about this gigantic shaft wanted to know whether a person going through it would emerge feet first or head first on reaching Australia, and his enquiry leads to many interesting and curious results.

I shall be glad to know what my readers think of this article, and to receive suggestions for other problems that are suitable for inclusion in the series. Problems submitted should not involve any mathematical calculations, and should be capable of being illustrated by a photograph or a drawing. Payment will be made for any problem accepted for publication.

Speeding Up Railway Services

It is interesting to find that on the sixth of this month the time required by *"The Flying Scotsman"* to travel from London to Edinburgh is to be reduced to 7¼ hours. This is 15 minutes less than the time now taken, which four years ago was reduced from the 8¼ hours that had been customary for many years. There is an even greater saving in the journey onward to Aberdeen, which is now brought 57 minutes nearer London. Similar changes have been made in the running of other L.N.E.R. main line trains, and also of the L.M.S.R. Anglo-Scottish trains. For instance, the time to reach Glasgow from London by *"The Royal Scot"* is to be reduced by 10 minutes, so that the journey will occupy only 7½ hours.

This news is distinctly cheering both to railway enthusiasts and to travellers. The actual reductions may not appear very large, but it must be remembered that in recent years trains have increased considerably in weight because greater attention is being paid to the comfort of passengers. Present-day locomotives have to deal with loads of 450 to 500 tons, or even more. With these they are making better times than those engaged in the famous races of half a century ago, when a few small coaches only had to be hauled, and the speeds attained were thought to be dangerous.

Day Trips By Air

However much railway services are accelerated, they can never compete with flying as far as speed is concerned. It is almost incredible to realise that most of Europe's capitals, including places as far away as Budapest, Rome and Madrid, can now be reached from London in a day by air, and to-day a new Imperial Airways service begins that adds Stockholm to this list.

It is even more remarkable to find that day trips can be made as far afield as Switzerland. One can fly over to Zurich in time for lunch, and after a short stay there return to London the same evening. Similarly an early service from Croydon enables several hours to be spent in Copenhagen before returning the same night.

Flying services indeed are opening up Europe to us. It is only a few years since a journey even to Belgium or Northern France involved a long and troublesome journey, partly by rail and partly by water. Ostend, Le Touquet and other seaside resorts across the English Channel can be reached in an hour or two, and are now as near London as Brighton was in pre-War days. In the course of a single week visits actually can be made by existing air routes to France, Switzerland, Italy, Spain, Germany and Scandinavia.

The Romance of the Jaffa Orange

A Growing Palestine Industry

By H. J. Shepstone, F.R.G.S.

THE story of the Jaffa orange is a romance of industry. Some 80 years ago the British Consular Agent at Jaffa sent a few boxes of Jaffa oranges to Queen Victoria. They were the first boxes of oranges to be shipped out of the country, and it was a little time before the Jaffa came upon the ordinary market, but by 1913 the export of oranges from Palestine totalled about half a million cases. The fruit was given its name because it is grown in the groves around Jaffa. Its production then was virtually an Arab industry, for Arabs were responsible for its cultivation, picking, packing and transport to the steamers at Jaffa.

A modern orange packing warehouse in Palestine.

After the War the number of cases exported fell considerably and the half-million mark was not reached till 1929. Since then the industry has gone ahead by leaps and bounds, and the number of cases of oranges now exported is between five and six million in a season, together with more than a million boxes of grape-fruit. No other fruit-producing country can point to such a phenomenal growth in any of its products. As an exporter of oranges Palestine is second only to Spain, and as an exporter of grape-fruit she heads the list.

The Jaffa orange has won universal favour because of its high qualities, for in juice content, flavour, fragrance and pleasant shape it excels all other varieties. Its cultivation to-day is the principal industry of the Holy Land. Not only is it the greatest factor in the economic life of the country, but it is fast becoming an important factor in the citrus industry of the whole world.

Fumigating the trees in the orange groves at Jaffa to destroy insect pests.

There is something attractive about an orange grove. The luscious fruit is grown on what is really an immense bush rather than a tree. At blossom time an orange grove is a fairyland picture come true, for it is one blaze of beautiful white flowers, intoxicating the air with their scent, which often can be detected miles away and off Jaffa even envelops ships far out at sea. The leaves of the plant are a beautiful dark, velvety green. At first the fruit is green, and it turns gradually to a lovely golden tint affording a striking contrast to the dark rich colour of the leaves.

The trees are grown from carefully selected seedlings, the seeds being planted in a seed bed in close rows. There the young plants remain for 12 months, by which time they are ready for transporting into the nurseries. At the end of the second year, they are budded to the variety desired, for even among Jaffas there are several varieties, and the tree is planted in the orchard or grove. It is carefully watched for the next two years, when it should be bearing its quota of fruit. The principal duty of the grower now is to keep the grove free of weeds and see that it is efficiently irrigated. This is done by means of furrows ploughed between the rows of trees along which the water is allowed to flow.

In gathering the fruit considerable care is called for. Oranges must not be plucked roughly from the tree. Each has to be clipped off carefully so as not to cut either the skin or peel of the fruit, or the buttons on the stem centre. Care is taken to avoid scratching the fruit on the limbs of the tree, or when placing it in the picker's bag, as skin punctures would result in rapid decay. From the pickers' bags the oranges are transferred to field boxes, which are carted to the packing houses, where the fruit is washed, dried, graded, wrapped, and packed ready for transport.

The packing houses are model establishments of their kind, possessing the latest labour-saving devices for the rapid and efficient handling of the fruit. At present there are some 70,000 acres under citrus fruit in Palestine, but the area is being rapidly extended. Mr. S. Tolkowsky, Chairman of the Jaffa Citrus Exchange, declares that if the present rate of planting continues—and there is no sign of its abating—the total available crop for export 10 years hence will be somewhere in the neighbourhood of 20 million cases. About 65 per cent. of the industry is in Jewish hands, the remaining 35 per cent. being controlled by the Arabs.

Reconstructing the ancient harbour at Jaffa. A portion of the foreshore is being reclaimed for the erection of a large orange and transit shed.

In order to facilitate the handling of this ever-increasing volume of fruit, some interesting improvements are being carried out at the port of Jaffa. In a word, what the engineers are doing is reconstructing the old harbour used by Solomon in Bible times. Strictly speaking, there is no harbour at Jaffa capable of accommodating modern steamers, but only a small rock-protected shelter. Running parallel to the town is a belt of rocks that lie awash, about 300 ft. to 400 ft. from the shore, forming a barrier that presents both a refuge and a menace. To the smaller craft, such as lighters and small sailing boats, capable of being steered by adroit seamen through their rocky gateway barely 20 yds. wide, the sheltered waters behind them are a haven of refuge; but to the modern cargo steamer the rocks, with their submerged extensions, constitute a peril to be avoided at all costs.

Gathering Jaffa oranges. The fruit is clipped off and care is taken to avoid scratching the skin, which would lead to decay.

The reef to-day is very jagged and broken, and consists of soft rock. In Hebrew times it probably was much more pronounced, running more evenly and standing higher out of the water, thus acting as a natural breakwater to shipping lying within the sheltered area. The engineers are restoring this old harbour of Solomon by converting the rocky reef into a massive mole or sea wall; the dangerous submerged extensions are being blasted away, a proper entrance is being constructed, and the sheltered water dredged to a depth of 10 ft. to 12 ft. The harbour will not be able to accommodate large steamers, but they will be able to lie to the north of the entrance in a much safer position than in the roadstead off the port. A portion of the foreshore also is being reclaimed, and upon it wharves are being built as well as a transit shed capable of holding 250,000 cases of oranges.

Another reason for carrying out these improvements at Jaffa is to attract the better type of cargo boat. Both the Palestine Government and the growers realise that if a market is to be found for their fruit it must be conveyed quickly to the markets of Europe. Whereas 19 to 20 days was the average duration of the voyage a few years ago, the best steamers engaged in the trade are now taking only 12 to 13 days from Jaffa to Liverpool or Glasgow, and even to Hamburg. The shorter the voyage, the less the waste.

Everything possible is being done to push the sale of the fruit in overseas markets. There is a special Government Inspection Service to see that only fruit in first-class condition is exported. Ugly and unshapely fruit is thrown on one side, and if an orange has to travel overseas it should have been picked and packed just before it is ripe. In order to increase the sale of the fruit the Government have created a fund for propaganda and advertising by a levy on the fruit exported. Thus the fine qualities of Palestine oranges and grape-fruit are being brought to the notice of people in the principal fruit-consuming countries of Europe. The cost of this inspection service and the administration of the propaganda fund is being borne by the shippers themselves, and not by the Government.

While these various schemes for quicker transport, an inspection of the fruit before shipment, and large-scale advertising campaigns may do much to increase the demand for the fruit, the shippers realise that it is doubtful if they can attain their aim of an export trade of 20 million cases unless they are prepared to accept lower prices. The cheaper they can sell their fruit the more will consumption be increased. Thus they are demanding through the Colonial Office and the British Parliament the grant of Imperial Preference—the same treatment as is meted out to the growers of South Africa and Australia. At present the fruit is subject to a Customs duty of about 3s. 6d. a box on grape-fruit and 1s. a box on oranges. The growers declare that their profits are small, only 4s. a box on grape-fruit and about 3s. a box on oranges. A reduction in the duty, or its abolition would enable them to place the fruit on the market more cheaply, to the benefit of the people of this country as well as the growers. At present this country takes 70 per cent. of the oranges and grape-fruit that are grown in Palestine.

The Magic of the Firth of Clyde

Glasgow to Ardrishaig by the "*Lochfyne*"

By O. S. Nock, B.Sc., D.I.C.

AN early morning start to any journey always gives an indefinable though quite definite sense of adventure; there is a nip in the air, and a feeling of elation. On going aboard the "*Lochfyne*" at 7 a.m. this feeling rises to a tremendous thrill of expectancy, for this stout little craft makes her daily voyage among high mountains, by firth and sea loch, carrying the Royal Mail to some of the remotest parts of the West Highlands. The scene at Bridge Wharf, in the heart of Glasgow, irresistibly fascinating as it is, gives not the slightest idea of the enchanting seascapes to which this rather grimy river leads; but one of the greatest charms of this voyage is that of infinite surprise.

The "Lochfyne," a Diesel-electric ship of 754 tons that carries the Royal Mail in winter from Glasgow, or Greenock, to Ardrishaig. Photograph by courtesy of David MacBrayne Ltd.

From the wharf on the opposite bank sail the Burns and Laird Line ships to Belfast; immediately beyond the Clyde bridge is the massive viaduct carrying the L.M.S. Railway into the Central station, and at this hour train after train is arriving with hundreds of city workers. The morning is as yet grey, but away to the west a broad rift of clear pale green sky gives a hint of brighter weather to come. There is just time for a look round the engine rooms before starting; this is as well, because throughout the voyage the passing scene is of such compelling interest that to go below at any time would be to miss much.

The "*Lochfyne*" is only a small vessel, with a gross tonnage of 754; she was specially designed for the summer service from Oban round the Isle of Mull to Staffa and Iona, but during the winter months she works on the Royal Mail route from Glasgow, or Greenock, to Ardrishaig. She is a Diesel-electric ship of about 1,600 h.p. To enable passengers and mails to be landed at short jetties at all states of the tide, and shallow waters navigated at full speed, she has been designed with a very shallow draught, and so the engine room control platform is level with the lower saloon deck instead of in the depths of the ship. There are two 5-cylinder Diesel engines, and each of these drives an electric generator; the latter have an output of about 750 amperes each, direct current, at 500 volts. Each of these dynamos supplies current to an electric motor that is directly coupled to one of the propeller shafts. Throughout a voyage the Diesel engines are kept constantly running so that full power is available at a second's notice. All that has to be done on receiving the signal from the bridge is to switch on the motors, an operation that is rather like starting up an electric train, except that with a ship you can put on full power immediately.

Loading the mails at Prince's Pier, Greenock.

The "*Lochfyne*" sails at 7.11 a.m.; that odd minute seems very curious, but so it has been for very many years, in fact the 7.11 a.m. departure of the Ardrishaig mail boat is quite one of the traditions of Glasgow. Just before starting time I was welcomed on the bridge by Captain Cameron, and a moment or so later the gangways were let down and we were under way. The first miles lead past a score of shipyards, vast warehouses, and docks to which come ships from the very ends of the earth. On the stocks at such famous yards as Barclay Curle's, the Fairfield Engineering Company, and Harland and Wolff's were to be seen vessels of all kinds: cruisers, huge Diesel-driven merchantmen, motor yachts. At some yards there were three or even four ships under construction, some nearly ready for launching, others scarcely advanced beyond the laying of the keel.

The Clyde is an amazing river. Past all these shipyards it is so narrow that even small vessels have to be launched into it slantwise to avoid hitting the opposite bank, and it can usually provide something in the way of vivid contrasts. Near Govan, where we called at the little pier to pick up passengers, a great 25,000 ton Anchor liner, the "*Transylvania,*" was berthed alongside one of the quays, while just ahead one of the gaunt vehicle-carrying ferries nosed its way across; these queer-looking craft are provided with a hoist so that the platform can always be brought level with the landing berths at any state of the tide. If the ferries are gaunt looking, even more so are the dredgers. The most remarkable thing about the Clyde is that by Nature it was anything but an ideal place to build ships, and in order to do so it has been artificially deepened and requires constant dredging. Between Glasgow and Dumbarton it is indeed more an excavation than a river. The dredgers are extraordinary looking implements—you could hardly call them ships! What passes as their deck is only a few feet above water level; two immensely tall funnels, placed abreast, rise from the stern, and on deck is what looks like a very thick-set version of a colliery winding wheel, up to which leads an endless chain of buckets. It is, thanks to the efficiency of such as these, that a vessel of the "*Queen Mary's*" size could be brought down the river successfully.

By the time we were approaching Clydebank, the birthplace of that beautiful ship, there was open meadow land on the south bank; the town of Renfrew slipped by, and to the north, behind the array of electric cranes at John Brown's yard, rose the Kilpatrick Hills, dark and solemn in the grey morning light. At Clydebank the river is considerably wider than nearer Glasgow, and right opposite is the mouth of the River Cart; but apart from this, the yard that has become world famous is little different from the others. At the time of my trip the light cruiser "*Southampton*" was in the fitting-out basin. Below this point the river winds considerably; round the S-curve at Bowling even the "*Lochfyne*" was reduced to half-speed, although of course it was low tide, and so we entered the long straight channel that leads past Dumbarton.

Far ahead the sky was now brilliant, but a slight mist hung over the widening firth and gave Dumbarton's isolated rock the appearance of a big cone-shaped island. Along this straight stretch artificial banks have been built on each side of the deep water channel and on these are fixed the gas buoys marking the course; at low tide the banks are exposed. As we passed abreast of Dumbarton there was a glimpse, through a gap in the hills, of Ben Lomond away to the north, his snow-capped summit sparkling in the sun. Port Glasgow now lay on our port bow. There is an almost continuous chain of shipyards from here onward to Greenock, at one of which the ill-fated French liner "*Atlantique*" was waiting to be broken up. Seen against the dark hillside, her appearance at first sight was not unlike that of many another merchant ship needing overhaul; but as we drew closer her hollow interior, smashed and twisted bridge, and scorched metalwork gave a terribly vivid suggestion of the horror of fire at sea.

The "Lochfyne's" bows swinging out as she leaves Greenock.

At 9 a.m. we were tying up at Prince's Pier, Greenock; here part of the mails is picked up, having come down from Glasgow by the G. and S.W. route of the L.M.S.R. Passengers who prefer to leave Glasgow as late as possible travel on the 8.35 a.m. train, via the Caledonian route, and join the ship at Gourock, where the bulk of the mails were taken on board. While we were at Gourock the changing lights on mountain and firth were of simply dazzling beauty; westward lay the Holy Loch, to the north was Loch Long, and just across the water near Helensburgh was the entrance to the Gare Loch. These inlets all point outward like the fingers of a human hand, and on the rolling hills between them shadows of the flying clouds were chasing each other over brilliantly green fields and purple-brown moorlands. Just astern of us at the pier was berthed another mail boat, bound for Lochgoilhead; this was the paddle steamer "*Mountaineer*" which, like the "*Lochfyne*," belongs to the fleet of David Macbrayne Ltd.

At 9.30 a.m. the ropes were cast off once more and we headed for Dunoon. We were now almost exactly half way to Ardrishaig, but the difference between the two halves of the journey is a much more striking one than a mere matter of time and distance. Up to now the interest of the trip had lain chiefly in the engineering wonders of the Clyde; glimpses of distant peaks and occasional splashes of brilliant colour on the hillsides had given only the merest suggestion of the glory of the West Highlands. But now, half way between Gourock and Dunoon, with smoky Greenock disappearing behind Kempock Point, the last link with industry was severed, and at the same time, far away to the south, the wild jagged mountains of Arran rose blue from the sea. Range upon range of brown hills were grouped round the northern inlets of the firth, and from the gently rising moorlands of the Renfrewshire coast rose the smoke of heather fires.

In the Kyles of Bute. The L.M.S.R. turbine steamer "Duchess of Argyll" is passing ahead of the "Lochfyne."

Both the L.M.S.R. and the L.N.E.R. operate steamer services on the Clyde, and as we approached Dunoon there was a vessel of each company at the pier. This popular resort, together with Rothesay on the island of Bute, can only be reached by water, and during the busy months six or eight ships can often be counted at once plying the firth on various routes. We berthed at Dunoon to the skirl of the bagpipes. This music has to be heard in its natural setting of mountain and loch to be really appreciated, and this morning amid the splash of the water and the scream of seagulls, its wild air, borne on the wind, was thrilling beyond description.

Southward bound now the green hills of Bute came into view, the island of Great Cumbrae lay out in the firth, and far down the eastern shore the sun was dazzingly reflected from a skylight in Largs. We called at Innellan, where solemn crags and pine woods rose from the water's edge; and then, rounding Toward Point with its gleaming white lighthouse, we entered Rothesay Bay. Here is a fair-sized town most charmingly situated round the sweep of the bay; its pier resembles a busy railway station, at which no less than five steamers can be berthed at once. In getting away from all these piers the forward ropes were cast off first and the engine driving the propeller farthest from the pier was put at "Full Astern," while the near engine was usually put at "Half Ahead." This swings the bow away from the quayside, and as soon as the vessel is pointing well clear the after ropes are cast off and both engines put ahead.

From Rothesay our course is due north at first, and right ahead of us is Loch Striven, a narrow fiord winding far into the mountains; but on passing abeam of Ardmaleish Point we swung north-west into the Kyles of Bute. The waterway here is never more than half a mile wide. On the hills rising smoothly to the heights of Beinn Bhreac the colour gradually deepened from brilliant green at the water's edge to the deep rich brown of heather in winter, as the summits were neared. Ahead, moorland fires spread a soft haze, while firth and sky were of a truly exotic blue. At the little pier of Colintraive we landed some mails, and on setting forth again we were soon threading our way through the Narrows. Beyond this point, although the Kyle widens considerably, there are two rocky islets, known as the Burnt Islands, that reduce the navigable waterway to two channels barely 100 yards wide.

Ahead now was a wall of great beetling crags, and leaving Loch Riddon on our right we turned southward into the western arm of the Kyles of Bute. At the turn the character of the scene changes entirely: smiling farm land at the waterside gives place to rugged outcrops of bare rock, and instead of smooth rounded hill tops there are rough overhanging crags. As if to harmonise with the wilder scene great clouds were racing across the sky, the rising wind whipped the sea into a welter of white caps and there was every sign of an approaching squall. Just beyond the narrowest part of the western Kyle is Tighnabruaich, an exquisitely pretty village of white cottages and trim villas straggling up the hillside. We called here at 11 o'clock, and then set out on our longest non-stop run since the Govan-Greenock stage, the enjoyable passage that brought us to Tarbert.

The Kyle widened out into the Sound of Bute, once again Arran loomed ahead, much nearer now, but a mass of cloud clung round its highest peaks and gave the whole island the appearance of a vast grey shadow. The land on our starboard side gradually tapered down to Ardlamont Point, and soon we were turning a complete half-circle round this promontory and heading up Loch Fyne. Looking north now the prospect was majestic in the extreme. Overhead were range upon range of cumulo-nimbus clouds separated by patches of the most intense blue, and beneath the loch was the colour of steel; the hills to the west were deep in shadow while the eastern shore was bathed in brilliant sunshine. In the early spring the lower hillsides are often of the palest yellow that in company with sea and sky produces some enchanting pictures.

The "*Lochfyne*" is now bearing towards the western shore of the sea loch after which she is named, and soon the little inlet of East Loch Tarbert can be distinguished against the dark hillside. "Tarbert" is a Gaelic word meaning an inlet of the sea, and there must be dozens of villages with the same name along the west coast of Scotland. At this Tarbert the long peninsula of Kintyre is almost cut into an island, for the two inlets, West Loch Tarbert from the Atlantic, and East Loch Tarbert from Loch Fyne, almost meet. The eastern loch is very pretty; it is fringed with trees and there is a noble background of hills. We reached the pier just after noon. There we found a motor coach was waiting, bound for Campbeltown near the southern end of the peninsula of Kintyre and nearly 50 miles away, and a large quantity of mails were put ashore, the bulk of them being for the islands of Jura and Islay, for the Campbeltown mails are taken direct by steamer. Passengers for Islay and Jura are taken by coach as far as West Loch Tarbert, and from there the steamer sails, reaching Islay about 4.30 p.m.

As we got away from Tarbert a squall swept across Loch Fyne, veiling the mountains in a curtain of rain; but in a very few minutes blue sky could be seen through the driving grey shroud, and the hills of Cowal on the eastern shore were in sunshine. Of all the phenomena produced by the weather in the West Highlands none is more beautiful than the clearing of a heavy shower of rain, and now, sailing up Loch Fyne, it was seen to perfection. The waters gradually changed colour from lead, through deep green, to the most vivid ultramarine, and the sunshine on the distant hills gave to their rich browns a purple tinge as of heather in bloom.

Tighnabruaich, in the Kyles of Bute. This village is one of the calling places of the "Lochfyne."

The village of Ardrishaig could now be distinguished some miles away up the western shore. The upper reaches of Loch Fyne wind far away into the hills for nearly 30 miles, beyond Inveraray, and to within 10 miles of the head of Loch Long. We were heading for the small inlet of Loch Gilp. Until quite recently the service from Glasgow to Oban was operated through the Crinan Canal, a short waterway that cuts across the isthmus from Lochgilphead to Crinan; a special steamer was used for the canal section, and then at Crinan passengers transferred to one of Macbrayne's well-known two-funnelled paddle boats. By far and away the most famous of these was the "*Columba,*" which worked on the Glasgow-Ardrishaig run for over 50 years and was described and illustrated on page 308 of the "*M.M.*" for May; the "*Chevalier*" was usually employed on the Crinan-Oban Service. Nowadays the whole journey from Ardrishaig to Oban is made by motor coach all the year round, by a delightful Highland road that is never far from the sea.

By now the little stone jetty of Ardrishaig with its lighthouse is at hand, there is great bustle on the wooden pier inside the harbour in anticipation of our arrival, and in just under six hours from Glasgow we are alongside and tying up. And so at this typical West Highland village, with its stone cottages straggling along the water's edge and the hills of Knapdale rising behind, ends one of the most enthralling voyages in Britain.

A Remarkable L.N.E.R. 4-4-0 Performance

By a Railway Engineer

At busy holiday seasons it not infrequently happens that engines of quite moderate power are called upon to perform first class express duty. Such a case occurred on the Thursday before Easter this year when the L.N.E.R. 1.20 p.m. "*Scotsman*" was run in five portions; the regular express, working to the ordinary schedule, had been preceded by four reliefs. The engine provided to work the fifth part forward from Newcastle was not a "Pacific," nor yet an N.E. "Atlantic," but a 3-cylinder 4-4-0 of the "Shire" class.

The 1.20 p.m. is by far the hardest train of the day between Newcastle and Edinburgh, being allowed 147 minutes to cover the 124½ miles, inclusive of two regular stops and two conditional stops that are usually made. To run the 57½ miles from Berwick to Edinburgh in 67 minutes, with two stops, is a stiff proposition with the normal load of 300-340 tons, even with a "Pacific" at the head of the train; but on Maundy Thursday last the load was no less than 412 tons tare, and 435 tons with passengers and luggage. An almost overwhelming task was therefore set to the 4-4-0 engine No. 249 "*Aberdeenshire,*" but by dint of superb enginemanship on the part of her driver, McKellop, of Haymarket shed, Edinburgh, the loss of time was amazingly small.

An Aberdeen express hauled by L.N.E.R. 4-4-0 locomotive No. 307, "Kincardineshire." Remarkable work by a similar engine is described in the accompanying article.

Getting away very smartly from Newcastle and sustaining 37 m.p.h. up the 1 in 200 of Benton bank, some cautious running was needed past Annitsford owing to colliery subsidences. Speed was picked up well to 66 m.p.h. at Stannington and then came the severe slowing round Morpeth curve. A single minute was all that had been dropped on this initial section and with engine and crew well warmed up to their work the running thenceforward was really magnificent. Sustaining 60 to 67 m.p.h. throughout the undulating stretch that succeeds the Morpeth slack, No. 249 reached Alnmouth, 34.8 miles, in 43 minutes, or 42 minutes net, a loss of only a minute on schedule.

On the next stage time was kept almost to the second. Starting up the formidable Longhoughton bank, 4½ miles at 1 in 170, the engine accelerated all the way up and breasted the summit at 35 m.p.h.; then a glorious dash for Berwick followed. Speed rose to 77 m.p.h. at Beal; for 17.8 miles from Christon Bank to Goswick the average was 68.1 m.p.h., and, most brilliant of all, the 4½-mile bank at 1 in 190 past Scremerston was mounted at a minimum speed of 54 m.p.h. So Berwick-on-Tweed, 32.1 miles from Alnmouth, was reached in 36 minutes. Up the 1 in 200 to Grant's House 46½ m.p.h. was sustained—a feat involving an output of 1,500 h.p.—but although 80½ m.p.h. was touched down Cockburnspath Bank time was lost to Dunbar. The last 17.8 miles, from Drem into Edinburgh, were completed in 24½ minutes.

Seeing the World

Cruising Holidays in Great Liners

ONE of the most cheerful scenes in the world can be seen when a cruising ship is about to leave her home port, carrying with her a happy crowd of holiday makers. The vessels usually are gaily decorated with bunting, and their white hulls glisten in the sunshine, as in our illustration of the "*Vandyck*," of Lamport and Holt Ltd., in the Mersey. This vessel and the "*Voltaire*" are sister ships of 13,200 tons, and their blue funnels with black tops immediately above a white band are familiar to all who know Merseyside or Southampton. The long list of ships now engaged in similar work includes representatives of many famous lines, among them the "*Franconia*" and other vessels of the Cunard White Star fleet that were intended originally chiefly for the North Atlantic service, and have been diverted to this newer form of holiday traffic.

A gaily-bedecked cruising steamer in the Mersey. The vessel is the "Vandyck" of the Lamport and Holt Line. Photograph by B. and A. Feilden, Blundellsands, Liverpool 23.

Formerly holidays by sea were almost entirely confined to those fortunate people who had at their disposal an ample supply of time and money. To-day wonderful opportunities of sea cruising are open to people of quite moderate means and who have only a few weeks or even a few days to spare.

It is rather curious to reflect that this new phase of short pleasure excursions by sea came about as the result of the depression in the shipping world a few years ago. Many fine liners had to be withdrawn from their usual services simply because there were not enough passengers for them to carry. As an alternative to laying up their vessels certain shipowners decided to experiment with short cruises, and the result was immediately and quite surprisingly successful. As is usually the case when any new scheme is brought forward, the croakers said that this kind of cruising was only a passing craze and would not last. Time has proved them wrong, however, and there is no doubt that the short cruise has come to stay, for the very good reason that it meets a genuine public demand. The shipping companies have spared no efforts to meet the requirements of this new class of ocean traveller, and their enterprise has been well repaid.

It is not difficult to understand why this new form of holiday should have become so popular. In the first place a cruise provides perhaps the easiest of all ways of taking a holiday. Once the ticket is bought there is absolutely nothing else to worry about. The ship is at one and the same time the means of locomotion and the hotel. At the various ports of call excursions are arranged, and there is nothing to do but step into the conveyance provided and revel in the new and strange scenes of a foreign port. While the ship is at sea sports and games of all kinds are arranged, and there is not a dull minute. Those who are full of energy can be active all day long; those who are fat and lazy can simply revel in doing nothing but drowse in the sunshine. To all alike comes the wonderful tonic effect of a holiday that is a complete change in every respect from normal every-day life.

It is quite astonishing to find how many countries can be visited in the course of quite a short cruise. Whatever the holidaymaker wishes to see, from the northern capitals of Europe and even the Arctic wastes of Spitzbergen to sub-tropical Northern Africa, is open to him. He can visit Portugal or sunny Spain and explore the Mediterranean Sea, or travel farther south to Morocco, Madeira or the Canary Islands.

The islands in the Atlantic Ocean off the African coast are indeed favourite ports of call for cruising steamers, particularly Grand Canary, one of the Canary Islands. There Nature has been lavishly generous, and the island is remarkable for the magnificent scenic effects of its formidable heights and its black volcanic gorges in which vineyards abound. Excursions amid its ravines and mountain slopes combine with visits to its beaches, carpeted with the finest white sand, to add to the pleasures of a cruise; and these are heightened by the pure and bracing air and mild equable temperature that has made the Atlantic islands famous health resorts.

It is not necessary to leave the British Isles in order to enjoy a holiday of this kind, and nothing could be more pleasant than to cruise among the mountains, lochs and islands of the West Coast of Scotland. The full beauty of the firths of that famous holiday region can best be appreciated from a deck of a steamer sailing into them, and to see them in this manner is one of the most delightful ways of spending a holiday. The ship calls at various places, at which interesting shore excursions are arranged.

Cruising indeed provides a magic carpet.

The World's Queerest Jobs

Achieving Realism on the Cinema Screen

By Andrew R. Boone

IN Hollywood there are more sane people performing crazy jobs than anywhere else in the world. No job is too "queer" for the workers behind the scenes in the city of celluloid, for the demands of the camera and microphone are many and varied. For instance, take horses' tails. Harold Lloyd selected a fine sorrel mare to pull his wagon in *"The Milky Way,"* but the cameraman soon registered a protest. Cameraman, director and owner of the animal conferred, and half an hour later Jerry Smith found himself busy making the tail blonde with the aid of a paint spray gun in order that it would register more clearly as it swished backward and forward across the actor's face. Thus was a new job added to the growing list of the cinema's already large number of unusual pursuits.

Occupations that would be queer in the average town are commonplace in Hollywood and Elstree. At the former, 500 men and women are listed in studio directories as owners of animals available for pictures at rentals ranging from £1 to £30 a day. There also are men who will catch anything that lives in Southern California on short notice and deliver their victims, alive and kicking, to any studio—for a price.

Bleaching cattle bones on the roof of a studio building in Hollywood. These bones were required for a picture introducing desert scenes in the wild west.

Not long ago a studio demanded delivery within 48 hours of 320 grasshoppers, 225 large red roaches, 430 spiders, 60 small roaches and 25 black beetles. The firm receiving the request devised ways and means of filling the order. Five experienced men took to the fields near Los Angeles and netted the grasshoppers during a two-day chase. Spiders were plucked from thick hedges. The basement of a large office building gave up the cockroaches, but only after a crew of men had moved scores of barrels and boxes.

"This," declared one of the men engaged in the task, "was the craziest order we ever got. Well, nearly the craziest. Sometimes a studio wants someone to be bitten by a rattler. For £10 a bite, I'll let 'em strike. When they're cold, they don't really bite. Anyway, I wear boots. So it's easy money."

Spraying flowers with dyes to give good photographic colours.

The story is told in Hollywood of an Italian organ grinder with three monkeys who had come to the United States hoping to eke out a livelihood. One day a director saw him in a side street, hired him with his three monkeys for a picture, and thereafter for seven years the Italian worked the little creatures regularly. Though he had trained them to perform only simple tricks, the monkeys drew larger pay than their owner, for every day they worked each earned £5, while the Italian only received £2. After seven years the organ grinder retired to Italy, having saved enough from his earnings to retire.

When I toured Hollywood recently to seek out the world's queerest jobs, and to talk with the men who perform these unusual tasks, I found a score of them earning their daily bread at things that seem silly, but have very definite values. For instance, on the roof of a great stage at the Paramount studio I discovered Fritz Dickie examining the bleached bones of a dozen steers killed a few weeks previously. It is Dickie's job to collect old bones and bleach them for use in western pictures. For several years he made regular trips to the Southern California deserts seeking old bones, but the desert no longer takes its historic toll of cattle, so now he obtains his bones from slaughter houses, and does his own bleaching.

Then there is the squeak eliminator. This is not a mechanical device, but a carpenter in the person of Robert Green. He ferrets out squeaks on each new set by pushing a roller over the floor. When he finds one, out come his hammer and nails, and he kills it before some actor releases the noise. Green has found and destroyed hundreds of squeaks, any one of which might have cost a month's wages in lost time and spoiled film if it had been heard and recorded while a part of a picture was actually being "shot."

All glass used on a motion picture set must be invisible, for otherwise the camera will pick up reflections and register the dirt. Not long ago an actress walked through a plate glass show window and fractured her nose. Immediately, Charles Beauchamp got a new job, and on every set involving the use of glass, it is now his duty to stretch strips of black tape in the form of crosses over all glass until the camera begins to turn.

No further glass accidents have been reported in that studio.

"Mirror spoiler" is the unusual assignment given William Witt whenever his studio films a picture requiring their use on the set, and with good reason, for no matter how carefully mirrors may be placed, they pick up light and reflect it into the camera. On the set a mirror usually need only look like one, and Witt therefore coats them all with a thin layer of liquid wax in order to stop this unwanted reflection.

A screen actress once walked through a glass window on the set. Now black tape is pasted over windows until the scenes are "shot."

While it is one man's job to save property from damage, it is another's to wreck things artistically and well. Arthur Camp breaks crockery and statuary so effectively that whenever a scene is shot in which a fight or storm supposedly has taken place, he is called upon to smash a score or more plates, statues and vases to small bits. Scattered around the set these fragments add to the appearance of confusion.

Everything appearing in a set representing an old English street, with houses built 100 years ago, or an old house, must be given the appearance of age. Carpenters, equipped with blow torches, grey paint and lampblack, burn off fresh paint and "dirty" the walls. When the set itself has been aged, property men bring in the smaller articles, such as chairs and pictures. These, too must give the appearance of long, continuous use, and this is the special task of Pat Delaney, who with his dark shellac and an assortment of paints has made more small objects look old than any other Hollywood property man. Delaney learned his job while reproducing antique furniture.

The official squeak detector at work in a Hollywood studio. Nailing down squeaky floor boards keeps him fully employed.

Suppose the director of a picture calls for a spider web-infested haunted house. After the agers have done their work and departed from the set, in walks a man spider to spin the web. Harry Thompson recently devised a novel machine with which he can fill a large room with interlaced webs in 10 minutes. This consists of an electric fan, with a container of liquid rubber fitted directly in front of the blades. Centrifugal force spins the rubber into a tiny thread, and the air current blows it out. Recently Thompson walked through 10 rooms and halls of a large set in which scenes of the picture *"Seven Keys to Baldpate"* were being filmed, and there spun an intricate web containing hundreds of yards of rubber more quickly than a spider can spin two feet of its fragile product.

It is the ambition of every director to see his picture and name on the screen, and every actor wishes his face to be shown registering comedy and tragedy in all the picture houses of the land. Yet there is in Hollywood one man who has directed thousands of pictures, not one foot of which ever reached the public; and there are several score actors, all busily at work, who have never appeared in any scene shot by the cameras.

The man who has filmed so many scenes that have never been exhibited is a test director, and from the beginning his work is destined for the scrap heap. To him come the principal players of pictures produced by the studio where he is employed, and he tests them to make sure that their make-up is of the proper colour and tone, and is properly applied; that they have selected suitable costumes; and that they read their lines in accord with the "mood" selected for each character. Those who "pass" are selected at high salaries for the picture, and a few weeks later the test film is discarded.

The actors never seen on the screen are known as "stand-ins." They are men and women chosen because each resembles some high-salaried star in size and features, and are paid moderate salaries for taking the places of their principals for long hours before the camera or while the cameraman studies angles and makes adjustments. At the last moment, when all is ready, the star, untired by these tedious preliminaries, appears and plays the scene.

A natural flower or blossom is seldom seen in a picture. Roy L. Hollis specialises in creating beautiful artificial flowers and trees, and these are made of lacquer, bamboo, copper and paper. Not long ago Hollis produced in a few days 10,000 branches of imitation peach blossoms, each consisting of wood-fibre flowers tied to natural wood, and he has been known to complete as many as 720,000 flowers and branches for a single movie production.

Because of the artistic appearance and long life of artificial flowers, less than one tenth of all seen on the screen are provided by nature. Many of the real flowers used do not photograph well in their natural colours, so at one studio Bill Tait not only keeps them fresh, but changes the colour to suit varying conditions of background and lighting. Using an ordinary spray gun and special dyes, Tait dyes roses blue, lilies purple or green, and performs other feats of magic while the camera waits.

Probably no studio worker has his ingenuity taxed more than the property man. He may be called upon one minute to supply an old champagne bottle, only to have the director follow this order with a demand for a cow bell. Irving Sindler, head property man at the Samuel Goldwyn studio, has developed several portable boxes which he keeps on the set near the cameras. From these he can produce anything from a doorbell to fog-making apparatus and pop guns.

These examples do not represent all the unusual pursuits behind the scenes at Hollywood, for there are many other experts who have similar strange tasks.

A Day at Croydon Airport

Now that the summer services of the principal British and European air transport companies are in operation, more than 60 aircraft fly in and out of Croydon Airport daily. They include newspaper carriers, cargo craft, specially chartered machines, air liners to and from the Continent, services to and from destinations throughout the Empire, and fast air expresses of the British internal air lines.

In the early hours of the morning the aircraft that carry newspapers to the Continent are taking on board their loads and vanishing over the hills on their way to the coast. After this there are the departures of early-morning passenger aeroplanes for the Continent. A Dutch service leaves for Amsterdam; a big machine departs for Cologne; a French air-liner ascends for Paris; other services are signalled out to Brussels and Lille.

Here is one of the fast expresses of our inland airways, bound from London to Glasgow. Then come aircraft outward bound for Paris, Zurich, Rotterdam and Budapest. By the Imperial Airways express services one can now reach Budapest or Brindisi in a day's flying. Passengers outward bound across the Empire mingle with those who are about to make trips over the Continent. Every now and then a specially chartered aeroplane will leave on an urgent flight. So the day wears on—big motor coaches arriving with fresh parties of passengers, and mail vans dashing up with bags of letters to be air-borne throughout Europe or for thousands of miles across the Empire. Now the air liners of the outward bound evening services are departing, and presently, with a drone from its powerful engines, a big night freighter is winging its way from Croydon on its flight to Berlin.

All this outward traffic has its counterpart in a stream of inward bound aeroplanes. Early-morning arrivals at Croydon are from cities such as Amsterdam and Brussels; then comes a large air liner from Berlin, followed by one from Paris. Now an air express arrives from Glasgow, its passengers effecting connections with services that will carry them to destinations on the Continent. Other big machines reach Croydon at intervals from Switzerland, Sweden, and Budapest, and gliding down to the landing ground they taxi to the arrival platform. Airway porters are ready to handle the luggage; postal vans stand waiting for the mails; Customs and other officials are very busy. Speed is the watchword of the airway on the ground as well as in the air, and soon motor coaches are carrying the incoming passengers into the heart of London.

Imperial Airways' air liner "Hengist," of the "Hannibal" class, at Malakal, Anglo-Egyptian Sudan. The natives are members of the Shiluk tribe. Illustration by courtesy of the American Colony Photographers.

Brisbane-Singapore Service Increased

The recent duplication of the Brisbane-Singapore section of the England-Australia Empire air line has provided two services each way weekly, and has already proved a great boon to air travellers in Australia. Residents in Western Queensland towns, for example, can travel by air to Brisbane, spend a day and a half in that city and then return home, all within three days. Before the advent of the air service the only link between Darwin and the South was a monthly steamer service. Australian business men can now fly to Singapore, spend 5½ days there and return to Brisbane in less than a fortnight. By sea a similar trip would take six weeks. Quantas Empire Airways Ltd., operate the Brisbane-Singapore air service.

Isle of Man Air Races

The two Isle of Man air races were carried out in bad weather. The first one was the London–Isle of Man handicap race on Saturday 30th May, and only 12 of the 20 competitors who had entered for it made the flight. The race was won by Mr. A. Henshaw in a D.H. "Leopard Moth," second place was taken by Flying Officer C. F. Hughesdon in a Hawker "Tomtit," and third place by Mr. W. Humble, who flew a Miles "Hawk."

The second race was flown on Whit Monday, 1st June. It was also a handicap event, and consisted of three left-hand circuits of the Island, totalling 161.3 miles. The race began and finished at Ronaldsway aerodrome. A total of 18 machines were entered, and the race took place in continuous drizzle and cloud. It was won by Mr. R. F. Hall, who flew a Hillson "Praga," a new type of high wing cabin monoplane, Flying Officer A. E. Clouston and Flt. Lt. W. D. Guyler, in an "Aeronca" light aeroplane, finished second, and Mr. L. Lipton in a D.H. "Moth" was third.

Airport for City of London

The City of London will shortly have its own airport, for its Corporation have decided to construct one at Fairlop, near Ilford, Essex. The site chosen is about 600 acres in extent, and it is estimated that the cost of buying the land and constructing the airport will be about £600,000. The work is to be put in hand immediately.

Giant Aerial Camera

An aerial camera that is claimed to be the largest of its kind in the world has been produced by the Fairchild Aviation Corporation, of America. It has been designed specially for aerial survey work, and has nine lenses, the shutters of which are operated electrically. When the camera is used at a height of 30,000 ft. the lenses can photograph simultaneously an area of 600 sq. miles, and the record is obtained on one sheet of film. The camera weighs 305 lbs. when loaded.

A New British Bomber

The upper illustration on this page shows the Armstrong Whitworth "Whitley," the latest British Bomber. It is 69 ft. 3 in. in length and 15 ft. in height. This military monoplane is of special interest because it is neither a high wing nor a low wing machine, the wing being in a mid-way position. This wing is of 84 ft. span and is built of a light alloy that is used also for a portion of the covering, the remainder being fabric. The fuselage also is of metal. The undercarriage is of the divided type and, like the wing flaps, is operated hydraulically; it can be drawn up when the aeroplane is in flight. There are three enclosed gun turrets, one in the nose, one on the underside of the fuselage and just to the rear of the wing, and the third at the extreme stern of the machine. The raised cockpit for the pilot provides a clear view over the front gun turret.

The "Whitley" has two Armstrong Siddeley "Tiger" IX engines, each of which develops 804 h.p. at 7,200 ft. They are mounted in nacelles that project from the leading edge of the wing, one on each side of the fuselage. Controllable-pitch airscrews are fitted. No details of the performance of this machine are available, but it is known to be exceptionally high considering the heavy load-carrying capacity.

The Armstrong Whitworth "Whitley" Bomber. It is a middle-wing machine, and has three enclosed gun turrets. Photograph by courtesy of Sir W. G. Armstrong Whitworth Aircraft Ltd.

Zeppelin Notes

The disasters to the *"Akron"* and the *"Macon"* turned public opinion in the United States against the use of giant airships, but the success of the *"Hindenburg,"* following upon the long series of regular ocean flights by the *"Graf Zeppelin,"* has revived interest there in the practicability of lighter-than-air aircraft. There is no indication of any similar revival in Great Britain, but Japan is said to be thinking of purchasing two Zeppelins and using them on a proposed five-day airship service between Tokio, Vancouver and San Francisco.

In Germany work on the LZ.130, a sister ship to the *"Hindenburg,"* is being pressed forward. When this latest Zeppelin is put into service the veteran *"Graf Zeppelin"* will be retired from the South Atlantic route, and will be used only as a training ship.

A splendidly-equipped airship port has been built at Frankfort-on-Main in connection with the German airship service to America. The *"Hindenburg,"* on the completion of her maiden return flight from America, was the first airship to land passengers at the new airport, and the *"Graf Zeppelin,"* on 11th May last, was the first to take passengers on board there.

The Royal Aeronautical Society have awarded the British Gold Medal for Aeronautics to Dr. Hugo Eckener, the famous Zeppelin designer, for his technical accomplishments in lighter-than-air aircraft.

Imperial Airways' 100 Pilots

There are now just over 100 pilots engaged in flying the aircraft of Imperial Airways on the company's European and Empire routes. Some of the pilots are Captains and others are First Officers. For organisation purposes the territory covered by those routes is divided into four divisions. No. 1 operating division covers Europe, and on it more than 30 pilots are employed. There are just over 30 pilots on No. 2 operating division, which covers the Mediterranean and extends as far as Karachi on the India route and Kisumu in Africa, and along the West Africa route. On No. 3 operating division, stretching from Karachi to Singapore and including the new air mail link between Penang and Hong Kong, the total number of pilots is about 20; and on No. 4 operating division, which covers the Africa route from Kisumu to Johannesburg, five Captains and five First Officers are now engaged. Several other pilots are on special duties in Africa, Newfoundland and elsewhere.

In addition to the pilots now in regular service, many more are in training at the "finishing school" mentioned in these pages last month. This was established by Imperial Airways to train pilots for new duties under the Empire air route expansion programme that will come into operation next year.

Dutch and Polish Summer Services

This summer Royal Dutch Airlines (K.L.M.) are operating six services daily between London and the Continent, and some very good timing is being maintained. Prague is reached from London in five hours, Vienna in six hours and Budapest in 7½ hrs. This swift journey is made possible by the service called the Blue Danube Air Express and operated every weekday, in co-operation with C.L.S., the Czecho-slovakian air transport company. Another of the six services is worked in conjunction with the Deutsche Luft Hans and links up London, Amsterdam and Berlin. The K.L.M. service between Amsterdam, Doncaster and Liverpool opens on the 1st of this month.

The summer services worked by L.O.T., the important Polish air transport company, include daily services between Danzig and Cracow, Warsaw and Katowice, and Warsaw and Berlin, and a thrice-weekly service linking up Warsaw and Salonica. New services planned for later in the year will give regular air transport between Warsaw and Moscow by way of Minsk, and between Gdynia, Malmo and Copenhagen. Douglas D.C.2s and Lockheed "Electras" are used.

This rear view of the B.A. "Swallow" with the wings folded back gives the machine an unusually angular appearance. Photograph by courtesy of "The Aeroplane."

Latest D.H. Aeroplane

The de Havilland company are now at work on their 91st design. This is a four-engined monoplane called the "Albatross," and two machines of this new type are being constructed for the Air Ministry. It is believed that they will be used for experimental flights across the Atlantic Ocean. The engines of the new aeroplanes will be of the D.H. "Gipsy Six" XII type.

The company's 90th design was the "Dragonfly," and an illustrated description of this twin-engined biplane appeared in last month's *"M.M."*

Avro Aircraft for Abroad

Avro aircraft are much in demand abroad, and several important orders from foreign countries are in hand at the Avro factory. Greece has ordered 30 "Tutors" and nine 626s, both types of equal-span single-bay biplanes designed for training duties. An order has also been received from Austria for three 626 machines. The Avro "Anson," the military version of the 652 twin-engined low wing cabin monoplane, has attracted attention abroad, and 38 machines of this type are to be supplied to Australia.

The Story of the Tramcar

From Horse Cars to Electric Traction

FOR many years electric tramways have provided the chief means of transport in our towns and cities, and they also have been extended to connect large centres of population with the surrounding districts. To-day they are being challenged vigorously by motor bus services, which in some towns have replaced them in part or even entirely. Tramway engineers are meeting this challenge by providing comfortable and speedy tramcars of large capacity and attractive appearance, and in view of the struggle now proceeding, it is interesting to trace the development of the rail vehicle that has served our needs so long.

One of the luxurious single deck tramcars of the Blackpool system. Current is collected by a pantagraph instead of the more usual trolley. Photograph by courtesy of the English Electric Company Ltd.

The iron rail may be said to have been developed to meet the requirements of the coal industry in Northern England and the Midlands. During the 18th century speedier means of transporting the coal brought to the pit head became necessary. Carts then were replaced by wagons of larger capacity running on specially constructed roadways along which heavy loads could be drawn with comparative ease by horses. The earliest of these larger wagons had wheels with smooth iron tyres and at first ran on ways made of stone flags. Later, planks laid on sleepers buried in the track were used, and as these soon became worn out thin plates of iron were nailed on them to protect their surfaces. It was then a natural step to make rails or plates entirely of iron.

The plates or rails of most of these early tramways had a vertical flange on the inner side of the track that formed a guide for the wagon wheels. The reverse plan of fitting the wheels with flanges also had been tried, however, and in 1789 William Jessop introduced cast iron edge rails in connection with a railway that he built near Loughborough. This kind of rail is used on our railways to-day.

A Liverpool horse drawn tramcar of other days. It is strangely in contrast with the modern electric vehicles now used, one of which is shown on the opposite page.

Tramways or railways in the streets of a town cannot be built in the same manner as the track of an ordinary railway, for rails above the ground would be in the way of wheeled traffic. No attempt therefore appears to have been made to develop them until 1832, when an experimental horse tramway for the convenience of passengers was laid down in New York, but was not a success. In 1852 Loubat, a French engineer, invented a heavy rolled iron rail with a groove in its upper surface in which the flange of a tram wheel could be engaged, and in the same year the scheme for street tramways was revived in New York. Europe's first tramway was not laid until 1860, when George Francis Train, an American engineer, constructed a pioneer track at Birkenhead. Only part of the rail first used could be kept flush with the surface of the road and the raised portion was found to be a great inconvenience to ordinary wheeled traffic. In 1864 it was replaced by a grooved rail. It is interesting to find that the shape of the upper surface of the tramway rail has remained practically the same ever since that time.

Train's success at Birkenhead encouraged him to build tramways between Marble Arch and Notting Hill Gate, and between Victoria Station and Kennington Gate, in London. In 1868 the Liverpool Tramways Co. Ltd. was incorporated, and other tramways then were built in various parts of the country. The cars were drawn by horses. They were small and slow in comparison with modern tramcars, and it was necessary to hitch on additional horses in order to pull them up steep inclines. For various reasons they survived until a comparatively late period and could be seen working in London as recently as 1912. The only horse-drawn cars now running probably are those in which visitors to Douglas, in the Isle of Man, travel sedately along the Promenade.

The next step in the development of the tramcar was to substitute some form of power unit for the horse. The steam engine was the first to be tried and steam tramcars made their first appearance in Great Britain in 1871 at Leith. They took various forms. One used in the Birmingham and Dudley district had a vertical boiler and engine in the middle, together with a coal bunker and a feed water tank, and the passengers sat in front and behind. Other systems employed separate engines, the lower parts of which were covered almost to the ground by a sheet metal casing, and these drew behind them cars with either one or two decks. The sight of these weird monsters rumbling noisily through our streets and emitting clouds of smoke would astonish us to-day.

Another type of engine tried out in 1876 in the Vale of Clyde was driven by compressed air, and in other places experiments were tried with tramcars driven by gas engines. A more interesting scheme that was employed for many years in Edinburgh made use of a cable in an underground conduit between the rails. The cable was hauled along continuously at a speed of about 8 m.p.h. by means of stationary engines, and the cars were provided with grips that descended through a slot between the rails. The grips were operated by turning large wheels on the driver's platform, and the cars were stopped when required by releasing the cable and applying the brakes. One of the drawbacks of the system was the lack of speed.

With the coming of the electrical age, it was natural to use the new power for tramways, for it promised to be cleaner and more convenient than steam. What is believed to have been the first experimental electric tramway for passenger use was constructed in Budapest in 1881. It was followed by a pioneer line between Giant's Causeway and Portrush, in Northern Ireland, that was opened in 1883, and this system was the first hydro-electric tramway or railway in the world. Another electric line was opened at Brighton Beach, also in 1883, but the first regular electric tramway system was that of Blackpool, service on which began in 1884.

A modern electric tramcar. This illustration and the lower one on the opposite page are reproduced by courtesy of Mr. W. G. Marks, M.Inst.T., General Manager, Liverpool Corporation Passenger Transport Dept.

Current was supplied to the tramcars of the Giant's Causeway line by means of a third rail carried at the side of the track on posts that raised it 17 in. above the ground. This system of course could not be used for street tramways and three main types of electric system have been tried in adapting electric traction to roads and streets. In one of these the electric cable or rail was laid in an underground conduit between the running rails; in the second surface contacts were provided; and overhead conductors were used in the third, which eventually proved best.

In the conduit system the current was collected by a trolley pole that was pressed down through a slot in the road by means of a spring, and made contact with the underground conductor. The original Blackpool tramway was operated on the conduit system and portions of the old track may still be seen in some of the side streets there. A similar system was formerly used at Bournemouth, where the conduit was under one of the track rails. It was difficult and costly to keep the conduit well drained, and its construction interfered with gas and water mains. The system therefore is now used only in certain parts of large cities where overhead wires are impossible or undesirable, and in this country is employed only in London.

A streamlined American tramcar that travels at 50 m.p.h. Photograph by courtesy of the General Electric Company of New York.

The surface contact system was introduced to avoid the cost and inconvenience of underground conduits. Current was supplied by an underground cable and tapped off from metal studs, 10 to 15 ft. apart, placed along the centre of the track and projecting slightly above the road surface. These studs were "alive" only when a car was passing over them, underground contacts then being made automatically by various means, and current was taken from them by sliding brushes beneath the car. The system was tried in London, Wolverhampton, Lincoln and elsewhere, but proved unreliable.

The first line with overhead wires was opened in 1889 in New York, and in 1892 the earliest to be used in this country was constructed at Roundhay, Leeds. Overhead conductors are now practically universal. The wires are supported by bracket arms projecting from standards, or by cross wires attached to buildings on each side of the road. Current is collected from them by a small grooved wheel at the end of a long trolley arm that is kept in position by means of strong springs, and the electric circuit is completed through the electric motors to the track rails. Current usually is supplied at 500 V. At distances from the generating station the voltage is reduced appreciably by the resistance of the conducting wires, and for this reason a system is divided into sections, each supplied with current at the required voltage through transformer stations fed with current at 5,000 volts.

Great improvements have recently been made, both in the track and in the tramcars themselves in order to provide speedy and comfortable transport The two-wheeled axle is being displaced by the four-wheeled bogie, so that instead of swaying wildly at high speeds the tramcars glide along smoothly with less wear and tear on the track, owing to the better distribution of their weight. Light metals and alloys are used in constructional work, and the introduction of rubber-cushioned seats has added greatly to the attractions of a tramcar journey.

Excellent examples of what has been done in this direction are the latest types of tramcar introduced in Liverpool, one of which is illustrated on this page. The luxurious cars designed by Mr. W. Luff, Transport Manager to the Blackpool Corporation, and supplied by the English Electric Co. Ltd. for service in Blackpool also are of outstanding interest. One of these is seen in the upper illustration on the opposite page. It is a closed single decker, but has sliding sections in its roof that can be opened when required and locked in any desired position. Passengers can be quickly taken up through the wide central doors. Inside they find a well ventilated atmosphere at all times, and electric heaters controlled by the driver provide a comfortable warmth in cold weather. Wide windows give an excellent outlook in all directions. On a straight track the new cars attain a speed of 31 m.p.h.

The call for speed on tramcar routes is not so great in this country as in some parts of the United States, where traffic congestion is being overcome by the use of streamlined speedy cars of almost revolutionary appearance. A type of car supplied with electrical equipment by the General Electric Co., of New York, and introduced for use in Brooklyn is illustrated on this page. This car is capable of travelling at 50 m.p.h. and starting from rest it can reach a speed of 17 m.p.h. in 5 sec. and attains 25 m.p.h. in 11 sec. High speeds can be employed safely, for three types of brakes are installed, working on the motors, the wheels and the track respectively, and when travelling at 32 m.p.h. the car can be stopped in less than 100 ft. Each car is equipped with four 55 h.p. motors and has accommodation for 60 passengers on its single deck. Its interior is well ventilated, and during the winter electrical resistance heaters are used for providing a comfortable temperature.

"King Edward VIII"

With the consent of His Majesty The King one of the well-known G.W.R. locomotives of the "King" class, No. 6029, has been named *"King Edward VIII."* This engine was the last of the class to be built and was originally named *"King Stephen."* It is attached to Old Oak Common (London) Locomotive sheds and takes its turn on the principal expresses worked by engines from that depot, including the *"Cornish Riviera Limited"* and *"The Bristolian."*

Among the named engines condemned in recent months were No. 3263, *"St. Michael,"* and No. 3288, *"Mendip,"* both of the 4–4–0 "Duke" class, and No. 3327, *"Marco Polo,"* and No. 3412, *"John G. Griffiths,"* of the "Bulldog" class. No. 3422 of the latter class also has been condemned. This engine was formerly named *"Aberystwyth,"* but lost its name as the result of the decision some years ago to remove "place names" from G.W.R. locomotives.

With the designing this year of a new class of 4–6–0 mixed traffic locomotives, several of the "43XX" series of 2–6–0 "Moguls" have been withdrawn. The first locomotives of this useful class were built at Swindon in 1911.

Locomotive News from Ireland

G.N.R. (I) 4–4–0 locomotive No. 172 of the familiar "Carrantuohill" series has been equipped for oil burning. This is an interesting development in view of the fact that coal for Irish locomotives has to be imported. The first experiments are being made with ordinary heavy oil fuel, but it is stated that there is a possibility of the use of the by-products of the oil refineries in the Irish Free State.

All the 2–6–0 locomotives on the N.C.C. section of the L.M.S.R., the work of which was referred to in the *"M.M."* last January, have now received names. These are as follows: No. 90, *"Duke of Abercorn"*; No. 91, *"The Bush"*; No. 92, *"The Bann"*; No. 93, *"The Foyle"*; No. 94, *"The Maine"*; No. 95, *"The Braid"*; No. 96, *"Silver Jubilee"*; No. 97, *"Earl of Ulster."*

New L.N.E.R. Rolling Stock

Since the beginning of the spring services new rolling stock has been in use on the L.N.E.R. *"Hook and Antwerp Continental"* service from Liverpool Street. This has been provided with the object of making the nightly Continental service of a high standard throughout for all passengers, and in order to combine in a single boat train accommodation ranging from the ordinary third-class to first-class Pullman. All compartments on the train provide seating for three passengers on each side, and arm rests are fitted throughout. The heating, ventilation and other arrangements for the comfort of passengers have been given special attention. Ample luggage accommodation is provided and the formation includes an all-electric kitchen car. The external design and finish of the train conform with the usual L.N.E.R. standards.

The latest type of corridor vehicles, as used on the principal main line services, are now employed on the trains between Leeds and Scarborough and between Newcastle and Carlisle. As in the boat train vehicles already mentioned, three-a-side seating is standard. Between Newcastle and Carlisle seven trains each way daily now have buffet cars attached; 4–4–0 "Hunt" class locomotives are largely used on this line.

"The Royal Scot" express on the southern ascent to Shap. The locomotive is one of the four-cylinder 4–6–2s No. 6204, "Princess Louise." Photograph by Mr. J. G. Muir, West Kirby, Cheshire.

L.M.S.R. Locomotive News

After several alternate weeks of duty on the Liverpool and Anglo-Scottish services respectively from Euston, the L.M.S.R. "Turbomotive" No. 6202 recently carried out a series of trials with the dynamometer car on the chief Anglo-Scottish trains. It was handled throughout by Crewe enginemen.

The later engines of the "Jubilee" class, Nos. 5665–5742, differ from the earlier ones in having boilers with the regulator valve situated in the dome, not in the smoke-box. The top-feed fittings are not now applied at the sides of the dome cover as previously, but are housed in a separate "hump" in front of the dome, as in the case of No. 6170, *"British Legion,"* which was illustrated on page 23 of the January *"M.M."* Unlike this engine, the latest "Jubilees" have the feed pipes concealed beneath the outer covering of the boiler barrel. Future engines of the 4–6–0 and 2–8–0 classes will incorporate this arrangement.

All new L.M.S.R. locomotives are to have a new style of numbering and lettering. The engine numbers, classification numbers on cab-sides, the Company's initials and the numbers on the smoke-box front will be executed in plain block style instead of in Roman characters. The letters and numbers will be in gilt, with black shading for red-painted passenger engines, and red shading for black-painted passenger engines. On the black freight engines the characters will be of plain block type in gilt, without any shading.

Extensive L.N.E.R. Orders

Large contracts have been placed by the L.N.E.R. for the supply of steel rails, including 750 tons of conductor rails. In addition two locomotive coaling plants are to be supplied; one, mechanically-operated, for Carlisle, and the other, electrically-operated, for Grantham. The locomotive depot at Ardsley, near Leeds, is to be provided with hot water boiler washing apparatus recently ordered. Outside builders are to supply 100 bogie bolster wagons.

the line of the bridge is almost due east and west. The most difficult part of the work of course was the construction of the bridge itself. This has 33 main steelwork spans, and these are flanked on the west side by seven intermediate spans, each of which has a length of 165 ft. Each of the main spans is 262 ft. 6 in. in length, giving this section of the bridge alone a length of more than 1½ miles, and the highest of them stands 27 ft. above high water level. The permanent way on the east bank of the river is higher than that on the west, and 19 of the main spans therefore were constructed with a slight incline, mainly of one in 216.

A panorama of the lower Zambesi River, showing the site of the bridge. There the river normally is about 5,000 ft. wide, but at high flood the total width is about 2½ miles.

The main spans are carried by 34 piers, two of which were founded directly on the rock of the left bank on the north side of the river. The remaining 32 were built in the bed of the river itself. No water flows on a large part of the southern side of this during the dry season, and there it was possible to work directly, material being brought to the positions of the piers by means of a constructional railway of 2 ft. gauge. The foundations of some of the other piers were built with the aid of cofferdams, which shut off the river from their sites and enabled these to be laid bare by pumping, but in some cases dredging was sufficient and it was unnecessary to remove the water. Pontoons and barges were moored alongside the pier sites and on these were placed concrete mixers and other necessary equipment.

The work of constructing each pier was begun by sinking an oval steel structure, shaped like the funnel of a steamship, into the bed of the river. This structure was 36 ft. in length and 20 ft. in width and formed a shield within which a strong steel-sided well was sunk. Mechanical grabs were then lowered down shafts to remove the material inside the well, which was built in sections and carried deeper as the excavation continued. The depths to which the wells were taken varied from 80 ft. to 110 ft. below water level and each was filled with concrete reinforced with steel rods as it was sunk, leaving only the shafts used for excavation purposes. Finally these were filled in, giving a solid foundation on which a reinforced concrete pier was built up to take its share in supporting the steelwork of the main spans of the bridge. This process was carried out for each of the piers and the steelwork of the spans was then erected by means of cranes.

In order to give access to the bridge from the west bank of the river a steel trestle viaduct was built. This is founded on ferro-concrete piles. It is level throughout and has a total length of 1,805 ft. 8 in. The seven intermediate spans already referred to connect it to the western end of the main spans. The approach to the bridge on the east bank consists of six plate girder spans carried on piers about 66 ft. apart, and having a total length of 399 ft.

Work on the bridge began in 1931, and the last span was erected on 12th October, 1934. Its total cost was more than £1,400,000. It is crossed by a single line of 3 ft. 6 in. gauge. The rails are set on sleepers made of native hardwood that are spaced not more than 2 ft. apart and are attached to the steelwork on the bridge by hook bolts.

Preparing for the building of a great bridge in a district remote from the great centres of industry is almost as formidable an undertaking as its actual construction, and the Lower Zambesi Bridge was no exception to this rule. Steel cranes, excavators, concrete mixers, forges and other equipment had to be transported to the site from Great Britain, in addition to the steelwork used in the erection of the spans of the bridge and the approach viaduct, and immense quantities of stores, including millions of nuts and bolts and office furniture specially treated to make it suitable for the hot moist climate. Two light draught stern wheel steamers, 20 barges and eight pontoons also were required, and most of these were shipped in parts and assembled at the site. Constructional railways also were laid down. These were of 2 ft. gauge and all the material necessary for them had to be sent out from Great Britain. One service on which this narrow gauge line was engaged was that of transporting the stone required for concrete making from quarries that were opened on each side of the river.

Piers on the right bank of the river in course of construction. The bridge has 33 main spans of 262 ft. 6 in. each.

Native labour was employed in building the bridge, and the men were housed in special camps on the two sides of the river that in themselves formed small towns, for the number of men engaged usually was 4,000 and at times rose to 6,000. Feeding this army of men and keeping them in good health was a heavy undertaking.

A Well-Equipped Fire Engine

The illustration on this page shows an interesting and well-equipped Dennis fire engine, commissioned recently by the Eastbourne Fire Brigade. The body is of the totally enclosed type now favoured by many brigades and affords complete protection for the firemen. It has seating accommodation for 10 men, and is provided with a remarkable variety of equipment, including a canteen cabinet with cups, kettles, Primus stove, etc., oxy-acetylene cutting plant, heavy-capacity sheer-legs with chain-lifting tackle, two searchlights and four cable reels with 700 ft. of cable. There are also two folding stretchers and provision for carrying four sets of breathing apparatus, while on the roof are three special ladders.

The chassis is equipped with a six-cylindered engine that develops 110 b.h.p., and the pump is a multi-stage high-pressure turbine, which is mounted in the forward position, near the driver, and has an output of 650-800 galls. per min. Inlet and two delivery valves are arranged at each side so that the machine can be readily brought into use, irrespective of the position of the water supply or the scene of the fire. A first aid hose is also part of the equipment, and this is fed by the main pump from a 40-gallon tank.

In addition a central gangway in the body carries rails on which runs a Dennis self-contained portable pump, which consists of a single-cylindered water-cooled engine mounted on a tubular frame, together with a turbine pump having an output of 100 galls. per min. This handy unit is very compact, and can be lifted out of the machine by three men.

A fire-engine of interesting design in service with the Eastbourne Fire Brigade. The body provides accommodation for 10 men and at the front is a high-pressure turbine pump that has an output of 650-800 gallons per minute. Photograph by courtesy of Dennis Brothers Ltd., Guildford.

Roofing the River Mersey

In order to solve the traffic problem presented by the narrowness of certain existing streets in Stockport, Cheshire, and the impossibility of widening them except at a prohibitive cost, a portion of the River Mersey is being roofed over to carry a road 75 ft. wide. The portion of the river to be covered in this manner extends for a distance of a quarter of a mile. The new highway, which is to be known as River Mersey Road, will provide a new east to west route through Stockport that by-passes narrow streets that now have to be negotiated by traffic.

The new road will be a continuous bridge structure with a reinforced concrete deck carried on reinforced concrete portal frames. The carriageway will be 45 ft. in width, and will be divided down the centre by island refuges 5 ft. wide, and will be flanked by footpaths each 15 ft. wide. Work has been in progress for some time on the first portion of the scheme, which consists of the covering of the river in Mersey Square and the reconstruction of Mersey Bridge, and these works have now been completed.

The entire scheme will cost about £128,400 and will require three years to carry out. When completed the new road will be placed in Class 1 category.

Rocket Assists Engineers

Rocket apparatus of the kind used in carrying a lifeline to a ship in trouble in rough seas has been used recently by engineers in South Africa for the purpose of carrying electric cables across 1,500 ft. of almost impassable mountain country. A thin line was attached to the rocket, which landed within 60 ft. of its objective, and the line was then used to draw a cable across the intervening space. The rocket was designed to give two propelling explosions, the first as it started its flight and the second when it was in mid-air.

Drilling for Oil in Britain

Great interest centres in the large scale experimental borings now being made in various parts of this country in an endeavour to find oil. Recently the D'Arcy Exploration Company, which is connected with the Anglo-Iranian Oil Company, began to sink a test drilling at Paulsgrove on Portsdown Hill, near Portsmouth, as several outcrops of rock formations to the east and west of this site gave evidence of petroleum impregnation.

The drilling plant installed at Paulsgrove includes a derrick 136 ft. high with a loading capacity of 400 tons, and designed to drill to a depth of over 12,000 ft. The depth to which the drilling is to be carried is one mile, but if oil is not reached the bore will be carried down to two miles later. The cost of drilling is estimated at between £5 and £8 per yard, and it is anticipated by the experts that drilling may continue without success for as long as two years! Other plants are in course of erection near Steyning in Sussex, and on sites in Derbyshire, Lincolnshire and Nottinghamshire.

Giant Suspension Bridge for Vancouver

This summer Vancouver, Canada's Pacific port, is celebrating its jubilee, and the occasion will be marked by the inauguration of one of the greatest engineering undertakings of recent years. A great suspension bridge is to be built across what are known as the First Narrows at the entrance to Vancouver Harbour. The bridge will be known as the Lion's Gate Bridge. It is claimed that it will be the largest structure of its kind in the British Empire, for it will have a central span 1,500 ft. long and 209 ft. high at the centre. The total length across the First Narrows will be just under a mile.

The bridge will carry a roadway wide enough for four lanes of traffic and two footpaths, and will cost approximately £1,250,000. When completed it will form a link in a highway system that is of great industrial importance in the Canadian Pacific trade, and which runs through some of the finest scenic country in the world.

Completion of World's Highest Dams

The great Boulder Dam across the Colorado River in the United States of America, the largest constructional work ever undertaken, and the highest dam in the world, is now officially completed. The building of the Dam occupied just 11 days less than five years and cost £11,000,000, and over 5,965,972 cu. yds. of earth and rock were excavated during the construction. The reservoir that is gradually forming behind the Dam has been named Lake Mead and already is more than 80 miles long. It will eventually reach 115 miles up the Colorado River, and will be 40 miles in width with an area of 229 sq. miles.

This huge lake will contain 30,500,000 acre-feet of water and will be the largest man made body of water in the world. In addition to driving huge turbo-generators for the supply of electricity, the water penned up by the Dam will be released as required into specially built canals, to provide an adequate all-the-year-round supply of irrigation water to the surrounding country.

Closely following the completion of Boulder Dam comes the news of that of the second highest dam in the world, the Sautet Dam at the headwaters on the Rhone River in the French Alps. This structure is a thin wall of concrete 414 ft. high, and is built across the narrow canyon of the Drac River. It is second to Boulder Dam in height and its successful completion reflects great credit on French engineering skill, for it is built upon treacherous limestone. In order to prevent water leaking through the rock and around the dam, hundreds of holes were drilled into the foundations near the structure, and 3,000 tons of cement were pumped into them under a pressure of 5,000 lb. per sq. in.

The power plant, consisting of six 13,000 horse-power generating units, is wedged into the bottom of the narrow canyon, and the space available is so narrow that the machines are remote controlled by cables.

The Carryall Scraper at Work

Le Tourneau Carryall Scrapers as described on page 351 of last month's "*M.M.*," are being used in building the world's greatest earth-filled dam at Fort Peck, in the United States. This machine is hauled by a Diesel-engined tractor, and not by one using petrol, as we inadvertently stated last month.

World's Largest Paper-Making Machine

In the "*Engineering News*" pages of the May 1936 "*M.M.*," we referred briefly to a great new electric paper-making machine that is installed at the Kemsley Paper Mills of Edward Lloyd Ltd., Sitt'ngbourne, Kent.

An impressive view of the world's largest paper-making mill, which is installed at the Kemsley Paper Mills, Sittingbourne. Photograph by courtesy of Edward Lloyd Ltd., Sittingbourne.

This wonderful machine is the largest of its kind in the world and forms the centre of interest in a big extension scheme that has recently been carried out at these mills. It can produce 320 in. news-print paper at a rate of 1,400 ft. per minute, or about 1,200 tons per week. The machine is nearly 500 ft. in length and weighs 2,000 tons, and is driven entirely by electricity. Some idea of its huge size may be obtained from the fact that when the machine was started up an initial charge of 4,000 gallons of oil was put into the lubricating system. This giant is housed in a specially designed building 550 ft. in length and 175 ft. in width.

The electrical power plant installed at these Mills is one of the largest industrial installations in the world, and has an annual output sufficient to meet the needs of a large city. The boiler plant includes four high-pressure boilers each capable of turning 45 tons of water per hour into steam.

This handsome concrete building is the De La Warr Entertainment Hall at Bexhill, Sussex. It has a structural steel framework that was erected entirely by welding. Photograph by courtesy of Murex Welding Processes Ltd., London.

New Exhibition Buildings at Earls Court

When the new Earls Court Exhibition Buildings in London are completed this year, it will be one of the largest permanent exhibitions and sports centres in the world dependent for all its lighting, power and heating requirements upon electricity. The area of the site is approximately 20 acres and the main building will cover over six acres, and the electrical energy will be supplied from the Grid through a new generating station now under construction at Fulham. Approximately five million units a year of electricity will be consumed in lighting and power, and the consumption of electricity for heating will amount to between eight million and eleven million units, thus making the total requirements of the new Earls Court almost equal to the needs of a town of 30,000 inhabitants.

Pavilion with Welded Steel Frame

During the last two years great advances have been made in the application of welding to structural steelwork, and many important steel-framed buildings have been erected in which welding has replaced riveted construction. One of the most notable and recently completed buildings of this kind is the handsome De La Warr Entertainment Pavilion at Bexhill, Sussex, which is shown in the lower illustration on this page. This fine entertainment hall is the first building of this nature in Great Britain to have a welded steel frame, and it includes a large auditorium 116 ft. long, 74 ft. wide and 30 ft. high, a conference hall, lounge, reading room and restaurant. The illustration shows a beautiful cantilevered balcony that forms an imposing part of the building.

Large Petrol Tank Floated to New Site

A large petrol storage tank 40 ft. in diameter and 35 ft. high was recently hauled to a new site 150 ft. away, the foundations of which were 9 in. higher. The moving was done by floating the tank on an artificial lake. The ground around it and extending beyond the new site was enclosed in an earth embankment, and this area was then flooded with water to a depth of 27 in., sufficient to float the tank and give it a clearance of 10 in. The water was placed in the tank itself, and by opening the tank valves was emptied quickly into the enclosure to avoid seepage. The tank was finally emptied by pumping.

The Fascination of York Railway Museum

Locomotives of Former Days

By a Railway Engineer

IN the closing years of the 19th century British locomotive design and performance had reached a very interesting and at the same time critical stage. Maximum speeds of 80 m.p.h. and over were for the first time in railway history daily events and train speeds generally had reached a high level that was not improved upon for over 30 years. The engines of this period are naturally of exceptional interest, and fortunately examples of some of the most notable types have been preserved and are now kept in the York Railway Museum. Historic feats of speed, no matter when or where achieved, lose a great deal of their glamour when the engines concerned have long since gone to the scrap heap, and only photographs of them remain; but at York some of these old racers can be studied at leisure, and their graceful lines appreciated from all angles.

"Columbine," a 2-2-2 "single-wheeler" of the former L.N.W.R. It was the first locomotive to be built at Crewe Works.

In many ways the most striking locomotive of the whole collection is the old Great Northern 8 ft. "single-wheeler." This engine, No. 1, was built by Mr. Patrick Stirling in 1870, and was the pioneer of a type that remained the crack express engine of the G.N.R. for 28 years. It is a remarkable fact that the Great Northern Railway, and its successor the London and North Eastern, have had but three locomotive engineers in the last 65 years, and each, in the early years of his chieftainship, has produced an engine of such outstanding design as to render any further type unnecessary for many years. Mr. Stirling produced the 8 ft. "singles"; Mr. Ivatt, who succeeded him, will always be remembered by the G.N. "Atlantics"; while the fame of Mr. Gresley's "Pacifics" is world wide.

The Stirling "8-footers" are among the most beautiful engines ever built. The huge single driving wheel, the bold sweep of the running plate over the wheel centre, the long domeless boiler, and the beautifully-shaped safety valve cover all combine to give a most elegant appearance at any time; but the sight of one of these engines at speed was a thing never to be forgotten. The footplate arrangements are most interesting. Only one water gauge is provided; the reversing gear is of the notched lever type, but with a very much coarser adjustment than on later Great Northern engines; and the regulator is opened by pulling out horizontally. This pattern was standard on all Great Northern engines with the exception of the Ivatt "Atlantics," and was used also on the earliest types designed by Mr. Gresley. The boiler is quite small, and the look-out ahead, interrupted only by the chimney, is almost as good as that of a motor car.

Cab view of the 2-4-0 "Tennant" locomotive of the former N.E.R., showing the convenient arrangement of the fittings and the neat finish generally.

After 25 years on the hardest express duties came the biggest test of their whole career, the "Race to Aberdeen" in 1895. Rivalry between the equivalents of the present-day "*Aberdonian*" and "*Royal Highlander*," at that time leaving King's Cross and Euston respectively at 8 p.m., grew so intense that in August timetables were scrapped altogether and each train went "all-out" for the Granite City. Throughout the culminating weeks the Stirling 8-footers greatly distinguished themselves by their unvarying excellence; but on the final night, Wednesday, 21st August, the Great Northern achieved the marvellous feat of reaching York, 188.1 miles from London, in 181 minutes. This time is only one minute more than the fastest time ever scheduled between the two cities, that of the "*Scarborough Flyer*" of last summer; but the 1895 time included a two-minute stop at Grantham to change engines. On this wonderful run No. 668 was the engine from London; and she passed Peterborough, 76.4 miles, in 72 minutes, and completed the 105.5 miles to Grantham in 101 minutes. Engines were changed like lightning in a little under two minutes, and with another 8-footer, No. 775, at the head of the train the 82.6 miles on to York were run in 78 minutes. The load on this historic occasion was one of six six-wheeled East Coast Joint coaches and an eight-wheeled sleeping car, a weight of about 140 tons.

The only other single-wheeler in the museum is a veteran of such hoary antiquity that the Stirling 8-footer seems a modern engine by comparison! This is "*Columbine*," a 2–2–2 of the London and North Western Railway, and the very first engine built at Crewe Works. This "tiny tot" of a locomotive was designed by Francis Trevithick, a son of the famous Richard Trevithick, and was turned out in 1845. At first sight it appears to have a domeless boiler, the only mounting between the chimney and cab being a safety valve column; but on climbing up on to the footplate the dome is discovered—inside the cab! At the time of construction "*Columbine*" was not even fitted with a weatherboard, let alone a cab; and the dome, a big copper geyser-like erection, is mounted over the fire-box. In the light of modern practice the footplate arrangements are singular indeed. The various steam cocks take the form of big brass taps; there is a total absence of gauges, and only the regulator and notched lever reversing gear have any resemblance to modern practice.

The driving wheels are only 6 ft. in diameter, very small for a single-wheeler; but perhaps the most distinctive feature of the engine is the massive double framing that supports the cylinders and leading axle-boxes, and encases the slide bars. This was the outstanding characteristic of all early Crewe engines, and it was faithfully copied on several of the Scottish lines for many years. Another interesting point is the use of a drop-down smoke-box door. *"Columbine"* remained in active service till 1902, and she has been preserved in the condition of that time. She is painted in the black livery of the L. and N.W.R., though at the time of construction the company's engines were finished in green. Although they are of very great historic interest, these Trevithick singles never achieved any great speeds; the L.N.W.R. engines that proved such formidable rivals of the Stirling 8-footers were the 2-4-0 "Precedents," but although one of these latter engines has been preserved it has not yet been placed in York Museum.

In the centre of this photograph is the 0-4-2 L.B.S.C.R. locomotive "Gladstone," restored to its original condition. On the left is the "Tennant" locomotive.

At the time of the "Race to the North," the London Brighton and South Coast Railway was not exactly distinguished for speed. That was not the fault of the engines, however, and it would be hard to imagine a finer example of 19th century locomotive craftsmanship than No. 214, *"Gladstone,"* which represents the company at York. The designer, Mr. William Stroudley, was one of those remarkable men who made every detail of the locomotive a matter of constant study and research, and the "Gladstones" were not only a striking and original design but also embodied many most ingenious details. To a modern observer the most arresting point about the whole engine is its colour—bright yellow ochre. This was known officially as "Stroudley's improved engine green"; and the title alone is sufficient to show that no detail of the engine was too trivial to escape Mr. Stroudley's attention. The wheel arrangement, 0–4–2, is unique as far as express passenger engines are concerned, and another curious feature is the use of inside bearings for the tender wheels. Mr. Stroudley was a great exponent of standardisation and these wheels are interchangeable with the trailing wheels of the engine.

Of the footplate fittings the regulator is of particular note. Under Mr. Stroudley at Brighton there served those equally famous engineers, the brothers Dugald and Peter Drummond, and much of Mr. Stroudley's practice was embodied in the subsequent designs produced by the Drummonds. The 4–6–0 *"Beaufort Castle,"* which featured in my footplate run on the Highland Mail, described in the *"M.M."* for May last, was fitted with an exact replica of *"Gladstone's"* regulator. The latter engine is fitted with a speed indicator of a novel and ingenious kind. A small water pump is driven off one of the axles and maintains a level of water in a vertical glass tube in one corner of the cab; as the speed increases, the quicker working of the pump causes the water level to rise in the tube. I was amused to see that the glass was not graduated above 60 m.p.h. Presumably this figure was not supposed to be exceeded, though actually the "Gladstones" were fast engines and regularly attained 75 m.p.h. and over.

One last point illustrates the striking changes that have taken place in locomotive working since 1882, the year *"Gladstone"* was built. Over the regulator are painted the words, "William Love; Driver." At that time every driver had his own engine and no other, and it was only in cases of emergency that man and machine were separated. What a contrast this makes with modern practice when, on the L.M.S.R. for example, a "Royal Scot" class engine may be handled by four different crews in the course of a single day's work!

In the 19th century tank engines very rarely appeared on fast trains, and so there are no records of speed exploits to compare with those of their brilliant modern counterparts, such as the L.M.S.R. 2–6–4s and the Great Western 2–6–2s. The only tank engine in the Museum has quite a remarkable history all the same. This locomotive, No. 66 *"Aerolite,"* belonged to the North Eastern Railway and was built as long ago as 1851; at that time it was a 2–2–2 with outside cylinders and two water tanks, one below the forward end of the boiler and the other under the coal bunker. In 1869, and again in 1886, the engine was successively modernised, but its present condition dates from 1907, when a very interesting rebuilding took place.

The cylinders had been moved to a position inside the frames in 1869, and in 1886 the old well tanks had been replaced by side tanks of conventional pattern, but throughout the first 56 years of its existence the engine had remained a 2–2–2 simple. In 1907 the engine was taken out of ordinary service, however, and drafted to work the Chief Mechanical Engineer's private saloon. To enable *"Aerolite"* to make the long runs sometimes necessary on such duty it was fitted with enlarged coal bunkers that in turn necessitated a trailing bogie to carry the increased weight.

The engine thus became a 2–2–4 and at the same time was converted to a 2-cylinder compound on the Worsdell-von Borries system. This system had been used extensively on the North Eastern Railway in the closing years of the 19th century both for express passenger and goods engines; it proved most economical and successful, but with the increasing weight of trains and the limitations imposed on the size of cylinders placed between the frames, the engines proved somewhat inflexible and with heavy trains were sluggish starters. But on such a duty as that of hauling the Chief Mechanical Engineer's saloon the system was ideal. The high pressure cylinder is 13 in. dia., and the low pressure 18½ in. dia., the stroke in each case being 20 in.

The Fletcher 2-4-0 locomotive of the "901" class.

In her present condition *"Aerolite"* is a very pretty little engine, but her principal claim to notoriety is that she is the last English survivor of the Worsdell-von Borries system and also of that rare species, a single-wheeler tank engine. These two unusual features combined make *"Aerolite"* quite a unique locomotive.

Right up to the end of the 19th century the most popular wheel arrangement for British express engines was the 2–4–0, and in York museum there are two very fine examples of the type, both North Eastern locomotives. The older, No. 910, was built in 1875 to the designs of Mr. Edward Fletcher. It has a sturdy, bull-doggy sort of look, while the stove pipe chimney tapering outward from the bottom, the safety valves on the dome, and a highly decorative finish give the engine a most distinctive appearance. The coupled wheels are 7 ft. diameter, in fact the "901s," as the class were known, were racers in every sense of the word. For many years they hauled the Scottish expresses between York and Edinburgh, and in 1888 frequently ran the hilly 57½ miles from Berwick to Edinburgh in less than an hour.

The cabs were quite roomy for the period, but it seems strange nowadays to have the rear coupled wheel splashers extending right inside; their presence considerably restricts the space available though they make good seats. The fittings are simple and straightforward, and the engines were always great favourites with the men. One particular point about their design deserves special mention. In order to soften the blast at speed, and reduce fire-throwing to a minimum, Mr. Fletcher fitted the cylinders with exhaust cocks, so that a certain amount of the exhaust steam was allowed to escape directly from the cylinder instead of passing through the blast pipe and up the chimney. It was most successful, and the coal consumption when working the heavy East Coast expresses was little over 25 lb. per mile. The popularity of the engines was such that, when Mr. Fletcher retired, indignation meetings were held all over the system to protest against the shortcomings of his successor's first new type!

Mr. Fletcher's successor soon resigned, and for some months the North Eastern was without a Locomotive Engineer. During this period however a committee of locomotive men under the chairmanship of the General Manager, Mr. Henry Tennant, was responsible for producing one of the finest examples of the 2–4–0 type that has ever run. The "Tennants," as they have always been known, were technically an enlarged and improved edition of the Fletcher "901" class, but outwardly they are of very much neater appearance. The cab interior is most ornate; the fire-box has a broad polished brass surround, the side sheets are finished to look like wood panelling, and a padded seat is provided for the driver. The reversing gear is a combination of a notched lever and screw, the former being used for large movements such as reversing the engine, and fine adjustment of cut-off obtained with the screw. Double sliding fire-doors are used.

The "Tennants" were not only handsome to look at, but also were magnificent performers on the road. They bore the brunt of the "Race to Edinburgh" in 1888, when *"The Flying Scotsman"* was pitted against the Edinburgh portion of what is now *"The Royal Scot."* These gallant little 2–4–0s made the 80-mile run from York to Newcastle in 79 to 82 minutes as a regular event with loads of about 140 tons. An even finer feat was to cover the 124 miles from Newcastle to Edinburgh in 127 minutes; this was a wonderful effort in view of the heavy climbing involved north of the Border. Standing on the footplate, looking through the big square window with slightly closed eyes, it is not difficult to recapture something of the thrill and excitement of the race—the little engine rolling and pitching like a live thing; driver and fireman keyed up to the highest pitch, and behind them a train of six-wheeled non-corridor coaches. It seems incredible to us to-day that at the time of the 1888 race the "Scotsman" was booked to stay 20 minutes at York for lunch; one can quite imagine with what impatience that stop was regarded! The "Tennants" also did good work in the early days of the 1895 "Race to Aberdeen," but as the speed increased the latest Worsdell 4–4–0s were used. The 2–4–0s regularly attained 75 m.p.h. and touched 83 and 84 in the 1888 race.

G.N.R. No. 1, the first of the famous Stirling 8 ft. single-wheelers

The greatest racer of all in the distinguished company in York Museum, the Great Western 4–4–0 *"City of Truro,"* is really a 20th century engine. She was built in 1903 and provides a most interesting connecting link between types such as the "Tennant" 2–4–0 and modern locomotive practice. Unlike most of the engines in the Museum, *"City of Truro"* has not been restored to her original condition; but although she looks extremely modern compared with the others, the changes are not so great as might at first be imagined. The boiler has been fitted with top-feed apparatus on the safety valve casing, the familiar Great Western chimney with its copper cap has replaced the original tapered pattern, and a Swindon superheater has been added. The exterior finish is just as decorative, perhaps even more so than the original. The engine was withdrawn from service in 1931, and at that time all the company's engines carried the full name "Great Western" on the tender; the recent change to a small monogram consisting of the letters GWR is a reversion to the practice in vogue when *"City of Truro"* was built, though the three initials were then interwoven in a series of artistic curves, strongly contrasting with the plain block letters of to-day.

The footplate arrangements are practically unaltered, and what is more remarkable, little change has taken place in Great Western practice since the engine was built; but for the absence of the audible cab signalling apparatus you might be standing on the footplate of a "Castle" or a "King." *"City of Truro"* is the only engine in the museum to have the actual percentages of cut-off marked on the reversing gear, though it is interesting to note that nothing lower than 25 per cent. appears. Double sliding fire-doors are used, operated by a mechanism exactly the same as that adopted on the L.M.S.R. 4–6–2s of the "Princess Royal" class; *"City of Truro"* has cast iron doors working in a plain slide, whereas in the recent L.M.S.R. engines the doors are of fire-clay and run on rollers. The regulator is of the standard Great Western pattern, wherein oil is fed into the steam and carried in the form of a fine spray to the cylinders and valves. By means of a link motion, operated by a roller working in a cam slot on the regulator quadrant plate, oil is only fed into the steam when the regulator is open.

Perhaps the most noticeable difference between *"City of Truro"* and the other engines in the museum is in the cab look-out. One narrow window on each side gives only a very restricted view on either side of the Belpaire fire-box; it is not only a poor view compared with the other engines at York, but also in comparison with big modern locomotives. The cab does not extend to anything like the full extent permitted by the loading gauge, however, and it is only by making the cab as wide as possible that engines with boilers of the size of *"Cock o' the North"* and *"The Princess Royal"* have been given such splendid look-outs.

"City of Truro" achieved everlasting fame by attaining the tremendous speed of 102.3 m.p.h. while hauling an Ocean Mail special from Plymouth to Paddington. This amazing feat took place on 9th May 1904 and was the culminating effort of a series of runs that put the 1895 "Race to the North" completely in the shade. In 1904 eastbound Transatlantic liners began calling at Plymouth, and the Great Western with the mails, and the London and South Western with the passengers, indulged in a race to London of the most thrilling kind imaginable. On 9th May *"City of Truro"* hauling a load of 148 tons ran from Millbay Docks, Plymouth, to Bristol, 127.8 miles in 123 min. 19 sec., including the very heavy grades of the South Devon line; the 75 miles from Exeter to Bristol were covered in 64 min. 17 sec., an average of 70.2 m.p.h. It was however after the train had mounted the ascent over the Blackdown hills that the pace became so exceptional, and on the descent to Taunton *"City of Truro"* reached 102.3 m.p.h. This marvellous achievement was not surpassed until 31 years later, when the L.N.E.R. Super-Pacific *"Papyrus"* attained 108 m.p.h. On *"City of Truro's"* part it was no brief spurt either, for the average speed from Whiteball summit right through to Bedminster, a distance of 54.5 miles, was 74 8 m.p.h.! It is amusing that this feat of speed was kept a secret for years, for fear of alarming the public!

Not the least of the many admirers of these grand old engines are the local drivers and firemen. Naturally to them the Great Northern and North Eastern locomotives appeal most, for many top link drivers of to-day have fired on the "Tennants" and Stirling 8-footers and retain a great affection for their old steeds; but the strangers also come in for their full share of attention. The Museum is quite close to the south locomotive yard, and on one of my earliest visits I found a Sheffield driver studying *"City of Truro"* intently. I have yet to meet the locomotive man who, whether on duty or off, was not ready to talk "shop," and in conversation with him I learned of the respect in which *"City of Truro"* is held among northern enginemen. It is not to be wondered at, and especially as at that time her epic feat had not been surpassed. This driver's interest was not merely that of a sightseer, for he was keenly critical of certain details, and to drive his points home more forcibly he took me outside and showed me the features of his own engine, an early G.C. Robinson 4–4–0, that he considered superior to those of the famous Great Western racer. The black livery and travel-stained appearance of the Great Central engine contrasted strongly with the superb finish and spotless cleanliness that is not the least attractive feature of the veterans inside. Thus in every way the York Railway Museum is a veritable treasure house of British locomotive history.

The Wimbledon "Fly-Over"

Improving the Approach to Waterloo Station

On Sunday 17th May last the S.R. brought into use the greater part of a scheme designed to improve the approach to Waterloo Station. This included a "fly-over" line near Wimbledon and various improvements in the track outside Waterloo, together with colour-light signalling between Malden and Vauxhall. The change-over is yet another of those apparently overnight transformations that seem to have become almost second nature to the S.R. engineering and signalling staffs during the past few years.

The policy of suburban electrification that was started on this Western Section of the S.R. by the former L.S.W.R. in 1915 has given rise to an increase in traffic; and this, with the necessity for providing for future developments, has made necessary the improvement of facilities for handling trains into and out of Waterloo. Some 200 more trains are being operated in and out of Waterloo during a normal 24 hours than in 1925, and until the new arrangements were completed this was being done over the same layout of lines as existed 10 years ago, and with ordinary normally-operated signalling except at Clapham and West London Junctions, where power operation had been in use for 25 years.

On the former L.S.W.R., now the Western Section of the S.R., it has long been the principle, where separate pairs of fast and slow roads are provided, to keep the fast lines in the centre. Ordinarily this is quite convenient, and it is easy to arrange connections between fast and slow roads in the same direction so that trains can be transferred from one to the other without difficulty. A disadvantage is that on reaching a terminus the slow trains have to be dealt with at platforms relatively far apart—an inconvenient arrangement—unless the track connections approaching the station allow the trains to and from the slow lines to be dealt with on adjacent roads. When this is effected by means of ordinary surface connections, trains from one or other of the slow lines either on entering or when leaving the station have to cross the fast lines.

This is exactly what was happening at Waterloo. Stopping electric trains going up to London had to cross the paths of the up and down steam and electric fast trains just outside the station. Another point of importance was that main line trains had become so long that they could only be accommodated at certain platforms; and on leaving Waterloo they had to cross all the up lines between there and Vauxhall, thus adding to the possibilities of delay to other trains. Again, only 10 platforms were available for main line trains, whereas 16 were really needed in order to permit of the smooth conduct of traffic.

It was therefore decided to take the bold step of altering the disposition of the running lines from a convenient point inward to Waterloo, and to effect alterations in the various track connections outside the terminus to conform with the new arrangements. The new scheme prevents up slow trains delaying the main line ones. It also provides the 16 platforms at Waterloo required by main line trains and reduces delays caused to up fast trains by those departing. In order to obtain the fullest benefit from the new track conditions, the colour-light system of signalling, recognised as the speediest method of moving the traffic through congested areas, is being installed all the way between Waterloo and Hampton Court Junction, but Waterloo Station section will not be completed until Autumn.

A point near Wimbledon was selected as the spot at which the change-over of the lines was to be effected in order to bring the up and down local lines together. To prevent delay to the fast trains, the up local line is carried over them by means of a fly-over, or viaduct with inclined approaches. The illustration on this page shows the commencement of the approach looking in the direction of Waterloo, the oblique crossing over the fast lines, and part of the downward slope beyond. From left to right the tracks in the foreground are up local, up fast, down fast and down local; those beyond the fly-over are the up fast, down fast, up local and down local respectively.

A general view of the new "fly-over" near Wimbledon by means of which the up local line is led over the two fast lines. It incorporates 850 tons of steel encased in 8,000 cu. yds. of concrete. Photograph by courtesy of the S.R.

It was in connection with this part of the work that troubles occasioned by the weather challenged the resources of the engineers, and added to the usual difficulties met with on transformations of this kind that have to be carried out without undue interference to traffic. Work on the fly-over, which is a steel and concrete structure, commenced last September. It will be recalled what severe weather was experienced during last winter. Frost hindered the making of concrete, so that fires had to be maintained round the concrete mixers and round the heaps of cement and sand; rain constantly flooded the holes dug for the foundations, which had to be pumped dry before work could proceed again; and fog also impeded progress. By hard and constant endeavour day and night the structure was completed, however, and it was brought into use on the scheduled date. Any delay would have seriously affected the conduct of the traffic in and out of Waterloo.

The final episode in this mighty effort occurred in the small hours of Sunday morning 17th May. From 1 a.m. till 7 a.m. Waterloo Station was closed for traffic, and during this time normal local services were covered by substitute buses. Victoria became the temporary terminus of Southampton and Salisbury trains, and the starting point for the important newspaper trains that usually depart from Waterloo. During this period of six hours track was slewed and lifted to make the final connections of the existing roads with the new fly-over line; the mechanical system of signalling was replaced by colour-light signals; and the improved layout outside Waterloo was finally completed. The alterations had already necessitated the closing of platforms Nos. 1 to 3 for 10 days, and Nos. 4, 5 and 6 also were out of commission from 6 p.m. on the previous Friday, 15th May. The new track layout had been put together at Mitcham, every piece being marked; and it was then dismantled, ready for the final assembly of the components in their destined position, and their connection to the existing tracks at Waterloo.

The colour-light signals are mostly of the three-aspect and four-aspect types. As compared with the mechanical system previously in use they permit of the reduction in the headway between trains from 4 min. to 2½ min., and in some instances even to 2 min. The new system incorporates certain notable features differing from those of previous S.R. installations. Instead of having separate "splitting" signals for each route at running turn-outs and crossovers, one signal only is now used with a route indicator. This combination avoids the need for many individual signals for which it would be difficult to find room, and also simplifies the driver's task.

Shunting signals are of special interest in that they consist of white enamelled discs having a red horizontal bar across them. The disc of one of these signals is moved so that the bar is sloped at 45 deg. when the road is clear. They display no lights, but each has a flood-lighting attachment that makes the position of the bar visible at night.

Excavating Under Water

Removing Rock from River Beds

By H. F. Kutschbach

If the dredging operations now carried on in most of the important trade rivers and harbours of the world were suspended, many of these waterways would soon become unnavigable to any but the smallest vessels, for the vast quantities of sand and silt carried in from the sea by each tide and deposited on the bed of the waterways would rapidly reduce the depth of water available for shipping. Constant and efficient dredging is a necessity in nearly every river and harbour of consequence to trade, and many interesting vessels and implements have been introduced to perform this work. The design of these dredging appliances is governed by the depth of water in which it is necessary to work, and the kind of material that has to be removed.

The German rock-breaking vessel described in the accompanying article, at work in shallow water.

Where the bottom is of a sandy or muddy nature, bucket or suction type dredgers are usually employed. The bucket dredger is a very old form of dredging vessel, the first of its kind being built and launched at Hull in 1778. The name of the inventor is not known, and the dredger itself was crude and primitive. It was fitted with 11 buckets, and the motive power was provided by two horses, which rotated a pair of horizontal beams on the deck of the dredger. The machine was able to work in 14 ft. of water and its output was about 30 tons per hour.

Some years later about the end of the 18th century, steam power was applied to dredging, the engine for the first steam-driven dredger being constructed by James Watt. This was a double-acting engine with a cylinder 18 in. in diameter by 16 in. stroke, and steam was applied at a pressure of from 5 lb. to 10 lb. per sq. in. The oak hull of the vessel was 60 ft. in length and 21 ft. in breadth, and the dredger could work at a maximum depth of 18 ft. A splendid proof of the excellence and durability of the workmanship of the men who built this vessel and engine is provided by the fact that the dredger was in use in the River Tay until 1905.

The rock-splitting tool and power cylinder suspended from the jib of the winch hoist. The tool guide post can be seen near the side of the vessel extending into the water.

During the last 50 years considerable improvements have been made to this class of dredgers in order to increase their efficiency and speed of working, and to-day many of the larger dredgers of this kind are capable of removing up to 1,000 cu. yds. of spoil per hour. In this type of vessel there is an opening in the bottom through which passes a girder that is suspended from a central superstructure and is pivoted at its upper end. The other end of the girder can be lowered down to the bed of the river to be dredged. At each end of the girder there is a heavy roller, round which passes an endless chain bearing at regular intervals metal scoops or buckets. These scoops are fitted with a steel cutting edge, and when the dredger is in operation the chain is set in motion and the scoops dig into the bed of the river, fill themselves, and then return along the upper side of the girder. On reaching the top of the girder the scoops tip over and discharge their contents either into holds in the dredging vessel itself or into barges moored alongside. In some instances means are provided for discharging the excavated material ashore by driving it through floating pipelines by means of powerful pumps.

Suction dredgers do not scoop up material from the river bed like bucket machines, but are provided with powerful pumps that suck up the spoil through long pipes. The pipes are pivotally mounted so that they can be lowered to the river bed.

The work of the pump is often assisted by a rotary cutter, which breaks up the material before this is drawn into the suction pipe. The cutter consists of a series of blades mounted on a rotating shaft, and means are provided for raising or lowering the cutter to work at different depths according to the depth of the bed that is being dredged.

A good example of the work done by large suction dredgers is provided by the great vessels employed to dredge the Bar at the mouth of the River Mersey. Dredging commenced there in 1890, when the depth of water at the Bar at low water of spring tides was only 11 ft.; and the operations have been so successful that under the same conditions there is now a depth of 25 ft.

Dredging has been carried on constantly over an area measuring about 8,000 ft. by 2,000 ft., the latter being the average width of the buoyed channel used by all the ships entering or leaving the Mersey. The material dredged includes both fine and coarse sand and mud.

One of the two largest dredgers employed on the work is the "*Hilbre Island,*" a vessel 330 ft. in length and 54 ft. in width. Its powerful pumping machinery is capable of removing 3,500 tons of sand in 50 minutes from a depth of 70 ft. The removed material is stored in huge hoppers aboard the dredger itself, the hoppers having a total capacity of 70,000 cu. ft.

Bucket, suction and grab type dredgers were described in the "*M.M.*" for June 1935, and they are in common use all over the world for deepening and maintaining waterways where the bottom is of a sandy or muddy nature. The beds of many rivers and harbours, however, are composed of solid rock, and when it is desired to deepen such waterways or to remove dangerous rocks other methods have to be employed.

A rock-breaking vessel in which two splitting tools and guide frames are attached to a superstructure that is arranged to travel on rails laid along the deck. The tools operate one on each side of the vessel.

Sometimes the work is carried out by divers operating from small boats. The divers are equipped with rock-splitting implements and blasting apparatus, and under favourable conditions quite satisfactory results are obtained. Owing to its slow nature, however, the process is very costly, and with the object of providing a cheaper and more efficient method of doing this work special rock-splitting and removing vessels have been introduced.

The rock-breaking device with which these vessels are equipped has been developed from the ordinary pile driver, and consists of a cylinder inside which works a reciprocating piston or ram that applies a hammering action to the shaft of a stout steel rock-breaking tool of special shape. The tool is held in a retaining device that prevents it from falling out of contact with the piston, and the whole of this apparatus is suspended over the ship's side by means of wire ropes that pass over a pulley at the head of a hinged jib, and are then wound round the drum of a steam or compressed-air driven winch mounted on the deck of the vessel.

A large piece of rock being removed from a river bed by a "Polyp" grab.

The vessel travels to the scene of operations under its own power, and is there anchored and the rock-breaking appliance lowered on to the rocks. If the waterway is shallow the cylinder of the rock-breaking device may not be completely submerged, and in this case it can be operated by steam power. When the water is deep, however, and the whole of the rock breaker, including the cylinder, is completely submerged, steam power is useless owing to difficulties caused by condensation, and the piston is then operated by compressed air, which is led to the cylinder through a flexible pipe. When the power is turned on, the piston hammers on the splitting tool, forcing it downward into the rock and gradually splitting this apart into pieces convenient for removal.

In order to prevent the tool from skidding off the rock while in action a guide is provided. This consists of a long vertical pillar that is attached at its upper end to the jib, and which may be extended by a further pillar when working in deep water. Brackets are provided on the cylinder of the splitting tool, and these encircle the guide post as shown in the illustration at the foot of the opposite page.

The winch for lowering the cylinder and splitting tool to the correct working level may be driven by either steam or compressed air, and the jib and guide post can be slewed to enable the splitting tool to be moved from place to place without moving the entire vessel.

After the rock has been broken, the next thing to be done is to bring up the boulders out of the water, and sometimes this is carried out by what is known as a "Polyp" grab. This has eight articulated arms and claws, which in action operate very like the claws of a crab, and are able to grip rocks of various sizes and shapes. The pointed arms rummage their way into the split rocks and boulders in such a manner that a good haul is always obtained, and as the arms have quite a lot of sideplay in their joints, and can incline themselves sideways when resistance is encountered in grabbing, the device is very flexible and capable of adapting itself to awkward situations. If one of the arms encounters a difficult obstacle when grabbing, it can not only slide up or down off it, but can also get round it sideways, without in any way affecting the movements of the other arms. Thus the grab adjusts its arms like human fingers in accordance with the job on hand. It is therefore unnecessary to provide the grab with guides, an advantage of great importance in dredging under water when the material to be dredged is out of sight. The "Polyp" is lowered on to the heap of broken rock lying at the bottom of the river by means of a crane mounted either on the rock-breaking vessel itself or on a separate pontoon or barge.

The illustration at the foot of this page shows the new grab in action and explains how the flexibility of its arms enables it to hold even the most irregularly shaped rocks.

Sometimes a bucket dredger is used to remove the broken rock after the rock-breaking vessel has done its work, and as an instance of this method of working it may be mentioned that a few years ago it was decided to deepen the entrance channel at Blythe on the Northumberland coast, a task that necessitated the removal of a million tons of solid rock, which was over-laid by large boulders. A vessel fitted with rock-breaking apparatus, working on a somewhat similar principle to that already described, was brought into use to break up the rock and afterwards a bucket dredger was set to work to remove the boulders. By this method 250 tons of rock were dredged per hour.

British Single-Seater Fighters

High-Speed Military Aircraft

THE various types of military aircraft are all of interest, as each has been designed to carry out some particular branch of air activity and possesses certain distinctive features of structure and equipment. In many respects the single-seater fighter is the most interesting of these types. Bombing and reconnaissance work call for the highest skill and the coolest judgment, but these qualities are required in the highest degree by the pilots of fighting machines, who must seek out combat, and fight for the protection of slower and more vulnerable machines engaged on other duties. During the War the fighting squadrons of the R.A.F. were chiefly employed in the protection of machines occupied in bombing and reconnaissance work, but an equally important part of their duties was to keep off marauding enemy aircraft and to attack the machines from which the fire of the enemy's artillery was directed.

The Gloster "Gladiator" General Purpose Fighter. The photographs on this page are reproduced by courtesy of "Flight."

The end of the War did not put a stop to the development of fighting aeroplanes. The tendency in these has been to keep to practically the same overall measurements, but to increase the amount of military equipment carried and to fit larger tanks in order that the machines should be capable of remaining in the air for longer periods. The additional weight that this extra equipment involves has made it necessary to use more powerful engines, and remarkable strides have been made in the efficiency of power units of all types.

The Gloster "Gauntlet" Day and Night Fighter, with which two R.A.F. squadrons are equipped.

Single-seater fighters are produced in many countries, and the British examples of this class of military aircraft are among the finest in the world. The types at present in use in the R.A.F. include the Gloster "Gauntlet," the Hawker "Fury" and the Bristol "Bulldog." The R.A.F. expansion programme now being carried out has provided an opportunity for acquiring a larger number of machines of certain types and of including new ones. For instance, a second squadron has recently been equipped with "Gauntlets," and several "Gladiators," the latest production of the Gloster Aircraft Co. Ltd. to be adopted by the R.A.F., have been put into service. Another fine type of British single - seater fighter is the "Firefly" produced by the Fairey Aviation Co. Ltd., Hayes, whose "Gordon" day bomber and "Seal" torpedo-spotter reconnaissance machines are standard service types in the R.A.F. A more recent production of this company is the "Fantome" single-seater fighter. In this article we describe the Gloster "Gauntlet" and "Gladiator," and the two Fairey machines just referred to.

The Gloster "Gauntlet" Mk. I has a span of 23 ft. 9½ in., a length of 26 ft. 6 in., and a height of 10 ft. 2 in. The wings are built up of light steel spars and ribs, with a covering of fabric secured to the wings by a method of "wiring-on" that has been patented by the Gloster company. The framework of the fuselage is also of metal and is oval in section; the forward part is covered with metal panels and the rear part with fabric. The powerful wheel brakes of the undercarriage can be operated either from the control column, or by means of pedals attached to the rudder bar.

The trailing edge of the centre section of the upper wing is cut away to provide adequate clearance for the pilot, as the cockpit is situated beneath this part of the wing. The equipment of the cockpit is very comprehensive, and in addition to the usual navigating instruments and the necessary gun sights and supply of ammunition, it includes night-flying equipment, a wireless transmitter and receiver, and a supply of oxygen. The two Vickers guns are mounted in troughs, one in each side of the fuselage, and are easily accessible to the pilot. There are also racks from which four 20-lb. bombs can be hung.

A Bristol "Mercury" VI.S engine is fitted in the nose of the fuselage. It is of the radial air-cooled type and develops 605 h.p., which gives the aeroplane a top speed of 230 m.p.h. at 15,800 ft. The "Gauntlet" has a very high rate of climb, as this is essential in a fighting machine, and it can attain an altitude of 10,000 ft. in four minutes, and takes only nine minutes to reach 20,000 ft. The service ceiling is 33,500 ft.

The Fairey "Fantome" in the air, photographed from another machine. Illustration reproduced by courtesy of "The Aeroplane."

A later version, known as the "Gauntlet" Mk. II, differs from the original machine in having the wing spars and rear part of the fuselage of the type embodied in Hawker aircraft. It may be mentioned here that early in 1934 the Gloster company was taken over by Hawker Aircraft Ltd., of which it is now a subsidiary company.

The "Gladiator" has been developed from the "Gauntlet," and although it carries more fuel and equipment it gives a much better performance with the same type of engine. It is very similar to the "Gauntlet" in regard to wings, fuselage and tail unit. The engine is a Bristol "Mercury" IX, and enables the aeroplane, fully loaded, to attain a top speed of 260 m.p.h. at 15,500 ft., which is 30 m.p.h. faster than the "Gauntlet." The fuel tanks are in the fuselage. The all-up, or loaded, weight is 4,400 lb. and although this is 450 lb. more than that of the "Gauntlet" when loaded, the new aeroplane takes only 9 min. 20 sec. to climb to 20,000 ft.

Fairey "Firefly" single-seater Fighter, as used in the Belgian Military Air Force. Photograph by courtesy of the Fairey Aviation Co. Ltd., Hayes.

There is no doubt that the "Gladiator" will be a very formidable foe in the air. In addition to being capable of a very high maximum speed and a fast rate of climb, it is armed with four machine guns. Two of these are placed like those of the "Gauntlet" and the other two are mounted below the lower wing, one on each side of the fuselage. The lower guns fire outside the radius of the airscrew.

Many types of British military aircraft have been adopted by the Air Forces of foreign countries. The Fairey "Firefly" single-seater fighter, for instance, is standard equipment in the Belgian Military Air Force, and the machines of this type required for that Force are produced by the Belgian Fairey company.

The "Firefly" has wings of unequal span and therefore is a sesquiplane. Literally a sesquiplane is a machine with one-and-a-half wings; in practice, however, the term is applied to all biplanes in which one wing is shorter than the other. The overall span of this aeroplane is 32 ft., and both wings are built up of metal components and have a fabric covering. The fuselage conforms to the general practice for fighting machines and has a metal framework of oval section. The front part is covered with aluminium cowling that can be removed easily and quickly for inspection of the framework, and the rear portion is, of course, covered with fabric. The well-equipped cockpit for the pilot is just aft of the upper wing.

A Rolls-Royce "Kestrel" engine is employed, and, as the lower photograph on this page shows, is completely covered by the cowling. The engine is of the water-cooled and supercharged type, and the necessary cooling system for it is fitted under the fuselage. The main fuel tanks are in the upper wing.

The armament of the "Firefly" consists of two Vickers guns, and these fire in a forward direction through two recesses, one in each side of the long cowling covering the engine.

Some time ago the Belgian Government organised a competition for single-seater fighters, and aircraft entered were required to have a top speed of at least 248 m.p.h. at 16,400 ft., and to be able to climb to 5,000 ft. in six minutes. One of the aeroplanes designed and built for this competition was the Fairey "Fantome" illustrated in the upper photograph on this page. It is an unequal span biplane, with the wings slightly staggered, that is, one wing is set a little ahead of the other. The overall span is 36 ft. 6 in., the length is 27 ft. 6½ in., and the height is 9 ft. 2 in. The wings, fuselage and tail unit are built on similar lines to those of the "Firefly," and the pilot's cockpit contains full night-flying equipment.

The armament is of especial interest, as it includes a .78 in. Oerlikon quick-firing gun, which is mounted in the "vee" of the Hispano-Suiza engine and fires through the airscrew boss. There are also four machine guns.

Here we review books of interest and of use to readers of the "M.M." We can supply copies of these books to readers who cannot obtain them through the usual channels. Order from Book Dept., Meccano Limited, Binns Road, Liverpool 13, adding 1/- for postage to the price. Postage on different books varies, but any balance remaining will be refunded.

"Electricity"

By W. L. Bragg, Sc.D., F.R.S.
(T. Bell and Sons Ltd. 8/6 net)

Professor Bragg gave a course of six lectures on electricity at the Royal Institution, London, at Christmas 1934, and has now expanded these lectures into book form. In doing so he has maintained the practical character that distinguishes Royal Institution lectures, which are famous for the number and interest of the experiments performed in them; and the result is a really fine book that will give its readers a complete grasp of electricity and magnetism and an understanding of its use in everyday life.

The author remarks in his preface that "Nature has not prepared us to study electricity." We are able to realise the meaning of light, heat and sound directly, but the electrical sense must be acquired if we wish to win the freedom of the modern world, in which electricity figures so prominently. His book is well calculated to help his readers in this respect. It begins by presenting the fundamental ideas of electricity as simply as possible and then deals with motors, dynamos and power stations. In these sections we learn not only how electricity is produced and distributed through the "Grid" scheme, but also how it is measured—a matter of importance and interest to everyone who pays electric light and power bills—and how it is used in simple domestic appliances.

The author then turns to the application of electricity to the transmission of signals and speech, with and without wires. He gives an excellent account of the working of the automatic telephone exchanges that are now being installed in various parts of the country; and the section on wireless covers a greater range than is usual, for it explains fully the production of wireless oscillations by means of Tesla coils and deals with their use in high frequency special furnaces.

The book is valuable not only because of the interesting and useful information it contains, but also because of the many neat and effective experiments described in it and the remarkably simple but sufficient manner in which every detail is explained. The general reader with practically no previous knowledge of electricity will have no difficulty in grasping the meaning of every experiment, and electrical principles are brought so clearly into relation to his daily experience that he will find it difficult to forget them. The book contains 138 illustrations, including explanatory diagrams in the text and a large number of plates reproducing photographs of electrical plant and instruments of all kinds.

This is a book that will appeal to every "*M.M.*" reader who is at all interested in electricity. It is attractively written, and is full of information that is both accurate and attractive.

Sparks from the terminal of a van de Graaff machine to which an electrostatic charge of 10 million volts is given. From "Electricity," reviewed on this page.

"The Locomotive Stock of the Main Line Companies of Great Britain"

This is a useful publication for railway-minded readers, particularly for those who like to keep records of locomotive numbers and of the different locomotive classes. The information given is correct up to 31st December of last year, and commences with a tabled analysis of the different locomotive wheel arrangements and the numbers of each type in use on the L.M.S.R., L.N.E.R., G.W.R. and S.R. A short review of British locomotive practice in 1935 is given, and then follow details of the types, classes and numbers of British locomotives. Not only are the four groups dealt with, but details of the locomotives of the M. and G.N. Joint line, the L.P.T.B., and the steam rail cars of the C.L.C. also are included.

Although locomotive names are not included, the names of the rail motor vehicles on the L.N.E.R. are shown. Special reference is made to the classes of locomotive that became extinct during 1935, and there is a total of 27 illustrations of typical members of these.

Copies of this useful and interesting publication can be obtained from Mr. D. R. Pollock, Publications Editor of the Railway Correspondence and Travel Society, at 102, Disraeli Road, Putney, London, S.W.15. The price is 1/2 post free.

"R.M.S. *Queen Mary*"

(B. T. Batsford Ltd. 2/6 net)

Few events in recent years have given rise to so much excitement as the completion of the "*Queen Mary*," the world's most wonderful liner, and her departure on her maiden voyage. The present volume is a remarkable memento of the appearance of this "Queen of the Seas," for in 84 magnificent pictures it traces her production from the time when she was merely a growing mass of steel plating and girders to the day when she was launched and named, and her memorable passage down the Clyde to meet the open sea for the first time. Impressive photographs of the wonderful halls, state rooms, swimming pools and other luxurious accommodation provided in her also are reproduced. Each illustration is adequately described, and an introduction by Mr. George Blake gives in brief the whole story of the building of this masterpiece of British shipbuilding.

"The Young Engineer"

By J. N. Digues La Touche
(The Technical Press Ltd. 5/-)

The author has had a wide and valuable experience of engineering in India, chiefly in connection with railway construction and maintenance, and here places the benefit of the practical knowledge he has gained there at the disposal of engineering students. The result is an unusual book that does not deal with the mathematical side of engineering, but only with actual practice and the daily life of the engineer at work, supervising contractors and handling large bodies of workers. No claim is made to literary excellence. In many places the writing indeed is somewhat awkward, with unnecessary repetitions; but the author provides a wealth of information and practical wisdom.

"Cradle of the Storms"

By B. R. Hubbard, S.J. (Harrap. 8/6 net)

The south-western tip of Alaska is one of the most interesting places in the world. There not only do the warm waters of the Pacific meet the icy Bering Sea, and thus give rise to violent storms, but the land surface itself is still in process of formation. The entire region is volcanic, and islands may yet disappear overnight, or emerge from the waters, in catastrophic eruptions and upheavals.

The district is the favourite exploring ground of Father Hubbard, famous throughout America as "The Glacier Priest," and in his lively and entertaining book he describes his latest expedition to this ever-changing corner of the world. He tells his readers thrilling stories of climbing great volcanic mountains, flying over active craters and even landing in them, and scaling precipitous pinnacles. At one point of his wanderings he was faced twice with the necessity of crossing a vast area swept by storms of such violence that not only was every stream swollen to almost incredible dimensions, but the land itself was turned into moving mud. He encounters giant brown bears, sees the birth of immense icebergs, is threatened with disaster by fierce blizzards, and finally camps in one of the greatest wonders of Alaska, the Valley of Ten Thousand Smokes. The Valley came into existence during a violent eruption, and then was covered with clouds of sulphurous steam rising skyward from cracks and craters in the ground. Now there are few of these "smokes" to be seen, but it is still a land of geysers and coloured pools that rival any to be seen in the famous Yellowstone Park in the United States.

The wonders of this amazing region and the struggles and hardships endured by the explorers traversing it are well described by the author. His book will not only satisfy the needs of readers who are in search of tales of adventure, but also will give them attractive and accurate pictures of the most amazing volcanic region in the world. It is exceptionally well illustrated by nearly 100 original photographs of intense interest.

The boiling lake in Akutan Crater, Alaska. The illustrations on this page are from "Cradle of the Storms," reviewed on this page.

"Foundations for the Study of Engineering"

By G. E. Hall, B.Sc.
(The Technical Press Ltd. 7/6 net)

An engineer can only be completely successful if he is able to combine theory with practice and to reason on scientific lines in dealing with the problems that confront him. He should therefore be given a thorough grounding in the principles involved, and to provide the young engineer with what he requires in this direction is the purpose of the book.

The contents range from the laws of motion, friction, simple machines and mechanisms to the steam boiler, the steam engine and the internal combustion engine. The treatment is thoroughly practical and is illustrated by a large number of carefully planned diagrams and photographs of machines and engines. The book should be particularly valuable to students preparing for preliminary examinations.

"South with Scott"

By Vice-Adm. E. R. G. R. Evans. (Collins. 2/6)

The story of Scott's last journey across the dreary wastes of the Antarctic continent and the Great Ice Barrier is one of the epics of exploration, and the determination and heroism displayed by that great leader and the four men who died with him will never be forgotten. The tale has been told on many occasions, but never so well as by Vice-Admiral Evans, who was second in command of the Scott expedition, and himself underwent terrible hardships when making his way back with a supporting party that had accompanied Scott to a point only 150 miles from the Pole itself. For this reason the re-issue of his splendid book *"South with Scott"* in the cheaper form now reviewed is to be welcomed.

Climbing a precipice on an Alaskan volcano.

The book gives a complete account of Scott's great expedition from the time when it left British shores in 1910 to the return, nearly three years later, of the last of those taking part in it. Although Scott's famous march to the Pole is an outstanding feature, it is by no means the only thrill in the book, for practically every one of Scott's little band of adventurers did sterling work and endured great hardships, whether they were sailors engaged in the work of exploration or scientists probing into the mysteries of the frozen South. The members of one party were compelled to spend an Antarctic winter of intense cold and appalling blizzards in a cave hacked out of an ice drift. One factor in keeping them alive in such terrible conditions was the immense cheerfulness and the fine spirit of comradeship that they displayed. This indeed was characteristic of every man in the Expedition, as almost every page in the book reveals. The story in fact is a magnificent record of great achievement, self-sacrifice, and heroism that should be read by every boy.

"How the Locomotive Works and Why"

By M. P. Sells, O.B.E.
(Locomotive Publishing Co. 3/6 net)

This book was originally written for the benefit of the locomotive staff of the Nigerian Government Railway, on which the author holds the position of Chief Mechanical Engineer. It has now been revised in order to render it generally useful to workers on other railways, and can be recommended to all who are interested in any way in its subject.

The contents cover every phase of locomotive working, from the combustion of coal and the duties of firemen to the distribution of steam and the function of the valve gear. Automatic brakes of the vacuum and Westinghouse types are described in detail. Lubrication is fully dealt with, and a particularly useful chapter describes systematic methods of locomotive examination.

The frontispiece of the book illustrates a three-cylinder 4–8–2 locomotive designed by the author, and there are two coloured diagrams in addition to many useful and interesting line drawings.

"More Potted Stories"

By Vera C. Barclay
(Brown, Son and Ferguson. 2/6 net)

Miss Barclay thoroughly understands the Scout mind and has written many books that are a source of inspiration to Scouters and Cub masters. Her most recent production is a further collection of stories that are suitable for telling to Scouts and Cubs on various occasions.

Only the gist of most of the stories is given, the idea being to leave the narrator to expand them and to add dramatic effects where desirable. In addition to these "potted" stories, there are longer ones that may be read aloud in full, or treated in the manner described. Most of the stories are true and all tell of inspiring deeds of courage or comradeship, while a particularly valuable feature is the inclusion of yarns dealing with patrol animals.

The most attractive mi and furniture ever

"DOLLY VARDEN" DOLL'S HOUSE

READY IN MID-JULY

The Couch Hammock, Tennis Net, Garden Seats, Dinky Toys Garage, Motor Cars and Figures, and the Hornby Trees and Hedging featured in the illustration below are not included with the Doll's House and Garden.

DIMENSIONS

The following are the overall dimensions of the "Dolly Varden" Doll's House when built up ready for play.

Length	1 ft. 6¾ in.
Depth	10¼ in.
Height	1 ft. 6¾ in.

The open container on which the house stands measures 3 ft. 3½ in. by 2 ft. 5½ in.

When the house is dismantled and packed in container, the overall dimensions of the complete parcel are ⅜ in. x 1 ft. 7½ in. x 2 ft. 5½ in.

MECCANO LIMITED
BINNS ROAD, LIVERPOOL 13

ure house duced

y Varden" Doll's House illustrated below has designed for use with Dinky Toys Doll's House

is collapsible and the exterior is designed to f-timbered dwelling, while the interior decora- e printed in nine colours, are in an attractive

leather board is the material of which the house and when set up it is as strong as a wood structure. which also is made of reinforced leather board, now a lovely garden with Tennis Lawn, Carriage kery, providing an exquisite setting for play with l Hornby Trees, Hedging, etc. House will be ready in mid-July. Price 9/6

NKY TOYS
DOLL'S HOUSE
URNITURE

extension of the range of Dinky Toys to include cale modern Furniture will be welcomed by all w the charm of these perfect miniatures. Much thought have been given to the design, finish entation of every article of this Furniture series. tone and individuality of style about them which il to appeal. Among the most attractive features pening doors and drawers. This furniture is far to anything of its kind that has ever before been for the delight and pleasure of young people. y Toys Furniture is now ready. See it at your

ROOM FURNITURE. Dinky Toys No. 101
Price of complete set 2/3

Table ...	5d. each
Sideboard (Opening doors) ...	9d. ,,
Carver Chairs ...	3d. ,,
Chairs ...	2d. ,,

Supplied in walnut finish only.

OM FURNITURE. Dinky Toys No. 102
Price of complete set 2/11

Bed ...	6d. each
Wardrobe (Opening door) ...	9d. ,,
Dressing Table (Opening drawers) ...	10d. ,,
Dressing Chest (Opening drawers) ...	6d. ,,
Dressing Table Stool ...	2d. ,,
Chair ...	2d. ,,

Supplied in two colour schemes—mauve and gold; light green and dark green.

KITCHEN FURNITURE
Dinky Toys No. 103
Price of complete set 2/6

No. 103a.	Refrigerator (Opening door) ...	8d. each
No. 103b.	Kitchen Cabinet (Opening doors and drawer)	10d. ,,
No. 103c.	Electric Cooker (Opening door) ...	6d. ,,
No. 103d.	Table ...	4d. ,,
No. 103e.	Chair ...	2d. ,,

Supplied in two colour schemes—light blue and white; light green and cream.

ROOM FURNITURE. Dinky Toys No. 104
Price of complete set 2/-

Bath...	6d. each
Bath Mat ...	1d. ,,
Pedestal Hand Basin ...	6d. ,,
Stool ...	2d. ,,
Linen Basket (Opening lid) ...	4d. ,,
Toilet (Lifting lid)...	6d. ,,

wo colour schemes—pink and white; light green and white.

NOW READY

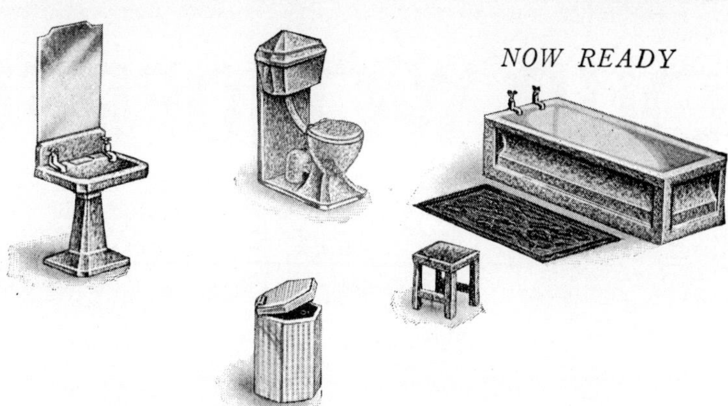

BATHROOM FURNITURE. Dinky Toys No. 104. Price 2/-

BEDROOM FURNITURE. Dinky Toys No. 102. Price 2/11

DINING-ROOM FURNITURE. Dinky Toys No. 101. Price 2/3

KITCHEN FURNITURE. Dinky Toys No. 103. Price 2/6

Salmon in Prehistoric Rivers

It has long been well known that the salmon alternates between fresh water and salt water, returning after its stay in the sea to spawning grounds in the upper reaches of the river in which it was born. Salmon that have been marked on their way to the sea have frequently been recaptured on entering the river down which they passed, both on the European shores of the Atlantic and on the Pacific coast of North America. This has been regarded as an instance of the cleverness or instinct that is so common in the animal world, but it has now been suggested that the fish is not really impelled by a knowledge of its original home and a desire to return to it. Its behaviour is even more remarkable than that, however, for it appears to be living in the world of the past, and to act as if unaware of the immense changes that have taken place in the configuration of land and sea during past ages.

The explanation that is now offered for the return of the salmon to the river that was its original home is simply that it never leaves it. In prehistoric times immense areas that are now under water were part of the Earth's land surface, and many of the rivers that we now know were very much longer. For instance, some of the salmon rivers of the east coast of Scotland made their way across a great plain, now sunk beneath the North Sea, to join a mighty stream formed by the union of the Rhine and the Thames that flowed northward to a sea coast that stretched roughly from the north of Scotland to Norway. The channels of these ancient rivers still exist under the sea, and it is believed that the fish follow them, just as their ancestors did in prehistoric ages when fresh water flowed along them.

This idea is strongly supported by the fact that salmon have never been found at sea outside the limits of what is known as the continental shelf. This is a comparatively shallow area extending from the continents to a kind of underwater coast or cliff beyond which are the deep waters of the ocean itself. The salmon appear to collect at the prehistoric estuaries of the rivers in which they were born, and between October and March they return along the underwater channel and up the present-day rivers to reach their spawning grounds.

A striking photograph of Lake Louise, a beautiful sheet of water in Banff National Park, the famous reservation among the peaks of the Canadian Rockies.

Photographing a Swordfish Attack

Turning from the salmon to a deep water fish of a far more ferocious disposition, I have been interested to find that the attack of one of these creatures has at last been photographed. Stories of swordfish driving their extraordinary weapons through the planking of boats are by no means uncommon, but this record actually showing the fish with its sword partly outside and partly inside a boat is unique. The fish was harpooned from a yacht and a man was sent out in a dory to bring it alongside. He experienced so much opposition that the master of the yacht anticipated trouble and got ready to take a photograph of anything of interest that might occur. He suddenly saw the flash of the fish in the water charging the dory and released the shutter, fortunately catching the fish exactly at the right moment. The attack that was photographed was not the only one made by the swordfish, for immediately afterwards it made a second lunge that ripped one plank entirely out of the boat and caused it to sink. When the fish was hauled on board it was found to weigh 350 lb.

A Ravenous Insect

Most readers of the "*M.M.*" will be familiar with pictures of the mantis, the insect that folds its forelegs in an attitude of prayer, and those who live in warmer climates than that of Great Britain may be familiar with the creatures themselves. In spite of the peaceful appearance this remarkable attitude gives it, the mantis is extremely bloodthirsty and has an enormous appetite for all kinds of insects. It lies in wait for its victims on a tree or shrub, with its head bent downward and inward and its long forelegs held before it. The instant a fly or other insect comes near its legs shoot out like lightning. Sharp spines on their inner sides fold round the victim, which is then immediately devoured.

The praying mantis has found its way to the United States. There it was accidentally introduced 30 or 40 years ago, and in many parts of the country has flourished to such an extent that it is now a common object in early autumn. Fortunately no ill effects are likely to follow its arrival there, for unlike many insects that have travelled from one part of the world to another, it is not a nuisance and does not damage crops. On the contrary, it is beneficial, for it devours insects that are destructive to vegetation.

The mantis is about 4 in. in length, and when its wings are spread to the full they have a span of 6 in. It is capable of strong flight and has even been found on the highest windows of skyscrapers in New York.

Putting the Sun to Work

Indirectly all our usual sources of power can be traced back to the Sun. Coal has been described as "bottled sunshine," for it consists of the carbonised remains of plants of millions of years ago. Oil also represents the solar energy of past ages, and even the wind and waterfalls owe their origin to the Sun, for both movements in the atmosphere and the fall of rain are due to its activities.

While we are steadily using up our sources of power, we are allowing the rays of the Sun, their creator, to stream unharnessed into space. Some day we may find that we shall have to make use of these rays, and no doubt efficient schemes will have been devised when that time comes. Many efforts have already been made to use Sun power directly. The principle in most of these had been to concentrate the Sun's rays by means of curved mirrors on to boilers of various shapes in which liquids are heated. In an extensive plant of this kind erected in Egypt many years ago, the boilers were long thin tubes placed within channel-shaped reflectors that were tilted by automatic gearing to enable them to follow the Sun and make full use of its rays throughout the day. The plant was more costly to erect and run than a boiler fired by coal, but it was a very promising attempt, the best output being one brake horse power for every 183 sq. ft. of surface.

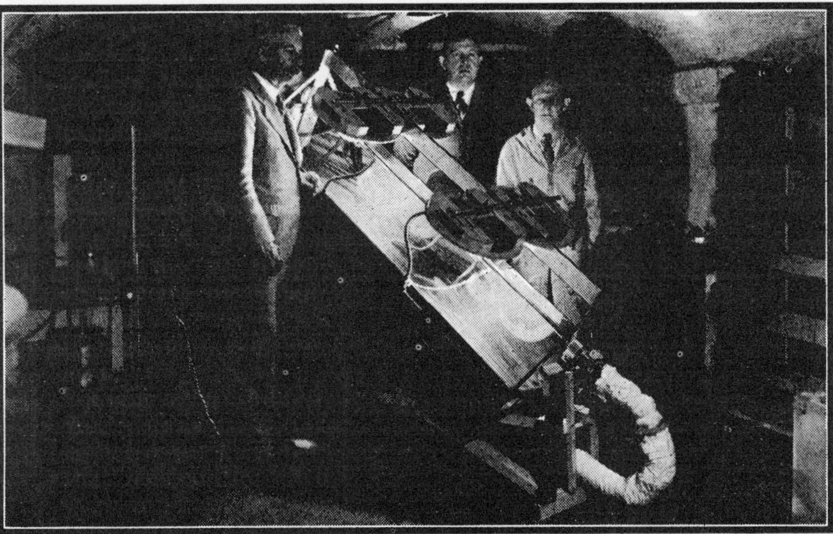

A solar heater designed by Dr. C. G. Abbot, Secretary of the Carnegie Institution, Washington, who is seen on the left. The four overhead mirrors and the lamps under them form an artificial Sun for demonstration purposes. Photograph by courtesy of Dr. Abbot.

A New Solar Engine

By far the most successful results yet achieved in this direction have been obtained with the aid of the simple solar heater illustrated on this page. This was devised by C. G. Abbot, Secretary of the Smithsonian Institution, Washington, who has been making experiments in the use of the Sun's rays for cooking and other purposes for 20 years. His reflector is a sheet of "Alcoa," a very light alloy made by the Aluminium Company of America. This reflects more than 80 per cent. of the Sun's rays, and exposure to the weather for a year has no appreciable effect on its surface. It is bent into the form of a parabola by screwing it down on a special frame, and it brings the Sun's rays to a focus along a line no wider than a lead pencil.

The greatest novelty in Dr. Abbot's apparatus is the form of heater he employs. This consists of three concentric tubes of pyrex glass fitted along the focal line of the mirror. The central tube is only ½ in. in width, and inside it is a black liquid called "Aroclor," a complex organic substance, in which a little lampblack is placed. When treated in this manner the liquid almost totally absorbs the rays focussed upon it. A vacuum is maintained in the spaces between the tubes, thus forming a kind of thermos flask in which little of the heat absorbed is wasted.

When the Sun's rays are directed on to the mirror and focussed on to the heater, the "Aroclor" becomes hot and circulates through the tube naturally, as in a domestic hot water system, passing away to the place where its heat can usefully be absorbed for cooking or for producing steam. When it has cooled it re-enters the central tube at the lower end. The heater shown in our illustration makes use of powerful electric lamps as a substitute for the Sun, as it is being used for indoor demonstrations. The rays of these lamps are concentrated by means of four overhead mirrors.

This little apparatus is three times as effective as the plant tried in Egypt. A ½ h.p. steam raising model is now being constructed, and it is believed that the success that has so far attended Dr. Abbot's experiments has brought us near the stage when the direct rays of the Sun will become a serious competitor with coal and oil. The Sun does not shine continuously, and some means of storing the energy it gives us therefore will be necessary. This can readily be arranged either by using its power to charge giant accumulators, to pump water to a reservoir on a convenient hill or mountain, or simply by some form of heat storage. Chemical methods of storing it also have been suggested.

A moose in Elk Island National Park, Canada. This animal benefits by the protection afforded it in the National Parks of Canada, where it lives a peaceful, un-hunted life.

The Monarch of the Deer Tribe

One of the characteristic creatures of Canadian life is the moose or elk. This is a large and magnificent animal, often standing 7 ft. high at the shoulders, and carrying a wonderful display of antlers. The elk is in fact the monarch of the deer tribe. It is now found only in North America and in parts of Northern Europe, but at one time was common in England, and also in Ireland, the now extinct Irish elk being even larger than the Canadian animal.

The elk is a powerful swimmer, and in summertime revels in deep swamps, where he tears up aquatic plants and frees his mouth and nose of mud and water by loud blowing that betrays his presence to the hunter. Like most game animals he is now protected, and many of the old tricks by which he was once tracked down and slaughtered are no longer allowed. For instance, it is forbidden to go out at night by boat with a flare to a place where an elk has betrayed his presence by blowing, in order to shoot him while he gazed at the flare in stupid wonder. The use of dogs also is not allowed, and the animal cannot be hunted by men on snowshoes when a thaw has been followed by a frost and the surface carries the weight of the hunter, but breaks under the hoofs of the elk and hampers his flight.

One curious trick the elk shares with the African buffalo. He has a very keen sense of hearing, and when he wishes to rest he turns to windward from his track so that he is in a position to scent pursuers following him. It is this trick that makes the African buffalo so dangerous, especially when wounded, for the hunter often then has been transformed into the hunted, and the elk makes use of it for his protection.

A Bean with 300 Uses

For centuries Man has been content to make use of trees and vegetable products for one or two obvious purposes only, but every year their value is being greatly increased as new applications are found for them. Wood of course is an excellent example of this. It no longer provides material only for the fire or for the carpenter, but is the raw material for paper and even for dress materials, as from it rayon or artificial silk is now made on an immense scale. Cotton also does more than provide a valuable fabric, for it enters into the composition of an almost endless list of articles from finger nail polish to high explosives. Another subject of surprising developments of this kind is the soya bean, long regarded only as a suitable food for pigs, but now providing also a plastic material and an oil that is largely used. Altogether more than 300 possible uses have been discovered for it.

I. *If a shaft were dug through the centre of the Earth from England to Australia, would anyone descending into it come out on the opposite side feet first or head first?*

THIS may seem a frivolous question, but finding an answer involves so many interesting problems that it is worth while to stop to consider it. In order to arrive at a solution it is necessary first to appreciate the startling fact that in space there is no absolute right way up. We feel that we are right when our feet are on the ground, and our heads are pointing to the sky, and soon become uncomfortable if we reverse the position and stand on our heads. It is easy to imagine conditions in which what we should regard as an upside-down position would be the only reasonable one, however. Suppose that a man enters a room in which gravity pulls objects towards the ceiling instead of the floor, or in which some artificially-created force of the same kind directed upwards overcomes gravity. Immediately a man entered such a room he would rise until his head came into contact with the ceiling. This probably would be painful, for the movement would be involuntary and could fairly be described as a fall. It would in fact be the same kind of movement that would happen if a man were to enter an ordinary room by the ceiling instead of through a door on the floor level.

A surprise for an Australian policeman. Would anyone making a journey through the centre of the Earth from England to Australia emerge feet first or head first? This question is answered in the accompanying article.

When the victim of this trick recovered and stood up, he would automatically place his feet on the ceiling with his head hanging downward towards the floor. If he became alarmed by this unusual position, and by vigorous struggles succeeded in attaining what he had previously thought to be the correct attitude, with his feet downward, he would experience the same uncomfortable sensations as we undergo when we stand on our heads. Profiting by experience, he would then resign himself to the upside-down position, which of course for him would really be right side up. He would then be perfectly happy. If a table and a chair were brought in, he would be able to place them with their feet resting on the ceiling, and would be able to sit down, write at the table, and in fact behave exactly as we do in the more ordinary rooms of the buildings in which we live. He would not feel that anything was wrong and in truth he would be right way up in his own little world.

This will make clear how it is that people in both England and Australia remain on the surface of the Earth and act in a perfectly normal manner, although they are on opposite sides of the great ball on which we live. Each of course thinks that he is right way up and the other is upside-down, and both are right. Strange as it may seem to us now, this was difficult to understand not very long ago, when the Earth was believed to be more or less flat. The suggestion that our planet is really round was then violently ridiculed on the ground that people on the opposite side of it would fall off! That anyone could live in what was then thought to be an upside-down position was regarded as utterly fantastic.

Now let us return to our large scale excavation and see what would happen if we dug a hole through to Australia. As the shaft grew deeper the temperature in it would rise, and long before the diggers reached the centre of the Earth they would be burned to cinders, or even converted into gases, chiefly carbon dioxide, and blown back up the shaft. Molten rock under high pressure also would be encountered deep down in the Earth, and dealing with this would be about as easy as trying to hold back the boiling lava that is thrown out with terrific force by a volcano.

Let us suppose that means of overcoming these and other difficulties are found, however, and that the shaft has been driven to the centre of the Earth. Up to that point the hardy adventurers making the trip would have been moving in the direction in which the force of gravity is exerted. As soon as they tried to go farther, however, they would be opposed by gravity, and would be compelled to cling to something if they wished to remain on the "floor" of their shaft. If they let go their hold they would drop back towards the centre, past which they would be carried by the impetus due to the fall. The direction of the force attracting them would again change as they passed the centre. They would therefore once more be pulled back and again would overshoot the mark, but this time in the opposite direction and by a smaller distance. They would continue to oscillate to and fro in this manner for a while before coming to rest.

Once they had settled at the centre of the Earth, in whatever direction they moved they would immediately be dragged back again by the force of gravity. For them there would be no "down," as any direction would be "up," and in this respect they would be in a somewhat similar position to that of a man standing at the North Pole, who would go south whether he stepped forward, backward or sideways.

If they had been sensible enough to fit the shaft with side ladders to enable them to cling to their working face, they would still be very uncomfortable, for the direction of the pull due to gravity on their bodies would be from their feet to their heads, and in effect they would be upside-down. For this reason progress with their work would be difficult. They also would be hampered by the necessity for attaching themselves to the ladder, and would be surprised to find that considerable effort would be required to push their picks and shovels, or whatever tools they were using, towards their feet.

If they could maintain this position while they are digging out the remaining 4,000 miles of their gigantic bore, however, they would astonish the policeman seen in our illustration by breaking ground in Australia feet first, and he would have every excuse for arresting them as dangerous lunatics threatening to turn everything in Australia topsy turvy. This of course is impossible and they would be compelled to reverse their positions, directing their heads towards Australia and their feet towards the centre of the Earth.

Even then their troubles would not be over. They would still have to lash themselves in some way to their ladder and, as their "floor" would have become a roof, they would have to "dig" above their heads. The one task that would be simplified would be the disposal of the spoil. Once they were past the halfway stage the material they broke loose with their tools would simply fall towards the centre of the Earth and there form an ever increasing plug in the long tube.

It will be realised that if our pioneers survived the hardships and terror of their immense task, they would emerge from their great bore head first.

H. A. ROBINSON.

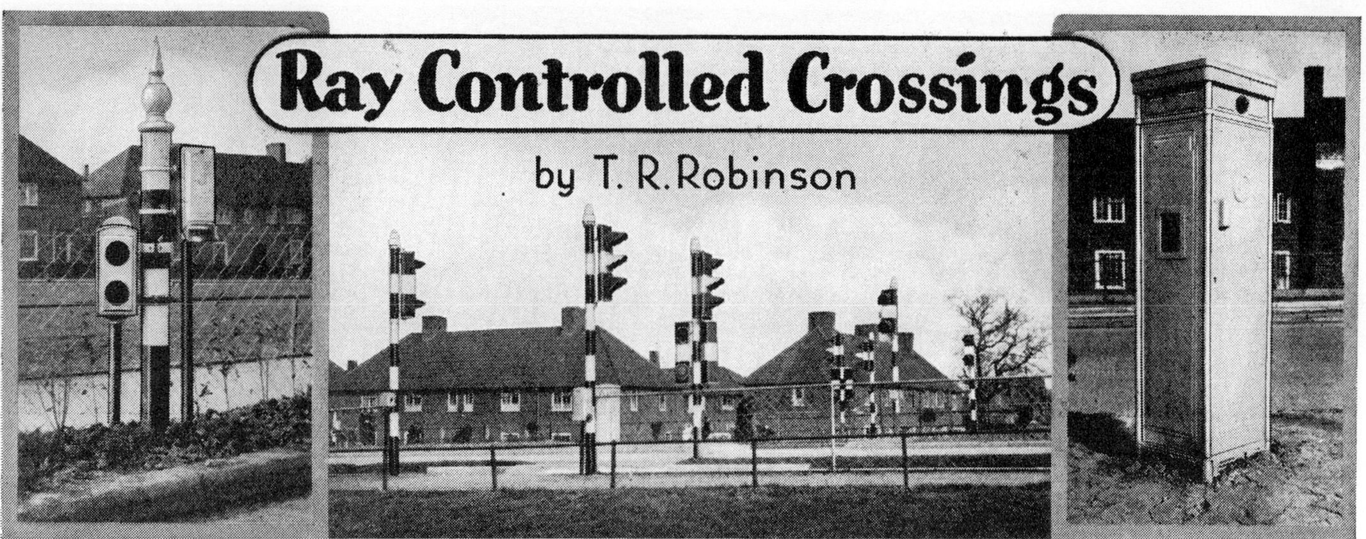

Ray Controlled Crossings

by T. R. Robinson

TRAFFIC SIGNALS THAT DIRECT PEDESTRIANS

CROSSING a busy road is nowadays a somewhat perilous adventure, and there may be danger even in walking across a street or lane in which traffic is not very dense or frequent, for modern vehicles move swiftly. Many schemes have been suggested in efforts to diminish the risk of accident, or to abolish it altogether. Special places for crossings of course have to be provided if control is to be exercised. The ordinary controlled crossing, familiarly known as the Belisha crossing, is not entirely satisfactory, however, for it is simply a zone in which motorists and the drivers of other road vehicles must respect the rights of those on foot, and no definite signals are given.

Crossings provided with signals for both road users and foot passengers have now been introduced. In these the signals directing pedestrians are of what is called the "two-aspect" type, showing one or other of the two instructions "*Cross Now*" or "*Do Not Cross.*" The usual red, amber and green signals are used for road traffic, and the two sets work in conjunction with each other. Anyone wishing to cross the road presses a special switch fitted on a post. This changes the lights against oncoming traffic to red, and causes the two-aspect signal to show "*Cross Now.*"

In practice it has been found that many pedestrians fail to use the switches at crossings of this kind, and either wait for a lull in the traffic or dodge in between passing vehicles and thus run unnecessary risks. An entirely new system therefore has been devised in which pedestrians automatically and involuntarily demand the right of way. The first crossing of this new type was put into operation in St. Helier Avenue, on the Sutton by-pass road, Morden, Surrey, and is illustrated at the head of the page. The crossing chosen connects two sections of a great housing estate and passes over a busy arterial road, with up and down carriage ways and a central dividing strip, and therefore is particularly suitable for the installation, which is somewhat in the nature of an experiment.

Barriers along the sides of the road ensure that the crossing is made at a definite place and the approach to this is spanned by a ray of light that is interrupted by anyone wishing to cross. The beam normally falls upon a device, known as a photo-electric cell that is sensitive to light. When the beam is interrupted the internal electrical resistance of the cell is lowered, and it permits sufficient current to pass through it to operate a relay. This action in turn completes a circuit that operates contacts in a master controller, and thus records the demand. If no traffic is approaching the signals change at once, showing first amber and then red on the roadway and altering the other signal indication from "*Do Not Cross*" to "*Cross Now.*" In other circumstances the pedestrian signals change in a very short time.

The entire crossing is controlled by means of light rays, for there also are beams across the up and down carriageways and these are arranged to detect the presence of vehicles at distances of from 85 to 110 ft. There are no unfair delays, either for traffic or for pedestrians. Unless a foot passenger actually is waiting to cross, the road lights remain at green, and are only interrupted when the pedestrian beam is broken. Even a more or less continuous succession of vehicles, each in turn operating the road signals, is interrupted automatically after a definite time when a pedestrian gives the signal that he wishes to cross, however. Similarly, when the signals have released the traffic, they cannot again be changed to favour the pedestrian until a certain time has elapsed. During the waiting period the presence of somebody on foot waiting to cross is noted and remembered, and he is allowed to proceed at the first opportunity.

The illustration at the head of the page shows the light-ray controlled crossing at Morden, with the ray transmitter for vehicles on the left and the receptor box on the right. In our lower illustration the twin light rays in the middle of the pedestrian crossing are being interrupted.

The light ray apparatus for the pedestrian crossing is seen in our illustration, which shows a double set installed on the dividing strip in the middle of the road. On one side is the box containing the ray transmitters, which are provided with small filament bulbs similar to those used for motor car headlamps. These are mounted with reflectors and lens systems that focus their beams on the windows of the receptor boxes opposite them. There they fall on the photo-electric cells, which are placed behind coloured glass screens.

The arrangement of the vehicle units is similar, but in this case lenses are fitted in the receptor box as well as the transmitter. These focus only the beams from the transmitter on the photo-electric cell, and thus interference due to the lights of passing cars is prevented. The beams actually are invisible, for the lamps are fitted with infra-red screens in order to prevent the ray transmitter lights from causing glare to approaching drivers. Two lamps are fitted to each vehicle transmitter, but only one of these normally is in service. The second comes into action automatically if the first fails for any reason, and a warning red light then appears on the side of the controller pillar.

An interesting feature is that the light beams cross the carriage ways at an angle. The result is that fast moving vehicles on the inner side of the road are detected when they are farther from the crossing than those moving more slowly, which of course usually are nearer the pavement. Thus the speedier traffic is given a greater distance in which to pull up if this course is necessary.

The pedestrian crossing units are four in number, one at each entrance to the crossing and two on a refuge in the central dividing strip. Anyone crossing the road therefore breaks four rays and the arrangement can be used to allow a pedestrian to cross one traffic lane and then to halt him at the road centre until the other lane is clear, at the same time releasing the traffic behind him.

The master controller is almost human in the way in which it responds to the various demands made on it. For instance, when one pedestrian is crossing, the passage of a second through the beam automatically causes the signal "*Cross Now*" to be shown for a longer time. The direction in which a crossing is made also is detected, so that traffic is not stopped by a foot passenger leaving the crossing as well as approaching.

These pages are reserved for articles from our readers. Contributions not exceeding 500 words in length are invited on any subject of general interest. These should be written neatly on one side of the paper only, and they may be accompanied by photographs or sketches for use as illustrations. Articles that are published will be paid for at our usual rates. Statements contained in articles submitted for these pages are accepted as being sent in good faith, but the Editor takes no responsibility for their accuracy.

"The Chicago Express" of the C.P.R.

The accompanying photograph shows Canadian Pacific Railway train No. 21, *"The Chicago Express,"* crossing the Don Valley Bridge between Leaside Station and Don Station, Toronto. This train is one of the finest on the North American continent. It leaves Montreal every night at 11.15 p.m., reaching Toronto at 7.45 a.m. next morning and arriving in Chicago, 852½ miles from Montreal, at 8.10 p.m.

"The Chicago Express" of the Canadian Pacific Railway crossing Don Valley Bridge, near Toronto. Photograph by J. Adams, Toronto.

The engine at the head of the train when the photograph was taken is No. 3100, and is one of two built especially for this run, and known as KIA class. Its wheel arrangement is 4–8–4. It was built in 1928 at the Angus Shops of the C.P.R. in Montreal and follows the standard practice of that railway in having nickel steel boilers and fittings. The steam pressure is 275 lb. per sq. in., the driving wheels are 6 ft. 3 in. in diameter, and the tractive effort is 60,800 lb. The total length of the engine is 97 ft. 5½ in., and the firebox is fitted with a mechanical stoker.

The train is always very heavy. Sometimes there are as many as 19 cars, of all-steel construction, and as each car weighs nearly 80 tons the total load behind the engine then is more than 1,500 tons. Even heavier loads are occasionally known, and I have a photograph of this train leaving Leaside with 20 cars.

The bridge over which the train is passing is 1,150 ft. long and was strengthened in 1928 to allow the passage of locomotives of the KIA class. It carries the mainline of the C.P.R. between Montreal and Toronto over the Don Valley, and its height may be gauged by contrast with the chimneys seen on the left. J. Adams (Toronto).

Brittany's "Emerald Coast"

I was very glad to be able to visit Brittany on holiday last year, and in excited anticipation conjured up thoughts of rocky and irregular coasts surrounded by a beautiful emerald sea. In this I was not disappointed and cannot think of a more suitable name for this famous holiday district than the "Côte d'Emeraude," the Emerald Coast.

During my short stay I was only able to see the district round Dinard and St. Malo. The latter is an old naval fortress. Its tortuous cobbled streets are very narrow, in few places being more than 10 ft. in width, and as the speed limit in the town itself is as low as 4 m.p.h., driving a motor car within its walls is not a very agreeable pastime. St. Malo is separated from Dinard by the River Rance. There is no bridge to connect the two towns and a ferry service conveys passengers, cars, luggage and mail across the river.

Mont St. Michel, a famous islet off the coast of Normandy. Photograph by A. Frodsham, Crowborough.

At its eastern extremity Britanny is separated from Normandy by the River Couesnon, and just within the Norman boundary stands the famous Mont St. Michel, crowned by a monastery of the 11th century. This is not really an island, as it is usually described, for it is now connected to the mainland by a long built-up road or causeway. At low tide the sea cannot be seen and indeed is believed to withdraw as much as 12½ miles from the mainland. As high tide approaches a wall of water suddenly appears on the horizon and within 20 minutes the mound is surrounded, only the causeway remaining above water.

The unique streets of the town that has grown up on the island are even narrower than those of St. Malo. A. Frodsham (Crowborough).

Gold Mining in South Wales

I recently visited the gold mine workings near Pumpsaint, Cardiganshire. These are situated in a cleft of the hills that rise from the Cothi Valley. The mines were worked at least as far back as Roman times. This accounts for the abundance of rock mosses in the neighbourhood, for these probably were cultivated by the Romans, who are believed to have used them for medicinal purposes. The old galleries are cut into the hillside in such a manner that accumulations of water could run out at the entrances, for the Romans do not appear to have used pumps. They extend over 4 miles through quartz that has been hewn by hand.

One of the entrances to the Roman gold mines at Pumpsaint, South Wales. Photograph by K. G. Bilbe, London, S.W.12.

The present workings are reached by a vertical shaft 260 ft. in depth. This pierces some of the lower levels of the Roman mines, and one cavern, known as the Cathedral, contains many rock pillars that were left to support the roof. The present company has suspended weighted lines over basins of water in this part of the mine to indicate movements in the rock strata. Examinations are made if the weights dip into the water.

The ore is grey or white in colour and contains lead, silver and mica in addition to gold. Work is carried on day and night in the light of acetylene lamps, and there are no gases to contend with, as there are in coal mines. The use of modern machinery has increased the output of the mine. This includes a huge Blackstone oil engine that drives air compressors feeding the ventilating system as well as the drills with which the ore is extracted. Another shaft has just been commenced.

I found the miners exceedingly friendly and helpful. They come from all parts of Wales and stay for weeks at a time on the premises, which include social rooms and a canteen, and they willingly showed me round their quarters.

K. G. Bilbe (London, S.W.12).

Erecting the steelwork of a giant building. Photograph by E. H. Coles, London, W.11.

A Perilous Climb

Recently I had the opportunity of visiting a site on which is being erected a new block of flats of modern steel frame construction. In this form of building the loads are carried down to the foundations by a framework of steel and it is fascinating to watch this grow.

Part of the steelwork of the new flats had been erected when I visited the site, and men were busy overhead fixing new parts in position, walking calmly along narrow girders and balancing themselves easily in the most precarious positions. As I watched them I thought that certain death awaited a false step. In spite of this, I made up my mind to see them at close quarters. Feeling extremely nervous, I climbed ladders, walked along girders where careful balance was needed, and clambered round stanchions until I reached a height of 50 ft. above the ground. There I kneeled down on a plank that bent alarmingly whenever I moved, and photographed the men at work.

Right over my head, and another 15 ft. higher, was the crane that hoisted the steelwork into position. The men working it invited me to go up and "take their pictures," but I made the excuse that I had run out of films, and in a very short time was again safely on solid ground. My little climb gave me a pleasant thrill, but I prefer to spend my days working a little nearer the earth.

E. H. Coles (London, W.11).

In a Devonshire Pottery

While on a recent holiday in Devon I joined in a very interesting visit to a pottery near Torquay. Our guide first showed us a machine in which the raw, red clay is mixed with water and passed through a very fine sieve that retains impurities. The liquid mixture formed is led through pipes to a machine in which the water is pressed out, leaving pure clay, or "slip," ready for use in the pottery. In appearance this reminded me of "Plasticine."

Certain articles, such as plates and ash trays, are formed in moulds of plaster of paris, which automatically absorbs surplus moisture from the clay. Vases and bowls must be shaped, and in the potter's room we watched the making of a vase. The potter or "thrower," as he is called, placed a lump of clay on his revolving wheel, and shaped it with his hands, being guided as to height and width by gauges projecting over the wheel. When the vase was satisfactory, he cut it from the wheel with a wire.

The next step is to smooth the surface and edges of the vase on a lathe, and we saw this process in operation with vases that had been dried. These were then dipped in a tank containing a coloured liquid, and designs were painted on them when they had dried. They were then ready for baking.

P. Hawks (Shortlands).

Electric Winders for Gold Mines

Raising Ore from a Depth of 6,600 ft.

THE general appearance of pithead hoisting gear is familiar to all who live within reach of a colliery district, or have visited or passed through one. It consists of two immense narrow wheels, set side by side at the top of the pithead buildings. Cables from the winding machinery pass over these and disappear vertically into the shaft up which coal is hoisted and men are lowered to their work and raised to the surface. When the gear is in operation the wheels revolve at high speed in opposite directions, for each of the two ropes supports a cage, and one cage is raised as the other is lowered.

Similar equipment is used in gold mines, and indeed wherever valuable products found in the depths of the Earth have to be raised to the surface through a shaft. Fascinating as it is to watch the great wheels spinning rapidly, it is still more interesting to see the powerful machinery that actually hoists the cages and to realise how it has been developed from the earliest days of mining. Then shafts were not very deep and a simple barrel or drum was sufficient for the single rope that supported the bucket or hopper in which ore was raised. The first improvement on this simple scheme consisted in winding two ropes on the drum in opposite directions and providing each with a bucket. As the drum was turned one bucket then was raised while the other was lowered. Thus the rate of working was doubled, and the task of hoisting was made easier, since the weights of the two buckets balanced each other.

As the depths of pit shafts increased, longer ropes or cables became necessary and eventually the weight of the cable itself became a matter of importance, for it produced an over-balancing effect that added to the difficulties of starting and stopping. For this reason, a new form of drum with conical ends has been introduced. In one type the central portion of the drum is cylindrical and the earlier turns of the cable supporting a cage that is being hoisted are wound on a short portion of small diameter, those following passing round the continually increasing diameter of the conical section until eventually the cylindrical part in the centre is reached. The effect of this may be compared to the use of low gearing in a motor car on starting, when power rather than speed is required. In the case of the conical winding drum, the speed at which winding begins is comparatively low, and increases as the cable winds itself round the conical portion, reaching its highest when the central cylindrical section comes into operation.

An electric winder, with 35 ft. winding drums driven by two 3,300 h.p. motors, constructed for the Simmer and Jack Mines of New Consolidated Goldfields Ltd., South Africa. Photograph by courtesy of Metropolitan Vickers Electrical Co. Ltd.

As the design of winding equipments was improved, their power was increased in order to enable them to cope with demands for greater production. Modern winding machinery is capable of dealing with heavy loads, and of drawing them from immense depths at very high speeds. This is well shown by the plant of which the winding unit is illustrated on this page. This forms part of the hoisting machinery built for the Simmer and Jack Gold Mines Ltd., part of the New Consolidated Coalfields of South Africa. There are actually three winders in the winder house of this mine, all of the same size as the one illustrated. They hoist three pairs of skips, each of which weighs 9,000 lb., and the weight of rock lifted in each skip is 16,000 lb. These immense loads are raised from a depth of 6,600 ft., which is greater than that to which any winder previously constructed works, and the speed at which they are carried upward is 3,000 ft. per min. throughout the greater part of the lift.

Of the three winders, one is used for raising or lowering men and the other two for rock, and all six skips work in the same shaft. The equipment is electrical in operation, and was constructed by the Metropolitan Vickers Electrical Co. Ltd., the mechanical parts being manufactured by Fullerton, Hodgart and Barclay Ltd., Paisley.

For convenience the winding unit of this equipment is constructed in two parts, and our illustration shows one of the two drums of which it consists, together with the motors that drive them. The second drum is behind the first. Each weighs 127 tons and is built up from 58 cast steel sections secured by means of 550 fitted bolts. The smallest diameter is 13 ft. and the greatest is 35 ft., and some idea of the immense size of the two drums is given by a comparison with the control platform, seen on the right in the accompanying illustration, where an engineman can be distinguished in the act of moving one of the control levers.

A cable from the shaft passes over each of the two drums of the winder unit, and these of course rotate in opposite directions when winding is in progress. In each case the end of the cable is attached to the narrow end of the drum and is wound up when this rotates in the appropriate direction. The first four or five turns can be accommodated on the narrow end, but as the momentum increases the cable is guided on to a spiral path on the conical section and thus is transferred to the larger diameter. Actually the cable is wound up along a spiral groove beginning at the narrow end of the drum and passing up the scroll, or spiral path on the conical section, to be continued along the cylindrical portion. The groove is carefully shaped to enable the lower half of the cable to fit into it, so that the latter forms a single layer on the drum and is subjected to as little wear and tear as possible. The steel cables used are 2 in. in diameter and weigh nearly 7 lb. per foot.

The winder unit is driven by two electric motors, each of 3,300 h.p., that are supplied with direct current at 660 v. by special motor generator sets and run at 225 r.p.m. They act through pinions to drive a large helical gear wheel that is 12 ft. 6 in. in diameter and has a face 3 ft. 4⅝ in. in width. The great main shaft carrying this wheel has a length of 37 ft. and a diameter of 2 ft. 4 in. It alone weighs 33 tons, although it has a 6 in. hole running right through it from end to end. The shaft passes through the two winder barrels and is supported by four self-aligning bearings. The drums are loose on the shaft, and are driven by means of a toothed clutch 8 ft. 4 in. in diameter that has 60 teeth.

The winding drum of hoisting equipment of this kind must be capable of exact control and very powerful brakes therefore are fitted to it. Each section is provided with braking gear and the drum of one of these, together with its immense brake shoes, can be seen immediately behind the gear wheel in our illustration. The drums are 18 ft. in diameter and 2 ft. wide, so that they provide a large and efficient braking surface. The shoes are applied by means of an engine consisting of a cylinder fitted with a piston that pushes a weight upward as oil is forced beneath it. The oil is released when the brakes are to be brought into use, and the fall of the piston then gives a steady controlled braking pressure. If this becomes too great a governor slows down the rate at which oil is released. Violent braking that might cause injury to men in the cages therefore is avoided. In addition many safety devices are fitted to protect the equipment.

ASTRONOMICAL MODELS

There is intense fascination in following the movements of the Earth round the Sun and the Moon round the Earth in a model that reproduces their relative rates of motion correctly. Meccano is particularly well adapted to the construction of models of this kind, which are known as orreries, and an excellent Meccano orrery was described in the "*M.M.*" for June 1927. In it the Sun is represented by a celluloid globe mounted on a fixed vertical standard. The Earth and the Moon are represented by balls mounted on arms, one rotating round the standard carrying the Sun, and the other round the one supporting the Earth. An electric motor drives the apparatus through suitable gearing to give the required speeds, and the actual movements of the Earth and the Moon are reproduced in a very realistic manner.

Similar models have been built by Meccano enthusiasts, and an interesting extension that might be suggested would introduce other planets, mounted on arms that would place them at their correct relative distances from the Sun, each driven at the appropriate speed round the centre of the system.

There is ample scope in models of this kind for novel and ingenious devices to illustrate the changes of the seasons and other events or happenings that depend on the motions reproduced in them. The model illustrated on this page shows one device of considerable interest that has been introduced not only to show how the seasons change, but also to illustrate the position occupied each month or season by the Earth during its annual journey round the Sun.

This fine model was built by Mr. J. Piesing, B.Sc., Manor Road Senior School, Wolverhampton. In general construction it follows the lines of the Meccano orrery already referred to. A Meccano Ball Bearing is secured to the centre of a stout board, and this supports one end of a strongly constructed arm that carries an electric motor and the structure supporting miniature representations of the Earth and the Moon. These move in their circular orbits in the correct manner, and it is fascinating to watch on the model the passage of a complete solar year in a very short time.

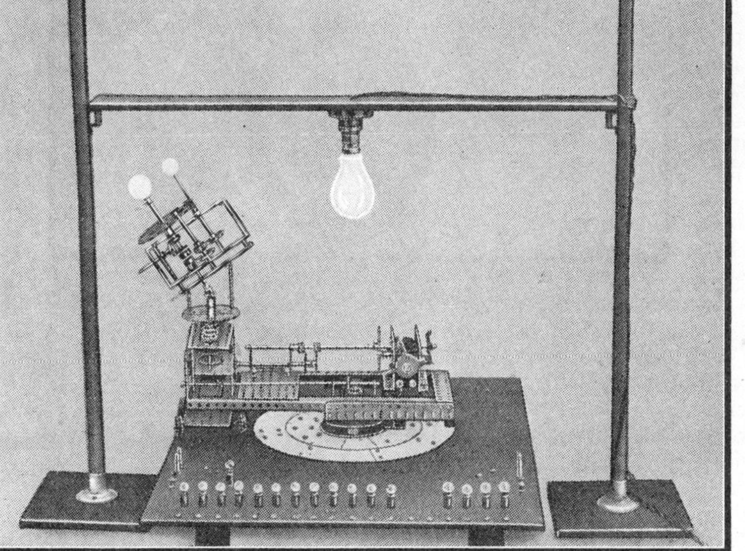

The Meccano Orrery described on this page. The electric lights in front show the passing of the months and the seasons of the year by automatically lighting up for the correct periods.

The novelty in Mr. Piesing's model is the use of lighted lamps to illustrate the succession of the months and the seasons. There are 16 lamps altogether, arranged in two groups of 12 and 4 respectively. Each of the lamps in the first group is labelled with the name of a month and is illuminated when the miniature Earth is in the correct position for the period it represents. Similarly the lamp for each season is lit up during the right period.

The mechanism by which this is done is simple, but interesting. Two brass slip rings are secured to the baseboard, and encircle the Ball Bearing. The inner slip ring is divided into 12 sections that are insulated from each other and are connected, in order, to the 12 lamps representing the months. The outer slip ring is similarly divided into four sections, each of which is connected to one of the lamps in the second group of four. Two spring brushes carried beneath the rotating arm make contact with the sections of the slip rings and complete circuits that illuminate the lamps in succession.

TAKING ONE'S OWN PHOTOGRAPH

Now that the long sunny days are here, the ardent photographer will be looking for fresh fields to conquer with his camera. Here is a plan devised by M. Orde, Switzerland, that will allow him to take a photograph of himself. This is always an interesting achievement, and pictures of scenes in which the photographer himself is included are ideal mementos of enjoyable holidays as well as interesting novelties.

M. Orde's device takes the form of an automatic shutter release. A camera, preferably of the box type, is clamped to a simple framework built up from two 12½" and two 7½" Angle Girders. This framework carries the Clockwork Motor, the speed of which is controlled by a fan, as described in Standard Mechanisms No. 116. The driving spindle of the Motor is connected by a step-down gear train to a horizontal Rod mounted, as far away from the camera as possible, in Flat Trunnions, and on the Rod is wound a length of Cord the free end of which is attached to the shutter lever of the camera.

The Cord is allowed to hang in a loop between the horizontal Rod and the shutter lever, and the Motor is wound up. When all is ready the Motor brake is released and the photographer moves to his pre-arranged position. The Cord is slowly wound up until it is tight and the shutter of the camera is released after a period of time that is governed by the amount of slack. A few trials will show how much slack must be allowed.

ROAD WHEELS FOR TRACTORS

A small model tractor that received a prize in a recent "Simplicity" Model-building Contest is of outstanding interest because of the means adopted to represent the large rear wheels. In the model these wheels consist of Townend Rings, Meccano Special Aeroplane Constructor Part No. 201, and the remainder of the structure is built to a scale corresponding to their size. The wheels are lock-nutted on opposite ends of a short threaded rod that is journalled in suitable bearings in the sides of the model tractor.

The rear wheels of many real tractors have projecting flanges crossing their treads at an angle. These can be realistically reproduced in small models by using 1½" Helical Gears, Part No. 211b, as wheels, for their teeth are curved in a similar manner.

MECCANO AIDS FOR THE WOODWORKER

Miniature cabinet makers and woodworkers in general can make good use of Meccano parts, for these are admirable for strengthening purposes, and also can be applied to advantage in actual constructional work. For instance, ½"×½" and 1"×1" Angle Brackets can profitably be fitted into corners and to corner posts. When used in this manner they save trouble in cutting and shaping special pieces of wood, and also add considerably to the strength of the work. Angle Girders and Girder Brackets can be used in a similar manner. It is a good plan to sink these parts slightly into the wood, and the necessary recesses can easily be made by means of a few judicious saw cuts and a little careful chiselling.

Sometimes it may be desirable to conceal the strengthening pieces. In that case they can be covered with a thin layer of plastic wood, and a perfect finish combined with maximum strength is obtained if this layer is carefully applied and sand-papered when thoroughly set.

Meccano parts also can be used in the construction of handles. One form can be made by securing Handrail Supports or Handrail Couplings to the woodwork and fitting in them the ends of Meccano Rods bent into any desired shape. Dredger buckets also make excellent small handles for similar purposes. These of course are fitted with their openings downward and fine screws are passed through the twin slots at the back and into the woodwork.

Other simple handles are formed by securing Double Angle Strips to the woodwork by means of ½"×½" Angle Brackets, the connections between the Double Angle Strips and the Angle Brackets being made by lock-nutted bolts. Crankshafts in conjunction with Handrail Supports also can be used for the same purpose.

A TURNTABLE FOR A WIRELESS RECEIVER

A little ingenuity will suggest other uses for Meccano parts in coping with the little problems that so often confront the woodworker. An interesting example of this occurred recently when the owner of a portable wireless set wished to construct a substantial turntable for it. A set of this kind is directive and must be turned so as to secure the best results from transmitting stations in various directions.

The base of the turntable designed for use in this case is a piece of wood, 12" sq. and 1" in thickness, to which the lower half of a Meccano Ball Bearing unit consisting of a Flanged Disc, was screwed. The upper portion of the ball bearing unit, a Geared Disc, was attached in a similar manner to the underside of the wireless set. A Bush Wheel was fitted in the centre of the Geared Disc and a Rod was secured in its boss. A Ball Casing was placed on the lower portion of the Ball Bearing, and the Rod then was passed through the centre hole of the Flanged Disc, and also through a hole drilled in the 12" square of wood. A Collar sunk in the lower face of the wooden base was fitted on the lower end of the Rod, to hold the two halves of the Ball Bearing together.

MECCANO WARSHIP ACCESSORIES

Much attention has recently been drawn towards naval matters, and this has had the effect of increasing interest in battleships, cruisers, and other vessels of the navy as subjects for model-building. Many suggestions for warships' fittings have been brought to our notice and these include the introduction of special funnels, ventilators, guns, and ships' boats.

Funnels are readily made from the present Meccano Funnels (part No. 138). If desired, these can be painted either light or dark naval grey. A piece of fine mesh wire gauze inserted in the top of the funnel, and held in place either by solder or Seccotine, could be used to represent the cinder catcher that in practice is necessary because of forced draught. Funnels for larger models can readily be made from specially painted Boilers that are secured to the deck of the ship by Angle Brackets, and to them can be bolted miniature searchlight platforms and sirens. Other naval accessories were described in the "*With the Model-Builders*" Section of the "*M.M.*" for November 1932.

In Search of New Models

Building Model Bicycles

EVERY boy loves a bicycle, and it is only natural that a model-building enthusiast should be attracted by the idea of constructing a miniature machine, especially if this will work like the one he rides. This opens out a really attractive field, for a beginning can be made with very simple but effective models built with small Outfits, and this can be followed by the construction of larger and more interesting representations that include reproductions of details of actual machines.

In some countries the design of bicycles is adapted to local conditions and the resulting machines often have a quaint appearance. Apart from this, really novel and interesting designs have been produced, especially on the Continent. In Great Britain there has been steady progress towards lighter and more reliable machines, which in general appearance have remained unaltered for many years, but novelties from overseas are now being introduced. These have received a full share of criticism, favourable and adverse, but have the advantage that they make exceptionally interesting subjects for reproduction in model form.

Fig. 1. A model of an unusual type of bicycle, the "Cycloratio."

One of these unusual bicycles is illustrated in Fig. 1. It is a scale reproduction of a Cycloratio machine, a strange-looking bicycle manufactured by the Cyclo Gear Co. Ltd. It may be added that this company a few years ago introduced another novelty into this country in the Derailleur Gear, an interesting bicycle gear mechanism that was fully described and illustrated in model form in the "*M.M.*" for October, 1931.

The rider of a Cycloratio machine does not sit upright, but reclines gracefully against a back rest, with his feet projecting forward and actuating cranks fitted in front instead of between the wheels. The machine is claimed to be more efficient than the usual design, and one fitted with an 8-speed Cyclo Gear recently put up a creditable performance in the "Concours Des Alpes," a 405-mile race over mountain roads. The Meccano model is based on this machine, but the Cyclo Gear is not reproduced and the gearing fitted to represent it does not work in the same manner.

Fig. 2. A simple model bicycle built with Outfit B.

An interesting feature of the model is the method of constructing the wheels. The rear wheel is formed from a Circular Strip, representing the rim, and two Bush Wheels, representing the hub. The rim of the front wheel is built up from 2½" Curved Strips. In each case the spokes are of 22 S.W.G. Copper Wire, fitted as shown in Fig. 1. Each spoke is passed through one of the holes in the Bush Wheels and its end fixed there by twisting, and the other end is secured to the rim in a similar manner after the wire has been straightened by stretching. A wheel of this design is remarkably strong and very easy to "true up."

The frame of the bicycle is built up from a number of Rods joined together by means of Couplings and Swivel Bearings. Other interesting features of the original machine that are reproduced in the model are its curved cranks, represented by 2½" small radius Curved Strips, and the brake and gear cables, which are indicated by lengths of Spring Cord. The back rest is a 2½"×1½" Flexible Plate, curved to the correct shape, and the seat is a Flat Trunnion held in place by a 1½" Strip and two Flat Brackets.

The early days of cycling have much to offer to the observant model-builder, and many interesting models can be made of pioneer machines. One of the very earliest was the dandy horse, which was merely a cast iron frame fitted with two wheels, and had no pedals. The rider sat astride a bar and propelled the machine by striking the ground with the feet in a kind of walking or running movement. This forms an excellent subject for small outfit model-builders. Later came the "penny-farthing," which had a small wheel behind a very large one. Many clever and often humorous reproductions of this have been illustrated from time to time in Manuals and the "*M.M.*" It is interesting to note that the Cycloratio bicycle resembles a "penny-farthing" in having wheels of different sizes, but in this case the small wheel is in front.

Fig. 3 illustrates a simple model of an early tricycle that can be constructed with a small outfit to which Artillery Wheels are added. The frame of this model is very simple, consisting of a series of short strips connected together in the manner shown. The method of representing the handle bars is worth noting. These are made of two Pawls, without bosses, secured to two ½"×½" Angle Brackets on the frame. If desired, the pedals and front forks can readily be made to work as in actual practice.

Fig. 3. A model of an ancient tricycle compared with a modern racing machine.

The introduction of the "safety" cycle did much to standardise the design of bicycles, and for a period of about 40 years they have had the appearance typical of most modern touring machines. Heavy frames, deep section mudguards and chain cases are the outstanding features of these, and the careful use of Curved Strips and some of the smaller Flexible Plates in reproducing them should result in first-class models.

With the coming of the craze for lightness and speed, cycle manufacturers introduced a variety of "light-weights." All Meccano model-builders will be familiar with these and will doubtless appreciate the clever reproduction, in model form, illustrated in Fig. 3. Although this is not built accurately to scale it conveys the desired impression. The excessively high saddle, low handle bars, and straight forks are the most outstanding features. The frame is built in a similar manner to that of the bicycle shown in Fig. 1, but fuller use is made of End Bearings and Small Fork Pieces. At each point where a Small Fork Piece is used, set-screws with Washers placed under their heads form the required connections. Each pedal is represented by a "spider," in one of the holes of which is screwed a ⅜" Bolt supporting a Collar carrying a Bolt.

Fig. 4. This simple model of a tandem machine is easy to make and is effective in appearance. Its construction is described in the accompanying article.

Larger scale models built up neatly in a similar manner look very effective. In these the wheels can be formed in the same manner as those fitted to the Cycloratio bicycle. Large scale models have the added advantage of giving greater scope for accuracy, and for the inclusion of many interesting accessories.

Tandems have become increasingly popular in recent years, and these form particularly interesting subjects for reproduction. A simple model tandem is shown in Fig. 4. Its frame is built up from Strips of various lengths, and the crossbar and bottom main member are built of duplicated 5½" Strips. The saddle supports are made of 3½" Strips. The inter-frame members and front forks consist of 3" and 2" Strips and the handle bars are 1" Threaded Rods. In this model good use again is made of Pawls without bosses, four being employed in building up each saddle. 1"×½" Angle Brackets represent pedals, and these are fitted in a similar manner to those of the model Tricycle.

An interesting addition that can be attached to all models of tandems takes the form of a small sidecar. The construction of this need only be of a very simple nature. A model so fitted has the advantage of being able to remain upright without supports. The introduction of figures built from Meccano parts also makes models more attractive and gives them a lively appearance. The construction of these can be quite simple, a few Strips for the limbs and body and a 1" loose Pulley for the head being all that is required to produce a really good effect. Much larger and more complete figures can be built by resorting to the bending of parts, but these are beyond the scope of the owner of small Outfits.

All the models illustrated are fitted with cross bars, but it is a simple matter to convert any of them into a lady's machine by removing the cross bar and doubling the down member from the head-lock to the bottom bracket. Tandems also can be treated in this manner, but in this case only the rear half need be altered.

A special type of bicycle that can readily be built with Meccano parts is the "triplet," in which provision is made for three riders. Machines of this type are seldom seen on the road, but are used on many tracks for the purpose of "pacing." When building a model "triplet" a very strong frame should be constructed and for this duplicated Strips can be used to advantage.

Model-builders in search of novel subjects could reproduce the Auto-wheel, a small power unit designed for fitting to cycles that at one time was popular. This consisted of a separate wheel, of about the diameter of a bicycle wheel, that was driven by a small single-cylinder petrol engine. The petrol engine drove the Auto-wheel through a leather belt and the entire unit was so built that it could be clamped to the frame of any bicycle close to the rear wheel. The engine was started by pedalling.

An auto-wheel can be reproduced easily with the aid of only a few Meccano parts. The wheel is best represented by an Artillery Wheel, and the cylinder by a Worm. The necessary framework is built up from Rods and Small Fork Pieces in a similar manner to the model light-weight bicycle. The petrol, air and ignition controls can be represented by Collars, fitted with bolts and secured to the handle bars. Lengths of Spring Cord connect them with the engine of the auto-wheel.

Two Meccano "Old Timers"

The Wright Biplane and an Early Motor Car

AEROPLANES and motor cars are among the most popular subjects for model-building, and both include a very wide range of machines that lend themselves well to realistic reproduction. The model-builder particularly enjoys building models of modern cars or aeroplanes, but equally good fun can be obtained by reproducing old time examples, many of which are noteworthy for their quaint and unusual appearance as well as for their historical interest. The two models dealt with in this article are excellent instances of this. One of them is a reproduction of the biplane in which the Wright Brothers made the first controlled flights more than 30 years ago. The other represents one of the earliest motor cars to be used in this country.

Fig. 1. A scale model of the Wright Biplane. The construction of this "old timer" is fully described in the accompanying article.

Construction of the model of the Wright Biplane is begun by building the simple fuselage of the machine. Two 12½" Angle Girders 1 are connected together by two 3½" cross members 2, each of which is built up from two 2½" Strips overlapping three holes, and two 1½"×½" Double Angle Strips 3 are secured to the inner ends of the Angle Girders. Two angle members 4 also are fitted.

Two 5½" Angle Girders are fitted at the outer end of the Girders, as shown in Fig. 1, and to the top of these are bolted 1"×1" Angle Brackets 5.

The lower main plane can now be built and fitted. This is formed from two 12½"×2½" Strip Plates overlapping three holes, and it is fitted with a 3½" Strip 6 in the middle and Flat Brackets at each end, as shown in Fig. 3. The purpose of the Strip and the Flat Brackets is to carry pairs of 12½" Strips that form the edges to the wing. The upper main plane is constructed in a similar manner, except that two additional 3½" Strips 7 are fitted for strengthening purposes.

Fig. 2. An effective model of an early type of motor car.

The under side of the upper wing carries six 3½"×½" Double Angle Strips, three on the leading edge and three on the trailing edge, as shown in Fig. 3. To these are bolted the upper ends of the interplane struts, the lower ends of which are attached to the bottom main plane by ½"×½" Angle Brackets. The struts at the ends are secured by means of Double Brackets.

To the under side of the top and bottom planes are bolted long compound girders 8 and 9. These two members form the trailing section of the fuselage. This carries the two rudders, which are represented by 5½"×1½" Flexible Plates, placed vertically and joined together by means of four 2½"×½" Double Angle Strips. Two of these Double Angle Strips are shown at 11, Fig. 3, and carry a Double Bent Strip 10, Fig. 1, and a Flat Bracket 12, Fig. 3. The Flat Bracket supports the upper end of a 3½" Rod 13, the lower end of which is journalled in one of the Double Angle Strips joining the rudders and the end of the member 9. The Double Bent Strip 10 forms a support for the 3½" Rod 14, the upper end of which is journalled in the same manner as the lower end of the Rod 13. Collars are used to hold both Rods in position.

The elevators are next fitted and it should be noted that, contrary to modern practice, these are placed forward of the main planes. A 5½"×2½" Strip Plate is first bolted to the 1"×1" Angle Brackets 5. This Plate carries two 2½" Small Radius Curved Strips 16 and 16a, and also four 2½"×½" Double Angle Strips, to two of which are bolted two 2½"×1½" Flexible Plates.

The propeller shafts are carried in frameworks secured to two of the interplane struts. Each is built up in the following manner. Two 2½" Strips 17, Fig. 1, are secured to the third rear strut from the outer ends of the planes. The Bolt joining these two Strips also holds one end of a 2½"×½" Double Angle Strip carrying a 3½" Rod 18 that forms the propeller shaft. This has secured to it at one end a 1" fast Pulley and at the other a Coupling. The Coupling is fitted with two ½"×½" Angle Brackets that carry 3" Strips representing the propeller blades.

The 1" Pulleys on the propeller shafts are connected

by belts of cord to a ½″ Pulley 19 that forms the flywheel of the dummy four cylinder engine, consisting of two Couplings carried on a horizontal 2½″ Rod. Four Washers are placed on the Rod between the two Couplings, which are secured by set-screws to two Double Bent Strips 20. The four cylinders of the engine are represented by Collars held in place by ⅜″ Bolts.

The controls can now be fitted. A 2½″×1″ Double Angle Strip 21 is first bolted to the lower plane to support a 3½″ Rod carrying a Coupling and a Collar 22, Fig. 3. The control column 23 is fitted to the Coupling by a Small Fork Piece, and a Swivel Bearing connects it to a compound rod. A second small Fork Piece is free to turn on the outer end of the compound Rod and is prevented from sliding off by means of a Collar. A nut, carried on a bolt passed into one hole of the Small Fork Piece prevents this part from sliding down the compound Rod by bearing lightly against the Collar already mentioned. This bolt also secures a Flat Bracket to the Fork Piece, and this is pivotally connected to the Crank 24. This Crank is secured on a Rod as shown and it represents the elevator control.

Fig. 3. An underneath view of the Wright Biplane illustrated on the opposite page.

Ailerons had not been invented when this machine was built, and the effect of banking was obtained by "warping" the wings. In the model this movement is obtained by moving the control column from side to side, thus rocking the Collar 22, carrying a Bolt. Two double cords 25 and 25a are used to connect the bolt to the ends of the upper plane. Two continuous cords 26 connect the two ends of the lower planes, and these pass through the top unoccupied holes of four interplane struts. The rudder bar 27, a 2½″ Strip, is coupled to the rudder by two cords 28.

List of parts required to build the Wright Biplane Model: 10 of No. 1; 20 of No. 2; 2 of No. 2a; 5 of No. 3; 6 of No. 4; 10 of No. 5; 2 of No. 6a; 8 of No. 8; 4 of No. 9; 5 of No. 10; 4 of No. 11; 22 of No. 12; 4 of No. 12a; 4 of No. 12c; 1 of No. 13a; 2 of No. 15b; 5 of No. 16; 1 of No. 17; 1 of No. 18a; 2 of No. 22; 1 of No. 23a; 2 of No. 35; 156 of No. 37; 6 of No. 37a; 22 of No. 38; 3 of No. 45; 1 of No. 46; 2 of No. 48; 10 of No. 48a; 6 of No. 48b; 8 of No. 59; 1 of No. 62; 6 of No. 63; 4 of No. 90a; 2 of No. 111; 6 of No. 111c; 1 of No. 116a; 2 of No. 165; 2 of No. 188; 2 of No. 189; 2 of No. 195; 4 of No. 197.

The second model can be built with D Outfit and is driven by a No. 1 Clockwork Motor concealed under the seats.

The side member 1 of the model consists of two 5½″ Strips overlapping seven holes. The other side member 2 is formed from two 5½″ Strips, also overlapping seven holes, but the rear strip is placed above the front one, the lower edge of the former resting on the upper edge of the latter. This arrangement is necessary in order to expose the winding spindle of the motor. The two Strips forming this side member 2 are held together by a Flat Bracket, secured in place by the bolts 3, and a 2½″×½″ Double Angle Strip 4 fitted with two Flat Brackets.

The lower bolts 3 and the corresponding one on the opposite side of the model secure in place a 2½″×½″ Double Angle Strip. This is fitted with a ½″ Reversed Angle Bracket 5 carrying a Double Bracket that is bolted between the side plates of the Motor. The Double Angle Strip also carries a 2½″×2½″ Flexible Plate, forming the floor of the car, and in addition two 2½″ Strips 6 and 7 are fitted. The Strip 6 is attached by means of two Angle Brackets to the side members. The front hole of the Strip 7 carries the lower end of the steering column.

One end of the Motor is secured to the Bracket 5 as already described, and the opposite end is secured by a Double Bracket to the Double Angle Strip 8. This is bolted to the member 1. The axle carrying the rear wheels is journalled in the side plates of the motor and the drive is taken to a 1″ Pulley on this by means of a Rubber Band from the motor driving shaft.

Fig. 4. This illustration shows how the power unit is fitted in the early model car.

The steering gear is arranged as follows. A 3½″ Rod 9 carries at its lower end a Bush Wheel to which is bolted two 3½″ Strips 10. Two 2½″ Strips are bent in the manner shown in Fig. 4 to represent the springs and fitted at each end of Strip 10. A Double Bracket secured to the lower member of each spring forms a bearing for the front axle on which the front wheels are free to rotate.

The "box" portion of the model represents the seats, and it consists of two 5½″×1½″ Flexible Plates bent in the manner shown in Fig. 2. The front ends of these plates are joined by a 2½″×½″ Double Angle Strip that supports one end of a 4½″×2½″ Flexible Plate. The other end of this Plate is held in place by an Angle Bracket. The back of the seats is secured in position by Angle Brackets.

List of parts required to build Model Car: 7 of No. 2; 2 of No. 3; 11 of No. 5; 2 of No. 6a; 7 of No. 10; 4 of No. 11; 12 of No. 12; 1 of No. 15; 2 of No. 16; 2 of No. 19b; 4 of No. 22; 1 of No. 24; 2 of No. 35; 65 of No. 37; 4 of No. 37a; 11 of No. 38; 1 of No. 48; 7 of No. 48a; 1 of No. 51; 1 of No. 59; 1 of No. 62; 2 of No. 90a; 6 of No. 111c; 1 of No. 115; 3 of No. 125; 2 of No. 126; 2 of No. 126a; 1 of No. 186; 2 of No. 187; 2 of No. 188; 2 of No. 189; 2 of No. 190; 1 of No. 191; No. 1 Clockwork Motor.

Prizes for "M.M." Readers

Can You Make This Model Work?

This month we announce the second of the special summer Meccano competitions. These Contests are of such a nature that boys and girls can prepare their entries just as easily while enjoying the fresh air out of doors as in the house. There is no model-building to do and no Meccano parts are required, the only things necessary being a good knowledge of Meccano model-building practice, a pencil and a sheet of paper. There are no restrictions as to age.

Several faults in the construction of this model lifting bridge prevent it from working. Several good prizes, details of which appear on this page, are offered to readers who can discover these mistakes.

The model illustrated on this page is a reproduction of a rolling lift bridge. It was built by a boy who is familiar with the uses of the various Meccano parts, but possesses little mechanical knowledge, and consequently has made a number of mistakes in the construction of the model, some of which are so serious that although at first glance the model appears to be correctly built, actually it will not work.

Competitors in this contest are asked to study the illustration of the model very carefully and then to write on a sheet of paper a list of all the mistakes they can find in its construction, stating in each case how the mistake interferes with the working of the model, and explaining briefly how they themselves would correct each fault in order to make the model work properly.

Entries will be divided into two sections as follows: A, for competitors of all ages living in the British Isles; B, for competitors of all ages living Overseas.

Each entry must bear the competitor's age, name and address, and letter A or B indicating the section for which it is submitted. Entries must be addressed to "Lifting Bridge Errors Contest," Meccano Ltd., Binns Road, Liverpool 13. Those for Section A must be posted in time to reach Liverpool before 31st August, 1936; the closing date for Overseas competitors entering in Section B will be 30th September, 1936.

Prizes will be awarded to those competitors in each Section who succeed in finding all the errors that prevent the model from working correctly, and who make the best suggestions as to how each mistake should be corrected. The prizes in each Section are as follows: First, Meccano Products value £2–2s. Second, Products value £1–1s. Third, Products value 10/6. There will be also five Prizes of Products value 5/–.

If no single competitor discovers all the errors the prizes will be awarded to the next best entries.

Meccano "Aeroplane Constructor" Model-Building Contest

This month we are arranging a competition for the benefit of owners of Meccano Aeroplane Constructor Outfits. The present contest is similar to previous Aeroplane Constructor competitions that have been organised, and in order to take part in it a would-be competitor should set to work to build a model aeroplane. This may be of any type, but should be based on a real machine of well-known make. The chief portions of the model, that is the fuselage and wings, must be constructed entirely from Meccano Aeroplane Constructor parts, but a few ordinary Meccano parts may be used for reproducing small details or for representing special features of certain makes of machines. If preferred, however, models may be built entirely from Aeroplane Constructor parts.

Each model must be assembled by the competitor without assistance from anyone. Competitors may submit two or more models if they wish, but no competitor will be awarded more than one prize, and all models sent in by one entrant will be grouped together and judged on their joint merits.

The actual model must not be sent. A photograph or a good drawing is all that is required. Competitors must write their age, name and address on the back of each photograph or drawing submitted, and must enclose a short description explaining how the model is constructed. Envelopes containing entries must be addressed "Aeroplane Constructor Contest," Meccano Ltd., Binns Road, Liverpool 13.

The contest is open to competitors of all ages, living in any part of the world, and all entries must be forwarded so as to reach Liverpool on or before 30th September, 1936. The prizes to be awarded for the most interesting and original models received are as follows: First, Meccano Products value £2–2s. Second, Products value £1–1s. Third, Products value 10/6.

Photographs or drawings of prize-winning models become the property of Meccano Ltd., but unsuccessful entries will be returned, provided that a stamped addressed envelope is enclosed with the entry.

Model-Building Competition Results

By Frank Hornby

"Winter" Contest (Sections B and C)

The results in Section A of the "Winter" Competition were announced in the May issue of the "*M.M.*" and this month we give the lists of awards in Sections B and C. These are as follows:

Section B (Home Competitors under 14)
1st Prize, Cheque for £2/2/-: Alan Bunce, Harpenden, Herts. 2nd, Cheque for £1/1/-: Leslie Rhodes, Retford, Notts. 3rd, Products value 15/- : K. M. Hill, Huddersfield.

Products value 10/6: A. Dawson, Edinburgh; H. Beckett, Exeter; P. Shovelton, Worcester; W. Stiling, Exeter; C. Ramplee-Smith, Leigh-on-Sea; J. Mayo, London, S.W.16.

Products value 5/-: J. Gunn, Timperley; J. A. Scowcroft, Blackpool; C. B. Edmonds, London, S.W.16; R. Symons, Plymouth; D. Wills, Exeter; T. Patten, Edinburgh.

Certificates of Merit: K. Lack, Darley Dale, Matlock; J. Evans, Clowne, Derbys.; M. Kasmir, London, N.W.1; H. D. Munson, Marlow, Bucks.; D. Langdon, Exeter; J. Bulley, Exeter; E. Shapland, Exeter; N. Legg, Jarrow; A. Dick, Brighton.

Section C (Overseas Competitors of all ages)
1st Prize, Cheque for £3/3/-: P. J. de Proft, Willebroek, Belgium. 2nd, Cheque for £2/2/-: R. Myburgh, Capetown, South Africa. 3rd, Products value £1/1/-: J. Nie, Shanghai, China.

Products value 10/6: B. Van 't.Land, Groningen, Holland; Melvin J. Maddock, Carbonear, Newfoundland; J. Rombach, Delft, Holland; Pablo Giese, Buenos Aires; W. W. Dussel, Groningen, Holland; G. Whitfield, East London, Cape Province, S. Africa.

Products value 5/-: Lars Linder, Stockholm; M. Nicholls, Natal; Y. Willems, Hoboken, Belgium; G. Stanley, Johannesburg; R. Borland, Peterboro, Canada; C. Fishburne, Edmonton, Canada.

Certificates of Merit: L. Edwards, North Auckland, N. Zealand; M. Orde, Chateau d'Oex, Switzerland; H. Young, Port Elgin, New Brunswick, Canada; F. Hinbest, Toronto; N. Hanning, Calgary, Canada; E. Azzopardi, Sliema, Malta; E. Norton, Vancouver; E. Andersen, Manitoba; D. Swan, Oak Bay, B.C., Canada; D. McLeod, Calgary, Natal.

The model that won First Prize in this competition owes its success to originality of subject and to the way in which the simple parts employed in it have been used. The subject of the model is a bell buoy used for indicating shoals and rocks and other dangerous conditions in rivers and harbour entrances.

The portion of the buoy that normally is beneath the water is made from two Ring Frames and 12½" Flat Girders. The Ring Frames form the upper and lower rims of a pontoon, and the Flat Girders are used for filling in the sides and are held in place by Flat Brackets. The top of the buoy is formed with 5½" and 3½" Flat Plates, and to the upper Ring Frames are secured a number of 12½" Strips, which are connected together at their upper ends by means of a Bush Wheel and at the bottom by curved Flat Girders. Two circles also made from 5½" and 2½" Curved Strips are used to strengthen the structure. Four 1½" × ½" Double Angle Strips are bolted to the Bush Wheel and a second Bush Wheel is bolted to their opposite ends. A Rod fitted with a Handrail Coupling and pushed through the bosses of the two Bush Wheels supports the bell, which is made from 5½" Strips bent into U formation and bolted to a circle of Strips. The model was built by A. Bunce.

The model built by L. Rhodes, who won Second Prize in Section B, also is simply constructed. It is a traction engine, the boiler of which is made of two Meccano Boilers bolted end to end. The gear-box and bunker are made from 5½" × 2½" Flat Plates bolted to one end of the boiler, and the cylinder is a Sleeve Piece fixed between two ¾" Flanged Wheels, in the bosses of which a short Rod slides. This Rod is fitted with a crosshead and is coupled to a Crank Shaft, which carries a 3" Wheel for a flywheel. Similar Wheels are used also for the front steering wheels of the engine, and the large driving wheels are made from Circular Girders fitted with 2½" Strips for spokes and Bush Wheels for hubs.

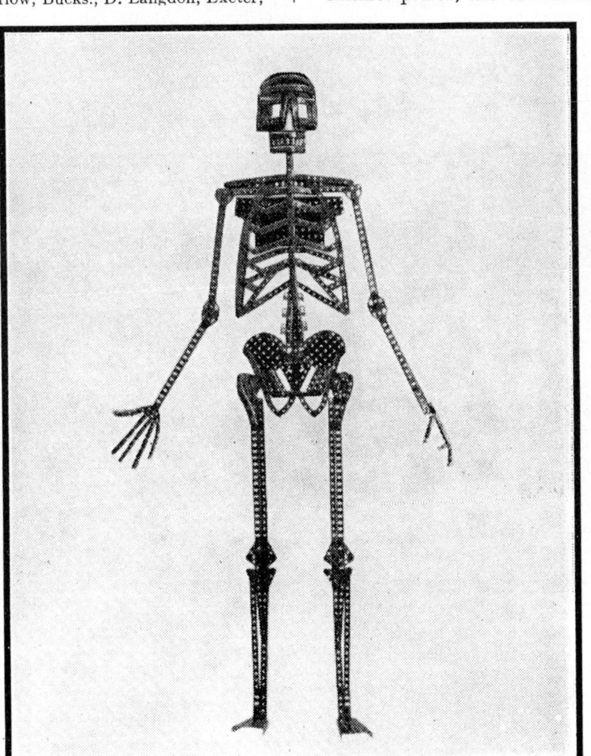

This remarkable model of a human skeleton is a splendid example of the adaptability of Meccano parts. It was built by J. Nie, Shanghai, for whom it won Third Prize in Section C of the "Winter" Competition.

K. M. Hill, the winner of the Third Prize in this Section, is to be congratulated on an excellent piece of work. His model represents a street organ-grinder and his pet monkey. The organ is built on a base made from a 5½" × 2½" Flat Plate, through which a 3½" Axle Rod is pushed and then fitted with two 3" Pulleys. The organ itself is made from 5½", 2½" and 2" Strips, and although it is rather crudely finished it looks quite realistic. The organ-grinder is made from Strips, and the monkey from ½" Reversed Angle Brackets and ½" × ½" Angle Brackets. Its head is a ½" loose Pulley, to which is fixed a ½" Pinion for a hat.

There are no really outstanding models among the winners of the smaller prizes, the best of these being those sent by W. Stiling and H. Beckett, both of whom are members of the Exeter Meccano Club. Stiling's model represents a gasometer at the local gasworks. It is octagonal in shape with uprights made from 18½" Angle Girders braced by means of 12½" Strips and 5½" Braced Girders. The gas container is constructed from 12½" Strip Plates bolted to a framework of Angle Girders and Strips.

H. Beckett's model was reproduced from photographs of a special omnibus that was designed for use on trackless desert country. The chassis is carried on six wheels and it hauls a long trailer that contains sleeping accommodation for a number of passengers.

In the Overseas Section there are many models that I should like to illustrate and describe in detail, but the space available for these notes permits only a brief mention of those most interesting to readers generally. Foremost among these models are a ship unloading machine and a Brownhoist coal-handling machine that were built by P. J. de Proft. The models are rather complicated, and it is impossible for me to give any useful constructional information concerning them in space of a few lines. Both of the models are original in subject, well built and neatly finished, and this I think, is the highest praise one can give to the work of this competitor.

R. Myburgh, who is well known to readers of this page as the builder of many fine competition models, submitted for the present competition a model of the oil tank vessel "*British Grenadier*" that plies between Singapore and Capetown. The hull of the model is 1½" high amidships and 3" at the bow and stern. The fore deck is complete with winches and a life-boat, and also with a support for an awning. The bridge amidships also is provided with similar supports, and the engine-room and galley in the stern have ventilators and stanchions as in an actual vessel of this type. Realism is given by the addition of Dinky Toys figures.

The skeleton illustrated on this page is the work of J. Nie. Although the model is far from correct anatomically it illustrates the adaptability of Meccano parts and the good effect that ingenious use of them can produce.

"Fun with Dinky Toys" Competition

On the Editorial page of the December 1935 "*M.M.*" the Editor offered a number of prizes for the best suggestions for tabletop fun with Dinky Toys. Among the many suggestions received are several original and interesting ideas, and I intend to refer to some of these in the "*M.M.*" The prizes were awarded as follows: 1st Prize, Cheque for £1/1/-: C. C. Forsyth, Bellville C.P., S.Africa. 2nd, Cheque for 15/-: Douglas Murison, Buenos Aires. 3rd, Cheque for 10/6: J. Halsall, Southport.

Sutton Valence Council School M.C.—Several Model-building Competitions have been held and all have been greatly enjoyed. In one Contest a special feature was made of working models, and those completed included a roundabout; trip hammer; lorry with brakes and gearing, and a hammerhead crane. Another model of a crane was equipped with two motors, one for lifting the load and the other for moving the crane. This fine display was inspected by the President, who also gave a short lecture on "*One-Piece Metal Work*" and exhibited some of the objects he had made from metal. The members were interested to learn that he had even invented the machines he used in this work. The future programme is being planned according to members' suggestions, and is expected to include, as last year, a Sports Meeting between the club and the school; Visits to local places of interest, and outdoor meetings during which model aeroplanes will be flown. Club roll: 25. *Secretary:* J. Chandler, "Herriard," Chart Sutton, Nr. Maidstone, Kent.

St. Thomas (Exeter) M.C.—Meetings have been held at the Leader's house, and most of them have been devoted to model-building. During the latter part of each meeting an instalment of a serial story is read. New members have to sign their names on the club Roll of Honour, which is framed and hangs on the club-room wall. Club roll: 24. *Secretary:* L. Robinson, 15, Brunswick Street, St. Thomas, Exeter.

Bexleyheath Boys' Central School M.C.—At one meeting a member brought along a clockwork railway he had built. It consisted of a spiral track that started at ground level and was carried upwards on Meccano supports to a height of 1 ft. above the ground. A novel feature of the railway was an automatic lift to lower the engine to the ground when it reached the top of the track. Another member has constructed a model workshop, driven by a small mains electric motor. Extensive preparations have been made for the School Open Day. Club roll: 30. *Secretary:* D. Hicks, 4, Audrey Avenue, Long Lane, Bexleyheath, Kent.

Members of St. Giles' Cathedral (Edinburgh) M.C. with Mr. R. Croall, Leader, who is eighth from the left on the second row. This club was originally known as St. George's (Edinburgh) M.C., and it acquired its present name in 1934 when it became associated with the St. Giles' Cathedral Club. It has been affiliated with the Guild almost six years, and the membership now totals 185.

Kidderminster M.C.—An illustrated lecture on "*Chenille Carpet Manufacture*" was given recently by Mr. C. P. Harris, the Chairman of the Kidderminster H.R.C. Branch, and was much enjoyed. Club roll: 12. *Secretary:* E. J. Watkins, "Elmar," Wolverhampton Road, Kidderminster.

Claremont Avenue School M.C.—The biggest event recently has been the club Exhibition, which attracted many visitors. The models included a motor chassis; bascule bridge; derricking crane; aeroplane and a striking Dinky Toy display. The visitors were also very interested in a display of model aeroplanes made of wood and balsa. Club roll: 13. *Secretary:* G. Furton, 5, Brookfield Crescent, Kenton, Harrow.

Plymouth M.C.—The club magazine "*The Gearbox*," has been divided into three parts, headed respectively "*Railway News*," "*Municipal Transport Notes*" and "*Shipping News*." Each part is under the direction of its own sub-editor. The first issue in which these three sections were featured also included a competition, and proved very popular. The Hornby section of the club have not laid down a permanent track, as they prefer to adopt a new layout frequently; and each new one seems better than its predecessor. The club provides only the track, and members bring their own locomotives, about six being available at most meetings. Club roll: 70. *Secretary:* R. G. Symons, 47, Lisson Grove, Mutley, Plymouth.

Barnard Castle School M.C.—This recently-affiliated club is doing well. The members are very enthusiastic, and many new ones are being enrolled. The club has been divided into two groups, one devoted to Meccano activities and the other to Hornby Train operations, and it is probable that a Cycling group will also be formed. Club roll: 15. *Secretary:* S. L. Wears, The School, Barnard Castle.

Enfield Grammar School M.C.—The Meccano section has completed a fine model of an overhead railway of the George Bennie Railplane type, and it is being used to supplement the club layout. This layout is now complete except for lineside accessories, and the Railway section are busily engaged in making them. A new section has been formed to deal with wireless for the club room. An interesting talk on "*Scale Model Wagons*" was given by Mr. Hemingway, a prominent member of the Model Railway Club, during a recent visit. He illustrated various points in his talk by partly building a scale model wagon. Club roll: 35. *Secretary:* J. H. Pettifer, 31, Goat Lane, Forty Hill, Enfield.

St. Stephens (Saltash) M.C.—Models recently constructed have included roundabouts, windmills and aeroplanes. At one meeting members were engaged in building railway rolling stock. Points are awarded for all models constructed, and the high efficiency of the members is shown by the fact that several have recently gained full points. The Woodwork section have been busy making a fleet of model ships, and have also constructed a cupboard in which the club stock of Meccano parts, etc., is now stored. A Cycling excursion is to be held to Kit Hill, a local vantage point where an excellent view of the surrounding country can be obtained. Club roll: 16. *Secretary:* B. Braund, 9, Homer Park, Saltash.

Wednesbury and District M.C.—This recently re-organised club continues to make good progress, and both the Meccano and the Fretwork sections are doing well under the guidance of their capable leaders. The Master of the local High School has accepted the Presidency of the club, and he is taking an active interest in the members. Cycling, Cricket and Model Aeroplane Sections are being formed to provide scope for outdoor activities during the summer. A Lantern Lecture on "*British Locomotives*" has been given by J. Lemaire, a member, and the secretary recently gave an interesting talk on "*Fretwork*." A Social and Games Evening during which various party games were played was greatly enjoyed by all present. Club roll: 28. *Secretary:* A. L. Morgan, 17, Cobden Street, Fallings Heath, Wednesbury.

St. James (Grimsby) M.C.—Model-building was the chief occupation during the second Winter session. At one meeting the members working in pairs began the construction of three large models. One pair decided to build a large travelling gantry crane driven by a steam engine; another a swivelling jib crane complete with luffing movement; and the third pair began a model of the quayside ship unloader illustrated in the February "*M.M.*" The ship unloader was driven by a clockwork motor in place of the electric one in the "*M.M.*," and the gear-box had to be specially adapted. The completion of these models kept the members busy for several evenings. Club roll: 6. *Secretary:* A. N. Dixon, 65, Yarborough Road, Grimsby.

Stationers' School M.C.—Outdoor activities have chiefly centred round the construction of a portable railway layout. The Model Railway section have been attending to the track and rolling stock, the Electrical section are responsible for the colour light signalling and controls, and the Meccano and General Engineering section have been busy building the bridges, stations and model village. Members enjoyed a Lantern Lecture on "*The Story of London's Underground*," in connection with which London Passenger Transport Board kindly supplied booklets describing the construction of the Underground railways. A Lecture has also been given on "*Track Circuiting and Automatic Signalling*." Outings have included Visits to the Science Museum, South Kensington, where the Curator had kindly arranged a special demonstration of the automatic telephone equipment, and to the L.N.E.R. Works at Stratford, the most popular department of which was the machine room. The secretary is compiling a history of the club, and this will be printed in the School magazine. The meetings have been well attended, and the membership has increased recently by almost 75 per cent. Club roll: 25. *Secretary:* R. J. Post, 8, Bourne Road, Crouch End, London, N. 8.

AUSTRALIA

Maylands (Perth) M.C.—The first Anniversary Exhibition was a great success, and the excellent display of models was much praised. The Meccanograph and a penny-in-the-slot machine were especially popular, and collected a total of 16/-. A Party was held after the Exhibition, and a few nights later a Parents' Social was held, both events proving most enjoyable. On Easter Monday a visit was paid to the Midland Junction Railway workshops, where the members were greatly interested in all they saw. Club roll: 22. *Secretary:* M. Thomson, 13, Kennedy Street, Maylands, Perth.

NEW ZEALAND

Christchurch M.C.—The membership is increasing rapidly and all are keen model-builders. Recent accomplishments have included some fine models of cranes. Another visit has been paid to the invalid boy mentioned in earlier reports, and he was again very thrilled by the working models that some of the members took with them and demonstrated. A delightful day in the open air was spent recently when the club tramped over the Cashmere Hills to Lyttleton Harbour and thence to Governor's Bay at the head of the harbour. Most of the members took their fishing tackle with them, and after having tea and feeding the seagulls they enjoyed some very successful angling from a little pier that juts out into the Bay. A walk home in the twilight concluded this ideal outing. Club roll: 24. *Secretary:* L. W. Best, 28, Circuit Street, Strowan, Christchurch.

SOUTH AFRICA

Pioneer (Pietermaritzburg) M.C.—The club has become officially associated with the Maritzburg Amateur Horticultural Society. This gives the club the privilege of staging displays of models at the two exhibitions held each year by the Society, and it is hoped that the publicity thus obtained will be the means of attracting many new members to the club. Club roll: 11. *Secretary:* A. H. Alley, 461, Burgers Street, Pietermaritzburg, Natal.

Malvern M.C.—Indoor meetings have been divided between Talks and Model-building. Models completed have included representations of many unusual subjects, such as a baboon, a street fiddler, a nurse and pram, a compass and a lighthouse. A most enjoyable visit has been paid to the Witwatersrand Technical College, where Professor Willowes-Munro gave a Talk on "*Mining*," during which the members learned many interesting facts about this great Witwatersrand industry. Afterwards they were conducted through the laboratories, where they saw many interesting scientific instruments in action. Outdoor activities have included a cross-country run over a course of about three miles. Club roll: 85. *Secretary:* B. H. Saunders, P.O. Box 8, Cleveland, Johannesburg.

Model Aeroplane Meetings

In reading the club reports during the first summer session I have been interested to note that several clubs are including model aeroplane meetings among their outdoor activities. This is not surprising, as interest in aeroplanes and air services is greater to-day than ever before.

The construction of model aeroplanes is an ideal hobby for the summer months, and can readily be carried on as a club affair. Models of varying degrees of complexity and difficulty can be made, ranging from simple machines of thin card to more elaborate aeroplanes with longerons and spars of wood strip, and plane covering of suitable fabric.

A further good point about the hobby is that it is especially suitable for competitions, as summer is the best time of the year in which to make the practical tests of flying ability that must be the chief consideration in awarding prizes. Ordinary open competitions may be run, in which competitors are asked to enter aeroplanes designed and constructed by themselves from any material, but others in which the materials to be used are restricted in character, or an aeroplane of a particular design is to be made, will provide great scope for ingenuity.

In deciding on the merits of the entries in any competition, marks should be awarded for good workmanship and ingenious methods of construction, while if the competition is an open one the merits of the design must be taken into account. First consideration must be given to airworthiness, however. An open space free from accidental air currents is required in order to carry out tests of this, and if possible aeroplane meetings should be held in conjunction with country excursions. In addition it will almost certainly be found that the proceedings will be lengthy, as the members are sure to be so interested in the winning models that they will want to see them in operation repeatedly, and ample time should therefore be allowed. Each entrant should be permitted three trials in which to demonstrate the stability and range of his machine in the air.

Meccano Club Leaders

No. 83. Mr. W. J. T. Watson

Mr. W. J. T. Watson was the founder of the Sydney (Australia) M.C., of which he has been Leader since 1933. The club programmes are very attractive and include Model-building, Games, Lectures, Debates, Social Evenings, and Visits to places of interest.

Summer Holiday Hints

One of the habits that engineers, whether amateur or professional, should cultivate is that of observing keenly and storing in mind information gained in this manner, of which good use may be made later. There are always opportunities for training of this kind, but perhaps the best of all come with the summer holidays, when most boys leave for a short time the surroundings with which they are so familiar, and find themselves in places where on all sides there is something new to be observed.

I should like every club member to keep a keen lookout during his summer holiday for something of interest that is new to him. By doing so he will form a basis for good model-building next winter, and the little time and trouble involved will then be fully repaid. In addition to this a holiday frequently affords ideas for other features of the programme, such as new lectures and papers, additions that will make Hornby train operation more realistic, and other hobbies and pursuits to increase the variety and interest of club work. There is nothing like variety to maintain interest in club affairs, and no opportunity of seeking means of increasing the enthusiasm of members and adding to the attractiveness of the programme should be overlooked.

Encouraging Club Photography

In practically every club there are members who own cameras, and the various summer excursions and outdoor meetings provide plenty of scope for them to practice their hobby. These members should be encouraged to learn how to make the best use of their cameras, and it is a very good plan to form a photographic section and give talks and demonstrations designed to help the beginners to get the best out of the hobby. These talks should be of a practical character, of course, and not merely lectures describing what happens when a photographic plate is exposed; and the senior members of the club will no doubt be able to help in this work.

Small prizes may be offered for the best collection of photographs taken during the summer sessions, for this develops a spirit of friendly rivalry among the photographers, and encourages them to take the necessary steps to secure good results. An important consideration is that an attractive record of the various activities of the club during the summer months can be obtained in this manner. I hope that this course will be followed in many clubs during this session, and while on the subject I wish to remind Leaders and secretaries that I am always pleased to see photographs showing their members at work or play, and if they are suitable, to make use of them in these pages. I should like to mention also that in most cases I can obtain a much stronger and clearer reproduction from the negative than from a print, and whenever possible the negative should be sent.

Proposed Clubs

Attempts are being made to establish Meccano Clubs in the following places, and boys interested should communicate with the promoters whose names and addresses are given below:

GUIST, S.O.—N. L. Everitt, High Street, Foulsham.
INDIA—R. K. Banerji, D40/5 Lachmanpura, Benares City, U.P.
MALTA—A. Cappola, 96, St. Vincent Street, Sliema.
NEW ZEALAND—C. C. Carncross, Graham Street, Eltham, Taranaki.
NEW ZEALAND—V. Hack, Pleasant Road, Glen Eden, Auckland.

Hornby Tank Wagons and their Uses

Miniature "Liquids in Bulk" Transport

THE distinctive nature and appearance of Hornby Tank Wagons make them of special interest to the miniature railway owner. Real tank wagons have been familiar objects on our railways for many years and are now being employed in increasing variety for the transport of liquids in bulk. Similarly the miniature Tank Wagons of the Hornby Series have grown in numbers, and this article deals with the variety of types available and the services on which they can be used.

One of the most attractive vehicles of this kind is the Milk Tank Wagon, which represents in miniature one of the most recent applications of the tank wagon for the bulk transport of liquids. Fleets of such tanks are now operated by various dairy organisations, and they run on each of the four group railways, bringing supplies from the concentration points in dairy farming areas to the town depots from which distribution is carried out. For large consignments passing regularly by rail the tank wagon indeed has almost entirely supplanted the familiar churn, but the latter is still employed for smaller quantities. The advantages of the new method are strikingly realised when it is remembered that the churns chiefly in use have capacities of 10 to 17 gallons, while tank wagons hold as much as 3,000 gallons or even more.

Milk traffic is an important feature on the layout of Mr. H. G. Ogden of Victoria, B.C., part of which is shown in this photograph. A Hornby Milk Tank Wagon is prominent in the siding in the foreground.

The Hornby Milk Tank Wagon consists of a large cylindrical tank supported on two bolsters mounted on a standard wagon base. As in real tank wagons, there is a beam at the top of two vertical pillars across each end of the tank and wire braces run diagonally from the beams down to a point near the centre of the solebars of the vehicle. These arrangements serve to retain the tank in position.

The miniature tank itself is complete with the usual manhole on top, and there are also representations of the inlet valve for filling and the safety outlet that are fitted to the real tanks. The details are completed by the fitting of the inspection ladder, which passes over the tank about the middle. The tank is painted white, in accordance with the usual practice for insulated vehicles or containers that have to be kept cool.

Milk Tank Wagons can be used in the formation of trains consisting entirely of such wagons, or of others that also include Milk Vans. Special milk trains of both kinds are run regularly in real practice and should therefore be included in the working timetables of any miniature railway system that makes a feature of perishable traffic of this type. Where a single Milk Tank Wagon is the only representative of its kind on the line, it can be attached to a convenient passenger train in order to work it up to the town depot. Real tank wagons are fitted with brake pipes and steam heating connections to allow of their inclusion in passenger train formations, so that the use in this way of a miniature Tank on a Hornby Railway system will be quite correct. In the operation of milk trains it is important that any shunting or other movements involved in attaching and detaching vehicles should be carried out with care, or the cargo may be spoiled. Similar precautions in miniature practice will add to the interest, so the injunction *"shunt with care"* should be obeyed literally by the "staff."

Efficient loading and unloading arrangements are essential to the success of milk tank wagon operation. If possible the lineside accessories of a miniature railway in which use is made of Hornby Milk Tank Wagons therefore should include buildings in which they can be accommodated at each end of the journey. The real rail tanks are fed from storage tanks by means of pipe line connections and similar means are employed for emptying them. These can scarcely be reproduced in miniature, but the provision of a building supposedly housing the pipe connections gets over the difficulty.

An interesting point in connection with milk tank traffic is the road collection of the churns from the farms for delivery to the depots where the tanks are filled, and the return of the necessary "empties." To assist in this process small loading platforms are erected at the roadside in dairy farming districts at points convenient for the farmers. The full churns are placed on these platforms for collection by lorry, and the empty ones similarly are returned there. On layouts where special attention is given to lineside effects and road services, such platforms would be an interesting and unusual roadside feature.

The lorry service could be efficiently performed by suitable vehicles of the Meccano Dinky Toys Series. The motor Wagon, Dinky Toy No. 25A, included in the Set of Commercial Vehicles No. 25 could be used, or the Flat Truck No. 25C. The Market Gardener's Van, No. 25F, with its open post-and-rail sides is typical of the motor vehicles frequently found in farming districts. The Trailer

No. 25G could be run behind any of these for loads heavier than usual.

The "Colas" Bitumen Tank Wagon is of similar construction to the Hornby Milk Tank Wagon, but is intended for a load of a very different character. This is the representative in the Hornby Series of the numerous wagons used in practice for the conveyance of tar and similar substances. The tank wagon operated by Colas Products Ltd. carries a special material used for the surfacing of drives and paths. The "Colas" Bitumen Tank Wagon forms an interesting addition to a mixed freight train in miniature, and can be worked to any station serving an area where "building developments" are supposed to be in progress. Tar and similar heavy liquids are sometimes carried in wagons having rectangular tanks. Modern practice favours the use of cylindrical tanks, however, and this is the type of tank wagon used exclusively in the Hornby Series.

Shunting in a local goods yard. The vehicle next to the engine is a Hornby "Colas" Tank Wagon of the type referred to in this article.

Simpler features of design and construction are embodied in the remaining Tank Wagons of the Hornby Series. These include the No. 1 Petrol Tank Wagons and the similar Oil Tank Wagons. In these the tank is mounted on a "saddle" or support that is fitted to the standard wagon base. Although the No. 1 Tank Wagons are less detailed than the larger Milk and "Colas" vehicles, they have a realistic appearance; each tank is provided with the characteristic manhole in the centre on top and is decorated in the style of the particular petrol or oil company that is represented.

A mixed freight train on a Hornby layout. The "Royal Daylight" vehicles are typical of the construction of Hornby Oil Tank Wagons, and form one of the latest additions to the range.

The range of Tank Wagons is completed by the MO Petrol Tank Wagon "Shell-Mex." This neat little vehicle, which was dealt with in detail in the *"M.M."* last December, conforms to the usual MO standards in size, wheelbase and coupling arrangements, and the tank is attractively finished in the style adopted for "Shell-Mex" rolling stock. Various realistic details are incorporated, among them a warning of the dangerous nature of the contents in the words: *"No lights to be brought near this tank."*

The working of tank wagons containing petrol and any other inflammable liquids is subject to special regulations in actual practice. A great deal of fun can be obtained if special rules are applied in miniature, and if necessary, certain restrictions could be imposed to suit special conditions on the lines of individual Hornby Railway owners. Petrol tank wagons in a freight train are usually marshalled away from the engine. Sometimes they are placed at the tail end of the train, but as their appearance there might be a source of danger in the event of a rear-end collision they are frequently about the centre of the formation. There are often restrictions on the passage of vehicles carrying dangerous or inflammable goods over sections of the line that traverse important bridges or bore through lengthy tunnels. In miniature the passage of a Hornby Viaduct or a big Meccano bridge might be forbidden; or the dangerous traffic might be restricted to certain times in order to avoid periods of "traffic pressure."

As in the case of the Milk Tank Wagon, the use of Petrol and Oil Tank Wagons is made more realistic if suitable lineside accessories can be arranged in connection with their traffic. Thus the addition of buildings representing refineries with their circular storage tanks, the whole plant served by sidings, would add considerably to the effect of the operation of miniature tank wagons over a Hornby Railway system. Shunting in the neighbourhood of such premises is invariably carried out by special fireless locomotives. These look much the same as the usual type of works shunting tanks except that they have no chimneys! An old Hornby Tank Locomotive minus this fitting could thus represent a fireless engine reasonably well, although strictly the bunker and side tanks also are unnecessary.

The remaining wagon of the Hornby Series that comes within the tank class is the Gas Cylinder Wagon, which represents the real vehicles used for the conveyance of oil gas. This gas is still used for lighting railway coaches and is extensively employed on dining cars for cooking purposes. It is carried under pressure in gas cylinders attached to the underframes on the vehicles. At points where the "gassing" of trains is regularly carried out storage tanks are let into the ground, and outlets at suitable spots make it possible for the gas cylinders on the coaches to be replenished by means of armoured hosepipes. These storage tanks are kept supplied by the conveyance of gas to them in gas cylinder wagons that are run between the producing plant and the gas filling stations. Such a wagon usually consists of two or three strong cylinders mounted on a standard underframe. The Hornby Gas Cylinder Wagon has three dummy cylinders and is an attractive and unusual piece of rolling stock. It can be run in passenger or goods trains as required, and it can be left at times at a terminal or junction station.

RUNNING SUBURBAN AND LOCAL SERVICES

SUBURBAN and local services that connect country districts and residential areas with cities and towns are of great importance in railway working, and there are many specially interesting features in their operation. In this article it is proposed to deal with useful points in connection with them that will be helpful to those who wish to run services of this kind on their miniature railways.

On Hornby Railways the type of locomotive and rolling stock equipment required for "local" trains will not vary much, whatever the particular group favoured by the individual owner, although certain practices may be peculiar to certain groups, or even to certain sections. Tank engines can invariably be employed, and then less platform length is necessary and turntables are not really required although they are useful in certain circumstances. More effective use therefore can be made of a restricted space. Advantage can be taken of the frequent station stops on clockwork railways for winding the engine, and with an appropriately organised service a great deal of fun can be obtained.

An "auto train" on a miniature G.W.R. system. This is composed of a No. 1 Tank Locomotive and a No. 2 Pullman Coach, the latter representing the centre-gangway type of car frequently employed on such duties.

For trains operating on the most important business or residential services on a Hornby Railway the No. 2 Coaches are ideal. The arrangement of the compartments is such that a complete train of these vehicles contains plenty of third-class accommodation; at the same time the first-class traveller—an important person on such trains—is by no means neglected. The first-third No. 2 Coaches contain first-class and third-class compartments in equal numbers, so that a three-coach train consisting of one first-third and two brake thirds ensures satisfactory accommodation for all. The brake thirds have a guard's compartment and just enough luggage accommodation. The guard's lookouts are placed at one end of the vehicle and give a typically "suburban" appearance to the formation.

The best engine for the more important suburban trains is the Hornby No. 2 Tank or, on electrically-operated lines, the E220 or E26 Special Tank. These three engines are of the same external appearance, and they represent the large passenger tanks in use on British railways. The clockwork No. 2 Special Tank is a powerful engine and has a very satisfactory length of run. A lively dash from station to station by one of these engines, with two or three No. 2 Coaches, will reproduce quite well the energetic running that is characteristic of most business trains. On electrically-operated railways much more realistic running is possible owing to the greater degree of control. The automatic reversing gear of the E220 Special Tank Locomotive also is of great advantage in the operation of suburban services. Apart from uncoupling the engine at each end of the trip no further handling of the train is necessary, as the Locomotive is reversed from the lineside by means of the speed regulator handle on the Transformer. Coupling up of course also is automatic when the vehicles are pushed together.

With regard to the actual services represented, much depends on the Hornby Railway owner and his personal preferences. Hornby No. 2 Tanks and No. 2 Coaches are suitable for the reproduction of the suburban services worked in and out of the London termini. Some of these services are more of a long-distance or "outer" suburban character, either because of the situation of the line, such as the G.W.R., or as the result of the electrification of the inner suburban area, as on the L.M.S.R. Euston services. Services centred on such places as Birmingham, Manchester and elsewhere where local traffic is heavy also can be reproduced.

On layouts where space is restricted it may be necessary to employ only four-wheeled locomotives and coaches. Suburban trains are readily made up of Hornby No. 1 Coaches and Guard's Vans. At times when the pressure of traffic increases it is quite easy to add one or two units to normal formations, and it is just as easy to detach them at slack periods. For regular working of the suburban services each standard formation or set train should be arranged with a Guard's Van at each end if possible. On some Hornby Railway layouts the owners have standardised four-wheelers for suburban traffic owing to their extreme handiness, although larger vehicles and locomotives may be in use for main line work.

It is frequently the practice to attach to the longer - distance suburban trains a van for any traffic, such as parcels, milk, or fruit in the season, that is to be worked into the towns or cities served. The addition of such a vehicle to a Hornby local train will add to the interest of its operation and a Milk Van, or other Van according to the traffic, can be employed in this way. A Hornby No. 1 Guard's Van also is very useful to represent many of the various types of vans that are used to convey parcels, milk in churns, and similar freights. In addition to its use in this way the No. 1 Guard's Van also can provide guard's and luggage accommodation on a train of No. 2 vehicles, if a bogie No. 2 brake-third is not considered necessary.

The arrival of a suburban train at the terminus. An interesting feature is the destination board on the No. 2 Special Tank Locomotive arranged as suggested in this article.

Owing to the complexity of routes and services in certain suburban areas various indications are carried on the engines of the trains in order that they may be readily identified. These indications may take the form of special route discs in place of the usual unlighted lamps by day, although lamps are of course necessary by night. Thus on the G.E. section of the L.N.E.R. both purple and white route discs are used on suburban trains in daytime, with corresponding purple and white lights at night, their arrangement varying according to the route served. Miniature discs can be made of circles of card, plain white or painted as required, and provided with a small "loop" of paper at the back to allow of their attachment to the lamp brackets on Hornby Locomotives.

A useful layout for a country terminus. The locomotive is being run round the branch train of No. 1 Coaches by means of a turntable and loop line.

Destination boards too are popular fittings on the locomotives of suburban trains. These are easily made of card and can be lettered according to the destination required on the miniature system. As the "stopping train" indication of the Standard Headlamp Code requires the use of the top lamp bracket only, the brackets above the buffer beam can be made to accommodate the destination board. If the board passes in front of the centre bracket and behind the two outside ones it will be held securely in place and will not be likely to be shaken off by the motion of the engine. Boards lettered on both sides are useful, needing only to be turned round to show a different destination. Care should be taken that the headlamp and the destination board are in the correct position for each trip. The necessary changing of boards at each terminal point and similar minor operations add greatly to the fun of suburban train working.

Various types of rail-motor vehicles have been developed from time to time specially for branch line service. Each coach has its own motive power, either enclosed within or attached to the coach body in the form of a small locomotive. Apart from the L.N.E.R. on which modern self-contained steam coaches of rather different type from the older vehicles enjoy quite a vogue, more recent practice has favoured a return to the less specialised type of motor train operated on the "push and pull" principle. With these the engine pulls its load in the forward direction, but pushes it when travelling backwards, the driver then riding in the end compartment of what becomes the leading coach, and controlling the engine from there by means of special apparatus. The G.W.R. specialise in this form of operation and have built quite recently new engines specially intended for "auto train" working, as it is termed on that line.

Such a train in miniature forms an attractive unit on any layout and working on this system is becoming more and more popular with "*M.M.*" readers. A Hornby No. 1 or M3 Tank Locomotive can be made to perform "auto" duties in conjunction with a No. 2 Coach, either a first-third or a brake-third separately, or the two together if required. The centre-gangway type of coach often is employed for this work on real railways, so that a No. 2 Saloon Coach or No. 2 Pullman can be used, if preferred. With this form of working the running round of the engine at its destination for the return journey is not required; thus the terminal equipment of branch lines can be simplified.

Apart from their use on branch services such units are often employed to supplement the ordinary local and suburban services between certain points. In miniature, "auto trains" can quite well be run in a similar manner.

Join the Hornby Railway Company and become eligible for the competitions announced on this page.

H.R.C. COMPETITION PAGE

Join the Hornby Railway Company and become eligible for the competitions announced on this page.

HORNBY LOCOMOTIVE KNOWLEDGE CONTEST

Our correspondence shows that every H.R.C. member possesses a wide and detailed knowledge of Hornby locomotives, even of types of which he does not possess examples. In order to put this knowledge to an interesting test we asked our artist to alter a photograph of one of the most popular locomotives of the Hornby range so as to introduce a large number of mistakes, and this month we invite competitors to find these. Most of the errors have been cunningly concealed, and entrants will be well advised to study the illustration carefully before regarding their entries as complete. When they think they have discovered all the errors they should make a list of them, using one side of paper only, and forward this to the address given in the next column.

The Contest will be divided as usual into two sections, Home and Overseas, and to the senders of the three longest correct lists in each will be awarded prizes consisting of any products manufactured by Meccano Ltd., to the respective values of 21/–, 15/– and 10/6.

In the case of a tie for any prize general neatness will be the deciding factor when the judges make the award. In addition to the main prizes a number of consolation prizes will be given.

Envelopes containing entries must be marked *"H. R. C. July Errors"* in the top left-hand corner and posted to reach Headquarters at Meccano Ltd., Binns Road, Liverpool 13, on or before 31st July. Overseas closing date, 31st October. Competitors are reminded that their H.R.C. numbers must be clearly indicated.

Railway Photographic Contest

Since announcing the first of the summer series of Photographic Contests in April we have received many excellent entries and each month the judges have had great difficulty in deciding which were the best. This month we expect even larger and better entries, for conditions at this time of the year usually are at their best for railway photography. As in previous contests, the subject is left to the competitor's own choice, and the only restriction is that the exposure must have been made by the competitor himself.

Competitors may send as many prints as they desire, but no competitor can win more than one prize in one contest. It is important that every print submitted should have on the back the name of the competitor, his H.R.C. membership number and his full postal address. A short description of the scene of the photograph also must be given. The best entries in these contests will be filed for possible publication in future issues of the *"M.M."*

The Contest will be divided as usual into two Sections, Home and Overseas, and to the winners in each will be awarded prizes consisting of Meccano or Hornby Train goods or photographic material if this is specially desired. The respective values of the three prizes awarded will be 21/–, 15/– and 10/6. A number of consolation prizes will be awarded in addition.

Envelopes containing entries must be marked *"H.R.C. July Photo"* in the top left-hand corner and posted to reach Headquarters at Meccano Ltd., Binns Road, Liverpool 13, on or before 31st July. The Overseas closing date is 31st October.

Summer Puzzle Contest

The strange-looking object shown here is actually a well-known product of Meccano Limited. The illustration is the first of a series of three mystery photographs, the second and third of which will appear in the August and September issues of the Magazine. A cash prize of £1/1/- will be awarded for the most complete solution of this three-fold puzzle.

There will be two sections in this contest, for Home and Overseas competitors respectively. As the last puzzle in the series will not appear until the September issue, the latest date for receiving solutions will be 30th September in the Home Section, and 31st December in the Overseas Section. Full directions for forwarding entries will be given in the September issue.

Competition Solutions

FEBRUARY "QUESTIONS" CONTEST No. 7.

The entries submitted in this contest were of a very high standard, Question No. 6 appears to have caused the greatest difficulty, and many competitors did not realise that Oxford was the station at which locomotives of all groups may be observed.

(1) Euston House, London. (2) 58.5 m.p.h. Paddington to Newport, G.W.R. (3) 14,000,000 tons. (4) 95 lb. (5) 2,112. (6) Oxford. (7) Diesel-electric express Berlin–Hanover 82.25 m.p.h. (8) Waterloo, London, covers 24½ acres. (9) Garston. (10) 60 ft. (11) G.W.R. (12) L.N.E.R. "Garratt" No. 2395.

MARCH "NAME AND NUMBER" CONTEST No. 6

We publish below a complete list of the correct names and numbers so that competitors can compare the solution with their own efforts.

6170 "*British Legion*" (L.M.S.R.), 3442 "*Bullfinch*" (G.W.R.), 921 "*Shrewsbury*" (S.R.), 5581 "*Bihar and Orissa*" (L.M.S.R.), 917 "*Hurstpierpoint*" (S.R.), 2597 "*Gainsborough*" (L.N.E.R.), 5627 "*Sierra Leone*" (L.M.S.R.), 4698 "*Loch Rannoch*" (L.N.E.R.), 5941 "*Campion Hall*" (G.W.R.), 6141 "*Caledonian*" (L.M.S.R.), 863 "*Lord Rodney*" (S.R.), 4082 "*Windsor Castle*" (G.W.R.), 5718 "*Dreadnought*" (L.M.S.R.), 6021 "*Queen Mary*" (L.N.E.R.), 6850 "*Hatton Castle*" (L.N.E.R.), 3358 "*Tremayne*" (G.W.R.), 2758 "*Northumberland*" (L.N.E.R.), 742 "*Camelot*" (S.R.), 2834 "*Hinchingbrooke* (L.N.E.R.), 2426 "*St. Albans Head*" (S.R.), 5428 "*City of Liverpool*" (L.N.E.R.), 9661 "*Ole Bill*" (L.N.E.R.), 4475 "*Flying Fox*" (L.N.E.R.), 6026 "*King John*" (G.W.R.), 923 "*Bradfield*" (S.R.), 2041 "*Peveril Point*" (S.R.), 6108 "*Seaforth Highlander*" (L.M.S.R.), 5032 "*Usk Castle*" (G.W.R.), 792 "*Sir Hervis de Revel*" (S.R.), 5593 "*Kolhapur*" (L.M.S.R.), 2511 "*Silver King*" (L.N.E.R.), 5642 "*Boscawen*" (L.M.S.R.), 4934 "*Hindlip Hall*" (G.W.R.), 796 "*Sir Dodinas le Savage*" (S.R.), 6017 "*Breadalbane*" (L.M.S.R.), 9256 "*Glen Douglas*" (L.N.E.R.), 5429 "*Prince Henry*" (L.N.E.R.), 5637 "*Windward Islands*" (L.M.S.R.), 4068 "*Llanthony Abbey* (G.W.R.), 938 "*St. Olaves*" (S.R.).

COMPETITION RESULTS

HOME

May "Locomotive Shadows Contest."—First: C. E. Wrayford (6039), Moretonhampstead, Devon. Second: K. E. Milburn (26029), Chingford, London, E.4. Third: G. H. Gill (36093), Chorlton-cum-Hardy, Manchester. Consolation Prizes: J. E. Heydon (47755), Ambergate; M. L. Harper (8718), Wood Green, London, N.22; R. B. Hayter (21630), Bedford; J. L. Makin (30933), Penwortham, Preston.

May "Railway Photo Contest."—First: D. Bayes (25638), Walthamstow, London, E.17. Second: V. L. Breeze (2134), Lewes, Sussex. Third: C. Spencer (44179), Sheffield, 11. Consolation Prizes: J. W. Hague (1258), Ripon, Yorks.; R. B. Hayter (21630), Bedford; A. C. Clements (31981), Tunbridge Wells; W. K. Holme (45888), Holsworthy; F. Hodson (9430), Bolton, Lancs.

OVERSEAS

February "Concealed Stations Contest."—First: H. R. Hondelink (25394), Oishi, Nada-Ku, Kobe, Japan. Second: W. G. Hallack (15578), Capetown, S. Africa. Third: D. J. White (9333), Christchurch, New Zealand. Fourth: I. Brough ((9112), Preston, Victoria, Australia. Consolation Prize: R. A. Wragg (7913), Bandikui, Rajputana, India.

February "Questions Contest No. 7."—First: A. G. Fellows (29952), Auckland, New Zealand. Second: G. E. Schulz (15425), Coromby, Australia. Third: A. McIntyre (30925), Winnipeg, Canada. Fourth: R. A. Wragg (7913), Bandikui, Rajputana, India. Consolation Prizes: W. G. Hallack (17578), Capetown, S. Africa; W. R. Hondelink (25394), Japan; D. Murison (37642), Buenos Aires, S. America.

February "Railway Photo Contest."—First: G. Healy (43145), Prince Albert, Canada. Second: G. E. Schulz (15425), Coromby, Australia.

Branch News

FIRST SHEFFIELD.—Much work has been done on various track extensions and improvements. Additions have been made to one of the terminal stations, new scenic effects have been incorporated, and miniature roads have been included on which are run associated services maintained by motor and trolley buses, and tramcars. The layout is modelled on an imaginary section of the L.N.E.R. in the neighbourhood of Carlisle, and both L.N.E.R. and L.M.S.R. stock are used. All new locomotives added to the Branch stock are fully tested before being put into regular service, so that the most suitable duties for them can be determined. Through the kindness of a friend interested in the Branch, members have the use of an excellent workshop where repairs and new construction can be carried out. Future arrangements include a visit to a local cutlery works; it is intended also to pay a visit to London and make a round of the various stations. Secretary: W. B. Hutchinson, 35, Linden Avenue, Sheffield, 8.

Members of the Hornby Railway section of the St. John's School (Bridgwater) Meccano Club. Chairman, Mr. C. J. H. Sanderson. Secretary, L. R. Temple. The keen interest taken in Hornby Trains by this club is shown by this photograph of the layout operated at a recent exhibition.

FOREST SCHOOL.—The Branch layout is now arranged on a raised substructure and the result is a great increase in the convenience of operation. It is proposed to work out a system of timetables for use when members are more accustomed to the running of the line. Definite duties will then be allotted to each member. In addition to the regular meetings, there are usually several members present in the Branch Room each night. Secretary: H. J. Pye, Forest School, Nr. Snaresbrook, E.17.

HOLYWELL (OXFORD).—With the commencement of the Summer Session indoor track meetings have been suspended and operations are now carried out on an outdoor line. Some interesting services have been operated and a discussion on real railways was a feature of one of the recent meetings. Successful visits have been exchanged with The Priory Branch, High Wycombe. Secretary: J. Spicer, 28, Holywell, Oxford.

THE PRIORY (HIGH WYCOMBE).—Important alterations have been effected on the Branch layout, and experiments have been made with a new timetable which provides for the running of more trains. A separate electric layout of gauge "OO" is being constructed. It is intended to finish this as soon as possible. Visits have been exchanged with the Holywell (Oxford) Branch and interesting work was carried out on each occasion. A visit was paid to the Model Railway Club Exhibition, and to the Bekonscot Miniature Railway that was described in the "*M.M.*" for April 1934. There is still room in the Branch for keen new members. Secretary: J. T. Cosgrove, 54, Priory Road, High Wycombe, Bucks.

ELMSIDE (EXETER).—Recent Branch meetings have followed the normal course. The method of conducting operations at track meetings is of interest, One member is chosen as Superintendent for the occasion. He selects a number of members as his staff to work the trains for a given period, and at the end of this time they are relieved by others. This process is repeated until all members present have had a turn at operating. The remainder of the time is spent in shunting operations, in working special trains and in general experimenting. It is proposed to allot names to the various expresses that figure in the Branch timetable. It is suggested also that some form of "ticket" or "working sheet" for members on duty would add to the general interest. Secretary: T. W. A. Smith, 98, Ladysmith Road, Exeter.

RAVENBURY (MORDEN).—Discussions on the various types of layouts have been held and track meetings have been arranged. Membership is increasing slowly, but it is hoped to arrange a series of Visits and other events that will attract further members. Secretary: A. M. Evans, 31, Arras Avenue, Morden, Surrey.

NORTHAMPTON.—In the last few meetings before the commencement of the Summer Session, Games and Competitions formed the chief interest. Outstanding matches were played off and the different contests finally concluded. At a track meeting a new system of awarding points for the work of members was tried and found satisfactory. A recent Lantern Lecture was greatly enjoyed, as were visits to Roade station and to Rugby Motive Power Depot, L.M.S.R. At Rugby members were conducted through the sheds and observed the new coaling plant in operation. A very popular feature of this visit was a detailed inspection of an L.M.S.R. Standard Compound locomotive, members being allowed on the footplate and also into the inspection pit below the engine. It is hoped to be able to arrange for a similar visit to Wellingborough Motive Power Depot. A Tennis Tournament has been proposed and it is suggested also to commence the publication of a Branch Magazine. Secretary: D. K. Adams, 8, Cedar Road, Northampton.

ST. STEPHENS (SALTASH).—Both indoor meetings and outdoor functions are held during the Summer Session, and it has been decided to arrange these alternately. Plans for a further section of the layout including 12 points have been approved. Indoor games were enjoyed at one meeting, and cricket and baseball are played out-of-doors. A Cycle Run was held to visit the Plymouth airport at Roborough. Plymouth Meccano Club have, through their Leader, extended to the Saltash Branch an invitation to combine with them for any works visits that may be held. Secretary: B. Braund, 9, Homer Park, Saltash.

Branches in Course of Formation

The following new Branches of the Hornby Railway Company are at present in process of formation, and any boys who are interested and desirous of linking up with this unique organisation should communicate with the promoters, whose names and addresses are given below.

BARNSLEY—G. Hunt, 65, Cope Street, Barnsley, Yorks.

EPSOM—J. Spooner, 20, Long Grove Road, Epsom, Surrey.

Branch Recently Incorporated

307. NEWTON ABBOT—H. W. Tompkins, 15, Union Street, Newton Abbot.

Early Coal Transport in the Midlands

Canals, Plate-ways and Railways

By T. G. Earp, B.Sc.

BEFORE 1780 the coal mined in the Leicestershire and Nottinghamshire coalfields was conveyed to market by horse and road transport. This method was extremely unsatisfactory; costs were high, roads bad, and the services so unreliable that the colliery owners were looking out for improved means of communication, especially for one which would favour their own coalfields. At first the Leicestershire coalfields were better situated for the Leicester market than were the Nottinghamshire mines. But later with the construction of canals Nottinghamshire coal could be conveyed very cheaply to Leicester by water, leaving the Leicestershire coal shut out of its natural market.

So strongly did the Leicester coalowners resent this intrusion that it was decided to construct a canal from the Swannington pits to Nanpantan by way of the north of Charnwood Forest. This canal, surveyed and directed by W. Jessop, was supplied with water from a reservoir situated in the Black-brook Valley and is now the site of the Loughborough water supply. Owing to the difference in height of 250 ft. between Nanpantan and Loughborough it was found necessary to construct a tramway to connect the canal with the River Soar. This tramway was designed by James Outram, and consisted of cast iron plates 3 ft. long mounted upon a stone foundation. In order to keep the trucks on the road the plates were shaped like the letter L, and were arranged so that the small lip or flange projected upward on the inside edge of each rail.

The material for the construction was delivered and work started on the 3½ miles of track, and then arose the question of crossing the London-Derby road, now "A6." Unfortunately Outram had not mentioned in his report to the Royal Commission that the flat plates were equipped with a flange or ledge that would stick up from the road and perhaps cause inconvenience to the users of the highway. When this was discovered by the Commission, they not only forbade the laying of rails with an upstanding ledge across the main road, but would allow no such obstruction on any other road. This resulted in the scheme being abandoned, and the plates already laid were taken up and returned to the foundry.

Jessop, the canal engineer, suggested that the flat type of wheel that was to run on the Outram-way should be replaced by the flanged type running on an edge-rail. Jessop therefore attended a meeting of the Royal Commission and asked "to be allowed to lay down two plates of iron, perfectly flat and level with the road, but each to have on the outside a groove ¾" wide and ¾" deep to control the guiding wheel," "guiding wheel" being the term used to denote the flange. Jessop's edge-rails were cast in 1788 and laid down in that year to the gauge of 5 ft. The original trolley used for the work had outside flanged wheels that were cast in one piece. During the construction of the line, however, Jessop realised the limitations of the outside flange, and decided to change to the inside-flanged wheel in order, as he reported to the Royal Commission, to avoid the use of fastenings for the wheels. This track was made up of iron rails mounted on wooden sleepers.

Scenes on the tramroad laid down by Jessop in 1793 for the Duke of Rutland. This line was in use until the War. (Top) The canal wharf and some of the old trucks. (Left) The type of rail joint and fastening. (Bottom) A standard length of the fish-bellied rail mounted on stone sleepers.

In 1790-91 Jessop surveyed the Nottingham-Grantham Canal with a view to opening up new markets for the Erewash coalfields via the Langley Mill - Nottingham Canal. The history of canals and railways teems with details of strong opposition from landowners, but the Duke of Rutland proved an exception. He not only approved of the passage of a canal through his estate, but desired a branch canal to carry coal to his own cellars. This was impossible, however. Too many locks would have been required, and also a pumping station to supply the canal with water. Jessop advised the Duke to have laid down an "edge-railway," now contracted to "railway," similar to the Loughborough line.

The Duke visited this track and consented to have a similar track laid down. The new line was to be 2½ miles long and made of rails mounted on wooden sleepers. At that time Jessop was a partner in the iron founders Outram, Jessop, Wright, and Beresford, of Buttery; and no sooner did Outram see the order for the rails than off he went to the Duke of Rutland and urged him to have laid down an "Outram way" instead of his partner's railway.

After hearing Outram, the Duke of Rutland had laid down two experimental tracks, one of each kind. He finally decided to adopt the railway proposed by Jessop, which was to be mounted on stone sets instead of wooden sleepers, in order to give the horses an unobstructed footway. This line was laid down in 1793 and one of the accompanying illustrations shows the type of rail used. These rails weighed 40 lb. and were 3 ft. in length and 3 in. deep at the ends; the depth increased to 5 in. at the middle.

Competition Corner

A NEW SKETCHOGRAM CONTEST

All the Sketchograms competitions we have featured in the past have proved exceptionally popular and because this intriguing form of sketching is a splendid means of whiling away an odd rainy half-hour, we are sure that all our artistic readers, and many of those who boast no drawing skill at all, will welcome this month's competition.

For the benefit of new readers we must explain that the production of sketchograms calls for no greater skill than the ability to include a given line in a simple sketch. To make the point clear, our accompanying sketch shows a sketchogram in the middle of the moon shining over the owl's right shoulder, and the sketchogram itself is incorporated in the outline of the owl's eyes and beak. For explanatory purposes it has been thickened considerably make it clearly visible.

Competitors are asked to submit original sketches in which this sketchogram is used. It may appear in the sketch as many times as the competitor desires, and may be tilted to any angle or turned upside down if desirable. Competitors who succeed in incorporating the sketchogram more than once will be given credit for the effort, but it is important to bear in mind that a simple drawing in which it appears effectively once, and is immediately obvious, will stand a better chance of success than a complicated drawing in which the sketchogram appears several times merely as a minor feature.

Each competitor may submit as many drawings as he wishes, but each must be on a separate sheet of paper, and on the back of each sheet the competitor's name, age and address must be given.

To give our younger readers an equal opportunity of gaining a prize the entries will be divided into two sections, A for readers aged 16 and over, B for those under 16. Cash prizes of 21/– and 10/6 respectively, will be awarded in each section.

Entries must be addressed "Sketchograms, Meccano Magazine, Binns Road, Liverpool 13," and must arrive not later than 31st July.

A similar set of prizes will be awarded in exactly the same conditions for Overseas entries, which must arrive not later than 31st October.

Competitors who desire their entries to be returned after the close of the contest must send a stamped addressed envelope of suitable size with the entry. Prizewinning entries are retained by the Editor and can be returned only in special circumstances.

July Photo Contest

Our photographic competitions this summer, as was announced in the April "*M.M.*," are open to photographs of any size or subject made with any make of camera, film, plate or paper.

The prizes are awarded each month to the best photographs submitted, and for the purpose of judging, the entries are divided into two sections, A for readers aged 16 and over, B for those under 16. Cash prizes of 21/– and 10/6 will be awarded in each section.

Only two restrictions are imposed: that the exposure shall have been the work of the competitor himself and that each print must bear a title. Prints may be professionally finished but, all other things being equal, preference is given to those entries that are solely the work of the competitor. Competitors who have developed and printed their own entries should mark the prints "Own work throughout."

Entries to the July competition must be addressed "July Photo Competition, Meccano Magazine, Binns Road, Liverpool 13," and must arrive not later than 31st July.

A separate set of prizes, to be awarded in exactly the same conditions, will be reserved for Overseas readers, whose entries must arrive not later than 31st October.

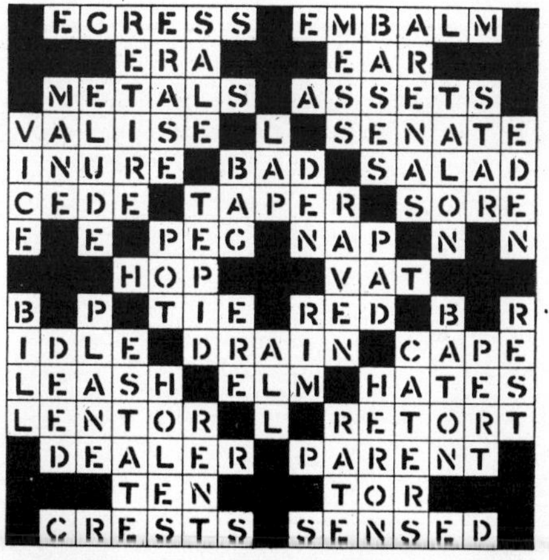

	E	G	R	E	S	S		E	M	B	A	L	M	
			E	R	A				E	A	R			
	M	E	T	A	L	S		A	S	S	E	T	S	
V	A	L	I	S	E		L		S	E	N	A	T	E
I	N	U	R	E		B	A	D		S	A	L	A	D
C	E	D	E		T	A	P	E	R		S	O	R	E
E		E		P	E	G		N	A	P		N		N
			H	O	P				V	A	T			
B		P		T	I	E		R	E	D		B		R
I	D	L	E		D	R	A	I	N		C	A	P	E
L	E	A	S	H		E	L	M		H	A	T	E	S
L	E	N	T	O	R		L		R	E	T	O	R	T
	D	E	A	L	E	R		P	A	R	E	N	T	
			T	E	N				T	O	R			
	C	R	E	S	T	S		S	E	N	S	E	D	

FEBRUARY CROSSWORD PUZZLE. To enable interested readers to check their solutions to this puzzle, we give herewith the solution. The results of the Overseas Section of the competition appear in the adjoining column; those for the Home Contest appeared in the April issue.

Note to Intending Competitors

Readers taking part in competitions that are divided into separate age groups are asked to note that it is not sufficient to indicate merely the group for which the entry is intended. The competitor's age must be stated on each entry.

COMPETITION RESULTS

May Photo Contest.—The popularity of our photographic contests is increasing year by year, and readers will be interested to know that the entries for the first two contests of this season, announced in the April and May issues, have shown a 50 per cent. increase in numbers over those of last year.

Many splendid photographs were submitted to the May Contest and the judges had considerable difficulty in deciding the final placings. The First Prize in the A Section was awarded to C. P. Silver of Exeter for a very pleasing picture entitled "*In Newlyn Harbour.*" J. R. Tottle of Taunton gained the First Prize in Section B for a rather unusual study entitled "*Landing,*" made in Weymouth Harbour. The subsidiary awards were as follows: Second Prizes: Section A, V. L. Breeze (Lewes); Section B, P. W. Sadler (Bromley). Special Prize: I. D. Moggach (London, N.W.2). Consolation Prize: D. R. Rooke (Goodmayes).

May Crossword Puzzle.—The more we study the entries to our crossword puzzles the more we marvel at the amazingly sustained interest that is taken in crossword puzzles. Certainly no other form of competition has achieved and retained such tremendous popularity, and it is evident that we cannot give our readers too many of them.

The "*M.M.*" puzzles are set for amusement only and, as our readers know, it is our practice to award the prizes to the correct entries showing the neatest and most novel presentation. It is always difficult to discriminate between the leading entries, and the four prizewinners in the May competition, whose names appear below, deserve every congratulation upon their success. The awards were as follows: 1. H. McLachlan (Edinburgh, 10); 2. B. Hardie (Bristol, 9); 3. R. Richards (London, E.5); 4. L. V. T. Medlin (Par, Cornwall).

OVERSEAS

February Crossword Puzzle.—1. J. R. Dingle (Halifax, N.S., Canada); 2. E. A. Fester (Wynberg, S. Africa); 3. J. D. Malan (Melbourne); 4. C. Keekok (Singapore).

PHOTOGRAPHY

TAKING ACTION PHOTOGRAPHS

MOST photographers like to take action pictures and during the summer will be on the look out for opportunities of doing so. These are not difficult to find in the outdoor season, when such events as school sports will give the possessor of even a small fixed focus box camera good pictures. A little thought is necessary before any attempt to take such photographs is made, however. The highest shutter speed of a camera of this kind is likely to be 1/30th or 1/25th of a second. An exposure of this length is useless for such an event as the finish of a mile cycle race if this is photographed from a short distance, for the speed of the competitors is so high that their figures will appear on the print as mere blurs. If a photograph of a speedy race must be taken with a slow shutter, it is best to work at a good distance, say, 40 yds., and to enlarge the small snaps.

There are dozens of incidents during a sports meeting that can easily be photographed well with a small camera, however. In many of the events there are moments when the motion of the competitor is practically suspended, and by acting quickly excellent results can be obtained. An instance of this is the start of a race, when the runners are crouched at their marks in readiness to move the instant they hear the starter's gun. Other examples are the change-over in the relay race and the action of taking the strain in the tug-of-war.

A tense moment on rough going during the Scottish Six Days' Trial. Photograph by courtesy of Ilford Limited.

Similar opportunities for successful snaps are provided by the high jump. In the former there is a moment when the jumper's upward movement ceases and he begins to drop towards the ground. Then is the time to obtain a good photograph, and this will be most effective if a low viewpoint is chosen in order to give the effect of height. A jumper who is deliberate in his movements should be selected as the subject rather than one who rushes at top speed towards the bar and flings himself over it.

The tennis court and the swimming pool are happy hunting grounds for the amateur in search of action photographs. There again it is best to wait for moments when little or no movement is actually taking place, and many good pictures taken at times such as this carry with them a surprisingly good suggestion of speed. The service of a tennis player provides an excellent example, and similarly first-class pictures can be obtained when a diver is poised for his plunge into a swimming pool. Such an event as a motor cycle trial also is well worth attention, and there the best pictures are those taken when the machines are tackling awkward corners, or making their way through water splashes or rough going.

Photographing railway engines in movement is particularly interesting, and will appeal strongly to many readers of the Magazine. The speed at which the engines travel is an important factor. It is useless to try to photograph a main line express travelling at high speed with an ordinary hand camera, but this need not deter the amateur photographer. If he resorts to strategy, and photographs an engine when it is emerging from a station, he will probably get more impressive results than if he were successful in photographing it at high speed, for it makes more fuss and gives out more steam and smoke when starting a heavy train from rest than when running along the level. Some of the most successful railway photographs are those showing a comparatively slow train just starting, or perhaps approaching the summit of a severe incline, where it is "breathing hard," and in all cases the impression of movement is very decided.

A splendid action photograph on the tennis court, taken with a Voigtlander camera.

Moving objects are difficult to centre on the plate or film with the aid of a small view finder, and for this reason the position from which to take an action photograph should be chosen beforehand. In the case of a train it is best to make the exposure when the engine reaches a certain point, marked by a signal or some other lineside object. This will spare the photographer the annoyance of finding that the engine has passed out of his picture, or appears only as a small object in the distance. A similar practice should be followed when taking other photographs of this kind, and all that is then necessary is to press the shutter release gently and firmly at the right moment. A hurried snatch at the trigger is almost sure to jerk the camera, and to displace the position of the image, so that above all things the photographer should keep a cool head. A few failures in timing may be expected in early attempts, but after a little practice the exact moment for exposure will be chosen almost by instinct.

Stamp Gossip
and Notes on New Issues

Bermuda Pictorials

Contrary to the rumoured intention of the authorities to use a portrait of King Edward VIII in certain of the new Bermuda pictorials, the new stamps have been issued bearing the portrait of King George V in the designs used for the 1d., 1½d., 2½d. and 1/– values. It is intended to substitute a portrait of King Edward in due course.

It is probable that this will be the last Colonial issue bearing King George's portrait, and thus there is a chance that there may fall to Bermuda the distinction of producing both the last King George issue and the first King Edward issue.

The new issue is a series of nine stamps, ½d. to 1/6 values, with designs as follows: ½d. and 1/6, a view of shipping in the harbour at Hamilton, capital of Bermuda; 1d. and 1½d. seacoast at South Shore, with portrait inset; 2d., a racing yacht under full canvas, a very happy design in view of the fact that Bermuda is a famous yachting centre; 2½d. and 1/–, Horse Shoe Bay, one of the island's most beautiful coral beaches, with King George's portrait; 3d., a typical homestead, built of white coral stone, with a specimen of the indigenous palmetto tree in front of the house; 6d., Par la Ville public gardens and library.

The library shown on the 6d. value was formerly the residence of Mr. W. B. Perot, the island's first postmaster, and the office building from which the famous Bermuda Postmaster stamps of 1848 were sold is still to be seen at the entrance to the gardens. The building is now used as a museum by the Bermuda Historical Society.

* * *

To celebrate the 40th anniversary of the founding of the Spanish Press Association, Spain has issued a series of commemorative stamps. The design that will appeal most to our readers is that illustrated here, used for the 2 p., 4 p., and 10 p. values. This shows Don Quixote and his trusty servant Sancho Panza on the wooden horse, an incident from "The Adventures of Don Quixote."

* * * *

To mark the completion of an important road-building programme, the Dominican Republic has issued a special commemorative series of four stamps each using the design illustrated here, showing the Avenue George Washington, one of the new roads.

A Stamp Yarn

In his book, *"The Memoirs of a Royal Detective"* (Hurst and Blackett), ex-Detective-Inspector Herbert Fitch of the Special Branch at Scotland Yard tells many good stories of his adventures when guarding royalty and other distinguished personages. One of these has a philatelic flavour and is worth repeating.

Mr. Fitch was one day on duty during a royal procession when he noticed a wild-looking man with a bag in his hand trying to force his way into the front rank of the crowd. The detective stopped him and asked to see the contents of the bag, thinking they might be of a dangerous nature.

The man explained that he was an American stamp collector and, opening his bag, displayed many thousands of postage stamps of all countries. With a cunning smile he added, "But the best are not in there!" and produced from his pocket a blue stamp which he said was *the* Twopenny Mauritius and added that he was in England to exchange it with King George.

Mr. Fitch pointed out that he could hardly expect the King to stop his State coach in order to exchange stamps in the street and suggested that he should approach His Majesty through the usual channels. The man appeared to agree, but when the royal coach drew near and everybody else began cheering, our American friend started bawling "Stamps! stamps!" at the top of his voice, to the amazement of the few people who could hear him. Evidently this appeal to his philatelic instincts did not reach the ears of the King, for the coach passed on and the American was lost in the crowd. Mr. Fitch adds that he never heard any more of the matter, but that he often wondered whether the enthusiast did eventually succeed in his formidable task of getting into touch with His Majesty and exchanging his stamps. —*Gibbons' Stamp Monthly.*

£30 Jubilee Stamp

Among all the millions of English Silver Jubilee Stamps issued last year, only one important variety has come to light, a 2½d. value printed in Prussian blue instead of the normal ultramarine. The Post Office has authenticated the error, which owes its existence to a curious mistake.

In the course of the preliminary colour trials, some of the sheets were printed in Prussian blue and others in ultramarine, and the latter was finally chosen as standard for the issue. In the ordinary course, nothing would have been seen of the Prussian blue stamps except for an imperforate block of four that was presented to the late King George. Inadvertently, however, three sheets of Prussian blue colour trials were mis-sorted among the normal sheets, perforated and distributed to a small Post Office in North Edmonton, London. Here they were noticed by a keen-eyed collector who purchased the whole of the 319 stamps remaining in stock.

Later he disposed of them to a prominent firm of London stamp dealers and specimens are now changing hands at £30 each.

New Zealand Anzac Commemorative

In our May Stamp Gossip notes we referred briefly to the issue from New Zealand to commemorate the 21st anniversary of the landing of the Australian and New Zealand Army Corps on the Gallipoli Peninsula. By courtesy of Mr. Errol A. Hamilton of Southland, N.Z., we are now able to give an illustration of the stamp.

The design is from a drawing by Mr. L. C. Mitchell of Wellington, N.Z., and depicts a private of the N.Z. Forces in battle order standing on a heap of sandbags, with Anzac Cove in the background. The picture is flanked on each side by laurel leaves, and the whole design is framed by a border of Maori carving. A private now serving with the N.Z. Army at Trentham Camp was chosen to act as photographic model for the design, and his accoutrements are a complete replica of those used in Anzac days.

A special first day cover was prepared for use with this issue and we have to thank several New Zealand readers for their kindness in sending specimens of this cover to the Editor.

See also stamp advertisements on page xviii.

A Darwin Commemorative

Although somewhat belated in its appearance, Ecuador's set commemorating the centenary of Charles Darwin's visit to the Galapagos Islands with the *"Beagle"* scientific expedition in September and October 1835 is none the less welcome. It is a most interesting series.

The Galapagos Archipelago lies some 600 miles from the South American mainland and the islands are remarkable for their unique fauna and flora. Almost all the reptiles found in the islands, and nearly half of the plant life and the fish found in the neighbouring seas, are peculiar to the islands and exist in forms that are not matched precisely in any other part of the world. There is no doubt that Darwin was greatly influenced by his researches in these islands when compiling his famous theory of the origin of species.

The set is comprised of six stamps, 2c. to 2 sucre values, three of which are illustrated on this page.

The lowest value, 2c., shows a map of the islands. A point of special interest in the design is that 10 of the islands are given their Spanish names, but that of the eleventh, Tower Island, is given in English.

The 5c. stamp shows the Marine Iguana, the more interesting of the two species of iguana that are found in the island. Darwin studied this reptile very closely and in a diary note dated 17th September, 1835, he writes "The black lava rocks on the beach are frequented by large (2-3 ft.), most disgusting, clumsy lizards. They are as black as the porous rocks over which they crawl and seek their prey in the sea. Somebody calls them 'imps of darkness.' "

This note implies that the iguana is carnivorous but in a later note dated 9th October Darwin corrected that impression: " 'The imps of darkness' live entirely upon seaweed. I suspect such habits are nearly unique in the Saurian race."

The 10c. stamp, illustrated on page 425, shows the giant Galapagos tortoise. As many as 15 different species of tortoise are found in the Archipelago, almost a distinct species for every one of the larger islands. At one time they existed in enormous numbers, but their food qualities were so excellent that they were greatly prized by visiting sailors and were killed almost wantonly. It has been estimated that in the last 200 years or so no less than 10 millions of the reptiles have been slaughtered, and to-day certain of the species are almost extinct and seem doomed to die out.

The species illustrated in the stamp is known to live 300 to 400 years and attains a length of 4 ft. and weighs up to 400 lb. In his diary under the date of 21st September, 1835, Darwin wrote "In my walk I met two very large tortoises (circumference of shell about 7 ft.). One was eating a cactus and then quietly walked away. The other gave a deep and loud hiss and then drew back its head. They were so heavy I could scarcely lift them off the ground."

The 20c. stamp gives a portrait of Charles Darwin and a small picture of *"H.M.S. Beagle"* in which he reached the islands. The portrait is a familiar one showing Darwin as an elderly man, but it should be remembered that he was only 22 years of age when he left the university to join the *Beagle* Scientific Expedition in 1831.

The higher values of the set, 1s. and 2s. respectively, show a portrait of Columbus and a view in the islands.

Australian Telephone Commemoratives

To celebrate the inauguration of the submarine telephone cable between Tasmania and the mainland, Australia has issued two commemorative stamps, 2d. and 3d. values, each bearing the design illustrated here. This shows Amphitrite, wife of the sea god Neptune, standing in a shell, and grasping a telephone cable in one hand. The cable is seen stretching away to its landing points, Apollo Bay, Victoria, in the left foreground, and Stanley, Tasmania, in the background.

The cable is 161 nautical miles in length and is the longest submarine telephone cable in the world.

The Magdeburg Hemispheres

The 250th anniversary of the death of Otto von Guericke, burgomaster of Magdeburg, one of the pioneers of electrical science, has been marked in Germany by the issue of a 6 pf. commemorative stamp.

Von Guericke is chiefly notable for the experiment with the Magdeburg hemispheres, by means of which he demonstrated the power of air pressure. He made a metal globe, divided into two hemispheres that fitted perfectly together, and by means of an air pump exhausted the air from inside the globe. Then, in the presence of the Emperor Ferdinand III, he invited anyone to pull the globe apart. Ultimately 25 horses were harnessed to it before the severance was achieved. Then Guericke showed that by turning a tap in one end of the globe and admitting air, the two hemispheres could be separated easily by one man.

Later von Guericke used his hemispheres and air pump to determine the weight of the gases of the atmosphere. He did this by weighing the globe before and after exhausting the air from inside.

Von Guericke also made interesting electrical experiments. In the most famous of these he charged a globe of sulphur with electricity by rotating it on an axis and rubbing it with his hand as it spun. A piece of paper then was attracted to the globe, but in turn became charged, after which it was repelled. Not until the paper had been discharged by contact with some other object was it again attracted by the globe.

The Best Designs of 1935

Recently *"Gibbons' Stamp Monthly"* held a competition to decide the 12 best stamp designs of 1935, and we think our readers will be interested to learn the results of the voting, which was as follows: 1. Southern Rhodesia, Silver Jubilee issue; 2. British Colonial Silver Jubilee, Windsor Castle design; 3. Belgium, Queen Astrid; 4. Cyprus, 45 pi. Forest Scene; 5. Ceylon, 15c. River Scene; 6. India, 2½ annas Silver Jubilee, Taj Mahal; 7. Canada, 10c. Silver Jubilee, Windsor Castle; 8. Cayman Islands, 5c. Hawksbill Turtles; 9. U.S.A., 3c. Boulder Dam; 10. Samoa; 3s. Falefa Falls; 11. Canada, 13c. Silver Jubilee, *Britannia.* There was a tie for the twelfth position between the French 1 f. 50 c. *S.S. Normandie* stamp and Canada's 10c. showing a Royal Canadian Mounted Policeman.

The following stamps followed closely in the list: New Zealand, 2½d. Mount Cook; Trinidad, 3c. Mount Irvine Bay; Australia, 1/6 Air Mail; and Bahamas, 8d. Flamingoes.

Obviously, the voting was greatly influenced by the interest taken in the Silver Jubilee stamps of the Empire, and it is clear that pictorial stamps are now preferred to portrait issues. It seems that beautiful or interesting scenes framed in a simple manner make the strongest appeal to the average collector.

Eight of the leading 13 designs were illustrated in the *"M.M."* during the year.

Dutch Summer Charity Issue

The Dutch "Summer Charity" issue that appeared in May last contains at least one portrait of interest to English collectors. This is on the 12½c. value featuring the famous scholar Desiderius Erasmus (1466-1536). Erasmus was probably the most famous scholar of his day, but spent only his childhood in Holland. Most of his time he lived in Switzerland, but on two occasions he visited England, where he became the friend of two great Englishmen, Cardinal Wolsey and Sir Thomas More.

The remaining three stamps of the series have designs as follows: 1½c. portrait of Kamerlingh Onnes (1853-1926), the well known physicist who was the first man to liquify helium (1908) and was awarded the Nobel Physics Prize in 1913. The 5c. shows Dr. Tahma (1864–1916), a statesman famous for his pioneering of social insurance principles. The 6c. shows Dr. Schaepman (1844-1903) a poet and a politician.

We thank Stanley Gibbons Ltd. for their courtesy in loaning the stamps from which the illustrations on this page have been made.

GOOD HUNTING

Mike had obtained a job at an observatory and spent most of the time watching the astronomers at the telescopes. One night an astronomer walked in, went to a telescope, and began to make observations. Just then a shooting star fell. Mike gasped. "Begorra, that was a fine shot, sir," he said with great admiration. "Why, ye hardly had time to take aim at it."

* * * *

Eager Playwright: "I wish I could think of a play to fill the audience with tears."

Theatre Manager: "I wish you could think of one to fill the tiers with audience."

* * * *

A Scotsman had to send an urgent telegram, and not wishing to spend more money than was necessary wrote this:

"Bruises hurt erased afford erected analysis hurt too infectious unconscious." (Ten words.)

The Scotsman who received it deciphered it as follows: "Bruce is hurt. He raced a Ford. He wrecked it, and Alice is hurt too. In fact she's unconscious."

* * * *

George and James were arguing about monkeys. George said that the monkey was the animal most resembling mankind.

"Monkeys!" scoffed James, "they are no more like human beings than I am!"

* * * *

Mother: "Now take your medicine like a man, Johnny."

Johnny: "No fear. It says on the bottle: 'Twice as much for adults.'"

* * * *

Teacher: "Every day we breathe oxygen. What do we breathe at night, Willie?"

Willie: "Nitrogen."

* * * *

Landlady: "Your egg is bad? Are you sure, Mr. Simpson?"

Boarder: "Well not absolutely, perhaps. I mean—er—I've only tried this end."

* * * *

"Father," said a young girl who had been to see her first football match, "how long does a man have to be a half-back before they make him a full-back?"

* * * *

GUILTY CONSCIENCES

Parker: "What's the idea of calling your dog Swindler?"

Barker: "Oh, just for fun. When I call him in the street, half the men nearly jump out of their skins."

* * * *

"Any complaints?" asked the orderly officer, looking in at the men's mess.

"Yes, sir," said a young private, "the bread's all wrong."

"What's wrong with it?"

"Well it defies the law of gravity, sir. It's as heavy as lead, but it won't go down."

* * * *

A girl who had just returned from a holiday in Egypt was telling her mother about the Pyramids and other wonders.

"Some of the stones, mother, were covered with hieroglyphics."

"I hope, dear," said her mother, anxiously, "you were careful not to get any of them on you."

* * * *

Mother: "And don't you know that King Solomon said, 'Spare the rod and spoil the child?'"

Tommy: "Yes, but he didn't say that till he was grown up."

* * * *

Soprano: "Did you notice how my voice filled the hall last night?"

Contralto: "Yes, in fact I noticed some people leaving to make room for it."

* * * *

Visitor: "Your son is rather small for his age, isn't he?"

Proud Mother: "Oh, no; most boys of his age are overgrown I think."

NASAL EVIDENCE

A dirty-looking boy walked into a chemist's shop, "I want some toilet soap," he announced.

"What kind?" asked the chemist.

"I want the strongest-smelling soap you've got," the boy replied. "Then mother'll believe me when I tell her I've washed my face!"

* * * *

Diner: "Waiter, what sort of bird is this?"

Waiter: "It's a wood pigeon, sir."

Diner: "I thought so. Get me a saw."

* * * *

Miss Howler: "I seldom think of my audience when I'm singing."

Miss Rapp: "But you ought to have some consideration for them, dear."

* * * *

Teacher: "Yes, Johnny, Lapland is rather thinly populated."

Johnny: "How many Lapps to the mile, teacher?"

* * * *

ELECTRICAL TERMS EXPLAINED

A GOOD EARTH CONTACT

Courtesy "A.E.I. News."

* * * *

Dentist: "Then you won't have gas, sir?"

Patient: "Certainly not! I am a director of an electric light company."

* * * *

A schoolmistress was giving her pupils a test on a recent natural history lesson.

"Now Dick," she said, "tell me where the elephant is found."

The boy hesitated for a moment, then his face lit up. "The elephant," he said, "is such a large animal it is scarcely ever lost."

* * * *

The tram conductor handed back the sixpence to the woman passenger. "That coin is no good, madam," he told her. "It's bad."

"Ridiculous!" she said, examining the coin. "Why, it's dated 1921. Someone would surely have noticed it before this if it were bad."

SAFETY FIRST!

"Why have you changed your name to Leslie Maurice Smith?"

"It's my wife's idea. She thinks we ought to have the initials that are on the towels!"

* * * *

Rural M.C.: "I beg to announce a small change in the programme. The interval of ten minutes will come now, after which the Reverend Mr. Peacock will sing to those of us wot comes back."

* * * *

Officer: "Now tell me, what is your idea of strategy?"

Private: "It's when you're out of ammunition, but keep on firing."

* * * *

Angler: "Yes, the fish was too small to bother with, so I got two men to throw it back."

* * * *

Visiting Captain: "Not much grass on the pitch."

Home Captain: "You came here to play football, not to graze."

* * * *

Welshman No. 1: "I never tasted such better beef in all my life any more."

Welshman No. 2: "So did I neither."

Welshman No. 3: "Neither did I too."

* * * *

Some engineers had been celebrating at a provincial hotel the completion of a big job. One old lady was somewhat shocked at their merriment as she said she had been told they were metropolitan vicars.

* * * *

Fat Man (in a cinema to little boy sitting behind him): "Can't you see, little fellow?"

Little Fellow: "Not a thing."

Fat Man: "Then keep your eye on me and laugh when I do."

* * * *

Tom: "I was shipwrecked once and lived for a week on a tin of sardines."

Bill: "You didn't have much room to move around did you?"

* * * *

EXPLAINED

"Pap," said the coloured youth, "A'd like ye to explain de way dat de telephone works."

"Dat's easy 'nuff, Rastus," said the old man. "Hit am like this. Ef dere was a dawg big nuff so his head could be put in Boston, an his tail in New York, den if you tramp on his tail in New York he'd bark in Boston. Understand Rastus?"

"Yes, Pap. But how am de wireless telegraph worked?"

"Jess prezactly de same way, Rastus, wid de exception dat de dawg am 'maginary."

* * * *

Billy (staying on uncle's farm): "There's a mouse in the milk pail."

Uncle: "Did you pull it out?"

Billy: "No; but it's all right—I put the cat in."

* * * *

A traveller entered the local inn and proceeded to shake the water from his clothes.

"Heavens!" he exclaimed. "Very rough weather for this time of the year, isn't it?"

One of the locals nodded and said: "Ay, that it is. Last night's storm were the worst as ever I seed. It blowed down trees as 'ad never been blown down afore."

* * * *

Teacher: "Tommy, how many bones have you in your body?"

Tommy: "Nine hundred."

Teacher: "Then you have a great many more than I have."

Tommy: "That is because you didn't have fish for breakfast as I did."

* * * *

A very fat man came in to bat and took his centre. The bowler started to bowl, stopped and turned to the umpire.

"Hang it all, Bill, what be I to do, his legs is clear, but his tummy is covering all the bails."

"It's all right, Garge, thee go on bowling, if thou hits him in front, it's leg afore, if thou hits him behind, it's a wide!"

MECCANO MAGAZINE

Editorial Office:
Binns Road, Liverpool 13
England

Vol. XXI. No. 8
August, 1936

With the Editor

Holidays and the "Silly Season"

By the time this issue of the "*M.M.*" reaches its readers, most of them will be on holiday, out in the open enjoying the sunshine. I ought perhaps to qualify this by adding "if the sun really is shining," for I am writing at a time when day after day, including the ill-omened 15th July, St. Swithin's day, seems to bring with it an undue share of rain. This may be gratifying to the water engineer, who no doubt chuckles as he watches his reservoirs filling; but it is scarcely what the holiday-maker wants. Whether the sun shines or not, however, holidays are holidays.

August is the time when the sea-serpent also takes a holiday, or at least ventures from the secret haunts in which he lurks during the greater part of the year. That is the only explanation I can find for the regularity with which stories of his appearance crop up during this month, in what is known as the "silly season." I hope that any amateur photographers among my readers who are fortunate enough to meet the sea-serpent will not be paralysed with excitement, as was the only man known to have had a camera with him when the creature showed himself. I should like to publish genuine photographs of the sea-serpent, so here is a chance for readers to enable their favourite Magazine to make what in newspaper circles is called a "scoop." They need not be deterred by fear of inclusion among the "credulous sailors, imaginative landsmen, and common liars" who, according to a well-known dictionary, have seen this elusive marine monster, for such a photograph would be good evidence that it really exists.

The Sligo Monster

A few days ago I read of the appearance at Sligo, on the west coast of Ireland, of a strange creature 51 ft. in length with a great elephantine head. Its lower jaw was armed with 44 teeth that rather surprisingly were described as resembling tennis balls, which does not suggest ferocity. I gather that the unfortunate creature was harmless, and probably, like the sea-serpent, it was merely out on a holiday tour when it came to an untimely end. A short time previously the "*Queen Mary*" had rammed what was believed to be a whale, and the presence of an enormous gash in the side of the Sligo monster has led some people to suggest a connection between the two events. If so, Britain's wonder ship may have relieved the Loch Ness monster of a possible rival. This is unfortunate, for competition might have spurred that old favourite to renewed activity. It is time we heard from him again!

The June Mystery Photograph Contest

There was a record entry in the "Mystery Photograph Contest" I announced in the June issue, and the variety of solutions was no less astonishing than their number. Most of the competitors thought the six mysterious objects were milk bottles with straws in them. Others were convinced that the liquid was more attractive than milk, and plumped for lemonade, ginger-beer and other "fizzy" beverages dear to the heart of the average boy.

Ash trays with matches, globes of goldfish, jam jars with spoons, pickle jars and inkpots were other unsuccessful efforts, but there were few suggestions completely wide of the mark. One competitor thought the objects were specimens of the first Edison electric lamp, which was introduced in 1879 and was then called the "red hot hairpin in a bottle," but the palm for originality must be awarded for the confident statement that the photograph showed birds and dogs looking out through holes in glass!

The photograph really was a view from above of Kemex flasks, each containing water and having a glass stirring rod in it. A lamp on the left and slightly above the level of the table cast long shadows, and the flasks acted as convex lenses, concentrating rays passing through them into bright spots and curved streaks of light within the shadows.

So many meritorious entries were submitted that I had great difficulty in making a final selection. The most complete solution was submitted by Donald MacKenzie, Peterhead, who wins the prize of 10/6. The entry of E. W. Oglethorpe, Harrow, was so near the winner's in merit that I have awarded him a special prize of 7/6, and in addition there are five consolation prizes of 2/6 each.

Air Liners Across the Oceans

The article on page 432 will be of special interest to all readers, in view of the schemes now being pushed forward for establishing air lines across the Pacific and Atlantic Oceans. It is written by Captain Sergievsky, a famous American test pilot, who explains how he tries out great flying boats before they pass into service.

The machines that Captain Sergievsky flies are built by the Sikorsky Aircraft Corporation, of which he is the chief test pilot, and include the famous "China Clippers" that will be used on the service from San Francisco to China by way of Honolulu. Trial flights have already been carried out, and next month I hope to publish an article explaining how machines are flown over the 8,705-mile route across the Pacific Ocean.

Europe's Largest Electric Generator

New 105,000 kW Unit at Battersea Power Station

A LARGE electric power station is one of the most fascinating places in the world. The huge machines in it work continuously at very high speeds, and the enormous power they generate passes outward through a network of underground wiring to light many thousands of electric lamps and to drive innumerable electric motors. The central feature of such a station is the turbo-alternator, the combination of turbine engine and dynamo that actually generates electricity, and the machines of this kind in large stations are now of great size and power.

The upper and lower sections of the intermediate pressure cylinder of the 105,000 kW turbo-alternator at Battersea Power Station. The photographs to this article are reproduced by courtesy of Metropolitan-Vickers Electrical Co. Ltd., Manchester.

The new Battersea Station of the London Power Company is a typical example of a modern installation. It is not yet finished, for only half of the scheme has been completed, but already it includes two units of 67,200 kW each, and a third, which was put into commission in September of last year, that has an output of no less than 105,000 k.W. This third unit is the most powerful ever installed in Great Britain, its capacity being 40 per cent. above that of the next in size in this country, and it also is the largest yet made for European installation. It was built by Metropolitan-Vickers Electrical Co. Ltd., to the design of Sir Leonard Pearce, Engineer-in-Chief of the London Power Company, and is a masterpiece of engineering that has contributed greatly to the remarkably high efficiency of the Battersea Station the three great sets of which have a total capacity of 239,400 kW.

Motor-driven extraction and drain pumps. The condensers can be seen behind them.

The tremendous power developed by the turbine of this great turbo-generator can best be realised from the fact that only 25 of them would be required to drive the whole of the generators at present in use in Great Britain for the production of electric light and power. No less than seven tons of water have to be changed into steam every minute to keep it running, and the steam enters them at a pressure of 600 lb. per sq. in. and a temperature of 800 to 850 deg. F.

A turbine dealing with this enormous quantity of steam must be exceptionally large, and that of the 105,000 kW set at Battersea has three separate cylinders, for steam of high, intermediate and low pressure respectively, and the steam passes through each in turn. It first enters the high pressure cylinder, and there passes in a zig-zag course over rows of curved stainless steel blades set round the circumference of a series of diaphragms or rings fastened to the rotor, which is set in motion by its pressure. Between the rows of moving blades are others, fixed to the cylinder casing, that serve to guide the steam so that it does its work efficiently.

The blades of each row are larger than those of the one before it in order to allow for the expansion of the steam as its pressure is reduced. For the same reason the intermediate and low pressure cylinders are larger than the first through which the steam passes, and the blades also are much longer. This can be seen in the upper illustration on the opposite page, which shows the rotors of these cylinders and gives some idea of their enormous size. The rotor in the foreground is that of the intermediate pressure cylinder, and behind it is the low pressure rotor, which is much larger.

Another interesting point is that the smallest blades of the low pressure rotor are in the middle. The reason for this is that the steam enters the cylinder at its middle and works its way towards the ends, instead of passing straight through from one end to the other, as it does in the two cylinders through which it has already passed. The largest blades of this rotor are about 2 ft. long and would have had to be made much larger if the flow of steam had not been divided in this manner.

The three cylinders are arranged in line and connected by pipes through which the steam passes from one to another. The connection between the high and intermediate pressure cylinders is provided by two tubes under the floor level. The pipes leading to the low pressure cylinder are overhead and are of enormous size, for the pressure on the steam has been considerably reduced, and its volume correspondingly increased, by the time it reaches them. These pipes can be seen in the lower illustration on the opposite page.

The intermediate and low pressure turbine rotors. The smallest rings of the latter are in the middle, as steam enters the low pressure cylinder in the middle and is exhausted at the ends.

Care is taken to prevent loss of heat as the steam passes through the turbine. For this purpose the high and intermediate pressure cylinders and the great tubes leading to the low pressure cylinder are lagged with plastic magnesia and asbestos, and covered with steel plating. The high pressure cylinder has a coating 1 in. in thickness of a special temperature resisting material.

The pressure of the steam leaving the last of the three cylinders is less than that of the atmosphere, owing to the action of extraction pumps included in the plant. Its temperature is roughly that of boiling water, but it is rapidly cooled when it comes into contact with the surface of the condenser into which it passes. There are two condensers, and each contain 7,000 tubes, 24 ft. in length and 1 in. in diameter, through which cooling water flows. Thus there are no less than 65 miles of tubing in the two units, giving a total cooling area of 90,000 sq. ft. Every minute 60,000 gallons of water are circulated through the tubes, this vast quantity being taken direct from the Thames. It passes through screens to a pumping station, from which it is delivered to a common main, and pipes 54 in. in diameter carry it to the condensers.

General view of 105,000 kW turbo-alternator. The overall length of the set is about 120 ft.

Three boilers are installed to supply steam for the turbine, and each is capable of evaporating 140 to 150 tons of water every hour. The quantity of coal required by each boiler is about 300 tons a day.

The three rotors of the turbine are coupled directly to each other and to the moving part of the generator they drive. In this set there are actually four generating units in line with each other, as can be seen in the lower illustration on this page. The largest is the 105,000 kW unit, and in front of it is a generator developing 5,000 kW at 3,000 V. that supplies power for certain auxiliary purposes in the station, together with two smaller units, known as exciters, that generate direct current for producing the magnetic fields required by the large generators.

An alternator comprises a moving part, known as the rotor, and one that is stationary and is called the stator. The latter carries the windings through which passes the current that produces a magnetic field in which the rotor spins, driven by the turbine, with the result that current is generated in its windings. The rotor of the 105,000 kW set weighs 82 tons, and this immense mass, together with the rotors of the turbine, spins round at the rate of 1,500 r.p.m. The speed of its rim is no less than 260 m.p.h. which means that every particle of metal on its edge travels 4½ miles in a minute. In spite of its enormous speed the rotor runs smoothly and easily, for it is very carefully balanced and before installation it was tested at a speed considerably higher than that at which it was designed to work.

The stator too is of enormous size. Its total weight is 148 tons and, with the exception of the steel yoke that carries the windings, it was built up on the site. The yoke itself was completed at the Metropolitan-Vickers works at Manchester. It alone weighs 42 tons, and is 24 ft. 1 in. in length, 11 ft. 4 in. in height and 12 ft. 6 in. in width. It is so bulky that special arrangements had to be made for its transport by rail to London, for its width is nearly 3 ft. more than railway standards allow. In some places the truck carrying it had to travel on the wrong line; in others the track had to be moved sideways to allow it to pass lineside structures; and in one instance a signal had to be partially dismantled. The journey was made at carefully selected times, and the passage through tunnels, past stations or under bridges where clearances were very small was made extremely slowly.

A Test Pilot at Work

Flying Giant Clippers of the Air

By Capt. Boris Sergievsky

AT my finger tips are the throttles, soon to unleash engines of 3,000 h.p. Underneath me is a wonderful structure of fabric, wood and alloy metals, weighing 40,000 lb. or nearly 18 tons. In the cabin, surrounding me and my assistants, are 90 instruments, each telling at a glance part of the composite story of performance; and as I sit in the upholstered pilot's seat I look at the three-bladed propellers ticking over in the afternoon sun, and wonder: "How will she fly?"

Test flying a great flying boat is like no other job in the world. I do not put the mammoth craft through thrilling evolutions, such as long dives and spins, but I do give her a thorough workout. For it is my duty to make sure that each new machine is airworthy, and that she will carry her cargoes of human beings and goods long distances with safety.

Before I take any new flying boat into the air, I make extensive taxiing tests, executing slow and sharp turns down, across and up wind. I speed the ship along the surface until she climbs up on the step ready to take off, but at this stage of the tests I have to make I do not permit the hull to clear the water.

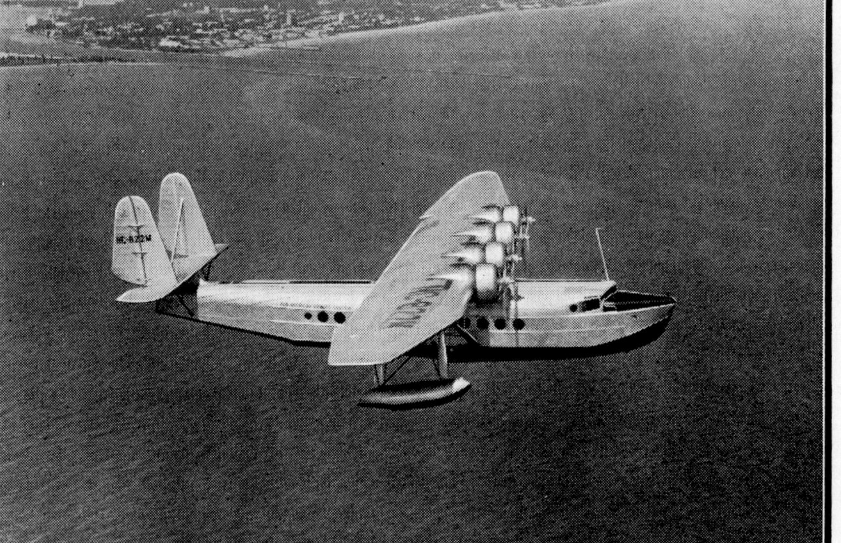
The "China Clipper" climbing above San Francisco Bay at the beginning of her flight to China.

My job is confined to handling the flying boat. Naturally I cannot attend to all the necessary tasks, and a crew of possibly six engineers accompanies me during taxiing runs. They observe the hull for leaks and the side floats and other parts for excessive vibrations, and watch the connections of wings and tail surfaces—in brief, they keep an attentive eye on all parts that might develop ailments.

Piloting any flying boat, no matter how large, is much like piloting a trim racing boat. I get up speed until she is on the step. At that moment the suction is broken, and I can get her away quickly. I have flown a lightly loaded 19-ton flying boat of the Sikorsky S-42 type off in less than seven seconds, and with a load of more than 19 tons, she took off in 18 seconds after a run of only 800 ft. That gives an idea of the tremendous power poured out by the four Pratt and Whitney "Hornet" engines of 750 h.p. each with which she is equipped, and the cleanness of her design.

Capt. Sergievsky is the Chief Test Pilot of the Sikorsky Aircraft Corporation, and in this article describes test flights in large flying boats and amphibians designed for service on air lines in America and across the Pacific Ocean.

Although we cannot know how such a giant flying boat will perform until she finally takes to the air, we do know through careful engineering that she is inherently stable. For instance, by weighing the machine on three scales we find where the centre of gravity is located, but the reaction of the airflow on the stabiliser, that is, whether it will cause the ship to be nose or tail-heavy, cannot be known until we are actually off the water.

Contrary to testing military aeroplanes, the first and cardinal rule in test flying amphibians and flying boats is to take no unnecessary chances. So, when ready to take off on the maiden trial flight, I first test the engines to make sure they are delivering full power. Then I set the stabiliser at the neutral position. With the engines ticking over rhythmically I reach upward to the four throttles, suspended from the cabin roof, and push all four forward together, opening up gradually.

As the flying boat gathers speed, and climbs up on the step of the hull, I begin to try the controls, moving ailerons, rudder and flipper slightly. Through the cabin windows I can see the ailerons move up and down—but will the plane respond? I know after running a very short distance. By that time the great pontoon has risen three feet in the water and we are skimming along at 50 m.p.h. on the step. Yes, the controls are beginning to "take hold." A moment later, with a crescendo of power, the big Pratt and Whitney "Hornet" engines pull the big machine into the air.

From that instant until we skim down to a landing I never have time to think of possible difficulties. True, unexpected things sometimes happen, particularly in trials of new equipment. For instance, when testing one of the 19-ton S-42 series, I was to try out the effectiveness of a new type wing flap. This lengthy "air brake" extends the entire length of the huge wing from aileron to aileron, a total distance of 64½ ft. The flap measures 32 in. from front to rear, and contains 172 sq. ft. of surface, far more than the wing of a small aeroplane.

As the machine roared forward at an altitude of 6,000 ft. I applied the flap, turning the lever that caused it to move downward. The resulting change in the angle of the air stream was expected to move the centre of pressure backward, thus creating a nose-heavy condition that would send the flying boat downward in a mild dive. In fact, before applying the flap I braced myself for the dive and prepared to roll the stabiliser up in order to help to pull out of it. Instead of going downward, however, the nose suddenly rose when the flap took hold, and the huge flying boat actually tended to turn into a vertical climb and loop the loop. I speedily pushed the control wheel forward and rolled the stabiliser down to overcome the climb and bring the machine once more into level flight.

"Why," I remember asking myself, "did the flap send us up instead of down, as expected?"

I tried to visualise what had happened, applying in a few seconds all the experience and engineering knowledge at my command in order to untangle the mystery. Soon I understood. The tremendous downwash from the lower side of the wing and the flap on the wide hull, which the flap almost touched when in the down position, and on the tail surfaces, produced very much the effect of a waterfall. The downward force in fact was so great that it created suddenly an extreme tail-heavy condition. With that knowledge, we were able to correct the trouble.

Flaps make possible amazing performances with these transoceanic flying boats. By winding down a flap to a maximum angle of 40 deg. the pilot converts a speedy wing into a wing of very high lift, enabling him to land at a speed of some 60 m.p.h. Without the flap, he would land at 90 m.p.h.

The flap is not the only mechanical novelty that is proving its worth on these giant machines. On the Sikorsky S-43, the first of a new series of twin-engine amphibians, we now have propellers that by means of governors can be made to turn at constant speeds, no matter whether the pilot is climbing, flying level or diving; brakes for stopping propellers in mid-air; and adjustable tabs for setting control surfaces at any desired angle. These relieve the pilots of wearisome duties in unusual conditions of flight.

For instance, suppose I desire all propellers to turn at 1,800 r.p.m. I make the desired speed-of-rotation setting, and after that, the hydraulic system fixed to the propeller hubs takes over the job. In taking off, I open the throttles and the propeller revolutions mount up to 1,800 a minute. Then as increased power from the engines pours in, which with the more common type of propeller would increase the speed of revolution further, the pitch of the blades changes automatically so that they take bigger bites of air and thus provide greater pull. If I dive, the blades assume an increased pitch, but do not spin.

The Sikorsky S-43 amphibian on the step, immediately before taking off. The twin-engines of this machine develop 750 h.p. each at a height of 7,000 ft. and give a maximum speed of 200 m.p.h.

Suppose on a long flight it becomes necessary to shut off an engine for adjustments or repairs. Ordinarily, when I merely close the throttle and break the electrical circuit, the propeller continues to mill around, and in time this wind-milling causes severe vibration that might hammer the engine to bits. A milling propeller located on the leading edge of the wing also blankets off a section equal to the diameter of the propeller itself. This is equivalent to pushing a disc of that size through the air. The four propellers on the S-42 actually blanket one-third of the carrying surface, and also spread a disturbance over the unblanketed area when they are milling.

What happens when I cut off one of the engines of the Sikorsky S-43, however. All I need to do then is to open an air valve. This starts a mechanical pump that by means of a belt and internal expanding pistons applies hydraulic pressure to the particular propeller involved, and in five seconds it stops.

Capt. Sergievsky in the cockpit of a giant flying boat ready to take off on a test flight.

Robot pilots save the human pilots much physical labour, but of course I handle the controls myself most of the time when testing. Recently we have added "tabs" to the control surfaces. These are really small auxiliary controls that when set in one direction tend to drive the control in the opposite direction. For instance, if the machine for some reason is flying left wing down, I set the "tab" on the left aileron in an upward position. The air stream then forces the aileron downward, and this in turn acts to raise the wing. Among the 90 instruments in the pilot's cabin is one that tells me at a glance the angles of all "tabs." At any moment I know exactly how each is placed, leaving no guesswork in their use.

It is a physical impossibility for one man to watch all instruments, however. Both when taking off and on a trial flight I watch the tachometers, which register revolutions of the engines, and the manifold pressure gauge most closely. Other instruments, including fuel pressure gauges and thermocouples, which tell at a glance the temperature of base and head of each cylinder of each engine, are located on panels in front of the mechanic, who is stationed directly behind me on a small seat.

Then I have other instruments that demand occasional glances. There are the ordinary and directional gyroscopic compasses, the sensitive altimeter, and indicators for the air speed, banks and turns and the rate of climb. All these are on a panel directly in front of the wheel, and there also are instruments that govern the automatic pilot, indicators for the flap position and others that show the oil pressure within the flap control system and the positions of the tabs. Two clocks are included for good measure.

The great flying boats of to-day are of giant size and of very large carrying capacity. In one flight I made in the Sikorsky S-42, the pay load was 16,608 lb. This is the equivalent of 93 passengers, or of freight consisting of 7 light motor cars. More than 5,000 sq. ft. of metal is required to cover the wing and hull of one of these flying boats, and the enormous extent of surface they possess can be realised from the fact that 600 gallons of paint are used on a single machine. This quantity includes the priming coat, lacquer and bituminous paint as well as the dope required for the fabric, and is sufficient to give 60 cottages of average size one coat each.

No fewer than 400,000 rivets are used in building each machine, and this contains more than 1¼ miles of cables and a mile or so of electric wiring.

The latest of the Sikorsky flying boats that I have flown in tests is the S-43, an amphibian that makes no concessions in performance or efficiency to land machines. In this amphibian Igor Sikorsky, the famous designer, has achieved the first large commercial passenger-carrying flying boat capable of a speed of about 200 m.p.h. It is a high wing monoplane with a two-step hull and an undercarriage of the retractable type. It has two Pratt and Whitney "Hornet" engines and, as I have already explained when describing my trial flights, the airscrew is of constant speed and its pitch is varied automatically to meet requirements.

Although the "Clipper Ship," as the great four-engined Sikorsky S-42 is often called, seems large compared with the liners that ply daily on the air routes from coast to coast, larger flying boats undoubtedly will appear in the near future. The two pilots and mechanic required to watch all the instruments undoubtedly will be able to fly them, however, for fortunately the number of indicators will not increase in proportion to the size of the machines.

In great 100,000 lb. flying boats of this kind, powered by six or eight engines, passengers one day will cross the Atlantic on daily flights and fly across the Pacific on regular schedules. Nor will that be the limit. Cost and economical operation only stand in the way of ocean air liners weighing from 150 to 250 tons, great machines many times larger than the present Clipper ships. These amphibians or flying boats of the future will fly 5,000 miles without landing for fuel and will carry 100 passengers in less than a day from America to Europe.

Whether we shall cross the oceans in the stratosphere, sealed like so many sardines within air-tight cabins, is a moot question. I rather expect these ocean crossings to take place at altitudes of 15,000 ft. to 20,000 ft., which is low enough for personal comfort, yet sufficiently high to avoid the storms of lower levels. In any event, I hope it will fall to my lot to test fly these great super-clippers.

How Great Bridges Are Built

Riveting Steel Plates and Girders

OUR cover this month shows a part of the great bridge across the St. Lawrence River, near Quebec, during its erection, and illustrates the manner in which steelwork is riveted together in building immense structures of this kind. This is the age of steel, and with this material engineers have been able to build mighty bridges with spans far greater than would have been possible with masonry. The construction of even a simple bridge of short span is more readily carried out with steel than with masonry, but the superiority of the modern material is best shown with large structures built in difficult situations. The bridge across the gorge of the Zambesi River below the Victoria Falls is an excellent example of this. In a sense this bridge may have been said to have been built, not in South Africa, but in the yards of the Cleveland Bridge Co. Ltd., at Darlington, for all the members were erected there before they were sent out to the site of the actual bridge.

The use of steel makes also for speedy work, which in many cases is essential. For instance, a road bridge had to be built in a remote part of South Africa over a waterway subject to sudden floods of such violence that uncompleted work would be swept away. The difficulties were overcome by rapidly erecting a steel bridge, and inserting bolts and drifts in the joints and connections in order to make it secure against the onslaught of the floods. Later the joints were riveted in the usual manner, and the temporary fastenings were then discarded.

The steelwork of modern bridges consists of plates, girders and other forms of rolled steel sections, and these are built up into members of the bridge structure that take various forms. Outstanding examples that will be familiar to many readers are the tubular main girders of the Forth Bridge, which were formed of plates bent to the correct form and riveted together. The tendency to-day is to use rectangular girders for the main members of bridges, for these are more economical to build, and girders of this kind are to be seen in the Sydney Harbour Bridge.

It is interesting to follow the progress of the steel from the works in which it is produced to the bridge itself. Great ingots, weighing perhaps 20 tons, form the starting point. These are made white hot and are passed on to the rolling mill, where they are reduced to the required sizes in the case of plates, or given the correct shape in the case of other special sections. The steel gives to the tremendous pressure of the rollers and is brought by stages to the form required by the bridge builder. The sections are then cut to length, and drilled and shaped in accordance with the working drawings, and each is given a mark or number for the guidance of the erectors.

In many cases much of this work may be carried out in workshops erected on the site of the bridge, as was done when the great Sydney Harbour Bridge was built. This is impossible when the scene of operations is in more remote country, to which access is difficult, and where skilled labour and other requirements are not available.

In the meantime work at the bridge goes on steadily, for the foundations must be prepared before the erection of the steelwork can begin. The foundations usually take the form of concrete, reinforced with a braced steel structure that acts as a rigid anchor for the visible parts of the bridge. If the structure has only one span, its foundations on the banks of the waterway can be built in ordinary excavations taken down to suitable rock or hard ground. When foundations have to be made in the waterway itself, the work is more complicated, for cofferdams have to be erected, or caissons sunk, to exclude the water from the site before the necessary excavation can be carried out.

When the foundations are complete the steelwork that has been accumulated at the site is then placed in position according to the plans, cranes of various sizes and types being used to raise it. Usually the parts are first bolted into their permanent positions. This method of fastening is only temporary, however, and at the first opportunity the bolts are replaced by rivets. These are made white hot in a special furnace, seized by means of tongs and pushed into holes passing through the plates or other sections that have to be joined. A heavy hammer is pressed against the head of each rivet as it is placed in position. The purpose of this is to keep it close up against the plates through which it passes, and the task of holding it there is that of the member of the riveting squad who is known as the holder-up. On the opposite side of the plate are two riveters, who hammer down the tail end of the rivet, so that the metal completely fills the hole, and shape it like a mushroom. In cases where the surface must be left flat, with no projections, the rivet holes are countersunk. The holder-up often has to work in very cramped quarters. For instance, he may have to creep inside the built-up rectangular members of a great bridge, and these are provided with manholes to allow him to enter, and also to give access for inspection and other purposes.

A riveting squad at work on one side of the main arch of the Sydney Harbour Bridge.

The plan followed in erecting the steelwork depends partly on the type of bridge, and partly on the conditions in which it is erected. In some cases special staging or falsework has been used to support the structure as it is built, and removed when construction is finished. In other cases entire spans have been built on land and floated out on pontoons in readiness for lifting into position.

Yet another method of bridge erection that is often employed is by overhang. A cantilever bridge is readily erected in this manner, for the two halves of a cantilever balance each other as they are built outward on each side from the supporting pier. Arch bridges sometimes are converted into temporary cantilevers, but this is not always possible and then other methods have to be used. In the case of Sydney Harbour Bridge immense cables anchored in tunnels on each bank were used to hold the sections of the arch in position as they were built out from the abutments. The steelwork was erected section by section with the aid of giant cranes, each capable of raising 120 tons, that crept steadily up the completed portion of the arches in order to be in a position to hoist and assemble the steelwork for the next section. The two creeper cranes met at the crown of the arch when this was completed and then slowly returned to their starting points, on their way taking part in the work of erecting the hangers and the deck of the bridge.

The Art of the Maori Carvers

Unique Features of Design

By A. P. Godber

The elaborately carved prow of a war canoe.

ONE of the most striking characteristics of the Maori is his carvings—handsome and intricate in design. Handsome is used advisedly, yet it may be that that description is only understood after some careful and sympathetic study of carving technique. The so-called decorative woodwork on many pakeha dwellings in New Zealand is far less interesting, and lacks those evidences of art which are found in Maori carvings.

The Maori who lived close to Nature had an imagination which had to find some form of expression. He had no written language whereby to transfer his thoughts to books. Thus he used the wood of the bush, suitably embellished with carved scroll-work, as a medium to express his thoughts. The Maori is very conservative and the designs seen in ancient carvings have, in the main, been followed by successive generations of carvers. Augustus Earle, who was draughtsman on H.M.S. "*Beagle*," visited New Zealand in 1827. From an artist's point of view he found much to praise in the Maori carvings he inspected. The symmetry of design and accuracy of the curvilinear details were features that especially excited his admiration.

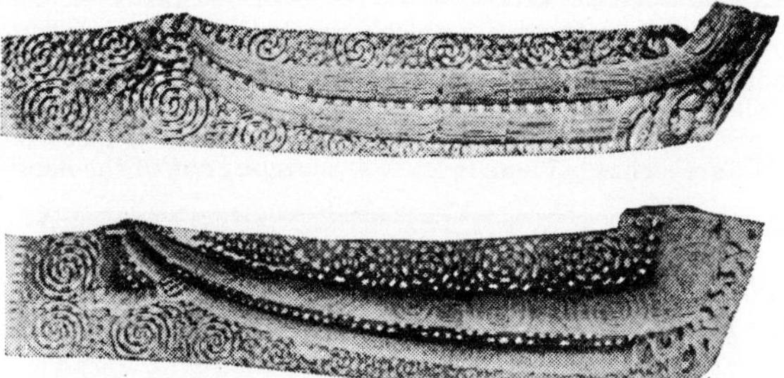
Ornamental carving on the stern.

In the old days the art of carving was looked upon with sacred awe. Only persons of good birth and breeding were initiated into the carvers' cult, and taught the intricacies of the art. A karakia, or incantation, would be recited at the felling of the tree. Further karakias were necessary at the commencement of the work, and during its progress. Mistakes were regarded as unlucky, both for the artisan and the owner of the work. If a hara (false stroke) were made ill fortune would inevitably ensue. It was equally disastrous to blow the chips from the work. They could only be removed by the hand, or by turning the work over.

The carver and his tools would be tapu during working hours. Even the chips from his stone chisels and gouges were highly tapu. When members of the Ngati-Awa tribe came from Whakatane to carve the Hoturoa house at Thames, a serious sickness befell them while the work was under way. Inquiry revealed the fact that some of the women had used chips from the carvers' workplace, wherewith to cook food. It was Mereana Mokomoko, wife of the chief Apanui, who, by reason of her mana, was able to carry through the necessary ceremony, which overcame the infringement of the tapu, and so stayed the pestilence. (This house, when completed, was a splendid example of the art of the Maori carver, and it is now housed in the Auckland Museum.)

When we consider that the old time carvers had only stone tools to achieve the results we so much admire to-day, we must credit them with an art sense above the average, coupled with a surprising facility in the use of their prehistoric tools. The tohunga carver had no patterns to guide him in his carvings. His fertile brain would imagine the design. Once conceived, the idea would be mentally projected on the object to be carved, the outline, traced with charcoal or other medium, and then the actual carving would commence.

It is interesting to note here that the human figure, with wide variations, predominates in Maori carving. A koruru, the huge figurehead seen on the gable of tribal meeting-houses, seems to be the outcome of the carver to express the features of a toa, or warrior, whose grimaces were calculated to instil fear into the hearts of his enemies.

Another point of interest is that the ancient tohunga scorned straight lines. On the oldest carvings the incisions were of rather a shallow cut, with notches, and lines between. Later methods were to cut deeper. The beautiful curved ground was introduced, turning itself round and round like a comma. It is marvellous how the expert carver would cut the double spiral with its attendant intricate curves without any geometrical aid.

A peculiarity to be noted in old carvings of the human figure are the hands, with only three fingers. In quest of information regarding this custom in old carvings, the writer sought the opinion of the late Mr. E. Best. His reply was that the meaning or reason of such was lost.

It is very difficult to find a Maori who can explain satisfactorily the various patterns and designs. Those who had that knowledge have passed away without handing it down to others.

This article is reprinted, with illustrations, from "*The New Zealand Railways Magazine*" by courtesy of the Editor.

Meeting House at Tokomaru Bay, North Island. The carvings for the house were made at the Government School of Maori Arts and Crafts, Rotorua.

Nature at Work and Play

Strange Rocks and Wonderful Caverns

By Sydney Moorhouse

WE are all greatly interested in such wonderful creations of Man as huge bridges, powerful engines and gigantic buildings. We must not forget that Nature can show us equally astounding examples of her handiwork, however, and in the holiday season of the year we cannot do better than endeavour to see some of the marvellous things that she has fashioned. For thousands of years she has been at work along our rock-bound coasts, among the great mountains, amid the white limestone scars and beside the rushing streams, with the result that Britain is a veritable treasure trove of natural wonders.

Sometimes Nature reveals the delicacy of the master craftsman in weaving intricate and beautiful patterns in crag and cliff; at others she is a playful designer, leaving in her wake fantastic designs of human and animal figures. It was in the latter mood that she fashioned the Toad Rock, which stands beside the main road from Sheffield to Hathersage. This weird creation resembles a gigantic toad crouched in readiness to spring into the Derwent Valley below, and has been modelled out of the gritstone by the combined action of wind and rain.

The Lion Rock, Dovedale, a striking example of natural rock carving.

Lions' heads are favourite subjects for Nature's chisel. There is a magnificent head guarding the entrance to the wonderful rock chine of Cheddar Gorge; and another in Dovedale, on the Derbyshire-Staffordshire border, forms an almost perfect representation of the head of the King of Beasts.

Dovedale is rich in natural wonders and has been said to rival Ancient Egypt for its marvels of architecture. Those in Egypt are the work of man, but in Dovedale are all natural. There are to be seen Tissington Spires, the Twelve Apostles, Reynard's Cave with its fine cathedral archway, and Ilam Rock, aptly described as Nature's own Leaning Tower of Pisa, all carved out of gleaming white limestone.

On a hillside above Dacre in Nidderdale, Yorkshire, are the Brimham Rocks, huge pieces of gritstone weathered into diverse shapes. Some are like great heathen idols, one has the form of a giant mushroom and another resembles a dancing bear. Most wonderful of all is the Druid's Idol, which weighs more than 200 tons and yet rests on a base only a foot wide.

Nature would appear to have been not quite so successful in her modelling of human heads, for in many cases the likeness is not easily recognised. Just off the main Beddgelert-Caernarvon road, and opposite the commencement of one of the tracks up Snowdon, is Pitt's Head, which is supposed to bear a resemblance to the head of William Pitt, one of England's most famous Prime Ministers. Near Llanberis is the Queen Victoria Mountain, with a remarkably good representation of her late Majesty, Queen Victoria, lying in state.

Gordale Scar, a remarkable rock cleft near Malham, in Yorkshire.

When seen from the Island of Bute, and from certain places on the mainland of Scotland, the skyline of the mountains of Arran look very much like a Sleeping Warrior with his arms folded across his breast. An even more impressive example of natural carving is the Witch's Head at Tintagel, Cornwall, the centre of many legends associated with King Arthur. It mounts guard over the mystic beach where they "found a babe upon the sand and that was Arthur," and the resemblance to the traditional witch is unmistakable.

The Cornish coast is indeed packed with fine examples of Nature's handiwork and there is no doubting the fact that the combined forces of the mighty Atlantic, the wind and the rain have had little mercy upon the rock-girt coast of England's westernmost county.

Kynance Cove, near the Lizard, is a remarkable spot. It is a palace of rocks, some perpendicular and others with sides sloping like those of church steeples and pyramids, rising out of a beach of pure white sand. To see it at its best it should be visited when the tide is out, otherwise much of its wonder will be lost. There is the Lion Rock, a couchant lion breasting the foam; the huge Steeple Rock; and the Devil's Post Office, where a piece of paper held near a fissure in the rock is snatched out of the hand and hurled far out to sea. Also at Kynance is the Devil's Bellows, a curious opening into a cave through which air is expelled at certain states of the tide with a roar that has been heard $4\frac{1}{2}$ miles away!

Between the Lizard and Cadgwith is the Devil's Frying Pan, a great cave with a hole in the roof. This cave is best reached by boat from Cadgwith. The sea forms its floor, and in stormy weather foams and hisses in a manner suggestive of satanic cookery. There is a similar feature on the South Welsh coast at Bosherton Mere, some six miles from Pembroke. This is a funnel-shaped opening in the rock that descends to a cave filled by the sea. In rough weather, great columns of water are thrown up and the spectacle is a very fine one.

In the vicinity of Land's End are many mighty rocks called by various fanciful names, such as the Armed Knight, the Irish Lady and Enys Dodman, the last being pierced by a natural arch some 40 ft. high. Eight miles south-west of Penzance is a fine example of a logan stone, that is a great boulder perched so precariously that it sways when it is touched. This example weighs about 65 tons, and is some 17 ft. long and 30 ft. in circumference. In 1824, Lieut. H. C. Goldsmith, a nephew of the poet Oliver Goldsmith, dislodged it with the assistance of a party of sailors. There was a great outcry as a result of this audacious piece of vandalism, and the lieutenant was compelled to replace the rock at his own expense, but it has not swayed so easily since this escapade. There are other logan stones in Cornwall, but the one mentioned is the finest example.

The colossal power of the sea has carved out many great sea caves amongst the cliffs of Britain. There is one at Land's End that penetrates through hundreds of feet of cliff, and Merlin's Cave, at Tintagel, runs right under the ruins of Arthur's Castle. There are other fine sea caves on the Pembrokeshire coast and among the white cliffs of Flamborough, in Yorkshire, and Great Ormes Head, in North Wales. Some of the best lie off the west coast of Scotland, and Fingal's Cave, on the lonely island of Staffa, is a wonderful spectacle. This penetrates 227 ft. into the island and the highest portion of the roof is 60 ft. above high water mark. The sides and roof of the cave are formed of black hexagonal and pentagonal pillars, and the only other places in the world where similar strange forms are found are at Giant's Causeway, Portrush, Ireland, and on the New Jersey shore of the Hudson River, opposite North York.

Not far from Aberdaron, on the Lleyn Peninsula, North Wales, are some whistling sands. As you walk along the beach the dry sands give out a shrill rasping note that is quite eerie. But beware of coming here just when the tide has gone out or you will be disappointed, for the wet sands do not produce any whistling effect. Only one other beach in the world has this singular property and that is in West Africa, but singing sands are found in the Arabian desert.

A splendid curtain of stalactites in Treak Cliff Cavern, Castleton, Derbyshire.

The Craven district of Yorkshire is rich in natural wonders. Some of the most remarkable are in the vicinity of Malham and include Gordale Scar, a great cleft in the rocks with beetling cliffs on each side, and Malham Cove, a wall of limestone some 300 ft. high, from the foot of which the Aire, or a tributary of that river, issues forth into the green dale. A few miles west are the Attermire Cliffs, where the limestone has been worn into an intricate system of rock protuberances that provides the nearest approach in England to the basaltic "organ-pipe" construction of Giant's Causeway.

In the Craven area also is the Ebbing and Flowing Well, on Giggleswick Scar, which possess the peculiar property of ebbing and flowing at irregular intervals. A sudden flow then completely fills the well, after which the water subsides and escapes. In rainy weather this may happen four or five times a day, but in times of drought days may elapse between successive displays. There is believed to be a natural double syphon in the limestone rock from which the water flows, and models made on this assumption have worked in the same fashion as the well.

The magnificent caverns of Craven were described in the *"M.M."* for December of last year, but there are almost equally fine underground systems in Derbyshire and among the Mendip Hills of Somerset. Near Castleton, Derbyshire, is the recently opened Treak Cliff Cave, which is packed with magnificent coloured stalactites and stalagmites. These are formed by the action of water that has penetrated the limestone rocks. The water is charged with a small proportion of carbon dioxide, and eats away the limestone to form a solution from which the mineral is again deposited when the gas is lost. This happens when the solution drips from the roof of a cave and there, and on the floor where it falls, these columns of limestone are gradually built. Their colours are due to traces of iron, manganese and other metals.

A scene on the Cornish coast, showing the Armed Knight, the rock in the distance, as seen from the Land's End.

In the same hillside as Treak Cliff Cavern are the Blue John Caves, where the transparent Blue John spar is found. This hillside is the only place in the world where this blue-tinted mineral is known to exist. It was known to the Romans, and vases made of Blue John have been discovered amongst the ruins at Pompeii.

Not very far away is the yawning gulf of Eldon Hole on the flanks of Eldon Hill. This is some 200 ft. deep and from it a long scree leads into an inner chamber 64 ft. lower. The height of this chamber is more than 50 ft. and the walls are covered with fine stalagmite deposits. There are no subsidiary passages.

For centuries this chasm had the reputation of being bottomless and there are records of an attempt to fathom its depths made in the reign of Queen Elizabeth, when the Earl of Leicester, who figures in Sir Walter Scott's *"Kenilworth,"* hired a peasant to be lowered into the cavern. We are told how the poor creature was lowered "two hundrel ells" and then hauled out "with great expectations of discovery." The hapless fellow was senseless when he reached the top, however, and died within eight days of a frenzy, never recovering consciousness. Probably he had been knocked on the head by a falling stone.

The whimsical Charles Cotton, Izaak Walton's boon companion, once attempted to plumb the depths with a line and recorded:

"But I myself, with half the Peake surrounded,
Eight hundred, fourscore and four yards have sounded."

It seems likely that Cotton allowed his line to coil itself on one of the ledges of the shaft, and so to give an excessive figure for the depth.

Peak Cavern is at the base of the cliff upon which are perched the ruins of Peveril Castle, and on the walls of its immense underground halls geologists have been able to trace a flow of lava. To the south of Buxton, on the slopes of Grinlow, is Poole's Cavern. This is more than 800 yds. long, and the stalactites and stalagmites in it are said to be larger than anywhere else in the country. There are also many interesting caverns, such as the Great Cumberland Cavern, Rutland Cavern and Great Masson Cavern, in the neighbourhood of Matlock.

At Bradwell, Derbyshire, is the Bagshawe Cavern, the full extent of which has not yet been determined, although passages in it have been explored to a distance of more than five miles. Many remarkable discoveries have been made there. One portion of the cave, known as Calypso's Grotto, is rich in a rose-coloured calcareous deposit about 5 ft. thick. When it is realised that thousands of years may be needed to form a layer one inch in thickness, one can only marvel at the age of this cavern.

The caves at Cheddar, Somerset, have been known to exist for centuries, for between 1125 and 1130 a monk known as Henry of Huntingdon wrote of the "caves under the ground at Cheddarhole" as one of the four wonders of England. These are now open to the public, as is Wookey Hole, another cave in the same neighbourhood. Wookey Hole is noted for the famous, or infamous, Witch of Wookey, now turned into a huge white pillar stalagmite gazing down into the ice-blue depths of the subterranean River Axe. Even more astounding is the chamber known as the Witch's Parlour, which has a span of 135 ft. without support, although its greatest height is but 14 ft. above floor level. Above it are the Mendip Hills, and for millions of years a stupendous mass of solid rock 500 ft. in thickness has borne down on this span, which to engineers seems impossibly flat, without disastrous results.

These Somersetshire caverns are lighted by electricity and this produces wonderful effects among the stalactites and stalagmites.

A Clover Leaf Road Junction in Stockholm

The diagram on the opposite page shows an interesting clover leaf road junction that has been constructed in Stockholm as part of a scheme to solve the city's traffic problems.

The oldest part of Stockholm is situated on an island, which is separated from a densely-populated district on the mainland to the south by a narrow waterway. The bridge formerly crossing this proved insufficient for the needs of modern traffic, which was frequently held up while barges were towed through the waterway. The area therefore has been reconstructed with a wide double bridge across the waterway.

The clover leaf junction forms part of the scheme adopted. It consists of two streets at different levels, which cross at right angles and are connected by three spiral ramps, a fourth ramp being omitted in order not to conflict with an adjacent underground railway station. There are also two straight ramps, one on each side of the group of spiral ramps. Between them the new roads provide routes without cross traffic in any direction between the approaches on the north and south sides of the waterway.

A new 17 h.p. Armstrong Siddeley limousine owned by Prince and Princess Arthur of Connaught, who are seen about to enter it. Photograph by courtesy of Armstrong Siddeley Motors Ltd., Coventry.

The roadways are supported on concrete viaducts which cover a space of about 16,750 sq. yds., and a restaurant and cinema are being built inside one of the arms of the clover leaf.

A Concrete Road 3,000 Miles Long

In the United States it has been suggested that a concrete road should be built from the Atlantic Coast to the Pacific. The proposal is to make this highway as straight as possible and to avoid cross-roads. It has been put forward by the Pittsburg Chamber of Commerce as a means of finding work for the unemployed, and it is estimated that its construction would keep 200,000 men busy for two years.

The suggested highway would be 3,000 miles in length and would cost about £80,000,000. Much of it would be elevated in order to clear existing roads and railways. It would be separated into two strips, each 45 ft. in width, by a channel through which telephone, telegraph and electric power lines were run, and each carriageway again would be divided into fast and slow traffic lanes. Feeder roads leading to adjacent towns would join the highway at intervals of about 10 miles, and if necessary the road would be forked at each end, the two branches on the eastern side of the continent serving New York and Boston, and those in the west leading to Los Angeles and San Francisco respectively.

There is already one great highway stretching across the North American continent in the United States. This is known as the Lincoln Highway. It was not planned as a separate road, however, and has many crossings, is extremely tortuous, and varies greatly in breadth and in the character of its surface.

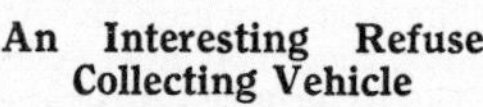

An Interesting Refuse Collecting Vehicle

The lower illustration on this page shows a huge semi-trailer refuse collector owned by the Glasgow Corporation. Its principal feature is a special Carrimore hopper body that has a capacity of 18 cu. yds. The trailer is coupled up to a Karrier Mechanical Horse tractive unit, which can be detached if desired and used with other vehicles and for other duties.

The main compartment of the trailer body is divided by a partition and each half is loaded through side openings screened by curtains made of strip rubber. An ingenious arrangement enables refuse to be discharged through trap doors in the bottom of the vehicle that are operated by winding a handle at the side. Receiving hoppers are provided at the discharge point, and the vehicle is driven over these on a runway.

The huge refuse collector in use in Glasgow, and described on this page. Photograph by courtesy of Carrimore Six Wheelers Ltd., London.

Rubber Company's 250 Million Motor Tyres

The Goodyear Tyre and Rubber Company at Akron, in the United States, recently completed its 250 millionth tyre. In making this immense number of tyres about 1,200,000,000 lb. of cotton and 2,750,000,000 lb. of crude rubber were used.

If all the tyres produced by the Company up to that time had been built up into a pile, they would have reached a height of 17,750 miles. Laid side by side they would have encircled the globe 4½ times, or would have extended nearly halfway to the Moon, and packed in railway wagons they would have made up a train nearly twice as long as the British Isles.

It is even more interesting to realise how much running capacity these 250 million tyres represent. If a single motorist, travelling an average distance of 10,000 miles a year, tried to wear them all out, he would find himself faced with a task that would last 75 million years, and in that time he would have to cover more than the distance involved in making 60,000 trips to the Moon and back again!

An Old Type Racer's Success

A new challenger for British and Continental motor racing honours has arisen in the form of an old Delage owned and driven by R. J. B. Seaman. This is one of the finest racing cars ever built. Its main features are of 10-year old design, for it was constructed under the Grand Prix formula of 1926, but at the Derby and District Club's meeting early this year it beat a field that included several of the modern E.R.A. machines, which have achieved such a great reputation.

A scene at Quarry Corner on the Ards circuit in Northern Ireland during the R.A.C. Tourist Trophy Race last year, showing a competitor swinging out wide to take the corner. Photograph by courtesy of Riley Record Ltd.

As though to prove that this success was no mere flash in the pan the Delage next won in handsome style the newly organised R.A.C. Isle of Man Race on 28th May, in which 19 cars competed. At one period it seemed that this race would result in a victory for Earl Howe's E.R.A., which held a good lead in the early stages. The Delage took the lead on the fifth lap, however, and held it until the end. Earl Howe's car had to retire halfway through the race owing to a fractured petrol tank, and from then onward the struggle was between the Delage and other E.R.A.'s driven by "B. Bira" and C. Paul, who finished second and third respectively. The average speed of the Delage was 69.76 m.p.h.

At the Nürburg Ring

Following its success in the Isle of Man the Delage was taken to southern Germany, where it took part in the famous Eifel Races, which are run over the mountainous Nürburg course, which has been described as the most wonderful in the world. On this occasion it had to retire early in the race owing to a crumpled oil tank and other damaged parts.

The chief events of the Eifel Races, so far as British cars were concerned were the international races for racing cars of 1,500 c.c. and 800 c.c. capacity, and sports cars, all of which started together, but competed in separate classes according to their capacity and whether they were supercharged or not.

Last year the 1,500 c.c. event was won by an E.R.A. driven by R. Mays. Four E.R.A. machines were entered this year, including one driven by the winner in 1935. Mays was soon in difficulty, however, and had to make a call at the pits owing to plug trouble. At that time another E.R.A. driven by "B. Bira" was holding second place to a Maserati driven by Count Trossi, but before the half-way stage was reached the British car had dropped to third, second place being taken by Tenni, who also was driving a Maserati, and these positions were held to the finish. Towards the end of the race Mays drove in furious fashion in a bold endeavour to make up lost time, but his efforts were unsuccessful. Trossi won the race with an average speed of 69.9 m.p.h., Tenni was second and "B. Bira" third.

The chief event of the day was the race for large cars such as Mercedes-Benz, Auto-Union and Alfa-Romeo. Among the many famous drivers who competed were Rosemeyer, Nuvolari, Stuck, Chiron and Brauchitsch. The latter driver holds the lap record for the Nürburg Ring with a speed of 80.73 m.p.h. set up during the German Grand Prix last year. No great speeds were set up in this year's event owing to bad weather, and the race was won by an Auto-Union driven by Rosemeyer. Nuvolari and Brivio, both driving Alfa-Romeos, were second and third respectively.

A Sweeping Victory for the E.R.A.

E.R.A. cars demonstrated their capabilities in a convincing manner by securing the first three places in the Picardy Grand Prix. In this race, which comprised two heats and a final, seven E.R.A. cars competed against Maseratis, Amilcars, Bugattis, several Salmsons and Seaman's Delage. In the first heat there was a terrific duel between an E.R.A. driven by P. Fairfield and a Maserati driven by Count Trossi, first one and then the other of these two gaining the lead. Trossi finally overhauled Fairfield, however, and went on to win comfortably, while "B. Bira" was third.

In the second heat an E.R.A. driven by R. Mays took the lead, but unfortunately had to retire with a broken oil pipe. Seaman, who in his Delage was following closely behind, immediately flashed into the first place, which he succeeded in retaining until the finish. E.R.A. cars driven by Earl Howe and Tongue were second and third respectively.

In the final the steering gear of Seaman's Delage went wrong during the fifth lap, and the car went over a heap of stones and dashed into a wall, but was not very badly damaged. At that time Fairfield's E.R.A. was in the lead, but struck a bank at one of the last bends. Fairfield was uninjured, but the accident cost him the race, for "B. Bira" immediately shot into the lead and held it to the end. Fairfield was second, half-a-minute behind the winner, Earl Howe was third and F. McEvoy, who drove a Maserati, finished fourth.

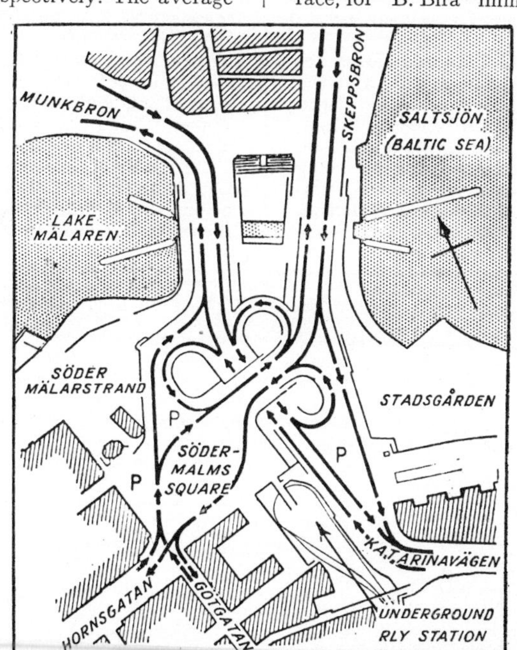

A diagram of a novel clover leaf road junction in Stockholm that is described on the opposite page. For this illustration we are indebted to the courtesy of "Modern Transport."

The French Grand Prix

This year's French Grand Prix, run on 28th June at Montlhéry, resolved itself into a struggle between three new streamlined Bugattis and nine Delahayes. The winner was J. P. Wimille, who drove a Bugatti and covered the distance, about 620 miles, in 7 hrs. 58 min. at an average speed of 77.85 m.p.h. Delahayes driven by M. Paris and R. Brunet were second and third respectively.

The record for the lap was broken eight times during the race and a Talbot car set up the final figure of 83.68 m.p.h. Three Riley cars driven by J. Trevoux, A. von der Becke and C. Paul were placed first, second and third in the group for cars of two litres capacity.

Racing Thrills in Store

Everyone interested in motor racing is now looking forward to the R.A.C. Tourist Trophy Race, which will take place over the Ards Circuit near Belfast on 5th September. This race never fails to provide exciting incidents and thrills in plenty for the great crowds of spectators that invariably line the course.

The Ards Circuit is used for the R.A.C. Tourist Trophy Race only, and consists of 13 2/3 miles of well-surfaced roads with many corners that give drivers opportunities of showing their skill. Last year the Trophy was won by F. W. Dixon's 1½ litre Riley, which covered the course at an average speed of 76.9 m.p.h. This is the second highest speed in the history of the race, the record being the 80.53 m.p.h. set up by Earl Howe in 1932 in a supercharged Alfa-Romeo, and Dixon's speed is the highest reached by a winning car not fitted with a supercharger Earl Howe's record speed was almost equalled last year by an unsupercharged car, E. R. Hall's Bentley achieving 80.36 m.p.h.

On the Footplate of a Southern Flyer

Efficiency of "Schools" Class Engines

By a Railway Engineer

THE 80-minute London-Folkestone service of the Southern Railway represents the fastest group of trains in the country still regularly worked by 4–4–0 engines. Occasionally a "King Arthur" may be seen on one of these expresses, but otherwise they are almost invariably hauled by the "Schools" class 4–4–0s. These remarkable engines are the most powerful examples of the type that have yet been built, and with three cylinders 16½ in. diameter by 26 in. stroke, combined with a working pressure of 220 lb. per sq. in., they have a tractive effort almost equal to that of the six-coupled "King Arthurs." They were designed primarily for the Hastings line, which abounds in steep grades and sharp curves; but whether it be in the realm of heavy collar work or fast running on the level their performance is equally good.

Down Kent Coast Express leaving Priory Station, Dover. The engine is No. 916, "Whitgift," on the footplate of which the run described in this article was made.

In order to conform to loading gauge restrictions on the sharply curved lengths of the Hastings line, the cab, although wide and roomy, is rather short, and the side sheets are inclined inward; they are arranged for left-hand driving and the reversing gear is operated by a vertical wheel like that of the "Lord Nelsons." An interesting feature of the cab fittings is the lubricators. The coupled-wheel axle-boxes are fed from oil containers fixed on the backplate of the fire-box in the driver's cab, the oil being conveyed down the connecting pipes by means of worsted trimmings. In the right-hand corner of the cab is a three-feed Wakefield sight-feed lubricator for the cylinders. In this apparatus live steam is supplied to the oil chamber of the lubricator; this steam condenses, sinks to the bottom as water, and in so doing displaces a quantity of oil which feeds in drops through a vertical glass tube. The rate of feed can always be seen by the enginemen and thus regulated to suit conditions.

The footplate of a "Schools" class locomotive, showing the convenient arrangement of the fittings.

I was privileged to ride on the footplate of No. 916, "*Whitgift*," while working the 12.55 p.m. express from Charing Cross, on which the load was one of eight corridor bogies and a Pullman car, 282 tons tare and 300 tons full. Driver Keel and Fireman Burgess of Ramsgate shed were in charge. Starting away very gently, we were barely across the Thames when cut-off was back to 20 per cent., and then, still running on arches after we had gained the Surrey side of the river, we were soon passing the impressive facade of Waterloo. As soon as we were past this point "*Whitgift*" was given full regulator. Running level with the roofs of dwellings and warehouses, and with the dome of St. Paul's and the spires of the City churches enobling the outlook northward, we accelerated rapidly until, nearing Borough Market Junction, one of the four-aspect colour-light signals showed us a single yellow. It quickly changed to green, but we were in any case easing a little for the sharply curved stretch of line ahead where the line from Cannon St. joins in, and where the railway almost brushes the side of Southwark Cathedral.

The London Bridge home signal showed green, indicating that at least three signal sections were clear, and Keel opened up to full regulator. As it was Saturday, the platforms were crowded with home-going City workers, electric trains were on all sides, and we went through the great station in fine style in a little under five minutes from Charing Cross, 1.9 miles. Once through the platforms the line becomes dead straight, the signal lights show up literally for miles, even in bright sunshine, and ahead of us three successive signals showed double yellow, single yellow, and red. Whistling shrilly, we were up to the single yellow and preparing to stop when the red changed to green, and then we were "right away" indeed. This is an amazing piece of line; no less than eleven parallel tracks run into London Bridge; on both sides of the railway there stretches a veritable sea of house-tops; while to the north the line of the River is marked by the Tower Bridge and farther eastward by the masts of ships lying in the London docks.

On the dead level, cut-off was brought back to 18 per cent., and we swung through New Cross at 52 m.p.h.; but just beyond here begins the 11-mile climb over the North Downs. Without securing the reversing wheel in any fixed position, the driver very gradually increased the cut-off; at Grove Park where the gradient steepens to 1 in 120 it was up to 27 per cent., and as we approached Elmstead Woods tunnel a final increase to 29 per cent. was made. Here speed was a steady 38½ m.p.h. The check at London Bridge had cost us a minute, but this was being gradually won back. Just beyond the tunnel the grade eases a little, and the driver took advantage of this to notch up to 20 per cent.; Orpington was passed at 49 m.p.h., and so we came on to the last stage of the climb, again at 1 in 120. Through deep cuttings where the banks are almost vertical walls of grey-white chalk, through Chelsfield tunnel, "*Whitgift*" responded finely to a gradually increased cut-off and came over Knockholt summit at 45½ m.p.h. The 16.6 miles from Charing Cross had taken 25¾ minutes, and throughout the 11 miles of ascent speed had averaged 44.7 m.p.h.—a very fine achievement considering that for only three miles of the distance cut-off was as much as 29 per cent.

Just beyond Knockholt we entered the long tunnel under Polhill. The engine was worked with the fire-doors closed except when firing was in progress, and in the tunnel we were in pitch darkness on the footplate; in the meantime the driver had changed over to the first valve of the regulator and cut-off was reduced to 18 per cent. We left the tunnel at 65 m.p.h., and running beneath the beautiful chalk escarpments of Polhill swept down to the valley of the Darent. Dunton Green was passed at 72½ m.p.h., but Driver Keel never let the cut-off remain in one position for long, and increasing to 22 per cent. we took the 2-mile rise at 1 in 160 to Sevenoaks flying, at a minimum speed of exactly 60 m.p.h. We were now dead on time, having covered the 22.1 miles from Charing Cross in 31 minutes.

At the entrance to the long tunnel under the southern ridge of the North Downs the descent to Tonbridge begins; cut-off was brought back to 17 per cent. and even the first valve of the regulator was practically closed. Speed steadily rose all through the tunnel, and at Weald signal box, half a mile beyond the south end, we were doing 69 m.p.h.; here the first regulator was opened to the full. The response of the engine to this modest increase was amazing—in less than three miles we were up to 78 m.p.h.! The hills were now left behind, we were down among the level meadows of the Weald of Kent; and approaching the River Medway steam was shut off and the brakes applied for Tonbridge curve. On this first descent "*Whitgift*" proved herself to be without question the smoothest riding engine I have ever travelled on, and at 75 m.p.h. my notes, even when made standing, were as steady as if written in a room; the driver told me that when she first came out of the shops she rode more like a limousine than a locomotive.

No. 912, "Downside," of the "Schools" class, taking up water at Dover.

Not a second was wasted over the slack; speed was carefully reduced to the prescribed figure round the curve, but the instant the engine was over the junction the regulator was opened again so as to take full advantage of the quarter mile down at 1 in 670 before the rise to Mile Post 31 began. Rapidly accelerating, we passed Tonbridge station, 29½ miles in 38 minutes. Beyond here the character of the line changes entirely; the sharply graded switchback of the route through the Downs gives place to a gently undulating road with no grade steeper than 1 in 240. Hop fields extend on both sides of the line, and many miles to the north the long green ridge of the Downs runs parallel with the railway; but perhaps the most unusual feature of this length is that from Tonbridge almost to Ashford the line is practically dead straight.

We were quickly up the rise from Tonbridge, and the driver then changed over once more from the main to the first regulator; but even on these gentle ups and downs cut-off was constantly varied between the narrow limits of 18 and 24 per cent., to suit every change in the grade. We maintained a beautifully even pace. Paddock Wood was passed at 71 m.p.h., 65 was maintained over the rise past Marden, and at Staplehurst we were doing 69 m.p.h. on the dead level. Approaching Headcorn, Driver Keel changed over to the main regulator, but only just half open, in readiness for the 8-mile rise to Chart Siding. On the final length, where the grade is 1 in 277, speed did not fall below 63 m.p.h., and a moment later we were approaching Ashford at 71 m.p.h.

A view of the driver's side of the cab showing the slanting side. The reversing wheel and brake valve are clearly visible.

There was a very severe permanent way slack in store for us beyond Smeeth, and the driver was wisely getting some time in hand. We passed Ashford, 56.1 miles from Charing Cross, in 62½ minutes, 2½ minutes early, and our average speed over the 26.6 miles from Tonbridge was 65.2 m.p.h. Considering the very moderate regulator opening that had been used, this was a very striking figure with a 300 ton load, for taken on the whole this length is decidedly against the collar. The relaying slack was in force right in the middle of the long 1 in 266 ascent to Westenhanger. For over half a mile we crawled along, and although Keel subsequently gave the engine 33 per cent. cut-off and opened the main regulator to three-fifths, we were doing barely 40 m.p.h. on topping the summit where speed rarely falls below 55 m.p.h. in the ordinary way.

Grey chalky downs rose ahead, the Western flanks of the most famous cliffs in England; we passed Sandling Junction, practically on time despite the check, and "*Whitgift*" was once again working on the first regulator. Accelerating rapidly on the 1 in 266 descent, we emerged from the long tunnel beyond Sandling at just over 60, touched 66 before Shorncliffe, and in 80 minutes almost to the second drew up at Folkestone Central. The net time for the 69.9 miles from Charing Cross was not more than 75½ minutes, however, and thus the average speed of 55.8 m.p.h. was maintained.

At Folkestone four coaches were detached, leaving a load of 170 tons to go forward; this of course provided a very simple task for the engine, but even so the journey worked up to a glorious climax. Ahead of us lay a magnificent range of chalk cliffs, those white walls that for centuries have stood as a symbol of England herself; and through these formidable bastions that great engineer Sir William Cubitt carried the line to Dover by one of the most daring pieces of railway engineering in the British Isles. Just after leaving Folkestone Central the line is carried high above the town on the stately Foord Viaduct, from which there is almost a bird's-eye view of picturesque old houses tier upon tier, of narrow streets winding down to the sea, and out beyond a glimpse of the harbour and cross-channel steamers.

Rapidly accelerating we sped through Folkestone Junction, whence the boat trains run down to the harbour, and a moment later entered Martello Tunnel; this of course takes its name from the famous towers, one of which stands on the cliff above. We emerged into Folkestone warren, a wild and lovely tract of land between the cliffs and the shore. On through deep cuttings with only an occasional glimpse of the sea; cliffs towering higher and higher above us on the left; then, with speed now up to 60 m.p.h., we dived under the great headland of Abbots Cliff, through the longest of the many tunnels on this route. It is dead straight, and right ahead was a tiny pin-point of light. Half way through the regulator was closed, and coasting freely we emerged on a high ledge with the sea right beneath; mist hung over the Channel and the breaking waves were of a green as brilliant as verdigris.

Shakespeare's Cliff now lay ahead, through which the line is carried by two single-line tunnels of a most curious pointed shape. Almost before there was time to appreciate the full beauty of the cliff scenery we were into the tunnel and slowing up for Dover. We came out in full view of the Admiralty Pier, and running abreast of the locomotive sheds crept over Archcliffe Junction at 10 m.p.h.; then swinging right round away from the sea there was just time for some fascinating glimpses of the harbour, the castle, and the cliffs of the South Foreland, before we entered Hawkesbury St. tunnel. This extends for half a mile under the chalk downs, and we emerged at the Priory station, as at Folkestone, dead on time; the 77.3 miles from London had taken 95 minutes. This run is typical of the fine locomotive work that is being done year in year out on these expresses, and it shows off well the efficiency of the "Schools" class engines.

A Notable British Canal Lift

Raising Barges 50 ft. by Electric Elevator

CANALS provide one of the oldest means of transport. Although traffic along them is comparatively slow, it is cheap, and in spite of the advantages of speedier means of transport they are being more extensively employed, especially in Germany, where a great national system of waterways has been built up.

Perhaps the greatest of the difficulties that the builders of canals have to contend with is that of linking up sections at various levels, or providing access to other waterways in similar conditions. Unlike a railway, a canal cannot be constructed at any point with a gradient, however slight, and locks therefore have to be built in order to enable barges to pass from one level to another. This is inconvenient when the height to which vessels have to be raised is large, for long and expensive flights of locks then have to be erected and the passage through them takes up valuable time.

This difficulty can be overcome by using a lift instead of a series of locks. The first lifts were hydraulic in action. Barges at both the higher and lower levels ran into tanks or troughs supported on rams that were moved by water pressure. The tanks were balanced, and the lower one could be made lighter by taking out some of the water. The upper and heavier tank then descended and the lower one was raised.

The Anderton Boat Lift after its reconstruction as an electric lift. We are indebted to the Weaver Navigation Trust for the illustrations to this article.

More recently canal lifts that are operated electrically have been introduced. In these tanks to hold one or more barges are suspended from ropes or cables passing over pulleys and are lifted by means of electric motors. Watertight gates at the ends of the tank enable barges to pass in or out. A famous lift of this kind is that at Niederfinow, in Germany, which was described and illustrated in the "*M.M.*" for December, 1934.

There is a particularly interesting example of a canal lift at Anderton, in Cheshire. This forms part of the Weaver Navigation System in Cheshire, and actually is more than 60 years old. For the first 30 years or so of its existence it was a hydraulic lift. It was then rebuilt as an electric lift, and has since given many years of excellent service. It connects the River Weaver with the Trent and Mersey Canal. The latter is 50 ft. 4 in. above the river, and before the lift was constructed there was much loss of time in the expensive process of transhipping goods from barges in the one waterway to similar vessels in the other.

The lift was opened in 1875. It is situated on an island in the basin of the river and for this reason it was necessary to build an aqueduct to carry the canal over the river to the point where the transfer of barges was to be effected. This aqueduct is 162 ft. 6 in. in length. It is built in three spans and a central web divides it into two channels, each 17 ft. 2 in. wide, that form the approaches to the two tanks of the lift itself.

The Anderton lift in its original form, when it was hydraulic in action.

The two tanks or caissons originally were supported on rams 3 ft. in diameter working in the cylinders of hydraulic presses communicating with each other through valves. They are of wrought iron, and are 75 ft. long and 15 ft. 6 in. wide. When the lift was operated by water pressure, one tank was always at the level of the canal and one at that of the river, except of course during the actual lifts, when they passed each other. A barge to be transferred from the canal to the river was floated into the tank at its own level, and the gates at the open end of the tank were then closed. In the meantime a similar operation was being carried out at the lower tank, if barges were there waiting to be transferred from the river to the canal. A small quantity of water was then drawn from the lower tank. This left the upper tank the heavier of the two and on opening the valves connecting the presses in which the rams worked, this tank moved downward, the lighter one being raised upward until the new levels had been attained. The watertight doors were then opened and the barges proceeded on their way.

Each tank when full of water weighed 252 tons, and only a slight difference in weight was necessary to bring about the change of level. It is calculated that about 5/6th of the power required for transfer were due to it, and the rest was obtained from a small hydraulic accumulator, with a ram 1 ft. 9 in. in diameter, that was used to assist in working the lifts.

In this form the structure remained in use for about 20 years, when corrosion and scoring of the rams made it necessary to replace the canal water previously used in the cylinders of the hydraulic system by condensed water. A small dynamo and battery were installed at the same time in order to supply light and power for warehouses and cranes on the adjoining wharves, and this also supplied power for raising the gates of the tanks and the aqueduct.

Early in the present century it became necessary to make several alterations to the lift, including the renewal of the main rams. This would have caused a lengthy interruption to traffic and it was therefore decided to transform the lift into one of the electrical type. Each tank therefore is now suspended by means of wire ropes passing round overhead pulleys. Counterweights consisting of 252 tons of cast iron hang from the free ends of the ropes, so that comparatively little power is needed to raise a tank, although the total weight moved, including the pulley wheels, is about 570 tons. This power is supplied by an electric motor of 30 h.p., and is applied directly to the pulleys over which the ropes pass.

The whole of the alterations were carried out with only three short stoppages, each lasting a fortnight. The work was completed in May 1907, and it not only reduced the cost of operation, but also speeded up the transference of barges from one waterway to the other. The lift is still working satisfactorily, after a period of operation in its new form of more than 31 years.

It is interesting to compare this veteran British canal lift with the one at Niederfinow to which reference has already been made. The Niederfinow canal lift was opened in March 1934 and is the largest in the world. It is designed to deal with barges up to 1,000 tons in displacement and lifts these to a height of 116 ft. in five minutes. The length of its giant steel trough is 278 ft., or nearly four times that of each of the tanks of the Anderton lift, and its width is 40 ft., the depth of water in it being 8 ft. 3 in. The total weight of this enormous structure is nearly 4,200 tons. Great blocks of concrete about 24 ft. long form the counterweights, but four 75 h.p. motors are sufficiently powerful to raise the huge mass, although the total weight moved is more than 8,000 tons.

Motor Boat's Record Run

Grimsby to Southampton at Over 36 Miles Per Hour

A TRIPLE-SCREW motor lifeboat cruiser built for the R.A.F. by the British Power Boat Co., of Hythe, Southampton, to the design of Mr. Hubert Scott-Paine recently accomplished one of the most remarkable voyages ever made by a motor vessel. This cruiser is 64 ft. long, with a draught of a little more than 3 ft. She has a designed speed of 35 knots, or about 40 m.p.h., and at this speed she can cover a distance of 500 miles without refuelling. At about 24 knots the range is some 800 miles.

The new boat is intended for rescue work in the event of aeroplanes with wheeled undercarriages being forced down at sea. Her high speed makes her particularly suitable for work of this kind, and she is well equipped for her task. Accommodation is provided for a crew of eight, and there is also a hospital bay for four stretcher cases, in addition to a wheelhouse, a chartroom and a wireless cabin.

Three "Power-Napier" Sea Lion engines are fitted in the vessel. These are based on the Napier Lion aero engine, which has been modified and adapted for marine work by the British Power Boat Co. Each engine develops about 500 b.h.p. at about 2,000 r.p.m., though it is believed that they are capable of working up to considerably higher power.

The new triple-screw 64-ft. R.A.F. Cruiser that made the record run from Grimsby to Southampton described on this page. The average speed over this distance of 373 miles was more than 36.2 m.p.h. Our photograph is reproduced by courtesy of The British Power Boat Co., Southampton.

The cruiser was taken on a trial run of well over 700 miles from Southampton to Grimsby and back round the south-east coast. The outward journey occupied a little more than 14 hrs. It was not easy running from the South Foreland up the east coast, and really heavy weather was encountered going across from Cromer to Spurn Head. Across the Wash the vessel was driven hard through confused seas by Mr. Scott-Paine, who was at the helm practically throughout the run.

The behaviour of the boat was so satisfactory on the outward trip that her designer decided to go all out for a record on the return trip. This attempt was remarkably successful, for the voyage of 373 miles from Grimsby to Southampton was completed in an actual travelling time of 10 hrs. 14 min. at an average speed of more than 36.2 m.p.h. This is probably the most remarkable performance ever put up by a motor craft of comparable size and speed.

It had been intended to make the return trip on Monday, 25th May, but owing to fog and cold sleeting rain the start was postponed until the following day. Tuesday turned out to be cold, with an overclouded sky, and visibility was only about six miles, but at 9 a.m. the engines were set in motion, and within 20 minutes the boat had left its mooring berth in Grimsby Inner Dock, passed through the lock and was in the Harbour. The actual voyage commenced at 9.30 a.m. With all three engines full out, a speed of about 30 knots was maintained, and Haille Sands buoy was passed in 18 minutes. A heavy swell was encountered outside the Wash, with occasional patches of severe broken water, and conditions became more and more difficult, visibility being reduced first to about two miles, and later to only a mile. In spite of this and of the high speed, the journey across the Wash was made without discomfort.

Cromer was sighted abeam at 11.43 a.m., and conditions then improved slightly. The sea became smoother, and the waves, from 4 ft. to 5½ ft. in height, lengthened considerably. At 12.15 p.m. the engines were stopped for five minutes to enable accurate petrol readings to be taken, a task that was undertaken every three hours. Up to that time the average speed had been more than 30 knots, or 34.5 m.p.h.

Soon after restarting, visibility further increased to six miles, and the boat passed Yarmouth at 12.44 p.m. riding the smooth swell without difficulty. The fog was gradually becoming thinner, and finally at Orford Ness at 2.8 p.m. the Sun broke through for the first time that day, only to be blotted out again by the time the Sunk Light Vessel was reached. Visibility now improved to 10 miles, however. The waves shortened and became choppy, and about 30 minutes later, when passing the Kentish Knock Light Vessel, quite a sea was working again. Speed had increased, and at this part of the course the average was more than 34 knots. At 3.15 p.m. a stop was made for the second of the three-hourly petrol soundings.

A few minutes after restarting, the vessel ran into heavy seas, which were white capped as far as could be seen. The North Foreland was passed at 3.21 p.m., and the Brake Light Vessel and the South Foreland were sighted abeam some 23 and 33 minutes later, respectively. The sea continued to be very heavy and, backed by a strong wind, was making it hard going for the shipping in the vicinity. Off Dover at 4.0 p.m. in the heaviest sea yet encountered, the cross-Channel steamer was seen throwing the waves rail high. Conditions eased a little after passing Dover Point, and at 4.11 p.m. Folkestone was sighted abeam. Off Dungeness the sea became quite as bad as at Dover, though going was easier as the waves had lengthened.

The clouds were now rapidly disappearing, and by 4.45 the sun was shining strongly, the overcast sky having been replaced by one of shimmering blue, rendering visibility excellent. The boat made a fine picture as she drove through the heavy sea, for the spray thrown up on each side sparkled in the sunlight, and the long pure-white wash left in her wake looked like a street of dazzling snow. The sea continued to be heavy and broken, and Mr. Scott-Paine was constantly at work playing the fast moving little ship with the sea in long and short tacks, for he and indeed all aboard were bent on putting up the best possible performance. Actually, first-class progress had been made, for the average speed was still more than 30 knots.

After passing Beachy Head at 5.50 p.m., the periodic stop was made at 6.15 p.m. to take the petrol readings. The sea was now getting calmer. Brighton was passed a few minutes after restarting. Sea conditions had further improved by 6.48 p.m., when Littlehampton was reached, and for the first time they became perfect off Selsey Bill at 7.7 p.m. Horse Sands Fort outside Portsmouth was sighted at 7.32 p.m., and Stokes Bay Pier and Calshot Light were reached 6 and 14 minutes later respectively. Another 13 minutes sufficed to see the boat at her mooring berth at the factory of the British Power Boat Co.

So regular had the running of the vessel been that she was only a minute ahead of the time set that morning by Mr. Scott-Paine for her arrival. Her average speed of more than 36.2 m.p.h. is a record that is likely to stand for a considerable time.

Imperial Airways Notes

According to the latest figures available, the eight Imperial Airways air liners of the well-known "Hannibal" and "Hercules" class have spent about 52,000 hr. in the air, and have flown a total distance of approximately 5,000,000 miles, since they were put into service in 1931. These splendid Handley-Page four-engined aircraft have been operating night and day, and in all kinds of weather and widely varying climatic conditions, with perfect reliability.

Powerful beacons are being placed at points 30 to 50 miles apart between the aerodromes on the Karachi-Rangoon section of the England-Australia air route to guide night-flying pilots traversing this section. Each beacon is 8 ft. in height and 4 ft. in diameter, and is rated at 1½ kW. The main optical system is surmounted by a red obstruction light, and as the beacon revolves, Morse light signals are flashed skyward.

Some fast timings have been accomplished on the new air mail service between Penang and Hong Kong, and on two occasions recently the full distance of 1,850 miles has been flown in a day. This service provides a connection at Penang with the England-Australia air service, and preparations are already in hand there for the introduction of the Short flying boats next year, as Penang will be one of the refuelling points on the Empire air route. The principal task being carried out is the erection of three huge petrol storage tanks, each of which weighs 11½ tons.

The work of the "finishing school" organised by Imperial Airways to train their pilots for new duties under the Empire air route expansion scheme, as described in the June *"Air News,"* has been taken over by Air Pilots Training Ltd., a new company formed specially for the purpose. The company have taken charge of the Short "Calcutta" flying boat at Hamble and the two Westland "Wessex" aeroplanes at Croydon, which are being used by the school. This step enables the school to be run separately from the ordinary commercial activities of Imperial Airways.

Air Ambulance for British Red Cross Society

The first aeroplane produced in this country solely for use as an air ambulance was christened *"Florence Nightingale"* by Mrs. Mollison at Hanworth recently. It is a Monospar S.T.25 machine, and externally is finished in white, with prominent red crosses to indicate its special purpose. The aeroplane was named in the presence of many Red Cross officials and members, and afterwards was placed at the disposal of the Society for use whenever occasion arises. There is much to be learned regarding the employment of aircraft as air ambulances, and it is expected that the experience to be gained with the *"Florence Nightingale"* will provide useful information.

A Junkers Ju.86 twin-engined air liner. It has a retractable undercarriage, and cruises at 193 m.p.h. Photograph by courtesy of Junkers Flugzeugwerk A.G., Dessau.

The Monospar S.T.25 is a twin-engined low wing monoplane with a span of 40 ft. 2 in., reduced to 14 ft. 10 in. when the wings are folded back. The length of the aeroplane is 26 ft. 4 in. and the height is 7 ft. 10 in. It can climb at the rate of 700 ft. per min., and the greatest height it can attain is 14,000 ft. Normally the cabin is equipped to seat five passengers, but this arrangement of course is altered in the air ambulance. The large door on the starboard side of the fuselage, and the hinged portion of roof immediately above it, together provide ample room for the easy entry of either passengers or stretcher cases.

* * * *

The total weight of flying cargoes carried last year in Canada was over 27,000,000 lb., and more than 18,000 prospectors were carried during the same period.

Air France Developments

Reference was made in the May *"Air News"* pages to the important additions being made to the fleet of Air France. According to the latest reports, the company have ordered a further eight Dewoitine 338 triple-engined monoplanes, carrying 25 passengers. When delivered they will be employed on the Baghdad-Saigon air route.

The two large flying boats ordered from the Loire-et-Olivier Company for the Air France air mail service between Dakar and northern Brazil have been completed. Both flying boats are of the four-engined type, and one, the Loire 102, has completed successful trial flights at St. Nazaire, where the maker's factory is situated. The other vessel is of the Loire-et-Olivier 47 type, and has been shipped to Antibes, where it will be assembled and will make its maiden flight. It can carry four passengers in addition to 10 cwt. of mail and a crew of five, and even against a 30 m.p.h. head wind it has a range of 2,000 miles. It is expected to prove capable of a top speed of 225 m.p.h.

Air France have not yet definitely decided in favour of flying boats for this South Atlantic service, and they have ordered two large four-engined landplanes for it, so that they will be able to compare the respective merits of the two types of aircraft in actual use.

Huge Sikorsky Flying-Boat Designed

The Sikorsky Aviation Corporation of America are said to have completed the designing of a huge six-engined flying boat suitable for trans-Atlantic service. It resembles the Short flying boats now being built at Rochester for Imperial Airways in having the wing mounted directly upon the hull. This wing will be of 180 ft. span. Each of the six engines will develop 1,000 h.p.

The new flying boat will be about 55 tons in weight, and it is anticipated that it will have a cruising speed of 170 m.p.h. At night the cabins in the great hull of the boat will provide sleeping accommodation for 48 passengers.

King Ghazi Buys a "Dragonfly"

King Ghazi of Iraq has bought a D.H. "Dragonfly" for his personal use. It was flown from this country to Iraq by Mr. P. de Havilland, and its arrival at the private royal landing ground, Baghdad, was witnessed by the King and other high officers. The appearance of the aeroplane is very striking, as the wings and fuselage are finished in gold, with the Iraq crown in gilt metal on each side. The King has appropriately named it *"The Golden Eagle."*

The cabin equipment is on a more luxurious scale than in the ordinary "Dragonfly," and includes a bookcase, a small cabinet to contain luncheon, and a folding table on which meals can be served or maps laid out and studied. The King makes most of his journeys about Iraq by air, and this further evidence of his appreciation of the advantages of air travel may do much to encourage civil aviation in that country.

King Ghazi of Iraq, in white suit and bareheaded, inspecting his D.H. "Dragonfly" upon its arrival at the private Royal landing ground, Baghdad. The photographs on this page are by our reader A. O. Kouyoumjian.

British Gliding Record

A new British gliding record was achieved on 5th July last by Mr. P. A. Wills, a young London shipping merchant. He took off from Dunstable at noon, and after a flight of about 110 miles he landed at Pakefield, in Suffolk, at 4.30 p.m. The highest altitude he reached was 3,600 ft. when near Whipsnade, but low clouds frequently forced him down several hundreds of feet. After each drop he regained the lost height by a wide circling movement. The glider flown by Mr. Wills was British-built and of a new high-performance type.

The previous record for a flight in a British-made glider was set up by Mr. A. L. Slater, of Matlock, who on Easter Sunday this year flew 75 miles and attained a height of 4,500 ft.

Badges for R.A.F. Machines

The aircraft of the many R.A.F. units will soon be adorned with the badge of the unit to which they belong, in addition to bearing the ordinary R.A.F. markings that have always been a familiar feature of Service aeroplanes. Under a scheme of the Air Council, a series of unit badges is being designed. Each completed design is submitted to the King, and on receiving his approval is endorsed with the words "Approved—Edward R.I." The reproduction of that design is then authorised, and after it has been registered at the College of Arms the original, bearing the King's words, is presented to the unit concerned. It is easy to understand that these original designs will be greatly treasured.

The badge of each unit will be different, of course, but a standard type of frame has been adopted. It consists of a circle coloured R.A.F. blue, bearing the name of the unit and a reproduction of the Imperial Crown, and bordered by a wreath of laurel in gold. The motto chosen for the unit appears in a scroll beneath the circle. The aircraft of operational units will be further distinguished by special backgrounds to their badges. In the case of bomber, torpedo-bomber and bomber-transport aeroplanes the background will take the shape of a bomb; for fighter squadron aeroplanes it will be in the shape of a spear-head and for army co-operation, general reconnaissance and flying boat squadron aircraft it will be a six-pointed star.

New Depot Ships for Deutsche Luft Hansa

The new depot ship *"Ostmark"* built by the Hamaldt shipyard at Kiel for the Deutsche Luft Hansa is now in service. After undergoing sea trials in the Gulf of Lubeck she sailed for Bathurst, in Gambia. The ship has been designed and built to take the place of the two regular depot ships *"Westfalen"* and *"Schwabenland,"* when either of them is withdrawn for overhaul. Her deck fittings include a catapult for sending off a loaded flying boat and a crane for hoisting it back on board when it returns. The *"Ostmark"* is of about 2,000 tons displacement, and her Diesel engines give her a speed of 15 knots. The construction of a fourth depot ship is now in hand.

The King of Iraq's "Dragonfly." The wings and fuselage are finished in gold.

The England-Johannesburg Race

The longest and most interesting air race since the MacRobertson event in October 1934 will take place next month, when an air race from London to Johannesburg, South Africa, will be flown. It is the idea of Mr. I. W. Schlesinger, a wealthy South African industrialist, and he has made it practicable by offering prizes totalling £10,000. The largest prize is £4,000, and it will go to the pilot who completes the flight in the shortest time. There will be a handicap section, and the prizes offered in this are £3,000, £1,500, £1,000 and £500 respectively.

The race is being organised by the Royal Aero Club of this country at the invitation of Mr. Schlesinger, and has the approval of the Air Ministry and of the Government of South Africa. The distance to be covered by the competitors is about 6,500 miles, and the route selected lies by way of Vienna, Cairo, Khartum and Salisbury, Rhodesia. All these places will be control points where landing will be compulsory, and it is probable that several intermediate points, where landing will be permissible but not compulsory, will also be established.

One important difference between this race and that to Australia in 1934 is that it is restricted to pilots and aircraft of the British Empire, whereas the earlier race was open to every country. Another point is that as the race is being organised at very short notice, there is not sufficient time for aircraft manufacturers to design and build aeroplanes specially for the event. The race will therefore be a thrilling test of current types of aeroplanes, and the result will be awaited with keen interest.

Long-Range Wireless on the Empire Air Routes

Remarkable examples of long-range wireless communication between air liners in flight on the Empire air routes, and between the machines and ground stations, occasionally occur under favourable conditions. Not long ago a wireless station in Cairo picked up short-wave signals sent out by an air liner flying more than 1,000 miles away, along the route to Capetown; and on another occasion two machines on the Africa route were in touch with each other by wireless when about 2,000 miles apart.

An Imperial Airways aeroplane flying across Africa has established communication with a wireless station in England, in this instance the distance being roughly 4,000 miles. Even longer range communication has taken place, as when a wireless amateur in Cape Province, South Africa, picked up short-wave messages sent out by an air liner flying 5,000 miles away.

How Seamless Steel Tubes are Made

Piercing and Rolling White Hot Ingots

WE are so accustomed to the presence in our streets of steel poles supporting lamps, or the trolley wires needed by tramcars, that we are apt to pass them unnoticed unless they have been erected in inconvenient positions. Yet they are of the greatest importance, for without them it would be difficult to find suitable positions for the lamps that light our towns and cities. They also provide the best means of suspending overhead wires of all kinds, and many of them are used to carry notices guiding motorists. They are really tubes and the modern practice is to make them in one piece, without seams or any other joints that have to be welded. Such tubes can readily be produced with "steps" in them that reduce their diameter in stages. These are lighter in weight and cheaper than tubes of the same diameter throughout their length, and have no ledges, pockets or traps in which moisture can collect and set up corrosion, as the easy flow at the shoulders of the steppings gives a free run for rain water.

Another advantage of providing steps is that the tubes are given a symmetrical streamlined appearance. It is therefore unnecessary to add collars or ornamental work that might form corners harbouring moisture, and even where these are thought desirable they can be cut down to a minimum, especially when brackets or arms have to be added to carry the lamps or other fittings supported by the poles. It is not essential that these seamless tubes should be perfectly plain, however, for ornamentation in the form of straight or curved fluting can be introduced while they are being made, and attractively shaped and designed base sections also can be produced and are very largely used.

Tagging the end of a tube with a steam hammer in preparation for drawing it through dies to make steps. The illustrations to this article are reproduced by courtesy of the British Mannesman Tube Co. Ltd.

Switch gear and automatic timing apparatus are now often placed in the bases of lighting standards, and this is so complicated and delicate in action that it must be well protected. There is no difficulty in cutting an opening in the base section of a seamless pole and fitting it with a door, complete with lock and key to give ready access to mechanism of this kind, and, weather strips can be fixed above the door to prevent water from entering in wet weather and interfering with the apparatus inside. Openings also can readily be cut below ground level, in order to allow cables or gas supply pipes to be passed through.

Seamless tubes combine strength and lightness, for they are made of high tensile steel. They are easy to handle when they are being taken over rough country and during erection, and their strength makes them practically unbreakable. They even survive the impacts of heavy motor vehicles crashing into them. Many accidents of this kind have occurred, and the poles have invariably maintained their upright positions, although in some cases they have been damaged. Usually there is no interference whatever with the purposes for which the poles were designed. For instance, lamp-posts of this type have continued in service after motor coaches have collided violently with them. The mere fact that in these circumstances the poles continue to stand up is in itself a great advantage, for they probably would do much damage, and cause injury to those passing by or standing near, if they were to collapse, especially in busy thoroughfares.

The interest of these poles extends to their manufacture, for they pass through many spectacular processes. They are made in one piece from hot steel billets or ingots. These are cast at the steel works, where molten metal is tapped from a furnace and run into a huge ladle holding several tons. From this the steel is poured into seamless vertical moulds, round in cross-section, that hold the exact quantity of metal required for making the tube, and there it is left to cool.

The ingot cast in this manner is the raw material of the pole maker, whose first task is to pierce a hole through it. He places it in a gas fired furnace until it is white-hot, and soft enough for his purpose. This takes several hours, but large furnaces are used and they hold a sufficient number of ingots to keep up a constant supply for the tube-making machinery.

When the ingot, or bloom, as it is called, is ready, it is lifted out of the furnace by the mechanical fingers of an overhead electric crane and carried away to the piercing mill. It is astonishing to see how easily these masses of white-hot metal are moved. There seems to be no more difficulty in placing one of them exactly where it is wanted than in lifting a lump of sugar in a pair of tongs and placing it in a teacup.

In the piercing mill the ingot, which may be about 3 ft. long and 18 in. in diameter, is firmly gripped between three rollers, set at slight angles to each other. The rollers are turned at high speed by a 2,500 h.p. steam engine acting through speed-increasing helical gearing, and they spin the white-hot ingot round. In the meantime the piercing head advances from the opposite end of the mill. This is a water-cooled steel bar, 3 in. or 4 in. in thickness, and has a sharp point that is forced into the end of the rotating bloom. The piercer may be withdrawn once or perhaps twice to allow it to cool, but eventually it is pushed right through from end to end, and in this one operation the ingot is changed into a crude tube, from 6 ft. to 8 ft. in length, with a hole about 4 in. in diameter passing through it.

The newly-made tube is still white-hot and is immediately carried on a electrically-controlled bogey to the tube mill, which also is known as the "Pilger" mill. There a mandrel or rod with a tapering leading end is forced into the hole to open it out to the size required. Hydraulic power is used for this operation, and the bloom is pushed steadily forward against the mandrel until it has passed right over the tapering point on to the part with parallel sides that forms the inside diameter.

The drawbench, on which tubes are stepped. The dies through which they are drawn are mounted on a face plate.

The Pilger mill carries out two operations, for while the hole is being widened out the tube itself is reduced to the required outside diameter. Pressing it forward over the mandrel brings it into engagement with specially designed rolls exerting enormous pressure, which squeeze the steel and roll it out. The whole operation must be completed while the metal is almost white hot, and the steady thumps of the rollers and the hiss of steam issuing from various openings as the metal is crushed into shape combine to strengthen the impression of the exertion of tremendous power.

The mill works from one end of the pierced ingot to the other until the whole mass has been dealt with, and the effect of this spectacular process is to stretch the bloom out into a narrower tube of greater length. From a billet of the size already suggested a tube 50 ft. to 60 ft. long may be produced, but one measuring 178 ft. in length has been produced in the ordinary course of operation in the mills of The British Mannesman Tube Company Ltd., makers of these weldless steel poles. This tube is $8\frac{5}{8}$ in. in outside diameter, and is the longest ever produced without seam or join of any kind.

The piercing head penetrating a white hot ingot in the piercing mill, and forming it into a crude tube.

The mandrel is then extracted from the tube, and this is carried forward to the cutting bench, where its ends are squared and it is weighed and allowed to cool down. Careful examination follows. The tube is supported at its ends on pairs of rollers that rotate and so turn it round, and it is then easy to see if it is straight. If necessary, irregularities of this kind are corrected in a press. At this stage the tubes are cut to the length required. It is more economical to produce them in great lengths and then to cut them than it is to make them in short pieces separately.

The steps that reduce the width of a finished steel pole in stages towards the top have now to be made. The sizes of the steps vary, but a pole with a width at its base of 8 in. may have upper sections 7 in. and 6 in. in diameter. The reductions are made by drawing the red-hot tube through a die. For this purpose one end of it is "tagged." This means that after heating the end is beaten down by a steam hammer to form a surface that can be gripped by toothed jaws. The end is threaded through the die on the drawbench, where this operation is carried out. It is then seized by jaws attached to a sliding carriage that is clipped to a continuous chain hauled by an electric motor, and these pull it through the die, which narrows it down, and produces the smooth symetrical step.

The size of the die used in this process of course is that required for the step being made, and the operation is repeated for the other steps to be given to the pole. All the dies required for any size of tube are set up in suitable positions around a face plate on the drawbench, so that the whole of the drawing operation can be finished quickly while the metal is hot enough. It may then be necessary to straighten the tube again, and in that case it is reheated and passed through a press.

The many types and varied designs of poles that can be seen in our streets are produced in this manner and their special features are introduced during the drawing operation or by other manipulation. For instance, lamp posts vary considerably in size and form according to the system of lighting in which they are to be used. Some carry the lamps on top and others have arms from 3 ft. to 10 ft. in length. In many cases the poles are fixed at the sides of the road, and wires are stretched between them so that the lamps can be suspended in the middle. The poles for these conditions require special designing and the loads they have to support must be taken into account in order that they are not deflected or bent to a noticeable extent when in service. Allowance also must be made for the effect of wind pressure both on the poles and on the lamps they carry. The bases of the poles rest upon horizontal steel plates placed deep in hard ground or set in concrete.

For the information contained in this article we are indebted to the courtesy of The British Mannesman Tube Co. Ltd., Newport, Mon.

Belfast to Liverpool by Air Liner

Impressions of a Cross-Channel Flight

By O. S. Nock, B.Sc., D.I.C.

It is one of the marvels of this age of speed that the fastest means of travel are incomparably the most soothing and restful. The smooth even pace of a really fast train like *"The Silver Jubilee"* dulls one's sense of speed completely, unless of course you are clocking the quarter-mile posts (!), but the progress of a modern air liner at 200 m.p.h. is so sedate that anyone seeking the thrill of sheer speed would be sadly disappointed. On a recent air journey from Belfast to Liverpool by Railway Air Services there was an entire absence of bustle, formalities were conducted in a quiet leisurely way, and the watchword as far as the passengers were concerned might well have been, "There's no hurry!" Yet from port to port we averaged 130 m.p.h.

One of the few disadvantages of air travel is that the ports are necessarily situated some miles from the centre of big cities. In his speech at the opening of Gatwick airport, in June last, the Secretary of State for Air said that there would never be an airport in Central London unless the population grew so air minded and so unæsthetic as to pull down every tree in Hyde Park. So it is with other cities. In this country, although the speed while in the air is infinitely faster than anything that has yet been regularly scheduled on land, unless you happen to live close to the aerodromes at each end the fastest means of travel between cities up to about 100 miles apart is still by train. It is when the distance exceeds 200 miles, or the sea has to be crossed, that air transport has such a tremendous advantage. The R.A.S. time of $5\frac{1}{2}$ hours from Glasgow Central Station to Victoria Station, London, including the road journeys at each end, is a big improvement on the $7\frac{1}{2}$-hour run of *"The Royal Scot,"* while $4\frac{1}{2}$ hours from Belfast to London puts the 12 hours 20 minutes of the *"Ulster Express"* completely in the shade.

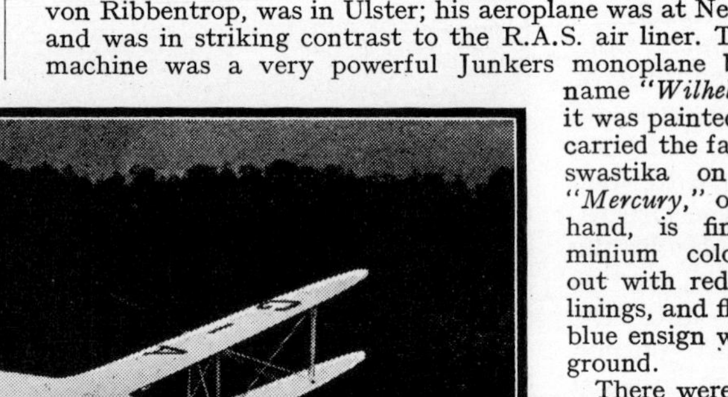

The Railway Air Services liner "Mercury," a de Havilland D.H.86 machine. The photographs on this page are reproduced by courtesy of Railway Air Services.

The Belfast airport was, until recently, at Aldergrove, on the shores of Lough Neagh near Antrim, but a short time ago it was transferred to Newtownards in County Down, much nearer the city, but still 10 miles out. A comfortable car picked up passengers in Belfast at about 8.15 a.m. and a pleasant run of about 25 minutes brought us to the airport. It was a very still morning; a hot sun was breaking through and slowly dispersing a mist that hung over the land after a night of rain. Scrabo Hill to the north of the aerodrome, crowned by a monument to a former Marquess of Londonderry, looked very lovely through a thin veil of cloud. Just as we arrived, the air liner *"Mercury"* was approaching, having left Renfrew, the Glasgow airport, at 7.50 a.m. She flew right across, circled round and made a beautiful landing facing what wind there was. *"Mercury"* is one of the well-known de Havilland D.H.86 machines, having four engines each of 200 h.p. and accommodation for eight passengers.

At the time of my trip the German Ambassador-at-large, Herr von Ribbentrop, was in Ulster; his aeroplane was at Newtownards, and was in striking contrast to the R.A.S. air liner. The German machine was a very powerful Junkers monoplane bearing the name *"Wilhelm Siegert"*; it was painted black and carried the familiar Nazi swastika on the tail. *"Mercury,"* on the other hand, is finished aluminium colour picked out with red and green linings, and flew the pale blue ensign while on the ground.

There were four other passengers besides myself, and while our luggage was being weighed and other formalities gone through the machine was being refuelled. The passenger compartment of these liners is most comfortable. It is just wide enough to accommodate two passengers abreast in cosy armchair seats, one on each side of the central gangway. Windows extend almost the whole length of the compartment and give a splendid look-out. Luggage and mails are carried in the tail end of the fuselage.

On the stroke of time, 9 a.m., we were off. First of all we ran across the grass to the extreme south end of the landing space. The machine floated smoothly over the uneven patches on the ground, and then it was neatly pivoted round in readiness to take off up wind. Then, full throttle; the engines roared, and after a very gentle start *"Mercury"* developed a truly lightning acceleration. In less than a quarter of a mile we were travelling at 90 m.p.h. and at this speed we took-off, though the exact moment was very difficult to judge.

"Jupiter," of Railway Air Services, at Speke aerodrome. This machine also is a de Havilland D.H.86.

We soared over the town of Newtownards, all the time swinging round on to our true course, which was approximately south-east; while the machine is banking you get the rather curious impression that the earth below is tilting up towards you—the machine seems perfectly horizontal. We were soon flying over Strangford Lough. Newtownards lies at the head of this long inlet of the sea and the country on both sides of the water is very flat. Fields showed as a chequered pattern; I could just pick out the ruins of Grey Abbey on the eastern shore, and westward a long line of white cumulus clouds sailed level with us where earth and sky blended in the haze.

The tide was out, and from the eastern shore curiously shaped spits of sand trailed out into the water; from above they looked like so many fantastic worms. The long peninsula that separates Strangford Lough from the sea is never more than five miles wide, and at about 9.6 a.m. we passed over the coast near Cloghy Bay. The whole Ards peninsula is very flat and it could be seen stretching away to the south in a long succession of capes and bays, without a sign of hill or cliff, until it faded into the distance.

And now sky and sea merged together in a soft blue haze; far below, the water was an intense ultramarine; a few detached little clouds sailed high overhead, and the sense of motion became almost imperceptible. With a complete absence of vibration, the cosy well-ventilated cabin and ever-present drone of the engines induced a strong desire for sleep, and several of the other passengers were nodding over their newspapers before long. Outside, the sun flashed on the silvery aluminium paint of the wings and spars, there was only the slightest motion on the sea below, and it seemed incredible that we were travelling at a land speed of 210 m.p.h.

Refuelling the air liner "Mercury" at Newtownards immediately before the flight described in this article.

The air speed of this machine is 143 m.p.h.; this is the actual speed at which we should travel in perfectly still air, but the land speed naturally varies according to the direction and strength of the wind. In the early stages of this flight conditions were most favourable and the Captain expected to reach Liverpool at 9.59 a.m. The motion was generally very smooth and this is usually the case over the sea in fine weather; occasionally the machine dipped slightly, giving a momentary sensation like that of a lift beginning to descend, but each time this motion was instantly checked.

In less than 10 minutes after our last sight of the Irish coast we were nearing the Isle of Man. Although we were flying at about 2,000 ft. the haze restricted visibility to about six or seven miles; this in a way was most fortunate, for we came upon the island quite suddenly, and a fascinating sight it was! Seen against the strong sunlight, coast and mountain appeared alike as one bluish-grey shadow; queer, devoid of all detail, it looked a veritable phantom isle riding out at sea. But we were approaching at nearly 200 m.p.h.; detail was quickly revealed. To the north was Niarbyl Bay, where the oddly named peak Cronk-ny-Irey-Lhaa sweeps down to the sea; we were heading straight for Port Erin, and at the southern end of the island lay the Calf of Man, a small rocky islet.

In less time than it takes to describe we had reached the coast and Ronaldsway aerodrome lay far below on our left. Port Erin lies on the western shore of a narrow isthmus only two miles wide, and as we crossed to the opposite coast the aspect of the land changed entirely. Looking backward now the sun was behind, and the whole countryside was picked out in a wealth of exquisite detail. Right below was the picturesque haven of Port St. Mary, its little stone jetty and lighthouse standing out vividly against the blue of the sea; southward to the Calf stretched a rock-wall of magnificent cliffs, while to the north behind Castletown rose the big hills that run northward like a backbone. A red-funnelled paddle steamer was making its way up the coast, leaving a foaming wake that from above looked dazzling white against the deep blue of the sea. It was just as though we had been taken for a novel and lightning tour of the southern end of the island, but although its geography had been so quickly unfolded and almost as soon lost again in the haze, there was none of the breathless haste in seeing beautiful country from a fast train, and the illusion that we were travelling quite slowly remained perfect.

Looking out through the starboard windows of "Mercury" approaching the Isle of Man. In the distance on the right is the Calf of Man.

Up to now the wind had been northerly and had helped us not a little in attaining our high land speed, but after we had passed over the Isle of Man it veered round eastward and became quite strong; our air speed of course remained constant at 143 m.p.h. but our land speed was reduced considerably and it was soon evident that we should not reach Liverpool airport until some minutes after what had been anticipated earlier. We came down to about 1,500 ft. and the Captain told me afterwards that the side wind became so strong that he had no less than eleven degrees of drift on. The angle of drift is the angle between the course and the direction the machine would be flying if there were no wind, and from this the navigating officer can calculate the strength and direction of the wind. Just as in the case of a ship, the Captain of an air liner has to make a log of the journey that includes all such particulars; the reports are handed in at each aerodrome where the machine calls, and from these notes weather conditions are wirelessed to all flying stations in the British Isles. The actual steering of these machines is done almost entirely by compass.

As we approached the English coast the haze, which had shown signs of clearing as we came eastward, slowly changed into a grey mist that foretold rain; the air was still too thick to see any great distance but the sea became covered in white breakers. The change in the weather was as surprising as it was complete. Over the Isle of Man it had every appearance of a sultry summer day, calm and quite settled; now the grey clouds were racing across the sky and the machine was bumping a little more frequently.

We were now flying over the steamer track leading to the Mersey; a big merchantman homeward bound was quickly overtaken, and just beyond, a graceful schooner was similarly overhauled. Then at 9.55 a.m. we passed over the Bar lightship. Here is the beginning of the narrow channel that leads through the shallows of the Mersey estuary into the port of Liverpool; it is fascinating enough when seen from the water, especially at night when the gas buoys are flashing red and white, but from the air the winding zig-zag course can be seen in its entirety. The worst bends are marked by the Crosby and Formby lightships, and the long double chain of buoys looks rather like the cork floats of a drift net when seen from an aeroplane. Between this chain of dots steamers were coming and going, and dredgers were at work in several places.

By now the Lancashire coast showed up as a long grey line, the clouds were quite low, there was a hint of rain, and then quite suddenly out of the mist we came upon the mouth of the Mersey, and New Brighton lay below on the right. We flew right up the course of the river, over miles of docks and the shipyards of the Wirral side. Smoke and the mist combined to give the impression that there was fog below though actually we were travelling through the fringe of a cloud. The speed seemed much higher now and familiar landmarks followed each other so quickly that many others went unrecognised.

After crossing the city the air cleared again, though it was now raining hard; we came out over the wide inner basin of the Mersey, past Garston docks, and then the engines went suddenly quiet and we began to turn and descend. Banking moderately we traced out a perfect circle, over the vast railway yard at Speke Junction where every wagon and siding stood out clear to the smallest detail, right out over the river again, and so down to make a beautifully smooth landing at Speke airport. It was 10.8 a.m. and we had covered the 147 odd miles from Newtownards in 68 minutes, an average speed of 130 m.p.h.

So ended a fascinating and most enjoyable trip. To the very end the impression that we had not travelled really fast persisted, though the striking weather changes alone were ample evidence to the contrary, quite apart from the brief time we were in flight.

Fine Performances on the Liverpool Services

A good example of the consistently fine running put up on the *"Liverpool Flyer"* occurred recently, when the train was divided. The first portion left Lime Street at 5.20 p.m. and was booked to run the 188.2 miles to Willesden Junction non-stop in 191 minutes. No. 6209, *"Princess Beatrice,"* a 4–6–2, was the engine, with that prince of drivers L. A. Earl of Camden at the regulator. The load was 390 tons behind the tender.

Speed was 71 m.p.h. as early as Allerton, 5.7 miles out of Liverpool, but a very severe check at Runcorn caused Weaver Junction to be passed nearly 3 minutes late. Wonderful running followed with speeds of 71 to 75 m.p.h. all the way up the gentle rise to Crewe, and despite a signal check approaching the station that important centre was passed on time, 35½ miles from Liverpool in 43 minutes.

With the most scrupulous observance of the slacks at Norton Bridge, Stafford and Polesworth colliery the 75½ miles on to Rugby took 73 minutes, the highest speed being 83½ m.p.h. near Tamworth; but after a brilliant recovery from the usual slowing through Rugby the train was brought practically to a dead stand by adverse signals at Weedon. In consequence Earl ran more moderately for some distance, but beyond Wolverton he opened out to some purpose and ran the 15 uphill miles from Bletchley to Tring at an average speed of 74 m.p.h.! The train passed Tring summit 161.9 miles in 165½ minutes, 2½ minutes early in spite of all delays.

Descending towards London speed was up to 83½ at King's Langley. Another severe delay was experienced at Watford, but a glorious finish with yet another maximum of 80 m.p.h. brought the train into Willesden on time. The net time for the 188.2 miles was only 177 minutes, the run having been made in 14 minutes under schedule at an average speed of 63.8 m.p.h.

The Liverpool expresses altogether have been distinguishing themselves recently and on one occasion the first part of the down *"Merseyside Express,"* loaded to 510 tons gross behind the tender, made one of the fastest runs ever recorded with so heavy a train. Signal checks made the time out to Tring 41¾ minutes for the 31.7 miles, but the 48.6 miles from there to Hillmorton signal box were covered at an average speed of 69.3 m.p.h.! This performance was all the more meritorious in that the engine was not a "Princess" 4–6–2, but a "Royal Scot," No. 6111, *"Royal Fusilier,"* ably handled by Driver Bishop of Camden. The lost time was more than regained by the time Rugby was passed, after which the express ran punctually all the way to Liverpool.

We are indebted to Mr. O. S. Nock for these timings.

"The Ulster Express" made a good run with a heavy load between Crewe and Euston recently. The train left Crewe 17 minutes late but arrived at Euston on time, having covered the 158 miles in 148 minutes, at an average start-to-stop speed of 64 m.p.h. The train was made up of 14 vehicles weighing 421 tons tare, or about 445 tons fully loaded, and the engine was 4–6–2 No. 6204, *"Princess Louise,"* in charge of Driver F. C. Brooker and Fireman R. Speed, of Camden. Between Rugby and Willesden the average speed was 70 m.p.h. for 77 miles.

G.N.R. of Ireland 4-4-0 compound locomotive No. 85 "Merlin" at Amiens Street, Dublin. The engine is painted in the striking blue livery referred to in these pages last April. Photograph by Mr. O. S. Nock.

Southern Summer Services

The provision of more and faster trains is the keynote of the S.R. Summer services that have been in operation since Sunday, 5th July. In addition improvements have been made in various through and cross-country services. The growth of traffic in recent years has been such that many of the trains previously introduced as reliefs are now included in the timetable as regular services.

Various West of England trains have been speeded up; 17 minutes have been deducted from the timing of the 10.35 a.m. from Waterloo to Ilfracombe on weekdays, and Weymouth is now reached in the fastest time yet achieved, 2 hrs. 54 min. The journey time of the up *"Bournemouth Belle"* Pullman express has been reduced by 8 minutes. An interesting feature of the new services is the standardisation of the departure times from Southampton Central of the up Bournemouth and Weymouth trains. These now depart at 20 minutes past each hour from 11.20 a.m. to 7.20 p.m. inclusive, each weekday.

The new signalling and track improvements between Waterloo and Surbiton, that were described in last month's issue, are proving their worth during the conduct of the heavy Summer traffic.

Additional electric trains are being provided as necessary at week-ends between London and various South Coast resorts. On Saturdays throughout the season intensive services to the Kent Coast are being maintained, and there is also a heavy list of extra trains on the Portsmouth route.

Cross-country and coastal services between Sussex and the West of England show a total saving of 210 minutes as compared with previous years. The through service between Margate and Ramsgate and Birmingham and Wolverhampton in conjunction with the G.W.R. is being duplicated on Saturdays.

Names for New G.W.R. Locomotives

After the "Castles" and the "Halls," "Granges" and "Manors" are to be added to the series of class names of G.W.R. locomotives, and 10 of each of the new classes are being constructed this year. Their numbers and names are as follows: No. 6800, *"Arlington Grange"*; No. 6801, *"Aylburton Grange"*; No. 6802, *"Bampton Grange"*; No. 6803, *"Bucklebury Grange"*; No. 6804, *"Brockington Grange"*; No. 6805, *"Broughton Grange"*; No. 6806, *"Blackwell Grange"*; No. 6807, *"Birchwood Grange"*; No. 6808, *"Beenham Grange"*; No. 6809, *"Burghclere Grange"*; No. 7800, *"Anthony Manor"*; No. 7801, *"Ashley Manor"*; No. 7802, *"Bradley Manor"*; No. 7803, *"Boston Manor"*; No. 7804, *"Baydon Manor"*; No. 7805, *"Broome Manor"*; No. 7806, *"Cockington Manor"*; No. 7807, *"Compton Manor"*; No. 7808, *"Cookham Manor"*; No. 7809, *"Childrey Manor."*

L.M.S.R. Locomotive News

In addition to the naming of class "5P5F" locomotives Nos. 5157 and 5158 *"The Glasgow Highlander"* and *"Glasgow Yeomanry"* respectively, No. 5156 of the same class has been named *"The Ayrshire Yeoman."* The "Royal Scot" class locomotive No. 6127 formerly *"Novelty"* is now *"The Old Contemptible."*

Recent withdrawals include three further rebuilt "Claughtons," No. 5957 and No. 6013, both fitted with Caprotti valve gear, and No. 5993 with Walschaerts valve gear. The ranks of the Horwich type four-cylinder 4–6–0s also are being depleted, and further 4–6–0 locomotives of the L.N.W.R. "Prince of Wales" and mixed traffic classes have been scrapped. The scrapping of the former L.N.W.R. "George The Fifth" and the similar superheated "Precursor" classes is proceeding with great rapidity. Engines recently withdrawn include No. 5270, *"Marmion,"* the last of the few "Precursors" that were superheated without being rebuilt. These engines retained their original slide valve cylinders and their short smoke-boxes. *"Engineer Watford,"* the last of the former L.N.W.R. engineer's service locomotives, has been scrapped. It was the last of the 2–4–0 "Jumbos" with 6 ft. driving wheels and straight-link motion.

L.M.S.R. two-cylinder 4-6-0 locomotive No. 5157 "The Glasgow Highlander." This engine is attached to St. Rollox Depot, Glasgow, and is fitted with tablet exchange gear for use on the Highland Section. Photograph by courtesy of the L.M.S.R.

L.M.S.R. Rolling Stock Programme

In addition to the building of 687 passenger vehicles that are to be completed this year, the L.M.S.R. are carrying out an extensive modernisation programme of the existing coaching stock. The low waistline, giving deeper windows and better observation facilities, that has characterised more recent vehicles, is being standardised as a permanent feature for main line stock.

Under a plan inaugurated in 1933 for the replacement of 70 of the older dining cars, 42 new cars have been put into service, and the remaining 28 will be built either this year or next. To replace the cars in Scotland formerly operated by the Pullman Car Company Ltd., but since taken over by the L.M.S.R., seven composite first-third dining cars are to be built during 1936-7. In addition 20 new kitchen cars for use in excursion trains are to be introduced.

A plan that was begun in 1934 for the replacement or renovation of the whole L.M.S.R. stock of sleeping cars will be completed this month. This has involved the building of 13 new first-class sleepers and of 13 composite cars; also the renovation of 64 first-class vehicles and of 12 composites. In a stock of nearly 17,000 passenger vehicles the L.M.S.R. have 200 dining cars and 232 sleeping cars.

The Fastest Train in the World

The record for the fastest start-to-stop run in the world, which has been held since May 1933 by Diesel articulated trains of the German State Railway, has passed to the United States. The *"Super-Chief"* of the Atchison, Topeka and Santa Fé system on its run from Chicago to Los Angeles is scheduled to cover the 202.4 miles from La Junta to Dodge City in 145 minutes, at an average start-to-stop speed of 83.7 m.p.h. A twin-unit Diesel-engined locomotive of 3,600 b.h.p. hauls the train of seven to nine cars weighing 500 to 650 tons.

Acceleration of *"The Granite City"*

With the acceleration from Monday, 6th July, of *"The Granite City"* express from Glasgow to Aberdeen by 33 minutes, a timing of 3 hrs. 12 min., the fastest on record, has been instituted between these cities. Stops are made at Perth and Stonehaven only. The 1.40 p.m. from Glasgow now makes the journey in 3 hrs. 18 min., an acceleration of 37 min., and stops only at Gleneagles, Perth and Stonehaven.

Other important L.M.S.R. improvements in Scotland include accelerations between Glasgow and Inverness, together with the running of a new express at 4.30 p.m. from Glasgow to Inverness. By connection at Perth, this train affords a one-day service from the Midlands and North of England to the Highland capital.

The giant name of 58 letters that distinguishes the North Wales station shown in the timetables as "Llanfair." The special canvas streamer seen in this photograph is in use during the Summer season only. (H.R.C. prize-winning photograph.)

Streamlined "Mikados" for the L.N.E.R.

The new series of four 2–8–2 passenger locomotives, the names of which were given in last month's *"M.M.,"* are generally similar in design to the existing No. 2002, *"Earl Marischal,"* in having piston valves instead of the poppet valves of No. 2001, *"Cock o' the North."* They are however streamlined in a similar manner to the A4 class "Pacifics" of the *"Silver Link"* series. This streamlining has been carried out in order to render the engines more suitable for service on the exposed parts of the line between Edinburgh and Aberdeen, where strong north-east winds are frequently encountered.

The first of the new 2–6–2 or "Prairie" type tender engines are now in service. An illustration and description of the first engine built, No. 4771 *"Green Arrow,"* appears on page 452 of this issue.

Brisk Work by a "Schools" Class Engine

Mr. O. S. Nock sends us the following notes:—

With the 80 minutes London-Folkestone expresses, the "Schools" class 4–4–0s of the Southern Railway continue to give striking evidence of their ability. On a recent run No. 917, *"Ardingly,"* had a load of eleven cars, 390 tons behind the tender, and yet ran the 25.6 miles from Smeeth to Paddock Wood at an average speed of 73.2 m.p.h. The maximum was a sustained 79 m.p.h. at Headcorn and the train passed Tonbridge, 40.4 miles from Folkestone, in half a minute under the very fast schedule of 39½ minutes; speed fell to 34½ in the 1 in 122 ascent to Sevenoaks tunnel, but a splendid finish with a sustained maximum of 75 m.p.h. near Chislehurst took the train through Hither Green a minute early, 62.7 miles in 65 minutes, and the 69.2 miles to Waterloo Junction were completed in 74¾ minutes instead of the 76 minutes booked. After a halt of 1½ minutes Charing Cross was reached in 79½ minutes from Folkestone. Morley of Ramsgate shed was the driver.

Buffet Cars for G.N.R.(I)

Two new buffet cars have been put into service between Dublin and Belfast on the G.N.R. of Ireland. These are furnished on modern lines and have removable tubular framed chairs. The kitchen compartment is well fitted up to enable refreshments and light luncheons to be served. The cars are constructed with timber body framing finished externally with sheet steel panelling. Overhung suspension gangways are provided and in general the cars are similar in appearance to the steel-panelled stock introduced last year. They were constructed in the Company's works at Dundalk.

The L.N.E.R. "*Green Arrow*" Locomotive

A New Design for Mixed Traffic Duties

THERE appears to be no limit to the originality of Sir H. N. Gresley, the Chief Mechanical Engineer of the L.N.E.R. To introduce successfully such striking designs as his "Pacifics" and freight "Mikados," "*No. 10000*," "*Cock o' The North*" and "*Silver Link*" constitutes a notable record; yet he again breaks new ground in the latest class of locomotive he has introduced. The new engines are of the 2–6–2 or "Prairie" type of which, as a tender design, only a single experimental representative has ever been in use on a British railway. Four of these new engines have been constructed at Doncaster and of these the first, No. 4771, "*Green Arrow*," forms the subject of our illustration. A further 28 are to be built at Darlington.

These engines, which form class "V2" on the L.N.E.R., are intended to form a "general utility" type, supplanting to some extent on certain main line passenger trains and express freight trains the 2–6–0s that have been the recognised engines for such duties for some years. The standard group engines of this type, class K3, were developed from the "1000" series of the former G.N.R. and have rendered excellent service. They are still doing so, but under modern operating conditions there has been an increasing need for locomotives having a greater boiler and fire-box capacity than it is possible to obtain with the 2–6–0 wheel arrangement, and economically more capable of sustained high-speed running. This explains the adoption of the "Prairie" or 2–6–2 wheel type, in which the small trailing wheels render possible the familiar features of Doncaster practice, the wide fire-box, as on the "Atlantics," "Pacifics," and "Mikados," the satisfactory development of the boiler itself and a well balanced distribution of weight. For easy running at higher speeds the driving wheels are 6 ft. 2 in. in diameter as compared with the 5 ft. 8 in. wheels of the K3 "Moguls."

The illustration above, reproduced by courtesy of the L.N.E.R., shows the first of the new 2-6-2 tender locomotives No. 4771, "Green Arrow." The appearance of the new class marks the first application of the "Prairie" wheel arrangement to tender locomotives in this country. They form a development of the familiar "Moguls" and incorporate features developed in recent L.N.E.R. locomotive practice.

The boiler is of the same general design as that of the A3 class "Super-Pacifics," and carries a working pressure of 220 lb. per sq. in. A similar type of steam collector is fitted, consisting of a steel pressing mounted above the barrel, and entrance to it is gained through a number of slots cut in the top of the boiler barrel. The main steam pipe is of generous dimensions, and a 43-element superheater of the Robinson type is provided. As might be expected there are three cylinders, each 18½ in. in diameter, and with a piston stroke of 26 in. The cylinders, steam chests, smoke-box saddle and all steam and exhaust passages are cast as one unit, this monobloc casting design being a special feature of L.N.E.R. practice. Each of the pistons is combined in a single forging with its piston rod, and the drive from the inside and outside cylinders is taken to the middle coupled axle, which is necessarily cranked and of built-up construction.

Piston valves are relied on for steam distribution and those of the outside cylinders are actuated by Walschaerts valve gear. The motion of the inside valve is derived from the outside valve spindles by means of the patent Gresley system of conjugated levers that has been applied so successfully to more than 470 other three-cylinder locomotives on the L.N.E.R. The lubrication of the cylinders and of the coupled wheel axle-boxes is effected mechanically by means of two Wakefield lubricators mounted on the running plate. The leading wheels, 3 ft. 2 in. in diameter, are mounted in a pony truck, which has a side play of 5½ in. to each side, grease lubrication being applied to all links and slides. The trailing wheels, 3 ft. 8 in. in diameter, have their axles carried in Cartazzi axle-boxes, as on the "Pacifics," which give a maximum side play of 2½ in. each side. The curving properties of the leading and trailing wheels and the central disposition of the coupled wheelbase result in a well-balanced flexible locomotive.

The cab design is of interest in that it follows the wedge-shaped formation of the spectacle plate that was first seen on the "*Cock o' The North*." A particularly good lookout is afforded through the front windows, which are of "Triplex" safety glass. The engine is arranged to be driven from the left-hand side. Hand-operated sanding gear supplies the leading pair of coupled wheels and steam sanding is applied to the centre pair. The sand-boxes are of welded construction, and this also applies to the ashpan.

The tender is a large six-wheeled vehicle similar in appearance to those provided for many of the J39 class 0–6–0s and "Shire" class engines, also the latest 4–6–0s of the "Football Club" series. Its wheelbase is disposed unequally, the centre and rear pair of wheels being spaced closer together on account of the concentrated weight of the water towards the rear. It accommodates 7½ tons of coal and 4,200 gallons of water. Screw-operated water pick-up gear is fitted. The tender weighs 51 tons loaded, and with the engine weight of 93 tons 2 cwt. this gives a total weight in working order of 144 tons 2 cwt. It is interesting to note that the new engines are only seven tons less in weight than the giant booster-fitted 2–8–2s, or "Mikados," Nos. 2393–4, of the same company, which regularly haul mineral trains with loads of 1,600 tons.

The complete engine and tender has a massive yet handsome appearance. It is less revolutionary externally than was "*Cock o' The North*," or "*Silver Link*," yet it has a distinctly modern look about it. A minor innovation is the selection of the side of the smoke-box as the position for the nameplate, there being no splashers above the driving wheels on which the usual curved plate could be mounted. The name itself of No. 4771, "*Green Arrow*," is significant and is well chosen in view of the fast goods duties for which these engines are partly intended. The "Green Arrow" service, as some readers will know, is the specially rapid registered transit for freight that is afforded by the railway companies. An additional charge of 2/6 is made on any consignment sent by this service, whether it is a small package or a complete train load, and the railway companies guarantee delivery on the next day to any town in England, Scotland or Wales.

A Veteran Forth Paddle Steamer

The "William Muir's" Great Record

By J. H. Sutherland

ALL who are interested in the vessels that ply in the Scottish firths no doubt were familiar with the *"Columba,"* the Clyde steamer described and illustrated on page 308 of the *"M.M."* for May last, and were aware of her 57 years of service before she went to the ship-breakers. It is perhaps not so widely known that the Forth can present a parallel to the career of this famous ship in that of the *"William Muir,"* a steamer that for 57 years has been as familiar to the people of Edinburgh as the *"Columba"* was to Glaswegians.

The "William Muir," the last of the railway steamers maintaining the ferry service across the Firth of Forth between Granton and Burntisland. This veteran has 57 years' service to her credit.

Before the Forth Bridge was built the main railway route from Edinburgh to Fifeshire and the North was interrupted by the Firth of Forth, across which a ferry service was maintained by the North British Railway between the ports of Granton and Burntisland, a distance of five miles. At one time as many as four steamers for vehicles and two for passengers were necessary to cope with the traffic on this service, and of these none was more popular than the *"William Muir,"* which was named after a director of the owning railway company.

This vessel began her period of long service in 1879. She was launched in that year from Kay's yard, at Kinghorn, in Fife, with full steam up, as was customary in the absence of a fitting-out basin. She was not without her share of good looks, possessing symmetrically placed twin funnels, a deck saloon, a spacious promenade deck and a well-moulded hull capable of weathering the winter storms in the Firth. Except for her rounded, whale-backed forecastle, her lines were those of the typical pleasure steamer. This roofed enclosure provided shelter for steerage passengers and was necessary for the horses and other livestock that were transported regularly.

The "William Muir" before her reconstruction in 1910.

The *"William Muir"* was closely associated with one of the most appalling disasters that occurred in Scotland during the nineteenth century. On Sunday, 28th December, 1879, the year in which she commenced service, she crossed from Granton to Burntisland in the teeth of a hurricane with about 75 passengers bound for Dundee. Not one of these was destined to return, for the central portion of the Tay Bridge collapsed as the train in which they travelled north passed over it, and all lost their lives.

For 13 years the *"William Muir"* shared the ferry duties with the *"John Stirling."* When the Forth Bridge was opened in 1892, the volume of ferry traffic decreased to such an extent that one passenger boat was taken off the service, and the *"William Muir"* alone was left to maintain the connecting link between the two ports.

In 1910, after 31 years of arduous employment, the old stager was re-conditioned at Leith, and on her re-appearance at Granton few would have recognised her if she had not carried the familiar name on her bows. Her two trim black funnels had been replaced by a single tall smoke-stack of greater diameter set abaft the paddle-boxes, and this was painted bright red with black top and an intervening white band, in accordance with the colour scheme of the N.B.R. Clyde steamboats. The disappearance of one funnel meant a gain of deck space forward for the accommodation of vehicles, but the alteration had affected her former harmony of outline.

Changes were made also below decks. There her venerable simple engine had given way to a compound that enabled her to attain a speed of about 16 knots. Her present-day running is more nearly at 10 knots, but now there is no passenger service between Waverley Station, Edinburgh, and Granton, and there is no vital necessity for a speedy ferry passage.

The Forth ferry steamer was designed and built for her special duties and never approached the all-round standard of excellence of the *"Columba."* Of the two the former can boast the more meritorious record as far as actual service is concerned, however. The *"Columba"* spent eight months every year at sheltered moorings, but the *"William Muir"* is in commission seven days a week practically throughout the year. Apart from her overhaul in 1910, and an annual renovation that occupies three weeks, she has therefore spent her 57 years of existence in continuous service.

A few years ago Diesel-electric ferry boats displaced the steamer that used to ply between North and South Queensferry, higher up the Firth, and the *"William Muir"* is the last railway-owned steamboat in service on Forth waters. She is the only remaining link with a service that was busy and famous for almost half a century, and cannot be brought to an end until the Act of Parliament that established it 90 years ago has been repealed. The old craft seems destined to continue her course indefinitely. After her annual overhaul, when the painters make her spick and span, her age would be difficult to conjecture were it not for the old-fashioned alleyways that separate the saloon from the bulwarks. She carries her years lightly, and, when she departs for good, Granton, where she lies overnight, will truly be incomplete without her.

Finnish Training Vessel

The *"Suomen Joutsen,"* the three-masted sailing vessel illustrated on this page, was built at St. Nazaire in France in 1902. She was purchased in 1931 by the Finnish Navy for use as a training ship. With a length of 260 ft. and a beam of 40 ft., she has a displacement of 2,259 tons. As is the case with other sailing ships still afloat, she does not depend only on the wind, but is fitted with two auxiliary Diesel engines that develop 400 h.p. and give her a speed of six knots. Her complement is 27 officers, and 60 cadets.

World's Largest All-Welded Tanker

An oil tanker recently put into service in the United States is claimed to be the largest all-welded vessel of this kind in the world. The vessel has been named *"Transoil,"* and has an overall length of 258 ft., a moulded beam 43 ft., and a moulded depth of 16 ft. 4 in. She is propelled by two 475 h.p. oil engines, giving her a speed of 9 knots when loaded.

Another recent addition to the world's fleet of oil tankers is the *"Standella,"* which is the first of 16 tankers being built on the Clyde to the order of companies associated with Scottish Oils and Shell Mex, Ltd. This vessel has been delivered to her owners after successful trials. The orders represent an expenditure of more than £2,000,000.

Motor Boat Records Broken

A world speed record for motor-boats with engines of 1,500 c.c. was recently created by Carmagnani, an Italian, who on Lake Maggiore covered a mile in 59 4/5 sec. The average speed in the runs that gave Carmagnani the record was 69 m.p.h.

The record for the highest speed ever attained by a motor-boat with a displacement of less than 350 k.g., or about 770 lb., stands at 74.4 m.p.h. It is held by Jean Dupuy, and there is some speculation at the moment as to whether he will break his own record within the next few weeks, as he has just had built a remarkable outboard craft, which is fitted with two Soriano engines each developing 110 h.p.

Drifting in Arctic Ice

One of the most famous ships the world has known is the *"Fram,"* in which Dr. Fridtjof Nansen, the great Arctic explorer, attempted to reach the North Pole. The vessel was built with rounded sides, and a keel that was practically sunk in the planking, so that it would be lifted up when caught between ice floes instead of being crushed between them. In her Nansen allowed himself to be imprisoned in the ice off the coast of Siberia, in the belief that she would be carried across the Pole by the drift of the ice. She spent between three and four years in the grip of the ice, but did not go as near to the Pole as Nansen had expected, and he left her with a single companion to make a memorable journey across the ice in which he attained what was then a farthest north record. The *"Fram"* meanwhile had drifted to Spitzbergen, where she was released from the ice, and then returned to Norway. She had been considerably farther north than any other vessel.

The famous drift of the *"Fram"* is recalled by the news that another vessel is being designed in the Arctic Institute, Leningrad, for the same purpose. This will have a displacement of 1,000 tons, and will be fitted with a 400 h.p. oil engine and sails. The egg-shaped hull and the removable rudder and screw of the *"Fram"* are being reproduced in her, and she will be towed into high northern latitudes by an ice-breaker in order to commence her Arctic drift.

The Finnish training ship "Suomen Joutsen" off the Manx Coast. Photograph by H. Elwell, Liverpool.

Coastal Motor Torpedo Boat Trial

The trials recently took place on the Thames of the first of a batch of fast coastal motor torpedo boats of improved design, which are being constructed and engined by John I. Thornycroft and Co., Ltd. for a Far Eastern Government.

The boats are of the single-step hydroplane type, and are built of mahogany. They have a length of 55 ft. and a beam of 11 ft., and the two 12-cylinder petrol engines of the latest Thornycroft type with which they are fitted have a total designed output of a little over 1,000 h.p. The engines are placed side by side, and an auxiliary cruising engine is coupled to one of the main engine shafts.

The trials were carried out with the boat in service conditions, loaded with the equivalent of two 18 in. torpedoes, two depth charges, machine guns and ammunition, and wireless equipment. The average speed over six runs was more than 45 knots.

A Mile a Minute Ambulance Boat

A streamlined motor ambulance boat said to be capable of a speed of a mile a minute has just been completed in America for the Portland Fire Department, Oregon. The hull of the vessel is described as aerodynamic in design. Below speeds of 30 m.p.h. it behaves normally, but at higher speeds lifting forces come into play and cause it to rise. At about 45 m.p.h. most of the hull of the craft is clear of the surface, and at 60 m.p.h. only the central keel section is in contact with the water.

An interesting feature is that below the waterline the hull is given the shape of an inverted "V." At high speeds the air in the hollow in the vessel's bottom is said to produce an air cushioning effect.

* * * *

Voyages by the Union Castle Line between Southampton and Capetown will be reduced from 17 days to less than 14 days this month, when the *"Athlone Castle"* will join the *"Stirling Castle,"* described in the *"M.M."* for May, and other liners that have undergone engine alterations.

"Queen Mary's" Steering Gear

The rudder of the *"Queen Mary"* weighs more than 140 tons, but the steersman on the bridge, more than 1,000 ft. away, can move it with ease by merely turning a small steering wheel. The massive electro-hydraulic steering gear that makes this possible is shown in the lower illustration on this page. It was built by Brown Bros. and Co., Ltd., of Edinburgh, and the figures seen behind it in the illustration give some idea of its immense size. It is indeed the largest ever installed in an ocean liner. Its weight is about 180 tons, and the power it exerts is approximately three times that of the largest gear previously built in this country.

This complicated steering gear is required to multiply the power exerted by the helmsman. The movements of the wheel control pumps that supply oil fluid to cylinders in which slide four cast steel main hydraulic rams. These can be seen in our illustration, arranged in pairs with two swivel crossheads, one on each side of the rudder stock, that transmit their movements to the arms of the tiller. The pumps used were manufactured by The Variable Speed Gear Co., Ltd., Elswick, and automatically provide the pressure fluid in the exact quantity required to move the rams to the extent indicated by the movement of the steering wheel.

There are two independent steering wheels on the bridge, and in addition there is one on the docking bridge near the bows, and three others placed on pedestals in different places. The gear can therefore actually be controlled from any one of six distinct wheels.

Motor Launches for River Police

The upper illustration on this page shows one of two Diesel-engined motor launches recently supplied to the Metropolitan Police by the Sittingbourne Shipbuilding Co., Ltd., Kent, for use on the Thames. Each boat has a length of 28 ft., a beam of 7 ft., and a draft of 2 ft. 3 in. They are constructed of teak planking on an oak framing, and are of round-bottom section. An A.E.C. six-cylinder oil engine is fitted. This develops 100 h.p. at 1,650 r.p.m., or 125 h.p. at 2,000 r.p.m., and gives the boats a maximum speed of 15 knots.

* * * *

A recent motor boat race at Oulton Broads, was started by Gar Wood by wireless from his home in Detroit. He first gave a short speech which was broadcast to mpetitors and spectators.

New Motor Vessels for the Belfast-Glasgow Service

Two new twin-screw motor vessels, the *"Royal Ulsterman"* and the *"Royal Scotsman,"* recently took up service on the Belfast-Glasgow service of the Burns and Laird Lines, Ltd. The ships were built by Harland and Wolff, Ltd., Belfast, and have a displacement of 3,244 gross tons. They have an overall length of 341 ft. 6 in., a moulded breadth of 47 ft. 6 in., and a moulded depth of 17 ft. 9 in., and their service speed is about 15½ knots.

The Harland-Burmeister and Wain two-stroke oil engines fitted in each of the vessels have a total designed output of about 5,500 h.p. They are eight-cylinder units with a bore of 500 m.m. and a stroke of 900 m.m. Poppet exhaust valves are incorporated and heat from the exhaust gases is recovered by using it in a special boiler.

A Metropolitan Police motor launch on the Thames. Her two Diesel engines give her a speed of 15 knots. Photograph by courtesy of the Sittingbourne Shipbuilding Co., Ltd., Kent.

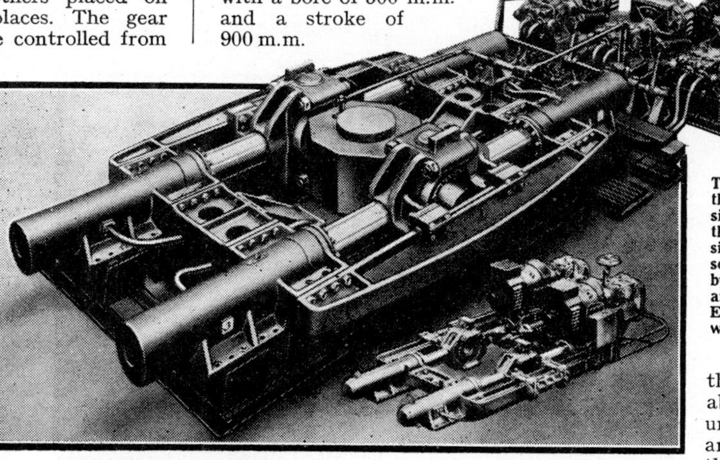

The steering gear of the "Queen Mary" side by side with that of a medium-sized passenger vessel. Both were built by Brown Brothers and Co., Ltd., of Edinburgh, to whom we are indebted for our illustration.

Streamlined Ferry Steamer

A ferry boat that is completely streamlined is being completed for the Virginia Ferry Corporation in the United States. The vessel has an overall length of 260 ft., a breadth of 59 ft. and a depth of 19 ft. It is constructed entirely of steel, and the streamlining includes the entire superstructure and funnel.

Leigh Bawley Becomes a Yacht

There are many types of fishing craft to be found round British coasts, each designed to operate in the conditions peculiar to their customary fishing grounds. Among these is the Leigh "bawley," which is built for shrimping and whitebait fishing in the Thames Estuary. This craft is locally built at Leigh-on-Sea, and can be distinguished by its characteristic high, straight stem and its wide, flat, transom stern. Both features are designed to fit this type of vessel for its work in the Estuary. Another peculiarity is the short lower mast and long top mast.

The number of bawleys in operation has greatly diminished during recent years, for while there were about 72 in 1914, two years ago there were only 22. Several have been converted into yachts, and in its new form the bawley is ideal for those who wish to acquire a seaworthy boat at less cost then would be involved in buying a new yacht.

An interesting conversion of this kinu was recently carried out by the Underwood Shipyard, South Benfleet, Essex, with a bawley that had seen 35 years' service. She is now fitted with a cutter rig of 750 sq. ft., and a two-cylinder poppet-valve Kelvin engine, developing 13 h.p. at 550 r.p.m. on paraffin, has been installed in a separate compartment in the stern. The fish hold has been transformed into a cabin, and in its new form the old vessel provides comfortable accommodation for seven persons.

Channel Steamer's Stabiliser

The Southern Railways newest channel steamer, the T.S.S. *"Isle of Sark,"* a vessel of 2,211 tons, has been fitted with the "Motora" stabilising system. Her first voyage with the new equipment was made early this year with satisfactory results.

The device consists of fins projecting into the water from the side of the hull at about the turn of the bilge. These fins are under the control of a gyroscopic detector and relay, and as the ship rolls, that on the side descending rises, while the one on the opposite side of the ship turns downward. The forward motion of the ship causes the water to exert an upward force on the fin tilted up on the descending side and a downward force on the fin tilted down on the side of the ship moving upwards, and the couple thus created acts to restore the ship to an even keel. As she recovers the fins resume their normal position, and as she heels over on the opposite side they reverse their tilt. When their stabilising action is not required the fins can be withdrawn into recesses inside the hull.

Cableway Drag-Line Excavators

Giant Machines for Open Pit Mining

ONE of the chief reasons for the leading position that Great Britain holds in the modern industrial world is that she has under her soil an immense store of hard coal that is an ideal fuel for industrial purposes. Other countries are not so fortunate in this respect, and in many of these the chief natural fuel supplies take the form of lignite, or brown coal, which represents an intermediate stage between wood and coal. This is soft compared with the coal with which we are familiar, and usually is comparatively light, friable and porous. Its heating value is very low, and when lighted in an open grate it smoulders, but it can be burned with little difficulty in specially designed grates using some form of forced draught.

General view of the tail tower of a cableway drag-line, showing the bucket discharging fuel into a crusher. We are indebted to Bleichert-Transportanlagen G.m.b.H., Germany, for the illustrations to this article.

Brown coal is not obtained from deep pits reached by shafts. It is found comparatively near the surface, at depths ranging from only a few feet to perhaps 200 ft., and usually is extracted by stripping off the covering layer of soil, or overburden, and then digging the fuel itself out of the open pit. There are immense deposits of this kind in many parts of the Earth, notably in Germany, where it is largely used in industry, in North America, and at Yallourn, Victoria.

The fuel is only economical when cheap mechanical methods of extracting it are used, and giant machines of many types therefore have been devised for use in the open pit mining by which it is won. These include powerful electric shovels and bucket excavators, for the material is sufficiently soft to be dug up readily by appliances of this kind, but in many ways cableway drag-lines are the most interesting of the machines employed. These are literally land dredgers. The excavating bucket is suspended from great cables that may be up to a quarter of a mile in length, and is dragged through the coal, which is scooped up in it and hauled to one of the towers supporting the cables. There it is dumped or delivered into wagons, and the bucket is hauled back to dig up another load.

A great area can be swept free of brown coal in this manner, or the covering layer of clay can be removed, as easily as mud can be dredged from the bottom of a lake or estuary. One advantage of the machine is that it not only digs out the coal or soil from the open workings, but also lifts it and carries it away in a single operation.

It will be seen that these giant machines combine the features of drag-line excavators, of the type that have often been described in the "*M.M.*," with those of cableways. The main cables that stretch across the open pit are supported at their ends by immense towers built of steel. These are known as head and tail towers respectively. The former carries the machinery that operates the bucket and may be as much as 60 ft. to 80 ft. in height, and the latter often is fitted with a bunker in which large pieces of coal are broken up, and a hopper from which the material is fed into the wagons waiting to receive it.

The digger bucket of a cableway drag-line excavator in use at Wolfersheim, Germany.

The towers are movable, and are carried on bogies with creeper tracks of large size. The usual plan is to make use of triple tracks for each tower, and the size of these can be gauged from the upper illustration on this page.

When the drag-line is at work the towers remain in one position held firmly by means of anchors or hold-fasts, until the long strip beneath the cables has been worked to the required depth. Then one of them is moved so that the bucket covers fresh ground, or if necessary both are made to travel sideways. The use of creeper tracks enables this to be done readily, and these have the further advantage that towers mounted on them can travel up gradients as steep as 1 in 15. Very little levelling therefore usually is necessary when a pit is being opened out, or when a change in the scene of operations becomes necessary. Some of the earlier drag-line excavators had their towers mounted on rails. They were not so easily adaptable as those now in use, and could not travel on such severe gradients.

The head tower of an excavator at the Altenbury workings in Borken, Hessen. The span of the cableway is 355 yds.

The excavating bucket of one of these giant excavators may hold as much as 15 cu. yds. of coal. It is carried by a travelling cradle that is suspended from the main cables, and can be pulled backward or forward by means of operating ropes. At the head tower the main cables pass over the top of a jib that can be raised or lowered as required. When the machine is working the jib is first lowered, causing the main cable to dip. The bucket is thus brought into engagement with the ground, through which it cuts its way as it is dragged along by the hauling cable. When it is full it is lifted from the ground by raising the jib, and is then pulled to the head tower or the tail tower to deposit its contents.

A cableway drag-line excavator at work removing debris at the Görlitz Pit, Silesia.

The movements throughout are controlled from an operating room in the head tower, in which are installed the winches by means of which the cables attached to the jib and to the cradle are hauled in. The work of lifting the jib is made easier by providing it with a counterweight. All the winches are electrically driven, and separate motors are employed for the different motions. In one excavator in which a bucket of 15 cu. yds. capacity is used, the motor that pulls it through the coal is of 345 h.p., while other motors of 380 h.p. and 275 h.p. respectively are employed for pulling the load along the cable and raising the jib. The discharge of the spoil from the bucket also is automatic and is controlled from the head tower; in this case a 25 h.p. motor operates the mechanism that brings this about.

The speed at which the bucket is dragged through the coal usually is 60 yds. per min., and hoisting and lowering take place at similar speeds. These movements are short in comparison with the distance travelled by the bucket when full, or when returning empty after discharging, and comparatively little time would be saved by speeding them up. The rate at which the bucket travels along the cable has been greatly increased since these excavators were first introduced, and is now from 300 to 400 yds. per min. when full and 500 yds. per min. when empty.

The entire operation of filling the bucket, raising it, and returning it to the ground after emptying its contents where required occupies from two to three minutes, and of this time only 10 sec. are spent in the actual excavation. The output of cableway drag-line excavators usually is very large, however, and is about half as much again as that of mechanical shovels employing the same number of attendants. Normally only three men are required to a drag-line. These are a driver in the control room of the head tower, a signaller in the pit who communicates with the driver by telephone, and a greaser. Possibly a fourth man may be required to manipulate the tracks on which the tail tower moves.

An interesting feature of the use of cableway drag-lines in open pit mining is the manner in which flooding is dealt with. Surface water is bound to be encountered in open pit working, and this would form a considerable handicap if it were allowed to spread through the mine. For this reason strips of ground are left intact between successive excavations in which water accumulates. These strips act as bars or dams, and prevent the flow of water from one section to another as the depth of the pit is increased.

These giant excavators also can be used with advantage for digging out deposits of gravel, sand and sandy clay that contain gold, tin and other valuable products.

Time By Telephone

How The Post Office Speaking Clock Works

By T. R. Robinson

A REMARKABLE new clock that announces the time in hours, minutes and seconds to telephone subscribers has recently been completed at the Dollis Hill Research Station of the Post Office, and is now in service telling the time to enquirers by telephone in London. All that they need to do is to dial "TIM" and listen. In a few seconds they hear an announcement such as, "At the third stroke it will be three twenty-six and forty seconds." Immediately afterwards three "pips" are heard, and the third gives the actual instant of the time announced. The wording changes 10 seconds later, so that those who then ring up are told that at the third stroke it will be "three twenty-six and fifty seconds."

The speaking clock is at work continuously. Its announcements are changed in this manner every 10 secs., and of course alterations in the minute and hour are made when required. A subscriber is cut off automatically after listening for from 90 to 180 seconds.

The words announcing the time in this new service are spoken in the voice of Miss Ethel Cain, but actually come from recorded sound tracks on a series of glass discs that are revolved by a special electric motor. Miss Cain was the successful competitor in a special contest to decide who should make the records, and she has become widely known as "The Girl with the Golden Voice."

Miss Ethel Cain, who has become known as "The Girl with the Golden Voice," speaking into the microphone when making the sound track records for the Post Office speaking clock. We are indebted to the Post Office for the illustration to this article.

The main mechanical part of the clock is shown in the illustration on the next page, in which the discs and their driving motor can be seen. Each disc has on it sound tracks, similar to those on "talkie" cinematograph films, and alongside them is a small lamp. The beam from each lamp passes through the corresponding disc, and falls on a photo-electric cell opposite. The recordings thus interrupt the light and cause the current in the cell to vary, with the result that the part of the spoken phrase represented by the part of the sound track opposite the light ray is reproduced in the receivers of listening telephones.

Separate discs are used for the hours, minutes and seconds announcements, and each complete phrase does not come from one disc alone, but is built up by cleverly fitting together the currents from the photo-cells alongside all of them. In the illustration, the minute discs are seen nearest to the driving motor. There actually are two minute discs, for it was found impossible to place the 60 sound tracks needed for a full hour on one disc. The two therefore share the work, each carrying 30 tracks, and in our illustration are seen nearest the driving motor.

They are driven directly and each makes one turn per second. The hour disc is next to them, and the seconds disc is on the extreme right. These are driven through enclosed reduction gearing placed between them and the minute discs, and run at half the speed of the latter.

In addition to rotating the discs, the motor also brings about the necessary changes of position of the lamps and photo-electric cells. The two shafts and skew gears that can be seen close to the motor are concerned in this movement. They act through a set of cams to move the carriers on which the lamps and cells are mounted, and thus to bring them into line with the correct sound tracks on their respective discs. The long shaft that in the illustration can be seen mounted in brackets across the front of the bed-plate rotates continuously, and is coupled to the cam-shifting mechanism by a simple trip release at the exact moment when a change of position is required.

The cams are in a row between the shaft and the discs, and attached to each is a ratchet wheel having as many teeth as there are steps on the cam. Stepping the ratchet one tooth therefore moves the cam one step, and changes the associated carrier, lamp, and cell to a fresh track on the disc.

The stepping mechanism for the ratchets consists of a small eccentric that runs loosely on the continuously rotating shaft driven by the motor, and a trip that can couple the eccentric to the shaft when the moment to change the lamp position occurs. The trip itself is an ingenious mechanism and is shown diagrammatically in the lower illustration on the opposite page. The motor driven shaft, which normally revolves idly, is marked A, and carries the ratchet wheel D fixed to it. The sleeve B is attached to the eccentric that steps the cam ratchet, and is stationary until the moment for a change arrives. On this sleeve is the pawl C, and this is held out of engagement with the ratchet by its tail, which rests upon the tip of the armature F of the release magnet E.

When the magnet attracts its armature, it withdraws the tip from under the tail of the pawl, and the latter then falls into the teeth of the ratchet wheel and locks the two together. The shaft and sleeve then revolve until they have made one complete turn. The tail of the pawl then again catches the tip of the armature and is knocked out of engagement with the ratchet wheel, the shaft being thus released to continue its idle motion. The spring-loaded safety catch H is fitted to act as a further guard, and to retain the tail of the pawl in contact with the armature tip.

This view of the speaking clock shows the glass discs carrying the sound tracks.

Three of these trips are fitted to the clock, one each for the hour, minute and seconds discs, and carefully timed cams and contacts control the energising of the appropriate release magnets. The two fixed lamps and cells that can be seen at the rear of the clock close to the first and fourth discs are used to give the "pips" and the words "At the third strike," which of course are common to all the announcements.

The accuracy of the clock depends on careful control of the speed of the driving motor. This is a special synchronous machine of the 8-pole type, arranged for separate excitation, and runs at the correct speed when it is connected to a supply having a frequency of four cycles per second. The current feeding the motor is generated by the swing of a special master pendulum that beats seconds, and carries at its lower end a transparent slide with wavy blackened portions. As this moves a varying amount of light is passed from a lamp to a photo-cell, and there generates a current that is amplified and used to feed the motor. This generation of current to operate a motor by means of a pendulum and photo-electric cells is a distinctly novel scheme, and one that seems to possess great possibilities in many directions.

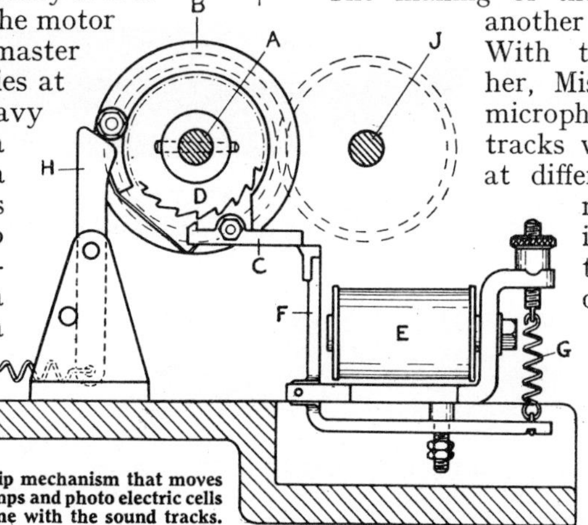

The trip mechanism that moves the lamps and photo electric cells into line with the sound tracks.

By a clever arrangement, the very current generated by the swing of the pendulum also is employed to keep it swinging, for as soon as the swing of the pendulum becomes too small the current fed to a pair of condensers becomes unbalanced, and an energising magnet then automatically restores the pendulum to its original arc. The pendulum also is checked if it swings too far, and the Greenwich time signal automatically speeds up or slows down its swing as necessary.

The current that flows through the photo-cell circuits is not powerful enough to be fed directly to subscribers' lines, and has to be amplified. It is then carried to a multiple contact board that allows up to 100 enquirers to obtain the time simultaneously. This ensures that in all normal times those calling will not have to wait, but will be connected at once. The clock has been installed at the London Tandem Exchange, Holborn, and really forms an additional exchange devoted to the distribution of time signals. Two clocks actually are installed, both of which will be kept running continuously. Only one will be in active service, however. The second will remain silent until something happens to cause the first to fail. The connections then will be transferred automatically and at the same time an alarm signal will sound as a warning that attention is needed.

The construction of the clock necessitated much careful experimental work by the engineers of the Post Office Research Station at Dollis Hill, and it is interesting to learn that Meccano parts were used in making many of the mechanical parts of the first experimental model. A framework of Plates and Strips with many Gear Wheels and other parts were prominent features of a counting mechanism that proved invaluable in determining many of the necessary points of detail. A card dial was mounted on the front of the Meccano framework, and spindles that projected through this carried pointers that recorded the desired information. This is not the first time that Meccano has been used at the Post Office Research Station, where it often proves of great assistance in experimental work.

The making of the glass sound-track records was another interesting part of the work. With typewritten sheets in front of her, Miss Cain spoke the phrases to a microphone, and from this the sound tracks were obtained. The discs revolve at different speeds, and the concentric rings of the sound track vary in length with their distance from the centre of the disc. This part of the work therefore had to be very carefully arranged for, more especially as the final phrase heard by the telephone subscriber is made up of the currents obtained from the sound-tracks of three different records carefully fitted together. To enable this to be done, the words and phrases chosen had to be carefully designed and spaced.

In addition to the London speaking clock, similar equipments are to be installed at Bristol and Manchester, and further clocks will follow at other centres as soon as the public demand justifies them. The American telephone service has a similar time distribution system, but employs manual operators who speak the time into microphones every 15 sec.

We are indebted to the Post Office Engineering Department, and the Research Station at Dollis Hill, London, N.W., for the information in this article.

This is Hornby Sp

HORNBY SPEED BOATS

Enjoy the Thrills of Sp

One of the few outdoor hobbies that can be carried on at any
friends, is model motor boating. This splendid hobby is within th
expensive of all summer pastimes, and it provides hours of fun

Hornby Speed Boats and Racing Boats are the best that ca
lines and beautiful finish are the outstanding characteristics of these
of excellence in British toys.

Hornby Speed Boat

1st - 8th August

Boys, you should visit your local dealers during Hornby Speed Bo
of Hornby Speed Boats and Racing Boats. What a grand range to
Boats are the best you can buy. Best not only in appearance
reliability. Another thing—if you buy a Hornby Boat during th
in the Hornby Speed Boat Club and presented with the
Badge—FREE! Fill in the Coupon on page xvi, and ca

SPEED BOAT CLUB HORNBY

Join the Hornby Speed Boat Club

If you own a Hornby Boat you should join the Hornby Speed Boat Club. You can do this by purchasing a special badge (illustrated on the right) from any Meccano dealer, or direct from Meccano Ltd., price 6d.

HORNBY RACING BOA

Hornby Racing Boats are superb! Compare these swift, pow
racing craft. You will see they have the same design, the same
The series of Hornby Racing Boats is composed of three exceptio
Each boat is extremely "quick off the mark," and maintains a high
throughout the whole length of its run.

Pennants

Pennants for Hornby Speed Boats Nos. 3 and 4 may be purchased separately. They add the final touch of realism to these boats. Price **2d.** each.

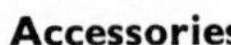

Accessories

The Hornby Speed Boat and Racing Boat Clockwork Motors and Propellers with Shafts can be obtained separately by boys who prefer to build their own boats.

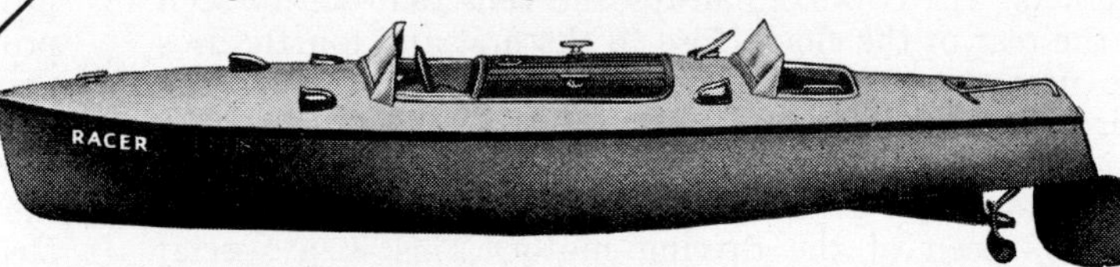

HORNBY RACING BOAT No. 3. "RACER III." Price **14/6**
Travels over 300 ft. at high speed on one winding. Finished in Red and Cream. Dimensions: Length 16½ in. Beam 3½ in.

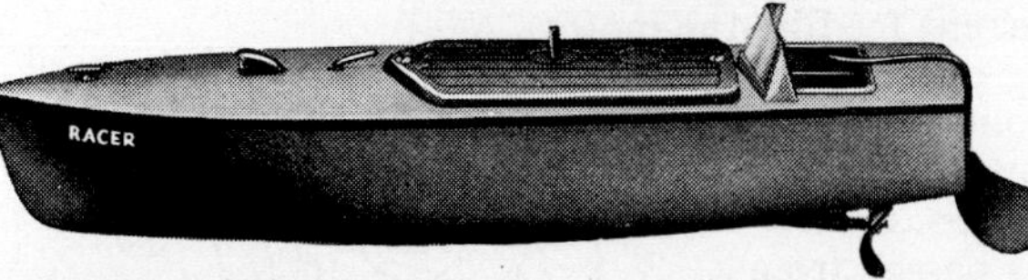

HORNBY RACING BOAT No. 2. "RACER II." Price **8/6**
Travels over 200 ft. at high speed on one winding. Finished in Blue and Cream. Dimensions: Length 12½ in. Beam 3 in.

HORNBY RACING BOAT No. 1. "RACER I." Price **4/6**
Travels over 120 ft. at high speed on one winding. Finished in Cream and Green. Dimensions: Length 8½ in. Beam 2⅜ in.

SWIFT

HORNBY SPEED
Travels over 300 f
schemes. Dim

HORNBY WATER TOY (DUCK). Price **2/6**
Travels over 100 ft. on one winding. Finished in appropriate colours. Dimensions: Length 9¼ in. Beam 3 in.

HORNBY SPEED BOAT No. 1. "HAWK."
Travels over 100 ft. on one winding. Choice
schemes. Dimensions: Length 9¼ in. B

MECCANO LTD. . . . BIN

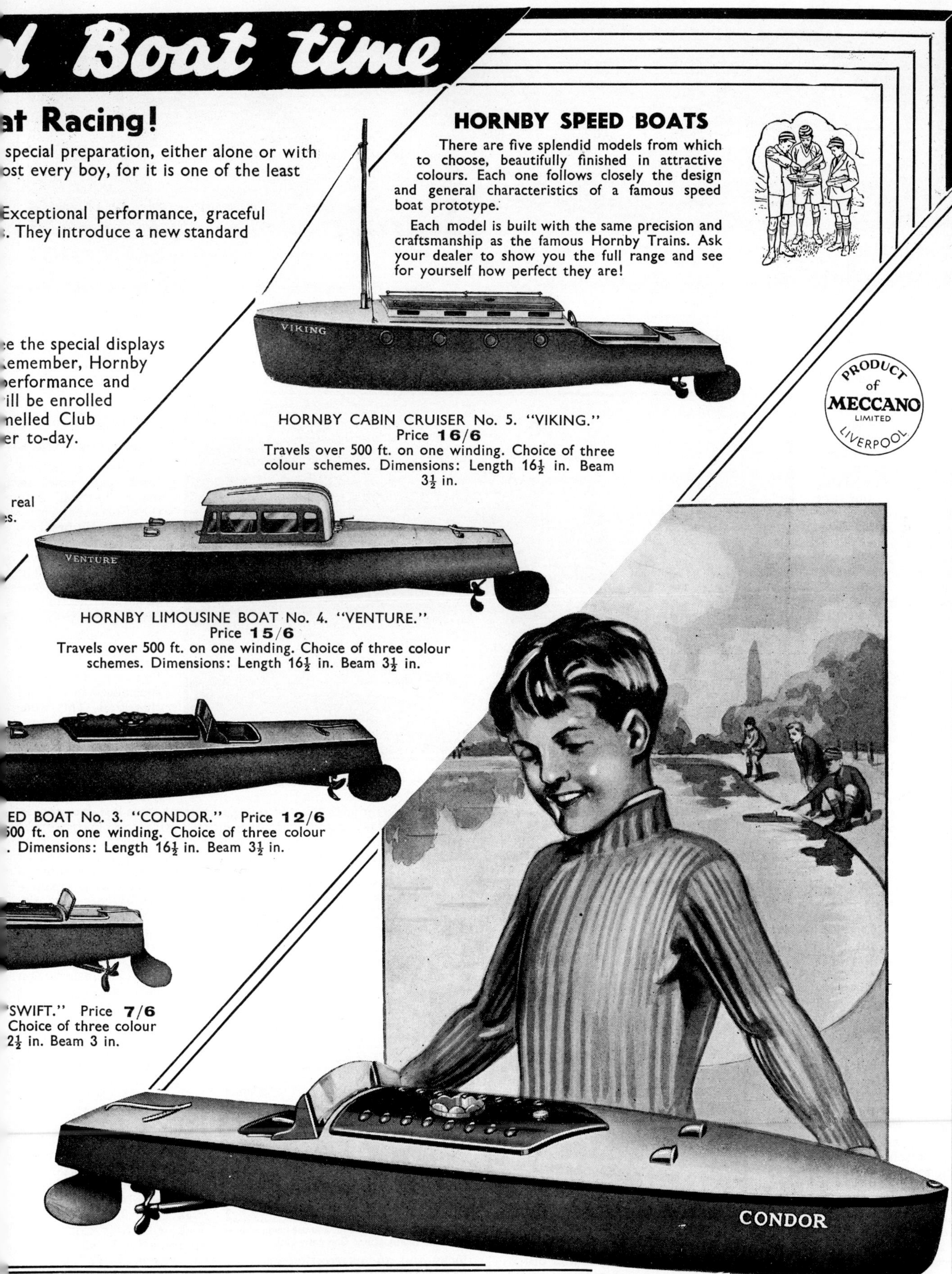

d Boat time
at Racing!
special preparation, either alone or with
ost every boy, for it is one of the least
Exceptional performance, graceful
. They introduce a new standard
e the special displays
emember, Hornby
erformance and
ill be enrolled
nelled Club
er to-day.
real
s.
HORNBY SPEED BOATS
There are five splendid models from which to choose, beautifully finished in attractive colours. Each one follows closely the design and general characteristics of a famous speed boat prototype.
Each model is built with the same precision and craftsmanship as the famous Hornby Trains. Ask your dealer to show you the full range and see for yourself how perfect they are!
VIKING
HORNBY CABIN CRUISER No. 5. "VIKING." Price 16/6
Travels over 500 ft. on one winding. Choice of three colour schemes. Dimensions: Length 16½ in. Beam 3½ in.
PRODUCT of MECCANO LIMITED LIVERPOOL
VENTURE
HORNBY LIMOUSINE BOAT No. 4. "VENTURE." Price 15/6
Travels over 500 ft. on one winding. Choice of three colour schemes. Dimensions: Length 16½ in. Beam 3½ in.
ED BOAT No. 3. "CONDOR." Price 12/6
500 ft. on one winding. Choice of three colour
. Dimensions: Length 16½ in. Beam 3½ in.
'SWIFT." Price 7/6
Choice of three colour
2½ in. Beam 3 in.
CONDOR
. . . LIVERPOOL 13

A Recording Studio on Wheels

The lower photograph on this page shows the interior of the wonderful recording van by means of which "His Master's Voice" gramophone records are made of events that cannot take place in the usual recording studio. In outward appearance the van is of the ordinary type, but it is full of expensive apparatus and devices to enable complete sound records of any kind to be made, and taking it to any place where sound records are to be made is equivalent to bringing the studio itself to the performers. It is often as many as 10 days away from its headquarters in London, and it is the duty of a special staff to see that it is at all times ready to go to any place where records are to be made.

A wonderful collection of more than 500 models collected by R. Lerry, Birmingham. Dinky Toys Motor Cars, a Telephone Kiosk, an A.A. Hut, Crossing Signs and other miniatures in this series can be recognised. Photograph by courtesy of the "Birmingham Post."

The recording apparatus is in duplicate, and each machine is fitted with a sapphire engraving needle for engraving the wavy line on the wax recording blank. Signal lights and buzzers are used to tell the engineers in charge when the apparatus has been adjusted and all is in readiness. This is necessary because for outside recording great lengths of armoured cable often have to be used to link the microphones picking up the sounds with the apparatus in the van. For instance, at such an event as the Aldershot Tattoo more than five miles of cables may be required. At times the cables cannot be taken direct to the van. It often happens that they have to be buried beneath a grandstand or under a football pitch, or carried over the tops of buildings, and on one occasion they had to be specially weighted and sunk in a river over which the van could not be taken.

The interior of the "His Master's Voice" mobile recording van. This photograph, and the lower one on the opposite page, are reproduced by courtesy of the Gramophone Company Ltd.

Every square inch of space in the van is used for batteries, battery chargers and other equipment, including a special cabinet for the wax blanks on which the records are made. These blanks have to be kept at a constant temperature and as soon as the van reaches its destination heating apparatus is brought into use to make sure that they remain in perfect condition. The van also is securely jacked up while recording is in progress in order to keep it perfectly steady, for the slightest movement would ruin the blank in use.

Strong Rooms that Defy Attack

Strong rooms and safes can now be made that will defy the efforts of an entire gang of safe-breakers armed with the most powerful tools yet introduced. The secret of their construction lies in the use of an alloy, known as "Tannsteel," that has been developed by John Tann Ltd., who for years have specialised in work of this kind. This wonderful metal is capable of withstanding attack by an electric drill, an oxy-acetylene blow pipe and even high explosives.

Great ingenuity is devoted to making great safes burglar-proof in every way. Their massive doors are fitted with combination locks capable of millions of variations, and also with several key locks so that they can only be opened by the concerted action of three or more men, each of whom is in possession of a separate key. Clocks prevent the doors from being opened except at specified times, but perhaps the most remarkable feature is a device known as an insurrection lock. This can be brought into use in the event of violent riots and disturbances, and prevents a strong room from being opened even if the keys have been extorted by force from their holders and the secrets of the combination locks have been discovered.

The doors of a modern strong room or vault often are of enormous size. One made recently for a foreign bank weighed 30 tons and was controlled by a time lock with four clocks, two combination locks, two key locks and an insurrection lock. Another was made of Tannsteel about 9 in. in thickness and its two combination locks provided one hundred million variations. Special bolting devices make violence of little use against doors of this kind.

Bottled Gas

Those who live in houses to which gas or electric mains have not yet been extended can now enjoy all the advantages of a regular gas service by purchasing their requirements in bottles. The gas used is not ordinary coal gas, but one known as butane that is specially suitable for bottling, for it becomes a liquid when it is subjected to a pressure of only 23 lb. per sq. in. at a temperature of 60 deg. F. It is colourless and non-poisonous, and is very heavy, so that in the event of an escape it simply remains in a layer on the floor. Leakages are readily detected, although the gas has no smell, because for commercial purposes it is mixed with another gas with an odour that gives warning of its presence.

The bottles used in this interesting new scheme are made of pressed steel without a weld, and are capable of withstanding a pressure of 700 lb. per sq. in. Thus there is an ample margin of safety, for the normal working pressure is only about 23 lb. per sq. in. A loaded bottle is only 16 in. high and weighs about 50 lb., and can readily be connected to gas cookers or gas fires by means of flexible reinforced tubing. A special valve is fitted to reduce the pressure of the gas.

Cutting a sound record on the "Simplat" disc. Records made on this disc can be played back immediately. Photograph by courtesy of the V.G. Manufacturing Co. Ltd.

The advantages of the scheme have already been appreciated so highly that many installations have been made in country districts, and several villages are considering the use of the gas for street lighting purposes.

A Gramophone Record Invention

A record made on the usual wax blank cannot be played over without destroying it, but a new recording material for sound tracks has been invented that is claimed to be free from this drawback. It is said that speech, music and other sounds can be played back 15 to 20 times from the discs on which they have been recorded, and that these can be used for at least 200 reproductions if the material is hardened and polished by means of special fluids.

The "Simplat" disc, as this invention is called, is made of glass and is coated with a special composition in which the sound grooves are cut. No elaborate equipment is required for making a record, all that is necessary being a microphone, a wireless set or amplifier, and a turntable with a pick-up, together with a tracking device to guide the cutter in the narrowing circles it makes round the disc. A special sapphire that will cut 24 double-sided records is recommended, but a steel cutting needle also can be used. The records made on the new discs can be played on any gramophone, and the discs themselves are not affected by climatic conditions. The glass always remains flat and this is of great importance in preventing irregular cutting and giving good reproduction.

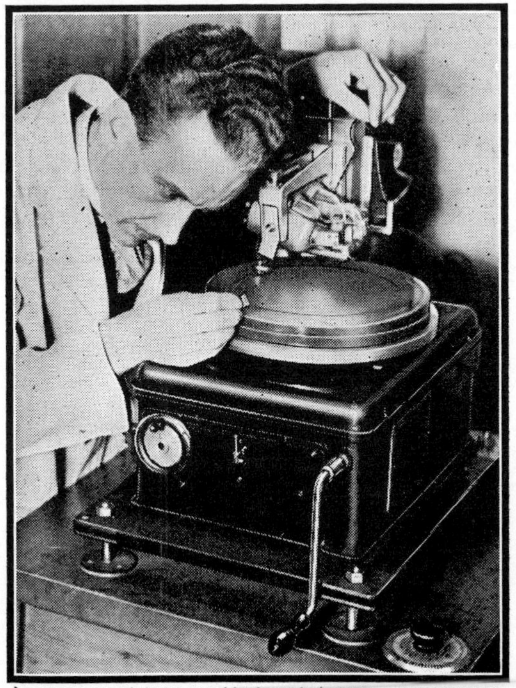

An expert examining a wax blank ready to have a sound track recorded on it in the "His Master's Voice" mobile recording van.

Building with Two Million Inhabitants

An interesting effort has been made in Australia to find how many termites, or white ants, as they are often wrongly called, make their home in an ant heap. The results are astonishing, for they reveal that from 750,000 to nearly 2,000,000 of the species of termites dealt with may inhabit a single mound, although the largest mound in which a census was taken was only 19 in. in height and about 3 ft. 4 in. in diameter. In view of their size and number, it is unnecessary to say that no effort was made to count the individual termites. Instead the mounds were dug up and their population found by a weighing method, allowance being made for absentees. It is interesting to find that the termites show a tendency to stay at home during the cooler months of the year, when the population of any mound is at its greatest.

A Robot Ear

A mechanical ear that listens only to the sounds that the human ear can take in has been constructed at the National Physical Laboratory. It looks like a portable wireless set and measures sounds by comparing them with a note of fixed pitch that is similar to the signal used for tuning purposes by the B.B.C.

This artificial ear has been designed to measure some of the noises that disturb us in our daily lives. One of the disadvantages of living in an age of machinery is that we are frequently assailed by such sounds as the clatter of pneumatic drills and the roar of engines. Some of these no doubt can be made less penetrating and annoying, and the robot ear will help to decide what can be done in this respect by measuring them accurately. We cannot hope to escape noises of this kind completely, but any scheme for limiting them would be welcomed.

I have been greatly interested to learn that measurements have been made in the National Physical Laboratory, of the minute crystals that build up a piece of steel. These crystals are far too small to be measured by any ordinary means, and it has been necessary to adopt complicated methods involving the use of X-rays to find how large, or rather, how small they are. They are so tiny that there may be from one million to 100 million of them in a cubic inch of steel, but in spite of their very small dimensions they break up when the metal is subjected to severe stresses. The fragments then produced appear to be of uniform size and it would take about one hundred thousand of them to make a strip an inch in length.

The larger crystals are entirely shattered into these fragments when the steel is more heavily stressed, and it is then that cracks begin to appear. These are the first outward signs of failure, and thus the breakdown through wear of a steel part in an engine or machine may be due literally to the shattering of the crystals of which it is built up.

A Scientific Detective at Work

I wonder how many of my readers realise how much care is taken in testing the working parts of engines and machinery of all kinds. This of course is specially important with aero engines, upon the performance of which the lives of aeroplane passengers and pilots may depend. An engine of this type is dismantled after it has been in operation for its allotted period, and is then carefully examined. In the case of Imperial Airways a complete overhaul is made after an engine has been in service for about 600 hours, and every part is then cleaned and thoroughly inspected. The first indication that any part is in need of replacement may take the form of a small surface crack. Fortunately such a flaw can be detected long before it can be seen with the naked eye by magnetising it and pouring over it a liquid, known as "detecting ink," containing a metallic powder that reveals the tiniest of flaws as thin black lines.

Steam Tramway Systems

A Once-Popular Form of Local Transport

By H. C. Casserley

IN this country the steam-operated tramway is almost extinct nowadays, although it is still met with in various parts of the Continent, in particular the rural districts of Belgium and Holland. It should not be forgotten, however, that during the later years of the past century steam power played a considerable part in the development of local passenger transport until it was superseded by electricity. At a comparatively early date the electric tramcar was found to be especially suitable for this sphere of activity, but in its turn it is now gradually giving way to the more mobile motor omnibus propelled by the internal combustion engine.

A passenger train as formerly operated on the narrow-gauge Glyn Valley Tramway in North Wales. The curious appearance of the locomotive is due to the prolongation of the side tanks and the presence of the casing round the wheels.

Steam-operated tramways may be said to have reached their hey-day during the eighties and earlier nineties of last century and at that time there were many such undertakings, operating both on the outskirts of London and in the provinces, particularly in the Midlands. Most of these have long since disappeared and are now only remembered by older members of the past generation. Some survived in a few out-of-the-way rural areas until comparatively recently, and even to-day one or two are still run for goods traffic only. One of these is the Wisbech and Upwell Tramway, formerly operated by the Great Eastern Railway, and now a part of the L.N.E.R. system. Running from Wisbech, in Cambridgeshire, this line follows a course along one side of the road for practically the whole distance of about eight miles to the villages of Outwell and Upwell. Goods trains only are run now and during the season a large volume of fruit and flower traffic is conveyed over its standard gauge track.

A scene on the Wisbech and Upwell Tramway, now part of the L.N.E.R. The locomotive is of the "boxed-in" tramway type, as described in this article.

The type of locomotive usually employed on steam tramways was of the 2–2–0 or 0–4–0 type, and was generally totally enclosed with iron sheeting in the form of an all-over cab, the top of the chimney projecting through the roof. The boiler was of the orthodox pattern common to larger steam locomotives, but in some designs a vertical boiler was used. The regulator and other controls were at one side of the boiler instead of at the rear of the fire-box, and this was the position occupied by the driver. The fireman took up his post on the opposite side, on which was to be found the fire-hole door and a small bunker containing the necessary coal. The wheels were enclosed with iron sheeting, this being necessary owing to the presence of straying animals on the public highway. Suitable holes or hinged flaps were provided where necessary to give access to the motion and working parts for oiling and inspection.

The upper illustration on the opposite page shows a Dutch tramway locomotive that may be taken as a typical example of the general arrangement, and is very similar to many tramway engines that were to be found in England 40 or 50 years ago. In spite of their diminutive proportions, these little engines were capable of drawing anything up to six or seven fully-loaded cars, often on gradients that were necessarily severe owing to the fact that the line generally followed the undulating contour of the highway. In some cases the whole or part of the track was constructed over the company's private property, and was fenced in as on a main line railway.

Passenger coaches were generally of the usual single- or double-decker tramway type, with longitudinal seats on the lower floor and "garden" seats on the upper storey, if there was one. The upper open-air passengers enjoyed the benefit—or otherwise—of the smoky exhaust from the locomotive!

One of the last passenger steam tramways operated in the neighbouring counties of London was the Wantage Steam Tramway, which was opened in 1875 to provide communication between the charming old country town of Wantage in Berkshire with Wantage Road station on the Great Western Railway's Swindon line. This station was about three miles distant, and the nearest point of main line communication that the town has ever enjoyed. Passenger trips making connection with the G.W.R. trains were operated as recently as 1925, when they were withdrawn and a service of omnibuses substituted. The engine generally in use was of the usual four-wheeled enclosed tramway type already described. Goods traffic is still carried, however, by two 0–4–0T locomotives of orthodox if somewhat ancient design. The one shown in the lower illustration on this page was in fact constructed as long ago as 1857 by Messrs. George England and Co., of Hatcham Iron-works, a London loco-motive-building concern that long ago ceased to exist. This interesting little engine is probably one of the oldest steam locomotives still in regular commission in this country.

A typical tramway locomotive in Holland, with a horizontal boiler and "all-over" cab. The driver rides on one side of the boiler and the fireman on the other.

The Swansea and Mumbles Railway is a good example of a former steam tramway that has been converted to electric traction, and it still carries a heavy traffic. The line is $5\frac{1}{2}$ miles in length and connects the industrial part of Swansea with the watering place of Mumbles on the Bristol Channel. It runs on its own private property and station platforms are provided, but at the same time it is a true tramway in that the old steam-hauled coaches were of the usual double-decked tramcar type; and the new electric cars are large bogie vehicles seating 106 passengers, 48 in the lower saloon and 58 on the upper covered deck. The conversion of the line to electric traction took place as recently as 1929.

The small and little-known Rye and Camber Tramway, formerly worked by diminutive steam locomotives of 2–4–0 tank design but now operated by a small petrol tractor, is situated on the Sussex coast. This little line of 3′ 0″ gauge runs from the outskirts of Rye, formerly a seaport, but now owing to the recession of the sea an isolated township situated in the Romney Marshes. The line runs over the flat sandy wastes to give access to the well-known Camber Sands. It is essentially a one-man concern, for the driver is not satisfied with his own duties, but also carries out those of a guard, conductor and stationmaster all combined!

A goods train on the Wantage Steam Tramway running alongside the public road. The locomotive is an ancient 0-4-0 tank built in 1857.

Many visitors to North Wales will have enjoyed a trip on the little Glyn Valley Tramway, which runs from Chirk up the pretty valley of the Ceiriog river to Glynceiriog. Like most other such tramways, the line ran for the most part along the side of the road, but diverged in one or two places and had a station and yard of its own at each terminus. Its three tramway-type engines differed slightly from the usual design in that the upper part was not boxed in and the driver's cab was at one end, as on an ordinary locomotive. A fourth engine was a 4–6–0 tank built by the Baldwin Locomotive Works, U.S.A., for service in France during the War, and was purchased from the Government at its conclusion. The passenger coaches were small vehicles of compartment design, many of them without side windows and some without roofs! The gauge of this line was only 2′ $4\frac{1}{2}$″ instead of the more common standard gauge of 4′ $8\frac{1}{2}$″. Passenger working ceased in 1933.

Turning now to Ireland, we may take a brief glance at the Giant's Causeway, Portrush and Bush Valley Tramway. This gives a connection between the popular watering place of Portrush and the wonderful Giant's Causeway on the north coast of Antrim. The perfect hexagonal formation of the rocks forming the Causeway is an extraordinary freak of nature. The tramway was built in 1880-1881. From the first it was intended to work this electrically, and it was in fact the first hydro-electric line in these islands; but for various reasons steam locomotives of the tramway type were used on it in its earliest days. Near by a second steam tramway connected Portrush and Portstewart. This was closed in 1926.

One of the last steam tramways to work for passengers in these islands was the Dublin and Blessington line, which ceased operation on the 31st December, 1932. During the later part of its existence there were three steam locomotives. One was of the ordinary four-wheeled box type and was not often used; the other two were powerful 2–4–2 engines of a unique "double-ended" design. Instead of having the usual arrangement, whereby the driver took his place on one side of the boiler, these locomotives were provided with two cabs and a duplicate set of controls so that the engine could be driven from either end. The cars in use were large bogie double-decked vehicles, and frequently the trains at weekends consisted of five or six carriages, Blessington being a popular resort for picnickers from Dublin. Curves were numerous and severe, and riding on the upper deck of one of the cars of these trains was a most enlivening experience, speeds of 30 m.p.h. often being attained. Traffic at other times was very light however, and various forms of petrol and oil-operated rail cars were tried with a view to economy, but eventually the line had to close down owing to omnibus competition.

The steam tram engine has played its part and its passing will be regretted by few, since its work can now be more successfully carried out by other forms of transport.

These pages are reserved for articles from our readers. Contributions not exceeding 500 words in length are invited on any subject of general interest. These should be written neatly on one side of the paper only, and they may be accompanied by photographs or sketches for use as illustrations. Articles that are published will be paid for at our usual rates. Statements contained in articles submitted for these pages are accepted as being sent in good faith, but the Editor takes no responsibility for their accuracy.

Railway Notes from Tientsin

The most important railway developments in China have taken place in the north, with Peiping and Tientsin as the centres. These cities are connected by a railway that is continued to the Manchurian border at Shanhaikwan, near the Great Wall, where connections are made for Moukden. Tientsin has two stations on this railway. These are called Tientsin East and Tientsin Central, and each has four covered platforms. Modern colour aspect signals are in use there.

An express train, headed by a "Pacific," at Tientsin East station. Photograph by D. Hall, Tientsin.

The locomotives are about 16 years old on the average, but are well kept and some are fitted with smoke deflectors. More than half of them are "Pacifics," and a description of engines of this type built for the Tientsin-Pukar railway by the North British Locomotive Co. Ltd. at Glasgow was given in the *"M.M."* for March of last year. These engines are doing excellent work on the expresses between Peiping and Shanghai, and can be seen regularly at the railway depot at Tientsin. All passenger trains are hauled by "Pacifics," but the locomotives have no definite class of work to do and these engines also can be seen at the head of goods trains. In addition there are several "Mikado" freight engines, some ancient tank engines that pull local trains and are used for shunting, and old 4–4–0s, dating from about 1910, that have stove pipe chimneys and large driving wheels.

Box cars somewhat similar to those of North American Railways are used; otherwise the rolling stock of goods trains is similar to that seen in Great Britain. The passenger services are very good. There are three classes. The first class coaches have red bands round them, and white and blue bands distinguish the second and third class coaches respectively. Coolies constitute more than 90 per cent. of the total number of passengers and they travel in the third class coaches.

Passenger trains generally consist of about 12 coaches with a total tare weight of about 420 tons. Speeds of 65 m.p.h. are attained with these loads and the fastest train service is that between Peiping and Tientsin, a distance of 86.5 miles that is covered non-stop in 110 min. at an average speed of 52.5 m.p.h. Automatic tablet exchange apparatus is now in use for single line running and this has speeded up traffic considerably.

Coal trains are made up of loads of more than 900 tons. High speeds of course are impossible with these heavy trains of mineral wagons. D. HALL (Tientsin).

Ice Cutting in Newfoundland

The practice of cutting ice from lakes in winter and storing it for use in summer suffered a severe blow when mechanical refrigeration became common. It is still carried on in many places, however, including Carbonear, Newfoundland, where I live. There the ice is obtained from a large pond and most of it is cut under the direction of one man, who has been in the business for nearly 50 years.

Sawing natural ice into blocks to be stored for use in summer. Photograph by M. Maddock, Carbonear, Newfoundland.

There are three stages in cutting out ice. The first cut is a straight one that serves as a guide line. Men armed with long steel saws then begin to work, cutting at right angles to the marked line at intervals of about 15 in. Finally blocks measuring about 15 in. each way are detached by striking the uncut sides with crow-bars.

The blocks are loaded on sledges and are conveyed to the ice house, where they are packed in sawdust to remain until they are needed for various purposes in the summer. M. MADDOCK (Carbonear).

The Foogous of Cornwall

The foogous of West Cornwall are artificial inland caves, and some of them are of considerable size. One near Bartinney indeed is capacious enough to shelter a fairly large herd of cattle. It has been suggested that the foogous were constructed for the storage of food, and another theory is that they were intended as hiding places. It seems fairly certain that use has been made of them by smugglers, and no doubt wreckers also concealed their plunder in them.

The entrance to a foogou, or artificial cave, in West Cornwall. Photograph by J. D. V. Ward, Oxford.

As a rule there are two or three entrances to a foogou and these are usually fairly well concealed, although there does not appear to have been any definite attempt to ensure secrecy. Inside is a stone walled passage of varying length, with one or possibly two chambers cut out at the side. Ancient wheels, chapels, stone circles or hut remains often are to be found in the vicinity of these ancient structures. It is doubtful if the one illustrated on this page is really antique, however, for no relics of a former age have been found immediately at hand. It stands in what is now a private garden and is about $1\frac{1}{4}$ miles from the nearest cove. J. D. U. WARD (Oxford).

Images of Buddha in Burma

Burma is known as the land of pagodas, and one of these, the famous Shway Dagone, in Rangoon, is one of the wonders of the world. The country is remarkable also for its many images of Buddha, and the people reverence them as much as their pagodas.

The lower photograph on this page shows the image of Buddha at Thongwa, which is about 20 miles east of Rangoon, and gives a good idea of the general appearance of these images. It is of immense size, as comparison with the figure of the man leaning on the table in front of it indicates, and is housed in a huge steel-framed structure covered with sheets of corrugated iron. The robes and headgear of such an image usually are gilded.

A giant Burmese image of Buddha. Photograph by T. Sike Shu, Thongwa.

There are many images of Buddha in other European countries, such as Siam, China and Japan, but these differ in many respects from those of Burma, which are unique. T. SIKE SHU (Thongwa, Burma).

Rambles in Sicily

During the Easter holidays last year I and 80 other members of the School Scout Troop spent an interesting holiday in Sicily. We arrived at Palermo, Sicily, early one morning and there motor coaches, sent by the Mayor, were waiting to take us to Mondello, which we reached in a short time. From there we drove round the bay to the Colonia Marina, which had been put at our disposal. It was built as a shipbuilding yard and barracks during the Great War and has since been used as a holiday "camp" for Italian children. We spent the remainder of the day exploring the district and in bathing.

Next day we went to Bottadefalco by motor coach, and from there walked up a mountain path. Progress was slow, as the day was very hot, but by lunch time we reached the monastery of San Martino. After a brief respite we followed a path over the hills to Monreale, where we quenched our thirst with abundant supplies of oranges, which we bought for little more than a halfpenny each. A thrilling motor coach ride back over the hills to Mondello completed our day's tour.

We set off next morning to climb Monte Peligrino, a steep height that overshadows Colonia Marina. When at last we reached the summit we saw many black snakes that darted across our path, and one member of our party narrowly escaped being bitten. From the mountain we had a magnificent view of the coast from Palermo to Mondello, and saw the Colonia Marina far below us. We had an early supper that evening, as we had been invited to go to the opera as guests of the Mayor of Palermo.

D. JENNINGS (Bristol).

A Visit to an Engine Shed

It was my good fortune recently to visit the L.N.E.R. Haymarket Engine Shed, Edinburgh. As I arrived the famous "Mikado" locomotive "*Cock o' the North*" was leaving for Waverley Station to take charge of the 9.55 a.m. Aberdeen express. For its brief run to the station it was coupled to a "Scott." This engine is a 4–4–0 of the former North British Railway. With its tender it weighs only 104 tons, against the 165 tons of its companion on this occasion, and the two locomotives were in striking contrast to each other.

Inside the sheds there were several engines awaiting repair, the most prominent being "Pacific" No. 2579, "*Dick Turpin.*" The big mechanical coaling plant attracted attention and it was wonderful to see the tender of a "Pacific" filled with nine tons of coal in a few minutes. We had a splendid time inspecting other locomotives, among them "Shires" and "Directors," and were sorry when the time came for us to leave.

W. McWHIR (Edinburgh).

The Sussex Iron Industry

Where Drake's Cannon Were Made

By W. A. Bagley

ANYONE asked to mention the chief iron districts of England probably would name among other places the Black Country, Cleveland in Yorkshire, Frodingham in Lincolnshire and Corby in the county of Northampton. These are in the North and Midlands, and many would be surprised to learn that the rich pastures and primrose-carpeted woods of Sussex were the chief iron producing district in England from the earliest times right up to the beginning of last century. The cannon in the ships of Drake and other great seamen who sent their shot crashing into the proud galleons of the Spanish Armada were cast there.

Few people realise how extensive the Sussex iron industry was. It is often referred to as the Wealden industry from the name of the district in which it was carried on, and the story of ironworking there goes back to very early times. In the British Museum there are specimens of British iron that the ancient Britons wore, not as ornaments, but as outward signs of wealth, and when the Romans came, they seized the existing holdings and exploited them for their own purposes.

The bay and sluice at Ashburnham Furnace, near Penhurst, Sussex. This was the last of the old Sussex iron furnaces to be kept at work.

In those early days the ore was dug in red clods out of shallow pits or hillsides, where its presence was betrayed by a rusty red colour. Sometimes bell pits were dug, but these were rarely more than 20 ft. deep or 6 ft. in diameter. The ore was first washed to remove dirt, and then "burnt," that is roasted or calcined. This treatment removed further impurities, and enabled it to be broken up into small pieces that were more easily smelted. Care had to be taken not to overheat the material, for this would have caused it to fuse into a mass.

The iron was smelted on what was known as the bloomery hearth. The term "bloom" is used to this day, and comes from an Anglo-saxon word *bloma* that in general terms means a lump of metal. The process is still used among primitive peoples, and in one direct operation produces a small piece of iron.

First of all a saucer-shaped depression from 7 ft. to 9 ft. in diameter was lined with blocks of rough sandstone and beaten clay. Upon this a conical heap consisting of alternate layers of iron ore and charcoal was raised, and the whole was covered with a thick coating of clay. Gravel and old slag were strewn on the ground around the heap to provide a platform for the workmen, and the nozzles of the bellows, which were made of ox-hide, were pushed into the pile near the bottom. Several pairs of bellows were used, and after the charcoal had been ignited the hearth was kept at full blast for about six hours.

The heat was not great enough to melt the iron set free, and this merely became pasty enough to trickle down to the floor of the hearth. The product was wrought iron. If by any chance the temperature became too high, the iron was converted into what we now call cast iron. This is more brittle than wrought iron, and as the people of the day did not understand how to work it, the bloom thus made was regarded as spoilt and thrown away.

After the smelting, the hearth was knocked down to obtain the iron. This was very impure, although only the richest ores were used, and was full of cinder that had to be beaten out. It was then sold to the smith, and was worked without any further treatment.

The process was a wasteful one, for the iron was never fully extracted. The cinder indeed was so rich in iron that in later times it was used instead of ore, and it also was a good source of slag that was valuable as a road-making material. The hearths were of a temporary nature, and few tools were used.

The industry declined in the Dark and Middle Ages, and survived only as a limited and almost domestic industry. During the 15th century a new process for extracting iron from its ores was introduced from the Continent, however, probably from the Liege district, in which the recently invented blast furnace was used. This is a tall structure that is fed with ore and fuel at the open top, and from which the molten iron is withdrawn at the bottom. A continuous blast of air is driven through the mass, and the iron tapped off is led into moulds. It is cast iron, containing a small proportion of carbon, and can be converted into the more malleable wrought iron by reheating.

The introduction of the blast furnace gave a tremendous impetus to the industry, which rapidly grew in importance. It reached its peak during the time of Queen Elizabeth, when it is estimated that not less than 7,000 people were employed in it. This was a very large percentage of the population of those days. The iron workers became prosperous, as the fine houses they built show, and great landowners entered the trade in order to make the most of their woodland and mineral wealth. This was the first step in changing England from an agricultural country into an industrial one.

None of these old furnaces actually stands to-day, but we

have many documents relating to them, although no accurate drawings are available. One of the best of them was 24 ft. square at the base, and 30 ft. high. It was shaped like a truncated pyramid, with thick walls, and inside was approximately egg-shaped, with a rectangular hearth of considerable depth.

The bellows that were so necessary for iron furnaces were worked by hand and foot until the 14th century, when water power was substituted. The furnaces were built on the banks of the streams, for water played a great part in the Sussex iron industry. It worked not only the bellows supplying the air blast, but also the hammer that beat the iron itself in the forge.

A small cannon and other relics of the Sussex iron industry. They are now in the garden of a house on the site of Robertsbridge Abbey Forge, where they were cast.

A water-wheel drove the bellows, the arms of which were pushed down by pegs or cams arranged round a barrel rotated by the wheel. A counterweight raised the arms of the bellows in readiness for the next stroke. It was possible to tap a swift stream and run the water along wooden troughs to the wheel. A sufficient head of water usually could not be obtained directly in this manner, however, so artificial ponds, known to-day as "hammer ponds," were made by throwing up a dam, or "bay," as it was called, across a narrow deep valley. An overflow, or spillway, was constructed, with sluices that could be raised or lowered in time of flood, and if the difference in levels was considerable, a series of steps were made to break the force of the fall, and thus to avoid undermining the bay. In west Sussex the spillways were made of stone, and traces of them still survive; those in East Sussex probably were made of wood, for they have vanished without leaving a trace.

The water was carried to the wheel in oaken chutes. The supply depended entirely on rainfall, and a man-driven treadmill had to be used if this proved insufficient. Few furnaces worked all the year round, and the ironmasters probably did a little farming and other work in the slack periods.

A gun of Sussex iron on Tower Wharf, London.

In time the hammer ponds became silted up, and the bays then were made higher with cinder and slag. If they broke, the expense of making new ones usually was too great for the owners of the furnace.

A forge was generally erected about half a mile below the furnace, but this was not invariably the case. The forging was carried out with a tilt-hammer driven by water-power. The hammer head weighed about 8 cwt. and was hafted or fitted to the shaft or helve in the same manner as that of an ordinary household hammer. The shaft of course was much longer, measuring about 9 ft. and was pivoted to the middle of a stout framework firmly bound with iron clamps and wedges. The water-wheel turned a second wheel provided with four projecting pegs that in turn caught the shaft just below the head, lifted it and then allowed it to fall. Additional impetus was given by means of a springy, laminated length of timber against which the shaft was forced as it was raised. The rebound of the timber made the blow on the hot metal resting on the anvil more powerful than if the hammer had been allowed to fall under its own weight.

The mainstay of the Sussex iron industry was the making of cannon, and a well-known piece of doggerel tells us how, at Buxted, in 1545,

"Master Huggett and his man John,
They did make the first can-non."

The cores for the moulds in which the cannon were cast were made up of successive layers of straw and clay, wound on a stick. At a later time the guns were cast solid and bored.

In 1573, Ralph Hogge, the Queen's gunmaker, complained that certain ironmasters were infringing his monopoly by exporting ordnance. In the year following this complaint, a Commission of Enquiry drew up a list of Sussex ironworks and this still exists. There was much smuggling and illegal trading in those days, and some Sussex cannon makers were charged with selling their products to friend and foe alike.

Peaceful homely firebacks, now much prized by collectors, also were cast at Sussex ironworks, and iron tombstones, or rather "headirons," were other products of this old industry.

There is a popular belief that the Sussex iron industry died out because the demand for charcoal threatened forests with destruction. This is a half truth. It is true that alarmists pointed out that there would soon be no timber left to make ships for the Navy if the forests continued to be cut down at the rate necessary to provide the charcoal, and it was then arranged that so many trees per acre were to be left standing when large areas were depleted.

The real cause of the waning of the Wealden iron industry was the invention of smelting processes in which coke was used. Charcoal was more expensive than the new fuel, and its transport costs were high. As a result valuable Naval contracts were lost to the industry and it died out after a long history that included 2,000 years of small things, and a period of 300 years in which it was of great importance. The last furnace to be shut down was that of Ashburnham, near Penhurst, which was closed about 1820. Wm. Hobday, the last surviving worker there, died as recently as 1883.

In Search of New Models

Ideas from Seaside Holidays

THE lively scenes on the sands and promenades of a seaside resort provide many interesting ideas for model-building of the lighter and humorous type, and model-builders on holiday should keep a keen look out for suggestions for novel and ingenious models. Piers and fairgrounds of course are already well known as prototypes of many splendid reproductions in Meccano, but they do not by any means exhaust the possibilities. Pierrots, minstrels and bathers are all excellent subjects for fascinating and effective model-building, and the exciting or humorous events that are always taking place at the seaside also can be turned to good account. Meccano figures of course play a prominent part in models of this kind, and careful arrangement of the parts representing the legs and arms often will transform a simple and uninteresting subject into one that is full of life and vigour.

Fig. 1. A Meccano ice-cream man.

The models described in this article show a few of the many possibilities that the seaside suggests to the model-builder, and many of these have the great advantage that they offer splendid opportunities to owners of small Outfits and others who enjoy devising models of the simplicity type.

The ice-cream vendor shown in Fig. 1 is a good example of an effective seaside model, in which the construction of the barrow and of the figure accompanying it is remarkably simple. The barrow is built up from three $3\frac{1}{2}'' \times 2\frac{1}{2}''$ and two $2\frac{1}{2}'' \times 2\frac{1}{2}''$ Strip Plates, Angle Brackets being used to form the connections between these Plates. The Wheels are held in position by Couplings, and Collars are used for carrying the roof supports and shafts. The curved roof is built up from two $5\frac{1}{2}'' \times 2\frac{1}{2}''$ Flexible Plates. The top of the ice-cream container consists of a large and a small Flanged Wheel, and this is placed on top of the barrow but is not secured in any way. The construction of the figure is typical of most Meccano models of this type. Strips of various lengths are used for the body, legs and arms, and a $1\frac{1}{2}''$ Strip surmounted by a 1" loose Pulley forms the neck and head. A neat use for the new Pawls, without boss, is that of shaping the back of the neck of this figure. The arms of course must be bent outward slightly in order that the hands, represented by $\frac{1}{2}'' \times \frac{1}{2}''$ Angle Brackets, can grasp the shafts. Many other humorous models can be built on similar lines.

Swimming, diving, and sunbathing are naturally the main attractions of a seaside holiday, and suggestions for a variety of new models can be obtained by watching those who take part in these pastimes. One of the most recent additions to water sport in this country is surf-board riding, and a simple, but effective model of a surf-board rider is illustrated in Fig. 2. The disposition of the Strips is of major importance in a model of this kind, for the whole atmosphere must be one of thrill and speed, and a streamline effect therefore is necessary.

The construction of the surf-board is very simple. A rectangle is first formed from two $5\frac{1}{2}''$ and two $1\frac{1}{2}''$ Strips. These support a $5\frac{1}{2}'' \times 1\frac{1}{2}''$ Flexible Plate, and the front end of the board is curved by making use of two Pawls, without boss. The figure is built up in a similar manner to that shown in Fig. 1, but $2\frac{1}{2}''$ large radius Curved Strips are used to form the body. Two lengths of Meccano Cord represent the reins.

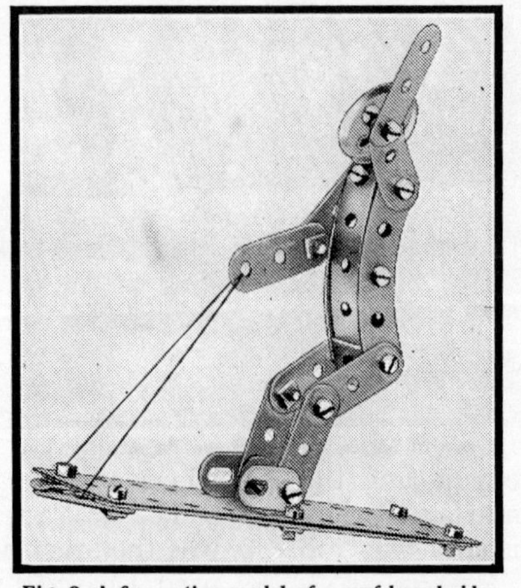

Fig. 2. A fine action model of a surf-board rider.

To increase the attractiveness of this model it is a good plan to show it being towed behind a Meccano model motor boat. The boat may be of the big cruiser type or it may be a smaller one fitted with an outboard motor. Motor boats of the second of these types are extremely popular, and many are now used for towing surf-board riders at high speed.

Surf-board riding came to this country from the South Seas, where it has been the general sport for hundreds of years. The inhabitants of these islands rely on the long Pacific rollers for carrying them and their surf-boards at high speed towards the beach. A model of a surf-rider of this type can be built in a similar manner to that shown in Fig. 2. The figure should lie flat along the board, however, and no reins need be provided.

Evenings at the sea-side may be enlivened by a visit to the pier or hall in which a concert party is performing. Here again are to be found many ideas for humorous models, and a good example is shown in Fig. 3. The figures in this represent a concertina player and a banjoist respectively. Both are shown dressed in evening clothes, and one wears a top hat.

The construction of these figures is simple. Each consists essentially of two large radius Curved Strips, connected together by one Double Bracket the centre portion of which forms a support for a $2\frac{1}{2}''$ Strip bent to the shape shown. Legs and arms are represented by $1\frac{1}{2}''$ Strips, and the long boots typical of most minstrels are formed from $1\frac{1}{2}''$ Strips. In both cases $1\frac{1}{2}''$ Strips and $1''$ loose Pulleys are used for neck and head, and the top hat carried by one is built up from a short Strip and a Single Bent Strip. The concertina is a Hornby Coach Connection, the ends of which have been filled in with small pieces of black cardboard cut to the required shape. This use of the Hornby Coach Connection is ingenious and effective and no doubt Meccano model-builders will find many other uses for it. The appearance of the model can be much improved by painting in a key board and stop manual on the "concertina."

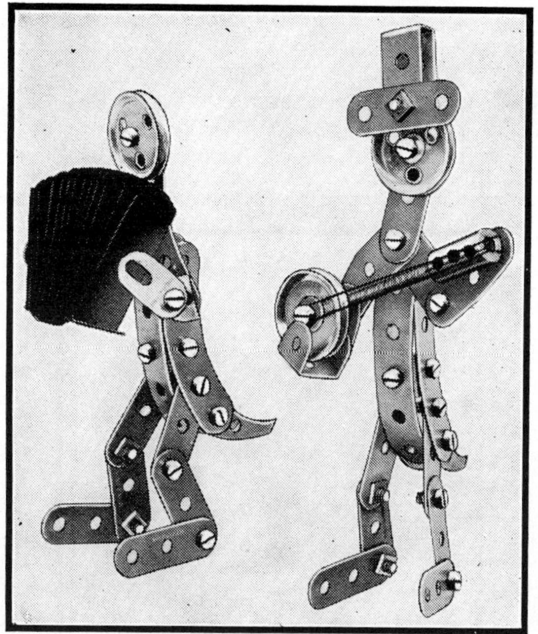
Fig. 3. A humorous minstrel troupe.

The banjo carried by the second figure can easily be built up from a $1''$ fast Pulley fitted with a $2''$ Screwed Rod. The Rod is fitted in one of the holes in the boss of the Pulley, and is locked in position by the set-screw. The upper end of the Rod is fitted with a Threaded Coupling locked in position by a nut, and a bolt is used to connect the Threaded Coupling with the $1\frac{1}{2}''$ Strip forming one arm of the figure. Banjo strings can be suitably represented by Meccano Cord.

These two models do not of course exhaust all the possibilities of stage shows and minstrel troupes. A model submitted in a recent competition is worthy of note. It was a miniature reproduction of a complete pierrot show, and the entire stage and seating accommodation were included. Marionettes operated by the builder of the model presented a variety concert and provided many hours of good fun both for the owner and his friends. No doubt many other Meccano enthusiasts will find the idea of sufficient interest to include in their future model-building programmes.

Illustrated post-cards sent by friends from the sea-side often have humorous sketches as their frontispiece. Here again are ideas suitable for reproduction in Meccano, and Fig. 4 gives some idea of possibilities of this kind. This model represents the traditional fat man on a thin donkey, and the hollow back of the animal is a graphic illustration of the evils of such a combination.

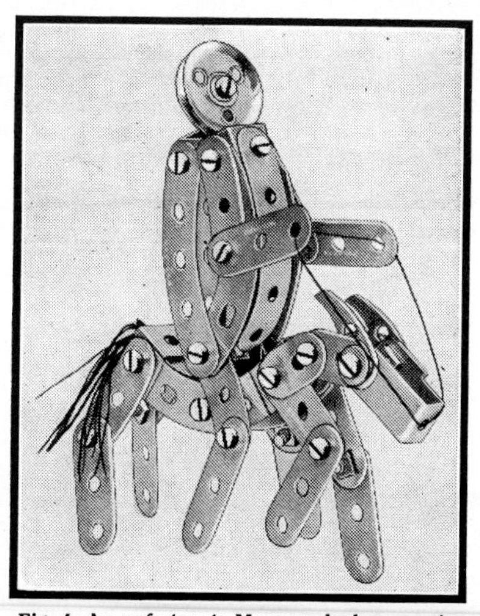
Fig. 4. An unfortunate Meccano donkey carrying a heavy load.

Careful arrangement of the legs, head, and ears of the donkey give a very humorous appearance to the model, and a final touch consists of a tail formed from a bundle of Meccano Cords. In this model use is again made of Pawls, without boss. They represent the ears of the animal and in the position shown in the illustration suggest stubbornness and temper.

The man mounted on the donkey is made to appear as fat as possible by making good use of Curved Strips. In front he is built up from two $2\frac{1}{2}''$ small radius Curved Strips, and his back is formed of two $2\frac{1}{2}''$ large radius Curved Strips. The space between each pair of Curved Strips is filled in by means of $2\frac{1}{2}''$ and $1\frac{1}{2}''$ Strips bent to the required shape.

Beach camera men and novelty hawkers can be reproduced in Meccano with excellent effect. Typical scenes of a few years ago also are attractive. Clumsy-looking bathing huts mounted on four massive wheels were the most conspicuous objects of old-style beach scenes, and these are specially effective when contrasted with representations of modern seaside resorts and the people who throng to them.

One aspect of model-building that has so far been very much neglected is the construction of miniature swimming baths. Of recent years swimming has become increasingly popular, and open-air and indoor baths have been instituted for the benefit of those who find seabathing rather boisterous. These baths feature largely in holiday advertising and so many photographs from every conceivable angle are available that the model-builder need never be at a loss when designing such a model. The high diving boards and the other structural portions of these models lend themselves admirably to reproduction in Meccano, and by the judicious use of Strip Plates and Flexible Plates excellent models of cubicles and galleries can be built. Extra interest is added by the addition of handrails, offices and entrances provided with turnstiles, and green rippled glass is an excellent substitute for water.

A glance through holiday catalogues issued by all railway companies and town authorities will result in a surprising crop of further ideas, for the photographs and pen sketches found in many of these publications give many aspects of holiday life by the sea. Plan views of gardens and promenades are to be found in great variety, and reproductions of these seldom fail to attract interest.

A purely structural model can readily be given a lively appearance by the addition of miniature figures carrying out suitable movements. For example, divers and sunbathers can be included in a model swimming pool, the divers being suspended by lengths of cotton from the high diving board. The figures are constructed in a similar manner to the surf-board rider shown in Fig. 2, but in many cases the arms will have to be secured in place by means of $\frac{1}{2}'' \times \frac{1}{2}''$ Angle Brackets. Figures of spectators can also be added with good effect, and in this direction there is considerable scope for the ingenious model-builder.

Meccano Suggestions Section

By "Spanner"

(356-7)—Photographic Devices (L. P. Storey, Bristol and R. M. Smith, Stanmore)

Spring and summer bring with them great activity in the ranks of photographers, and gadgets that are likely to shorten the time spent in carrying out the routine work associated with their hobby are always acceptable. The two mechanisms described and illustrated in this section have been designed for the purpose of eliminating tedious work of this kind.

The first of these mechanisms will be appreciated by those who develop their own roll films, for it gives the necessary movements to films that are being developed. It also can be adapted to rock a photographic dish in which films and prints are being fixed.

The construction of the apparatus is fairly simple and is commenced by building up a rectangle from two 12½" Angle Girders and two 5½" Angle Girders. An additional 5½" Angle Girder is bolted in place between the two 12½" Angle Girders 1, Fig. 356. Two 5½"×2½" Flanged Plates are now fitted, and these form supports for an Electric Motor.

A ½" Pinion on the armature shaft of the Motor meshes with a 57-teeth Gear 2, and this drives at a slow speed the shaft 3 through the medium of four 3 : 1 reduction gears. Each stage of reduction consists of a ½" Pinion and a 57-teeth Gear. The shaft 3 is journalled in reinforced bearings formed from two Cranks, and carries at one end a Rod Socket 4. This part is used as a right-angle connection, and in it is locked the 3½" Rod 5.

A second Rod Socket is carried on the 2½" Rod 5, and this forms a support for a short Rod 6 on which are mounted three 1" loose Pulleys. These are spaced apart by two Washers each, and are prevented from slipping sideways along the Rod by means of two Collars.

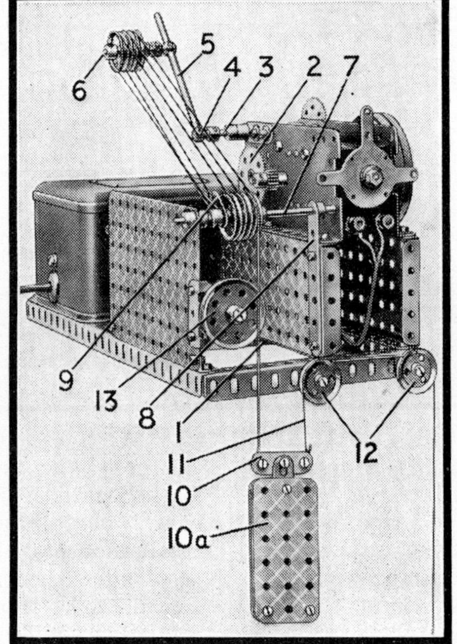

Fig. 356

A 5½"×3½" Flat Plate fitted as shown, supports at one corner a 3½" Rod 7, the opposite end of which is journalled in the upper hole of a 3½" Strip 8. On the Rod are mounted a Flat Bracket 9 and a second set of three 1" loose Pulleys spaced by Washers in the same manner as those mounted on the Rod 6.

The operating cord is attached at one end to the Flat Bracket 9, and is then passed alternately round the Pulleys on the Rod 6 and the Pulleys on the Rod 7. The resulting arrangement is similar in every respect to a three sheave pulley system. The free end of the cord is clamped to the 1½" Strips 10, which also are attached to a cord 11 that passes over the two Pulleys 12, and carries at its lower end a large bull-dog clip. Two clips are required, one being attached to the Plates 10a. The film to be developed or fixed is clipped at each end and allowed to hang in a loop dipping into the developing or fixing solution. As the arm 5 rotates, the cord passing round the Pulleys is alternately lengthened and shortened and produces the required see-saw movement of the film. A Flywheel on the armature shaft of the Electric Motor prevents undue variations in the speed of the apparatus.

A Pulley 13 is fitted in order to adapt the movement to the rocking of the dishes used. When the model is used for this purpose the cord is passed round only one set of Pulleys, that is, round one Pulley on the Rod 6 and one on the Rod 7. The Rod 6 is moved inward along the Rod 5 until its travel is about ½". After passing round the Pulley 13 the cord is attached to a platform carrying the developing dish.

The second mechanism, Fig. 357, submitted by R. M. Smith, Stanmore, is a dish rocker for use when developing plates, or fixing plates and roll-films. Films must of course be cut before being placed in the dish.

The device is built by bolting together two 9½" Angle Girders and two 5½" Angle Girders to form a framework. Three further Girders are secured in place across this framework in the positions shown in the illustration, and two of these form supports for two 3½"×2½" Flanged Plates that carry at their upper ends a 2½"×2½" Flat Plate. A 2½"×½" Double Angle Strip 1 also is bolted to the Flanged Plates. A third 3½"×2½" Flanged Plate is secured to the base of the model, and this forms a support for two ½"×½" Angle Brackets that carry the ends of two 4½" Strips, one of which is shown at 2. The other ends of these Strips are bolted to the two central Flanged Plates.

An E1 Electric Motor drives a 57-teeth gear that is mounted, together with a 1" Sprocket 4, on a 3½" Rod. The 1" Sprocket is connected to a similar part on the Rod 5 by means of a length of Sprocket Chain. A ¾" Pinion is mounted on the same Rod as the last mentioned Sprocket, and this is meshed with a 50-teeth Gear 6. A ½" Pinion on the same Rod as the Gear 6 engages with a 1½" Contrate Wheel locked on the Rod 7 that carries a Worm, driving two Bush Wheels 8 by means of a ½" Pinion 9.

Each Bush Wheel 8 carries a Threaded Pin that forms a pivot for the lower end of a 2½" Strip 10, and the upper end of this Strip is lock-nutted to a horizontal 7½" Strip. The 7½" Strip is pivotally mounted on a 3½" Rod as shown, and carries at its free end a 2" Strip 11. This 2" Strip forms the link connection between the rocking table and 7½" Strip. It is connected to the table, together with the opposite 2" Strip, by a 6½" Rod, Collars being used on both sides of these strips to prevent side movement.

Fig. 357

The framework of the rocking table is built up in a similar manner to the base of the model, but is filled in by means of three 5½"×3½" Flat Plates. It is fitted with a Flat Trunnion on each side, and each of these can be adjusted slightly to prevent the dish from sliding. The complete table is pivoted at its centre on a 6½" Rod 12.

The range of movement of the table on which the dish is carried can be adjusted by altering the position of the Strips 11. These Strips are secured, as already described, by means of a 6½" Rod journalled at each end in the centre hole of a 1½" Strip bolted to the side Girders of the table. By replacing the 1½" Strips with longer ones it is possible to alter the position of the 6½" Rod. In this way the leverage between the Strips 11 and Pivot 12 can be increased or decreased, and the movement of the dish varied proportionately.

It is inadvisable to fill the photographic dish to capacity. Only sufficient solution for the purpose should be used, and in order to protect the Meccano parts from possible damage by the solution a layer of felt should be placed on top of the table. The speed of rocking can be controlled by incorporating a Resistance Controller between the motor and the source of the current driving it.

(358)—Clock Escapement (J. Wheldon, Newcastle-on-Tyne)

Meccano clocks always excite great interest among Meccano model-builders, who are continually experimenting and trying out new ideas. Among the novel devices recently submitted is a Meccano Escapement, by J. Wheldon, Newcastle-on-Tyne, in which an attempt is made to increase the length of run of a Meccano clock by making use of an escapement wheel with a large number of teeth.

Fig. 358

Fig. 358 shows this mechanism, which is extremely simple to construct. The escapement is a 2″ Sprocket Wheel, and this is mounted on the final shaft of the clock gear-train. The pallet is built up from a 1½″ × ½″ Double Angle Strip that is attached by means of two ½″ × ½″ Angle Brackets to two Cranks. The Angle Brackets are bolted together to form a double bracket, and the Cranks are locked on the ends of two short Rods. The outer ends of the two Rods are carried in suitable bearings mounted on the frame of the model clock, and great care is necessary when fitting these to see that they are exactly in line. In the illustration only one bearing is shown in order to make the construction and pallet setting quite clear.

The crutch is locked on the end of one of these two Rods, and is built up in a similar manner to that incorporated in the Super Model Grandfather Clock, Leaflet No. 14a. Care must be taken when adjusting the ends of the Double Angle Strip, and the exact position of the pallets in relation to the escapement wheel must be gauged very accurately. Correct adjustment is best accomplished by mounting the entire clock mechanism on screw feet.

The builder claims many advantages for this movement. The chief of these are compactness, and long running. The mechanism is remarkably silent and absorbs very little of the initial power.

(359)—Intermittent Motion

(K. Robinson, Fishguard)

By means of this mechanism, submitted by K. Robinson, Fishguard, intermittent motion of almost any duration and in a variety of sequences can be imparted to a rotary rod. As will be seen on reference to Fig. 359, a 57-teeth Gear fitted with four Threaded Pins is mounted on a Pivot Bolt and driven by means of a Worm that is in constant engagement with the Gear. The Worm is mounted on a Rod that is rotated from a shaft, running at right-angles to it, by means of a pair of ⅞″ Bevel Gears. The end of the Rod protruding from the Worm carries one half of a Dog Clutch, the other portion being secured to the inner end of a sliding Rod.

As the Rod driven by the Bevel Gears rotates, the Threaded Pins on the 57-teeth Gear push forward a second sliding Rod attached by Cranks to that carrying one half of the Dog Clutch. A compression spring on this Rod returns the Dog Clutch into engagement as the pressure of each Threaded Pin in turn is released. The number and disposition of the Threaded Pins decides the sequence of the intermittent movement of the rotating Rod.

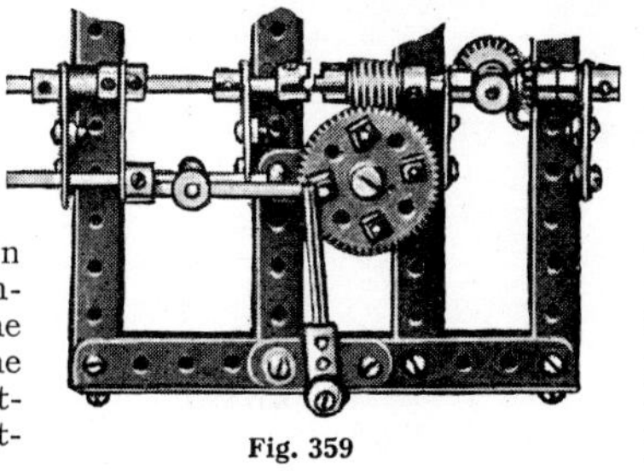

Fig. 359

The short Rod that is mounted approximately at right angles to the sliding Rod is carried in a Coupling that is free to turn on a short vertical Rod. It is held in position by Collars on the vertical Rod, which is secured to the base by means of a Double Arm Crank. The ends of the sliding shaft and the pivoted Rod are in contact with each other during the period that a Threaded Pin is moving the two Dog Clutches out of engagement. At other times the pivoted Rod is free.

(360)—A Novel Display Mechanism

(F. Barlow, Rhyl)

The special window display mechanism illustrated in Fig. 360 has been submitted by F. Barlow, Rhyl, who made use of it in a large advertising model. In this a large drum carrying advertising slogans had to be rotated so that each slogan appeared for a period in an opening cut in the background of the display. The mechanism was built entirely of Meccano parts.

The drum is mounted on a long Rod 1, on one end of which is locked a Face Plate 2, carrying four Threaded Pins, which engage with a built-up hook 3. This hook is bolted on the lower end of a compound Strip 4 pivotally attached at its upper end to a second Face Plate 5 that is driven at a slow speed by an Electric Motor.

The Strip 4 is held in engagement with the Threaded Pins by a short length of Spring Cord 6. A 12½″ Strip is fitted in order to prevent the drum rotating after receiving an impulse from the hook 3, and this is held in engagement with the Threaded Pins by a Spring. As the Hook 3 is raised by the Face Plate 5 it engages with one of the Threaded Pins in the Face Plate 2, and lifts it. As the Hook descends it rides over the bottom Threaded Pin.

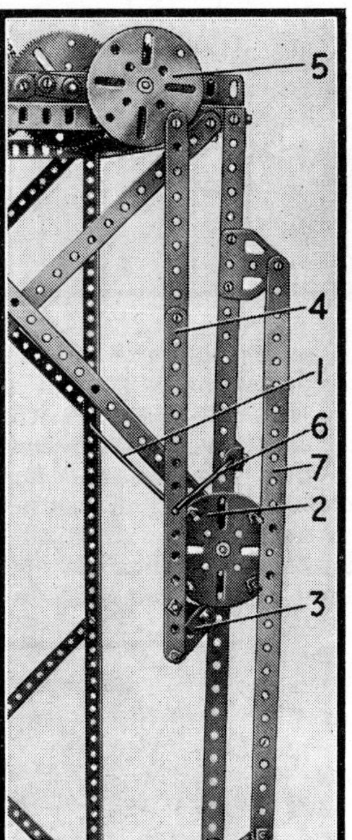

Fig. 360

Miscellaneous Suggestions

Under this heading "Spanner" replies to readers who submit interesting suggestions regarding new Meccano models or movements that he is unable to deal with more fully elsewhere. On occasion he offers comments and technical criticisms that, he trusts, will be accepted in the same spirit of mutual help in which they are advanced.

(M.190.) A Built-up Eccentric.—In the construction of very large Meccano model steam engines, the fitting of Eccentrics of suitable size is a point of considerable importance. Meccano Eccentrics are often too small, but W. Avory, London, W.11, has succeeded in building up an Eccentric that works satisfactorily and has a good appearance. It can be recommended to any Meccano model-builders who have experienced difficulty in constructing a suitable unit of this type.

The suggested Eccentric consists of a 2″ Pulley, across the centre of which is bolted a Crank. The boss of this Crank is in line with one of the round holes in the Pulley, and the groove of the latter accommodates a "strap" that is built up from three 2½″ small radius Curved Strips. When these Curved Strips are in position, a gap of 1½″ exists between the ends of the strap they make. This is bridged by a Flat Trunnion, the apex of which points outwards, away from the centre of the 2″ Pulley Wheel. The Connecting Rod is bolted at one end to the Flat Trunnion, and at the other it is linked-up with the valve or valve-gear. Before being used, the groove of the Pulley and the "strap" must be thoroughly lubricated.

(M.191.) Creeper Track.—The fitting of creeper tracks to Meccano models of tanks, tractors, etc., continues to interest Meccano Model-builders. The latest suggestion in this connection has been submitted by G. Garvey, Redcar, Yorks., who has made use of elastic trouser belts in order to represent the caterpillars of his model tractor.

The belts were obtained for a few pence from the local general stores and were then cut down the centre into two strips. The two ends of each strip were then cut square and joined together by means of a strip of adhesive rubber similar to that supplied in cycle puncture repair outfits. The complete track passes round two large diameter wheels of double width, one of which must consist of Pulleys fitted with Meccano Dunlop Tyres and must be coupled-up inside the tractor to the driving motor. The rear set of wheels carrying the belt may consist of Sprocket Wheels, Pulleys or Wheel Flanges and, if desired, an intermediate jockey pulley can be fitted to take up slackness. A device of this kind is to be found in nearly all modern, high-speed tanks and tractors. A 1″ Pulley carried in a spring-mounted framework will be found suitable for use with this Caterpillar Track, and is easily fitted. This Pulley is so placed that it presses on the inner surface of the track between the main front and rear Pulleys.

New Outfit Models

Ideas for Small Outfit Builders

THE new models to be described this month are intended primarily for boys who possess medium sized Outfits. Two of the models are fitted with Meccano Clockwork Motors, and the Breakdown Lorry can readily be fitted with a Meccano *"Magic Motor"* if desired.

The first model, illustrated in Fig. 1, has as its prototype one of the train-ferries that operate between Ipswich and Ostend. The model is built with Outfit E, and its appearance can be greatly improved by the addition of a number of Dinky Toy Coaches, the scale of these Coaches approximating to that of the train-ferry. The construction is commenced by building the framework of the lower portion of the hull. Each side consists of two 12½″ Angle Girders 1 overlapping 15 holes. One bolt is used in the centre of these two Girders to hold them together, and the two complete compound Girders are connected together by three 5½″ Strips. These Strips, together with the side Girders, form supports for the deck, which is built up from two 12½″ × 2½″, and two 5½″ × 2½″ Strip Plates and one 12½″ Strip. This last part fills in the gap between the two 12½″ × 2½″ Strip Plates that are arranged longitudinally on the deck.

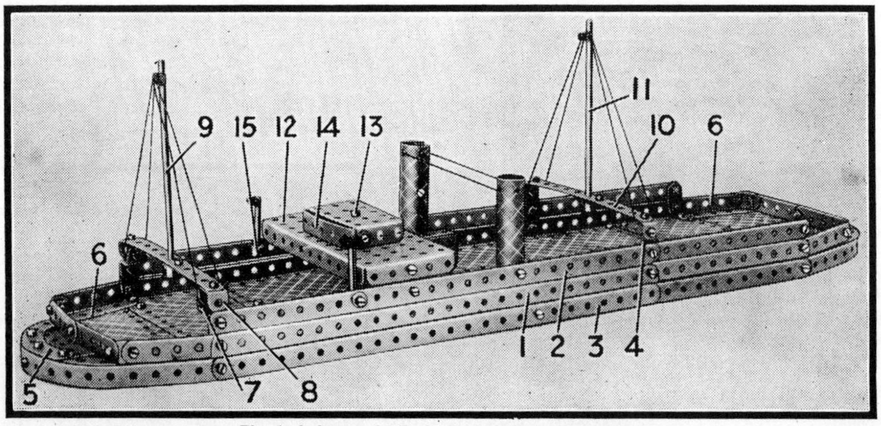

Fig. 1. A fine model Train Ferry built with Outfit E.

The sides of the model are increased in depth by the addition of two compound strips 2 and 3 each of which is formed from two 12½″ Strips overlapping 15 holes. They are attached to the Girders 1 by Flat Brackets at each end on the top, and Angle Brackets are used on the undersides. The 1½″ Strips 4, carrying the after bridge, also help to secure the upper Strips 2 in position.

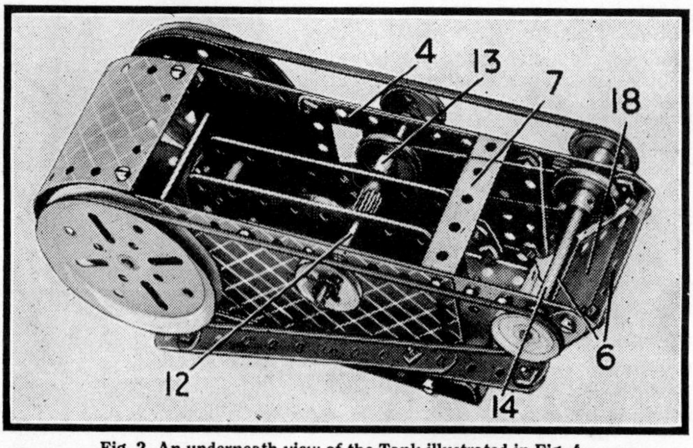

Fig. 2. An underneath view of the Tank illustrated in Fig. 4.

At each end of the Strips 3, two 5½″ Strips are bent to form the bows and stern, and where these are connected together an Angle Bracket is fitted in place to form a support for the 2½″ large radius Curved Strip 5. This is bolted at each end to a 2½″ small radius Curved Strip that carries a 2½″ Strip 6. The ends of the Girders 1 are extended by 2½″ Strips that carry ½″ × ½″ Angle Brackets forming supports for two 2½″ Strips bolted together and overlapping one hole. These Strips represent the barriers fitted to the actual vessel, when under weigh.

Two ½″ Reversed Angle Brackets 7 are now fitted and each of these carries a Double Bracket 8. The two Double Brackets form supports for a 5½″ Strip that carries at its centre a Crank supporting the fore-mast, a 4½″ Rod 9. A second bridge, built up from a 5½″ Strip 10 supported at each end by Angle Brackets, is secured to the 1½″ Strips 4, and it carries at its centre a Crank in the boss of which is gripped a Rod 11, forming the after-mast. The rigging is represented by short lengths of Meccano Cord secured to the masts by clips.

The bridge is built up from a 5½″ × 2½″ Flanged Plate 12 bolted to the Strips 2 by Flat Brackets in the position shown in Fig. 1. To the upper side of this Flanged Plate is bolted a 2½″ × 1½″ Flanged Plate by means of a ¾″ Bolt 13, and a curved Double Angle Strip 14 is used to represent the front of the bridge proper.

The addition of ventilators and funnels is all that is required to complete the model. Each ventilator is represented by a 1½″ Rod carrying a Spring Clip, held in a vertical position by a Collar 15. The funnels are each built up from a 2½″ × 2½″ Flexible Plate bent round into the form of a short tube, and when complete they are braced together as shown by two short lengths of cord.

Parts required to build the Train Ferry: 8 of No. 1; 11 of No. 2; 2 of No. 6a; 4 of No. 8; 6 of No. 10; 2 of No. 11; 12 of No. 12; 4 of No. 12c; 2 of No. 15; 2 of No. 18a; 3 of No. 35; 85 of No. 37; 6 of No. 37a; 6 of No. 38; 5 of No. 48a; 1 of No. 51; 1 of No. 52; 2 of No. 59; 2 of No. 62; 2 of No. 90; 4 of No. 90a; 1 of No. 111; 5 of No. 111c; 2 of No. 125; 1 of No. 176; 2 of No. 188; 2 of No. 190; 2 of No. 191; 2 of No. 195; 2 of No. 197.

In Fig. 3 is shown a model Caterpillar Tractor built with Outfit D. This model is driven by a No. 2 Clockwork Motor and is representative of many farm tractors used on the great farms of Canada and South America. The construction of the model is commenced by building the main side members 1 and 1a, the 5½″ Strips 1a being secured to the 3½″ Strip 1 by two Flat Brackets. Two further Flat Brackets form the connections between the 5½″ Strip 2 and the Strip 1a. Two 2½″ × ½″ Double Angle Strips held in place by the bolts 3 and 4 are used to connect the two complete side members together. A 2½″ × 1½″ Flanged Plate held in position by the

Bolts 5 is used to represent the rear platform, and it forms also a third strengthening piece between the main frames.

The side of the model not seen in the photograph is built up from a 5½″×2½″ Strip Plate and a 2½″×2½″ Flexible Plate, part of which is shown at 6. The lower edge of the large Strip Plate is attached by bolts to the 5½″ Strip opposite to 2. The near side of the Tractor is built up in a slightly different manner in order to expose the winding spindle of the Clockwork Motor.

The Motor is supported by passing two Rods 7 and 8 through the Strips 1, and through the next to end holes in the bottom edges of the Motor side plates. The Rod 7 carries a 1″ fast Pulley inside the main frames of the model, and this is connected by a driving band to a 1″ Pulley on the driving spindle of the Clockwork Motor. The 1″ Pulleys on the outer ends of the Rod 7 transmit the drive to the endless tracks, which may be represented by large Meccano driving bands or lengths of Cord.

Parts required to build the Caterpillar Tractor: 7 of No. 2; 2 of No. 3; 4 of No. 5; 1 of No. 6a; 2 of No. 10; 7 of No. 12; 1 of No. 12c; 4 of No. 16; 4 of No. 20b; 4 of No. 22; 2 of No. 22a; 1 of No. 24; 45 of No. 37; 14 of No. 38; 3 of No. 48a; 1 of No. 51; 2 of No. 59; 1 of No. 90a; 1 of No. 111c; 1 of No. 126; 1 of No. 189; 3 of No. 190; 1 of No. 191; Clockwork Motor No. 2; 2 large Driving Bands (not included in Outfit).

The next model to be described is a Tank, shown in Fig. 4. This is built with Outfit D, and is driven by means of a No. 1 Clockwork Motor. Fig. 2 shows an underneath view of the model. The side of the tank seen in Fig. 4, consists of a 5½″×2½″ Strip Plate fitted at its lower edge with a 5½″ Strip 1. This Strip overlaps for a distance of four holes, and it carries a 2½″ Strip 2 together with a 1½″ Strip. The compound Strip 3 is bolted at its upper end to Strip 2, and at its lower end to the end of the Strip 1. The opposite side of the model is shown in Fig. 2. This consists of two 2½″×2½″ Flexible Plates secured together by means of a 5½″ Strip 4, and the rear is built up in a similar manner to that described for the side shown in Fig. 4.

As will be seen from Fig. 2, three 2½″×½″ Double Angle Strips 6 and 7 form connections between the two sides of the model. The Double Angle Strips 6 carry a 2½″×2½″ Flexible Plate 8, and this represents the sloping rear portion of the model.

The Clockwork Motor is held in position in the model by the Rod 12, Fig. 2, and is prevented from turning round the Rod by the top edges of the side plates bearing lightly against the underside of the Flanged Plate 5. The driving spindle of the Motor is replaced by the Rod 12 and it carries a 1″ fast Pulley 13. The ends of this Rod are fitted with 1″ loose Pulleys held in place by Spring Clips and spaced away from the sides of the model by five Washers. The Pulley 13 drives a second similar Pulley mounted on the Rod 14 by a length of Cord. Each end of the Rod 14 carries a 1″ fast Pulley that drives the caterpillar track formed from a large Meccano driving band. At the front of the tank this band passes round a 3″ Pulley.

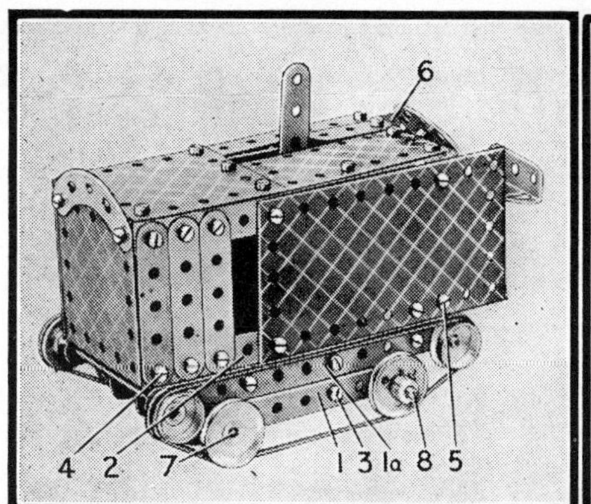

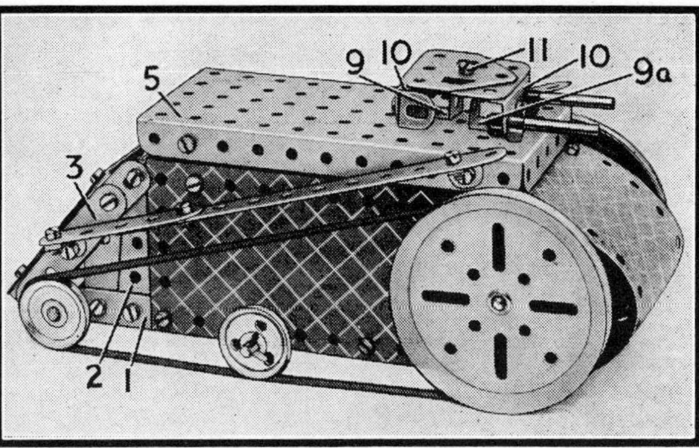

Fig. 3. (Left) The construction of this model Tractor is described in this article.
Fig. 4. (Right) A neat model Tank built with Outfit D.

Parts required to build the Tank: 4 of No. 2; 6 of No. 5; 2 of No. 6a; 8 of No. 10; 2 of No. 11; 8 of No. 12; 3 of No. 16; 2 of No. 18a; 2 of No. 19b; 4 of No. 22; 2 of No. 22a; 6 of No. 35; 52 of No. 37; 12 of No. 38; 1 of No. 40; 3 of No. 48a; 1 of No. 52; 2 of No. 126; 2 of No. 126a; 3 of No. 190; 1 of No. 192; 1 of No. 195; No. 1 Clockwork Motor, 2 large Driving Bands (not included in Outfit).

The last model to be described is a simple reproduction of a Motor Breakdown Lorry, built with Outfit B. Much additional fun can be gained by fitting a Meccano *"Magic Motor"* to the underside of this lorry, and connecting it up to a 1″ Pulley on the rear axle by means of a short length of Cord.

The model is begun by joining together a 5½″×2½″ Flanged Plate and a Flanged Sector Plate by means of two 5½″ Strips. Each side of the crane is built up from two 5½″ Strips arranged in the manner shown in Fig 5, and the upper end of the jib carries a 2″ Rod on which is mounted a ½″ loose Pulley. This Pulley and the Rod are prevented from moving laterally by four Spring Clips. Each side of the lorry is represented by 5½″×1½″ Flexible Plates, and two of the upper holes of this carry a Crank Handle round which is wound a length of cord. The cord passes over the ½″ Pulley at the top of the jib and is fitted with a Small Loaded Hook at its outer end.

Fig. 5. A simple Meccano Breakdown Crane.

The cab is built up at each side from three 2½″ Strips and one 2½″ small radius Curved Strip. Two Angle Brackets 1 and a Double Angle Strip 2 secured in the position shown form points of attachment for a 4½″×2½″ Flexible Plate. The bonnet is built up from a Trunnion 4 and two 2½″×1½″ Flexible Plates joined by an Obtuse Angle Bracket.

Parts required to build the Breakdown Lorry: 6 of No. 2; 6 of No. 5; 1 of No. 11; 5 of No. 12; 2 of No. 16; 1 of No. 17; 1 of No. 19s; 4 of No. 22; 1 of No. 23; 6 of No. 35; 32 of No. 37; 2 of No. 37a; 5 of No. 38; 1 of No. 40; 2 of No. 48a; 1 of No. 52; 1 of No. 54a; 2 of No. 90a; 1 of No. 111c; 1 of No. 126; 2 of No. 126a; 2 of No. 188; 2 of No. 189; 1 of No. 191.

Competitions for All Readers

A Novel "Dinky Toys Layout" Competition

This month we announce the third of the special summer competitions. These contests are of such a nature that entries may be prepared either indoors or out in the open. There is no model-building to do and all that a competitor requires to enable him to prepare his entry are a copy of this issue of the *"M.M.,"* a pencil, and a sheet of paper.

The illustration on this page shows a complex Dinky Toys road and traffic layout, which is fully equipped with various Road Signs, Traffic Signals, Motor Vehicles, and other appropriate items from the Dinky Toys Series. In designing the layout and arranging the traffic several ridiculous mistakes have purposely been made. For example, some of the Road Signs are in the wrong places and Traffic Signals are facing the wrong directions. If the illustration is carefully studied a large number of other errors will become apparent, and readers are invited to test their powers of observation by trying to find as many of these as possible. Many of the mistakes are obvious and will be seen at a glance, but some of them will only be revealed by a very careful examination of the illustration.

Numerous errors have been made in the arrangement of this Dinky Toys traffic layout and prizes are offered to readers who can find the greatest number. Full details of the contest are given on this page.

The competition is open to readers of all ages, living in any part of the world, and all entries will be grouped into one section and judged together.

The following instructions should be noted. On one side of a sheet of paper competitors should make a list of all the mistakes they can "spot," and explain exactly where each occurs in the layout. They must then write their name and address on the other side of the sheet, and enclose it in an envelope addressed to "Dinky Toys Layout Competition," Meccano Ltd., Binns Road, Liverpool 13.

The following prizes will be awarded to the competitors who discover the greatest number of errors, in order of merit. First, Meccano Products value £2/2/–; Second, Products value £1/1/–; Third, Products value 10/6. Prizewinners will be notified by letter, and the result will be announced in due course in the Magazine.

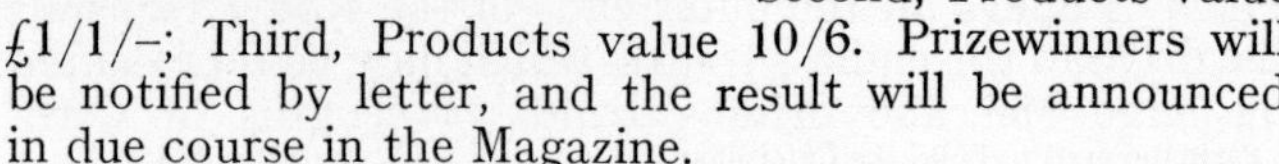

In the event of a tie for any of the prizes the judges will take into consideration the neatness of the entries concerned.

All entries must be posted in time to reach Liverpool on or before the 31st October, 1936. Any received after that date will be disqualified.

"August" General Model-Building Competition

In this competition prizes are offered for models of any kind whatever built entirely from Meccano parts. All a competitor has to do is to think of some new and original subject and then set to work to build it in Meccano as neatly as possible. Any number of parts may be used, but all models submitted must be the competitor's own handiwork both in design and construction.

The competition will be divided into two Sections as follows: Section A, for readers of all ages living in the British Isles; Section B, for readers of all ages living Overseas. The age of each competitor will be taken into consideration when judging.

When the model is completed a photograph or a good drawing of it should be sent to "August General Model-Building Contest," Meccano Ltd., Binns Road, Liverpool 13. Photographs or drawings need not be the competitor's own work, but the model must be built by the competitor himself, without assistance from anyone. More than one model may be submitted, but no competitor may win more than one prize. If two or more models are submitted by one entrant they will be considered jointly. The competitor's age, name and address, and letter A or B indicating the Section for which the entry is eligible, and the name of the competition must be written clearly on the back of each photograph or drawing submitted. It should be clearly understood that actual models must not be submitted for consideration.

Prizes will be awarded in each Section of the competition as follows: First, Meccano Products value £3/3/–; Second, Products value £2/2/–; Third, Products value £1/1/–. There will be also Five Prizes of Products value 10/6, and Five Prizes of Products value 5/–, in each Section.

Readers living in the British Isles must forward their entries so that they reach Liverpool not later than 30th September, 1936. In order to give Overseas readers plenty of time in which to build their models the closing date for Section B has been extended to 30th November, 1936.

All prize-winners will be notified by post as soon after the closing dates as possible, and the full lists of awards, together with illustrations and descriptions of prize-winning models, will be published in due course in the *"M.M."* Prizewinners will have the opportunity of choosing any items they like from current price lists. Models that already appear in any of the Meccano publications are not eligible for entry in this contest.

Photographs or drawings of prize-winning models become the property of Meccano Ltd., but unsuccessful entries will be returned if a stamped addressed envelope is enclosed for that purpose.

Model-Building Competition Results

By Frank Hornby

"Ingenuity" and "Meccano—Dinky Toys" Contests

"Ingenuity" Contest (Home Section)

The principal prizewinners in the Home Section of the March "Ingenuity" Contest are as follows:

1st Prize, Products value £3/3/–: F. R. Hilton, Cowes, I. O. Wight; 2nd, Products value £2/2/–: J. Maguire, Belfast; 3rd, Products value £1/1/–, P. Hands, Hillingdon.

F. R. Hilton owed his success mainly to the simplicity and realism of his model of an ordinary household water tap, which is illustrated on this page. The nozzle of the tap is made from Curved Strips and 4½" Strips bent into the required shape. The bent Strips that form the base of the tap are secured to 1½" Pulley Wheels with the aid of ½"×½" Angle Brackets. A Rod is pushed through the boss of the 1½" Pulleys, and on it are carried two 1" loose Pulleys, a Bush Wheel, a hexagonal prism made from Obtuse Angle Brackets, another 1" loose Pulley and a Chimney Adaptor, a Worm, a ¾" Pinion fitted with a Socket Coupling, and finally a built-up handle. The Worm is pushed inside the Chimney Adaptor and represents the screw thread usually found at the top of taps of this type. The handle is made of four 2½" Strips with their centre portions bent round the Socket Coupling, and their ends secured together by means of bolts. The tap is mounted on a 2" Sprocket.

The Second Prize was awarded to J. Maguire, whose model of a microscope attracted favourable attention by reason of its realism, and the fact that it is built with very few parts.

The stand is made from Curved Strips and is held in place on the base plate by Trunnions. The microscope itself consists of two Sleeve Pieces mounted end to end on a Rod, which is provided at its upper end with a ¾" Flanged Wheel and a Chimney Adaptor and at its lower end with a ¾" Flanged Wheel and a Collar. It is held in place on the upper end of the stand by means of Double Brackets and two Flat Trunnions. The specimen holder consists of a 2½" Flat Girder fixed in place by Strips and underneath it is a ½" Pulley Wheel that represents the mirror. The ½" Pulley Wheel is mounted between the prongs of a small Fork Piece secured to the base of the stand by a Double Bracket.

A little model of an electric fire was constructed by P. Hands. It consists essentially of two end frames made from half circles of 2½" Curved Strips, which are joined together by 5½" Strips. The reflector is made from two 3½"×5½" Flat Plates overlapped by four holes and bent to the same curvature as the end frames. The heating element is a Rod provided with a number of Couplings and clamped at each end between two 1½" Strips that are bolted to the end frames. The end holes of the 1½" Strips are connected in pairs by means of Rods that represent the guard bars used in actual electric fires. The legs of the model are composed of Strips.

Other models of interest among the winners of the smaller prizes are a telephone receiver, which was built by J. Dinwoodie, a silver cup by R. H. Thorpe, a hearth companion set by P. Bunce, and a small traction engine by S. Girling. R. K. Martin selected a household water tap for his subject and although this is somewhat similar to the model that won First Prize it is not nearly so neat or ingeniously constructed as the latter model.

The "Meccano—Dinky Toys" Contest produced many interesting entries, one of which is shown above. This dock scene is the work of P. Giese, Buenos Aires. (Right) A domestic tap provided F. R. Hilton of Cowes, I.O.W., with a unique subject for his entry in the "Ingenuity" Competition. The model was awarded First Prize.

"Meccano—Dinky Toys" Contest

The "Meccano—Dinky Toys" Competition was announced in the February 1936 issue of the "*M.M.*," and readers were asked to submit models of any kind incorporating standard Meccano parts and any of the Dinky Toys. The entries received are of outstanding interest, and a selection of them is described below. The lists of the principal awards in the Home and Overseas Sections of the competition are as follows:

Section A (Home competitors of all ages)

1st Prize, Products value £3/3/–: A. Aikman, W. Worthing, Sussex; 2nd, Products value £2/2/–: Miss L. Slater, Portsmouth; 3rd, Products value £1/1/–: A. Smith, Inverurie, Aberdeenshire.

Section B (Overseas competitors of all ages)

1st Prize, Products value £3/3/–: L. Linder, Stockholm, Sweden; 2nd, Products value £2/2/–: L. Edwards, North Auckland, N. Zealand; 3rd, Products value £1/1/–: E. Azzopardi, Sliema, Malta.

The entries generally were of outstanding interest, and illustrate the fine effects that can be obtained by combining Meccano with Dinky Toys in model-building. First Prize in Section A was awarded to A. Aikman for an exciting race game in which excellent use is made of Dinky Toys Racing Cars. The model consists of a motor racing track equipped with a number of Racing Cars, the track being 4 ft. 2 in. in length and 2 ft. 2 in. wide. The surface of the track is made of cardboard and is banked. It is provided with five slots that run completely round the track. Beneath the cardboard a number of Sprocket Wheels are fitted at equal distances along each of the slots, and on them run lengths of Sprocket Chain. The Chains are driven by means of an E6 Electric Motor and are held in correct tension by jockey pulleys mounted on spring arms. Meccano Dinky Toys Racing Cars (Nos. 23a and 23b) are placed on the baseboard and are attached to the Chains by pieces of wire that pass through the slots, and as the Chains move the cars are caused to travel realistically round the track.

A realistic dock scene forms the subject of the entry submitted by Miss L. Slater, and it includes a warehouse made from Flat Plates and Strip Plates bolted to a framework of Angle Girders, a wharf and a baseboard painted to represent water. Various Dinky Toys Motor Vehicles are placed in suitable positions on the quay and figures from the Station Staff Set are used to represent ships' officers.

A model entitled "Joyride" was submitted by A. Smith, and won Third Prize. It has a baseboard with two slots in which run endless lengths of Sprocket Chain driven by a Clockwork Motor fixed underneath. Dinky Toys Motor Cars are attached to the Chains that draw the cars too and fro across the board.

With the exception of those that won the principal prizes the entries in the Overseas Section, while quite interesting, generally are below the standard of those submitted for the Home Section. By far the best effort is L. Linder's model of a canal, complete with a lock and a Dinky Toys ship. The lock gates are made to open by means of a handwheel operated from the canal bank, and the ship slides along a platform that represents the surface of the water. It is hauled by an endless belt that is operated from a hand winding gear.

The dock scene illustrated on this page is the work of P. Giese, and is particularly interesting because of the skilful way in which Dinky Toys have been incorporated in it.

Pennthorpe School (Chislehurst) M.C.—An excellent model of the Meccano Motor Chassis has been completed. The keenness of the members ensured the success of the club's first Exhibition, to which added interest was given by the inclusion of a large model Transporter Bridge on loan from Headquarters. Several excellent Lantern Lectures have been given, including one by Mr. S. G. Braby, Headmaster of the school, on "*Locomotive Construction.*" Another Lecture described "*Eastern Canada,*" and was illustrated by slides kindly lent by the Canadian National Railways. Club roll: 27. *Secretary:* J. G. Slater, Sunny House, Clarence Road, Bickley, Kent.

St. James' (Grimsby) M.C.—A model ship-unloader, based on the Meccano Super Model, but provided with a special gear-box devised by the members provided good fun when put into operation. Models of a naval quick-firing gun and a derricking crane also have been completed. A Visit has been paid to the Grimsby Telephone Exchange. There is much enthusiasm for stamp collecting, and many exchanges of stamps are being made between members. Club roll: 5. *Secretary:* A. N. Dixon, 65, Yarborough Road, Grimsby.

Mary Swanwick School (Chesterfield) M.C.—Outings during the past club year have included a week's holiday at Tenby, which was so greatly enjoyed that many members asked for it to be repeated this year. Visits have been paid to Messrs. Firth's of Sheffield, and to Messrs. Pearson's Pottery. At the close of the Pottery tour Mr. Pearson very kindly showed the party his workshop, where they were delighted to see a model electric railway, complete with docks, boats, and even a lifting bridge. At one meeting a Tea was held, the meal being followed by games and competitions. On another occasion an amusing feature was a cooking competition, in which each entrant had to fry his own egg and bacon and then eat it. During the second winter session visits were paid to the L.M.S. Locomotive works at Derby, a local foundry and to a printing works. Club roll: 18. *Leader:* Mr. T. E. John, "Mary Swanwick" Modern School, Old Whittington, Chesterfield.

St. Oswald's (Norbury) M.C.—Model-building has been continued with unabated enthusiasm, and 46 models have been completed in one month. Occasional Games Evenings give variety to the programme, and several summer excursions have been arranged. A local gentleman has generously placed his garage at the disposal of the club for use as a club-room. The football team had a very successful season, and finished at the top of the local league. Club roll: 15. *Secretary:* R. H. Smart, 14, Kensington Avenue, Thornton Heath.

Fraserburgh M.C.—Additional tables have had to be acquired to provide sufficient accommodation for model-building and Hornby Train operations. A complicated railway layout has been planned in which three stations will be used, one being situated in the garden. It is intended to make the layout large enough for all the L.M.S.R. and L.N.E.R. engines available to be used simultaneously. One Saturday each month is now devoted to cycling, but the club room is open for members who do not wish to take part in the outings. Club roll: 28. *Secretary:* W. H. Dawson, Phingask, Fraserburgh.

Sid Vale M.C.—Members have been busy building Motor Show models and stands on which to display them. The Show was open to the public, and attracted many interested visitors. The vehicles on view included buses, vans, lorries and sports and streamlined cars. Club roll: 20. *Secretary:* L. R. J. Gliddon, Sheffield House, Sidmouth.

Old Charlton M.C.—A Talk on motor cycles proved very interesting, and a Debate on "*Steam Traction v. Electric on Railways*" brought forth some very good arguments for both sides, ending with a vote in favour of steam. An impromptu talks meeting, at which the subjects were written by the Leader on slips of paper drawn from a hat by the members, proved so amusing and interesting that other similar meetings are to be held. Each speaker was given two minutes in which to discuss the subject stated on his slip. An excellent Exhibition has been held, when an attractive display of models was staged. At one meeting four members who are in employment gave interesting 15-min. talks about their work. Club roll: 26. *Secretary:* W. Jaques, 60, Gurdon Road, Charlton, London, S.E.7.

Mall School M.C.—Several Meetings have been devoted to outdoor activities, and these have included a treasure hunt, which was much enjoyed. A mock trial has been held, and resulted in the prisoner being acquitted. Club roll: 32. *Secretary:* D. Rubin, Mendip Lodge, 33, Clifden Road, Twickenham.

Hornsea M.C.—An enjoyable visit has been paid to the locomotive sheds at Dairycoates, where Assistant Superintendent Swan permitted the members to enjoy the thrill of a ride on the footplate of an engine. The senior engineers recently visited the local gas works, where they were shown round by the Leader. Each member of the party received a rough plan of the works, and the features indicated on it were fully explained during the tour. One member, who has had the good fortune to visit Belgium and Holland, gave a very interesting Lecture on his trip and illustrated it by means of lantern slides and a film. The Leader gave a Lecture on "*Photography,*" in the course of which he showed his audience how to take indoor photographs. Mah Jong has been played at several meetings, and a film show has been held. Club roll: 15. *Secretary:* Mr. P. Thom, 5, Alexandra Road, Hornsea.

A group of members of the XXVIII (Edinburgh) M.C., with Mr. B. McCall Barbour, the President, in the centre. Mr. J. M. Ferguson, Leader, is standing at the right end of the group. This club was affiliated in March 1930.

Exeter M.C.—Cycling runs are very popular, and a total of 105 miles has been covered in a month. Interest in model-building continues to be keen, in spite of the attractions of the long light evenings, and models completed recently have included a large version of the liner "*Queen Mary,*" a railway station, ship, crane and an aerodrome. A Radio Circle has been formed, and the members of this will specialise in building various kinds of wireless sets. Work has already begun on the construction of a one-valve set. Club roll: 44. *Secretary:* K. Milton, 18, Baker Street, Heavitree, Exeter.

Islington M.C.—Owing to the great popularity of Lectures, they continue to form an attractive feature of this club's programme. Subjects dealt with recently have included the "*Post Office Railway,*" "*The Cutting of the Panama Canal,*" "*The Railway System at York*" and "*Britain's Largest Railway.*" Other activities have been model-building, fretwork, model aeroplane construction, chemistry and games. Club roll: 14. *Secretary:* K. Dines, 70, Mornhill Road, Islington, London, N.1.

Plymouth M.C.—The time of meeting has been changed from Saturday afternoon to Saturday evening. The club has also been re-organised and is now divided into three sections devoted to Meccano, Hornby and general activities respectively. The last named section includes the woodworking and printing branches of the club. It has been decided to acquire a new rotary type printing press that will print pages double the size of those accommodated by the present machine. Club roll: 68. *Secretary:* R. G. Symons, 47, Lisson Grove, Mutley, Plymouth.

Todmorden Road Central School (Burnley) M.C.—A debate on "*Hornby* or *Meccano?*" ended in favour of Meccano, by one vote. The Hornby section is making good progress, and becoming quite expert in railway operations. It is hoped to arrange for visits to the local Bus depot and the Rosegrove (L.M.S.R.) locomotive shed. Club roll: 28. *Secretary:* L. Hinton, 4, Thirlmere Avenue, Butland Avenue, Burnley.

St. Stephens (Saltash) M.C.—Games are very popular and are played for 50 min. at each meeting. Table tennis has been played with the local Y.M.C.A., who won by three games to two. The construction of the model of Millbay (G.W.R.) terminus is proceeding satisfactorily. Some enjoyable cycling runs and rambles have been held. An account of the activities of the club is to be published at the end of each month in the "*Saltash Gazette.*" Club roll: 15. *Secretary:* B. Braund, 9, Homer Park, Saltash.

Enfield Grammar School M.C.—The club participated in a school excursion to Southampton, where a tour of the Cunard White Star liner "*Aquitania*" was immensely enjoyed. After lunch on shore the party visited the great floating dock, the working of which was explained to them. They then had a trip on a paddle steamer down the Solent to Calshot, and during the sail they saw several R.A.F. flying boats. Tired but happy, the party eventually boarded the train for home, and had a last-minute thrill when the train was detained by signals at a point that gave everybody a splendid close view of the famous R.M.S. "*Queen Mary*" in dock. Club roll: 34. *Secretary:* J. H. Pettifer, 31, Goat Lane, Enfield.

Wednesbury M.C.—Model-building and Fretwork continue to be the chief indoor activities. A cabinet is to be made in which to store the club stock of Meccano, etc. A lantern lecture on "*Imperial Airways*" has been given by a senior member. On a recent Surprise Evening a member brought his Table Tennis outfit, and a very jolly time was spent with it. Several of the members took part in a Cycle Run to Lichfield, where they inspected the fine cathedral and afterward made a tour of the surrounding countryside. Club roll: 24. *Secretary:* A. L. Morgan, 17, Cobden Street, Fallings Heath, Wednesbury.

CANADA

Montreal Y.M.C.A. M.C.—Considerable model-building activity has centred round preparations for the club's display at the Montreal Boys' and Girls' Hobbies Show. Special models have been built for club demonstration purposes, and an improvised projector has enabled Lantern Lectures to be given. On several occasions members have spent enjoyable times in the excellent swimming pool at the Central Y.M.C.A. Club roll: 9. *Leader:* Mr. J. Rodriguez, 1900, Tupper Street, Apt. 4, Montreal P.Q. Canada.

SOUTH AFRICA

Malvern M.C.—On Magazine night members showed their literary ability in articles on various subjects, some of which were humorous in character. The Leader expressed his pleasure at the high quality of the contributions, and the next Magazine night is eagerly awaited. A hiking expedition to Bedford View by 12 members was much enjoyed. During the outing the party visited an important dairy, where they took snapshots of the work carried on. The many excellent models completed during a recent Bridge evening included road bridges, a footbridge with electric lights, a suspension bridge and a model of the Tower Bridge, London. Club roll: 85. *Secretary:* B. Saunders, P.O. Box 8, Cleveland, Johannesburg, S. Africa.

EGYPT

Zagazig M.C.—The club continues to make good progress, and meetings are held every week. A Lecture on "*What Industrial Chemistry Means*" has been given by the Leader. Another dealt with "*The Primary Materials of Perfumes,*" and was a prelude to much activity by members of the chemistry section, who have been busy experimenting in the preparation of perfumes. Club roll: 20. *Leader:* Mr. A. Mangourie, 39, B'Gannabiet Sikka Hadid Avenue, Zagazig, Egypt.

Club Not Yet Affiliated

Rangoon M.C.—Meetings are being held at the home of one of the members, and at one of the early meetings a helpful discussion was held on "*How to make the Club well known.*" Club roll: 6. *Secretary:* P. Swan, c/o Burma Dental Supply Co., 124, Sule Pagoda Road, Rangoon, India.

The Holiday Month

August is the great holiday month of the year, when many members are away at the seaside or in the country, and those who stay at home spend as much time as possible out of doors. Club room activities are restricted, and the programmes consist chiefly of games and excursions of all kinds. Whatever form these take, I hope that every member of every club is having a thoroughly good time.

In this country there is always the possibility of unfavourable weather to contend with, however. It is well, therefore, for Leaders to have ready some form of indoor entertainment that can be arranged quickly and easily in the event of rain causing an outdoor programme to be abandoned. In such circumstances indoor games are about the most satisfactory substitute, but an unexpected hour or so indoors also could be devoted to a series of two-minute talks by the members, or the reading of an excellent detective story, each member dealing with one chapter. A mock trial provides plenty of fun, but requires a certain amount of planning beforehand. If the members are "bursting" with energy a pleasant way of expending it indoors is in overhauling the club material and carrying out improvements in the club room so that it will be more comfortable and enjoyable to work in during the coming winter.

Meccano Club Leaders

No. 84. Mr. K. A. Blackman

Mr. K. A. Blackman is Leader of the Pennthorpe School (Chislehurst) M.C., of which he was the founder. The club was affiliated as recently as February last, but has already held a very successful Exhibition.

Making Club Reports Interesting

I am very pleased to say that there has been a good response to my appeal in the March *"M.M."* for more really interesting club reports. One result of this improvement is that I am now much better informed concerning the work and achievements of many clubs from which only scrappy notes on routine events used to reach me.

There are still a few secretaries who are content to remark that "the club continues to progress and the meetings are well attended," but I am sure that eventually they will come into line with the others. I am well aware that secretaries of Meccano Clubs are busy individuals, and that their duties are extremely varied in character. For this reason I suggest that any official who feels that he is unable to spare time to write adequate reports should delegate the duty to an assistant. This assistant could also act as minute secretary. He should take care to note down at each meeting the chief events of the evening, and he would then find it a very easy task to compile from his records a monthly report that does justice to the efforts of officials and members, and is sufficiently full and interesting to enable me to include an attractive notice in the "Club Notes" page.

It is important that secretaries should send me reports as regularly in the summer as in the winter, especially if a club is carrying out a programme that is keeping the interest of its members at a high level. Every year there are many young clubs making the experiment of keeping together throughout the summer for the first time, and they are greatly encouraged to persevere by reading accounts of successful summer sessions of other clubs, in addition to often gaining valuable hints for their own programmes.

Another New Lantern Lecture

I have received from the Publicity Manager of Imperial Airways Ltd., a copy of a lantern lecture entitled *"The Empire's Airway."* I am glad to recommend this fine lecture to Leaders of Meccano clubs, for it gives a fascinating account of the Empire air routes and of the elaborate organisation by which the services are carried on throughout the year. It is illustrated by 100 slides, many of which show the varied territory covered and the chief ports of call, while others give excellent views of the great air liners employed.

This lecture is contained in a special booklet *"The Empire's Airway,"* and a copy of this can be obtained on application to the Publicity Manager's Office, Imperial Airways, Airways House, Charles Street, Lower Regent Street, London, S.W.1, to whom application also should be made for the loan of the necessary slides. The lecture is certain to be very popular in view of the great interest that is taken in Imperial Airways' services and aircraft, and it is advisable to give at least three weeks' notice of the date of the lecture, so as to ensure that the slides will be available in time.

Secretaries in search of attractions for the winter sessions are reminded that a list of lectures that can be obtained on loan from various firms and railway companies is available, and I shall be pleased to send a copy to Leaders and secretaries who do not already possess one. The list not only indicates the nature of each lecture, but gives full information concerning the steps to be taken in order to obtain the slides and the accompanying descriptive matter. Usually application must be made well in advance, as in the case of Imperial Airways' lecture to which I have referred, and it is wise to have a copy of this list on hand when planning the forthcoming winter sessions.

Lone Members

I have received several letters recently from boys living in remote places, who have written expressing regret that they are unable to join the Guild because there is no club in their vicinity. This idea is, of course, quite unfounded, for any boy who owns a Meccano Outfit or a Hornby Train Set may join the Guild, although he may live hundreds of miles away from the nearest Meccano Club, as is the case with many overseas members. These "lone members" are just as much members of the Guild as if they belonged to a Meccano Club, and they find compensation for their unavoidable isolation in correspondence with Headquarters and other enthusiasts who have joined the Guild Correspondence Club. Full details of this Club, together with entry forms, will be sent to every applicant.

Extending a Hornby Railway

Improvements on a Notable North Wales Layout

A REALISTIC feature of a miniature railway system is that there is always scope for some improvement, either in the layout, equipment or operations, even when it has reached a more or less complete state and boasts a regular service of trains. Additions are constantly being made in order to keep abreast of growing traffic, or to anticipate demands for more goods and passenger accommodation, and this accounts for many changes of great interest.

An excellent example of the development on these lines of a Hornby railway is given by the miniature L.M.S.R. system operated by W. Southwell, Holyhead, a keen H.R.C. member, and Mr. J. Southwell, his equally enthusiastic father. A description and photographs of the system appeared on page 613 of the "*M.M.*" for October of last year. It is an outdoor railway, and its special feature is the manner in which it is laid out as an actual terminal-to-terminal line with several branches. Remarkably complete services of passenger and freight trains are provided, and both "Winter" and "Summer" timetables are operated, the Summer services incorporating an increased number of trains in view of the demands of holiday traffic. The workings throughout are based on the real L.M.S.R. timetables of the routes represented, and through services and connections are worked by the appropriate trains.

It will be recalled that on this miniature line the geography of the real L.M.S.R. system is modified for reasons of space, and "Shrewsbury" is brought into a position on the main line between "Stafford" and "Crewe." The most important traffic is the "Irish Mail" service between "Euston" and "Holyhead." "Stafford" is another through station on the main line, and branches serving separate terminal stations designated "Swansea," "Liverpool" and "Manchester" give very interesting "cross-country" workings.

A recent development has been the inclusion of a new terminal station representing Stoke. This can be reached direct from "Stafford" by trains going north, and direct from "Shrewsbury" by trains going south. The tracks from these two stations converge like the arms of a letter Y just before reaching "Stoke," and the platform line there occupies the position of the main stem of the Y. Trains can thus run into "Stoke" from the north and from the south, and if required they can stop there, but through journeys in both directions can be made by reversing. For working of this kind a fresh engine is backed on to the tail of the train on arrival in the station. This addition provides a new route that can usefully be employed when the through main line via "Stafford" is being occupied to capacity, as is frequently the case at the height of summer week-end traffic.

Improved facilities for freight traffic have been provided at "Stafford," "Shrewsbury" and "Crewe," and additional stations have been erected at "Craven Arms" on the Swansea branch, and north of Shrewsbury at "Whitchurch," where the "Manchester" line now diverges. The main terminals of the line, "Euston" and "Holyhead," also have received special attention. "Holyhead" has been modified and provided with an additional platform. This is arranged to join up the original platform at the landward end, and the two make a V-shaped formation with the railway lines along the outer sides, the space between the platforms representing the harbour. Ships and trains are accommodated on opposite sides of the quay at Holyhead, as described and illustrated on page 310 of the "*M.M.*" last June. This characteristic layout is now well reproduced on the miniature layout and the "Irish Mail" services that are operated regularly on it are dealt with in the same manner as the trains and steamers used in actual practice, arrivals and departures being effected at separate quays.

Two views of the reconstructed "Euston" terminus on the miniature L.M.S.R. system at Holyhead operated by Mr. J. Southwell and his son. Details of the latest developments on this system are given in the accompanying article.

The miniature "Euston" on this layout has been entirely rebuilt, and the illustrations on this page show the effective appearance of the new terminus. This has two platform roads and separate goods accommodation, and an all-over roof covers the platforms and tracks. The platforms are more than six feet long, so that trains of exceptional length can be dealt with. The usual offices and buildings are provided, and the thoroughness with which the details have been planned and carried out is shown by the fact that the windows of the "Refreshment Rooms" are provided with miniature curtains! The whole station has been painted in the bright and effective fashion now commonly adopted in actual practice, and its appearance blends well with its garden surroundings.

These improvements make it easier to handle traffic on the line, and one result of this has been an increase in the number of services operated. It has been necessary to put further stock into use in order to provide for this increase. A Hornby No. 1 Special Locomotive and Tender is the latest addition on the motive power side, and its capacity for work makes it a valuable member of the engine stud. In the rolling stock section there have been added four No. 1 Pullmans, and a No. 1 Passenger Coach and Guard's Van.

Hornby Signals and their Uses

By "Tommy Dodd"

WE have come to regard railway signals as the symbols of safety, and rightly so, for the almost perfect system of signalling that has been developed over the course of years has made British railways the safest in the world. There are no lives at stake on Hornby Railways, but signals are equally necessary on them, for they would not look at all realistic without miniatures of these familiar lineside features, which also are essential in order to enable traffic to be run in true railway fashion.

Each of the various types of signal in the Hornby Series is made in three different patterns, No. 1, No. 2, or No. 2E. The No. 1 Signals are the simplest and are quite realistic, although they lack some of the detail of those of the No. 2 type, which include a dummy lamp attached to the post and a ladder for the use of the "lampman." The semaphores of the No. 2 Signals also are of improved construction as compared with those of the No. 1 pattern, for they have transparent "spectacles" of the appropriate colours mounted in a frame of the correct type instead of solid tinprinted ones. The No. 2E kind are more elaborate, for they are fitted for electric lighting in addition to having the details standard on the No. 2 pattern.

A stopping train on a Hornby layout passing a No. 2 Signal Gantry of the "home" type. The taller signals apply to the main lines shown, and each of the shorter ones indicates that there is a divergence to the left a short distance ahead.

The arm or semaphore of the ordinary "home" signal has a plain square end, and when in its normal position must not on any account be passed by a driver. On the side that faces an approaching train the semaphore of this signal is painted red, and it has a plain vertical white stripe at a short distance from its outer end. At night a red light is displayed when the arm is in the "danger" position, and a green light tells a driver that the line is "clear."

In order to give due warning of the aspect displayed by the "home" signal, its indication is repeated by what is known as a "distant" signal, which is placed sufficiently far in advance of the "home" signal to allow a driver to pull up at the latter if this is necessary. A "distant" semaphore in the danger position is therefore a warning or caution indication.

To enable "distant" signals to be recognised their semaphores have fishtailed notches cut in their outer ends. For many years this was the only distinction, and at night drivers had to rely on their knowledge of the route, for all signals showed red when in the danger position. In modern standard practice, however, the semaphore of a distant signal facing the train is painted yellow, with a black stripe following the contour of the fishtailed end, instead of the red with a plain white stripe of a home semaphore. At night "distant" signals now display an orange light for "caution," and this makes them quite distinct from the "home" signals. Green is used to show "line clear" for both types.

Hornby Signals are made with "home" or "distant" semaphores as required. The "distant" semaphores are correctly coloured yellow with the characteristic black stripe, and the electrically-lighted No. 2E Signals of this kind display the correct orange and green lights.

The Double-Arm Signal is an interesting type, carrying a "home" semaphore at the top of the post, with a "distant" arm below it. These signals are used in practice where the section ahead is so short that the distant signal applying to the next signal could not be placed in its correct position. It is therefore mounted on the same post as the preceding home semaphore. If the latter only shows "line clear" a stop is likely at the next "home" signal, but if both the semaphores show "line clear" the next "home" signal also will be in this position. The "distant" semaphore must never show "line clear" when the "home" arm on the same post is at "danger."

Divergences to the right or to the left are indicated by junction or "splitting" signals, one for each route. The signals at the junction or points are of the "home" type. Sometimes they are preceded by a single distant, although the junction signal itself has two semaphores, and on some routes complete "splitting" or junction distants are provided. Both "home" and "distant" Junction Signals are available in the Hornby Series, so that actual practice can be correctly followed by the Hornby Railway owner who specialises in signalling. An interesting point is that the No. 1 Junction Signal of the Hornby Series has the shorter post on the left-hand side, indicating that the less important or branch line diverges on that side, but the No. 2 and No. 2E Junction Signals have it on the right-hand side. Branches to the right or to the left thus can be correctly signalled.

A signal gantry is practically a bridge on which several short signal posts are mounted, and is used where there are several lines or divergences to be signalled. The Hornby Signal Gantries have four signal posts mounted on the actual gantry portion. The tall posts for the more important lines are in the centre, those for the less important or diverging roads are on the outside.

SUMMER SERVICES ON HORNBY RAILWAYS

MOST readers will be enjoying themselves at the seaside or in the country when they obtain this month's issue of the "*M.M.*" On their holiday journeys by rail they will probably have seen various forms of special working and interesting train operations that are peculiar to the period of summer traffic, and are sure to wish to reproduce them on their own Hornby Railways. Very attractive schemes on these lines can be developed, and in this article we give a few suggestions that will help them.

During the summer there is a great deal of through working, not only of coaches but also of locomotives. Traffic is heavy and at times unusual locomotives, and possibly rolling stock, are used for certain duties. Through running now takes place between different sections of the same group, and also between the groups themselves, to a much greater extent than ever before. This is particularly so where trips are being run to some seaside or inland resort, possibly in connection with some special event, and there are numerous instances of such through working by "foreign" engines and stock on excursion trains.

Summer service operations on a Hornby S.R. layout. The G.W.R. train arriving at the station represents a through working of the kind frequently observed in actual practice.

A great deal of fun is to be had in miniature if similar schemes are followed on a Hornby Railway. This is easily possible where two or more H.R.C. members operate their engines and stock together on a layout arranged by combining their rails and other equipment to form one system, for the locomotives and vehicles of different companies are then invariably represented.

The exact services to be reproduced may vary according to the tastes and ideas of the operators. For instance, G.W.R. excursions are worked with that company's engines over the S.R. into Bournemouth. Similarly S.R. engines and vehicles return the compliment by working over G.W.R. metals in the West, particularly in connection with the "sight-seeing" excursions that are now so popular. A round trip may follow the route of one company on the outward journey, returning over the metals of the other. A "sight-seeing" excursion, bearing the special decorations on the engine that are always used nowadays for such purposes, would be an unusual train in miniature, and its working could be made very interesting by keen Hornby Railway owners.

There also are exchanges of traffic and the working of regular through trains that involve the use of the engines of one group with the stock of another. For example, the "*Sunny South Express*" consists of L.M.S.R. stock that is taken over by S.R. engines at Willesden Junction, and hauled to the South Coast. Such arrangements give attractive working in miniature, especially when the locomotives of different companies appear side by side. This is shown in the illustration on this page, in which a Hornby S.R. No. 2 Special Locomotive and a G.W.R. No. 2 Special Locomotive are seen at the same station, each with a train of appropriate rolling stock. The designs of the two engines are quite different, although both have the 4–4–0 wheel arrangement.

The summer season is essentially the time for organised outings and similar excursions, and in many instances special trains are chartered for the conveyance of parties. A development of modern times has been the complete tour or "land cruise," made by train, the journey occupying perhaps several days. The trains used are of special formation, according to requirements, and it usually is the custom to decorate or distinguish in some suitable manner the locomotives that haul them. A favourite form of decoration is a large circular board that can be mounted in front of the smoke-box, bearing on it details of the particular train.

Additions of this kind are particularly attractive in miniature, and the lower photograph on the next page illustrates an interesting plan that could be followed on any Hornby layout for the decoration of the engine of a Hornby Railway Company "cruising" train or any other "special" of this kind. The "board" shown is a circle of white card, 1¼ in. in diameter, with a reproduction of the familiar H.R.C. badge pasted in a prominent position in the centre. This badge can be taken from any publication in which it appears; and a disc cut from a plain postcard will be suitable for the "board" itself, which can be hung by a small loop of cotton from the top lamp bracket of the engine, or from the small hand-rail that on some designs of locomotive passes straight across the front of the smoke-box door. Other details are carried out in Indian ink. Hornby railway owners can easily make boards of their own design, incorporating more detail if necessary, and also some reference to the purpose and destination of the train. A board of this kind is easily changed when necessary.

Away to the West! A Hornby S.R. express of No. 2 Coaches hauled by a No. 3C "Lord Nelson." The Hoarding in the lineside field displays the slogan "It's Quicker By Rail."

A point of importance in connection with the running of special trains of this kind is that publicity arrangements should be made to draw the attention of the Dinky Toy "public" to the facilities offered. Suitable "bills" and posters can be prepared by keen miniature railway operators and displayed on the Poster Boards and Station Hoardings. Very pleasing results can be obtained with ink and paints, and it is frequently possible to make use of cuttings from real timetables and the holiday guide books and folders that are so numerous nowadays. The advantages of a particular route or the attractions of a certain district may be stressed, and the familiar phrase *"It's Quicker By Rail"* certainly should not be overlooked. The creation of a "Publicity Department" indeed increases the fun of miniature railway working, and the results of its efforts strike a topical note, and add considerably to the air of realism of the operations generally.

A cruising train in miniature. The locomotive, a Hornby No. 2 Special L.N.E.R., "The Bramham Moor," is decorated with an appropriate board, as described in this article.

There is a great demand for Pullman, buffet and restaurant cars during the summer season. Good use therefore can be made of Hornby Pullmans, which are typical of the luxurious stock operated on the L.N.E.R. and S.R. by the Pullman Car Co. Ltd. Buffet and restaurant cars of railway companies' stock can be represented by Hornby No. 2 Saloon Coaches. These vehicles in fact can be used extensively for holiday traffic, for they are of the centre-corridor type that is so popular in actual practice for the composition of long-distance excursion trains.

Another use to which No. 2 Saloon Coaches can be put is to represent sleeping cars, which are required in large numbers on the routes to Scotland, especially during August. The commencement of the grouse shooting season on 12th August causes a northward rush on the days, or rather the nights, immediately preceding the magic date, and several trains consisting perhaps of "sleepers" only are run in addition to the regular *"Royal Highlander"* from Euston and the *"Highlandman"* from King's Cross. The introduction of such "Twelfth" traffic in miniature will add to the enjoyment to be obtained from summer operations on a Hornby L.M.S.R. or L.N.E.R. system.

A scheme already suggested in these pages can be employed to make the standard Saloon Coaches look more like the actual sleeping cars. On one side of the coach a strip of tissue or thin white paper is placed between the metal side of the Coach and the strip of celluloid window "glass." This gives a realistic reproduction of the windows on the compartment sides of sleeping cars. The scheme is very effective and the appearance of a train of several Saloon Coaches so fitted is quite distinctive.

In addition to extra traffic of this kind, during summer there are lively "rushes" from the cities to seaside resorts, especially at weekends. As an instance, specially intensive services to the various Kentish Coast resorts are maintained by the S.R. Train after train actually becomes a "Kent Coast Express," and the work demands the best of the Eastern Section locomotives.

A very good representation of a typical Kent Coast train can be made up of Hornby No. 2 Coaches in S.R. colours. At its head can be placed the E220 Special tender Locomotive, or the corresponding No. 2 Special Clockwork engine, both in S.R. colours, for these are representative of the Ashford 4-4-0 type that for a long time has put up fine work on these duties. More recently bigger engines have been in common use over the Coast lines, however, so that a No. E320 or No. 3C Locomotive in S.R. colours can be used quite well, if preferred.

The working of through coaches to various destinations sometimes accounts for remarkable train formations, although at the height of the holiday traffic the number of passengers may require almost a separate train for each place normally served by a through coach.

Join the Hornby Railway Company and become eligible for the competitions announced on this page.

H.R.C. COMPETITION PAGE

Join the Hornby Railway Company and become eligible for the competitions announced on this page.

MYSTERY STATIONS CONTEST

As most H.R.C. members are on holiday during August, our competition this month takes the form of a word puzzle that will provide interest and amusement for them while they are at the seaside or in the country, and perhaps far away from books and their copies of past issues of the Magazine. It is based on station names that do not give any indication of the town or city in which they are found. Waterloo and Liverpool Street are typical examples of names of this kind. Both stations are in London, but the names by which they are known to every railway enthusiast give no direct clue to this fact.

MELSITERTE	**ROGNAPA**
SWENTRTEE	**PADMTELEMES**
ROSAQUTEFSRER	**RAWDESTLOWN**
DACLITE	**DANLORDOON**
SACLET	**RIPOYR**
EHTSCON	**GINLEWLONT**
SOWDODIE	**KAPTNBO**
LANGREE	**YAUKBNQA**
RYEWVEAL	**GONTANDIDP**
TIRVACIO	**GIKARKET**
FYARRI	**TSHNERRUFCTCEEH**

In the panel on this page are the names of 22 well known stations of this type, but in each case letters have been jumbled, and competitors are invited to discover the identity of these stations, and to state the town or city in which they are placed. The initials of the railway company owning each station now and before grouping took place in 1923 also must be given.

Prizes consisting of any products manufactured by Meccano Ltd. to the value of 21/–, 15/– and 10/6 respectively will be awarded to the senders of the three best entries. In the case of a tie for any prize, this will be divided equally between the successful competitors. Consolation prizes also will be awarded to the senders of the next best solutions.

Envelopes containing entries must be marked *"H.R.C. August Mystery Stations"* in the top left hand corner, and posted to reach Headquarters at Meccano Ltd., Binns Road, Liverpool 13, on or before 31st August. The closing date for competitors in the Overseas Section is 30th November.

Entries, which should be written out on postcards, must have on them the H.R.C. numbers of their senders, and those not distinguished in this manner will be disqualified.

Railway Photographic Contest

The summer series of Photographic Contests, which closes next month, has produced many remarkably good entries, some of which have already been published in the *"M.M."* This month we expect a larger number of entries than ever, for the holiday season gives ample opportunities for making use of cameras. Competitors are reminded that any railway photograph, either large or small, may be submitted. The exposure must have been made by the competitor himself, but development and printing may be the work of professional photographers.

This month's Contest will be divided as usual into two Sections, Home and Overseas. The prizes to be awarded in each will consist of products manufactured by Meccano Ltd., or if preferred photographic material, to the respective values of 21/–, 15/– and 10/6. A number of consolation prizes also will be awarded.

On the back of all entries submitted for this contest must be written a short description of the scene shown in the picture, the competitor's name, full address and his H.R.C. membership number.

Envelopes containing entries must be marked *"H.R.C. August Photo Competition"* in the top left hand corner, and posted to reach Headquarters at Meccano Ltd., Binns Road, Liverpool 13, on or before 31st August. The latest date in the Overseas Section is 30th November.

Summer Puzzle Contest

The accompanying illustration is the second in our series of three Mystery

Photographs, the first of which appeared last month. The third puzzle picture will be given in our September issue, and in each case the object shown is a well known Hornby Train component.

The Contest is divided into two sections —Home and Overseas—and a cash prize of £1/1/– will be awarded to the competitor in each section who gives the best solutions to the three puzzles of the series. Full directions for sending in entries will be given in the September issue.

COMPETITION SOLUTIONS

APRIL "SIGNALLING CONTEST"

A diagram giving the solution of the April "Signalling Contest" appears at the foot of the page. As there are many variations in railway signalling practice, the actual number of signals required was specified when this contest was announced. In spite of this, many competitors failed because they introduced signals that are unnecessary. The results generally show a high standard of knowledge of signalling requirements, and there is no doubt that this important branch of railway practice is well understood by Hornby Train enthusiasts.

COMPETITION RESULTS

HOME

June "Dream Journey" Contest.—First: J. C. Button (10335), Crewe, Ches. Second: K. Costain (5108), Bolton, Lancs. Third: J. Fraser (2267), Exeter. Consolation Prizes: M. L. Harper (8718), Wood Green, London, N.22; E. H. Frewin (25098), Oldbury, Nr. Birmingham; W. W. Pollard (45922), Datchet, Nr. Slough, Bucks.; E. R. Dudley (37680), Carshalton, Surrey; A. W. R. Coomber (8098), Bedford; K. L. Milburn (26029), Chingford, London, E.4.

June "Railway Photographic Contest."—First: T. Fletcher (6057), Perry Barr, Birmingham. Second: C. Spencer (44179), Sheffield 11. Third: E. W. Oglethorpe (46851), Harrow, Middlesex.

OVERSEAS

March "Name and Number Contest No. 6."—First: I. Brough (9112), Preston, N.18, Victoria, Australia. Second: W. S. Eagle (31779), Byculla, Bombay, India. Third: G. Hallack (17578), Capetown, South Africa. Consolation Prizes: D. J. White (9333), St. Albans, Christchurch, N.1, New Zealand; H. C. Key (24764), Park Circus. Calcutta, India.

March "Railway Photographic Contest."—First: R. M. Perry, Park View, Johannesburg, South Africa. Second: Nils Söderberg (43551), Falun, Sweden. Third: G. E. Schulz (15425), Coromby, Victoria, Australia.

March "Drawing Contest."—First: M. Conly (24290), Dunedin, N.W.1, New Zealand. Second: Nils Söderberg (43551), Falun, Sweden. Third: E. C. Heath (29104), West Pennant Hills, New South Wales, Australia.

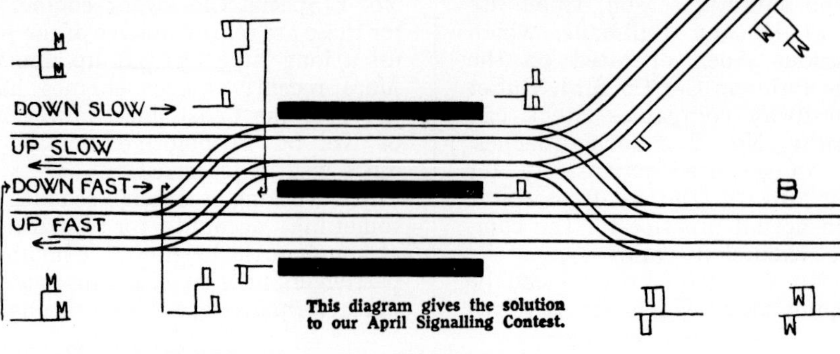

This diagram gives the solution to our April Signalling Contest.

Branch News

RUTHERGLEN (GLASGOW).—Several meetings have been devoted to the construction of a new layout. The track has now been completed and has been found generally satisfactory. It consists of an oval main line having a terminal station with four platforms. There are two goods stations and two goods yards and the locomotive depot is situated in a central and convenient position. A suitable table for indoor games has been added to the equipment of the Branch and a series of table-tennis matches has been held. Cycle runs have been inaugurated and will continue throughout the summer months. A visit to the Clyde paper mills is proposed. Secretary: R. G. Langmuir, 11, Afton Street, Shawlands, Glasgow, S.1.

WATERLOO (DUBLIN).—At recent track meetings normal services have successfully been operated. At the conclusion of one recent meeting a series of speed tests of several different locomotives was carried out. A visit has been paid to the Kingsbridge terminus of the Great Southern Railways and members followed with interest the working of various trains in and out. Several successful photographs were taken on this occasion. Secretary: Mr. S. B. Carse, 38, Oakley Road, Ranelagh, Dublin.

FOLKESTONE.—On the Hornby layout considerable attention is being given to the harbour works and other items of marine interest at "Folkestone." Good progress has been made with the construction of various ships to be used in conjunction with boat trains and other services. The flags flown by these vessels are to be painted to represent different companies. Cruises and other special services are to be arranged. A Meccano Outfit won by the Secretary of the Branch has been added to the Branch stock of Meccano parts and the construction of several improved models has been the result. Secretary: Mr. F. E. Saunders, 79, Dover Road, Folkestone.

FOREST ROAD CABIN (SOUTHPORT).—For the time being Branch members make use of the track belonging to the Secretary. This consists of a double track continuous main line with various sidings and loop lines. It is situated in a shed specially built for the purpose so that the maximum of scenic effect can be obtained. The interior of the shed is decorated with railway, shipping and airways posters, and is provided with special illumination that is very effective. Secretary: K. F. Pyett, 46, Forest Road, Southport.

ARDSLEY.—Train running is carried out in the orthodox manner by means of real signals and miniature block telegraph instruments. These were constructed by the Secretary, who is to be congratulated on his successful reproduction of the real instruments. Two sets of these are at present in use and members find operations with them very instructive. Secretary: G. Etherington, 3, Oxford Street, Ardsley, Barnsley.

Part of the Hornby railway layout operated by P. Lancaster of Hull (H.R.C. No. 22023). The line is conveniently situated on a raised baseboard, and is attractively arranged with ballasted tracks and suitable scenic and lineside details.

CHORLTON-CUM-HARDY.—A social meeting held at the Secretary's house was greatly enjoyed by the members. Track meetings have been run on the usual lines and various types of layouts have been tried, each proving very satisfactory. Various visits to places of interest are being arranged for the future. Secretary: G. H. Gill, 56, Highfield Road, Chorlton-cum-Hardy.

ELMSIDE (EXETER).—At meetings of Directors, special attention has been given to plans for improving working on track nights and as a result the general standard of train operations has improved to a considerable extent. A special display was given at a Fete arranged by a local church. The track laid down included 12 stations and members of the Branch attended in relays to work the trains. The display attracted much attention and added appreciably to the revenue. An interesting feature is that as a result of careful consideration of the services arranged for this display, means of improving the schedules at present in force on track nights have been discovered. Summer train services have been run at recent meetings, the number of heavily-loaded long-distance expresses being a feature. Secretary: T. W. A. Smith, 98, Ladysmith Road, Exeter.

OVERSEAS

PERTH (W.A.)—The Branch layout now consists of 540 ft. of track. This is completely electrified and is signalled by means of automatic colour lights. The four stations on the layout are connected in a realistic manner by electric telegraphs. Special attention has been given to the provision of suitable lineside scenery. Members are particularly keen on train operation, and track meetings are greatly enjoyed. Visits have been paid to the workshops of the Midland Railway at Perth and to the local railway signalling school. It is hoped to arrange further visits to the signal boxes at Perth Central Station and the locomotive running sheds at East Perth. The Commissioner of Railways, Mr. Ellis, takes a keen interest in the Branch and it has also been visited by the instructors of the Perth and Fremantle Signalling Schools. Secretary: J. Stanbridge, 285, Lord Street, Perth, W.A.

Branches in Course of Formation

The following new Branches of the Hornby Railway Company are at present in process of formation, and any boys who are interested and desirous of linking up with this unique organisation should communicate with the promoters, whose names and addresses are given below:

BICKLEY—J. A. Whyte-Venables, St. Hugh's, Bickley, Kent.

GREENFORD—R. A. Capps, 89, Halsbury Road West, Northolt Park, Greenford.

HUDDERSFIELD—D. Sandland, 12, Dryclough Road, Crosland Moor, Huddersfield.

NEWPORT—G. Williams, 69, Queens Hill Crescent, Newport, Mon.

Branches Recently Incorporated

308. ACTON—S. Simmons, 7, Alfred Road, Acton, London, W.3.

309. ARDSLEY—G. Etherington, 3, Oxford Street, Ardsley, Barnsley.

II. *Can a Policeman shoot a bandit in the car he is pursuing if both cars are travelling at the same speed as that at which the bullet leaves his gun?*

THIS is an old puzzle that has appeared in many disguises. One of these pictures an exciting situation in which the guard of a train aims over the top of a line of open coal wagons at the engine driver, who of course is unconscious of his danger as he peers ahead. Is it possible for the guard to shoot the driver if the muzzle velocity of the bullet is equal to the speed of the train? In this form the problem is a little more convenient to deal with, and we shall see what happens to the engine driver before considering the problem of the policeman and the motor bandit.

To many people the solution to the problem seems easy; they cannot see how the bullet can ever reach its target, since both are travelling at the same speed. But let us think what this would involve. Suppose the guard repents of his murderous designs on the driver and decides instead to commit suicide. If then he happens to turn his back on the engine and tries to shoot himself in the middle of the forehead the bullet apparently could never reach him, because he is travelling away from it at a speed equal to its own. Thus his only hope of success would be to face the engine, so that he and the bullet would be travelling in opposite directions.

Can the policeman in the pursuing motor car shoot the bandit if both cars are travelling at 80 m.p.h. and the muzzle speed of the bullet in his gun also is 80 m.p.h.? This problem is dealt with in the accompanying article.

This is not exactly a matter for trial by experiment, and fortunately this is not necessary, as the problem can be reasoned out quite easily. It is clear that there is a flaw in the obvious solution already suggested, for it is absurd to suppose that the guard would have to be so careful and calculating about putting an end to his own career. The clue is to be found in the fact, often overlooked, that before the trigger is pulled the bullet itself is travelling at the same speed as the train. The effect of the explosion is to give it an extra kick forward, so that its speed is increased.

There is no difficulty in realising the truth of this by a few experiments with more harmless apparatus than a revolver. Anyone who is walking moves ahead more quickly if he is given a violent push in the back, and his extra speed is exactly the same as that which would have been given to him if he had been standing still when he was the victim of the blow in the rear.

As another example, suppose a heavy object, such as a small brass weight, is placed on a sheet of card and the two are moved rapidly through the air. What happens when the card is suddenly stopped? A single trial will show that the weight immediately shoots forward. The reason of course is that the weight shares the speed of the card, and in spite of its innocent appearance, it cannot be stopped except by force.

Exactly the same thing happens in many similar circumstances. If a lorry laden with bales of cotton or trusses of hay charges violently into a solid iron post that brings it to a standstill, the bales will topple forward because they are moving as fast as the lorry and there is nothing to stop them. The opposite happens when a lorry laden in this manner is started with a violent jerk, for the bales then tend to topple backward. Everybody who has travelled in a tramcar or a motor car has had similar experiences. A man standing up in a swiftly moving vehicle is shot violently forward when the brakes are applied suddenly, and he is thrown backward if it starts forward with a jerk.

Now let us see how this applies to the problem of the murder of the driver of a train by the guard. When the latter stands up and takes aim his bullet is already travelling at the speed of the train, say 60 m.p.h. As soon as he pulls the trigger an extra force is applied to the bullet that alone would be capable of giving it a speed of 60 m.p.h. The result is that its speed now is 120 m.p.h. It has no difficulty in travelling as far as the engine driver, for it speeds ahead of the guard's van at the rate of 60 m.p.h., that is to the extent of 88 ft. in every second, so that it would reach the driver in four seconds if the length of the train were 352 ft.

Returning to the policeman and motor bandit, suppose that the two cars are travelling at 80 m.p.h. This also is the speed at which the bullet leaves the policeman's gun—when the gun is still. As the gun has a speed of 80 m.p.h., it is clear that in this case the actual speed of the bullet is 160 m.p.h., and the motor bandit cannot hope to escape.

The penetrating power of a bullet is conferred upon it by its speed. In the case of the guard and the engine driver, the bullet is a deadly missile even when it seems to be lying innocently in the guard's gun. Why then does it not kill anybody, or at least make a hole in the woodwork of the train? The answer is that everything around it is moving at the same speed as itself, and it cannot become dangerous until it is given a much higher speed by the power derived from the explosion of the powder in the cartridge. If by any means it could be taken out of the gun and so placed that it could be intercepted by the hand of a man standing at the lineside, it would pass through his flesh and bone as easily as if it were fired from the gun when this was held still by the lineside.

The problem of course is one of relative velocity, and it is curious to think that even if the bullet were lying idly on the ground instead of in a moving train, it would be travelling at a very high speed, unless it were at one of the two Poles. For instance, at the Equator it would be carried round by the revolution of the Earth at a speed of more than 1,000 m.p.h. Yet it would be harmless, for it would have no speed relative to everything around it until fired from a gun. Then it would be effective, whether it were fired in the direction in which the Earth rotates or not. H. A. ROBINSON.

Competition Corner

AUGUST CROSSWORD PUZZLE

CLUES ACROSS

1. Comprehends
9. Organ of hearing
10. Artificial silk
11. Daub
14. Vessel
15. Denial
16. Yield
17. Health resort
19. Loaded
21. Voter
23. Challenges
25. Habituates
26. Objected
28. Poem
29. Messages
33. Animal
35. Annoyed
37. Skill
38. Moulds
40. Church dignitary
41. Moves
43. Point
44. Continually
45. To Freeze
46. Fixes
47. A tract of land
50. Holidays
51. Evening (abbrev.)
52. Varieties

CLUES DOWN

2. Cherish
3. Embankment
4. Before
5. Compels
6. Juice
7. Arrange
8. Anxiety
12. Expert
13. Perform
14. Prophet
17. Nail
18. Part of verb "to be"
20. Low hill
22. Affords
24. Fit
27. Entertain
30. Settled down
31. Stupefy
32. Speech
33. Reacnes
34. Stage
36. Resident
37. Suitable
38. Fondle
39. Observes
42. Mistake
46. Flood
48. Calm
49. Figure

All *"M.M."* crossword puzzles have enjoyed exceptional popularity, principally, no doubt, because they are set for amusement rather than strenuous competitive effort. This month's puzzle will be found to follow the lines of those set in previous issues in that it is fair and interesting. The clues are all perfectly straightforward, and every word used can be found in Chambers' or any other standard dictionary. The rules that govern the solution of crossword puzzles are so well known that it is unnecessary to give any further explanation of the requirements of the competition.

Cash prizes of 21/–, 15/–, 10/6 and 5/– respectively will be awarded in order of merit to the senders of the four correct solutions that are neatest or most novel in presentation. The prizes will be duplicated for the Overseas section, which is open to all readers living outside Great Britain, Ireland, and the Channel Islands.

Entries should be addressed "August Crossword Puzzle, Meccano Magazine, Binns Road, Liverpool 13," and must be sent to reach this office not later than 31st August. Overseas closing date 30th November.

Competitors need not mutilate their magazines by cutting out the crossword illustration. Instead they may make a copy of the square on the same scale or larger, and use that in submitting their entries for the contest.

August Photo Contest

As we announced in the April Magazine, each month throughout the summer we are offering prizes for the best and most interesting photographs submitted, and in this issue we announce the August Contest in this series. As in the previous competitions, this is divided into two groups, Home and Overseas, and each group again is divided into two sections, A for those aged 16 and over, B for those under 16. Cash prizes of 21/– and 10/6 are being awarded in each section.

The photographs may be of any subject and may be taken with any make of camera, while any kind of film or paper may be used in making the exposure and producing the prints. Each photograph must bear the reader's name, age and address, and a title on its back.

Entries must be addressed "August Photo Contest," Meccano Magazine, Binns Road, Liverpool 13, and must arrive not later than 31st August. The Overseas closing date will be 30th November.

Competition Closing Dates

HOME

August Crossword Puzzle	...	31st August
August Photo Contest...	...	31st August

OVERSEAS

May Crossword Puzzle	...	31st August
May Photo Contest ...	...	31st August
June Doublets Contest	...	30th September
June Photo Contest ...	...	30th September
July Sketchogram Contest	...	31st October
July Photo Contest	...	31st October
August Crossword Puzzle	...	30th November
August Photo Contest...	...	30th November

Watch the Closing Dates:

Competitors, both Home and Overseas, are particularly requested to make a careful note of the closing dates of the competitions.

In sending entries to competitions that are divided into age groups, competitors should take particular care to mark their ages clearly on the back of the entry. It is not sufficient merely to indicate the age group, as age allowances are given to ensure equality of opportunity for the younger competitors.

COMPETITION RESULTS

HOME

June Doublets Contest.—1. C. E. Wrayford (Moretonhampstead, Devon); 2. F. F. Round (Southfields, London, S.W.18); 3. E. R. Andrew (Wellingborough); 4. L. Martin (Bournemouth).

June Photographic Contest.—First Prizes: Section A, R. F. Freke (Folkestone); Section B, J. R. Tottle (Taunton). Second Prizes: Section A, J. Hampson (Edgware); Section B, P. Sheldon (Hull). Special Prizes: R. H. Warr (Willaston, Wirral); H. H. Lees (Selly Oak, Birmingham).

OVERSEAS

February Drawing Contest.—First Prizes: Section A, S. D. Kurlawala (Bombay); Section B, A. Puntman (Arnhem, Holland). Second Prizes: Section A, M. Conly (Dunedin, N.Z.); Section B, M. O. Akinsehinwa (Ibadan, Nigeria). Consolation Prize: J. Parminter Wairoa, N.Z.).

Meccano Limericks.—Last Line Section.—1. D. Murison (Buenos Aires); 2. G. M. Healy (Prince Albert, Sask.); 3. R. B. Latimer (Rangoon, Burmah); 4. A. Rutherford (Sumner, Christchurch, N.Z.). **New Limerick Section.**—1. Barbara Hulley (Nantes, France); 2. Mrs. F. D. Mitchell (St. George's, Grenada, B.W.I.); 3. B. T. Roberts (Vancouver); 4. S. R. Thompson (Sydney).

March Drawing Contest.—First Prizes: Section A, M. Conly (Dunedin, N.Z.). Section B, R. Dickison (Roslyn, Dunedin, N.Z.). Second Prizes: Section A, C. Cali Corleo (St. Julians, Malta). Section B, R. L. Lowson (Caledon, Cape Province, S.A.).

PHOTOGRAPHY

SEASIDE PHOTOGRAPHY

IT is safe to assume that the majority of our readers will spend a considerable part of this month on holiday at the seaside, and probably many will be using a camera for the first time. No better starting point could be chosen, for under-exposure, the bugbear of most newcomers to photography, is almost non-existent at the seaside in August. The light rays are so strong that even with the cheapest of box cameras an ample exposure can be given at any time on any reasonably sunny day.

It is not possible to lay down definite rules for exposure, but as a rough guide 1/25 sec. at F/11 would prove ample when snapping open seascapes at any time between 10 in the morning and 4 in the afternoon. The exposure should be doubled if beach scenes containing dark rocks or near boats or figures are included. These are merely suggestions, however, and we would recommend all our readers to use an exposure meter or a table such as is given in the Burroughs Wellcome handbook.

At the seaside there is no lack of subject matter for photographs. Indiscriminate and careless snapshotting should be avoided, however, for it is better to obtain a dozen really good pictures than 50 poor ones spoiled by over-eagerness.

Rounding the mark. A typical yachting scene. Negative on Selochrome roll film, reproduced by courtesy of Ilford Ltd.

It is a good plan to work out a scheme that will cover all the main features of the holiday, such as the departure from home, and arrival at the holiday resort. These pictures should be followed by a sequence of characteristic views of the resort, such as the launch and return of the lifeboat, yachting and bathing scenes, children playing on the sands or at the model yachting pool, coast scenery and so on. Such views should be varied with snaps of personal incidents, of course, for these after all must be the main feature of the holiday story. Finally the series can be completed by pictures of the return home.

Novices should not be tempted to waste films on wide rolling expanses of sea. However attractive they may appear to the eye, they are very difficult indeed to translate into satisfactory snapshots. It is better to concentrate on beach and rock scenes.

Most of our readers no doubt will be using roll film cameras, and only a few of them will be fortunate enough to possess a camera in which the focussing is visible up to the moment of exposure. The focussing problem, therefore, calls for some consideration.

The simple box camera with its so-called fixed focus does not present great difficulty. The makers have fixed the relative positions of the lens and the film to give the best average result, and usually with such cameras it may be assumed safely that everything beyond six feet away from the camera will be in focus.

The folding camera, with which focussing is achieved by altering the distance between the lens and the film, calls for more care and experience. Usually this type of camera is fitted with a focussing scale marked for distances of 6, 9, 15 and 25 feet, and beyond that with the letters "INF" representing "Infinity" or extreme distance.

When the camera is set at, say, the point on the scale marked 15 feet, all objects 15 feet distant from the camera are in sharp focus, but objects slightly nearer and beyond also are in focus. This range of distance is known as "depth of focus," and it is the salvation of the photographer who cannot accurately estimate distances. It is helpful, therefore, and not at all a difficult matter to ascertain the depth of focus of one's own camera.

The exact depth of focus is dependent upon the "focal length" of the lens and the size of the shutter "stop" employed. The focal length is ascertained by setting the camera at "infinity" and measuring the distance from the lens to the film. In the case of cameras using "double," rapid rectilinear, or "anastigmat" lenses, the measurement is made from the shutter. The sizes and positions of the various "stops" are usually marked on the front of the lens mount, but, if they are not so marked, they can be ascertained by dividing the diameter of the shutter opening into the distance from the shutter to the film. The usual "stop" sizes available on cheaper types of cameras are known as F/8, F/11, F/16, F/22 and F/32. Box type cameras rarely have a larger stop than F/11.

Water for the castle moat. A "Kodak Snapshot."

The focussing point that will give the greatest possible depth of sharp definition, or the hyperfocal distance, as the photographer calls it, is ascertained by multiplying the square of the focal length by 100, and dividing the result by the F number of the stop multiplied by 12.

To illustrate this point let us assume that we have a camera in which the depth from lens to film is five inches, and the shutter aperture is five-eighths inch. The stop number of the aperture is therefore F/8. The hyperfocal distance is $5 \times 5 \times 100$, or 2,500, divided by 8×12, or 96. This works out at 26 ft.

If we set our camera focussing scale at 26 feet and use stop F/8, all objects from 13 ft. (half the hyperfocal distance) to infinity will be in focus, and the point of sharpest focus will be at 26 ft. If we set the camera scale at Infinity everything beyond 26 ft. will be focus. This is more difficult to describe than to do, and readers will find it a very simple matter to work out the figures for their individual cameras and stops.

There is one final word of advice for every reader, and that is to make sure that the camera is in thorough working order before the holiday starts. It also is a good plan to allow a local photographic dealer to develop the first spool of film. If the results are good, the photographer can then go ahead, happy in the knowledge that his exposures are correctly judged.

OLYMPIC GAMES STAMPS

THE outstanding international event this month is the 11th series of Olympic Games that will be held at Berlin from 1st to 16th August. It is therefore appropriate to devote this month's talk to Olympic Games stamps, of which there are so many that in themselves they constitute a sports stamp collection of the greatest interest.

The story of the Olympic Games goes far back into dim antiquity, so far back indeed that we read of their being reorganised in the 9th century B.C., and records have been preserved since 776 B.C. They were held every fourth year at Olympia, one of the great religious centres of Greece, and in the Greek calendar each period of four years was known as an Olympiad, the individual years being described as the first, second, third and fourth of their particular Olympiad. Then, as now, the honour of a victory at the Olympic Games was its own reward and the only trophy was a garland of laurel.

In ancient times the Games were largely confined to a few field and track sports, such as running, jumping, discus throwing and javelin throwing, but since their revival in the modern world almost every athletic game and pastime has been included. Cricket is a notable exception, but this game is peculiar to the British.

The first of the present International Series of Olympic Games was held at Athens in 1896 and the event was celebrated by a special commemorative stamp issue, the first ever produced by Greece. The designs were devoted largely to pictures of ancient Olympic scenes, such as a gladiator fight (1c. and 2c.); a discus thrower in action (5c. and 10c.); and a chariot race (25c. and 60c.). In addition the series included a view of the ancient Stadium at Olympia (1 dr.), and various allegorical figures depicting victory and youth.

Since 1896 the International Games have been held every fourth year, in accordance with the Greek tradition, except in 1916, a break for which the Great War was responsible. In 1900 the games were held in Paris, in 1904 at St. Louis, U.S.A., in 1908 in London, and in 1918 at Stockholm. After the end of the war the games were resumed in 1920 at Antwerp, and in honour of the occasion the Belgian Post Office issued a short series of three charity stamps with designs showing a discus thrower (5c.); a chariot race (10c.); and a runner (15c.). Each of the designs was based on early Greek pictures.

Belgium may be considered to have founded the custom for the country acting as host to the Olympic Games to issue commemorative stamps, for each subsequent series of games has been so honoured. In 1924, when the Games were held at Paris, France issued four stamps, 10c. to 50c. in value. The designs for these stamps were confined to allegorical features, on the lines of our illustration of the 10c. value, in which a laurel-garlanded athlete is seen with saluting arm outstretched towards the Olympic Stadium and the Arc de Triomphe. Another interesting stamp in this series is the 30c. value, which shows a magnificently built athlete splitting a tree trunk with his bare hands.

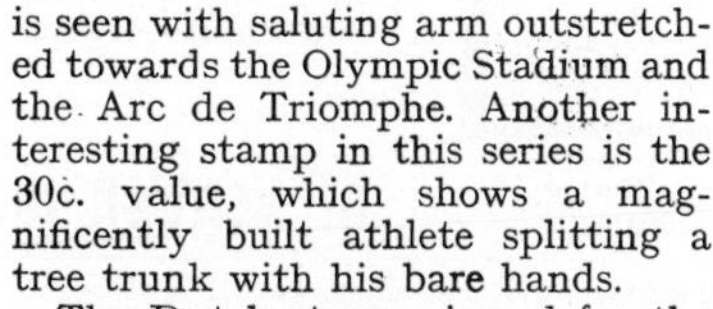

The Dutch stamps issued for the Amsterdam Games of 1928 were devoted to sporting types. There were eight designs, the list being as follows: 1½c., Sculling; 3c., Association Football; 5c., Yachting; 7½c., Putting the Weight; 10c., Running; 15c., Riding and 30c., Boxing. The 7½c. value is illustrated on page 491.

Winter sports, such as ski-ing, skating, sleighing and ice hockey, came into the programme for the first time in 1924, but this section was not marked by commemorative stamps until 1932. In that year the Games were held in the United States. Lake Placid, New York, was the scene of the Winter Games, and the Summer Games were celebrated at Los Angeles. The 2c. stamp, bearing a striking ski-ing scene that is illustrated here, was issued in connection with the Winter Games, and two stamps, 3c. and 5c. appeared later in commemoration of the Summer Games. The 3c. design, showing a sprinter on his mark, which also is illustrated here, is a splendid action picture and probably is the finest sports design ever issued on a stamp. The 5c. shows a statue of an ancient Greek discus thrower over a map of the American Continent.

Germany is acting as host this year and three stamps, 6pf., 12pf. and 25pf. values, were issued in November last for the Winter Games at Garmisch-Partenkirchen. These show skating, ski-jumping and bob-sleighing scenes respectively, and the second and third of these stamps are illustrated here. For the Summer Games at Berlin a long series of eight stamps, 3pf. to 40pf., have been issued. Two specially good designs are those of the vaulter on the 3pf. and the javelin thrower on the 8pf., but the most interesting of all is the 12pf., featuring a relay runner bearing a lighted torch.

The design of the 12pf. stamp has no connection with the competitive sports, but is intended to symbolise the bearing of a torch of "sacred fire" from Olympia, the original home of the Games, across Europe to the Stadium at Berlin. No fewer than 3,000 runners are taking part in this, and the last will carry the torch into the Stadium at the moment when the competitors from 50 nations march into the arena for the inauguration of the 1936 Games. An Olympic Flame on the Summit of the Stadium Tower will be lighted from the torch, and simultaneously there will be unfurled a great white flag, bearing five linked rings to symbolise the five continents of the world. This symbol can be seen on the fronts of the tunics worn by the figures shown on the stamps. The remaining designs in the series are as follows: 4pf., Diving; 6pf., Football; 15pf., Fencing; 25pf., Rowing; 40pf., Steeplechasing. *(Continued on page 491)*

YOUR LAST CHANCE TO GET "JUBILEES" CHEAPLY!

On September 1st the prices of the popular SILVER JUBILEE stamps on our special SILVER JUBILEE APPROVAL SHEETS will be raised. For August **only** you can get them at the old prices. Definitely your last chance, so write **to-day** for a SILVER JUBILEE APPROVAL SHEET.

STANLEY GIBBONS LTD.,
Dept. S15, 391 Strand, London, W.C.2

Stamps Bought, Sold, Exchanged.—Burley, 21, Jardine Road, Aston, Birmingham, England.

PRINCESS ELIZABETH & ROYAL FAMILY PACKET FREE!

You should send for this wonderful packet immediately. It contains 32 different stamps, including our beautiful little Princess, who may one day be Queen Elizabeth II, her father, the Duke of York, the present Heir-Apparent, King Edward VIII in Colonel's uniform, and an old King Edward VII. There are five different Jubilee stamps, long sets of Spain and Bohemia in this packet and, finally, a large, beautiful pictorial Jubilee depicting both the late King George and Queen Mary. Absolutely all free. Just send 2d. for postage and request approvals. *(Stamp Collections and Loose Lots Purchased.)*

LISBURN & TOWNSEND (Dept. M.M.), LIVERPOOL 3

FREE WONDERFUL 1936 OFFER 25 NEW ISSUES AND NOVELTIES

Including **Andorra** (1935), fine new **Cayman Islands** (map of Islands), obsolete Austria, China, Denmark, **Gwalior** Service, Hungary (Statesman Szechenyi), **new Kenya** (Kavirondo Cranes), **Roumania** (new portrait of King Carol), and many others. I will send this collection **absolutely free** to all stamp collectors sending 2d. postage (abroad 4d.).

G. P. KEEF, Willingdon, EASTBOURNE

THE "DIAMOND" PACKET IS THE ONLY PACKET

OF UNSORTED STAMPS ON THE MARKET with 15 years' reputation behind it. It contains approx. **1,000 UNSORTED STAMPS** from Convents abroad. **MANY RARE STAMPS** have been found in it. 1 pkt., 1/6; 3 pkts., 3/9; 5 pkts., 6/–. All post free inland. Colonies 3d. per pkt. extra. Foreign, 6d. extra.

Ask your stationer for the "Diamond" packet.

SPECIAL: TURKS IS. JUBILEES complete set, used or unused, 5/6.

O. NERUSH (Dept. A), 68, TURNPIKE LANE, HORNSEY, LONDON, N.8

THE 'SHIP' PACKET

This marvellous packet is offered under cost as an advertisement, **45 different stamps each with a ship on it.** A regular armada. **GABOON**, New Issue **SENEGAL** (Canoe), wonderful flotilla of caravels from **DENMARK** (complete set), **NEW CALEDONIA, IVORY COAST, COSTA RICA**, a fleet of **7 CHINESE** junks usually sold at 10d., **TRINIDAD & TOBAGO, MAURITIUS, SOUTH WEST AFRICA, NEWFOUNDLAND, U.S.A., B. GUIANA**, set of **S. AFRICA, GREECE, POLAND, INDO-CHINA, FRENCH OCEANIA**, etc. Price **4½d.**, postage 1½d. (abroad 3d. extra). Purchasers of this packet asking for approvals receive **FREE** set of **4 SPAIN** (Columbus, each with his ship on it). Senders of addresses of stamp collectors receive **FREE** set of **6 VENEZUELA** or **6 PERSIA, 100 BRITISH COLONIALS 1/–, 20 AIRPOST 6d., 6 TRIANGULARS 6d., 50 PERSIA 4/–, 2 ASTRID** (mourning stamps) **2½d., VOLUMES OF B.O.P. CHEAP.**

H. C. WATKINS (M. Dept.), Granville Road, BARNET

SETS (POSTAGE EXTRA)

5 Cameroons ...	3d.	5 Togo	3d.
10 " ...	6d.	10 "	6d.
5 Gold Coast	3d.	15 "	10d.
10 " " ...	6d.	20 "	1/2
15 " " ...	10d.	25 "	1/6
20 " " ...	1/2	5 Syria ...	2d.
1 " " Jubilee	2d.	10 " ...	5d.
5 Nigeria ...	3d.	15 " ...	8d.
10 " ...	6d.	4 Lebanon ...	2d.
15 " ...	10d.	5 Palestine ...	2d.
20 " ...	1/2	10 " ...	5d.
1 Nigeria Jubilee	3d.	10 New Zealand	2d.
5 Sierra Leone...	3d.	15 " "	4d.
10 " " ...	6d.	20 " "	6d.
15 " " ...	10d.	10 Ceylon ...	2d.
1 Sierra Leone Jubilee ...	3d.	15 " ...	4d.

J. RUSSELL
23, Shanklin Drive, Westcliffe-on-Sea

ONE THOUSAND STAMPS ON APPROVAL

From which you may select any 100 for 3/–. This selection is not made up of the very commonest varieties, but contains stamps catalogued at 1/– each or more. (I do not sell less than 100.) During this month I will include in all selections a stamp catalogued at least 3/–. Can you find it?
H. HARDY, "Hoyland," Potter Heigham, Norfolk.

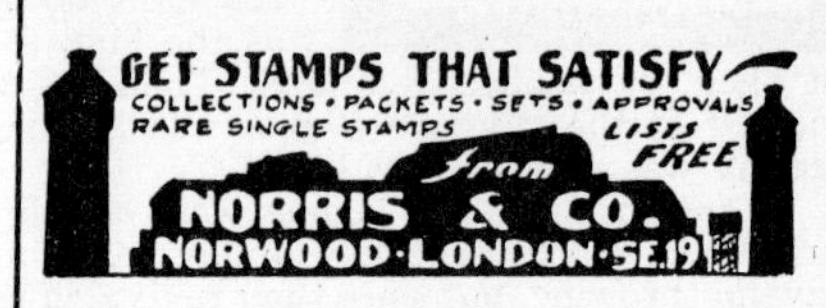

ARE YOU AIRMINDED ? ? ?

Yes! Then send for the greatest Airmail Packet we have ever offered. Besides the attractive △ **Air Stamp of Mozambique**, the packet includes **Egyptian, Indo-China, Latakia, Ecuador, Spain** and **Syrian Airmails.** Some of the most famous aircraft built are depicted on the beautiful stamps of this magnificent packet.

1/6 **USUALLY SOLD AT 1/6. FREE AND POST FREE** to approval applicants. **THE UNIVERSITY STAMP CO., 13, WALTON WELL ROAD, OXFORD.** **FREE**

AIR MAILS

We offer a unique air mail service under which air mail covers (including first flights) can be sent to you from any country in the Empire and from most foreign countries. Cost: 25 per cent. above face value of stamps used.

Write for full particulars of this service and of supplies of **first day covers** of all **King Edward VIII stamps** as issued.

ARCHIBALD F. McQUARRIE,
83, Cliff Road, Wallasey, Cheshire.

FREE. Hong-Kong Jubilee. Send P.C. only.—Pukka Stamp Co., Normandy Avenue, Barnet.

FREE.—Four different Iraq to applicants for ½d. Approvals.—Cox, 21, Dennis Mansions, Westcliff.

FINE APPROVAL SELECTIONS

My Stock contains fine condition medium and scarce stamps of nearly all countries. Now breaking several Colonial and Foreign collections at real **Investment Prices.** Mention your interests and References, please.
B. Max Campbell, B.P.A., Haldon Avenue, Teignmouth.

FREE SETS of STAMPS

6 Cuba or 6 Imperial China or 6 Straits Settlements or 6 old French, etc. Just send stamps value 2d. and ask for my Approval Sheets containing some high value stamps at low prices and with progressive discounts. State which set of stamps desired to be sent free.

P. ILLINGWORTH,
TRANMERE PARK, GUISELEY, near LEEDS.

MINT ST. LUCIA NEW ISSUE FREE

This handsome stamp together with 25 other fine **BRITISH COLONIALS** (including soon to be obsolete King George issues) will be sent FREE to all genuine applicants for my **MODERN** approvals and sending 2d. Postage (6d. Abroad).

S. CAMPBELL, 71, Manor Rd., Tankerton, Kent.

CHEAP APPROVALS

My beautiful Approval Selections are ideal for filling those vacant spaces. Pictorials, Colonials, and hard to get items. Selections from 4 a 1d. Free Gift Bi-coloured Persia all applicants.

A. V. TAPP,
108, CHESTERFIELD RD., BRISTOL

SPECIAL AUGUST OFFERS

JUBILEES. CANADA Used **COMPLETE** set	2/–
15 COLONIAL JUBILEES, used, different ...	1/6
20 BRITISH COLONIALS, Mint, New Issues	1/4
100 PERSIA, all different, incl. Air	2/9
4 BELGIUM, "Queen Astrid"	6d.
6 MONGOLIA, Pictorials (Cat. 3/4)	7d.
6 BERMUDA, ½d.-3d. K.G. Pictorials, new issue	1/3

Cash with order. Postage extra.
T. R. HUGHES, 'Ibis Cottage,' Long Park, Amersham

EVERY COLLECTOR NEEDS THIS ILLUSTRATED BOOK

Zoo in a Stamp Album—Ship Stamps—Watermarks—The Aerodrome—Single Country Collections—Olympic Games—Loose-Leaf Albums—Earthquake Stamps—Washing Day in the Stamp World—Three-cornered Market Place—British Empire Albums—Rare Stamps—Overprints and Surcharges—To Correspondents Abroad—Treasure Trove—Triangular Packets—Packets of British, French, Italian, Portuguese, Spanish and German Colonials—Building a Collection—West Indian Packets—Triangular Stamps—Philately Royal—Albums for Beginners—Penny Sets—English Men on Foreign Stamps—Emergency Papers—Shilling Sets—Advertising Stamps—Strip Pocket Books—Glossary—Stamp Tongs—Punctured Officials—etc., etc., etc. These are only a few Headings out of my **SIXTY-PAGE BOOK,** which is **WELL ILLUSTRATED THROUGHOUT** and so full of the right sort of useful and interesting Philatelic information that **EVERY STAMP COLLECTOR MUST HAVE THIS BOOK,** FREE and POST FREE from

EDWARD SANDELL, 10, EVELYN GROVE, SOUTHALL, MIDDLESEX, ENGLAND.

For other stamp advertisements see page xvi.

Stamp Collecting—(*Continued from page 489*)

In addition to the stamps issued in connection with the International Olympic Games series proper, there have been associated issues from other countries, either to commemorate participation or to celebrate an important victory in the Games. There also have been many other sports stamps relating to semi-international sports meetings, such as Austria's beautiful winter sports issues, the striking Philippine Islands series of 1934 issued in connection with the Far Eastern Championship Games series, the 1935 Central American Olympic Games issues from Colombia, Cuba and San Salvador, and the Balkan Olympic Games issue of 1931 from Bulgaria.

We have selected one or two stamps from these issues for illustration here, but unfortunately there is not space in this article even to deal briefly with the general nature of the designs of these issues. We dealt with many such stamps in an article on Sports Stamps in the April *"M.M.,"* however, and readers who wish to form a complete collection of stamps bearing sports designs will find that article very helpful.

United States "Heroes" Stamps

This month the United States will commence the issue of a series of 10 commemorative stamps, to be known as "Heroes" stamps, in honour of celebrated figures in American naval and military history.

The first of the stamps, two 1c. values, one with a naval and the other with a military design, will appear about 1st August. The other stamps will follow at monthly intervals, two 2c. values on or about 1st September, two 3c. on 1st October, two 4c. on 1st November and two 5c. on 1st December. There will be 17 portraits in all, the list comprising nine naval and eight military "heroes." Seven of the stamps will carry two portraits each and one three, and the remaining two will have on them pictures of military and naval academies.

Four of the naval commemoratives will have on them portraits of the following: 1c., John Paul Jones and John Barry; 2c., Thomas MacDonough and Stephen Decatur; 3c., David Glasgow Farragut and David Dixon Porter; 4c., George Dewey, William Thomas Sampson and Winfield Scott Schley. The fifth, the 5c. value, shows the United States Naval Academy at Annapolis.

The heroes in the Army list are as follows: 1c., George Washington and Nathaniel Greene; 2c., Andrew Jackson and Winfield Scott; 3c., Ulysses Simpson Grant and William Tecumseh Sherman; 4c., Robert Edward Lee and Thomas Jonathan ("Stonewall") Jackson.

Stamp Gossip
and Notes on New Issues

Buying Stamps Abroad

This month many of our readers will sample the delights of sea-cruising for the first time, and most of them will desire to bring back souvenirs of their trips in the form of stamps from each country visited. Few souvenirs can be so interesting, more especially in those cases where the stamps bear pictorial designs. We should advise our readers to be cautious, however, should they desire to buy other than current stamps from local post offices. Occasionally it may be possible to pick up bargains from itinerant vendors, but in the long run it will prove more economical to go to the local stamp dealer and pay higher prices for reliable specimens.

We read recently of a young collector who picked up some odds and ends of Greek stamps from a seaside hawker in Greece. He was shrewd enough to confine his purchases to Greek stamps, but when he returned to England and ventured to soak the stamps off their paper, he found to his disgust that every single specimen consisted of two parts skilfully patched together!

Stanphil Stamp Books

Readers who are specialising in subject collections, such as we have recommended on many past occasions, will be interested to know that Stanley Gibbons Ltd. have published three additions to the Stanphil Series of books dealing with stamp designs.

The first of these is *"Land Transport in the Stamp Album,"* by A. E. Gould, and deals with the various methods of carrying goods and passengers that have been employed throughout the ages. Stamps illustrate every stage of progress from the chariots of ancient Greece and Rome, and the reindeer sledges of the Russian steppes, to modern streamlined Diesel-electric trains, represented by the *"Flying Hamburger."* This is demonstrated in the book, which will be invaluable to every collector of engineering stamp designs.

The other additions to the series are *"The Stamp Zoo,"* Parts I and II, by L. P. W. Renouf. In them the author has made the most of an ideal subject for a specialised subject collection, as many countries have depicted on their stamps the more notable wild creatures found in them. Part I deals with Beasts, and Part II with Birds, Fishes and Reptiles. Stamp illustrations of every creature mentioned are included, together with special drawings by the author.

Stanley Gibbons Ltd. also have published a third edition of Mr. Stanley Phillips' popular handbook *"Stamp Collecting for All."* This edition has been completely revised and new plates have been added.

These books can be obtained from any stamp dealer, price 1/- each, or 1/1½ post free from Stanley Gibbons Ltd., 391, Strand, London, E.C.2.

South Australian Centenary

To celebrate the centenary of the foundation of the city of Adelaide and the State of South Australia, the Commonwealth Post Office will issue a special commemoration stamp issue on 2nd August.

There will be three values, 2d. red, 3d. blue, and 1/- green, each using a design showing a composite picture of the original site of Adelaide and King William Street, the city's main street, as it is to-day. The old gum tree at Glenelg, under which the proclamation founding the State and its capital city was read, will be shown in the foreground.

New Stamps for Fiji

Designs for a new series of stamps for Fiji were invited in a recent official notice in the Fiji *"Royal Gazette."* Fiji is one of the few British Colonial Possessions that hitherto have remained loyal to the King's Head design, but a change to pictorial stamps in the projected new series is foreshadowed by the intimation that the new designs may feature characteristic scenery and industrial or agricultural pursuits. The King's Head must be included in each design.

* * * *

It has been announced that the Vienna Educational Council is arranging that each school under its control is to have at least one experienced philatelist upon its teaching staff. The value of stamp collecting as a means of acquiring a sound knowledge of the world appears to be well recognised in Vienna, and stamp collectors among the boys attending schools there will appreciate the opportunities the arrangement will give them of discussing their hobby with a master who is an expert.

The Gibbons 1937 Catalogues

Stanley Gibbons Ltd. advise us that owing to the unprecedented demand for their 1936 catalogues, which resulted in supplies being exhausted very early, it has been decided to issue the 1937 editions on 1st September of this year.

It will be remembered that the 1936 issue of the Simplified Catalogue met with so great a demand that supplies were entirely sold out in February last. An entirely new edition was then produced, but this in turn was sold out in a few weeks, making a further printing necessary. A large reprint of the full catalogue was ordered on the day on which it was published, but this has been out of print for some months.

We thank Stanley Gibbons Ltd. for their courtesy in loaning the stamps from which the illustrations for our stamp pages have been made.

TOO TRUE

Customer: "That man that's just left tried to make me believe he'd driven the same car for five years and never paid a penny for repairs. Do you believe that possible?"

Garage Proprietor: "It's possible, all right! I'm the man that's done his repairs."

* * * *

"What's the shape of the earth?" asked the teacher, calling suddenly on Wee Wullie.

"Round," said Wee Wullie.

"How do you know it's round?" asked the teacher.

"Well, it's square then; I dinna want any argument about it."

* * * *

Caller at Telephone Exchange: "These flowers are for the 'phone girls."

Supervisor: "Oh, thank you, sir, you flatter our service."

Caller: "Flatter nothing, I thought they were all dead."

* * * *

The chairman of a village council announced that the clerk wanted a supply of ribbons for the typewriter. Immediately a member protested against such extravagance. "She may be a nice girl," he said, "but I don't see why she should be provided with finery at the expense of the public."

* * * *

Teacher had been explaining the Order of the Bath, which is a decoration given by the King.

"Now, Freddie," she asked, "what is the Order of the Bath?"

"Well, Miss," replied Freddie, "in our house it's baby first, then Peter, Johnny next, and I come last."

* * * *

Inexperienced Mountaineer (pointing from door of hotel): "I'm going to scale that peak to-morrow, and I want your advice. Tell me, what preparations must I make?"

Hotel Proprietor: "You must pay me in advance for your stay, sir!"

* * * *

Riley met with an accident, but the next day managed to crawl to work.

"Why didn't ye stay home for a week or two?" said Finnigan. "Worn't ye carryin' an accident policy?"

"I wor not, bad cess to me carelessness!" said Riley. "I had left it at home on the kitchen dresser."

* * * *

CAUSE AND EFFECT

A very thin man met a very fat one in the hotel lounge.

"From the look of you," said the latter, "there might have been a famine."

"Yes," was the reply, "and from the look of you, you might have caused it."

* * * *

After buying a railway ticket a woman was asked by the booking clerk whether she would take an insurance ticket.

"No thanks," she replied, "We are always taking tickets for this and that, and we never have any luck."

A SHORT STORY

Act One. "Good evening, Officer."

Act Two. "Good morning, Your Honour."

Act Three. "Good day, Warder."

* * * *

Employer: "You don't seem to have had enough experience to suit me."

Applicant for work: "Experience? Why I have been in 13 places in three months. Surely that ought to be enough experience."

* * * *

ON THE SCENT

An Irishman, whose wife was fond of moving from one house to another, was met by a friend while walking behind a vanload of household goods.

"Halloa, Mick, shifting again? Where might you be going this time?"

"I don't know," said Mick. "I'm following the furniture to find out."

* * * *

Tom: "My uncle was a great man. He dug the Mississippi River and threw the dirt out and made the Rocky Mountains."

John: "That's nothing; you know the Dead Sea? Well, my father killed it."

* * * *

Old Gentleman (having fallen downstairs at a big stores): "Help! Help! I've broken my leg."

Shop Walker: "Artificial Limb Department three doors on the left, sir."

* * * *

"Why are these envelopes addressed so badly?" an employer asked his office boy.

"The new nibs won't write, sir."

"And why have you let my fire go out?"

"The new coal won't burn, sir."

"And what new thing caused you to be late this morning?"

"Neuralgia, sir."

* * * *

Stan.: "Did you go ahead with your singing lessons?"

Les.: "No. The teacher told me it would take years of hard study to sing as well as I thought I could sing already."

* * * *

Teacher: "Now Charlie; in front of you is east, at your right south, at your left north; what is behind you?"

Charlie: "Please, sir, it's a patch on my trousers. I told mother you'd notice it."

* * * *

"Your handwriting is very bad," said a man to a young college friend. "You ought to learn to write better."

"Yes," replied the young man, "but if I were to write better, people would be finding out how badly I spell."

* * * *

Camper: "Well, what's on the menu?"

Camp Cook: "Why, we have thousands of things to eat."

Camper: "What are they?"

Camp Cook: "Beans."

ON THE MARCH

The new lance-corporal, watched by his sergeant, had the squad marching away from him. The men had gone some distance, and it appeared that the corporal had forgotten how to give the command, "About turn."

At last, when the men were about 100 yards away, the exasperated sergeant yelled: "For 'eaven's sake say something, even if it's only 'good-bye.'"

* * * *

Teacher: "Thomas, make up a sentence using the word 'archaic.'"

Thomas: "We can't have archaic and eat it too."

* * * *

A young typist had just obtained employment and was taking down letters for the first time. "I didn't quite get that," she said, after the first letter had been dictated.

"What didn't you get?" her employer asked.

"Well, I'm not quite sure what comes between 'Dear Sirs' and 'yours truly.'"

* * * *

Smith: "Johnson's address was well timed, wasn't it?"

Brown: "Yes, two-thirds of the audience had their watches out before he finished."

* * * *

White: "What is the best way to make your dog walk behind you?"

Black: "Walk in front of him."

* * * *

Sandy had been on a foraging expedition, and had returned with a good fat hen under his arm. He was about to decapitate it for roasting when another Scotsman interfered.

"Will ye no bide a wee, Sandy?" he suggested cautiously. "Leave that bird till the morning. She micht lay an egg."

* * * *

A lady on a cruise, noticing that the boat was moving rather slowly, asked the reason. She was told that it was because of the fog.

"But it is quite clear above," she persisted.

"Yes, madam," replied the officer to whom she had spoken, "but we're not going that way unless the boilers burst."

* * * *

Inspector: "Now who can tell me what are raised in wet climates?"

Jimmy: "Umbrellas, sir."

* * * *

HIS BEST

Burglar (displaying trophies): "I got this for one of my best efforts—a hundred yards race against three coppers, with ten yards start."

* * * *

Covered with grime, the motorist emerged scowling from beneath the car. His smiling friend, fresh and debonair, beamed down upon him, waving an oil can. "I've just given the cylinder a thorough oiling, old man," he said. "Thought that might help to make the old bus go."

"Cylinder be hanged," yelled the enraged one, "That was my ear."

NEXT MONTH: "SPINNING IRON AND CONCRETE PIPES." PUBLISHING DATE: 1st OCTOBER

MECCANO MAGAZINE

Editorial Office:
Binns Road, Liverpool 13
England

Vol. XXI. No. 9
September, 1936

With the Editor

A Romance of Science and Business

The life story of Sir Henry Wellcome, who died on 25th July last at the age of 82, can fittingly be called a romance of science and business. It begins in the midst of Indian tribes in Dakota, in the United States, where Sir Henry was born. While he was still a youth, Sioux warriors massacred more than 1,000 white settlers near his home, and in the war that followed he was captain of the boys employed in casting rifle bullets.

During this Indian warfare Sir Henry helped his uncle, then a well-known surgeon, in treating the wounded, and afterwards turned his mind to chemistry and pharmacy, in which he achieved a great reputation. He travelled to South America in order to study the forests from which quinine was obtained, and subsequently decided to make his home in England, where with Mr. S. M. Burroughs he founded the firm of Burroughs Wellcome and Co., now world-famous as manufacturers of fine chemicals. The majority of my readers will be familiar with the firm's many photographic products.

Sir Henry Wellcome, LL.D., F.R.S., 1853-1936.

Fighting Tropical Diseases

Business success did not satisfy all Sir Henry's desires by any means, and he was ever on the look out for some means of employing his knowledge and wealth to good advantage. He was particularly interested in Africa, and was friendly with Stanley and others whose explorations in that continent made them famous. Soon after the conquest of the Sudan, he established laboratories in Khartoum to study the diseases that ravaged the continent. He also supported exploring expeditions in practically all parts of the world—many of the great expeditions of modern times were medically equipped by him—and he himself carried out extensive explorations in the upper Nile region of Africa, excavating ancient sites and unearthing relics of Stone Age men in Ethiopia.

Good Things In Store For Readers

I have many interesting articles in store for my readers. Among these is one dealing with a wonderful pipeline, 248 miles long, built to carry water from the Colorado River across great deserts and under mountains to supply Los Angeles and other cities of Southern California. Another attractive contribution will describe a visit to Iceland.

Railway enthusiasts will be glad to know that "A Railway Engineer" has in preparation further footplate articles, which become more popular month by month. Another railway article of outstanding interest will describe the provision at Leeds New Joint Station of colour-light signals, power-operated points, track circuits and a new signal cabin. Readers who enjoyed Mr. O. S. Nock's account in the August issue of his flight from Belfast to Liverpool will find even greater interest in his forthcoming description of an air trip from Amsterdam to Croydon. Other aviation articles will deal with the new "direct-lifting" Autogiro, capable of a big vertical jump, and with recent types of British military aircraft.

Retaining Old Favourites

Whenever the *"M.M."* appears without *"Engineering News,"* or some other old favourite, I invariably receive a shoal of complaints and enquiries. This is not surprising, for practically every page of the Magazine is the result of imperative demands from readers. My difficulty is that I am called upon to provide articles and contributions on so many different topics that it is impossible to find room for all of them in every issue. I can assure readers that the absence from any issue of a regular feature does not mean that it is to be discontinued, and they can look forward to its re-appearance the following month.

Boring the Severn Tunnel

How the Engineers Fought Floods

THE day on which this issue of the *"M.M."* appears can be regarded as the fiftieth birthday of the Severn Tunnel of the G.W.R., for the first goods train ran through it on 1st September 1886. The Severn Tunnel is the longest in Great Britain, apart from the London tubes, and is still the longest under-water tunnel in the world. Its opening greatly improved communication between England and South Wales. Before it was brought into use the quickest rail journey between Bristol and Cardiff took 2 hrs. 14 min. and involved crossing the Severn by ferry, while freight trains had to go round by Gloucester. When train service on the new route was established, the time required for travel between the two cities was reduced to 80 min.

The building of the Severn Tunnel was the most difficult engineering achievement of the whole of the G.W.R. system, and the contractor engaged in the task held that "one such tunnel, with its strangely contorted strata and dangers from floods above and floods below," was enough for a lifetime! Only the dogged perseverence of those in charge, and the courage and resource of the men who worked in the tunnel, enabled it to be completed in the face of a succession of difficulties, disappointments and even disasters.

A G.W.R. up South Wales express emerging from the English mouth of the Severn Tunnel. This tunnel is 4 miles 624 yards long, and is the longest under-water tunnel in the world. Photographs by courtesy of G.W.R.

The story of communications across the Severn estuary is very interesting. The Romans established a ferry on the road from Bath to their military stations at Caerwent and Caer leon. This was closed during the Civil War by Cromwell, because some of his soldiers had been lost there owing to treachery on the part of the ferrymen. It was reopened in the following century, and took the name of the New Passage, a ferry near Chepstow upstream then being known as the Old Passage. The channel at New Passage was open for navigation at any stage of the tide, and therefore was selected by the Bristol and South Wales Union Railway as the site of a steam ferry that commenced to operate in 1863, and continued to work for 25 years. The transfer from train to steamer and vice-versa took place on wooden piers.

The Bristol and South Wales Union Railway later became part of the G.W.R., and eventually powers were obtained to construct a tunnel to replace the cumbersome ferry. Boring under the Severn did not promise to be an easy task, for the range of tides in the Severn estuary is large and on the Monmouthshire side there is a deep-water channel, a quarter of a mile wide and 58 ft. deep at low water, that is known as the "Shoots." It was intended that there should be a depth of 30 ft. between the top of the tunnel and the lowest part of the river bed, and long approaches therefore were necessary in order to avoid a gradient of more than 1 in 100, the maximum proposed. Originally it was planned to sink a shaft in the estuary on a rock that was uncovered at low tide. The rock was covered by 28 ft. of water at high tide, however, and the currents were so strong that this scheme would have been expensive. Because of this, and of the interference to navigation that would have been occasioned by the presence of the shaft, the scheme was abandoned and all the shafts used were on land and outside the influence of tide water.

Work was begun on the Welsh side of the river, the sinking of a brick-lined shaft 15 ft. in diameter and 200 ft. deep being commenced in March 1873 at Sudbrook. The tunnellers soon made their first acquaintance with water, which was to be a constant source of trouble and delay during the work, for they encountered a spring yielding 12,000 gallons per hour, and twice that amount came from a second struck lower down. Two steam pumps were installed, the first to deal with the upper spring, and the second to take away the water of the lower one.

By the end of 1874 the headings of the tunnel itself were begun, and they had been carried nearly a mile under the river bed by August 1877. At first they were driven by means of hand drills and blasting, but later compressed air drills were brought into use. The compressed air required was carried along the headings in a six-inch pipe, and on release from the drills served to keep the air fresh at the working face. Other shafts were sunk on both sides of the Severn, and headings were commenced from them to join up with those from the foot of the Sudbrook shaft, now known as the Old Shaft. By October 1879 there were five shafts altogether, and the original headings from the Old Shaft had been lengthened by two miles, only 130 yds. then separating them from the working face of the headings driven from the Sea Wall Shaft, on the Gloucestershire side.

Then came a disaster. An underground reservoir, afterwards called the Great Spring, burst into the workings, flooding them at the rate of 6,000 gallons a minute. The men had to run for their lives, but fortunately were able to escape through a cross heading into a pumping shaft. Soon the water was 150 ft. deep in the shafts. It was found to be fresh, and at the time when it poured into the tunnel many of the streams in the district dried up. The River Neddern, a tributary of the Severn, actually became dry for a distance of five miles!

After this disaster Sir John Hawkshaw, hitherto Consulting Engineer, was put in charge. The first step was to deal with the water flooding the workings, and heavy oak shields were placed in position by divers at each heading entrance at the bottom of the Old Shaft, while more powerful pumps were installed.

In the efforts to master the incoming water, heroic feats were performed by a diver named Lambert, who is described as "a fair-haired man of few words and great courage." A special flood door had been provided in the heading, the idea being that in case of emergency this would be closed and two valves also screwed down to keep flood water within bounds. These had been left open in the rush to safety when the Great Spring broke in, however, and now had to be closed. In his first attempt Lambert had to make his way into the heading past all the material left behind in the miners' race for life, dragging his air pipe after him. Two other divers assisted him, one being stationed half way along the heading to feed the pipe forward and the other at the bottom of the shaft to turn the frail tube into the heading. Lambert could not approach nearer than 70 ft. from the door, and had to return, bringing his air pipe with him and spending anxious moments when it caught in various obstructions on the way.

Another attempt was then made by Lambert in company with Fleuss, the inventor of a self-contained diving apparatus. They reached the bottom of the shaft, but owing to inexperience Fleuss could venture no further. Lambert reached the flood doorway, however, and removed one of two tram rails passing through it, but was not able to do more. He went back two days later, removed the second rail and operated the valves. After this, it was a great disappointment to find that the pumps still had considerable difficulty in reducing the amount of water in the workings. When, a month later it became possible to inspect the valves, it was found that one of them had a left-hand thread, and that Lambert had opened it to its fullest extent instead of shutting it down, as he imagined. The works were gradually cleared of water, and the Great Spring was sealed in for the time being by means of head walls of brickwork and cement.

The 12 Lancashire boilers in the No. 1 pumping house at Sudbrook. These boilers supply steam to the pumps that deal with water from the Great Spring.

Hawkshaw decided to place the tunnel 15 ft. deeper under the Shoots, considered to be the critical part of the work. This made it necessary to increase the slope on the Welsh side to 1 in 90, and the lower of the two headings already driven then became the top heading of the tunnel. Work was resumed, but the troubles of the tunnel builders were by no means ended, for in April 1881 the river broke into the workings from a pool known as the "Salmon Pool," where the water is only 3 ft. deep at low tide. A number of men joined hands and waded about the pool at low tide in order to find the hole. One of them discovered it by falling into it, but he was quickly pulled out and the opening was then filled up with clay, loose and in bags.

Later difficulty was caused by a four days' strike and a severe snowstorm in January 1881, during which the coal supplies for the pumping engines gave out, and wood and almost anything else at hand that would burn was thrust into the furnaces in the effort to keep the pumps going. Satisfactory progress was made with actual tunnelling, however, and in September 1881 the two headings, each about 7 ft. square, were joined up to make a clear passage 2¼ miles long from Sudbrook on the Welsh side to Sea Wall Shaft in Gloucestershire. The work of opening out the headings to the full width was then begun, 3,744 yds. of tunnel being completed by the end of 1882.

The ever-threatening water again put a stop to proceedings in the following October, for the Great Spring once more broke through, this time in greater quantities, 27,000 gallons pouring into the tunnel every minute. Diver Lambert again was prominent in the task of stemming the invading water. After the pumps had gained ground, he went down to close a flood door in the special heading that had been provided in the earlier draining operations.

In the meantime what might have been a more serious disaster took place, for during a storm a tidal wave swept over the Severn banks, putting out the fires of all the pumping engine boilers and pouring down one of the shafts to fill the tunnel to within 8 ft. of the top. Two or three of the men at work climbed the shaft with water flowing down over them; the remainder, 83 in number, were trapped in the tunnel, where they took refuge on raised staging. Next day a small boat was lowered down the shaft end-on, but the rescuers in it could only approach the marooned workmen after some of the submerged staging had been sawn through. Fortunately no further trouble prevented the men from making their way to the surface in safety. The pumps again cleared the workings of water and the Great Spring was restrained by head walls.

Good progress was then possible both in the tunnel and in the approach cuttings, which required the excavation of more than 800,000 cu. yds. of earth. Steam shovels were used in the latter task. These had never before been employed in Great Britain and their appearance aroused great interest. Eventually the threat of the Great Spring was dealt with by driving a special heading into which the water was allowed to flow through the sluices in the head wall. The pumps then available were masters of the situation, so that it was possible to complete the tunnel without further trouble from this cause. On 18th April 1885 the last length of brickwork was keyed in, and some months later a special train carrying Sir Daniel Gooch, then Chairman of the G.W.R., and other officials, travelled through the tunnel from the Welsh to the English side and back.

An important part of the construction of the tunnel was the lining, which accounted for half of the cost of the complete work. It was made of vitrified bricks laid in cement, and some idea of the immensity of the work carried out in building the tunnel is given by the fact that no fewer than 76,400,000 bricks and 37,000 tons of cement were used. Water pressure on the brickwork caused a considerable amount of trouble. Showers penetrated through the joints in several places, and at one time pieces of the tunnel lining broke off and jets of water shot right across the bore. The water that spurted in all directions sometimes made it impossible to have any lights burning. Work then had to be carried out practically in darkness, but an electric lighting system was installed in the Sea Wall Shaft in 1880, and in the workings at the Welsh end of the tunnel later. This was a remarkable step, for electric lighting was then in its infancy.

In order to avoid mishap from this source it was decided to add to the pumping plant. This meant the sinking of a new shaft 29 ft. in diameter at Sudbrook, and the installation of six large pumps. This provision added to the cost of the tunnel and delayed its opening for traffic by about 12 months, but the plant installed was capable of dealing with all the water of the Great Spring and averted danger of further disaster.

On the left is a view of the approach to the Severn Tunnel on the Welsh side. Below is the exterior of the No. 1 pumping house at Sudbrook.

On another occasion the deaths of three tunnel workers caused a "bad ventilation" scare, and experiments were conducted with a fan 12 ft. in diameter and 7 ft. wide in efforts to improve the air supply underground. This was fixed over the New Shaft at Sudbrook and drew air through from the Sea Wall Shaft 2¼ miles away. It continued to work for four years and was of ample capacity, but in 1886 it was replaced by a much larger fan 40 ft. in diameter and 12 ft. wide. This fan was in continuous use until 1924, when the present still more powerful installation was provided, having a capacity of 800,000 cubic feet of air per minute. This is driven by a tandem compound engine supplied with steam from three Lancashire boilers, two being used at once.

Finally, after 13 years of hard work and disappointments, the courage and enterprise of the builders of the tunnel was rewarded by complete success. The full length of the workings is practically 7 miles, with 4 miles 624 yards actually in tunnel, and the total cost was more than £1,800,000. An experimental coal train from Aberdare to Southampton was run through the tunnel early in 1886, but the opening for traffic was delayed until 1st September owing to the necessity of completing the pumping arrangements.

The Clipper Ships of the Pacific

By A. R. BOONE

ALTHOUGH public attention of late has been centred on aerial accomplishments on this side of the globe, our airminded American cousins have been hastening the final conquest of the air by their latest achievement in opening up the 8,705-mile route from California to China. This has been done by spanning the vast Pacific Ocean with 25-ton flying boats in which the world traveller is as safe as in a railway carriage on land.

Americans call these monster air liners "clippers," and they are building a large fleet of them in order to cope with future freight and passenger traffic between California and China. Already there have been several trial flights carrying mail and freight, and passenger service will start within a few months. Then one will be able to travel around the globe in 17 days in comfortable, luxurious air liners. Suppose a start is made in New York. From there it will be possible to cross the Atlantic via Montreal, or to reach Marseilles by way of Bermuda, the Azores and Lisbon. The flight will be continued across Europe to Bangkok, by scheduled services already in operation, and thence to Manila over a line soon to be inaugurated. Then will follow the journey by air from Manila across the Pacific to California, and finally a dash across North America back to New York. It is the age-old dream of mariners come true!

In the pilot's cabin of the Pan American Clipper, the flying boat engaged in experimental flights across the Pacific Ocean.

Engineering science has made these Pacific Ocean flights as safe as the proverbial houses, for nothing is left to chance. Here are a few interesting features of the giant air ships employed on the service. They cruise at 157 m.p.h., each crankshaft making 1,800 revolutions in every minute of the flight. This means that the crankshaft of each engine revolves 6,500,000 times during the 60-hour flight from Alameda, in California, to Macao, off the southern coast of China, making a total of 26 million revolutions for the four 12-cylinder engines. Further, there are 900 explosions in each of the 56 cylinders each minute, or a total of 181,441,000 power strokes between California and China. Any three of her engines will keep a "clipper" in the air, no matter how heavily she may be loaded.

Five specialists will man each air liner when the passenger service is inaugurated, and each will be capable of taking over the job of nearly every other. The captain, for instance, may fly the ship, serve as flight engineer, navigate or work the radio. A "flight engineer" is a comparatively new job on air liners, and on this particular route he takes over many of the former duties of the pilot. He sits in his cabin, above the passengers' compartment and directly beneath the leading edge of the huge wing, and within easy reach has the instruments and controls by means of which he starts the engines, feeds them with petrol, controls them and finally shuts them off at the end of a flight. The removal of all these gadgets from the pilots' cabin has left the men who actually fly the machines only 50 instruments and controls at their fingers' tips.

The flight engineer knows every quirk and rivet in the ship. Not only is he capable of performing any necessary repairs, but each hour during flight he takes 70 recordings, including the rate of petrol consumption, head and base temperatures of two cylinders on each engine, and oil temperature and pressure. His is a busy life, from the time he takes off until he lands.

Once a "clipper" is in the air, vigilance does not relax until the machine is reported safe at her destination. Everyone realises the important part the weather plays in air safety, and perhaps nowhere in the world is such a vast weather forecasting service maintained as that which covers the entire northern Pacific. From Eastern Siberia, Japan, China, the Philippines and the mandated islands south and east of Japan, wireless flashes twice daily reports of local weather and wind conditions.

There are observers at Macao, the terminus, and at Manila, Guam, the tiny island of Wake, Midway and Honolulu, all calling places on the Pacific air route. These men take surface observations four times daily and upper-air soundings, noting wind direction and velocity to great altitudes, twice a day, and they report their observations to Alameda. Then the United States Weather Bureau collects weather information at the same hours from ships at sea, from shore stations in Alaska, and from places all over the United States.

With these reports before him, the meteorologist at the Alameda airport charts the weather as it will develop during the next 12 hrs., and he can then follow the progress of storms as they develop thousands of miles away and direct air liners so that they may shape their courses to avoid these disturbances.

In the chart room of the Pan American Clipper. The navigator is working out his position after taking night sights of the moon and a star.

When a flight actually starts, the weather experts multiply their efforts to provide up-to-the-minute information. Starting three hours before each flight, and continuing throughout, the stations of departure and arrival make observations every hour. More than once they have steered a machine in service from a storm area into calm air, thereby not only saving the crew from distress, but also speeding up the flight. On one occasion a "clipper" was at Midway ready to take off for Wake, when at Alameda indications were discerned of a tropical storm brewing 6,000 miles to the south of its starting point. The disturbance was moving north-westward towards the liner's course at a speed of about 20 m.p.h. News of its approach was despatched by radio to Midway, where a new course 100 miles west of the regular route was quickly planned to enable the machine to avoid it.

When on shore the giant clippers are towed by tractors. This illustration gives some idea of the immense size of their tails.

When the liner on its new course was half way between Midway and Wake huge storm clouds and heavy rain squalls were seen 100 miles away on the starboard beam. The storm was 200 miles in diameter. It crossed the path of the air liner before the return flight to Midway two days later, and the machine then flew along its eastern boundary, thus missing it completely on both flights as the result of information collected and charted 4,000 miles away.

Even if weather changes are sent by radio to the navigators, how do they change courses and yet bring the big air liners into port on time and with unerring accuracy? How important exact navigation is may be realised from the fact that the tiny island of Wake is only 4½ miles long and 2½ miles wide. It is indeed a tiny dot in the vast Pacific Ocean, 1,138 nautical miles west of Midway and 1,309 miles east of Guam. Yet it is reached without hesitation, and similar precision marks every stage of the long flights the "clippers" are called upon to make in maintaining the new service.

In order to achieve this remarkable accuracy, during the day the navigator takes observations every hour of the Sun and Venus, and at night of the Moon and Venus. Intersecting lines indicate within an error of a few miles where the machine was at the precise instant he held his octant toward the sky and got a "fix." These observations serve as a check on radio messages, by means of which the machine's position is determined every 30 minutes. To make sure that all is well, Alameda calls the liner every quarter of an hour.

Although the machine might be on the true course at the moment, cross-winds may be blowing her gradually off her flight path. Whether this is so, and in what direction she is being driven off her path, is determined by an ingenious flask built like an air bomb and containing 1 lb. of aluminium powder. The navigator attaches his drift indicator to a window sill, and casts the flask into the sea. It shatters on impact, the powder quickly forming a tiny, glistening island. Speedily he determines from the scale on the indicator the extent to which the liner is drifting. Still the wind may be coming in ahead from the bow, or astern off the tail, holding the liner back or speeding her along. So the navigator calculates where she would be 15 min. later were there no wind, and after that time has elapsed he determines her position by radio messages and celestial observation. The difference in these positions represents the drift. Air liners can always tune in on some radio station and determine in a few seconds whether they are flying on the charted path or not.

Any of these American "clipper" air liners could circle the globe to-day at the Equator in nine days were it possible to refuel at intervals. Yet to-morrow's round-the-world air liners will be even larger and faster. English and American engineers already are planning huge ships to weigh 150,000 lb., with cruising speeds exceeding 200 m.p.h. They will fly well over the clouds and above storms, at heights of four to five miles, thus permitting passengers to enjoy smooth and comfortable flight.

Centenary of a Famous Bridge

How the Avon Gorge at Bristol was Spanned

By F. R. Winstone

THE foundation stone of the Clifton Suspension Bridge across the Avon Gorge at Bristol was laid 100 years ago on 27th August 1836, in the presence of thousands of people. The annual meeting of the British Association was being held in Bristol that year, and the Marquis of Northampton, the President, was given the honour of laying the first stone of the bridge, which marked the beginning of the construction of the abutment on the Leigh Woods, or Somerset side of the river.

The story of the Clifton Suspension Bridge began in 1753, when Mr. William Vick, a Bristol spirit merchant, left £1,000 in the keeping of the Society of Merchant Venturers of Bristol to accumulate at compound interest until it reached £10,000, when it was to be devoted to building a stone bridge to span the Avon Gorge. By 1829 the bequest had grown to £8,000, and a committee was then formed to consider how the scheme could be carried out. A stone bridge proved to be out of the question because of the high cost, and as one of the most widely discussed topics of the day was the recently completed Menai Straits suspension bridge, Telford's great triumph, it was decided to build the Clifton venture on similar lines. Accordingly designs for a suspension bridge were invited, and one of those who entered the competition was Brunel, who later created the Great Western Railway and built the "*Great Eastern.*"

The Clifton Suspension Bridge outlined by illuminations at night. Below it is the Avon Gorge, and the tracks of the headlights of motor cars on the road by the river can be seen.

At that time Brunel was only 23 years of age. He designed four bridges with single spans varying from 760 ft. to 1,180 ft. in length, and it seemed as if one of his designs would be adopted. Unexpected opposition came from Telford, who when asked to judge the designs argued that a span of more than 600 ft., that of his own Menai Straits bridge, was inadmissible. Telford favoured the erection of two enormous Gothic towers on the banks of the river, to give a central span of 360 ft., but his design did not satisfy the committee and a further competition was held. This time Brunel was successful. The suspended span of his proposed bridge was 600 ft., but in the final plans this was extended to 702 ft.

The estimated cost of the bridge was £57,000, or more than seven times the sum to which the Vick legacy had amounted; but more money was raised by means of gifts and loans, and operations began in January 1836, after Brunel had suggested decreasing the width of the bridge and dispensing with some of its ornamental features. Unhappily all the money available was spent by 1840, when the two towers had been completed. Great efforts were made to collect funds, but no more work was done for some 20 years when a new company was formed by prominent members of the Institution of Civil Engineers, who wished to complete the work as a monument to Brunel. The opening of the bridge took place in 1864.

Shortly after the foundation stone ceremony, efforts were made to connect the two sides of the Avon Gorge by means of an iron bar 1,800 ft. in length and 1½ in. in diameter. The purpose of this was to enable workmen to pass from one side of the river to the other in a car suspended from the bar. At the first attempt a hawser broke and one end of the great rod fell into the river. It was raised into position next day, but was then found to be bent in the middle to such an extent that it was practically useless. A new bar was passed over the river in September, however, and the great occasion was marked by Brunel making the journey across the Gorge, along with a youth named Claxton.

As can be imagined, the novelty of the trip was a great attraction, and crowds of people wished to follow the engineer's example. They were allowed to do so at a charge of 5/–, which eventually was reduced to 1/–. There was great eagerness to experience this 19th. century thrill, and in Bristol 100 years ago the first question people asked of their friends and acquaintances on meeting them was; "Have you crossed the Gorge?" It is said that on one occasion a bride and bridegroom essayed the trip on their wedding day. Unfortunately, the hauling ropes refused to work when the couple were half way across, and there they were left for several hours to contemplate the beauties of the Avon Gorge and the hills of Somerset on the horizon. They began to discuss the prospect of staying in their novel and uncomfortable position all night, but fortunately they were rescued in time to avoid this.

Taking toll from a motorist about to cross the bridge.

The bar stayed in position nearly 20 years, and on one occasion during a general election practical jokers hung an effigy of one of the rival candidates on it over the middle of the river. As this could not be reached by ordinary means it was necessary to engage a rifleman to sever the rope by shooting bullets through it in order to appease the injured dignity of the candidate concerned.

Since its completion the bridge unfortunately has proved a favourite place for suicides. There is a sheer drop of 45 ft., so that there is little likelihood of anyone leaping from the bridge landing safely on the ground. Yet this actually happened on one occasion to a Victorian lady of 60 years ago who determined to take the plunge to death. She was fashionably dressed in the crinoline of the period, and this saved her life, for as she fell it opened out like a parachute and the breeze lifted her clear of the river and landed her unhurt on the bank. The few spectators of this unique event thought it was an advertisement for a circus, and on learning the truth were relieved to find that the would-be suicide had been cured of the desire to end her life.

Although Brunel did not complete the Clifton Suspension Bridge, his connection with it gave him the opportunity of making a name in his profession. In subsequent years he used to say that his success was due to his victory in the second competition for designs for this bridge.

A Machine that Tests Roads

Lorry with the Energy of a Six-inch Shell

OUR roads have been restored to importance by the coming of the motor car and the motor lorry, and to-day they are crowded with vehicles of various sizes travelling mostly at high speeds. The resulting wear and tear on their surfaces is so considerable, however, that no less than 50 million pounds are spent annually in Great Britain on road-making and upkeep.

In view of this enormous expenditure it has become necessary to carry out experiments to find the best materials with which to build roads and the most effective ways of making use of them. The chief need is to learn how experimental road surfaces will stand up to the actual strain of traffic passing over it. It is only by tests on full scale roads that we can find whether they are really suitable for the task they are given. In the ordinary way tests of this kind require many years to complete, however, and for this reason machines have been devised that concentrate the wear of years into a comparatively few hours. Three of these machines have been built at the Road Research Laboratory, Harmondsworth. The largest, which is illustrated on this page, employs a full-sized 12-ton lorry running at high speed over an experimental road track. The impression it gives is rather like that of a greyhound racing track in which the electric "hare" has been replaced by a lorry, for this is tethered to a central post by means of a steel arm, and swings round and round on its circular course at a speed of 40 m.p.h. As regards the weight of the vehicle and its speed, the machine is the largest of its kind in the world.

The steel arm of the large road testing machine at the Road Research Laboratory, Harmondsworth. This has to withstand a pull of 25 tons as it whirls a 12-ton lorry round at a speed of 40 m.p.h.

The lorry consists of an A.E.C. chassis in which the engine has been replaced by a 180 h.p. electric motor. It is attached to one end of a steel arm by means of a ball joint, and runs on a track 10 ft. wide in a circle with an average diameter of 110 ft. Each circuit is completed in six seconds.

The steel arm by which the lorry is tethered is an immense girder weighing 5 tons. It has to withstand a pull of 25 tons when the lorry is whirling round at its maximum speed, and if the lorry broke away from its centre post it would shoot from its track, as a stone leaves a sling, with as much energy as is possessed by a shell fired from a 6-inch gun. For this reason special safety devices have been incorporated. The building in which the machine is housed is surrounded by an earth bank, except where the control room adjoins the track, and there a heavily reinforced concrete "crash" wall is provided. The control room itself is of reinforced concrete, with a small safety glass window through which the machine and the road under test can be watched.

As the lorry has to follow a circular course, the steering is locked in the correct position when tests are in operation. A further aid in keeping it on its course is provided by a steel stay attached at one end to the front of the lorry and at the other to a point on the steel arm. This stay usually carries only a light load, and its chief purpose is to act as a safety measure in the event of such an accident as the bursting of one of the tyres.

The centre post around which the lorry swings is bedded in a heavy reinforced concrete pier 6 ft. deep and 8 ft. in diameter. This is connected to concrete foundations under the outer track by eight arms of heavily reinforced concrete, and thus the whole structure rests on a great concrete wheel, 100 ft. in diameter, sunk into the ground.

The wheels of a lorry rotating at the end of a fixed arm would run throughout in the same tracks, and would produce ruts in the road instead of testing a reasonable expanse of surface. This is avoided in the road testing machine at Harmondsworth by moving the end of the connecting arm slowly backward and forward over the central post. The full traverse is made in five minutes, and its effect is to cause the lorry to wear two tracks, each about 2 ft. 6 in. in width.

The electric motor that drives the lorry is supplied with current from pick-up gear surrounding the central post, through cables that run along the steel arm; and the speed can readily be varied from the control room. The opening of the gate leading to the track automatically cuts off the current and brings the machine to rest, and a similar result follows failure of any part of the electrical equipment. Special precautions have to be taken to keep the back axle of the lorry supplied with oil, for this is flung outward by the centrifugal force developed by the immense speed at which the vehicle makes its circuits. As the oil swirls to the outer end of the axle it is fed back again to the inner end by a specially fitted oil pump.

Trials can be carried out in all weathers, for the track is roofed. In fact the engineers in charge may be said to make their own weather, for artificial water sprinklers have been installed to imitate the fall of rain.

Discharging Grain From Ships

New Plant at a London Flour Mill

THE greater part of the wheat that goes to the making of our daily bread is grown in Canada, Australia, South America and other distant parts of the world, and is brought to this country in ships specially fitted for carrying grain. This trade supplies cargoes for the last of the sailing ships that traverse the great ocean routes. Every year several of these vessels bring wheat to this country from Australia. Keen interest is taken in their passages, and an unofficial grain race has been waged annually for many years past.

Grain formerly was shipped in sacks, and loading and unloading it were laborious processes. To-day sacks are seldom used. Instead the grain is treated in bulk, and is simply shot into the holds of the ships. Special precautions have to be taken in loading these vessels in order to prevent shifting of the cargo, which might give rise to danger in rough weather.

When the handling of grain in bulk was first introduced, unloading was carried out by means of shovels and scoops, or buckets, which were lifted by cranes on the quayside. Later grabs capable of holding as much as 2 tons of grain were introduced. These also were handled by cranes, and were provided with special gear for closing the grab when it was lowered into the hold, and for opening it again on swinging it over the place where the grain was to be deposited.

The next step was to introduce elevators consisting of continuous vertical belts provided with buckets that scooped up the grain as they were pulled through it at the bottom of their travel. These elevators were suspended from arms projecting from quayside buildings. They delivered the grain to chutes, down which it passed to band conveyors leading into the silos, as the special buildings in which grain is stored are called. One of the disadvantages of this system was that the grain in the hold of a vessel in process of unloading had to be brought to the foot of the elevator.

Wheat is no longer transferred from ship to shore by shovelling into skips lifted by cranes, and even bucket elevators are now seldom employed. Instead the grain is sucked out in the same manner as dust is extracted from carpets by an electric vacuum cleaner. On the wharves or quays where unloading takes place, are towers that run on rails. These carry overhead booms from which are suspended long vertical pipes with nozzles that are dropped into the wheat. Powerful pumps suck air through the pipes, and the wheat is as readily drawn up these as if it were a liquid.

A modern pneumatic grain discharging plant of this kind includes many interesting and novel features, and how these work is illustrated by an improved type of plant that has been installed at the Millennium Flour Mills of Spillers, Ltd. (W. Vernon and Sons' Branch), at Victoria Docks, London. This was built by Henry Simon, Ltd., Cheadle Heath, Stockport. It transfers grain from the holds of ships to the silo at the rate of 240 tons per hour, but when necessary it can be speeded up to deal with 280 tons in the same time.

Unloading operations at the Millennium Flour Mills, Victoria Docks, London. The grain is delivered to the two closed conveyors seen on the jetty. We are indebted to Henry Simon, Ltd., for the illustrations to this article.

The concrete jetty alongside which grain ships lie at the Millennium Flour Mills is entirely surrounded by water, a barge dock separating it from a quay in front of the mills, along which run railway tracks. There was already an unloading plant on the jetty, and the new plant was erected while the old one continued to work. The change-over was effected in two stages at week-ends, in order to avoid loss of time.

In designing the new plant it was decided to make use of the two travelling towers already in existence on the jetty. These run on rails alongside the ship to be unloaded, and have been specially strengthened in order to enable them to carry heavier pipe booms to take larger quantities of wheat. They are driven by electric motors and can move along the jetty at a speed of 50 ft. a minute. Each of the structures carries its own motors, together with winches by means of which the booms are hoisted or lowered as required. The necessary electric current reaches their motors through trailing cables, which are mounted on spring drums that allow a certain amount of give and take, in whatever direction the towers are moving.

Each of the two booms of the travelling towers ends in

a vertical telescopic pipe that is lowered into the holds of ships at the quayside and moved about as required. At the end of each of these pipes is a flexible tube carrying at its end a nozzle that is dipped into the grain when unloading is being carried on. The grain is sucked up into the nozzle and passes through the telescopic pipe into the boom. When it reaches the tower it enters a junction box leading to a pipe by means of which it is delivered on to a conveyor that runs along the whole length of the wharf. The movements of which the booms and the telescopic pipes are capable enable every corner of the holds to be scoured without difficulty, and it is not necessary to push grain towards the nozzles.

Another view showing grain being unloaded, with the flour mills in which it is used on the right. A gantry connects the mills with the jetty.

One of the most interesting features of the plant is the manner in which the unloading is controlled. Formerly this was from a cabin on the pneumatic plant structure. Now the entire operation is in charge of a man stationed on the deck of the ship, immediately above the hold, where he has a full view of the whole of the proceedings. He can easily watch the booms in order to make sure they are in the most convenient positions, and a glance down the hatchway keeps him fully in touch with progress in the hold itself. He makes use of a small master controller, first selecting the motion he requires, and then turning a crank handle to put it into effect.

Several interesting safety devices are fitted, and the control is as nearly foolproof as possible. Electric brakes come into operation automatically when necessary, and a change cannot be made from one winch to another unless the first is stopped. In addition, the connections are so designed that operation is stopped as soon as the man in charge leaves the controller, while the cutting of a cable or its short circuiting to earth has a similar result.

A travelling tower extracting grain from the hold of a ship. From the conveyors beneath the tower the grain passes to an elevator that carries it to the site.

The grain sucked up the pipes and booms of the travelling towers passes through flexible telescopic pipes on to one of two conveyors, which are of special design and act as air pipes under vacuum. Each conveyor is air-tight, and all moving parts are enclosed in a heavy steel box. The two conveyors run along the length of the jetty, between the rails on which the towers are moved, and they are mounted on steel supports. At intervals of 16 ft. there are cast iron inlets that can rapidly be connected by means of quick-coupling flanges to the pipes through which the grain comes, and from each tower the wheat drops through the one of these that is in use on to the conveyor, which carries it along the bottom of its housing to what is called the intake house.

The air sucked in with the grain also passes through the conveyor, and reaches the intake house along with the wheat. An overhead gantry connects the jetty with the mainland at this point, and there the two are separated. The grain is extracted by an electrically-driven tipper provided with special mechanism to avoid stoppages due to any foreign matter that may be mixed with it, and is then delivered to bucket elevators. The elevators in turn deliver to band conveyors, which transfer the grain to the storage bins in the silo. The air passes on into steel cyclones in which it is whirled round to get rid of the dust it contains. After this cleaning it enters welded steel air pipes, which are carried under the gantry, and lead to vacuum pumps in a special house built between the barge dock and the railway tracks on the mainland.

The vacuum pumps are a very important part of the plant, for they produce the suction that unloads the grain and feeds it to the conveyors. There are two sets, each of which is driven by an electric motor with an output of 170 b.h.p., and they work with high efficiency, lowering the pressure on the vacuum side to about a quarter of that of the atmosphere. The motors are equipped with automatic starters, and these can be operated either from the jetty or from the room in the silo in which the grain is automatically weighed. The two conveyors also are electrically driven, each being equipped with a 35 h.p. motor that acts through a train of gearing. These motors are placed in a separate house outside the intake shed.

The plant can be started and stopped from the jetty or from the weighing room in the silo.

Important Aerial Surveys

By the use of aerial methods large tracts of land can be surveyed accurately in very much less time than if the work is carried out by survey parties on foot. In settled countries such as England, air surveys have proved of great value to town planning authorities and in the revision of Ordnance maps, and they have been employed in ascertaining the mineral wealth of undeveloped territories in Africa and elsewhere. At the present time a survey of an area of 3,000 sq. m. in the Belingwe mining district in Southern Rhodesia is being carried out.

In Canada a company has been formed to survey about 25,000 sq. miles of territory in Labrador for signs of minerals. In this case two seaplanes will be employed in the preliminary work of photographing the country from the air, and later in transporting equipment and men from place to place as the survey proceeds, a method that will result in a great saving of time and labour.

The advantages and value of aerial surveys also are becoming recognised in China, and at Tungchi University a fully equipped Institute for Aerial Survey will shortly be established under the direction of a German expert.

First British Night Air Mail Service

The first British night air mail service began on 27th July last, when a D.H.86 aeroplane of British Airways Ltd., left Gatwick for Cologne and Hanover. The service is being worked in co-operation with A.B. Aerotransport, of Sweden. The machines leave Great Britain at 10 p.m. on Mondays, Wednesdays and Fridays, and set out from Sweden at 1.30 a.m. on Tuesdays, Thursdays and Saturdays. The mails flown from England are handed over to the Swedish company at Hanover, where those for England are collected a few hours later. Eventually a through air mail service to and from Stockholm is to be operated.

"Bristol"-Engined Military Aircraft

At least 14 of the various types of military aircraft now on order by the Air Ministry in connection with the R.A.F. expansion scheme have Bristol engines. Orders recently placed include a large number of Gloster "Gladiator" multi-gun fighters fitted with Bristol "Mercury XI" engines, and several of the Fighter squadrons of the R.A.F. will be equipped with these machines. The "Gladiator" was described and illustrated in the "*M.M.*" of July last. Many Westland "Wallace" general purpose aeroplanes, which have Bristol "Pegasus" engines, also are on order, and one of the new Bomber squadrons will be provided with Vickers "Vildebeest" torpedo bombers, with Bristol "Pegasus III" engines, a type of military aircraft supplied to two of the squadrons stationed at Singapore.

A busy scene in the assembly shop at the Junkers aircraft factory, Dessau, Germany. The light-coloured air liners in the foreground are Junkers Ju.52/3ms, and in the background is a D.L.H. machine. This illustration is reproduced by courtesy of Junkers Flugzeug Und Motorenwerke A.-G.

Large Aerodrome for Rangoon

A new aerodrome is to be built near Rangoon at an estimated cost of about £70,000. The existing aerodrome is at Mingaladon, about 12 miles from Rangoon, and is used by Imperial Airways, Air France and K.L.M. It has become inadequate, and the new aerodrome will be larger, with a runway 1,130 yd. in length, whereas that at Mingaladon is only 800 yd. in length.

Air Transport in New Guinea

It is 10 years since the first prospectors in New Guinea forced their way inland through the jungle and discovered the rich goldfields in the Wau area of the mountainous interior. Their discovery resulted in the opening of important gold mines in that district, but until recently the lack of efficient transport for equipment and food supplies hindered full and efficient working. It took the native bearers 14 days to carry loads up from the coast town of Salamaua to Wau.

The introduction of air transport has changed all this, and the district is now served by air services that fly regularly between Salamaua and the gold mines. Each load has to be flown over jungle-clad mountains, but in spite of this one of the companies operating the services has carried a total of 30,000 tons of freight and considerably more than 30,000 passengers. In addition to ore and mining equipment, the freight aircraft carry a remarkable variety of loads. One batch of cargo recently flown up to Wau included barrels of cement, tins of kerosene, bags of rice and flour, sheets of corrugated iron, cases of tinned food and meat, and metal telegraph poles!

When the loads are landed at the aerodrome at Wau, portions are now transferred to other aeroplanes and flown on to Rama, Watut, Roaring Creek and other subsidiary landing grounds. Surveyors and prospectors are penetrating steadily farther inland, and several thousand Europeans in New Guinea now depend upon air transport for rapid conveyance and for regular receipt of their supplies.

Newcastle Airport Lighting Equipment

The municipal airport at Newcastle-upon-Tyne will shortly be provided with extensive lighting equipment. This will include a complete installation of boundary and obstruction lights, an illuminated wind indicator, three fixed and powerful floodlights, and automatic switch-control gear.

A Famous French Pioneer Airman

The recent death of M. Louis Blériot removed one of the earliest French pioneers of aviation. Many excellent monoplane types of aircraft have been produced to his designs, but it is as the first man to fly across the English Channel that he is best remembered in this country.

Blériot was born in 1873, and when in his twenties began to devote his spare time and money to designing and experimenting with aeroplanes, chiefly of the monoplane type. In spite of many failures and crashes he persevered until he won success. He accomplished his first notable flight in October 1908 when he flew from Toury to Artenay, a distance of nine miles in a Blériot monoplane. The return trip was also made by air. In 1909 he set up an aircraft establishment at Neuilly aerodrome, and the same year created a sensation by making a flight with two passengers. Interest in the man and his machine was heightened by the public exhibition of his No. 11 monoplane at the Paris Salon. This machine was only 28 ft. in span, and was fitted with a 25-h.p. Anzani three-cylinder air-cooled engine.

The same year Blériot and Latham, another enthusiast, competed for the *"Daily Mail"* £1,000 prize offered for the first successful cross-Channel flight. Latham tried first, and although he made a good take-off he eventually came down in the sea, but fortunately he was rescued. Blériot made his attempt shortly afterward and used the machine that had been shown in Paris. He took off from Baraques, near Calais, at 4.40 a.m. on 25th July, in the presence of a group of well-wishers who had come to see him start upon his great adventure. The navigating equipment of his machine was very meagre compared with that of a modern aeroplane, and did not even include a compass. He had to rely upon his spectators, therefore, to point out to him the direction of Dover as soon as he was in the air, and the French destroyer *"Escopette"* steamed across the Strait as a guide.

Blériot flew at an altitude of about 250 ft., and his speed averaged 45 m.p.h. Only a few people were about when he flew over the English coast near Dover, and a policeman on night duty was the only person who actually witnessed the airman's descent. He landed in a field at 5.20 a.m., and in doing so broke the airscrew and undercarriage of his machine. These misfortunes were negligible, however, for his success had won him a fortune. A concrete monument on which is a representation of his aeroplane now stands upon the spot where he landed.

During the next few years he made several other excellent flights, but eventually he gave up flying and concerned himself solely with aircraft design and production.

Imperial Airways liner "Delia," one of the "Diana" class, drawn up outside the Customs offices at Croydon airport. This class of aeroplane is employed on the company's London-Cologne-Zurich route. Photograph by courtesy of Imperial Airways Ltd., and Kodak Ltd.

Wind Tunnel Tests of "Flying Flea"

The criticism of the "Flying Flea" ultra-light aeroplane designed by M. Henri Mignet that has followed upon several crashes of small machines of this type gave special interest to the full-scale tests carried out recently in the wind-tunnel at the Chalais-Meudon research station, in France. The tests revealed that the safety factor of the machine can be much increased by equipping the front wing with controls to increase the angle of incidence from 9 to 14 deg. A description of the wind tunnel in which the test was made was given in the *"M.M."* of July 1935.

The latest *"Pou-du-Ciel,"* or "Flying Flea," produced by M. Mignet differs in several respects from the first of the type, as experience has shown some of the improvements necessary to make it an efficient flying machine. In the early machine the upper and lower wings overlapped, but in the latest there is a vertical gap between them. The performance of this new machine is said to be much better than that of its predecessors.

Renault "Bengali Junior" inverted, air-cooled aero engine, the type fitted in the Caudron "Aiglon" monoplane described in the article on page 518. Photograph by courtesy of Societé des Avions Caudron, France.

The Johannesburg Air Race

The Schlesinger air race from England to Johannesburg, South Africa, will not be held on the 15th of this month as originally planned, but at the end of the month. The later date will give competitors the benefit of a full moon on the night-flying stage of their trip.

Many interesting entries have been received, including that of Flt. Lt. T. Rose, who will fly a B.A. "Double Eagle," a new cabin monoplane with two D.H. "Gipsy Six" engines. Percival and Miles aircraft are expected to be well represented. It is probable that Mr. David Llewellyn and Mrs. J. Wyndham will fly a Percival "Vega Gull," and Major Allister Miller, the founder of South African Airways, has entered a "Mew Gull." A Miles "Sparrhowhawk" is to be flown by Victor Smith, the young South African airman who has flown to England to take part in the contest.

Wireless Stations on the East Africa Coast Route

Important technical surveys, carried out in connection with the forthcoming flying-boat route of Imperial Airways down the east coast of Africa, have just been completed by Captain Durrant, Superintendent of Empire Air Routes Wireless, and Mr. R. A. Munday, aviation expert of the Marconi Company. During these surveys arrangements were made for new wireless stations, containing the latest forms of equipment at eight places along the route, including Mombasa, Dar-es-Salaam, Beira and Lourenco Marques.

Capt. Durrant will next concern himself with wireless developments along the Persian Gulf sections of the England-Australia route. It is interesting to note that he was wireless officer in the British airship R.34 when she made her double flight across the Atlantic in July 1919.

Air France Traffic

During 1935 Air France carried a total of 55,664 paying passengers, 1,075 tons of freight and excess luggage, 272 tons of mail and 245 tons of newspapers. The cross-Channel service between London and Paris proved the most popular, and accounted for 16,042 of the passengers, while the quantity of freight carried on it, 413 tons, was more than double the amount on any other of the company's services. The greatest quantity of mail was transported on the Toulouse-Casablanca route, and averaged 1½ tons per week.

French West African Air Service

Chargeurs Réunis, a French air transport concern, are planning to establish a regular air service between Dakar and Pointe Noire to link up with the passenger and mail service to South America operated by Air France. They will use three Sikorsky S.43 amphibians which have been ordered specially for the new air line.

Footplate Run on an Irish Compound 2-4-0

Smart Work by 46-year-old engine

By A Railway Engineer

NEARLY all the footplate journeys that I have so far described in the *"M.M."* have been made on big modern locomotives; the veterans that have featured in the series, such as the Highland "Castles" and the Great Northern "Atlantics," are fair-sized engines even by modern standards. The run about to be described, however, was made on one of the smallest standard gauge (Irish) engines still in service, much less on express duty. But the journey has a greater interest even than this, for the engine in question, No. 57 of the Northern Counties Committee section of the L.M.S.R., is one of the few remaining two-cylinder compounds on the Worsdell-von Borries system.

L.M.S.R. (N.C.C. Section) 2-4-0 compound No. 57 "Galgorm Castle," on which the trip described in this article was made. The engine is shown outside the running sheds at Belfast.

This sturdy little engine, which bears the name *"Galgorm Castle,"* was built as long ago as 1890 by Beyer Peacock and Co. Ltd. At that time Mr. T. W. Worsdell was Locomotive Superintendent of the North Eastern Railway, and his two-cylinder compounds were greatly distinguishing themselves. Mr. Bowman Malcolm, the Locomotive Engineer of the Belfast and Northern Counties Railway, as it was then, decided to try some engines of the same general type; and they proved so successful that no further simple express engines were built for the N.C.C. until 1914. *"Galgorm Castle"* has one high-pressure cylinder 16 in. in diameter and one low pressure 23¼ in. in diameter, each with a stroke of 24 in., and both of course inside the frames. About 10 years ago the engine was fitted with a new boiler a little larger and pitched rather higher than the original, but otherwise she remains substantially as built 46 years ago.

Cab view of one of the 2-4-0 compounds. The low-pitched boiler with the large lookout windows above it is in striking contrast to the cab_layout of modern engines.

Only one of the class, No. 56, which is illustrated on the next page, remains entirely unaltered, though the style of painting has been changed twice since the engine was built. Before the Belfast and Northern Counties Railway was taken over by the English Midland Railway, the engines were painted a bright myrtle green picked out with red and yellow lining, and all had polished brass domes. Then came the new livery that was adopted under the Midland regime. It was known officially as "invisible green," but the actual colour was a dark brownish olive. Finally, when the Midland, and with it of course the N.C.C. section, became part of the L.M.S.R. in 1923, the colour was changed to Midland red. Whereas on the parent system only the crack express locomotives are painted red, on the N.C.C. this fine livery is borne by all engines.

It is strange that these little 2–4–0s, which were the first compounds built for the line, should be the last to survive. The more powerful 4–4–0s that were put on the road in 1903 have all been converted to simples of a type almost identical in appearance with the "Castle" class, a footplate run on one of which I described in the *"M.M."* for February last. A point of exceptional interest about these rebuilds is that they use the original valve gear, and this gear was Walschaerts. It was fitted to all Mr. Malcolm's compounds, and must have been one of the earliest applications of the gear in the British Isles.

For some time now *"Galgorm Castle,"* with two others of the same class, has been stationed at Cookstown, County Tyrone; that shed has the unique distinction of housing only three engines, and all of them two-cylinder compounds. Their most important turn is the working of the 12.40 p.m. through train to Belfast, and returning with the sharply-timed 4.20 p.m. down; these trains travel on the N.C.C. main line to Londonderry as far as Cookstown Junction. Between Belfast and Dunadry the 4.20 p.m. runs at real express speed to a schedule as fast as that of the *"Portrush Flyer."*

"Galgorm Castle" is in every way a contemporary of the famous engines in York Railway Museum, and riding on her footplate seemed almost like stepping back into the nineteenth century. But at the same time the working of this compound engine was intensely interesting. The regulator is of the single-handle type that the driver pulls over towards him when starting up; it has two ports, like the "Moguls" and other N.C.C. engines, though this feature was introduced when the larger boiler was fitted. The small port or "first regulator" does not give simple working as in the case of the Midland compounds, but is used for light steaming; these N.C.C. engines are all started up full compound. The reversing gear is of the notched lever type, and one operation only is necessary to link up the valves in both high and low-pressure cylinders. The fire-box seemed tiny by modern fashions.

On the occasion of my trip Driver Harkness and Fireman Nelson of Cookstown shed were in charge. The load was of course a very light one by present-day standards—three bogie coaches weighing 85 tons all told—but counting the tender as part of the train the little engine was pulling quite 3½ times its own weight. Working on the same proportion an L.M.S.R. 4-6-2 "Princess Royal" would have 300 tons behind the tender.

We got away from Belfast in true *"Portrush Flyer"* style. Driver Harkness almost immediately opened out to practically full regulator, and for the first hundred yards or so the engine was working in full forward gear, with 79 per cent. cut-off in the high-pressure cylinder and 82 per cent. in the low. With only one low-pressure cylinder there are but two exhausts per revolution of the driving wheels, instead of the usual four in a two-cylinder simple engine. This unfamiliar effect is very curious, and to anyone watching from the lineside it gives a most deceptive idea of the speed at which the train is approaching.

As the speed rose these isolated exhausts developed into a tremendous noise, but about half a mile out the lever was brought three notches back, giving 62 per cent. cut-off in the high-pressure cylinder and 67 in the low; in an ordinary simple this would be equivalent to about 40 per cent. cut-off. We accelerated in fine style along the level beside Belfast Lough, and passed Whitehouse 3.3 miles out in 5¼ minutes at 49 m.p.h., but then came the formidable ascent over the Greenisland loop line, where the gradient is 1 in 76 for 3 miles.

L.M.S.R. (N.C.C. Section) No. 51, one of the three remaining 2-4-0 compounds mentioned in this article. This photograph shows very clearly the tablet exchange apparatus on the cab side.

As we passed Whiteabbey the reversing lever was advanced one notch, thereby increasing cut-off to 68½ per cent. in the high pressure cylinder and 73 per cent. in the low. Climbing splendidly over the stately reinforced concrete viaduct at Bleach Green, speed settled down to a steady 32 m.p.h. on the steepest part of the bank. This was really fine work; it compares in a most interesting way with the run on the *"North Atlantic Express"* that I described in the January number of the *"M.M."* On the latter run one of the powerful "Moguls" hauling 190 tons fell to 36½ m.p.h. on this same ascent, even though being worked with full regulator and 40 per cent. cut-off. So *"Galgorm Castle"* passed Ballyclare Junction, which marks the end of the worst climbing, in 13½ minutes from Belfast, 8.2 miles; this was half a minute less than the schedule of the *"Portrush Flyer."*

After passing Ballyclare Junction a very severe permanent way slowing was in force, where speed had to be reduced to 15 m.p.h.; but just beyond this point the long descent to Antrim begins and speed was regained very quickly on the 1 in 180 grade. In barely 1¾ miles we accelerated from 15 to 57 m.p.h., and on passing Doagh, Driver Harkness changed over to the first regulator, for the only time on the whole run, and the lever was brought still farther back, giving cut-offs of 48 per cent. in the high-pressure and 54 in the low-pressure cylinder.

This photograph of 2-4-0 No. 56 is of special interest, as it shows the original condition of these compounds, as built in 1890. The small boiler and the generally diminutive characteristics will be noted.

Riding on a 2–4–0 engine at 60 m.p.h. and over can be a tempestuous business, and between Doagh and our first stop, Dunadry, *"Galgorm Castle"* really ran wild. She did not become violently rough like some engines of which I have previously written, but developed a peculiar bouncing action. Near Templepatrick speed rose to 65 m.p.h., and at this pace the slightest curve set up a hearty sideways roll in addition! So we reached Dunadry, 15.9 miles from Belfast, in 22¾ minutes—three-quarters of a minute early despite the check. Our net time of 21½ minutes gave an average speed of 44½ m.p.h., a fine figure, including as it did the Greenisland ascent.

Restarting, I was treated to the rare spectacle of a steam locomotive being driven absolutely "all out"; wide open regulator, full forward gear. The engine was a little bit sluggish for the first 50 yards, but after that we got away in tremendous style, and about three-quarters of a mile out the lever was pulled four notches back, giving 48 per cent. cut-off in the high-pressure cylinder and 54 per cent. in the low. We passed Muckamore, 1.4 miles, in the remarkable time of 2½ minutes, and with a top speed of 53 m.p.h. reached Antrim 3.4 miles in 5¼ minutes—a smart time over so short a distance. Inclusive of the stop at Dunadry the 19.3 miles from Belfast had taken 28½ minutes.

From Antrim onward we called at all stations, but the run became more interesting than ever. Few railway enthusiasts realise the strenuous and exacting work required on the footplate with a stopping train, especially where, as in this case, the station to station timings are tight. Full regulator and full forward gear was used in getting away from every station, but the reversing lever was usually brought to the third or fourth notch after the first half mile or so; on every section, however, full regulator was used from start to finish.

Such a run demands not only skilful enginemanship, but real physical effort on the part of the driver. A regulator under steam takes some shifting, and a notched lever reversing gear is worse; both controls were being altered every few minutes, and I noticed that *"Galgorm Castle"* had been fitted with a steel plate on the front of the reversing rack, so that by putting one foot against it the driver can get more purchase on the lever. Very sound judgment is needed in stopping at intermediate stations, for the platforms are short, and even with a three-coach train care is needed in drawing up. At the same time whole minutes may be lost by too slow an approach, but on this journey I was astonished at the way in which Driver Harkness maintained full speed until the latest possible moment and then made a perfect stop, every time. Added to all this, in the one and a half minutes we stood at Cookstown Junction the crew actually found time to take water!

How well the strenuous task of working this train was discharged is shown by the very smart runs made on the branch. We had to pick up a four-wheeled van at Antrim, which meant backing right into the sidings of the adjoining Great Northern station; it made us 3 minutes late away, but sure enough we were into Magherafelt on time. The first lap of 3.1 miles to Cookstown Junction took 5¾ minutes, speed rising to 49 m.p.h. on the 1 in 213 rise. The branch is single-tracked, but tablets were of course exchanged by hand while standing at the stations.

From Cookstown Junction the branch swings away westward from the main line, and in the first short run of 2 miles, to Randalstown, we attained 48 m.p.h.; this length was completed in 4¼ minutes. On the next section the line approaches the shores of Lough Neagh. This great lake is very wide, and being surrounded by low-lying country looks just like the sea; far away to the south could be seen the mountains of County Armagh, and on a serene evening in late spring with scarcely a cloud in the sky it made a very lovely picture. The freshness of the trees and the brilliance of gorse newly in bloom formed a serious counter-attraction to the exploits of *"Galgorm Castle,"* which by now was racing along in gallant style. We ran the 5½ miles from Randalstown to Staffordstown in 8¼ minutes with a well-sustained maximum speed of 57½ m.p.h., and some even faster running was made on the next section, where the 3¾ miles on to Toome took only 5¾ minutes start to stop; in this short distance speed rose to 58½ miles per hour.

(Continued at foot of next page)

Footplate Terms Explained

The Economical Use of Steam

THE articles by *"A Railway Engineer,"* describing footplate trips, are among the most popular that have ever appeared in the *"M.M."* Large numbers of readers have written to express their keen enjoyment of these articles and to demand more. Among these letters have been some from younger readers asking for explanations of some of the expressions used by the author, and in order to make matters clear to every reader we deal in this article with the points that have most often been raised in correspondence.

A phrase that is often used by *"A Railway Engineer"* refers to running at a "cut-off" of so much per cent. This phrase is connected with the supply of steam to the cylinders. Steam is not admitted to each cylinder throughout the movement of the piston from one end to the other. Instead it is cut off by means of the valves after a certain proportion of the stroke has been completed. The point at which this occurs is always expressed as a percentage of the stroke of the pistons, and is described briefly as the cut-off. Thus a "cut-off of 25 per cent." means that the steam supply ceases when the pistons have each completed 25 per cent., or a quarter, of their stroke. For the remaining three-quarters of the stroke the steam already in the cylinders is xpanded, driving the piston forward or backward until it reaches the end of its travel. The expanded steam is then exhausted as the piston makes its return journey.

A typical footplate view showing tne regulator handle, screw reverse gear, driver's brake valve, the firehole door and numerous other important fittings. The water gauges can be seen, one at each side of the regulator handle. Photograph by Mr. O. S. Nock, Bushey.

This expansive use of steam is much more economical than its admission throughout the piston stroke. The degree of expansion permitted is regulated by the valve gear and is controlled from the cab by the driver. The apparatus provided for this purpose on modern locomotives invariably takes the form of a wheel or handle on the driver's side of the cab, operating on a screwed rod connected to the valve gear. On the standard or bracket supporting the wheel and screw, it is now usual to fit a scale marking the position of the valve gear from full forward to full backward gear. As the wheel or handle is revolved, an indicator or pointer is traversed on the screw along the scale, and from this the degree of cut-off can be seen.

The term "notching up" is frequently used to denote the action of shortening the cut-off, or making it occur earlier in the stroke. This term is a reminder of the fact that at one time the valve gear was controlled from the footplate by means of a tall lever mounted on a notched quadrant, a catch handle fitted to the lever allowing a block to engage in any one of the notches from full forward to full backward gear, and thus to hold the lever in the desired position. As the notches have to be spaced relatively far apart, this method of valve gear control does not allow of such a fine degree of adjustment as is possible with a screw gear. The lever arrangement is still found on older locomotive designs, and also is used on shunting engines, where quick reversing is a necessity.

The term "cut-off" in descriptions of footplate trips often is associated with the words "full regulator." The regulator valve of a locomotive admits the steam from the boiler to the main steam pipe, and so to the cylinders; and the driver opens it to the extent required by means of a long handle, known as the regulator handle, that is more or less centrally placed and is one of the most conspicuous fittings in the cab of a locomotive. "Full regulator" means that the handle is pulled over to its limit, opening the steam admission valve as widely as possible. Sometimes the regulator valve is of special construction, with two ports, one small and one large, and one or the other is brought into use according to the setting of the regulator handle. The "first port," or "first regulator," is used for light steaming, and the "second port," or "main regulator," is brought into action for the fast and heavy work necessary on the level or on rising gradients.

The regulator handle may stand up above its spindle, as in the cab of the 2–4–0 compound illustrated on page 504. With large high-pitched boilers the spindle is necessarily high up in the cab, however, and the handle then hangs downwards at a convenient angle for the driver's management, as is seen in the illustration on this page. A short tail-piece is formed at the spindle end of the handle and this usually works over a small quadrant provided with stops at each end. The position of the tail-piece between these stops does not always accurately represent the degree of regulator opening, however, and in such cases adjustments of the regulator position have to be made by the driver more by the "feel" than by the "eye."

The dials of the pressure, steam heating and vacuum gauges are sometimes referred to as "clocks," their circular faces and the moving fingers making comparison with the ordinary time-piece irresistible. The first of these three gauges shows the driver what steam pressure, in lb. per sq. in., he has to work with, and the fireman's job is to keep this pressure up to the working limit, or as near it as possible. The steam heating gauge shows the steam pressure in the pipe leading to the train; before entering this pipe the steam passes through a valve that reduces its pressure. Two pointers on the vacuum gauge show how little pressure there is in the train pipe and in the vacuum chamber respectively. Its record is given in inches, corresponding to the scale of a barometer.

The water gauge is of different form. It consists of a glass tube connected to two cocks mounted on the boiler back or doorplate, so that the height of water in it indicates the level of the water in the boiler. The gauge is commonly referred to as the "glass," and the term "half glass," for instance, means that the water is half-way up the gauge tube and thus stands at about half the normal working level in the boiler.

Another locomotive term connected with the fuelling and watering of the engine is "dip," the word used to denote the water scoop that is lowered from the tender to pick up water from track troughs.

Footplate Run—*(Continued from previous page)*

Immediately after leaving Toome the railway crosses the outlet from Lough Neagh; this is the River Bann, which flows due north to enter the Atlantic beyond Coleraine. A lively run was made on to Castledawson, 4¼ miles in 6½ minutes with a top speed of 54 m.p.h.; on this section the lever was not brought back beyond the third notch. The last section is all uphill; ahead is the splendid height of Slieve Gallion and there are rolling hills stretching far away to the south. The 2¼ miles into Magherafelt took 4¾ minutes, and we arrived almost on the stroke of 5.33 p.m.

From here it is only 10 miles on to Cookstown, but I was bound for Coleraine, via the Derry Central line. Thus finished an excellent trip. It illustrates the strenuous work needed to operate a stopping train, but is chiefly of note as showing what these historic little compounds can do. Their days are numbered, however, for in addition to the three 2–4–0s, only one other standard gauge compound express engine remains, the 7 ft. 4–4–0 *"Parkmount."*

How Locomotives are Cleaned

Spraying with Hot Water at High Pressure

THERE are few finer sights than a magnificent modern locomotive that has been polished up in readiness for a long and speedy run at the head of a famous train. A well-groomed engine is a source of delight to the railway enthusiast, and gives even the most casual observer or traveller an impression of smartness and efficiency on the part of the company owning it.

Most drivers and firemen commence their careers as engine cleaners, working in gangs under the general supervision of a chargeman cleaner. The materials used are simple when cleaning is carried out by hand, as it is almost exclusively in this country. Cleaning oil is drawn from storage tanks at the sheds, and is applied by means of the familiar hand cloths that appear to be part and parcel of the equipment of every locomotive man! The oil used includes paraffin for removing dirt, and the degree of finish imparted to the wiped surface depends a great deal on the condition of the paint, and also on the skill exercised by the cleaners.

Of what we may term the spectacular parts of the locomotive, as opposed to the working parts, perhaps the easiest portions to deal with are the cab and tank sides, splashers and similar details. The boiler is the most prominent part of the modern locomotive, and if its jacket is in good condition and well cleaned the whole of the engine has a good appearance. Unfortunately the upper surface of the boiler is liable to suffer from the effects of smoke and soot from the chimney, and therefore tends to blacken on an engine that is finished in colour. The surface underneath the boiler barrel is protected from smoke from the chimney, but is liable to be blackened in patches from making acquaintance with the small flares used by enginemen and shed staff as aids to inspection. Dirt tends to accumulate also at any joint or raised surface, such as the bands encircling the boiler casing, especially if wiping is carried out across them.

A cleaner at work on the boiler of an L.N.E.R. "Pacific." The upper part of the boiler requires vigorous treatment, as it becomes blackened by the soot and smoke from the chimney.

The tender sides present a broad flat unbroken surface that at first sight would appear to be ideal for good cleaning effects. It is difficult to maintain a permanently good effect on the sides, however, for several reasons. Dust thrown up by the engine in course of travelling settles on the tender sides, which also are subject to splashes when water is picked up. Coal dust from the footplate is blown back when on the run, and the tender is so near the footplate that it collects ash when fire cleaning or fire dropping is carried out. A point of interest is that oil is frequently flung off the rapidly moving rods of modern locomotives having outside valve gear, when travelling at high speed. This is blown back in streaks on to the tender, and sometimes on to the train, where dirt sticks to it.

An interesting practice is now followed on the L.M.S.R. with a view to preserving the finish of a cleaned engine. This consists in applying a special preparation developed after a considerable amount of work on the part of the technical research authorities at Derby. The preparation is viscous, and smells strongly of ammonia, and it deposits a coating of wax on the cleaned surfaces. A splendid finish is given to engines treated with it, and it helps to preserve their paintwork as well as making them easier to clean subsequently. Two kinds of this "wax" are in use. One is for black engines, and the other is employed on the more select classes of engines that are finished in red, such as the "Princesses," "Royal Scots" and "Jubilees."

Cleaning a large express engine thoroughly involves much time and labour. To make a big tender engine presentable means a day's work for perhaps three or four cleaners, and they will use anything up to 48 hand cloths on the job! It is not surprising therefore to find that efforts have been made to speed up the work, especially in America and Canada, by the introduction of spray cleaning. Steam and hot water under pressure are projected on to the dirty surfaces by means of a special portable spraying gun, and its forcible application removes the accumulated dirt in a fraction of the time required for hand wiping. Similar equipment has been experimented with on the L.N.E.R., and with it two men can completely clean an engine in a short time. As time goes on it will be interesting to see whether the mechanisation of running shed equipment is extended to include the installation of such apparatus as a regular feature.

Perhaps the most interesting application of this form of cleaning comes from Canada, where a special engine cleaning plant has been installed at the Turcot Engine Shed of the Canadian National Railways in Montreal. In this the engine is driven past the installation while a number of jets spray a cleaning fluid on to all parts. The fluid is applied at high pressure. It is a mixture of hot water and a special compound that dissolves oil and grease, which is washed away, and a light film of wax is left on the clean surface.

The operation of the plant is simple and automatic. After closing the cab windows and ventilator, the man responsible for the cleaning takes the engine slowly over the length of track past the apparatus. When the engine reaches a certain spot the jets come into play, and these only cease operation when the last wheel of the tender has passed off the apparatus, and the whole length of the engine has been subjected to a thorough cleaning. If certain parts of the engine are particularly dirty, and require more attention than the rest, the engine is moved more slowly than usual for these to be dealt with. This in no way affects the working of the apparatus, the jets remaining in action all the time. Passenger locomotives are wiped down by hand after passing through the plant, but this is not considered necessary with shunting engines.

Modern locomotives are far less "showy" than the engines of former days, which carried many copper and brass fittings to be polished up. Copper-capped chimneys and brass domes, safety valve casings and splasher beadings were favourite forms of decoration, but they added very largely to the labour of cleaning. In order to reduce the amount of attention necessary, it became the custom to paint over such details, although the G.W.R. still retain polished copper and brass fittings on their principal express locomotives. In recent years there also has been a tendency to abandon the use of colour for all except the most important locomotive classes.

ENGINEERING NEWS

Transporting a 20-Ton Glass Disc by Rail

A 20-ton glass disc 200 in. in diameter and 26 in. thick was recently conveyed by railway from the Corning Glass Works, Corning, New York, to Pasadena, California, where it will be prepared for installation in a 200-in. reflecting telescope, by far the largest ever constructed. The casting of the giant glass disc was described and illustrated on page 512 of the "*M.M.*" for September, 1935.

The transportation of this valuable scientific freight across the United States was undertaken only after more than a year of planning by packing and transporting specialists. The disc was packed in a steel crate that weighed 10 tons, and was constructed of ½ in. plate steel reinforced by heavy angle and channel section girders. During the journey across the continent great care had to be exercised in operating the special train, owing to the fact that the bottom edge of the crate was only 6 in. above the rails, while the top had only a 3-in. clearance in some of the tunnels and bridges along the route. The train was a New York Central three car special.

Dialling Ships at Sea

A new system of telephony for use in calling ships at sea has been developed in America. Under the new system each ship has a three-figure number assigned to it, and only the particular ship it is desired to call receives the message. When an operator wishes to speak to a ship he simply dials its number, as if using an automatic telephone, and this action sends out a series of tone pulses that are received by all the ships within range. The ship called is the only one that receives an audible signal, however, and in it a bell warns the operator, who picks his handset off the hook and replies in the usual manner. When the telephone conversation is finished the handset is returned to its hook, and the call signal receiving apparatus is automatically reset.

A Telford Bridge to be Preserved

A stone arch bridge built by Thomas Telford to carry the Glasgow-Carlisle road over the River Clyde, is to be closed to traffic and preserved as a permanent example of his work. It is only 18 ft. 6 in. wide and is unsuitable for present day traffic. The road is to be diverted and a new ferroconcrete bridge with a single span of 96 ft. is to be constructed. The width between parapets of the modern bridge will be 60 ft. The whole scheme will cost £58,000.

An Edgar Allen hot saw cutting red hot metal at the Glengarnock works of Colville's Ltd., to whom we are indebted for the illustration.

World's Longest Aerial Railway

The first portion of a new aerial railway that when completed will be the longest and highest of its kind in the world is now in operation in the north of Italy. It commences at Cervinia, and goes up the mountain ridge that forms the Swiss-Italian frontier towards the Matterhorn. The section now completed ends at the ski-ing runs on the Maison Plain, but eventually the cableway will extend to the Theodule Pass, 11,000 ft. above sea level, from which the stiffest part of the climb to the summit of the Matterhorn 4,000 ft. above it begins.

10 Tunnels Under New York River

Work will commence soon at New York on the construction of a new tunnel that is to be driven under the East River between Manhattan Island and Queensborough, on Long Island. There are already nine tunnels underneath the East River, and five bridges across it, and another bridge is now being built. The existing tunnels carry only railway traffic, however. The new one will be the first under this river to accommodate motor vehicles, and will provide a direct route between New Jersey and Queensborough. It is expected that the new tunnel will be completed in time to serve as a means of transport to the great World Fair that is to be held on Flushing Meadows, Long Island, in 1939.

Colours for Submarines

In future British submarines are to be painted to suit the particular light reflecting properties of the water in which they are intended to operate. Until now they have all been painted grey-green, but experience has shown that the vessels show up clearly in some seas when painted this colour, although in others they are not easily visible. Under the new system submarines for service in the Atlantic will be painted green-grey, and those to be stationed in the Mediterranean royal blue. Black appears to be the most suitable colour for submarines operating mainly in the Red Sea.

Giant South African Dynamite Factory

Modderfontein, near Johannesburg, will shortly possess the largest dynamite factory in the world. An enormous plant already exists there and it is now to be extended by new works on which £1,000,000 is to be spent. These will include at least one new factory and additions to the ammonia plant, which is now inadequate to meet demands.

With the exception of the great steel works at Pretoria, the dynamite factory employs more workpeople than any factory in South Africa, and at present is turning out 800,000 cases of dynamite each year. When the proposed extensions are completed the output will reach 1,600,000 cases annually.

A Titan Crane for Harbour Work

The upper illustration on this page shows a 90-ton Titan Crane that has been specially built by Werf Gusto Ltd., Schiedam, Holland, for service in the harbour of Las Palmas, in the Canary Islands. It is intended for placing concrete blocks required in the construction of quay walls and piers, and is of the travelling type with portal legs that can be turned through an angle of 90 degrees. The load is suspended from a travelling trolley that is moved along the jib by means of winding mechanism. The blocks can be deposited in any required position, and can be lowered to a depth of about 63 ft. below the water level.

The 90-ton electrically driven crane described on this page, at work on harbour construction at Las Palmas, in the Canary Islands. Photograph by courtesy of Werf Gusto Ltd., Schiedam, Holland.

A New Use for Stainless Steel

Stainless steel has been applied to a great variety of purposes, ranging from the making of cutlery to the lining of the interiors of giant milk tanks and high-pressure steam pipes. One of its most recent applications is in facing two Venturi-flume meters that have been constructed by the Derwent Valley Water Board at Yorkshire Bridge in connection with a new reservoir at Ashopton, Derbyshire. The meters are used for measuring the flow of water in the river, and the lower illustration on this page shows the two flumes, one of which is in the background and is partly submerged, while the other is in the foreground and is seen dry. It is important in meters of this kind that the measuring throat should maintain its original contour, and stainless steel is being used in order to prevent changes due to erosion and accumulations of moss, algae and other fresh-water growths.

The steel facing is bedded on concrete, and is constructed of Firth-Vickers "Staybrite" steel plates, covering a total area of approximately 320 sq. ft. The length overall measured along the bottom is 26ft. 4in. The plates were all very carefully shaped before despatch from the makers' works, and numbered to facilitate erection.

Two Venturi-flume meters on the River Derwent that have been lined with stainless steel. That seen in the foreground of our illustration is dry, and the other is partly submerged. Photograph by courtesy of Industrial Units Ltd., Sheffield.

Four 82,500 kVA Generators for Boulder Dam

Although construction of the great Boulder Dam in the United States of America is now completed, engineers are still at work installing the mighty generating plant. This includes four huge hydro-electric generators, each of 82,500 kVA capacity, all of which are expected to be in operation before the end of this year. These machines are twice as large as any of their kind previously constructed, and they will supply electricity to many towns and cities over a wide area, including Los Angeles.

Giant Omnibuses for Moscow

In the near future two new systems of transport are to be introduced in Moscow. In one of these, giant buses 34 ft. 6 in. in length and capable of carrying 100 passengers will be used. The bodies of these vehicles will be made of steel sections welded together and faced with aluminium. The windows will be of unbreakable glass, and the doors will be wide enough to allow three persons to enter at the same time.

In addition to these vehicles, a number of semi-trolley electric goods trucks are to be introduced. These will be able to operate either on power taken from overhead conductor wires, or from batteries carried in the trucks themselves. When using the overhead trolley wires they will be able to travel at speeds up to 30 m.p.h., with a full load, but the maximum speed, when operating on their own storage batteries, will be 10 m.p.h.

* * * *

The Government have granted to the Anglo-American Oil Company, Ltd., marketers of Esso products, licences to search for petroleum covering nearly 500 square miles in the south of England.

World's Highest Multiple Arch Dam

A fine multiple arch dam that when completed will be the highest of its kind in the world, is to be built in the United States of America. It will form part of an important reclamation scheme that is being carried out in connection with Salt River, and will be built across the Verde River in Arizona. It will have a height of 270 ft., and a crest length of 750 ft., and will consist of 10 reinforced concrete arches supported by nine hollow reinforced concrete buttresses spaced 60 ft. apart. The new structure will be known as the Bartlett Dam and will cost £450,000.

A New Canadian Industry

The manufacture of a peculiar substance known as rock wool, which is one of the most effective insulation materials yet discovered, is now being carried on in two separate plants in Ontario. At one of these plants electric furnaces are used in conjunction with a special mechanical spraying device for converting molten rock into fibres, from which is produced a long-fibred wool that weighs from three to four pounds per cubic foot. The product made at the other plant is a heavier short-fibred material. The greater part of the material from the two plants is being used for building insulation and soundproofing, and for the acoustical treatment of offices, theatres and broadcasting studios.

Lighting and Cooking by Bottled Gas

Many of the crofters of the Western Highlands of Scotland are now cooking, heating and lighting their homes by means of bottled butane gas, referred to on page 463 of the August Magazine. The gas is distributed in liquid form in steel containers, which when full, weigh under 50 lb. and contain enough gas to last a family of three for six to 10 weeks, and will keep an ordinary gas mantle alight for 450 hours.

Upon installation the consumer is supplied with two containers of gas and one regulator. The regulator is attached to one of the containers and this is then ready for service, the other container being held in reserve until the first is exhausted. When the first container is empty, the regulator is disconnected and attached to the full container. Before the second container has become exhausted a further full container is delivered to the consumer, and the empty is taken away for refilling.

There is actually nothing new about this gas, for it has been used for many years in remote districts of America and on the Continent.

"Things to Come"

A World Ruled by Scientists and Engineers

By I. O. Evans

WHAT will the world be like at the end of the present century? That is a question all Meccano boys must have asked themselves, and they will find a fascinatingly interesting answer to it in the film *"Things to Come,"* which has already appeared in London and is now being shown all over the country. In it H. G. Wells, the famous writer of scientific romances, forecasts a world ruled by engineers and scientists, who rebuild bombed cities and reconstruct civilisation after a devastating war. They banish poverty, abolish war altogether and make life complete and happy with the aid of marvellous inventions. Not content with mastery over their own Earth, they turn to other worlds, and their crowning achievement is a great space gun to fire a shell to pass round the Moon.

One of the aeroplanes used by the engineers' government is shown descending near "Everytown," the city in which most of the scenes in the film take place. It is the first of the inventions we see in the picture, a "small new 1970 type" with its wings curved back like a swallow's. It is jet black and glossy, built of some new alloy, and its method of flight is new. The whole thing is "different" and strange, and the uniform worn by its pilot is equally remarkable, for he is clothed in black gas-proof material with great gauntlets, and his chest and head are enclosed in a huge circular shield that makes him look over seven feet high. This shield is a 1970 gas mask, and when he swings the visor down to talk, it looks like a black halo behind him.

The airmen have their headquarters at a great airport at Basra, where they are seen loading their machines and crowding up the huge gangways into them in readiness for conflict with a war lord in "Everytown," who is preparing to resist the new government of scientists and engineers. In the picture we go back there and from a drift of cloud across the sky we hear the distinctive throb of some new type of engine. Then, sweeping out of the cloud, huge and black and terrible, comes a great bomber. It flies very steadily and with an air of being irresistible; it looks less like an aeroplane than an air battleship. Behind it come others, with their many roaring propellers and their far-spreading wings.

The old-style aeroplanes of "Everytown's" war lord cannot resist these mighty creations of the engineer and fall in flames, or are forced to earth. The pilots of the government fleet pull levers that release bombs containing neither explosives nor poison nor disease germs, but a harmless gas that produces sleep, and then hundreds of airmen leap out of the machines and descend by means of parachutes, to disarm the sleeping people.

These great aeroplanes are fascinating to watch, but the giant machines by which the new "Everytown" is built are no less attractive. Great mechanical excavators burrow into the hills, blasting and hurling rocks aside. As the illustration on this page shows, they are like nothing we use to-day. They consist of immense cylinders, moving on huge tractor-carriers and supplied with explosives and power by great flexible steel-ribbed tubes. Below them are the control rooms that house their crew, and these seem small and unimportant in comparison with the machines themselves. Nozzles like the muzzles of great guns project jets of explosive liquid against the surface rock. Then spider-like metal arms move great rods of carbon close against it. There is the flash of an electric spark and an explosion, and masses of rock crumble, break away, and crash heavily down as the huge machine recoils upon its springs.

Giant excavating machines at work on the mountain side, preparing the site for the new underground city of "Everytown," the chief scene of events in the film "Things to Come."

The houses of the new city are built of huge sheets of metal made by pouring the molten material into a great container, carried on a wheeled trolley. The sides of the mould are supported by pistons moving in narrow cylinders, and as they separate they reveal a thin sheet of glowing metal, newly-cast and fit for use as soon as it has cooled. This slides along on a carrier, while the walls of the mould return to their place ready for a new sheet to be cast. The work of erection is carried out by a machine that seems to be a combination of a tank and a crane. From the front of its body projects a long arm, tipped with a suction pad that is pressed against one of the great metal sheets, to grip it and lift it high into the air before placing it against a metal framework.

Thus the homes of the city are built, the wall of a whole apartment being placed in position in one operation. The people dwell in flats each provided with a balcony overlooking the streets. The new "Everytown" is not a city of skyscrapers or of concrete blocks of dwelling-houses and offices, however, for it is built, not up into the air, but underground, leaving the surface of the earth unspoilt for cultivation, games and sports. In its streets are moving ways, a series of platforms like those at the top and bottom of a modern tube escalator, by which its people can travel about conveniently. Overhead are railplanes, swift torpedo-shaped cars running on rails suspended from girders of latticed steel, and the flats and the different levels of the town are reached by lifts travelling in transparent shafts. All work in silence, for it has been recognised that noise in a machine is a sign of waste.

The giant mould used for casting the huge metal sheets of which the buildings of "Everytown" are made.

The new "Everytown" is a place where most of us would like to live. But some of its citizens think it "unnatural" and long for the "good old days." They are distressed because new things are always being done and new inventions made. A great gun has been cast to fire shots round the Moon, and a young man and a girl are to make the first adventurous journey into space. Thousands of volunteers have clamoured for this privilege, but an artist who hates "all this progress" uses the city's system of broadcast-television to rouse the people to smash the great space-gun, and so put an end to the rule of the scientists and engineers. Stepping into a dark studio, he waves his hand to the electrician to show that he is ready. As the studio light flashes on, his voice is heard in receiving sets all over the world and his image appears on their screens.

The great space gun designed to shoot a shell carrying human beings on a voyage round the moon. The shell is lowered into the gun by means of the hammerhead crane on the right.

The people are impressed by his arguments and rush off to destroy the great gun. Word is taken to the leading engineers; and the young people who have volunteered for the expedition are anxious to be fired into space at once before the mob can do any damage. They set off for the gun in a helicopter, looking something like an Autogiro with a closed-in torpedo-shaped body. Really its principle is very different; for during flight the horizontal screw above it is driven, not by air-pressure, but directly by an engine. As the pilot moves a switch the screw revolves, and the helicopter rises vertically and hovers in the air, noiseless except for the whirring of its screw. The tail-screw now propels it forward through the clouds until it reaches the space-gun, and as it sinks to the ground the great girders and cables and machinery around seem to be rising past it.

The gun itself is a triumph of engineering. Supported by immense shock-absorbers and pointing vertically upward, it towers high into the air, and beside it stands a complicated mass of lattice-girders, with a swinging arm to load it. The whole thing looks as though giants had been experimenting with a super-Meccano set. The engineer and the adventurers travel upward in one of the transparent lifts to the loading platform. The great shell is lowered to their level and with a purring of motors its great steel door swings open. The two young people who are to travel in it are strapped inside to supports, which they are to clutch with all their muscles tensed to break the shock of the discharge. The door is shut, and the shell is lifted slowly into the air.

Now it is a race against time; the mob who wish to destroy the complicated machinery that actuates the gun are scrambling down the cliffs and rushing towards its base. The moving arm of the loading tower swings the shell round until it is exactly above the muzzle. The great pistons of the shock-absorbers slide out ready to take the recoil, the shell vanishes into the mouth of the gun, and the grip that held it returns empty and the moving arm swings clear to one side. In a concussion chamber, safe from the shock of the discharge, the engineer has his hand on the firing-switch, but there is a clock before him and he dare not throw the switch until the proper moment, lest the shell, instead of circling the Moon and returning to Earth, be lost forever in outer space. Its two young passengers clutch their supports, tense with expectation, not knowing whether the next moment will find them dragged ignominously out to face the scorn of the crowd, smashed lifeless to the floor by the concussion as the gun is fired, or drifting weightless but unhurt about the shell as it moves swiftly through space. Meanwhile the mob have entered the control tower—but it would spoil the story to say more.

This exciting scene is the climax of a film suggesting many mechanical marvels of the future that will give Meccano engineers new ideas for model-building.

Liverpool to Dublin by "*Lady Leinster*"

Fine Work by Veteran Steamer

By O. S. Nock, B.Sc., D.I.C.

A CHAIN of unusual circumstances combined to make this cross-channel trip of the most exceptional interest. In the ordinary way the night Irish steamers sail from Liverpool landing stage, and the simultaneous departure, at 10.15 p.m., of the Belfast and Dublin boats provides the fascinating spectacle that I described when writing of the "*Ulster Queen*" in the "*M.M.*" for October 1935. On this occasion, however, the Cunard White Star liner "*Samaria*" was sailing from the landing stage at about 10 p.m., and so the Dublin steamer left from Gladstone Dock, three miles down the river and right opposite New Brighton.

I was interested to find that our ship was the "*Lady Leinster*," whose departure from Liverpool I had previously watched from the bridge of the "*Ulster Queen*." She was berthed in the most southerly branch of the dock, and although it was after 10 p.m. there was still sufficient light to distinguish the colour of her funnels, that brilliant grass green that gives the British and Irish Steam Packet Company's ships such a distinctive appearance. The Gladstone Dock is used principally by the Canadian Pacific and Cunard White Star lines, and berthed just ahead of the "*Lady Leinster*" was a 16,000-ton C.P.R. liner, the "*Montcalm*."

It was just before the Whitsun holidays, and traffic for Ireland was extremely heavy. Most of the connecting trains were running in duplicate, and it was well after our advertised departure time when the last of the vans bringing passengers' luggage raced up alongside the berth. When I met Captain Hawkins on the bridge a few minutes later he sounded a note of tremendous enthusiasm. "She's the finest vessel on the British coast" were almost his first words to me, and the "*Lady Leinster*" went a long way towards justifying such a claim by making a magnificent crossing.

The "Lady Leinster" approaching the Prince's Landing Stage, Liverpool. The landing stage is afloat, and vessels can berth alongside at all states of the tide.

She is not large as cross-channel ships go, for her gross tonnage is only 2,284, but she draws a good deal more water than most vessels of her class and consequently travels more steadily in rough weather. She was built no less than 24 years ago, for the Belfast Steamship Company, and bore the name "*Patriotic*." For the bulk of her career she has worked on the Liverpool and Belfast service, and it was only a few years ago, when the new motorships "*Ulster Monarch*," "*Ulster Queen*" and "*Ulster Prince*" were commissioned, that the older steamers were transferred to the Dublin route.

It was 10.53 p.m. when the gangways were let down. We were berthed very close to the "*Montcalm*," and our bow had to be worked away from the quay very carefully; but an even more tricky piece of navigation awaited us at the dock entrance. The lock leads out into the river in a direction almost due south, and coming out of No. 1 branch of the dock there is very little space in which to swing the ship round. The big liners are of course always assisted by tugs, but Captain Hawkins had to rely entirely on manœuvring with the engines. We slipped quietly past the "*Montcalm*"—although not a big ship by modern standards she towered above us—and a moment later were heading straight for a jutting-out corner of the dock wall near the lock gate. For a few thrilling seconds it seemed as though we must collide, but then both engines were put full astern, the ship was pulled up within a few feet of the wall, and the starboard engine put full ahead. The "*Lady Leinster*" swung beautifully in the confined space, and a few minutes later we were safely in the lock.

"It's the only way, with a north wind," the Captain explained. "You've got to let her go right up to the wall, then"—with most expressive gestures—"pull her up sharp and swing her round!" The lock is big enough to take the largest liners that come to Liverpool, and it was no less than twenty minutes before we were lowered to river level. During this time our progress was in the care of a dock pilot who was shouting orders from the quayside through a megaphone. At last the gates ahead of us were opening; the pilot gave the orders necessary to get us under way again, and then finally . . . "Half-ahead port." A pause, then "Half on both. Good night, Sir!"

"Good night!"

So we steamed out into the Mersey. It was 11.22 p.m. when we left the lock, and by the time we had described a complete semi-circle and were heading north past New Brighton it was fully an hour later than if we had left the landing stage on time at 10.15 p.m. Timekeeping is of no little importance on this service because the boat connects at Dublin with two important expresses of the Great Southern Railways, the 7.0 a.m. English Mail to Cork, which also serves Killarney and the south-west, and the 7.20 a.m. "Limited Mail" to Galway. So every effort was made to regain lost time, and the "*Lady Leinster*" was soon doing a good 19 knots.

As we threaded our way down the ever-fascinating channel that leads out of the Mersey, between the long line of flashing buoys, Captain Hawkins talked of his experiences and of the healthy rivalry between the Dublin and Belfast boats. He told how one night the two ships left at exactly the same moment, and after manœuvring from the quayside came abreast of each other in the river. Then—"I rang down to the Chief: 'The *Ulster Queen's* just level with us. Let her have it.'" I can quite imagine how the challenge was taken up in the rival ship, and Captain Hawkins went on to tell how they raced neck and neck almost to the Crosby lightship. But there the "*Lady Leinster*" put on a tremendous extra spurt, was first at the turn, and afterwards led the way to the Bar Light, where their courses diverged.

* * * *

I went down to the engine-room shortly after we passed the Formby Lightship. The "*Lady Leinster*," in contrast with most cross-channel ships, is driven by a four cylinder compound triple expansion steam engine. There is one high-pressure cylinder, one medium-pressure, and two low. One screw is driven by the two low-pressure cylinders, while the other is driven by the high and medium. The cylinders are placed vertically above the crankshaft, just as in the latest marine oil engines; but with only four cylinders to drive the ship they are necessarily very big. I was interested to see that the valves were operated by the Stephenson link motion, which at one time was almost universally used on British locomotives; in the case of the "*Lady Leinster*," however, the valve gear is so tremendously heavy that a small subsidiary engine is necessary to reverse the main engines.

The working of this triple expansion compound engine makes a most interesting comparison with that of a railway locomotive. All four cylinders have a stroke of 36 in., the high-pressure cylinder is 21½ in. diameter, the medium pressure 35 in., and each of the low-pressure no less than 41 in. diameter. Such dimensions put in the shade even the greatest of American locomotives. Speed is controlled entirely by the regulator, which is operated by the usual form of horizontal wheel. There is no need in a ship for adjustment of the point in the piston stroke at which steam is cut off; on a railway, with rising and falling gradients, the output of power required from the engine is constantly varying, but at sea it is quite steady. In the *"Lady Leinster,"* steam is cut off after the piston has travelled 65 per cent. of its stroke in the high-pressure cylinder, 70 per cent. in the medium, and 55 per cent. in each of the low-pressure cylinders; this is equivalent to about 20 per cent. in a simple engine, so that the steam is very thoroughly expanded. Piston valves are used on the high and medium-pressure cylinders, but the low-pressure are fitted with double port slide valves.

The "Lady Leinster" in the Mersey. This cross-channel steamer has a gross tonnage of 2,284. Her funnels are green with black tops.

A reciprocating steam engine at full speed is a thrilling sight. Even when riding on the footplate of an express train you never get an opportunity of standing close to the pistons and connecting rods, but on the control platform of the *"Lady Leinster"* you are right between the two pairs of cylinders. At 19 knots the crankshafts are making 160 revolutions per minute, and the huge rods are flying up and down, a mass of shining steel almost too rapid for the eye to follow. There is surprisingly little noise—the bulk of what there is comes from the pumps—but the atmosphere is thick with the all-pervading smell of hot oil.

Just ahead of the main engine room are the boilers. The furnaces are oil fired, and about 24 tons of fuel are used in making the crossing. They use a very thick black treacly oil that is the residue after petrol and higher grades have been distilled off, but with the efficient type of burner fitted it is a first-rate steam raiser.

The *"Lady Leinster's"* engines develop about 6,500 horse power. Comparing this with the 16,000 horse power of the L.M.S.R. ships on the Holyhead-Dun Laoghaire mail service, the disparity seems incredible, but it is a remarkable example of the price you have to pay for speed at sea. The L.M.S.R. boats of course have a tonnage of 3,500, but the difference in speed, 23 knots as against 18 to 19, does not seem much at first sight. But even in a ship of the *"Lady Leinster's"* size to increase speed by one knot means developing an extra 1,000 horse power! An even more striking fact was emphasised at the time of the *"Queen Mary's"* maiden voyage; with a modern giant liner, to increase speed from 30 to 35 knots would mean putting in engines of exactly double the power!

* * * *

When I came up on deck again we were just off the north coast of Anglesey. After passing the Bar Lightship our course is almost due west right across the Irish Sea, and although the strong north wind was catching us heavily, the *"Lady Leinster"* rode as steadily as though she were steaming in quite sheltered waters. Vivid stabs of light to the south showed the whereabouts of the Skerries lighthouse, just to the north of Holyhead; we passed abeam at about 3.0 a.m. and a rough calculation showed that we were picking up lost time well and should, with reasonable luck, make our connections in Dublin safely.

A view in the engine room, showing the medium pressure cylinder. The small lever like a locomotive regulator is for operating the reverse engine. The log of the trip is chalked on the cylinder wall.

After passing the Skerries I turned in for a while, but was on the bridge again shortly after 5 a.m. It was a grey stormy morning. A great bank of leaden clouds hung in the west, effectively veiling the Irish coast; small detached rain clouds were racing across the sky and the sea was a heaving mass of greyish-green and white. Far away to the south-west was the L.M.S.R. mail steamer heading for Dun Laoghaire and leaving a trail of black smoke that in the damp air hung, so it seemed, fo rmiles behind. Watching her through the glasses I was soon able to pick up the Kish lightship, by which she passed very close as usual.

We were steaming towards the Howth peninsula, though it was some little time before any land showed up at all. Then gradually the rocky headland called the Nose of Howth took shape out of the shroud of rain, and at the same time a clearing in the sky revealed the Wicklow Mountains away to the south. Soon the whole coastline of Dublin Bay was visible; we watched the mail steamer turn into Dun Laoghaire harbour, and a long rift of clear sky away in the west silhouetted the towers and spires of the city itself.

We had passed abeam of the Kish at 5.42 a.m., and although the *"Lady Leinster"* had come at a great pace it was still touch and go as to whether our connections would be made. We passed within half a mile of the coast at Howth Head, getting a fine view of the lighthouse that is built right out on the extreme nose of the rocks. This lighthouse is called the Bailey. The hills on the south side of the bay were now looking very fine; a shaft of early morning sunshine was glinting on the water just off Dalkey, and with the glasses I could pick out every detail of Dun Laoghaire harbour. In the meantime the heavy rain clouds were slowly rolling up the slopes of the Dublin Mountains, and the westernmost summits stood out sharply against the sky.

The channel leading into the river Liffey is bounded by two very long breakwaters. As we reached the entrance speed was reduced to one half, but our race was practically won, for it was barely 6.20 a.m. The sky was rapidly clearing, and although isolated squalls of rain were still sweeping across from the north-west, the reft clouds in all directions showed patches of brilliant blue. As you draw nearer the city the prospect develops into a curious mixture of elegance and gaunt industrialism. Near at hand are the electricity works and, just upstream, what is surely the world's most colossal gasometer; farther ahead is the magnificent classical pile of the Custom House, and beyond that the famous tower of the Four Courts.

We were now approaching the quay at North Wall. In the ordinary way the steamer is swung round in the river, but to save time Captain Hawkins decided to berth at once with the bow pointing upstream. So we rode straight up to the quayside, and at 6.43 a.m. the gangways were run across. Fully 47 minutes of lost time had been made up, and our passengers were able to catch their various trains with time to spare.

As soon as all these early passengers were ashore, the gangways were let down again and the ship swung round. I went down to the engine room to watch this operation. Telegraph signals from the bridge came very rapidly; the Chief and the Second Engineer with deft turns of the regulator wheels adjusted the steam pressure to give the speeds required on the port and starboard engines. Changes in direction were frequent, and I was astonished to see how quickly the valve gear was shifted and how silently the main engines restarted; but when one engine was going ahead and the other astern the effect when seen from a short distance away was odd in the extreme!

Canadian National Streamlined Locomotives

Locomotive streamlining has been introduced in Canada with the building of five new 4–8–4 engines for the Canadian National Railways by the Montreal Locomotive Works. These are the largest streamlined locomotives in the world. The outward form adopted was developed by the National Research Council at Ottawa in collaboration with officers of the C.N.R. Motive Power Department after a series of wind-tunnel tests, and the photograph reproduced on this page shows in a striking manner how all the familiar front-end features have been concealed beneath the streamlined casing. The pilot or "cow-catcher" is absent, for the rounded front extends to within a few inches of the rails, and the automatic coupler fitted to the front of the engine disappears behind a door when not in use. All pipes formerly exposed are covered by a casing that extends from the smoke-box to the cab of the engine at the usual running board level above the driving wheels, but the wheels and the running gear are left exposed for easy inspection.

The chimney, bell and other boiler-top equipment except the whistle are concealed in another casing running along the boiler from the smoke-box front to the cab. This casing has a louvred front end with the object of inducing a draught when the engine is running to throw the smoke and steam from the chimney well upward and clear of the cab and train. The front window on the right-hand side of the cab is of a special type consisting of a disc of high-grade glass, which revolves at a very high speed and gives clear vision to the driver.

The new engines, Nos. 6400-6404, have been given a striking appearance by the adoption of a new colour scheme. The front and smoke-box of the engine and the wheel centres are black. The cab, the running board apron and the tender are the same shade of green as C.N.R. passenger stock, with gold lining. The wheel rims are aluminium in colour, and the boiler and casing above it are of unpainted planished steel that has merely to be wiped with oil to retain its natural blue-grey colour. The number of the locomotive appears in bronze on a red background on the running board apron, and the familiar tilted "label" bearing the words "Canadian National" appears on the tender sides, gold lettering being used on a red background.

These giants are intended for use between Montreal, Toronto and Sarnia on the route of *"The International Limited."*

The striking front end of the first Canadian streamlined locomotive. Photograph by courtesy of the Canadian National Railways.

The "Earl" Class on the G.W.R.

Ten 4–4–0 engines named after various West Country Earls have been added to the series of G.W.R. locomotives that bear distinguished titles. Although the four-coupled locomotive was pronounced obsolete for main line express work on the G.W.R. some years ago, and such famous 4–4–0s as the "Cities" and "Counties" have all been withdrawn, there is still much work for which the "mixed traffic" type of 4–4–0 of moderate weight and with wheels of medium diameter is suitable. This is especially so on the hilly routes in Central Wales and on the Cambrian Coast, where weight restrictions apply.

On the G.W.R. this 4–4–0 type of locomotive originated with the "Duke" or "Devon" class in 1895, and was developed in the "Bulldog" series. Now that it has become necessary to replace many of these engines, the opportunity has been taken to evolve the "Earls." These engines conform to the traditional type of G.W.R. 4–4–0 with outside frames, for they incorporate certain usable parts from "Duke" and "Bulldog" engines now broken up. Briefly the general impression of the appearance of the first engine completed is that "Bulldog" outside frames and running gear generally have had mounted on them a "Duke" domed boiler, but without the top-feed apparatus.

The cylinder and boiler dimensions of the "Earls" correspond to those of the "Dukes," and as the working pressures and driving wheel diameters are the same the tractive efforts are identical. The total weight of an "Earl" is 49 tons in working order, or nearly 2 tons more than that of a "Duke." The tenders provided are of the 3,500-gallon type and accommodate 6 tons of coal.

As might be expected, the engines have a somewhat Victorian appearance as compared with modern designs, and the building of small 4–4–0s will no doubt come as a surprise to many G.W.R. enthusiasts. The "Earls" have however been produced to meet the special requirements of the routes over which they are to run and represent an interesting instance of the economical use of material.

The first 10 engines thus dealt with are Nos. 3200-09, and they bear the following names:—*"Earl of Mount Edgcumbe," "Earl of Dunraven," "Earl of Dudley," "Earl Cawdor," "Earl of Dartmouth," "Earl of Devon," "Earl of Plymouth," "Earl of St. Germans," "Earl Bathurst," "Earl of Radnor."*

Diesel Railcars for L.P.T.B.

The London Passenger Transport Board has placed an order for two A.E.C. Diesel-engined railcars generally similar to those of the same make that are in use on the G.W.R. They are to be employed between Chesham and Chalfont, where one of the G.W.R. vehicles was given a trial last March, as it was completed a little before it was actually required by the G.W.R. The introduction of these cars will enable additional connections to be made at Chalfont with main line trains to London, without interfering with existing through services from Chesham to Baker Street and Marylebone.

Each car, driven by two 130 h.p. 6-cylinder oil engines, will seat 70 passengers and will incorporate such safety devices as dead man's handle control, automatic brake trip cock gear and air-operated doors. An interesting variation from the standard equipment of the G.W.R. cars will be the fitting of standard L.P.T.B. automatic couplers. These cars will be the first Diesel railcars to be put into service by the L.P.T.B.

Speeding by a "Sandringham"

The latest "Sandringham" class engines that have recently taken over the hardest duties at Leicester (G.C.) shed are putting up some remarkable work. On the 6.20 p.m. from Marylebone No. 2849, *"Sheffield United,"* in the able hands of Driver Newall and Fireman Lees, recently made some brilliant running with a 9-coach train weighing 310 tons tare and 325 tons loaded. Northolt Junction was passed on time in 17 minutes from the start, and then No. 2849 went up the 1 in 175 of Gerrards Cross bank at 56 m.p.h. After slacking to 35 m.p.h. through High Wycombe and taking the ascent to Saunderton at a steady 50 m.p.h., Driver Newall completely eclipsed his previous fast running with Atlantic No. 5363, described in the June *"M.M.,"* by averaging 76.7 m.p.h. over the 15.3 miles from Princess Risborough to Grendon, with a top speed of 85 m.p.h. So Finmere, 59.0 miles, was reached in 63½ minutes.

On the next stage, to Woodford, the maximum was 74 m.p.h. at Culworth Junction, and then came a thrilling finish. Speed rose to 85 m.p.h. at Braunston, 77 was reached beyond Rugby, and going up Lutterworth bank the minimum speed was 58½. The culminating effort of a superb run was a top speed of 88 m.p.h. on the final descent into Leicester. The 34 miles from Woodford were run start to stop in 32 min. 55 sec., and for 27 miles of this distance speed averaged 73 m.p.h.

This run was recorded by Mr. O. S. Nock.

The upper illustration on this page shows L.N.E.R. 2-8-2 locomotive No. 2003 "Lord President," which is streamlined in a similar manner to the "Silver Link" series of "Pacifics." Photograph by courtesy of the L.N.E.R. The lower photograph, by H. C. Casserley, shows one of the few remaining rail-motor vehicles of the combined engine and coach type. This L.M.S.R. unit was built by the former Lancashire and Yorkshire Railway.

L.N.E.R. Developments

The L.N.E.R. have placed an order for a new turntable to be installed at Norwich. This turntable will be of the latest design with a diameter of 70 ft. and therefore will be capable of turning the largest engines in service on the line.

A contract also has been placed for the electrification of the new coaling plant to be installed at Nottingham, where the Colwick Locomotive Depot is in course of modernisation. The new plant will have a capacity of 500 tons.

In view of the actual and prospective activity in the coal, iron and steel trades the L.N.E.R. recently placed special contracts for the building of 1,800 open goods wagons of 12-tons capacity, 1,400 12-ton hopper coal wagons, and 100 20-ton hopper coal wagons.

An extensive programme of wagon building during the forthcoming year has been approved after a special survey of the existing and prospective conditions in each of the many branches of industry served by the L.N.E.R. This survey has taken into account the withdrawal of a number of existing wagons not of the most modern design, and provides for the construction of 7,550 open goods wagons, 300 of which will be specially suitable for the conveyance of road-rail containers. It includes 430 covered goods wagons all of which will be fitted with the continuous brake, and 150 special wagons for the conveyance of the increasing fish traffic. There also will be 1,265 bolster wagons for the conveyance of iron, steel and timber traffic, of which 15 will be of a special design for the conveyance of exceptionally long girders and steelwork up to 90 ft. in length. In addition 700 new cattle wagons, 1,600 coal wagons and 14 special trolley trestle wagons for the conveyance of exceptional loads are to be constructed, and other items include 250 goods brake vans, 59 horse boxes of modern design, and 300 large covered containers.

L.M.S.R. "Bedrooms on Wheels"

Composite sleeping cars of the most up-to-date design have recently been put into service from Derby Works. The underframes and six-wheeled bogies are built up of rolled steel sections and electric arc welding is used instead of riveting. The body structure forms an integral part of the underframe and welded steel members enter very largely into its construction. The outside panels are of steel sheets. Special measures have been taken to eliminate noise, the vehicles running on wooden-centre wheels of Mansell type. The heating, lighting and ventilation have been the subject of special attention.

The number of new cars is 13. Each accommodates six first class and 14 third class passengers, and there is also an attendants' compartment. A distinctive external feature is that the hot air and cold air distributing ducts of the ventilating system are carried outside the roof of the vehicle.

Unusual Loads

A chain measuring over a mile (1,895 yards) was recently moved by rail from Cradley Heath to Millbrook. It was loaded on to four close-coupled open goods wagons, enough slack being allowed between the wagons to permit of tension on the drawbars during conveyance. The chain links were 6 in. long, 3¾ in. wide and 1⅛ in. in diameter.

A Georgian red brick house, Brooks Hall, Ipswich, and the furniture and effects in it have been moved from Suffolk to Somerset by rail, seventeen wagonloads of bricks and masonry, fruit trees, bins and outhouses, and four container loads of furniture travelling from Ipswich Station to South Cheriton. The Hall has now been re-erected, and this is believed to be the first occasion on which a complete house and its contents have been transported by rail.

The *"Green Arrow"* Freight Service

The *"Green Arrow"* system for freight was introduced by the railway companies for the purpose of speeding up traffic. Delivery is in accordance with a prearranged schedule. It is generally effected next day, but this is not guaranteed, as was inadvertently stated on page 452 of the *"M.M."* last month.

Blowing Up a Brick Arch Bridge

Novel Operation on the G.W.R.

By a Railway Engineer

AN engineering job of a most unusual kind was carried out recently on the Great Western Railway near Overton-on-Dee, Flintshire. In a shallow cutting on the single line between Ellesmere and Wrexham a single span brick arch bridge was becoming unsafe. It was what is known as an accommodation bridge, provided for the use of a farmer whose land had been severed by the construction of the railway. In recent years the land on one side had been sold and so the bridge was no longer required, and in view of its condition the novel course was taken of blowing it up.

Naturally it was necessary to reduce the amount of brickwork to be demolished by explosion to an absolute minimum, and so the parapets and earth filling were removed before the day fixed for the final operation. This left only the actual arch, but even this contained about 9,500 bricks. The preliminary work had been carried out without any interruption of train service, beyond the necessity of putting on a speed restriction. On a Sunday in April, the engineers obtained absolute possession of the line in order to carry out the final demolition, and on that day I was privileged to witness not only the operations at the site, but also the preliminary work, which in itself was very interesting.

The headquarters of the Divisional Engineer responsible for the job are at Oswestry, and here at 6.15 a.m. the special train was ready. It consisted of a ballast brake van at each end and about a dozen low-sided wagons, with drop-down doors; it was hauled by an old 0–6–0 goods engine. The explosives, 10 lb. of ammonal, were carefully loaded into the rear brake van. The driver had to be warned not to be too violent in starting and stopping, for the train was of course loose coupled; even with the greatest care the rear brake van got plenty of shaking up.

We got away just after 6.30 a.m. A trip in a permanent way brake van can be quite an entertaining experience: only a dim light, from four narrow windows, a small cheery party gathered round the enclosed fire, and all the time the van riding almost as hard as a locomotive. We stopped at Ellesmere to pick up a permanent way gang, and here the engine was run round the train in order that we might proceed in the opposite direction up the Wrexham branch; this joins the line from Oswestry in a trailing junction. At about 7.20 a.m. the site was reached.

Stripped right to the arch, what was left of the bridge had a most singular appearance. The first job to be done on arrival was the packing of the charges. A row of 10 holes $1\frac{1}{2}$ in. in diameter had previously been drilled along each of the lines where the arch joins the abutments; this line is called the springing of the arch. Another double row of 16 holes had been drilled along the crown. These holes were about 12 in. deep, and into each was packed a small charge of ammonal that occupied about half the depth of the hole; the space remaining above the charge was plugged up with clay after the detonating fuse wire had been attached to the charge. While the packing was in progress it was quite a novel experience to clamber up to the crown of the arch, and from rail level those working on the top seemed to be in a precarious position. Two detonators were used, and 18 of the charges were wired up in series to each of these by fuse wire along which the speed of detonation is no less than 40,000 ft. per second.

In the meantime the permanent way gang were making a temporary platform of old sleepers underneath the arch to catch the bulk of the debris from the explosion, and protect the track. The train was now divided, half on either side of the bridge. At the actual point the railway is on a rising gradient in the direction of Ellesmere, and half the wagons, together with the rear brake van, were left on the rising side, with the nearest wagon 150 yds. from the bridge; on the opposite side, the engine drew the remaining trucks away to an equal distance. After the explosion the line would be completely blocked, and the train was divided in this way so that a truck could be brought up on each side of the debris, and the work of clearing up made much quicker.

The upper illustrations show the preliminary dismantling and the packing of the explosive charges. The explosion is seen taking place in the central photograph, reproduced by courtesy of the G.W.R., and the result is shown below.

It took nearly two hours to pack the charges, and then the detonators were wired up by long flexible leads to a small 50-volt portable hand generator that was placed about 100 yds. to the side of the line, in a field The finishing touches were put to the wiring, the "C" and "T" signs which had indicated the speed restriction past the bridge were removed out of harm's way, and the engineers, platelayers, and spectators retired to a distance of 150 yds. on either side; only the intrepid press photographers and movie camera men ventured nearer than this.

In a few minutes the whole scene was hushed; men talked in whispers. Then—a sharp whistle. For a second the atmosphere was electric, and suddenly came an explosion that shook the ground beneath us, a cloud of dust, and an eruption of bricks like a miniature volcano. It was all over in a few seconds, but one of my most vivid recollections of it was the sight of the photographers calmly filming the event amid a perfect hail of bricks; The explosion was too well done to be really spectacular, however. The bulk of the arch was severed cleanly at the springings and fell solid across the temporary platform, and it was only a very small proportion of the bricks that provided the principal thrill for the spectators. One or two individual bricks were thrown a tremendous distance; one fell right beyond the engine, fully 250 yds. away, and another hurtled down the track in the opposite direction nearly to the far brake van, causing workers to take cover between the trucks.

The speed with which the line was cleared was not the least notable feature of this interesting job. The engine pushed its half of the train up the rising gradient towards the bridge, while a number of wagons were detached from the other half and allowed to run downhill by gravity, though of course a man walked by the side of each one periodically applying the hand brake to keep the speed dead slow. In this way wagons were quickly brought on either side of what was left of the bridge, and it was then a comparatively easy matter to shovel up the bricks from the wooden platform. The explosion took place shortly after 9.30 a.m. and by 11 o'clock the line was clear enough for the train to pass through; if necessary an ordinary train service could have run, for only the final tidying up remained. Every little detail of the operation was of interest, however, as showing the careful organisation that attends the carrying out of an engineering job on a railway.

Powerful Crushing Machinery

Breaking Up Rock, Stone and Ore

THE equipment used at mines and quarries generally includes powerful machines for crushing rock, stone or ore into pieces of the required size. Various types of machines are available for this work, some of which incorporate a rapidly revolving rotor fitted with swinging hammers, while others have reciprocating steel jaws, between which the stone or ore to be broken up is fed. A machine of the latter type is illustrated on this page. It is made by Hadfields Ltd., of Sheffield, who are probably the largest manufacturers of this class of breaker in this country, and is available in various sizes, the largest of which is capable of dealing with 300 tons of material an hour. The machine shown in the illustration is a $24'' \times 13''$ machine, the dimensions denoting the size of the opening through which the stone is fed, and it has an output capacity of from 20 to 25 tons of hard stone an hour, when set for $2\frac{1}{2}''$ ring product.

A powerful stone and ore breaking machine in which the material is crushed between reciprocating steel jaws. For our illustrations we are indebted to Hadfields Ltd., Sheffield.

The stone or other material is crushed between a pair of toothed jaws, one of which is fixed rigidly inside the body of the machine, and the other in a swinging holder, or stock, that has a reciprocating motion imparted to it when the machine is in operation. The swing stock is suspended from a strong steel shaft that is rigidly secured at each end to the top sides of the frame and acts as a pivot upon which the swinging jaw rocks when the machine is working. The necessary movement is produced by the action of an eccentric shaft in a pitman, which imparts motion to two toggles situated between the back end of the breaker frame and the bottom of the swing stock. The eccentric shaft is fitted with two fly wheels and is driven by a belt pulley attached to one of these wheels.

Solid steel construction is used throughout and except in the case of very large machines, the frame is made in one solid piece in toughened cast steel. This use of steel makes the machine extremely strong and light in weight for its capacity, features that render these Breakers ideal for portable plants for use in road making and in situations difficult of access, such as are frequently met with in mines.

Stone and ores are very abrasive substances and in order to give the crushing jaws and certain other parts of the machine a high resistance to the wearing action of these materials, they are made of special manganese steel. Lubrication of the eccentric shaft bearings is accomplished by a high pressure central feed lubricator, fitted at the back of the machine.

A front view of the Hadfield ore and stone Breaker, showing the opening into which the material to be crushed is fed.

Other types of jaw breakers made by the firm include a double-action machine, in which both the crushing jaws oscillate. This machine is known as the "Shearar" double-action jaw crusher. In it the jaws are driven from separate eccentric shafts, which run at different speeds, with the result that one jaw makes approximately twice the number of crushing strokes as the other in a given period. One of the swing stocks is driven at the top end and the other at the bottom, and the motion of each is controlled by toggles. Adjustments are provided that enable the size of product to be varied at will, and the machine therefore can be used for both fine and coarse crushing.

French Light Aeroplanes

Types of Caudron Machines

THE aeroplanes with which we deal this month are made by the well-known Caudron Company, of France. This company was one of the pioneers of French aircraft and dates back to the earliest days of aviation in that country. Caudron military aeroplanes played an important part during the Great War, but although the firm have produced some interesting military types since then, they have paid more attention to light aeroplanes designed for the use of civilian flying schools, clubs and private owners. These machines range from two-seaters to six-seaters, and although certain structural details patented by the company are common to most of the types, the latter are sufficiently varied to be easily identified.

The "Luciole" is the only biplane produced by the Caudron Company, of France. It has a top speed of 110.5 m.p.h. The illustrations to this article are by courtesy of Societé des Avions Caudron.

The engines fitted in all Caudron aircraft are produced by the Renault Company, who were among the earliest builders of aero-engines in France, and even before the War had become noted for their important part in the development of the air-cooled Vee type aero engine. The Renault engines of Caudron aeroplanes, however, are of the "in-line" inverted air-cooled type, with four or six cylinders.

For several years monoplanes have been much more popular than biplanes in France, and the Caudron Company are now engaged almost entirely in producing them. Probably one reason for this preference is that a monoplane gives a much better view than is obtainable from a biplane, which is a great advantage. The absence of the struts and rigging necessary in a biplane, accounts partly for this, and it also lessens the weight of the aeroplane, and the cost of production.

One of the few types of high wing monoplanes made by the company is the "Fregate," shown above. It is a cabin machine with seating for three passengers.

Most of the monoplanes produced by the company are of the low wing type, the only high wing ones being the "Phalène," and two others, the "Fregate" and the "Pelican," that have been developed from it. These three are single-engined cabin aeroplanes. The "Fregate," shown in the lower illustration on this page, is not the usual cantilever monoplane, as the wings are not only attached to the top of the fuselage, but also are supported by four inclined struts fixed at their upper ends to the undersides of the wings and at their lower ends to the bottom of the fuselage. The wings are made of spruce, with a covering of fabric, and can be folded back. Their trailing edges are hinged along the full length, but only the outer portions are used as ailerons, the centre portion being hinged merely to facilitate folding back.

The length of the "Fregate" is 26 ft. 11 in., and its height 6 ft. 11½ in. The fuselage is a spruce structure, with the usual covering of fabric treated to make it weatherproof. The cabin seats three passengers, one near the pilot and the other two on a wide seat that extends across the back of the cabin, as in certain British light aeroplanes. A large door on each side of the cabin gives easy access to the interior. The engine, which is mounted in the nose of the aeroplane, is a Renault "Bengali," with four cylinders in line, developing 140-150 h.p. With this engine the aeroplane has a top speed of 130.4 m.p.h., and cruises at 115 m.p.h. There are two fuel tanks, one inside each wing, and sufficient fuel is carried for a flight of 528 miles. The greatest height to which the aeroplane can climb is 14,760 ft., or almost three miles.

The two other Caudron monoplanes illustrated here are

of the low wing type. The "Aiglon" is particularly attractive in appearance, and is an ideal machine for a private owner who does not demand the comfort and protection provided by an enclosed cabin, but nevertheless requires a machine in which he can take a friend for a flight. The two open cockpits, one for the pilot and the other for his passenger, are arranged in tandem, and there are two luggage compartments forward of the front cockpit. The span of the "Aiglon" is 37 ft. 4 in. and the wing is built in three sections, the centre section having the same chord and thickness throughout, while the two outer ones taper in both chord and thickness towards their tips. The spars and ribs of the wing are of spruce and plywood, and those of the centre section fit into special recesses in the underside of the fuselage. Wing flaps are attached to the trailing edge of this section, and ailerons are fitted to the remainder of the wing. The short, rather stumpy legs of the undercarriage are enclosed in streamlined fairings and have balloon-tyred wheels and powerful brakes.

A fine photograph of the "Aiglon," in which the deep fuselage and the thick wing are well brought out.

The engine is a Renault "Bengali-Junior" of 100-112 h.p., and gives the aeroplane a top speed of 133.5 m.p.h. and a cruising speed of 111.7 m.p.h. The service ceiling is 13,120 ft. The fuel tanks are fitted in the centre section of the wing, one on each side of the fuselage, and carry enough fuel for a non-stop flight of 435 miles.

The "Simoun" Caudron low wing monoplane. The curved roof of the cabin gives the machine a humped appearance.

The other low wing monoplane is the "Simoun," a slightly larger machine than the "Aiglon." It is designed to carry four passengers, and therefore is excellent for use on internal air lines and for air taxi work. The structure of the wing follows the general Caudron practice, being of wood and in three sections, with the centre one attached to the underside of the fuselage. A light metal alloy is used extensively in the construction of the fuselage framework, and the roof and bottom are of magnesium sheeting; the whole is covered with fabric. The enclosed cabin has large windows that give a wide outlook, and the seats for the passengers are arranged in pairs. There is the usual luggage compartment, which in this instance is behind the cabin. The undercarriage is of the divided type, and the legs and the upper halves of the wheels are covered with streamlined fairings.

A Renault "Bengali-Six" engine of 170-195 h.p. is fitted on a special detachable mounting in the nose of the aeroplane, and a variable pitch airscrew is employed. The "Simoun" has a top speed of 186.3 m.p.h., and a cruising speed of 167.6 m.p.h. The all-up weight, that is the weight of the aeroplane when fully loaded and ready to take off, is 2,706 lb., and the service ceiling is 19,860 ft.

The current types of Caudron aircraft include only one biplane. This is the "Luciole," shown in the upper illustration on the previous page. It is a two-seater light biplane of the kind that has long been favoured for training purposes. The two open cockpits are situated one behind the other, and dual control is provided. Another point about the machine that is important to those in charge of flying schools and clubs, and also to private owners, is that it occupies only a small amount of hangar space. The wings can be folded back easily and quickly, and the width of the machine is then reduced from 32 ft. 5½ in. to only 9 ft. 6 in. It is an equal-span biplane, and the upper wing is flat. The wings, the fuselage and the elevator of the tail unit are made of spruce, but the rudder, another part of the tail unit, is of welded tubular steel; fabric is used as the covering for the machine.

The "Luciole" is 32 ft. 5½ in. in length and 9 ft. in height, and employs the same type of Renault engine as the "Fregate" monoplane. The petrol tanks are in the centre section of the lower wing and hold enough fuel for a flight of 410 miles. The aeroplane has a top speed of 110.5 m.p.h., and cruises at 96 m.p.h.

In addition to the types described in this article, the company have produced many other commercial aeroplanes, and since the winning in 1933 of the Coupe Deutsch de la Meurthe, an annual European air contest for light aircraft, by a Caudron aeroplane, they have become actively interested in the production of light racing monoplanes. Up to the present only one type has been designed for racing purposes. This is the Caudron C.460, a low wing monoplane with a top speed of 314.2 m.p.h.

A Lake in a Volcanic Crater

The illustration on this page and the upper one on the opposite page show two views of Crater Lake, high up in the Cascade Mountains in Oregon, in the United States. How it got its name is explained in a report issued by the Carnegie Institution of Washington, which describes it as a lake "cupped in the heart of what once was a great cone-shaped mountain, built up by successive outflows of volcanic lava and ashes, which met with disaster, it is believed, through the blowing off of its top in a mighty explosion. It is probable that a lake formed in the crater directly thereafter, but it was a lake, not of water, but of red hot, seething lava which gradually cooled, solidified, and in part receded into the depths whence it came.

Crater Lake, in the Cascade Mountains in the United States. This photograph and the upper one on the opposite page are reproduced by courtesy of the Carnegie Institution, Washington.

"As unmistakable evidence of a volcanism that must have continued throughout countless centuries geologists point to crater walls, 2,000 ft. high, which are composed of layers of lava, of pumice, and of volcanic breccia, indicative of recurrent eruptions; to instances such as the Devil's Backbone where the molten lava has broken through fissures in the mountain side, leaving fillings which are harder than the surrounding rock and which remain after the softer materials have washed or weathered away; and to cinder cones, such as Wizard Island, approaching or rising above the surface from the lake floor, 2,000 ft. beneath.

"The lake has no known intake or outlet. Rain and melting snow are the sole sources of supply; seepage and evaporation are the sole agencies of depletion. Apparently also these conditions are in remarkable balance, for the water level of the lake changes little from year to year.

"No one fails to express astonishment at the incredible blueness of its water. Indeed, the intensity of the colour so deeply impressed the first white men who saw the lake, a party of prospectors seeking gold who chanced upon it in 1853, that they named it the Deep Blue Lake. As seen from the rim above, the water, a lovely turquoise blue along the shallow borders, shades by myriad gradations into darkest Prussian blue in the deeper parts. Upon descending the crater wall to the lake and viewing the water from a boat, one notes that the colour deepens to dark indigo."

Why is Crater Lake so Blue?

The Carnegie Institution decided to find why the water appeared to be so blue, and asked Dr. Edison Pettit, a famous American astronomer, to look into the problem. The explanation he gave showed that its colour and that of the sky are due to the same cause. In the words of the report already referred to: "The blue of Crater Lake and the blue of the sky are due to the selective scattering of rays of light which have been diverted from a straight course by molecules of water, in the one case, and, in the other, by molecules of air.

"If light should strike particles that are comparable in size with the wave-length of light—one fifty-thousandth of an inch or smaller—then an interesting change occurs. The direction of travel of the long waves of the light beam, the waves that produce the sensation of red when they fall upon the eye, will be shifted slightly, but only very slightly, by the particles as the waves pass on; whereas the direction of travel of the short waves of the light beam, the waves that produce the sensation of blue, will be profoundly changed by the particles. It is these short waves that, reaching the eye of the observer, account for the blue colour.

"It is just this selective scattering of light, the scattering caused by extremely fine particles of dust and of water vapour in the air and even by the molecules of the air itself, that gives us the various colours of the sky, its fundamental blue, and the red and gold of sunrises and sunsets."

Our Drifting Continents

If Columbus had waited until the present day to set sail for the unknown West, he would have had to make a longer voyage before finding America, for in the interval that continent has drifted farther away from Europe. The difference in distance would not have troubled him greatly, however. The westward motion of the New World is slight, and during the 70,000 years since it is believed to have begun the North Atlantic Ocean has become only a foot wider every year. Other lands are wandering at higher speeds. For instance, it is believed that the distance between Africa and the great island of Madagascar is increasing by as much as 30 ft. a year; and Greenland appears to be moving away from Scotland at the rate of 60 ft. a year.

This drifting of great land masses provides evidence for the belief that at one time the continents formed a single great mass, which eventually broke up into fragments that gradually receded from each other. A glance at a map shows that in places they have surprisingly similar coast lines that can be fitted into each other. The east coast of South America and the west coast of Africa are good examples of parallel coast lines of this kind, and no doubt my readers can find others. Peculiarities in the plant and animal life of the two continents mentioned also suggest that in some past ages they formed part of a single land mass, and it has been calculated that South America actually began to separate from Africa about 30 million years ago, and has receded at a speed of about 9 in. a year.

World's Largest Insect

What is believed to be the world's largest insect is 15 in. long from the tips of its feelers to the end of its hind legs. It is a kind of stick insect, with a long thin body, and its home is the island of New Guinea. It would be difficult to give the measurement of the smallest insect for comparison with this giant, for many species are microscopic in size.

A Roaming Minor Planet

The inner slopes of Crater Lake. The black ridge in the centre is the "Devil's Backbone," and was formed by molten lava breaking through a fissure. The lake occupies the crater of an extinct volcano.

I wonder how many of my readers know that in February of this year a projectile weighing more than 100 million tons rushed past the Earth, not more than 1,500,000 miles away, at the rate of 20 miles a second. Even the astronomers who keep track of the movements of heavenly bodies did not know this until the projectile was rushing away from us again. Then they realised that a very small change in its course might have caused a disastrous collision. It is startling to realise that such a huge mass should have come so close without our realising it, but it is perhaps a comforting thought that if any similar wanderer in the skies ever does crash into the Earth at high speed, we shall have no warning of the impending disaster.

The visitor who nearly called upon us is a minor planet that almost seems to have gone astray. It does not keep to the general track of such bodies, between the paths of the Earth and of Mars, but at times is very near the Sun and at others runs away to a distance from the centre of our system that is considerably more than twice that of the Earth. The chances against an actual collision of course are very large. Fortunately for us the track of the minor planet is inclined to that of the Earth, but a shift of only $1\frac{1}{2}$ deg. would bring the two into the same plane. Even then the risk of trouble would be remote, and it has been calculated that there is only one chance in 50,000 of a collision.

Bubbles of Lava 30 ft. in Width

The lower illustration on this page shows a bubbling pool of lava in the crater of Vesuvius. Some of the bubbles shown are 30 ft. wide. There is little difficulty in reaching the crater to see pools of lava of this kind, for a wire-rope railway leads to within 150 yds. of its summit. The crater itself is a walled plain a mile or more in circumference. It is visited by many tourists, and outbursts of steam from small cones forming in it, with an all-pervading sulphureous smell make a visit to it one to be remembered.

Bubbles of boiling lava in the crater of Vesuvius. Some of the bubbles are 30 ft. in diameter. Photograph by H. Elwell, Liverpool.

Can Fish Hear?

Whether a fish can hear or not is a question on which there has been much argument. No fish with ears, or with any organs that seem to correspond to them, has yet been discovered, but careful fishermen do not make unnecessary noises, believing that these may scare the fish away.

The problem aroused the curiosity of a Russian experimenter, who set out to find out whether there was any foundation for the fisherman's precaution. He tethered a fish in an aquarium by means of a flexible lead that was long enough to allow it to swim about freely. A telephone diaphragm submerged in the water was made to emit sound waves by touching a key that at the same time sent a very mild electric current through the fish. Every time the key was closed the fish jumped. This of course might have been due to the electric shock, but after many trials of the double apparatus, the electric shock was omitted and only the sound produced. Still the fish jumped. It must therefore have detected the sound in some manner, and learned to associate it with an electric shock, so that finally the sound alone was sufficient to cause it to jump.

Similar tests with an electric bell suspended above the tank in which the fish lived also made it leap, so that it seems as if we must credit it with ability to hear.

When the Strait of Dover was Dry Land

The British Isles seem to have been separated from Europe almost by chance less than 8,000 years ago. Where the Strait of Dover are now was then a stretch of hilly country, and the only part of the present channel in existence at that time formed a deep bay of the Atlantic Ocean between Cornwall and Devon on the one hand, and Normandy and Brittany on the other. There was a valley along the line of the present strait, and this was invaded by the sea when the land began to sink, with the formation of a narrow waterway. The tides in the North Sea and in the western ocean ebbed and flowed at different times, and the four tidal currents that swept through the channel daily scoured it out to greater width, cutting it back to the cliffs of Dover on the north and those of the present French coast on the south.

The disappearance of the land bridge between Great Britain and Europe stopped the advance of many creatures then making their way westward towards the moist and comparatively warm lands on the shore of the Atlantic Ocean. Among these were many insects, such as that well-known butterfly, the Camberwell Beauty. The climate of Great Britain is suitable for this butterfly, but it arrived too late to make its home there. The specimens captured in the country reach it by long flights across the North Sea from Scandinavia, chiefly in the autumn.

Ireland also was cut off from Great Britain about the same time, with similar results. Less than two-thirds of British plants are found in Ireland, for they spread westward too late to reach that country. An even more interesting case is that of the common hare. This is not found in Ireland, and the Irish hare is a different variety that seems to be a survivor from the days of the Ice Age, when the climate of the British Isles was arctic.

A Perpetual Block of Ice

In the warm climate of New Mexico, in the south west United States, there is a cave that contains a bed of ice that never melts. To add to the mystery of its occurrence there, the ice is embedded in lava, which of course was molten when it was formed.

The explanation usually given for this curiosity is that lava on cooling becomes porous owing to the expulsion of gases from it, and tunnels and large openings are formed in it. During a cold spell at some time in the past, a great space formed in this manner in the New Mexico lava bed. This was filled with water that froze and was then protected from surface heat by the lava itself, which is an excellent insulator. The mass of ice therefore probably is a relic of the most severe winter ever experienced in the region in which it is found. It is blue in colour and streaked with dark lines believed to consist of layers of dust and ashes.

Masses of so-called "fossil ice," which probably are much older than that in the cave in New Mexico, are found deeply buried in certain districts in Central Asia.

HORNBY

CL

They're just like

A Selection of HORNBY ELECTRIC TRAIN SETS (20-volt and 6-volt)

EM120 (20-volt) or EM16 (6-volt) GOODS TRAIN SET (non-reversing). Price 15/-

EM320 (20-volt) or EM36 (6-volt) TANK GOODS TRAIN SET (reversing). Price 24/-

HORNBY No. EO20 (20-volt) PASSENGER TRAIN SET (reversing). Price 30/-

HORNBY No. E220 (20-volt) MIXED GOODS TRAIN SET (automatic reversing). Price 47/6

HORNBY No. E120 SPECIAL PASSENGER TRAIN SET (20-volt). Price 47/6

HORNBY No. E320 (20-volt) RIVIERA "BLUE" TRAIN SET (automatic reversing). Price 67/6

HORNBY No. E320 (20-volt) PULLMAN TRAIN SET (automatic reversing). Price 72/6

Hornby Electric Trains

Playing the game of railways with Hornby E'ectric Trains is the best fun in the world. No matter which you choose from the many models available, you can be sure that it will give you the utmost pleasure and satisfaction.

The performance and durability of the Hornby Electric Trains place them in a class entirely of their own. Each locomotive is fitted with a powerful motor that will haul heavy loads at high speeds, always under perfect control.

Hornby Train Sets are ava
Electric models an

A se
HOR

ELECTRIC MODELS

EM120 (20-volt) or EM16 (6-volt) L
(non-reversing)
EO20 (20-volt Locomotive (reve

E120 (20-volt) Tank Locom
versing)
E120 (20-volt) Spec
Locomotive (autor
versing)
E220 (20-vol

MECCANO LTD. -

K TRAINS

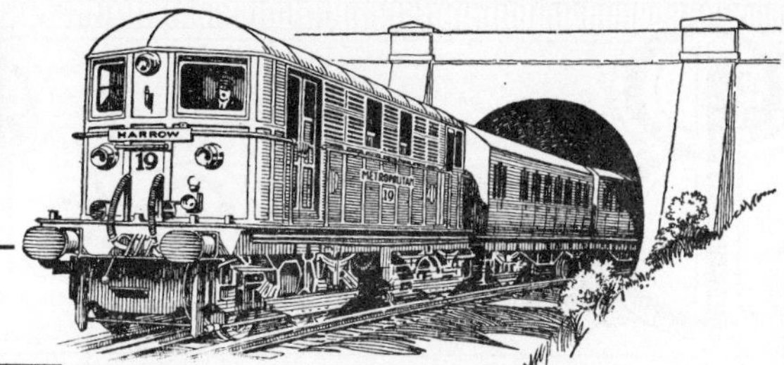

real trains, boys!

Hornby Clockwork Trains

Hornby Clockwork Trains are the longest-running spring-driven locomotives in the world. The motors fitted are of the highest quality, being perfect mechanisms with accurately-cut gears that ensure smooth running.

The splendid range of Rolling Stock, all fitted with patented and exclusive automatic couplings, and the wealth of Accessories, make the Hornby System complete in every detail.

ging from **15/-** to **75/-** for Clockwork models.

e of
IVES
otive (automatic reversing) Price 32/6
olt) Special Locomotive (automatic Price 37/6

CKWORK MODELS
motive (reversing) Price 4/6
ocomotive (reversing) Price 7/6
motive (reversing) Price 10/6
cial Locomotive Price 27/6

An illustration of a Hornby No. 2 Special Train Set, hauled by a Hornby No. 2 Special Locomotive, the latter being a true-to-type model of the real L.M.S.R. Standard Compound Locomotive.

AD - LIVERPOOL 13

A Selection of
HORNBY CLOCKWORK TRAIN SETS

MO CLOCKWORK GOODS TRAIN SET (non-reversible). Price 4/11

M1 PASSENGER TRAIN SET (reversing). Price 8/11

M3 TANK PASSENGER TRAIN SET. Price 13/9

HORNBY No. O GOODS TRAIN SET (reversing). Price 17/6

HORNBY No. 1 PASSENGER TRAIN SET (reversing). Price 25/-

HORNBY No. 2 TANK PASSENGER TRAIN SET (reversing). Price 40/-

HORNBY No. 3C PULLMAN TRAIN SET (reversing). Price 62/6

Books to Read

Here we review books of interest and of use to readers of the "M.M." We can supply copies of these books to readers who cannot obtain them through the usual channels. Order from Book Dept., Meccano Limited, Binns Road, Liverpool 13, adding 1/- for postage to the price. Postage on different books varies, but any balance remaining will be refunded.

"Famous British Trains"

By R. Barnard Way
(Ivor Nicholson and Watson. 5/- net)

Famous trains are an endless source of attraction, and their interest is not restricted to railway enthusiasts, for ordinary travellers also are eager to read about their journeys and the engines that haul them. Mr. Way's book is well calculated to satisfy these needs. It is described as a chronicle of the daily work of named British expresses, and deals with the history and routes of all the named trains of the four railway groups. There are no fewer than 56 of these, ranging from old-established favourites such as *"The Flying Scotsman"* and the *"Cornish Riviera Express,"* to such innovations as the cruising *"Northern Belle"* of the L.N.E.R., and the same company's latest introduction, *"The Silver Jubilee,"* a train that has made railway history by its speed achievements. The electric *"Brighton Belle"* also is included, and readers are taken across the Irish Sea for journeys in Northern Ireland on named trains of the N.C.C. section of the L.M.S.R.

The book is one that will be valuable to all who are specially interested in trains. No technical knowledge is demanded from its readers, and every traveller would find it a fascinating companion on any railway journey dealt with in it. It is well illustrated, as all railway books should be. A coloured reproduction of *"The Silver Jubilee"* emerging from a tunnel forms the frontispiece, and in addition there are 60 reproductions of photographs and a sketch map to illustrate the routes described.

"Gradients of the British Main Line Railways"

(The Railway Publishing Co. Ltd. 5/- net)

This publication consists of the reproduction in book form of the series of gradient profiles that appeared in the issues of *"The Railway Magazine"* during 1929 and 1930, covering nearly 9,000 route miles of track in Great Britain and Ireland. All the main line systems are included, together with the chief branch and other lines on which fast trains run. An interesting feature is that a uniform scale of inclination has been adopted, so that the difficulties of different routes can readily be compared. In addition to the gradients and the distances appearing on each profile, such details are given as the permanent speed restrictions, areas where reduced speed may be necessary owing to colliery workings, and single line sections.

As an aid to ready reference, the profiles of each group, joint lines and the Irish railways are printed on paper of different colours. Information as to the location of the mile posts on each route is included, and there is a complete index to the various profiles. The book forms a useful work of reference and is invaluable to those who make a habit of recording the locomotive work during a journey.

L.N.E.R. 2-8-2 locomotive No. 2002, "Earl Marischal," emerging from a tunnel. This and the upper illustration on the next page are from "Famous British Trains," reviewed on this page.

"Camp Devotions"

By K. C. Sparrow, B.Sc.
(Brown, Son and Ferguson Ltd. 1/- net)

Mr. Sparrow is an experienced Scoutmaster, and for many years was a keen and successful Meccano club Leader, so that his knowledge of boys and their requirements is thorough and extensive. He has already written an excellent book dealing with instructional play and games for Scouts, and he has now followed this by one dealing with the religious side of life in camp. His aim is to include everyone in camp in the devotions he suggests, and he gives schemes for suitable services in which the Scout Law plays a prominent part. He expresses the hope that his booklet "may help Scoutmasters to make camp devotions an inspiring and natural part of the day," and his sincerity and thoroughness should lead to the fulfilment of his wish.

"Woodcarving and Design"

By Lynn Miller. (Pitman. 7/6 net)

Woodcarving is an attractive craft that provides training in the use of tools, and at the same time encourages the development of artistic ability and the capacity to appreciate sound design. Mr. Miller's book is well calculated to satisfy these requirements, and a budding craftsman who follows its instructions should acquire skill in all branches of this handicraft.

After a preliminary chapter on design, the author deals more particularly with the woodcarving craft, describing the tools employed and their preparation, and giving details of actual work on the bench. Then follow exercises designed to give the learner command over his chisels and gouges, and these lead to actual examples of the production of models of various kinds, such as tables and frames. The book is admirably illustrated by means of 31 plates, chiefly of magnificent examples of woodcarving, and 89 drawings of designs and the tools with which they are executed.

"Parasites of Ponte Bello"

By Ernest W. Prangley. (Stockwell. 3/6 net)

This is a story of a desperate struggle with robbers and cut-throats who terrorised Ponte Bello, a valley in the wild foot-hills of the Drakensburg range in South Africa. Saunders Hope, the hero, almost single-handed frees the valley of brigands in spite of their attempts to drive him out, and even to murder him, and unmasks the rascally manager of a banana plantation who has been their chief ally. The finish is wildly exciting. There is a desperate gun fight in which the brigand leader is shot, and an invading horde of fierce natives is swept away by a torrent of water set in motion by the opening of the gates of a gigantic reservoir.

The story is full of thrills, and the unusual scene in which it is laid adds greatly to its interest.

"Exploring the Stratosphere"

By Gerald Heard. (Nelson. 3/6 net)

The stratosphere is a region of the atmosphere, beginning at a height of from seven to ten miles, in which the temperature is nearly constant at about 50 deg. to 60 deg. C. below freezing point. Its existence was revealed by temperature measurements made by means of small sounding balloons carrying safety-recording instruments, and the story of its discovery and of daring balloon ascents made into it is told by Mr. Heard in his latest book. One of the balloons reached the great height of 14 miles, or nearly three times that of Mount Everest. Aeroplanes also have reached the stratosphere, and the whole story of ascents into this strange region is one of fascinating adventures in the cause of science that can be compared with the great voyages of Columbus and Magellan.

The "Cornish Riviera Express" hauled by "King" class locomotive No. 6012, "King Edward VI." The train is travelling on the remarkable stretch of railway laid on the sea wall near Teignmouth.

From stratosphere voyages the author turns to the uses that we can make of the knowledge gained by them. There is reason to believe that our weather depends very largely on what happens in the stratosphere, which also is the approach to the mysterious ionised layers, such as the Heaviside layer, that reflect wireless waves of various lengths back to earth and make communication round the world possible. A complete knowledge of the conditions prevailing at any time in this region of the atmosphere therefore will be of the utmost service to us.

The stratosphere also may become a great highway of the air, for in it there will be less resistance to the passage of an aeroplane than at lower levels. The air at great heights is too thin to support life, so that these machines will have sealed cabins supplied with oxygen, and airmen who ascend into it will wear special suits, such as that shown in the lower illustration on this page, reproduced from Mr. Heard's book. Looking still further ahead, the stratosphere, in the author's own words, can be looked upon as the "training ground for rocket flight." It is not a ceiling, to be reached by persistent endeavour, but a floor or platform whence to launch ourselves into empty space. It also supplies the answers to many scientific questions, each of which is dealt with fully in the book. One of special interest concerns the mysterious cosmic rays, which are much more in evidence in the stratosphere than at the Earth's surface.

The task of giving a popular account of the stratosphere could not have been better done than by Mr. Heard, whose fascinating story will show his readers that the adventures into the skies that he describes have literally opened up new worlds. There are 10 excellent photographic illustrations, chiefly of high altitude balloons, and a diagram of ascents into the stratosphere.

"Every Boy's Book of Aeroplanes"

(Sampson Low. 3/6 net)

This book is a pictorial survey of the principal new aeroplanes of all the chief countries in the world. It contains 135 half-tone illustrations, and each is accompanied by a caption giving the dimensions and constructional details of the aeroplane illustrated. In addition to being an excellent book for the young air enthusiast, it is ideal for the model-maker, who will find it invaluable in building realistic models of the various types of aeroplanes shown.

"Walking Tours and Hostels in England"

By Sydney Moorhouse. (Country Life Ltd. 3/6 net)

There is no way in which the beauty of English country can be seen to better advantage than by walking through its lanes and over its ancient tracks, and those who enjoy this increasingly popular recreation will find Mr. Moorhouse's little book very useful. The fourteen tours described cover selected areas ranging from the English Lakes, the Peak district and the mountains of North Wales to the Chilterns, Devon and Cornwall, and the Downs. Each is planned to last a week. In each case the route is marked on a specially drawn map, and the walk for each day is carefully arranged to take in as many places of real interest as possible.

The practical value of the book as a guide is increased by the association of each tour with a group of youth hostels where accommodation for the walker can be found. The book indeed has been compiled with the help of the Youth Hostels Association, by whom it is officially recognised, but suitable hotels, farmhouses and other places in which to stay also are indicated in it.

[Photo: Keystone.

Wiley Post, the American aviator, in his Stratosphere suit.

"Pictorial Britain and Ireland"

(H. K. McCann and Co. Ltd. 8/6)

This attractive pictorial record of the roads of Great Britain and Ireland has been issued on behalf of the Anglo-American Oil Co. Ltd., and has for its outstanding feature a series of eight double page plates in colour, each 18¼ in. by 12⅛ in., reproducing road maps by Mr. Alfred Taylor. These maps are a delightful blend of artistry and wording, for along the motor roads shown on them are quaint designs and pictures illustrating points of special local interest, together with appropriate quotations and rhymes. In addition Mr. S. P. B. Mais supplies interesting notes on the chief towns and villages marked, and these form brilliant word pictures telling in brief the story of the British and Irish countryside. The combination of author and artist has produced a guide that is more attractive than the ordinary technical book, and at the same time is full of value to the motorist planning or making a comprehensive tour.

"The Electrical Handicraftsman and Experimenter's Manual"

By H. R. Langman and J. H. Moore (Technical Press. 7/6 net)

This book explains how to make fascinating working models from comparatively simple materials, and is remarkable both for the ingenuity displayed in constructional details and the wide range covered. Every type of electrical component is dealt with, from switches and joints to cells and condensers, and the making of electro-magnets and many different kinds of motors and dynamos is fully described. A special chapter is devoted to a simple universal electrical outfit that will enable experimenters to obtain a thorough grasp of the scientific principles behind these models.

Constructional work is explained with the aid of carefully-planned diagrams that show how each model is made and works.

Calling the Fire Brigade

How Modern Street Alarms Work

By Louis E. Calvo, M.I.Fire E., M.J.Inst.E.

"BREAK Glass—Pull Handle—Wait Here." These are the instructions on a modern street fire alarm. When they are followed in the event of a fire, news of the outbreak is flashed at lightning speed to the fire station and in an incredibly short time motor fire engines heralded by their clanging bells arrive, and are directed to the fire they have come to fight. How do the drivers of these familiar and speedy motor vehicles know which fire alarm to go to for this information?

Modern fire alarm signalling has evolved from the use of the hammer and gong used by the look-outs on watch-towers. Prior to 1850, watch-towers were erected in large cities, and these commanded a clear view of the district. It was the duty of each watchman to look out for fires, and when he discovered one to tap his tower bell with a hammer. The number of taps was the number of his district, and they were repeated by the other watchmen, thus spreading the alarm over the whole city. This is important, as it was the origin of the numerical signal system.

The transmission of alarms by electric telegraph was first introduced in Berlin in 1849, and indicators in the fire stations then showed the number of the alarm box from which the call was sent. This system has been steadily developed, and to-day in the area covered by a fire brigade there are many alarms at convenient points, from which news of a fire in the district is swiftly and automatically despatched to the central station by the mere pulling of a handle. The message sent over the wires in this manner does more than transmit the news of the outbreak; in addition it tells the station officials and firemen from which box the alarm came, and the engines and escapes race there to learn the exact position of the blaze.

The interior of a street fire alarm box, showing the clockwork mechanism by which the alarm is transmitted to the fire station. The illustrations to this article are reproduced by courtesy of the Automatic Electric Co. Ltd.

Let us look at a typical street fire alarm box. There are several different types, but an examination of one like that seen in the lower illustration on the opposite page will show the general principle. When the glass is broken, a small projecting door falls clear of the handle, which can then be pulled without fear of the hand being cut by fragments of broken glass. As we want to see how the alarm works, but do not wish to call out the fire brigade, we must refrain from pulling the handle at this juncture.

When the outer door of the box is opened by means of a key another box is revealed, and the door of this has to be opened to enable the mechanism to be seen. This is shown in detail in the illustration on this page. The main instrument is enclosed in a case with a glass front, and the triple metallic cases, insulated from each other, provide protection for it against extreme weather conditions. These cases are practically dust-tight. The air partitions between them shelter the signal movement from the effect of changes in temperature and prevent the deposition of moisture on it.

On the insulated panel at the bottom of the box is a telephone jack A. An official who wishes to call the fire station inserts the terminals of a portable hand telephone in the jack, and presses the button marked "Telephone—Press Once." The part marked "Test" is known as the silent test plug, and when this is pulled outward, the box is disconnected from the receiving apparatus at the fire station. A tapper key for signalling purposes, using a pre-arranged code, is provided at D, and at E there is a sounder that enables anyone at the box to hear if another call is being transmitted on the circuit. In that case nothing is done that would prevent its receipt at the station.

The incoming and outgoing cables of the box are fixed to the two outer terminals at the foot of the panel and an earth plate connection is made at the terminal between them. A plug switch is shown at H, and the plug for use with it is mounted at I. The incoming or outgoing cable can be earthed, or the box short-circuited, by inserting the plug in the appropriate hole in the switch. If the corresponding terminals in adjoining boxes are earthed, the section of cable between the two can be subjected to the operations of linesmen without risk of interference with the alarms.

The corresponding terminals at the top of the panel form the connections to the signal mechanism proper above them. This is known as a succession non-interference movement, for it is possible to start simultaneously several boxes on the one circuit, and to receive the signals correctly in succession without interference.

When the handle is pulled, a trip on the inside of the outer door depresses the lever J. This brings the clockwork drive into action, and it rotates the code wheel K in a clockwise direction. Round the rim of the code wheel are teeth that work the signal lever L and are spaced to give the number of the box in code. This lever is pivoted and actuates the break signal contacts through the medium of insulating pieces. The code is transmitted three times per call in one revolution of the code wheel spindle, the speed being four impulses per second. If re-operated, the box will make 16 calls before the clockwork mechanism is run down.

The design of the alarm provides several important safeguards which ensure that a box cannot be introduced into the circuit until the apparatus is entirely normal. For instance, when the plug I is removed from its holder, a catch falls and prevents the inner door being closed, and the box therefore cannot be left with the plug in one of the holes of the plug switch H. Again the silent test key is pressed into position by the closing of the door. The outer door cannot be closed until the spring is rewound; it then presses on the inner door and a shorting plug is pushed between the springs M, immediately below the telephone jack A, thereby removing the resistance of the mechanism from the line circuit.

The watchroom of a fire station. Incoming code impulses from fire alarm boxes are automatically recorded on the tape of the registering mechanism in the foreground.

Having replaced the glass and closed the box, let us proceed to the watchroom of the fire station and observe what happens there. This room is shown in the upper illustration on this page. The lines of the circuits terminate on the switchboard, a slate or marble polished panel. This carries switches and instruments for testing the conditions of the circuit and localising faults, together with means for regulating the charging and discharging of the batteries; and the associated apparatus of the switchboard actually informs the watchroom attendant of any particular circumstance as it arises, by means of visual indicators and supervisory lamps.

When the handle of an alarm box is pulled, its code wheel rotates and a train of code impulses is automatically recorded at the station on the paper tape of a punch register, the time and date also being added. Simultaneously, the code number is sounded on a gong, and visually indicated to the Brigade. This can not only be done in one station, but can be repeated automatically to several stations.

The punch register mechanism is driven by clockwork. It is in circuit with the alarm boxes and an electro-magnet is released at each impulse, punching a hole in a paper tape. The impulses are arranged to punch up to five per second.

The paper tape passes through a stamp that automatically records the minute, hour, day, month and year, and then on to a clockwork apparatus that collects it as it is fed out of the register, to form a permanent record of the calls received. The code number is received in 6 seconds and double checked in 20 seconds.

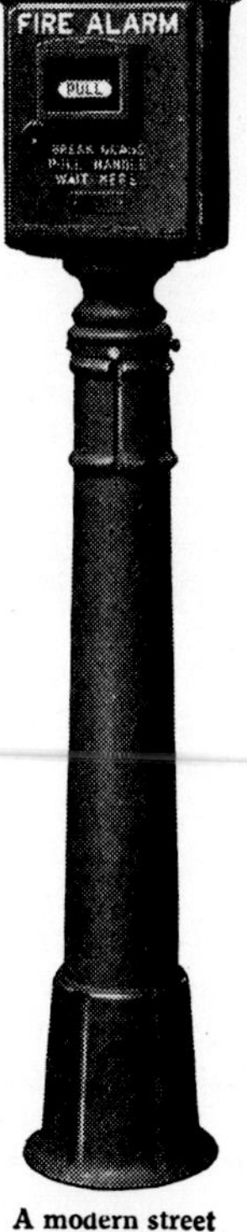

A modern street fire alarm.

The gong that sounds the alarm by giving the code number is electro-mechanical in action. It also is connected in the circuit and operates once for each impulse. The visual indicator that also comes into play when an alarm is given is a frame containing the code numbers or the addresses of the boxes, or both, and the particular indicator concerned is illuminated on the operation of the call-box. This does not exhaust the work that can be carried out from a box, for in addition its electrical impulses can be made to operate alarm bells, door opening gear, engine starters, automatic station lighting, and traffic signals to give the "all red" sign to clear the roads for the engines. Ambulance calls are also included on many circuits. In these cases the boxes contain a compartment at the rear in which there is a telephone, and access to this is obtained by breaking a small pane of glass.

Power for the circuits and watchroom equipment is supplied by accumulators in open glass boxes. These are installed on substantial stands, and all cables are protected by bead type alarm fuses, which cause an alarm bell to ring immediately a fuse operates. All batteries are trickle-charged by copper oxide metal rectifiers, which are silent in operation and require no attention when once set. The capacity of the charger is sufficient to carry the load in the event of battery failure, or during the period of changing a battery. If on the other hand the charger or the mains supply fails, the batteries will continue to provide the power for several days, or until the defects have been remedied.

There is no doubt that the installation of a modern fire alarm system is an essential part of fire fighting equipment, and it forms the quickest, safest and most reliable means of calling the fire brigade. It will be noted that the main object is to provide the public with means of giving a perfect fire call. The safety devices incorporated in the alarm ensure that normal conditions are certain when the door is closed, and all fire calls will be received in spite of disconnection or earthing at one point. Even if both these faults occur at one and the same point, the fire alarm service continues in working order, as it does also when an alarm box is short-circuited. The system described has been in experimental use at the Headquarters of the London Fire Brigade since 1931, and during that time not one false call due to any fault of the apparatus has been received.

And now, I wonder how many readers can say where is the nearest fire alarm to their homes.

FROM OUR READERS

These pages are reserved for articles from our readers. Contributions not exceeding 500 words in length are invited on any subject of general interest. These should be written neatly on one side of the paper only, and they may be accompanied by photographs or sketches for use as illustrations. Articles that are published will be paid for at our usual rates. Statements contained in articles submitted for these pages are accepted as being sent in good faith, but the Editor takes no responsibility for their accuracy.

South African Witch-Doctors

"Muti," or medicine, is responsible for many strange purchases from South Africa curio dealers. The witch-doctors who make them prefer to send deputies to obtain what they want, for they shun publicity. That is the reason why some of their more unusual methods continue to remain mysteries. Lions' fat smeared on the body is said to conquer pimples, but what special virtues there are in the bits of tortoises and ostrich eggs that these men use is a problem Europeans cannot solve. The tails of certain animals, especially the giraffe and the wildebeeste, are in great demand, and the horns of certain small buck are hollowed out to serve as containers for "muti."

A South African witch-doctor in full regalia. Photograph by Lynn Acutt, Durban.

Certain mineral stones rejected from gold mines are prized by witch-doctors, who also buy the teeth of crocodiles and lions and use them for "throwing the bones," the method they follow in looking into the future. For the fashionable witch-doctor the hind legs of ant-bears and baboons also are necessary, for they add much to his prestige.

Assortments of roots and herbs are used by witch-doctors and also by native herbalists. By far the most common native complaint is the humble but troublesome stomach ache. The remedies for this are bewildering in their number and variety, ranging from barks and herbs to portions of frogs. Madness is sometimes treated by burning a bat and making the patient inhale the smoke. Many of the remedies used are poisonous, if incorrectly taken. Mistakes seldom occur, however, and when they do a charge of murder may follow.

Like all other professions, that of the native witch-doctor has its quacks and crooks, but most of those who practise it are genuine in their beliefs and methods. It is slowly dying out, however, for the traditional belief of the natives in the witch-doctor's powers is being vanquished by the spread of European ideas among them. D. C. KIRKLAND (Durban).

Bird Life in the Welsh Hills

My friends and myself derive much pleasure from tramping over fields, along lanes and through the many little woods around our homes in the Welsh Hills. We take special delight in looking for birds' nests. We never rob these of their eggs, however, and are careful to disturb the birds themselves as little as possible, contenting ourselves with examining the nests and on occasions photographing them.

There are few birds among those to be met with in the neighbourhood whose nests we have not found and inspected. The peewit, or the lapwing plover, eluded our most diligent searches for a long time. The first of the names by which this bird is known is derived from its peculiar call. Its usual haunts are marshy or ploughed fields, but it builds its home so cunningly, and the eggs blend in colour with the ground so well, that it is possible to stand within a few paces of a nest without seeing it. The birds are extremely wary, and feign injury and limp about in order to attract intruders and lead them away from their nests. When we did find a peewit's nest on the edge of a cornfield, it was more by good fortune than skill in searching. In it were four eggs, greyish in colour and marked with black blotches. They were pear-shaped and their pointed ends were together in the centre of the nest. While we looked at the eggs, the owners circled around, uttering their high-pitched cry.

Other nests we have seen have included those of the curlew, the tawny owl, and the sparrow-hawk, as well as those of more common birds. It is curious to find that the nests of the smaller birds are more elaborate than those of the larger ones. For instance, the common wren, one of the smallest of British birds, weaves scores of feathers into the lining of its home, but a few blades of grass are sufficient for the curlew. I have found it very interesting indeed to make comparisons of this kind between the nests of the various birds I have been able to watch.

G. E. FANTHORPE (Newtown).

A Unique Water Supply System

The farmers in the Eburru district of Kenya rely almost entirely on the condensation of natural steam jets for drinking purposes, for bathing, and for giving to their cattle. An adequate supply of fresh water is essential to farming, and there must be few farms that have no normal water supply, and make use of a source so curious as this.

The mountain slopes above the farms are full of jets of natural low pressure steam, and these have been harnessed to supply a constant flow of water that has enabled thousands of acres of land to be occupied. Previously the district was thought to be completely useless, but now it supports a large population engaged in agriculture.

Tapping natural steam to supply pure water. The photographs on this page are by S. Hemsted, Kenya.

The apparatus for making use of the steam is remarkably simple. A jet is capped by a large tank, which is placed upside-down over it and has a hole cut in its side, to which are soldered lengths of corrugated iron piping of large diameter. In some cases several jets close together are capped in this manner by a single tank. The steam passes along the pipe, and the longer this is the better, for the steam then is given more opportunity to condense. A trickle of water forms in each pipe, and this is collected and led where it is required.

The rate of condensation varies from day to day. It is more rapid when a strong wind blows across the pipes, and is less complete on hotter days, when the water supply is correspondingly diminished.

S. Hemsted (Gilgil, Kenya).

The natural steam collected in the manner illustrated above is passed through long pipes in order to condense it. The water of this unique supply is always warm.

A French Seaside Holiday

Last August I was privileged to spend a short time at the seaside holiday home of a friend in France. I travelled first to Paris by way of Boulogne, and in the Nord station there boarded a train for Quend Plage, my destination. Most of the locomotives I noticed in the station carried smoke deflectors. I travelled third class and found the metal seats of my compartment very uncomfortable in comparison with those of third class trains in Great Britain. At the end of a journey lasting 45 minutes the train drew up in a wayside station resembling those to be seen in the English countryside, except that the plants were shrivelled up and the high platform was replaced by a raised gravel structure only six inches above the track.

My friend met me at the station, and I found that it was necessary to travel two miles by bus to complete the journey. The country there is very flat and sandy, and it is for this reason that the railway remains so far inland. The sand is held together in dunes by means of a special grass, sown by the peasants. One interesting result of the flatness of the land is that at night six lighthouses can be seen, ranging from Cape Gris Nez in the north to Dieppe in the south west.

The journey of two miles occupied 15 minutes, but at last on rounding a curve the village came into view. It has been built during the last eight years as a holiday resort, and is small, its population being about 72 in winter and 1,500 in summer. The main road runs straight through to the sea. It is macadamised in the centre, but is bordered by wide gravel paths. The houses of the village interested me greatly. They are scattered about, and are of all sizes, shapes and colours. The medley seems to be typically French, and in some ways is more picturesque than the more symmetrical layout of houses resembling each other that make up similar places in many parts of Great Britain. I thoroughly enjoyed my stay there with my French hosts. H. Drabble (Mosborough).

A Swiss Salt Mine

There are salt mines at Le Bouillet, south of the Lake of Geneva, and I was greatly interested in their working when I visited them recently. They consist of underground passages, or galleries, in which the rock is known to contain salt, and this is extracted by flooding them with water and leading off through pipes the brine that is formed.

The entrance to the mine is a narrow tunnel driven straight into the side of the mountains, and from it the various underground passages branch off. Some of the galleries are fitted with electric light, and acetylene lamps are carried to light the way along the others. The pipes are made of hollowed-out tree trunks, one end of each section being pointed, like a pencil, to enable it to be fitted into the blunt end of the next portion. Some of the pipes are 100 years old. Experiments recently have been made with cement and cast iron pipes, however.

During my passage through the mine I saw a large drill in use to obtain samples of rock for examination. Black diamonds are used at the boring end of this drill.

The visit was very enjoyable, but I was glad when I emerged into the bright sunshine after my stay underground. M. S. Bonford (Harpenden).

OLD TIME STEAMSHIPS

The illustration on this page shows a simple but effective Meccano model of the first Cunard steamer, "*Britannia*," which began her service in 1840. This model was intended to be displayed with the well-known Meccano demonstration model of the Cunard White Star liner "*Queen Mary*," illustrated on page 230 of the "*M.M.*" for April last, and therefore was built to the same scale. Apart from this comparison, the "*Britannia*" forms a very interesting subject for reproduction, and the model will introduce the model-builder who is looking for new subjects to a field that has been little explored.

The construction of these old-time ships need only be simple to give excellent results. The judicious use of a few Strips and Strip Plates produces an excellent hull, paddle boxes are well represented by Curved Strips of suitable size, and Pulleys can be used to form paddles. If desired, the shaft carrying the paddles can be connected through a high ratio reduction gear to one of the small Meccano Electric or Clockwork Motors. This greatly increases the interest of the model.

Early steamships were fitted with masts and sails, and these can readily be reproduced in Meccano with Rods and Couplings. The rigging can be secured to the masts and yards by means of Anchoring Springs, and small accessories such as masthead lamps, sidelights, and crows-nests can be built up from Collars and Couplings. Funnels, part No. 138, are suitable for most models of this type.

The appearance of these model ships can be greatly improved by fitting sails cut from good quality white paper and fitted to the yards by means of gum or cotton.

An interesting model of this type recently submitted was that of a Mississippi side-wheeler. These vessels are well known to Meccano boys. They were of shallow draught and had enormous superstructures that make them particularly suitable for reproduction in Meccano. The model submitted was a very fine effort, and the typical moving beam of the engine, protruding from the top of the superstructure, was cleverly represented by a number of Meccano Strips. The beam was driven by an Electric Motor and was connected to the crankshaft by a long coupling rod. The paddles carried at the ends of the shaft operated in exactly the same manner as those fitted to the prototype.

A Meccano model of tne "Britannia," the first vessel of the Cunard line.

DISPLAY MECHANISMS

A working Meccano model is always a great attraction, whether it is an imposing super model, or a smaller one incorporating an ingenious or humorous movement. It is therefore not surprising to find that Meccano models of all kinds are largely used for display purposes. In addition, the adaptability of Meccano enables novel movements to be devised that can be incorporated in special displays. Many examples of these have come to our notice, and the details of the two models now described may suggest similar schemes to other model-builders.

A model Grandfather Clock, built with the aid of Super Model Instruction Leaflet No. 14a, was recently loaned by a Meccano enthusiast, P. W. Mills, Lowestoft, for the purpose of advertising a brand of self-rising flour. The clock was displayed in a shop window, and there attracted considerable attention, much to the satisfaction of the shop owner. An interesting feature of the model was the face. This was cut from blue cardboard, on which were mounted gold Roman numerals, and the result was very effective.

An example of the use of Meccano mechanisms for operating non-Meccano displays that has been brought to our notice by E. A. Tooke, Peckham, was exhibited recently in the window of a London chemist. It took the form of a working model leg that moved in a similar manner to that of a human leg in the act of walking. The leg was arranged in front of a screen in which was cut a slot, and the cranked end of a Meccano Crank Handle projected through the slot. This end had a covering of thin rubber, and as it rotated it pressed against the underside of the leg while it was sweeping out at an angle of 90°.

The inner end of the Crank Handle was connected at right-angles to a long Rod by means of a Coupling. One end of this Rod was fitted with a counterpoise, and the other end was connected by a pivotally mounted Strip to a rotating Face Plate that formed a crank, and was driven at slow speed by an Electric Motor.

MECCANO GRUBS AND INSECTS

Snails, flies, mosquitoes and other small forms of life are seldom looked upon by Meccano enthusiasts as potential subjects for new Meccano models, but they have been chosen by Victor Nabb of Market Drayton as prototypes for a series of very interesting models. Nabb is interested in the study of insect life, and occasionally gives illustrated talks on the subject. For this purpose he has constructed a number of large size models of certain insects from Meccano parts, and it will readily be understood that these have made his talks very much more attractive to his hearers. A similar plan could of course be followed with many other subjects, and no doubt model enthusiasts with a second hobby will find the idea of interest.

Considerable ingenuity has been exercised in the construction of the Meccano insects, and good use has been made of Strip Plates, Spring Cord, and such small parts as Centre Forks and Handrail Couplings. One model, representing a locust, is of particular interest, as it has been built with extreme care and the finished model is correct in every detail. The body is relatively long and is formed in the centre from a Meccano Boiler, without ends. The head, which is built up from two 2½" Triangular Plates and two 2½"×1½" Flexible Plates, is secured to one end of the Boiler by means of Flat Brackets, and to the other end of the Boiler is attached a representation of the long tapering rear portion of the body, formed from a number of 12½" Strips secured to circles of 5½" and 3½" Strips.

The legs presented some difficulty at first, but finally were made to look very much like those of an actual locust by making use of a number of Reed Hooks and two Special Screwdrivers. The handle of each Screwdriver was extended slightly by a Sleeve Piece opened out at one end. The blades were then bent slightly to the required shape, and "hairs" represented by short lengths of Copper Wire were fitted where required.

Each of the four wings, when completed, represented many hours' delicate work. A frame was first built up from Rods, and these were also used to form the main structural members of the wings. Lacings of thin copper wire was next woven inside the wing frames, and after one or two failures, four really beautiful wings were ready for fitting to the body. Each wing was secured in place by means of two Handrail Supports. Pieces of Spring Cord were used in building up the wings and also formed the smaller legs and antennae. In order to preserve the shape of these, pieces of Spring Cord, twin lengths of 22 S.W.G. Copper Wire were passed down their centres.

In building models of moths and butterflies, Nabb introduces somewhat different methods from those already described. For instance, the fat and comparatively stumpy body of a large model Emperor Moth he has made recently has been reproduced by constructing a suitably shaped framework and covering it with a series of narrow frills of the required colours. These frills are cut from any light material and stained with ordinary coloured writing ink. The wings are simple frameworks built up in sections and covered with artificial silk that is cut into narrow strips as required. Later the colouring is added, and Spring Cord is used in forming the legs and antennae.

WIRELESS CABINET DESIGNS

For the wireless enthusiasts who wish to design their own cabinets the following ideas, from B. Bennett, Belfast, are of particular interest. The usual method of building up a cabinet of this sort is to construct a strong wooden box and fit this at the back with a removable panel. A second panel, to be screwed in position, is cut for the front of the cabinet and this usually consists of a sheet of three-ply wood, the centre of which has been cut away to form a design or fret.

These designs are liable to break, and to guard against this Bennett has constructed frets from Meccano parts to replace the wooden ones of his own cabinet and those of some of his friends. Curved Strips and short straight Strips were used largely in making these, and a few special parts such as Ring Frames and small Corner Brackets were incorporated in one or two examples. One of the most attractive cabinet fronts takes the form of a set of organ pipes built up from Strips covered with thin gauze.

LINK MOTIONS (J. CARROTHERS, BELFAST)

In the past many excellent demonstration models of valve gears and link motions have appeared in the "*M.M.*" and these have always created much interest. Mr. J. Carrothers, Belfast, is a keen model-builder who has taken full advantage of the possibilities offered by these motions, and one of his recent efforts is a reproduction of the link motion fitted to Atkinson's Differential Gas Engine, which enables a four-cycle stroke to be obtained for every revolution of the crankshaft.

The construction of this gear is simple. A crank 2" long is built up from a 1½" Strip and a Crank. This is mounted on the driving shaft of the engine, and is pivotally secured to a 3" Strip that carries a Simple Bell Crank at its lower end. The Strip and Crank overlap two holes, and one end of a second 3" Strip is pivoted in the centre hole of the Crank. The free end of this Strip is secured by a bolt and lock-nuts to the frame of the model. The lower end of the Bell Crank points away from the cylinder, and is linked up with the piston by a 4½" Strip. The vertical distance between the centres of the Simple Bell Crank and crankshaft must be 3½", the former being 1" forward of the latter.

A Meccano Wall Clock

A Simple Weight Driven Time-keeper

As a result of many requests for an accurate but simple clock, we describe in this article a Meccano Wall Clock that will interest specially model-builders who have a limited supply of Meccano parts at their disposal.

The frame is formed from two 12½" Angle Girders 1, fitted with two 5½"×2½" Flanged Plates, one of which is shown at 2. The near side Plate has been removed in order to expose the gear-train. A 5½" Angle Girder 3 is bolted across the upper flanges of the Flanged Plates 2, and two further Girders of similar size are bolted to the inside edge of each Plate. One of these Girders is shown at 4, and they both form supports for two 4½"×2½" Flat Plates. One 5½"×2½" Flat Plate and two 5½" Strips are bolted between the two rear flanges of the Plates 2, Fig. 2. Two 4½" Strips 5 are fitted as shown.

Two 12½"×2½" Strip Plates are secured to the Girders 1, and bridged at the bottom by a 5½"×2½" Strip Plate. At the top two 5½"×2½" Strip Plates are fitted as shown in Fig. 1, and they are connected together at their upper corners by a 2½" small radius Curved Strip. Fancy work is added to the bottom of the clock and this is formed from five 2½" small radius Curved Strips and two 4" Curved Strips.

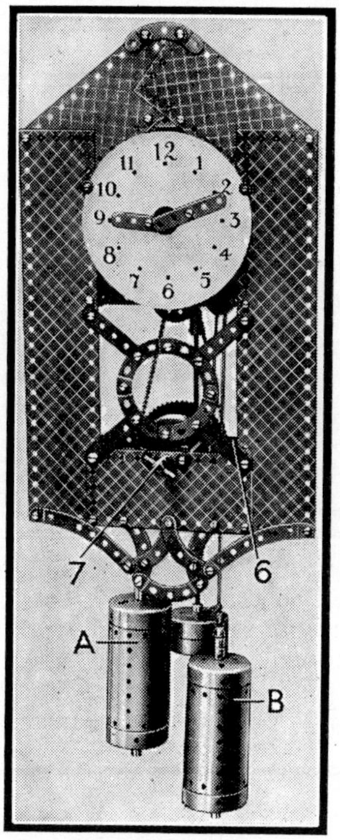

The lower end of the Girders 1 each carries a 2½"×2½" Flat Plate, the outer edges of which are fitted with 2½" Angle Girders. The Flanges of these Angle Girders point inward, and at their upper ends they are bridged by a duplicated 5½" Strip, a portion of which is shown at 6, Fig. 1. Two Double Arm Cranks are now fitted to form reinforced bearings, and one of these is secured to the centre of the 5½" Strips 6. The other is bolted to the lower 5½"×2½" Strip Plate as shown.

Fig. 1. This simple Meccano Clock is fully described on this page.

The winding barrel consists of two Wheel Flanges and two Face Plates, bolted together by two ¾" Bolts, to form a large diameter drum. The boss of one of the Face Plates is turned inward so that it is accommodated inside one of the Wheel Flanges, and the complete winding barrel is mounted on a 3½" Rod that carries also a Ratchet Wheel and a 3" Sprocket. The Ratchet Wheel is locked on the 3½" Rod with its boss pointing to the back of the model; and the Sprocket Wheel, free to turn on the Rod, is mounted in a similar manner, but is spaced away from the Ratchet Wheel by a Washer. In one of its outer holes a Pivot Bolt is secured and on this is carried a spring-loaded Pawl. The front end of the 3½" Rod carries a Coupling 7, fitted with a 1½" Rod, forming the winding handle.

The 3" Sprocket drives, through a length of Chain, a ¾" Sprocket Wheel mounted on the same Rod as a 1½" Sprocket 8. A second length of Chain connects the Wheel 8 with the Sprocket Wheel 9, and this is mounted on a 3" Rod, together with a 57-teeth Gear that is in mesh with a ½" Pinion locked on the same Rod as a second 57-teeth Gear. This last Gear is carried on the front end of its Rod immediately behind the face, and is in engagement with a ½" Pinion mounted on the same Rod as the Gear 10. The Rod is carried at one end in a bearing formed from a Double Bent Strip. A ½" Pinion on the escapement rod is in constant mesh with the Gear 10.

The Gears that transmit the movement from the minute hand to the hour hand are now fitted. The Rod carrying the Sprocket 9 is fitted with a ½" Pinion that meshes with a 57-teeth Gear 11 on the Rod 12. This Rod is 3½" in length and carries the minute hand at its outer end. At its centre is a ¾" Pinion, meshing with a 50-teeth Gear on the Rod 13, and also a 1" Gear that engages with a similar part on the Rod 14 carrying a second ¾" Pinion. This Pinion drives a 50-teeth Gear on the Rod 15, which carries on its front end a ½" Pinion. A 57-teeth Gear, that is free to turn on the Rod 12, meshes with this latter Pinion, and is fitted with a ½" Reversed Angle Bracket. This part is bolted to the 57-teeth Gear and it protrudes through a hole in the centre of the face. A 1½" Strip represents the hour hand.

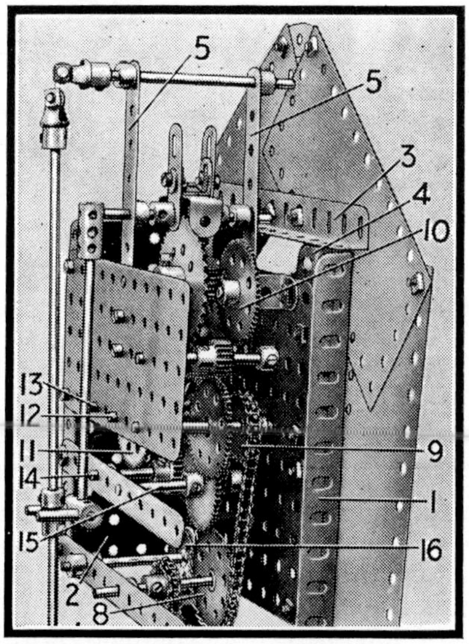

The escapement wheel and pallet are fully described in the Suggestions Section on page 473 of last month's "*M.M.*". The mounting of the pendulum will be apparent from the illustration. The flexible connection at the top of the pendulum consists of two short lengths of flexible steel wire. The pendulum itself is built up from one 8", one 11½" and one 3½" Rod joined together by Couplings. The "bob" is built up from two Boiler Ends in which is placed a small quantity of lead scrap.

The driving weights, shown in Fig. 1, are formed from Boilers filled with lead scrap and are attached to the driving cords by End Bearings. The cord from the weight A is taken to the drum, round which it is wound in an anti-clockwise direction. The cord from B passes over the Pulley 16 and is wound anti-clockwise on the drum.

Fig. 2. The gearing of the Wall Clock.

In Search of New Models

Countryside Figures and Scenes

LAST month we described a number of models of typical people seen at the seaside; this month we turn to the country. The same general idea is followed, the models representing figures and machinery that can be seen during a holiday in the countryside, where there is no lack of interesting subjects for reproduction with Meccano.

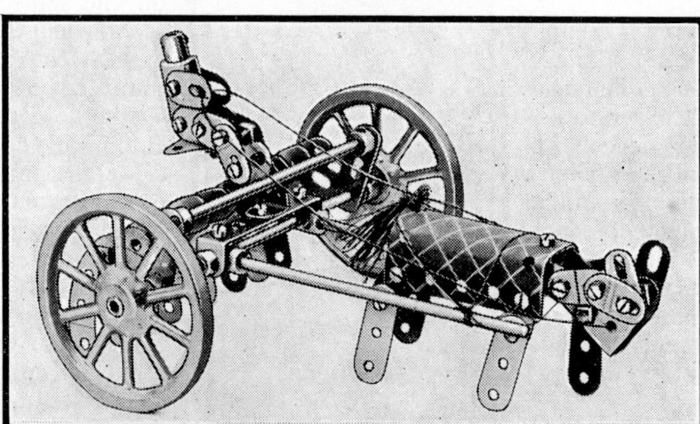

Fig. 1. A simple but realistic model of a horse rake at work.

A hay-field is the source of the first models to be dealt with. The old way of cutting grass was by means of a scythe, and this method is illustrated in miniature in Fig. 2, which shows a simple but clever reproduction of an old-time farmer plying his scythe. No difficulty should be experienced in building this and similar models. The body of the farmer is formed from four 2½" large radius Curved Strips. These are secured together at the top by means of two Double Brackets and two Flat Brackets, and at the bottom a Double Bracket and two 1½" Strips are used for a similar purpose. The shoulders are cleverly reproduced by means of 1" Corner Brackets, secured to the body by Angle Brackets. The scythe is built of a 4½" Rod and a 4" Curved Strip, joined by means of a Collar fitted with a bolt. An amusing feature is the spring-mounted head, which moves almost continuously and lends an atmosphere of quaintness to the figure. A Flexible Coupling Unit is secured at each end in the longitudinal hole of a Coupling, the lower one of which is bolted to the inside of the body by a ½" Bolt and nut. The upper Coupling is attached by means of a 1" Rod to a Bush Wheel forming the hat.

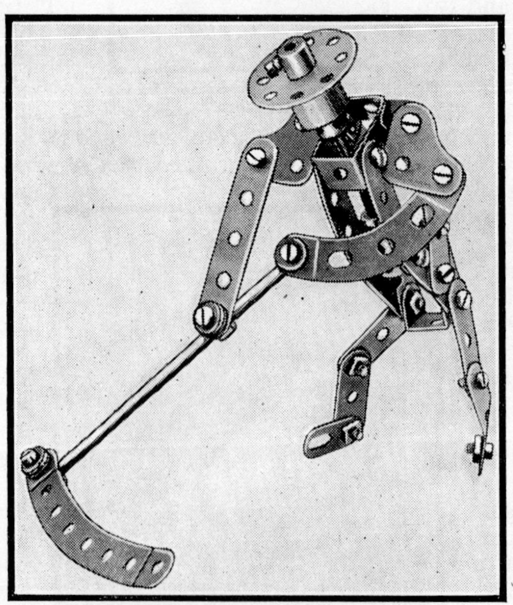

Fig. 2. A Meccano farmer wielding a scythe.

Other figures suggesting different farming occupations can readily be constructed on similar lines. Such simple actions as digging, hoeing and cutting with the aid of a sickle form excellent subjects for reproduction, and the builder will find ample scope for ingenuity when arranging the arms, legs and heads of his figures. Models of this kind do not rely for their successful appearance on the inclusion of a great number of parts, but rather upon the builder's imagination and ability to put a few parts to good use.

Modern methods of grass cutting on a large scale offer splendid opportunities for the agricultural model-builder, for many large and interesting machines have been devised for this purpose. The small horizontal cutting machine or mower in general use in this country forms an excellent subject for the small Outfit owners. A large wheel mounted to one side of the machine operates a cutter fitted at right-angles to the wheel, acting through a series of bevel gears. A right-angle drive formed from cord can be used in a simple model.

Before the hay is gathered in and stacked it must be dried by turning it, and is made up into swathes and haycocks. The specially designed machines, drawn by horses or tractors, that are used to carry out the necessary operations form excellent subjects for Meccano models. A hay tedder has four or six large rakes, mounted to form a long drum and rotated through spur gearing from the wheels. The rakes are fitted with a parallel link motion so that they turn the hay without throwing it into the air.

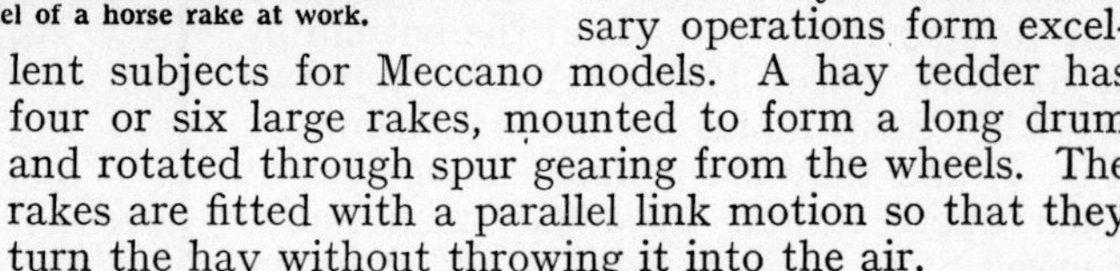

Horse drawn rakes are used for making the swathes or long ridges of hay, and a clever reproduction of a machine of this kind is shown in Fig. 1. This is a simple model and, with the addition of a few Curved Strips and 3" Wheels, is quite suitable for the small Outfit owner. The forks, or tines, are represented by 2½" small radius Curved Strips mounted on a Screwed Rod, and this is attached at each end to a Simple Bell Crank pivoted at its centre on the main axle. The driver is formed from a series of Flat Brackets and Double Brackets and a Rod Socket represents his head. The construction of the horse is very simple. A "U" Section Curved Plate forms the body, and each leg is built up from a Flat Bracket and a 1½" Strip. The tail, reins and harness are represented by short lengths of Meccano Cord.

Fig. 3 at the top of the next page shows a Meccano model in which the atmosphere of a favourite country scene has been successfully captured. Carting hay from the field to the stackyard is so typical of country life that no article of this nature would be complete without some mention of it. The design of hay carts has remained unchanged for generations, and their simplicity and solidity make them eminently suitable for reproducing in Meccano.

The sides of the model cart are built up on a $5\frac{1}{2}'' \times 2\frac{1}{2}''$ Flanged Plate, and the carrying frames are secured to the upper edges of these by Obtuse Angle Brackets. The front and rear carriers are represented by $2\frac{1}{2}''$ Flat Girders and those at the side by means of $5\frac{1}{2}''$ Strips. Hay of course must be added to give a final realistic touch. This can readily be represented by six bundles of Hornby Fibre, and real straw or grass also can be used.

The familiar reapers and binders used in harvesting wheat and other grain are ideal model-building subjects, for they are picturesque in appearance and incorporate interesting mechanisms. The cutter is similar to that of the grass mower, and is driven through a crank and gearing connected to the large wheel of the machine. Rotating arms press the grain against the cutter and lay it flat on the conveyors. These arms form what is called the reel and are driven by a secondary set of bevels, but in small models, cord can be used for this purpose. The conveyors carry the grain up to the sloping platforms on the offside of the machine on which it is bound into sheaves. Many interesting models of this kind have been described in the *"M.M.,"* an excellent example that won a prize in a Model-building Contest being illustrated on page 293 of the May, 1936 issue, and any keen model-builder who has spent a holiday in the country and has seen the machines they represent at work will find great pleasure in trying to build one for himself.

Fig. 3. A familiar countryside feature well reproduced in Meccano. The hay consists of six bundles of Hornby Fibre.

When they were first introduced these machines were drawn by horses, but to-day tractors are freely used, and a combination of a tractor and a reaper and binder would make a very attractive model. More recently, machines that actually thresh the corn as it is gathered and deliver it into sacks have been introduced, and the reproduction of one of these in miniature would be an interesting piece of work.

Fig. 4. A sturdy Meccano farmer following the plough. The attitude of the model horse is suggestive of the slow steady motion characteristic of ploughing, and the figure typifies strength.

A farming scene entirely different from those already described is reproduced in Fig. 4, which shows a very simple model plough together with a horse and ploughman. Little difficulty should be experienced in constructing an attractive model of this kind.

The plough blade is formed from two $1\frac{1}{2}''$ Strips, bolted together as shown, and secured by means of two $\frac{1}{2}'' \times \frac{1}{2}''$ Angle Brackets to two Collars. The Collars carry the shafts, which consist of two 5″ Rods bent to the required shape. The outer ends of these Rods pass into the end plain holes of two Couplings that form part of the ploughman's arms and are attached by two bolts to the upper ends of a Small Fork Piece. A Rod passing through the longitudinal hole of this Fork Piece carries at its upper end a $\frac{1}{2}''$ Pinion, representing the ploughman's head, and at its lower end a Coupling to which are secured the legs formed from Flat Brackets. The horse is built in the same manner as that hauling the rake and the traces can readily be fitted in the manner shown in the illustration.

A large number of machines are used in conjunction with the plough, and illustrations of these are to be found in the advertising sections of many farming and engineering periodicals. They include spring tine harrows, potato diggers, cultivators and drilling machines, all suitable prototypes for new models, and those who are searching for new ideas for entries in model-building contests will be well advised to consider one or more of these.

The construction of a miniature spring tine harrow is not difficult, and only very few parts are required. The large horizontal frame is best built up from a series of Strips set on edge, and connected together by two Angle Brackets. The finished frame forms three sides of a square and carries three long Rods disposed laterally. These Rods, which are mounted in the upper holes of Flat Trunnions bolted to the frame, are prevented from sliding by means of Collars.

The tines are now added, and these can be fitted to the three Rods already mentioned in a similar manner to those in the model horse rake. They are curved to a greater extent, however, and therefore are best represented by Strips bent to the required shape. Three Cranks are now fitted, in line, to the three Rods, and all are coupled together by a long Strip. This Strip is lock-nutted to the Cranks and it is linked up to a lever at its rear end. By moving the lever the tines can be adjusted to work at any depth. In large harrows two levers are often provided, each of these controlling half of the tines.

The addition of one or two horses and a farmer will add considerably to the appearance of the model and these can be built on exactly similar lines to those shown in Fig. 4. The reins and traces may be represented by short lengths of cord.

Attractive New Models

Motor Ice Yacht and Deep Sea Diving Suit

THE models to be described this month are varied in type and two of them are completely novel, for their subjects have not previously been represented in the Magazine. The new models are a Diving Suit for deep sea work, and a Motor Ice Yacht, and are illustrated in Figs. 2 and 4. The other two models dealt with are a Motor Launch and an Arch Bridge.

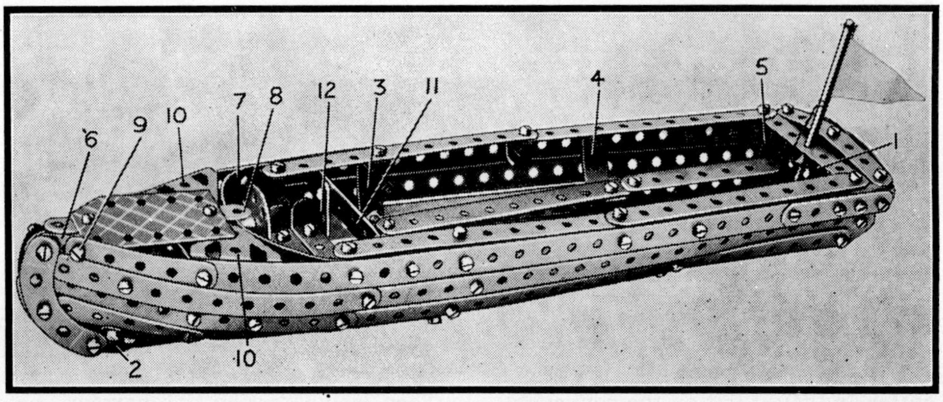

The Motor Launch, shown in Fig. 1, is a particularly neat model built with Outfit F. Its building is commenced by constructing the keel, which is formed from two 12½" Angle Girders bolted together, at their round holes, to form a "T" section Girder. Between the two Girders at the forward end, a 2½" Strip is inserted for a distance of three holes and is held in place by means of two nuts and bolts. At the rear is a Flat Bracket to which the rudder, a Flat Trunnion, is afterwards attached. This end of the keel is fitted with two Angle Brackets bent outward slightly, and secured in place by bolts passing through the end slotted holes. The two Brackets form supports for a 2½"×1½" Flanged Plate 1 representing the transom.

Fig. 1. A Meccano Motor Launch built on excellent lines. Its construction is described in detail in the accompanying article.

The bows of the boat are formed from three 2½" small radius Curved Strips, one of which is bolted by its end hole to the 2½" Strip carried at the front end of the keel. This Curved Strip is shown at 2, and the two other similar Strips are attached to it and overlap four holes.

The ribs are now secured to the keel. Two of these are shown at 3 and 4, and two others are fitted to each side, one represented by a 2½" Strip at the bow and the other, a 1½" Strip 5, at the stern. The lower end of the 1½" Strip at the stern is secured to the flange of the Plate 1.

When the ribs are in position the "planks" can be fitted, and the lengths of these are shown in the illustration. The top-most plank is fitted first. It is built up from one 12½" Strip and two 2½" Strips, and is extended at one end by means of a Flat Bracket 6. The second plank from the top consists of one 12½" and one 5½" Strip overlapping each other five holes. The third or centre plank is formed in a similar manner, but is secured in position slightly nearer the bows. Of the two remaining planks, one consists of a 12½" Strip and 2½" Strip, and the other of two 5½" Strips that overlap each other three holes.

The fore-deck is now constructed. A 5½" Strip 7, curved in the manner shown, is first secured across the hull and this carries at its centre hole a ½"×½" Angle Bracket locked in place by means of a Threaded Pin carrying a Bush Wheel, which represents the steering wheel. The Angle Bracket forms a support for one end of the 3½" Strip 8, the opposite end of which is bolted to a further ½"×½" Angle Bracket held in position by the Bolt 9. The 3½" Strip 8 carries a 2½"×1½" Flexible Plate, the corners of which are bent slightly in order to preserve the shape of this part of the model. The fore-deck is completed by the addition of the two Trunnions shown at 10 in the photograph.

Seats and flag-staff are all that are now required to complete the model. The flag-staff is represented by a 4" Rod that is held in position in the boat by means of two Collars, and a flag cut from a piece of coloured paper is fitted by means of a short length of Meccano Cord. The seat for the helmsman is formed from two 2½"×½" Double Angle Strips held together and secured to a 3½"×½" Double Angle Strip 11 by means of two 1"×1" Angle Brackets. One of these Angle Brackets is shown at 12. Each side seat is built up from a 5½" and a 3½" Strip, overlapping one hole, and is secured to the bottom of the boat by two Reversed Angle Brackets.

Parts required to build the model Motor Launch: 8 of No. 1; 15 of No. 2; 4 of No. 3; 2 of No. 4; 11 of No. 5; 2 of No. 6a; 2 of No. 8; 5 of No. 10; 12 of No. 12; 2 of No. 12a; 3 of No. 12c; 1 of No. 15b; 1 of No. 24; 97 of No. 37; 2 of No. 37a; 5 of No. 38; 2 of No. 48a; 2 of No. 48b; 1 of No. 51; 1 of No. 59; 2 of No. 90; 3 of No. 90a; 1 of No. 111; 2 of No. 111c; 1 of No. 115; 4 of No. 125; 2 of No. 126; 1 of No. 126a; 1 of No. 188.

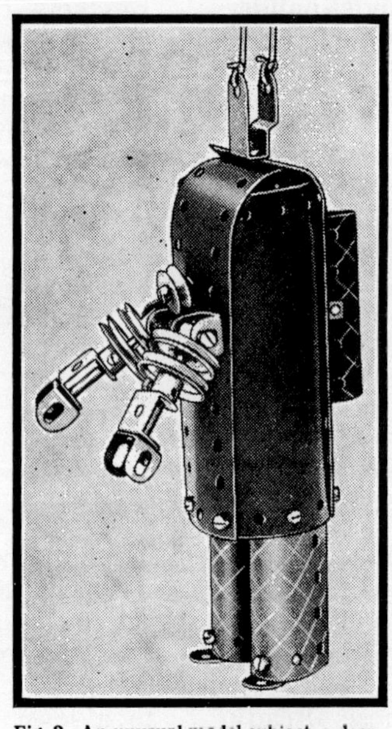

Fig. 2. An unusual model subject, a deep-sea diver.

The strange-looking model shown in Fig. 2 is based on a form of diving dress of the type invented by German engineers, and used by the Italian divers of the "*Artiglio*" in their search for the gold of the ill-fated "*Egypt.*" The dress is designed for salvage work in very deep water, and the man who descends in it is suspended in a position from which he can direct the use of explosives or of the grab employed to dig out treasure from a sunken vessel. Great strength is necessary at the enormous depths at which work is carried on with the aid of this dress.

The model can be constructed with Outfit B. The body

is built up from two 4½"×2½" and two 5½"×1½" Flexible Plates bolted together, and the upper edges of the 5½"×1½" Plates are joined by means of a nut and bolt that also holds in position a Cranked Bent Strip to which are secured the Cords representing the hoisting ropes. Each arm consists of a 1½" Rod fitted with two Pulleys, a Double Bracket and two ½"×½" Angle Brackets. One of the Pulleys is fitted with two bolts and the shanks of these pass through the slotted holes of two ½"×½" Angle Brackets that are attached to the body by a nut and bolt. The two ½"×½" Angle Brackets on the outer end of the 1½" Rod are retained in position by means of a Spring Clip. A compressed oxygen cylinder is represented by a 2½"×1½" Flexible Plate bent into the shape of a U and secured to the model by two Cords.

Fig. 3. An interesting arch bridge that can be built with the parts included in Outfit D.

The legs are fitted last. Each of these is represented by a U section Curved Plate, part No. 199, and the feet are reproduced by Reversed Angle Brackets.

Parts required to build the model Diver: 1 of No. 10; 2 of No. 11; 8 of No. 12; 2 of No. 17; 4 of No. 22; 1 of No. 23; 2 of No. 35; 20 of No. 37; 6 of No. 38; 1 of No. 44; 2 of No. 111c; 2 of No. 125; 1 of No. 188; 2 of No. 189; 2 of No. 190; 2 of No. 191; 2 of No. 199.

A fine model Arch Bridge built with Outfit D is shown in Fig. 3. This is suitable for incorporation in a Hornby Railway if only a single line is to be used in the section in which it is included.

Each main side member of the model is formed from two 12½" Angle Girders joined together by a 5½" Strip that overlaps each Girder two holes. Two 12½"×2½" and one 5½"×2½" Strip Plates are used to connect them, and six ⅜" Bolts protruding upward, and fitted with Cord as shown, represent handrails. Each end support of the roadway is formed from two 12½" Strips that are secured in position at their upper ends. The lower ends of the Strips carry ½"×½" Angle Brackets and a 2½"×½" Double Angle Strip also is fitted. The Angle Brackets form the connection between the vertical 12½" Strips and a 3½"×2½" Strip forming the base.

The arch may now be fitted. This is built up from four 12½" and two 5½" Strips, and is attached by bracing strips of varying lengths to the underside of the roadway. Additional bracing is added, and this takes the form of lengths of Meccano Cord.

Parts required to build the model Arch Bridge: 10 of No. 1; 13 of No. 2; 4 of No. 3; 4 of No. 5; 2 of No. 6a; 4 of No. 8; 8 of No. 10; 8 of No. 12; 92 of No. 37; 6 of No. 37a, 1 of No. 40; 7 of No. 48a; 2 of No. 53; 6 of No. 111c; 1 of No. 195; 2 of No. 197.

A neat model Motor Ice Yacht, built with Outfit B, is illustrated in Fig. 4. This model is characteristic of the ice yachts that in winter frequent the frozen lakes and rivers of Canada. Ice yachting is great sport, for high speeds are attained and remarkable feats of balancing by their crews are called for.

The base of the model is a Flanged Sector Plate fitted underneath, at its widest part, with two Angle Brackets and two Flat Brackets 1, which support a 2½" Strip 2 representing the rear runner. At its narrow end the Sector Plate is fitted with two Trunnions 3 that carry the 5½" Strips forming the outriggers. The outer end of each Strip has bolted to it a ½"×½" Angle Bracket and a Flat Bracket, and to the Flat Bracket is secured a 2½" Strip.

A Magic Motor 4 is bolted to the wide portion of the Sector Plate by Angle Brackets, and to the upper end of this Motor two Flat Trunnions are secured by means of Reversed Angle Brackets. These Reversed Angle Brackets are bolted to the two upper lugs of the Motor by their round holes, and their slotted ends are so arranged that they are ½" apart. The Flat Trunnions, bolted to the slotted ends of the Reversed Angle Brackets, carry two Double Brackets, and these form bearings for a 3½" Rod representing the propeller shaft. A ½" fast Pulley gripped on this shaft is connected by means of a Driving Band to tl e pulley on the driving spindle of the Motor. The propeller consists of a Bush Wheel, secured on the propeller shaft and fitted with four 2½" Strips representing the blades. If desired, these Strips can be twisted slightly to improve the effect.

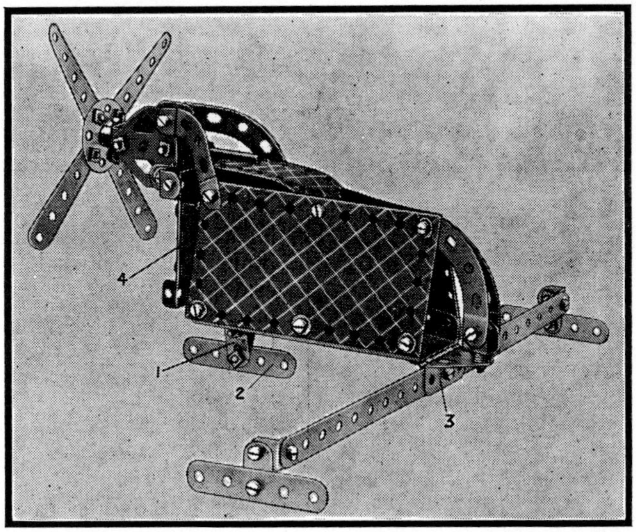

Fig. 4. The prototype of this power ice-yacht is to be seen in winter on the frozen lakes of North America.

The cabin is built up from two 4½"×2½" Flexible Plates bolted to the side flanges of the Flanged Sector Plate that forms the base of the model. Each of the top centre holes of the Flexible Plates is fitted with a bolt carrying a ½"×½" Angle Bracket, and these form supports for a 2½"×1½" Flexible Plate as shown. The rear portion of this Plate is held in position beneath the protruding end of the propeller shaft. The top of the Flat Trunnions, carrying the propeller shaft, is braced by two Curved Strips.

Parts required to build the Ice Yacht: 2 of No. 2; 9 of No. 5; 4 of No. 10; 2 of No. 11; 8 of No. 12; 1 of No. 16; 1 of No. 23a; 1 of No. 24; 42 of No. 37; 1 of No. 37a; 12 of No. 38; 1 of No. 54a; 4 of No. 90a; 1 of No. 111c; 2 of No. 125; 2 of No. 126; 2 of No. 126a; 1 of No. 186; 1 of No. 188; 2 of No. 191; 1 Magic Motor.

Meccano Model-Building Competitions

"General" Contest for Models of All Kinds

In the "General" Model-building Contest announced this month, competitors may choose their own subjects and any number of parts may be used. It is not necessary to own a large Outfit in order to win one of the splendid prizes offered, for small models often prove the most original and interesting, and they receive just as much attention from the judges as the larger ones. Competitors should simply try to think of a suitable subject, preferably one that has not previously appeared in model form in the Meccano Manuals or in the "*M.M.*," and then should give their imaginative powers full rein and put forward their best creative efforts.

This fine model of a naval gun was built by Robert De Wilde of Antwerp, and won a prize in a Meccano Competition.

As is the case with all model-building competitions announced on this page, this Contest is open to "*M.M.*" readers of all ages living in any part of the world. The only condition is that models submitted must be the unaided work of competitors, both in regard to design and construction.

When an entry is completed, it is only necessary to have it photographed or, if this is not possible, to make a good drawing of it, and these need not be the work of the competitor himself. A short explanation of the constructional details of the model should then be written, and this, together with the photograph or drawing, should be posted to "September General Model-building Contest," Meccano Ltd., Old Swan, Liverpool 13. The competitor's age, name and full address must be written on the back of each photograph or drawing sent in.

The contest will be divided into two Sections as follows:—A, for competitors of all ages living in the British Isles; B, for competitors of all ages living Overseas. The age of each competitor will be taken into consideration in judging the entries. The prizes to be awarded in each Section will be: First, Meccano Products value £3/3/–; Second, Products value £2/2/–; Third, Products value £1/1/–. There also will be a number of consolation prizes in each Section.

Entries for Section A must be posted in time to reach Liverpool on or before 31st October, 1936. The closing date for Section B is 31st December, 1936.

We advise intending competitors to commence work on their models immediately so as to have plenty of time to prepare and submit illustrations before the closing dates.

"Familiar Home Objects" Model-Building Contest

This Contest will provide splendid opportunities for all model-builders to show their skill in the use of Meccano parts, for entries must represent something that is to be found in almost every home. There is a very wide choice of subjects, ranging from articles of furniture, vacuum cleaners, and carpet sweepers to electric heaters and gas cookers, and the almost endless variety of appliances and utensils to be found in kitchens.

Every owner of a Meccano Outfit can take part in the competition. All that is necessary after building a model of the chosen object, is to have it photographed, or to make a good drawing of it, and to forward it to "Familiar Home Objects Contest," Meccano Ltd., Binns Road, Liverpool 13. There are no restrictions in regard to the size of the Outfits that may be used in building the models, and competitors may submit more than one model if they wish. Small and simple models will have just as good a chance to win prizes as more complicated and elaborate structures, for the deciding factors will be the degree of accuracy and realism with which the original is reproduced, and of the skill with which Meccano parts are employed. A model that contains a large number of parts that do not serve any useful purpose has little chance of success.

When sending in his entry each competitor must remember to write his age, name and full address clearly, preferably in block letters, on the back of each photograph or drawing submitted. These need not be the work of the competitor, but the model itself must be entirely the result of his or her own unaided efforts.

The competition will be divided into two sections as follows: A, for competitors of all ages living in the British Isles; B, for those of all ages living Overseas. The prizes in each Section will be, First, Meccano Products value £3/3/–; Second, Products value £2/2/–; Third, Products value £1/1/–. In addition there will be consolation prizes in each section.

In section A the last day on which entries can be received is 31st October, 1936. The closing date for Section B is 31st December, 1936.

Prize-winners will be notified by post as soon after the closing dates as possible, and lists of awards, together with illustrations and descriptions of principal prize-winning models, will be published in due course in the "*M.M.*" Prize-winners will have the opportunity of choosing any items they like from the current price lists. Models that appear in any of the Meccano publications are not eligible for this contest.

Model-Building Competition Results

By Frank Hornby

May "Simplicity" and "Small Outfits" Contests (Home Sections)

May "Simplicity" Contest (Home Section)

The results in the Home Section of the "Simplicity" Model-Building Competition, details of which were announced in the May 1936 issue of the "*M.M.*," are as follows:

1st Prize, Meccano or Hornby Products value £3/3/–: A. Spring, Cainscross, Nr. Stroud. 2nd, Products value £2/2/–: A. Audsley, Cobham. 3rd, Products value £1/1/–: R. Cathmore, Dundee.

Products value 10/6: W. Houghton, Daventry; J. Maguire, Belfast; A. Aldridge, Hook, Nr. Basingstoke; R. Rish, Wallasey; A. Tipper, Exeter.

Products value 5/–: E. Helby, Jersey; A. Kennett, Richmond, Surrey; P. Wickham, Countesthorpe, Leicester; R. Dent, Cambridge; R. Morley, Dorchester.

I was greatly pleased to find a large collection of ingenious models submitted for this competition, and the variety of subjects represented made it a pleasure to examine them. First Prize was awarded to A. Spring, who submitted a group of three models, two of which are intended to show the contrast between modern wireless sets and those that were considered the "latest thing" only a few years ago. The older type of receiver is represented by a box having 5½″ × 1½″ Flexible Plates for the top and ends and 2½″ Angle Girders and Strips for the back and front. The control dials are bolts fitted with washers and ½″ loose Pulleys, and the loud speaker, which is of the cone type, is made from a Road Wheel mounted on the end of a short Rod held in the boss of a 1½″ Bevel Gear. The cabinet of the modern wireless set has 2½″ × 1½″ Flexible Plates for its top and ends, and 2½″ × 2½″ Strip Plates for the back and front. The front Strip Plate is decorated with a border of Angle Girders, and a 1½″ Flat Girder fitted with a 1″ Triangular Plate and three bolts, on each of which are two washers, forms the control panel and tuning controls.

The quaint model of a man "turning the mangle" shown above was sent by G. B. Thompson of Sheffield. The realistic searchlight on the right is the work of R. Cathmore, Dundee.

The third model submitted by this competitor is a miniature vacuum cleaner, the body of which is made from two Sleeve Pieces connected end to end by means of a Chimney Adaptor. Chimney Adaptors also form the ends, and the handle and supports are made from stout wire. A short length of Spring Cord wrapped with a binding of thin twine represents the flexible suction pipe, and is provided at one end with an End Bearing and a 1″ Triangular Plate to form the nozzle. The electric lead is a piece of cord and a Collar is used to represent the point plug.

"*Crikey, another record by Shell!*" is the title given by A. Audsley to the amusing model with which he won Second Prize. This model is based on the humorous advertisement design for Shell petrol that was popular a short time ago. The actual advertisement shows a man watching a motor car moving at a terrific speed. An impression of the speed at which the car is moving is given by the fact that the man is shown with two heads, facing in opposite directions, as though he has swung his head very rapidly from left to right to follow the movement of the car. The model consists of a Flat Trunnion with 1″ × ½″ Angle Brackets bolted to its lower corners and two 1½″ Corner Brackets attached to its apex. The two 1½″ Corner Brackets are connected by a 1″ Triangular Plate, and to this are bolted two 1½″ Strips, each of which is fitted with a 1″ loose Pulley. The 1″ Pulleys form the two heads.

The Third Prize model built by R. Cathmore is a small searchlight. It is provided with a flashlamp bulb, which is fitted inside a lantern made from three Boiler Ends placed one on top of the other, the centre one being provided with two Threaded Pins in diametrically opposite holes to form a pivot. The pins engage in a "U" shaped frame of Strips that is mounted on a swivelling base.

Outstanding models among the entries that received prizes of 10/6 are a simple chiming clock, which was sent by W. Houghton, and a biplane by R. Rish. A. Tipper won a prize with a fine model of a 4–6–2 locomotive.

"Small Outfits" Contest (Home Section)

The list of prizewinners in the "Small Outfits" Contest (Home Section) is as follows:

1st Prize, Meccano or Hornby Products value £2/2/–: R. Walford, Newton Abbot. 2nd, Products value £1/1/–: K. Fielding, Retford. 3rd, Products value 10/6: W. Raybould, Bloxwich.

Products value 5/–: P. Dowell, Atherstone; P. Frost, W. Bridgford; P. Wickham, Countesthorpe, Leicester; R. Clarke, Nottingham; B. Thompson, Sheffield; A. Turner, Derby; L. Summers, Birmingham; G. Yates, Kingswinford; C. Halstead, London, E.10; J. Maguire, Belfast.

A model dragline built with Outfit F and submitted by R. P. Walford secured First Prize, and although the subject is not original, splendid work has been done in its construction. The model is very small, and is driven by a number of miniature hand winches, which actuate the various motions.

K. Fielding was awarded Second Prize for a model of a sack lifting machine of the type used in warehouses for lifting sacks of flour and bales of various materials and placing them in neat stacks. The model is rather like a porter's truck running on two wheels, and in addition to the usual tongue is provided with a second tongue which is movable. In use the tongues are pushed underneath the sack to be moved, and the sack is then wheeled to its destination. If it is necessary to unload the sack at a height above floor level a handle mounted on the truck shaft is rotated and this operates a length of chain running on Sprockets, which movement raises the upper tongue and its load to the required height. The model is neatly constructed and works in exactly the same manner as the actual truck on which it is based.

A floating crane forms the subject of one of four models submitted by W. Raybould. It incorporates a simple pontoon constructed from 3½″ × 2½″ Flanged Plates bolted between two 12½″ Angle Girders. The jib and the bearings for the winches are made from Strips, and the method of construction ensures that these are quite rigid. The model is driven by means of a Meccano Magic Motor, and as the jib is fitted with special multi-sheave pulley blocks the crane is able to lift considerable loads. The other models sent by Raybould are a steam roller, heavy oil engine, and a folding foot pump. The cylinder of the pump is a Sleeve Piece fitted with two ½″ Flanged Wheels through the boss of one of which slides a Rod. This is pivotally connected to the base frame and has a Collar at its cylinder end to represent the piston. The cylinder is attached to the foot lever, and this is held in the raised position by Spring Cord. A clip made from 1½″ Strips serves to hold the pump closed.

Among the winners of prizes of 5/– is a model of a deck hoisting gear similar to that found on small vessels. It was built by J. Maguire, and includes a small steam operated winch and a mast that supports a boom or jib. The model was built from parts in an Outfit F, and as the builder lacked sufficient small Pulleys for the sheaves he overcame the difficulty in a very clever manner, by means of specially designed pulleys. These were made by pushing pieces of stout wire through Collars and then binding the wires on to the Rod that forms the boom. The hoisting cord passes round the Collars, and as the cord is wound in the Collars revolve freely on the wire.

The winding drum consists of a Sleeve Piece, through the centre of which is a Rod that is held concentric by means of bolts passed through the holes in the Sleeve Piece and screwed into Collars on the Rod. The Rod carries a 57-teeth Gear Wheel and a ¾″ Flanged Wheel that forms the belt pulley.

As this contest proved so popular it is intended to organise further competitions of a similar nature, and I hope that all those who submitted entries for the present contest will watch for announcements concerning these in future issues of the "*M.M.*"

Wednesbury M.C.—Most meetings have been held out-of-doors, and some enjoyable cricket matches have been played. On Empire Air Day a party visited Castle Bromwich aerodrome, where a tour of the hangars, machine shops, armoury and photography departments was followed by a display of aerobatics and a fly-past of aircraft. The programme also has included a cycle run to Brewood, and Model-building and Fretwork. Club roll: 20. *Secretary:* A. L. Morgan, 17, Cobden Street, Fallings Heath, Wednesbury.

Sid Vale M.C.—Some excellent models were produced during a recent "Meccano Robot" Contest, and the largest one was about 3 ft. in height. A Fire Engine Contest held during another meeting also produced some fine models, and the first prize was won by a streamline fire engine. Club roll: 20. *Secretary:* S. R. J. Gliddon, Sheffield House, Sidmouth.

St. Stephens (Saltash) M.C.—The Meccano, Hornby and Woodwork sections have combined during recent outdoor meetings, when cricket and baseball have been played. A cycle run was made to Plymouth Airport to see the demonstration flights of Clem Sohn, the "bird man." The club has been invited by Mr. Ellis, the Leader of Plymouth M.C., to combine with that club in regard to visits to local works and other places of interest. Club roll: 11. *Secretary:* B. Braund, 9, Homer Park, Saltash.

Old Charlton M.C.—Recently-completed models have included a mechanical advertisement and a crane. A very enjoyable indoor Entertainment Evening has been held, during which a "thriller" game was played. The "criminal" had to drop one clue for the two boys chosen to be the detectives, and their subsequent investigations resulted in an arrest being made and a Mock Trial held that lasted two weeks! The dropped clue was a small piece of paper on which were written the answers to some general knowledge questions. At the trial the charge against the accused was so well contested that finally he was acquitted. Members greatly enjoyed a Lecture by Mr. Fish, a local gentleman, on his model railway, built by himself and worked by 14 model locomotives, including both steam and clockwork types, of his own construction. Mr. Fish has kindly consented to display and operate his layout at the next club Exhibition. Club roll: 22. *Secretary:* W. Jaques, 60, Gurdon Road, London, S.E.7.

Claremont Avenue School (Kenton) M.C.—Cricket has been played at most outdoor meetings, and at indoor ones the study of a large Meccano model has been the chief interest of members. Materials are being collected for building the model Belisha crossing illustrated in the "*M.M.*" of March last. Club roll: 14. *Secretary:* G. Turton, 5, Brookfield Crescent, Kenton.

St. James' (Grimsby) M.C.—Indoor meetings have been devoted chiefly to constructing a chassis of a large steam lorry. Ackermann steering gear was fitted, but it was worked by a crank instead of the worm and 57-teeth gear wheels. The Leader built an excellent model of a pair of scales, an interesting feature of which was that the scales remained parallel irrespective of the extent to which the beam was tipped. Other models completed included a windmill with sails that revolved slowly, in a very realistic manner, and two racing cars. Club roll: 5. *Secretary:* A. N. Dixon, 65, Yarborough Road, Grimsby.

Plymouth M.C.—The club quarterly magazine "*Gearbox*" is rapidly increasing in popularity, and many excellent contributions for it have been received from members. The Birthday celebrations this year will include a club Party and an Open Evening. The Meccano section have decided to build a "set piece" for the occasion, and this will be a dockside scene. The decision has been made known to all members in order to give them ample time in which to find out the advantages and disadvantages of the different types of models it is proposed to include in the scene. Club roll: 25. *Secretary:* R. G. Symons, 47, Lisson Grove, Plymouth.

Kidderminster M.C.—A debate on "*Talking versus Silent Pictures*" led to a lively discussion that ended in favour of the "talkies." A Lecture by the secretary on "*Trevithick*" and the engines and machinery he supplied to the Peru silver mines was much enjoyed. On another occasion one member brought a microscope, and with it the others viewed some of the minute creatures that exist in pond water. A Visit to the Parish Church has been arranged, and the party will be conducted by Mr. Hodgkins, a local antiquarian, who will tell them many interesting historical facts about the building. Club roll: 12. *Secretary:* E. J. Watkins, "Elmar," Wolverhampton Road, Kidderminster.

Fraserburgh M.C.—Meetings continue to be well attended. Plans for the Exhibition are going ahead, and several good models have been completed and painted. They include a large vertical drill, a crane and a beam engine. Others being built include a steam shovel, a new motor chassis and an aeroplane. Additional crossovers and left-hand points have been bought for the club layout, and a signal gantry has been made. Interesting timetable operations have been carried out. Club roll: 28. *Secretary:* W. J. Dawson, Phingask, Fraserburgh.

Officials and members of Regent Street Central School (Heywood) M.C. This club was affiliated in April 1930, and now is one of the largest in the Meccano Guild, the number of members totalling 150. Model-building and Lantern Lectures are the most popular features of the programmes.

Bexleyheath Boys' Central School M.C.—The fine display staged on the School Open Day included a clockwork spiral railway; a model workshop driven by a small mains motor; three model steam engines and a Dinky Toys layout. The display was a great success and attracted many visitors. Club roll: 30. *Secretary:* D. Hicks, 4, St. Audrey Avenue, Long Lane, Bexleyheath, Kent.

St. Oswald's (Norbury) M.C.—A Cycling Section has been formed, and has proved helpful to the Cricket Section, as most of the club cyclists are cricketers. The Cricket Section have played four matches, all of which they have won. Games Evenings have been introduced. A Visit has been paid to the local Telephone Exchange, and a photograph of the members was taken, by permission, while they were on the roof of the building. Other excursions to local places of interest have been arranged. Club roll: 21. *Secretary:* R. A. Smart, 14, Kensington Avenue, Thornton Heath, Surrey.

Islington M.C.—Interesting talks have been given, one by the Leader on "*The Making and use of Charcoal*" and another by a member who described his holiday in Russia. Model-building has been continued, though to a lesser extent than during the winter. At one meeting model aeroplanes with Meccano parts attached were made to run along a length of cord. Club roll: 10. *Secretary:* S. H. Gardiner, 3, Tiverton House, Pleasant Place, Canonbury, London, N.1.

Sutton Valence Council School M.C.—The club has been occupied chiefly with a Sports and Games Contest against the remainder of the School. It included six-a-side football, running, jumping, and cricket-ball throwing, and ended in a victory for the club by 166.5 points to 131.5. A silver medal offered by the club for the best individual performance was won by a member of the School team who scored 26 points. A Safety First Exhibition is being arranged, one of the chief features of which will be a miniature town with Dinky Toys traffic signs, etc. The School playground is also to be marked out for traffic, to be represented by boys on toy motor cars or cycles. It is hoped to have a small cinema in one of the classrooms, and the screen holder and many of the necessary fittings will be made of Meccano parts. Club roll: 24. *Secretary:* J. Chandler, "Herriard," Chart Sutton, Maidstone.

Exeter M.C.—In spite of the light summer evenings, model-building activities have been continued as energetically as ever, and during a recent month 19 models were completed. They included a clever reproduction of the German airship "*Hindenburg*," a Belgian cargo vessel and a tennis umpire's chair. A small party, including the Leader and secretary, recently visited Liverpool for a tour of the factory and a talk with the Guild Secretary. Club roll: 30. *Secretary:* K. Milton, 18, Baker Street, Exeter.

AUSTRALIA

Melbourne M.C.—At one meeting a member brought along a model bucket excavator and demonstrated its efficiency in scooping up coal, which was represented by sunflower seeds. Meetings have been devoted chiefly to operating the Leader's Hornby layout. Each member in turn has acted as a train despatcher and has been responsible for arranging a programme of operations. Later he has taken a turn as signalman, and as usually there are three trains running at the same time this official has been kept very busy! There are now four stations on the layout. Club roll: 10. *Secretary:* L. Ison, 8, Hayes Street, Northcote, N.16, Victoria, Australia.

Nhill Xlcr M.C.—When a local display was organised to advertise the Anzac Sports and Cycling Carnival, the club assisted by exhibiting models of a big wheel with advertisements on each car, a cycle track with two cyclists travelling at different speeds, and working models of vertical nad horizontal steam engines. The models were driven by a $\frac{1}{4}$-h.p. electric motor, and ran continuously for $7\frac{1}{2}$ hrs. The exhibits were very favourably commented upon by the local press. Arrangements have been made for Visits to a power house, a flour mill, and to the printing works of the "Nhill Free Press." A series of interesting Lectures on different subjects, including the "*Uses of Meccano parts and mechanisms*," is in progress. Club roll: 16. *Secretary:* F. Haustorfer, Leahy Street, Nhill, Victoria, Australia.

SOUTH AFRICA

Continental (Capetown) M.C.—A talk has been given by the secretary on "*How the 'Empress of Britain' was launched.*" Open Nights and meetings spent in playing Games have been very popular, but Model-building has not been neglected, and some excellent cranes and windmills have been completed. Preparations for the club's first Exhibition are well advanced. A Library is being organised. Club roll: 6. *Leader:* Mr. R. H. Woodley, 10, Stirling Street, Capetown, Cape Province, South Africa.

NEW ZEALAND

Christchurch M.C.—Another visit to the invalid boy friend of the club has been paid by four members, who took several new models with which to entertain him. A very enjoyable outing was held on Easter Monday, when a party went to Godley Head Lighthouse and to Lyttleton, where some of the boys visited an English ship in port there. Model-building and Hornby Train contests have been included in the programme, and a fine display of models has been arranged for the club's seventh Birthday Party. Club roll: 20. *Secretary:* L. W. Best, 28, Circuit Street, Strowan, Christchurch, N.W.1, New Zealand.

Preparing for the Winter Sessions

In the Meccano Guild, as in most youth organisations, September is a period of transition. At the beginning of the month members are still enjoying summer activities, but at its close they are eagerly anticipating, and in some instances have already begun, the varied indoor activities that make the club winter meetings so very enjoyable. I always think of September as the "conference" month, when Leaders, officials and members get together to discuss club policy and the programme to be followed during the forthcoming winter sessions.

A good scheme that can be adopted as a preliminary to such a conference is for the secretary to send a postcard to each member informing him of the date and time of the meeting, and asking him to send to the Leader before that date one or more written suggestions for new schemes, or for the improvement of old ones. The Leader should then sort out these suggestions into groups, each dealing more or less with one subject, so that at the conference he is able to put the various subjects before the members quickly and without overlapping or repetition. The proposals should be made out and discussed, and then voted upon. The sudden popularity of some particular hobby may have produced many requests for its inclusion in the club programme, and a unanimous or majority vote will secure its adoption. Some of the members may be so keen on it that they would drop other equally interesting pursuits on one side in its favour, but the Leader and officials must exercise tact, and allot the new hobby only a fair share of the time available during the sessions.

Opinions will be divided with regard to other proposals, and in such cases also a good deal must be left to the discretion of the Leader. It is unwise to "swamp" the club programme with some new scheme that is extremely popular at the moment; on the other hand, it is foolish to turn down too hastily any scheme on which the members are not unanimous, for that particular scheme may, on trial, prove to be a great success. Members should agree at the beginning of the conference that any plan which receives a certain number of votes, this number depending upon the number of members present, should be given a fair trial, and finally rejected or adopted permanently strictly on its merits.

Meccano Club Secretaries

No. 37. J. G. Slater

J. G. Slater is Secretary of the Pennthorpe School (Chislehurst) M.C. Model-building is the chief activity of this young and very enthusiastic club. Lantern Lectures also are greatly enjoyed.

Value of the Personal Visit

It is all to the good if the Leader is able to find time to visit the parents of as many of the members as possible before the opening of the first of the winter sessions. He is able to give parents a much better knowledge of the club and its officials than they are likely to have formed from the accounts given by their enthusiastic sons. By his personal account of the club's activities, and his testimony as to their constructive nature, the Leader is able to arouse the interest of the parents and to give them the satisfaction of knowing exactly what their sons will be doing on club nights. Time spent in such visiting is never wasted, for parents who are kept in touch with the progress of a club in this manner invariably become its keen supporters.

Another point is that at such visits the Leader is very likely to come in contact with gentlemen who are not only qualified, but also willing, to give lectures to the club from time to time. Many interesting talks on their daily work and experiences by engineers, mechanics, sailors and others have been secured in this way, while permission to visit factories also has been obtained from owners or managers who have similarly become interested in club work.

Gaining Friends and Recruits

This matter of making known the splendid aims and the good work of the clubs has been carried further by some enterprising clubs. In their endeavours to gain the support of local residents who take a practical interest in the hobbies and amusements of boys, they prepare a circular letter giving a short account of the club's history and activities, and outlining its plans for the coming session. This letter is printed if possible, or duplicated in some way, and a copy is sent to local residents, inviting them to visit the club and see the members actually at work. In some instances a definite "Visitor's Night" is arranged early in the session, and the letter contains an invitation to attend on that particular night. This method involves some small expense, but in most cases it brings the club excellent results, financially and otherwise.

The beginning of the winter session is also an excellent time for a general recruiting campaign. The entire membership of the club should take part in this, and as every member is in the happy position of being able to speak from personal experience, his efforts to persuade his friends of the advantages of association with the Meccano Guild should be very successful. Just one bit of advice to the recruiting member: always remember to have an application form handy so that when you do find a recruit you will be able to make sure of him on the spot! For my part, I shall be very pleased to send secretaries supplies of the leaflet that explains the aims and organisation of the Guild, to pass on to club members. The application form that must be filled in and signed by a recruit is on the back of this leaflet.

Merit Medallions

By the end of this month Leaders will be able to let me have their nominations for Merit Medallions for the summer sessions. I would mention, for the benefit of new Leaders, that in every affiliated club, at home and overseas, two Medallions are available each session for any kind of good service to the club or the Guild movement generally. The recommendation of the Leader is sufficient, and the names of the members concerned are inscribed on their Medallions, and are made known to all the Guild in the special list published annually on this page. I should like to receive the nominations immediately after the close of the present session.

Proposed Clubs

Attempts are being made to establish Meccano Clubs in the following places, and boys interested should communicate with the promoters whose names and addresses are given below:

AUSTRALIA—R. McLean, Marion St., Charters Towers, Queensland.
INDIA—N. S. Narang, Shish Mahal Road, Lahore.
NEW ZEALAND—L. Gilmore, Arney Street, Greymouth.

The Kensington Model Railway

An L.M.S.R. Garden System

By C. Dodds

IT is always interesting to a miniature railway owner to trace the progress of his line from its beginnings and to record the successive steps leading up to the latest state of development. The Kensington Model Railway, which I own and operate, is a good example of the manner in which miniature railway systems grow. In its earlier days it was an indoor track, and it graduated from a table railway through the intermediate stage of a portable line laid on the floor to a permanent system in a room of its own. Now it has been transformed into an outdoor railway that is still being extended.

The line began as a simple oval, and was operated by a small tender engine and coach. During the course of the first three years additional rails were obtained from time to time, until it became possible to stage an interesting layout on the dining room table. In 1921 a Hornby "Zulu" Tank Locomotive and a few trucks were added, and by 1924 it had assumed too great a size for the table, and was laid more or less permanently on my bedroom floor. The general form of the layout was then a fairly large oval with one or two sidings.

Later, after a house removal, my one ambition became that of having a system laid in the attic that was now available. During the course of the next few years this materialised, and a single track was laid down round three sides of the room, with a terminus at each end. At this time the original small-radius curves were abandoned for larger ones, so that a Hornby 4-4-4 No. 2 Tank Locomotive bought in 1926 could be used. There were then about nine trucks, but still no passenger stock. I now wanted to run passenger trains, so the track was doubled, and with the two engines it was possible to run an interesting service by timetable between the two termini.

Soon I had enough rails to go right round the attic, so in 1929, at the expense of a few sidings, the railway was made a continuous double track circuit about 22 ft. by 18 ft. Two stations were built of wood and cardboard, and at each there were appropriate sidings. The railway became gradually more realistic, and I had a lot of fun out of it. Two signal boxes were installed, one having 14 levers, and the other 8, and there was communication by means of Morse Code tapping keys between them. The rails were ballasted with granite chips; this deadened the noise a lot and greatly improved the appearance.

In 1930 I decided that the line should represent L.M.S.R. practice, and in that year was fortunate to get a Hornby No. 2 Special Standard Compound. Curiously enough the number of the engine that used to haul my train to school every morning was 1185, the same as that of my Hornby model! This engine pulled with ease five wooden bogie coaches twice round the layout, and was used exclusively for express passenger trains. The 4-4-4 Tank was used on goods trains, and the "Zulu" Tank still did excellent work as a shunter.

I then became interested in electric engines, so my father built for me an electric locomotive of the 4-4-4 wheel arrangement. The motor was a Meccano one, geared to the driving wheels. Overhead wires were put up over the down line, and the engine was fitted with a pantograph collector. In consequence of another move, this time to a house without an attic, the railway was dismantled for a time and its parts lay disused in a number of packing cases. But in 1934 I decided to make a layout as near the real thing as possible in the garden, and set about the whole job systematically, making full use of my experience with the attic layout. A site was selected giving a run of about 200 ft. that was dead straight, except for a right-angled turn mid-way. I began to level the route with the aid of a spirit level, but found it necessary to incorporate a gradient of 1 in 90 for 70 ft.

The railway is to represent in its final form the stretch of main line between Stafford and Manchester. So far there are three stations, "Stafford," the principal terminus, "Sandbach," a small passing station, and "Wilmslow," the temporary terminus until the line is completed to "Manchester." South of "Stafford," the lines converge into a single track and pass underneath a small path into a wooden hut, on the floor of which extensive sidings are laid in Hornby Rails for the storage of goods and passenger rolling stock, and locomotives.

"Stafford" station has four platforms, covered by wooden awnings, and at the entrance to the station there is a concrete road, with a three-storey office building surmounted by a tower. The platforms are of concrete, and their average length is seven feet, so that each easily accommodates a train of six bogie coaches. The points are operated mechanically from a signal box at the north end of the station.

Scenes on the Kensington Model Railway, operated by C. Dodds, Harborne, Birmingham. The illustrations at the top and on the left show "Stafford" and "Sandbach" stations respectively. Part of the indoor line from which the outdoor railway was developed is seen below.

From "Stafford" there is a double track main line all the way to "Wilmslow," and this line is electrified by means of a brass centre rail. The electric control panel at Stafford is mounted on the garden fence at a convenient height above the signal box. The panel incorporates one controller for the down line and one for the up, an automatic cut-out in case of a short circuit, an ammeter, and seven section switches. These section switches are used to connect either controller with any platform line in the station, also various sections of the line leading to the hut. This means that at any given moment, three trains can be held in "Stafford" on 'dead' sections of the line while another train is being moved.

From "Stafford" to "Sandbach" there is a straight run of 54 ft. up an incline of 1 in 90. This section of the line is on an embankment on which grass has been cultivated to prevent washing out by rain. "Sandbach" is a small two-platform station, 4 ft. long, and is used only by local stopping trains. From "Sandbach" the line curves to the left through a right-angled turn with a radius of 10 ft., and the line is "banked" or super-elevated. At this point there is a cutting, followed by a tunnel 10 ft. long, and the line then is level all the way to "Wilmslow." From "Sandbach" to "Wilmslow" is about 45 ft. "Wilmslow" has two main platforms and one bay.

North of this station the lines consist temporarily of well-painted Hornby rails to provide extra siding accommodation and sufficient room to turn large trains until the line is completed to "Manchester." At "Wilmslow" the controllers are similar to those at "Stafford," and they are housed in a small watchman's hut. Power for the line is obtained from a dynamo supplying 16 volts and this is brought from the generating hut to "Wilmslow" by means of telegraph wires, which give the line a very realistic appearance. There is electric bell communication between "Stafford" and "Wilmslow" and this is used for signalling train movements.

Containers for Hornby Railways

By "Tommy Dodd"

THE new Hornby Containers are an important introduction to the Hornby Series that I am sure will be welcomed by all Hornby railway owners. A railway container is similar to the body of a railway van or wagon, and can be carried on a suitable rail vehicle, or on a road lorry, as required. Its handiness has earned for it the appropriate title of "*the suitcase of commerce.*" Cranes lift it from lorry to rail, or back again as required, and thus goods packed in it are carried right through to their destination, without being disturbed on the way. They are in fact "*despatched in bulk and delivered in detail,*" as we are told by a railway poster advertising this road-rail container service.

With the miniature Containers now available, this "door-to-door" service can be provided on Hornby Railways. Hornby Containers are of four different representative types, one for each group, and the distinctive colours, lettering and other details adopted for their containers by the four groups are accurately reproduced on them.

The L.M.S.R. is represented by a Furniture Container "K61." The finish of this reproduces the timber contruction with vertical boarding of the real thing. All the details of the original are shown. The ironwork, such as the strapping on the sides and the door hinges on the rear end, is in black, and all lettering is in yellow, giving a very smart effect on a background of the familiar Midland red.

The possibilities of the publicity afforded by the carriage of real containers through the streets have not been neglected by the railways. Almost all containers now are decorated with concise wording, calling attention to the special advantages of this form of transport, and in comparison with most of the earlier more or less experimental containers they look quite gay affairs. Thus on the Hornby L.M.S.R. Container the words "Furniture Removal Service," and other phrases amplifying them, are prominent in addition to the initials of the owning company. This Container is distinguished also by carrying the L.M.S.R. Coat-of-Arms on each side.

Steel container construction is represented by the Hornby L.N.E.R. Goods Container "BLS297." The corrugations pressed out in the sides and front end of the original are well reproduced, as are the courses of rivets and the ventilating bonnets at each end. The design of the rear end shows two upper doors and the usual drop-down loading flap, with the necessary hinges and fastenings. This Container is finished in the familiar L.N.E.R. "red oxide" shade used for brake-fitted and "piped" wagons. The lettering is in yellow, and on the sides appears the full title of the company. Words emphasising the door-to-door nature of L.N.E.R. container transport and its advantages also are shown.

The G.W.R. representative is an Insulated Container "FX1642," as used for the transport of frozen meat imported from overseas, and has doors at the sides as well as at one end. It has a neat and clean appearance, for it is finished in white with black lettering and, like nearly all G.W.R. equipment, it bears the neat and up-to-date monogram of the company. It is very complete in detail, for its design includes the locking bars and other fittings for securing the doors, even to the minute hooks that hold these back when they are open for loading or unloading. The word "Insulated" appears on the side doors, and the other wording emphasises the special importance of container service for perishable traffic.

THE NEW HORNBY CONTAINERS THAT ARE DESCRIBED IN THE ARTICLE ON THIS PAGE. EACH IS SHOWN ON AN APPROPRIATE FLAT TRUCK.

The finish of the Hornby S.R. Ventilated Container, "M644," like that of the L.N.E.R. one, represents steel construction. This container is of the type used for the carriage of fresh meat and other similar traffic that requires to be kept cool. Two rows of ventilating slits therefore are represented along the sides and on the ends. Both side and rear-end doors are provided, with the hinge and locking arrangements characteristic of S.R. containers carefully reproduced. The finish is striking, giving a smart exterior and the impression of a cool well-ventilated interior, for it is carried out in aluminium all over, the lettering being in S.R. dark green. The initials of the company appear at the front end and on the side doors. On the latter also appears the word "Ventilated," together with an invitation to "Enquire at any S.R. station for details," and the initials of the Company.

The Hornby Miniature Containers are fitted with lifting tackle on the roof in the form of chains and a ring for the crane hook. When loaded on Hornby Flat Trucks they look very effective, as can be seen from the photographs reproduced on this page. They can be obtained mounted in this way on Flat Trucks, and also are available separately.

The complete units can be used singly as parts of freight or passenger trains as required; and they can be used also to make up complete trains, particularly of Insulated and Ventilated Containers for perishable traffic. Trains with containers of this type will form excellent miniature reproductions of those "freight flyers" that run from Plymouth and Southampton Docks with frozen meat, and from the West and South-West with freshly-killed meat and perishable produce to keep London's markets supplied.

Containers for general goods also can be used to form complete trains if required. A complete train of Furniture Containers is not perhaps a common sight on real railways. There is no reason why such a train should not appear on a Hornby railway, however, for it can be supposed to consist of returning "empties," or to be engaged in a special "removal in bulk" such as might be involved in moving complete the effects of a large mansion, or a school, or some similar institution. Examples of extensive removals on these lines have been undertaken by all groups, and the speed and convenience of the operations have demonstrated the efficiency of the container system.

The addition of Hornby Containers adds considerably to the fun and realism of freight working in miniature. A feature of modern practice has been the development of special flat wagons for container traffic only. These are fully fitted with automatic brake gear for running in passenger or fast goods train formations. The Hornby Flat Truck represents very well this type of vehicle, but in addition is a wagon of more general utility. It would be an interesting plan to reserve one or two Flat Trucks specially for container service, and these should be classified as "brake-fitted" on the lines of the suggestion that appeared in the article "*Special Freight Working In Miniature*" on page 238 in the "*M.M.*" of last April. In a fast freight train composed partly of wagons supposed to be brake-fitted, such wagons should always be placed next to the engine.

Occasionally containers are to be seen loaded on ordinary open wagons. This practice can be followed in miniature if desired; Hornby No. O or No. 1 Wagon can be pressed into use in this way if a Flat Truck does not happen to be available at the particular time.

L.M.S.R. (G.S.W.R. SECTION) SERVICES

THIS month we return to a type of article that from our correspondence appears to be very popular with Hornby Railway owners. From time to time we refer to special features of a real railway group, or a section of a group, and show how these can be reproduced in miniature with Hornby components. In this article we deal in this manner with the part of the L.M.S.R. that was formerly the Glasgow and South Western Railway, still familiarly referred to as the "Sou' Western." This is an interesting section that is particularly suitable as the prototype of a Hornby railway, for practically all L.M.S.R. locomotive types up to and including "Royal Scots" are to be found on G.S.W.R. metals, and the standard Hornby L.M.S.R. Locomotives therefore can be used on its miniature representative.

On the main line of this section between Glasgow (St. Enoch) and Carlisle, pride of place always has been held by trains run in association with the Midland services to and from St. Pancras. The present-day *"Thames-Clyde Express"* is worked over this route, and therefore should not be missed from the timetables of a miniature G.S.W.R. line. A miniature *"Thames-Clyde Express"* composed of Hornby No. 2 Saloon Coaches in L.M.S.R. colours has a very smart appearance, especially if the vehicles are fitted with train name boards. Making suitable boards is not a difficult task, and the lettering can be carried out in Indian ink on plain white card.

For motive power the first choice should be a Hornby *"Royal Scot"* No. E320 or No. 3C Locomotive, according to whether the layout is operated electrically or by clockwork. This type of engine is fitted with smoke deflectors and has quite an impressive appearance at the head of a train, as the upper illustration on the opposite page shows. Additional interest is given by the use of a miniature route indicator of the semaphore type on the front of the engine, as shown in the illustration. These interesting fittings formerly were peculiar to the Caledonian Railway, now also part of the L.M.S.R., but since grouping they have been adopted for the G.S.W.R. Section. The indicator consists of a central stem, with two small semaphore arms pivoted to it that can be made to take up various positions in a similar manner to the hands of a clock. The central stem serves as a means of attachment to a lamp bracket of the locomotive.

An express entering a station on a Hornby layout representing the G.S.W.R. Section of the L.M.S.R. The main line is single, but becomes double track at the station in order to provide a passing loop.

In miniature the central stem of the route indicator can be omitted. The two semaphore arms are best cut out of white card or stiff paper, with one end rounded and with the projecting semaphore portions slightly wider at their outer ends. The arms should be ½ in. long and should be ⅛ in. wide at their outer ends. When cut out, one should be placed on top of the other and a hole pierced through both at the rounded end with a stout pin. They should be fitted together by means of a very small paper fastener, the two projecting legs of which are bent flat after passing through the semaphore arms, and then doubled back so as to fit on the lamp bracket of a Hornby Locomotive.

When the head of the fastener has been touched up with white paint the indicator is ready for use. The arms can readily be set as required for the route to be indicated. Trains between Carlisle and St. Enoch have the arms in the "quarter-to-four" position as seen from the front of the locomotive, and this setting is shown in the photograph previously referred to.

If a "Royal Scot" is not available the chief passenger trains can be handled by a Hornby L.M.S.R. E220 Special Locomotive or the corresponding No. 2 Special Clockwork engine. This type of locomotive is a splendid representation in miniature of the well-known L.M.S.R. Standard Compounds that now perform a great deal of the main line work on the G.S.W.R. section. Readers no doubt will remember the sound performance of Compound No. 914 between Stranraer and Glasgow that was described in the article *"Belfast to Glasgow by L.M.S.R."* on page 72 of the *"M.M."*

for last February. This difficult route has always been distinguished by the splendid work of the locomotives running over it, and the traditions set up by the feats of one-time G.S.W.R. engines are ably carried on by the present-day Compound and Class "2P" 4-4-0 engines.

The association of the Stranraer line with the "Short Sea Route" to Ireland via Larne renders it of special importance, and the train services run in connection with the steamer sailings are of distinct interest. The principal services between Glasgow and Stranraer are included among the L.M.S.R. named trains, *"The Fast Belfast"* and *"The Irishman"* supplying the afternoon and evening services respectively. The Irish services generally were long known by the expressive nickname of the "Paddies," a title that needs no explanation. L.M.S.R. No. 2 Saloon Coaches can be used to make up these trains in miniature, and No. 2 compartment-type Coaches also are suitable. The route indicator is set at the "ten past two" position.

A Hornby No. 3C "Royal Scot" Locomotive hauling a miniature express. The engine carries a semaphore route indicator, constructed in the manner described in this article and mounted on the top lamp bracket.

A feature of this route is that much of it is single track, with passing loops situated at certain stations. This state of affairs is found on many miniature railway systems, so that the realistic representation of this line is not difficult. The working of the up and down trains must be so arranged that no undue delays occur at crossing places, and passing loops must have sufficient capacity for the longest trains operated, or some awkward operating problems may crop up. Single line working on the staff or tablet system could be instituted on the miniature line if desired, and will be found very fascinating. The exchanges on this route are carried out by hand. Stops therefore will have to be made at the "tablet stations" on a Hornby railway while a suitable "tablet" for one section—represented by a Meccano Collar perhaps, or some similar small Part carried in the tender—is exchanged for that belonging to the succeeding section.

A train of Hornby No. 2 Coaches hauled by a No. 2 Special L.M.S.R. Locomotive. This engine represents the real Standard Compound class that performs much notable work on the main line routes of the G.S.W.R. Section.

Another important route cuts across from Dumfries, on the Glasgow and Carlisle main line, to Challoch Junction on the Stranraer line. Single line working again applies here, but through traffic between England and Ireland via Stranraer passes this way. For miniature purposes the rolling stock and motive power of the Glasgow and Stranraer route can be used with good effect.

Between Ayr and Glasgow there is a remarkably heavy service of business and residential trains, with restaurant cars at suitable times of the day, in addition to the through expresses and other trains for Stranraer that also travel via Ayr. This traffic should be represented on a miniature G.S.W.R. system, and No. 2 Coaches are specially suitable for the composition of the trains. Restaurant facilities on this route formerly were provided by the Pullman Car Company Ltd. The L.M.S.R. have taken over their interests on this and on the Caledonian Section, but the Pullman cars themselves are still in use as L.M.S.R. vehicles. Hornby No. 2 or No. 2 Special Pullmans therefore can be employed in miniature. Most if not all the Pullmans thus taken over have been painted in L.M.S.R. colours, but there is no reason why vehicles in the standard Pullman finish should not be used on a Hornby layout.

The E220 Special L.M.S.R. Standard Compound is the first choice in the matter of locomotive power. Those readers who have in use locomotives of the old Hornby No. 2 type can employ them for the slower and more local trains, on which they will represent such G.S.W.R. 4-4-0s as still remain in service. The route indication for the Ayr trains requires the semaphore arms to assume the "ten past two" position, when seen from the front of the engine.

In spite of the short-distance character of much of the G.S.W.R. running, few tank engines are employed on this section. This was so in pre-grouping days, and conditions have not altered much in this respect. But if tank engine designs are few, this is made up for by the presence of some of the biggest engines of this type in service in this country. These are the large G.S.W.R. "Baltic" tanks, which are used on express work between Glasgow and Ayr. Hornby E220 Special Tank Locomotives can take the place of these giants on a miniature system. An inevitable result of the scarcity of tank engines is that a great deal of local and even of branch work is carried out by tender locomotives, which frequently have to perform much "tender first" running. This is a convenient practice from the operating point of view on a miniature system, and it saves the constant turning of tender engines.

Join the Hornby Railway Company and become eligible for the competitions announced on this page.

H.R.C. COMPETITION PAGE

Join the Hornby Railway Company and become eligible for the competitions announced on this page.

Model Railway Photograph Voting Contest

Voting competitions are always very attractive to Hornby Railway Company members, and this month we are giving them a further opportunity of expressing their opinions upon a series of photographs that have been used to illustrate the variety of railway topics dealt with in the "*M.M.*" The 12 photographs reproduced on this page show interesting scenes on Hornby railways. Some of them concentrate attention on the locomotive or on the train, their principal features being interesting formation or working. In others the lineside structures and the surrounding scenery are of greater importance, and these combine with the trains to form realistic railway scenes. We are asking members to examine these photographs and to place them in order of attractiveness according to their own views on building up realistic layouts.

Each competitor is only asked to do two things. The first is to decide the order in which he thinks the photographs should be placed, and to make a list in this order, representing each photograph by the number marked on it. The second is to state in as few words as possible his reason for selecting the photograph that he has placed at the head of his list.

Prizes of any products manufactured by Meccano Ltd., to the value of 21/–, 15/– and 10/6 respectively, will be awarded to the three entrants whose lists are nearest to the one decided upon by taking into account the votes of all the competitors. In the event of a tie for any prize, the award will be made to the competitor whose entry is presented in the neatest or most novel manner. This is a point worth remembering, as it sometimes happens that an entry good in other respects is handicapped by untidy presentation.

Envelopes containing entries must be marked "*H.R.C. September Voting Contest*" in the top left-hand corner and posted to reach Headquarters at Meccano Ltd., Binns Road, Liverpool 13, on or before 30th September. The closing date for competitors entering in the Overseas Section is 31st December.

Railway Photographic Contest

The coming of September may be said to herald the approach of the end of the outdoor photographic season, for the days now are shorter and the light generally is not too good. This month's Photographic Contest therefore is the last of the present series. In it we offer prizes for the best photographs of "*Any Railway Subject.*" Entrants may submit as many prints as they desire, but no competitor can receive more than one prize. As usual, the actual exposure must be the work of the competitor himself, but it is not necessary that he should have done his own developing or printing.

The Contest will be divided as usual into two sections—Home and Overseas—and prizes of any products of Meccano Ltd. to the value of 21/–, 15/– and 10/6 respectively will be awarded in each section. Every print submitted should have on the back the name of the competitor, his full address and his H.R.C. membership number.

Envelopes containing entries should be addressed "*H.R.C. September Photo Contest,*" Meccano Ltd., Binns Road, Liverpool 13. The closing date in the Home Section is 30th September. Overseas, 31st December.

Summer Puzzle Contest

The accompanying illustration of a well-known Hornby product is the third and last in this series of mystery photographs, the first and second of which were published in the July and August issues respectively. Competitors are now invited to forward to Headquarters on a postcard their solutions to the three puzzles.

The Contest is divided into two Sections, Home and Overseas, and a cash prize of £1 1s. 0d. will be awarded to the competitor in each section who gives the best solution to the three puzzles of the series. The closing dates are 30th September in the Home Section, and 31st December in the Overseas Section, and all entries should be addressed "*H.R.C. Summer Puzzle Contest,*" Meccano Ltd., Binns Road, Liverpool 13.

Competition Solution

MAY "LOCOMOTIVE SHADOWS CONTEST"

(1) 4–6–2 "Silver Link," L.N.E.R. (2) 4–6–2 "Turbomotive," L.M.S.R. (3) 4–6–2, L.N.E.R. (4) 4–6–0 Victoria Government Railways. (5) 4–4–2, L.N.E.R. (N.B.). (6) 4–6–2T. S.R. (7) 4–6–0, "Royal Scot," L.M.S.R. (8) 4–6–0, Palestine Railways. (9) 4–4–2, L.N.E.R. (G.N.). (10) 4–6–0, "Lord Baltimore," B. and O. Railway. (11) 4–4–0, M.R. Smith Compound. (12) 0–8–0T., S.R. (13) 4–4–2, L.N.E.R. (G.N.). (14) 4–6–2, German State Railways. (15) 2–6–0, L.N.E.R. (16) 2–6–0, L.M.S.R. (N.C.C.). (17) 4–6–2, Nord. (18) 2–8–2, "Cock o' the North," L.N.E.R. (19) 4–6–0, Streamlined "King," G.W.R. (20) 4–8–4, Class K, N.Z.R. (21) 4–6–4 German State Railways. (22) 4–6–2, L.N.E.R. (23) 4–6–2, Indian State Railways. (24) 4–4–0, L.M.S.R. (M.R.). (25) 4–6–0, "King," G.W.R.

COMPETITION RESULTS

HOME

July "Locomotive Knowledge Contest."—First: K. Costain (5108), Bolton, Lancs. Second: J. N. Leedam (43458), Burnley. Third: J. T. Fraser (2267), Exeter. Consolation Prizes: H. A. S. Cowles (47636), Goudhurst, Kent; S. Holloway (79), Plymouth; B. S. Jones (18593), Duffield, Derbyshire; J. C. Button (10335), Crewe, Ches.

July "Railway Photo Contest."—First: C. Spencer (44179), Sheffield 6. Second: V. L. Breeze (2134), Lewes, Sussex. Third: D. Fear (18477), Taunton, Somerset. Consolation Prizes: P. Andrew (22670), New Barnet, Herts.; S. H. Gardener (47996), Canonbury, London, N.1; J. W. Hague (1258), Ripon, Yorkshire.

Branch News

Bedford School.—The Branch layout represents the main line of the Midland Section of the L.M.S.R. from St. Pancras to Leicester, and a branch line representing the Tilbury section has recently been laid down. It is hoped to complete the doubling of the main line in the Autumn, and to instal goods yards at "Leicester" and "Cricklewood." Further locomotives are to be obtained and the whole layout will ultimately be electrified. At the School Exhibition a complete terminal station with five platforms, constructed by the "Chief Engineer" of the line, was highly commended and secured the highest obtainable prize. This station is now installed as "St. Pancras" on the Branch layout. Secretary: J. E. D. Rothwell, 6, Kimbolton Avenue, Bedford.

Folkestone.—Excellent progress is being made with the harbour works at "Folkestone" on the Branch layout, and the harbour is to be served by two lines of rails. "Boat Train" services are already in operation and are run to a special timetable. Night mail trains are regularly operated and the principal one is now named the *"Midnight Mail Express."* Goods and local services are run in addition. Improvements to the signalling of the line have been under consideration, and it has been decided to instal several new signal cabins. The Autumn Session commences this month and an attractive programme of track meetings, visits and other functions is being arranged. Secretary: F. E. Saunders, 79, Dover Road, Folkestone.

Elmside (Exeter).—A model road system complete with traffic signals and controlled crossings has been built, and Dinky Toys motor vehicles keep up a constant service on it. Road working is on an organised basis in co-operation with the rail services. During a recent spell of intensive traffic, 30 trains were run in a period of two hours and scheduled times were observed throughout. It was decided that the Branch track, which has been in its present position for three years, should be taken up and rearranged, and this was done after a general clean-up during the holiday period. Secretary: T. W. A. Smith, 98, Ladysmith Road, Exeter.

Islington.—After several meetings in which particular attention was given to track laying, some very satisfactory train running has been experienced. The arrangement of various accessories, including stations, goods depots, and locomotive sheds, has added considerably to the realism of operations. At one track meeting trains of all kinds were run and the locomotives and rolling stock of all groups were represented. A popular feature recently was a trip to Southend. This was greatly enjoyed, and is to be repeated in the Autumn. An interesting Lantern Lecture dealt with *"Britain's Greatest Railway."* The slides were kindly loaned by the L.M.S.R. Future arrangements include a Concert and an Exhibition, and preparations for both are well in hand. Attendance continues to be excellent, but there is room in the Branch for more keen members. Boys in the neighbourhood who are interested should communicate with the Secretary. A trial has been given to the assignment of particular duties to each member in turn, so that all will gain a knowledge of all aspects of operation. Secretary: F. H. Gardener, 3, Tiverton House, Pleasant Place, Canonbury, London, N.

Members of Bedford School H.R.C. Branch No. 310 with their Chairman, Pay-Captain W. H. Coomber; Secretary, J. E. D. Rothwell. This Branch has recently been incorporated, and is developing a realistic layout based on the Midland main line of the L.M.S.R. Some of the Branch stock used is shown.

Glengorse (Battle).—At a recent meeting a complicated track was arranged with the aid of additional Hornby material that has been obtained. On this occasion a new Hornby No. 3 *"Lord Nelson"* was given its first run, its finish and the realistic appearance of the smoke deflectors fitted being greatly admired. Subsequent track meetings have been held out-of-doors; the most successful arrangement incorporated a large continuous main line with two terminal stations, and many interesting train operations were carried out. Secretary: P. B. Bollard, Glengorse, Battle, Sussex.

Rutherglen (Glasgow).—A great variety of trains has been operated at recent meetings, the chief express passenger service being maintained by a special four-coach set train formation. The working of goods trains has not been neglected and shunting also has proved popular with many members. The most interesting outing yet enjoyed by the Branch was a visit to the Polmadie Motive Power Depot of the L.M.S.R. The locomotive sheds and repair shops, the coaling plant and the turntable also were inspected, and members were allowed to go on the footplates of engines of three different classes. One of these was a "Royal Scot" No. 6121 *"H.L.I."*; another was a 2–6–0 standard "Mogul," and the remaining one an 0–6–0 goods engine. At the final meeting of the Summer Session games were indulged in, and the results of prize competitions announced. Secretary: R. G. Langmuir, 11, Afton Street, Shawlands, Glasgow, S.1.

Whitgift School.—Interesting meetings with good timetable running have been held. Competitions devised by the members themselves have been greatly enjoyed. There was great excitement at a recent track meeting when comparative tests between various locomotives were carried out. It is hoped that members will be able to inspect the electric signal box at London Bridge. Secretary: J. C. Watson, 23, Addiscombe Avenue, Croydon, Surrey.

Branches in Course of Formation

The following new Branches of the Hornby Railway Company are at present in process of formation, and any boys who are interested and desirous of linking up with this unique organisation should communicate with the promoters, whose names and addresses are given below.

Chingford—G. Flowers, 1, Hortus Road, Chingford, London, E.4.

Peterborough—R. Garner, 128, St. Pauls Road, New England.

India—N. S. Narang, Shish Mahal Road, Lahore.

Branches Recently Incorporated

310. Bedford School—J. E. D. Rothwell, 6, Kimbolton Avenue, Bedford.

311. Umzinto—A. Payne, Umzinto Rail, Natal, South Africa.

LAND TRANSPORT IN THE STAMP ALBUM

tells you all about

LOCOMOTIVES ON STAMPS!

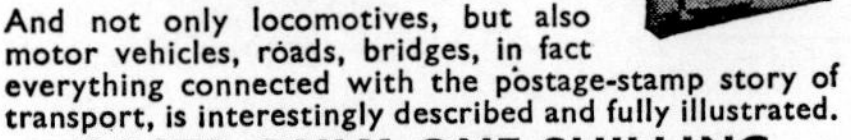

And not only locomotives, but also motor vehicles, roads, bridges, in fact everything connected with the postage-stamp story of transport, is interestingly described and fully illustrated.

COSTS ONLY ONE SHILLING
from your dealer.

Other Fine Shilling Books:

1. By Air Through the Stamp Album.
2. Native Races of the Stamp Album.
4. The Stamp Zoo. I. Beasts.
5. The Stamp Zoo. II. Birds, Fish, Reptiles.

All 1/- each, post 2d. extra.

In case of difficulty order direct from:

STANLEY GIBBONS LTD.,
DEPT. S.15 391 STRAND LONDON.

THE ABYSSINIA & QUEEN ASTRID PACKET FREE

With the African war over, stamps from Abyssinia are now obsolete and will become scarce. There is a large pictorial stamp from that country in this fine packet of 35 different stamps; a beautiful portrait stamp issued to perpetuate the memory of Belgium's lovely Queen whose tragic death shocked the world; a stamp depicting her husband King Leopold and also King Albert; a historical stamp depicting our War Memorial in Whitehall, and one from the new Asiatic country, Manchukuo; British Colonials, many fine sets; Chili Guatemala; Boy King of Jugo-Slavia, and set of Bohemia. Finally there is a Queen Victoria stamp issued 95 years ago. All free. Just send 2d. postage requesting new free 1936-7 Catalogue.

LISBURN & TOWNSEND LTD. (M.M.), LIVERPOOL

FREE WONDERFUL 1936 OFFER 25 NEW ISSUES AND NOVELTIES

Including **Andorra** (1935), fine new **Cayman Islands** (map of Islands), obsolete Austria, China, Denmark, **Gwalior** Service, Hungary (Statesman Szechenyi), **new Kenya** (Kavirondo Cranes), **Roumania** (new portrait of King Carol), and many others. I will send this collection **absolutely free** to all stamp collectors sending 2d. postage (abroad 4d.).

G. P. KEEF, Willingdon, EASTBOURNE

THE "DIAMOND" PACKET IS THE ONLY PACKET

OF UNSORTED STAMPS ON THE MARKET with 15 years' reputation behind it. It contains approx. **1,000 UNSORTED STAMPS** from Convents abroad. **MANY RARE STAMPS** have been found in it. 1 pkt., 1/6; 3 pkts., 3/9; 5 pkts., 6/-. All post free inland. Colonies 3d. per pkt. extra. Foreign, 6d. extra.

Ask your stationer for the "Diamond" packet.

SPECIAL: TURKS IS. JUBILEES complete set, used or unused, 5/6.

O. NERUSH (Dept. A), 68, TURNPIKE LANE, HORNSEY, LONDON, N.8

THE 'SHIP' PACKET

This marvellous packet is offered under cost as an advertisement, **45 different stamps each with a ship on it.** A regular armada. **GABOON,** New Issue **SENEGAL** (Canoe), wonderful flotilla of caravels from **DENMARK** (complete set), **NEW CALEDONIA, IVORY COAST, COSTA RICA,** a fleet of **7 CHINESE** junks usually sold at 10d., **TRINIDAD & TOBAGO, MAURITIUS, SOUTH WEST AFRICA, NEWFOUNDLAND, U.S.A. B. GUIANA,** set of **S. AFRICA, GREECE, POLAND, INDO-CHINA, FRENCH OCEANIA,** etc. Price 4½d., postage 1½d. (abroad 3d. extra). Purchasers of this packet asking for approvals receive **FREE** set of **4 SPAIN** (Columbus, each with his ship on it). Senders of addresses of stamp collectors receive **FREE** set of **6 VENEZUELA** or **6 PERSIA, 100 BRITISH COLONIALS 1/-, 20 AIRPOST 6d., 6 TRIANGULARS 6d., 50 PERSIA 4/-, 2 ASTRID** (mourning stamps) **2½d., VOLUMES OF B.O.P. CHEAP.**

H. C. WATKINS (M. Dept.), Granville Road, BARNET

SETS (POSTAGE EXTRA)

5	Angola	2d.
10	,,	5d.
15	,,	8d.
5	Azores	2d.
10	,,	5d.
15	,,	8d.
5	Cape Verde	2d.
10	,, ,,	5d.
15	,, ,,	8d.
5	Guinea	2d.
10	,,	5d.
5	India Port	3d.
5	Mozambique	2d.
10	,,	5d.
15	,,	8d.
5	,, Com.	2d.
10	,, ,,	4d.

10	Ceylon	2d.
1	,, Jubilee	2d.
5	Cyprus	3d.
10	,,	6d.
1	,, Jubilee	3d.
3	Charkari	2d.
5	Gold Coast	3d.
10	,, ,,	6d.
1	,, ,, Jubilee	2d.
3	Grenada	2d.
1	,, Jubilee	2d.
5	Hong Kong	2d.
10	,, ,,	5d.
1	,, ,, Jubilee	3d.
5	Kenya	3d.
1	,, Jubilee	3d.

J. RUSSELL
23, Shanklin Drive, Westcliff-on-Sea

NOW READY! - - -

THE 1937 EDITION OF THE STANDARD CATALOGUE of POSTAGE STAMPS OF THE WORLD - -

Enlarged, Further Improved and Completely Revised

The ideal Reference Catalogue for the beginner and general collector. Records every issue of the World's Postage and Air Mail Stamps, but omits all confusing minor varieties. The Jubilee Stamps and latest New Issues described and priced right up to date.

Start the season well by placing your order now, or ask for descriptive leaflet and free copies of our interesting price lists.

Price **5s.** Postage 6d. extra Abroad 10d.

Whitfield King & Co., Ipswich, Eng. Established 1869

ALL BRITISH COLONIAL APPROVALS

Fine **BRITISH COLONIAL NEW PICTORIAL SETS OF CAYMAN ISLANDS AND BERMUDA, FREE** to all Collectors sending 1½d. stamp and requesting **ALL BRITISH COLONIAL APPROVALS, BRITISH COLONIALS ONLY** on approval at bargain prices, including **JUBILEE** and new **PICTORIAL** issues, West Indies, East and West Africa, Cyprus, Iraq, Newfoundland, Papua and many other fine Colonials. (No stamps sent Abroad.) **C. H. SHAW (Dept. M.9), 95, CHRISTCHURCH AVENUE, KENTON, HARROW.**

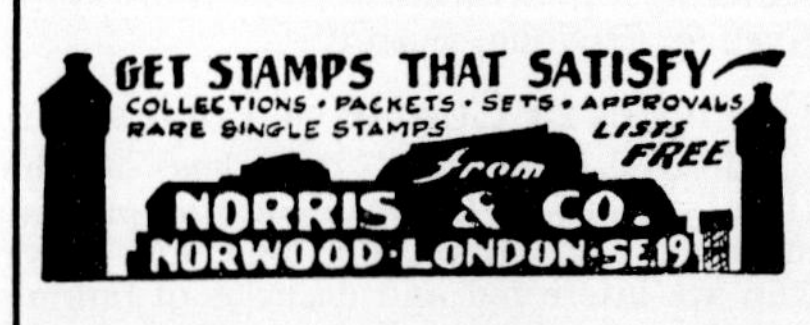

AMAZING PICTORIAL OFFER!

GLOBE-TROTTER AGAIN LEADS THE WAY—JUST THINK—The most beautiful selection of Pictorials and commemoratives **FREE**—including unused **Sarajevo** 1914 Assassination Commemorative, beautiful Silver Jubilee, some lovely stamps from South America, Morocco, Reunion, Madagascar, Syria, Andorra, Guiana, Air Mail, and other attractive varieties. The Surprise Packet of the year. Send 1½d. postage for Globe-Trotter approval selections, famous for sensational value. Ask for particulars of FREE stamps every 14 days!! Write now—there's a stamp treat in store for you.

GLOBE-TROTTER, 17, Winchester Road, Birchfield, Birmingham

Common and Rare Stamps

Bargain Hunters' Approvals. Pick attractive space-fillers or rare items from ⅓ to ⅛ S. G. Cat. **You will come again!**

CAMPBELL, Halden Avenue, Teignmouth.

ONE THOUSAND STAMPS ON APPROVAL

From which you may select any 100 for 3/-. This selection is not made up of the very commonest varieties, but contains stamps catalogued at 1/- each or more. (I do not sell less than 100.) During this month I will include in all selections a stamp catalogued at least 3/-. Can you find it?

H. HARDY, "Hoyland," Potter Heigham, Norfolk.

FREE! 4 DIFFERENT IRAQ to applicants for ½d. approvals.—Cox, 21, Dennis Mansions, Westcliff.

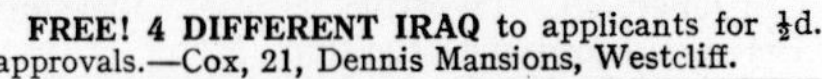

600 BRITISH COLONIALS on approval. Pick at ½d. each.—Sanders, 90, Newlands Avenue, Southampton.

GREAT NEWS

FIRST DAY COVERS KING EDWARD VIII

You can receive the new stamps on letters posted direct to you on the first day of issue from every one of the 63 British Colonies at prices from:

½d., 1d. and 1½d. stamp (or equivalent) from every colony **30/-**

½d. to 2d. stamp (or equivalent) from every colony **45/-**.

Single Colonies. Terms on Application.

Special Terms for Shareholders in Investors' Stamp Club.

A. F. McQUARRIE, 161a, STRAND, LONDON, W.C.2.

JUBILEES FREE

This magnificent FREE collection contains fine K. GEORGE SILVER JUBILEE issues, including a set of CANADA (Royal Family); AUSTRALIA (K. George on his horse Anzac) as well as the WINDSOR CASTLE issue. Also, this pkt. contains EGYPT (late K. Fuad); GREECE (Hermes); SIAM (Ex-King Prajadhipok); CHINA; JUGO-SLAVIA (Croatia); RUSSIA (Thunderbolts); JAPAN; BULGARIA; KENYA & UGANDA (obsolete K. George) etc., etc. Absolutely **FREE** to all genuine applicants for one of our famous 'Grey' booklets of stamps on approval who enclose 2d. stamps, or without approvals, P.O. 2/6. SPECIAL OFFERS, 25 Newfoundland 1/-, 50—5/-; 50 Japan 1/3, 100 5/-; 10 Japanese China 1/-; 50 Luxembourg 1/6, 100 5/-; 10 Vatican 1/-; 50 Spain 1/-, 100 3/6.

WINDSOR STAMP CO.
(M.M. Dept.), 59, Lee Road, Blackheath, S.E.3.

ORGANISED STAMP COLLECTING

WITHIN the next few weeks the popular stamp collecting season will be in full swing once again. No doubt many of our readers who have collected stamps in a haphazard way in past years have made up their minds to start on proper lines this season, and our article this month is directed to help such readers particularly. A well-kept collection provides its owner with an unlimited amount of pleasure.

An album and some stamp mounts form the only essential equipment for a commencement in stamp collecting, and it is advisable to buy the best that can be afforded. Unnecessary economy in this direction is a mistake. A loose-leaf album is better than one that has a fixed number of leaves and definite spaces devoted to various countries, for it permits expansion of the space devoted to any particular country, and the pages and stamps may be re-arranged as the growing collection demands.

This illustration, and that immediately beneath, are examples of stamps best left on their covers, the upper one because the cover is a souvenir of a most unusual type of mail service, and the other because the postmark indicates the stamp was used on the first day of issue.

The only satisfactory stamp mounts are those that can be peeled cleanly away from the stamp or the album page when it is necessary to make a change for any reason. Such mounts can be purchased at 8d. per 1,000, only a copper or two more than the cheap, dangerous bits of gummed paper that are frequently sold as stamp mounts. Cheap mounts will not peel off cleanly; either they tear a piece of the surface from the album page or they cannot be removed from the back of the stamp without risk of damage to the stamp itself. Any apparent saving achieved by the use of cheap stamp mounts is quickly lost when one or two stamps are ruined.

One word of warning must be given in connection with the use of stamp mounts, however. Even a good mount will not peel cleanly away from an album page or stamp unless it is perfectly dry. In no circumstances should an attempt be made to remove a mount while the gum is still damp.

There is a host of other accessories that a keen stamp collector can find useful, but only two of these are really required by the beginner—a catalogue and a pair of tweezers. The catalogue is a guide that simplifies the identification and arrangement of the stamps in their proper order, as well as listing details of perforation and watermarks that often are the sole means of distinguishing between various issues of the same country. It is just as helpful to the stamp collector as a compass is to a mariner. Young collectors are well catered for in the Gibbons "Simplified" catalogue and the Whitfield King "Standard" catalogue, both of which are priced at 5/–.

A splendid example of a used stamp. Note how perfectly the design is centred on the stamp and that the postmark is so light as not to obscure even the slightest feature of the design.

A pair of tweezers is often the last piece of equipment that the younger collector considers a necessity, and yet, in our view, it ranks almost next to the album itself. Stamps can so very easily be soiled, and their value is so quickly depreciated by dirtiness, that the use of tweezers is really important as a guard against fingermarks that would quickly deprive a stamp of its "mint" condition. At first the tweezers may seem a very clumsy tool, but after a little practice they are quite easy to use and in time their use becomes semi-automatic. Other items of equipment that the collector will find necessary as he progresses are a perforation gauge, watermark detector, a magnifying glass and a colour guide. Every one of these is really an essential to the serious collector, but the young collector can manage without them quite well for a considerable time. In a later article we hope to deal in greater detail with their employment in identifying stamps.

Having got together the essential equipment, the next stage in organising the collection is the mounting of the stamps that have been accumulated already. If it is intended to include both used and unused (mint) stamps in the collection, the two types should not be mixed together, but kept in separate rows on the page or, better still, on separate pages. A hard and fast rule should be made that dirty, heavily postmarked, or torn stamps shall not be included. The aim of the collector must be to make his collection neat and clean looking, and nothing detracts more from this object than heavily obliterated specimens. We do not agree with those who contend that only the most lightly postmarked stamps should be included, but somewhere between the lightly postmarked specimen and the dirty one there is a point that the young collector can adopt as the standard below which his used stamps may not fall.

If it is desired to retain stamps that fall below the standard set for the collection proper, there is no reason at all why the other specimens should not be put into a reserve collection that is retained for reference only. Here also may go the fiscal stamps, the meter frank specimens, and the odd curious charity stickers that every young collector seems to cherish. After all, those things have their interest, and there is no reason why anyone who desires to enjoy their possession should not do so, provided he does not consider them a legitimate inclusion in his stamp collection.

In the ordinary way every scrap of paper must be removed from a stamp before it is mounted in the collection, but there are certain exceptions to this rule, such as interesting postmarks, advertising cancellations, stamps on flown covers, etc., and in an early article we propose to deal with the handling of items such as these, and with the arrangement of the collection in the album.

In this article we have indicated certain general lines of action that every young collector should take to put his stamp collecting on to a proper basis. Inevitably, however, other points will arise in the experience of individual readers and in all matters of doubt on such points readers should not hesitate to write to the Editor of the "*M.M.*" for assistance.

10 DIFF. (NO G.B.) SILVER JUBILEE FOR 3½d. (Postage 1½d. Extra) TO ALL APPLICANTS FOR OUR BARGAIN APPROVALS CONTAINING OTHER JUBILEES, etc.

Don't delay, write at once for this wonderful packet, to: **THE PUKKA STAMP CO., 27, Normandy Ave., BARNET.**

PHILATELIC PHASCINATION

200,000 Stamps, what a pity we have no time to sort them through! We have purchased a huge accumulation, formed, for goodness knows what purpose, by an elderly collector. The collection dates back to the early days of Stamp Collecting. Even in the very brief glance we have allowed ourselves, we have noticed many high catalogue, some rarely seen nowadays. This is at a glance, we have no time at all to gauge the perforation, colour and other varieties which must abound. There is nothing to equal the pleasure of sorting a large accumulation such as this, so, as we are denied the pleasure ourselves, we are making it over to our customers. We have weighed the mixture into bags and offer it just as it stands, at 6d. (there's a chance for you boys and girls). 1/3, 2/9, 5/3, 10/3, and 25/– a bag. There is both the chance of some pleasant finds (we ourselves have seen three stamps catalogued over £4, while turning the mixture over, also some penny blacks and early Colonial Imperfs.) and the certainty of some real philatelic enjoyment. We especially urge our own customers to take as big a bag as possible, as we should not like them to miss it and there will be insufficient stock for repeat orders.

LIQUIFACTORS
43, Rectory Road, London, S.W.6 (England)

100 Different Stamps Free to Approval applicants. Liberal discount.—Cuthbert, Newsham Lane, Broughton, Preston.

Entirely free. 30 British Colonials including modern pictorials. Request approvals.—G. Kingsmill, New Barnet, Herts.

FREE SETS of STAMPS

6 Cuba or 6 Imperial China or 6 Straits Settlements or 6 old French, etc. Just send stamps value 2d. and ask for my Approval Sheets containing some high value stamps at low prices and with progressive discounts. State which set of stamps desired to be sent free.

P. ILLINGWORTH,
TRANMERE PARK, GUISELEY, near LEEDS.

New Greek Air Mail FREE

along with 25 other different stamps. Say whether British Colonial or Foreign preferred—to applicants sending 2d. in stamps and requesting our Booklets of Stamps. Special discounts allowed.

The BRAMLEY STAMP CO.,
TOWN END, BRAMLEY, LEEDS.

SENT BY AIR MAIL

Celebrated "Richemont" 6d. and 1/– packets, sets and singles, sent on approval by Swiss Air Mail. 50 Swiss, 1/–; 50 U.S.A., 1/–; 40 Canada, 1/–. Complete pictorial Swiss set of 7, 4d.

A. M. PHILLIPS,
Richemont, St. Légier, sur Vevey, Switzerland.

PICTORIAL STAMPS—FREE!

Make sure that you obtain this delightful series of pictorial stamps.
Two **ALGERIA** (Street in the Kasbah); Two **ANDORRA** (Notre Dame de Meritxell); One **ANDORRA** (Recouvrements); Two **GUADELOUPE** (Sugar-refinery); One **REUNION** (Waterfalls); Two **TCHAD** (Panther in ambush); Two **SENEGAL** (Bridge over river).
ALL OF THESE SENT **FREE** to applicants for our approvals who enclose 2d.
THE STANDARD AND UNIVERSAL STAMP CO. (SM9), 16, Gloucester Place, Greenwich, S.E.10.

CHEAP APPROVALS

My beautiful Approval Selections are ideal for filling those vacant spaces. Pictorials, Colonials, and hard to get items. Selections from 4 a 1d. Free Gift Bicoloured Persia all applicants.

A. V. TAPP,
108, CHESTERFIELD RD., BRISTOL

ANOTHER OUTSTANDING OFFER!

We always celebrate the opening of the Philatelic Season with a real **Bumper Gift** and this year we offer the **OCEANIA PACKET,** brimful of magnificent **Pictorials** from the Southern Seas. Here are some specimens included—Australia, **1/- Lyre Bird** and a **1936 Commemorative** of the Submarine Telephone to Tasmania; **Toga,** Coat of Arms mint; **Papua,** pictorial depicting Motuan Girl; **New Zealand,** Pied Fantail and Kiwi bird stamps; **Nauru,** view of island; **West Samoa,** showing Samoan girl with Kava Bowl; Australian comm. Centenary of Victoria, 2d. This packet would cost **1/6** from some approvals but is **FREE AND POST FREE.** Just send a P.C. requesting approvals to

THE UNIVERSITY STAMP CO., 13, WALTON WELL ROAD, OXFORD

TRIANGULAR PACKET FREE!

As a special opening offer for the new Season, we are presenting this wonderful collection **absolutely FREE.** The contents include—**Mozambique Triangular** as illustrated; Reunion (Waterfall); Middle Congo (**Train steaming over Viaduct**); Straits (Tiger); Belgium (**Rare Railway commemorative**); China (Sailing Boat); **2 Mint Air Mails,** and many other wonderful stamps. To obtain this fine gift, simply request approvals, and include 2d. postage. (No approvals sent abroad.) Price of packet alone 9d.

MICHAEL HERBERT (M.M.),
8, Woodstock Road, Walthamstow, London.

Mint BERMUDA New Issue Packet FREE

Magnificent opening season's offer: **Grand Packet** of 28 **British Colonials** inc. above handsome stamp, a **Rare Silver Jubilee, Cyprus** (1934 Salamis) and soon to be obsolete K.G. issues. Write now for this grand free gift. Send 2d. post (6d. abroad) and ask for my **Modern** approvals.

CAMPBELL, 71, Manor Rd., Tankerton, Kent.

BRITISH COLONIAL PICTORIAL PACKET FREE!

This packet contains stamps from **Bermuda, Cayman Islands, Ceylon, Nigeria, St. Lucia,** etc. All unused. Send postcard for cheap approvals. Prices ½d. upwards. Postage paid both ways. All applications received before noon will be despatched same day.

T. F. WILLIAMS
7, ISLINGTON ROAD, TOWCESTER, NORTHANTS.

MECCANO LUBRICATING OIL

Before commencing to operate a Meccano model, or to run a Hornby Train, all gears and bearings should be oiled thoroughly with Meccano Lubricating Oil. This oil is specially prepared and is of the right consistency for the purpose
Price per bottle 6d

Meccano Ltd., Binns Road, Liverpool 13.

Stands for HORNBY SPEED AND RACING BOATS

Every owner of a Hornby Speed or Racing Boat who prides himself on taking care of his model should obtain a Hornby Boat Stand on which to place his boat when it is not in use. The Stands are available in the following sizes: No. 1 for No. 1 Speed Boats; No. 1R for No. 1 Racer; No. 2 for No. 2 Speed Boat and No. 2 Racer; No. 3 for Nos. 3, 4 and 5 Speed Boats and No. 3 Racer. They can be obtained from any Meccano dealer price 9d. each (any size).

MECCANO LTD., Binns Road, Liverpool 13

100 diff. Stamps Free to approval applicants, good discount.—Gosling, 21, Powling Road, Ipswich.

"ABBEY" on a packet spells VALUE!

Unused Pictorials (Colonial, Air, and Foreign), 15 for 6d., 35 for 1/–. Special Mixture Used and Unused, 15 for 6d. Postage extra.

ABBOTT BROS., 16, Sedgemoor Road, Liverpool, 11.

FINE BRITISH COLONIALS

A collection of 700 different for 25/–, or pick where you like at ½d. each stamp—willingly sent on approval on request. Address:

S. F. BICKERS, 201, HILL LANE, SOUTHAMPTON.

BARGAIN OFFERS

Jubilees.—15 Colonial, all different, Used ... 1/6
Used **Sets Complete. Canada** or **Hong Kong** 2/–
Mint Sets. Bechuanaland, Swaziland, each 2/6
The **'Different'** packet of **British Colonials** containing 60 different fine used **Jubilees, Commemoratives** and **Recent Pictorials** 3/3
100 Iran (Persia), **2/9**; 50 for **1/6**
100 French Colonials (all bright pictorials) 1/6
Cash with order. Postage extra.
T. R. HUGHES
'Ibis Cottage,' Long Park, Amersham

MINIATURE AEROPLANE PILOTS

Aeroplane Parts Nos. P99 and P100

Miniature Pilots are now available for fitting to all open cockpit machines built with the Nos. 00, 0, 1, 2, 1 Special and 2 Special Aeroplane Constructor Outfits. These attractive little figures, which add a wonderful touch of realism, are supplied with green coat and orange cap, blue coat and red cap, or red coat and green cap. Aero Part No. P99, which is suitable for fitting to the Nos. 00 and 0 Outfit models, is fixed to a special bracket that takes the place of the Propeller Shaft Bracket in the Outfit. The special bracket is secured by passing bolts through the sides of the fuselage into the threaded holes in the bracket. The Propeller Shaft rests in the bearing socket formed in the Pilot's body.

Part No. P100 (illustrated above) is used in Nos. 1, 2, 1 Special and 2 Special Outfit models. The Pilot is fixed to a double angle bracket ready for bolting to the sides of the fuselage.

Prices:

P99	Aeroplane Pilot	each 4d.
P100	„ „	„ 4d.

Meccano Ltd., Binns Road, Liverpool 13

Stamp Gossip

and Notes on New Issues

New French Issues

Among recent French issues are several of exceptional interest. Pride of place in British collectors' eyes must be taken by the 75c. and 1 fr. 50c. values commemorating the unveiling of the Canadian War Memorial at Vimy Ridge, but unfortunately at the time of going to press specimens were not available for illustration here. Both stamps bear the same design, a simple front view of the complete memorial. The framework of the stamp is rather heavy and has the effect of dwarfing the noble dimensions of the memorial, but our Canadian readers particularly will join with us in appreciation of this very graceful French tribute.

Next in interest come two stamps commemorating the centenary of the death of Claude Joseph Rouget de L'Isle, composer of the French national anthem *"La Marseillaise."* There are two values, 20c. and 40c.

The 20c., illustrated here, shows a portrait of de L'Isle, who was a Captain of Engineers stationed at Strasbourg when he wrote the song in 1792. In company with his brother officers, he dined one evening with the mayor of the city, who expressed regret that no special marching song had been composed for the Army of the Rhine. On his return to his quarters de L'Isle sat down at his desk and in a moment of inspiration composed his famous revolutionary song. The full beauty of the stirring words and music were revealed when the song was sung by a battalion of 600 men from Marseilles who marched to Paris, to strengthen the revolutionary cause, and the song has ever since been known as the *"Marseillaise."*

The 40c. value depicts Francois Rude's famous sculpture *"La Marseillaise,"* from the Arc de Triomphe.

A third new French issue a 75c. stamp, illustrated here, commemorates Jean Francois Pilatre de Rozier, one of the world's pioneer aeronauts. De Rozier's special claim to fame is that he achieved the first successful ascent in a balloon. This was in Paris in November, 1783, when he made an ascent in a hot air balloon along with the Marquis d'Arlandes, remaining in the air 20 to 25 minutes.

King Edward VIII Stamps

We understand that definite preparations are in hand in Australia for the production of the new King Edward VIII stamps, and it is probable that these will appear for the first time on the Coronation Day next year.

The design will show a head and neck profile of King Edward facing left, bordered by a wreath of intertwined oak and wattle with other symbolic emblems. The stamps will be produced by the line engraved process with the usual inscription "Australian Postage" at the top and the value tablets at the foot. The values will range from ½d. to £2.

Shortly the Commonwealth stamps will appear on a paper bearing a new watermark depicting the correct Imperial Crown. The present Australian watermark shows an incorrect type. New paper has already been ordered.

Colonial First Day Covers

So great has become the demand for lightly cancelled used colonial stamps that the work of the postmasters in many colonies has been in danger of becoming disorganised by requests from collectors and dealers in other countries to have letters stamped and returned through the post. As a result, the Colonial Secretary has issued an instruction that in future such requests shall not be complied with.

In the ordinary way this instruction would have had the effect of making used stamps from the colonies, particularly those used on the first day of issue, scarcer and dearer, and to overcome this difficulty our advertiser, Mr. A. F. McQuarrie, of Wallasey, has devised a scheme whereby First Day Covers of the new stamps of King Edward VIII will be available to collectors at cheaper rates than ever before.

This has been made possible by the taking of orders in advance on a large scale, and the collaboration of some of the largest business firms abroad who will post letters all over the Empire on the correct date. The network of the scheme provides for the despatch of letters from any part of the Empire to any other part, and already orders have been received for despatches from Newfoundland to Nauru, from Papua to Pimlico, and from Aden to the Virgin Islands, in addition to other exchanges.

Mr. McQuarrie will be glad to send full details of this scheme, and of similar arrangements for the despatch of air mail covers, to any *"M.M."* reader who is interested.

Dutch Triangulars

Holland has marked the tercentenary of Utrecht University by issuing two very striking triangular stamp designs, 6c. and 12½c. values.

As our illustration shows, the 6c. bears an effigy of Pallas Athene the Goddess of Wisdom. The 12½c. stamp bears a similar design, but in this case the portrait is of Gisbert Voetius, an eminent Dutch theologian who played a large part in the foundation of the University.

* * * *

On 22nd June last, in connection with the race for the "Brown Ribbon of Germany," the German Post Office issued a special Charity stamp for sale at the Munich-Riem race course and a number of specially selected Post Offices.

The design, as our illustration shows, depicts a horse race in progress. The nominal value of the stamp was 42 rpf. plus a charity premium of 42 rpf., but actually the stamp was sold at 1 rm. 50.

U.S. Centennials

The latest issue in the long series of U.S. stamps marking the centennials of the various States of the Union is the 3c. Arkansas commemorative, illustrated here. The central plaque shows the Old State House at Little Rock, the capital. On the left is seen a representation of the old Arkansas Post, the first white settlement in the State, while in the right-hand panel appears a view of the recently erected new State Capitol.

Air Mails Growth

The Post Office returns for the quarter ending 30th June show a great increase in the weight of air mail flown from Great Britain to the Continent. The weight of letters flown was nearly 99,000 lb., an increase of 170 per cent. on that for the corresponding quarter in 1935. The increase is due very largely to the fact that first class mail to Scandinavia can now be sent by air without surcharge.

* * * *

Australia is to celebrate the 150th anniversary of the founding of New South Wales by a special stamp issue in January.

We thank Stanley Gibbons Ltd. for their courtesy in loaning the stamps from which the illustrations on this page have been made.

SOMETHING TO THINK ABOUT

III. Is it possible to go up in a balloon on a perfectly still day, and to remain immovable for a time while the Earth beneath rolls round, descending when some desired spot comes directly below?

THERE is something attractive in the idea that a cheap and easy means of travelling would be simply to step off the Earth and wait until the destination in view comes directly underneath. Anyone wishing to reach New York, say from Lisbon, would not actually go there, but would simply wait until New York came to him.

Travel of this kind would be very speedy—if it were possible. Let us suppose for a moment that it is, and see what happens. The Earth turns round once in every 24 hours, and every place on the Equator therefore travels at the rate of about 1,050 m.p.h. Lisbon travels more slowly, for it is on a smaller circle of latitude than the Equator, but nevertheless its speed is the high one of a little more than 800 m.p.h. A balloon released above that city therefore would be over New York, which is practically due west of it, in four hours, although the distance between these two places is about 3,000 miles.

Balloon travel by waiting at a great height would have the drawback that it would only be possible to go due west. Our imaginary traveller need not worry about that, however, for he could easily return to Lisbon by ascending in New York and letting the rest of the Earth go by under him! Although in effect he would travel nearly round the Earth, this would only take the remaining part of a day, that is about 20 hours. The fastest ships take a much longer time to complete the journey, even when travelling by the direct route eastward across the Atlantic Ocean.

Another interesting point is that New York could not be reached from London in this manner, for the balloon traveller going directly westward from the latter city would soon find himself over Labrador. If he went farther he would reach the prairie region of Canada, and he would have to complete his journey by train, car or aeroplane. Balloon voyages also would be completely out of the question for travelling north or south, say from London to Aberdeen or to South Africa, but within limits they would be very valuable.

A terrible disappointment. After ascending to a great height in the hope of reaching Canada by letting the Earth turn round beneath them, the balloonists find that they have not moved from their starting point. The reason for this is explained in the accompanying article.

Unfortunately the prospect of crossing the Atlantic Ocean in a balloon high up above the Earth in a few hours is only a dream. If an enthusiastic reader decided to give the plan an experimental test, he would be doomed to suffer a disappointment similar to that of the balloonists shown in our illustration, who are astonished to see below them the familiar features of the place they thought they had left far behind them.

The truth is that it is impossible to step off the Earth by any simple means of this kind. Although we cannot see anything but clouds above the solid ground on which we live, the Earth really extends for many miles above its apparent surface; the invisible blanket of air that surrounds it is as much a part of it as the solid rock mass of Mount Everest, and rotates with it. Every particle is subject to the gravitational attraction of the Earth, and we could only escape by allowing ourselves to be shot off at a rate of no less than seven miles a second. Such a speed is unattainable, for space guns and rockets packed with the tremendous amount of energy required have not yet been invented. They are the dream of those who look forward to the time when we shall be able to travel to the Moon, or to other destinations in space, and are found only in sensational stories of the future.

The balloon itself also must be regarded as part of the Earth. When it is tethered to the ground, in readiness for its ascent, it is travelling with the Earth at the same speed as everything else in the neighbourhood. It is not left behind as soon as it is released, but continues to move eastward, just as every solid object in its neighbourhood does, and with undiminished speed.

This may not be easy to realise, but here is an experiment that any reader can try for himself without expense or danger. Suppose a boy stands in front of a wall facing east, and leaps as high into the air as possible. If the time during which he loses actual contact with the Earth is only one tenth of a second, the wall will sweep on eastward to a distance of 88 ft. while he is in the air. If the jumper really were free of the Earth, in the manner suggested for a balloon, he would therefore be struck violently by the wall and his face would suffer severely! Nothing of the kind happens in reality, for the simple reason that the jumper continues to maintain his own eastward velocity while he is in the air.

Like the boy jumping into the air, a balloon when released is carried round in the air surrounding the Earth. Of this there is no doubt. Balloons that have been set free in Great Britain have stayed in the air for several hours, but have always descended in that country, or very near it. If they had not retained their Earth speed while in the air, they would have been swept away westward, or rather left behind, and would have come down in the Atlantic Ocean, if not in America.

The objection may be made that these balloons have not gone high enough. The answer to this is that no balloon, whatever its height, has ever shown the slightest trace of being left behind by the Earth. One indication of this would be a tremendous gale as the air rushed at high speed past the stationary balloon. Even at heights of 13 or 14 miles nothing but calm has been experienced, apart of course from normal winds of the kind familiar to everybody. These do not blow at 1,050 m.p.h., but they offer the only known means of causing balloons to move through the air, and only then in an aimless drift.

The only way in which one could remain still above the Earth would be by travelling at high speed. This sounds an absurdly contradictory statement, but it is worth considering. Suppose that an aeroplane ascends above some point on the Equator. The surface of the Earth then would whiz past the pilot of the machine at the rate of about 1,050 m.p.h. if he were really still, and as his machine would start with this eastward velocity, it would be necessary for him to fly westward at equal speed to neutralise the effect. The pilot then would be able to argue that he remained still, and that the Earth below him was travelling eastward at 1,050 m.p.h. On the other hand those on Earth watching him would think they were still, for its rotation gives no sense of movement, and that the airman was travelling round the Earth at a speed of about 1,050 m.p.h. H. A. ROBINSON.

ANOTHER "POINT WORDS" CONTEST

Several readers have written to ask for another competition of the "Point Words" type that we introduced some three years ago. They found it more puzzling than the average word competition, and readers who have not yet tried their skill in a contest of this kind will find it a distinctly teasing novelty.

In this competition readers are required to take from this issue of the "*M.M.*" any phrase or sentence containing exactly 25 letters, and to rearrange the letters to form a square in which as many complete words as possible are formed in the vertical and horizontal lines. For each word of five letters in one line 10 points are awarded; for a word of four letters, five points; for a word of three letters, two points; and for a word of two letters, one point. A line containing two words of three and two letters respectively thus scores three points. The maximum possible score is 100, but a score of 60 points from an average phrase may be considered quite satisfactory.

Letters may appear in the square only as many times as they occur in the original sentence, and short words forming part of a longer word in the same line do not count in reckoning up the score. Only genuine English words in current use may be used; proper nouns and coined or slang words are ineligible.

Competitors are at liberty to select any suitable sentence or phrase in this issue of the "*M.M.*," but in submitting their entries they must indicate the page and line from which the words are taken.

In order to make clear what competitors are asked to do, we have taken the phrase "in a car suspended from the bar," from the third line in the second column on page 498 of this issue, and in the centre of this page we have given a specimen "Point Words" working from this phrase. Our example is framed so that the full system of scoring is revealed. We have deliberately chosen this phrase to give what we consider to be an average result, and it will be seen that the total score is 58. The Magazine contains other phrases that will give much larger scores, and readers will find it useful to choose one with a fair sprinkling of letters such as T, R, S and E.

	10	10	2	1	—
10	C	R	A	B	S
10	R	A	T	E	D
5	U	P	O	N	F
5	S	I	N	E	H
5	E	D	R	A	M

Total: 58

There are two Sections in this Contest, for Home and Overseas readers respectively, and in each cash prizes of 21/–, 15/–, 10/6 and 5/– will be awarded to the four best entries in order of merit. In the event of a tie, preference will be given to the entries displaying the neatest or most novel presentation.

Entries should be addressed to "Point Words, Meccano Magazine, Binns Road, Liverpool 13." Those from competitors at Home, that is in Great Britain, Northern Ireland, the Irish Free State and the Channel Islands, must be posted to reach this office not later than 30th September. Entries for the Overseas Section must arrive not later than 31st December. The awards in the Home Section will be announced in the November "*M.M.*"

September Photo Contest

This month's competition is the last of the 1936 series of Photo Contests, and we hope that all of our readers who have not yet submitted an entry will make a point of sending along one of their holiday snapshots this month.

The conditions of our photo contests are so very simple that every camera-owning reader should take part. Any subject is eligible, and any make of camera, plate, film or paper may be employed. The only restriction is that the exposure must have been made by the competitor himself. Developing and printing may have been done professionally, but readers who do this part of the work themselves should mark the back of the print "own work throughout." Any number of prints may be submitted but the competitor's name, age and address must appear on the back of each print. It is not sufficient to indicate the age group only. The actual age must be given.

The entries will be divided into two sections: A, for competitors aged 16 and over; and B, for those under 16. Cash prizes of 21/– and 10/6 respectively, will be awarded in each section.

Entries should be addressed "September Photo Contest, Meccano Magazine, Binns Road, Liverpool 13," and must be sent to reach this office not later than 30th September. A separate set of prizes will be reserved for competition among Overseas readers, whose entries must arrive not later than 31st December.

COMPETITION RESULTS

HOME

July Sketchogram Contest.—First Prizes: Section A, T. R. Hayes (Nottingham); Section B, C. Buttery (Grantham). Second Prizes: Section A, J. Browne (Luton); Section B, A. M. Adam (London, N.6).

July Photo Contest.—First Prizes: Section A, D. H. Warner (Richmond, Surrey); Section B, B. P. Furley (London, W.1). Second Prizes: Section A, R. P. Tonkin (London, E.18); Section B, G. Arnold (Burgess Hill). Consolation Prizes: E. C. Haywood (Carlton, Notts.); C. P. Silver (Exeter).

OVERSEAS

Vocation Voting Contest.—1. J. C. Oleaga (Buenos Aires). 2. W. A. Carpinter (Christchurch, N.Z.). 3. A. Rutherford (Christchurch, N.Z.). 4. W. L. Jarvis (Capetown). Consolation Prize: A. G. Fellows (Auckland, N.Z.).

April Photo Contest.—First Prizes: Section A, G. C. Taylor (Sydney); Section B, C. Galdes (Valletta, Malta). Second Prizes: Section A, A. Hagg (Falun, Switzerland); Section B, M. Nicholls (Natal, S.A.). Consolation Prizes: G. S. Davies (Dunedin, N.Z.); B. B. Silan (Ipoh, F.M.S.); M. Abdul Wahid (Mysore, S. India); L. B. de Lancastre (Lisbon, Portugal).

A SOFT SPOT

The farmer had given an old Irishman permission to sleep in his barn, and at night found him lying on a heap of straw with a drainpipe for a pillow.

"Don't you find that pipe hard?" asked the farmer.

"No, yer honor," said Pat. "I've filled it with straw."

* * * *

Schoolmaster (suspiciously): "Is this essay all your own work, Jones?"

Jones: "No, sir, Dad wrote it, and I corrected it."

* * * *

Waiter: "How do you like your coffee, sir?"

Guest: "Without cream."

Waiter: "Sorry, sir, we've no cream; would it do if I gave it you without milk?"

* * * *

Master: "Now, boys, this is a very difficult problem. Watch the blackboard carefully while I go through it."

* * * *

Judge: "It seems to me that I have seen you before."

Prisoner: "You have, your honour; I gave your daughter singing lessons."

Judge: "Thirty years."

* * * *

"Do you know where little boys go to who fish on Sundays?"

"Yus, but I ain't lettin' you in on a good thing. You'll 'ave to find out for yerself, same as I did."

* * * *

Mark Twain had the best recipe for insomnia. He said: "If you cannot sleep, try lying on the very edge of the bed; you might drop off."

* * * *

Applicant: "And if I take the job am I to get a rise in salary every year?"

Employer: "Yes. Provided of course that your work is satisfactory."

Applicant: "Ah, I thought there was a catch in it somewhere."

* * * *

There had been a car smash; one driver had been pitched on to the road, the other into the hedge.

Voice from hedge: "Roadhog!"

Voice from road: "Hedgehog!"

* * * *

Two doctors lived together, one a doctor of medicine, the other a doctor of divinity.

A caller from the village, asking the man-servant if he might speak to the doctor, was asked: "Do you mean the doctor who preaches or the doctor who practises?"

* * * *

Jimmy: "That problem you helped me with last night was all wrong, Dad."

Dad: "All wrong? Well, I'm sorry, son."

Jimmy: "You needn't exactly worry about it, because none of the other fathers got it right either."

* * * *

SOUNDLESS

Customer: "I've brought back this music stool you sold me."

Shopkeeper: "Why?"

Customer: "Well, I've twisted and turned it in all directions, but I can't get a single note out of it."

SOME SHOT

Mike was before the bench on a charge of poaching.

"Do you admit that you killed the bird?" asked the judge.

"Indade Oi don't, sor," said Mike. "The only bird I shot with me gun was a rabbit, and that Oi killed with me stick."

* * * *

AN AWFUL PROSPECT

Man falling from skyscraper: "Catch this mirror, Tom! If I break it I'll have seven years' bad luck."

* * * *

New Recruit (to chief gunner): "Tell me, sir, is it true that the harder you pull the trigger the farther the bullet travels?"

* * * *

Auntie: "Which one of you children ate those grapes I had in the cupboard? No use denying it, I saw the seeds and skins on the floor."

Willie: "It wasn't me, Auntie, 'cause I ate the seeds, skins and all."

* * * *

"A moth leads a curious life."

"How come?"

"He spends the summer in a fur coat and the winter in a bathing suit."

* * * *

"Jimmy, dear," whispered the burglar's bride, as he started on his evening's work, "try to be a little quieter when you come in to-night."

"Certainly," replied the husband. "Did I wake you up last night?"

"No, but you wakened Mother, and I don't want her running up to prison and complaining to father that I married an amateur."

* * * *

"I hear you have a garden; I suppose things are growing very rapidly."

"Yes, the neighbour's hens; every time they get into it they grow fatter."

* * * *

Teacher (trying to teach boy manners): "Where do you keep your hat, Willie?"

Willie: "On my head."

Teacher: "Where should it be?"

Willie: "On father's."

* * * *

A wireless expertlet from Bristol
In error once swallowed a crystal;
This caused oscillation,
So in desperation
He "earthed" himself, using a pistol.

* * * *

"I can tell the age of a chicken by the teeth."

"But they haven't any teeth."

"No, but I have."

* * * *

Talkative Lady: "A big man like you might be better occupied than in cruelly catching little fish."

Angler: "Perhaps you're right. But if this fish had kept its mouth shut it wouldn't be here now."

* * * *

"Now, Willie, give me that sweet you are eating."

"I c-can't, teacher. It belongs to Harry Williams!"

GONE

He had gone into the manager's office to inquire if he could have the Saturday morning off for the purpose of digging his garden.

"But my dear man," said the manager, "Smith told me only a day or two ago that you hadn't a garden."

"Well then," was the reply, "someone must have taken it off the window sill."

* * * *

Jim: "All the prizes at the swimming gala were carried off by one man."

Jack: "What did he get?"

Jim: "Six months."

* * * *

"My boots were guaranteed for four months," said Sandy to the boot-maker, "and they need easin'."

"But they seem to fit."

"Ay, they're fine on me, but tight for my brither on night shift."

* * * *

Employer: "What do you mean by telling me that you had seven years' experience at a bank when actually you have never had a job before?"

Applicant: "Well, sir, you advertised for a man with imagination."

* * * *

Voice on Telephone: "My son will be unable to attend school this morning; he is not well."

Master: "I'm sorry. Who's speaking?"

Voice: "My father, sir."

* * * *

Peter: "May I have twopence for a man who is crying out in the street?"

Mother: "Certainly, sonny. What is he crying about?"

Peter: "Cream ices, twopence each!"

* * * *

Uncle: "So you finished bottom of the class at spelling to-day?"

Nephew: "Yes, I put too many Z's in 'scissors'."

* * * *

Mother: "Aunt Mary wants to know if you will carry her train at her wedding."

Small Son: "I will if it's a Hornby!"

* * * *

Customer: "Waiter, it's almost half an hour since I ordered that turtle soup."

Waiter: "Sorry sir, but you know how slow turtles are."

* * * *

"I'm buying this fountain-pen for my wife," he explained.

"A surprise, eh?" beamed the shop assistant.

"Rather! She's expecting a new car."

* * * *

Constable (to speeding foreigner): "Ere, you mustn't go rushing abaht like that. What's yer name?"

Speeding Foreigner: "Je ne comprends pas."

Constable: "Ow d'yer spell it?"

* * * *

NOT LIKELY

Q.M.S.: "Where are you going?"

Private: "To fetch water."

Q.M.S.: "In those disreputable trousers?"

Private: "No fear, in this 'ere pail."

MECCANO MAGAZINE

Editorial Office:
Binns Road, Liverpool 13
England

Vol. XXI. No. 10
October, 1936

With the Editor

The Indoor Hobbies Season

The long nights are with us again, and my readers will be turning their attention seriously to Meccano, Hornby railways and other indoor hobbies. It is always rather exciting to unearth boxes of material from cupboards and other places where they were hastily stowed on the approach of summer. Invariably some articles are missing. We are quite sure we put them away all right, and everybody else in the house denies having touched them; evidently the articles walked out of the box of their own accord! As a rule, however, the missing items are discovered hidden away in some unexpected corner, and operations then can be commenced in earnest.

Every year I am more impressed with the fact that the boys who get the greatest fun from their hobbies are those who adopt some sort of system. As regards Meccano, I think the best scheme is to decide upon building a series of models of one particular type—cranes, bridges, ships, motor vehicles, or whatever may be of most interest at the time. This is far better than just sitting down to play with an outfit without any particular object in view. The same thing applies to Hornby railways. It is not much fun running the same old layout that one had during the previous winter; a new scheme should be planned out and laid down bit by bit as new material can be obtained.

And here I want to remind all readers that, whatever their hobbies, I am always ready to help. Meccano enthusiasts who find difficulty in getting a particular model to work; Hornby railway owners who want suggestions for new layouts—I want these and all others to write to me without hesitation.

Photographs for Model-Building Contests

In order to enter one of the *"M.M."* model-building competitions it is necessary to send either a photograph or a drawing of the model to be submitted, and I find that this prevents many readers from taking part in these contests. I hear of many cases where a boy builds quite a good model and would like to enter it in a competition, but does not do so because he is no good at drawing and does not possess a camera. A satisfactory drawing of a model may be beyond the powers of many boys, but there should be no difficulty about a reasonably good photograph. I am sure that almost every reader either has a camera of his own, or has a friend who possesses one and could be induced to undertake the necessary photographic operations.

The main thing required in photographs of models is sharpness of focus, and this can be secured with any type of camera, even the very cheapest box form. I am anxious to encourage readers to tackle this photographic bogey and see how easily it can be overcome; and with this object in view I am preparing a helpful article, which I hope to include in next month's issue. In this article I shall deal only with the very simplest types of camera, and show how they can be made to produce really satisfactory photographs.

Readers often ask why it is that the models illustrated on the "Competition Results" page are in many cases not first-prize winners, but those that have been awarded second or third prizes. When this occurs the reason is that the photographs of the first-prize models are too poor to be reproduced. It is always a great disappointment to me to be unable to illustrate a really original model, and I hope that in future serious model-builders will take more care about their photography, with a view to their work appearing in the *"M.M."*

By the way, I am always glad to receive suggestions from readers for new competitions. In regard to such contests it is necessary to bear in mind that they must be of general interest and likely to appeal to the majority of Meccano model-builders. Another point is that they must be of such a nature that owners of small outfits can compete with a reasonable chance of success.

The Southampton to Capetown Record

We are all delighted that the *"Queen Mary"* has recovered the "Blue Riband" of the Atlantic. In our enthusiasm for this wonderful ship, however, we are in danger of overlooking the extremely interesting feat of the Union-Castle liner *"Stirling Castle"* in completing the voyage from Southampton to Capetown in 13½ days, and thus breaking a record established 43 years ago by the Union Steamship Company's liner *"Scot."* The *"Scot's"* fastest time for the trip was 14 days 18 hrs. 57 min. This fine vessel was built in 1889 by Harland and Wolff Ltd., and six years later the firm carried out with complete success the task of lengthening her by 54 ft., thereby adding 1,000 tons to her tonnage.

The Union Castle Line came into existence in 1900, as the result of the amalgamation of the Union Steamship Co. Ltd. and the Castle Mail Packets Co. Ltd. The Castle Line commenced operations in 1872 with two small ships, and it is interesting to know that the postage rate to the Cape was then one shilling per half ounce, and the contract period for delivery was thirty-seven days! The *"Stirling Castle's"* time of 13½ days is to be the regular mail ship time under the new South African Government contract.

The Maoris of New Zealand

A Fine Race of Hunters and Warriors

EXACTLY when or from where the Maoris came to New Zealand is uncertain. According to native legends their tribal ancestors discovered the islands 1,200 or 1,300 years ago, in the course of long canoe voyages. The Maoris did not invade the country until about 1350, however, when, their legends relate, they sailed from Rarotonga in a fleet of many canoes. Rarotonga is one of the Cook Islands, far out in the Pacific Ocean, and is about 2,250 miles from the North Island of New Zealand. With the help of the trade wind the emigrants probably accomplished the long voyage in about a month. The Maoris are Polynesians of the same race as the Tahitians, Rarotongans, Nawaiians and other natives of the Eastern Pacific. They found New Zealand inhabited by a people, quite different from themselves, who probably were Melanesians from the Western Pacific. The exact fate of these inhabitants is unknown, but they were either exterminated by the Maoris or eventually absorbed by them.

Feeding the tohunga, or medicine man. A scene at Rotorua, North Island, New Zealand.

In New Zealand the Maoris followed their natural pursuits of fishing, hunting, agriculture and fighting, and under the influence of the bracing climate they developed physically, and became one of the finest races in the world. They were of a warlike disposition, and conflicts between some of the many different tribes were always going on. As fighting was such a prominent feature of their life, it is not surprising that they were always as prepared against attacks as they were to be the aggressors. Their villages were protected by deep trenches and fortified by stockades, of which the Maoris were expert builders, and watch towers about 20 ft. high were built at points particularly open to attack. The storehouses were kept well stocked with food and weapons in case the villages were suddenly besieged, and the inhabitants were regularly practised in warlike exercises.

Armed with hatchets and heavy wooden spears, the Maoris on the war-path were a formidable foe. Often the women followed the men into battle and by their indifference to danger increased the fervour of the warriors. Both sides fought hard, as one would expect of such a sturdy and militant people, and the vanquished were made the slaves of the victors or suffered the more horrible fate of being cooked and eaten.

The whole of North Island and part of South Island were occupied by the Maoris, and the land was portioned out among the numerous tribes, who cultivated part of their territory. No stranger could settle on Maori land without the permission of the tribe to which it belonged, nor could he presume to claim any right to it. Even the tribal chief could not transfer any part of the land without the permission of his followers.

Te Keepa Puataata, an old Maori chief, standing beside a fine example of native wood carving.

The establishment of whaling stations on the coast of New Zealand in the early part of the 19th century brought the first European settlers to that country. The Maoris received the newcomers hospitably, and from them gained a knowledge of metals. Hitherto all their implements and weapons had been of wood, stone, bone or shell. They also learned of the existence of firearms, and obtaining them by trading with the white men, they used them in their fierce tribal wars with deadly effect. The heavy casualties caused by this change in the method of warfare was one of the causes of a serious decline in the Maori population during the period 1769-1840.

Occasionally there were conflicts between the natives and the Europeans, arising out of disputes concerning the transfer of land bought by the latter, but in 1840 British rule was established in New Zealand by the Treaty of Waitangi, which was signed by an assembly of Maori chiefs at the Bay of Islands. In return for this submission the tribes were guaranteed possession of their lands and fisheries. Friction continued, however, and on two occasions flared up into serious warfare, but since 1872 there has been peace.

The Maoris living in proximity to Europeans have adopted many Western ideas. They have shown themselves as capable intellectually as their white neighbours. Some of them have entered into professional life, and there are four Maori members in the House of Representatives. Modern tendencies are much less in evidence in the more remote districts of North Island, and the Maoris living there still maintain many of the customs of their ancestors.

Typical Maori costumes and carvings.

The Maoris are very artistic, and in the old days they adorned their principal houses, their tools, weapons, canoes, and ornaments with elaborate carvings. A particularly fine example of a Maori canoe with beautifully carved prow and stern pieces is in the Otago University Museum, Dunedin, New Zealand, and was described in the "*M.M.*" of January 1935. Some further interesting examples of this branch of native art are given in a special article on page 435 of the August 1936 issue.

All smiles! Maori woman and child.

Most Maori villages still have at least one principal house, with the posts, ridge pole, rafters and lattice walls richly adorned with carvings. The decorative work consists chiefly of black and red scroll work, with here and there grotesque heads with lolling tongues and leering mouths, and effigies of tribal heroes. These carved houses are used for village assemblies, entertainments, council gatherings and for accommodating important guests. The ordinary Maori houses, or "whares," have thatched roofs and walls built up of strong reeds bound together, but they are being superseded by more modern and less picturesque timber structures. The floors are covered with matting skilfully woven from the leaves of the New Zealand flax plant by the women. These leaves grow to a height of 5 ft. to 8 ft. Their fibres are considered to be the next strongest to manilla hemp. The laborious task of taking the best of them from each leaf by hand has now given place to the easier and swifter method of extracting them by machinery, and the fibres are made up into balls of twine for convenient use. Flax twine is used also for making clothes. The chief garments woven are a kind of kilt, which sometimes is the only apparel worn by the women, and a type of blanket shawl decorated with brightly-coloured feathers.

The Maoris have always been famous for their tattooing. The forehead, cheeks, nose and even the chin of a Maori chief were covered with finely tattooed curves and spirals, which gave him a barbaric dignity when he was decked out in his "war paint." The elaborate patterns used varied according to the family and rank of the warrior.

Rotorua, the chief town in the remarkable thermal springs region of North Island, is famous as a centre of Maori life, and only a few miles distant are two villages, Whakarewarewa and Ohinemutu, where the natives live in almost primitive state. The temperature of the volcanically-heated water that gushes up in the springs and geysers, and forms warm pools in cavities in the earth, ranges from 60°F. to over 200°F., and the Maoris use the water for cooking their food and washing their clothes. The mineral waters of these thermal springs are famous for their healing properties, and the State spas at Rotorua, Te Ahora and Hanmer are visited by people from many countries seeking relief from various ailments.

The Maoris long ago discovered the beneficial quality of the mineral waters. One of their many interesting legends relates that when the Moon "dies" each month she goes to the great Lake of Aewa to bathe in the Wai-ora-a-Tuna, or "Living Waters of Mankind." The Moon emerges from the lake renewed in life and strength, to traverse once more her familiar path through the heavens. According to Maori mythology Ruakimo, the seventh child of Rangi (Heaven) and Papa-tua-huku (Earth), is the deity personifying volcanoes and hot springs, and the thermal springs, geysers and pools are the breath of his nostrils.

The extensive forests of giant kauri pine trees in North Island have provided the Maoris with a basis for some strange legends. According to one of these the trees themselves are the limbs of Tane-mahuta, the Maori deity personifying the trees and birds of the forest.

Laying the Bass Strait Cable

Shore Lines Landed by Ship's Rockets

IN November of last year a new submarine telephone cable 162 miles long was laid across the Bass Strait between Apollo Bay, on the Australian mainland, and Stanley, in Tasmania. By connecting the land lines of the Australian mainland with those of Tasmania, this provided the final link in telephonic communication between all the States of the Commonwealth, and it is connected with wireless services that enable subscribers in Tasmania and King Island to telephone through to Great Britain.

The cable was manufactured entirely at the Woolwich works of Siemens Brothers and Co., Ltd. It contains one conductor only, and is of outstanding interest on account of the fact that over this single wire it is possible to transmit at the same time at least five telephone conversations, a wireless broadcast programme, and seven high-speed telegraphic communications. In the past, 14 separate conductors would have been necessary to carry out all these services.

The central copper conductor of the cable is composed of a circular wire, 0.138 in. in diameter, on which six copper strips are wound spirally. Each strip is 0.077 in. in width and 0.015 in. in thickness, and the whole weighs 508 lb. per nautical mile. Around the central conductor is the paragutta insulation weighing 690 lb. per nautical mile, and over this is the return conductor, which consists of six copper strips each 0.336 in. wide and 0.018 in. thick, applied as nearly straight as possible.

The Bass Strait cable and ropes hanging from the bow sheaves of the C.S. "Faraday" during the final splicing operation. For the illustrations to this article we are indebted to Siemens Brothers and Company, Ltd., London.

Each copper strip was shaped to form a segment of the circumference of a circle, so that when closed around the insulation the six strips formed a smooth tube, enclosing the centre conductor and weighing 852 lb. per nautical mile. As a protection against attacks by the teredo or ship worm, thin copper tape is applied with the edges overlapping immediately over the return conductor. The whole cable is armoured with steel wires embedded in jute to protect it from mechanical injury.

The cable crosses the Bass Strait in two sections divided at Sea Elephant Bay, King Island, which lies about midway across the Strait. The northern section is laid from the Island to Apollo Bay, Victoria, and from there communication is continued by means of overhead lines and underground cable to the trunk exchange at Melbourne, a distance of 127 miles. The southern section of the cable is laid from King Island to Perkins Bay near Stanley, on the northern coast of Tasmania, where connection is made to landlines running to the Launceston exchange, 139 miles away.

The completed cable weighed 1,395 tons. It was loaded into the tanks of the cable ship *"Faraday"* at her berth opposite the Woolwich Works, and the ship then sailed for Australia. The programme was to lay the northern portion of the cable in two parts, paying out from the shores towards the centre, and making a splice about half-way. The southern cable was then to be laid in a similar manner. As no tugs and lighters were available, the ship's own hauling gear was to be used for pulling the cable ashore and to the repeater station.

Work was begun at Apollo Bay. A strong south-westerly wind was blowing and a heavy surf was pounding on the beach, but a landing was made at the pier and two sand anchors were buried about 100 yds. apart. Heavy under-running sheaves were attached to the anchors by lengths of strong chain. By this time the weather had become so much worse that the ship's life-saving rockets had to be used to get a line ashore. Six attempts were necessary before this was done, and a 4-inch manila rope was then fastened to the rocket line and hauled ashore through the surf. A second landing rope was laid with the assistance of the local Life-Boat crew, who fired one of their large life-saving lines from the shore to the ship's cutter lying about 400 yds. out. The line was quickly picked up and made fast to a 4-in. manila rope, and to this a series of lengths of compound wire ropes were connected on board the ship. These were then hauled by the ship's cable gear through the two sheaves on shore and back to the ship, until the complete landing line consisted of the compound wire ropes.

The end of the cable was then attached to the landing line and lashed to it over a length of about 75 yds., the distance from the water's edge up the shore trench into the repeater station. The cable was then hauled ashore,

with empty watertight steel oil barrels lashed to it at 12 yd. intervals. It was laid in the trench and rove through a duct under a road, and its end was connected in the repeater station. The oil barrels were then cut away to allow it to sink.

Next morning the *"Faraday"* weighed anchor and commenced paying out the cable over the stern sheave at a rate of about 5 knots. A perfect course was made in spite of a long swell to which the ship rolled heavily, and towards evening this section of the cable was paid out and the end safely buoyed.

The next two days were occupied in recovering the mark buoys and mooring them again in position for marking the line from Sea Elephant Bay, King Island, to the buoyed end of the Apollo Bay section. Preparations also were made for laying the shore end on the Island. The landing place there was much more sheltered than that at Apollo Bay and there was less surf to negotiate. The landing ropes therefore were taken ashore by the ship's cutters.

This illustration and that at the top of the page show the Bass Strait cable being loaded into the tanks of the C.S. "Faraday" at Woolwich, prior to leaving for Australia.

The laying of the second half of the northern section now began. As the cable was being paid out over the stern sheave, the *"Faraday"* was steered for a distance of 200 fathoms beyond the buoy attached to the Apollo Bay end of the cable. At this point the ship was stopped and the cable cut and buoyed. The ship was then turned round and a boat was lowered to pick up the buoy, after which the cable was brought in over the bow sheaves and coiled back into the tank as the ship slowly steamed up to the buoy marking the end of the Apollo Bay section of the cable. The end of this also was brought aboard and the final joint was made after electrical tests had given satisfactory results. The entire northern section of the new cable was then safely slipped and sank to the sea bed in 50 fathoms, or 300 ft., of water.

It remained now to lay the southern section of the cable, from King Island to Perkins Bay in Tasmania. Soundings taken by a local vessel after the original cable line had been decided upon showed that the sea bottom at one part of this section appeared to be rough and unsuitable. Further soundings and dragging operations were therefore carried out by the *"Faraday,"* and in the end a new route was marked out by a line of buoys.

The ship then returned to Sea Elephant Bay, King Island, where the two ends of the landing rope were successfully taken ashore, joined together, rove through the sheaves, and buoyed off between the ship and the water's edge.

A strong wind and a choppy sea made the subsequent operation of heaving the cable ashore very difficult. Eventually however sufficient cable to connect with the repeater station was landed, and the laying of the first section from King Island to Perkins Bay then commenced. The weather gradually improved and when the last turn of the cable came out of the ship's tank, chain moorings were attached and the marking buoy slipped from the stern of the ship.

At the Tasmanian end, a 600 yd. length of cable from the Perkins Bay repeater station to the beach had already been laid, and the trench filled in. For three days the weather was too bad to attempt a landing, however. When conditions improved, the *"Faraday"* was manœuvred to within a distance of 1,565 yds. of the repeater station and anchored. The cable was then started on its way to the shore, where it was quickly placed in the trench and stoppered off.

The last stretch of cable was then laid, the ship steaming towards the buoyed end of the King Island section. The final splice was then made and after testing, the cable was lowered into the water.

The Cierva "Direct-Lifting" Autogiro

Solving the Aerodrome Problem

DURING the past few years many types of light aeroplanes have been developed of special suitability for private use. Some of these machines, on account of their small wing span, or the fact that the wings can be folded back, can be housed in hangars little larger than an ordinary garage for two motor cars. Unfortunately this compactness has been offset by the serious drawback that all such machines require a considerable amount of space in which to take off and land. For instance, the average light aeroplane requires room for a forward run of about 60 yards in order to take off safely. The result has been that even the smallest machines have had to be housed at aerodromes often at a considerable distance from the home of the owner. Recently a solution to the private owner's problem has been put forward in the shape of the direct-lifting Autogiro, the latest version of the interesting type of aircraft invented by Senor de la Cierva, a Spanish aircraft designer. This remarkable machine can both rise and descend vertically, and can be operated from any space sufficient to allow the rotor to turn, that is to say from a square piece of ground having sides each about 30 ft. long.

The "direct-lifting" Autogiro built by G. and J. Weir, Ltd., Glasgow. It can rise straight up into the air to a height of 25 ft. to 30 ft. The illustrations to this article are by courtesy of the Cierva Autogiro Co., Ltd.

The original Autogiro was produced as a result of an ordinary type of aeroplane that de la Cierva had designed for the Spanish Air Force crashing through stalling. The mishap convinced him that aeroplane flight in which safety depended upon speed was very unsatisfactory, and he began to consider carefully possible alternative methods of flight. This investigation led him to eliminate in turn all the known types of flying machines. Finally he decided that the solution lay in a machine having wings in the form of blades capable of rotating round a vertical axis, and early in 1920 he began experimenting with a view to producing such a machine.

Many varieties of revolving blades were devised and tested on various aircraft, but no practical result was obtained until he devised an Autogiro that embodied the principle of articulated blades; this eventually proved to be the main solution of the problem. It had a single rotor with four blades hinged at the root, so that they could move freely up and down in the vertical plane without any change in their angle to the airstream. Lateral control was provided for by tilting the axis to right or left, but this control proved to be too difficult for the pilot to operate, and many crashes resulted. Eventually a better system of lateral control was provided, and in January 1923 an Autogiro was completed that flew across the aerodrome at Getafe, Spain. It subsequently carried out an officially observed and controlled four-minute flight over a closed circuit at the Cuatro Vientos aerodrome, Madrid. Several other machines were produced after this, assistance being given to de la Cierva by the Spanish Government. One of these machines was demonstrated successfully at Farnborough, in England, and a similar machine constructed in 1925 by A. V. Roe and Co., Ltd., was demonstrated at the Hendon Air Pageant in 1926. The British Cierva Autogiro Co., Ltd., was formed in this country in that year, and since then 18 different types of Autogiros have been constructed.

In the earliest Autogiros the rotor was started to revolve by winding a rope round the axis and then setting six or eight men to haul on the rope. The machine then had to taxi round the field several times before the speed of the rotor became sufficient to lift it into the air. Later the rotor was started rather like a top by means of a mechanical contrivance on the ground; and an attempt was made also to start it by attaching rockets to the tips of the blades. Subsequently it was found that the rotor could be started by taxi-ing the machine round and round until the rotor was in operation, but this was a tedious business. Then the idea was conceived of constructing the tail plane and the elevator so that they could be brought together by the pilot to deflect the engine slipstream to the rotor while the machine was held stationary by means of wheel brakes.

This improvement was followed by a quite different and much more effective one, the adoption of a mechanical self-starter that derives its power direct from the engine crankshaft through a mechanically-operated clutch, and brings the rotor up to speed in less than 30 seconds. When the Autogiro is in flight the clutch is completely disengaged and has no connection whatever with the rotation of the blades, thus eliminating all the torque reaction found in helicopters. A simple braking arrangement similar to the familiar wheel brake stops the movements of the blades after the machine has landed.

The ability of the Autogiro to descend straight down and so slowly that it could land safely on even the roughest ground, or in any confined space large enough to permit the blades to revolve, was recognised as a great advantage in the event of a forced landing being necessary. Critics pointed out, however, that under other circumstances it would be useless for the machine to land where conditions were too bad, or the space too small, for it to take off again. De la Cierva therefore sought to overcome this limitation to the usefulness of the Autogiro by devising one that could take off without requiring even the short forward run of the existing types, and in March 1934 he announced that he had accomplished this. Actually the first take-off without forward run took place in August 1933, but many months of further patient research and tests were necessary before the "direct-lifting" Autogiro was perfected. At present this machine can rise straight up into the air to a height of about 25 ft., but theoretically it will be able to rise to a height of 100 ft. or more when certain modifications have been carried out.

A C.30 Autogiro, converted to "direct-lifting," taking off without any forward run.

This remarkable development has been accomplished by sloping outwards the hitherto vertical hinges about which the blades of the rotor swing sideways. When the rotor is being driven, by the aero engine, the blades tend to lag behind, and as they swing backwards the angle of incidence is reduced to nil owing to the sloping position of the blade hinges. The elimination of this angle of incidence enables the blades to be speeded up very rapidly to 350 r.p.m., which is about 60 per cent. higher than their speed when the machine is in flight. The pilot then presses a release that declutches the driving shaft from the rotor. The blades swing forward and in doing so they resume their normal angle of incidence, and the lift generated by this movement is sufficient to raise the Autogiro 25 ft. to 30 ft. into the air before the rotor has slowed to the normal flying speed of 210 r.p.m. During the brief time that the rotor has been speeding up and lifting the machine off the ground, the airscrew has been running normally, and it now begins to exercise its proper function of driving the machine through the air.

The C.30 "direct control" Autogiro, which requires a short forward run when taking off, but can descend vertically.

One type of "direct-lifting" Autogiro has been built by G. and J. Weir, Ltd., of Cathcart, Glasgow, and is known as the W.3. In addition to being able to lift itself off the ground it can, like earlier Autogiros, descend vertically to earth.

It will be seen from the accompanying illustrations that it is a single-seater machine and that the fuselage does not differ greatly from that of the ordinary light aeroplane. Instead of wings it has a two-bladed rotor mounted on a pylon structure that meets above the cockpit. The blades are hinged at their attachments to the supporting pylon head to give them full freedom in both the vertical and the horizontal plane, and they provide the total lift of the machine when it is travelling at a high forward speed. Even if the controls are misused a stall or crash cannot result, and when the Autogiro has ceased to move forward, there are still forces acting on the blades that enable it to drop at less than the rate of descent of a parachute, and therefore so slow that a perfectly safe landing can be made.

The cockpit is equipped with all the usual navigating instruments and, in addition with certain controls special to the Autogiro. The controls for starting the rotor are mounted on the left wall of the cockpit and are arranged so that it is impossible for the pilot to operate them in the wrong order. The machine carries sufficient fuel for a flight lasting about 2½ hr. at a cruising speed of 80 m.p.h.

The safety and ease of operation of the Autogiro makes flying possible for many people who are unable to develop the necessary skill to pilot an ordinary aeroplane. The small space occupied by the machine, and its ability to lift itself off the ground, enable it, as we have said, to be entirely independent of aerodromes or specially prepared grounds. In addition to being ideal for the private owner and the flying club, the Autogiro can be used as a machine for reconnaissance work in co-operation with an army in mountainous country, or with a fleet, for it can take off from, and alight upon, the deck of an aircraft carrier or warship. The Autogiro has also proved practicable for directing traffic from the air, and a machine of this type has been used by the police at Epsom Downs on the occasion of the last two Derby Days.

Dublin to Belfast on the Footplate

High Speed by the "Limited Mail"

By a Railway Engineer

THE presence of one of Mr. Glover's superb-looking three-cylinder compounds at the head of the train would give a tremendous fillip to the very dreariest of journeys, but the line from Dublin to Belfast is no ordinary route. The Great Northern of Ireland holds a unique position among the railways of the British Empire in that it is to all intents and purposes an international line. The boundary between Northern Ireland and the Irish Free State is a frontier in every sense of the word, and crossing it involves all the formalities of passing from one country into another. Since the creation of the Irish Free State the distinction between North and South has become increasingly marked, so much so that the Great Northern Railway is one of the few remaining institutions common to both political divisions of the island. This interesting state of affairs, combined with the charm of the scenery and the excellence of the locomotive work, makes a journey from Dublin to Belfast a most exhilarating experience.

G.N.R. No. 85, "Merlin," one of the compound engines referred to in this article. In this photograph it is shown standing at Goraghwood station where the northbound "Limited Mail" stops for Customs examination.

I was privileged to ride on the footplate of the compounds while working some of their hardest and fastest turns. Until recently these engines were painted black in common with all other G.N.R. locomotives, but, as recorded in the "Railway News" page of the *"M.M."* for August last, they are now resplendent in a brilliant blue finish very similar in shade to that of the former Caledonian Railway in pre-grouping days. The Irish compounds are fine-looking, amply - proportioned engines that would show up well in any colour, but in this new livery, which is maintained in spotless condition, they look really grand.

My first run was on the 9 a.m. express from Dublin loaded to eight corridor coaches, 255 tons tare and 270 tons with passengers and luggage; the engine was No. 85, *"Merlin,"* in charge of Driver Batten and Fireman Burns of Dublin shed. These engines are in many ways an Irish counterpart of the standard L.M.S.R. Compounds, and although the footplate arrangements look very different, the methods of driving are exactly the same. The Great Northern engines have a fine roomy cab, and as the firebox is round-topped there is an excellent lookout ahead. An interesting fitting is a pressure gauge for the intermediate steam chest, or receiver as it is called, through which the steam passes to the low-pressure cylinders after being exhausted from the one central high-pressure cylinder. When the engine is working full compound this gauge tells the driver the pressure at which steam is entering the low-pressure cylinders.

Getting the "right-away" sharp on time, Driver Batten opened up only to the first port of the regulator. This admits boiler steam to all three cylinders and operates the engine as a "simple," but the port is only small, and the steam is so throttled that although the boiler pressure is 200 lb. per sq. in., it enters the three cylinders at about 100 lb. As in the L.M.S.R. Compounds, it is only used for starting up, and as such provides a very useful extra bit of tractive effort; on this run of mine the driver changed over to the main regulator, which gives full compound working, about a quarter of a mile out. The very characteristic sound of the Midland Compound exhaust is reproduced exactly in the Irish engines—a harsh staccato beat when working as a simple, softening into a tuneful "burr" immediately the regulator was opened to the full.

In the meantime we were getting away in fine style. The line rises high above the docks, and the extensive view of Dublin Bay extends far to the south-east, where the Holyhead mail boat could be seen steaming out of Dun Laoghaire harbour. The regulator was brought back to about three-quarters open, cut-off was 65 per cent. in the high-pressure cylinder and 54 in the low, and less than five miles out we were travelling at 60 m.p.h. Descending almost to sea level at Malahide we touched 66 m.p.h., and sweeping across a broad tidal inlet there was a glorious view of golden sands with the Hill of Howth jutting far out to sea. The line cuts inland after passing Donabate, and there are over three miles rising at 1 in 170; but without being opened out at all *"Merlin"* took the bank in her stride and speed never fell below 51 m.p.h.

Soon after passing this summit the coast is approached again and the prospect was simply entrancing. After a night of rain the atmosphere was astonishingly clear, the fields sparkled a most vivid green in the sunshine, and the sea running high under a strong wind was the deepest blue. Far to the north, 40 miles away, were the Mountains of Mourne; clouds hung on their summits, and with their flanks of a blue that almost matched the sea, they made as splendid a picture as I have ever seen through the front glass of an engine cab. Flying through Skerries at 66, we then kept up a steady 69 to 70 m.p.h. along the sea shore; on past Balbriggan, where a picturesque stone jetty shelters a little fishing haven; and soon we were approaching Drogheda, our first stop. This initial 31¾-mile stretch was run exactly to time in 35 minutes, a smart average of 54.3 m.p.h.

A 15-ton van was added to the rear of the train, bringing the load up to 285 tons, and at 9.37 a.m. we were once more under way. Almost immediately the line leads on to the great viaduct over the River Boyne. Until recently this consisted of three lattice girder spans, the central one being 267 ft. long; but the rebuilding of this fine old structure, which had done duty for nearly 80 years, was completed in 1932, the wrought iron girders being replaced by modern steel spans. The original structure was designed for a double track, but now the viaduct carries the up and down roads in interlaced form, or gauntletted as it is usually known, thus avoiding the necessity of points at each end. Crossing the river 90 ft. above the water-line, to the west there is a magnificent view of country famed in every age of Irish history. Not only Ireland but the fate of all Europe was concerned when the Battle of the Boyne was fought in 1690, and centuries before this another battle, of a very different kind though equally momentous, was decided on the Hill of Tara. Here, in the very dawn of Christianity in these islands, St. Patrick met the Druids and utterly confuted them. Tara is indeed symbolical of the spirit of Ireland all down the ages.

From the Boyne valley the line rises at 1 in 177 for four miles, to Kellystown signal box. A little longer cut-off was used here, and *"Merlin,"* responding well, accelerated steadily to 43 m.p.h. at the summit. Then the regulator was closed to one-half and cut-off brought back to the 65 mark, and we were soon tearing down to Dunleer. "The're great engines for speed," the driver shouted across —75 m.p.h., 77, and then with a long shrill get-out-of-my-way sort of scream on the whistle we roared through Dromin Junction at 79. There was a slight drop in speed on the level beyond, but on the continuation of the descent the engine raced away again and we flashed through Castlebellingham at 81 m.p.h. Despite the stiff initial rise to Kellystown, the 16.5 miles from Drogheda had been covered in 17¾ minutes. But a very long slowing for permanent way repairs spoiled this fine burst of speed, and eventually we took 27¼ minutes to complete the 22.6 miles from Drogheda to Dundalk; the net time was only 25 minutes, another very smart average of 54.2 m.p.h.

Here, although *"Merlin"* worked right through from Dublin to Belfast, enginemen were changed. I have rarely travelled with a more entertaining crew, and Driver Batten's farewell to me was characteristic. "Well," he said as he stepped down from the footplate at Dundalk, "It's wishin' ye always the height of good luck I am!" Driver Muckian and Fireman Rooney of Dundalk shed now took over, and by the detaching of the rear van and the Enniskillen through coach the load was reduced to one of 235 tons. This reduction is fortunate, for the hardest work of the whole run is required on the next stage, to Goraghwood.

A view of the footplate of one of the G.N.R. compounds showing the neat and convenient arrangement of the fittings. The wide cab and round-topped fire-box give the driver a good lookout ahead.

The line climbs into Northern Ireland amid the heights of County Armagh; these are really a westward continuation of the Mountains of Mourne, though separated from the main group by the deep fiord of Carlingford Lough. As we got away from Dundalk, dark majestic hills lay ahead; the rich farming country that had been so predominant a feature of the landscape up to now gave place to rougher pastures, and queer-shaped peaks rose against the western sky. We made a fine start out of Dundalk, attaining 45 m.p.h. on the first part of the ascent, but as the grade steepened and the scene grew more desolate speed fell off. Cut-off was increased to 72 per cent. in the high-pressure and 62 per cent. in the two low-pressure cylinders, and on the 1 in 100 gradient we sustained 33 m.p.h.

On the stiffest part of the bank we crossed the frontier, the exact point being marked by a white strip painted on the wall of a rock cutting. The setting is perfect; a wide expanse of purple moorlands, relieved by just a few reed-encircled pools that mirrored the towering mass of Slieve Gullion to the west. In such a setting the train itself was a striking picture. Seen from the footplate, the handsome varnished coaches winding round the curves behind us, and the portly blue boiler of the engine as seen through the front glass, made a fine colour-scheme. Soon after passing into Northern Ireland the grade eases; we worked quickly up to 52 m.p.h. past Adavoyle, and the final climb through deep rock cuttings to the summit of the line was taken under quite easy steam. Speed fell to 45 m.p.h., and the 11.2 miles from Dundalk had taken 18¼ minutes.

This photograph is specially interesting as it includes the author of the article, who is grasping the tender handrail. Driver Muckian is looking over the cab side.

Down the steep descent that follows we were very soon travelling at a mile a minute. The view opened out on the right giving some delightful glimpses of the town of Newry lying far below, at the head of the Carlingford estuary, and right abreast of the line was the whole range of the Mourne mountains. Meanwhile we were careering downhill at ever-quickening speed; Bessbrook was passed at 75 m.p.h., and we had just reached 79 when the brakes went on for Goraghwood. With a smart stop we completed the 17.6 miles from Dundalk in 24½ minutes, a gain of 1½ minutes on schedule time.

Here the British Customs officials make their examination and a stop of ten minutes is scheduled for this purpose. This gives comfortable time to take water and also to pick up the through carriage from Warrenpoint to Belfast, the latter being attached "inside the engine." This queer-sounding phrase is quite commonly used among railwaymen to describe the operation of adding a coach or coaches to a train between the engine and what had been up to now the front coach. From Goraghwood onward to Belfast our load was 265 tons.

The restart is on steeply falling grades at first, and in two miles we were up to 67 m.p.h.; but there is a sharp curve through Poyntzpass station that entails slowing to 30 m.p.h., and speed has hardly recovered from this when there comes a similar curve at Scarva. After that we got going well, and sustained 64 m.p.h. until we were nearing Portadown. This is an important junction; a branch from Armagh and Cavan comes in from the south, the Londonderry route approaches from the west, and the main line swings round almost a complete right angle to run in a north-easterly direction thence to Belfast. We completed the 15.8 miles from Goraghwood in 19¾ minutes, quite a smart run considering the slacks at Poyntzpass and Scarva.

We were on the last stretch now, and Driver Muckian got the train away in first-class style. Despite a mile rising at 1 in 196 we were doing 53 m.p.h. at Boilie signal box, less than three miles out, but a long slowing for permanent way repairs followed right through Lurgan. Recovering splendidly on the 1 in 200 rise, and getting some splendid views of Lough Neagh to the west, we were up to 47 m.p.h. in two miles, and then once more *"Merlin"* began to gallop. Maze was passed at 68 m.p.h., there was a careful easing round the curve through Lisburn, and on the gentle final descent into Belfast we ran at a steady 66 m.p.h. Coasting through suburb after suburb, with the crags of Black Hill and Black Mount towering on the left, we drove right into the very heart of the city and reached Great Victoria St. station in 2 hrs. 35 min. from Dublin, 112.6 miles. On the last stage the 25 miles from Portadown had taken 31 minutes, a gain of a minute despite the bad check at Lurgan.

Going south, I had a fine trip on the 5.40 p.m. up "Limited Mail." This train takes a very composite load out of Belfast, as in addition to the main portion for Dublin there is a through carriage and mail van for Dun Laoghaire pier, and through carriages for Cookstown and Warrenpoint. On this occasion the total load was nine coaches, 289 tons tare and 305 tons loaded; the engine was another compound, No. 84, *"Falcon,"* with Driver Kyle and Fireman Tweedie of Belfast shed in charge.

In spite of a heavy shower of rain that made the rails slippery we got away in good style up the rising gradients, passing Lisburn at 53 m.p.h., and on the gentle ups and downs from there on to Lurgan kept up a general average of a mile a minute. The next 4.9 miles on to Portadown are very sharply timed, in seven minutes start to stop. The driver quickly opened out to full regulator and *"Falcon,"* getting off the mark in brilliant style, was doing 53 m.p.h. two miles from the start. With a maximum speed of 57 we kept time exactly, a fine piece of work for a 4-4-0 engine hauling 305 tons.

The principal interest of this journey however lies in the next stage where the 33.4 miles from Portadown to Dundalk are allowed only 38 minutes; this section of course includes the tremendous climb to Adavoyle summit. Going south, the Customs examination

No. 87, "Kestrel," another of the 4-4-0 compounds of the G.N.R. of Ireland. This illustration gives a good idea of the handsome proportions of these engines, and shows how they were originally turned out, with the words "Great Northern" on the tender. The initials "G.N." only are now used, and the tender sides are higher and turn inwards.

takes place at Dundalk, and to avoid the necessity of stopping at Goraghwood the Warrenpoint coach used to be detached by slipping; but in recent years this practice has been discontinued and the through coach is now left behind at Portadown. So for this really stiff booking our load was reduced to seven coaches, 230 tons tare and 245 tons full; but there was a severe permanent way slack in store for us just beyond Adavoyle, and even with this load it was going to mean very hard running to maintain the booked average speed of 52.8 m.p.h. over this difficult road. But by dint of one of the most thrilling runs I have ever had in Ireland time was kept, with a minute and a quarter in hand.

"Falcon" roared heartily out of Portadown, but as we swung over the south junction, half a mile from the start, Kyle opened out to full regulator and compound working began. Accelerating in brilliant style on the level speed was up to 69 m.p.h. at Tanderagee, 5.7 miles out, and then came those hampering slacks through Scarva and Poyntzpass, but once through the latter station engine and crew got to work with a vengeance. There are just three miles in which to get a run at the big bank, and accelerating magnificently from the Poyntzpass slack we attained 68 m.p.h., and directly we came on to the rise Kyle increased cut-off from 60 to the 63 mark. The figures on the reversing rack refer to the high-pressure cylinder; the low-pressure cut-off is generally speaking about 10 or 11 per cent. lower.

The fall in speed in the first few miles of ascent was barely perceptible, and we stormed through Goraghwood at 58 m.p.h. At Bessbrook, 2¾ miles farther on, we were still doing 53, and here cut-off was advanced to 65 per cent. in the high-pressure cylinder; throughout from Poyntzpass the regulator had been full open. Now on the final stage, where the gradient averages 1 in 105, speed fell steadily off; the Mountains of Mourne away to the south-east looked magnificent in the evening light, great heather-clad hills rose ahead, and in the deep rock-cutting that leads to the summit speed fell to exactly 40 m.p.h. On this really splendid climb the complete 8½ miles of ascent had been covered at an average speed of 51.2 m.p.h., and without any increase in cut-off beyond the 65 mark; in simple engines such as the Southern Railway "Schools," or the L.N.E.R. "Shires" this would be equivalent to about 27 per cent.

Once over the summit the regulator was brought back to about two-fifths open, still retaining compound working, and we approached Adavoyle station at 66 m.p.h.; just beyond here the relaying slack was in force by which we lost over a minute of precious time. Directly we were clear of the affected length the engine was given full regulator once more and on the falling gradient the acceleration was electrifying; but as soon as we were doing 60 again the regulator was brought back to about two-fifths.

Well might the engine's name be *"Falcon,"* for his final thrilling swoop down to Dundalk was in the very best traditions of the species! At a distance of 2½ miles from the site of the relaying work we were doing 80 m.p.h.; a very gentle application of the brake was made to steady the train round the curve past Mount Pleasant, and this reduced speed to 75, and then once more we blazed away. With the regulator pulled right back, giving the cylinders the merest wisp of steam, *"Falcon"* worked up to 82 m.p.h. So we left the mountains behind; ahead was the sea and the brilliant green meadows of County Louth, and once more we were in the Free State. A moment later we were running into Dundalk, where the G.N.R. locomotive and carriage works are situated.

This excellent locomotive work brought us from Portadown in 36¾ minutes, a gain of a minute and a quarter despite the Adavoyle check, and the net time for the 33.4 miles was only 35½ minutes. This gave the remarkable average speed of 56.4 m.p.h. during which the train had been worked over the 522 ft. altitude of the summit just north of Adavoyle. At Dundalk Driver Kyle and Fireman Tweedie were relieved by a Free State crew to work the express onward, but for me, as well as the Belfast enginemen, Dundalk was journey's end.

Meals on Wheels

Catering plays an important part in express train operation, and over 600 restaurant cars and more than 50 buffet cars are operated by British railway companies to provide for the needs of travellers. A highly developed organisation is necessary in order to maintain the restaurant services, and to provide for all possible fluctuations in demand. It is one of the wonders of modern railway travel that it is possible to prepare and to serve, from a kitchen 10 ft. long and 6 ft. 6 in. wide, a complete luncheon for perhaps 250 people and then follow this up with possibly an equal number of teas. It is all the more remarkable when it is remembered that the cooking is all done on board the train, the dining car staff joining the train well before starting time in order to commence their preparations.

Sometimes the kitchen forms part of the complete dining car, but for services where there is a heavy demand on the restaurant facilities a separate kitchen car is run in conjunction with the actual dining cars. Cooking is done largely by means of gas that is stored in the familiar cylinders below the car, and the water required is carried in tanks in the roof. Cooking by electricity is a feature of L.N.E.R. practice, as is the application of the articulated principle to restaurant and kitchen car sets. The smoothness of riding so obtained is much appreciated by both diners and the crew.

An L.M.S.R. kitchen car. The complete equipment of these vehicles provides a full restaurant service for a whole train of passengers.

Current for electric cooking is obtained from accumulators while stationary, and from axle-driven generators when the train is in motion. On the G.N.R. of Ireland two interesting experiments are in progress. In one town gas that is stored at high pressure in removable cylinders is being used, and in the other scheme a special anthracite cooker is employed.

In recent years there has been a growing demand for the provision of facilities for light meals, especially on trains where the running of full restaurant services would not be justified. Thus after certain experimental introductions there has developed the modern buffet car. The L.M.S.R. has recently put into service four buffet cars of a new type in which light meals and refreshments can be obtained. Each car is 57 ft. long, and in addition to the service arrangements and kitchen there is space for chairs and tables accommodating 24 people. Wide and deep windows giving an unobstructed outlook are provided.

A Holiday in Iceland

A Land of Glaciers and Hot Springs

By E. D. Bailey

TO the average reader Iceland is best known as the home of the deep depressions, heralding unpleasant weather, with which wireless weather forecasts have made us familiar. The association is as unfortunate as the name of the island, which lends weight to the false impression that it is a country of snow and ice. Actually its climate is very temperate in summer, affording welcome relief to those who cannot withstand the effects of heat waves, and the island has many attractions as a holiday centre.

Iceland boasts of having the oldest Parliament in the world. It is called the Althing, and its first meetings were held in 930. The island was discovered by the Norsemen about 850, but the first settlers, Ingolf and Hjorleif, came about 25 years later. Their memory is immortalised by two headlands bearing their names that stand out from the south-east coast and provide the first glimpse of Iceland from the approaching steamer.

The capital of Iceland is Reykjavik, a town of some 30,000 inhabitants. The snow-capped mountains of the island are sighted after a voyage of about 600 miles from the British Isles, and in fine weather the reflection of the Sun on the great snowfield named Vatnajökull can be seen many miles out at sea. This is the largest of Iceland's many snow-fields. It covers an area of 3,300 sq. m., and a glacier in it covers about 200 sq. m.

Iceland is a little larger than Ireland, and Reykjavik is not reached until nearly a day after sighting the island. The older buildings in the capital are of wood and corrugated iron. New buildings usually are constructed of reinforced concrete, which is not finished off, but is left just as it sets in the wooden moulds into which it is poured. There are no brick buildings, but in a few of the larger structures stone or rock quarried locally is used. The town is very well equipped. The plentiful supply of water-power enables electricity to be generated cheaply, and the telephone service is well developed, and constitutes a boon not only to the town dwellers, but also to scattered farms in outlying districts where the lack of roads makes travel slow and painful.

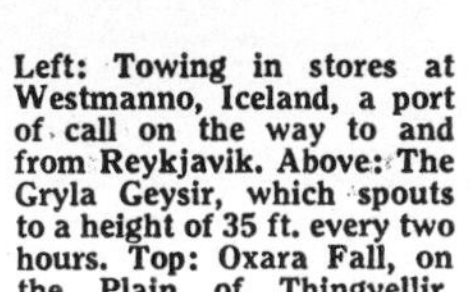

Left: Towing in stores at Westmanno, Iceland, a port of call on the way to and from Reykjavik. Above: The Gryla Geysir, which spouts to a height of 35 ft. every two hours. Top: Oxara Fall, on the Plain of Thingvellir.

The chief attraction in Iceland undoubtedly is the magnificent scenery of the mountain regions, and the natural splendours of the falls, hot-springs and geysers that are found throughout the island. The Plain of Thingvellir is one of the places most favoured by tourists, mainly owing to its many historical connections. It was the scene of many struggles and feats of heroism, when arguments among the Norsemen culminated in pitched battles. At one spot there stands a large rectangular stone, bearing the word "Logberg," which means Law Stone. This marks the place where the "President" of the Althing or Parliament had his dais when presiding over the annual deliberations.

The Plain is reached after a 30-mile ascent over glorified cinder tracks, which form the only roads from the coastal lowlands on to the high plateau, and before descending into the Plain, wonderful views can be obtained from rocky promontories overlooking it. Tremendous fissures in the rocks remain as evidence of the violent subterranean subsidences of past ages. Towards the west the strip of water known as Thingvallavatn, 27 sq. m. in area, glistens in the sunlight, reflecting the most exquisite shades of the deepest blue. The road into the Plain crosses a narrow bridge spanning a rushing torrent flowing from the basin into which falls from a height of 150 ft. the beautiful cascade of Oxara. The water in the basin is crystal clear owing to its passage over rocks. Farther down on the actual Plain there is a large pool in which the water is 30 ft. deep. A legend says that the visitor who throws in a small coin will surely return to Iceland. The coins that have been dropped in can be discerned clearly, a testimony to the exceptional clarity of the water.

The largest and most impressive waterfall in Iceland, and indeed in Europe, is the Gullfoss, which is about 80 miles inland. It is difficult to describe this magnificent and awe-inspiring spectacle, which must be seen to be fully appreciated. The fall stands at an altitude of about 2,000 ft. above sea level on the White River, and its immense torrent plunges madly in two sheer drops into the depths of a narrow chasm almost 500 ft. deep. Enormous showers of spray shoot up to a height of 100 ft. above the surrounding banks, and provide indescribably beautiful rainbow effects when the sun is shining.

Gryla Geysir, which can be visited en route to Gullfoss, is evidence of the violent subterranean eruptions that are still proceeding in Iceland. With the regularity of a clock, a huge column of boiling water spouts from an underground reservoir every two hours, rising to a height of about 35 ft. Its appearance is heralded by rumblings that are heard for about half an hour previously before the outbreak, and the display lasts for eight minutes, ceasing as suddenly as it begins. The surrounding ground is warm and it is said that snow never lies at this spot for this reason.

There are many hot-springs in the hills, and columns of steam rise perpetually at a dozen different points, demonstrating the forces of nature more spectacularly than in other more settled regions of the world. The boiling water in the hot-springs, or "hver," has a sulphurous taste and the whole atmosphere has the smell of sulphur in it.

The streams from the hot springs that abound in Iceland are harnessed for domestic use. Near Reykjavik the finest flowers are cultivated in conservatories heated by them, and they provide a constant supply of hot water for the municipal wash-houses and baths of the capital. Some consolation is due for the privations forced upon the people by the barren nature of the land. Dairy farming and fishing are the main occupations. The drying and salting of fish provides work for many girls and women, in the coastal towns and villages. The fish are hung up in the sun to dry after preparation, and are then stored in huge stacks with alternate layers of salt and fish awaiting export, mainly to Continental countries.

In mid-June the sun sets only for about 15 min. at this time of the year, so that to all intents and purposes there is no night. The summer is short, however, and in the winter there can only be about three or four hours of daylight, which on dull days, of which there are many, is reduced to a twilight. The weather is normally very variable, and although one day may be brilliant, by the next morning a depression may have formed, accompanied by a cyclonic wind whipping up the dust from the loose surfaced roads, to alter the whole aspect.

In Iceland the school holidays extend from May to October. In the former month scholars congregated in the towns return to their homes in the country and stay there until the arrival of the dark days, when they once more make their way to the towns to continue their studies. Even then, school hours are confined to the morning, the afternoon and most of the evening being given over to private study and "prep."

"Qu en Mary" Wins Blue Riband

Once more the coveted "Blue Riband" of the Atlantic is held by a British ship, having been wrested from the "*Normandie*," record holder since June 1935, by the "*Queen Mary*." The last British ship to hold the record for the Atlantic crossing was the "*Mauretania*," which enjoyed 22 years of supremacy before the "*Bremen*" beat her time in 1929. Four years later the Italian liner "*Rex*" crossed at a new record average speed of 28.92 knots, only to give way last year to the "*Normandie*."

On the round voyage during which the record was made, the "*Queen Mary*" left Southampton on Wednesday, 19th August, and arrived at New York on the following Monday, having made the passage from Bishop Rock to Ambrose Lightship, a steaming distance of 2,907 miles, in 4 days 27 minutes, at an average speed of 30.14 knots. On her return eastward the "*Queen Mary*" took the shortest time ever recorded for a voyage between the two points, taking only 3 days 23 hrs. 57 min. for the passage. Her average speed over the distance of 2,939 miles was 30.63 knots, compared with the "*Normandie's*" 30.31 knots for the previous record passage of 3,015 miles. The difference in the distances covered by the two vessels is due to their following different courses across the Atlantic.

Faster Voyages to South Africa

The acceleration of the England–South Africa mail service, referred to in the August "*M.M.*," took effect on Friday, 21st August. The Union-Castle liner "*Stirling Castle*" sailed from Southampton on that day, and accomplished the fastest passage to Capetown ever made, completing the voyage in 13½ days. This is now the regular mail ship time under the Union-Castle Line's new contract with the South African Government.

The "*Stirling Castle*" surpassed a record established 43 years ago by the Union liner "*Scot*," which in 1893 completed the trip from Southampton to Capetown in 14 days 18 hours 57 minutes.

A third new vessel for the South African mail service of the Union-Castle line recently laid down at the Belfast yard of Harland and Wolff is to be larger than either the "*Stirling Castle*" or her sister ship the "*Athlone Castle*." She will be 6 ft. to 8 ft. longer, and is expected to be of 26,000 tons or more. The "*Stirling Castle*" is of 25,500 tons. The name that has been suggested for the vessel now under construction is "*Glamis Castle*."

The "*Dunnottar Castle*"

The liner illustrated on this page is the "*Dunnottar Castle*," a new ship built this year for the Union-Castle Mail Steamship Co. Ltd. by Harland and Wolff Ltd., Belfast, and now in the London, South and East African service. She is a twin screw vessel with a gross tonnage of 15,007, an overall length of about 560 ft., and a moulded breadth of 71 ft. 6 in. She is based on modern designs, and has a well-raked rounded stem and a cruiser stern, two masts and a single low type streamlined funnel. The hull is divided into 10 watertight compartments, and there is a continuous double bottom for the carrying of fresh water, water ballast and oil fuel. A streamlined semi-balanced rudder is fitted, which is operated by electro-hydraulic steering gear.

The "Dunnottar Castle," a twin-screw vessel of 15,007 tons at present operating between England and South and East Africa. Photograph by courtesy of Harland and Wolff Ltd., Belfast.

The two main engines of the "*Dunnottar Castle*" are of the well-known Harland-Burmeister and Wain type, each having nine cylinders with a bore of 450 m.m. and a stroke of 1,200 m.m. The electric supply is taken from four 350 kw generators, driven by Harland-Burmeister and Wain Diesel engines running at 330 r.p.m. All the deck and engine room auxiliaries are electrically operated, the motors ranging from 2 h.p. to 90 h.p., and totalling over 800 b.h.p.

The lifebuoys on the vessel can be electrically released from the Captain's bridge, or locally for the prompt rescue of anyone falling overboard.

The "*Dunvegan Castle*," a sister ship of the "*Dunnottar Castle*," also has been built at Belfast by Harland and Wolff Ltd. This vessel had her trials in August, and recently ran her maiden voyage on the South African service.

Lifeboat Launched Like a Torpedo

Davits from which to launch the lifeboats of vessels in distress have been the subject of many inventions. These have been intended to make launching speedy and safe, and to overcome the difficulties encountered when a vessel is sinking, or has a heavy list. In a novel scheme suggested by an American inventor the lifeboat actually is shot from the deck of a vessel into the sea. The lifeboat designed for this purpose is shaped like a torpedo and is closed in. A liquefied gas is used for launching purposes. This is stored in a container in the lifeboat itself, and when it is released by opening a control valve the pressure developed on stationary plungers in the launching device shoots the lifeboat outward.

Cross-Channel Services

The cross-Channel fleet operating between England and France during 1935 comprised 37 vessels, including three train ferries. On all routes last year these vessels made 9,106 single trips, conveying 1,106,782 passengers and 191,727 tons of cargo. In addition, 38,044 passengers travelled by the Jersey–St. Malo service, and 39,373 by other routes, mainly between Jersey and Guernsey. For the maintenance of connection between the mainland and the Isle of Wight, twelve vessels were employed. Nine of these were paddle steamers, while the other three had motor propulsion.

New Zealand's Speediest Steamship

The fastest ship owned by any company registered in New Zealand or Australia is the twin-screw passenger steamship *"Awatea"* of the Union Steamship Company of New Zealand Ltd. This vessel is shown in the upper illustration on this page. She was built and engined by Vickers-Armstrongs Ltd., at their Naval Construction Works, Barrow-in-Furness, and is the second vessel to be built there for the Union Steamship Company. She recently completed successful trials in the Firth of Clyde before being handed over to her owners.

The length overall of the *"Awatea"* is 545 ft., the breadth moulded is 74 ft., and her displacement is about 16,000 tons. Her hull is divided into watertight compartments by eight transverse bulkheads, and in the usual double bottom there are tanks for fresh water, water ballast, feed water and fuel oil.

The vessel is propelled by twin screws driven by two sets of Parsons' turbines through single reduction gearing. The four-bladed manganese bronze propellers run at about 125 revolutions per minute on services when developing 20,000 s.h.p. On trial the two sets of turbines developed 22,500 s.h.p. at 130 r.p.m. Steam is generated by six Yarrow high-pressure boilers using oil fuel, and constructed for a blow-off pressure of 450 lb. per sq. in. at the safety valve.

Though primarily a passenger vessel, the *"Awatea"* has accommodation for a certain amount of cargo, including holds for carrying mails, livestock and motor cars; and insulated space is provided for the storage of provisions and fruit cargoes. The steering gear fitted is of the latest four-cylinder electro-hydraulic design of Brown Brothers and Co. Ltd., and operates a semi-balanced rudder. Two pumps are incorporated, and with one pump unit and four cylinders in operation the rudder may be turned through 70 degrees in about 30 seconds with the vessel steaming full speed ahead. The same manœuvre can be accomplished in 18 seconds if both pumps are used simultaneously.

The life-saving equipment includes 10 lifeboats, each to hold 80 persons, and two 22-ft. emergency boats. The boats are constructed of Birmabright corrosion-resisting alloy, and buoyancy tanks have been built into the hulls, dividing each into six watertight compartments.

Submarines Launched at Barrow

Two submarines were recently launched at Barrow-in-Furness, at the Naval Construction Yards of Vickers-Armstrongs Ltd., who built the vessels. The two vessels, which are named *"Lembit"* and *"Kalev,"* entered the water in that order at an interval of 15 minutes. They are identical in construction and design, and after fitting out will be handed over to the Estonian Naval Authorities for whom they have been built.

The *"Lembit"* and *"Kalev"* were ordered in 1935, and each has a surface displacement of 620 tons. Their length is 190 ft., with a breadth of 24 ft., and a depth of 11 ft. Diesel engines developing 1,200 b.h.p. are fitted, giving the vessels a surface speed of 13.5 knots, and a submerged speed of 8.5 knots. The *"Lembit"* and the *"Kalev"* are respectively the 168th and 169th submarines launched at the Barrow Yard.

The twin-screw steamsnip "Awatea," which holds the distinction of being the fastest ship owned by a company registered in New Zealand or Australia. Photograph courtesy of Vickers-Armstrongs Ltd., Barrow-in-Furness.

Another submarine recently launched at the Barrow Yard was named H.M.S. *"Rorqual."* This vessel is of the "Porpoise" class, and it has a length of 271 ft. 6 in., a breadth of 25 ft. 6 in., and a surface displacement of 1,520 tons. The craft was laid down in May 1935 under the Admiralty's 1934 programme. The propelling machinery is estimated to develop 3,300 h.p., giving a surface speed of 16 knots.

The deck of the four-masted barque "Pamir" in the East Float, Birkenhead. This vessel is one of the fleet of sailing ships owned by Captain Erikson, Mariehamn, and in 1932 was the leader in the unofficial Australian grain ship race. Photograph by courtesy of A. F. Burr, Mill Hill, London.

The Institute of Marine Engineers

Arrangements are now being made for the next annual examination for admission to the student class of membership of the Institute of Marine Engineers, which will be held in June 1937 in London and other centres. The examination for admission to Associate Membership to the Institute is to be held on 16th–19th November next. Full particulars of these examinations and of any exemptions that are allowed may be obtained on application to the Secretary, the Institute of Marine Engineers, the Minories, London, E.C.3.

All apprentices and students who wish to become marine engineers should endeavour to qualify for membership of the Institute of Marine Engineers. The first step is to become a Student Member of the Institute, which can only be done as a result of examination. Applicants for admission to the Student Section must be under 25 years of age and have completed at least one year of attendance at day or evening classes at an approved educational institution, as part of a regular course of training in the science of engineering or naval architecture. The possession of certain degrees or diplomas exempts the holder from sitting for the preliminary examination.

The Australian Grain Fleet Race

Every year the end of an unofficial race is heralded by the arrival at Falmouth or Queenstown of the earliest of a fleet of sailing vessels bringing wheat from Australia. These vessels include most of the sailing ships yet afloat, and make the voyage round the Horn or by way of the Cape of Good Hope. The passage home occupies about 85 to 125 days, and the earliest arrival usually is in April. Most of the vessels now employed in this trade are owned by Captain Gustaf Erikson, of Mariehamn, in the Åland Isles of the Baltic Sea.

One of the most famous of the grain fleet was the *"Herzogin Cecilie,"* which was the first to arrive in home waters this year, but went ashore near Salcombe. This ship won the unofficial race in 1927, 1928 and 1931.

The *"Pamir,"* a fine deck view of which is shown on this page, led the grain fleet home in 1932. She is a steel four-masted barque built in 1905 by Blohm and Voss at Hamburg. She has a length of 316 ft. and a tonnage of 3,020, and was formerly owned by a Hamburg merchant, who in 1931 sold her to Captain Erikson.

Motor Vessel for Lake Windermere

The twin screw motor vessel *"Teal"* recently entered the L.M.S.R. passenger service on Lake Windermere. The vessel was built by Vickers-Armstrongs Ltd. at Barrow-in-Furness, and taken in sections by rail to Lakeside and re-assembled there. The *"Teal"* has a length of 141 ft. 9 in., and a displacement of 230 tons. Two 8-cylinder Gleniffer Diesel engines are installed.

Pipeline 248 Miles in Length

Giant Tube with Streamlined Sides

By H. J. Shepstone, F.R.G.S.

OUT in the deserts of Southern California the engineer is carrying out a daring feat. He is building a mighty pipeline, 248 miles in length, to supply famished cities with a much-needed water supply. This line covers a distance equal to that from London to Cornwall, and on its way crosses vast stretches of desert and pierces many mighty mountains, in tunnelling through which the men at work on it have had narrow escapes from drowning. Unforeseen difficulties were encountered in the laying out of the canals and conduits and in the erection of the great siphons, and all the skill and ingenuity of the engineer were required to overcome them. Not the least of these difficulties is that the interior surface of the great tube has to be finished throughout to the smoothness of steel, with no sharp curves or rough places, in order to give a steady and easy flow of water; in other words, the pipeline has to be constructed and finished in perfect streamline form throughout its entire length of 248 miles.

Building the great pipeline from the Colorado River to the Californian coast. Our photograph shows the steel forms around which concrete is cast to form the arch of the 16-ft. tube.

Supplying large cities with water is one of the great problems of the engineer to-day. To do this he often has to tap lakes or springs many miles away and bring the precious liquid to the city through huge tubes. Manchester, for example, obtains its water from Thirlmere, in the Lake District, at a distance of 96 miles from the city, and Birmingham relies on Welsh lakes 73 miles away for its supply. The great pipes required in these cases were rightly regarded as clever engineering achievements, but they pale into insignificance when compared with the great project now in progress in California. This is evident when it is realised that it will be six years before the American scheme is completed, and an expenditure of £44,000,000 will be necessary.

Through this colossus of pipelines a million million gallons of water will flow daily to 13 different cities. This vast quantity of water is being taken from the Colorado River at a point some 150 miles below the great Boulder Dam, the construction of which was described in articles in the issues of the *"M.M."* for February, March and September, 1934. At that point another barrier, known as the Parker Dam, is now in course of erection. This alone will cost £2,600,000, and it will create what engineers call an intake, or reservoir, from which the water will flow into the pipe, wriggling its way like a gigantic snake across the desert and through tunnels under the mountains. Each of these tunnels will be 16 ft. in diameter, or large enough to accommodate a modern locomotive. There will be 29 of them altogether, with a total length of 92 miles, and the two longest will penetrate the East Coachella and San Jacinto Mountains. The lengths of the tunnels under the ranges will be 18 and 13 miles respectively.

The canal concrete paver at work. The concrete is poured through the slot into position at the bottom of the canal.

To have drilled these two tunnels in the ordinary manner, that is from each end simultaneously, would have taken too long. From 15 to 20 years would have been required for the one that is 18 miles long. So the engineers have attacked the mountains not only from each end, but also from the sides and from the top, in each case sinking shafts down to the tunnel level and driving borings from them into the very heart of the mountain. The East Coachella tunnel is being bored from eight different points simultaneously, and that through the San Jacinto Mountains has six working faces.

The very latest types of machinery and labour-saving devices are being employed in driving the tunnels. The great drill carriages mount as many as four to eight pneumatic drills, and with these machines from 20 to 60 holes, each from 6 ft. to 12 ft. deep, are drilled in the hard rock at the same time. The holes are loaded with explosives and fired, and after the blast the shattered rock is loaded into waiting cars and hauled out to the dump. The "muck," as the shattered rock is termed, is lifted into the cars by electrically-operated dippers.

Boring the 13-mile tunnel through San Jacinto Mountain is proving a particularly tricky proposition. To facilitate a more rapid completion of the boring, two shafts were sunk into the mountain to the tunnel level, one 246 ft. and the other 796 ft. in depth, and water was unexpectedly encountered in drillings from these borings. Every day enough water pours into the tunnels, drenching men and equipment, to supply a city of 100,000 inhabitants.

To cope with this rush of water it was found necessary to blast away the rock at the bottom of the shafts and instal powerful pumping stations, each as large as a small bungalow. These stations are guarded by massive steel doors that are never opened except for delivery or removal of machinery, and attendants enter them through tiny openings inside the doors, each scarcely large enough for a man to crawl through. By means of the pumps installed in them the engineers are locking large quantities of water within the mountain, and removing the vast volume that pours into the tunnel.

Before the pumping plants were installed the men had several narrow escapes. On one occasion a blast resulted in a cave-in, releasing a vast quantity of pent-up water into the tunnel. The men had no option but to down tools, hurry to the shaft, and make for the top as fast as they could. The water climbed the shaft to a height of 647 ft. and many of the workers barely escaped with their lives in their frantic climb to a height of 800 ft., beyond its reach. On another occasion the tunnel filled with water, and only after months of pumping was it dry enough for the drillers to proceed with their hazardous job.

Every safety device and method known to mining stands ready to guard the lives of the 600 men toiling in the tunnels. At the shafts special hoists have been installed so that the men can be brought to the surface quickly. Huge ventilator pipes carry 50 cu. ft. of air per man down the long bore every minute. After blasting, the system is reversed, and sucks out the poisonous and acrid fumes.

When treacherous ground is encountered holes are drilled 36 ft. ahead. This is done in order to ascertain the nature of the rock and what lies beyond. If water is tapped, precautions can be taken to deal with it. Where the tunnel passes through moving or "soft" ground, it is lined with timber and given a thick coat of concrete, and in faulty or fractured rock its walls and roof are strengthened with ribbed steel bent to fit them.

Another view of the concrete paver, which forms a moving bridge across the canal and lays concrete on the bottom and sides at the rate of a foot a minute.

Work in the tunnels has to be constantly checked, as the slightest deviation in grade or angle might prove serious. The surveyors found it difficult to get sufficient light to enable them to read their delicate instruments. This trouble was got over by the introduction of a powerful lamp allowing only a fine vertical beam of light to escape, and transit men are able to sight upon this slender beam from great distances down the tunnel. For other types of observation, pocket flashlamps are suspended from the roof of the tunnel.

Tunnel driving is by no means the only important phase of the undertaking. In addition to the 92 miles of tunnels that are being bored through mountains, there are 62 miles of canals, 55 miles of conduits and 29 miles of siphons. Then at five different points elaborate pumping machinery is being installed. By the aid of these pumps the water that will pass through the pipeline will be raised 1,539 ft. during the first 130 miles of its journey. At the fifth point, known as Hatfield Lift, it will be forced nearly straight up through a height of 440 ft., and from there the water will flow by gravity to its destination, through tunnels, siphons and conduits.

The siphons, the largest ever designed, are built of reinforced concrete many yards in thickness. Their work is to help the water across declivities in the desert terrain. The name "siphon" is actually a misnomer, as they do not exert any siphonic action. In design they resemble the letter "U" on an immense scale. The water flows down one side and rushes up the other to just below its own level, and the siphons have to be made very strong in order to withstand its great pressure.

The horse-shoe arch of one of the tunnels of the 248-mile pipeline.

It is necessary for the siphons, conduits, tunnels and canals to be finished as smooth as glass. There must be no sharp curves, projections or rough spots, for these would greatly retard and consequently reduce the flow of water. If the tunnels were left in the "rough" to cope with the proposed flow, they would need to be 18 ft. in diameter instead of 16 ft. Special machines were designed for the construction of the canals in order to ensure this streamlike effect. One of the most interesting of these is the trimming machine, which straddles the 60 ft. canals and moves on rails. After a canal is "roughed out" by a drag-line shovel, the trimming machine swings into operation. As it runs backward and forward, a series of knives slice away thin sections of earth, and an endless chain dumps the "shavings" along the banks. When the canal has been cut to the desired depth of 11 ft. 7 in., with a width at the top of 60 ft., its sides and bottom are quite smooth. Steel reinforcing rods are then laid down and all is ready to receive the concrete.

In the past the bottom of a canal was paved after it had been smoothed by hand, and the concrete then was laboriously set on the sides by hand. Now all this is accomplished in a single operation by means of an ingenious mechanical device known as a paver, which not only lays the concrete, but spreads it evenly and tamps it down. In design the paver resembles a huge rolling bridge mounted on trucks running on rails laid parallel to the canal banks. It is a colossal piece of machinery weighing some 48 tons, and is formed to the shape of the finished canal.

Concrete is supplied from a giant mixer mounted on creeper tracks that allow it to follow the paver as this moves along. The concrete runs down through special hoppers on to the floor of the canal. As it emerges from the machine, a series of revolving steel rods are brought into play, and these spread the concrete over the ground evenly, and also tamp it down firmly, giving to it a finish as smooth as glass. The concrete for the canal sides is delivered through a number of small apartments, or pockets. There another series of revolving rods come into play, and these are so designed that they not only distribute the concrete evenly, but also prevent the plastic material from moving sideways down the slopes. As the machine progresses, finishers follow behind, and from framed wooden "jumbos," or movable scaffolds mounted on rails, they work over the surface of the concrete with hand trowels to produce the desired hard finish.

When moving at a speed of about 1 ft. per min. one of these machines paves approximately 500 ft., placing over 700 cu. yd. in position during one eight-hour shift, whereas the abandoned hand-placing method could only account for an advance of 200 ft., during which only 282 cu. yd. could be laid.

Within the tunnels, conduits and siphons, workmen grind down inequalities, particularly at joints, with high-speed emery wheels; and finally the concrete is rubbed to a high lustre. Nowhere throughout the length of this 248-mile winding tube, whether in the desert or in the heart of the great mountains, is there a sharp corner. Thus friction will be reduced to a minimum, and water will flow through the great pipe with little restraint.

Before work could be started on the undertaking surveying parties spent two whole years in the desert and among the mountains mapping the course of the pipeline. It proved arduous and trying work. All supplies, including provisions, water and tools, had to be carried with them. In the desert the thermometer often registered 130 deg. F. in the shade, and on the mountain tops the party had to force a path through deep snowdrifts at a temperature far below zero. Then came the making of hundreds of miles of surface highways over which men and heavy machinery and material could be conveyed to the construction camps scattered along the route. Water is carried to these camps from 22 wells drilled in the desert, and the electric power used for operating the machinery in the tunnels is brought a distance of 450 miles.

At the various construction camps an army of 4,400 men is now at work. The tunnels are being driven at the rate of 3½ miles per month. and the pipeline is to be completed within six years. Water will then flow through the 248-mile channel into a great reservoir, from which it will be distributed through 144 miles of distribution mains to 13 cities in Southern California.

Hard Work on the G.W.R. in South Devon

The G.W.R. West of England main line between Newton Abbot and Plymouth has some of the most severe grading in the British Isles. Engines of up expresses have a particularly severe task in starting practically "cold" up the 1 in 41 ascent from Plympton to Hemerdon siding, and the kind of running made over this route is well illustrated by two recent runs timed by Mr. O. S. Nock.

On one of these trips, with a train weighing 365 tons gross, the engine was No. 5053, *"Bishop's Castle,"* one of the newest "Castles," but with this load a pilot was necessary, the limit for "Castles" in this direction being 350 tons. The pilot was No. 3342, *"Bonaventure,"* an old "Bulldog" class 4–4–0 with 5 ft. 8½ in. driving wheels. On the second trip, No. 6007, *"King William III,"* had to tackle 390 tons without assistance, although 385 tons is the limit for this class. Both trains ran very gently down the incline from Plymouth to Laira Junction and Plympton, the foot of the Hemerdon bank, was passed at 48 m.p.h. by the "Castle" and his pilot, and at 50 m.p.h. by the "King." The latter engine fell right down to 17¼ m.p.h. on the two miles at 1 in 41, but even the double-headed train dropped to 22. Beyond Hemerdon the line continues to rise but at much easier grades; speed rose to just over 50 m.p.h. on both runs, and Wrangaton summit 14.1 miles from Plymouth was passed in 22¼ min. by the "Castle" and "Bulldog" together, and in 24½ min. by the "King."

On the descent to Totnes, as steep as 1 in 60 in places, the speeds did not exceed 67 and 64½ m.p.h. respectively, and on passing through the station the double-headed train had slightly increased its lead. Then came the climb to Dainton tunnel, 4¾ miles of continuous rise, the last mile of which is at 1 in 37! The "King" did remarkably well to cover this length in 6½ min., speed falling to 22¼ at the summit, but the "Castle" and his pilot made a most exceptional effort, taking only 5½ min., and did not fall below 30½ m.p.h. These two engines had now taken 37 min. to cover the 28 miles from Plymouth to Dainton; the "King" took 40¼ min. So the double-headed train reached Newton Abbot, 31.8 miles, in 42 min., a gain of 4 min. on schedule from the Plymouth start.

The "King," which was working the up *"Cornish Riviera Limited,"* passed through Newton Abbot at reduced speed in 45¼ min., but then was badly delayed by signals and permanent way operations all the way to Exeter. On the other run the load was made up to no less than 505 tons, but on the level grades along the sea shore a pilot was no longer needed, and *"Bishop's Castle"* ran the 20¼ miles to Exeter in 25¾ min. start to stop. Speed was carefully reduced round the curves on the winding stretch between Teignmouth and Dawlish and then rose to 60 m.p.h. on the level at Exminster.

An S.R. Eastbourne express entering Lewes station. The starting signal shown on the left incorporates a shunting arm below the main semaphore, the purpose of this being indicated by the letter "S" shown attached to the arm. (H.R.C. prize-winning photograph.)

Motor Cars by Rail

With the rapid development of the motor industry there has been a great increase in the number of new motor vehicles conveyed by rail. Motor vehicle agents and manufacturers are more and more entrusting the initial transport of motor cars to the railways, who have provided specially-designed covered vans for the transport of this traffic. Some of the special motor car trucks are capable of carrying two standard type cars. They are equipped with vacuum brakes for express freight train running, and end doors to expedite loading and unloading. In some instances, where numbers of cars are to be conveyed at the same time, they are driven through the length of a whole train of covered motor car vans, the end doors and tread plates fitted to the vehicles making this possible.

New Fast Freight Locomotives for the S.R.

The S.R. have put into service 10 further 4–6–0 locomotives of class "S.15" for fast freight and mixed traffic working. These are Nos. 838–847 and differ only in details from the previous engines of the class, Nos. 823–837, which were built in 1927. The first five of the new batch have large flat-sided bogie tenders similar to those provided for some of the "Nelson" class express passenger engines. The latest tenders however have tanks built up by electric welding and run on disc wheels. They carry 5,000 gallons of water and five tons of coal. The other five engines have 4,000 gallon six-wheeled tenders taken from certain of the "King Arthur" class passenger locomotives, the latter receiving new bogie tenders in exchange. The six-wheeled tenders had been provided in order that these "King Arthurs" might work over the Central Section of the S.R., and they have now been transferred to the "S.15" engines for the same reason.

These new locomotives have been built in the Company's Works at Eastleigh to the design of Mr. R. E. L. Maunsell, the Chief Mechanical Engineer. The 1927 batch of the same class also were built at Eastleigh. They were developed from the original 20 "S.15" mixed traffic engines built in 1920 by R. W. Urie for the former L.S.W.R., but incorporated various improvements in motion design and smokebox arrangements and had a higher boiler pressure, being in fact practically "King Arthurs" with smaller driving wheels.

Speedier Anglo-Scottish Services

The fastest journey time that has ever applied by rail between Glasgow and London has been instituted by the L.M.S.R. by the acceleration of the up *"Royal Scot"* from Glasgow to a schedule of 7 hrs. 25 min. This represents a saving of 15 min. over the corresponding allowance last winter. A departure time of 10 a.m. is still maintained for this train at both Glasgow (Central) and Edinburgh (Princes Street), but the arrival at Euston is now made at 5.25 p.m.

On the East Coast Route the up *"Flying Scotsman"* now observes a similar timing from Edinburgh, this also showing a saving of 15 min. on former running times. In the down direction the allowance has been cut by 25 min. to 7 hr. 20 min.

L.N.E.R. "Football Club" Engines

At the time of writing 13 three-cylinder 4-6-0 locomotives named after famous football clubs have been put into service on the L.N.E.R. Each of these engines carries on the centre splashers the representation of a football and in addition the colours of the club after which the engine is named. The miniature football is shown in the upper illustration on this page.

The numbers and names of the engines are as follows: No. 2848, *"Arsenal"*; No. 2849, *"Sheffield United"*; No. 2850, *"Grimsby Town"*; No. 2851, *"Derby County"*; No. 2852, *"Darlington"*; No. 2853, *"Huddersfield Town"*; No. 2854, *"Sunderland"*; No. 2855, *"Middlesbrough"*; No. 2856, *"Leeds United"*; No. 2857, *"Doncaster Rovers"*; No. 2859, *"Norwich City"*; No. 2860, *"Hull City"*; and No. 2861, *"Sheffield Wednesday."*

It will be noted that No. 2858 is missing from this list. This locomotive has been named *"The Essex Regiment,"* so that although it belongs numerically to the above series it is not a "Football Club" engine. Nos. 2848-61 were built at the Darlington Works of the L.N.E.R. Another batch is on order from Robert Stephenson and Co. Ltd., but none of these has yet appeared in service.

The upper illustration, reproduced by courtesy of the L.N.E.R., shows the three-cylinder 4-6-0 locomotive No. 2848, "Arsenal," the first of the "Football Club" series of the "Sandringham" class. In the lower photograph a G.W.R. Penzance-Shrewsbury train is seen at Chacewater in charge of No. 4966 "Shakenhurst Hall." (H.R.C. prize-winning photograph.)

Further G.E.R. type "B12" class 4-6-0 locomotives rebuilt with larger boilers and round-topped fireboxes include Nos. 8541, 8550, 8559, and 8566. Two of the "E4" class 2-4-0 mixed traffic locomotives of the former G.E.R., Nos. 7411 and 7478, have been provided with enlarged cabs having side windows. This is to afford better protection for the enginemen when working over the exposed route between Darlington and Tebay to which these engines have now migrated. A short article describing this class of locomotives appeared in the July 1935 *"M.M."*

L.M.S.R. Locomotive and Rolling Stock Developments

The L.M.S.R. construction programme for 1937 provides for 105 new locomotives, 751 carriages, and 12,105 wagons. Included among the locomotives will be five more of the 4-6-2 "Princess Royal" class; these will be built at Crewe Works. For the most part the new stock will be built in the Company's shops, but orders have been placed with private firms for 2,195 wagons. The majority of the new carriages will be of main line vestibule and corridor types. In addition 17 new restaurant cars will be added to complete a scheme that has been in progress for some years to improve and increase the travelling restaurant facilities on the L.M.S.R.

Four engines of the "5X" "Jubilee" class Nos. 5739-42 that will be turned out towards the end of this year will be named respectively *"Ulster," "Munster," "Leinster,"* and *"Connaught."* The new series of class "5P5F" mixed traffic 4-6-0 locomotives numbered in the 5200s are being delivered from Sir W. G. Armstrong Whitworth and Co. Ltd., and are being put into traffic, as are the 2-8-0 mineral engines of the "8000" series on order from the Vulcan Foundry Ltd. New passenger tank locomotives of the 2-6-4 type continue to appear, both from the North British Locomotive Co. Ltd., and from Derby Works.

With the commissioning of so much new motive power the disappearance of many of the locomotives of pre-grouping days continues rapidly. L.N.W.R. "Princes" recently scrapped include No. 25627, *"Lewis Carroll"*; No. 25660, *"Kestrel"*; and No. 25685, *"Persia"*; No. 25697, *"Richard Cobden"*; and Nos. 25721, 25726 and 25796, which had no names. Among the 4-4-0s of L.N.W.R. design now broken up was No. 5278, *"Precursor,"* the first of a well-known class originated by Mr. G. Whale in 1904. The non-superheated engines of this class as originally built became obsolete last year, but No. 5278 was one of those that had been provided with superheating equipment and assimilated to the "George The Fifth" class, which were the superheated development of the "Precursors." "Georges" now withdrawn include No. 5337, *"T. J. Hare"*; No. 5349, *"British Empire"*; No. 5353, *"Staghound"*; No. 5355, *"South Africa"*; No. 5385, *"William Froude"*; No. 5399, *"Lord Stalbridge"*; and No. 5394, *"Phaeton."* Superheated "Precursors" also withdrawn are No. 5309, *"Fame"*; No. 5316, *"Viscount"*; and No. 25207, *"Eglinton."*

The M.R. "Kirtley" 2-4-0s of the old "800" class with outside frames are now obsolete, the last survivor No. 20060 having been withdrawn.

G.W.R. Notes

The 25 G.W.R. "Castle" locomotives built this year are Nos. 5043-5067 inclusive, and the names selected for them appeared in these pages last March. No. 5053, which was to have been named *"Hatherop Castle,"* was turned out as *"Bishop's Castle"* instead.

Recent withdrawals include No. 3255, *"Excalibur,"* and No. 3271, *"Eddystone,"* of the 4-4-0 "Duke" class, and No. 2678, one of the 2-6-0 inside-cylinder "Aberdares."

Winter train services came into operation on the G.W.R. on 28th September. A notable feature is that almost all the services operated by the 17 streamlined railcars are retained. These, including the parcels railcar referred to in *"Railway News"* in the June issue, will cover a mileage of 3,584 as compared with the corresponding figure of 1,235 last year. Four trips are now made daily, except on Saturdays and Sundays, by a streamlined railcar between Bristol and Cardiff, via the Severn Tunnel. This is the first regular railcar service to be operated through the Tunnel.

The non-stop run of the *"Cornish Riviera Limited"* to Plymouth is now cut short by a stop at Exeter to detach a coach for Kingsbridge. Slip coaches again serve Weymouth, Taunton, Minehead and Ilfracombe.

A Cruise in the Mediterranean

Replacing a Lost Propeller Blade

By Harold Elwell

WE boarded the gleaming white cruising liner at the Liverpool Landing Stage on a Saturday afternoon. Passengers and friends were hurrying on board, bunting fluttered gaily from the masthead and everyone had a holiday feeling, except the seamen working at top speed hauling trunks and stores aboard. The interest of the cruise began immediately, for the Mersey was full of shipping of all kinds, from great liners lying at anchor and cargo steamers passing up and down the river, to the busy ferry vessels and the fussy tugs, some of which were hovering round the cruising ship.

Gradually the winches stopped chugging. The bell boys cried "All visitors ashore, please," the gangway was raised after the inevitable last passenger had rushed aboard, and amid the hooting of sirens and farewells from our friends the tugs carefully nosed the vessel out against the tide downstream. The engineers on watch below kept a careful eye on the engine room telegraph as the pilot rang down from the navigating bridge "Half Speed Ahead," and not until we had negotiated the difficult Mersey channels did they receive the order "Full Ahead." Early in the evening off the Welsh Coast the pilot boat hailed us, and we slowed down for the cutter to "pick up the pilot." This was rather thrilling to watch, as the pilot clambers down a swinging rope ladder, and more often than not he has to make a leap for the cutter as it draws alongside.

The rock of Gibraltar seen from a cruising liner, with the town resting on its lower slopes.

Now we were for the open sea, and when all had found their bearings there was life-boat drill, which all had to attend, wearing lifebelts. About noon on Sunday we had the Scilly Isles abeam and passed the "first and last English lighthouse," that on the lonely Bishop Rock. By nightfall a slight roll warned us that we were in the Bay of Biscay, the troubled stretch of water bounded by the west coast of France and the north coast of Spain. Our course lay in a south-westerly direction, but even so we did not miss the swell, the tail-end of an Atlantic storm many hundreds of miles away, which made our otherwise steady ship pitch forward in uneven jerks.

Now and again the stern rose out of the sea and hit each wave tremulously. Seamen say "She's catching the short ones," when this happens. Just after one of these "short ones" the ship lurched, and instead of the steady throb of the engines and the even spin of the propellers there came an irregular bumping felt all over the ship. An engineer told us not to worry. "She's only dropped a fin off her starboard prop," he said, meaning that one of the blades had snapped off a propeller. Instead of both shafts keeping an almost even speed of, say, 78 r.p.m.—actually one shaft is always a little slower to prevent kick and erratic steering—the damaged propeller now raced unevenly. In a very short time the engineers down below adjusted both port and starboard engines, however, and we proceeded at about half speed. No sooner was the excitement over than the Bay also seemed to have calmed down. This was all to the good, for we had to make for Lisbon, the nearest port, for repairs.

Although every big ship must carry a spare propeller blade, not every port has a dry dock large enough to accommodate a ship of our size. Portuguese officials boarded us as we neared Lisbon, and after much gesticulating and arm waving they decided to allow the Captain and Chief Engineer to manœuvre the ship into DOCA No. 1. The reason for the officials' anxiety was that the dock was really too small to allow the vessel to settle properly on keel chocks on the bottom. She just managed to get in, however, and passengers were then able to enjoy unexpected tours of Lisbon, or visits to the Casino at Estoril.

The ship was lightened by emptying ballast tanks, and trimmed by pumping the fuel oil from the after into the forward tanks. This left her down by the head and with her stern higher, and the propeller shafts came into sight when part of the water in the dock had been pumped out.

Dock workers floated pontoons in position under the ship's stern, and engineers went down to examine the damage. Unfortunately the blade had snapped off at an awkward place just on the boss, and the massive bolts that still held the remnant in position had to be drilled out of the shaft. This meant extra work and delay, but after fitters had worked all through the night, early morning saw the shaft clear. The new blade, made of phosphor bronze alloy and costing £200, was then lowered ready to be bolted on. This took only an hour or so, and all tackle then was cleared away, the pontoons were hauled up, and gradually the dock was filled again with water.

An unusual feature of the dock in which this work was

carried on is that the gate is hollow and does not swing on pintles or hinges, but is sunk in position with its ends fitting in sockets in the walls by pumping water into it. The sides of both the dock and the gate are inclined, and thus a water-tight joint is formed. When the dock is to be opened the water is pumped out of the gate, which rises free of its sockets and is hauled out of the way by man power.

Two powerful tugs were waiting in the River Tagus to ease the ship out of the dock as she was pulled out inch by inch. Shore workers dropped fenders between the wall and the ship's side, and we cleared the entrance by a small margin. By the afternoon we were out to sea again, everyone marvelling at the rapidity with which such a ticklish job was effected.

The lighthouse at Cape St. Vincent, on the coast of Portugal. The light, which is tended by monks, is 232 ft. above high water.

It was full speed ahead now in an endeavour to make up for some of our lost time. On our way southward we passed within a mile or so of Cape St. Vincent, the scene of a great British naval victory, in which Nelson played a great part, nearly 150 years ago. The lighthouse on top of the cliff is tended by the monks of a monastery established there. It is not easy to secure a photograph of it from the sea, owing to the height of the cliff. The one reproduced on this page was taken with the aid of a high-power telephoto lens on a film about the size of a postage stamp, and only the central portion was enlarged.

We reached the Strait of Gibraltar early in the morning, and by breakfast time the Rock loomed above us, making the naval vessels and our own liner appear like toy ships. We went ashore by tender, and were taken up the narrow winding streets by horse carriage to see some of the fortifications and the huge reservoir for storing rain water.

Naples was our next port of call, and after skirting the southern coast of Spain we cut right across the Mediterranean between the islands of Corsica and Sardinia. We steamed into the Bay of Naples in blazing sunshine. On our right, or starboard side, Mount Vesuvius stood out boldly, belching out great puffs of steam and flames at regular intervals. The cloud assumes curious shapes according to the weather. Sometimes it is like a great mushroom; at others it trails out seaward in a perfectly straight line for hundreds of miles.

Manœuvring the gate of the dry dock at Lisbon in which the cruising liner's lost propeller blade was replaced.

We had two or three days' stay in Naples to enable us to explore the remains of the ancient city of Pompeii, which was overwhelmed in 79 A.D. by showers of hot ashes from Vesuvius. Some of the bolder ones among us ascended to the summit of the volcano itself by the funicular railway, which takes them within 150 yds. of the crater, and there looked down into a boiling inferno of sulphurous smoke with great pools of bubbling molten lava.

After leaving Naples we passed another interesting volcano at night time. This was Stromboli, the only European volcano that is continuously active. Its summit showed a reddish glare, which fully justified its name of the Lighthouse of the Mediterranean. The volcano is about 2,000 ft. high, and in spite of its activity peasants live on the sheltered side of the small island on which it stands.

Passing through the Straits of Messina, where it generally is very windy, and under the heel of Italy across the mouth of the Adriatic Sea, we arrived within sight of Athens four days after leaving Naples. The beauties of the Acropolis, an ancient walled Greek city set on a hill, which later became the shrine of Athena the patron goddess of Athens, are world famed, and we all went ashore to see them. One of the most famous of the buildings of the Acropolis was the Parthenon, the Athenian treasure house in ancient times. It was used by the Turks as a powder magazine during a siege of the city by the Venetians in 1687, and was then blown up by a violent explosion that damaged it severely.

Then followed a long run from Athens to Ceuta in North Africa. The name of this town is pronounced "Soota." It shelters under a rocky hill that forms one of the "Pillars of Hercules" guarding the entrance to the Mediterranean Sea. The other Pillar of course is Gibraltar. From Ceuta we went inland to see the Moorish town of Tetuan, at the foothills of the Atlas mountains. Tetuan is a maze of twisting passages, and it was almost impossible to find our own way around without a native guide.

When we arrived back on board ship in the evening, we found native vendors making last minute sales of leather bags and trinkets to passengers anxious for souvenirs of their tour abroad. In the meantime the engineers had been busy taking in hundreds of tons of oil by pipeline, and at midnight we left our last port of call and turned homeward. This time we found the Bay of Biscay as calm as the proverbial millpond, and we arrived in Liverpool on schedule time in spite of the delay due to the loss of a propeller blade.

A New Colour Photography Process

A film for colour photography that has been introduced by Ilford Ltd. can be used with ordinary cameras and gives coloured transparencies of high quality, reproducing the full brilliancy of colouring of the subjects photographed.

In the Dufaycolor process, as the new method is called, colour is introduced by means of a fine transparent pattern of alternating blue and green squares and red lines that is printed on the sensitive emulsion of the film. This is called the "reseau." It is formed by printing parallel blue and green lines, which are so thin that there are 508 of each to the inch, and across these and at right angles to them even narrower red lines are placed.

Before light can fall upon the emulsion it must pass through the reseau. Only red light can penetrate the red lines, and blue and green light therefore do not affect the emulsion beneath them. The squares of blue and green act in a similar manner, so that the emulsion on development gives a record in black and white of the intensities of the coloured lights falling upon the tiny areas beneath the coloured pattern. On development the film forms a transparency. The picture is seen on holding it up to the light with the reseau nearer the eye, with the result that the light passing through the film is given its appropriate colour.

Roll films and film packs in addition to cinematograph films are now available for colour photography by this process. Cameras are loaded in complete darkness, and special filters are employed to adapt the film for use with daylight or any artificial light, but the transparency only gives correct colour when viewed in daylight, unless a special viewing filter is used. Focussing must be very sharp, but there is good latitude in exposure, and the new film is not slow, the exposure required in daylight being only about twice that of ordinary Selo roll film. The transparencies can be viewed by holding them in front of a diffused light, preferably in a box that cuts off stray light on the side from which they are seen, or projected on to a screen either as stills or moving pictures.

The model saw mill in the Black Forest, Germany, described in the article on page 606. It is driven by water power. Photograph by J. M. S. Risk.

Bull Transformed into a Unicorn

For centuries the unicorn has been regarded as the typical mythical animal, and there has been much speculation as to how the belief in its existence sprang up. So far as we can tell, no creature of this kind with a single horn set in the middle of its forehead has ever existed, and it has been suggested that the error began with confusion with the rhinoceros, which has a single horn and great strength, but in other respects has no claim to the powers and characteristics of a unicorn.

In view of this it is very interesting to find that a "unicorn" actually has been produced in the United States. This amazing creature is an Ayrshire bull that was transformed by an operation carried out when it was a calf a day old. The knots of tissue that normally develop into a pair of horns were then cut out and placed together at the middle of the calf's forehead. They grew into a single horn, and the change seems to have endowed the bull with many of the characteristics of the fabled unicorn, for it has a regal carriage and appears to rule over the cattle with which it associates, but is not aggressive. This is remarkable, for the unicorn of tradition was always represented as combining nobility and even docility with strength and power.

The biologist who carried out this operation is inclined to believe that unicorns actually were produced in ancient times by an operation similar to the one that he has carried out.

Fighting Fire with Fog

Artificial mist is now used in America for extinguishing fires. It is produced by means of two jets of water at high pressure which are made to collide, when the streams are broken up into tiny particles. The mist begins near the jet and extends 15 ft. away. A fireman holding the nozzle producing it stands this distance from the fire to be extinguished, and convection currents then suck in the mist and carry it through the fire.

Fog for fire fighting has the further advantage that it is effective with chemical fires, against which water is practically powerless. In one case a tank of blazing petroleum, from which flames and smoke were rising hundreds of feet into the air, was extinguished in eight seconds by means of a single fog-making nozzle, and another fire that had continued to rage for hours when fought by ordinary methods was put out in 10 min. by the new process.

An extraordinary feature of the use of fog is the small quantity of water required. It is said that a nozzle delivering one gallon of water a minute as mist is as effective as hoses pouring 250 times as much water in the form of streams. Most of the damage caused by a fire usually is directly due to the water used in extinguishing it. This is avoided when the new method is used, for only a slight deposit of dew remains on walls and furniture, and this can easily be wiped off.

The cause of the remarkable efficiency of fog or mist in fire fighting is believed to be the cooling effect that it produces.

Safety Razor Blades of Glass

Safety razor blades have now been made of glass. The introduction of these solves the old problem of what to do with discarded blades, for they can simply be crushed to powder under foot and then are harmless.

Many astonishing uses for glass continue to be found. Gramophone discs of glass were described in the August "*M.M.*," and this useful material also has been made into a kind of wool and fibres of it have actually been woven into fabrics. Even bricks have been made of glass. These are very strong and as they are transparent, buildings erected with them require no windows. A block of offices built of glass bricks was exhibited recently in America.

Timing Watches by Electricity

A clever instrument that will enable watchmakers to time and regulate a watch in a very few minutes has recently been produced by the Western Electric Company. The regulation of a watch has always been the longest process in both manufacture and repair, the chief reason being that after each adjustment the watch has to be run for some hours before its error can be checked. The "Watch Rate Recorder," as the new instrument is called, is shown in the lower illustration on this page. It dispenses with this trial and error method, the timekeeping of the watch being shown directly by a line on ruled paper that reveals at once the number of seconds a watch gained or lost per hour.

Concrete sheet piling placed in position by a new method in embankment work. The ground to receive the piles is washed out by high pressure jets of water.

The main part of the instrument is a special electric motor, which is kept rotating at an exact speed in synchronism with a vibrating tuning fork. The fork is used to generate an alternating current, which is amplified by valves similar to those used for radio sets, and the amplified current operates the motor. The motor drives a drum round which the ruled paper is wrapped. The watch itself is mounted in a clamp, seen on the right in the illustration, and listened to by a microphone, the current from which also is amplified and used to control a marker or stylus fitted just below the drum.

Most modern watches have an "18,000 train," which means that they beat 18,000 times per hour, or five times per second. The drum is rotated at this speed, and the mechanism is so constructed that the paper is marked at each beat. If the watch is keeping time, its beats are in step with the revolutions of the drum, and as the marker is moved slightly along the drum after each beat, the dots form a straight line across the paper. If the watch is losing, so that each beat comes a little later than it should, a sloping line of dots is produced and the angle this makes with the straight line of an exact timekeeper reveals the degree of error. The beats of a watch that is gaining occur too soon, and a watch with an error of this kind produces a line sloping in the opposite direction when tested by this instrument.

A watch with an irregular action gives an uneven line, and defective parts or incorrect adjustments can be traced in this way. Those familiar with the instrument can even determine the incorrect part or the nature of the faulty adjustment of a watch by the type of line it draws, and this makes examination of damaged watches much easier.

The microphone clamp in which the watch is mounted for testing is movable, enabling watches to be tested in several positions. The paper is ingeniously stored inside the drum so that it can be pulled out and clipped in place rapidly and easily, and the chart for each watch can be cut off and stored as a permanent record of its performance.

T. R. Robinson.

The Watch Rate Recorder described on this page, with the cover removed to show the amplifiers.

Street Name-plate in the Kerb

An experimental installation of a novel form of street name-plate has recently been made by the Corporation of Kingston-on-Thames. In conformity with the present day trend towards locating road signs as near the surface of the carriage way as possible, this street name is actually placed in the kerb, a kerb-stone having been removed and the name plate assembly put in its place. The name appears on an oblong panel of plate glass in black letters on a translucent yellow ground, and behind it is a tubular filament lamp. The period of illumination is controlled by a suitable time-switch. A second transparent glass plate serves as additional protection, and guards against the entry of water from the gutter. The bottom and sides of the plates are sealed in, but a small space is left open at the top for ventilation and for the escape of air expanded by the heat of the lamp.

A heavy steel plate, level with the top of the adjoining kerb stones, covers the assembly, and this is secured by bolts that allow it to be removed to give access to the lamps for adjustment or renewal.

The visibility of the name-plate is distinctly good. The bright bar of light located in the kerb attracts attention from both vehicular and foot passengers, and the name can be read from a considerable distance. A further advantage of the name-plate is that drivers of vehicles need not take their eyes from the road in an endeavour to find out the name of a street. In addition, it is a useful aid in locating the position of the kerb in foggy weather.

T. R. Robinson.

Sheet Piling Without Pile Driving

In a new method developed in Germany, concrete sheet piling is put down without digging or driving, the ground in which it is to be placed being simply washed out by jets of water at high pressure. Only a quarter of the time required for ordinary pile-driving operations is required in the new system, which also is less costly and arduous.

The upper illustration on this page shows ground being prepared for the insertion of concrete piles by this method. The pump used has an output with a free discharge of up to 15,500 gallons per hr. When working at a pressure three times that of the atmosphere, and with a $\frac{3}{4}$ in. nozzle, the rate of discharge is 4,700 gal. per hr. The pump is driven by a two-stroke heavy oil engine of $5\frac{1}{2}''$ h.p. and at the high pressure developed the jets of water quickly make way for the piles.

H. F. Kutschbach.

Substitutes for Rubber and Petrol

It may not be long before we shall be independent of the two natural products that in the past have been essential in making and running motor cars. These are rubber and petrol, without which cars could not have been developed to their present pitch of efficiency and comfort.

A fuel entirely suitable for use in motor cars is now being produced in quantities from coal in both Great Britain and Germany, and the success that has been achieved in the plant erected for this purpose at Billingham by Imperial Chemical Industries Ltd. suggests that the time is coming when we shall be independent of overseas supplies, brought over in huge tankers.

Another possibility is that alcohol also will be developed into a fuel for internal combustion engines. There are many sources of this liquid, for many vegetable products yield alcohol by various fermentation processes, and if these were carried out on a large scale they would give immense quantities of comparatively cheap fuel. The liquid also is a by-product in the distilling industry, and a petrol mixture containing it is already in use.

Turning now to the other important natural product, the search for synthetic rubber has been carried on for many years with more or less success. It is claimed that artificial rubber has already been produced in Germany, and in the United States there is a factory producing a material of this kind at the rate of more than 400 tons an hour. It is claimed that this synthetic rubber is better in many respects than the natural product.

One curious feature is that its base is a compound of acetylene that was discovered by Father Nieuland, of the University of Notre Dame.

Riley Success in the T.T.

For the second year in succession the International Tourist Trophy Race, organised by the R.A.C. and held on the Ards Circuit in Northern Ireland, resulted in a win for a Riley car. This year's race was run on 5th September, and the winning machine was driven for more than half the distance by F. W. Dixon, and for the final laps by his reserve driver C. J. Dodson. E. R. Hall's Bentley was second for the third successive year, and A. F. P. Fane's Frazer Nash B.M.W. was third. The average speed of the winner was 78.01 m.p.h.

Several lap records were made and broken during the race. In the early stages Fane made a record lap of 75.65 m.p.h. for the 1,500 c.c. to 2,000 c.c. class. Shortly afterwards Prince Birabongse of Siam, who races in the name of B. Bira, in his little Frazer Nash B.M.W. broke Fane's record by covering a lap at an average speed of 78.81 m.p.h.; but Fane soon recaptured the record by covering a lap in 10 min. 23 sec., which gave him an average speed of 78.93 m.p.h. Two laps later the same driver beat his own record by raising the average to 79.57 m.p.h.

As the race was nearing its close, L. Lebeque, the French driver of a Delahaye, in a terrific burst of speed completed a lap at an average speed of 85.52 m.p.h., which is the highest ever attained on the course.

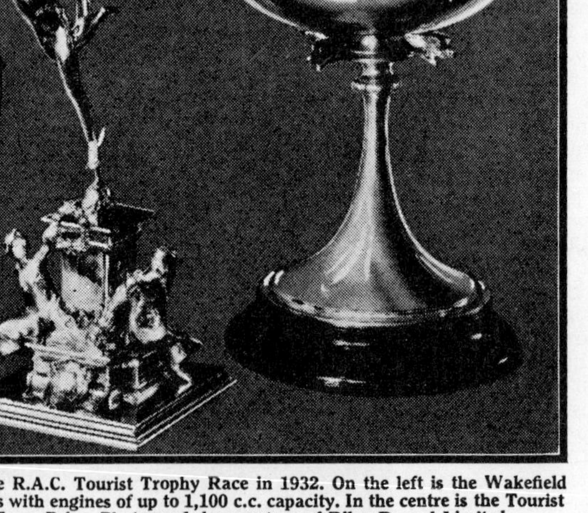
Three trophies won by Riley cars in the R.A.C. Tourist Trophy Race in 1932. On the left is the Wakefield Trophy for the winner of class G, for cars with engines of up to 1,100 c.c. capacity. In the centre is the Tourist Trophy, and on the right is the Team Prize. Photograph by courtesy of Riley Record Limited.

World's Fastest Motor Cycle Race

The outstanding feature of this year's Ulster Grand Prix, which is claimed to be the world's fastest motor cycle road race, was the amazing high speeds set up by the winners. The race is run in three groups, for 500 c.c., 350 c.c. and 250 c.c. machines respectively. The 500 c.c. race resulted in a runaway victory for F. L. Frith, who on a 499 Norton achieved an average speed of 92 m.p.h., more than a mile an hour above that of last year's winner. Frith probably would have improved on this if there had been any serious challenge for leading place in the closing stages, but his nearest rivals were so far behind that he was able to reduce speed towards the end. Second and third places were obtained by J. W. Breevers and W. G. Wright respectively, also on Nortons.

The race for 350 c.c. machines was won by E. R. Thomas, riding a Velocette, who completed the course at an average speed of 86.81 m.p.h. In the 250 c.c. group there was a very close finish between S. Woods and H. R. Foster, both on New Imperials. Woods finished first, his average speed being 78.76 m.p.h.

An Auto-Union Wins German Grand Prix

The race for the German Grand Prix, which was run over the Nürburg Ring at Eifel, ended in a magnificent victory for Auto-Union cars. Last year the race was won by Nuvolari's Alfa-Romeo, and the Germans were keen to avenge the defeat then suffered. In addition, the prospect for this year's race was made particularly interesting by the fact that in six previous important races the three leading makes of Grand Prix cars, the German Auto-Union and Mercedes-Benz and the Italian Alfa-Romeo, had each scored two victories.

After a hard and fast race Auto-Union cars came in first, second and fourth. The winning car was driven at an average speed of 81.75 m.p.h. by Rosemeyer, whose skilful and daring driving was an outstanding feature of the race. A long way behind was the second Auto-Union, driven by von Stuck, who in turn held an even longer lead over an Alfa-Romeo driven by Brivio. The Auto-Union placed fourth was driven by G. Hasse.

183 m.p.h. in Acerbo Cup Race

Following his success in the German Grand Prix, Rosemeyer in his Auto-Union competed in the famous Acerbo Cup race, at Pescara, Italy, and again won the day after a terrific battle with Nuvolari's Alfa-Romeo. Two other Auto-Unions piloted by E. von Delius and A. Varzi came in second and third.

During the sixth lap Rosemeyer flashed past the pits at 170 m.p.h., and overtook first Varzi and then Nuvolari to take the lead. Nuvolari's Alfa-Romeo continued to press hotly behind, however, and in a final endeavour to overhaul the leader Varzi accelerated to 183.64 m.p.h. So hot was the pace that shortly afterwards the engine of Nuvolari's car gave trouble and he had to retire, an event that robbed the race of what had promised to be a very thrilling finish.

In the class for cars not exceeding 1,500 c.c. R. J. B. Seaman, driving his famous Delage, repeated the victory of last year by defeating several Maseratis and three E.R.A.'s driven by "B. Bira," Embiricos and Tongue.

Racing Car Wheel Lost at 125 m.p.h.

After an exciting duel with Earl Howe, R. J. B. Seaman scored a further success with his Delage, when he won the historic 200-Miles Race organised by the Junior Car Club, at a speed of 69.28 m.p.h. Earl Howe's E.R.A. was second, and an E.R.A. driven by D. L. Briault and K. D. Evans was third. The race was run at Donnington Park, near Derby, and the winner completed the course without a single stop.

Austin Dobson had a remarkable escape from disaster when one of the front wheels of his Alfa-Romeo flew off while he was travelling at a speed of 125 m.p.h. The wheel with the tyre still intact on it, leaped over a fence crowded with spectators, bounded over the pits, and finally fell on the road in front of several oncoming competitors.

A Four-Wheeled Morgan

One of the most distinctive British small cars introduced this year is the attractive "Morgan 4-4" two-seater shown in the upper illustration on this page. The car is unusually low in build and has a graceful sporty bonnet and a tail streamlined to match the contour of the rear wings. Independent front wheel springing based on that used in the Morgan three-wheeled car, the Stevenson jacking system, and Girling brakes are other features of the chassis. The engine is a 9.8 h.p. Coventry Climax water-cooled unit fitted with overhead valves, and transmits its power through a single-plate clutch and an enclosed shaft to a four-speed gear-box, with syncromesh for easy changing on third and top gears. The car has a wheelbase length of 7 ft. 8 in. and an overall length of 11 ft. 8 in.

The distinctive "Morgan 4-4" sports car referred to on this page. Photograph by courtesy of The Morgan Motor Co., Ltd., Malvern Link.

Britain's Great Motor Industry

We are so accustomed to the sight and use of motor vehicles that perhaps few of us realise the enormous part the motor car manufacturing industry plays in the life of the country. Nearly 500,000 workpeople are employed in the actual manufacture of motor vehicles, and if others engaged in the driving and repair of vehicles and in allied engineering and body-building trades also are taken into account, the number of employees connected with the industry reaches well over a million.

The value of the motor products manufactured in England during 1935 was over £15,000,000. Last year 311,544 cars were produced, and it is anticipated that during the present year this number will be exceeded by over 50,000.

New Racing Track in South Africa

Preparations are now being made for a great motor race that is to be held in South Africa on 16th January next year. Drivers from England are being invited to enter, and the race will be run over a new track, now under construction at Muizenberg, near Capetown, which will be one of the finest of its kind in the world. It will include ample pits and a road racing circuit with interesting bends and corners, and there will be accommodation for many thousands of spectators.

A scene during the British Racing Drivers Club 500-Miles Race last year. A Riley that was second in the race being started from the pits after refuelling. Photograph by courtesy of Riley Record Limited.

Racing at Donnington Park

Very soon now the motor racing season will be ended, and the exhausts of cars flat out on road or track circuits will not be heard again until next spring. A few important fixtures still remain to be decided, however, and of these probably the most interesting is the International Grand Prix, which is likely to provide plenty of excitement for spectators at Donnington Park on 3rd October. Both supercharged or unsupercharged cars are eligible for this race, provided that they have suitable types of open bodies, four wheels and fulfil all essential racing requirements. The race will be run over 120 laps of the Donnington Park course, which is about 2½ miles in length, thus making a total distance of 300 miles; and a prize of £250 is offered to the winner. Last year the race was won by R. O. Shuttleworth, who drove an Alfa-Romeo. His average speed was 63.97 m.p.h., and he was closely followed by a Bugatti driven by Lord Howe.

As the race is open to foreign racing drivers, it is hoped that some of the famous Continental "aces" will take part in this year's event.

The Manx Grand Prix Races

The Manx Grand Prix Junior and Senior races, which are run over a 226 mile course in the Isle of Man, never fail to provide thrills for the thousands of spectators who line the course. The outstanding feature of this year's races was the remarkable riding of Austin Munks, an engineer of Boston, Lincolnshire, who won both the Junior and the Senior events. This is the first time the two races have been won by the same competitor since E. N. Lea accomplished the feat in 1929, and Munks's great performance is made all the more remarkable by the fact that he has the sight of only one eye. In the Junior Grand Prix he rode a Velocette and completed the 226 miles in 3 hrs. 3 mins. 47 secs. at an average speed of 73.92 m.p.h. Only seven seconds behind him was J. H. Blyth on a Norton, who averaged 73.88 m.p.h.

Simultaneously with the Junior Grand Prix a light-weight race was run for a trophy presented by relatives of D. J. Petrie, who was killed in a T.T. race last year, and this was won by D. Parkinson at a speed of 65.68 m.p.h., his machine being an Excelsior.

In the Senior Grand Prix Munks rode a 490 c.c. Norton, and the race was a keen duel between him and J. H. Blyth, also on a 490 c.c. Norton. Munks covered the six laps of the 226 miles course in 2 hrs. 52 mins. 14 secs., at an average speed of 78.88 m.p.h. Blyth finished 10 secs. later, his time and speed being 2 hrs. 52 mins. 24 secs. and 78.80 m.p.h. respectively.

K. Bills on a Norton, the fourth rider to start, was the first to complete the first lap, which he covered in 4 secs. under 29 mins., at an average speed of nearly 79 m.p.h. When Munks came roaring past the grandstand his time was six seconds more than that of Bills, who thus held the lead, but in his second lap Blyth averaged 78.85 m.p.h., and became 6 secs. ahead of Bills. During this lap Munks was even faster than Blyth, however, and his riding thrilled the crowds as he took corners at a tremendous speed. He finished his second lap 7 secs. ahead of Blyth, and then maintained the lead until the end of the race.

There was considerable excitement in the closing stages when it was learned that Munks' petrol tank developed a leak while he was on his fifth lap, and he had to stop to refuel. By the time he had restarted Blyth and several other riders had finished the course, and there was a thunderous cheer from the crowd when the red light over Munks' number on the score board showed that he had reached Governor's Bridge, less than a quarter of a mile from the finish. He had scarcely flashed past the finishing line before the timekeepers had worked out their calculations, to show that Munks had won by 10 seconds from Blyth. It was revealed after the race that there was less than a quart of petrol in the tank of the winner's machine when he reached the end of the course.

Ancient Tombs in Central America

Remains of Maya Civilisation

LAST March the Carnegie Institution of Washington announced that its specialists in Maya archæology, working near Guatemala City under the immediate direction of Dr. A. V. Kidder, head of the Institution's Division of Historical Research, were excavating a buried, stucco-covered structure of pyramidal form, the first of its kind ever to have been discovered in the highland region of Guatemala. The mound marking the site, located just outside Guatemala City, is one of a group of 100 mounds, large and small, dotting an area about 1½ miles in length and half a mile in width. The site has hitherto been known generally as Miraflores, or Miraflores-Arevalo, from the names of two of the principal farms or "fincas," but it is now proposed to call it "Kaminaljuyu," which means in the Quiche Indian tongue, freely translated, "Hills of the Dead."

The mound was brought to special notice through the laying out of a football field. A site between two mounds had been selected, but the distance was not sufficient, so a portion was cut from each to make room for the two sets of goal-posts. Upon digging into the edge of the westernmost of the two mounds, the corner of a structure was revealed which was faced with a hard, cement-like substance, and covered with fine white stucco.

The Carnegie Institution was invited to undertake excavation. As the digging progressed, pyramid after pyramid was revealed, until it is now certain that instead of there being three such superimposed structures, as originally announced, at least four actually exist. Owing to the destructive effect of torrential summer rains and of the penetration of the roots of trees, the outermost of these structures has been almost completely destroyed. By careful work, however, it was learned that originally it had been a large pyramid with steps and sloping lower walls, the latter having been constructed of blocks of pumice-stone, or tufa, laid in mud-mortar. The few blocks that remained were cleaned, noted, photographed, and stripped away, laying bare an older structure, also of pyramidal type.

A figurine of baked pottery discovered in a Maya tomb. The illustrations to this article are reproduced by courtesy of the Carnegie Institution of Washington.

This second pyramid was found to be in excellent condition in respect to its basal step and first terrace. Its upper walls, however, had been despoiled of their facing of cut stone, presumably by the builders of the outermost pyramid. By great good luck a small section remained, and this bit yielded invaluable information as to the nature and position of the missing portions, showing that the pyramid rose steeply in three levels to a surmounting platform.

The frontal stairway of this pyramid had also been torn down in ancient times, a loss which greatly distressed the excavators when it was discovered, but which led indirectly to the making of their most important finds. For example, the gap caused by the removal of the stairway permitted a trench to be run inward without damaging the beautifully finished basal slope of the pyramid. And this trench had been pushed but a few feet when it encountered the wall of another pyramid—Pyramid No. 2, counting from the innermost outward—which was in an even better state of preservation, inasmuch as its stairway was intact.

This pyramid has only been partially excavated, but enough work on it has been done to show that it differs from the two outer ones in that it rises to its summit platform in a single slope, which carries a balustraded stairway of 12 very steep steps. There is definite indication, moreover, that this pyramid, in turn, was built around yet another pyramidal structure, but the remainder of the mound will have to be excavated before detailed information about the latter can be obtained.

While puzzling over the reasons why the ancient builders removed the stairway of Pyramid Number 3 instead of covering it up, as was done with the stairway of Pyramid Number 2, the archæologists noticed that in the space originally occupied by the stairway the fill of the outermost pyramid ran somewhat deeper than elsewhere. Following this clue, the investigators sank through the floor of their original trench and found themselves coming down into a great square pit which proved to be a tomb. Fearing that they had overlooked other pits of similar nature, the workers recleaned and reexamined the floor of their trench, whereupon two more tombs were found. At a later time, a fourth tomb, located directly below the stairway of Pyramid Number 2, was also discovered, but it was not possible to enter it before work was brought to a close by the onset of the rains. It awaits excavation during the coming season.

The first tomb to be cleared, Tomb I, was a vertically-sided pit, dug into hard, volcanic deposit, 12 ft. square and 12 ft. deep. Originally it had been roofed with logs which had rotted away, long since, letting down stones and earth upon the contents. The pit was found to have been lined with rush matting, and its floor covered with a half-inch layer of brilliant red paint.

The personage who had been interred had apparently

been placed in a sitting position in the middle of the floor. In close association with the skeleton were 13 pottery vessels, nine beautiful obsidian spear-heads, several obsidian knives, a slate-backed mirror faced with iron pyrites, jade beads, a carved jade pendant, and what had evidently been two jade mosaic ornaments, perhaps ear-plugs. On three sides of the skeleton lay single human skulls and on the fourth, the skull of a jaguar.

A partially excavated mound that was found to consist of four pyramids. The stairway led to the summit of the second of these pyramids.

The second tomb to be opened, Tomb III, was both larger and deeper than the first. Like the first it had been roofed with logs and lined with matting made of rushes. Its excavation yielded a wealth of information regarding the burial practices of the period among the ancient people of this highland region.

The principal skeleton in it was that of a middle-aged male, presumably a priest or ruler. Apparently the body had been placed in the middle of the tomb in a sitting position with legs crossed. Also, when the body was interred it had evidently been loaded with ornaments: shells, crystals, ear-plugs, plaques inlaid with iron pyrites, beads of jade, and beautifully carved pendants, likewise of jade.

At the side of the skeleton was a heap of pottery in which two human effigies of clay were found. One of these represents a richly clothed personage, perhaps a deity, who is beating a ceremonial drum. At the feet of the skeleton lay the bones of a young woman, also vessels for serving food, and a milling stone for grinding corn —utensils evidently intended for use of the master in his home in the hereafter. And in a corner of the tomb reposed the bones of a small dog.

The third and last tomb to have been opened, Tomb II, is located at a point that was covered by the edge of the outermost pyramid, the one first discovered. In this connection an extract from a letter which Dr. Kidder sent to Dr. Merriam, President of the Carnegie Institution, is of interest, not only because of the information which it gives about the tomb and its contents, but also for the side light which it throws upon the work of "dirt archæologists."

A Maya incense burner from a tomb in Guatemala. The smoke issued from the mouth and armpits of the figure.

"In some ways Tomb II is the most interesting of all. It contained many unique pieces of pottery—a fish-effigy, a double-spouted jar with a carved serpent, wonderfully executed, a human effigy with a beard like that of the Tuxtla statuette—and much other material. Everything was in rather better condition than in Tomb III, so it was possible to get fuller data regarding the position of the principal skeleton and those of the two other persons, presumably slaves, who were buried with him. All three had been in sitting positions, cross-legged, facing the south.

"The laboratory is full of the material from the three tombs. Of pottery there are upward of 60 pieces; there are strings of jade beads, sheaves of obsidian flake-knives, chipped implements and many other objects.

"The pottery has been a great problem. Many of the vessels were coated with fine plaster, upon which were painted, figures apparently of priests or rulers or gods, performing what appear to be ceremonial acts. But these pots were wedged in among rocks fallen from the roof of the tomb; many were broken into small pieces or even crushed flat. . .

"We removed the vessels, as a rule, by undercutting them and raising the whole lump of earth, nesting the lump in a basket and transferring it to the laboratory, where the cleaning was done bit by bit and the plaster set in place by spraying it with a preservative solution. At the same time Tejeda, the artist, made colour notes, for the painting fades upon drying.

"It will take months to get the collection into exhibition shape, but it will prove a tremendous addition to our knowledge of Maya life, ceremony, dress, and art. The mound itself has been sectioned by deep, narrow trenches, in order not to destroy the outer constructions. So the data are recorded principally by plans and sections, while the photographs are mostly of details of masonry, stratification and such. If the rains will only hold off! Fortunately they did not come before the tombs were finished. A good hard shower, at some stages of the work, would have been calamitous."

From the position of the tombs in this mound in relation to the several pyramids, comes the suggestion of a possible explanation of the puzzling practice, common throughout the Maya area, of erecting successive pyramidal structures on and around one another in superimposed manner. Hitherto the procedure has been thought to be linked somehow with the termination of important periods, but the location of the tombs suggests the possibility that upon the death of a priest-ruler his body was interred towards the east and the pyramid with which he was associated, and which indeed he may have built, sealed by enclosing it within a new one.

We are indebted to the Carnegie Institution of Washington for the information in this article.

The Empire Flying Boats

The illustration on this page is an artist's impression of *"Canopus,"* the first of the Empire flying boats for Imperial Airways, in the air. This machine has completed the necessary trial flights and is now being fitted with the cabin equipment that will make it the most luxurious air liner in the world. Short Bros. (Rochester and Bedford) Ltd. are building 29 of these vessels.

A detailed description of this new class of flying boat will be published in an early issue of the *"M.M."* It will be seen from the photograph that the machines are of the high wing monoplane type, with four engines carried in streamlined nacelles faired into the leading edge of the great wing. There are two decks in the massive hull, an upper one for the crew and a lower one for the passengers, and sleeping accommodation will be available for passengers travelling long distances.

Imperial Airways have announced that the following registration letters and names will be given to the first 14 of the Empire flying boats: G-ADHL *"Canopus"*; G-ADHM *"Caledonia"*; G-ADUT *"Cavalier"*; G-ADUU *"Centaurus"*; G-ADUV *"Cambria"*; G.ADUW *"Castor"*; G-ADUX *"Cassiopeia"*; G-ADUY *"Capella"*; G-ADUZ *"Cygnus"*; G-ADVA *"Capricornus"*; G-ADVB *"Corsair"*; G-ADVC *"Courtier"*; G-ADVD *"Challenger"*; G-ADVE *"Centurion."*

An artist's impression of "Canopus," the first of the Empire flying boats for Imperial Airways. Twenty-nine of these are being built by Short Bros. (Rochester and Bedford) Ltd. Photograph courtesy of Imperial Airways Ltd.

Aero Engine Developments at Coventry

Coventry is destined to become an important centre for the manufacture of aero engines and aircraft. A large aero engine factory that will cost at least £500,000 is under construction there for the Daimler Co. Ltd., who will run it in co-operation with the Air Ministry. The factory will adjoin the present Daimler motor car works at Radford, and will provide employment for about 1,000 people. Other Coventry firms are joining in the Air Ministry scheme. The Standard Motor Co. Ltd., have begun construction of a large factory, and the Humber-Hillman Company and Rover Co. Ltd. are expected to do so shortly.

The Latest Douglas Air Liner

Details are now available of the latest type of Douglas air liner. It is called the DC.3 and is a slightly larger machine than the DC.2 described and illustrated in the *"M.M."* of September 1935. The span is 95 ft., the length 64 ft. 5 in. and the height 15 ft. It is similar in construction to the DC.2, and aluminium alloys have been used extensively for the structural parts. The undercarriage is retractable and can be raised or lowered in about 25 seconds.

The pilots' cockpit forward of the long cabin gives an unobstructed outlook, and behind it are two mail and cargo compartments with a total capacity of 146 cu. ft. These are separated by a narrow central gangway that leads to the passenger cabin, a soundproof structure 23 ft. long and 6 ft. 6 in. in height. The cabin can be converted into a sleeper for 14 passengers when the machine is required for night flying. It is then divided into seven compartments, each accommodating two passengers in upper and lower berths respectively. The compartments are ranged three on one side of a central passage and four on the other.

A Giant Russian Airport

Work has begun on the construction of a new commercial airport at Tuchino, near Moscow. This has been planned on similar lines to that at Gatwick in this country. It will be 1,400 acres in extent, and will be capable of dealing with 1,000 passengers a day. The construction of the airport is not likely to be completed until early in 1939.

R.A.F. Vacancies for Aircrafthands

The Air Ministry announce that owing to the expansion of the Royal Air Force 500 new aircrafthands will be required each month until further notice. Of these 150 will be entered for training as armourers and wireless operators. The age limit for these branches is 17 to 32 years, and the period of service is six years. Previous trade experience is not necessary, but applicants must have received a good general education. The other 350 will be entered for general duties as aircrafthands, the age limits in this case being 18 to 26 years. Applicants selected will have an opportunity, after about a year's service, to be trained in one of a number of trades, such as storekeeper, motor driver, fabric worker, or fitter's mate. Aircrafthands (general duties) are enlisted for seven years, and those selected for trade instruction are required to extend their engagement to nine years on completion of their training.

Detailed particulars of entry can be obtained from the R.A.F. Recruiting Depot, Victoria House, Kingsway, London, W.C.2, or from the provincial recruiting depots at Glasgow, Birmingham, Liverpool, Manchester, Newcastle, Leeds, Belfast, Plymouth and Cardiff.

Seaplane Channel at Singapore

At Singapore Harbour a special seaplane channel is to be provided to enable the new Empire flying boats of Imperial Airways to alight and taxi across the water to the slipways and hangars. The channel will be about a mile in length, and it will be clearly marked and protected by booms and kept clear of junks and other small native craft. Considerable quantities of reinforced concrete piling will be used in making the approach channel and anchorage, and this work will shortly be put in hand. Rapid progress has already been made in the construction of the seaplane slipways and of the hangars.

The whole scheme will be completed early in the coming year, and the event may be celebrated by an air race between Singapore and London.

Record Atlantic Flights

After an interval of about a year the North Atlantic has again been crossed by air, two record flights having been accomplished last month. The first was a west-to-east flight by Mr. Harry Richman, of New York, and Mr. Dick Merrill, the chief pilot of Eastern American Airways, who had been granted a month's leave to enable him to take part in the adventure. They took off from New York in their low wing monoplane *"Lady Peace"* on 2nd September, with the intention of flying non-stop to Croydon, and flew practically all the way to England at a height of 11,000 ft. Severe storms were encountered, and lightning put their wireless equipment out of action when they were about 500 miles from Ireland. Visibility was bad, and they flew through almost continuous cloud and rain, never sighting the Atlantic for more than an hour at a time. They did not see Ireland at all, and lacking this valuable check on their course they got lost. After anxiously circling around for 1½ hrs. they were forced to descend owing to their fuel supply being almost exhausted, and they landed safely in a field at Llandilo, a village in Carmarthenshire. Their flight from New York to Great Britain had been accomplished in the record time of 18 hrs. 8 min., at an average speed of 210 m.p.h.

This front view of the Armstrong Whitworth "Whitley" Bomber shows the great thickness of the huge wing and the totally enclosed gun turret in the nose of the fuselage. Photograph by courtesy of Sir W. G. Armstrong Whitworth Aircraft Ltd.

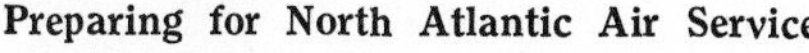

The second ocean flight was made in the reverse direction by Mrs. Beryl Markham, who took off from Abingdon aerodrome, in Berkshire, on the 4th September in a Percival "Vega Gull" monoplane named *"Messenger,"* and reached Baleine Cove, Cape Breton Island, where the machine was badly damaged on landing.

Mrs. Markham is thus the first woman to fly solo across the North Atlantic in an east-to-west direction. Since the above was written Richman and Merrill have accomplished the return flight. They made a forced landing near Musgrave Harbour, Newfoundland.

A fine picture of a Fairey "Fantome" in flight, taken from another machine. This type of modern single-seater fighter was described in the "M.M." for July 1936. Photograph by courtesy of "The Aeroplane."

New High Speed Monospar Aeroplane

The latest addition to the range of Monospar aircraft is a twin-engined low wing cabin monoplane with a top speed of 203 m.p.h. It is 59 ft. 6 in. in span and 43 ft. 3 in. in length, and the cabin has seating for 10 passengers. There is an armchair with adjustable back for each passenger, and above each seat is a reading lamp. The pilot's cabin is situated well forward in a raised position, giving a good outlook in three directions, and has dual control.

Heston Air Traffic

The growing importance of Heston Airport is borne out by the latest traffic figures. During the first half of this year 7,072 passengers passed through the Customs, an increase of 4,116 over the corresponding period last year. There were 19,900 aircraft arrivals and departures during the normal working hours of the airport, and this figure does not take into account the activities of the flying school machines.

French Airman's Altitude Record

The world's aeroplane height record of 47,350 ft. achieved by Commandant Donati, of Italy, in April 1934, was exceeded on 17th August last by M. Georges Detre, a French airman, who reached a height of 48,600 ft. He flew a Potez 50 machine fitted with a Gnôme-Rhône K.14 engine, and made the record flight from Villacoublay aerodrome. M. Detre would probably have climbed to an even greater height but for the fact that his oxygen supply became almost exhausted and he wisely decided to descend.

From 1932 until Commandant Donati's success in 1934 the record stood at 43,956 ft. and was held by England, having been won for this country by Capt. C. F. Uwins, the chief test pilot of the Bristol Aeroplane Co. Ltd. It will be interesting therefore to see how long the new record is held by France, as an attempt to regain it for England may be made shortly with a new low wing monoplane that has just been built by the Bristol Company for the Air Ministry, for research in flying at great heights.

More Machines for U.S. Army

The large number of new aircraft ordered this year by the United States Government include 85 Seversky P.35 single-seater fighters. This is a new Seversky type of military machine, and most details about it are withheld. It is known, however, that it has a retractable undercarriage and a Pratt and Whitney "twin-Wasp" engine of 1,000 h.p., and is capable of a top speed of 315 m.p.h.

Karachi Airport Progress

Good progress is being made with the important developments and improvements being carried out at Karachi Airport, and the huge new hangar is practically completed. The installation of the airport night lighting equipment is well in hand, and when it is ready the movement of a few switches at the control points will bring the entire lighting into use. The new airport, with its extensive landing area, roads and buildings, will cover a total area of about four square miles.

Preparing for North Atlantic Air Service

In preparation for establishing the North Atlantic air route, observations of upper-air conditions have been made in Newfoundland and above the mouth of the St. Lawrence. In these observations the British Air Ministry, and the Canadian and Newfoundland authorities have been working in conjunction with Imperial Airways. Pilots and aircraft have been stationed in Newfoundland since the autumn of 1934, and a Canadian Government meteorologist has been conducting the upper air investigations, the aircraft being flown by Imperial Airways pilots.

Fog reporting stations have been established in Newfoundland, both round the coast and inland. All-year observations indicate that although conditions rendering flying difficult are apt to persist in areas round St. John's, there is a central zone in Newfoundland where fog is much less prevalent. It is considered that some place in this more favourable area will be chosen for the island's airport on the trans-Atlantic service.

A Flying Laboratory

The Bristol "Pegasus"-engined Vickers "Viastra" cabin monoplane formerly owned by the King has been fitted up as a laboratory for use in elaborate experiments in connection with wireless and direction finding. This has been done at the request of the Aeronautical Research Committee.

HOW THINGS ARE MADE:

Spun Iron and Concrete Pipes

The Stanton Company's Plant

SINCE the first days of civilisation, the provision and maintenance of adequate water supplies has been one of the most important tasks of the engineer. At various periods of history, water was supplied through pipes of clay, terra-cotta, wood, lead and stone. For well over a hundred years, however, cast iron pipes have been generally used for the conveyance of both water and gas. Their great strength and durability is established by the fact that large numbers of cast iron pipes more than a century old are still in use. Cast iron is a material in which engineers place great faith, and to-day every civilised community depends for essential services on underground networks of cast iron gas, water and sewage mains.

The extension of these cast iron mains, and their frequent replacement by others of larger diameter, is responsible for a continuous demand for cast iron pipes. In this country the Stanton Ironworks Co., Ltd., of Stanton, near Nottingham, each week produce many miles of cast iron mains. No doubt most readers will have seen the company's pipes, bearing the word "Stanton" in white letters, lying ready to be laid down in trenches excavated by the roadside.

Pouring molten iron into the tilting ladle of a pipe spinning machine. We are indebted to the Stanton Ironworks Company Limited for the illustrations to this article.

The Stanton Company own their own ironstone mines, limestone quarries and blast furnaces, and are thus able to superintend every stage in the manufacture of cast iron pipes, from the extraction of raw materials to the despatch of the finished product.

Until about 15 years ago all cast iron pipes were cast in sand moulds contained in metal boxes, which were arranged vertically around the walls of a pit. This was a slow and arduous process, however, in which a great deal was left to the individual skill of the workmen. For example, if the "core," or inner part of the mould, were allowed to shift slightly, the wall of the resultant pipe would be thicker in one place than in another. Great care had to be exercised also to keep the surface of the mould free from flaws, dirt or other foreign matter that would produce faults in the finished pipe. Owing to the lengthy preparation of the moulds, and the slow cooling of the metal, production was naturally slow.

In 1922 the Stanton Company became interested in the Delavaud system of pipe-casting invented by M. Sensaud de Lavaud, a Brazilian engineer. This method, which at that time was in an undeveloped stage, utilises centrifugal force to dispense with the use of sand moulds and inner cores. Sufficient molten metal to make a single pipe is introduced into a revolving cylindrical mould, against the sides of which it is held by centrifugal force. The metal cools rapidly, and as soon as the pipe has been withdrawn the mould is ready to be used again. In this manner continuous production is secured and overhead costs are greatly reduced.

Even more important than these manufacturing improvements is the great advance that centrifugal casting has made in the technical properties of the pipes. The process has none of the disadvantages of that involving the use of sand moulds, to which reference has already been made, and the centrifugal action gives the metal a dense, close-grained structure that greatly increases its tensile strength.

Recently the Stanton Company have introduced an additional operation known as the Mairy process, in which the revolving mould is provided with a thin layer of ferro-silicon before the metal is introduced. This prevents the outer surface of the pipe from being chilled by direct contact with the surface of the mould, and greatly increases its resistance to shock and impact. The improved pipes made by this process are known as Stanton "New" Spun Iron Pipes.

With these general principles in mind, the reader will be better able to appreciate the following more detailed description of the spun plant at Stanton.

The pig iron used for the manufacture of the pipes is graded in concrete bunkers according to its silicon content. Hoists transfer it to cupolas in which it is heated, the molten iron attaining a temperature of 1,400 deg. C. It is then tapped into 1½-ton casting ladles, which are conveyed by telpher cranes to the spinning machines in the casting shops. There are 20 spinning machines, in which the pipes are made in lengths of 4 yds. and 6 yds., and in diameters ranging from 3 in. to 21 in. Pipes are made also in metric sizes for export to foreign countries using metric standards.

At the head of each machine is a casting ladle, into which the molten metal is poured. The ladle is tilted, and the metal runs down a cantilever trough into a revolving cylindrical mould, which has been coated with powdered ferro-silicon. As the mould revolves, it commences to move away from the spout of the trough, so that the metal flowing into it is deposited over its surface in the form of an even spiral, which knits together and so forms the pipe.

Molten metal flowing into the revolving mould in which the pipe is cast. The mould moves away from the tilting ladle as the pipe is formed.

The pipe solidifies in a few seconds, and is secured by internal grips. The mould then moves back to its original position, leaving the red-hot pipe behind it. The pipe is then transferred to gantries, and rolls slowly through a gas-heated normalising furnace. This serves to relieve casting strains and improves the structure of the metal. On emerging from the furnace the pipe is cleaned, and coated, while still hot, with tar solution. Water pipes are coated both internally and externally, but only the outside surfaces of gas pipes are covered.

Before leaving the works each pipe is tested hydraulically to approximately double its normal working pressure.

To enable the pipes to be jointed, one end is provided with a bell-shaped socket; the plain end is known as the spigot. When the spigot is entered into the socket, a narrow space is left between the outside of the spigot and the inside of the socket. Into this space is introduced molten lead or lead wool, which makes a leaktight joint.

The rigidity of the lead joint is a disadvantage where the pipes are to be laid in subsoil affected by heavy traffic vibration, or where ground subsidence is likely to occur. To meet such conditions, the Stanton Company have introduced a flexible type of joint known as the Stanton-Wilson Self-adjusting Joint. In place of lead, this joint employs a lead-tipped rubber ring, which enables the joints to be deflected without leakage under pressure.

The pipe making machine at the end of the cast. It has moved right back, leaving the metal pouring trough behind it.

The extent to which spun iron pipes are used is indicated by the fact that the Stanton Company have produced sufficient to make a giant tube over 18,000 miles in length. More than 1,000 miles of this piping has been fitted with the flexible Stanton-Wilson Joint.

Iron is not the only material that lends itself to the manufacture of pipes by this ingenious method. For sewage conveyance, and also for the supply of water under moderate pressures, concrete pipes are widely used, and these are made at Stanton by a process based on the centrifugal principle utilised in the manufacture of spun iron pipes.

The concrete is made from British Portland cement, clean-washed sharp sand, and Leicestershire granite. These materials are stored in damp-proof concrete bunkers, and are mixed in automatic travelling mixers. The wet concrete is introduced by hand, or fed automatically, into revolving moulds, and the centrifugal action not only flings it against the sides of the mould, and holds it there, but also greatly increases its density, and therefore its strength. During spinning, all surplus water is expelled from the concrete into the centre of the mould. After spinning, the concrete pipes are matured in stockyards for at least one month before they are allowed to leave the works.

Until a few years ago, concrete pipes were usually "grouted," or jointed, with cement. To-day, however, a proportion of Stanton concrete pipes are supplied with the Stanton Cornelius Flexible Joint, in which grout is replaced by a joint-ring made of special rubber. By the use of this joint concrete mains can be deflected without leakage, and thus accommodate themselves to the ground movements caused by traffic vibration or subsidence.

For the conveyance of certain types of water it is advisable to use iron pipes that have been provided with a thin lining of concrete. At Stanton, iron pipes are lined with concrete by the centrifugal process, the concrete being fed into the bore of the revolving pipes.

In addition to centrifugally made iron and concrete pipes, the Stanton Company also make large diameter cast iron pipes by the sand-cast process. Cast iron mains require not only straight pipes, but also bends, tees, angle branches, and other "specials," as such castings are called. These are produced in a mechanised foundry, in which as many operations as possible are carried out by mechanical means, thereby eliminating the various defects that are due to unsystematic production.

HORNBY ROLLING

"BOYS! A Hornby

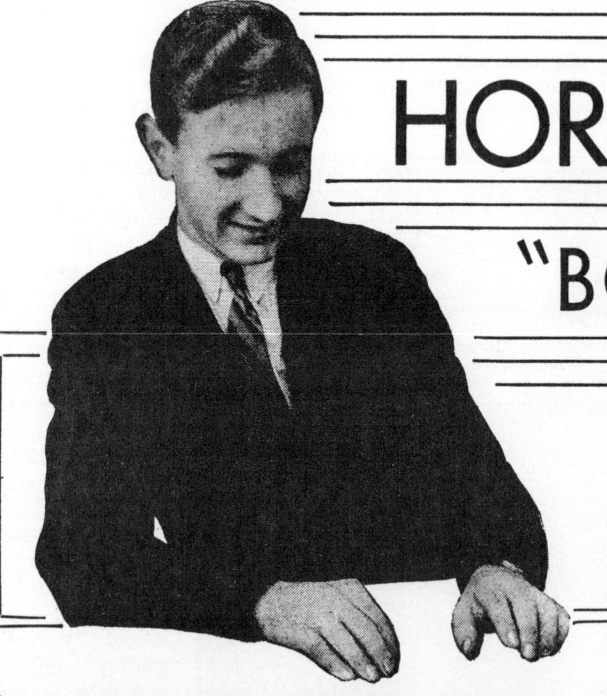

PERFECT MINIATURE RAILWAYS

Playing the great game of railways with Hornby Trains is the best fun in the world. Almost every operation in real railway practice can be carried out in miniature with the Hornby system.

From the day of their introduction Hornby Trains have always represented the latest model railway practice. Designs are continually being improved and new items added so that the system is complete in practically every detail. There are Locomotives for all duties, driven by electric motors or by clockwork. There is Rolling Stock of all kinds, including Pullman Cars, ordinary Coaches and Guard's Vans for passenger services; and numerous and varied Wagons and Vans for freight working.

THE COMPLETENESS OF THE HORNBY SYSTEM

Hornby Accessories are now better than ever before. Stations, Signals and Signal Cabins, Engine Sheds, Level Crossings and other items can be obtained wired for electric lighting. Cuttings and Tunnels add realism to the track; miniature Railway Staff and Passengers give "life" to station platforms; and there are Animals for lineside fields. The Rails, Points and Crossings make it possible to construct an almost endless variety of attractive and railwaylike layouts, for both Electric and Clockwork trains.

Many interesting illustrations and much useful information regarding Hornby Railway layouts are given in the booklets entitled "How to plan your Hornby Railway," and "Hornby Layouts—One Hundred Suggestions." Each of these booklets is obtainable from any dealer, price 3d., or from Meccano Ltd., Binns Road, Liverpool 13, price 4d. post free.

ACCESSORIES FITTED FOR ELECTRIC LIGHTING

The Hornby Accessories fitted for Electric Lighting make possible a new development in realism. By means of them, Stations, Engine Sheds, Signal Cabins and Goods Platforms can be lighted up, and goods yards and sidings illuminated by Lamp Standards. The various Signals can be made to show their red and green or yellow and green lights, and red lamps fitted to Buffer Stops and Level Crossing Gates will show their warning as in actual practice. No Hornby Railway is complete without some of these Accessories.

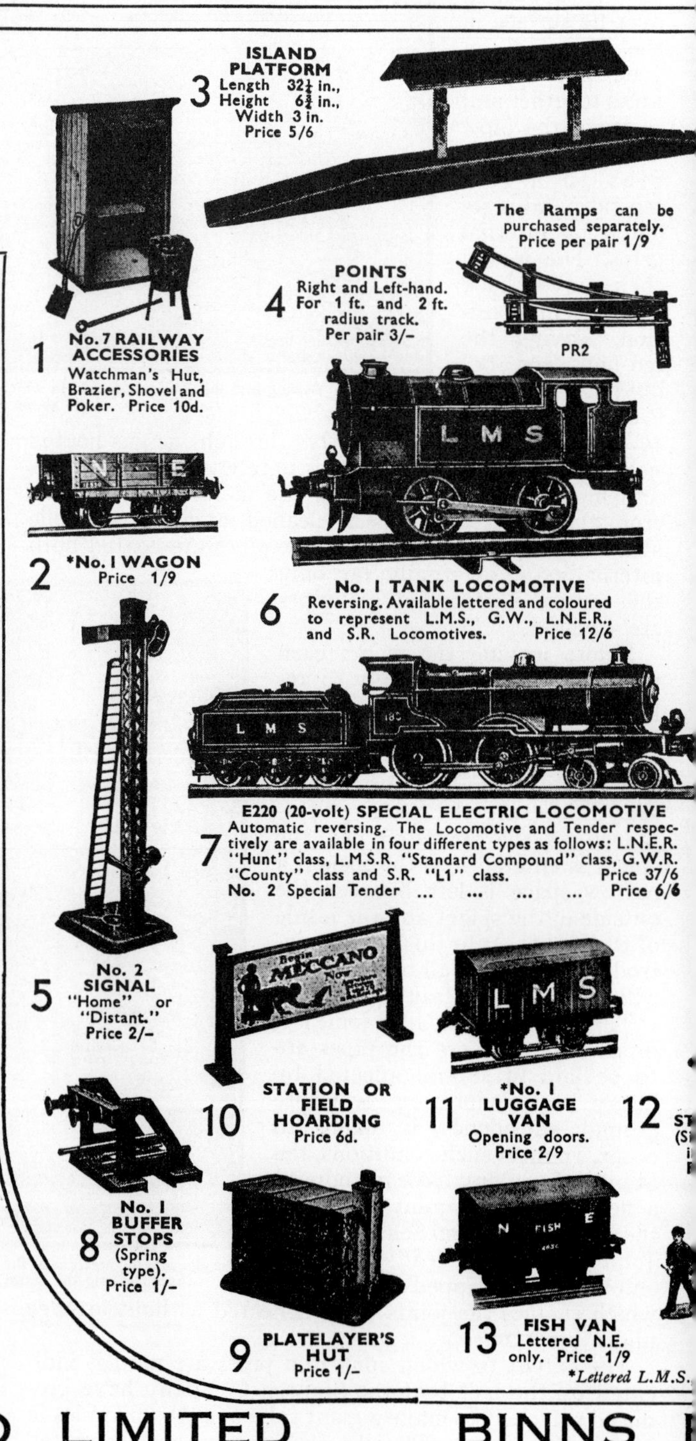

1 **No. 7 RAILWAY ACCESSORIES** Watchman's Hut, Brazier, Shovel and Poker. Price 10d.

2 ***No. 1 WAGON** Price 1/9

3 **ISLAND PLATFORM** Length 32½ in., Height 6¾ in., Width 3 in. Price 5/6

The Ramps can be purchased separately. Price per pair 1/9

4 **POINTS** Right and Left-hand. For 1 ft. and 2 ft. radius track. Per pair 3/–

5 **No. 2 SIGNAL** "Home" or "Distant." Price 2/–

6 **No. 1 TANK LOCOMOTIVE** Reversing. Available lettered and coloured to represent L.M.S., G.W., L.N.E.R., and S.R. Locomotives. Price 12/6

7 **E220 (20-volt) SPECIAL ELECTRIC LOCOMOTIVE** Automatic reversing. The Locomotive and Tender respectively are available in four different types as follows: L.N.E.R. "Hunt" class, L.M.S.R. "Standard Compound" class, G.W.R. "County" class and S.R. "L1" class. Price 37/6
No. 2 Special Tender ... ... Price 6/6

8 **No. 1 BUFFER STOPS** (Spring type). Price 1/–

9 **PLATELAYER'S HUT** Price 1/–

10 **STATION OR FIELD HOARDING** Price 6d.

11 ***No. 1 LUGGAGE VAN** Opening doors. Price 2/9

12 ST (S i

13 **FISH VAN** Lettered N.E. only. Price 1/9

*Lettered L.M.S.

PRODUCT OF **MECCANO LIMITED** BINNS

OCK AND ACCESSORIES

el Railway is the *Real* Thing"

15
No. 2 SIGNAL GANTRY
"Home" or "Distant."
Price 10/-

16
No. 5 RAILWAY ACCESSORIES
Gradient Posts and Mile Posts.
Price 2/-

STAFF
. No. 1
ete set 1/6

18
COACH, No. 2 PASSENGER
For 2 ft. radius rails only. First-third, or Brake-third. Available in the colours of each of the four railway groups.
Price 7/6

17
TELE-GRAPH POLES
Price per pair 3/6

HOW TO GET MORE FUN FROM HORNBY TRAINS

Dinky Toys can be used very effectively in conjunction with a Hornby Railway. Apart from the Station Staff, Engineering Staff, Farmyard Animals, etc., a delightful touch of realism can be given to the roads along the lineside by the addition of the numerous motor vehicles of all kinds that are now available. Your dealer will be pleased to give you a copy of the Dinky Toys Folder containing illustrations and prices of the full range.

LIVERPOOL 13

Books to Read

Here we review books of interest and of use to readers of the "M.M." We can supply copies of these books to readers who cannot obtain them through the usual channels. Order from Book Dept., Meccano Limited, Binns Road, Liverpool 13, adding 1/- for postage to the price. Postage on different books varies, but any balance remaining will be refunded.

"By '*Cornish Riviera Limited*'"

By W. G. Chapman. (Routledge. 5/- net)

Mr. Chapman is well known as the writer of the G.W.R. series of booklets on railway matters "For Boys Of All Ages," and in this volume he sets out to explain many of the interesting features of modern railway working by means of an imaginary journey by rail. The G.W.R. "*Cornish Reviera Limited*" is the train selected for this purpose, and on the run westward under Mr. Chapman's guidance the reader learns how the regular and safe operation of this famous train is ensured. The interesting story of its origin is given. It may be said to have begun with the non-stop run at 63.4 m.p.h. of a Royal Special from Paddington to Plymouth 33 years ago, and it is amusing to learn that the high speed of this and other trains of that time caused great alarm in certain quarters.

The chapters dealing with the modern train begin with an account of the preparation of the locomotive and rolling stock for their long run. Then the author turns to the actual journey, and there is little in connection with train operation in general, and with the working of the "*Cornish Riviera Limited*" in particular, that he does not describe in an entertaining and satisfactory manner. He shows his readers how the track is laid and how signals work, and explains the G.W.R. system of automatic train control, which repeats signals in the cab and makes it impossible to run past adverse signals, even in fog. Track water troughs, slip coaches and the vacuum brake are among other topics that receive attention. Most of the story of course refers to passenger express working, but other types of trains that may be met in the course of the journey are not overlooked. In addition, a glimpse is given of the driver and fireman at work on the footplate of the locomotive, and throughout Mr. Chapman finds time to point out interesting lineside features and to refer to famous or important places that are passed through en route.

The book is illustrated by 47 excellent reproductions of railway photographs, chiefly of the "*Cornish Riviera Limited*" itself, with a map of the route followed and several explanatory diagrams.

The "Cornish Riviera Express" emerging from a tunnel on to the sea wall near Dawlish. This and the lower illustration on the opposite page are from "By Cornish Riviera Limited," reviewed on this page.

"Muskwa The Trail Maker"

By H. Mortimer Batten. (Moray Press. 5/- net)

Muskwa, the hero of Mr. Mortimer Batten's story, was a Canadian black bear in the Great North West of Canada, a country that the author knows and loves. We begin with Muskwa in his cub-hood days, following his mother on the bear trails, continually getting into trouble, and from time to time being soundly cuffed for insolence and disobedience, but all the time learning how a bear should live. The terror of an immense forest fire in which his mother loses her life while protecting him brings Muskwa into contact with human beings for the first time, and when he has grown up he joins forces with a youthful Indian hunter in a fierce midnight struggle for life with a hungry pack of wolves. Finally we see him as a grim and grizzled veteran of the mountain solitudes, and he ends his life, taking with him half a pack of wolves, in a heroic plunge from the top of a cliff on to the ice of a frozen lake in a desperate effort to shield his mate.

The story is vividly written and is a fascinating romance of animal life, marked by sympathetic insight into the character of the many wild beasts that roam the solitudes of the Great North West. It is admirably illustrated by drawings, many of them deliciously humorous, depicting incidents in the life of Muskwa.

"A First Electrical Book for Boys"

By A. Morgan and C. L. Boltz, B.Sc. (Harrap, 5/- net)

All keen boys desire to know something about electricity, and in recent years many books have been written to tell them of its uses and wonders. Some of these books have shown a tendency to become overcrowded and too technical. The authors of this volume have avoided this error, and have produced an excellent introduction to electricity for boys of 10 to 13 years of age. It covers a wide range, but the matter is carefully selected and the explanations are simple and easily followed, and well calculated to develop keen interest to learn more.

The opening chapters deal with frictional electricity, magnets and electric batteries. The relation between electricity and magnetism is next explained, and then come interesting accounts of telegraphy, electric bells and simple electrical measurements. How electricity gives us heat and light and the story of the telephone are the next subjects taken up, and these are followed by simple accounts of the generation of electric power, and its use in motors, electric tramcars, the electrical system of a motor car, wireless, electric furnaces, X-rays and other miscellaneous applications of electricity.

An interesting feature of the book is the introduction of a large number of experiments that can be made with simple apparatus that is always at hand or is easily obtainable. The illustrations include nine full page plates in addition to 138 drawings in the text. Excellent use is made of diagrams illustrating the construction of the apparatus required for the experiments, and in addition there are many ingenious pictorial illustrations of the meaning of the electrical terms and units in common use.

This is a practical book that can be thoroughly recommended.

"Airdays"

By John F. Leeming. (Harrap. 7/6 net)

Mr. Leeming is one of the pioneers of gliding and light aeroplane flying, and in this book he relates the story of his many interesting and often thrilling experiences in the air. His first four gliders crashed after very brief hops, but in 1922 he began another on a more ambitious scale, in the construction of which he was helped by a small group of enthusiasts who eventually formed a gliding and flying club.

From this small beginning sprang the Lancashire Aeroplane Club, of which Mr. Leeming was Chairman for four years. The struggle of the new organisation for public recognition was very severe, and the anxiety of those responsible for it was increased by crashes and other untoward events during club flying and at the air pageants they organised. Some of these mishaps had their humorous side, however. The gallant struggle was continued until the club gained public recognition and was firmly established.

Upside-down flying at an air pageant. From "Airdays," reviewed on this page.

One of the schemes adopted to draw attention to the club and its work was a landing on the summit of Helvellyn. Bert Hinkler, the famous Australian pilot, joined Mr. Leeming in this enterprise, which was carried out under great difficulties. The first attempt was thwarted by a severe storm, but a further effort was successful, to the astonishment of a solitary climber encountered on the summit of the mountain, and the author gives a thrilling account of this remarkable feat.

When Mr. Leeming retired from the club he formed an Air Lines Company. In addition to flying on regular air routes, the Company organised joy-riding and pageants for which novel events and stunts were devised, and in all these activities the author played an important part. He tells the story of his adventures in this connection with great gusto. Unfortunately the company was not successful and was compelled to close down.

This joyously written book will be of the greatest interest to all who wish to obtain a glimpse from the inside of the difficulties that beset the early days of civil aviation in this country. It is illustrated by 20 photographs, chiefly of machines and adventures described in the text.

"Trooper Useless"

By Patrick Greene. (Harrap. 5/- net)

This is a book of adventure in Rhodesia that is based on the author's own experiences. The hero, whose real name is Ouless, is an English boy who distinguished himself at games, but otherwise was the despair of his masters. He solved the difficulty of finding a career by enlisting as a trooper in the British South African Police. We follow his progress as he is schooled in the ways of animals and men, and watch him change from an ignorant recruit, continually making himself a laughing stock to his comrades, into a keen trooper who shows himself capable of dealing with difficult problems affecting both natives and white men. Eventually he achieves a reputation by a patrol in an area that has been prescribed because of an outbreak of a dreaded cattle disease, during which he outwits a cunning white man who attempts to run a herd of cattle under his very nose. The story of this and of other adventures is brilliantly told, and reproductions of the maps that Useless himself draws adds greatly to the clarity and interest of the narrative.

The character of Useless and of his comrades, white and black, is admirably developed, and the background of the story gives evidence throughout of the author's knowledge of the scenes in which these actions take place. There is an excellent coloured frontispiece, and spirited drawings in line illustrate the chief events in the development of Useless into a keen "duty" trooper.

An unusual view looking through one of the main trusses of Brunel's Royal Albert Bridge, Saltash, joining Devon and Cornwall.

"Elementary Seamanship"

By Peter Clissold (Brown, Son and Ferguson Ltd. 3/6 net)

Mr. Clissold's book is intended chiefly for apprentices and boys about to go to sea. In it he explains the elements of the seaman's art, so far as they can be dealt with in writing, and he does so in very simple language that makes the book suitable also for amateurs who sail for pleasure. He deals thoroughly with every phase of life at sea, from work with anchors, cables and boats and the stowing of cargo to steering, signalling and ships' engines and boilers. A full and excellent glossary of sea terms is included, and there are 28 useful diagrams in addition to a coloured plate of flags and signals.

"The Air Dope Hunters"
"The Desert Air Raider"
"The Air Spies"

By Jack Heming
(A. and C. Black Ltd. 3/6 each net)

These three stories from the publishers' "Air Adventure Series" are well-written, exciting yarns that will appeal to every boy. *"The Air Dope Hunters"* tells the story of a detective and his youthful assistant engaged in tracking down a desperate gang of dope runners. *"The Desert Air Raider"* concerns the exploits of a young Assistant Consul who learns of a vast scheme to overthrow the power of the white man in the East, and, after a succession of flights, fights and escapes, outwits his enemies and ruins their plans. A long and thrilling struggle against international spies who are threatening England is described in *"The Air Spies."* The descriptions of actual flying in this story are particularly good, and excitement piles up rapidly. All three books have black-and-white illustrations by Alfred Sindall.

"Tips for Turners"

By W. F. Watson. (The Manual Press. 2/6)

The centre lathe designed 150 years ago by Maudeslay is still the key machine of industry, in spite of the introduction of such marvels of ingenuity as automatic and turret lathes, and skill in its use is one of the hall-marks of the complete mechanic. The full instructions and hints given by Mr. Watson, a practical turner with 30 years' experience of his craft, will help to give complete mastery over this universal tool. Every operation that can be carried out on a centre lathe is dealt with, and the text is illustrated by a series of well-chosen and clearly reproduced diagrams.

These pages are reserved for articles from our readers. Contributions not exceeding 500 words in length are invited on any subject of general interest. These should be written neatly on one side of the paper only, and they may be accompanied by photographs or sketches for use as illustrations. Articles that are published will be paid for at our usual rates. Statements contained in articles submitted for these pages are accepted as being sent in good faith, but the Editor takes no responsibility for their accuracy.

Unloading Locomotives at Capetown

Unloading a big locomotive from a ship is interesting work, as the accompanying photograph suggests. This was taken in the harbour at Capetown, and the locomotive of which the chassis is shown was one of a batch of 20 of the 4–8–2 type built by Robert Stephenson and Co., Ltd., Darlington, for the South African Railways.

The vessel in which these engines had been brought to Capetown was the *"City of Exeter."* The task of unloading the sections of the engine shown was slow, for the hatch through which each part had to be passed was small in comparison with the lengths of the chassis and the huge boiler. The lifting was carried out by means of a floating crane, capable of bearing a load of about 60 tons, which was manœuvred into position by a tug before operations could be commenced. The chassis gave most difficulty, and it had to be raised and lowered several times before it could be manœuvred through the hatchway.

D. V. Sevenoaks (Eastbourne).

Unloading the chassis of a locomotive from the "City of Exeter" at Capetown. Photograph by D. V. Sevenoaks, Eastbourne.

How Electric Lamps are Made

I had the good fortune recently to be one of a party taken on a tour of the "NOX" Electric Lamp Factory, Leeds. The first department we passed through was the furnace room in which the bulbs were blown. We looked into the furnace through small doors, and could see the molten glass used. A sufficient quantity of this is picked up on the end of a long rod while it is in a condition similar to that of a jelly, and is swung about until it is cool enough to be placed in a mould. The moulds normally are sunk into the floor of the room and are covered with water when not actually in use. They are raised by means of a foot pedal, and the lump of glass on the end of the rod is then inserted and rotated as the bulb is blown. After about half a minute the correctly-shaped bulb can be taken out of the mould.

We were then taken to the upper storey of the building, where the brass fittings of the lamps were being made by a wonderful machine. Then we were shown how the arms that hold the filament are fixed. The filament actually is a minute coil of wire, the wire itself being so thin that it is almost invisible when stretched out in a straight line. At a later stage we saw the coils being made. For this purpose the thin wire is wound round a thicker one, which is then dissolved out by means of chemicals that do not affect the filament.

Fitting the filament with its supports into the bulb of the lamp is a process that is carried out with almost uncanny speed by another remarkable machine. After watching this in operation for some time, we passed on to see how the bulbs are exhausted of air and filled with a special inert gas. The first lighting test follows, and we saw the lamps that passed this being fitted with their metal tops.

B. C. Ward (Leeds).

Loading Logs at Vancouver

The boat on which I left Vancouver took on board a load of Douglas fir logs. These lay in great booms in the harbour below, and on them men maintained what seemed a precarious balance with the aid of spiked poles. The work was carried on at night, brilliant arc lights illuminating the scene. The logs averaged five tons each in weight, and each was lifted over the ship's side by means of huge cables and lowered into its place in the hold. It was necessary to take care to preserve the balance of the ship, and when the holds were a third full, the remainder of the logs were swung on deck to be chained down. One rolled threateningly across the deck, but swift work with the hoisting cable retrieved the situation.

At last a large part of the deck space was filled with the logs, and we were able to depart. Very soon all that we could see of the country we were leaving was the dark shapes of great pine trees on the hillsides.

I. Pennie (London, N.W.7).

A New Australian Bridge

The suspension bridge shown in the upper illustration on this page connects Indooroopily and Chelmer, near Brisbane, and replaces a ferry that offered only slow and restricted means of crossing the Brisbane River, which flows between them. It cost about £85,000 to build, and was opened in February of this year. The span of the bridge is 600 ft. and is the longest in Queensland. The structure actually is the largest suspension bridge in Australia, and is second in span only to the Sydney Harbour Bridge. The cables used weigh 144 tons, and altogether about 1,000 tons of steel and 18,000 tons of concrete were required in the construction of the bridge.

The Indooroopily Bridge across the Brisbane River, Queensland. This fine suspension bridge was opened in February last. Photograph by courtesy of "The Telegraph," Brisbane.

The pylons supporting the cables are impressive in size and appearance. The Chelmer pylon, seen in the foreground of the photograph, is 126 ft. high and is built on 168 piles, each consisting of a slab of concrete 4 ft. thick. Its walls vary from 3 ft. 6 in. to 5 ft. 6 in. in thickness, and in constructing it more than 4,000 tons of concrete and 62 tons of steel reinforcement were used. G. MILNE (Brisbane).

Touring Rhodesia

I saw many things of great interest during a recent tour in Southern Rhodesia. Among these was the Khami Dam, behind which the water supply of Bulawayo is impounded. The Dam can be raised 4 ft. by means of steel sections. Each section is about 20 ft. long, and all are connected by levers to a main shaft that is turned to raise or lower them.

My tour extended to the Victoria Falls of the Zambesi River, where I was interested to see the great arch bridge, 400 ft. above the water in the gorge into which the river is precipitated. The accompanying photograph shows the main fall, with the mist that gave rise to the native name of "Mist That Thunders" for the Falls. I had to wait nearly 15 minutes before the mist subsided sufficiently to enable me to take a photograph.

The Victoria Falls of the Zambesi River, Rhodesia. Photograph by E. R. Füsslein, Zululand.

In the Matopo Hills, the last resting place of Cecil Rhodes, I saw the memorial to Allan Wilson and the men under his command who were ambushed and practically annihilated during the Matabele War of 1893. The stone of the memorial is of granite and was quarried on the hillside about 100 yds. away. Carved on it are reliefs depicting scenes that occurred during the expedition that ended so disastrously, and afterwards were described by the few survivors.

On my outward journey by rail I travelled 1,540 miles in 71 hours running time. Leaving my home at 8 o'clock on Friday morning I arrived at the Falls at 6 o'clock on the following Tuesday, after spending a day each in Johannesburg and Bulawayo. On my return, the train on which I travelled from the latter place to Mafeking consisted of 17 coaches.

E. R. FÜSSLEIN (Zululand).

A Visit to a Fish Preserving Factory

I have often seen Iceland cod being unloaded from trawlers, and sold by auction in the Aberdeen market, and was very pleased when I was able to visit one of the many large preserving factories and to learn what happens to the fish after they are bought. They are cleaned as soon as they are taken from the nets, and on reaching the factory are put into a machine worked by hand that removes the head. The men engaged in this work are so expert that they seldom miss a stroke. Splitting and boning follow, and I noticed that the men who do this wear gloves on their left hands to prevent cuts from the sharp bones. The fish are passed to girls, who finish the cleaning.

The actual curing then begins. The fish are thickly salted and piled in cupboards. There they are left for a certain period, and are then removed, slightly sprinkled with salt, and again placed in piles. Next they are washed in a machine in which they pass between revolving brushes, coming out clean and free from the salt that covers them on entry. Salting makes them so hard that a circular saw has to be used to cut them when the curing is finished.

After washing, the fish are hung up in a huge oven-like place through which hot air passes. There they are partially dried before they are piled up and pressed by means of heavy weights. They are hung up to dry a second time in a long room heated by means of coke fires, and I was surprised to learn that the room in which I saw this process being carried out contained nearly 10,000 cod. Finally the fish are packed in boxes and barrels for export. Each of these containers holds several hundred cod, and in the few days just before my visit to the factory 950 boxes had been sent to South America. G. GARDINER (Aberdeen).

L.M.S.R. Works Fire Brigades

Fighting Flames by Train

IN common with most owners of large properties, the L.M.S.R. maintain fire brigades composed of members of the staff at their more important premises, including passenger stations, goods depots, large blocks of offices and workshops, in the belief that a fireman on the job is worth two in the fire station.

The fire train at the Horwich Works of the L.M.S.R. This train includes a rail tank full of water and is completely equipped with fire-fighting apparatus.

At the locomotive, carriage and wagon works, with their large and multifarious risks, a greater degree of efficiency on the part of the fire brigade is necessary than is usually expected in staff brigades. The training and performance of the members is comparable with that of many municipal brigades maintained by quite important townships—in fact, in two instances the works fire brigades act as the town brigades in their area. These works, each covering many acres with buildings housing expensive plant, machinery and materials, represent a not inconsiderable portion of the company's assets and provide employment for many thousands. The fire risks are many and varied, and a fire not checked in its incipient stages might easily entail the loss of thousands of pounds, delay the output of important work, and cause days or weeks of unemployment for the shop staff.

There is no more effectual means of destruction than fire, and while great care is taken by the management and the local staff in guarding against risk of fire, even those who have not the opportunity of visiting such works will readily realise that by their very nature some of the operations carried on constitute potential fire risks. Some of the risks called to mind are oil-fired furnaces, cellulose spray-painting, welding and cutting by electricity and oxy-acetylene, and the storage of large stocks of timber, highly inflammable liquids, calcium carbide and fabrics.

Travelling accommodation on the Horwich fire train.

The fire protection arrangements in a large works are mainly centred in the works fire brigade, recruited from the works staff, and in many cases captained by a whole-time fire brigade officer operating under the direct control of the fire superintendent of the area. The members of the brigade are instructed in the principles of fire prevention, with special reference to the risks applicable to the individual works concerned. They are trained in the use of fire-extinguishing apparatus, and make themselves familiar with the whole of the premises, the positions of the fire appliances provided, and hydrants and other water supplies, and the manipulation of power pumps. Generally they are capable of acting singly in an emergency, or as a unit in a brigade. They assist in the upkeep of the appliances and the testing of fire alarms, hydrants and sprinkler systems, try out the stationary pumps driven by electricity or steam, and the petrol driven portable fire pumps. In some cases they carry out the duty of auxiliary watchmen.

The firemen reside in close proximity to the works, and in the majority of cases are provided with full fire brigade uniform, including helmets and jack boots. They drill regularly with the appliances, such drills ranging from the fixing up methodically but speedily of a single line of hose from a hydrant, to major operations with pumps, escapes, and life lines. In the latter case the evolutions carried out are such as might be necessary in dealing with a fire, say, in a large building; and in addition to training the firemen these regular drills provide necessary tests for the equipment and ensure that it is properly maintained and ready for instant use whenever required.

Most of the works are equipped with some system of fire alarm, the one most frequently met with being on the lines of the well-known street fire alarm, the calls being received at some central point in the works from which the firemen can be summoned. For this purpose either loud-sounding bells in the shops or the works hooter may be used, in conjunction with electric bells in the firemen's houses.

On an alarm of fire the members of the brigade quickly assemble at the recognised "fire station," where they are informed of the position of the fire together with any other details available, and take action accordingly. Often, when a fire is discovered in its early stages, it is only necessary for the firemen to use the nearest available hose and appliances, such equipment being provided at numerous points throughout the works. In other cases it may be necessary to bring the fire pumps and other equipment from the fire station into operation; but whatever the nature of the fire or equipment required to be used the members of the brigade know the particular part they have to play and immediately get to work.

When a fire has been extinguished it is often necessary for one or more firemen to remain to cool down the debris, or assist in salvage operations; while the captain of the brigade, after assuring himself that all is safe, is required to report on the fire, having ascertained, if at all possible, the cause of the outbreak.

Horwich firemen with their comprehensive equipment. This includes gas masks to protect the men from smoke and fumes.

Generally speaking, the main water supply for fire-fighting purposes is piped throughout the works with hydrants fixed at suitable points. In some cases the pressure is augmented by means of stationary pumps that can be immediately operated in the case of fire, while at five of the works petrol-driven pumps of the trailer type form part of the fire brigade equipment. These pumps can be readily taken by tractor or by man-handling to any point in the works, and obtain water either from the hydrant supply or from any other source available, such as tanks and canals.

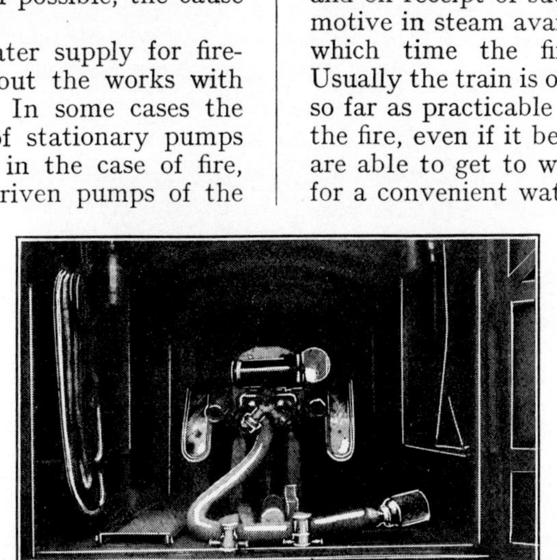
The fire pump in the van of the L.M.S.R. fire train at Horwich.

Horwich and Wolverton are the two places where the works fire brigades act also as the fire brigades for their respective towns. At Horwich the town authority has provided a motor-driven fire engine, complete with escape and appliances, and also a motor-driven tender. The latter, it is understood is to be substituted shortly by a new motor-driven tender with an auxiliary pump. At Wolverton the fire engine, motor tender and trailer pump belonging to the company are used, the town authority recompensing the company for their use. In both cases the services of the men called to fires in the town are paid for by the respective Councils, and although fires in these towns are not very frequent it may be accepted that the arrangements are to the mutual advantage of the company and the Councils concerned. Each of the local authorities has the services of a well-trained fire brigade at a comparatively nominal cost, while the company have a brigade whose members gain more actual fire experience than would be the case if their activities were confined to the works.

In addition, at three of the works, namely Crewe, Derby and Horwich, equipment is available to transport firemen, together with a petrol-driven fire pump, a rail tank of water and a large assortment of useful appliances, by rail to fires which may occur within a reasonable distance of the works.

These fire trains, as they are called, have on many occasions proved extremely valuable, particularly in dealing with fires on the line not readily accessible to a local authority's brigade. The procedure is for the District Control Office to call out the fire train concerned when it is considered assistance is necessary, and on receipt of such a call at the works the first locomotive in steam available is coupled to the fire train, by which time the firemen have generally assembled. Usually the train is on the way within a few minutes, and so far as practicable is given a clear road. On arrival at the fire, even if it be in an isolated position, the firemen are able to get to work immediately, without searching for a convenient water supply, as the tank which forms part of the train carries several thousand gallons, and by means of a simple connection between tank and pump this water can be immediately projected on the fire.

On several occasions a fire train has been called to a fire among wagons forming part of a train, and through being able to run right alongside with pump and water has enabled the line to be cleared in a comparatively short time. In other cases the blazing wagons have been taken off the main line to a convenient siding to be dealt with. These fire trains of course are called out to all manner of fires, including stations, goods sheds and viaducts, and on several occasions their assistance has been requested by local authorities' brigades, and by owners of private property, where premises adjoining the railway have been on fire.

With the exception of watchmen, who are generally required to be members of the brigade, all works firemen are volunteers and chosen for their interest in the work and physical fitness for it.

We are indebted to the Editor of the *"L.M.S. Magazine"* for permission to reproduce this article, and for the accompanying illustrations.

Meccano Suggestions Section

By "Spanner"

(361)—Four-Cylinder Solenoid Engine (A. Lockhowe, Edinburgh)

In the June issue of the "*M.M.*" there appeared a fine model of a five-cylinder radial engine built up with Elektron Magnet Coils and Cores. This model created a considerable amount of interest, and many model-builders have since sent in suggestions for other types of engines built on similar lines. Among these was A. Lockhowe, Edinburgh, who submitted the model 4-cylinder V-type engine illustrated in Fig. 361 on this page.

The bottom of the crankcase consists of a 2½"×1½" Flanged Plate, each flange of which carries a Flat Trunnion. One of these Flat Trunnions is indicated at 2. Four ½"×½" Angle Brackets are also secured to the Flanged Plate, two on each side, and to them are attached Flat Girders 1. Two 2" Angle Girders 2a are fitted to the upper edges of the Flat Girders by means of Obtuse Angle Brackets. The 2" Angle Girders carry the Girder Brackets 3, which are secured to them by ½" Bolts, and on the shanks are Collars for spacing purposes.

Before proceeding further with the frame of the model the crankshaft must be made and fitted. Two Couplings are attached to each other, side by side, by means of two 1" Threaded Rods. The Threaded Rods must protrude on opposite sides of the pair of Couplings to form the cranks, and they are locked in position by means of nuts. Each Threaded Rod is passed through the end holes of two 1½" Strips, forming connecting rods, and when these are in position a second nut is screwed part-way on to each. This nut is followed by a Coupling 4, the Threaded Rod being screwed into the end threaded hole of this. The centre plain hole of the Coupling 4 accommodates a Rod 5. This construction is duplicated at the opposite end of the crankshaft, and both Rods are journalled in the centre holes of the Flat Trunnions fitted to the crankcase.

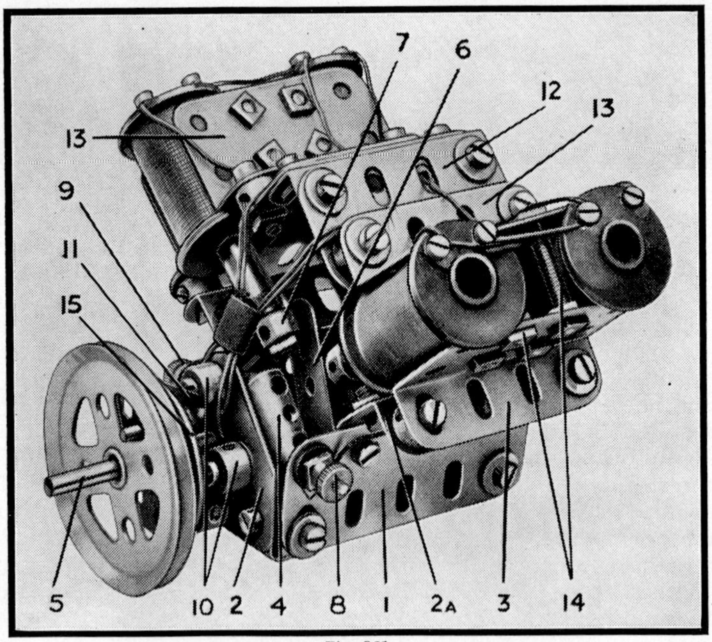

The Magnet Coils are now fitted. A second Girder Bracket 13 is secured to each Girder Bracket 3 by means of four 1" Threaded Rods, shown at 14, double nuts being used to lock each end in position. Before the Rods are tightened permanently, the Magnet Coils are placed between the pairs of Girder Brackets. When the four Coils are in position the Flat Girders 12, forming the top of the crankcase, must be attached to the Girder Brackets 13 by means of ½" Bolts. A Collar is passed on to the shank of each Bolt for spacing purposes, and the two Flat Girders 12 are joined together at their upper edges by means of a 2" Angle Girder.

Everything is now ready for inserting the "pistons." These consist of Magnet Cores (Elektron Parts No. 1539) on the threaded portions of which are carried Collars, indicated at 7. Each Collar is locked in position on its Magnet Core by the 6BA Nut supplied with the Core, and the free end of the 1½" Strip 6 is linked to the Collar by means of a bolt. Great care must be taken to see that all connecting rods and pistons move freely, and that the crankshaft does not turn unevenly. Strict attention must be given to these points before continuing with the construction.

The distributor, shown at the near end of the engine, is now added. Four Collars, two of which are shown at 10, are each mounted on a 6 B.A. Bolt, by means of which they are secured to the Flat Trunnion 2. Each Bolt also carries on its shank an Insulating Bush and Washer, by means of which it is insulated from the metal of the engine. A Bush Wheel 15, clamped on the Rod 5, has mounted on it a Pendulum Connection 11 that is bent slightly so that it acts as a brush, making light contact with each of the Collars 10 in turn when the engine rotates in a counter-clockwise direction. The Rod 5 also carries a light flywheel that consists of a 2" Pulley.

The electrical connections are now made. All the inner terminals of the Magnet Coils are first joined together, and connected to an insulated Terminal 8 mounted on the Flat Girder 1. The top Collar 10 is now connected to the remaining terminal of the nearer Magnet Coil on the right, and the bottom Collar is connected to the remaining terminal of the adjacent Magnet Coil. The left-hand Collar, not shown in the illustration, is connected to the free terminal of the nearer Magnet Coil of the second pair, and the unwired terminal of the fourth Magnet Coil is similarly connected to the last of the four Collars.

A Terminal 9 is fitted on the second Flat Girder 1, and is in electrical contact with the frame of the model. Wires from the source of supply are connected to the two terminals. The current passes from Terminal 9 through the frame of the model to the brush 11, and from this is distributed to the Collars 10 as the crankshaft rotates. After passing through each Coil in turn the current returns to the source of supply by way of the Terminal 8.

It is important to set the "timing" of the engine accurately in order that it may work efficiently. This is carried out by loosening the Bush Wheel 15 on its Rod 5, and rotating both the Bush Wheel and the Rod until the brush makes contact with the top Collar 10 when the piston of the near right-hand Coil is commencing its upward movement. The Bush Wheel is then locked in position.

Before setting the model in motion all the moving parts must be oiled, and a little vaseline smeared on the rubbing surface of the brush 11. Only Meccano oil or other high-grade light oil must be used for lubricating this model.

The Magnet Coils are designed to work on voltages not higher than four. If a Meccano T6 Transformer or other 6-volt Transformer is used for operating this model, the control lever therefore must never be moved beyond the third stud from the "minimum" position.

The engine as shown in Fig. 361 can be considerably improved by constructing the framework to represent a motor car or aeroplane engine. This is a simple matter and entails very little alteration to the existing model. The switch gear must be first covered in by means of 1"×1" Angle Brackets, so that it has the appearance of a gear-box or supercharger, according to the type of engine required. A Boiler End can be employed with good effect as a supercharger. The addition of end covering pieces for the crank-case, imitation cam-shaft covers, magneto and dynamo, will give the model a very realistic appearance.

Fig. 361

Photographic Devices

In the Suggestions Section of the August "*M.M.*" there appeared two interesting photographic devices submitted by R. M. Smith, Stanmore, and L. P. Storey, Bristol. Unfortunately the names were transposed by error. The builder of the model shown in Fig. 356 actually was R. M. Smith, and that shown in Fig. 357 was built by L. P. Storey.

(362)—Four-Wheel Steering Mechanism (J. Brown, Dundee, and S. Crane, Hull)

Many small Outfit owners have been deterred from building models of eight-wheeled lorries because of the comparatively complicated front wheel steering movement required. In these large lorries all four front wheels are controlled from the steering column, and as each must be able to turn independently, the fitting of the connecting links is fairly complicated. Two model-builders, J. Brown, Dundee, and S. Crane, Hull, have submitted simple wheel mountings suitable for small models, however, and they should prove useful to constructors of Meccano lorries.

The first of these, by J. Brown, is illustrated in Fig. 362, and is shown wrong way up for the sake of clearness. The underside of the model lorry is represented by a $5\frac{1}{2}'' \times 3\frac{1}{2}''$ Flat Plate, and to the ends of this are bolted two $4\frac{1}{2}''$ Strips. The outside holes of these Strips accommodate $\frac{3}{8}''$ Bolts, on the shanks of which are secured three Cranks 5 and one Boss Bell Crank 5a. The ends of the Cranks are linked in pairs, as shown, by $4\frac{1}{2}''$ Strips 1, the connection in each case being made by means of a lock-nutted bolt. Two Simple Bell Cranks 2 and 3 are now added, and these are attached rigidly to each other by a 3″ Strip 4. It will now be seen that the three Cranks will all turn on their pivots when the free arm of the Bell Crank 5a is moved.

The road wheels, 2″ Pulleys and Dunlop Tyres, are free to rotate on the shanks of $\frac{3}{4}''$ Bolts screwed in the tapped holes in the bosses of the Cranks, and two lock-nuts are used to hold each of them in position. If the road wheels do not lie parallel to each other it will be necessary to turn the bosses of the Cranks slightly.

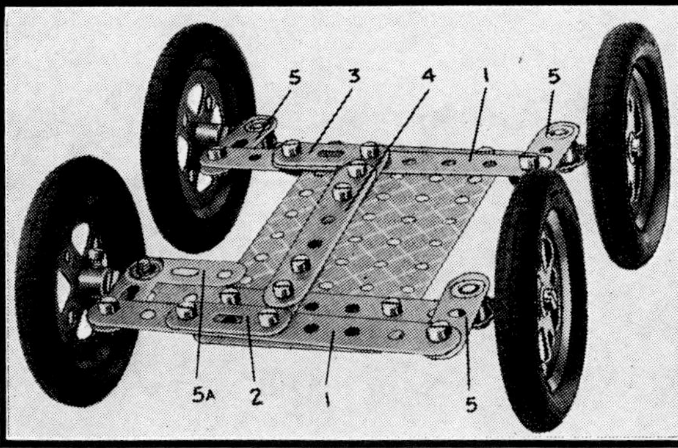

Fig. 362

The second suggestion, by S. Crane, is somewhat simpler than that already described, but is more suitable for smaller models. The Cranks 5 and the Boss Bell Crank 5a, Fig. 362, are replaced by 1″ Pulleys, and these are connected together by a single length of Cord passed round each Pulley twice.

(363)—Automatic Drag-Line Bucket (M. Bysouth, Manchester)

In the August issue of the "*M.M.*" there appeared a description of a cableway drag-line excavator used chiefly in the brown coalfields of Germany. M. Bysouth, Manchester, has submitted a neat model of the bucket used in this drag-line excavator, and he has employed it successfully in connection with a simple model cableway of his own design.

The bottom of the bucket consists of a $5\frac{1}{2}'' \times 2\frac{1}{2}''$ Strip Plate fitted on each side with a $5\frac{1}{2}''$ Angle Girder. These Girders carry $5\frac{1}{2}'' \times 1\frac{1}{2}''$ Flexible Plates 2 as shown, and a $2\frac{1}{2}'' \times 1\frac{1}{2}''$ Flexible Plate, placed across the ends of these, is held in position by means of two $1\frac{1}{2}''$ Angle Girders secured vertically in the corners of the bucket. To the centre of the end Flexible Plate is bolted the Flat Bracket 4. The front edge of the Strip Plate forming the bottom of the bucket carries three $1\frac{1}{2}''$ Strips representing the digging teeth, and to the front edge of the Plates 2 are bolted two vertical $2\frac{1}{2}''$ Strips. These are bent slightly at their upper ends and are bridged by a curved 3″ Strip 5.

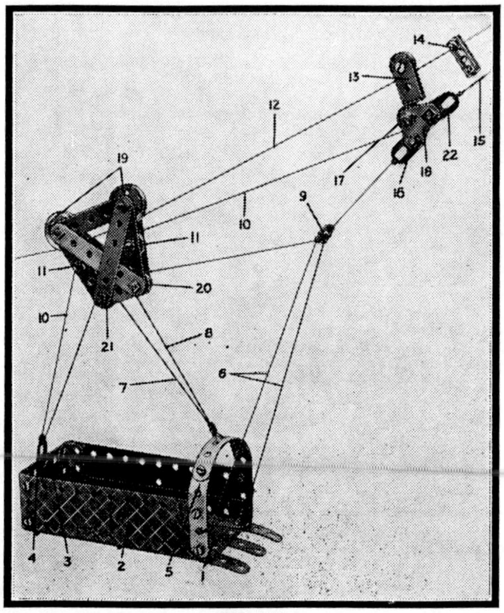

The traveller from which the bucket is hung is next constructed. The two Pulleys 19 are mounted on $\frac{3}{4}''$ Bolts between two $2\frac{1}{2}''$ Strips. Each $\frac{3}{4}''$ Bolt also supports a 3″ Strip and a $2\frac{1}{2}''$ Strip on each side of the Pulley, and lock-nuts are added at their outer ends. The 3″ Strips form bracing members of the traveller, and their lower ends, together with the lower ends of the $2\frac{1}{2}''$ Strips, are fitted on $\frac{3}{4}''$ Bolts carrying $\frac{1}{2}''$ Pulleys 20 and 21. These Bolts are joined by two $1\frac{1}{2}''$ Strips, as shown. The centre holes of the $2\frac{1}{2}''$ Strips carry further $\frac{3}{4}''$ Bolts 11, on the shanks of which are $\frac{1}{2}''$ loose Pulleys, which are free to rotate.

Fig. 363

The small pulley frame is built up from two 1″ Corner Brackets 18, held together by a $\frac{1}{2}''$ Bolt on which is mounted a $\frac{1}{2}''$ loose Pulley 17. Two further $\frac{1}{2}''$ Bolts are added to form supports for the Flat Brackets 16 and 22. A Single Bent Strip 13, in the outer holes of which is a $\frac{1}{2}''$ Bolt, carries a $\frac{1}{2}''$ loose Pulley that is free to turn, and is held in position by lock-nuts. The $\frac{1}{2}''$ Pulley runs on the rope 12, on which a Strip Coupling 14 is clamped by means of two set-screws to act as a stop.

(*Continued from previous column*)

The cable rope 12, a length of Meccano Cord, on which run the large pulley frame and bracket 13, is between two fixed points at an angle of about 30°, the lower section of the rope being arranged to bring the drag bucket into contact with the ground. The operating cord 15, the distant end of which in the complete cableway is passed round a hoisting drum operated by the main engine, is secured to the Flat Bracket 22, and a second hoisting and tipping cord 10 is attached to the Single Bent Strip. The rope 10 passes round the underside of the Pulley 17, over the two Pulleys mounted on the Bolts 11, and finally is fastened to the Flat Bracket 4. From this point a second cord 7 passes over the Pulley 21 and down to the bridge 5. The cord 8, which is attached to the same point as 7, passes over the Pulley 20 and is tied finally to the Flat Bracket 16. A Washer 9, carried on this rope, in the position shown, forms a point of connection for the cords 6, the bottom ends of which support the drag bucket.

When first attaching the various cords, it is a good plan to secure them only temporarily in place until they are all fitted. The bucket can then be suspended from the rope 12 and the cords adjusted in length until the bucket takes up the position shown in the photograph. The cord 15 is later fastened at its free end to the winding barrel.

(364)—Simple Free Wheel

(F. Anthony, Venice)

Many suggestions for free wheels built with Meccano parts have been submitted from time to time, and the best of these have been described and illustrated in the Suggestions Section. An exceptionally neat and efficient mechanism of this kind, devised by F. Anthony, Venice, is shown in Fig. 364. It is shown built on a 2″ Sprocket Wheel, but it will fit equally well on a Bush Wheel or 57-teeth Gear.

A Rod, free to turn in the boss of the Sprocket Wheel, carries a Ratchet Wheel, and this is held in contact with the face of the Sprocket Wheel by means of a Collar on the opposite end of the Rod. The Pawls are formed by mounting two Spring Clips on $\frac{3}{8}''$ Bolts in opposite holes of the Sprocket Wheel. The Spring Clips are so adjusted that the ends of their lugs press lightly against the teeth of the Ratchet Wheel, and drop into the gaps between the teeth when the gear is turned slowly. They are then fixed rigidly in position by tightening the Nuts on the $\frac{3}{8}''$ Bolts.

Fig. 364

In Search of New Models

Unusual Locomotives and Railway Signals

THE reproduction of railway subjects is a very attractive form of model-building, for the combination of two hobbies that it provides adds greatly to the fascination of constructional work. There is no lack of individual subjects of all kinds. Great express locomotives convey a stirring idea of power and energy; powerful goods engines and the fussy little tank engines used for shunting purposes are equally interesting; and the more modern electric and Diesel engined locomotives attract those who are in search of novel or experimental subjects. Yet another thrill can be obtained by building models of historic locomotives, many of them differing strangely in appearance and in essential features from those of modern times; and there is a wealth of material for the model-builder in the signals and signal gantries, stations, cabins, bridges and lineside structures of all kinds that are to be seen on any railway.

Fig. 1. A clockwork driven model of a heavy-oil shunting engine, the prototype of which is a converted steam 0-6-0 tank locomotive.

The examples of railway models described and illustrated in this article do not cover every aspect of so vast a subject. They will give inspiration to enterprising model-builders, however, and in particular they show what can be done by the owners of small Outfits. It is easy to construct new models if a large selection of parts is available, for the field of possible subjects is very wide. Those who have to rely upon a limited number of parts must make greater use of their imagination, and show their skill and ingenuity in making the best possible use of every individual part at the builder's disposal.

Fig. 2. A simple but attractive model of a rail-motor coach, the construction of which is fully described on this page.

A realistic model of a rail-motor vehicle of the combined engine and coach type is shown in Fig. 2. Vehicles of this kind are now seldom seen, except on small local lines, but they are excellent prototypes for interesting Meccano models. That shown in Fig. 2 is extremely simple, but ingenious, and the larger and more complete reproductions that can be built are very attractive. Practically all are fitted with outside cylinders and Walschaerts' valve motion, and this makes them still more interesting from the model-building point of view. An excellent photograph of an L.M.S.R. rail-motor vehicle appeared in the September issue of the "*M.M.*"

The main frame of the model shown in Fig. 2 consists of two 7½" Strips connected by Flat Brackets. The boiler is clamped in position on this frame by means of Angle Brackets, two of which are bent to the shape shown to represent the saddle. The steam dome consists of the shank of a Spring Buffer, and the chimney is a ½" Bolt partially screwed into the threaded hole at one end of a Socket Coupling. Gas cylinders under the coach are represented by Couplings held in position by two bolts each, and the underframe stays consist of short lengths of 22 gauge copper wire.

The two bogies are attached rigidly to the model by means of Flat Brackets. The main member of the front bogie consists of a 2½" Strip that carries at its front end two Flat Brackets. These form supports for the cylinders, represented by two Rod Sockets. Connecting rods and piston rods are reproduced by means of short lengths of heavy gauge wire.

The early days of engineering provide much attractive material for model-builders, and no better example of this is to be found than in locomotive engineering. The efforts of pioneer locomotive designers resulted in a wide variety of engines that are freaks, judged by modern standards, and no hunter after new ideas should miss any opportunity of searching through old railway books and periodicals for illustrations or drawings of these almost forgotten oddities.

In Fig. 4 is shown a model of a very early attempt at constructing an articulated locomotive. This was one of four built in 1832 by an American, Horatio Allen, for use on the South Carolina Railway, and was known as the *"South Carolina."* To all intents and purposes it consisted of two engines placed back to back, and its many remarkable features included four separate boiler barrels, joined at their inner ends by the fire-box and at their outer ends by the smoke-boxes. The fire-box door was at one side, where the fireman stood, and the driver's position was at the other. Four-wheel bogies were carried on substantial pivots, mounted directly beneath the boilers, and the connecting rods from the cylinders were provided with spherical bearings to allow for swivelling. An illustration of this remarkable engine appeared in the October 1932 issue of the *"M.M."*

The model is extremely simple, and its construction is commenced by building the fire-box. The top of this is a 2½" × 1½" Flanged Plate carrying two 2½" Angle Girders, to the projecting flanges of which are bolted 2½" Flat Girders. 1½" Flat Girders are bolted to the ends of the fire-box, and these are secured at their centre holes to the 2½" Flat Girders by means of ½" × ½" Angle Brackets. Each boiler barrel is built up from two Sleeve Pieces, and two Chimney Adaptors, down the centres of which is passed a 3½" Threaded Rod. This Rod, which carries a 1½" Strip at its outer end, as shown in the illustration, forms the connection between the boiler and the fire-box. The bogies are built up of short Strips, and each is pivotally secured to a 1½" Strip fixed beneath the boiler by a ⅜" Bolt. The axle supporting the small wheels is mounted in a 2½" × ½" Double Angle Strip, and Couplings are used for carrying the Pivot Bolts of the large wheels.

Two unusual railway subjects have been chosen for the models shown in Fig. 3. These are ground signals, and their construction is very simple. The signal arms are Meccano Parts No. 158b, reduced in length by one inch and with a white band and edging added, as shown. The white edging is continued round both spectacle glasses. If desired, these signals can be adapted for use in conjunction with a built-up signal cabin and lever frame by incorporating, at the rear of each signal arm, a series of cranks that can be made to operate in the same way as those fitted to Hornby Signals.

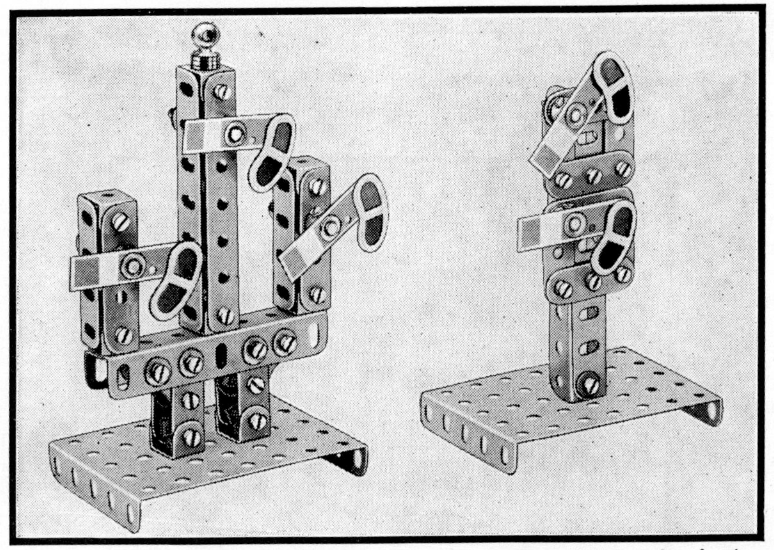

Fig. 3. Ground signals are excellent subjects for models incorporating a limited number of parts. Two good examples are shown in this illustration.

Fig. 4. A model of the "South Carolina," one of four articulated locomotives built in 1832 for use on the South Carolina Railway. These were the first locomotives of this type.

Larger and more detailed working models of full-size signals and gantries are very attractive. Visits to the lineside, especially at busy and complicated junctions, will give the model-builder all the information necessary for many models of different types of signalling apparatus.

The many changes that are taking place on modern railways, especially in connection with rolling stock, provide a never-ending source of fresh inspiration. New types of coaches, streamlined locomotives, heavy-oil engines of all types and many other novelties also give ample material, and those who are interested in railway affairs need never be at a loss for interesting subjects. The heavy oil units now in regular use include many that are admirably suited for reproduction in Meccano. Fig. 1 shows an excellent example of a model of this kind. It is a scale reproduction of an old 0–6–0 tank locomotive that has been re-constructed and fitted with a heavy-oil engine. The Meccano model shows the typical square appearance of its prototype. It is powered with a No. 2 Clockwork Motor that drives two cranks, set one on each side of the locomotive between the wheels, and these are coupled up to the connecting rods by means of Threaded Pins.

The Clockwork Motor is attached, in an inverted position, to the front end of the main frames of the model by ½" Reversed Angle Brackets and 1" × ½" Angle Brackets. A ¾" Sprocket Wheel on the driving spindle of the Motor is connected by Sprocket Chain to a 1½" Sprocket locked on a 3" Rod. This Rod is mounted in bearings formed from two 2½" × 2½" Flat Plates, one being bolted to each main frame.

The 3" Rod also carries a ½" Pinion meshing with a 57-teeth Gear that is mounted on a second 3" Rod together with a ¾" Sprocket Wheel. By means of a short length of Sprocket Chain this ¾" Sprocket drives a 1" Sprocket on the Rod carrying the main driving cranks.

The controls are arranged in the following manner. The brake lever has mounted on it a 2" Strip at right-angles and this carries a Collar. A 2" Rod is locked in this Collar, and protrudes from the front of the locomotive, a second Collar being fitted to it as shown in Fig. 1. The reversing lever is arranged similarly.

New Outfit Models

A Chemical Balance and an Unusual Aeroplane

THE chief feature of the four models described this month is their variety. They range from a chemical balance and a coal-handling crane to a cinematograph camera and a novel aeroplane in which the customary propeller is replaced by paddle wheels, and should interest a wide circle of model-building enthusiasts.

The first of the four models is the chemical balance, built with Outfit E. This will be of use to many who carry out experiments in chemistry. The base of the model, a $5\frac{1}{2}'' \times 2\frac{1}{2}''$ Flanged Plate, carries two $2\frac{1}{2}'' \times \frac{1}{2}''$ Double Angle Strips that form points of attachment for four $12\frac{1}{2}''$ Strips. These are connected at their tops, in pairs, by two $\frac{3}{8}''$ Bolts that carry the 1" loose Pulleys 1 on their shanks. Two $2\frac{1}{2}''$ Strips are bolted to the $12\frac{1}{2}''$ Strip for strengthening purposes.

A $2\frac{1}{2}''$ Strip 2 has attached to it at each end a Flat Bracket 3, and the bottom edges of these Flat Brackets are filed so that they are able to rest in the grooves of the Pulleys 1. The centre of the $2\frac{1}{2}''$ Strip 2 is clamped between two Cranks, placed with their bosses at opposite ends of the assembly and held together by the Bolt 6. The upper boss forms a support for the Rod 4, which is used to carry balancing weights consisting of 1" fast Pulleys.

Fig. 1. A useful Meccano chemical balance that any owner of an E Outfit can build without difficulty.

The boss of the second Crank carries the $11\frac{1}{2}''$ Rod 7 that represents the balance arm, and at each end of this are fixed two Spring Clips spaced apart the thickness of a Meccano Strip. In each of the spaces between the Spring Clips rests a Double Bracket 8. A slight nick is made in the lower edge of the Double Bracket where it rests on the Rod 7, and a sharp knife edge is formed there by filing, as in the case of the Flat Brackets 3. Each Double Bracket has secured to it two $5\frac{1}{2}''$ Strips, and these are disposed vertically as shown. To the bottom of each $5\frac{1}{2}''$ Strip two further Strips are bolted, and these are bent slightly so that their free ends can be attached to the $3\frac{1}{2}'' \times 2\frac{1}{2}''$ Flanged Plate 9. The two Plates 9 form the scale pans.

When the model has been assembled it is balanced by sliding the Spring Clips and Double Brackets 8 slightly along the Rod 7 as necessary. The final adjustment is made by varying the positions of the Pulleys 5 on the Rod 4.

Parts required to build the model Chemical Balance: 4 of No. 1; 8 of No. 2; 3 of No. 5; 2 of No. 10; 2 of No. 11; 1 of No. 13; 1 of No. 15; 2 of No. 22; 2 of No. 22a; 4 of No. 35; 27 of No. 37; 2 of No. 37a; 2 of No. 38; 2 of No. 48a; 1 of No. 52; 2 of No. 53; 2 of No. 62; 2 of No. 111c.

The strange looking model shown in Fig. 2 also is built with E Outfit, and has as its prototype a new form of aeroplane that makes use of two huge paddle wheels for propulsion purposes. This machine has an orthodox fuselage, on which is mounted a tall framework supporting a horizontal shaft that carries at each end a large wheel with paddles placed at equal intervals round its rim. The cross section of each paddle is similar to that of an aeroplane wing, and the assemblage is driven by an engine mounted in the fuselage.

The construction of the Meccano model is commenced by building the fuselage. A Double Bracket 1 has secured to it a $\frac{1}{2}'' \times \frac{1}{2}''$ Angle Bracket 2, and each lug of the Double Bracket carries a compound strip 3. This member consists of a $5\frac{1}{2}''$ and $3\frac{1}{2}''$ Strip overlapping one hole and the $3\frac{1}{2}''$ Strips at the end are drawn together and held in position by a nut and bolt. This nut and bolt also secures a Trunnion, representing the rudder, in position.

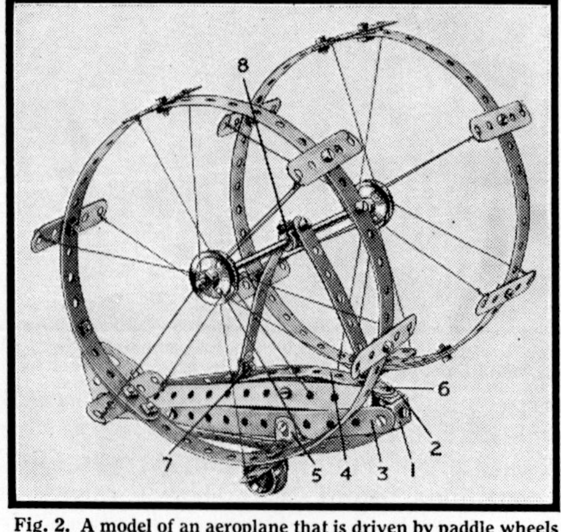

Fig. 2. A model of an aeroplane that is driven by paddle wheels instead of a propeller.

A Bush Wheel carrying seven $\frac{1}{2}'' \times \frac{1}{2}''$ Angle Brackets round its edge is now fitted in position between the two members 3 by means of two of the Angle Brackets, and the four curved $5\frac{1}{2}''$ Strips forming the body of the fuselage are similarly attached, two above and two below the compound Strips 3. The rear end of these Strips are held in position by short lengths of Cord that pass through suitable holes in the rear $3\frac{1}{2}''$ Strips. A further $5\frac{1}{2}''$ Strip 4 is attached by means of two Nuts and Bolts, one of which passes through one of the Angle Brackets of the Bush Wheel and the other through the Angle Bracket 2 on the Double Bracket 1.

Obtuse Angle Brackets 6 and 7 carry two 3½" Strips that are fixed at their upper ends to a Coupling 8. The centre longitudinal hole of the Coupling carries the inner ends of two 3½" Rods that support the paddle wheels. The construction of these wheels is shown in the photograph.

The undercarriage is formed from two Reversed Angle Brackets 5 that carry two ⅜" Bolts, and on these are mounted two ¾" Flanged Wheels that represent the landing wheels of the actual aeroplane.

Parts required to build the model Paddle Aeroplane: 4 of No. 1; 7 of No. 2; 4 of No. 3; 12 of No. 5; 1 of No. 11; 8 of No. 12; 2 of No. 12c; 2 of No. 16; 2 of No. 20b; 2 of No. 22a: 1 of No. 24; 45 of No. 37; 3 of No. 37b; 4 of No. 59; 1 of No. 63; 3 of No. 111c; 2 of No. 125; 1 of No. 126a; 7 ft. of Copper Wire.

In Fig. 3 is shown a fine model cinematograph camera built with Outfit D. This of course is not a working model, but its remarkably realistic appearance makes it well worth building. The body of the model is built up of Flexible Plates, each side comprising one 2½"×2½" and one 2½"×1½" Flexible Plate. The four corners of each side carry ½"×½" Angle Brackets, and to these are attached 2½"×1½" Flexible Plates forming the ends, one of which is shown at 1.

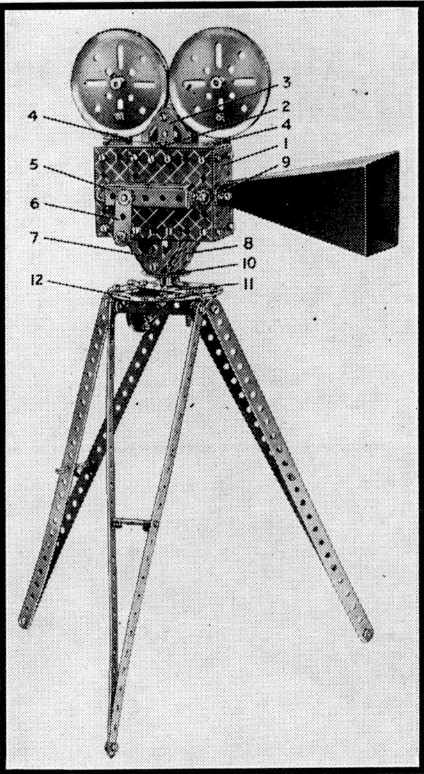

Fig. 3. A splendid model of a cinematograph camera built with Outfit D.

The side plates are bridged by a 1½"×½" Double Angle Strip indicated at 2, and this carries two 3½" Strips and two Trunnions 3. The 3½" Strips form two thirds of the top of the camera, the remaining one third consisting of the flanges of the Trunnions 3 and two 1½" Strips. Four Flat Brackets are secured across the ends of all the Strips forming the top. The side of the model not seen in the photograph carries two 2½" Strips, portions of which are shown at 4. The upper ends of these support the 3" Pulleys that are used to represent the reels, a notable feature of actual cinematograph cameras. The connections between the Pulleys and Strips 4 consist of ⅜" Bolts, and four Washers are used on each for spacing purposes.

On the side of the camera visible in the illustration is an imitation casing built up from three 2½"×½" Double Angle Strips carrying at their ends ½"×½" Angle Brackets by means of which the unit is attached to the camera. Before fitting this part of the model in position a ⅜" Bolt is passed through the second hole of the centre Double Angle Strip, counting from the rear. This ⅜" Bolt carries a Crank 6 that on its outer end has a second ⅜" Bolt held in position by a nut, and forms the operating handle. The hood is made from black cardboard, and is fixed by two nuts and bolts to a Double Bent Strip 9.

Two Flat Trunnions 7 are now added, the lower ends of which carry ½"×½" Angle Brackets. These form points of attachment for a bent 5½"×1½" Flexible Plate 8, and a Bush Wheel 10. The boss of this Bush Wheel is free to turn about a pivot consisting of a Threaded Pin that is locked in the centre hole of a 2½" Strip 11. The ends of this Strip are bolted to two further 2½" Strips, and these are carried on a circle of 2½" small radius Curved Strips 12. Two 1"×1" Angle Brackets, bolted to the underside of the circle 12, carry three 2½"×½" Double Angle Strips joined by Obtuse Angle Brackets and to these are attached the legs of the tripod, the construction of which is clear from the illustration.

Parts required to build the model Cinematograph Camera: 6 of No. 1; 2 of No. 3; 5 of No. 5; 2 of No. 6a; 4 of No. 10; 2 of No. 11; 12 of No. 12; 2 of No. 12a; 3 of No. 12c; 3 of No. 18a; 2 of No. 19b; 1 of No. 22; 1 of No. 23; 1 of No. 24; 6 of No. 35; 7 of No. 37; 4 of No. 37a; 12 of No. 38; 1 of No. 45; 1 of No. 48; 6 of No. 48a; 1 of No. 62; 4 of No. 90a; 6 of No. 111c; 1 of No. 115; 2 of No. 126; 2 of No. 126a; 2 of No. 188; 1 of No. 189; 4 of No. 190; 1 piece of black cardboard 10"×6".

The fourth of this varied selection of models is a coal-handling crane, built with Outfit C. The base of the rotating superstructure is built on a 2½"×1½" Flanged Plate that is secured, together with a 2½"×½" Double Angle Strip to a 3" Pulley 1. Each upturned flange of the Plate 2 and Double Angle Strip carries a 4½"×2½" Flexible Plate 3 and three Strips, two of which are 2½" long and one is the 5½" Strip 4. Two Sector Plates 5 are now added in the manner shown, and the upper flanges of these carry two 2½"×2½" Strip Plates forming the roof.

The jib consists of four main members, formed from 12½" Strips and these are all secured together at their upper ends by means of a Double Bracket. Each side pair of 12½" Strips is braced together as shown by two 2½" Strips. A 3½" Crank Handle is now journalled in two holes at the front edges of the Sector Plates 5, and this has mounted on it, between the Plates, a Spring Clip and an Anchoring Spring. Outside the Plates a Bush Wheel is secured in position and a 3½" Strip presses lightly against the periphery of this. Thus a light, constant braking effort is applied to the Crank Handle.

Fig. 4. An effective Meccano coal-handling crane that can be built easily with parts included in Outfit C.

The hoisting cord, which is fixed at one end to the Anchoring Spring on the Crank Handle, passes over a ½" loose Pulley situated at the upper end of the jib. It carries a Small Loaded Hook and from this are suspended the four lifting cords that are held apart, as shown in Fig. 4, by two 5½" Strips. The bottom ends of the lifting cords are attached to the buffers of the truck to be lifted.

The 3" Pulley 1, upon which the superstructure is built, rests on a second 3" Pulley 6 that is connected to a 5½"×2½" Flanged Plate in the base by means of two ½" Reversed Angle Brackets. A short Rod passes through the centres of both Pulleys.

Parts required to build the model Crane: 4 of No. 1; 8 of No. 2; 1 of No. 3; 9 of No. 5; 1 of No. 11; 5 of No. 12; 2 of No. 16; 2 of No. 18a; 1 of No. 19s; 2 of No. 19b; 4 of No. 22; 1 of No. 23; 1 of No. 24; 4 of No. 35; 61 of No. 37; 8 of No. 38; 1 of No. 40; 6 of No. 48a; 1 of No. 51; 1 of No. 52; 2 of No. 54a; 1 of No. 57c; 2 of No. 125; 1 of No. 176; 2 of No. 188; 2 of No. 189; 4 of No. 190; 2 of No. 191; 2 of No. 192.

Meccano Competitions for All Readers

"Autumn" Model-Building Contest

The coming of October and the dark evenings heralds the start of the great Meccano model-building season, and although many of us will regret the storing away of cricket bats, tennis rackets and other symbols of summer, all Meccano boys will welcome the opportunity of returning once again to the greatest of all indoor hobbies, and of participating in the model-building competitions announced every month in the *"M.M."*

During the summer many model-builders will have discovered new subjects of all kinds suitable for Meccano models and they will wish to put their ideas into practical form at the first opportunity. This month's competition therefore is open for models of any kind whatever, and the competitor is not limited to any particular size of Outfit or number of parts. He may use just those parts that he finds necessary to make his model as perfect as possible.

This B.S.A. three-wheel car was built by M. Powley, Sunderland, and forms the subject of the novel "Nuts and Bolts" Competition announced on this page.

Actual models must not be sent. It is only necessary to submit either a clear photograph or, if this is not possible, a good drawing of the model, together with a brief explanation of any constructional or mechanical features that are not shown in the illustration.

The photograph or drawing need not be prepared by the competitor himself, but it is absolutely essential that the model itself is his own unaided work.

Competitors may, if they wish, submit more than one model, but in this event all entries must be sent under the same cover. No single competitor will be awarded more than one prize, and if two or more models are submitted they will be considered on their joint merits.

Entries will be divided into two sections. Section A will comprise competitors of all ages living in the British Isles, and Section B those of all ages living Overseas.

The prizes to be awarded in each section are: 1st, Meccano or Hornby products value £3/3/–; 2nd, products value £2/2/–; 3rd, products value £1/1/–. In addition, there will be a number of consolation prizes of products value 5/–. Prizewinners will be notified by letter as soon after the closing dates as possible, and will be allowed to choose any goods they like from current Meccano price lists to the value of the prizes awarded to them.

The competitor's name, age and address must be written clearly in block letters on the back of each photograph or drawing sent in, together with letter A or B to indicate the section for which the entry is eligible. Envelopes containing entries should be addressed "Autumn" General Model-Building Competition, Meccano Ltd., Binns Road, Liverpool 13. December 31st, 1936, is the last day on which entries will be received in the Home Section, and the closing date for the Section for Overseas entries is 27th February, 1937.

It should be noted that photographs of prize-winning models become the property of Meccano Ltd. Those of unsuccessful entries will be returned to the senders after the close of the contest, provided that a stamped addressed envelope is enclosed for that purpose.

"Nuts and Bolts" Competition

This contest is open to all readers and it is not necessary to possess a Meccano Outfit in order to prepare an entry. There is no model-building to do, and any boy or girl who has a good idea of how a Meccano model should be built stands an excellent chance of winning one of the fine prizes to be awarded.

All it is necessary to do is to estimate the number of nuts and bolts used in building the model three-wheel car shown on this page. This is really a much easier task than may at first appear, for although some of the nuts and bolts cannot be seen in the illustration, the method of construction of the model provides clues to the number of bolts used in the portions that are out of sight. If no reader gives the correct number, the prizes will be awarded in order of merit to the competitors whose estimates are nearest correct. It should be remembered that all competitors have to work under the same difficulties, and the chances of success are therefore alike for all.

The prizes to be awarded are as follows: 1st, Meccano or Hornby products value £2/2/–; 2nd, products value £1/1/–; 3rd, products value 10/6.

Entries, which must be by postcard only, should be addressed "Nuts and Bolts" Competition, Meccano Ltd., Binns Road, Liverpool 13, and should be posted in time to reach Liverpool on or before 31st December, 1936.

Model-Building Competition Results

By Frank Hornby

An Ingenious Clock Mechanism

March "Piston Mechanism" Contest

On page 172 of the "*M.M.*" for March last appeared a diagram showing two pistons A and B working in a single cylinder. Piston A had a stroke of 3 in., and competitors in this contest were asked to design in Meccano suitable coupling gear to connect the two pistons so that each stroke of the piston rod attached to piston A would cause piston B to move through a distance of 14 in., but in an opposite direction to piston A.

The most interesting and ingenious entries were submitted by the competitors named in the following list, and they have received prizes as indicated.

1st Prize, Meccano or Hornby products value £2/2/–: D. R. Heeramaneck, Bombay. 2nd, products value £1/1/–: E. Armitage, Liverpool; 3rd, products value 10/6: A. C. Tipper, Exeter.

D. Heeramaneck's model is built up on a strong base plate, 9½ in. wide and 5 ft. 2½ in. long, constructed with Flat Girders and Angle Girders. At one end of the base are two rigid bearings made from 2½" Triangular Plates held in place by 2½" Angle Girders, and these support a triple-throw crankshaft, consisting of four large wheels, the centres of which are Hub Discs and the spokes and rims Strips bent as required. To one spoke of each wheel is fixed a Double Arm Crank so placed that its boss is 7 in. from the centre of the wheel, and 1" Rods secured in the bosses of the Cranks connect the wheels together in pairs. A further Double Arm Crank is bolted to the outside of each pair of wheels with its boss 1½ in. from the axis of the crankshaft, and these are then joined by a 2½" Rod.

The cylinder, which is 22½" long, is built up from five Boilers, and Boiler Ends are used for the pistons. As nuts and bolts would project inside the cylinder and prevent the piston from sliding, the builder experienced some difficulty in fixing the Boilers in position. He eventually overcame the trouble by clamping them in place with straps made from Flat Girders and Strips. A Rod is secured at one end to one of the pistons and its other end is connected to a crosshead, which is made from two pairs of Eye Pieces connected by 1" Rods that carry Couplings. The 1" Rod farther from the cylinder carries also a small Fork Piece, and this is coupled up by a Rod to the centre pin of the crankshaft.

Long Rods mounted on the two outer pins of the crankshaft are coupled to crossheads that move backward and forward on slides situated on each side of the cylinder. The slides are 18½" Angle Girders, and each crosshead is each made from four 2½" Angle Girders joined in pairs, one inside the other, by bolts passed through their elongated holes. These holes enable a slot for the crosshead guides to be formed, and the bolts hold Double Arm Cranks joined by 1" Rods provided with Couplings that are attached to the connecting rods. The rod of the piston that has a 14 in. stroke carries at its outer end a large crosshead made from two Girder Frames. This is fixed to the piston rod by Handrail Supports, and the small side crossheads are coupled to its ends by long compound rods.

When the crankshaft is rotated, its centre pin causes the piston it operates to move through a distance of 3 in., and the two outer crank pins operate the other piston through a stroke of 14 in. As the crank pins of each piston are placed on opposite sides of the centre axis of the crankshaft the pistons move simultaneously but in opposite directions.

An interesting feature of the contest was the ingenious manner in which many entrants constructed their mechanisms to scale.

"Clock Mechanism" Contest

In spite of the difficult nature of the subject, the "Clock Mechanism" Competition that was announced in the April issue of the "*M.M.*" attracted a considerable number of entries, many of which are most interesting and ingenious. The entry that won First Prize is a particularly good example of neat and compact construction, but unfortunately the photograph submitted is not sufficiently clear to enable me to reproduce it.

The chief prizewinners in the competition are as follows:

1st Prize, Meccano or Hornby products value £3/3/–: D. J. Hofsommer, The Hague, Holland; 2nd, products value £2/2/–: D. Berkin, Ki, China; 3rd, products value £1/1/–: J. Westhead, Brinnington, Stockport.

An ingenious gear mechanism that has a ratio of 12 : 1, and consists of only two built-up Meccano gears. It was designed by D. Berkin, of Ki, China, and won Second Prize in the "Clock Mechanism" Competition.

Competitors were invited to try their skill in reproducing the gearing illustrated on page 232 of the April "*M.M.*," by means of which a ratio of 12 : 1 can be obtained by the use of only two gears. The reproduction had to be built up from Strips, Angle Brackets or other Meccano parts, and the illustration on this page shows the mechanism for this purpose that was designed by D. Berkin and was awarded Second Prize. It incorporates an 11-tooth gear consisting of a ring of eleven 1½" Strips, with ½"×½" Reversed Angle Brackets at each connecting point. A 2" Slotted Strip and a 4½" Strip are attached to the ring so that the 4½" Strip projects outside the gear and the Slotted Strip inside. A Triple-Throw Eccentric is bolted to the Slotted Strip, the slot enabling it to be centred easily. Through the Eccentric boss marked "¾" throw" a 6½" Rod is passed, and this runs in bearings in the framework, as shown in the illustration.

The other gear has 12 teeth and is made up from a Hub Disc, which is fitted with a Face Plate at its centre and 12 equally spaced Flat Brackets round its rim. The Hub Disc runs freely on the 6½" Rod, but is spaced from the 11-teeth gear by a Collar, so that the teeth of both just engage.

A Socket Coupling attached to the boss of the larger gear is provided with a 3½" Screwed Rod to form the hour hand of the clock, and the minute hand is a 6½" Screwed Rod held in a Collar on the end of the Rod on which the Hub Disc is mounted. The 4½" Strip that is bolted to the 11-teeth gear slides in an Eye Piece that is fixed to the framework.

If the 6½" Rod is rotated 12 times, the 12-teeth gear is made to rotate once so that the mechanism is suitable for use as the gearing between the minute and hour hands of a clock. If the mechanism were built into a clock, a cardboard face could be bolted to the Ring Frame shown in the illustration.

Most of the other prizewinning entries follow similar methods of construction, the chief variations being in the selection of parts used for reproducing the two gear wheels and in the carrying out of minor details.

"Ingenuity" Model-Building Competition

The following is a complete list of the prizewinners in Section B of the "Ingenuity" Competition:

1st Prize, Meccano or Hornby products value £3/3/–: J. Oleaga, Buenos Aires. 2nd, products value £2/2/–: L. Linder, Stockholm. 3rd, products value £1/1/–: J. Carter, Capetown.

Products value 10/6: H. Dressler, Breslau X, Germany; F. Barry, Ocean Falls, Canada; P. Kett, Melbourne; P. Giese, Buenos Aires; J. Nie, Shanghai.

Products value 5/–: G. Philpott, Rangiora, N.Z.; D. McLeod, Natal; J. Hulley, Nantes; D. Murison, Buenos Aires; J. Capelli, Buenos Aires.

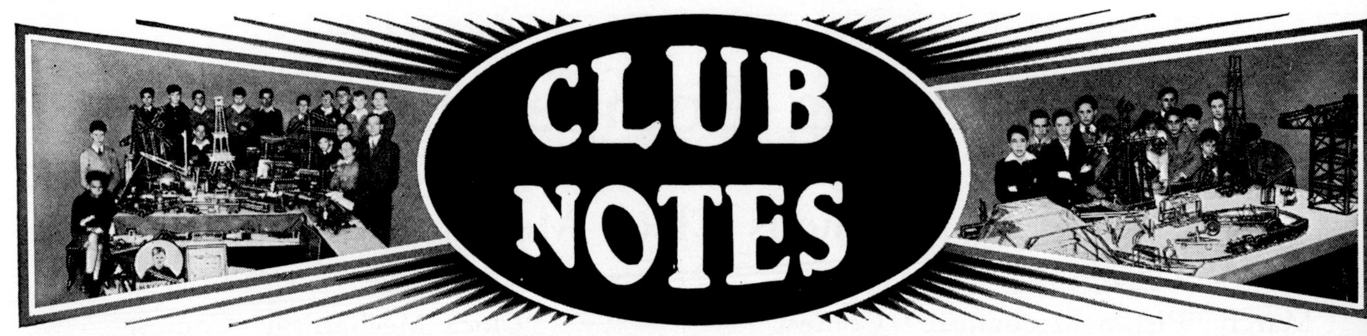

Regent Street Central School (Heywood) M.C.—This year the annual excursion took the form of a trip to Port Sunlight and Chester. Lectures have been well attended, and included one on "*The North of Spain*" by a gentleman who has lived there, and others on "*Jerusalem*" and "*The Railways of Germany*," both of which were excellently illustrated. Model-building has been chiefly in connection with a Display arranged for Parents' Day. An intensive recruiting campaign is to be carried out early in the next school term. Club roll: 150. *Secretary:* R. Nobbs, 6, Broadfield Street, Heywood.

Kendal M.C.—A delightful outing to Lake Windermere was thoroughly enjoyed. A sail on the Lake was followed by tea, and afterwards a round of miniature golf was played, during which the Leader was heavily defeated! A club-room has not yet been obtained, but enquiries are still being made, and it is hoped that suitable premises will be obtained shortly. Club roll: 10. *Secretary:* L. Haslam, Middleton, Kirkby Lonsdale, Carnforth.

Wednesbury M.C.—At the quarterly meeting of officials, the President expressed his pleasure at the continued good progress of the club. Recent activities have included enjoyable games of cricket. A small party of senior members joined with the Kidderminster Model Railway Branch in a tour of the "*Birmingham Gazette*" printing works. Mr. F. J. Inns, Vice-President of the club, has kindly presented a fretwork machine, and as a result there will be considerable activity in the Fretwork section during the forthcoming winter session. The Aeroplane section have purchased a stock of balsa wood and other requirements, and the construction of many interesting and efficient model aeroplanes is being planned. It is probable that an Exhibition will be held late in the autumn. Club roll: 20. *Secretary:* A. L. Morgan, 17, Cobden Street, Fallings Heath, Wednesbury.

Islington M.C.—The varied programme carried out has included model-building, games and a visit to Southend. Interesting talks have been given on "*How Goods Traffic Works at Night*," and on the Exhibition to be held this month, Club roll: 10. *Secretary:* K.V. Vines. 70, Thornhill Road, Barnsbury, London, N.1.

South Parade Modern School (Cleckheaton) M.C.—The club Exhibition on the School Open Day was a great success. The excellent display of models built by the members was supplemented by models of a Horizontal Engine and o Watt's Beam Engine, kindly loaned by Headquarters, and which were much admired by the many visitors. An attractive programme is being drawn up for the winter sessions, and it is hoped to recruit many new members. Club roll: 24. *Secretary:* R. Ellis, 2, Tennyson Place, Cleckheaton.

St. Stephen's (Saltash) M.C.—Cricket and baseball have been the main occupations of the members during outdoor meetings. Model-building has been continued on other occasions, and when the subject chosen was "*Familiar Objects*" one member built an excellent reproduction of an organ and another a dog kennel. A fleet of model battleships is being constructed with the help of the Leader. A prize is to be offered for the best attendance during the present half-year. Club roll: 9. *Secretary:* B. Braund, 9, Homer Park, Saltash.

Old Charlton M.C.—A recent Model-building Evening was spent in devising simple models, and one of the best constructed was a grindstone that consisted of only 17 Meccano parts. A very enjoyable visit has been paid to Croydon Airport. Recent talks have included an amusing one by the Leader on "*How to be witty*," and one on "*Patents*" that was followed by an interesting discussion, during which several members suggested types of humane rabbit traps that were subjected to criticism. A General Knowledge evening dealt with such questions as "*What is the gear ratio between a worm and a ½ in. pinion?*" and "*What wheels should be used for running on rails?*" Afterwards, Mr. Leverett, the new Vice-Leader, showed the members an illuminated map dial he is making for his wireless set, and explained how he proposed to work it. Future plans include a Debate on "*Are Big Ships Worth While?*", a talk about Boats by Mr. Fish, and a Table Tennis Tournament. Club roll: 25. *Secretary:* W. Jaques, 60, Gurdon Road, London, S.E.7.

Fraserburgh M.C.—The models for the club Exhibition have been completed and painted. A considerable length of new track has been acquired for the Hornby layout, and a tunnel and a bridge, both wide enough for double track, are being made from plywood. Club roll: 28. *Secretary:* W. J. Dawson, Phingask, Fraserburgh.

Bryntirion School M.C.—The club has developed an international character, as it now includes members from Peru, Belgium and New Zealand. Some excellent models have been built during recent meetings. Members hope to arrange an Exhibition during the autumn. Club roll: 22. *Secretary:* H. Williams, Bryntirion School, Bridgend, Glam.

A group of officials and members of the Hornsea M.C. In the centre is Mr. R. W. Shooter, who has been Leader of the club since its formation and affiliation with the Meccano Guild in 1928. Model-building, Games, and Lectures upon a wide variety of subjects are the chief features of the club programme.

St. Giles' Cathedral (Edinburgh) M.C.—Almost 50 new members have been enrolled during the past club year, and all meetings have been well attended. Model-building has not been carried on as much as in previous years, but is to be a prominent feature during the coming winter. The railway layout has been partly electrified and considerable experience gained in the working of it. The senior members deserve special mention for their part in this improvement. Club roll: 180. *Secretary:* H. W. Govan, 18, Revelston Park, Edinburgh, 4.

Hornsea M.C.—During the summer meetings have been devoted almost entirely to games. Cricket and bowls have been the most popular out-of-doors, while mah-jong is the favourite indoor game. Lectures continue to be given periodically, and the varied and interesting subjects dealt with recently have included "*The Automatic Telephone Exchange*," "*Australia*," "*The Army Rifle*," "*Aeroplanes*" and "*The Lake District*." Other activities included a day's outing to Swine, which proved very enjoyable. Club roll: 15. *Secretary:*. Mr. P. Thom, 5, Alexandra Road, Hornsea.

AUSTRALIA

Nhill Xlcr M.C.—The club has been divided into Senior and School (Junior) Sections. Excellent recruiting has been accomplished by the secretary and treasurer, each of whom has enrolled nine new Guild members. A new club-room has been obtained. It is equipped with electric light, and has two rows of shelves along each wall. The stock of nickelled Meccano parts has been enamelled, and a Meccano Electric Motor has been added to the equipment. Club roll: 16. *Secretary:* F. Haustorfer, Leahy Street, Nhill, Victoria.

Maylands (Perth) M.C.—An election has been held to elect a new President and a Vice-President. Several of the members are competing in a Meccano model-building competition organised by a local dealer. A Debate on "*Is War Worth While?*" aroused great interest, and some excellent speeches were made. Club roll: 23. *Secretary:* M. Thomson, 13, Kennedy Street, Maylands, Perth.

CANADA

Rosemount (Regina) M.C.—Very favourable reports of the club's Annual Exhibition appeared in the local press. The fine display of models included a Dutch windmill, log saw, loom that weaved ties and hat bands, reproduction of George Washington Bridge and stage coaches. A further attraction was an electrically operated model railway layout. Club roll: 16. *Secretary:* J. Watson, 974, Athol Street, Regina, Sask.

EGYPT

Zagazig M.C.—A pleasantly varied programme has been carried out, the chief features of which have been fretwork, games and talks. Lectures on "*Electricity*" and "*Benjamin Franklin*" were appreciated. A special silver Medallion and a Merit Diploma have been awarded to the Zagazig and Cairo M.C.s for the very fine joint display of models that they staged at the recent Exhibition of Egyptian Industry. Club roll: 18. *Secretary:* A. Yousig, Gannabiet Sikka Hadid Avenue, Zagazig.

NEW ZEALAND

Christchurch M.C.—At one meeting two Lectures loaned from Headquarters were read and were much enjoyed. Further visits have been paid to Eric Broomfield, the invalid friend of the club mentioned in earlier reports. A "Surprise Outing" provided much fun, the route followed leading to a coffee stall for refreshments. This unexpected climax proved immensely popular, and it is probable that another mysterious outing will be arranged during the winter. The President recently gave a Lantern Lecture describing a tour through New Zealand, and illustrated by a set of beautiful slides, kindly loaned by the New Zealand Government Tourist Bureau. A Debate on the controversial subject "*Should Boys and Girls be Educated Together?*" proved exceptionally interesting, and the arguments for and against the motion were very well thought out. Members have been busy in connection with a Fete the club are organising to help the Epworth Homes. Club roll: 23. *Secretary:* L. W. Best, 28, Circuit Street, Strowan, Christchurch.

Ashburton M.C.—Many interesting outings have been held, including a visit by eight of the members to Christchurch M.C., to participate in the Birthday Night celebrations of that club. The Model-Building section entered 11 models in the Models contest at the local annual Winter Show, and five of them were awarded prizes. Club roll: 25. *Secretary:* Miss P. Kruse, Cameron Street, East, Ashburton.

SOUTH AFRICA

Malvern M.C.—Excellent super models are being built for the club display at a forthcoming Fete. Meetings are well attended, and good progress is being made in establishing a Junior section. Club roll: 85. *Secretary:* B. Saunders, P.O. Box 8, Cleveland, Johannesburg.

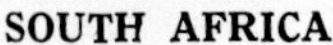

Pioneer (Pietermaritzburg) M.C.—The club staged a display totalling 15 models at the Maritzburg Horticultural Society's show. The Correspondence section continues to flourish, and two evenings each week are devoted to Boys' Brigade work. Club roll: 11. *Secretary:* A. H. Alley, 461, Burgers Street, Pietermaritzburg, Natal.

Club Not Yet Affiliated

Charters Towers M.C.—A copy of the club rules has been hung in the club-room. Two very interesting models recently completed were a merry-go-round and a steam engine. *Secretary:* R. C. McLean, Marion Street, Charters Towers, Queensland, Australia.

Producing a Club Magazine

I am a firm believer in the value of the club magazine, and therefore I am always very pleased to receive copies of such publications. One most interesting club magazine that reaches me regularly is *"The Gear Box,"* the official organ of the Plymouth M.C. It is a quarterly magazine started several years ago, and is notable for the variety and high standard of its contents. Every issue contains a summary of recent club events, pages of notes concerning local railway, tram and bus activities, a page of shipping news and, by way of lighter fare, a clever "home-made" crossword puzzle. In addition to these regular features, there are always one or more special articles, chiefly of engineering interest.

I should like to see a magazine started in every established club. Actual production offers little difficulty, although in most cases printed magazines are out of the question. Satisfactory reproduction can be obtained by the use of stencils cut on a typewriter, and copies taken from these with the aid of a duplicator have a very neat appearance and can be read with ease. A jellygraph also may be employed. The results are not so good as those given by the method already described, but with care they are satisfactory, and the system has the great merit of being inexpensive.

Mr. A. Singh is Leader of the Ranjit (Lahore) M.C. This Indian club was affiliated in October 1931. Its members are keen model builders, and recently displayed an excellent selection of large working models during the Jubilee celebrations of their school.

Attractive Features

It is impossible to lay down definite rules in regard to the contents of a club magazine, for the character of these depends on the tastes of members themselves—and also on their capacity for providing the editor with contributions. Apart from items of club news and the general articles of an attractive type that should always be included, special attention should be paid to features of local or topical interest, and in this respect the railway, tram and bus notes of *"The Gear Box"* might well be imitated.

If it proves difficult to maintain the interest of the members in running a club magazine, the less ambitious plan of issuing a monthly Bulletin should be adopted. This may include short reports of recent events, together with a programme of meetings to be held the following month, and it also should contain comments on any features of interest in connection with club work. A regular production of this kind is more satisfactory than a magazine that is excellent one month and dull the next. Copies should be distributed as widely as possible in order to keep members and friends of the club in touch with progress, and it may be enlarged into a regular magazine when a suitable opportunity arises.

Membership Cards and Report Forms

This is the time to replenish the stock of club literature, and I shall be glad to forward membership and subscription cards to all secretaries who are in need of them. Report forms also are necessary. I am sending supplies to all affiliated clubs, and any secretary who has not already received his copies, or does not receive them during the next few days, should write to me immediately.

I have several times mentioned the great advantages of submitting regular club reports, and I must again emphasise that I cannot give satisfaction to club members by accounts of their work in the *"Club Notes"* page unless I receive sufficient and regular information from secretaries. Another point is that good reports help members to feel they belong to an important club, and so stimulate their enthusiasm. They also attract other Meccano boys, some of whom may possess gifts for model-building or organising powers that can be turned to good account in club life.

Forming New Clubs

One interesting feature of my correspondence during the past summer has been the steady flow of enquiries from new members of the Guild for details of the nearest available Meccano club. I have given the required information wherever possible, but there have been several instances in which no suitable club existed. For this reason I strongly urge all members of the Guild who live in populous districts where no club has been established to give serious thought to the possibility of forming one. It is almost certain that in the same neighbourhood will be other Meccano boys in similar positions, and it is only necessary for these to be brought into contact to enable a successful club to be formed. The present is an ideal time to take this step.

I am always very pleased to help any enterprise of this kind by publishing the details in these columns, and so bringing them to the notice of boys who wish to enjoy Meccano club life, but at present have not the opportunity of doing so. Even if only small clubs that are not qualified for affiliation are possible at first, there is no need to be discouraged, for many of the largest and most successful Meccano clubs have grown from very humble beginnings.

New Lantern Lectures

From the British Railways Press Office I have received news of three interesting lantern lectures that are now available on loan. These are entitled *"The Railways of Great Britain," "British Railway Locomotives,"* and *"Railway Wonders of Great Britain"* respectively. The first set of slides illustrates the many and varied activities of the railways; and the second deals with the development of the locomotive down to modern times. The third set is particularly interesting. It includes slides of famous locomotives, interiors of railway workshops, signal boxes, control rooms, marshalling yards, famous railway bridges and tunnels and train ferries, and 12 of these are coloured.

A descriptive booklet is supplied with the slides to enable the lecturer to give an interesting running commentary upon them. Leaders who wish to obtain the loan of the lectures should apply to the British Railways Press Office, 35, Parliament Street, Westminster, London, S.W.1. There is certain to be a great demand for them, and application should be made well in advance of the date for which they are required.

Proposed Clubs

Attempts are being made to establish Meccano Clubs in the following places, and boys interested should communicate with the promoters whose names and addresses are given below:

GREENFORD—H. Smith, 63, Halsbury Road, W., Northold Park.
INDIA—Mr. N. S. Narang, Shish Mahal Road, Lahore.

Preparing for Winter Activities

Cleaning and Oiling Locomotives

ABOUT this time of the year Hornby Railway owners turn with renewed interest to their layouts, and become busy with plans for extensions, and improvements, or for running more intensive services. Before putting these into operation, the equipment should be examined in order to ensure that it will give satisfaction in the busy times ahead.

On any layout successful operation depends primarily on a good track. The rails therefore should be carefully examined, whether they are laid down permanently or are put down only from time to time when required. On a permanent layout inspection of the rails is easy to carry out. They probably will not require any adjustment of level, but should be tested for truth to gauge, a very important point. For this the combined Rail Gauge, Screwdriver and Spanner packed with all Hornby Electric Locomotives must be pressed into service on an electric layout, and the winding key handle of Hornby Clockwork Locomotives form a rail gauge for the tracks on which they are used. By sliding either of these along between the rails of Hornby Track, defective places can be detected immediately, and the rails should be eased apart gently where they are tight. A portable layout should be tested in a similar manner. It is much easier and quicker to make an examination of a track in position than to test numerous separate rails; so the track components of such a layout should be set out and then tested.

A Hornby express on a miniature L.M.S.R. system passing along a high embankment. The train is formed of Hornby No. 2 Coaches and the Locomotive is an L.M.S.R. No. 2 Special "Standard Compound."

The process of laying down the line in this manner will bring to notice another item of importance, the loss of any of the connecting pins fitted at the ends of the rails. Where these are loose they should be tightened up by pinching the rail head with a pair of pliers. Any missing pins should be replaced by new ones, which can be obtained separately, and are far better than the match sticks that are sometimes used for the purpose. The hollow rail heads for receiving the pins also should be inspected. The frequent assembly and disassembly of the track of portable layouts is liable to cause them to open out. They should be closed up carefully with a small pair of pliers, a spare pin being inserted in the rail head to prevent it being distorted while the pliers are being used.

The rails that have been out of use for some time may be dirty, their heads showing traces of a black deposit due to the action of the wheels rolling over the oil that sometimes finds its way on to the rails, followed by the settlement on it of dust. As this prevents satisfactory running it should be removed from the rails, and of course from all wheels, by wiping with a rag that has been soaked with a small quantity of petrol. Paraffin is of no use for this purpose, as its more oily nature tends to start the whole process again, apart from the wheel slip that it causes.

Where electric locomotives are in use axles, gears, coupling rods and wheels should be cleaned of any dirt that may have collected on them, particular attention being paid to the wheel treads and collector shoes. After cleaning up, engines should be tested and any slight defects dealt with according to the instructions packed with each Hornby Electric Locomotive.

The connections to the line from the power supply should be examined, and any loose contacts tightened. Plug connections that may have become loose in their sockets can be tightened up, after being withdrawn from the sockets, by placing the blade of a penknife or thin screwdriver in the longitudinal slot in the plug in order to separate slightly the two sections of the fittings. Any connections made by means of terminals should be examined and tightened up if necessary. Terminal Connecting Plates may require their fuses renewed, and it is very important that the appropriate fuse wire should be used as specified in the instructions packed with the Locomotive and the Transformer.

On clockwork railways the mechanism of the locomotive should be washed out with petrol in order to remove any old oil that may be in it, together with any accumulated dust that would tend to clog the mechanism and prevent the free working of the engine. Operations involving the use of petrol always should be performed out of doors. Petrol can be introduced into the mechanism in the same way as lubrication is carried out, that is from a small oil can kept specially for the purpose. When all dirt has been removed the engine should be allowed to stand until the petrol has evaporated, leaving the mechanism clean and dry. Lubrication of the various spindles, bearings and gear wheels with Meccano Oil should then be undertaken, and Meccano Graphite Grease applied between the coils of the spring.

The cleaning and examining of rolling stock and accessories is equally important if the best results are to be obtained. A little cleaning here, a little adjustment there, and a spot of Meccano Oil or Graphite Grease on the bearings frequently work wonders with a wagon or signal that does not move easily. Operations such as those briefly detailed above will be found interesting, and the results will repay the miniature railway owner for his trouble.

New Hornby High Capacity Wagons

By "Tommy Dodd"

THREE exceptionally interesting No. 2 High Capacity Wagons have been added to the range of bogie goods vehicles in the Hornby Series. The new vehicles will be very popular with Hornby Railway owners, for they are extremely realistic in appearance, incorporating several features that have not previously been included in the design of Hornby No. 2 Goods Stock, and their use will enable attractive features of modern goods practice to be reproduced in running operations.

The new Wagons are finished by means of the tinprinting process, which allows the reproduction of so much of the detail that appears on real wagons, and are handsome in appearance. The accuracy in detail of these new vehicles indeed reaches a very high standard, as the illustration on this page shows. The bogies fitted are of the usual No. 2 type, but these have been improved by the addition of axle-boxes and by the provision of die-cast spoked wagon wheels. These two features in conjunction add considerably to the ease and steadiness of running of the Wagons. Hornby Automatic Couplings of course are fitted, and the underframe equipment of the new Wagons is completed by standard oval-headed buffers, as frequently used on bogie stock of this kind.

THE NEW HORNBY HIGH CAPACITY WAGONS

The L.N.E.R. vehicle represents the well-known L.N.E.R. timber-bodied 50-ton brick wagon. Its main purpose is clearly indicated by the word "Brick" that appears prominently on the sides, although the wagons also can be used for road metal, iron-stone and other heavy traffic. On the prototype the sides are divided into three sections, each section being arranged to drop in a similar manner to the side doors of an ordinary wagon, and the necessary support between the adjacent ends of these sections is obtained by pressed steel stanchions attached to the underframe. The representation of this feature has been carried out very well in the printed design on the miniature Wagon, the three sections with the stanchions, hinges and strapping details all being shown. The necessary bolt heads also are included, and even such minute details as the pins and chains for securing the hinged sections in place are shown. There also are stop plates on each of the door sections, with corresponding fittings on the solebars, the purpose of these in actual practice being to prevent the doors being damaged when let down.

The lettering and similar items are completely carried out, the Company's initials "N.E." being shown in large characters, together with the running number, tare weight and the capacity of the vehicle. The latter, 50 tons, represents the respectable load of some 20,000 bricks.

These wagons are particularly associated with the brick traffic conveyed by the L.N.E.R. from the Peterborough district, where there are numerous brickfields, to King's Cross and other parts of the system. Many of the wagons are fitted with automatic brakes and can therefore be run at express speeds. An up "brick express" is in fact operated regularly from Peterborough.

The Hornby L.N.E.R. High Capacity Wagon is finished in the correct colours of the prototype, the red-brown shade used on the L.N.E.R. for brake-fitted and "piped" freight vehicles.

The Hornby G.W.R. High Capacity Wagon represents the all-steel 40-ton wagon used for the conveyance of the Company's locomotive coal. It is interesting to note that in the sides of this wagon there are five openings, each fitted with a drop door to the lower part and double doors opening sideways above it. The addition of the upper doors is a comparatively recent feature, so that the Hornby Wagon represents the G.W.R. 40-ton "loco coal" vehicle in its most recent form.

Although this Hornby Wagon is similar in outline and construction to the L.N.E.R. Brick Wagon, its design includes the underframe stays that are a prominent feature of the real G.W.R. vehicle. These fittings are not incorporated in the Hornby High Capacity L.M.S.R. and L.N.E.R. Wagons, the underframes of which are made deeper between the bogies.

On the Hornby G.W.R. Wagon the various details characteristic of Swindon practice are all reproduced. The hinges and other door fittings, together with the rivets that secure the various parts, are all shown, and altogether the effect is very convincing, especially as the Wagon is finished in the dark shade of grey used for G.W.R. goods stock. The familiar initials "G.W." appear on each side, together with the tare weight, the running number, and the word "Loco," an abbreviation that suggests the purpose of the vehicle.

The Hornby L.M.S.R. High Capacity Wagon represents another variation of the same general type, having three drop doors on each side. The prototype is the 30-ton all-steel wagon developed for the conveyance of locomotive coal and similar duties, on the Midland Division. The strapping, corner plates and other details are shown, and the whole of the tinprinted features show up well on a background of light grey, as used for L.M.S.R. freight vehicles. A striking feature that adds greatly to the realism is the reproduction on each side of the wheel for the use of shunters in setting or releasing the hand brake.

CONTAINER TRAFFIC ON HORNBY RAILWAYS

In the *"M.M."* last month "Tommy Dodd" described in detail four new Containers that have recently been added to the Hornby Series, giving also brief suggestions for their use. In this article other ways in which Container traffic on Hornby Railways can be operated are explained and illustrated. The use of containers in actual practice has developed to a surprising extent in recent years, particularly in connection with the numerous fast freight services that are operated by our railways, and the reproduction on a miniature scale of services of this kind is the first to be dealt with.

An interesting scene at the goods depot on a Hornby Railway. Flat Trucks with G.W.R. Insulated Containers are prominent among the various items of rolling stock.

Among the best known of the trains that can be described as freight flyers is the L.N.E.R. "3.40 p.m. Scottish Braked Goods." This provides a rapid service between London, intermediate stations, and Scottish destinations, delivering its freight in Edinburgh and Glasgow early on the morning following its departure from King's Cross. It has long been one of the fastest freight trains in the world and therefore is worthy of reproduction on a miniature L.N.E.R. system.

In making up a "3.40 Scotsman," as this train is often called, on a Hornby Railway, L.N.E.R. Containers loaded on the appropriate Flat Trucks should be prominent. The rest of the train may consist of various vans, with perhaps on ordinary Wagon or Open Wagon B with its load shrouded in a Hornby Wagon Tarpaulin, the whole being completed by an N.E. Brake Van.

Preparing a fast freight train for its run on a miniature S.R. system. The train represents one of the numerous express goods services that are run for the conveyance of perishable traffic.

Motive power will depend on the resources of the system; on larger layouts an E320 or E220 Locomotive can be used, the latter in particular representing the standard practice of the L.N.E.R. Passenger locomotives are being used to an increasing extent to-day on fast freight services and this is a matter of great convenience on a miniature railway. The E120 Special Locomotive is a very suitable one for fast freight work, and in fact for mixed traffic duties of every kind. It can be used therefore to represent the "K.3" 2–6–0s of actual practice, or the 2-6-2 "Green Arrow" locomotive that forms the latest development on the L.N.E.R. for this kind of duty.

Containers are of special value in the transport of perishable traffic, for they provide conveyance with the least amount of handling and this avoids delay and possible damage. The Containers of the Hornby Series include two of the kinds used for perishables; these are the S.R. Ventilated Container, and the G.W.R. Insulated Container. The former is particularly well-known in connection with the various fast trains that come up nightly from the West Country bearing their perishable freight for the London markets.

Readers will no doubt remember the run described by *"A Railway Engineer"* in the article *"On the Footplate of a Night Goods"* that appeared in the *"M.M."* for January, 1935. This was on the 7.38 p.m. from Exeter, the chief train for London market traffic, which has connections from most of the Western stations. It stops at Templecombe for connections from East Devon and from the Somerset and Dorset Joint Line, and at Salisbury; thence it runs to Nine Elms, the chief S.R. depot in London for West Country freight traffic. The rostered load is 55 vehicles, 15 of which fitted with continuous brakes are next to the engine.

A "Market" freight flyer in miniature would be an interesting train to operate on a Hornby layout representing the S.R. The chief freight of the real "Market" train is fresh meat. S.R. Ventilated Containers on Flat Trucks are exactly what is required for this traffic, with perhaps an S.R. Refrigerator Van in its characteristic pink colour. An S.R. Luggage Van also can be made use of, either the No. 2 bogie type or the four-wheeled No. 1. On this, as on other trains of this kind, the Open Wagon "B" or an ordinary No. 1 Wagon covered with a tarpaulin will be quite suitable and realistic.

The L.N.E.R. "3.40 Scottish Braked Goods" in miniature. A Flat Truck carrying one of the new Hornby L.N.E.R. Goods Containers is attached next to the engine.

Perhaps the most suitable locomotive of the Hornby Series for these S.R. West Country "Market" trains are the E320 and No. 3C types according to whether the layout is electric or clockwork. This type of engine can be used very well to represent on a Hornby layout the big "S.15" and "H.15" fast freight engines of actual practice. The handy 2–6–0s of various classes also take a part in the working of S.R. express goods trains, and on Hornby layouts these engines can be represented by the E120 or No. 1 Special Locomotives.

The G.W.R. insulated container is particularly intended for the conveyance of frozen meat imported from abroad, and similar traffic. A complete train of Flat Trucks carrying Hornby G.W.R. Insulated Containers would be an interesting sight on a miniature railway. Alternatively a train consisting partly of these, and partly of the well-known Hornby Refrigerator Vans with G.W.R. lettering, could be assembled to form a miniature "Meat Special." The G.W.R. is well-known for its custom of bestowing names not only on its special types of vehicles, but on its freight trains also. Thus there is "*The Meat,*" the purpose of which is indicated by its title, that runs regularly from Birkenhead to Smithfield.

A farm removal on a Hornby Railway. L.M.S.R. Furniture Containers are employed for the "household effects," while the live stock and equipment are provided with appropriate vehicles.

For such trains in miniature a Hornby G.W.R. Insulated Container is specially suitable and the inclusion of a named freight train in the working timetables of a miniature layout would add considerably to the interest of operations. The G.W.R. code name for refrigerator vans incidentally is "Mica. B," the word "Mica" being suggestive of the insulated construction of these vehicles.

"Hall" class engines are particularly associated with these duties on the G.W.R., but other 4–6–0 classes, and of course the "Moguls," also are to be seen on such trains. On Hornby layouts the E320 and E220 Specials or the corresponding clockwork Locomotives can be used to represent the named classes, with the E120 or No. 1 Special as the counterparts in miniature of the "Moguls."

The Hornby L.M.S.R. Furniture Container makes possible various operations of a particularly interesting kind. Mounted on an L.M.S.R. Flat Truck it can of course be conveyed by passenger or freight train as required in the ordinary course of traffic. Alternatively several of them can form a "special" for the conveyance of a large consignment; the imagination of Hornby Railway owners will enable them to devise various reasons for the running of trains of this kind.

Perhaps the most interesting uses of the furniture container are in connection with the "removal in bulk" of the whole of the stock and equipment of a farm or estate. By means of container transport, in conjunction with suitable rail and road vehicles, such removals can be made practically from one end of the country to the other with little difficulty, provided that arrangements for feeding and watering farm stock on the way are made. On a Hornby layout some very good fun can be had carrying out in miniature wholesale removals of this kind, and the lower illustration on this page shows typical loading operations for a "farm removal" in progress. Hornby Furniture Containers will be required to carry the "household effects," and they will invariably be loaded on to Flat Trucks intended for their conveyance. This type of Wagon also will be useful for carrying such items as the Tractor, Dinky Toys No. 22E. When loading operations are completed, the load on a Wagon of this kind should be covered with a Hornby Wagon Tarpaulin.

The use of the Farmyard Animals of Dinky Toys Set No. 2 and of the components of the Shepherd Set, Dinky Toys No. 6, is an obvious suggestion for representing the farm stock. These can be loaded into Hornby No. 1 or No. 2 Cattle Trucks.

Join the Hornby Railway Company and become eligible for the competitions announced on this page.

H.R.C. COMPETITION PAGE

Join the Hornby Railway Company and become eligible for the competitions announced on this page.

SHARP EYES CONTEST

This month we are introducing a new competition that we are sure H.R.C. members will find fascinating and enjoyable. It is not difficult, requiring only sharp eyes, combined with a reasonable amount of knowledge of Hornby Trains. In the illustration on this page, 34 parts used in making Hornby Products are shown. These should be recognised without difficulty by Hornby Train enthusiasts, and competitors are invited to discover the identity of each part illustrated, to give its name, and to state on which locomotive, coach or other component in the Hornby Series it is to be found.

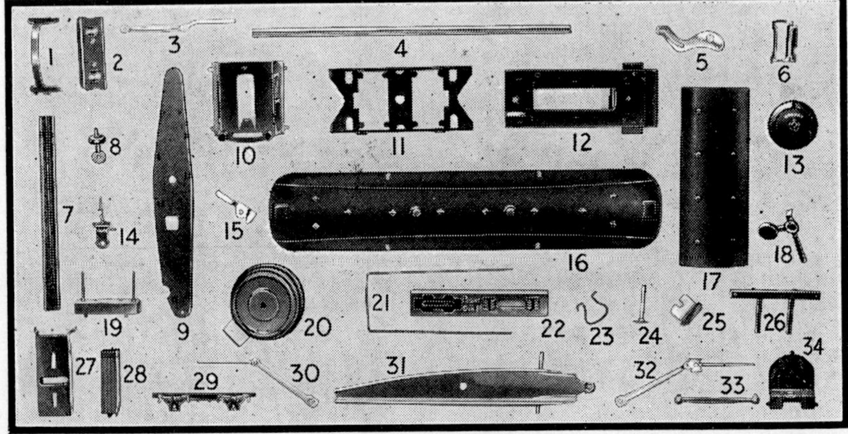

When a competitor has discovered what each figure represents, or has identified as many as possible, he should make a list of them in numerical order on a postcard, giving with each the name and other information required. No descriptive matter is required, and solutions should be brief, containing only the details asked for. Provided the conditions of the contest are observed, the shorter these are the better.

The Contest will be divided into the usual two Sections for Home and Overseas members. Three prizes will be awarded in each Section, and in each case those to whom they are awarded will be able to choose any products manufactured by Meccano Ltd. to the value of 21/–, 15/– and 10/6 respectively. In addition, there will be several consolation prizes, and these will be awarded to competitors whose entries show merit, but do not quite reach the standard attained by the winners of the chief awards. In the event of a tie for any prize, neatness and style in setting out solutions will be taken into consideration by the judges when making their final decision.

Postcards on which solutions have been written, or envelopes containing entries, must be marked *"H.R.C. October Sharp Eyes Contest"* in the top left-hand corner. Each entry must have the name and full address of its sender clearly marked on it.

Entries in the Home Section must be posted to reach Headquarters at Meccano Ltd., Binns Road, Liverpool 13, on or before 31st October. The closing date in the Overseas Section is 30th January, 1937.

Questions Contest No. 8

This contest is the eighth of a popular series in which questions on railway matters have been set. The questions are 12 in number, and form a simple test of the knowledge of H.R.C. members of interesting features of railways and railway working.

(1) On which railways in the British Isles are Pullman Cars run? (2) Some wagons are fitted with red brake pipes instead of black. What is indicated by this? (3) What does a diamond-shaped sign attached to a signal post mean? (4) What does a white diagonal painted on a wagon side indicate? (5) What is a sand-drag? (6) The levers in a signal box are usually painted different colours. What are they, and what type of lever does each colour represent? (7) Between which two towns does the L.N.E.R. operate the longest through coach journey, and what is the distance covered? (8) In what year was the Severn Tunnel opened for traffic? (9) What are catch points for? (10) What is a "Tommy Dodd"? (11) Which railway or railways operate slip coaches? (12) Who are the owners of the Forth Bridge?

There are two sections in the contest—Home and Overseas—and to the senders of the three best sets of answers received in each will be awarded Meccano or Hornby Train products to the value of 21/–, 15/– and 10/6 respectively.

Answers should be written on one side of paper only, on the back of which must appear the competitor's name, full address and his H.R.C. membership number. It is not necessary to go into great detail; provided the conditions are satisfied, the shorter the answers are the better. If more than one competitor sends in an all-correct set of answers, the prize awards will be made to those whose entries are submitted in the nestest or most novel manner.

Envelopes containing entries must be marked *"H.R.C. October Questions Contest No. 8"* in the top left-hand corner and posted to reach Headquarters at Meccano Ltd., Binns Road, Liverpool 13, on or before 31st October. The closing date for the Overseas Section is 30th January, 1937.

COMPETITION SOLUTION

"June Dream Journey Contest"

This contest aroused much interest among H.R.C. members. It also left us with no doubt that they are wide awake, for between them the competitors tracked down every error in the story reproduced in the June issue, in spite of the fact that many of these were cunningly concealed. In the space at our disposal it is impossible to give a detailed list of the errors, but it is of interest to mention that the winner of the first prize, J. C. Button (10335), Crewe, succeeded in discovering 79 mistakes.

COMPETITION RESULTS

HOME

August "Mystery Stations Contest."—First: W. Lobb (11765), Broadley, Rochdale. Second: D. H. Wakely (17486), Cheam, Surrey. Third: O. J. Otway (48585), Farnham, Surrey. Consolation Prizes: D. D'Arcy (34560), Padiham, Nr. Burnley; J. C. Button (10335), Crewe, Ches.; C. W. Lex (14033), Kingston-on-Thames; R. H. Sedgwick (39165), Cricklewood, London, N.W.2.

August "Railway Photo Contest."—First: C. Spencer (44179), Sheffield, 6. Second: D. Fear (18477), Taunton, Somerset. Third: E. W. Oglethorpe (46851), Harrow, Middlesex. Consolation Prizes: A. Banwell (33434), Oxhey, Watford, Herts.; H. W. West (99), Newport, Mon.; V. L. Breeze (2134), Lewes.

OVERSEAS

April "Signalling Contest."—First: H. R. Hondelink (25394), Nada-Ku, Kobe, Japan. Second: G. E. Schulz (15425), Coromby, Victoria, Australia. Third: H. C. Key (24764), Calcutta, India.

April "Railway Photo Contest."—First: R. Pearson (29199), Richmond, E.1, Victoria, Australia. Second: P. N. Roy, Calcutta, India. Third: W. S. Eagle (31779), Bombay, India.

May "Locomotive Shadows Contest."—First: R. A. Wragg (7913), Bandikui, Rajputana, India. Second: W. B. Moore (20918), Toronto, Canada. Third: I. Brough (9112), Preston, Australia. Consolation Prizes: D. Parker (38595), Brussels, Ontario, Canada; A. McIntyre (30925), Winnipeg, Canada; H. Bennett (10615), Auckland, New Zealand.

May "Railway Photo Contest."—First: R. B. McMillan (9592), Melbourne, Australia. Second: F. D. Aria (12362), Tardeo, Bombay, India. Third: H. Bennett (10615), Auckland, New Zealand. Consolation Prizes: J. Jasper (42664), Manly, Queensland, Australia; G. E. Schulz (15425), Coromby, Victoria, Australia; A. A. Boult, Wellington, New Zealand; R. Myburgh (37538), Claremont, Cape Province, South Africa.

Branch News

SUTTON COLDFIELD.—During the Summer months Hornby Speed Boat meetings were popular and some interesting events were held. These meetings are being continued, although with the commencement of the miniature railway "season" the operation of Hornby trains forms the chief interest. Future arrangements conform to the regular programme that has proved so satisfactory in the past. Secretary: G. C. Low, 272, Boldmere Road, Erdington, Birmingham.

ST. STEPHENS (SALTASH).—Further outdoor games meetings have been held. At the indoor meetings the reconstruction of the track has made good progress, the old formation being entirely taken up and the rails relaid to a new design. This has necessitated the rebuilding of the baseboard in certain places. Members have indulged in Table Tennis and other games at recent meetings, and attendance continues to be satisfactory. Secretary: B. Braund, 9, Homer Park, Saltash.

WATERLOO (DUBLIN).—The progress of the Branch generally and the operation of the Branch layout continue to be satisfactory. An interesting development has been the installation of a single line branch in connection with the main line system. This is laid out in a similar manner to the real Kent and East Sussex Railway between Headcorn and Robertsbridge. Several locomotives have been allocated to operate the miniature branch line, and these bear names taken from suitable prototypes of actual practice. The passenger and goods rolling stock provided for the branch system are kept separate from the stock used in main line running. Secretary: S. B. Carse, 38, Oakley Road, Ranelagh, Dublin.

Members of Sutton Coldfield H.R.C. Branch No. 303 with their Chairman, Mr. G. Harper; Secretary, C. C. Low. This Branch was incorporated in February of this year and is making satisfactory progress. Track meetings provide the chief interest of indoor meetings, and outdoor meetings for the running of Hornby Speed Boats also are held.

THE PRIORY (HIGH WYCOMBE).—A new layout plan has been developed that differs slightly from the arrangement previously in use. The doubling of the track in one section has added considerably to the convenience of operation. Great attention is paid to scenic and other details, and a feature of one of the terminal stations is the provision of a row of Dinky Toys Telephone Call Boxes. The first stage of electrification has been completed with satisfactory results. Timetable working is carried out successfully, and it has been found that other methods of operation tend to cause congestion on the line. Several members made a tour during August of the North Eastern Area of the L.N.E.R. The operating practice in various centres was observed with keen interest. Train working at local stations in the neighbourhood of the Branch premises is regularly watched. Secretary: J. T. Cosgrove, 54, Priory Road, High Wycombe, Bucks.

NEWTON ABBOT.—Good progress is being made in recruiting. A Branch Library is being formed, and members are busily engaged in collecting suitable interesting literature for it. Owing to its situation the Branch takes special interest in G.W.R. matters, and it is proposed to compile an engine book for the use of Branch members giving details of all G.W.R. locomotives from 1895 up to date. It is hoped to visit the Newton Abbot locomotive sheds and marshalling yard of the G.W.R. in the near future. Secretary: H. W. Tompkins, 15, Union Street, Newton Abbot, South Devon.

ARDSLEY.—The Branch layout now incorporates about 135 ft. of main line track. Considerable interest is shown in the operation of joint L.M.S.R. and L.N.E.R. services. A refinement of interest has been the fitting of suitable clips to all goods rolling stock in which small labels can be fitted showing the destination of the individual vehicles. Passenger trains are operated to timetables and their actual arrival times are entered up, together with explanations of any undue delays. Younger members of the Branch undertake duties as shunters and have also formed the break-down gang. Future arrangements include the provision of block telegraph instruments and telephones on the L.M.S.R. section of the layout, and it is proposed also to introduce a motor train for shuttle services between Sheffield and Barnsley. Secretary: G. Etherington, 3, Oxford Street, Ardsley, Barnsley.

WHITGIFT SCHOOL.—In a novel competition held recently, about 30 types of locomotives had their names, numbers and group lettering covered up and competitors had to identify the locomotives and to give as many important particulars as possible. Several meetings have been devoted to railway operations, and have included timetable working. A visit has been paid to the works of Metal Propellers Ltd., Croydon, where the party had a most interesting time. Secretary: J. A. Watson, 23, Addiscombe Avenue, Croydon, Surrey.

NORTHAMPTON.—Visits enjoyed by the Branch recently have included one to the factory of Bassett-Lowke Ltd., where the firm's showroom and the special department dealing with ship models were inspected. The L.M.S.R. Motive Power Depot at Wellingborough also has been visited, and members were conducted through the running sheds, fitting and repair shops and the forge, and inspected the coaling stage and water softening plant. The footplates of several locomotives were examined with great interest, particularly those of two of the "Garratt" articulated locomotives stationed at the depot for use on heavy main line coal trains. Secretary: D. K. Adams, 8, Cedar Road, Northampton.

Branches in Course of Formation

The following new Branches of the Hornby Railway Company are at present in process of formation, and any boys who are interested and desirous of linking up with this unique organisation should communicate with the promoters, whose names and addresses are given below.

LEICESTER—J. E. Duggan, 4, Belton Close, Park Estate, Leicester.

NORTHWICH—H. Tomlinson, 44, Northway, Winnington, Northwich, Ches.

WEST HADDON—M. Bush, "Stonelea," West Haddon, Nr. Rugby.

Branch Recently Incorporated

312. SWAN (KIDDERMINSTER)—A. Hamblin, Black Bull Hotel, Swan Street, Kidderminster.

Afoot in the Black Forest

Visiting a Youth Labour Camp

By J. M. S. Risk, B. Com.

LAST year I was fortunate enough to enjoy a tour of the Black Forest. With other members of my party, I stepped out of a train one sunny afternoon at Ottenhofen, a charming little village in the Northern Black Forest, and with our rücksacks on our backs we made a short day's walk up to Mummelsee, a lake that occupies the crater of an extinct volcano.

The entrance to a Work Camp in Southern Germany. The sentry is armed with a spade.

The days that followed were full of interest. As we tramped along we would see picturesque carts drawn by oxen moving slowly up a narrow road to some upland farm; then we would pass a party of Hitler youth, complete with Nazi emblems and short bayonets. The people we met wore quaint costumes and had many pleasing customs. Living as they do, surrounded by trees, they are adepts at utilising this abundant raw material in countless different ways. Fences, paths, bridges, gates, houses, carts, water troughs, signposts, clocks, farm implements—all are made from wood; and the people have a happy knack of exercising their skill for the benefit of the visitor. An attractive little saw mill we came upon near Todtnauberg was evidence of this. It is only about 2 ft. high, and its mill wheel revolving under the impulse of a jet of water from above drives a vertical saw blade for cutting up miniature logs.

We left the Black Forest by way of the Feldberg, or "field-mountain," its highest point. As its name implies, this mountain is completely covered with grass, although it is over 450 ft. higher than Ben Nevis, the highest mountain in Great Britain. At its summit there is a restaurant.

The second part of our trip was spent at Staad, where there is a water tower from which the higher parts of Constance are supplied with water. We passed two nights in this tower, for its seven lower storeys form a most excellent youth hostel. From the seventh floor an external spiral staircase, shown in the lower illustration on this page, leads to the top of the tower. There is no lift, but energetic visitors who climb up to the summit are amply repaid by a magnificent view of Lake Constance and the surrounding country.

A water tower at Staad, near Lake Constance. The lower portion is used as a youth hostel.

During our visit we were given the opportunity of visiting a labour camp for youths, an invitation that we readily accepted. All young Germans now spend six months in such a camp doing manual labour, followed by their army service. We were shown through their barracks, at the gate of which there stood a sentry with a spade over his shoulder. We noticed that there was barbed wire round about the building. The rooms themselves appeared to be spacious, and on the walls of the living room were to be seen team slogans, such as "Struggle," "Faith" and "Justice."

According to a notice in the hall reveille is at five o'clock, but we were told later by members of the camp that in reality it was at 4.30 a.m. Physical drill occupies the first 20 min., and before breakfast beds have to be made and a visit paid to the wash room, the concrete floors of which do not impress one as being particularly inviting so early on a cold winter morning. Second breakfast comes after work for 3½ hrs., and at 1 p.m. all return to camp in time for dinner at two o'clock. The members are free for the rest of the day, with the proviso that everyone has to be in bed not later than 10 p.m. Saturday afternoon and the whole of Sunday also are free time. Board and lodging of course are provided, and in addition a nominal payment of about threepence a day is made. Bathing parades are held twice weekly on the shores of Lake Constance.

The members of this camp, about 150 in number, were engaged on the preparation of a piece of waste ground for a housing scheme. This involved the construction of roads and drains, and later houses for the accommodation of working class people were to be built on the site. The youths worked in groups under the direction of qualified artisans, and all seemed to be quite content with their lot. New members pass through a preliminary period during which their hours of work are gradually raised from two to the full number.

From Constance we sailed up the lake to Friedrichshafen, where the Zeppelin airships are built.

Competition Corner

OCTOBER CROSSWORD PUZZLE

CLUES ACROSS

2. Reason
6. Sea
9. Burden
10. Gift
11. Rushing stream
14. Poisons
17. Point of the compass
19. Lake
20. Seaman
22. Beverage
24. Shade of brown
25. Beast of burden
26. Discovers
28. Lofty
31. Shoot out
33. Conspirator
36. Gasp
39. Prepare
40. High mountain
41. Liable
44. Consume
45. Withhold
46. Claw
48. Solitary
49. Penetrate
51. Supplement
53. Retreat
54. Excuse
55. Incline
56. Country house

CLUES DOWN

1. Endeavour
3. Gathers
4. Cathode
5. To provide
6. Marsh
7. Wander
8. Implant
12. Rustic
13. In motion
15. Period
16. Understanding
18. Occupant
21. Isolated mass
23. Total
26. Alarms
27. Elementary
29. Past
30. Disclose
32. Metal
33. Machine
34. Rage
35. Bar
37. Article of clothing
38. Disloyalty
40. Receptacle for ashes
42. Domestic utensil
43. Ownership
45. Kingdom
47. Incline
50. Remove
52. Climbing annual herb

All *"M.M."* crossword puzzles have enjoyed exceptional popularity, principally, no doubt, because they are set for amusement rather than strenuous competitive effort. This month's puzzle will be found to follow the lines of those set in previous issues in that it is fair and interesting. The clues are all perfectly straightforward, and every word used can be found in Chambers' or any other standard dictionary. The rules that govern the solution of crossword puzzles are so well known that it is unnecessary to give any further explanation of the requirements of the competition.

Cash prizes of 21/–, 15/–, 10/6 and 5/– respectively will be awarded in order of merit to the senders of the four correct solutions that are neatest or most novel in presentation. The prizes will be duplicated for the Overseas section, which is open to all readers living outside Great Britain, Ireland, and the Channel Islands.

Entries should be addressed "October Crossword Puzzle, Meccano Magazine, Binns Road, Liverpool 13," and must be sent to reach this office not later than 31st October. Overseas closing date 30th January.

October Drawing Contest

Our artist readers will have been awaiting with eager anticipation the first of our new season's series of drawing and painting competitions. For the benefit of new readers, we must explain that each month throughout the coming winter we shall feature a drawing or painting competition that will provide every reader with an opportunity of displaying his artistic skill. No special subjects will be set, and the monthly prizes will be offered simply for the best drawings or paintings submitted during the month.

The entries each month will be divided into the usual two sections, A for readers aged 16 and over and B for those under 16, and cash prizes of 21/– and 10/6 will be awarded in each section. A separate set of prizes will be reserved in the Overseas section.

Entries to the October competition must be addressed "October Drawing Contest, Meccano Magazine, Binns Road, Liverpool 13," and must arrive not later than 31st October. Overseas closing date, 30th January, 1937.

Competition Closing Dates

HOME

October Crossword Puzzle ...	31st October
October Drawing Contest ...	31st October

OVERSEAS

July Sketchogram Contest ...	31st October
July Photo Contest	31st October
August Crossword Puzzle ...	30th November
August Photo Contest... ...	30th November
September Point Words Contest	31st December
September Photo Contest ...	31st December
October Crossword Puzzle ...	30th January
October Drawing Contest ...	30th January

Watch the Closing Dates:

Competitors, both Home and Overseas, are particularly requested to make a careful note of the closing dates of the competitions.

In sending entries to competitions that are divided into age groups, competitors should take particular care to mark their ages clearly on the back of the entry. It is not sufficient merely to indicate the age group, as age allowances are given to ensure equality of opportunity for the younger competitors.

COMPETITION RESULTS

HOME

August Crossword Puzzle.—1. J. K. Robinson (Dunton Bassett). 2. D. Morley Davies (Maesteg). 3. B. Hardie (Bristol 9). 4. E. Hooper (Exeter). Consolation Prize: R. Richards (London, E.5).

August Photo Contest.—The standard of entries to this competition was probably the highest that we have ever experienced and the judges had considerable difficulty in deciding the destination of the prizes. The work generally showed considerable interest of subject and high technical quality. The awards were as follows: First Prizes: Section A, A. B. Bishop (Bristol 4); Section B, R. F. Y. Randall (Oxford). Second Prizes: Section A, J. R. Tottle (Taunton); Section B, R. Bowler (London, W.4.). Consolation Prize: V. L. Breeze (Lewes).

OVERSEAS

May Photo Contest.—First Prizes: Section A, F. D. Aria (Bombay 7); Section B, E. W. Honey (Palmerston North, N.Z.). Second Prizes: Section A, K. J. Orams (Wellington, N.Z.); Section B, E. Azzopardi (Sliema, Malta).

May Crossword Puzzle.—1. J. R. Dingle (Halifax, N.S., Canada). 2. H. W. Galea (Alexandria, Egypt). 3. G. E. McKinnon (N. Sydney, N.S.W.). 4. J. A. Rodriguez (Montreal, Canada).

NOTICE TO INTENDING COMPETITORS: Entrants to drawing and similar competitions are asked to note that unsuccessful entries can only be returned if a stamped addressed cover is sent with the entry.

How Sugar is Extracted from Beet

By R. Cox

In recent years the sugar beet industry has been greatly developed in this country, and I was very pleased to have an opportunity of seeing how sugar is produced at the Felsted Factory. The beet is stored in silos of 1,000 tons capacity, and at this particular factory there are 10 of these stores. Each silo consists of a very long trough, perhaps 20 ft. in depth, along the bottom of which runs a narrow trench about 3 ft. deep. A stream of water rushing through the trench carries the beet into the factory.

On reaching the factory the beet is held up by grilles, the water proceeding onward to the filtration plant, whither it emerges to be used once more. A total of 8½ million gallons of water is used daily. The beet is lifted from the stream by a wheel, resembling a waterwheel, that scoops it on to a belt conveyor leading to a washer inside the factory. This consists of a long tank through which passes a swift stream of water that is whipped into fury by steel arms, and from it another conveyor carries the beet to a picking table, where skilled workmen remove any stones and other foreign matter.

The beet is now ready for cutting up. It is carried to the top of the building by a bucket conveyor and tipped into a hopper that automatically inverts itself when half a ton of beet is inside. This measures the amount of beet passing through the factory. The roots drop into slicers, which are armed with whirling knives that chop them into shreds, known as "cossettes," from which the sugar is dissolved out in longitudinal tanks fitted with stirring gear and filled with boiling water. The exhausted cossettes still contain 2 per cent. sugar. They are taken to another part of the building, where they are dried in ovens for use as cattle food.

The sugar solution is run into tanks. Lime is added, and carbon dioxide is then passed in until a precipitate is formed. The carbonated juice is then filtered, and the material removed by the filtration is called lime-cake. This process is repeated three times, and its purpose is to remove any earthy taste from the sugar.

The juice has 15 per cent. of sugar in it, and is next evaporated to form a syrup containing 60 per cent. After filtering this is transferred to the sugar boilers where it is boiled until the sugar crystallises out. Along with the crystals is a thick syrup. The mixture is whirled round at high speed in centrifugal machines, which separate out the best crystals of white sugar and free them from molasses and small crystals. These are taken back to the boilers, and further treatment there, followed by centrifuging, give brown sugar crystals. The final residue of the process is molasses.

After crystallising the sugar is sent to the refinery. The quantity of beet treated daily in the factory at the time of my visit was 2,000 tons. This yielded 325 tons of sugar and 150 tons of pulp, and in the season 450 men were employed in three shifts for 100 days.

According to the most recent figures the world's production of sugar from beet is about 9,000,000 tons, of which the United Kingdom produced 600,000 tons.

Aboard H.M. Aircraft Carrier "Glorious"

By E. Azzopardi

The first thing that impressed me when I visited H.M. aircraft carrier *"Glorious,"* off Malta last year, was the vastness of the decks. There are two decks, and the upper one is wider than the lower one. It has three white lines painted along its full length, one in the middle and two at the sides. These lines are to guide the aeroplanes when landing upon the deck. I was interested to see a jet of steam rising from a hole in the middle line, and I learnt from the lieutenant who was my guide that it served to indicate the direction of the wind, a matter of great importance when the aircraft aboard are about to take-off.

When not engaged in flying the aircraft are stored in vast hangars on the lower deck, and they are taken down to these one at a time by two lifts, the floors of which form part of the top deck of the ship. Fully equipped aircraft repair shops are also situated on the lower deck.

While the lieutenant was explaining these and other things to me several aeroplanes from the ship were droning overhead, and I was permitted to watch them carry out certain exercises. I was greatly interested in the landing practice, during which each machine flew so low that it almost touched the deck, but did not actually land; then each machine landed three times in succession. Special palisades consisting of wires carried on bars extend outward from the side of the ship so that if an aeroplane runs off the deck it does not fall into the sea. During the exercises a destroyer, referred to as a "finder," followed the aircraft carrier, presumably to give aid in the event of any of the machines landing in the sea instead of upon the ship.

Immediately each aeroplane touched the deck at the conclusion of the exercises, the men of the special handling party assigned to it, who had been waiting alongside the palisades, got hold of the machine and pushed it on to one of the lifts. The wheel chocks were quickly put in place, the wings folded back, and the aeroplane taken below. When the elevator ascended again a signal was given for the next machine to land; and this process was repeated until each machine was safely housed below.

The Vogue of the Miniature Camera

An old Chinese proverb says: "One picture is worth ten thousand words," and certainly holiday-makers seem to be realising the truth of this saying if one may judge by the eager way in which snaps are shown to friends. The most remarkable thing about cameras is the way in which they have decreased in size. The modern high-class camera, weighing only a few ounces and producing a negative measuring no more than 1 in. by 1½ in., is so remarkably efficient and so easy to use as to make larger instruments unnecessary except for certain special purposes.

The Zeiss Ikon Contax is a prominent example of this type of miniature camera. For this beautiful little instrument a series of 13 interchangeable lenses have been specially constructed at the famous optical works of Carl Zeiss, Jena. One of these lenses is so rapid—f/1.5—that with it instantaneous pictures can be obtained of such subjects as express trains travelling through stations at night, acrobats performing at the circus, or machinery at work in factories, all with the ordinary artificial lighting. The definition given by these lenses is amazingly keen. At a recent exhibition of enlargements one picture measured 6 ft. by 4 ft., 1,370 times larger than the original negative, and the definition was practically perfect.

The best miniature cameras of this type, fitted with very rapid shutters, are necessarily expensive, but a Zeiss Ikon miniature camera, with many of the advantages of more expensive instruments, can be obtained for as little as 18/6. This camera will take first-class photographs within its limitations, and it is constructed with the same excellent workmanship that distinguishes all Zeiss Ikon cameras, full details of which can be obtained from Zeiss-Ikon Ltd., 46, Mortimer House, Mortimer Street, London, W.1.

FIRESIDE FUN

NOT WHAT SHE WANTED

Tommy: "Mother, here is a parcel marked C.O.D."
Mother: "Tell the postman to take it back, I ordered herrings."

* * * *

Pupil: "Please teacher, I ain't got a pencil."
Teacher: "How many more times must I tell you not to say that? Listen: I haven't one, you haven't one, we haven't one, they haven't one."
Pupil: "But teacher, ain't nobody got one?"

* * * *

A young Naval officer was showing a lady friend over the ship.
"Awfully interesting," she said, "but tell me, do you close the portholes when the tide rises?"

* * * *

Mother was reproving her small son.
"You really must be more contented," she said. "You are always wishing for something you haven't got."
"Well, Mummie," pleaded young hopeful, "what else can I wish for?"

* * * *

Pat and Mike were walking along an old road in Ireland when they came to a gibbet. "Now, Pat," said Mike, "if that gibbet had its due, where would you be?"
"Arrah," replied Pat, "I'd be walking home by myself."

* * * *

Billy: "Dad, I'm going to be a detective. Can you tell me a good disguise?"
Dad: "Yes, wash your face."

* * * *

Irish motorist, puzzling over his petrol indicator. "It's at the half-way mark and I can't remember if that means half-full or half-empty."

* * * *

Little Jimmy (to old lady newly arrived, and whom he had never seen before): "So you're my grandmother, are you?"
Old Lady: "Yes, on your father's side."
Jimmy: "Well, you're on the wrong side; I can tell you that right now."

* * * *

Constable: "Stop; both your tyres are flat."
Cyclist: "I know; I let them down because the saddle was too high for me."

* * * *

Servant (to lion tamer in cage): "That grocer is here again demanding payment of his bill."
Lion Tamer: "Send him in."

* * * *

George: "Mother, may I go out in the street? Dad says there is going to be an eclipse of the sun."
Mother: "Yes, but don't get too close."

* * * *

THE CLUE

"Name of a dog," said the foreigner fiercely, as a porter dropped a trunk on his toes.
"Ow many letters?" replied the porter, who was a cross-word puzzle enthusiast.

PAST THE MARK

Lady: "You said you were so weak from hunger that you did not feel equal to work. Now that I have given you such a good dinner, surely you feel equal to doing some work in return?"
Tramp: "Madam, after your excellent repast I feel more than equal to work. I feel superior to it."

* * * *

A TALL STORY

Constable: "What are you doing there?"
Burglar: "A fortnight ago I picked up a front-door key, and now I'm trying to find out which house it fits so that I can give it back to the owner."

* * * *

Gentleman (at railway booking-office): "One first return—quick!"
Clerk: "Return to where, sir?"
Gentleman: "Why, here, you ass!"

* * * *

Little Girl: "Packet of pink dye, please."
Grocer: "For woollen or cotton goods?"
Little Girl: "It's for mother's indigestion. The doctor says she's to diet, and pink is her favourite colour."

* * * *

Dick: "Does your watch keep the correct time, old man?"
Jim: "Well, it did until I began to compare it with the radio broadcasts!"

* * * *

MacTavish: "I see ye're advertisin' life-size enlargements for 5/-."
Photographer: "Yes, sir!"
MacTavish: "Well, ah've brought along ma snap of the '*Queen Mary*.'"

* * * *

The village grocer was interviewing applicants for the post of messenger boy, and to each one he put questions to test his intelligence. "Well, my lad," he said to one bright-looking youth, "what would you do with a thousand pounds?"
The lad scratched his head thoughtfully. "I don't know, sir," he replied. "I didn't expect so much for a start."

* * * *

Workman (using pneumatic road drill): "I wish you'd stop humming, Harold. You get on my nerves."

* * * *

Speed Fiend (slowing down): "Gosh! Don't you feel glad you're alive!"
Timid Passenger: "'Glad' isn't the word—I'm amazed."

* * * *

Mother (preparing dinner): "Whatever have you done with the jelly, Tommy."
Tommy: "It was shivering, so I put it in front of the fire."

* * * *

"Won't you have a fork?"
"No, thanks, I never use forks; they leak so bad that they ain't no use."

* * * *

Old Lady: "Isn't it wonderful how these garage people know exactly where to set up a pump and get petrol!"

OF COURSE

Tom was rather inattentive, so the teacher asked him a test question. "Where was Solomon's temple?"
"On the side of his head, sir, the same as mine," replied Tom.

* * * *

Scotchman: "Doctor, what can I do to prevent seasickness?"
Doctor: "Have you a sixpence?"
Scotchman: "Yes, sir."
Doctor: "Well, hold it between your teeth."

* * * *

Bill: "I hear you are looking for work, Tom."
Tom: "Not necessarily; but I'd like a job."

* * * *

"If I'd been offered a plate wi' twa cakes on it, I'd have taken th' smaller."
"Weel, an' ye've got it," replied Jessie's greedy little brother, "so what's a' th' fuss aboot?"

* * * *

A little girl accompanied her mother into the Post Office, and thoughtfully surveyed the lady clerks behind the counter grille. "Mummy," she said after a while, "do all the people who have to go to prison come here?"

* * * *

Rastus: "Say, Sambo, what time in your life does yo' think yo' was scared de wust?"
Sambo: "Once when ah wuz callin' on a hen-house an' de farmer come in an' caught me. Boy, wuz ah scared!"
Rastus: "How are yo' shuah dat wuz de worstest yo' evah been scared?"
Sambo: "Cause de farmer grab me by de shoulder an 'say, 'White boy, wha' yo' doin' heah?'"

* * * *

The labourer at the top of the high building shouted down to his mate at the bottom, "I say, Jim. Come up here and listen!"
Slowly his mate climbed the ladder, and arrived at the top breathless. "What is it?" he panted. "I can't 'ear nothing."
"No," said the first. "Ain't it wonnerful quiet?"

* * * *

1st Girl: "Look at these cows, aren't they lambs?"
2nd Girl: "Yes, perfect ducks."

* * * *

"Terribly rough," said the lawyer on board the ocean liner.
"Well," said the farmer, "it wouldn't be near so rough if the captain would only keep in the furrows."

* * * *

Thomas had called on his tailor. "Isn't this bill rather steep?" he said.
"You should know best, sir," said the tailor, "for it was run up by you."

* * * *

P–LEASE C–ONSTABLE!

Small boy: "Will you go in there for me, Mister?"
Constable: "What for?"
Small boy: "I want a catalogue and the advert. said 'send a P.C.'"

SETS (POSTAGE EXTRA)

5 Angola ...	...2d.	10 Ceylon ...	...2d.
10 ,, ...	...5d.	1 ,, Jubilee	...2d.
15 ,, ...	...8d.	5 Cyprus ...	...3d.
5 Azores ...	...2d.	10 ,, ...	...6d.
10 ,, ...	...5d.	1 ,, Jubilee	...3d.
15 ,, ...	...8d.	3 Charkari	...2d.
5 Cape Verde	...2d.	5 Gold Coast	...3d.
10 ,, ,,	...5d.	10 ,, ,,	...6d.
15 ,, ,,	...8d.	1 ,, ,, Jubilee	2d.
5 Guinea ...	...2d.	3 Grenada ...	...2d.
10 ,, ...	...5d.	1 ,, Jubilee	2d.
5 India Port	...3d.	5 Hong Kong	...2d.
5 Mozambique	...2d.	10 ,, ,,	...5d.
10 ,, ...	...5d.	1 ,, ,, Jubilee	3d.
15 ,, ...	...8d.	5 Kenya ...	...3d.
5 ,, Com.	2d.	1 ,, Jubilee	...3d.
10 ,, ,,	...4d.		

J. RUSSELL

23, Shanklin Drive, Westcliff-on-Sea

THE "OLYMPIC" GAMES PACKET FREE!

This splendid packet of 36 different stamps includes a fine COMPLETE SET of stamps issued to commemorate the Olympic Games, and you should secure them FREE immediately. Included also is one of the beautiful Canadian Mounted Police stamps, sets of Bohemia and Spain, many British Colonials, Brazil (aeroplane), Belgium (late King Albert), Set Hungary (crown of St. Peter), Australia (beautiful large Centenary Stamp), and a fine pair of Jamaican Stamps. Finally, to just 500 applicants we are including a fine green unused Bulgaria and the scarce Costa Rica Map Stamp. This offer cannot be repeated. Send immediately 2d. for postage, requesting approvals and free Price List. *(Stamp Collections and loose lots purchased.)*

LISBURN & TOWNSEND LTD. (Dept. M.M.), LIVERPOOL, 3

FREE WONDERFUL 1936 OFFER 25 NEW ISSUES AND NOVELTIES

Including **Andorra** (1935), fine new **Cayman Islands** (map of Islands), obsolete Austria, China, Denmark, **Gwalior** Service, Hungary (Statesman Szechenyi), **new Kenya** (Kavirondo Cranes), **Roumania** (new portrait of King Carol), and many others. I will send this collection **absolutely free** to all stamp collectors sending 2d. postage (abroad 4d.).

G. P. KEEF, Willingdon, EASTBOURNE

THE FIRST STAMP Ever Issued

(British 1840 Penny Black) for P.O. 3/3! It is guaranteed genuine in every respect. Its companion stamp (1840, 2d. blue) for a further **5/–** (cat. 15/–)! Other "Classics" which every Collector should have are the **Cape of Good Hope Triangulars**; we offer 1d. rose (cat. 40/–) for **12/6**; 4d. blue (cat. 15/–) for **5/–**; and 6d. pale lilac (cat. 40/–) at **12/6**. Superb approvals of any country against approved English References or a deposit. **Full Lists Free.**

NORRIS & CO. (Dept. M), Norwood, London, S.E.19.

THE "DIAMOND" PACKET IS THE ONLY PACKET

OF UNSORTED STAMPS ON THE MARKET with 15 years' reputation behind it. It contains approx. **1,000 UNSORTED STAMPS** from Convents abroad. **MANY RARE STAMPS** have been found in it. 1 pkt., 1/6; 3 pkts., 3/9; 5 pkts., 6/–. All post free inland. Colonies 3d. per pkt. extra. Foreign, 6d. extra.

Ask your stationer for the "Diamond" packet.

SPECIAL: TURKS IS. JUBILEES complete set, used or unused, 5/6.

O. NERUSH (Dept. A), 68, TURNPIKE LANE, HORNSEY, LONDON, N.8

THE 'SHIP' PACKET

This marvellous packet is offered under cost as an advertisement, **45 different stamps each with a ship on it.** A regular armada. **GABOON,** New Issue **SENEGAL** (Canoe), wonderful flotilla of caravels from **DENMARK** (complete set), **NEW CALEDONIA, IVORY COAST, COSTA RICA,** a fleet of **7 CHINESE** junks usually sold at 10d., **TRINIDAD & TOBAGO, MAURITIUS, SOUTH WEST AFRICA, NEWFOUNDLAND, U.S.A., B. GUIANA,** set of **S. AFRICA, GREECE, POLAND, INDO-CHINA, FRENCH OCEANIA,** etc. Price **4½d.,** postage **1½d.** (abroad 3d. extra). Purchasers of this packet asking for approvals receive **FREE** set of **3 SPAIN** (Columbus, each with his ship on it). Senders of addresses of stamp collectors receive **FREE** set of **6 VENEZUELA** or **6 PERSIA, 100 BRITISH COLONIALS 1/–, 20 AIRPOST 6d., 6 TRIANGULARS 6d., 50 PERSIA 4/–, 2 ASTRID** (mourning stamps) **2½d., VOLUMES OF B.O.P. CHEAP.**

H. C. WATKINS (M. Dept.), Granville Road, BARNET

OCTOBER SPECIALS

1 Abyssinia ...	1d.	1 New Guinea ...	1d.
1 Antigua ...	1d.	2 New Hebrides...	2d.
1 Ascension ...	1d.	2 Niue Island ...	3d.
2 North Borneo...	2d.	1 Nyasaland ...	1d.
1 Br. Honduras	1d.	2 Palestine ...	1d.
1 Brunei ...	1d.	2 Papua	3d.
5 Cayman Islands	4d.	1 St. Helena ...	1d.
2 Cook Islands ...	3d.	1 St. Kitts Nevis	1d.
1 Dominica (Br.)	1d.	1 St. Lucia ...	1d.
2 Falkland Is. ...	2d.	3 Sarawak ...	3d.
3 Fiji Islands ...	3d.	2 Seychelles ...	2d.
1 Gambia ...	1d.	1 Sierra Leone ...	1d.
1 Gibraltar ...	1d.	1 Tanganyika ...	1d.
1 Gilbert & Ellis	1d.	2 Trans-Jordan ...	2d.
1 Jaipur	1d.	1 Tonga	1d.
1 Leeward Islands	1d.	1 Trengganu ...	1d.
1 Montserrat ...	1d.	2 Turks & Caicos	2d.
7 Morocco Agencies	5d.	1 Virgin Islands...	1d.
5 Nauru	8d.	2 Western Samoa	3d.
2 Nepal	2d.	1 Zanzibar ...	1d.

10 Different TRIANGULAR Stamps 1/2

10 Different Australian Commemoratives 7d.

Packet of 35 French Colonials, all 25c. values, all different, all mint and many obsolete. Cheap at 3/11. All Orders Postage Extra.

Packet of Mounts FREE with all orders of 2/6 or over. Purchasers of 5/– worth or over will receive ALSO a MIDGET POCKET CASE, FREE.

EDWARD SANDELL,
10, EVELYN GROVE, SOUTHALL, MDX.

Business by Post. No Callers.

NOW READY! - - -

THE 1937 EDITION OF THE STANDARD CATALOGUE of POSTAGE STAMPS OF THE WORLD - -

Enlarged, Further Improved and Completely Revised

The ideal Reference Catalogue for the beginner and general collector. Records every issue of the World's Postage and Air Mail Stamps, but omits all confusing minor varieties. The Jubilee Stamps and latest New Issues described and priced right up to date.

Start the season well by placing your order now, or ask for descriptive leaflet and free copies of our interesting price lists.

Price **5s.** Postage 6d. extra Abroad 9d.

Whitfield King & Co., Ipswich, Eng. Established 1869

ONE THOUSAND STAMPS ON APPROVAL

From which you may select any 100 for 3/–. This selection is not made up of the very commonest varieties, but contains stamps catalogued at 1/– each or more. (I do not sell less than 100.)

*Special offer of 30 different Scandinavia and Iceland, post free, 7½d. (The Iceland stamps alone are Cat. at least 3/–.)

H. HARDY, "Hoyland," Potter Heigham, Norfolk.

Mint BERMUDA New Issue Packet FREE

Magnificent opening season's offer: **Grand Packet** of **28 British Colonials** inc. above handsome stamp, a **Rare Silver Jubilee, Cyprus** (1934 Salamis) and soon to be obsolete K.G. issues. Write now for this grand free gift. Send 2d. post (6d. abroad) and ask for my **Modern** approvals.

CAMPBELL, 71, Manor Rd., Tankerton, Kent.

The NEW "TRANSPORT" Packet

Contains a wonderful assortment of 44 foreign and colonial stamps including the following which depict various means of transportation, **Tunis** (water carrier), **Senegal** (bridge and boats), **Mauritania** (crossing desert), **Mid. Congo** (train and bridge), **Sth. Africa** (ship), **Germany** (aeroplane), **Austria** (horseman), **Indo China** (boat), **Mozambique** (aeroplane), **Gaboon** (raft), **Greece** (bridge and liner), **St. Pierre and M.** (trawler), **Fr. Guinea** (native carriers), **Dutch Indies** (Steamboat), **Madagascar** (native transport), **Brazil** (aeroplane), **Belgium** (train), **Roumania** (aeroplane), **Newfoundland** (steamship), **Fr. Morocco** (camels). Price **6d.** All purchasers asking for approvals will receive large **Ceylon** pictorials free.

BURDOCK & FLURY,
4, MARLBOROUGH ROAD, LONDON, S.W.19.

6 Bermuda Pictorial to 3d., mint...	1/1
7 Kenya Pictorial to 50c., used	6d.
4 Queen Astrid Mourning, mint	6d.
1 Holland Triangle, 6c., used	2d.

Post 1½d. extra. Selections sent on request.

J. R. MORRIS, 9, Audley Road, Folkestone, Kent.

"ABBEY" on a packet spells VALUE!

Unused Pictorials (Colonial, Air, and Foreign), 15 for 6d., 35 for 1/–. Special **Mixture** Used and Unused, 15 for 6d. Postage extra.

ABBOTT BROS., 16, Sedgemoor Road, Liverpool, 11.

Tanna Touva Triangular Pictorial Packet—FREE!

Another Globe-Trotter luxury surprise gift—**Tanna Touva** (Northern Mongolia) Picturesque Triangular, **Mozambique Air Mail,** Mint **Tanganyika** Pictorial, large mint pictorials from **Madagascar, Morocco, Re-union, Martinique, Syria, Andorra, Gaboon,** some lovely stamps from **South America, Belgian Mourning Stamp,** and others—a veritable stamp feast—**FREE.** Send 1½d. stamp postage for Globe-Trotter approval selections, famous for sensational value. Ask for particulars of **FREE** stamps every 14 days!! Write now—you must not miss the treat in store for you.

GLOBE-TROTTER, 17, Winchester Road, Birchfield, Birmingham

ALL BRITISH COLONIAL APPROVALS

Fine BRITISH COLONIAL NEW PICTORIAL SETS OF CAYMAN ISLANDS AND BERMUDA, FREE to all Collectors sending 1½d. stamp and requesting **ALL BRITISH COLONIAL APPROVALS, BRITISH COLONIALS ONLY** on approval at bargain prices, including **JUBILEE** and new **PICTORIAL** issues, West Indies, East and West Africa, Cyprus, Iraq, Newfoundland, Papua and many other fine Colonials. (No stamps sent Abroad.) **C. H. SHAW (Dept. M.10), 95, CHRISTCHURCH AVENUE, KENTON, HARROW.**

THE HISTORICAL SIDE OF STAMP COLLECTING

ALL stamp collectors, whether beginners or experts, realise that the history of the civilised world since the introduction of stamps can be traced in their collections. Until 1914 this historical interest was largely confined to changes of monarchy, the accession of a new king or emperor naturally being followed by the issue of new stamps; but on rarer occasions there were also sudden changes or revolutions that led to the production of new and interesting stamps.

A French war orphan charity issue of 1917.

All previous records of this kind have been surpassed during the years since the outbreak of the Great War, and a complete collection of stamps issued since 1914 would be very extensive. An album containing it would be a guide book to history, for it would remind its owner of practically every event of importance and also of many minor happenings that now are almost forgotten. For instance, how many people still remember that in 1918 a Siamese Expeditionary Force left for Europe? Collectors who possess a Siamese stamp specially overprinted at that time with a Geneva Red Cross are almost the only people who have not forgotten this interesting event, of which they also are reminded by the existence of a series of stamps of the same country over which the word *"Victory"* is printed. The overprint is in English and Siamese.

A Hungarian stamp issued in 1920 to raise funds for prisoners of war in Siberia.

Overprinting has always been a favourite device for devoting a stamp issue to special purposes. Readers no doubt are familiar with stamps of British colonies and dominions on which the words *"War Tax"* or *"War Stamp"* have been overprinted. This draws their attention to the practice followed during the War in many countries of increasing postal charges in order to bring in extra revenue. An excellent example is the green 1 cent Canadian stamp illustrated on this page. The presence of stamps of this class in collectors' albums helps to bring home the fact that wars are luxuries that must be paid for.

Another reminder of the difficulties caused by the War is given by the numerous charity stamps issued by European States in which distress was rampant. A very interesting example of a stamp of this kind is illustrated on this page. It is a brown 60 filler Hungarian stamp, and the inscription at the bottom shows that on it there was a premium of two korona. The purpose to which the extra charge was to be devoted is well indicated by the pathetic picture on the face of the stamp of prisoners of war behind a formidable barbed wire fence.

One of the early issues of Czecho-Slovakia.

An interesting issue of charity stamps was made in France in 1926, and one of these is the 50c. stamp illustrated on this page. The premium of 10c. was collected for the support of French war orphans.

Several existing countries were broken up and new states were created as the result of the Great War, and these changes can easily be traced by a careful examination of stamps issued during that period. A good example is the change from the Imperial Russian Empire to the Union of Soviet Socialist Republics. The last Czarist stamps were overprinted on the back in order to make them legal currency when ordinary coins were scarce, and many of them were issued by the first Revolutionary Government. A new stamp issue also was planned in order to mark the changed conditions, but before it was introduced a further revolution brought the Bolsheviks into power.

The first definitive issue produced by the Irish Free State.

From 1918 to 1921 no stamps of any kind were produced, the Soviet Government having abolished them in order to make the posts free. Since 1921, however, an extensive series of stamps of all kinds has appeared. These include charitable and commemorative stamps, in addition to those designed for ordinary postal use. From a historical point of view the most interesting are those on which appears the portrait of Lenin, the founder of modern Russia. The violet 5,000 rouble stamp illustrated is not one of these, but is typically Russian. It was issued in 1922 and is symbolic in character, the design being suggestive of the crafts and industries of a modern state.

An early Soviet Russian issue.

A curious feature of this stamp is its large nominal value. A similar stamp issued at the same time actually had the nominal value of 22,500 roubles. At pre-war rates this would have been equivalent to about £2,400 sterling. This did not mean that the stamp was very valuable, but that the rouble was practically worthless for international exchange purposes.

Perhaps the most interesting of the new States that came into existence as a result of the Great War is Czecho-Slovakia, one of the countries carved out of the old Austrian empire. The orange 60 heller stamp illustrated is a typical Czecho-Slovakian stamp. It appeared in 1919, only six months after the revolutionary Committee of Prague had issued the first Czecho-Slovakian stamp.

In many respects the history of Italy after the War is as interesting as that of any country. The 5 lire Italian stamp illustrated on the next page is one of a special issue that appeared in 1923 in commemoration of the triumph of Mussolini the Fascist leader. It is bold in design, and leaves no doubt of its origin, for on each side are shown the bundles of rods, or fasces, bound round an axe, from which the name of the modern movement was taken. These rods were carried before the higher magistrates of ancient Rome as a symbol of authority.

Changes due to conquest also may be traced by means of stamps. Thus during the War British, Belgian and Portuguese troops took part in the attack on German East Africa, and overprinted stamps of all three countries were used during the campaign. Similarly, the postal changes made as the British advanced and the Turks retired in Mesopotamia form an accurate record of events in this theatre of the War.

A very interesting case occurred in the Marshall Islands in the Pacific Ocean. These were German possessions until 1914, when they were taken by the (*Continued on next page*)

A special Canadian War Tax issue of 1915.

Stamp Collecting—(*Continued from previous page*)

Japanese and handed over to Australia. The first stamps issued after the change took place actually were German in origin and were overprinted "G.R.I." to indicate British ownership!

Nearer home than either Italy or Russia, an event that to us is of equal importance led to the introduction of an entirely new issue of stamps. This was the creation of the Irish Free State, and we illustrate one of the stamps to which the change gave rise. This is the 1d. carmine stamp, issued in 1922, the immediate successor of a series of British stamps overprinted in Gaelic characters for use in the newly created state.

The 5L. value of Italy's 1923 issue, commemorating the establishment of the Fascist Regime.

The post war stamps of Turkey and particularly the issues of 1926 are illustrative of one of the most astonishing revivals in history. At the close of the War, Turkey appeared to be at the last gasp. It seemed quite certain that no scrap of European territory would remain to her, and later she was faced with the prospect of the loss of more of her territory, this time in Asia. The genius of one man not only prevented the break-up of the country, but enabled Turkey to take effective possession of the little that remained to her of her former possessions in Europe. Through his efforts Turkey is now well governed, and is going ahead rapidly in regard to industry and to social conditions.

The higher values of the 1926 issue bear the portrait of Mustapha Kemal Pasha, the dictator who has led Turkey back into the forefront of near Eastern nations. A point of interest is that the portrait shows the present ruler of Turkey in European dress, and at the foot of the stamp there is a value inscription in Roman characters. These two features were significant of the change from the old Ottoman Regime to modern progressive methods.

Incidentally it is possible to trace in the 1926 issue an interesting compliment to the quality of British printing. The Turkish issue of 1913 was engraved and printed in London by Messrs. Bradbury, Wilkinson and Company. During the war the Turks necessarily had to go to their Austrian allies for fresh supplies of stamps. With the cessation of hostilities and the resumption of friendly trading relations between Britain and Turkey, the Turkish Government again placed their stamp printing contracts with the British firm.

In the space at our disposal in this article it is impossible to deal with more than a few of the interesting historical stories and developments that are portrayed in stamp issues. Almost every country can provide such a story, however, and readers who follow up the illustrations we have given will find a wealth of fascinating material.

Stamp Gossip

and Notes on New Issues

King Edward VIII Stamps

The whole philatelical world was taken by surprise by the appearance of the new King Edward VIII stamps on 1st September. Only five days' warning were given by the Post Office, and previously only a few Post Office officials and the printers had the slightest inkling that the stamps were ready.

The design of the new stamp is reproduced on this page. Three values only, ½d., 1½d. and 2½d., each using this design, were issued experimentally on 1st September and were available generally for five days. Subsequently supplies were obtainable on demand. A penny value followed on 14th September. Three thousand million of the stamps have been printed, which supply should be sufficient to last until the New Year.

The outstanding feature of the stamp is its simplicity. This was achieved by using the head of a specially posed photograph taken by the Hugh Cecil Studios. All the scrolls and curls of the King George and King Edward VII issues have been swept away, and the stamp relies for its attractiveness upon its simple dignity and the rich colour achieved by the photogravure process.

Another point of special interest in the stamp is that the paper bears the new Royal cipher *E 8 R* followed by a crown. The watermark runs throughout the paper and several portions of separate watermarks will be found in each stamp.

There has been much criticism of the design in quarters where the photographic basis of the stamp was not appreciated, but an official announcement made a few days after the appearance of the stamps showed that public opinion was overwhelmingly favourable.

A London Stamp Exhibition

Readers within easy reach of London will be interested to learn of the Stamp Exhibition that is being staged at the Dorland Hall in Lower Regent Street from 17th to 24th October.

Many fascinating exhibits have been arranged, including a demonstration of stamp printing and a model Post Office at which special cancellation marks will be applied to all correspondence posted at the Exhibition. Competitions will be held for the best displayed and written-up set of pictorial or commemorative stamps laid out on not more than three sheets.

Particulars of the competition and free invitation tickets of admission to the Exhibition can be obtained by "*M.M.*" readers from Mr. T. Todd, Organising Secretary, 36, Camomile Street, London, E.C.3.

We thank Stanley Gibbons Ltd. for their courtesy in loaning the stamps from which the illustrations for our stamp pages have been made.

New Season's Catalogues

With the publication of the 1937 catalogues, the popular stamp season may be said to have opened officially, and those collectors who have neglected their stamps throughout the summer must make a special effort if they are to make up leeway.

As a result of the heavy demand for stamps of all varieties since the Silver Jubilee issues started, the greatest boom stamp collecting has ever known, the new large Gibbons' Catalogue shows 22,000 price alterations, affecting common and rare varieties alike. The most interesting of the new pricings are the figures quoted for Silver Jubilee stamps. These will startle the laggards who have delayed completing their sets in the hope that a dying boom would bring easier prices.

The large Gibbons' Catalogue, or, to give it its correct title, Gibbons' Priced Catalogue of the Stamps of the World, is the standard philatelical reference book. Although it now contains 1,816 pages, the price remains unaltered at 15/–.

The 1937 edition of the Gibbons' Simplified Catalogue appears simultaneously with the larger one. This publication has achieved an amazing success, and has reached its fifth edition in 2½ years. The secret of its success is that it caters for the average collector, who does not wish to be bothered with minor differences of shade, perforation or watermark. The present edition comprises 1,046 pages and lists 55,376 different stamps. The price remains unaltered at 5/–.

Both of the Gibbons catalogues may be obtained from any stamp dealer or direct from the publishers, Stanley Gibbons Ltd., 391, Strand, London, W.C.2.

The new edition of the old favourite catalogue of young collectors, the Whitfield King Standard Catalogue, was published on 1st September. It retains all its familiar features, and now includes an index that will prove a popular innovation. It includes all important watermark and perforation details, but avoids the minor varieties that so frequently confuse beginners.

The total number of stamps listed in this catalogue is 62,155, of which 1,380 are new varieties. Europe heads the list with 19,727 stamps, of which 517 are new issues, and Africa comes next with 13,657 stamps, including 242 new varieties. Then follow Asia, 11,280 stamps and 127 new varieties, America, 10,822 and 371, West Indies, 3,594 and 81, and Oceania, 3,075 and 42.

The Whitfield King catalogue can be obtained from any stamp dealer price 5/–, or direct from Whitfield King and Co., Ipswich, price 5/6 post paid.

MECCANO MAGAZINE

Editorial Office:
Binns Road, Liverpool 13
England

Vol. XXI. No. 11
November, 1936

With the Editor

Mr. Frank Hornby

I find it difficult to express adequately my feelings in regard to the death of Mr. Frank Hornby. The severing of a close association extending over a great number of years comes as a great shock, and it takes time to adjust oneself to the new circumstances resulting from the loss of a strong personality.

I feel that I cannot do better here than quote the following gracious tribute from Emeritus Professor H. S. Hele-Shaw, D.Sc., LL.D., D.Eng., M.Inst.C.E., F.R.S., Past President of the Institution of Mechanical Engineers. It was to this famous engineer that Mr. Hornby first submitted his invention, and his quick appreciation of the unlimited possibilities of this constructional toy gave help and encouragement at a time when it was badly needed.

Dr. Hele-Shaw writes: "It is always a sad thing, although alas! it often happens, that when a man has reached success, even beyond his wildest dreams, the hand of death deprives him of a well-earned, happy and peaceful old age. Such is the case of the late Mr. Frank Hornby.

"It must be well over 40 years ago that I first met him, when I was Professor of Engineering at the Liverpool University. I am not sure if I was actually the first to whom he appealed for help from his little workshop below stairs, where I think there was a small lathe and a few tools, and where he began a work which has brought not merely enjoyment to young and old, but, to the young especially, something beyond mere amusement—the laying of the foundations of sound principles in mechanics which has been of incalculable service to the world.

"I forget what I wrote about Mr. Hornby's work and ambition, but he told me, when he proudly showed me round the Meccano Works during the visit of the Institution of Mechanical Engineers in 1934, that he had been able to borrow £5 as a result of my letter; and with a twinkle in his eye, assured me it had been promptly paid back again!

A Trade given to this Country

"It is with no little pride that his fellow workers can look upon the trade that 'Meccano' and Hornby trains have given to this country—namely, mechanical toys, which trade had before been largely in the hands of foreign countries. Although these countries had a long start, it is owing to him, and in later years to the help which he received from many able men, that Meccano and the name of Hornby are universally recognized as in advance of anything previously achieved in model-making.

"It was a great triumph for Mr. Hornby when the American Courts decided that his work, although not perhaps protected by impregnable patents, was of such national importance as to secure the protection of the American Government in the face of powerfully organized imitation.

"These few remarks have been written at short notice in appreciation of a man whose brave and uphill work to establish a great industry will never be forgotten. It is safe to say that the work of Frank Hornby, and the name 'Meccano' associated with his name, is secure for all time on the Roll of Fame."

A Message to all Readers

The news of the death of my father, Frank Hornby, has been received in all quarters, and especially in that great and wonderful country called Meccanoland, with the deepest regret, and I wish to thank very sincerely all those who have written to express their sympathy.

As the inventor of Meccano, and the head of the Meccano Guild and the Hornby Railway Company, the great organisations founded by him, he came into close and affectionate contact with the youth of the whole civilised world. The responsibility of maintaining this contact falls upon me as his elder son and the first Meccano boy, and I accept this responsibility as a great and sacred trust. I look back to the days when my father first began to see dimly the outlines of his great invention; and I recall vividly the wonderful evening when I helped him to cut out from a sheet of copper the very first Meccano parts.

I send my cordial wishes to readers of the "Meccano Magazine," to members of the Meccano Guild and of the Hornby Railway Company, to all Meccano boys, and to all to whom my father's invention and its developments have brought pleasure. I assure them that I shall do my utmost to further their interests and to carry on the high traditions associated with the name of Frank Hornby.

Yours very sincerely,

Roland G. Hornby

Frank Hornby

Inventor of the World's Most Famous Toy

MECCANO, like all other inventions that time has proved to be of real worth, did not emerge complete as the result of a sudden inspiration, but developed slowly as an idea, at first crude and dimly outlined, grew more and more sharply defined.

Frank Hornby was born in Liverpool. From his early boyhood he was interested in mechanical matters, and later, when to his great joy he became the owner of a little workshop of his own, his happiest hours were spent in making devices of his own contrivance. About this time he came across the famous book "*Self-Help*," by Samuel Smiles, in which are described the difficulties encountered by various inventors, and the way in which these were overcome. These stories appealed to young Hornby's imagination and fired him with the ambition to become an inventor. His first effort in this direction was a bold one—nothing else than the invention of a perpetual motion machine! Not knowing that he was attempting the impossible, he worked away at one scheme after another. Finally, of course, he had to admit defeat, but his time had not been wasted, for he had greatly improved his mechanical knowledge and skill. Turning now to simpler matters he produced various small inventions, all interesting, but of no practical value; there was always some flaw in each one that made it useless. For instance, he spent a great deal of time on a submarine that was to submerge and rise automatically. When it was tried out it submerged beautifully, but by no means could it be persuaded to come to the surface of its own accord!

Frank Hornby.

Frank Hornby commenced work in an office, and in due course rose to be chief managing clerk of a Liverpool firm of importers. He never abandoned his mechanical pursuits, however, and as the years passed by he gradually acquired a useful equipment of tools and a good all-round knowledge of engineering principles and methods. As his two sons grew up he delighted in making toys for them, but found it difficult to meet their continual demands for new ones. The trouble was that for every new toy new parts had to be made, because most of the parts of previous toys were useless for any but their original purpose. While casting about for some way of reducing this waste of time and material he happened to notice a large crane in operation. As he watched it he was struck by the essential simplicity of its construction, and the idea occurred to him that a model of it could be built with a comparatively small number of easily-made parts. Eagerly following up this idea, he gradually thought out a scheme of perforated parts that could be bolted together in any required positions, and afterwards could be unbolted and reassembled in different arrangements.

Full of enthusiasm for his new idea, Frank Hornby bought a large sheet of copper and a pair of shears, and hurried home to experiment with a series of perforated strips. Mr. Roland G. Hornby, his elder son, has often described to the writer the excitement that prevailed on that and many subsequent evenings, as he helped his father to prepare his parts. The strips were all cut to a width of half an inch, their lengths being $2\frac{1}{2}$ in., $5\frac{1}{2}$ in., and $12\frac{1}{2}$ in. respectively; and they were perforated with equal-sized holes at half-inch intervals, this being the special task of the son, who thus became in a real sense the very first Meccano boy.

Suitable rods and bolts were obtained from a watchmaker, but although Frank Hornby sought high and low he could not obtain nuts of the correct size, and therefore was obliged to make these himself. Angle brackets for fastening the strips together at right-angles were cut out of sheet copper. Wheels provided the next problem, for none of suitable size and construction could be bought; so the inventor had to work out his own design and have the wheels cast for him in a local brass foundry and then turned in the lathe. The next difficulty was to devise a suitable method of fixing the wheels on the rods. The usual collar and setscrew would of course have been satisfactory, but at the time this method seemed to him to be too expensive for his requirements, and he adopted a steel clip for the purpose. Subsequently he abandoned the clip in favour of the setscrew.

It was a long and weary time before all the parts were ready for trying out, but he was encouraged by the growing certainty that he was working along right lines. At last came the great day when he built up the first Meccano model, a crane, which ran on wheels and luffed and jibbed in the same manner as a real crane. It may be imagined what delight Frank Hornby and his sons took in building the crane, taking it to pieces, and building it up again! Before they attached the jib, the base of the crane looked so much like a truck that they added a few more strips and made it into a real truck that could run on rails formed of strips. Then it was found that the parts could be used to construct a whole range of other models.

The next step was to consult a patent agent and to obtain the necessary protection for the great idea. An English patent was granted in January 1901, and foreign patents followed in due course.

In later years Frank Hornby often said that he wondered if he would ever have tackled the task of developing his invention if he had foreseen the trouble and difficulties he was destined to encounter. At first matters seemed hopeless. He approached one firm after another with a view to their manufacturing and marketing the toy, but without success. He then had the happy idea of submitting photographs and details of the toy to Professor Hele-Shaw, who at that time was Professor of Engineering at the Walker Engineering Laboratories, University College, Liverpool. In his reply Professor Hele-Shaw expressed the opinion that the scheme was based on sound engineering principles, and that it should have great success as a constructional toy. This letter was of great assistance to the inventor in enabling him to obtain the financial assistance necessary to have the parts manufactured for him.

The toy, to which he gave the name *"Mechanics Made Easy,"* was now actually in being, but troubles came thick and fast. The parts were made by different manufacturers, and it was impossible to ensure uniformity of finish, or to rely on all of them being ready at the same time. Soon it became clear that the only satisfactory course was to produce all the parts in one factory, and so Frank Hornby took the step of transforming himself from an inventor into a manufacturer.

The first "factory" was so crude that it seems marvellous that anything was ever produced in it at all. It consisted of a single room, equipped with a few hand presses, a lathe or two, and a small gas engine which, as the result of a vast amount of humouring, was persuaded to produce the necessary power. The actual making of the parts with this crude machinery provided plenty of excitement, but this was nothing to the thrills of cleaning the finished wheels and other brass parts. When these came from the presses they were dirty and tarnished, and in order to give them a bright finish they were first dipped in strong acid to clean them, and afterwards lacquered to prevent further tarnishing. Frank Hornby and his chief assistant used to stay behind in the one-roomed factory after the other employees had gone home, and bring out the acid vats to dip the wheels. There was no proper system of ventilation, with the result that the fumes from the acid often became choking. When matters got too bad, both men had to dash out into the open air to recover!

It was about this time that the name *"Mechanics Made Easy"* was changed to the handier and shorter one of *"Meccano."* This name was registered in England on 14th September 1907, and ever since has been the mark of the genuine Hornby system.

This first factory soon proved utterly inadequate, and a move was made to larger premises. Frank Hornby has told us that the size of these premises terrified him, and that he never thought he would fill them. As he put it, the building seemed more suitable for building locomotives than for making the small Meccano parts! In spite of these forebodings, however, the demand for Meccano increased so rapidly that not only was the building crammed with machinery, but also it became evident that in a very short time still larger premises would be required. Then Frank Hornby, looking to the future and now confident of success, took the bold step of buying a plot of land and building a factory for himself. So there came into being the great Meccano Factory in Binns Road, which is familiar by name to hundreds of thousands of boys all over the world. To the end of his life the factory was Frank Hornby's great pride, and he was delighted to welcome to it the thousands of Meccano boys who visit it every year.

Frank Hornby explaining the manufacture of Meccano Parts to the Duke of York, on the occasion of His Royal Highness' visit to the Meccano Factory in 1930.

The addition of Hornby Trains to the range of products of the Meccano factory is another romance of the toy trade. The idea originated in a little Meccano locomotive, and from this developed first the clockwork trains and later the electric trains which, with their accompanying range of track, rolling stock and accessories, have reached world-wide fame.

Most men would have been satisfied with these two phenomenal successes, but Frank Hornby's active brain was always searching for new ideas. The result was the rapid development of the many other Hornby products—constructional motor car and aeroplane outfits, chemical and electrical outfits, and the most fascinating of all miniatures, the famous "Dinky Toys." He never lost his enthusiasm and up to the time of his death was full of schemes for new products.

One of the greatest achievements of Frank Hornby's career was his success in welding together Meccano boys of all nationalities into the world-wide fellowship of the Meccano Guild. A few years later he founded the Hornby Railway Company, the purpose of which is to guide young railway enthusiasts along right lines in developing their miniature railways, and thus enable them to obtain the greatest enjoyment from their hobby. There can be no doubt that these two organisations have brought a vast amount of joy into the lives of thousands of boys.

Frank Hornby used to say that he believed he had a million boy friends; and one cannot help feeling that he was right.

Four Bridges In One

An Elevated Roadway Seventeen Miles Long

NEW YORK has grown with amazing rapidity since its foundation little more than 300 years ago. Then it was merely a settlement on Manhattan Island, which has a frontage to New York Harbour and is flanked on one side by the Hudson River and on the other by the East River. To-day it is the second largest city in the world. It covers the whole of Manhattan Island, and has spread across the East River, into Long Island where are the boroughs of Brooklyn and Queens, and also to the mainland, north of the Harlem River, where the Bronx is situated.

There is an enormous flow of traffic between the various sections of the city, and the waterways that have made it into a perfect seaport have proved serious obstacles to communication on land. As a result of this New York has become a city of bridges. On the west side the George Washington Bridge, the greatest suspension bridge in the world, connects Manhattan with New Jersey. The East River is spanned by three immense structures known as the Brooklyn, Manhattan and Williamsburg Bridges respectively, and also by Queensborough Bridge, which gives direct communication between Manhattan and Queens. There are also several small bridges across the Harlem River. These structures have proved inadequate, however, particularly for communication at the north end of Manhattan Island; and it has been found necessary to embark on a great scheme to improve matters on that side. The construction of a single bridge would not have solved the problem, and instead a great system of bridges and highways has been built across the junction of the East and Harlem Rivers to connect Manhattan, Queens and the Bronx. The structure is known as the Triborough Bridge because it joins these three boroughs.

There are two islands at the junction of the East and Harlem Rivers, where the three boroughs approach each other, and the engineers have made good use of them in working out their schemes. Four bridges have been erected over the adjoining waterways, one connecting the two islands and the others joining them to the three boroughs, and a viaduct unites the four bridges into a great highway. The entire structure is more than 17½ miles in length and includes 3½ miles of bridges. It has cost over £12,000,000, but this huge expenditure is justified by the use that will be made of it. Even in 1935 about 25,000,000 vehicles crossed between the boroughs, although the only direct connections were provided by ferries, and long detours had to be made to cross the existing bridges, all of which were overburdened with traffic.

Fastening the ends of one of the main cables of the East River suspension bridge. The illustrations to this article are reproduced by courtesy of The Chief Engineer, The Triborough Bridge Authority, New York.

The most outstanding structure is the suspension bridge over the East River. This section of the waterway has the picturesque name of Hell Gate, and the bridge across it has a main span of 1,380 ft. and is designed for a total load of nearly 11 tons for every foot of its length. The structure is wide enough to accommodate eight lines of traffic. Its deck is 135 ft. above water level, and is supported by two parallel suspension cables, each nearly two feet in diameter, which are slung between two steel towers 300 ft. high. Each tower consists of two columns connected by bracing, and rests on concrete foundations laid on bedrock and faced above ground with granite masonry. Twin anchorages are provided for the giant cables. These also are founded on rock and have a width of 150 ft. and a length of 225 ft.

An interesting feature of the erection of the bridge was the manner in which the towers were built. That at the Queens end was built up to roadway level with the aid of a derrick supported on a temporary steel framework. The derrick then was dismantled and moved to the opposite bank of the river for use in erecting the lower part of the tower built there. In the meantime riveting proceeded on the Queens tower, and the men engaged in this task were not exposed to any danger from erection work carried on over their heads. Afterwards the derrick was returned to the Queens end for the erection of the upper part of the tower there, finally being used in completing the second tower, and throughout riveting and erection were never carried on together.

The wire cables were built up of single strands of cold-drawn galvanised steel wire, 0.196 in. in diameter, of high tensile strength. These wires were laid in groups or cores of 248 strands, and each cable consisted of 37 of these cores. This assembly of wires had a total cross sectional area of 277 sq. in. After spinning and adjustment in the saddles on the towers and at the anchorages hydraulic machines squeezed them together, the final diameter of each cable being 20¾ in. A temporary footbridge seven feet wide and suspended by ropes 2¼ in. in diameter was built for the use of the men engaged in this work.

The steel floor of the bridge was placed in position in

two stages in order to avoid excessive deflection of the cable due to unbalanced loading. The work was done by travelling cranes working from the towers. On the one hand these advanced toward the centre of the main span, and on the other toward the anchorages at the shore ends of the side spans. Thus as far as possible the increasing load was suspended from the cable symmetrically. Part of the steelwork was hoisted to the roadway level of the towers and placed in position during this stage of the proceedings and the remainder was erected as the travelling cranes made the return journeys to the towers.

The supporting pillars of part of the viaduct under construction. This view was taken from the top of one of the towers of the East River suspension bridge.

Of the remaining three bridges, the most interesting is that crossing the Harlem River. The main span of this is only 310 ft. in length, but it can be lifted vertically from its normal height of 55 ft. above the water to give a clearance of 135 ft. The purpose of this is to allow the passage of vessels with high masts, an infrequent occurrence. Heavy piers 50 ft. in height support the bridge towers, which are unusually substantial and reach a height of 220 ft., and the main span is flanked by two others 152 ft. 9 in. and 241 ft. 9¼ in. in length respectively. The vertical lift span of this bridge was constructed on floats and hoisted bodily into position. Its deck area is 29,000 sq. ft., and in this respect it is the largest of its kind ever built.

The bridge giving communication with the Bronx has three spans, the central one being 350 ft. long and the total length 600 ft. The clearance above high water is 50 ft. The Bronx Kills, the waterway beneath this bridge, is not navigable. For this reason a fixed bridge was sufficient, but the central span has been so designed that it can readily be converted into a vertical lift span if the Bronx Kills should ever be made into a highway for shipping.

Travelling cranes at work on the erection of the floor steel of the suspension bridge crossing the East River.

The viaducts joining these bridges consist of a series of plate girder spans varying from 64 ft. to 125 ft. in length, and six similar spans of 125 ft. bridge Little Hell Gate, the narrow waterway between the two islands. It was necessary to build cofferdams in order to construct the piers of this bridge. Each cofferdam was circular and was made of steel. It was driven right down into contact with the rock bottom of the waterway, and was sealed by placing specially-prepared concrete between the steel and a timber framing inside it. The timber then was removed and the water inside the cofferdam was pumped out, after which the concrete required for the pier bases was pumped into the space within the steel cylinder.

The most interesting feature of the great viaduct is the junction of the Manhattan branch with the section that sweeps straight across the islands from the East River bridge to that leading to the Bronx. This is the key to the entire system of bridges and roads. It is built entirely of reinforced concrete and is a massive structure containing 70,000 cu. yd. of concrete and 5,900 tons of steel supported on over 1,700 concrete columns. The roads on it have been laid out to avoid crossings. The four tracks from the Manhattan branch join the straight through portion of the viaduct system by means of great sweeping curves, and two of them burrow under it in order to form the junctions on the correct side to give a continuous and easy flow of traffic.

The toll gates are placed at this junction, 10 between Queens and Bronx and 12 on the branches leading to Manhattan. All the roads are of ample width, that connecting Manhattan with the junction being 200 ft. wide. The road deck consists of a 7 in. concrete structural slab covered by a 4 in. concrete wearing surface, and is laid in panels averaging 75 ft. in length. Most of the great system of thoroughfares crossing the rivers and islands is built at the same elevation, and ramps have been built at the approaches from the three boroughs it unites in order to give easy access to it.

The outstanding feature of the Triborough Bridge is not the size or novelty of the bridges and viaducts of which it consists, but the immensity of the undertaking as a whole. Planning the work and organising it was a stupendous task. The staff of designing engineers under the authority constructing the bridge numbered 85, and in addition consulting engineers gave advice and assistance in regard to special features.

Constructional work actually began in the autumn of 1929, but lack of funds caused it to be suspended in 1932. Early in the following year the Triborough Bridge Authority was constituted and operations were resumed. The peak of activity was reached last spring, when work was in progress at the same time under 28 separate contracts, with a total value of more than £4,000,000. The bridge was opened for traffic on 11th July this year, and its value was quickly shown by the great use made of it.

The Royal Air Force

Work and Equipment of the Service

THE Royal Air Force expansion scheme now being carried out has drawn renewed attention to the many and varied duties of this, the youngest of the Services, and public interest in the types of military aircraft employed is greater to-day than ever before.

The first step towards the formation of an Air Force in this country was taken in 1911, when an Air Battalion, Royal Engineers, was formed, with headquarters at South Farnborough; and in the same year a Naval Flying School was established at Eastchurch. The new branches of the Army and Navy proved so successful that within a year they were separated from those Services and formed the first units of a new one, called the Royal Flying Corps. This Corps consisted of a military wing made up of an airship squadron and two aeroplane squadrons, a Naval wing, an aircraft factory and a flying or training school; and, with the exception of the Naval wing, it was controlled by the War Office. The aircraft of the Corps included a Nieuport monoplane and three Avro training biplanes, each fitted with a 50 h.p. Gnôme engine, and a Breguet biplane with a 60 h.p. Renault engine. There was also a B.E. (British Experimental) biplane, the first heavier-than-air machine produced by the Royal Aircraft Factory.

The Blackburn "Perth" on the slipway. It is a three-engined flying boat designed for reconnaissance and coastal patrol work. This photograph and the upper one opposite are by courtesy of the Blackburn Aeroplane and Motor Co. Ltd.

In July 1914 the Naval wing was separated from the Royal Flying Corps and renamed the Royal Naval Air Service. The aircraft of this new Service took part in the Naval Review of that year, and gave the first demonstration of formation flying. At the outbreak of the War the R.N.A.S. had 39 aeroplanes, 52 seaplanes and six airships, and the R.F.C. had 179 aeroplanes.

The various types of British aircraft employed during the War have long since become obsolete, but it is interesting to recall them, as although they were much less efficient than the military aeroplanes of to-day, they gave a very good account of themselves. During the early part of the War the R.F.C. were engaged chiefly in reconnaissance work, and the R.N.A.S. in coastal patrolling for submarines and in acting as aerial escorts to troopships crossing the Channel. As improved or entirely new types of aeroplanes were produced, the scope of the flying Services was extended. The R.F.C. carried out air photography, day and night bombing and aerial combats. The R.N.A.S. co-operated with the Fleet during bombardments, by spotting and reporting enemy gun positions; and carried out bombing expeditions, at first from vessels adapted to carry aircraft, and later from specially-built aircraft carriers.

Reference to all the many types of aeroplanes used would make this article into a catalogue, and therefore mention will be made only of some of the types that were of outstanding design, or an account of their high efficiency were produced in very large quantities. The Sopwith 1½-Strutter, for instance, was the first British aeroplane designed as a fighter, and the first to have a fixed gun firing through the airscrew by means of synchronising gear. It was employed also very successfully on air photography flights, bombing expeditions, reconnaissance and escort duty. The French Government were so impressed by its excellent performance that they adapted and standardised the type so that a large number could be produced quickly for their own Air Force. The unusual name was chosen because the aeroplane appeared to have one long and one short interplane strut on each side of the fuselage, when viewed from the front.

A later Sopwith fighter that also was produced in great quantities, but for the R.F.C., was the "Camel" single-seater. This was the first British aeroplane to carry two machine guns synchronised to fire through the airscrew. One of the most interesting aeroplanes was the Sopwith triplane, which was the British reply to the Fokker triplane of the enemy. The three wings of the English machine were staggered, the top one being the most forward and the bottom one the least. It had a maximum speed of 114 m.p.h. and could climb to 15,000 ft. in 19 minutes. The D.H. 4 two-seater fighter, bomber and reconnaissance aeroplane was used chiefly for long-distance bombing, and helped materially to establish the superiority of the R.A.F. during the last year of the War. It was a two-seater single-engined biplane with a top speed of 136.5 m.p.h. Another interesting de Havilland type that gave good service was the D.H.5 single-seater fighter. The wings of this biplane had a pronounced backward stagger, the upper wing being set well back and the lower one more forward than is usually the case.

Some notable types of bombers were used with good effect, one of the most successful being the Handley Page 0/400 long-distance night bomber. It was a formidable aeroplane, and in addition to carrying 16 bombs each weighing about one cwt., it was armed with four Lewis machine guns. The crew consisted of a pilot and two observers. Another big aeroplane of this kind was the Vickers "Vimy," which carried over a ton of bombs and had a range of 900 miles.

Various types of seaplanes and flying boats were used by the R.N.A.S. Many of the seaplanes were produced by the well-known Short company, and their 320 type was the first seaplane to carry a torpedo.

Broadside view of the Blackburn "Shark" Coastal Protection aeroplane. There is also a seaplane version of this machine.

The R.F.C. and the R.N.A.S. grew so enormously that in April 1918 they were amalgamated to form the Royal Air Force. The rapid development continued, and by November 1918 the R.A.F. equipment included the enormous total of 22,647 aeroplanes. The reduction of this number to a peace-time footing was carried out rapidly, however.

During the 18 years that have passed since the end of the War, the R.A.F. have been far from idle; in fact they have been engaged almost continuously in active service, first in one distant part of the Empire and then in another. The control by this country of Iraq, and later of Palestine, gave the squadrons there many responsibilities. In addition the R.A.F. carry out a great deal of air patrolling along the north-west frontier of India, where the swift reprisals made possible by using aircraft have proved very effective in suppressing warlike tribes. The rapid transport of troops to disaffected areas, the relief of besieged towns and garrisons, and searches for lost long-distance civilian fliers are other urgent tasks performed by the R.A.F. overseas. They also played an important part in surveying the Empire air routes now flown regularly by Imperial Airways.

The Hawker "Fury" single-seater interceptor fighter. It has a top speed of 240 m.p.h. Photograph courtesy of Hawker Engineering Co. Ltd.

These varied duties overseas are reflected in the several types of squadrons that comprise the Service. There are fighter, bomber, bomber-transport, and Army co-operation squadrons, and in the Fleet Air Arm, or Naval branch of the R.A.F., there are corresponding squadrons known as Fleet fighter, Fleet torpedo-bomber and Fleet-spotter-reconnaissance, and several flying boat squadrons.

Under the expansion and reorganisation scheme referred to at the beginning of this article many of the aircraft of these squadrons are being replaced by machines of the latest types. The following notes will indicate the wide range of aeroplanes employed.

The fighter squadrons have several types of single-seater fighters, including the Gloster "Gauntlet" and "Gladiator," described and illustrated in the July 1936 "*M.M.*," and the Hawker "Fury." The Fleet Air Arm employ the Hawker "Nimrod," an adapted version of the "Fury." The work of the Army co-operation squadrons is perhaps less obvious than that of fighter squadrons. They help the Army by obtaining for it air photographs of enemy positions, and also carry out reconnaissance flights. Several types of light aeroplanes are employed, including the Hawker "Audax" and "Hector," and the Westland "Wapiti."

The equipment of the bomber squadron includes day and night bombing machines. Among the former are the Hawker "Hart" and "Hind" "general purpose" biplanes, and the Westland "Wallace." Some of the squadrons have the Boulton Paul "Overstrand." The night bombers are larger machines and include the twin-engined Handley Page "Heyford," which has a top speed of 142 m.p.h. and a range of 920 miles.

The Fleet-spotter-reconnaissance squadrons employ the Fairey "III.F" and "Seal," and the Blackburn "Shark." Blackburn aircraft figure also among the equipment of the Fleet torpedo squadrons, as both "Ripons" and "Baffins" are in service. The coastal-reconnaissance squadrons use several types of flying boats, including the Blackburn "Perth" and the Short "Singapore."

The striking cover to this month's issue is reproduced by courtesy of the Blackburn Aeroplane and Motor Co. Ltd., Brough. It represents an artist's conception of a future type of naval aircraft acting in co-operation with a submarine flotilla.

Railway Working in Holland

Steam, Electric, and Diesel Traction

By a Railway Engineer

ONE of the most outstanding characteristics of the Dutch railways is the curious mixture of English and Continental practice that one finds on almost every route. It is not that practice as a whole is a kind of half-way house between the two; the differences are as clear-cut as could be imagined, some features being wholly English, others just as definitely Continental. They run on the right-hand track, use upper-quadrant signals of a shape very strange to English eyes, and the rails are flat-bottomed; but the stations, especially those serving the bigger towns, with their high platforms and quiet serene atmosphere might easily be in the suburbs of London or Manchester, but for the prevalence of a foreign language. Most English of all are the locomotives, with their clean handsome lines and copper-capped chimneys; and one is not in the least surprised to see "Beyer, Peacock" or "Sharp, Stewart" on their makers' plates.

On all the principal services within the country, steam haulage is gradually being superseded. Along the shores of the North Sea the network of electrified lines is slowly extending, while farther east the chief internal services are being worked by Diesel-electric trains. The distances between large towns are so short that nothing in the shape of corridor restaurant car expresses is needed, and a fast and convenient service can be most satisfactorily maintained by multiple-unit vestibule trains, whether Diesel or electrically driven. With the international trains it is quite different. The famous *"Rheingold"* and *"Edelweiss"* expresses begin their journeys to Switzerland at Amsterdam; the cross-country express from The Hook of Holland to Berlin is a very popular service with English travellers; and all these trains are made up of very heavy all-steel coaches, and are steam hauled. On the less busy lines to the east of the Zuider Zee steam traction is still exclusively employed, though no doubt it is only a matter of time before Diesel trains are used here.

Amsterdam Central Station, showing an express for North Germany ready to start. The locomotive is a large 4-6-0 and, like most Dutch engines, follows British practice in many respects.

The short run from the Hook of Holland up to Rotterdam forms a very striking introduction to the Dutch railways. This is the latest section to be electrified, and the service is operated by some of the most remarkable multiple-unit trains that have been put into service anywhere in the world. The trains are made up of two-car articulated sets; each end is carefully streamlined and an additional cowling is provided over the bogies to assist in reducing air resistance. The power supply is 1,500 volts D.C., using overhead conductors. The coaches are finished externally in a handsome colour scheme of grey and scarlet, while the interior effect is entirely grey, relieved by a liberal amount of chromium plating. In addition to being good to look at and supremely comfortable to ride in, these trains are capable of really startling performance. In some trials carried out on the main line between Rotterdam and Amsterdam, one two-car set attained a speed of 100.6 m.p.h.! Of course the speeds demanded on the service between The Hook and Rotterdam are very much less than this, but after each station stop the acceleration was perfectly astounding. Every time we were up to 55 m.p.h. in about three-quarters of a mile from the start, and then the motorman eased up for the rest of the distance on to the next station.

I was bound for Amsterdam, and so alighted from this remarkable train at Schiedam, a junction just on the outskirts of Rotterdam where the main line comes in from the north. There are alternative routes between Rotterdam and Amsterdam. The western one is electrified and runs through The Hague and the university city of Leiden; the eastern route goes via Utrecht, and the inter-city service is worked by Diesel-electric trains. On the line to Amsterdam via The Hague the older electric trains are used. These are not nearly so attractive in appearance as the stock working on the Hook branch; they are rather American-looking and are painted a dull olive-green. But they are fast comfortable trains, and their big windows give fine views over the countryside.

The landscape is of a most astonishing flatness. In every direction as far as the eye can see there is not the slightest undulation, let alone as much as a hill; and it all lies below sea level. Every few miles the railway crosses canals; along their banks are built picturesque little villages, and there are usually one or two windmills in sight somewhere on the broad horizon. In the fields are numerous dwarf windmills. These look like large scale-models of the full-sized ones and are used for pumping work where only a small amount of power is required. They do not stand more than 10 ft. or 12 ft. high.

By now the train is nearing Delft, one of the most picturesque cities in all Holland; and there are pleasing glimpses from the train just after leaving the station. The town is intersected by a number of canals, the banks of which are lined with trees; two glorious church towers rise above the red-tiled roofs, and alongside the canal that runs parallel to the railway for some distance is a very fine windmill, right in the town. Just beyond this point is a notable example of a modern Dutch signal box. It is built in reinforced concrete, almost entirely glazed on three sides, and the flat roof is overhung to provide an awning over the windows. There is no ground floor at all; the cabin proper is perched high above the track, supported on four slender reinforced concrete pillars.

There are some very interesting features in modern Dutch signalling. Except in one or two very big stations, where electric point machines are used, the points are everywhere worked on the double-wire system. The underlying principle of this method of operation is that of an ordinary belt drive. The point lever, instead of being pulled through a small angle as in English practice, is moved through a full semi-circle, and to the lever is fixed a pulley wheel that revolves about the same centre as that round which the lever pivots. Adjacent to the points is a corresponding pulley wheel which is turned through half a revolution when the cabin lever is operated. The points are operated off this pulley by a mechanism just like the piston rod and connecting rod of an engine; in the case of double-wire worked points however the action is reversed, for the wheel drives the "piston." The work of throwing a pair of points is far too great for a simple belt to be used, and the wire is stoutly coupled to the pulleys at each end. The same principle is used for working signals.

At a distance of 5½ miles beyond Delft is The Hague. Here a cross-country line from Utrecht comes in, over which the service is worked by Diesel-electric trains. As befits the capital city of Holland, The Hague has a fine station, very English in appearance, with of course the difference that trains run on the right-hand track instead of the left. Just as we arrived the southbound *"Edelweiss Express"* was leaving. This famous train is composed entirely of Pullman cars, and leaving Amsterdam at 8.6 a.m. serves Antwerp, Brussels, Luxemburg, Metz and Strasburg, reaching Basle at 6 p.m. Over the Dutch portion of the journey the load is one of only four coaches, but farther south it becomes a very heavy train. This western route between Rotterdam and Amsterdam is also used by the through expresses from France, of which *"L'Etoille du Nord"* is the most celebrated.

These trains are hauled by handsome four-cylinder 4–6–0s, the design of which was prepared by Beyer, Peacock and Co. Ltd. in consultation with the Dutch authorities. Steam train schedules in Holland, though quite smart, do not demand any very high speed, and a diameter of 6 ft. for the coupled wheels has been standardised. The cylinders of these particular engines are 15$\frac{3}{4}$ in. in diameter by 26 in. stroke, and these ample dimensions coupled with a boiler pressure of 170 lb. per sq. in. give them a high accelerative capacity. The *"Edelweiss Express"* has no run longer than 40 miles in Holland, but on each section speed usually rises to over 60 m.p.h. The engines are painted olive green, but this rather drab colour is wonderfully set off by the copper-capped chimney and polished brass dome and safety valve casing. The numerous "gadgets" usually found on and around the boiler on Continental engines are conspicuous by their absence, and the only feature that differs in any way from English practice is the use of large electric headlamps.

One of the Diesel-electric articulated trains bound for Utrecht, at Amsterdam. These trains consist of three-coach units, the centre vehicle containing the engine and the luggage compartments.

From The Hague the line runs north through Leiden and Lisse to Haarlem. The country throughout is dead flat, and one is never far from the sea. In many places can be seen the long range of sand dunes that act as a natural bulwark to the low-lying country inland. In a comfortable electric train we bowled along at a steady 50 m.p.h. with surpassing smoothness, and then, approaching Haarlem, we passed through the world-famous bulb fields; it was August and the gladioli were a magnificent sight. Haarlem is an important junction; a short branch from the seaside town of Zandvoort comes in from the west, and another electrified line runs northward to Alkmaar, famed for its cheese. The main line swings round due east, and a run of 11$\frac{3}{4}$ miles brings us to Amsterdam.

This last stretch has a most unusual interest. For almost its entire length there are parallel tracks for five different modes of transport. On the extreme left, looking towards Amsterdam, is the railway; then in order comes a canal, a highway for fast motor traffic, a special track for bicycles, and last of all a path for pedestrians. As if this were not enough, a few miles to the north is the big sea level canal that connects Amsterdam with the sea; along this waterway ocean-going ships can often be seen.

A picturesque scene in Delft, including a typical windmill and showing a fast electric train on the run between Rotterdam and Amsterdam.

At Amsterdam Central station practically every phase of Dutch railway working can be observed. On the western side electric trains from Rotterdam, Zandvoort, and Alkmaar are coming and going every few minutes. Important international expresses arrive from all parts of Europe. The dark sepia cars of the Northern Railway of France are familiar objects; there are coaches of the International Sleeping Car Company, and all coming in on trains drawn by the English-looking 4–6–0 engines. The eastern end of the station bears a different complexion altogether. Here are to be seen expresses destined for all parts of Germany, some carrying through coaches for places still farther afield. The very distinctive Mitropa stock is largely used on these trains; all-steel construction is employed for ordinary carriages, dining cars, and sleeping cars alike, and they are painted a reddish-maroon colour that makes them recognisable anywhere. To an English traveller, accustomed to much timber work in coaches, they take some getting used to, with the clanging of steel doors and a chill to the touch; but they ride superbly and the internal decoration of the dining cars is most ornate.

On the routes running east from Amsterdam the latest type 4–6–0 engines are extensively used. They are slightly more powerful than the "Beyer, Peacock" type previously mentioned, having four cylinders 16$\frac{1}{2}$ in. in diameter by 26 in. stroke. The boiler is pitched considerably higher, and smoke deflecting plates are fitted at the front end, but still they are definitely English in appearance. This is perhaps more remarkable than in the case of the earlier engines, for the new type have all been built by the German firm of Henschel and Sohn of Cassel. Quite recently one of them was completely streamlined, not with a view to any ultra-rapid running, but in an attempt to reduce coal consumption.

Alongside these handsome steam-hauled trains may be seen the Diesel-electrics. In outward appearance they are very similar to the latest electric trains working on the Rotterdam–Hook service. They consist of three-coach articulated sets in which the centre coach contains the engines and luggage compartments. There are two engines to each three-car set, driving on to the two centre bogies. Each engine is of the Maybach 12-cylinder V-type, using airless injection, running at 1,400 r.p.m. and driving a D.C. generator that supplies current to the four motors, each of which is coupled direct to one of the bogie axles. These three-car trains develop no less than 820 h.p. and they have been tested up to 87 m.p.h.; in ordinary service however the speed rarely exceeds 60 m.p.h.

By way of contrast to these ultra-modern developments the branch lines in quiet country districts provide a most interesting study. Here traffic moves very sedately, the rolling stock consists chiefly of very spartan four-wheelers, and speed rarely exceeds 35 m.p.h. But for all that there is a wealth of interest about these placid branches. The historic seaport town of Hoorn, on the western shore of the Zuider Zee, is a fascinating railway centre. One evening when I was returning to Amsterdam a very odd collection of engines was on view. There were two "Beyer, Peacock" 4–4–0s built as long ago as 1892; they sported very tall chimneys and tiny boilers, but what made them still more ancient-looking was a huge bell-shaped dome. One of them was working a cross-country local to Alkmaar that consisted of three four-wheeled coaches!

Slightly more modern was a double-framed "Sharp, Stewart" 4–4–0, and then, just as I was studying this old "bus," what would rank as a fast train on this line arrived behind a handsome Dutch-built 4–4–0. In outward appearance this could best be described as a much enlarged edition of the early "Beyer" type, including even the bell-shaped dome. My own train, which consisted of only two coaches, was drawn by a 4–4–4 tank engine that bore a strong family likeness to the 4–4–0 just mentioned. We jogged along at a merry 27 to 28 m.p.h. between stops, and so reached Zaandam, where the electrified line from Alkmaar to Amsterdam is joined.

Even on these quiet unhurried routes traffic though slow is very punctually operated. So Zaandam, where the two extremes meet and one transfers from the placid "steamer" to the rapid bustling electric, is a good place to take leave of the Dutch Railways.

Furnaces that are Rocked at Work

Melting Metals by the Electric Arc

DURING the last 20 years or so the study of the structure of metals and the processes of refining them have both made great progress. One important result has been the development of many valuable new alloys, each possessing qualities that make it particularly suitable for some definite industrial purpose. The special features of an alloy depend to a great degree on the purity and consistency of its ingredients. Considerable skill and care are required in making them, and the necessary processes usually are carried out in enclosed furnaces heated electrically. In these the metal is not "burned" or oxidised, as it might be when heated in an ordinary furnace, and the product therefore is pure.

A Birlec-Detroit rocking arc melting furnace in which 1,000 lb. of metal can be melted at a single charge.

The main types of electric furnace are the induction, the resistance, and the rocking arc furnace, each of which has its special uses. Induction furnaces owe their heating effect to eddy currents induced in the metals placed in them by means of high-frequency currents in special coils. They are used to a great extent for the manufacture of high grade steel, and are made with capacities ranging from about 100 lb. to 5 tons. About 90 furnaces of this kind are in use in various parts of England. Furnaces in which heat is produced by passing current through resistances are employed principally for heat treating iron, steel and other metals, and for pottery making.

The rocking arc furnace is used when comparatively small castings in metals such as high test malleable or cast iron, nickel silver, and various bronzes are required. The illustrations on this page show two examples of the Birlec-Detroit furnace, which is made in this country by Birmingham Electric Furnaces Ltd., Birmingham. In a furnace of this kind the metal is melted by means of the heat of an electric arc formed or "struck" inside a cylindrical chamber that is rocked about its axis. In this manner rapid heating of the metal is obtained and the constituents of the alloy are evenly distributed. Two important advantages of this method are that a rocking arc furnace can be installed in any part of a works or laboratory, and that it permits the rapid production of alloys of consistent composition and quality without the necessity for skilled operation.

The furnace is lined with special heat-resisting bricks and is provided with a combined charging, opening and pouring spout. The electric arc is formed between two graphite electrodes that enter the chamber at opposite ends, and as the chamber is effectively closed there is little loss of heat and very high efficiency is obtained, while no air can enter to oxidise the molten metal. The furnace can readily be cleaned out after emptying it of its charge, and different alloys can be melted in consecutive heatings, a great advantage in a foundry producing a wide range of castings in different metals.

The melting cylinder is mounted at each end on steel rollers in such a manner that it is free to rotate on its axis. The rocking motion is imparted to it by an electric motor, which is provided with a patented reversing mechanism, and its speed is increased, either automatically or by hand, as melting progresses. A special control device enables the rocking motion to be controlled in a suitable manner for every type of charge, starting with a small oscillation and increasing at a controlled rate to the maximum value. The movement stirs the molten metals, giving thorough mixing that ensures uniformity in the charge, so that every casting from it has exactly the same composition and properties. It also serves to bring every portion of the charge into contact with all parts of the heated furnace lining. The result is that the rate of melting is greatly increased, and at the same time overheating of any part of the lining is prevented. A charge of brass can be melted in about 25 to 30 minutes, while the melting time for iron is from 50 to 60 minutes. The electrodes are arranged either for hand or automatic control.

Pouring molten metal from a Birlec-Detroit rocking arc furnace. For the illustrations on this page we are indebted to Birmingham Electric Furnaces Ltd., Birmingham.

Flying Nearly 9½ Miles High

Britain Regains World Altitude Record

THE first aeroplane flight officially confirmed as a world altitude record for heavier-than-air aircraft was achieved by Hubert Latham, an English airman, at Rheims on 29th August, 1909. He flew an Antoinette monoplane and reached a height of 509 ft. During the 27 years since then the height to which aircraft can climb has increased enormously, and the record for the highest flight has been held successively by various countries, including France, Germany, England (from 1932 to 1935), and Italy. It was won from Italy in August this year when M. Detre, a French airman, reached a height of 48,698 ft. He flew a Potez aeroplane fitted with a Gnôme-Rhône engine. On 28th September last the record was regained for Britain by Squadron Leader R. F. D. Swain, of the Experimental Section of the Royal Aircraft Factory, Farnborough, who flew to a height of 49,967 ft., or nearly 9½ miles.

The Bristol 138a single-engined low wing monoplane in which Squadron Leader F. R. D. Swain regained the world altitude record for Britain. Photographs on this page by courtesy of "Flight."

He took off from Farnborough at 7.30 a.m., clad in a special sealed suit that could be inflated to a pressure adequate to sustain life at any altitude. This suit was essential, as at heights above 43,000 ft. it is necessary to resort to some means of artificially increasing the pressure in the lungs. The lower illustration gives a good idea of the appearance of the suit, which is made of rubberised fabric and is fitted with a helmet that is of the same material and has a large curved double window. The suit is made in two pieces, and is joined at the waist. A panel is incorporated in the helmet to enable the occupant to free his head quickly in an emergency. Oxygen is fed into the breathing circuit at the required rate, the oxygen jet being the driving element of a small injector that produces rapid circulation of gas round the system. The gas passes from the injector through a flexible tube, enters the helmet on the right-hand side of the face, and passes across the face to an outlet on the left. It now contains the exhaled breath, and passes down a flexible tube to a canister containing chemicals that absorb the carbon dioxide and moisture from the breath. The gas then issues from the canister outlet in pure condition, ready for recirculation.

After taking-off Squadron Leader Swain climbed in wide circles until he reached a height of 40,000 ft., when he turned south-east and climbed about another 5,000 ft. He said afterward that at that height the light was almost dazzling, but he had taken the precaution to guard against the glare by having all the external parts of the aeroplane that could catch his eye painted black. He added that the sky above appeared a very deep blue, but that no stars were visible. The deep colour was due to the air being free from dust and moisture, and to the complete absence of cloud above 35,000 ft. The exceptional height enabled him to see a great distance, and when flying about 10 miles north of Brighton he could see northward as far as the Wash and westward as far as Land's End.

A strong north-west wind was blowing, and heading his machine into it he climbed steadily until he reached the record height of 49,967 ft.

The flight back to earth was exciting. When he began it he was almost over the Bristol Channel. He had glided downward about 5,000 ft. when the window of his helmet and those of the cockpit became misted over, only the brilliant sunlight penetrating them and he was forced to fly blind. A growing feeling of suffocation caused him to believe he was running short of oxygen, and when he found he could not press the release lever that would open the roof of the cockpit, or open the panel of his helmet, he became desperate. In spite of his failing strength he managed to grasp the sheath knife hung in the cockpit for use in emergency, and he cut open the window of his helmet. Immediately there was a welcome inrush of fresh air that revived him and relieved his fear of suffocation.

A glance at his altimeter showed that he had descended to 14,000 ft., and he also observed that he was flying in the neighbourhood of Yeovil. He therefore turned eastward, and still gradually descending, he eventually arrived over Salisbury; and landed safely at Netheravon, with barely two gallons of petrol left. He found that he had been mistaken in thinking that his oxygen supply was running out, and that the feeling of suffocation had been due to his exhaustion.

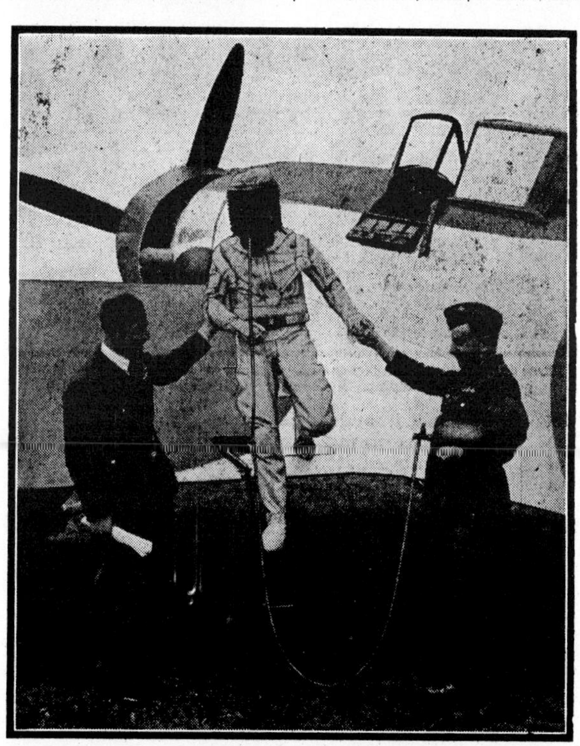

Squadron Leader Swain, clad in his special suit, descending from the aeroplane after his record flight.

The aeroplane used by Squadron Leader Swain was a new low wing cantilever monoplane designed specially for flights at heights of 50,000 ft. and over, and produced by the Bristol Aeroplane and Motor Co. Ltd., to the order of the Air Ministry. It was also designed so that it could be used in an attempt to break the altitude record for heavier-than-air aircraft, and now that this has been accomplished it will be used to investigate the special problems involved in the operation of aeroplanes, and in the functioning of aircraft equipment and instruments, at extreme altitudes. The Bristol 138a, as it is called, is one of the largest single-seater aeroplanes ever built, and has a wing span of 66 ft. It is exceptionally light for an unbraced monoplane of such large span, as it is built throughout of wood, except for the engine mounting and the cowling.

At the time of writing preparations for a further flight are being made, and Sq. Ldr. Swain's record may have been beaten before this issue appears.

Four-Decker Cages for South African Gold Mine

The illustration on this page shows three four-decker duralumin mine cages recently built for Daggafontein Mines Ltd., South Africa, by Vickers-Armstrongs Ltd. Each cage weighs 3½ tons and is capable of carrying 80 men. Some idea of their size is given by comparison with the work-people shown in them. Each is 26 ft. 11 in. in height, 4 ft. 8¼ in. in width, and 5 ft. 11 in. in depth from back to front. The principal tension supporting and lifting members of the cages consist of mild steel angle and channel sections, and the deck plates, which also are of mild steel, are laid on duralumin supports suitably secured to the main members.

On each of the four decks rails are fitted, so that the cages can be used as required for raising ore in trucks only or for a combination of ore and workmen. The sides of the cages are of 1/16th-in. thick duralumin plate, and combination hinged and sliding doors are fitted at back and front.

A Giant American Generator

A new 110,000-kw turbine generator built by the General Electric Company of New York was recently placed in service in the River Rouge power generating plant of the Ford Motor Company at Fordson, Michigan, U.S.A. The new generator is the first large unit in the world to operate at a steam pressure of 1,200 lb. per sq. in. and 900 deg. F. With the additional capacity afforded by the new generator the Fordson station is now the largest industrial high-pressure steam generating installation in the world, having a total output of 325,000 kw.

The new plant consists of a high-pressure turbine and generator mounted directly on top of a low-pressure turbine and generator. Superheated steam is fed to the upper turbine at 1,200 lb. per sq. in. pressure and 900 deg. F. The generator driven by this turbine is of 55,000 kw capacity, and the steam then flows down into the low-pressure unit, which generates another 55,000 kw. The steam is then exhausted to condensing equipment.

Lock that Cannot be Picked

In a novel safety lock that has been introduced in Germany, the code or safety device is not in the lock itself, but in the key. This is a narrow strip of light metal, with five wards or racks that can be adjusted in various positions, and the lock automatically adapts itself to the key when this is used to close it. A similar key cannot be used for opening the lock, since the arrangement of the key parts is known only to the owner, and the chances that a burglar or any other intruder will find the combination he has selected are very remote, since the locking bolt of the key allows a choice of 99,999 positions.

As a further protection the lock casing is armoured with special steel that cannot be drilled, and it is claimed that it is impossible to pick the lock itself. The lock was exhibited at the Danzig Autumn Fair, where it attracted considerable attention.

Three duralumin four-decker man cages, built for service at a South African gold mine. Photograph by courtesy of Vickers-Armstrongs Ltd.

Progress on New York Arch Bridge

Rapid progress is being made with the construction of the Henry Hudson arch bridge over the Harlem River at New York. The main span of this bridge will be 800 ft. in length, and will be supported by two arch ribs consisting of silicon steel box girders, 12½ ft. deep, 3½ ft. wide, and spaced on 50-ft. centres. The bridge will give clearance of 140 ft. to shipping in the river, and at each end of it there will be steel viaduct approaches each 300 ft. in length.

Building a Deep-water Harbour in Trinidad

For some months past work has been in progress on the construction of a deep-water harbour for Port-of-Spain, Trinidad. At present ocean-going liners have to disembark their passengers at the anchorage, which is three miles out, but on completion of the new harbour they will be able to reach the quayside, and the inconvenience of a three-mile trip in a small tender will be avoided.

The work now in progress includes the construction of a wharf wall 3,100 ft. in length, the dredging to 30 ft. below water of an approach channel about two miles in length, and the construction of a wide basin in front of the wharf wall. In addition an area of 140 acres behind the wharf wall is being reclaimed and five transit sheds with the necessary rail and road service tracks are being erected.

The wharf wall is of concrete deposited between two rows of interlocking steel sheet-piling. The constructional work is being carried out from timber stagings on each side of the wall. Railway tracks laid from these stagings and connected with the local railway system carry the necessary plant for pile-driving, excavation, and concreting.

Sheets of interlocking steel piling at the front and back of the wall site are first driven. The enclosed material is then excavated by grab cranes and deposited behind the wall to form a bank on which narrow-gauge rail tracks were laid for bringing out concrete and other constructional materials from the shore.

The dredged approach channel will have a bottom width of 350 ft., and will be marked by beacons mounted on greenheart stages at the sides of the channel, and by a pair of lights fixed on shore towers. In dredging the channel and the basin in front of the wharf wall over six million cu. yds. of material have to be removed, some of which will be deposited in the reclaimed area at the back of the wharf wall, while the remainder will be dumped at sea in deep water. It is expected that the entire scheme will be completed towards the end of 1938.

Gearless Buses for London

The London Passenger Transport Board has ordered 100 oil-engined buses from Leyland Motors Ltd. The buses will all be similar in outward appearance, but 10 of them will be fitted with Leyland hydraulic torque converters in place of gear transmission systems.

Jarrow's New Coal Shipping Staith

The illustration at the top of this page shows a new coal shipping staith recently constructed by the Tyne Improvement Commission at Jarrow. It has two loading berths, one of which is intended for coaling small ships and is equipped with a single loading tower, while the other has two towers and is suitable for dealing with larger vessels. The staith has a river frontage of 1,309 ft., and provides ample space for two vessels to be loaded simultaneously.

Coal is brought from the collieries in railway wagons to new standing sidings situated about a quarter of a mile from the river. These sidings provide accommodation for 2,000 tons of coal in 20-ton wagons, and for about 127 similar wagons empty. The full wagons gravitate along the sidings to discharging hoppers, and after discharge are raised by automatic electric lifts to the deck of an elevated structure from which they gravitate into the "empty" sidings.

From the hoppers the coal is carried by means of an electrically-driven belt conveyor system over a public street and adjoining land to the three shipping or loading towers on the bank of the river. The towers are mounted on two four-wheeled bogies that run on flat-bottomed rails and are driven through a rack and pinion, with brakes to prevent horizontal movement when strong winds are blowing. Each tower is provided with a sliding loading boom, which is slung by wire ropes at its outer end, and can be raised or lowered to suit all sizes of vessels at any state of the tide.

Tunnelling under the Thames

Work will soon begin on the boring of the new tunnel under the River Thames between Dartford and Purfleet. At present there is no bridge or tunnel below Blackwall Tunnel, which is 35 miles from the mouth of the Thames, and as the site of the new tunnel is about 12 miles lower down the estuary it will provide a much needed link between the north and south sides of the waterway.

Work will commence with the boring of a pilot tunnel with an internal diameter of 12 ft., and a length of 900 yds. Two ventilation shafts will be constructed, one on each side of the river, and at the foot of each shaft a chamber 35 ft. in internal diameter will be excavated to serve as a starting-off point for the main tunnel. Each of these shafts will be 100 ft. in depth, and the depth of the pilot tunnel below the bed of the river will be from 20 ft. to 25 ft.

The pilot tunnel will provide valuable information regarding the strata under the river at this point and will give the engineers some idea of the conditions in which the main tunnel will have to be built.

The main tunnel will be rather more than a mile in length. On the north side of the river it will connect with the Purfleet-Grays road; on the south side the approach will be linked with the Dartford Southern by-pass.

A glass-lined milk tank being "fired" in a gas-heated furnace, as described on this page. Photograph by courtesy of the British Commercial Gas Association. The illustration at the head of the page shows the new coal staith at Jarrow, and is reproduced by courtesy of the Tyne Improvement Commission.

Glass Linings for Milk Tanks

Now-a-days there is an increasing tendency to handle widely-used materials in bulk rather than in small quantities. For example, petrol used to be delivered to garages in 2-gallon cans, but now-a-days it is distributed in huge tank wagons to roadside tanks and pumps. Milk formerly was handled in bulk only in the familiar churn, but now it is frequently transported in large tanks mounted on lorries or railway wagons, and similar tanks are used also for storage purposes in food factories.

The tanks usually are lined with glass, and the lower illustration on this page shows the lining of such a tank being fired in a large gas furnace in a Yorkshire works. The inside of the tank is first sprayed with vitreous enamel by an operator wearing a gas mask, then dried by means of a stream of hot air from a flexible pipe and finally vitrified at about 800°Cent. in the gas-fired furnace shown.

World's Steepest Inclined Railway

What is believed to be the world's steepest inclined standard gauge railway is in operation near Ripple, Oregon, U.S.A. It is 3,421 ft. in length and is used for carrying timber logs down the side of a high mountain ridge to the bottom of the canyon of the Salmonberry River.

The railway is designed to operate on the double-track counterbalanced principle, in which a loaded car descends while an empty one ascends, the extra weight of the loaded car being utilised in hauling the empty car. The track commences with a gradient of 1 in 3.6, continues at 1 in 1.3, and finishes at 1 in 2 as it nears the top of the ridge.

The cars weigh 14 tons each when empty and, with 28-ton loads of logs, their descending weight is 42 tons. An average car load is 9,000 ft. of timber, and about 250,000 ft. of timber can be hauled daily.

The mountainous nature of the country made an ordinary railway unsuitable.

How Cotton Driving Ropes are Made

Work on a Modern Rope-Walk

ROPE-MAKING is one of the oldest of industries, reaching far back into prehistoric times. Possibly the first ropes were simply the long vines of the forest. Later they were made of the hides of animals, and the art of rope-making began when some early man twisted two or more strands together in order to obtain greater strength.

The Egyptians certainly used ropes, for there are carvings on old monuments showing ropes being spun by hand in a similar manner to that practised to-day in small country rope-walks. The great granite blocks of which the pyramids were built 5,000 years ago were hauled by means of ropes made from palm fibres and papyrus. References to rope-making appear in the Bible, and in verse 12, Chapter 4, of the book of Ecclesiastes we read "A three-fold cord is not quickly broken." In this connection it is singular that although to-day ropes are made of three-ply, four-ply and seven-ply construction for different purposes, a three-ply combination actually is the strongest.

Part of the main rope-walk at the Lambeth Rope Works, of Thomas Hart Ltd., Blackburn, to whom we are indebted for our illustrations and the information in this article.

Many different fibres are used in the manufacture of ropes, and wire also is employed, but ropes of this material are outside the scope of this article. Hemp ropes are generally used on ships. These are made chiefly of Manilla hemp, but Italian hemp, sisal and coir fibre also are used. Manilla hemp, or manilla, as it is simply called, comes from the Philippine Islands, and the fibre is obtained from the trunk of the manilla plant, which resembles a banana tree and grows to a height of from 15 ft. to 25 ft.

Sisal is obtained from the leaves of a cactus-like plant from Yucatan in Mexico. These leaves are about 6 ft. long and are cut down every year after the plant is about four years old. The growth of sisal is now being fostered by the British Government in Kenya, and very large portions of the British supplies are being obtained from there. The fibre is lighter in colour than manilla and is being very largely used for twine making. Coir is the fibre of the husk of the coconut.

Splicing cotton driving ropes. The splice used takes 9 ft. to 15 ft. of rope.

During the last 70 years ropes of cotton have become very popular. This is largely due to the introduction of power transmission by ropes, for cotton is far more suitable than any other material for this purpose.

In the making of ropes, the fibre is first spun into an even yarn, and this is transformed into rope on the rope-walk. The system employed is the oldest and best, and formerly was carried out by hand, usually in a long narrow shed of wood with a tarred felt roof. At one end of the walk was a spinning wheel to which the spinner attached a few fibres of hemp by means of hooks. The bunch of hemp was placed round the spinner's waist, and as the wheel turned, twisting the fibres into yarns as they were automatically drawn from the bunch, he backed slowly down the walk, regulating the quantity of fibre drawn and spun by the movements of his hands.

Nowadays rope-making is carried out in factories equipped with intricate and ingenious machines. A modern rope-walk is of immense size. The raw material to be converted into rope on it is first treated in various machines, which clean and straighten the fibre and make it into an endless ribbon or sliver that is reduced by spinning into an even yarn. A sufficient number of yarns are laid out on the walk, and there they are first twisted into strands of the thickness required for the size of rope that is to be made. The strands are then twisted into the finished rope, again on the walk. Ropes of all diameters are made in this manner for different purposes, ranging from $\frac{1}{4}$ in. ropes for use as clothes lines and for similar purposes, up to larger ones 3 in. or even more in diameter.

Power transmission by ropes has been in vogue about 70 years. For large powers it almost entirely superseded driving by flat belts, one great advantage, especially for textile factories of several storeys, being that from one flywheel a sufficient number of ropes can be taken to each floor to drive the machinery there. There are some Lancashire cotton mills, with engines of over 2,000 h.p., employing 40 to 50 ropes of say 1¾ in. diameter, which is a very common size to use; and in one case 64 ropes were used on the one flywheel.

Rope-driving of course is not confined to textile factories, and steel rolling mills, tin-plate works, flour mills and similar works employ this system on a large scale. It is sufficiently positive for all practical purposes, being superior to a belt in this respect, and in addition is shock-absorbing, thus saving wear on engines, motors and machinery.

In designing a rope drive perhaps the first thing to keep in mind is that the pulleys should be as large as possible, within the limits of the speeds allowable at their rims. The ropes should be of such a diameter that they will bend around the pulleys easily. An old rule, and a good one, is that the diameter of the pulley should be not less than 30 times that of the rope used. This rule need not be taken too literally, however, for no one ratio of rope size to pulley diameter can apply universally.

A large rope on the coiling winch after manufacture.

A rope will bend with less detriment to itself at a slow speed than when it is moving more rapidly. Generally speaking, the larger the pulleys the easier the bending of the rope and the longer its life. Special tables have been prepared to show what may be considered the minimum diameters of pulleys for particular sizes of ropes at various speeds.

What may be called the standard shape of pulley groove has a width and depth respectively of 1 1/12th and 1½ times the diameter of the rope used with it. The pitch is one-third larger than the thickness of the rope, and the angle of the groove is 45 deg., although some engineers use grooves with an angle of 40 deg.

The load that ropes can carry depends primarily on the speed, although the sizes of the pulleys also is a factor. An interesting feature is that it is better to use the ropes with their driving sides at the bottom and their slack sides at the top, for then they are in contact over a greater length of the grooves of the pulleys.

It is very important with a rope drive that there should be no girders, beams, wheels or intervening shafts on which the ropes could touch, for they always run with a sag. Plenty of room should be allowed, for the ropes would soon wear out if they were to touch on obstructions. The usual allowance for sag is about 8 per cent. of the distance between the shafts connected by the ropes. Drives may be either long or short. The pulleys connected may be almost touching, but if they are large enough they may be 80 ft. to 100 ft. apart.

Cotton ropes at work in a cotton mill. The flywheel is 30 ft. in diameter and from it driving ropes run to different floors.

In order to avoid differential driving, in which the ropes do not pull uniformly, it is important that all the ropes of any one drive should be of the same diameter. If the driving and driven pulleys are equal in size, this is not of great importance, but where one pulley is larger than the other, the smaller ropes, sinking deeper into both grooves, attempt to give the driven pulley a slightly different speed than the thicker ropes. Uneven driving and friction are thus introduced.

This point sometimes arises in the mixing of new ropes with old ones. If one or two new ropes are set to work with others that have been in use for some time, where the driver is larger than the driven pulley, the new ones, if thicker, often drag behind the others and carry the slack on the wrong side. The new ones then have to be tightened in order to get them to work evenly with the rest. Where possible it is better to replace all the ropes on a drive at the same time.

Wear in grooves, especially when some are more worn than others, often is a cause of differential driving, and the effect is much greater with a small pulley running at a high speed than with a large pulley working at a correspondingly low speed. This also applies to new pulleys, if all the grooves have not been turned exactly to the same template. Ropes generally run with great steadiness. If any surge, bounce or mounting occurs, the cause usually can be traced to unsteadiness of the engine, shaft, or load.

Rope driving is special work, and suitable construction of the rope used is advisable. It must be reasonably strong, very pliable and, most important of all, must have a low rate of stretch. Cotton is now almost exclusively used for driving ropes because it has a much softer nature and is not so subject to atmospheric influences. In order to obtain pliability a rope must not be too hard in the "lay" or twist. There is no rope that is absolutely stretchless, but this is achieved as nearly as possible in the "Lambeth" design, where the central portion of each strand has practically no twist in it, and is protected by an outer covering of twisted threads that take the friction with the grooved pulleys. This is one of the oldest and best known driving ropes, and is extensively used in all parts of the world. It is made with three or four strands, as some users prefer the one form and some the other.

There is no satisfactory rope coupling for driving ropes, and in order to join them they are spliced with what is known as a "long" splice. This takes 9 ft. to 15 ft. of rope, the length depending upon the thickness, but when finished is no thicker than the main body of the rope. Making a long splice is a job for an expert.

A well-designed rope drive is really a no-trouble drive. The average life of a set of ropes may be given as 10 years, but on some drives it frequently reaches 20 to 30 years.

Old Locomotives and Where to See Them

Veteran Engines in Retirement

By R. D. Gauld, M.Eng., A.M.Inst.C.E.

In the issue of the "*M.M.*" for July last there appeared a description of some of the old locomotives in the Railway Museum, York, which contains the finest collection of railway relics in this country. The present article, which may be regarded as an extension of the previous one, is believed to include all the other old locomotives in the British Isles that are preserved for their historic interest.

Not on account of number, but because of age and historical value, the leading collection of old locomotives is that in the National Science Museum, South Kensington, London. This Museum is open to the public without charge. Of the collection the "*Rocket*" is the most famous member, but unfortunately it is incomplete. This engine was built in 1829 and won the £500 prize awarded by the directors of the Liverpool and Manchester Railway to the best locomotive running in the Rainhill trials of that year. It was purchased by them, and worked on their line till 1836, when it was sold to the Midgeholme Railway, near Carlisle. It ceased running there in 1844, but was not brought to South Kensington until the year 1862.

A group of the old locomotives mentioned in this article. The first is the G.W.R. "North Star"; then come the L.N.W.R. "Columbine" and "Cornwall," and finally the M.R. Johnson single-driver, as exhibited at the Liverpool and Manchester Railway Centenary Celebrations in 1930. Photograph by courtesy of the L.M.S.R.

A replica of the "*Rocket*" showing what the original complete engine looked like is on view. From the descriptive label we learn that the driving wheels were of oak with cast iron bosses and iron tyres, and that a 300-gallon water barrel was carried.

Another famous exhibit is "*Puffing Billy*," built at Wylam Colliery in 1813 by William Hedley. It worked until 1862 between the colliery and the River Tyne. It has two vertical cylinders driving four wheels through a series of rods and gear wheels. The engine weighed 8.3 tons in working order, and usually hauled about 50 tons at 5 m.p.h. The four-wheeled tender weighed 4.3 tons when loaded. Owing to the weakness of the cast iron plateway track on which it ran, the engine was rebuilt in 1815 with eight wheels, each group of four wheels being carried in a separate truck, and two more gear wheels were used. About 1830 it was altered back to four wheels, the line being at that time relaid with cast iron edge rails, on a short length of which the engine now stands.

The "*Sans Pareil*" ("without equal") was built in 1829 by Timothy Hackworth for entry in the Rainhill trials. It was afterwards bought by the directors of the Liverpool and Manchester Railway and used until 1831, when it was transferred to the Bolton and Leigh line. In 1837 the wood-spoked wheels were replaced by cast iron wheels. In 1844 it was removed to Coppull Colliery, near Chorley, and used to drive pumping machinery. At this duty it worked until 1863, when it was remodelled as a locomotive, and presented to the Museum. There are four coupled wheels with two vertical cylinders.

The "*Novelty*," by Braithwaite and Ericsson, which also competed at Rainhill, has been reconstructed, as parts were missing. After a short period on the Liverpool and Manchester line this engine went to the Longridge and Preston Railway. A peculiar feature of it is the closed ashpan, into which air was forced by a bellows worked off a bell crank. There are four wheels, and two vertical cylinders, but the wheels are not coupled. The exhaust was direct into the air, not up the chimney; and in working order the engine weighed just under 4 tons.

Leaving the Museum, we may now note individual engines that are to be found in various places. There is "*Lion*," now established on a pedestal in Lime Street Station, Liverpool. This engine, which is of the 0–4–2 type, was built for the Liverpool and Manchester Railway by Tod, Kitson and Laird, of Leeds, in 1838. After four years' service it was sold to the Mersey Docks and Harbour Board for £400, and for 70 years was used for driving a set of pumps at the Princes Dock, Liverpool. It was fixed on trestles, the coupling rods being taken off and the driving wheels used as flywheels. It was recovered and restored as a locomotive for the Centenary celebrations of the Liverpool and Manchester Railway in 1930.

Outside Barrow-in-Furness station is an elaborate ornamental iron and glass pavilion, in which is housed "*Copper Nob*," so called because of its polished copper-domed firebox. It was numbered 3, and built by the celebrated Bury, an early builder of many locomotives. It was first run in 1846, and saw 52 years' service on the Furness Railway, being withdrawn in 1898.

In Dane John Gardens, Canterbury, "*Invicta*" is mounted in a small railed enclosure. This locomotive was built by Robert Stephenson in 1830 for the Canterbury and Whitstable Railway. It has been altered at various times, and for a period was housed in Ashford Works. There are four coupled wheels, and the boiler was originally similar to that of the "*Rocket*," with fire tubes, but was afterwards replaced by a boiler with a single flue tube.

In the Scottish National Museum, Edinburgh, is preserved Hedley locomotive No. 2, very similar in appearance to "*Puffing Billy*." The engine has eight wheels, driven by gearing, with vertical cylinders, and an arrangement of overhead rocking levers.

The L.N.E.R. station at Bank Top, Darlington, contains the famous engine "*Locomotion No. 1*," built by George Stephenson in 1825. It had a fairly short life, as it ceased running in 1846. There are two vertical cylinders and four wheels, coupled together; the original weight was 7 tons. It is estimated to have developed 10 h.p., and it used to haul a load of 60 to 70 tons at 5 m.p.h. The tender is of wood, on four cast iron wheels, and held 15 cwt. of coal and 240 gallons of water. Engine and tender together weighed in working order, 10 tons.

Next on the list is the engine preserved by the L.N.E.R. in their station at Newcastle. This is the locomotive called "*Derwent*," numbered 25, and built to Timothy Hackworth's design by Alfred Kitching in 1845. It has six wheels coupled, and inclined cylinders driving forward.

Two very interesting locomotives are preserved at the Crewe Works of the L.M.S.R. "*Cornwall*," built by Francis Trevithick in 1847, has the 2–2–2 wheel arrangement, and the driving wheels are 8 ft. 6 in. in diameter with openwork splashers. On her trials this engine attained a speed of 79 miles per hour. She was rebuilt in 1858, and from then until the end of December 1905 she ran 928,838 miles. From November 1890 until May 1902 "*Cornwall*" worked the 40-minute expresses between Liverpool and Manchester.

The upper illustration shows the C.R. 4-2-2 and the H.R. 4-6-0 locomotives that are preserved at the St. Rollox Works of the L.M.S.R. in Glasgow. "Locomotion No. 1" of the Stockton and Darlington Railway appears in the lower photograph, which is reproduced by courtesy of the L.N.E.R.

The other locomotive preserved at Crewe is "*Hardwicke*," of the famous "Precedent" class built by F. W. Webb. These engines were fitted with Allan's link motion, and "*Charles Dickens*" of the same class ran well over two million miles in 26 years. "*Hardwicke*" gained fame by taking part in the "Race to Aberdeen" in 1895. On the last day of the race, 22nd August, this locomotive took the West Coast train of 70½ tons from Crewe to Carlisle at an average speed of 67.2 miles per hour, thus materially helping this train to win the race.

At the Swindon Works of the G.W.R. is housed "*North Star*," built in 1837, and reassembled for exhibition purposes in 1925. This engine was made for the original broad gauge track of the G.W.R., and the single pair of driving wheels are 7 ft. in diameter. The builders were R. Stephenson and Co. and the locomotive started work in June 1838, when the line was opened to Maidenhead. It remained at work for 32 years, during which a mileage of 429,000 was run.

At one time most of the fastest trains in this country were hauled by the class of engine known as the "single drivers," because the whole of the tractive effort was exerted through one pair of driving wheels. This arrangement gives the minimum of internal friction, and as the wheels could be made very large, it is not surprising to learn that these engines were noted for very fast running. The Great Northern and Midland designs were probably the most notable, and one of each has been preserved for the admiration of future generations of railwaymen. The Great Northern one is at York, as described in the earlier article on the Railway Museum. The Midland engine is kept at Derby Works, and is restored to its original condition and painted in the former Midland colours, which greatly enhances its appearance. The designer of the locomotive was S. W. Johnson, who for many years was responsible for the Midland motive power and did much distinctive work. This particular engine was built at Derby in 1900. It has steam sanding gear. This was somewhat of a novelty in 1900, but as slipping was the main fault with single drivers when hauling loads that taxed their powers, a reliable supply of sand under the wheels was very important.

Early in 1936 the L.M.S.R. decided to save two notable engines from the scrap heap, and these have now found a home in the St. Rollox Works, of the former Caledonian Railway. One of these is the Caledonian engine numbered 123, of the single-driver type and the last of this pattern to be used on passenger services in Great Britain. It was running in Scotland up till 1935, and completed a total mileage of about 780,000. The engine was built by Neilson and Co. of Glasgow in 1886, and was bought by the Caledonian Railway after it had been shown at the Edinburgh Exhibition. It took part in the "Race to Edinburgh," between the East and West Coast Routes.

The other locomotive at St. Rollox was formerly Highland Railway engine No. 103, and is notable for being the first 4–6–0 engine to be built for service in Great Britain. It was designed by Mr. David Jones, for working on the heavy gradients of the Highland line.

Portsmouth-Johannesburg Air Race

The air race to Johannesburg, South Africa, promoted by Mr. I. W. Schlesinger as an item in the celebrations of the Jubilee of Johannesburg, was won by Mr. C. W. A. Scott and his companion, Mr. G. Guthrie. They covered the 6,150 miles in 52 hr. 56 min. 48.2 sec., at an average speed of 116 m.p.h., and set up a new record for a flight from this country to South Africa. By this fine flight they won the Schlesinger Cup and the first prize, £4,000.

Mr. Scott is well-known as the winner, along with the late Mr. T. Campbell Black of the England-Australia air race in 1934, and he now has the distinction of having flown from England to both Australia and to South Africa faster than any other airman. Scott and Guthrie flew one of the two Percival "Vega Gull" low wing monoplanes that took part in the race. The other was flown by Major A. M. Miller, who withdrew after getting as far as Belgrade.

Until a late stage in the race the lead was held by Captain S. S. Halse, flying a Percival "Mew Gull," but he crashed when only about 680 miles from the finishing point. Unfortunately the largest machine taking part, an Airspeed "Envoy," crashed when taking off from Abercorn, in Northern Rhodesia, and two of the four occupants, Captain M. Findlay and Mr. A. H. Morgan, the wireless operator, were killed. The disaster probably would not have occurred but for the fact that shortly after the airmen landed at Abercorn to refuel the wind changed, and it became necessary for them to take off in a direction that involved an uphill run across the aerodrome. The airmen were advised not to attempt the difficult take-off, but did so in the hope of overtaking Captain Halse, then the only competitor ahead of them. The "Envoy" got off the ground, but failed to clear a belt of trees bordering the aerodrome.

As none of the other competitors in the race succeeded in reaching Johannesburg before the time limit expired, the £6,000 provided by Mr. Schlesinger for second and third prizes is to be divided between the dependants of the two airmen who were killed.

Wireless and the New Empire Air Scheme

Many important developments and improvements are taking place in wireless communication, as part of the improved ground organisation for the big new Empire air scheme to be brought into operation next year, and about 20 new wireless stations are now being erected at various points along the Empire air routes. The wireless equipment being fitted in the new Empire flying boats is the most modern and efficient ever constructed for use in commercial aircraft.

These important developments make it necessary for Imperial Airways to increase their highly-skilled wireless personnel. In addition to pilots entering the company's service and studying at the instructional school to obtain their official certificates in wireless, specially-chosen operators are being drafted from the marine service into that of the air. They are being given additional and specialised coaching to enable them to pass their examinations for obtaining, as air-liner wireless operators, the aviation equivalent of the official certificate held by wireless operators on ships. A special article describing the work of Imperial Airways' school will appear in next month's *"M.M."*

This broadside view of the Bristol 130 Transport-Bomber gives a good idea of the great depth of the fuselage and breadth of the wings. When used as a troop carrier the machine can convey 24 soldiers with complete equipment. Photograph by courtesy of The Bristol Aeroplane Co. Ltd.

"Hindenburg" to Carry More Passengers

The regular trans-Atlantic airship service maintained by the *"Graf Zeppelin"* and the *"Hindenburg"* has become so popular that the passenger accommodation of the *"Hindenburg"* is to be increased by the addition of 10 more double cabins and two single ones. The airship will then be able to carry 72 passengers. The service is not operated during the winter.

Winter Air Services

Internal air services that are being continued throughout the winter include the Croydon-Glasgow and the Isle of Man lines of Railway Air Services. The Croydon-Glasgow trip is flown daily, the aeroplane leaving Croydon at 9.30 a.m. and reaching Glasgow at 1.40 p.m. In the reverse direction the aeroplane leaves Glasgow at 7.50 a.m. and arrives at Croydon at noon. The trip between Liverpool and the Isle of Man is made twice daily on weekdays and once on Sundays.

A thrice-weekly service between Belfast and Carlisle also is being operated by Blackpool and West Coast Air Services Ltd.

There have been seasonal reductions in the air services to and from Europe. Swissair are continuing their daily London-Zurich service, but only on weekdays, although the trip will be made on Sundays during the winter sporting season. The flight takes just under four hours. During the autumn and winter the Amsterdam-Batavia service of K.L.M. is a twice-weekly one, the aircraft leaving Amsterdam on Wednesdays and Saturdays, and departing from Bandoeng, the Batavia termini, on Mondays and Thursdays. The outward trip takes 6½ days and the return only 6 days.

Monospars for Canadian Air Service

Five Monospar S.T.25 aeroplanes have been built for Eastern Canada Air Lines Ltd., and will be employed on a twice-daily circuit of the Maritime Provinces. These twin-engined low wing monoplanes are fitted with Pobjoy "Niagara III" engines, and have a cruising speed of about 130 m.p.h. The five machines built for Canada have specially strengthened floors and cabin sides, as they will be used chiefly for freight transport, but they can easily be fitted with seating accommodation if required for passenger flights. The aircraft have been named after the principal Canadian cities on the Atlantic coast, and before being despatched from England were christened at Hanworth aerodrome by Lady Shelmerdine, wife of the Director-General of Civil Aviation.

G.E.C. Wind Direction Indicator

One of the most important features of the lighting equipment of a modern airport is the illuminated indicator designed to show pilots the direction of the wind, by day and night. The upper illustration on this page shows the G.E.C. illuminated wind direction indicator installed at Gatwick Airport. It consists of a "T" shaped metal framework 20 ft. in length, with a 20 ft. crosspiece, the whole framework mounted at its centre of gravity on a pivot and further supported by means of compression struts. The pivot is constructed of steel tube and is fitted with enclosed heavy duty ball bearings and thrust races. The apparatus is operated by the direct action of the wind on a streamlined vane fixed to the tail of the indicator. The upper surface of the "T" shaped framework is covered with sheet metal and is painted white, and the remainder of the indicator is finished black.

At night the indicator is brilliantly lit by 40 15-watt Osram lamps, which are mounted along the upper surface of the "T" shaped framework, and are protected by weatherproof cover glasses.

Trans-Pacific Air Service

Pan-American Airways have organised a regular passenger air service between San Francisco and Manila. Martin flying boats are being used, and stops are made at Honolulu, Midway Island, Wake Island and Guam. The total distance is 8,200 miles, and it is covered in six days, including a 24-hr. stay at Honolulu.

More Aircraft for Netherlands Navy

The Dutch Government have ordered six triple-engined Dornier aeroplanes for the Netherlands Navy. They will be used for the defence of the Netherlands East Indies. When the builders have completed these machines a further order for 36 aircraft will be given to them. Half of this number will be produced at the Dornier factory and the remainder will be built in Holland under licence.

Iraq Internal Air Services

An important step toward the development of internal air services in Iraq was taken recently, when the Iraqi Economic Council decided to form an air transport company. The regular air services it is proposed to operate will link up the chief towns in Iraq, and will also give communication by air between Baghdad and important towns on the Mediterranean coast. The scheme also includes the establishing of a flying school for the training of commercial air pilots.

Growth of Air Transport in Canada

In 1924 there were only 39 licensed aeroplanes in Canada, and only a little over 500,000 lb. of freight was carried by air in that country. By last year the total of licensed aircraft had increased to almost 400, and the quantity of freight carried in 1935 was over 25,000,000 lb. In the same 10 years the amount of air mail dealt with annually increased from 1,080 lb. to 1,126,084 lb.

Commercial air transport has proved of great value to Canadian mining, and in connection with the Canadian fisheries. Civil aircraft are also being used increasingly for aerial survey work.

The upper illustration is of the G.E.C. illuminated wind direction indicator at Gatwick Airport, and is reproduced by courtesy of the General Electric Co. Ltd. The lower photograph shows a B.A. "Eagle" in flight, with the undercarriage retracted. Photograph by courtesy of "The Aeroplane."

New Italian Military Aerodrome

An important military aerodrome has been constructed at Forli, an Italian town near the Adriatic coast. It covers an area of about 296 acres, and the preparation of the site involved the demolition of four villages and some woods, and the levelling of several hills. The extensive equipment of the aerodrome includes air raid shelters, and underground fuel and oil tanks sufficiently large to hold several month's supply of those commodities. The aerodrome was officially opened by Signor Mussolini, who is a native of Forli, and striking formation flights and demonstrations were then carried out by 250 aircraft of the Aquila Air Division of the Italian Air Force.

Second Empire Flying Boat Launched

"Caledonia," the second of the Empire flying boats under construction by the Short company, was launched recently at the maker's works at Rochester. It immediately made a preliminary test flight lasting about 30 min., during which time it circled over the town. It was piloted by Captain A. L. Parker, a test pilot of the company, who was accompanied by a crew of six. Other necessary test flights have been carried out since.

The *"Caledonia"* has been fitted with extra fuel tanks in the wings, as it will be used early next year for long-distance test flights to obtain technical information in connection with the proposed North Atlantic air service.

British Air Transport Record

An Imperial Airways liner *"Danae"* has set up a new British air transport record by covering 2,070 miles in one day. This air liner is in service on the London-Marseilles-Brindisi route, and on a recent outward journey from Croydon was delayed overnight by bad weather at Marseilles. The following morning the pilot, Captain E. R. D. White, who was accompanied by an assistant pilot and wireless operator, flew on to Brindisi, where a load of mails was picked up. Making a quick turn-about he arrived back at Croydon shortly before midnight on the same day. The 2,070 miles were covered in 18 hrs., in spite of five halts for re-fuelling and freight purposes.

"Danae" is one of the company's "Diana" class air liners, and is fitted with four D.H. "Gipsy Six" engines.

Homeward Bound

Up the Thames on a Cunard White Star Liner

By O. S. Nock, B.Sc., D.I.C.

THE *"Georgic"* rode a calm sea. But for an occasional quiver, the distant purr of the engines, and the swish of the waves, I might have been sitting in the lounge of a hotel, so smooth was our progress. We were in mid-Channel, homeward bound from New York, and were due at Havre in a few hours. I went into the Palm Court. This kind of forward lounge is just beneath the bridge and commands a splendid view of the sea ahead; the superstructure is rounded at the front, giving a degree of streamlining and a very pleasing effect from inside. The sky was overcast, the sea deep green, and right ahead the French coast showed up as a grey line.

The *"Georgic"* and her sister ship the *"Britannic"* operate what is known as the "intermediate" service to America, as distinct from the "express" service worked by the *"Queen Mary," "Aquitania"* and *"Berengaria."* They sail from London, and call at Southampton and Queenstown in addition to Havre. As their names show, these vessels belonged to the White Star Line—indeed they still carry the old colours, buff funnels with a black band at the top; they are magnificently appointed and are among the most popular ships on the North Atlantic.

The *"Georgic"* is a motorship of 27,760 tons, built as recently as 1932 by Harland and Wolff's at Belfast; she is designed for moderate speed and makes the crossing from New York to Queenstown in a week. Her normal speed is about 18 knots. An hour before we were due at Havre I met Mr. Horsburgh, the Chief Engineer, who took me down to the engine room to watch the ship being manœuvred into port. We went down by an electric lift, in a cage just big enough to take three men, and as we neared the bottom passed several galleries that are needed for maintenance purposes owing to the great height of the engines.

The Cunard White Star motor passenger liner "Georgic" in the River Mersey.

The ship is driven by two 10-cylinder Diesel engines each of which develops 10,000 horse power. They work on the four-stroke cycle, on what is known as the "solid injection" principle. The fuel oil is sprayed into the cylinders and vaporised by means of compressed air, the "blast air" they call it, at a pressure of 800 lb. per sq. in. The cylinders are 33⅝ in. in diameter with a stroke of no less than 5 ft. 3 in.; and the propeller shafts, which are coupled direct to the engines, make only 98 revolutions per minute when going full speed.

When we got down to the control platform both engines were going full speed ahead, but the warning signal had been given from the bridge and the engineers were standing by ready for any changes that might be wanted. Each engine is in two halves, there being two 5-cylinder units; each half of the engine is controlled separately but the regulating levers are placed close together so that both can be operated simultaneously by one man. The telegraph signal dials are placed close to the regulating levers, near the middle of each engine.

Soon the telegraph rang indicating half speed; we were slowing up to take a French pilot on board to get us into Havre. Signals now followed rapidly, and two visual revolution indicators were switched on to show the actual movement of each propeller shaft. These devices consist of a ring of electric lamps behind a frosted dial. As the shafts revolve the lamps are lighted consecutively, and give the impression of a point of light travelling round and round in a circle. The engines are entirely encased, and the engineers on the control platform have no means of seeing exactly when the shafts have ceased to revolve. If the valve gear were to be reversed and an attempt made to restart the engine before it had completely stopped, the result would be some terrific back-firing.

The engines are restarted by compressed air. The regulating levers are moved to a particular notch on the quadrant plate; then with a sharp hissing the engines start, and as soon as each has made one complete revolution, as indicated on the dial, the levers are moved still further over and full Diesel working begins. Four 800-h.p. Diesel engines are provided to drive the compressors that supply the blast air, though actually only three are used. These three engines should strictly speaking be included in the total horse power of the ship, making it up to 22,400, but even this is quite a small figure considering the size of the *"Georgic."* But here again it is entirely a question of speed. Only 22,400 h.p. are needed to drive a ship of 27,760 tons at 18 knots, compared with the 16,000 h.p. required to take the 3,470-ton Irish Mail boats from Holyhead to Dun Laoghaire at a top speed of 25 knots. The difference seems incredible! Then, in addition to the air compressors, the auxiliary Diesel engines drive four 500-kilowatt generators for supplying electricity through the ship. As the Chief Engineer expressed it, they generate sufficient power for a town of 30,000 inhabitants.

Now both engines were stopped; for a moment all was quiet, and then, full speed ahead on both engines. The pilot was on board. As we manœuvred up to the berth, with tugs assisting of course, I tried to visualise the scene above; often the two engines were running in opposite directions, while the ship was being swung. Both were stopped, severally, to be restarted with the loud accompanying exhaust of the compressed air. In the upward current of ventilating air it was beautifully cool; Mr. Horsburgh told me that when they were in New York during the terrific heat-wave earlier in the year the engine-room was the coolest part of the ship! So we came into Havre.

The quay where the Transatlantic liners berth is remarkably equipped. A ship is moored against a number of buttresses so that it is kept six feet or more from the quayside, and instead of the usual type of gangway a sliding bridge is run across from an elevated gallery so that passengers go ashore from the promenade deck of the liner. Cargo is unloaded very quickly by powerful travelling cranes. One of the big C.G.T. liners, the *"Paris,"* was berthed just astern of us, and three tugs, two at the bow and one at the stern, were waiting ready to help us off. Our stay at Havre was brief indeed; at 6.25 p.m., barely 40 minutes after we had berthed, the gangways were withdrawn. During this brief time the customs and immigration formalities had been carried out for a hundred or more passengers, and cargo unloaded.

While we were in Havre I was introduced to Captain Townley. He told me that he expected to be off Dungeness about 1 a.m., and that there the Channel pilot, Mr. Anderson, would take over. The Thames estuary requires very skilful navigation and a most intimate knowledge of the currents, the difficulties beginning as far out as the Straits of Dover. I should explain that in such cases, although the pilot sets the courses and gives all the necessary orders for navigation, he never takes full charge of the ship; he is the local expert taken on board to advise, but he is in all things responsible to the Captain. It is just the same in the case of the harbour pilots taken at Havre, Southampton, and Queenstown.

Now, the two tugs at the bow were pulling away at right angles to the length of the ship; belching smoke and churning the water into a welter of foam they fully earned the description "fussy," which is so often applied to their kind. The one at the stern was hauling too, and soon we were well clear of the quay; then the steel hawsers were cast off and two of the tugs steamed away to the opposite side of the dock. The third went careering out to sea in front of us ready to lend a hand when we dropped the pilot.

A fascinating glimpse of the Engine Room of the "Georgic."

The evening sun was now brilliant, and as we put out to sea the picturesque French port was looking its very best. Groups of sightseers gathered on the nearest quays to wave us farewell, the docks used by merchantmen were alive with shipping, and right away in the inner harbour at the Quai de Southampton was the little Southern Railway cross-Channel boat. The sun was gleaming in the windows of the hotels and fashionable villas along the esplanade as we passed abreast of Cap de la Hève; we passed the Whistle Buoy, and then just short of the lightship the pilot cutter was waiting. Our little tug was still tearing on ahead, but when we began to slow he dropped astern. A rowing boat was put out from the pilot ship and in a few minutes we were practically at a stop; the little boat approached on our starboard side, a rope ladder was lowered, and a moment later the Havre pilot had clambered down and the boat was being pulled away vigorously.

The "*Georgic*" was once more under way. The cliffs stretching away to Cap d'Antifer glowed a warm red, almost the colour of those of South Devon; the sun was sinking in a cloudless sky. The strong light from the west threw the wavelets into dark relief, the sky overhead changed, through the most glorious shades of pink, blue, and purple, and as it neared the horizon the sun's flaming disc developed an elongated shape like a Rugby football. A vivid green spread into the western sky after the sun had disappeared. Then the long line of cliffs changed colour to a wondrous violet blue, and the lighthouse on Cap d'Antifer began to flash. We were making a course almost parallel to this part of the coast, and now the beautiful chalk cliffs beyond the cape, of Etretat, and away towards Fecamp could be seen. Far astern Cap de la Hève light was now flashing, sky and sea blended into the deepest blue, and so we rode on into the night.

After dinner I came up on deck for a while. Four great lighthouses were flashing away to the south, Fecamp showed up as a row of shimmering lights, the sky was bespangled with stars, but—the lounge looked very cosy and inviting and I went inside again. The main lounge of the ship is a delightful place. The pervading colour-scheme is one of soft greys and browns; the style is essentially modern—the "*Georgic*" was not built till 1932—and the lighting very subdued and effective. The principal lights are carried on octagonal pillars of polished wood, and the lamps themselves contained in funnel-shaped shades; along the walls these are so arranged that the light throws into bold relief the moulding round the ceilings. Just outside is the long gallery, with its grey tapestry-covered walls, colourful bookcases and some curious Chinese ornaments. Here you are more conscious of being on board ship; wind-blown figures pass occasionally along the promenade deck just outside, there is the ever-present swish of the sea, and through the windows are seen the lights of a passing ship. In the Palm Court the heavy curtains were tightly drawn, an orchestra was playing in the lounge, and with this pleasant impression of the last night at sea I went early to bed.

Close-up of the "Georgic" at her berth, Ocean Dock, Southampton.

In the middle of the night there was a knock at my door. A steward came in with tea, and "We're approaching Dungeness, Sir." I looked at my watch; it was 12.15 a.m. I dressed hurriedly and went up aloft. In the passenger quarters it was most eerie; the lounge bore the same deserted look as a big hotel when you leave at dawn to catch an early train or boat. But up above things were very much awake. I could just distinguish the outline of the bridge, muffled figures were pacing to and fro, and a chink of light showed the whereabouts of the chart-room. Every now and then its curtains would be brushed aside as somebody passed, and then other figures inside the wheelhouse were silhouetted against the light. In the still night air voices carried to a remarkable degree and I could hear almost every word spoken on the bridge.

When I came up on to the boat deck Dungeness lighthouse was just abeam. The powerful shaft of light, travelling round, lit up the whole ship. Another vessel just on our port bow was picking up her Channel pilot. In our case Mr. Anderson had come aboard at Southampton, but ships not calling at any Channel ports stop off Dungeness, and their pilot is brought out on a Trinity House cutter. We drove on. We picked up Folkestone harbour lighthouse, and soon a long chain of twinkling lights revealed the positions of Hythe, Sandgate, and Folkeston itself; then farther ahead were the lighthouses of Dover Admiralty Pier, and the South Foreland.

A little to the north-east of the South Foreland are the Goodwin Sands, at low water left high and dry enough to play a cricket match. Between the Goodwins and the coast is the deep water channel known as the Downs. In times of storm this channel provides a placid anchorage, and then from Deal the sight of thirty or more vessels sheltering, of all sizes and shapes, is an extraordinary one indeed. But to-night, as one of the officers explained, we had plenty of time and so would take the longer course east of the sands. As we approached Dover the revolving beams from the lighthouses could be watched sweeping round. There was mist about, and try as we could to locate it, there was not a sign of the mightiest light hereabouts, the giant at Cap Griz Nez across the Channel. The Thames estuary is notorious for fog, and although it may be merely an early morning mist there is nothing for it but to drop anchor and wait till it lifts. The Goodwin sands are marked by three lightships and we were now approaching the "South Goodwin"; its watchmen also were apprehensive of fog, for the sound of the siren came moaning across to us. The channel through the Downs is marked by a chain of gas buoys, but a ship taking the outer course steers in a straight line from one lightship to the next.

Although the beams from the lightships shone yellow in the misty haze, it was most brilliantly clear overhead and the sky was bespangled with stars. Right across the heavens like a great arch stretched the Milky Way, Orion was ascending in the south-east while the Great Bear drooped towards the north. The fog siren of the "East Goodwin" came booming over the water, and this lightship has also a submarine bell by means of which vessels can calculate their bearings by wireless in dense fog. But the tide was turning, and this change of water seemed to disperse the mist for by the time that the "North Goodwin" was abeam the lights of Ramsgate stood out with astonishing clearness.

From now onwards, amid the shallows and mud banks of the Thames estuary, our progress was enthralling in the extreme.

To be continued)

Snow Scenes At Hollywood

Machine That Creates Winter Blizzards

By Andrew R. Boone

ICY winds beat against the walls of a backwoods cabin, carrying snowflakes that swirl past the windows and pile up in drifts around the stoop. In front of the door, a snow-encrusted bridge spans a narrow expanse of glistening ice. Men and women, bundled up in heavy winter clothing, lean against the force of the gale as they move about, breathing puffs of fog into the wintry air.

When you witness the scene on the screen of your cinema, it will have an air of grim reality. And, as far as physical conditions go, this is a genuine blizzard that is being photographed. Wind, snow and ice, and even the icicles that fringe the eaves of the house, are real. The cameramen and technicians behind the battery of lights stamp booted feet and wave their arms to keep warm. Yet, only a few feet away, beyond the insulated walls of the stage where the picture is being made, the Southern Californian sun is shining with all its summer heat.

A winter scene of snow and ice in the refrigerated stage in Hollywood. Cooling pipes are suspended from the ceiling, and the walls and roof are insulated by granulated cork.

The refrigerated stage is Hollywood's latest aid in bringing realism to motion pictures. Instead of spending vast sums of money to send players and technicians "on location" to the snow fields of the Californian mountains, or even as far away as Alaska, producers now can film their winter sequences right in Los Angeles, only a short distance from their home studios.

The first of these ice-box stages utilises the interior of an ice-storage plant, which was stripped of its load of 10,000 tons of manufactured ice and studded with studio lights and painted sets. Snow slingers and wind machines were installed, making it possible to create at the wave of a hand any of the scenes common to lands of boisterous winters.

The building is 140 ft. long, 100 ft. wide, and 40 ft. high, with walls and roof completely insulated by a 14-in. layer of granulated cork. Three miles of coiled pipes lie in triple banks three deep suspended from the ceiling, forming a cooling system that can reduce the temperature of this vast room to 10 deg. F. above zero, and hold it there indefinitely.

A portable snow machine makes actual snow out of 25-lb. cakes of ice that are tossed into a hopper in which spiked cylinders crush them and chop them into flaky white chips. The snow is hurled through a centrifugal slinger 60 ft. out over the sets, where it drifts naturally upon roofs, fences and ground and clings realistically to trees and shrubs. Impelled by gusts from a wind machine, this man-made snow is said to be indistinguishable from the outdoor variety. The machine eats 300 lb. of ice for each minute of snow.

The cabin of a Canadian trapper can be reproduced now in Hollywood in midsummer. The icicles that hang coldly from its eaves are chill and brittle. They have been made and frozen in a water mould, and "pasted" on the set wherever needed by means of a little water that quickly freezes them solidly in place.

Making an artificial snow storm. The machine grinds blocks of ice into fine flakes, which are sprayed over winter settings for film scenes.

Before the advent of the refrigerated stage, a chemical known as "hypo ice" was used wherever the appearance of an ice sheet was needed on an indoor set, and white gypsum fluttered down out of a dull sky as a crude imitation of snow. But the effect was often destroyed by the unlifelike setting. "Fog-breath"—one of the touches of realism never before possible with indoor winter scenes—comes as a natural consequence of the low temperatures maintained on the set.

Even the Eskimo's igloo is faithfully reproduced with blocks of ice, laid like stones in a wall and then covered with a blast of snow from the snow-throwing machine. The frozen surface of a lake or stream is almost instantly made by flooding water upon the required spot. The ice withstands skate runners on its flinty surface.

The Midland and Great Northern Railway

An Interesting Joint Line

ON 1st October last there came to an end the independent operation of the Midland and Great Northern Joint Railway, for since that date the L.N.E.R. have been responsible for its working. Previously the system was managed by a Joint Committee consisting of L.M.S.R. and L.N.E.R. representatives, as the successors of the former partners the Midland and the Great Northern Railways. It is of great importance in East Anglia, particularly in connection with the agricultural, fishing and flower-growing industries, and during the Summer months it deals with much holiday traffic from the Midlands and the North to Cromer, Yarmouth and elsewhere.

The M. and G.N. passes from an end-on junction with a former Midland line near Little Bytham across to Yarmouth. On the way it receives a branch from Peterborough, and there are in addition branches from Melton Constable to Cromer, and to Norwich.

A typical M. and G.N. 4-4-0 of former Midland design. The photographs on this page were taken by our reader D. Redshaw of Spalding.

It was as a result of the amalgamation of several independent small lines in Norfolk that the system eventually became the joint property of the Midland and Great Northern Railways. In 1883 an amalgamation of several local lines formed the Eastern and Midlands Railway. Owing to a shortage of engines, an arrangement was made for the lines of this railway east of King's Lynn to be worked by the Eastern and Midlands Company, and those west of that point by the Midland and the Great Northern Railways. The lines west of King's Lynn were once nearly purchased by the Midland Company but this aroused protests from the Great Northern, with the result that joint working was established on this section in 1889 and on that east of King's Lynn in 1893. Until 1895 each section had a separate manager, the western section headquarters being at Spalding and those of the eastern section at King's Lynn. In that year a Traffic Manager for the whole line was appointed, with offices at King's Lynn, and until this year the M. and G.N. was worked as a separate concern, with its own engines and stock.

One of the Great Northern type 0-6-0 engines of the M. and G.N. This engine is practically unchanged from its original condition.

The Eastern and Midlands Railway originally had only 26 engines to work about 140 miles of railway. With the commencement of the interest of the Midland and Great Northern companies there appeared several 4-4-0 express locomotives typical of Midland design of the period. In the course of time they have been rebuilt according to the prevailing Derby practice, and some are now fitted with the "stove-pipe" chimneys that appeared on the new L.M.S.R. 0-4-4 tank locomotives that were constructed in 1932.

The first really suitable goods engines possessed by the joint concern were of Derby pattern. The G.N.R. section of the L.N.E.R. also is represented among the goods locomotives. In 1900 an arrangement was made whereby several standard G.N.R. engines then under construction should be passed over to the Joint line. These engines still retain the characteristics that marked the Ivatt classes of engines on the G.N.R. In view of the lengths of single track included in the main lines, all locomotives are fitted with tablet exchange apparatus, which is a prominent feature on the tenders. At one time the engines were finished in light brown, but this has now given place to very dark brown and black.

At the time of the formation of the Joint Committee, coaches from each partner were contributed to the stock already owned; and as the Doncaster and Derby locomotives differ, so also do the coaches originating at these places. More modern vehicles of course also have been provided, and these are typical of the standard practice of the representative groups. The through express services from the L.M.S.R. and the L.N.E.R. systems are formed of stock belonging to those Companies. The signalling equipment too is "joint" in character, some signals being of Midland pattern and others of the G.N.R. "somersault" type.

The engineering offices and workshops of the line are at Melton Constable. There the engines and stock are maintained and some of the "specialities" of the system in reinforced concrete are produced. This material has been used extensively for signal and fencing posts, gradient and mile posts, telegraph poles, crossing gate posts and for various other lineside items of this kind.

A feature of the line is the number of level crossings, of which there are 155. A little way away from the junction with the L.M.S.R. near Little Bytham is Toft Tunnel, which is 330 yd. long and is the only one on the line. Other engineering features include two large swing bridges, Breydon viaduct, which has five spans in all, and Cross Keys Bridge, which has three. The latter crosses the River Nene at Sutton Bridge and provides a way for road vehicles as well as the railway.

There is heavy traffic in vegetables and potatoes on the line, and the carriage of fruit has received special attention. A road collection service for this traffic started in 1934, has been greatly extended.

The L.M.S.R. "Turbomotive"

The turbine-driven 4-6-2 locomotive No. 6202 of the L.M.S.R. has become a familiar sight on the Euston and Liverpool expresses. It has worked on these services almost exclusively since its introduction, although trials were carried out earlier in the year with the dynamometer car on Anglo-Scottish trains.

From the "*L.M.S. Magazine*" we extract the following details of a run made by No. 6202 on the 5.25 p.m. up "*Liverpool Flyer,*" after having made the corresponding down journey on the 10.40 a.m. from Euston the same morning. The schedule of the "*Flyer*" involves a start-to-stop average of 64.5 m.p.h. over the 152.7 miles from Crewe to Willesden. On this occasion No. 6202 had a 'oad of 11 vehicles with a tare weight of 315 tons, and was manned by Driver Fryer and Fireman Bodey of Edge Hill Depot.

In spite of greasy rails owing to the showery weather the 10.5 miles from Crewe to Whitmore were covered in 12¾ min., a steady acceleration to 61 m.p.h. being recorded up the 1 in 177 gradient. Signal checks through the Stafford area were experienced as far as Milford; after a maximum of 82 m.p.h. at Lichfield the Polesworth pitfall slack caused a reduction to 30 m.p.h. and Nuneaton was passed 4 min. late, but Willesden was reached a minute early, the 124.1 miles thither from Milford having been covered at an average speed of 69.4 m.p.h. Over the most favourable section of the journey, from Welton to Wembley, the average was 76 m.p.h., 83½ being recorded twice—before Weedon and before Wolverton respectively—and 82 m.p.h. at Hemel Hempstead. Rapid acceleration from slacks and a scrupulous observance of the latter were features of the run.

On another occasion No. 6202 regained 5 min. on this schedule with a tare load of 472 tons behind the tender.

The L.M.S.R. 4-6-2 "Turbomotive" No. 6202 on the 5.25 p.m. "Liverpool Flyer." The train is approaching Wavertree station. Photograph by the Rev. E. Treacy, Liverpool.

Records of "*The Silver Jubilee*"

During its first 12 months' service, which began on 30th September 1935, Britain's first streamlined train, "*The Silver Jubilee*" of the L.N.E.R., covered 132,397 miles, or more than half the distance from the Earth to the Moon.

The service has been so successful that it may be extended to Edinburgh on a 6-hour schedule, and similar services may be introduced on other routes. To this end tests have been made with the dynamometer car added to the usual seven-coach formations, and on 27th August last a new high speed record for British railways was set up when a maximum of 113 m.p.h. was reached by the streamlined No. 2512 "*Silver Fox*" in charge of Driver Haygreen. The load behind the tender totalled 270 tons, and the record was made on the descent from Stoke to Tallington on the up journey. The train ran at over 100 m.p.h. for 11 miles, and lunch was actually being served during this high-speed period, but the smooth and steady running of the train made it impossible to detect any undue increase of speed above the normal.

The previous highest speed of this now famous train was the 112½ m.p.h. attained on a trial run before it was put into service last year. The new record speed therefore is easily the highest ever attained by a British train in ordinary running.

On the corresponding down journey it was arranged not to exceed 90 m.p.h. in order to see the effect of this, in conjunction with an increase in load, on No. 2509 "*Silver Link.*" Some remarkable running was the result, Driver Sparshatt being in charge on the footplate. An average of 82.6 m.p.h. was maintained over the 15.3 miles up from Tallington to Stoke, 90 m.p.h. being actually attained when the climbing had already begun. All slacks were carefully observed throughout and Newcastle was reached 4 min. inside schedule.

Subsequently successful trials were carried out between Newcastle and Edinburgh. These were carried out on a Saturday, on which day the train does not make the London run.

So far only one set of "*Silver Jubilee*" coaches has been available and it is a remarkable tribute to their sound design and construction that practically the whole of the mileage has been performed by them. The working of the train devolves chiefly on three of the four streamlined "Pacifics" built for the service. These are No. 2509 "*Silver Link,*" No. 2510 "*Quicksilver,*" and No. 2512 "*Silver Fox,*" all attached to King's Cross shed; No. 2511 "*Silver King*" is allocated to Gateshead and stands by to relieve any of the others as may be necessary.

"The Railway Handbook 1936-1937"

The 1936-1937 issue of this handbook maintains its reputation as a most useful work of reference. It contains statistical information relating to the railways of Great Britain and Ireland. Its contents are by no means confined to masses of figures, however, and it also includes general particulars of the principal systems and their development, and a brief history of railway events arranged in chronological order. Various aspects of railway working are dealt with and different forms of motive power are considered, and there are some useful details relating to locomotives and rolling stock generally, permanent way and signalling. In addition such items as fastest runs, greatest altitudes, steepest gradients, largest stations and many others are included.

Although the contents deal primarily with the railways of Great Britain and Ireland, international comparisons are necessarily made in certain sections. The matter is very comprehensive and the "Handbook" fairly claims to be the cheapest publication available that presents so much information in convenient form. It costs 2/6 nett and is published by The Railway Publishing Company Limited, 33, Tothill Street, Westminster, London, S.W.1.

A New "*Patriot*" Locomotive

L.M.S.R. No. 5500 is to be named "*Patriot*"; the name was originally applied to a "*Claughton*" in honour of the L.N.W.R. men killed in the War, but this engine was scrapped last year.

High Speeds with "Football Club" Locomotives

Reference has been made several times recently in the *"M.M."* to the excellent work being done on the Great Central section of the L.N.E.R. by engines of the "Football Club" series of the 4–6–0 "Sandringham" class, and readers will no doubt be interested to learn that these fast runs are being made with the utmost ease.

On a recent run with the up Manchester express due into Marylebone at 1.10 p.m., No. 2851 *"Derby County"* was worked at 15 per cent. cut-off for practically the whole distance, and this with a load of nearly 300 tons. From Rugby to Woodford the 14.1 miles, half of which are rising at 1 in 176, were run in 17¼ min. start to stop, and 20 per cent. cut-off was sufficient to sustain 51 m.p.h. up the long bank through Catesby tunnel. The next two sections, Woodford-Brackley and Brackley-Aylesbury were covered entirely on a cut-off of 15 per cent. and yet the former stretch of 9.8 miles was run in 12½ min., and the latter, 21.3 miles, in 23 min.

Starting away from Aylesbury, up the stiff rise at 1 in 110 on to the Chilterns, 25 per cent. was used as far as Stoke Mandeville, where speed had risen to 40 m.p.h., but from there to the summit 20 per cent. was enough. Fast running followed with the engine now working on 15 per cent.; a top speed of 72 m.p.h. was reached at Great Missenden, and Amersham summit was passed at 50 m.p.h. After that things were so well in hand that no higher speed than 70 was reached on the descent to Rickmansworth, and the 38 miles from Aylesbury to Marylebone were completed in 46 min., three minutes inside schedule time.

The driver who was responsible for this good work, Green of Leicester shed, made some brilliant running later with No. 2855 *"Middlesbrough."* The train this time was the 4.55 p.m. from Marylebone, loaded to 300 tons, the journey being recorded from Leicester onwards. A very rapid start was made, speed rising to 50 m.p.h. up a gradient of 1 in 176 as early as Belgrave, 2¼ miles out. Really high speed followed with 81 m.p.h. through Loughborough, 62½ over Barnston summit, and a well-sustained 77 near Ruddington. Nottingham (Arkwright St.), 22½ miles, was passed in 21 min. 55 sec. from the start and in spite of a signal check right at the finish, the 23.4 miles from Leicester to Nottingham (Victoria) took exactly 24 min. Here again the engine was worked at little over 15 per cent. cut-off all the way.

These runs were timed by Mr. O. S. Nock.

An L.N.E.R. Harrogate express passing Barnby Moor. The locomotive is No. 2833 "Kimbolton Castle," one of the 4-6-0 "Sandringham" class.

Brighter Railway Stations

Following a series of experiments, the L.M.S.R. have adopted a range of six standard colours for painting their 2,500 passenger stations in a more cheerful and more attractive style than has hitherto been employed. These colours include two light shades, either of which can be used in conjunction with any one of three dark shades. The sixth colour, golden brown, is being used sometimes by itself and sometimes in conjunction with another paint; it is particularly useful at stations where there are electric trains, for there the air contains a certain amount of iron dust, which causes a rust-like stain on paint work. The effects of this are reduced when golden brown paint is used. Ultimately all L.M.S.R. passenger stations will be painted in accordance with the new colour scheme.

Continuing their general policy of "brighter stations" the L.N.E.R. have recently placed contracts for the painting and cleaning of a number of stations in Scotland. These include St. Andrews, Buchlyvie, Kilsyth, Campsie Glen, Strathblane, Aberfolye, Gartmore, Port of Menteith, Blanefield, Balfron, Gartness, Dumgoyne, Killearn, and Gargunnock.

An L.M.S.R. Blackpool excursion train from the Midland Division passing Dore West Junction. The illustrations on this page are from H.R.C. prize-winning photographs by C. Spencer, Sheffield, H.R.C. No. 44179.

A New "Coronation" Engine

One of the L.M.S.R. engines of the 4–6–2 "Princess Royal" class is to be named *"Coronation"* in honour of the coronation of His Majesty King Edward next May. This step follows the precedent established in 1911, when one of the L.N.W.R. express engines then being built at Crewe Works was so named in honour of the coronation of King George V and Queen Mary.

The earlier "Coronation" engine was the 5,000th locomotive to be built at Crewe. It is now L.M.S.R. No. 25348 and is stationed at Chester, but will shortly be withdrawn from service, as this type of engine has become obsolete. It was illustrated on page 348 of the June 1935 issue of the *"M.M."*

The new *"Coronation"* and its tender will weigh over 160 tons. The corresponding weight of its older namesake is less than 100 tons, and the two *"Coronation"* engines will typify the progress of a quarter of a century in locomotive design and construction.

By Train Ferry to Paris

On 14th October, the Southern Railway introduced a new Channel Train Ferry Service between London (Victoria) and Paris (Nord). Through first and second class sleeping cars now leave London at 10 p.m. and Paris at 9.50 p.m. nightly, completing their journeys at 8.55 in Paris and 8.30 in London the following morning. Customs and passport examinations are carried out aboard the trains, which cross the Channel on board 3,000-ton train ferries having accommodation for 500 passengers. Each ferry can accommodate 12 sleeping cars, or 40 loaded goods wagons, and has a fireproof insulated garage for 25 motor cars, as well as fully equipped restaurants and other accommodation.

As the daily rise and fall of the tide on both the French and English sides of the Channel is between 10 and 20 ft., new locks have been constructed to enable the ferry vessels to be operated at any time.

The G.W.R. "Grange" Locomotives

The G.W.R. have just introduced a new class of 4-6-0 mixed-traffic locomotives designed to ensure the more expeditious working of the Company's already speedy freight services. The new engines have been built at the Swindon Works, and are known as the "Grange" class. The names selected for the first 10 engines were given in the August *"M.M."* this year. The "Granges" will be used for hauling market produce from Cornwall, Worcestershire and other districts, and also for excursion traffic. They replace the condemned 2–6–0s of the 4300 class.

Oil from Shale

An Important Scottish Industry

THE mention of oil suggests deep wells and forests of steel derricks in Iraq, Iran, Burma, Mexico and many parts of the United States, from which come millions of gallons of petroleum. The great wells in these immense oil fields are not the only sources, however, for in Scotland there is a large industry in which oil and sulphate of ammonia are produced from a mineral known as oil shale, which is mined in much the same way as coal. The shale sometimes crops out at the surface, and is worked as deep as 1,500 ft.

The story of oil from shale began in the middle of last century, the industry owing its origin to James Young, a Glasgow chemist who had distilled an illuminating oil from an underground source in Derbyshire. Young's experiments were the foundation of the modern petroleum industry, for he believed that natural oil was produced from some kind of coal by underground heat, and tried to make it artificially. This led to the establishing of a plant at Bathgate, in West Lothian, Scotland, for distilling illuminating oil from Boghead Coal or Torbanehill mineral mined there. The supply of this material soon gave out and attention was next directed to oil shale beds discovered at Addiewell, Broxburn and in other places, principally in West Lothian and Midlothian. The shale did not give such a good yield of oil as the Boghead Mineral previously used, but it was so abundant and cheap that the new industry flourished, and by 1865 there were 120 works in operation producing oil from it.

At the working face of a mine in the Scottish oil shale field. The illustrations to this article are reproduced by courtesy of Scottish Oils Limited

Then came the discovery of the prolific oil fields of the United States. The petroleum obtained directly from the earth was cheaper than the oil distilled from shale, and as a result of its competition many of the mines and works in the shale field were abandoned. The survivors turned their attention to other valuable products, such as lubricating oils, paraffin wax and sulphate of ammonia, and their enterprise brought renewed prosperity to their undertakings.

In 1913 3¼ million tons of shale were mined and used in the distillation of oil and other products, but for a time further development was checked by the outbreak of the Great War. At the end of the conflict the six companies at work were brought under one management, forming Scottish Oils Ltd., and to-day the company works 13 mines, the output of which is dealt with in five crude oil works and a central refinery. A coal mine supplies part of the fuel required, and the plant also includes two sulphuric acid works and a candle factory.

The shale is dark brown in colour and can be cut with a sharp knife, curling like a wood shaving. It has been formed in successive layers, pressed together like the leaves of a closed book, and its structure is more easily seen when it has been distilled in a retort than when it is in its natural state. It is difficult to work, and can only be dislodged by blasting. To mine a ton of shale requires almost ¾ lb. of explosive.

The largest mine is that at Westwood, near West Calder. This has an output of 700 tons a day, in which two shifts are worked, but is designed to yield a higher output. The mine covers an area of about 500 acres and works two seams, known as the Broxburn and Dunnet Seams. These are 5 ft. and 11-12 ft. in thickness respectively, and are separated by 380 ft. of sandstone and other minerals.

The Westwood pit has two shafts, which were sunk between the years 1915 and 1917. The downcast shaft is 16 ft. in diameter, and the upcast is 14 ft. across. Both are sunk to a depth of 700 ft. and are lined with brick from top to bottom. The downcast shaft is used for winding shale and men, and the upcast shaft carries water pipes and electric cables, and is only used in case of emergency. Two single deck cages work in the downcast shaft, each carrying two hutches that together weigh about 10 cwt. and carry about 36 cwt. of shale. The steel wire ropes used to wind the cages in the shaft are 1⅜ in. in diameter and in addition there are three guide ropes and two rubbing ropes between the cages, all being of the same size as the winding rope.

The visitor to the Westwood pit finds himself on the main haulage road as soon as he steps out of the cage that carries him down the shaft. Alongside are the pit pony stables, the pump rooms and the haulage rooms, in which is the machinery that drives the endless ropes used in hauling the hutches to and from the working faces. These are now well away from the pit bottom, some of them fully a mile distant. The shale is worked by what is known as the "stoop and room" method, the shale seam being formed into pillars or "stoops" in the first operation, the pillars or stoops being extracted in the second operation. In working the Dunnet Seam, a thickness of only 9 ft. is taken when the stoops are formed, and the full thickness when extracting the stoops.

No mechanical contrivances have yet been found advantageous for working the shale. The shot holes are bored with hand boring machines, which the miners are experts at working. After blasting the shale is worked off by picks and "pinches."

The pit is ventilated by means of a single inlet Sirocco fan that is connected to the upcast shaft by means of a drift, or airway. The fan is nearly 9 ft. in diameter and runs at 140 r.p.m., driving 100,000 cu. ft. of air through the mine every minute.

The two shafts and pithead buildings of the Westwood Pit. The shafts are sunk to a depth of 700 ft.

The shale reaches the surface in pieces that are too large for the treatment it has to undergo, and these are reduced to about the size of a man's fist by heavy toothed rollers or "breakers" in crushing machines. Then it passes on to the retorts. These are of giant size, measuring 43 ft. 6 in. from top to bottom, with a width of 2 ft. at the top and 2 ft. 9 in. at the bottom. Each holds about four tons of shale. Its upper portion is of cast iron and the lower part of firebrick, and at the top and bottom are hoppers for charging the retort and removing the spent shale respectively.

The retorts are built up in towering banks, four in a set and 13 sets in a bench, and at the Deans Oil Works, one of the five in which crude oil is made, there are six benches, making a total of 312 retorts in all. The shale comes from the Westwood Pit, which is 3½ miles away, and two other mines nearer the works. It is carried over the intervening distance by means of endless rope haulage, and on arrival is shot from the trucks into the steel charging hopper of one or other of the retorts. There it passes slowly downwards, taking 24 hrs. to travel from top to bottom, so that the shale is treated in each retort at the rate of four tons a day. As it moves downward it is gradually heated to a temperature of 1,300 deg. F. The oil vapour is given off long before this stage is reached, however, a temperature of 650 deg. F. to 900 deg. F. being sufficient for this purpose.

Making bricks from spent shale from the retorts in which oil is distilled.

As the shale descends and becomes hotter it meets an upward current of steam that converts the nitrogen in the shale into ammonia. About 90 to 100 gallons of steam are introduced into the retorts for each ton of shale. In addition to converting the nitrogen in the shale to ammonia, it cools the spent material, distributes the heat evenly through the discharge hopper, and carries the oil vapour away quickly and thus prevents it from "cracking."

The shale is passed through the retorts continuously, and the oil vapour and gases are drawn out at the top by means of the exhausters that carry them into condensers, where liquid oil and water are condensed and collected. The incondensed gas still contains ammonia and light spirit. The first is removed by scrubbing with water and the second by scrubbing with oil. The permanent gas is returned to the retorts for heating and is augmented by producer gas. Steam is passed through the ammonia liquor, and the gas thus expelled from it is absorbed in weak sulphuric acid to make sulphate of ammonia, a valuable fertiliser. The spent shale also is turned to good account, for it is made into bricks of excellent quality.

The oil distilled from the shale in this manner is too crude to be used and requires further treatment in order to separate it into fractions that can be used for motor fuel, as solvents for use in the rubber and linoleum industries, and oils suitable for burning or for Diesel engines. The first step in refining the crude oil is distillation, and this is carried on at a special plant at Pumpherston, where the crude oil from the Deans and other retorting plants is dealt with. A bench of five boiler stills is used, each having a capacity of about 6,000 gallons. The crude oil runs continuously into the middle still of the five and the residue is fed into the two stills on each side of it. As the distillation continues, the liquid remaining in these is again run off into a range of smaller stills in which it is heated until only coke remains. Steam is injected into all the stills, partly to check the decomposition or breaking up of the oil and partly to stir the liquid up and thus prevent the deposit of the carbon formed during distillation.

The carbon or coke left behind in the coking stills is particularly suitable for making the best class of electrodes for electric furnaces. Resin also is formed, but the greater part of the crude oil is vaporised and condensed separately. Even yet it is not suitable for any definite purpose, however, and it has to be washed with sulphuric acid and caustic soda, and again distilled, in order to separate it into a crude burning oil, a heavy oil containing solid paraffin and a coke that is an excellent household fuel. Further refinement transforms the crude burning oil into grades suitable for domestic and power use, lighthouses, railway signals and other purposes, and paraffin wax also is obtained from it.

These pages are reserved for articles from our readers. Contributions not exceeding 500 words in length are invited on any subject of general interest. These should be written neatly on one side of the paper only, and they may be accompanied by photographs or sketches for use as illustrations. Articles that are published will be paid for at our usual rates. Statements contained in articles submitted for these pages are accepted as being sent in good faith, but the Editor takes no responsibility for their accuracy.

A Canoe Trip Down the Severn

Our party consisted of three boys and a master, and our boats were a falbot, a canoe of German make, and a three-seater Canadian canoe that was hired from Shrewsbury.

We started from Newtown, which is 42 miles from the source of the river, amid the jeering of many who had turned out specially to see us. Progress during the first two days was slow, and we covered only five miles. This was because we lacked experience. On approaching a rapid, we would tie up the boats and wade across it to find the deep channel. This entailed a certain amount of risk, owing to the speed of the current as it rushed a foot deep over the slippery stones. If we found a sufficient depth of water we would paddle the boats through without more ado, but in some places the boats had to be lifted over.

On a canoe expedition down the Severn. Photograph by M. Sayers, London, W.C.1.

At weirs and dangerous bends it was necessary to make a portage, unloading everything from the boats and carrying them across the land, and loading up again on launching. Later we became more skilled in finding the deep channels, and then we shot through without preliminary investigation.

On one occasion our daring was rewarded by catastrophe, the unfortunate occupants of the falbot being thrown into the water when it capsized after being swept into a current that ran deep under a low-lying row of willows. There were some hectic moments while they rescued themselves, the boat, and its contents and the paddles from the torrents. A coat in which most of our money was kept was only just saved. We landed to dry our clothes and discovered that we had lost our only Primus stove, a deck-cover, two rain-coats and a leather bag containing spares and some money.

We then proceeded very carefully, and our only further mishap was the breaking of a paddle, which was repaired with a piece of over-size curtain rod discovered after a long hunt through garages and scrap heaps. After passing the last rapid at Bridgenorth we did 28 miles in one day, which was good, as the current was slow. In all we covered 114 miles, and finished at Worcester, although we had planned to go on as far as Gloucester.

M. Sayers (London, W.C.1).

How Cigarettes Are Made

During a tour of a cigarette factory that I enjoyed recently, I was greatly impressed by the order and cleanliness to be observed everywhere. The care shown for the welfare of the employees also was noteworthy. Doctor's and dentist's rooms are provided and there is an excellent restaurant.

The leaf tobacco arrives in the factory in large casks containing about 800 lb., and many of these were being opened in the storeroom during my visit. The leaves are passed through large revolving cylinders, in which they are steamed, and from there are taken by lift to the stemming room, where hundreds of girls sit at long tables stripping off the stalks. The stripped leaves are placed in canvas buckets, weighed and checked, and then sent down chutes to a large room in which they are stacked in "blocks" according to the kind of cigarette to be made from them.

The tobacco is now transported by a belt into the cutting room, and is placed on a slow travelling belt that guides the leaves between rollers about two inches apart by which they are compressed. As they emerge they are cut into thin shreds by oscillating knives. The blades of each cutter have to be removed and re-sharpened by a special machine every ten minutes. The cut tobacco is now fed at the rate of 10 lb. per min. into a heated revolving cylinder, fitted with radial bars, which breaks up and dries the shreds.

Then follows actual cigarette making, which is carried out on fascinating machines that work with uncanny precision. The tobacco is placed in a hopper, and a roll of cigarette paper is placed on a spindle below it. The tobacco shreds are teased out and fed into the paper, on which is printed the name of the maker and the brand of cigarette, and the wrapper then is curled round the tobacco and sealed up. An oscillating knife then cuts off the length to form a cigarette. The output is delivered on two moving bands. The machine also counts out cigarettes in bundles of 25 and weighs them, defective cigarettes being rejected.

The cigarettes are placed in trays and wheeled to the packing room, where they are wrapped in moisture-proof transparent material and packed into cartons.

L. Wright (Pengam).

The Zoo at Cairo

The upper photograph on this page shows a family of elephants, consisting of a mother and two sons, and was taken when I visited the Cairo Zoo. The elephants were from India and are used for giving rides to visitors.

The Cairo Zoo is in Gizeh, a suburb of Cairo on the road to the pyramids. Most of the creatures in it come from the African forests and form an interesting collection, many beautiful parrots being a particularly attractive feature. Most of the exhibits are in cages, but the hippopotamus is a notable exception, as it has a large pond in which to disport itself and an island where it can bask in the sun.

Elephants at the Zoo at Gizeh, Cairo. Photograph by D. F. Gresham, Bickley.

Although the climate of Egypt is so hot, there are polar bears in the Zoo, living in quarters that have been equipped with cooling apparatus in order to make them more congenial. The bears, and indeed all the animals in the Zoo, were in a very healthy condition when I saw them, and are well cared for by their Sudanese keepers.

D. F. GRESHAM (Bickley).

A Swiss Metre Gauge Railway

When I was in Switzerland I was greatly interested in the Furka-Oberalp Railway. This is of metre gauge and is operated by steam, as it was found that the cost of electrification would never be cleared in a railway such as this, which is closed in winter. The line is about 50 miles long, and extends from Brig to Dissentis by way of Andermatt, where the main Swiss railway lines are touched not far from the portals of the St. Gotthard Tunnel.

Locomotive No. 1 of the Furka-Oberalp Railway at Andermatt. Photograph by J. D. Fage, Teddington.

The railway follows the valleys of the Rhone, Reuss and Rhine, and besides taking sight-seers through a region of mountain peaks and glaciers, it forms an important link in Switzerland's communications from east to west. It was built in 1910-14, but was not opened until 1926 owing to the effects of the Great War. The locomotives are all 2-6-0 tanks and the rack system is of the Abt type, which allows combined rack and adhesion working. The carriages are saloons with end platforms and are very roomy. Goods trucks follow British practice, but are generally attached singly to the ends of trains. The line rises to an altitude of 7,000 ft. at the Furka Pass, the steepest gradient being 1 in 10.

The stations are simple, in many cases consisting merely of a shed or even an excavation in the hillside. That at Andermatt is an exception, however, for it has fine station buildings, three covered platforms and an engine shed.

J. D. FAGE (Teddington).

A Film in the Making

When I visited the film studios at Welwyn Garden City I saw carpenters at work making the sets before watching the actual production of part of a film. Anything from a fully equipped theatre to an old world cottage can be modelled in full size in the workshops, and in one corner I saw what appeared to be a delicious meal, but was disappointed to find that the good things it included were made of plaster!

On the set a theatre scene was to be taken, and when I arrived the members of the audience, themselves part of the cast of course, were already in their seats. The chief actors then arrived and the scene was rehearsed several times before the producer announced that he was ready. Three cameras were then placed in position for taking views from different angles, and the sound-recording apparatus in a little room at the top of the studio was made ready. In the meantime final instructions and advice were given to the cast by the producer and his assistant, and a few scenic alterations were made.

Then the arc lamps bathed the stage in a flood of amazingly bright light that to me seemed like concentrated moonlight. An assistant standing in front of the set gave the signal to start "shooting" by sounding a clapper three times and then dropped out of camera range; switches clicked over, and for a few minutes there was dead silence except for the voices of those taking part in the scene.

Suddenly the producer called out "Cut." Lights faded out, for the current consumption of the arc lamps is very high and their heat is unpleasant; the cameras were switched off and their operators began to replace the used film. Something was wrong with the set. Workmen were summoned and 10 minutes later the trouble had been corrected, lights again were switched on, and filming was restarted.

This time the scene was nearly completed, but was then stopped to allow some alteration to be made in the acting. The new version was rehearsed and filming began once more, to be carried through successfully, both for sound and camera.

This was not the end of the scene, however, for some of the theatre seats were then removed to allow close-up views to be taken, after which "stills" were photographed with an ordinary camera. The entire scene lasts only a few minutes in the finished film, but it took nearly three hours to shoot.

The films were developed as soon as they were finished, ready for showing in the private cinema of the studio.

P. WARE (Hoddesdon).

Books to Read

Here we review books of interest and of use to readers of the "M.M." We can supply copies of these books to readers who cannot obtain them through the usual channels. Order from Book Dept., Meccano Limited, Binns Road, Liverpool 13, adding 1/- for postage to the price. Postage on different books varies, but any balance remaining will be refunded.

"Further Heroes of Modern Adventure"

By T. C. Bridges and H. H. Tiltman (Harrap. 7/6 net)

The authors have already written four books dealing with modern adventure, but have found no lack of material to enable them to compile a fifth, for the spirit of adventure thrives as strongly as ever. Like its predecessors, this volume contains stories of recent exploits of travellers and explorers in all parts of the world, and is a wonderful record of heroism and resource in dangerous and unusual situations.

In it we read of Sven Hedin's journeys across deserts in unknown Asia, and of explorations by Dr. Baker in the depths of caves. Captain Benyon's race by car to India in an attempt to beat an ocean liner; the experiences of Reginald Campbell in the snake-haunted teak forests of Siam; Douglas Carruther's hunt in Arabia for the oryx, which is probably the fabled unicorn; and Major Cheeseman's tracing of the Blue Nile from its source in Abyssinia, form other absorbing sections of the book. Further thrills are provided by stories of encounters with man-eating tigers, of a visit to the lair of Chinese pirates, and of other amazing adventures in unknown lands and seas and in the air. The book is well illustrated by means of 30 full-page plates.

Alligator hunting in America. From "Further Heroes of Modern Adventure," reviewed on this page.

"Gradients of British Main Line Railways"

(Railway Publishing Company Ltd. 5/-net)

The demand for copies of this publication, which was reviewed in the "M.M." last September, was so great that a second edition has already become necessary. In this some useful revisions have been effected. An additional page has been inserted dealing with the G.W.R. line from Salisbury to Bathampton, and an up-to-date touch is given to the book by the transference of the gradient profiles of the Midland and Great Northern Joint Railway from the joint section to that dealing with the L.N.E.R., in view of the fact that this company is now working the line. As in the first edition, paper of different colours is used for the profiles for each group, the joint lines and the Irish railways. This paper is suitable for the addition of notes.

"Claudius the Bee"

By John F. Leeming. (Harrap. 5/- net)

This is an unusual story that will delight everybody, youngsters and grown-ups alike. It is set in the world of bees, into which is introduced Mr. Tawney, who was kind to a bumble bee, and in gratitude was invited to the nest in which it lived and given a drink that made him shrink until he was only about half an inch in height. In this form he was entertained at a banquet, and thoroughly enjoyed himself with Claudius, the master of the nest, and his new friends. Unfortunately that moment was chosen by Black Michael, a rival of Claudius, to let in a gang of bandit wasps by a secret entrance. Mr. Tawney and Claudius are captured by this black villain, but the former manages to free himself and in the end he saves the nest from destruction.

Before Mr. Tawney creeps into the cavernous interior of his discarded clothes and drinks the mixture that restores him to his normal size, he learns many interesting things about the creatures of the world into which he penetrates, and takes part in a variety of amusing episodes.

The book is attractively written, and the reader will find it difficult to put it down until he has read it from beginning to end. Its interest is greatly increased by the amusing drawings that appear on almost every page.

"The Untold Story of Exploration"

By Lowell Thomas. (Harrap. 8/6 net)

All "M.M." readers who delight in stories of exploration in distant parts of the world will enjoy this book. The author has chosen as his subject the achievements of travellers who are not very well known, but nevertheless lived exciting and romantic lives; and he throws an interesting light on many parts of the world that even yet are not familiar to us.

The book begins with the story of Chang K'ien, the first Chinese explorer, who ventured into the wilds of Central Asia more than 2,000 years ago. Then come the adventures of Hans Schiltberger, a Bavarian who travelled in Siberia in the 15th century. Juan Fernandez, sometimes spoken of as the first Robinson Crusoe; Captain Bertram Thomas, who in 1930 crossed the great Arabian Desert; Pytheas, the Greek of Marseilles, the first traveller in the Arctic Regions; and William Dampier, the buccaneer who became a great explorer, are others whose deeds are described.

The book is illustrated by 12 full-page plates.

"Ships of the Narrow Seas"

By Edmund Vale

The romance and interest of the sea is not confined to the great ships that cross the oceans, but also can be found in the vessels that maintain cross-channel services around our shores. The men who direct these have to contend with storms, strong tidal currents and winds, and must find their way through tortuous and often crowded shipping lanes leading to their ports. How their work is carried on is well explained in this interesting booklet published by the L.M.S.R., dealing with the cross-channel services.

The story begins with a general account of cross-channel practice and then deals in turn with the Irish Mail route between Holyhead and Dublin, with the Heysham-Belfast and Stranraer-Larne services, and with the steamers that ply on the Clyde and on the lakes of Scotland and the Lake District. The vivid descriptions given by the author of scenes on the bridge, in the engine rooms and in the cabins of the vessels engaged in these services will delight all who have been, or propose to be, passengers in them; or indeed all interested in the sea.

The booklet can be obtained free of cost by sending a postcard to the Advertising and Publicity Department, L.M.S.R. Euston House, London, N.W.1.

"The Modern Book of Lighthouses, Lightships and Life-boats"

By W. H. McCormick. (A. and C. Black. 5/- net)

The story of the lighthouses and lightships that guard our shores, and of the life-boats that put out in the wildest weather to save the lives of sailors in distress, is of absorbing interest, and it is told fully in this fascinating book by the Editor of the *"Meccano Magazine."*

Lighthouses occupy a great part of the volume. After tracing their development from the crude lights of early days, the author turns to the lighthouses of the British Isles, explaining how these are controlled and worked, and giving stirring accounts of the building of several of the most famous of them. Chief among these is the Eddystone, probably the most famous lighthouse in the world; and the story of the four towers that have been erected on the Eddystone Rock illustrates the dangers and difficulties of lighthouse construction on an exposed and often wave-swept rock. Other British lighthouses the building of which is described include the Bishop, Longships, Lizard, Wolf, Bell Rock, Skerryvore and Fastnet. All these are dealt with fully and in the most interesting manner, and graphic descriptions are given of exciting incidents connected with them. Passing farther afield, the author devotes chapters to some of the more famous lights along the United States coast, to French lights, and to the famous Rothersand lighthouse at the mouth of the Weser River, Germany, which was built on a foundation of shifting sand. Another chapter deals with lightships and their work.

A section of special interest deals with the mechanism by which the warning beams are sent out from lighthouses and lightships, and with the variety of signals used during fog. Automatic unattended lights that switch themselves on at nightfall and off with the return of daylight are described, and a full account is given of the different types of buoys that mark the channels leading to our great ports. Equally interesting is the description of the use of wireless for guiding ships at sea and in narrow waterways.

The remainder of the book is devoted to the story of the life-boat, one of the greatest romances of the sea. The development of the modern unsinkable life-boat, down to the latest Diesel-engined vessels of the Royal National Life-boat Institution, is described in full, and thrilling accounts are given of many rescues carried out by the heroic members of the Life-boat Service.

The many attractions of this well-written book are greatly increased by its numerous photogravure illustrations. D. G.

The Aldeburgh motor life-boat. This is designed for launching off the beach and is illustrated in "The Modern Book of Lighthouses, Lightships and Life-boats," reviewed on this page.

"Chiseltooth the Beaver"

By J. W. Lippincott. (Harrap. 5/- net)

Well-told nature stories are always attractive and interesting, and no more suitable hero for a book of this kind could be found than the beaver, Nature's greatest engineer. The author of this volume, who is a distinguished explorer, traces the career of a pair of beavers in a North American creek, who build a new home for themselves and bring up a family, and emphasises well their courage and industry, and their devotion to each other. In the end they are compelled to give way before the advance of Man. The last act of Chiseltooth and his companion is to exercise their natural skill and cunning in repairing a breach in a great dam built to impound a reservoir. They thus save an entire valley from destruction by flood. Then they dramatically disappear, but in honour of their achievement the reservoir is named Beaver Lake.

The book is a fascinating picture of an unusually interesting creature that until recently was in danger of becoming extinct. It is illustrated by a coloured frontispiece and many attractive woodcuts.

The Southampton floating dock. From "Great Scientific Achievements," reviewed on this page.

"The Lion of the Frontier" By John Grant
"Sea-Plane Base" By M. E. Miles
"Flying Dawn" By Dorothy Carter

(A. and C. Black. 3/6 each net)

These three further volumes in the publishers' "Air Adventure Series" are as full of thrills and excitement as those reviewed last month. The scene of *"The Lion of the Frontier"* is the turbulent north west of India, where Colonel Challenger and his son Richard fall into the clutches of a local chieftain notorious for his cruelty. Richard escapes and succeeds in rescuing his father after a dramatic attack on the chieftain's stronghold, in which R.A.F. machines give valuable unofficial aid. Aeroplanes play a greater part in *"Sea-Plane Base,"* which deals with the efforts of a gang of international spies to blow to pieces a wonderful new British sea-plane undergoing secret trials from a base in the Hebrides. Their evil intentions are thwarted, after a breathless chase through burning heather and a perilous voyage in an open boat, by three determined youngsters who stumble on their headquarters by chance during a motor-boat holiday. *"Flying Dawn"* concerns the adventures of two enthusiastic girl flyers during a trip abroad by air. One of them is kidnapped, but after many adventures and misunderstandings is rescued by her companion, who makes effective use of her machine in her pursuit of the kidnappers.

Black and white illustrations by Alfred Sindall illustrate each of the books.

"Great Scientific Achievements"

By Professor A. M. Low

(Nelson. 3/6 net)

Professor Low has chosen varied and interesting subjects for treatment in this book, which contains non-technical accounts of recent great achievements in science and engineering. The erection of great buildings, the *"Queen Mary"* and feats of salvage begin the story, which is continued with descriptions of wonderful bridges and floating docks, and accounts of the manner in which the forces of nature have been harnessed to give us electric light and power. The wonders of wireless, the conquest of the stratosphere and travel across the Atlantic Ocean by air are the subjects of other interesting chapters, and interesting details are given of the coming of science into farming. The many-sided story is completed with an account of the gyroscope and its uses at sea and in the air, and special attention is given to the Iraq pipe-line and the Mersey Tunnel.

The book is vividly written and is easy to read, but is packed full of useful information. It is illustrated by 12 plates.

Diamonds from Sugar

In view of the value that is attached to gems, it is scarcely surprising to know that repeated efforts have been made to make the more valuable of them artificially. These efforts have been conducted on genuine scientific lines. Sir Charles Parsons, the inventor of the turbine, was one of those interested in this subject, and he spent over £20,000 in experiments on making diamonds that continued for 24 years.

The diamond of course has the greatest attraction for artificial gem makers, but so far they have been unable to produce a rival to the natural product, which is a crystalline form of carbon. Artificial diamonds have been made, but they were almost microscopic in size and of no value, although they were costly and difficult to produce. The most famous experiments were made by Moissan, a French chemist who dissolved pure carbon from sugar in molten iron at a temperature of about 7,000 deg. F. and plunged the mass into molten lead in order to cool it. This seems a curious method of cooling, but lead melts at a temperature of little more than 600 deg. F., and thus there was a fall in temperature of more than 6,000 deg. F. Water could not be used for this purpose, for the layer of steam that would have been formed would have prevented the mass of iron from cooling.

The result of plunging the iron into molten lead was to solidify its outer surface, and as this shrank it exerted a pressure up to 20 tons per sq. in. on the carbon in the interior, causing it to crystallise. Even this high pressure was insufficient, and it seems as if diamonds will never be made until the conditions of temperature and pressure existing deep under the surface of the earth can be reproduced.

An unusual view of a barge crossing Barton Aqueduct, which carries the Bridgewater Canal across the Manchester Ship Canal. The Aqueduct is turned through a right angle when necessary to allow large vessels to pass up and down the Ship Canal. Photograph by A. Phillips.

Making Artificial Gems

Efforts to make rubies, sapphires and other precious stones have been more successful, and artificial gems to the value of £20,000,000 are now produced annually. Rubies and sapphires consist of the oxide of aluminium known as corundum, which in crystalline form is second in hardness only to the diamond. Corundum is colourless and the ruby owes its colour to the presence of small quantities of chromium. Artificial rubies are built up by melting the tip of a piece of corundum by means of a small, intensely hot flame, and blowing powdered corundum mixed with a little chromium on to the molten drop. When this is allowed to cool slowly, and is cut, a stone that cannot readily be distinguished from a natural ruby is obtained.

Artificial sapphires are made in a similar manner, substituting titanium for chromium, and artificial or "oriental" emeralds also can be produced from corundum by adding a larger proportion of chromium than when making artificial rubies and heating to a different temperature.

The Earliest Known Englishman

Until recently the honour of being the earliest known inhabitant of England belonged to Piltdown Man, a being who is thought to have lived about a million years ago near what is now Piltdown Common, Sussex. The only traces of him that we possess are a few of the bones of his skull that were found in a gravel bed. These were sufficient to enable us to picture him in some degree, however, and we know that his head approached that of modern man in shape and in other respects, while his jaw was like that of a chimpanzee.

Now Piltdown Man is in danger of losing the honour that so far has been accorded to him, for two bones of the skull of what may have been an earlier inhabitant have been discovered at Swanscombe, Kent. The first was found in June 1935 in a seam of gravel at a depth of 24 ft. below the surface, and the second was found in the same seam in March of this year. The two bones fit together perfectly and are sufficient to show that Swanscombe Man was more primitive than Piltdown Man, for his skull was smaller and lower in the crown and his brain was not so well developed. The conclusion from this is that he lived at an earlier date, and thus he was the earliest Englishman of whom we have any direct knowledge.

The World's Gold Output

The gold reef on which Johannesburg stands is believed to be an immense golden bowl, the rim of which touches the surface in places, while the bottom may be more than 10,000 ft. deep. This bowl probably is the dried-up bed of a great inland lake of prehistoric times, into which a river flowing from the north west carried gold in suspension and solution.

About one-third of the gold dug out of the earth annually comes from the mines of the Rand, which yield about 10,500,000 oz. a year. The next greatest output comes from Russia, which produces 4,300,000 oz. of the world's total production of 27,500,000 oz. As existing mines are carried deeper and new ones are opened the amount of gold being won is increasing, and it is expected that in four years the Rand output alone will reach 15,000,000 oz. a year.

Why Do Lost People Travel in Circles?

It has long been known that people who are lost in forests or deserts show a tendency to walk in circles instead of going straight ahead. This has been tested by experiments with blindfold people who were asked to walk straight across a large and level field. None of them succeeded, their paths invariably being spirals. An interesting variation of these experiments was carried out on ground covered with a light fall of snow, when the tracks were readily seen to be spiral in form, some curving to the left and others to the right. Even blindfold swimmers in similar trials followed spiral courses instead of swimming along straight lines.

These experiments seem to point to the existence of some kind of steering mechanism in the body that automatically causes people to travel in circles instead of straight lines when it is allowed full control, and it is interesting to find that animals appear to possess a similar mechanism that makes them move in spiral paths when unable to rely upon their senses.

A Reversing Waterfall in the Arctic

At the mouth of the St. John River, New Brunswick, there is a barrage of rock that has transformed the estuary into a reversing waterfall. When the tide is low the water of the river pours into the bay, and the flow is in the reverse direction at high tide.

This reversing fall was thought to be unique, but another has now been discovered in a fjord in Baffin Land. A group of rocky islets stretches across the narrowest part of the fjord, and at low tide the water that has been pent up in the inner reaches pours down the rocks in a foaming cataract. When the tide rises the levels become equal and the disturbance subsides. There is peace for only a few minutes, however, for as the tide rises further the direction of the current is reversed and the water flows inward in a turbulent mass of great waves.

The constant motion of the water prevents the formation of ice, in spite of the severity of the climate of Baffin Land, and the Eskimo name for this reversing fall means "The Place That Never Freezes."

A petrol station on road from Berlin to Potsdam. The road was formerly at the level of the top storey of the building, but when a new road was made at a lower level another storey was added under the original structure. Photograph by J. M. S. Risk.

Fire Fighting in San Francisco

The thrilling spectacle of fire engines dashing through the streets at high speed, with bells clanging and all the traffic held up to allow their passage, will no longer be seen in San Francisco, for fire-fighting mains delivering water at high pressure have been installed in the city. It is therefore unnecessary to take pumps to a fire; instead the firemen connect their hoses to the hydrants of the special mains, and are immediately able to send jets of water as high as the tops of twelve-storey buildings.

The new system is entirely distinct from that providing the normal water supply. It includes a main storage reservoir with a capacity of 10,000,000 gal., and two intermediate reservoirs, from which the fire-fighting mains are directly supplied, and these are at heights giving pressures ranging up to 150 lb. per sq. in. The mains vary in diameter from 12 in. to 18 in. and they surround the central business quarter of the city and cross it in all directions.

One reason for the creation of an independent water system is the possibility of earthquakes that may disorganise ordinary services. Much of the destruction of the famous earthquake of 1906 actually was due to fires that broke out when buildings crashed to the ground, and for some time raged practically unchecked because of the failure of the water supply system. Even if the special mains are broken in any future disaster, an independent supply of water is assured from pumping plants built on the shores of San Francisco Bay. These are entirely self-contained, for sufficient oil to keep their pumps in operation for 96 hours is stored in underground steel tanks, and reserves of fresh water for the boilers are kept in special concrete reservoirs. Huge wells also are being constructed at various points in the city. Each will hold 75,000 gal. of water, which will be available if ordinary supplies are cut off by the destruction of the mains.

The Horse Power of the Sun

Every square yard of the Sun's surface radiates 75,000 h.p., and the nearest approach to this intensity that is commonly found on Earth is the one horse power per square inch, or 1,300 h.p. per square yard, exerted on the piston area of the average motor car engine. In spite of the best efforts of scientists and engineers, none of the Sun's energy is used directly for producing power, except in the few plants in which sunlight is concentrated on boilers by means of mirrors, as in the device described and illustrated on page 401 of the "*M.M.*" for July last. When we burn coal or oil we are using Sun power indirectly, however, for these fuels are the result of the Sun's activities in past ages, and windmills and hydro-electric stations depend upon it for their power.

The continuous flow of energy from the Sun is stupendous. On a clear day in June the amount falling on the County of London is 352,000,000 h.p., or 88 times the maximum that can be developed by Niagara Falls, and this of course is only a minute fraction of the total that falls upon the Earth. Even allowing for absorption of the Sun's rays by the atmosphere, they carry about 3,000,000 h.p. to every square mile of the Earth's surface illuminated by them. Most of the Sun's energy streams away unheeded into space, however, for the planets intercept only a small proportion of it, the Earth's share being one part in 2,200 million.

A novel clock in a French shop. The figures in the small square gives the number of minutes to wait before the shop is opened. Photograph by Mrs. J. Williams.

Clock that Tells Time to Come

The lower illustration on this page shows an ingenious method that has been adopted by a French shopkeeper for telling his customers how much longer they have to wait before his shop is open. When he leaves for lunch or any other purpose he fixes a novel clock in a position where it can be seen by those approaching the door. This clock does not record the minutes that have passed, but those that are to come. Thus if the owner is to be away for an hour, he sets it to show the number 60 in the small square, and the number decreases minute by minute until zero appears, and with it the shopkeeper—if he is punctual.

Automatic Gun Detector

It is impossible to take a gun or any concealed metal weapon or tool into the Alcatraz Prison, in San Francisco Bay. Any attempt to do so would be detected at once, not by searchers, but by an automatic device.

The gun detector is electrical in action, and consists of three loops of wire hidden in the framework of a door. High voltage current is passed through the middle loop, inducing currents in the two outside loops, and all the circuits are carefully balanced. The introduction of any metallic object, such as a gun, a knife or a file, disturbs the balance and causes current to flow through an alarm device. Alternatively the current may be made to switch on a light, and persons entering the prison can be searched without knowing that they are being examined.

A Million Inches of Ruling on a Glass Screen

The largest half-tone screens in the world are nearly 5 ft. in diameter. There are only three of them, and they are used in one of the largest cameras ever made for the production of half-tone blocks. Blocks of this kind are used in printing illustrations similar to those in the "Meccano Magazine," and the screen breaks up the picture into the dots of various sizes and shapes that render light and shade.

Each screen consists of two sheets of glass ruled with parallel lines and placed face to face, so that the lines of one sheet are at right angles to those of the other; and there are more than a million inches of ruling on a single screen.

How to Photograph Competition Models

Making Sharp Pictures with a Box Camera

NOW that the long dark evenings are here again hundreds of Meccano model-builders will be busy building models for entry in the competitions announced each month in the Magazine. When a suitable model has been built, the next step is to send details of it to "*M.M.*" headquarters in Liverpool in order that the judges of the contests in which it is entered can give it consideration. For this purpose drawings may be made of it, or a photograph can be taken.

It is not easy to make drawings of a Meccano model that will give the judges a clear idea of its design and how it is built. A photograph therefore is much more satisfactory, and fortunately it is easy to take suitable photographs with the most simple cameras, such as a Kodak Brownie or any other camera of this kind, provided that a few elementary precautions are taken.

The photograph reproduced above was taken with a box camera fitted with a portrait attachment, and is a good example of the satisfactory work that can be done with the most simple apparatus.

A good photograph to be used in an entry in a model-building competition should not be too small to show the model itself distinctly. It must be free from dense shadows on the one hand, and from high lights on the other and, above all, it must be sharp. Examples of really good photographs in which all these features are present are the illustrations on this page and the upper illustration on the opposite page.

It may at first appear difficult to obtain a photograph possessing these qualities with a box camera, but it is really quite easy as the examples illustrated here prove. Those on this page and that at the foot of the opposite page were all taken with a Kodak Brownie box camera under conditions likely to be encountered by the average boy in his own home, and were specially prepared to show what can be done with simple cameras of the fixed focus type.

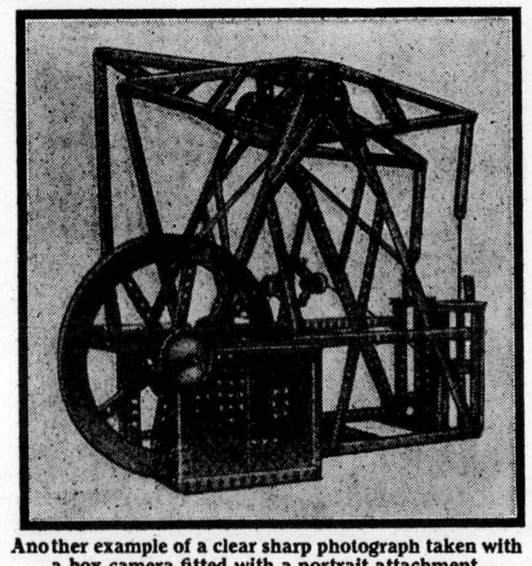

Another example of a clear sharp photograph taken with a box camera fitted with a portrait attachment.

A great fault with most photographs taken with box cameras is that the image is too small to show the details clearly. This is due to the fact that these cameras are of what is known as the fixed focus type, in which the lens will not focus sharply any object nearer than about 8 ft. This distance is too great to give a reasonably large image of an average model, and in order to increase the size it is necessary to work nearer to the model. Unfortunately, if this is done the resulting picture is all blurred, through being out of focus. The difficulty can easily be overcome, however, by fitting over the regular lens a simple supplementary lens, known as a portrait attachment. With the aid of a portrait attachment the camera will focus sharply objects placed as close as 3 ft. from the lens, and will give a large image. Such attachments suitable for use with almost any make of camera can be obtained from any photographic dealer. One for use with a Kodak Brownie costs 3/–, and is provided with a spring mounting by means of which it is held in position in front of the ordinary lens. The attachment does not affect the operation of the camera in any way; its object is simply to reduce the focal length of the regular lens to permit of working closer to the subject.

When working with a portrait attachment it is most important to see that the model is the correct distance from the camera. If a Brownie box camera fitted with a No. 1 Kodak portrait attachment is used, the model should be placed at a distance of 3 ft. from the lens. This distance should not be guessed at, but should be measured carefully from the front of the subject to the lens along the centre line of the camera. No part of the model should be nearer than 3 ft. from the lens. Any parts of the model within this distance from the camera will appear blurred in the negative and will ruin the photograph both for competition purposes and for reproduction in the "*M.M.*"

A model being photographed with the aid of a portrait attachment is so near the lens that the view-finder cannot be used as a guide in the ordinary manner. The best plan is to sight the model along the top of the camera, allowing for the fact that this viewpoint is slightly above the lens. A little practice will make the method easy.

The model should, of course, occupy as much space on the film as possible. If the model is a very large one, however, that is, if it exceeds 4 ft. in length or height, it will be found that when the camera is placed only 3 ft. away the image more than fills the view finder. In this case it is best to take separate photographs of each half of the model. These should overlap in the centre so that together they show the entire model. Such photographs will be of greater help to the competition judges than a single photograph that shows only a section of the model.

If a suitable situation is available it is best to take the

photograph indoors in order to avoid the dense shadows cast by strong outdoor light. A good place is near a large window, the model being so placed that the main light falls on to it from the front.

The next thing is to arrange a suitable background. Often photographs are submitted in which the models, having been taken out-of-doors, appear to be hopelessly entangled in a mass of foliage; others, at first sight, appear to be a view of somebody's house, but close scrutiny brings to light a model extended in delicate tracery against the bricks! An example of this kind of thing is shown in the lower illustration on this page. In this case the photograph was taken out-doors and the situation was deliberately chosen to illustrate the bad effect of an unsuitable background. The iron railings at the rear are so mixed up with the Strips and Girders of the model itself that it is difficult to make out even the general outline of the model, while the finer constructional features are completely lost.

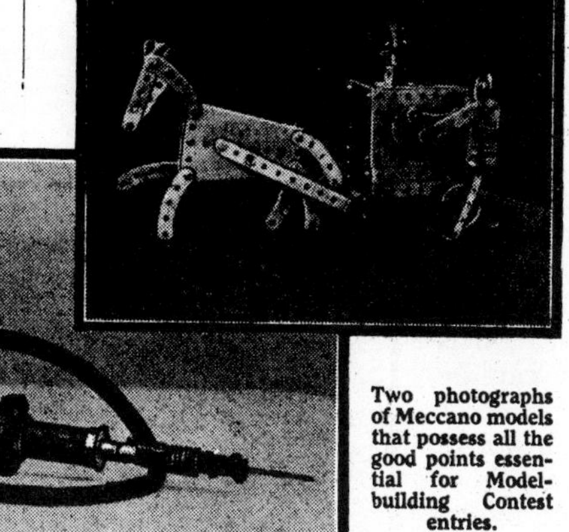

Two photographs of Meccano models that possess all the good points essential for Model-building Contest entries.

The background used for the illustrations on the opposite page was merely a sheet of white rough-surfaced paper, such as cartridge drawing paper. This was hung immediately behind the models, and it will be seen that it throws up the various parts of the models quite distinctly. One or two sheets of similar paper were placed at each side of the models so as to reflect light on to them from all directions.

If a suitable situation indoors is not available, good photographs can be taken out-doors provided that care is taken to avoid strong sunlight, and to arrange a satisfactory background.

The angle at which the model is photographed is of great importance if the best results are to be obtained. It is advisable therefore to study the model carefully from all sides until the viewpoint that shows most clearly the essential details is found. Usually a three-quarter front view, taken at eye level, is the most satisfactory.

When a suitable background has been arranged and the model has been set up, the next thing is to place the camera in position. It is important that the instrument should be firmly supported, as a time exposure will be required. It should therefore be placed on a table that is firm on its legs, so that it will not wobble through vibration caused by passing traffic or by the photographer's footsteps, or on some equally secure support. It should be at such a height that its lens is approximately in line with the centre of the model, and when the correct position has been found one hand should be placed on the camera to make sure that it is kept absolutely still while the shutter is being operated.

This illustration shows the effect of photographing a model against an unsuitable background.

In order to obtain the greatest possible degree of sharpness and to show the smallest details in the photograph, it is necessary to use the smallest aperture or "stop" with which the camera is provided. This is usually F/16, and owing to the small amount of light this stop can pass, a long exposure has to be given. It is not possible to give definite instructions as to the exposure required, as this depends entirely on the particular lighting conditions and the kind of film being used. The best plan is to make use of an exposure meter of some kind. A simple form of this instrument only need be used, and the well-known meter made by Burroughs Wellcome is quite suitable. Guidance in regard to indoor exposures is given in many of the handbooks and leaflets issued by camera makers, and these will give useful help.

When it is not possible to photograph the model by daylight, artificial lighting can be employed. For this purpose ordinary electric lamps are the most suitable. If only a single overhead lamp is available, the model should be placed in such a position that the light falls on it from the front at an angle of about 45 degrees. If a second lamp, such as a portable table lamp, also is available, it should be used in conjunction with the overhead light and should be placed a little to one side of the model. In order to avoid heavy shadows it is better to use a pearl or opal globe than a clear one, and to arrange one or two sheets of white paper at each side of the model so as to reflect light on to it from different directions.

If gaslight only is available, this may be used quite satisfactorily, but a very long exposure will be required. No matter which source of illumination is used, however, the correct exposure time should be ascertained by a calculator.

Where neither electric light nor gas is available, the best alternative is magnesium ribbon. This is easy to use, and may be purchased in small quantities in special holders provided with an arrangement for feeding out the length of ribbon required. Heavy shadows can be avoided if the burning ribbon is moved slowly from side to side while the exposure is made, care being taken to hold it slightly behind the camera so that the light from it does not fall directly on to the lens. A tin or an old plate should be held under the burning ribbon to avoid trouble if a blazing piece should break off and fall.

It is quite as important to obtain a good print as it is to obtain a sharp negative. The most suitable prints are those on glossy paper, as these not only show the finer details more clearly than a print on matt or rough paper, but also reproduce better.

In Search of New Models

Meccano in the Home

THE brilliant colouring of Meccano parts lends itself well to decorative effects, and model-builders will have no difficulty in finding opportunities for exercising their skill in making simple models that are both useful and picturesque in appearance. This month we are dealing with several models that will suggest what can be done in this direction.

The Reading Lamp shown in Fig. 1 is an excellent example of a useful type of Meccano model and will look well on a bureau or on the table of a study, where it will retain its lustre for many years. The globe that forms its base is constructed of 1½" Strips. Five of these are first bolted together to form a pentagon, and from each corner of this radiate five others. It is a good plan to use gold coloured parts for the pentagon, and green enamelled parts for the radiating Strips and the "figures" of which they form part. The pleasing contrast in colour that results is suggested in the photograph of the model. The green radiating Strips are extended by further Strips to form five six-sided figures, each based on one of the sides of the original pentagon, and these are further extended to form a set of five and six sided figures. Throughout this construction the 1½" Strips must be curved slightly as necessary.

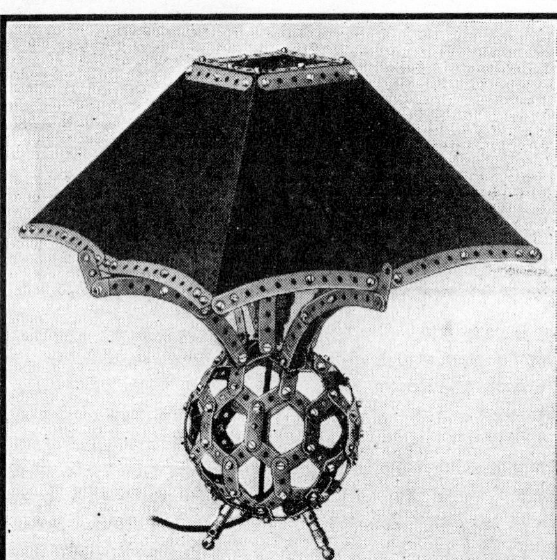

Fig. 1. A cleverly designed table lamp that can be put to practical use.

This completes one half of the globe, and it is then duplicated, and the two halves are joined together by green 1½" Strips, as shown. The colour scheme of this part of the model is of course optional, and if desired, gold or green parts can be used throughout.

Each of the three legs is built up as shown from a Rod Socket, Handrail Coupling and the shank of a Buffer. The arms supporting the shade are built of 4" Curved Strips fitted to the globe by means of Double Brackets. The shade of course can be made to suit individual requirements. Any good semi-transparent paper, carried in a framework of straight and curved Strips, can be used, and a shade of better quality can be made from coloured celluloid, which is obtainable in sheets of varying size from most stationers. Good effects can be obtained by drawing or painting simple designs on the panels of the shade.

The electric lamp can be carried in either a "batten" type lampholder, or in a combined switch and lampholder of the "pendant" type. Whatever type is used, a simple framework of Strips will be required to secure it to the globe. The flex connecting the lamp to the mains supply passes through the centre of the globe. This should be new, or at least in very good condition, and it is best to use rubber covered wiring in order to be sure that there will be no accidental short circuits.

Many variations of this lamp are possible and its design offers ample scope for the ingenious model-builder. Lamps with vertical stands, such as are seen frequently on dining tables, and bowl lamps hanging from wall brackets can readily be built by the use of only a few parts. The Meccano wall bracket shown in Fig. 4 can be adapted to this purpose.

A different type of model is shown in Fig. 3. This is a simple but efficient barometer that can be built in a variety of different designs. The model can be fitted into any odd corner of a hall and, if desired, a graduated scale can be added that will simplify readings. The general appearance of this model is that of a flower, the stem of which consists of a 12 in. length of Glass Tubing, Kemex Part No. K15, that forms the barometer tube. The bottom of the tube is connected by a short length of rubber piping to an "L" shaped glass tube, for which Kemex Part No. K12 is suitable, that is passed through a cork into the neck of an inverted bottle. This can be one in which minerals are supplied, and the cork must fit tightly. The bottle is partly filled with water coloured with red ink. This liquid flows into the tube forming the stem of the flower, and the level in the tube is raised slightly above that in the bottle by blowing down the tube until a small air bubble passes into the bottle.

Fig. 2. A form of barometer that is easy to build and simple in operation.

When wet weather is impending, and the pressure of the atmosphere becomes less, the column of water in the glass tube of the barometer rises proportionately. A period of dry, warm weather causes a fall in the level in the tube, owing to the increased atmospheric pressure. The best results are obtained when the bottle is about a quarter full of liquid. The colour of the latter is not important, but if green or gold parts are used in the construction, a red liquid gives a good colour effect and is more easily seen than clear water.

This barometer should be kept in a room in which the temperature does not vary greatly, for if it is exposed to the varying heat from the sun or a fire the air in the bottle expands and confuses the readings by forcing up the level in the tube. Even grasping the bottle with the hand will cause the liquid to rise in the tube, but this does not mean that there is a probability of rain!

A different type of barometer is shown in Fig. 2. In appearance this is of the form usually seen and it works on a simple but very interesting principle. The framework consists essentially of a 4" Circular Plate carrying round its circumference two 5½"×2½" and two 2½"×2½" Flexible Plates. These are secured in position by means of ½"×½" Angle Brackets and ⅜" Bolts. The upper part of the frame does not effect the working of the barometer, but forms a housing for a small thermometer.

The moving part of the barometer is a disc of light, non-warping card of 3¾" diameter, through the centre of which is passed a needle or pin sharpened at both ends. The card is suspended vertically in the barometer case, the ends of this needle being carried in pointed bearings in the centres of Elektron Magnet Yokes, Part No. 1555. Two of these Yokes of course are required, and they are held in place inside the model by 6BA Bolts and Nuts. On the right hand side of the disc, and behind it, is fixed a shallow cardboard box, not more than ¾" in length, filled with rock salt. The box must be open at the side facing the rear of the model, and after it is filled with rock salt the opening is covered with some finely woven material so that the salt is in contact with the atmosphere.

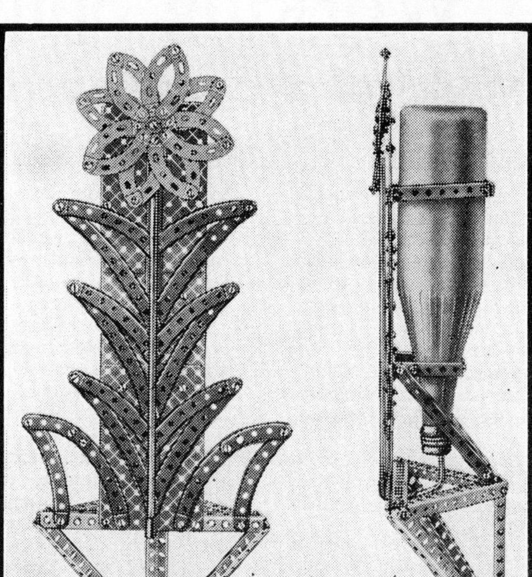

Fig. 3. The stem of the "flower" in the Meccano model seen on the left of this illustration is the tube of a novel barometer, the working parts of which are shown on the right.

The disc is balanced by adding small weights at a point directly opposite the box containing the rock salt. This balancing must be done in a warm, dry room after the disc has been dried in an oven for a few minutes, and the counterbalancing weights must be heavy enough to bring the box of salt to the highest possible position. When the barometer is in use, the box remains in this position during dry weather, but falls below it in wet weather because the salt absorbs moisture from the air and increases its weight, the disc then rotating in a clockwise direction when seen from the front. When dry weather returns, the moisture in the salt evaporates and the disc returns to its original position. The card of course is marked with the usual weather indications, as shown in Fig. 2, and the words at the top tell the user what he may expect in regard to weather conditions.

Another form of useful ornament that can be built with Meccano parts is shown in Fig. 4. This is a flower or fern basket, and looks very attractive when hung in an elevated position out of doors with a suitable plant or fern in it. Many different designs are possible, and that shown in Fig. 4 can easily be modified to suit individual requirements.

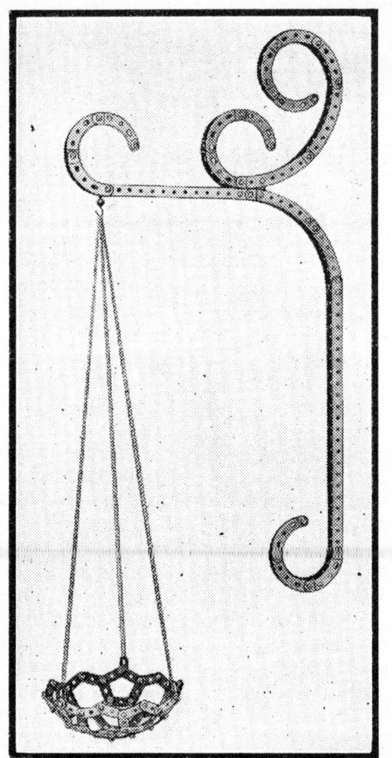

Fig. 4. An attractive Meccano hanging basket suitable for ferns and other plants.

The wall bracket consists of two 12½" Strips and two 7½" Strips joined together at right angles by means of four 4" Curved Strips. The outer ends of the 7½" Strips and the bottom ends of the 12½" Strips are fitted with additional 2½" large radius Curved Strips. These represent the bent iron work typical of fittings of this type. A subsidiary curved bracing bracket is bolted to the top of the main bracket, and this is formed from 4" Curved Strips and 2½" Curved Strips, large and small radius.

The hanging basket is built up in a similar manner to one half of the globe built into the model shown in Fig. 1. The arrangement of 1½" Strips is altered slightly, however, so that the edge of the flower basket has a serrated appearance. The basket is suspended by three lengths of Meccano Sprocket Chain, the lower ends of which are fixed to the 1½" Strips by Flat Brackets. The upper ends of the chains are carried on a Small Loaded Hook.

An excellent small hanging lamp can be formed by inverting the basket and covering it inside with different coloured sections of celluloid or paper. A small lamp mounted inside the inverted basket by means of a batten type lamp holder will give an artistic coloured effect if the sections of the material are carefully arranged.

The possibilities of building new models along the lines set out in this article are numerous and many new ideas are to be found in such well-known household articles as pipe racks, tie racks, candle sticks, etc. Novelty pipe racks can be made in the form of nigger minstrels, piccaninnies, clowns and a host of other characters, and two pipes, placed in concealed racks, can be arranged to look like legs. Coloured parts are used to advantage in these models especially when making the faces.

A minstrel's face, for example, may consist of a blue enamelled Face Plate, on which are bolted a large radius and small radius Curved Strip, in gold, to suggest a mouth. The "nose" a 1" Triangular Plate, and "eyes" two 1" loose Pulleys, complete the appearance. The addition of a large "top hat" of Strips, and small "body" represented by a Flat Trunnion, will bring to life a caricature of very humorous appearance.

The Meccano figures are shown to best advantage when arranged before a background of Blue and Gold Flat Plates, the lower portion of which is constructed to form the pipe rack. A piccaninny, built along similar lines but supplied with a skirt of 2½" Curved Strips, is suitable for enlivening any dark corner of a room.

A tie rack, on which any small article can be hung before the fire to dry, can be built with only a few parts, to represent a two-door stable. The front of the stable only need be represented and from each door the head of a Meccano horse "looks out." Halters from the heads of the horses to the centre of the stable wall form the lines for carrying the articles to be dried.

A Meccano Working Spinning Mule

Accurate Model of a Complicated Machine

FROM time to time we have described in the *"M.M."* notable models built by readers that demonstrate the remarkable accuracy with which great engineering masterpieces can be reproduced in model form with Meccano parts. The illustration on this page shows another model of this kind, which was built by Mr. A. Lord of Petersham, New South Wales. It is a reproduction of a modern spinning mule, one of the most complicated machines used in the textile industry, and was referred to briefly in the *"M.M."* for March 1935. Recently Mr. Lord sent the model to us for examination, and as it contains several ingenious mechanisms that are easily adaptable for use in other kinds of models, we now give further details of it.

The purpose of the spinning mule in the manufacture of cotton or woollen thread is to spin smooth strong material, suitable for weaving, from the rough weak thread produced by the earlier processes of carding, drawing and slubbing.

The thread is placed in the mule wound on a spool, and from this it is led to a revolving spindle that applies a peculiar twist to the fibres and winds up the finished material in the form of a conical-shaped bobbin, known as a cop. Mr. Lord's model carries out all these operations in exactly the same manner as an actual mule. The cop is formed on a spindle 3, which is mounted on a travelling carriage that consists of a Strip bent to form a $3\frac{1}{2}'' \times 1\frac{1}{2}''$ double angle strip. The carriage slides on a horizontal Rod 2, and a second Rod 4, which at one end has a Collar that engages the slot of a special cam 5, causes a wire finger attached to a pivoted $3\frac{1}{2}''$ Strip to move up and down the cop spindle 3. The spindle is a Rod filed to a point at its upper end, and it revolves in bearings in the carriage. The drive is taken from the main gear-box by means of cord.

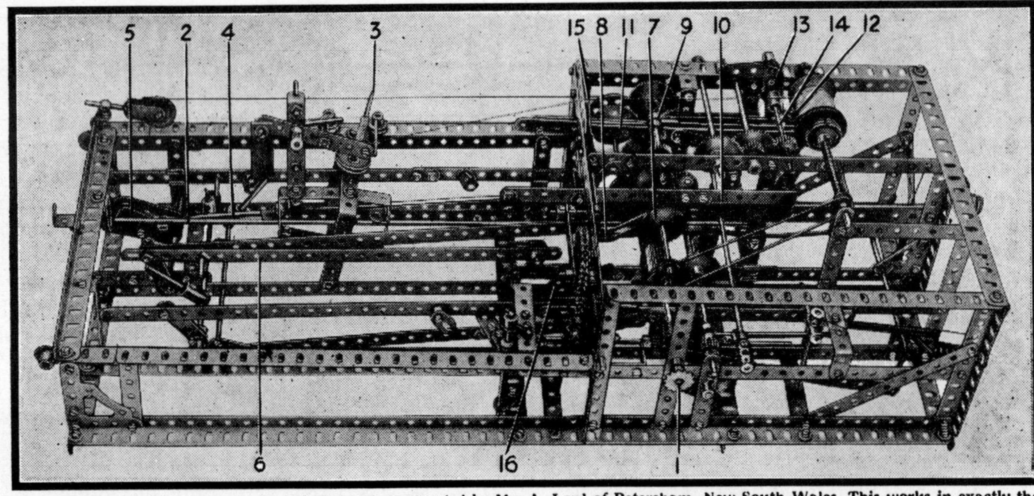

A remarkable model spinning mule designed and constructed by Mr. A. Lord of Petersham, New South Wales. This works in exactly the same manner as the spinning mules installed in textile factories.

The following is a brief description of the operations that take place. The cop carriage commences operations at the right-hand end of its slide. It first of all travels slowly to the left. Thread is drawn from the spool, and at the same time the cop spindle revolves at high speed. When the spindle first begins to rotate, the fact that the cop is tapered and inclined from the vertical, causes the thread to travel upward and finally to slip off the end of the spindle. It is this slipping-off movement in conjunction with the rapid rotation of the cop spindle that applies the necessary twist to the thread.

At the end of its travel the carriage strikes a stop and operates mechanism that causes the finger on the pivoted arm to travel rapidly down the cop, drawing all the upper turns tightly together and placing a binding thread down the cop in a steep spiral. The carriage then travels slowly back to its original position and winds the thread on to the cop, and simultaneously the Rod 4 allows the wire finger to rise slowly. At the end of the travel cam 5 rises quickly and lifts Rod 4 and the wire finger, so that the latter is well clear of the cop and ready for the next draw.

The carriage is operated by an ingenious return mechanism. A Strip attached to the carriage slides in an Eye Piece, and has a short length of Rack Strip bolted to it. At each end of the travel of the carriage the Rack Strip is just out of mesh with a Pinion that is driven continually, but in opposite directions during each half of the complete cycle of operations. The carriage is pushed forward slightly by means of a system of Strips provided with projecting pins as in the case of Strip 6, until its Rack Strip engages the rotating Pinion, which carries it along until it is thrown out of gear at the other end. Another pin then throws it into mesh again, to travel in the reverse direction.

One of two interesting reverse gears incorporated in the model is shown in the illustration at 9. It is used for altering the gear arrangements that control the cop spindle and the cam 5. A reciprocating Strip 11, bent so that its ends are parallel but about $\frac{1}{8}$ in. out of alignment engages between two Collars 9 on a Rod that slides sideways across the machine. It is actuated by a Rack and Pinion mechanism and as it travels, the sliding Rod is moved a distance equal to the misalignment in the ends of the Strip, and its movement is utilised to throw certain gear trains into reverse.

The second of the two reversing gears is actuated by a special slotted Strip 8 that is bent roughly at 60° to the axis of the Gear Wheel 7. The Rod of this gear passes through the slot in the Strip, and a Collar on the side of the Strip opposite from the gear prevents the Rod from sliding freely. The Strip is bolted to the assembly 6, to which the travelling carriage imparts a reciprocating motion. As the Strip moves from right to left, or vice-versa, the gear and its Rod slide through a distance of about $\frac{3}{8}$ in., and the various gear arrangements are altered.

During the operation of changing from one of the main gear trains to the other, a gear wheel on the sliding Rod engages momentarily with a special narrow-faced pinion that forms part of the driving mechanism of the cop spindle. The result of this action is a momentary increase in the speed of rotation of the cop at the end of the draw.

As the model was required to work continuously for display purposes, Mr. Lord devised an ingenious gear for re-winding the thread from the cop on to the spool at the end of every 80 draws. This operates as follows. At the end of each draw the Angle Bracket 12 makes contact with the lower end of the $2\frac{1}{2}''$ Strip 13 that is bolted to a Crank on Rod 14. The assembly 13 is provided with a Pawl that engages a Ratchet Wheel, and each time the Strip 13 is struck the Rod 14 is rotated 1/20th of a revolution. A 4 : 1 gear reduction between this and a Rod that operates the rewinding gear ensures that 80 draws are completed before rewinding takes place. The final Rod of the 4 : 1 gear train has a pointed striking cam secured to its end, and as it rotates this forces down a lever that throws the mechanisms that control the carriage and cop out of gear. The cop spindle now being free to revolve the thread is rewound on to the spool and the distributing arm 15 guides the thread backward and forward and fills the bobbin evenly. The rewinding of the thread on to the spool is automatic, as during the whole of the normal spinning period the spool is rotated against the action of the spring clip clutch. When the cop is thrown out of gear the clutch friction is strong enough to turn the spool.

While these operations are being performed, the pointed cam 16 is rotating slowly, and when all the thread has been wound on to the spool, the cam returns the various gears to their original positions.

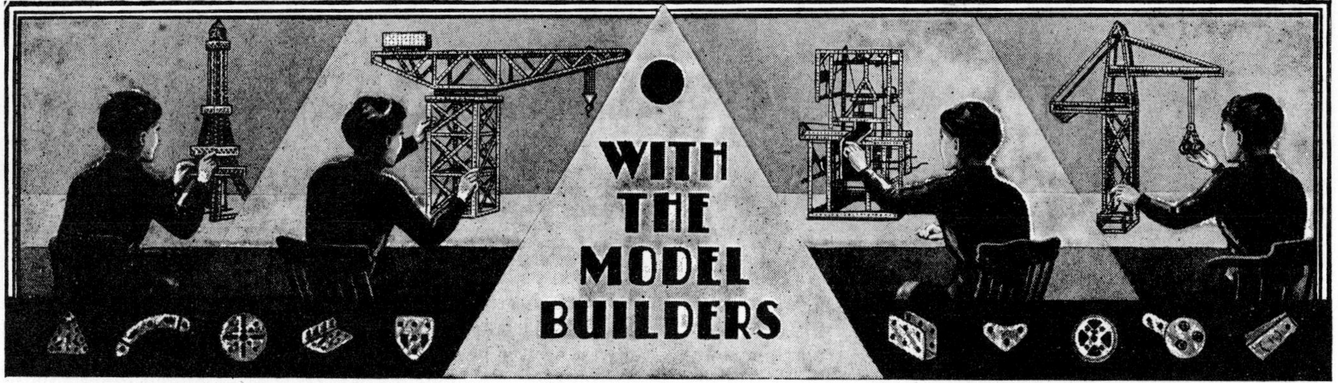

CUCKOO CLOCK MECHANISM

Meccano clock making still holds the interest of model-builders, and the latest development in this direction is a cuckoo clock built by H. Lloyd, Toronto. In general appearance Lloyd's clock is similar to the Wall Clock described in last month's issue of the "*M.M.*," but the top portion of the frame is modified slightly in order to allow a small double door to be fitted. Each side of this door is a $2\frac{1}{2}'' \times 1\frac{1}{2}''$ Flexible Plate suspended on a vertical length of elastic to form a hinge. The elastic is clamped to the door by two Flat Brackets, and at each end is fitted to the frame of the clock by Collars.

The chief novelty of Lloyd's clock, of course, is the cuckoo mechanism itself, in which Meccano bellows supply air to two note tubes adjusted to give the required notes. The cuckoo is one taken from an ordinary cuckoo clock, but no doubt many ingenious Meccano enthusiasts will be able to design a Meccano "bird" that will be quite efficient.

The note tubes are ingeniously built up of Kemex and Meccano parts. Each consists of a Kemex Test Tube, Part No. K2, partially filled with water, and it is easy to adjust the cuckoo notes by varying the amount of water in them. The pitch of the note is raised by adding water, and lowered by the reverse operation.

The test tubes are suspended from their upper ends by means of clamps built from $2\frac{1}{2}''$ Strips, and in building the model care must be taken to see that these clamps are not too tight, so that there is no possibility of the glass being fractured. The quality of the notes can be improved by placing strips of thick felt between the clamps and the test tubes. The two pipes down which passes the air for blowing the notes are made by rolling lengths of paper round a pencil and gumming the edges to prevent unrolling. The ends of the pipes adjacent the top of the test tubes must be flattened to give two long narrow openings. The lower edge of each opening rests on the edge of the test tube, and a musical note is produced when the pipe is lightly blown. A little adjustment will be necessary before a perfect note results.

Each of the two sets of bellows operating the "cuckoo" is formed from two Boiler Ends joined together by a tube of flexible material. This tube may be formed from a small sheet of very thin rubber, such as that from which toy balloons are manufactured. The lower Boiler End is secured rigidly to the frame of the clock and the upper Boiler End is carried on the lower end of the operating lever, which is moved by a quick action cam.

GRANDFATHER CLOCK

A fine Meccano Grandfather Clock, built by F. Botting, Glen Osmond, Australia, was so attractive that it was described and illustrated in the local press, in addition to being displayed in a large store in Adelaide, where it gave rise to favourable comment.

The illustration on this page shows F. Botting with his model. It will be seen to be similar in design to the standard Meccano model described in Super Model Instruction Leaflet No. 14a, but the framework has been modified slightly and the driving weight is enclosed in a large box.

A SIMPLE SCREW MOVEMENT

The usual method of obtaining a screw traverse with Meccano parts is by passing a Threaded Rod down the centre of a Nut or Threaded Boss, when the two threaded parts can be moved in either direction by rotating the Rod. Both schemes are simple, but when building a large model the necessary parts cannot always be spared and some other expedient is desirable.

B. Everest, Walsall, suggests a simple screw movement that will doubtless be useful to many model-builders. A length of copper or steel wire is bound tightly round a Threaded Rod over a length of about $\frac{1}{2}''$. The resulting wire "nut" is similar in appearance to an Anchoring Spring, Part No. 176, and acts like a Threaded Boss. One end of the wire forming the coil is next turned into a loop and through this passes a bolt, attached to a short Strip by a nut. A Washer is placed between the head of the bolt and the wire loop.

This screw movement is suitable for small, light mechanisms, and when oiled thoroughly will work very smoothly on its Threaded Rod.

MECCANO SHOOTING RANGE

From Canada comes a suggestion for miniature shooting ranges that will interest Meccano enthusiasts who possess small calibre sporting rifles or air guns. H. Roland, Montreal, who has submitted the suggestion, has graduated through air guns and small shot guns to full bore sporting rifles, and has made use of his Meccano parts to build an automatic clay-pigeon thrower and a "flying-bird" shooting range in order to improve his marksmanship.

This fine Grandfather Clock, built by F. Botting, Glen Osmond, Australia, has created considerable interest among the many people who have examined it.

The clay pigeon thrower is a small but very powerful catapult that flings into the air a disc of hard-baked clay about the size of a small dinner plate. The base consists of four H girders, each built from four $24\frac{1}{2}''$ Angle Girders, connected together at six points by means of $7\frac{1}{2}''$ Angle Girders. On this solid base is pivoted the catapult, built from a number of $12\frac{1}{2}''$ Angle Girders, and this is controlled by a battery of powerful coil springs. It is drawn into its "firing" position by an Electric Motor, geared down to give the required power. A clay-pigeon then rolls on to it, releasing an automatic catch, and is flung high into the air to form a target for the marksman. Resetting and firing is carried out automatically by the Motor at intervals of about three minutes.

The model shooting range built by H. Roland also is operated by an Electric Motor. It takes the form of an endless belt of Sprocket Chain passing round two 3" Sprocket Wheels. The Rods carrying the Sprocket Wheels slope backward at an angle of about 10 deg. Lengths of Cord are secured to the Chain at intervals and from these hang small cardboard "birds." When the Cords and birds are moving along with the upper length of Sprocket Chain they are hidden behind a sheet of heavy metal, and only come into view when travelling with the lower section of the Chain. The Chain is driven slowly by the Electric Motor through suitable gearing, and the birds suspended from it form lifelike, moving targets.

A BUILT-UP CRANKSHAFT

The construction of large and small Crankshafts for Meccano model engines cannot always be carried out by using Couplings or Cranks. An alternative is suggested by W. Crowther, Birmingham, who makes use of Strips, Flat Brackets and Rod Sockets. These Rod Sockets are accommodated in the end holes of the Strips or Flat Brackets and protrude on opposite sides. Two or more Strips can be used for crankshafts with a more massive appearance, or Triangular Plates and Flat Trunnions can be employed. Short Rods are used to join the various sections of the crankshaft together.

A UNIQUE MECCANO PIANO

Something really new in Meccano model-building comes from S. Thompson, Rugby, an enthusiastic model designer who has made use of Meccano parts in a unique "piano," each note of which is produced by striking a jam jar or wine glass in which water is placed. The jars or glasses are the only non-Meccano sections of the model. The key-board covers three octaves and includes sharps and flats. It is built up from $12\frac{1}{2}''$ and $24\frac{1}{2}''$ Angle Girders. Each "white" key is represented by a $5\frac{1}{2}''$ Strip pivotally mounted three holes from its inner end on a Double Bracket, and is held in its normal position by a short length of Spring Cord. Two Silver-tipped Contact Screws are brought together when it is depressed, and this completes an electrical circuit and excites the coil of a magnetic hammer. The hammer mechanism is built very simply and consists of an Elektron Magnet Coil, Part No. 1538, and a Magnet Core, Part No. 1539. The Core slides freely in the centre bore of the Magnet Coil and to its threaded end is fastened the hammer, which is held away from the glass jar by a very light spring. When the hammer is raised and allowed to fall quickly, the weight of the mechanism overcomes the spring and strikes the jar. The spring then lifts the hammer clear of the jar until the note is again struck.

Shorter Strips are used to represent the black keys, and these are arranged in a similar manner to the white keys, above which they are raised slightly.

The casing of the model has an extremely pleasing appearance and is built up from a number of Strip Plates and Curved Strips of various sizes. Two "stops" are provided for increasing or decreasing the power of the notes. These act in the same manner as the swell stop of a real organ and control the amount of current passing to the Magnet Coils.

This model seems to open up a new field for ingenuity in model-building. No doubt this will be explored by many Meccano enthusiasts full of ideas for new effects worked out on similar lines.

IMPROVED CLOCKWORK MOTORS. (Reply to J. Fallowfield, Sompting, Sussex.) The size and shape of the present Meccano Clockwork Motors does not permit them to be built into certain small Meccano models without considerable trouble, and for this reason J. Fallowfield has suggested the introduction of motors similar to those fitted in No. 2 Special Hornby Locomotives, but with slightly modified side plates.

The idea has much to recommend it, but it is doubtful if the demand for motors of this size would justify their introduction. With a little ingenuity the existing range can be made to fulfil practically all requirements. For instance, the Magic Motor is suitable for driving small models, and two of these Motors can be joined in tandem, that is with their driving shafts linked-up by a Coupling or connecting gear train, if greater power is required and space is limited. A small Meccano Motor Chassis is a suitable model for driving in this manner.

SMALL HUB DISCS. (Reply to M. Fellows, Lancaster.) The introduction of Hub Discs, $3\frac{1}{2}''$ in diameter, has been under consideration for some time but up to the present nothing definite has evolved. These parts would be used primarily in conjunction with 4" Circular Plates to form intermediate size flanged wheels.

New Outfit Models

A Submarine and Two Unusual Aeroplanes

THE four models to be described this month are based on vessels and aeroplanes that with one exception are unusual in type and not very widely known. The one that will be familiar to model-builders is a submarine, and the other subjects are a Mississippi steam-boat, an aeroplane without a tail and an interesting American aeroplane in which the fuselage and tail unit are of special design.

The first of these models to be dealt with is the Mississippi steam-boat, a splendid miniature reproduction of a stern-wheeler built with Outfit G. Its construction is commenced by connecting two Flanged Plates 1 and 1a by means of the compound strips 2, each of which carries a 3½"× 2½" Flanged Plate 3. Three Double Brackets are bolted to the inside of each strip 2, and these support the outside of the lower deck and also the 12½" Strip Plate 4. To the forward end of the Strip Plates are bolted two 2½"×2½" Flexible Plates, and these are curved in the manner shown. At the rear of the lower deck two 2½"×2½" Strip Plates, connected by a 4½"×2½" Flexible Plate, are secured in position. Together with the Plates 4, these carry two 12½" Angle Girders 5, to the unoccupied flanges of which are fitted the 12½" Strips 6 by means of Flat Brackets.

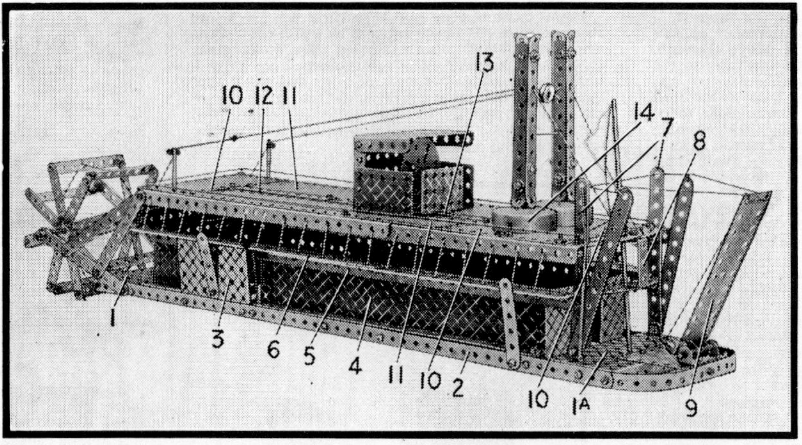

Fig. 1. This model reproduces the typical features of a Mississippi steamer, a vessel of shallow draught driven by a paddle wheel at the stern.

The after end of the middle deck is represented by a 5½"×1½" Flexible Plate, and this carries along its upper edge a 5½" Angle Girder. This in turn has bolted to it the double 12½" Angle Girders forming the sides of top deck. The free ends of these Girders are fitted with Angle Brackets that are attached to vertical 5½" Strips 7. These also form derrick-stumps.

The forward ends of the middle and upper decks are rounded by the addition of four 2½" large radius Curved Strips, which are bolted in pairs to Angle Brackets that in turn are bolted to the Strips 7, and a 1½"×½" Double Angle Strip 8 is fitted as shown. The gang-plank consists of a 5½"×1½" Flexible Plate that is bolted at its lower end to two ½" Reversed Angle Brackets in the manner shown in Fig. 1. The lower holes of these Reversed Angle Brackets accommodate a short Rod forming a pivot.

The upper deck of the model is built from three 5½"×2½" Strip Plates 10 and two 12½"×2½" Strip Plates 11. Down the centre of the deck passes a compound strip 12. The wheel house is carried on this deck. It is built up from two 3½"×2½" Flanged Plates and two 2½"×1½" Flexible Plates and is secured in place by means of a ½"×½" Angle Bracket. Its forward end consists of a 2½"×1½" Flanged Plate held in position by a Reversed Angle Bracket 13. The inner portion of this Bracket has bolted to it a 1"×1" Angle Bracket, and to this the "wheel," represented by a Face Plate, is attached by means of a ⅜" Bolt.

Four 5½" Strips, turned over at their ends, are used for each funnel. These Strips are fixed to Couplings at their upper and lower ends, the lower Coupling accommodating a 3" Rod in its longitudinal bore. The 3" Rod passes through the centre of the Boiler End 14, and is held in position on the underside of the top deck by means of a ¾" Flanged Wheel.

The framework for carrying the stern paddle-wheel is built up from six 5½" Strips, three of which are used on each side. The arrangement is shown in the illustration. Each side of the paddle-wheel consists of a Bush Wheel, from which radiate eight 2½" Strips, and when both sides of the wheel are complete they are mounted 3½" apart on a 6½" Rod. The ends of each alternate pair of radiating 2½" Strips carry 3½"×½" Double Angle Strips, and the remaining pairs of 2½" Strips have 3½" Strips fitted to them by means of Angle Brackets.

Parts required to build the model Missisipi steam-boat: 11 of No. 1; 19 of No. 2; 2 of No. 2a; 4 of No. 3; 2 of No. 4; 18 of No. 5; 2 of No. 6a; 8 of No. 8; 2 of No. 9; 7 of No. 10; 5 of No. 11; 19 of No. 12; 3 of No. 12a; 1 of No. 13a; 1 of No. 14; 2 of No. 16b; 3 of No. 17; 2 of No. 20b; 1 of No. 23; 2 of No. 24; 2 of No. 35; 170 of No. 37; 6 of No. 37a; 12 of No. 38; 2 of No. 40; 1 of No. 45; 2 of No. 48; 2 of No. 48a; 4 of No. 48b; 1 of No. 48d; 1 of No. 51; 2 of No. 52; 4 of No. 53; 8 of No. 59; 2 of No. 62; 5 of No. 63; 4 of No. 90; 1 of No. 109; 3 of No. 111; 6 of No. 111c; 1 of No. 115; 2 of No. 125; 2 of No. 162a; 2 of No. 188; 2 of No. 189; 2 of No. 190; 1 of No. 191; 3 of No. 193; 3 of No. 195; 4 of No. 197.

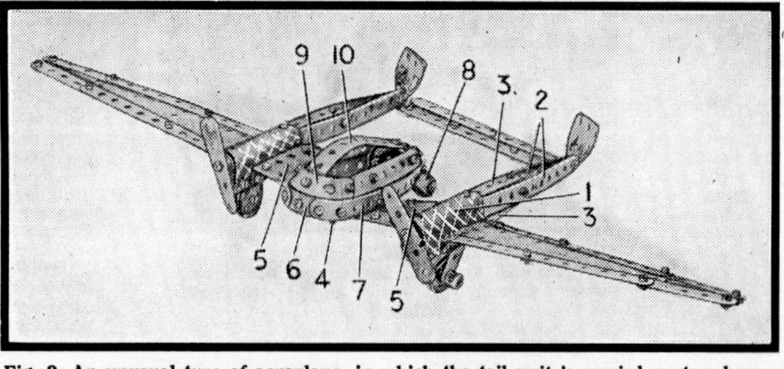

Fig. 2. An unusual type of aeroplane, in which the tail unit is carried on two booms instead of on the rear section of a fuselage of the normal type.

The second model to be described has as its prototype an unusual type of aeroplane, the American-built Gyro "Crusader," a four-seater cabin monoplane. The model, which is shown in Fig. 2, is built with Outfit D.

The first part of the model to be built consists of the two tail-booms, on the forward ends of which the engines are carried. Each boom is constructed of a U-Section Curved Plate 1, and to this is bolted two 5½" Strips 2 and three 2½" Strips, two of which are shown at 3. The rear ends of the Strips are drawn together and held in position by a Nut and

Bolt, and the Bolt also carries a Flat Bracket, a Flat Trunnion, and a ½"×½" Angle Bracket. The Flat Trunnion represents one of the rudders, and the ½"×½" Angle Bracket carries one end of the tail-plane.

When both tail-booms are complete they are connected together at their forward ends by means of four 2½"×½" Double Angle Strips. These parts are arranged in pairs and are joined together by their turned-over ends at the centre. One point of connection is indicated at 4. Two 2½"×1½" Flexible Plates are fitted to the Double Angle Strips as shown at 5, Fig. 2, and between these two Strip Plates is carried the cabin, which is built up in the following manner. A 2½" Strip 6 is bent as shown, and is bolted at each end to a bent 5½" Strip 7. The rear ends of these 5½" Strips are connected together by a ½"×½" Angle Bracket, and a second Angle Bracket forms the connection between a Cranked Bent Strip 8 and the cabin. The two outer holes of the Cranked Bent Strip accommodate a Threaded Pin on which is mounted a ½" loose Pulley. A 5½" Strip 10 is now added and this carries a bent 2½" small radius Curved Strip 9. To the ends of this Curved Strip are bolted two 3½" Strips, and these are fixed in position by means of Flat Brackets and Obtuse Angle Brackets.

The construction of the wings is shown in the photograph. Each propeller is represented by a 2½" Strip free to turn on a ⅜" Bolt. This Bolt is locked in the upper hole of a Flat Bracket, bolted to a Double Bracket that in turn is attached to the front end of the tail-boom.

Parts required to build the model Aeroplane: 13 of No. 2; 2 of No. 3; 13 of No. 5; 9 of No. 10; 4 of No. 11; 9 of No. 12; 2 of No. 12a; 4 of No. 12c; 2 of No. 22a; 1 of No. 23; 89 of No. 37; 4 of No. 37a; 10 of No. 38; 1 of No. 40; 1 of No. 44; 4 of No. 48a; 2 of No. 62; 2 of No. 90a; 4 of No. 111c; 1 of No. 115; 2 of No. 126a; 2 of No. 188; 2 of No. 189; 2 of No. 199.

Fig. 3. A neat and interesting model of a submarine. An extremely realistic effect is obtained by the skilful use of only a few parts.

The model submarine shown in Fig. 3 is built with Outfit D. Each side of this model is built up from three 12½" Strips 1 and 2, the two Strips 1 being overlapped one hole. The Strip 2 is also connected at the point of joining of the Strips 1, and a 2½"×½" Double Angle Strip is fitted. This Double Angle Strip, together with an Angle Bracket indicated at 3 and a Sector Plate indicated at 4, carries a 12½" Strip 5 forming the deck. The forward ends of the Strips 1 and 2 are joined together by two Angle Brackets and a Flat Bracket. The 12½" Strip 6, forming part of the fore-deck, is bolted at its after end to the central 2½"×½" Double Angle Strip already mentioned.

The upper portion of the deck of the model is represented by two 12½" Angle Girders and a 12½" Strip 7. The rear end of the upper deck carries two 3½" Strips 8, and also a 5½"×1½" Flexible Plate bent in the manner shown. The conning-tower is built up from two 2½"×1½" Flexible Plates secured at each end to a 1½" Strip, and also to the upturned flanges of a Double Angle Strip forming the top, by means of four Obtuse Angle Brackets. The small Flexible Plates are fitted to the upper deck of the model by means of ½"×½" Angle Brackets. The central mast is a 6½" Rod held in position by two 1" Pulley Wheels, and the periscope is a 3½" Rod held in place by Spring Clips. The after-mast, a 5" Rod, is carried in one hole of a 2½" Strip and held in position by a 1" Pulley and Anchoring Spring. A length of Cord is used to represent the aerial and mast stays.

The miniature gun consists of a 1½" Rod mounted in a Double Bracket and held in place by two Spring Clips.

Parts required to build the model Submarine: 10 of No. 1; 2 of No. 3; 1 of No. 5; 2 of No. 6a; 2 of No. 8; 3 of No. 10; 4 of No. 11; 7 of No. 12; 1 of No. 14; 1 of No. 15; 1 of No. 16; 1 of No. 18a; 3 of No. 22; 1 of No. 23; 1 of No. 24; 5 of No. 35; 56 of No. 37; 6 of No. 37a; 5 of No. 38; 1 of No. 40; 1 of No. 48; 3 of No. 48a; 1 of No. 54a; 6 of No. 111c; 1 of No. 176; 2 of No. 188; 1 of No. 189.

Tailless aeroplanes resemble the pterodactyl, or "flying dragon" of prehistoric times in appearance and they have been developed in efforts to provide a machine that is stable in itself and proof against errors in piloting. The prototype of the model shown in Fig. 4 is the Westland-Hill "Pterodactyl" MK.V, a two-seat fighter. The fuselage is constructed from two 5½"×2½" Strip Plates that are curved slightly at their rear ends and joined together by a U-Section Curved Plate. The front ends of these Plates are joined in a similar manner. Two 2½" small radius Curved Strips 1 are next fastened to the bottom of the fuselage, and these carry two 1½" Rods on which 1" loose Pulleys are free to rotate. These Pulleys represent the landing wheels. A 2½"×1½" Flexible Plate 2, bent into the shape of a U forms the front of the cockpit, and the front of the rear cockpit consists of a Double Bracket 3 and two Flat Brackets.

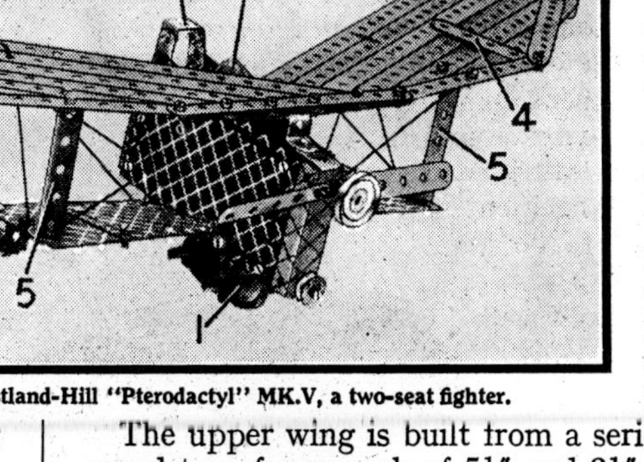

Fig. 4. A clever representation of the Westland-Hill "Pterodactyl" MK.V, a two-seat fighter.

The upper wing is built from a series of 12½" Strips secured to a framework of 5½" and 3½" Strips and clamped neatly in position by the 2½" Strips 4. The outer ends of the wings carry steering fins that are built up from Trunnions and Flat Trunnions. The lower wings are each formed from two 2½"×2½" Strip Plates connected to the upper wing by means of the Double Angle Strip 5. A 2½" Strip 6 is now added, and this is secured to the end of the wings by a 1½" Strip and ½" Reversed Angle Bracket. The 1½" Strip is extended by means of an Obtuse Angle Bracket, and the Bolt securing this part to the Strip 6 also clamps in position a ⅜" Bolt disposed horizontally.

Parts required to build the model "Pterodactyl": 8 of No. 1; 12 of No. 2; 2 of No. 3; 12 of No. 5; 2 of No. 6a; 3 of No. 10; 1 of No. 11; 6 of No. 12; 1 of No. 12a; 1 of No. 12c; 2 of No. 17; 1 of No: 22; 2 of No. 22a; 1 of No. 23; 8 of No. 35; 64 of No. 37; 2 of No. 37a; 5 of No. 38; 1 of No. 40; 2 of No. 48a; 2 of No. 90a; 2 of No. 111c; 1 of No. 115; 3 of No. 125; 2 of No. 126; 2 of No. 126a; 1 of No. 188; 2 of No. 190; 2 of No. 191; 2 of No. 193; 2 of No. 199.

The Ewbank Carpet Sweeper

British Firm Offers Cash Prizes for Meccano Models

AMONG the furnishings and equipment of the average home are many objects that make splendid subjects for Meccano models. One of the most familiar of these is the domestic carpet sweeper which, while not difficult to reproduce, provides scope for ingenuity in the choice of Meccano parts used for building it. This month we are offering handsome cash prizes in a special contest in which competitors are asked to submit models of the well-known Ewbank Sweeper, which possesses features and movements that make it attractive to model-builders. Entwisle and Kenyon Ltd., Accrington, the makers of this sweeper, are greatly interested in the competition and have kindly offered to give the prizes in the Home Section.

The illustrations on this page show a general view and an underneath view of a Ewbank "Success" Sweeper. Sweeping is effected by a brush that revolves inside a polished wooden casing, and is driven by friction from the four wheels on which the sweeper travels. The wheels are provided with rubber treads and these make contact with brass collars mounted on the ends of the brush shaft. In action the sweeper is simply pushed over the carpet and the motion of the wheels is transmitted to the brush, which is caused to revolve rapidly and flick any dust or dirt it encounters into the dust pans. It is necessary that the brush should revolve at a high speed, and this is effected by making the brush collars much smaller than the wheels.

The brush spindle is mounted in steel bands at each end of the casing, and the wheel spindles are journalled in a simple spring suspension system consisting of curved spring steel wires fixed in position outside the ends of the casing. The purpose of this arrangement is to enable varied pressure to be put on the sweeper brush according to the thickness of the carpet being swept. Only slight pressure is necessary on a thick carpet, and heavier pressure is applied when a thinner one is being cleaned.

Along each side of the brush there is a hinged dust pan, each dust pan being carried on a pivot fixed in each end of the casing. The dust pans close the space between the brush and the casing. To remove dust collected in them it is only necessary to depress a small lever at one end of the casing. This causes the hinged pans to snap outward under the action of powerful springs, and to throw out the dust. By sliding this lever forward when fully depressed the dust pans are locked open to permit internal examination of the container. For the purpose of removing fluff and bits of cotton from the brush a strip of metal with projecting teeth spaced about $\frac{1}{2}$ in. apart is fixed to the inside of the sweeper. The teeth project between the hairs of the brush and make an effective scraper.

These illustrations of the Ewbank "Success" Carpet Sweeper will help entrants in the model-building competition announced on this page. One gives a general view of the Sweeper and the other shows the underside, with the dust pans opened to reveal their construction.

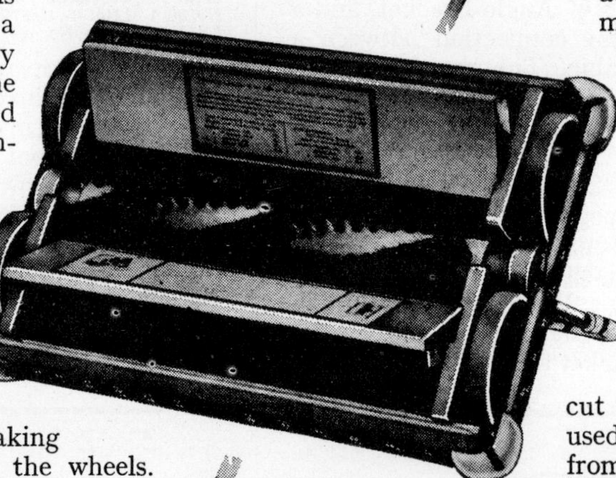

The handle is screwed into a metal yoke that is pivoted in a hole in a metal plate at each end of the casing. In order to prevent damage to articles of furniture through the sweeper bumping against them, the sweeper is provided with a number of resilient rubber cushions. These are fixed in a special manner at the corners of the case and on the handle yoke, as shown in the illustration, while the end of the handle itself is fitted with a rubber cap.

It is not expected that competitors will be able to reproduce accurately every mechanical detail of these sweepers or that they will be able to make their models actually sweep, and so long as a model demonstrates the essential features of their construction and outward appearance it will stand a good chance of winning a prize. There is a good opportunity for showing originality in devising suitable materials for representing the rotating sweeping brush, and no restriction is enforced on the choice of materials for this purpose. For example, on models of suitable size a piece cut from a bottle brush could be used. These brushes can be obtained from any chemists for a few pence. Another idea would be to build up a brush from pieces of springy wire.

Entries will be divided into two Sections, A for readers of all ages living in the British Isles, and B for readers of all ages living Overseas. The age of each competitor will be taken into consideration in judging the entries in order to give the younger competitors an equal chance of success.

A separate and complete set of prizes as follows will be awarded in each Section. First Prize, Cheque for £3/3/–; Second, Cheque for £2/2/–. Third, Cheque for £1/1/–. There will be also a number of consolation prizes.

The actual model must not be sent. What is required is a photograph or drawing giving an adequate impression of the design and construction of the model, and this may be accompanied by a few words of description if considered necessary. The model must be built by the competitor himself without any assistance, but the drawing or photograph may be prepared by others if necessary.

The competitor's age, name and full address must be written on the back of each photograph or drawing sent in. Entries should be addressed to "Carpet Sweeper Contest," Meccano Ltd., Binns Road, Liverpool 13. The closing date for entries in the Home Section will be 31st December, 1936, and for Overseas entries 27th February, 1937.

The entries will be judged by Entwisle and Kenyon Ltd. and Meccano Ltd. jointly.

Model-Building Competition Results

By "Spanner"

Ingenious Small Models by Overseas Readers

May "Simplicity" Contest (Overseas)

A notable feature of the Overseas Section of the Competition was the large number of competitors who were sending in entries in "*M.M.*" Model-building Contests for the first time. Many of these were successful in winning prizes, and I hope that their early successes will encourage them to become regular competitors and that other model-builders will follow their example.

The list of awards is as follows: 1st Prize, Meccano products value £3/3/–: L. Dumont, Charlottetown, Canada. 2nd, products value £2/2/–: D. Murison, Buenos Aires. 3rd, products value £1/1/–: H. Guallart, Buenos Aires.

Products value 10/6: A. Turton, Ottawa, Canada; H. Dressler, Breslau X, Germany; J. Oleaga, Buenos Aires; J. Cruse, Wellington, N.Z.; G. Myburgh, Claremont, Capetown.

Products value 5/–: R. Hill, Toronto; N. Vung, Shanghai; L. Edwards, Hokianga N.Z.; B. Walsh, Nelson, N.Z.; R. Plewman, Johannesburg.

Three of the most interesting models entered in the contest are illustrated on this page. The base of the simple hammer-head crane built by L. Dumont consists of four 1″×1″ Angle Brackets bolted together by a ⅜″ Bolt that projects upward. Loose on this bolt is a Double Bracket locknutted to keep it in position. Two 3½″ Strips bolted to the Double Brackets as shown form the jib, and at one end they are connected by a Double Bracket and at the other by two ½″×½″ Angle Brackets. The winding drum is a ¾″ Bolt and the travelling carriage from which the hoisting hook is suspended is made from two ½″×½″ Angle Brackets bolted through their elongated holes. The hook is a small piece of bent wire. The judges were impressed by the clever way in which the builder had reproduced in a simple manner the main features of such a large prototype.

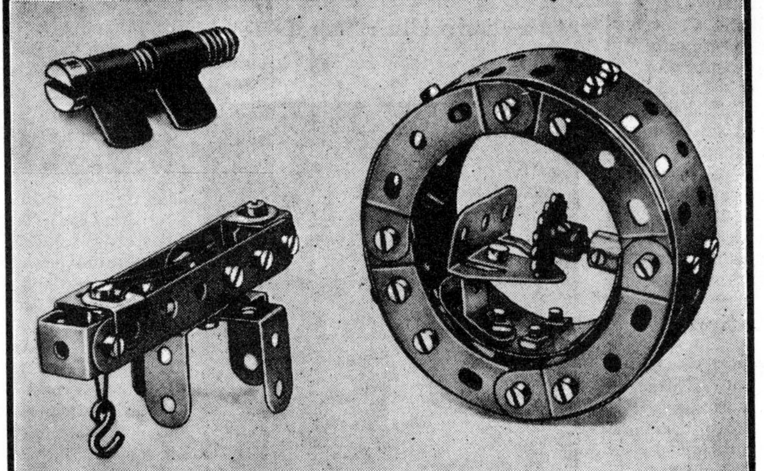

Ingenious models that won prizes in the May "Simplicity" Competition. In the top left corner is a Dachshund by D. Murison, and beneath it is L. Dumont's hammerhead crane. The simple dynasphere on the right was built by H. Guallart.

One of the smallest "simplicity" models that I have yet seen was submitted by D. Murison. It is the Dachshund illustrated on this page, and awarded Second Prize. No doubt readers with imagination will see in it a likeness to several other members of the animal and insect kingdom, but it certainly gives a very good impression of one of these lengthy German dogs. It consists of only three parts, one ¾″ Bolt and two Spring Clips, and is an outstanding example of what can be done with limited resources.

The third model illustrated is a reproduction of the dynasphere shown on the cover of the "*M.M.*" for February 1935, and was built by H. Guallart. The large wheel consists of two built-up circles of 2½″ small radius Curved Strips, which are connected round their rims by Flat Girders bent to shape. The power unit, which in the real dynasphere remains horizontal while the road wheel is revolving, is a 3″ Flat Girder, fitted with a Rod Socket and a Double Bracket. The former holds a ¾″ Bolt on which is a ¾″ Sprocket for the steering wheel. The driver's seat is a Trunnion bolted to the Double Bracket, and the whole unit is held inside the wheel by two 1″ Screwed Rods. Underneath the power unit are four ½″ loose Pulleys that are bolted to the circles of Curved Strips. This competitor submitted also a miniature merry-go-round and a small monoplane, but I think the dynasphere is the most cleverly built model of the three.

The base of the merry-go-round is a geared disc taken from a Ball-bearing, the flanged disc of which is used for the roof. A Sleeve Piece held on a Rod by means of a ¾″ Flanged Wheel and a Chimney Adaptor forms the centre pillar, and Eye Pieces are used to represent the cars.

"Small Outfits" Competition (Overseas)

This contest was designed specially to encourage younger model-builders and those who possess only the smaller Meccano Outfits to try their skill in building models based on their own ideas. The large number of entries received shows that the opportunity thus provided for these boys and girls to add to their stock of parts by winning a prize was fully appreciated. The successful competitors are as follows:

1st Prize, products value £2/2/–: J. Winborn, Christchurch, N.Z. 2nd, products value £1/1/–: W. Ingle, Johannesburg, S.A. 3rd, products value 10/6: D. Hutt, Hamilton, N.Z.

Products value 5/–: J. Forrester, Montreal; J. Carter, Capetown; J. Nie, Shanghai; Y. Nai Kong, Shanghai; R. Miller, Claremont, Ontario; E. Aronson, Hedemora, Sweden; J. Walter, Fort Brown, S. Africa; M. Nicholls, Pietermaritzburg; M. Choon, Kingman, Alberta; M. Jones, Melbourne.

I am sorry that I am unable to illustrate the interesting motor cycle model that won First Prize. It evidently is copied from a very old type of machine, and it gives the impression of being a miniature of one of the first produced. The body of the model is formed with a No. 1 Clockwork Motor, which is fitted at one end with Strips that support the rear wheel axle, and at its other end with a strong projecting arm of Strips reinforced to form the head-lock bearing. The rear wheel axle is driven from the Motor by means of a belt. The model is rather crude, but this is only natural considering the few parts used in building it, and it is obvious that Winborn has endeavoured to make the best use of the parts at his disposal. He deserves encouragement and the prize that he has won in this contest will enable him to construct much more elaborate models. I hope that he will submit some of these for future competitions.

An amusing model representing a policeman on point duty earned Second Prize for W. Ingle. Neat construction is the main feature of this entry, which although simply built is remarkably life-like and gives a good impression of action. The policeman is mounted on a 5½″×2½″ Flanged Plate and his body consists of two Flanged Sector Plates and his legs and arms of Strips, one arm being raised to hold up traffic.

After examining the first two models I should not have been surprised to find that the next was either a "black-maria" or an ambulance! Actually, however, it is a fine little model of a Schneider Trophy seaplane, the fuselage being a boxlike structure made from four 5½″ Strips and Double Brackets. The tail is made from two Trunnions, and each main plane consists of three 2½″ Strips. Strips are used also for the propeller, undercarriage and floats.

Novel "Short Story" Contest

1st Prize, products value £2/2/–: Miss M. Robinson, Dunton Bassett. 2nd, products value £1/1/–: L. Wright, Pengam, Glam. 3rd, products value 10/6: W. Whitaker, Hornsea.

Products value 5/–: M. Maddock, Carbonear, Newfoundland; D. Murison, Buenos Aires; F. Phillips, Ashton-in-Makerfield; A. O'Neill, Glasgow, S.2; J. Woods, Liverpool 21; D. Byrne, Brynteg, Nr. Wrexham; G. Ashwell, London, S.W.4; F. Giles, Sheffield 8; G. B. Milling, Lindsay, Ontario; N. Adamson, Wairoa, N.Z.

"Most Useful Parts" Voting Contest

1st Prize, products value £2/2/–: J. Reid, Pietermaritzburg, S. Africa. 2nd, products value £1/1/–: C. Brett, Great Coates, Lincs. 3rd, products value 10/6: L. Edwards, Hokianga, N. Zealand.

Products value 5/–: D. Webb, Transvaal, S. Africa; J. Riddell, Glasgow E.1; B. Turner, Henfield Sussex.

The Guild President

All members of the Guild will join with me in sincere regrets at the passing of Mr. Frank Hornby, its founder and first President. Few men have done more for boys than Mr. Hornby, who provided them with really worth-while hobbies and, through the Guild and the Hornby Railway Company, encouraged them to think and act for themselves, to help others and to prepare to play their parts in life thoroughly and manfully.

Many members have written anxiously enquiring who is to take Mr. Hornby's place as President of the Guild and Chairman of the Hornby Railway Company. I am glad to take this opportunity of announcing that his son, Mr. Roland Hornby, has undertaken to fill these responsible positions. Thus the name of Hornby will continue to be linked with these world-wide organisations of boys. On page 613 appears a message from Mr. Roland Hornby, who, I am sure, will be able to command the support of every member of the two organisations in his great task of furthering their interests.

The Christmas Exhibition

The first winter session is now well on its way, and the Meccano, Hornby Train, fretwork and various other sections of club life have got thoroughly into their stride. The Leaders and secretaries of many clubs are already making preliminary arrangements for an Exhibition toward the close of the session. It is advisable to make a start at once with these preparations, particularly if it is intended to obtain demonstration models on loan from Headquarters, as at least five weeks' notice is needed to ensure their being available by the required date. Time also is saved by giving full details of the electric supply available, in order that a suitable motor can be fitted to each model.

Those who do not already possess a list of the models available for loan to clubs for display at Christmas and New Year Exhibitions can obtain one on writing to me. The list is comprehensive and varied, and the models themselves are of very handsome appearance. For the information of new clubs, I would like to mention again that very little expense is incurred in including one or more of these splendid working models in a club display, for it is only necessary to pay the return carriage, the amount of which depends on the size of the models and in no case is more than a few shillings.

I am very pleased to publish on this page a notice concerning the forthcoming Sid-Vale M.C. Exhibition, and I shall be delighted to perform a similar service for any other club, if the Leader of it will send me particulars. On several occasions notices of this kind have led to the acquisition of keen Meccano enthusiasts as new members. The *"M.M."* goes to press early, and notices therefore should be sent to me at least a month in advance of the date of publication, but I can still include notices of Exhibitions in December in the next issue if I receive details within the next few days.

Meccano Club Secretaries

No. 38. H. W. Govan

H. W. Govan is secretary of the St. Giles' Cathedral (Edinburgh) M.C., one of the largest clubs in the Guild. Model-building, Games and Lectures are among its many activities, and with the associated Branch of the H.R.C. operates two extensive Hornby layouts.

A Meccano "Safety First" Demonstration

There is a refreshing originality in many of the schemes devised in modern Meccano clubs, especially those in which members keep in touch with current events and plan their model-building and other activities to serve some practical purpose. I should like officials to keep a keen look out for opportunities of introducing novelties of this kind into their programmes.

Sutton Valence Council School M.C. have set a fine example in this respect by a carefully planned "Safety First" demonstration. The grounds of the school were marked out by chalk lines to represent a typical section of a town, including island blocks of shops and offices, with main and secondary roads and pedestrian crossings. Traffic signs were erected where necessary and Belisha beacons, with real oranges as their heads, were also in place, while traffic signals constructed from Meccano parts were in operation at two cross-roads. The club members were employed as "police," or as attendants and guides to the many visitors to the demonstration, and other boys from the school, seated in toy motor cars or astride bicycles, provided the necessary road traffic.

It is a credit both to the "police" and to the traffic that the demonstration passed off without a single accident. There were several cases of excessive speeding, however, and these were dealt with by Meccano solicitors and magistrates at the "police court," one of the classrooms in the school. In another room was a Safety First village, elaborately laid out and planned to provide for the needs of modern traffic, with Dinky Toy models to demonstrate the rules of the road and the need for "Safety First."

Visitors to this topical and original display praised the efforts of the club very highly, and dwelt particularly on its practical value as a help in reducing the number of road accidents.

* * * *

The Sid-Vale M.C. will hold their Annual Exhibition in the Congregational schoolroom, off Church Street, Sidmouth, on 10-13th November, 1936. On the 10th, 11th and 13th it will be open from 6 p.m. to 9.30 p.m., and on the 12th from 2.30 p.m. to 9.30 p.m. Admission will be free, but a collection will be taken in aid of club funds.

Proposed Clubs

Attempts are being made to establish Meccano Clubs in the following places, and boys interested should communicate with the promoters whose names and addresses are given below:

BELFAST—T. M. Emery, Bedell House, Methodist College.
CANADA—T. K. Campion, 102, Queen Street, St. Catherines, Ontario.
INDIA—N. S. Narang, Shish Mahal Road, Lahore.
NELSON—D. Holt, "Ivy Lea," Barkerhouse Road.
SOUTH SHIELDS—R. Gale, 11, Cedar Grove, Cleadon Park.

Wednesbury M.C.—Inclement weather has reduced outdoor activities, and most meetings have been held in the club-rooms, when model-building and fretwork have occupied the members. The seniors have re-decorated the rooms. The upper half of each wall has been painted white and the lower half brick-red, with striking effect. Some good games of Cricket have been played, and a ramble from Wolverhampton, during which the party walked about 12 miles, proved a very enjoyable outing. Visits to several local places of interest, including the Central Fire Station, Birmingham, have been arranged. A recruiting campaign is to be organised. Club roll: 18. *Secretary:* A. L. Morgan, 17, Cobden Street, Fallings Heath, Wednesbury.

Sid-Vale M.C.—Some very interesting rambles have been held, games being played when the destinations were reached. During a ramble along the permanent way to Tipton St. John, for which permission was obtained, the party were shown over a junction signal box. In a "Buildings" Contest many excellent models of churches, houses, and a railway station were entered. Club roll: 20. *Secretary:* L. R. J. Gliddon, Sheffield House, Sidmouth.

Plymouth M.C.—Visits have been paid to the Friary (S.R.) Engine Sheds, and to the Dewerstone, one of the Dartmoor tors, at Shaugh, where members were also interested in the old railway. A Visit to Yelverton was made specially enjoyable by a Treasure Hunt and races across the moor. A "backward" race across rough moorland for officials only greatly amused members, those taking part carrying out many remarkable unintentional gymnastic feats. A special issue of the "*Gear Box*" is to be produced to celebrate the club's 10th birthday. A second magazine is to be produced on the club press, and special editions of it will be sold to clubs in Devon and Cornwall who do not issue one. It has been decided to elect an Advertising Manager to seek advertisements for the magazines. The Library is to be re-opened. *Secretary:* R. G. Symons, 47, Lisson Grove, Mutley, Plymouth.

St. Stephen's (Saltash) M.C.—Games have been played during two outdoor meetings, and Model-building and Table Tennis have been the chief features of indoor work. Models completed include a yacht, revolving hammerhead crane, and a tennis umpire's seat; and the main block of buildings on the model of Millbay (G.W.R.) Station has been completed. The Model-building Section continues to be busy making cupboards in which to store the club stock of Meccano parts. One member is building a model of a United States cruiser. Club roll: 8. *Secretary:* B. Braund, 9, Homer Park, Saltash.

Members of the Maylands (Australia) M.C. building models for display at an Exhibition. This club was affiliated in February 1936, and is making excellent progress. Photograph by courtesy of West Australian Newspapers Ltd., Perth, West Australia.

Exeter M.C.—Special attention is being paid this session to operations with Dinky Toy vehicles on the model road layout. Recent models completed have included one of Blackpool Tower, an air liner, cabin motor boat, speed indicator and several types of motor vehicles. Club roll: 36. *Secretary:* E. Ashwood, 188, Pinhoe Road, Exeter.

Bexleyheath Boys' Central School M.C.—A visit to the Science Museum, South Kensington, proved very enjoyable, and the party were specially interested in the model of Stephenson's "*Rocket.*" A fine model of a gantry crane, driven by an electric motor, was exhibited at one meeting, and at another a Talk on "*How an Aeroplane Flies*" was enjoyed. Club roll: 30. *Secretary:* D. Hicks, 4, St. Audrey Avenue, Longlane, Bexleyheath.

Enfield Grammar School M.C.—The club's second Exhibition was held in connection with the School Fête. It was arranged in two rooms, and the chief features in the first were the ever-popular Meccanograph, an electric crane, model aeroplanes, and a ¾ in. scale model of a G.N.R. "Atlantic" locomotive, complete with train. This locomotive can haul six adults at 8 m.p.h., and it is hoped to have it working at the next Exhibition. The second room contained other attractive Meccano models, and the club layout, which was operated to timetable. At the end of the day the club was able to hand over £3/10/- to the School fund. The track used at the display is to be replaced by a new one completely track-circuited and controlled from a signal box worked on the system now in use on the L.N.E.R. at Thirsk. Club roll: 35. *Secretary:* J. H. Pettifer, 31, Goat Lane, Forty Hill, Enfield.

Islington M.C.—The Leader has given an interesting talk on "*Curious Jobs.*" The chief feature of recent Model-building meetings has been the construction of various types of aeroplanes, but other subjects have not been neglected, and an excellent model of a gantry crane has been completed. Fretwork and chemical experiments have been carried out. Preparations are in hand for the club Exhibition. Club roll: 18. *Secretary:* K. V. Dines, 70, Thornhill Road, Barnsley, London, N.1.

St. Giles' Cathedral (Edinburgh) M.C.—New club-rooms have been obtained in a central part of the city. Partitions have been erected to divide the space available to the best advantage, and two of the rooms created have been named "H. N. Gresley Railway Room" and "Cecil J. Allen Railway Room" respectively. Both have been equipped with strong baseboards at a height of about 3 ft., and about 200 ft. of Hornby track has been laid in the Gresley room. Another room contains two heavy benches and is used for model-building, fretwork and wireless, and a fourth one is utilised for games, lectures and committee meetings. Many new members are required so that full advantage can be taken of these excellent facilities, and the secretary will be glad to hear from any local Guild member who would like to join. *Secretary:* H. W. Govan, 18, Ravelston Park, Edinburgh 4.

Hornsea M.C.—Outdoor activities have included a picnic in a wood and a cycle run to Burton Constable Hall, where the party were greatly interested in the old furniture and many fine pictures in the various rooms. They also inspected the extensive gardens. During an excursion to Hull the members visited the Alexandra (L.N.E.R.) Dock, where they were allowed to inspect a Danish ship. In the town they visited the Regal Cinema, and by kind permission of the Manager they were privileged to see inside the projection room. Another outing was to the residence of a Mr. Drys, who possesses a fine model railway. He allowed the members to take their "Flying Scotsman" with them and to operate it on his steel track. Much interest was taken in an excellent steam locomotive owned by Mr. Drys. Club roll: 12. *Secretary:* P. Thom, 5, Alexandra Road, Hornsea.

Fraserburgh M.C.—At one outdoor meeting a member of the flying section brought his "Frog" aeroplane and a model Bird-man. Both models flew exceptionally well. A visit was paid to the Empire Air Display promoted by the late Mr. T. Campbell Black when it visited the locality, and many members enjoyed flights in spite of the very cold weather. Club roll: 28. *Secretary:* W. J. Dawson, Phingask, Fraserburg.

Mallow M.C.—A grand Reunion was held to mark the opening of the first winter session. The club stock of Meccano and Hornby has been overhauled. Several interesting lectures by local gentlemen have been arranged. An extensive and varied programme has been planned for this and the second winter session, and members are very enthusiastic. Club roll: 12. *Secretary:* M. D. Hickey, 42, Ballydaheen, Mallow, Co. Cork, I.F.S.

AUSTRALIA

Thebarton (Adelaide) M.C.—This club is making rapid progress, and all members are very enthusiastic. Lectures are very popular, and as there is no lack of volunteers to give them, they figure prominently in the club programme. Some of the many and varied subjects dealt with have been "*The Building of the Forth Bridge,*" "*Glass Blowing,*" "*Gold Fish Breeding*" and "*Bee Keeping.*" Places of interest visited recently by the club include the locomotive works of Southern Australian Railways, a motor body-building factory, a telephone exchange, newspaper printing works, engineering works and foundry, and a reservoir under construction at Mount Bold. Club roll: 65. *Secretary:* D. C. Tweedie, Technical High School, Ashley Street, Thebarton, Adelaide, South Australia.

Maylands M.C.—A model harbour complete with docks, quays, cranes, railways and warehouses is to be an outstanding feature of the next club Exhibition, for which preparations are being made. The club has been visited by a representative of "*The Western Australian,*" and as a result a detailed and very favourable account of the club and its useful activities appeared in that paper. A Debate on "*Is War Worth While?*" produced some very interesting speeches. A Visit to the "*Daily News*" offices was much enjoyed. Club roll: 30. *Secretary:* M. Thomson, 13, Kennedy Street, Maylands, West Australia.

EGYPT

Cairo M.C.—Good progress is being made and the membership is increasing. The most popular activities are model-building, stamp collecting and correspondence with Guild members in other countries. Visits have been paid to Alexandria, Port Said and other coastal places, and a moonlight trip to the Pyramids was greatly enjoyed. While the party rested there before making the return journey one of the members entertained the others by singing songs. At one meeting the Leader gave an interesting talk on "*The uses of collecting Stamps and Coins.*" Club roll: 30. *Secretary:* Mohed Kamel Salem, 14, Bibars Street, Cairo.

Zagazig M.C.—Interesting competitions and debates have been held. When the subject "*Is Road Transport better than Rail?*" was debated, there was a very lively discussion, and the final result was a majority in favour of railways. A Mock Trial proved very amusing. It is proposed to establish a club library, each member giving a few books to provide an opening stock. Members camped at Bebasta Hill for several days, and there inspected ancient monuments and carried out simple excavation work, discovering interesting relics. Club roll: 19. *Secretary:* Miss B. Mangourie, 39B, Gannabiet Sikka, Hadid Avenue, Zagazig.

INDIA

Ranjit (Lahore) M.C.—The membership is increasing, and all are very enthusiastic. A trip by road and rail to the hill stations of Kulu and Simla, a total distance of 430 miles, has been arranged. On the way the party will visit Jogindar Nagar, the head of the hydro-electric scheme for the whole of the Punjab, where they will inspect the power station and see the huge generators at work. Club roll: 21. *Secretary:* S. Harbhajan, 689, Krishna Bazar, Gowalmandi, Lahore.

SOUTH AFRICA

Pioneer M.C.—Model-building and the Boys' Brigade continue to be the chief activities. Preparations are in hand for an Exhibition, and the members are working in pairs on the construction of the many models required. Club roll: 10. *Secretary:* A. H. Alley, 461, Burgers Street, Pietermaritzburg, Natal.

Passenger Trains on Hornby Railways

Their Formation and Running

ON most miniature railways pride of place is given to the passenger train services, and these can be carried out in a thoroughly realistic and interesting manner. The planning of services, the correct formation and despatch of trains, and the arrangement of specials for various purposes, form a very fascinating part of the general working of the line. In this article it is proposed to deal with various points of interest in connection with this subject.

The most important trains on many layouts are made up of Hornby No. 2 Special or No. 2 Pullman Coaches. With these practically all the business or pleasure services of real practice on which Pullman accommodation is the rule can be operated. On miniature L.N.E.R. systems the *"Queen of Scots"* or the *"Yorkshire Pullman"* can be run, and the correct naming of such trains by means of specially prepared name-boards will add considerably to their interest. An unusual type of Pullman train, also on the L.N.E.R., is the *"Eastern Belle,"* which runs during the Summer season on various routes of the former Great Eastern Railway from Liverpool Street, and serves a different resort on each day of the week! Similar traffic is catered for by the *"Bournemouth Belle"* of the S.R., which, from being a seasonal train only, has now developed into a regular all-the-year-round service.

A main line stopping train on a Hornby layout representing the L.N.E.R. The No. 2 Coaches composing the train are correctly arranged with a Brake-Third vehicle next to the engine.

Particular interest is attached to trains that run in connection with steamer sailings, and for this reason *"The Golden Arrow Limited,"* or any of the Southampton *"Ocean Liner"* specials of the S.R., are well worth reproducing in miniature. It is distinctly thrilling to run such trains as "The Boats," as they are known to the staff, for "Continental" or "Transatlantic" traffic on a miniature railway! The completeness of Hornby equipment makes it possible to follow closely the formation and running operations of real practice. *"Pullman Race Special"* trains are operated frequently on the S.R. and on the L.N.E.R. in connection with the most important meetings. Their running in miniature would be a novelty, while the making of the arrangements necessary for including specials of this kind among the regular trains is always fascinating.

When assembling such trains as these with Hornby No. 2 Special Pullmans, care should be taken to see that the Composite vehicles are marshalled at the ends. The guard's and luggage accommodation provided by them will then be situated in the correct position, and the trains will have the neat and well-finished appearance that characterises the all-Pullman expresses of real practice.

In addition to the various trains that are composed exclusively of Pullmans, there are many others made up of railway companies' stock that also include Pullman accommodation to the extent of one or two cars. The contrast in colours is then very striking, the umber and cream Pullman livery showing up well against the L.N.E.R. teak brown, or the S.R. green, as the case may be. The L.N.E.R. Continental services that operate between Liverpool Street and Parkeston Quay convey Pullmans in trains otherwise composed of standard stock. In miniature the Hornby No. 2 Saloon Coaches and No. 2 and No. 2 Special Pullmans can be used to reproduce such formations, and an interesting point is that these different vehicles can be correctly vestibuled together by means of the Corridor Connection with which they are provided. This helps to maintain the atmosphere of importance that always surrounds a Continental Boat Express, even in miniature.

The No. 2 Saloon Coaches are in fact extremely useful vehicles for a number of different purposes. They can be used for restaurant or sleeping cars, and they represent very well the end-vestibule corridor type of vehicle that is so popular nowadays for main line travel. Centre corridor vehicles are largely used for excursions, and the No. 2 Saloon Coach is typical of many vehicles of this kind that are found in actual practice. The organisation of special excursion working is always interesting and during the Winter there are many long-distance football and other excursions that can be run on Hornby Railways. For the formation of such trains the No. 2 Saloon Coach is ideal.

Coming now to non-corridor stock, the best vehicles of this type in the Hornby Series are the No. 2 Coaches. These represent the familiar compartment type of coach, and can be employed for almost every kind of ordinary passenger train, including long distance residential and business services. On layouts where there is plenty of accommodation, and a corresponding amount of stock, No. 2 Coaches can form the ordinary suburban and local trains. The No. 2 Coaches are made as First-Thirds or as Brake-Thirds, so that the complete trains can be correctly assembled.

A feature of interest that should not be neglected is the placing of a tail lamp on rear vehicles of a train of these No. 2 Coaches. These and the No. 1 Coaches are fitted with lamp brackets for the purpose, and are supplied with appropriate tail lamps. The presence of the tail lamp shows that the train is complete, and it has to be looked out for by the real signalmen as the trains pass them. It is important therefore on a Hornby Railway to see that the tail lamp is in position before the train leaves the carriage sidings.

Cable Drum Transport in Miniature

By "Tommy Dodd"

THE miniature Cable Drum introduced into the Hornby Series some time ago is an extremely popular accessory. Its prototype, which will be familiar to all readers, takes the form of a large wooden "reel" on which is wound cable used for the distribution of electricity. When this "reel" is filled with coils of cable, boards are fixed across the edges and form a drum. The cable is thus completely covered in and is protected from any damage in transit. With the ever-increasing use of electricity these cable drums have become familiar items of freight on our railways.

The Hornby Cable Drum is a most effective accessory and is finished in a realistic manner to represent the drums used for the transport of the cables manufactured by the well-known firm British Insulated Cables Ltd. Both sides of the Hornby Drum bear the inscription "B.I. Cables" in large letters arranged to cover practically half the circumference of the side, so that there is room for the words to appear twice. Separating the two inscriptions round each side there are two "B.I." trade marks, and within the ring thus formed the full name of the firm appears, thus forming practically a full inner circle. These details are common to both sides, but on one side of each drum there appears a very necessary instruction "*Roll drum this way,*" the direction being indicated by an arrow. This ensures that the drum is placed the right way round for the laying of the cable. Round the actual edge of the Hornby Cable Drums the boards used to cover in the cable are shown in a realistic manner.

A train conveying Cable Drums on a Hornby Railway. These are shown loaded on a Flat Truck, and also on a Trolley Wagon, which has die-cast wheels and axle-boxes, as described in this article.

As might be expected these Cable Drums make quite an imposing load on the Flat Trucks that are provided for their transport. The Flat Truck is an interesting piece of rolling stock, typical of the low-sided goods wagons that are in common use on all our railways. It is therefore available finished and lettered to represent each of the four groups. It conforms generally to the usual standards of Hornby Goods Rolling Stock and is of course fitted with automatic couplings. A feature that is of special importance in connection with securing loads such as Cable Drums is the provision of four wire rings, two to each side, to which miniature ropes or chains can be attached. These fittings correspond to the ring plates that are found on real wagons for the same purpose.

The method of securing the Hornby Cable Drum is shown in the accompanying illustration, and is the same as that followed in actual practice, "ropes" of Meccano Cord being passed from the rings on one side to those on the other side of the vehicle through the hollow centre of the Drum. This results in the firm fixing of the load, although additional security is obtained by the use of scotches or wedges nailed to the floor of the real wagons to prevent any tendency of the drums to commence rolling.

The Hornby Cable Drums make suitable loads on any layout and they are particularly applicable to electric systems. Many miles of cable are required for real electrification schemes, so that the number of cable drums involved reaches quite high figures. Laying the cable alongside the track is an interesting process and is carried out by means of a "cable-laying" train. This consists of wagons on which special supports or frames are fixed that allow the cable drums to be revolved. The train moves slowly along and the cable is paid out from the wagons to the lineside, where it is housed in the special troughing prepared for it. This is usually of wood above ground, or of concrete where it is necessary to bury the cables.

For such bulky loads as large cable drums it is often necessary to employ special low-built machinery trucks, or trolley wagons. Their low construction reduces to a minimum the amount of lifting when loading and unloading, which is a point of importance. Special interest is therefore attached to the Hornby Trolley Wagon that is now available loaded with two of the standard Hornby Cable Drums. The Cable Drums are accommodated in the well portion of the Trolley Wagon, and they are secured by miniature "ropes" passing through the centre of the Drums and through the slots that are provided in the well for this purpose. Loaded thus the two Cable Drums present an imposing appearance and add considerably to the realism of any freight train to which the Trolley Wagon is attached. A train load of Cable Drums on Flat Trucks or Trolley Wagons could be run if required.

The Trolley Wagon itself, which is a familiar vehicle to all Hornby Railway owners, has been improved in an important detail for this season. The bogies are now provided with axle-boxes and in place of the tinplate wheels formerly used die-cast spoked wagon wheels are substituted. These greatly improve the realistic appearance of the vehicle and in addition the ease and smoothness of its running.

Similar improvements are also being made to other items and Hornby No. 2 Rolling Stock. These are the Breakdown Van and Crane, and the No. 2 Pullman and Saloon Coaches. The passenger vehicles are provided with Mansell pattern solid wheels.

STATION WORKING ON HORNBY RAILWAYS

A LARGE proportion of the queries received from readers that are dealt with at H.R.C. Headquarters refer to the planning of layouts, their signalling and the train operations that are possible on them. Many of these queries are concerned with stations, particularly terminal stations. These are necessary in any layout, for without them trains would have nowhere to leave or at which to arrive, and their running would have no object. They are of special interest in planning a miniature railway, for it is not always easy to decide on a layout, especially if space is limited. This month therefore we are describing a station layout that was devised to meet the special requirements of a member of the H.R.C. because it has many features that make it of interest to all miniature railway enthusiasts, and in this article it is proposed to deal with some of the operations that can be carried out on it.

This station layout is illustrated at the top of the opposite page. It consists of three main platforms, the centre one being an island, and there is available a total of four platform faces. Arrival and departure platforms are not kept separate, the platforms being used as convenient according to the demands of traffic. This reduces the amount of shunting necessary with empty trains, and is a method that is necessarily adopted on many miniature systems. The rails between each pair of platform faces consist of Hornby Double Track. The inner end of the platforms beyond the extreme right-hand edge of the illustration the rails terminate in Hornby No. 2 Buffer Stops, which reproduce so well the chief features of the hydraulic buffer stops found in real termini. At the outer ends of the platforms the rails of each length of Double Track converge by means of Hornby Parallel Points. A connection is then thrown off each of the two single tracks thus formed towards the centre of the layout by means of ordinary Points, the curved branches of these Points joining up to the corresponding arms of a pair of Double Symmetrical Points. Thus both lead to the No. 2 Turntable shown, and this in turn gives access to an Engine Shed by means of Parallel Points. The double track engine roads continue for one or two rail lengths beyond the shed and terminate in buffer stops.

A busy terminal station on a Hornby Railway. Trains of various kinds are being dealt with at different platforms, and an all-Pullman express is seen arriving.

The effect of this arrangement is that the locomotive accommodation is centrally situated, with ready means of access to the station and to the sidings outside it. The main lines pass on each side of the turntable and shed roads, and each incorporates a slight reverse curve formed of two Curved Half Rails in order to clear the turntable. Beyond the limits of the diagram on the left-hand side these lines are again brought nearer together by means of similar reverse curves. Full length Curved Rails then bring them nearer together, and they are resolved into single track by means of Double Symmetrical Points. These are applied in the same manner as those leading to the locomotive shed that we have already considered.

Main lines consisting partly or wholly of single track are not uncommon on miniature railways. In this case the arrangement of track connections gives trains on the single main line access to any of the station platform lines by means of the approach roads. With the methods of working adopted, this results in the rapid handling of traffic, both in and out. Trains therefore habitually travel in either direction over the tracks connecting the platform lines with the single track main line section. Such "reversible" working is not unknown in real practice in the neighbourhood of busy terminals. Considerable lengths of track are sometimes arranged for it, the flow of traffic at busy periods settling whether such lines are to be used for up and the down traffic for any particular period, but of course special attention has to be given to signalling.

If the miniature terminus is required to handle in quick succession a series of arriving trains constituting "business rush" traffic, these could proceed from the single main line along either of the tracks alongside the Engine Shed as convenient. We will consider the movements during a typical "peak period" and assume that the first train enters the terminus by means of the approach line above the

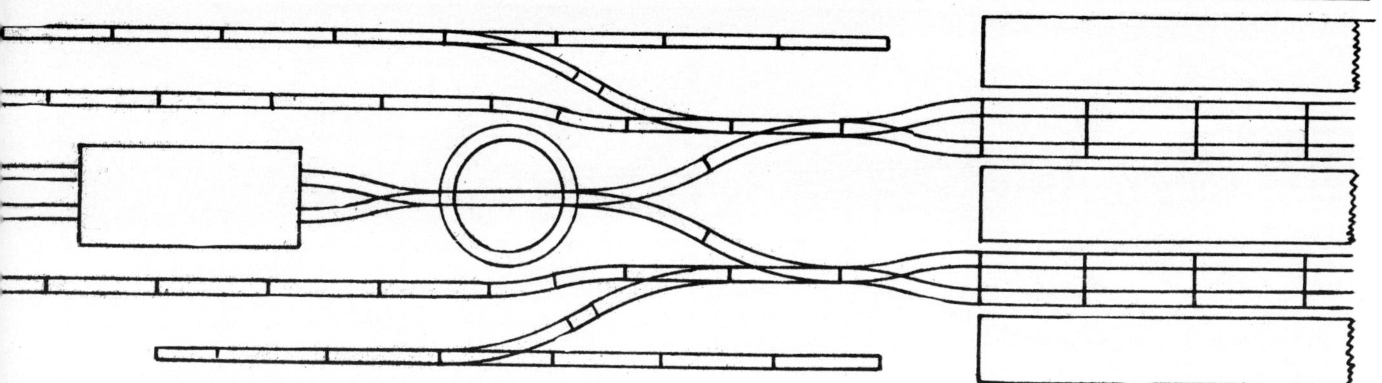

engine sheds in the diagram. It comes to rest alongside the upper single-faced platform at what we will term for convenience the north side of the station. The engine is uncoupled, but as its coaches are required for an outgoing service and running round facilities are not provided owing to the limits of space, another locomotive proceeds from the engine yard and is attached to what now becomes the head of the train. This move is carried out immediately in the interval between the arrival of this train and the next, which follows the same path, but is turned into the platform road adjacent to the northern face of the central island platform.

Almost at the same time similar operations have been going on in the south side of the station, so that we have the arrival of four trains at quite short headways. Possibly departures have to be effected equally rapidly, so that the first arrival with the fresh locomotive at its head leaves the north platform. This movement releases the engine that brought this train in. This engine follows the outgoing train until just clear of the Parallel Points beyond the platform end. These Points are changed, the engine is reversed and then backs on to the second arrival at the upper or northern face of the central island platform. The engine that brought this in has been uncoupled and on the departure of the train it is switched into the locomotive yard. From there it proceeds in turn to back on to one or other of the trains in the south side of the station. A similar cycle of operations to those we have just followed is repeated, the last move being the release of the fourth arriving engine on the departure of its train. This engine runs out into the locomotive yard and waits there until the arrival of a further train, when another spell of duty commences.

The upper illustration on this page shows the station layout referred to in this article. In the lower photograph train working is shown in progress at a station, with a stopping main line train arriving.

This method of operation is known as turnover working, and engines so employed are known as turnover locomotives. It is necessarily adopted when running round facilities for engines are not provided at a terminus; running round invariably requires Crossover Points and in terminal layouts it is often difficult to find room for them. They require in addition an engine length or so of track between them and the buffer stops, to allow the engine to draw forward from its train clear of the Points before reversing to the other end of the station.

At other less busy periods an arriving train perhaps may not be required for a departure until later on, so the engine backs it out of the station into one or other of the sidings according to the platform at which the train arrived. At the end of the siding a locomotive can be waiting, having previously proceeded there from the Shed or after release from the station on the departure of a train brought in previously. This locomotive is coupled to the shunted train which is thus ready to be backed from the siding into the station when required for a departure.

Workings of this kind with variations, can be indulged in to almost any extent, the planning of different movements being very fascinating. The layout also could be altered without difficulty to suit other conditions. For instance, the dead-end sidings at the extreme edges of the layout could be prolonged into running loops. These would be useful in affording separate roads for the up and the down traffic, and in addition might be used to separate different classes of traffic, then becoming relief lines more particularly intended for parcels, milk, and other similar freight trains that would be dealt with at the terminus. On a layout worked entirely by tank engines the turntable in the locomotive yard would not be really necessary. It was provided in this instance as tender and tank locomotives were in use together.

Effective terminal stations can be arranged with the aid of Hornby components. The standard lengths of Passenger Platform are very useful, whether they are employed with the Paled Fencing supplied with them as an ordinary platform, or without it as an island. In the illustration on the previous page both uses of the Passenger Platform sections are shown. They also can be laid end to end to make a long platform, and are then secured together by means of the special locking device at each end. This device also is provided on the platforms of the No. 2 Station, on the ramps, and on the Island Platform. In addition, the front edge of the No. 2 Station platform has these fittings, so that lengths of Passenger Platform can be attached at right-angles to it. This enables the Hornby Railway owner to assemble a terminal station without difficulty, the centre of the No. 2 Station forming the circulating area.

Branch News

Plymouth.—The annual general meeting of the Branch has been held and the Branch Committee and Officials for the current year's work have been elected. Several track meetings have been enjoyed and each member has taken a fair share in the various operations. Recent outdoor activities have included visits to the S.R. Friary Locomotive Sheds at Plymouth, where members were allowed to inspect various locomotives at close quarters, and to climb on to their footplates. On an outing to Yelverton part of the track of the old Plymouth and Dartmoor Railway was explored. The Branch recently celebrated its birthday with a special concert. Future arrangements include the Annual Exhibition in December and in the same month a railway Lantern Lecture. Secretary: R. Symons, 47, Sisson Grove, Mutley, Plymouth.

Cottesmore.—During the Summer members who were in camp at Cromford made a special study of the Cromford and High Peak line, and also of the traffic over the main line of the Midland Division of the L.M.S.R. that passes through Cromford station. Good progress has been made by the Branch and a very full programme for the Winter Session has been arranged. This will include regular Track Meetings, Socials and Special Cinema and Lantern Slide Displays. Visits are to be paid to places of interest, and one that is eagerly anticipated is that to the Meccano Factory. A Study Circle for the reading of the "*M.M.*" and railway and engineering books has been instituted. Secretary: J. S. Butler, Cottesmore Central School, Lenton, Nottingham.

Elmside (Exeter).—The relaid track is proving a great success and improved working has resulted from the incorporation of additional sidings and connecting lines. The relaying of tracks is carried out as in actual practice, without suspending the train services. Modified workings are adopted to suit the special conditions, and this adds considerably to the realism of operations. Secretary: T. Smith, 98, Ladysmith Road, Exeter.

Whitgift School.—A recent visit that was greatly enjoyed was paid to the Signal Box at London Bridge (S.R.). Members were shown over the Box and were greatly interested to watch the progress of various trains on the large electrical indicator. After observing the working of the trains, the locking arrangements and power plant were inspected. The day was completed by a visit to the Science Museum, South Kensington. Train running to timetable has been a feature of recent track meetings, and Winter session activities are now in full swing. Secretary: J. C. Watson, 23, Addiscombe Avenue, Croydon, Surrey.

Folkestone.—An increase in membership is recorded and a good start has been made with the Winter service on the Branch track. "Folkestone Harbour" station is now complete and a new station representing "Folkestone Junction" is under construction. "Margate" and "Brighton" stations are to be improved. It is possible that new services will be introduced representing the Dover Train Ferry workings of real practice. New signals are under construction and most of the existing ones have been repainted. Various track improvements are to be made that will be a considerable aid to high-speed running. New telegraph poles are being installed, and water storage tanks are being provided at all stations. Secretary: F. E. Saunders, 79, Dover Road, Folkestone, Kent.

Some of the members and friends of Sydney Branch, No. 146. Chairman, Mr. H. H. Matthews; Secretary, Mr. W. J. T. Watson. This photograph was taken on a joint excursion by rail with the associated Meccano club. On these occasions a special coach decorated internally in the club colours and with the club badge prominently displayed on the outside is always used.

Swan (Kidderminster).—Stations made of wood have been added to the Branch layout, and at one of these colour-light signals have been installed experimentally. Through the generosity of a local gentleman who is interested in the Branch, a specially painted scenic background 18 in. high has been provided all round the track. Trains are operated to represent G.W.R. services, and as the result of experience one or two modifications to the track plan have been effected. At some meetings games are played, and a Branch Library has been formed. Secretary: A. Hamblin, Black Bull Hotel, Swan Street, Kidderminster.

Waterloo (Dublin).—The attendance of meetings continues to be satisfactory, and for the present the usual arrangements are being followed. The Branch layout has been overhauled and cleaned up, and the Branch room generally prepared for the intensive activities of the Winter Session. For the accommodation of the various tools belonging to the Branch the "shadow board" system as employed in actual practice, has been adopted with success. Secretary: S. B. Carse, 38, Oakley Road, Ranelagh, Dublin.

AUSTRALIA

Parramatta.—The proposed electrification of the Branch layout has now been carried out. The Hornby 20-volt system has been adopted and the Locomotives have proved so powerful that additional rolling stock is to be obtained. A Visit has been paid to the Branch layout by the members of the Sydney Branch. The Branch extends an invitation to visit the layout to any "*M.M.*" readers who care to do so. The Branch room is open for this purpose every evening and on Saturday afternoons, and appointments should be made by writing to the Branch Secretary. Future arrangements include the provision of additional siding accommodation and improved facilities for handling goods traffic, and the installation of colour-light signals, and the electro-mechanical locking of points. Lineside effects are to be the subject of special attention. Secretary: H. H. Matthews, 27, Ross Street, Parramatta, N.S.W., Australia.

Branches in Course of Formation

The following new Branches of the Hornby Railway Company are at present in process of formation, and any boys who are interested and desirous of linking up with this unique organisation should communicate with the promoters, whose names and addresses are given below.

Aberdeen—J. Geddes, 26, Argyll Place.
Greenock—J. Agnew, 122, Dunlop Street.
Southampton—N. Guilmant, 69, Shirley Park Road, Shirley.
Sunbury—J. S. Mathieson, 5, Kempton Avenue, Staines Road.

Join the Hornby Railway Company and become eligible for the competitions announced on this page.

H.R.C. COMPETITION PAGE

Join the Hornby Railway Company and become eligible for the competitions announced on this page.

PLANNING A HORNBY RAILWAY

The central feature of any Hornby railway is of course the layout of the track. This must be so designed that interesting and realistic working can be carried out on it, and only when this is the case can the owner of a miniature railway derive the full pleasure and enjoyment that comes from adding accessories and scenery.

This month we give H.R.C. members an opportunity of showing their skill and ingenuity in planning a Hornby layout with this purpose in view. The space that is supposed to be set apart for this purpose measures 15ft. by 10ft. There are no fireplaces or other obstacles to contend with, and in order to give competitors free scope for designing a really useful and interesting Hornby railway no restrictions are imposed in regard to cost. At the same time it must be remembered that a carefully planned layout in which every component serves a definitely useful purpose is more likely to be successful than one that is merely crowded with tracks, points and crossings.

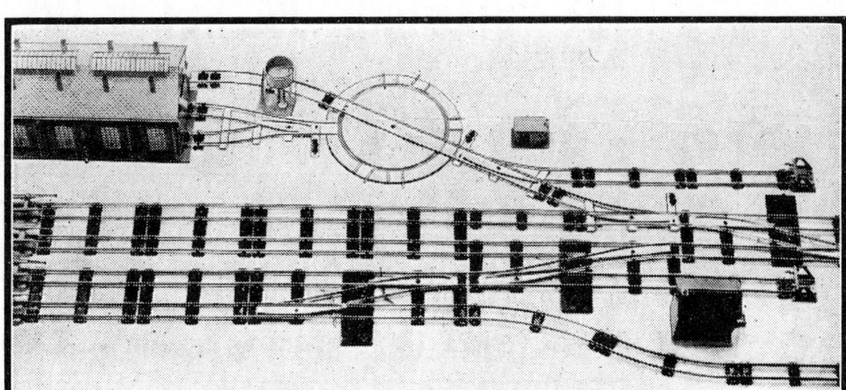

Competitors may introduce as many features as they wish. A good terminal station is almost a necessity, and a well-planned arrangement of such a station is shown in the accompanying illustration. This is reproduced as a guide to show the features that must be kept in mind in station designs; but of course it must not be copied. Only 2 ft. radius track should be used on curves, and no signals need be indicated.

The drawings submitted should not only indicate track arrangements, but should show also the positions of station buildings, engine sheds, bridges, crossings and other important features. Boys who are poor at drawing need have no hesitation about entering this Contest; entries will be judged strictly on the layouts and not on the quality of the drawings.

The Contest is divided as usual into two sections, Home and Overseas, and the senders of the three best layouts in each will be awarded prizes consisting of any products manufactured by Meccano Ltd., to the respective values of 21/–, 15/– and 10/6. In the case of a tie for any prize, the prize money will be equally divided. A number of consolation prizes also will be awarded.

Envelopes containing entries must be marked *"H.R.C. November Layout Planning Contest"* in the top left-hand corner, and posted to reach Headquarters at Meccano Ltd., Binns Road, Liverpool 13, on or before 30th November. The closing date in the Overseas Section is 27th February, 1937.

Word-Building Contest

The two Word-Building contests held during 1935 were very popular with H.R.C. members, and for our second contest this month we are arranging a third of this type. The requirements are very simple, all that competitors are asked to do being to make as many different words as they can, using the letters that appear in *"Hornby Electric Trains."*

Only standard English words are admissible in this contest, and proper names, and faked or slang words are not allowed. Entries should be written on one side of the paper only, and the total number of words submitted must be stated at the end of the list.

The contest will be divided into the usual two sections, Home and Overseas. To the three competitors in each section who submit the longest list of words will be awarded prizes consisting of any products of Meccano Ltd. to the respective values of 21/–, 15/– and 10/6. In addition a number of consolation prizes will be awarded.

Envelopes containing entries must be marked *"H.R.C. November Word-Building Contest"* in the top left-hand corner, and posted to reach Headquarters at Meccano Ltd., Binns Road, Liverpool 13, on or before 30th November. The closing date for competitors in the Overseas Section is 27th February, 1937.

COMPETITION SOLUTION

"July Errors Contest"

This contest produced a remarkably large number of entries, and competitors showed great keenness in hunting for the errors introduced by our artist into his illustration. Some entrants in fact were too sharp-sighted, for they spoiled their efforts by discovering errors that did not exist.

Unfortunately space does not permit us to give a complete list of the errors. The largest number was found by K. Costain, of Bolton, who detected 43 genuine mistakes, and his entry was awarded first prize. Second prize was won by J. N. Leedam, of Burnley, who found 41 errors, and the third prize was awarded to J. T. Fraser, of Exeter, whose entry indicated 39 mistakes.

COMPETITION RESULTS

HOME

September "Voting Contest." First: G. Masterson (47859), Leytonstone, London, E.11. Second: D. James (39923), Northenden, Manchester. Third: H. Wilson, Leek, Staffs. Consolation Prizes: J. C. Button (10335), Crewe, Ches.; J. C. Baker (36514), Ryde, I.O.W.; J. West (46770), Hipperholme, Nr. Halifax.

"Summer Puzzle Contest." In view of the fact that several competitors submitted all-correct solutions in this contest, the judges have decided to divide the First Prize of £1/1- between the two competitors whose entries were most complete and presented in the neatest and most eligible manner. Special Consolation Prizes have been awarded to the remaining competitors whose entries were correct, but not quite up to the standard of the two winners in regard to presentation. First Prize: divided between L. T. A. Bern (347), Portsmouth and J. F. Taylor (42922), Beckenham, Kent. Consolation Prizes: P. T. Jackson (46596), Hornsey, London, N.8; J. C. Button (10335), Crewe, Ches.; F. J. Hearn (33614), Southgate, London, N.14; V. H. Cutts (624), St. Albans; P. L. Baldwin (32479), New Malden, Surrey; J. E. Allen (31359), Leytonstone, London, E.11; C. E. Wrayford (6039), Moretonhampstead, Devon; A. M. Adam (44544), London, N.6; S. Evans (21924), Bosham, Sussex; W. H. Cook (2249), Kensal Rise, Willesden, London, N.W.10.

September "Railway Photo Contest." First: D. F. Forbes (14092), Leith, Edinburgh 6. Second: D. Fear (18477), Taunton. Third: C. Spencer (44179), Sheffield 6. Consolation Prizes: J. W. Hague (1258), Ripon; T. G. Cook (43441), Shirley, Croydon; G. L. Wilson (2478), Wormit-on-Tay, Fife; H. S. G. Darke (4461), Hampstead Garden Suburb, London, N.W.11; H. C. M. Clements (31981), Tunbridge Wells.

SETS (POSTAGE EXTRA)

10 Australia ... 2d.	5 Fiji Is. ... 3d.
1 „ Jubilee 1d.	1 „ Jubilee 4d.
5 Barbados ... 2d.	5 Gold Coast ... 3d.
1 „ Jubilee 4d.	10 „ „ ... 6d.
4 Bermuda ... 3d.	1 „ Jubilee 2d.
1 „ Jubilee 4d.	3 Grenada ... 2d.
5 Brit. Guiana ... 3d.	1 „ Jubilee 2d.
1 „ Jubilee 2d.	5 Hong Kong ... 2d.
10 Canada ... 2d.	10 „ „ ... 5d.
3 „ Jubilee 4d.	1 „ Jubilee 3d.
4 Cayman Is. ... 6d.	20 India ... ... 6d.
1 „ Jubilee 3d.	4 „ Jubilee 6d.
10 Ceylon ... 2d.	5 Jamaica ... 2d.
1 „ Jubilee 2d.	10 „ ... 5d.
5 Cyprus... ... 3d.	1 „ Jubilee 2d.
10 „ ... ... 6d.	5 Kenya ... ... 3d.
1 „ Jubilee 3d.	1 „ Jubilee 3d.

J. RUSSELL
23, Shanklin Drive, Westcliff-on-Sea

THE "QUEER COUNTRY" PACKET FREE!

Have you got stamps from Trans-Caucasia, Georgia, Azerbaijan, Iran in your collection? There is a stamp from each of these queer, outlandish places in this excellent packet of 35 different stamps. They are good stamps, too. For instance, the Trans-Caucasian is catalogued at least 1/6. There are also sets from Bohemia, Kenya Colony, Magyar, South Americans, Manchukuo, Holland (Jubilee), Persia (Lion of Judah), British Colonials, including the famous "Mountie" stamp of Canada. Set of Denmark, including King Christian and Coravel, Norway (Spitzbergen). Finally a beautiful Mongolian stamp and Jugoslavia (new Boy King) ABSOLUTELY FREE. Just send 2d. for postage, requesting approvals. We also send new Price List free.

LISBURN & TOWNSEND LTD. (Dept. M.M.), LIVERPOOL 3

Stamp Collections purchased for prompt cash.

ABYSSINIA

A timely offer, which should not be missed, of a superb **MINT** set of 30 diff. stamps from this mysterious country, mostly 1917-31 issues (cat. over £1), with scarce **AIR STAMPS, COMMEMORATIVES, PICTORIALS, ETC.** Price 5/- only, secure them while you can. We offer superb collections of any country at bargain prices. Full lists FREE.

NORRIS & CO. (Dept.M), NORWOOD, LONDON, S.E.19

500 STAMP MOUNTS FREE to bargain approval applicants.—Winter, 89, Cobham Road, Seven Kings.

FREE WONDERFUL 1936 OFFER 25 NEW ISSUES AND NOVELTIES

Including **Andorra** (1935), fine new **Cayman Islands** (map of Islands), obsolete Austria, China, Denmark, **Gwalior** Service, Hungary (Statesman Szechenyi), **new Kenya** (Kavirondo Cranes), **Roumania** (new portrait of King Carol), and many others. I will send this collection **absolutely free** to all stamp collectors sending 2d. postage (abroad 4d.).

G. P. KEEF, Willingdon, EASTBOURNE

THE "DIAMOND" PACKET IS THE ONLY PACKET

OF UNSORTED STAMPS ON THE MARKET with 15 years' reputation behind it. It contains approx. **1,000 UNSORTED STAMPS** from Convents abroad. **MANY RARE STAMPS** have been found in it. 1 pkt., 1/6; 3 pkts., 3/9; 5 pkts., 6/-. All post free inland. Colonies 3d. per pkt. extra. Foreign, 6d. extra.

Ask your stationer for the "Diamond" packet.

SPECIAL: TURKS IS. JUBILEES complete set, used or unused, 5/6.

O. NERUSH (Dept. A), 68, TURNPIKE LANE, HORNSEY, LONDON, N.8

THE 'SHIP' PACKET

This marvellous packet is offered under cost as an advertisement, **45 different stamps each with a ship on it.** A regular armada. **GABOON,** New Issue **SENEGAL** (Canoe), wonderful flotilla of caravels from **DENMARK** (complete set), **NEW CALEDONIA, IVORY COAST, COSTA RICA,** a fleet of **7 CHINESE** junks usually sold at 10d., **TRINIDAD & TOBAGO, MAURITIUS, SOUTH WEST AFRICA, NEWFOUNDLAND, U.S.A., B. GUIANA,** set of **S. AFRICA, GREECE, POLAND, INDO-CHINA, FRENCH OCEANIA,** etc. Price **4½d.,** postage **1½d.** (abroad 3d. extra). Purchasers of this packet asking for approvals receive **FREE** set of **3 SPAIN** (Columbus, each with his ship on it). Senders of addresses of stamp collectors receive **FREE** set of **6 VENEZUELA** or **6 PERSIA, 100 BRITISH COLONIALS 1/-, 20 AIRPOST 6d., 6 TRIANGULARS 6d., 50 PERSIA 4/-, 2 ASTRID** (mourning stamps) **2½d., VOLUMES OF B.O.P. CHEAP.**

H. C. WATKINS (M. Dept.), Granville Road, BARNET

NOVEMBER SPECIALS

2 Afghanistan ... 2d.
1 Aitutaki ... 2d.
3 Bahamas ... 3d.
2 Bahrain ... 2d.
4 Barbados ... 3d.
2 Barwani ... 2d.
3 Basutoland ... 4d.
4 Bechuanaland ... 5d.
4 Queen Astrid ... 10d.
3 Belgian Olympic Games... ... 9d.
6 Belgian Congo ... 3d.
5 Bijawar ... 10d.
3 Bolivia ... ... 2d.
5 British Honduras 6d.
2 British Somali ... 3d.
2 Brunei ... ... 2d.
2 Cape Juby ... 1d.
5 Cayman Islands 4d.
3 Chili Airmails ... 3d.
3 China, Postage Due ... ... 2d.
3 Chinese Turkestan 2d.
3 French Levant 2d.
5 Hejaz-Nejd ... 6d.
6 Manchukuo ... 3d.
2 Morvi ... ... 2d.
4 Negri Sembilan, mint ... 6d.
6 New Guinea ... 9d.
1 N.Z. Air, used ... 2d.
3 N.Z. Air, 1d., 3d., 6d. mint ... 1/3
4 Pahang, mint ... 6d.
4 Papua Ann., cpte 1/3
4 Perak, mint ... 6d.
5 Port Said ... 4d.
12 Porto Rico ... 7d.
2 Raratonga ... 4d.
7 San Marino ... 5d.
1 Saxony ... ... 2d.
4 Selangor mint ... 6d.
9 Soloman Ids., ½d. to 1/- mint ... 3/6
5 Spanish Morocco 3d.
5 Szechuan ... 3d.
5 Timor ... ... 3d.
3 Tonga ... ... 4d.
7 Transjordan ... 8d.
5 Vatican ... ... 4d.
15 Different Mozambique Company, **AIR ONLY,** Price 1/10.

All Orders Postage Extra.

A BONUS of 25 best quality sorting envelopes will be given free to purchasers of not less than 2/6 worth, and a BONUS of 50 ditto., a good assortment of sizes, will be presented to all purchasers of not less than 5/- worth from this advertisement.

EDWARD SANDELL, 10, Evelyn Grove, Southall, Mx.

Business by Post. No Callers.

LIBERIA PACKET FREE!!

This packet contains a fine mint **TRIANGULAR LIBERIA** (cat. 1/6); set of the attractive **DENMARK** Hans Andersen commemoratives; mint stamps from **PARAGUAY, MOZAMBIQUE CO.** (airmail), **GABOON** (surcharged Afrique Equatoriale Française), **PORT. GUINEA** (Ceres), **OCEANIC SETTLEMENTS** (native spearing fish), large **PERSIA,** set of **INDIA** (service), **CEYLON** (King George), **ITALY** (Foundation of Rome), etc. This packet will be sent free **ONLY** to those requesting approvals who send 2d. postage and packing (Overseas 1/-).

HELY. HUTCHINSON (M.2), HURROCK WOOD, KENTS BANK, GRANGE-OVER-SANDS.

BERMUDA PACKET

This packet contains a splendid selection of recent stamps, including many pictorials. **New Bermuda, mint,** as illustrated, 10 cent Canada 1935 (Mounted Policeman), New Zealand 1935 (Kiwi Bird), **Australia 1936 (Telephone),** Hungary, prisoners of War pictorial, Denmark, set of 3 Hans Andersen (Fairy Tales) commemoratives, Nigeria 1935 pictorial, Roumania (King Carol), Ceylon 1935 (Native tapping rubber tree), Siam (double head), Set of 3 China, **Australia (Jubilee),** Set of 10 Canada including the above and **Canada Jubilee.**

The packet for the discriminating collector.

Offered for 4½d. only to genuine applicants for our approval sheets. (Without approvals 9d.) **SHIRLEY STAMP CO., 19, SANDRINGHAM AVENUE, LONDON, S.W.20.**

Tanna Touva Triangular Pictorial Packet—FREE!

Another Globe-Trotter luxury surprise gift **repeated** for one more month—**Tanna Touva** (Northern Mongolia), Picturesque Triangular, **Mozambique Air Mail,** Mint **Tanganyika** Pictorial, **British Guiana** and **Trinidad** Pictorials, large mint pictorials from **Madagascar, Morocco, Martinique, Syria, Andorra, Gaboon,** some lovely stamps from **South America, Belgian Mourning Stamp,** and others—a veritable stamp feast—**FREE.** Send 1½d. stamp postage for Globe-Trotter approval selections, famous for sensational value. Ask for particulars of **FREE** stamps every 14 days! ! Write now—you must not miss the treat in store for you. **First 100 applicants** receive unused set Montenegro (cat. 1/-).

THE GLOBE-TROTTER

GLOBE-TROTTER, 17, WINCHESTER ROAD, BIRCHFIELD, BIRMINGHAM

The NEW "TRANSPORT" Packet

Contains a wonderful assortment of 44 foreign and colonial stamps including the following which depict various means of transportation, **Tunis** (water carrier), **Senegal** (bridge and boats), **Mauritania** (crossing desert), **Mid. Congo** (train and bridge), **Sth. Africa** (ship), **Germany** (aeroplane), **Austria** (horseman), **Indo China** (boat), **Mozambique** (aeroplane), **Gaboon** (raft), **Greece** (bridge and liner), **St. Pierre and M.** (trawler), **Fr. Guinea** (native carriers), **Dutch Indies** (Steamboat), **Madagascar** (native transport), **Brazil** (aeroplane), **Belgium** (train), **Roumania** (aeroplane), **Newfoundland** (steamship), **Fr. Morocco** (camels). Price **6d.** All purchasers asking for approvals will receive large **Ceylon** pictorials free.

BURDOCK & FLURY, 4, MARLBOROUGH ROAD, LONDON, S.W.19.

Try an "ABBEY" Packet for VALUE!

8 Egypts (with Air), 2 Normandie, 5 Persia, Ceylon (picts.), Aus. Cable, Breton, Le Puy, Cayman, Congo, etc. 25 for 1/- post free.

ABBOTT BROS., 16, Sedgemoor Road, Liverpool 11.

FINEST EVER APPROVALS

Mention the class of stamps you want and get by return the cheapest and best selection ever! Thousands different at ¼d., ½d., and 1d. each; also rare to £1 each. Prices from ⅓rd. to ⅛th Catalogue.

CAMPBELL, HALDON AVENUE, TEIGNMOUTH.

600 BRITISH COLONIALS on approval. Pick at ½d. each.—Sanders, 90, Newlands Avenue, Southampton.

ONE THOUSAND STAMPS ON APPROVAL

From which you may select any 100 for 3/-. This selection is not made up of the very commonest varieties, but contains stamps catalogued at 1/- each or more. (I do not sell less than 100.)

*Special offer of 30 different Scandinavia and Iceland, post free, 7½d. (The Iceland stamps alone are Cat. at least 3/-.)

H. HARDY, "Hoyland," Potter Heigham, Norfolk.

100 Different Stamps Free to Approval applicants. Liberal discount.—Cuthbert, Newsham Lane, Broughton, Preston.

ALL BRITISH COLONIAL APPROVALS

Fine **BRITISH COLONIAL PICTORIAL SETS OF CAYMAN ISLANDS and GAMBIA FREE** to all Collectors sending 2d. in stamps and requesting **ALL BRITISH COLONIAL APPROVALS. BRITISH COLONIALS ONLY** on approval at bargain prices, including **JUBILEE** and **NEW PICTORIAL ISSUES,** West Indies, East and West Africa, Cyprus, Iraq, Newfoundland, Papua, and many other fine Colonials. (No stamps sent Abroad.) **C. H. SHAW (Dept. M.11), 95, CHRISTCHURCH AVENUE, KENTON, HARROW.**

For other stamp advertisements see pages 668, 670 and xxxi

BEGINNING STAMP COLLECTING

THIS is the time of year when there are most newcomers in the world of stamp collecting. They usually begin with a small album and a miscellaneous collection of loose stamps, and they set to work to fill in as many of the blanks as possible on the pages of the album devoted to different countries. This is quite good fun at first, but before very long, when the first supply of stamps is exhausted and the process of blank-filling slows down to the rate at which fresh stamps are received from various sources, the young collector begins to be more critical, and to wonder whether he is on the right lines towards making a really good collection. Many beginners who have reached this stage get the idea that they would do better to concentrate on one or two countries, and they write to ask our advice about this. Our reply is always the same, namely, that it is far better to continue with general collection until a good album full of stamps has been obtained. After all, the main purpose of the hobby is to give pleasure to those who follow it; and to begin to specialise, even to a small extent, at such an early stage makes the whole business too serious. This is specially so for boys whose opportunities of obtaining good stamps are limited, because then the process of completing any particular set is apt to be so slow that the collector becomes tired of it and gives up stamp collecting altogether.

For general collectors the stamp itself and the story it has to tell are the things to keep in mind. The six stamps reproduced on this page give some indication of the attractive designs of modern stamps and the wide range of topics they illustrate. The first one is particularly interesting as a reminder of one of the greatest engineering feats ever accomplished. This is the building of Boulder Dam across the Colorado River in the United States, which stores up behind it the flood waters of the river in order to enable vast areas of desert to be irrigated in dry seasons, and uses the flow to provide electric light and power on a large scale. Both features are illustrated by the stamp, which shows the immense lake 113 miles in length that is forming behind the Dam, and the range of buildings at its foot in which the generators are housed. The mountainous nature of the surrounding country can be realised, and the stamp that tells this story is well-designed and attractive in appearance.

The two German Railway Centenary stamps shown at the foot of the page illustrate another aspect of stamps. The 6pf. shows the first German locomotive, and on the 40pf. stamp is a representation of the most recent product of German railway engineering, a thoroughly modern streamlined train. Each is excellent in itself, but together they have the added interest of illustrating the history of railways in Germany.

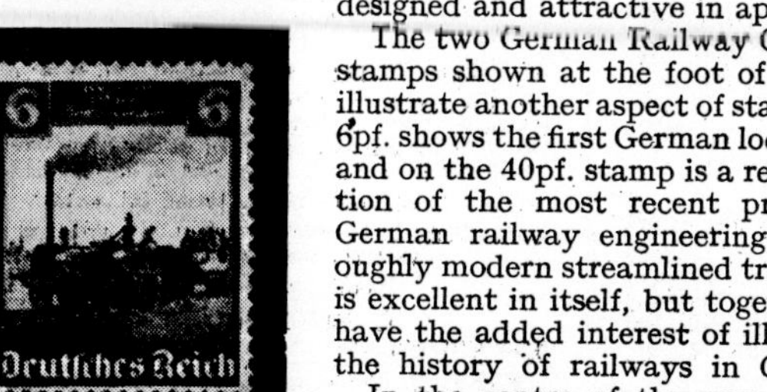

In the centre of the page are two stamps of a different kind, chosen from an immense range of stamps carrying maps, one of the favourite devices of stamp designers who have a special purpose in view. The lower of the two stamps, the 1p. Argentine stamp, rather surprisingly reveals a political dispute between the British and Argentine Governments over the Falkland Islands, in the South Atlantic Ocean. These are a part of the British Empire, but are claimed by the Argentine and in the stamp are shown of the same colour as the territory of that country on the mainland of South America.

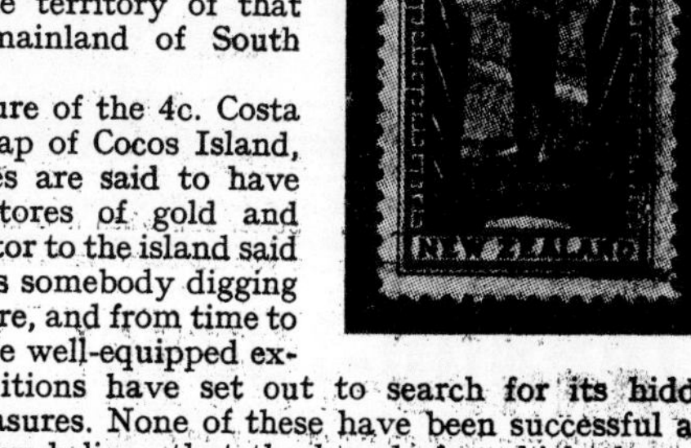

The central feature of the 4c. Costa Rica stamp is a map of Cocos Island, where many pirates are said to have buried immense stores of gold and silver. A recent visitor to the island said that there is always somebody digging there, and from time to time well-equipped expeditions have set out to search for its hidden treasures. None of these have been successful and many believe that the hoards for which they are looking do not really exist, but a glance at this attractive stamp will always conjure up romantic stories of piracy and adventure.

The remaining stamp illustrated this month is of an entirely different type from many of those already referred to. It is one of a series of New Zealand stamps issued with a purpose, and its attractive design is symbolic, showing sunshine, the Key to Health, through a keyhole.

Stories of native life, the development of special industries and important and romantic historical events are among other topics that have been illustrated by means of special stamps and stamp series, and it is scarcely possible to turn to any page of a general stamp collection without finding some of these.

Young collectors usually are greatly interested when they read of the fabulous prices that have been offered for rare stamps. They should not be misled into regarding stamp collecting as a certain means of making money, however. Its greatest reward is the enjoyment to be derived from the stamps themselves. If, in time, the value of the collection increases, that fact should be regarded merely as an incidental happening.

In later articles this winter we shall deal in greater detail with stamps of special interest, and with the problems that often puzzle younger collectors. It is impossible to meet the special requirements of every individual stamp collector in this manner, and any reader who would like to have stamps identified, or would like information of any kind in connection with his hobby, should write to the Editor about it, enclosing any stamps concerned in his query. He will receive a full reply as soon as possible, and any points raised in letters from readers that are likely to be of interest to others will be referred to at greater length in *"M.M."* stamp pages.

The Finest Stamp Album You Ever Saw!

A SEPARATE SPACE FOR EVERY BRITISH EMPIRE POSTAGE STAMP — 384 PAGES — THOUSANDS OF ILLUSTRATIONS

Costs Only 12/6—The NEW IDEAL BRITISH EMPIRE ALBUM

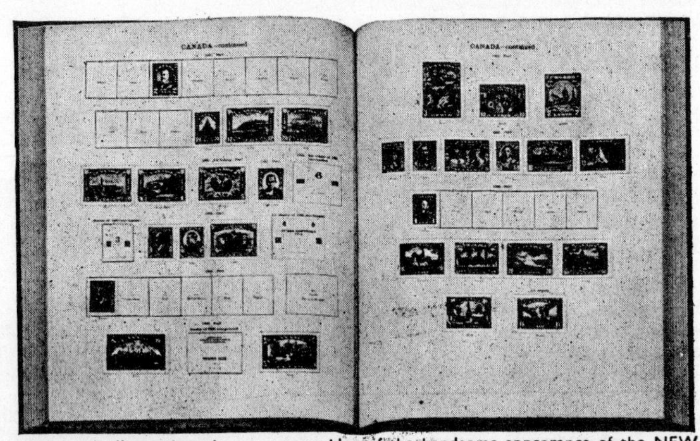

This small illustration gives you some idea of the handsome appearance of the NEW IDEAL—but it looks better still when it is filled with **your** collection.

A wonderful new permanent album (replacing the old "Ideal" volumes) for British Empire postage stamps from 1840 to the end of King George's reign, with the following outstanding features:

(1) Straightforward alphabetical arrangement.
(2) Exclusion of Postage Dues, Officials and minor differences of shade, perforation, etc. (3) Provision of a separate space for each postage stamp, each space containing either a full-size illustration, or details as to colour and value, so that the correct position can be instantaneously found. (4) Strong and handsome cloth binding, well guarded.

Get this album for Christmas and find a new zest in your collecting.

ORDINARY EDITION: 12s. 6d.
Post U.K. 8d., abroad wgt. 5 lb.

INTERLEAVED EDITION: 17s. 6d.
Post. U.K. 9d., abroad wgt. 6 lb.

Two Foreign Countries volumes also in preparation —WRITE TO-DAY FOR FULL PARTICULARS TO

STANLEY GIBBONS LIMITED
Dept. S.15, 391 STRAND, LONDON, W.C.2

TANNOU-TOUVA! TANNOU-TOUVA!!

This month you have an opportunity to secure the magnificent △ Pictorial of Tannou-Touva. It is being presented with a host of other New issues and Pictorials such as **MONGOLIA**, beautiful stamp, Perak new issue, **NIGERIA**, depicting Tin Dredger at work, **TRINIDAD**, view of the first Boca. **CEYLON** 2c. and 6c. with views of Rubber Tapping and Colombo Harbour, Luxemburg, Spain and Suriname (new issues). **ALL FREE AND POST FREE** to applicants requesting approvals.

THE UNIVERSITY STAMP CO., 1, PLANTATION ROAD, OXFORD

IMPROVED

THE "MYSTIC" PACKET

1000 UNKNOWN UNUSUAL UNSORTED 1/6

(Over 200 diff. guaranteed.)

Stamps on paper, etc. Just as received from Convents, Missions, Banks, etc. Guaranteed unpicked. Chance of a **FIND** in every lot. Send to-day for your treasure hunt to-morrow. 3 for **4/3**, 6 for **8/-**. **Abroad 1/9** pkt. **FREE!** 25 Br. Cols. including the new reign issues to approval applicants. Enclose postage. Overseas 3d. Also **FREE EXCHANGE.**

ASTLEY & CO.
(M), LOWHILL, WOLVERHAMPTON

WAR

Just eighteen years ago the World War of 1914-1918 finished. This terrible War caused many special issues of stamps to be made and during this month we are giving **FREE** a selection of these scarce items. We are calling it the 'War' packet and it includes **AUSTRALIA** (Anzac landing at Gallipoli, Whitehall Cenotaph); **BELGIUM** ('Tin Hat' and German Occupation issues); **CANADA** (War Tax); **CEYLON** (1c. War Stamp sur. on 5c.); **HUNGARY** (1915 surcharge for Widows and Orphans and 1916 War Charity depicting Soldiers in action); **JAMAICA** (War Stamp ovp.); **JUGO SLAVIA**; **NEWFOUNDLAND** (War Memorial); **NEW ZEALAND** (Victory and Peace comm.); **PALESTINE** (Occupied Enemy Territories ovpd.); **RUSSIA** (Northern Army); **TURKEY** (Soldiers off to the front), and **UKRAINE.** While stocks last, we will send this historic collection absolutely **FREE** to all genuine applicants for one of our famous 'Grey' booklets of stamps on approval who enclose 2d. for post, etc.

WINDSOR STAMP CO. (Dept. M), 59, LEE ROAD, BLACKHEATH, S.E.3.

HONG-KONG JUBILEE PACKET

Contains 7 Large **JUBILEE** Pictorials, from **HONG-KONG, SOUTH AFRICA, CEYLON, BR. GUIANA, Australia, India** and **Canada;** Also **Large AIR MAIL** Pictorials from **CUBA, PARAGUAY** and **CHILE**, a fine **New Liberia, TRIANGULAR AIR MAIL;** Large **ABYSSINIAN** Provisional, surcharged in Addis Ababa; Hindenburg **Mourning** **Fine** set of 5 **HONG-KONG** (K.G.); **Belgian Congo;** Large **BR. NYASALAND** Pictorial; **Scarce ST. VINCENT;** China **Sun Yat Sen,** etc. **ALL** for 1/- only!! (Postage 1½d. extra.) Purchasers asking for **BARGAIN** approvals will receive 2 **Large SPANISH AIR MAILS FREE.**

THE PUKKA STAMP CO., 27, NORMANDY AVENUE, BARNET.

MORE BARGAINS.

3 **ABYSSINIA.** Italian Colony Issue ... **8d.**
6 **LIBERIA** Air Mail Commem. Triangles **1/4**
25 **BRITISH COLONIALS,** Mint New Issues **1/9**
8 **NORTHERN RHODESIA,** ½d.-1/- used **1/-**
14 **SOUTH AFRICA** Pictorials, ½d.-1/- ... **8d.**
7 **KENYA,** 1c.-50c., Used, **1/-; 6** (without 30c.) **9d.**
9 **CEYLON** K.G. Pictorials, 2c.-30c. used **1/-**
100 **PERSIA 2/9;** 100 **FRENCH COLONIALS 1/9**
JUBILEES (Colonials), 15 at **1/6;** 20 at **2/-**
Cash with order—Postage extra.

T. R. Hughes, 'Ibis Cottage,' Long Park, Amersham.

BRITISH COLONIAL PICTORIAL PACKET FREE!

This packet contains stamps from **Bermuda, Cayman Islands, Ceylon, Nigeria, St. Lucia,** etc. All unused. Send postcard for cheap approvals. Prices ½d. upwards. Postage paid both ways. All applications received before noon will be despatched same day.

T. F. WILLIAMS
7, ISLINGTON ROAD, TOWCESTER, NORTHANTS.

Four Different Iraq free to applicants for ½d. approvals.—Cox, 14, Broadmead Avenue, Worcester Park.

SEND FOR OUR

"ZOOLOGICAL" PACKET

Containing a selection of 45 Foreign and British Colonial Stamps, much better than those usually found in packets of this class, including the following pictorials: **Kenya** (Cranes), **South Africa** (Springbok), **Tchad** (Panther), **Turkey** (Wolf), **Poland** (Eagle), **Madagascar** (Zebus), **Cameroons** (Cattle), **Australia** (Sheep), **Hungary** (Turul) also (Eagle), **Fr. Indo-China** (Ox), **Barbados** (Sea-Horses), **Finland** (Lion), **Epirus** (Eagle), **W. Australia** (Swan), **New Zealand** (Kiwi) also (Fantail), **Mauritania** (Oxen), **Fed. Malay States** (Tiger), **Sweden** (Lion). **Price 6d.** Ask for approval sheets and receive **Andorra** pictorials **Free.**

BRETT & CO.,
201, Uxbridge Road, West Ealing, London, W.13.

FREE! 8 New Zealand 1915-29 K.G., ½d. to 1/-. Request approvals. 25% discount. Enclose 2d. postage. Special bargains for beginners—Stanley Gibbons Album, holds 3,000 stamps. Illustrated. 7½d. 100 different stamps 5½d.—A. R. Dickie, Dept. M., 23, Winscombe Crescent, Ealing, W.5.

---

50 DIFFERENT STAMPS FREE, ask for 4 a 1d. Approvals.—Adams, 100, Banbury Road, Oxford.

He Who Hesitates is Lost

All George V current colonials will very shortly be obsolete. Don't leave it until it is too late. Here's your chance to get them before they become scarce Buy an Empire Packet, guaranteed to contain only unsorted British Colonials sent out exactly as received from Banks, Trading Stations, and other Outposts of the Empire.

An Empire Packet is the cheapest and best way to fil up the gaps in your British Colonial Collection includes Silver Jubilees, Commemoratives, New and Obsolete Issues, and heaps of other attractive stamps 100 for 1/-; 250, 2/-; 500, 3/9; 1,000, 7/3.

All Post Free (Abroad 3d. extra).

I am giving to all purchasers of 3/9 and over a Queen Victoria Labuan stamp cat 2/6.

Remit by Postal Order only.

K. HUMPHRIES (Dept. M.),
East Wittering Road, East Wittering, Chichester, Sussex

FREE. 40 Zoological Stamps to applicants for our superior Approvals. Good discount and bonus.—M Riley, 10, Stricklands Road, Stowmarket, Suffolk

---

For other stamp advertisements see pages 666, 670 and xxxi

Stamp Gossip

and Notes on New Issues

Music on a Stamp

Two very striking designs have been used for the Brazilian stamps issued to commemorate the centenary of the birth of Carlos Gomes, composer of the Brazilian National Anthem, *"Il Guarany."*

The design shown on this page, and used for the two 700r. values, includes a fragment of the original manuscript for *"Il Guarany."*

There are also two 300r. values showing a medallion bust of the composer, the medallion being surrounded by the inscription *"Brasil Correio 1836-1936 Centenario de Carlos Gomes."*

Algerian Pictorials

A newly issued set of 26 Algerian stamps forms a pictorial presentation of life and scenery in that part of Northern Africa.

We illustrate the 1f. 25 value, showing the Admiralty Buildings and Penon Lighthouse. This design also was used on the 10c., 50c., and 5f. values. The remaining designs are as follows: 1c., 65c. and 2f. 25, a Halt in the Sahara; 3c., 90c. and 2f., L'Arc de Triomphe, Mzab; 5c., 30c., and 1f. 75, Lambese, Ghardaia; 15c., 40c. and 20f. Marabout, Touggourt; 25c., 1f. and 3f. 50 El Kebir Mosque, Algiers.

All the foregoing stamps have horizontal designs. The following are vertical: 2c., 75c., 1f.50 and 10f. Colomb Bechar-Oued; 20c., 45c. and 3f., Moslem Cemetery, Tlemcen.

Mobile Post Office

In recent years the British Post Office has been a model of enthusiastic enterprise. Its latest innovation is a mobile Post Office consisting of a motor van that can be despatched to race meetings, agricultural shows and other outdoor gatherings where postal facilities are necessities. The van contains the full equipment of an ordinary post office including telephone kiosks.

South Australian Centenary

This month we are able to reproduce the design of the South Australian Centenary commemorative stamp to which we referred in our *"Stamp Gossip"* notes in the August *"M.M."*

The Oregon Trail

The United States have issued a special 3c. stamp, illustrated on this page, to mark the centenary of the State of Oregon. The design shows a map on which the Oregon Trail is indicated.

The Oregon Trail is the most famous of all the great roads of America leading from the east to the west. It was the route from St. Louis to the fur country of Oregon and was first travelled over by white men in 1811. Later the covered wagons of settlers went in a constant stream along the road, and in the border panels of the stamp there are representations of a settler's wagon and of a mounted redskin, typifying the constant struggle that went on between the settlers and the Indians in those early days.

The completion of the railway across the United States in 1869 led to the decline of the famous trail, but even to-day there are places in the Western States where grooves worn by wagon wheels may be seen on the prairie.

N.Z. Commemoratives

To celebrate the holding of the 1936 Congress of the British Empire Chambers of Commerce in Wellington, New Zealand issued a special series of five commemorative stamps on 1st October. The stamps were to remain on sale for one month only.

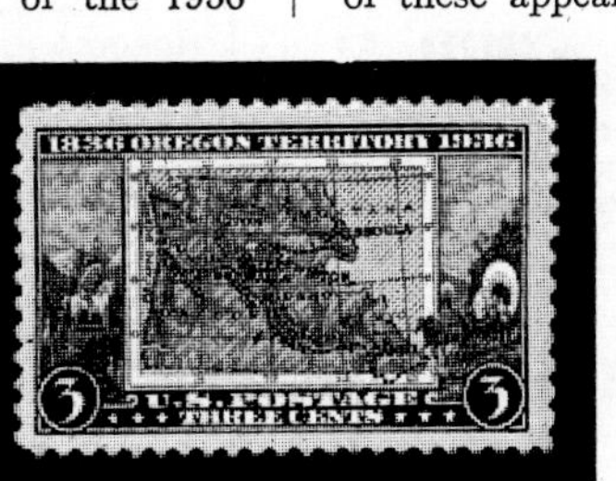

The stamps were of the same size as the New Zealand Silver Jubilee issues and presented striking designs typifying various N.Z. industries. Each of the designs shows a subsidiary vignette in the top left corner and, beneath, a panel containing the inscription "Chamber of Commer e Empire Conference, Wellington, Oct. 1936." The designs were as follows: ½d., the wool industry. A motor lorry loaded with bales of wool, with a sheep shearer at work in the top left corner. 1d., the butter industry. Churning and packing butter, and the head of a prize cow. 2½d., sheep farming. A sheep farm and the head of a prize sheep. 4d., fruit farming. Apple grading and packing and a portrait of a typical farmer's daughter. 6d., shipping. A dockside scene, with a medallion representation of an old-time trade ship in the top left corner.

Each of the five designs is beautifully produced and the set comprises a most striking issue.

Australian stamp illustration:

We thank Stanley Gibbons Ltd. for their courtesy in loaning the stamps from which the illustrations on this page have been made.

French Air Mail Stamps

We illustrate on this page one of the two designs issued by France to commemorate the 100th crossing of the South Atlantic by French airmail service. The design shows a mail aeroplane flying over an old time caravel, and bears the inscription *"Conquête Aerienne de l'Atlantique Sud."*

The other stamp is a 10f. value in horizontal format showing an aeroplane in front of a hemisphere on which the route of the trans-Atlantic air mail service is indicated.

At the moment France has two newly issued 50f. air stamps in current use. One of these appeared on 29th July in small format, and carried the design illustrated on the *"Stamp Gossip"* page of our issue of June last; the other, a larger stamp using the same design surrounded by a network of wavy lines that give it the appearance of a tiny bank-note, was issued on 10th July.

The explanation is that the smaller stamp was actually printed last December, but the Minister of Posts would not agree to its being placed on sale, as he considered the word "Francs" in the design was barely readable. In order to use up the printed stock he proposed surcharging it for use as a 10f. or 15f. provisional, and meanwhile had the stamp prepared in the larger size.

Following the change of Government, the new Minister of Posts decided that the original stamp was suitable for issue, and it was released in spite of the fact that the 50f. "bank-note" stamp was already on sale.

The Bermuda Pictorials

Some little commotion has been caused by the discovery that the yacht illustrated on the 2d. value of the Bermuda pictorial issue, to which we referred in our *"Stamp Gossip"* notes for July last, is the American-built yacht *"Lusie"* owned by a Mr. B. S. Cunningham, of Connecticut, and not Mr. K. Trimmingham's *"Viking,"* the winner of the Prince of Wales Cup, that it had been intended to depict. How the mistake occurred has not yet been explained, but the unfortunate error really signifies nothing, as the object of the stamp was simply to emphasise the importance of Bermuda as a yachting centre.

For other stamp advertisements see pages 666, 668 and xxxi

"MODERN INVENTIONS" VOTING CONTEST

We are living in an age of invention, and almost every year sees developments in all branches of science and engineering. These enable us to travel about more quickly and comfortably, add to our pleasures, and generally make life easier and brighter, and many of them have led to the foundation of great new industries.

The present century has been rich in inventions of all kinds, and readers of the "*M.M.*" are in a particularly good position to appreciate their value and importance, for they are kept in touch with the work of inventors by articles appearing in its pages. This month therefore we are giving them the opportunity of expressing their opinions on the value of the chief of the outstanding inventions of modern times.

In the panel in the centre of this page is a list of eight of the more important inventions that have appeared since the beginning of the century. Each competitor is invited to state A, which of these, in his opinion, has brought the greatest benefit with it, and B, his idea of the order of importance in which the votes of all the competitors will place them. Those taking part in the competition should note that it is not necessary to place the invention of their choice in the first part of the contest at the head of the list to be given under B, unless of course they think it will be favoured by more entrants than any other.

1. **Automatic Traffic Signals**
2. **Broadcasting**
3. **Stainless Steel**
4. **Talking Pictures**
5. **Television**
6. **Unbreakable Glass**
7. **The Gyro Compass**
8. **The Pre-selector Gear-Box**

Entries should be written on postcards and competitors should refer to the items by their numbers in the accompanying list. Prizes of Meccano products to the value of 21/–, 15/–, 10/6 and 5/– respectively will be awarded to the four entries that come nearest to the general opinion of the relative importance of the eight inventions named, as revealed by the voting. In addition there will be several consolation prizes.

Entries should be addressed to "Modern Inventions" Voting Contest, "Meccano Magazine," Binns Road, Liverpool 13," and must reach this office not later than 30th November.

A separate set of prizes will be reserved for entries from Overseas readers, those living outside Great Britain, Ireland and the Channel Islands. Closing date, 27th February.

A Humorous School Story

In our school days, much as we loved the long sunny days on the playing fields and mourned their passing, the winter term was the one we enjoyed most of all. Somehow it seemed productive of more real fun than all the rest of the year put together.

We do not know whether the winter term is still the same prolific source of fun, but we are quite sure that every one of our readers has encountered in the present school term at least one funny incident worth recounting. We therefore offer prizes this month for the best humorous true story of an incident at school this term.

The prizes will consist of Meccano products—this description covers all articles featured in the current Meccano and Hornby Train catalogue—to the value of 21/–, 15/–, 10/6 and 5/– respectively.

Entries, which should be written on one side of the paper only, should be as brief as possible and should be addressed to "School Story, Meccano Magazine, Binns Road, Liverpool 13." A specially late closing date, Friday, 1st January, has been appointed and this will give readers the opportunity to send in the best story of the term.

A separate set of prizes will be available for Overseas readers whose entries must arrive not later than 27th February, 1937.

November Drawing Contest

This month we announce the second of the monthly drawing and painting competitions that we are holding throughout the winter. Competitors may select any subject they like for their entries in this contest and full details of the conditions and the prizes offered were given on page 607 of our October issue.

Entries in this month's competition must be addressed "November Drawing Contest, Meccano Magazine, Binns Road, Liverpool 13." Closing date, 30th November. Overseas, 27th February, 1937.

The Overseas section now having closed, we give above the solution to the May Crossword Puzzle.

COMPETITION RESULTS

September Photo Contest.—The September Photo Contest, the last of the 1936 season, was easily the most popular of the series, and the entries in it were of such outstanding merit that the prize list has been extended and includes nine more awards than were originally offered. Five of these are special prizes of 7/6 each in the A Section, in which the entry was not only the heaviest in number but also the most impressive in quality that we have ever received in a "*M.M.*" photographic contest.

First Prizes: Section A, D. H. WARNER (Richmond); Section B, D. EARLE (Wembley Park, Middx.). Second Prizes: Section A, C. P. SILVER (Exeter); Section B, D. A. WOODS (Bexhill). Special Prizes: E. H. COLES (London, W.11); D. MORLEY DAVIES (Maesteg); D. FEAR (Taunton); B. HOMER (Birmingham, 8); C. M. SINCLAIR (Glasgow, S.W.2). Consolation Prizes: T. BROOKS (Halifax, Yorks.); D. PHAYNE (Wokingham); MISS G. PENNETHORNE (Haywards Heath); E. M. READ (Edinburgh 10).

September "Point Words" Contest.—1. W. G. B. EDMONDS (London, S.W.16). 2. C. J. B. BRETT (Great Coates, Lincs.). 3. K. FORD (Waleswood). 4. L. W. CHITTY (London, S.W.20).

OVERSEAS

June Photo Contest.—First Prizes: Section A, B. PARKER (Montreal); Section B, D. N. MUNRO (Sydney). Second Prizes: Section A, P. NATH ROY (Calcutta); Section B, S. P. WALLACE (Capetown).

June Doublets Contest.—1. E. K. SHORROCK (Vancouver, B.C.). 2. R. RUSSELL (Whangarei, N.Z.). 3. D. TOLKOWSKY (Tel-Aviv, Palestine). 4. R. BURBERY (Christchurch, N.Z. 1).

NOTICE TO INTENDING COMPETITORS: Entrants to drawing and similar competitions are asked to note that unsuccessful entries can only be returned if a stamped addressed cover is sent with the entry.

The Newfoundland Banksmen

Deep Water Fishing from Dories

By D. G. Lyon

THE schooners operating from Lunenburg, Nova Scotia, the home of Canadian deep water fishermen, show many differences in design and equipment when compared with English vessels engaged in similar work. This is chiefly due to the greater distance of the fishing grounds from their home port, and the extension of their activities into fresh water fishing in lakes and rivers during the winter months. Although practically all these fishing schooners have deserted sail, and instead use Diesel engines, they are still built with attractive lines and carry tall tapering spars.

One of the largest schooners of the Lunenburg fleet is the *"E.F.Zwicker,"* which is shown in our illustration. Native woods were used in the construction of the hull of this vessel, which has a length of 142 ft. and a beam of 27 ft. 6 in., with a hold 11 ft. in depth. The keel and frames are of hard woods, with planking of birch and beech and white pine decks, and a point of constructional interest is the use of trenail fastenings in the planking instead of the less expensive galvanised bolts used by English builders. There are comfortable quarters for the captain and crew of 24 men, and a galley of ample dimensions is provided, for the schooner may remain at sea as long as two months in one trip, during which time the cook has to prepare 100 meals a day for hungry men.

The "E.F.Zwicker," a Diesel-engined schooner from Lunenburg, Nova Scotia, that is employed in line fishing on the Grand Banks of Newfoundland in summer and on lakes and in rivers in winter.

Deep water fishing is generally carried on in the neighbourhood of the Grand Banks of Newfoundland. This region, where the Gulf Stream meets the cold current flowing down the coast of Labrador, is one of the world's great fisheries, for an abundance of the plankton, or plant life, on which fish feed, is carried down into it from the open Polar waters to the north. Line fishing is employed, and most of the fish caught are those frequenting the sea bottom, among them being cod, halibut and haddock.

When a schooner arrives on the Banks, small boats called dories are launched, each manned by two fishermen who proceed to set lines. The *"E.F.Zwicker"* has 11 dories nested on her deck. From each dory a main line, with short lines carrying hooks branching off at every 5 ft., is anchored to the sea bed and marked with buoys. A single crew may set up to two miles of line equipped with 2,000 to 3,000 hooks, and altogether in one setting there may be a total of more than 20 miles of line and 30,000 baited hooks. Hauling in takes several hours, especially if the tide is strong or the sea rough, and fishing in this manner is not without its dangers, for if fog comes down there may be difficulty in picking up all the dories that have been sent out.

The centre section of the schooner, 43 ft. in length, is reserved for the catch. During the fresh fishing season ballast is carried to a depth of 5 ft., leaving only 6 ft. of hold for storage; and to ensure prime quality this is again divided into small bins by vertical and horizontal partitions so that the greatest depth to which fish can be piled on each other is only 3 ft. More than 100,000 lb. of fresh fish can be iced in these compartments. The tables on which the crew bait their lines are arranged along the centre of the hold, but if fish are plentiful this section also is utilised for storage. The crew then give up their comfortable working quarters and bait their lines on deck, as their fathers and grandfathers had to do in the old-time schooners of the Newfoundland Banks fishing fleets.

During salt fishing in summer, all gear is handled on deck and ballast is removed. This gives an increased carrying capacity, enabling the crew to pull 1,000,000 lb. of fish out of the sea, salt them and dress them in a single trip. The largest catch of fresh fish ever landed at Halifax was discharged there recently by the *"E.F.Zwicker,"* and amounted to 210,000 lb.

The main engine of the vessel is a 240 b.h.p. five-cylinder Diesel of British make, and is controlled by a single hand wheel so that it can be started ahead or astern at any desired speed from a quarter to full. The manoeuvre from full ahead to full astern, or vice versa, can be carried out in from five to seven seconds. The fuel tanks have a capacity of 3,880 gallons, allowing a range of 3,500 miles at the full speed of 10½ knots.

Power for essential services such as electric lighting throughout the vessel, and a supply of sea water under pressure for washing down decks and hold, are supplied by auxiliary machinery. The pumps and lighting dynamo are driven by a small 5 b.h.p. Diesel engine, and the dynamo charges 16 storage batteries of 13 plates each that supply current to operate the vessel's wireless as well as the lighting system.

Hamley's Model Aero Contest

Those of our readers who are interested in the construction of scale model aeroplanes will be pleased to know that Hamley Bros. Ltd. have decided to hold an annual competition for model aeroplane construction. The first of these competitions is now in progress and will remain open until 31st December next.

Competitors are required to construct models from one or another of certain specified construction kits, and challenge trophies and cash prizes will be awarded to the successful entrants.

Full details of the competition and entry forms may be obtained from Hamley Bros Ltd., 200-202, Regent Street, London, W.1.

New Cycle Accessories

Bluemel Bros. Ltd., are again to the fore with additions to their famous range of lightweight cycle accessories. Several of these, and particularly an extra-long rear mudguard, will satisfy a long-felt want among riders of lightweight cycles.

The new mudguard is both efficient and neat in appearance. It is similar in many ways to standard Bluemel lightweight guards, but is thirteen inches longer and is secured in place on the machine by three, instead of two, stays. Its additional length will be a great boon to club riders in checking back-flung water and mud.

Lightness and freedom from rattle are outstanding features of another new rearguard, known as the "Duplex," in which the rear reflector actually forms part of the guard. This idea not only saves weight but also eliminates the crevices that seem to invite mud deposits on the average guard with a separate reflector.

Bluemel Bros. Ltd., Wolston, Nr. Coventry, will send full details of these new accessories to any "*M.M.*" reader who is interested.

The Ceuta-Tetuan Railway

By J. S. Scruton

The railway between Ceuta and Tetuan, in northern Africa, is about 20 miles long, and is single track except at wayside stations, where there are passing loops. At Ceuta the line runs along the whole length of the main quay, so that passengers disembarking from touring liners can board trains immediately if they wish to visit Tetuan. The locomotives in use on the line are old American ones. The coaches are of the standard length, and have no glass in the windows, and are comfortable to ride in although they have wooden seats, as the track is remarkably good.

The five wayside stations have no platforms, but only small neat buildings painted in green and white. A chain is the only guard provided at road crossings. This is rather surprising, for the roads are used by many cars and trains run frequently. The chain at each crossing is in charge of an official, who usually seems to spend the remainder of his time with his goats, which graze by the lineside. The signals, of which there are very few, are all worked by hand.

Waiting for the starter's signal in a Hornby Speed Boat Race at Westgate-on-Sea. The starter is Mr. Clay Thomas, of the "Sea-Mews" Concert Party, who organised the races. Photograph by Mr. E. Owen.

A City of Cyclists

By B. Unne

This summer saw the realisation of what had long been one of my ambitions—a visit to a foreign country. I travelled by cargo boat from Hull to Copenhagen and was fortunate in having ideal weather for my sea voyage of about 600 miles, which occupied about 50 hours.

On my first view of the city I was impressed by the number of high ornamental towers and mellow green domes that are to be seen. Most of these are on churches or public buildings, and have galleries on them at different levels.

A channel that divides the city into two parts is crossed by lift bridges carrying footpaths and roadways with tramcar tracks. These bridges can be raised and lowered very rapidly, and this is necessary because of the large amount of traffic on the waterway. During the short periods when road traffic is stopped, long lines of cyclists assemble on both sides of the bridges. Almost everybody in Copenhagen seems to ride a bicycle, and in proportion to its population the city has more cyclists than anywhere else in the world.

As a capital city and port, Copenhagen is a natural centre of the culture and commercial life of Denmark. No activity is more picturesque than the local fishing industry, which seems to penetrate to the very doors of the houses through the many small canals and waterways that run right into the city.

Steelstrand Expanders

The National "Keep Fit" campaign that is now gathering momentum, gives special interest to the advertising of Herbert Terry and Sons' Steelstrand Expanders that appears in our current issue. Messrs. Terry, who have specialised in the manufacture of all types of springs for more than 80 years, have developed an attractive series of spring exercises for boys and adults.

Our advertisers have sent to us a range of the exercise charts that are packed with each of their exercisers, and we have been interested to see the beneficial series of exercises that can be carried out.

Herbert Terry and Sons Ltd., Redditch, will be pleased to send full details of their exercisers to any reader who writes mentioning the "*M.M.*"

Bond's 1937 Catalogue

The latest edition of Bond's General Catalogue contains a mine of information of help to all who are interested in model making and model railways. The catalogue, in addition to listing hosts of complete models, mechanisms, castings, fittings, gears, machine and hand tools, marine engine and electric pumps, includes a new 14-page feature of hints and tips on model making and the maintenance of a model workshop. The catalogue can be obtained price 6d., including postage, from Bonds O'Euston Road Ltd., 254, Euston Road, London, N.W.1.

A LITTLE BIT INDEPENDENT

Thompson: "There goes the most independent man I ever met; he takes orders from nobody."
Jones: "Who is he?"
Thompson: "A commercial traveller."

* * * * *

Repair Man (having pushed door button repeatedly without response): "Fancy ringin' me up to come and mend the doorbell and then goin' out!"

* * * * *

Here lies the body of William Jay,
Who died maintaining the right of way;
He was right, dead right, as he sped along,
But he's just as dead as if he was wrong.

* * * * *

Madame: "Liza, why didn't you sweep the cobwebs down?"
Liza: "Why, ma'am, I thought it was part of the radio."

* * * * *

Tom: "I've had a most exciting time with my car."
Dick: "Yes?"
Tom: "I bought a carburetter that saved 50 per cent. of petrol, an induction gadget that saved 30 per cent., and a sparking plug that saved 25 per cent., and after I had gone 10 miles my petrol tank was overflowing!"

* * * * *

Mrs. I. Swank: "My first husband was a man of distinguished bearing. He was known as 'Thompson of the Guards.'"
Mrs. Sar. Castic: "Indeed! Goods or passenger?"

* * * * *

First Workman: "It's a new thing for the foreman to praise me."
Second Workman: "What did he say?"
First Workman: "He says me work's been very perfunctory."

* * * * *

"Are you a doctor?" asked a young lady, stepping into a chemist's shop.
"No," replied the youth behind the counter. "I'm just the fizzician."

* * * * *

An enthusiastic supporter of the local football team arrived at the ground one day and saw a load of bricks there. He approached the club secretary and asked: "Wouldn't half-bricks have been better?"
"Half-bricks?" replied the secretary. "We couldn't build a pavilion with half-bricks."
"Oh, I see," said the supporter. "I thought they were for the referee."

* * * * *

Mother: "Did you put 'Love to Grandpa and Auntie Dorothy' at the end?"
Betty: "Yes, Mummie."
Mother: "You didn't forget Uncle John, Cousin Bill, and the others?"
Betty: "No, I just put 'and Co. Ltd.,' for them."

* * * * *

A WARM WELCOME

Servant (to lion tamer in cage): "That grocer is here again demanding payment of his bill."
Lion Tamer: "Send him in."

A SUITABLE INMATE

Fat Gent.: "Am I all right for the Zoo?"
Johnnie: "You look all right to me, mister, but I'm not running the place."

* * * * *

House-owner: "I'm glad you stopped complaining about the plaster falling."
Tenant: "It's all down now."

* * * * *

NOTHING TO HOWL ABOUT

A bricklayer was working on a scaffold when suddenly a brick slipped from his hand and dropped on to the head of his workmate, who was mixing mortar below. The unfortunate man started dancing about and groaning in his agony. The bricklayer stared down with contempt in his eyes.
"Come, come!" he yelled at last. "It can't have hurt as much as that, man. Why, it wasn't on your head half a second!"

* * * * *

Boss (to office boy who is late): "You should have been here at nine o'clock."
Office Boy: "Why, wot 'appened?"

* * * * *

The lecturer paused a moment, and then remarked: "Of course you all know what a corpuscle is like."
"Most of us do," remarked the chairman, "but you'd better explain it for the benefit of those who have never been inside one."

* * * * *

Father: "Son, can't you cut down on your college expenses? You know you are almost ruining the family."
Son: "Well, I might possibly do without any books."

* * * * *

"If a Chinaman went to a dentist to have a tooth drawn, what time would it be?"
"Give it up."
"It would be half past two, of course."
"How do you make that out?"
"Half past two is two-thirty, isn't it?"

* * * * *

"Why does your wife always close her eyes when she is singing?"
"Well, you see, she reaches such high notes that she becomes giddy."

* * * * *

Johnson had just returned from a trip abroad and was making his report to his employer. Presently his expenses-sheet came under review. "What is this large item? "asked the employer.
"That's my hotel bill, sir," replied Johnson.
"Huh! Don't buy any more hotels next time you go abroad."

* * * * *

Perks: "You say he's very sure of himself?"
Jinks: "I'll say he is. He does crossword puzzles with a pen."

* * * * *

Small voice from pantry: "Mummy, you know when it says break six eggs?"
Mother: "Yes, darling."
Small Voice: "Well, I've done that."

A SAFE RETREAT

First Dentist: "What do you think of my new offices? You see, the fire escape here makes my waiting room one of the safest rooms in the building."
Second Dentist: "Safe nothing! I lost twelve patients that way."

* * * * *

Dr. Kiddem: "How did that diagnosis machine work you had installed in your surgery?"
Dr. Killum: "Oh, I treated a man for three months because that old machine said he had yellow jaundice."
Dr. Kiddem: "And was it correct?"
Dr. Killum: "No, he was a Chinaman."

* * * * *

Teacher: "Now Bobby, tell me the names of some stars."
Bobby: "Football or film, miss?"

* * * * *

"Doctor, how am I?" quavered the patient. "Oh, you're much better," replied the medico, breezily, "but I wouldn't start reading any serial stories if I were you."

* * * * *

Belle: "I've taken three lessons in French from a correspondence school."
Agnes: "Could you carry on a conversation with a Frenchman?"
Belle: "Oh, no, but I could talk to anybody else who had had three lessons."

* * * * *

Employer: "Rather strange, Jones, that your uncle should be buried on Cup Final day."
Jones: "Yes, good old uncle—a sportsman to the end."

* * * * *

An Irishman got a job at a railway station. When the first train came in, however, he forgot the name of the station, so he called out: "Here ye are for where ye are going. All in there for here, come out."

* * * * *

Tutcham: "I asked you for a loan of twenty pounds! This is only ten."
Smith: "I know it is, but that's the fairest way; you lose ten and I lose ten."

* * * * *

Teacher: "Now, if I subtract 25 from 37, what's the difference?"
Jimmy: "That's what I say. Who cares?"

* * * * *

A man went up to a railway porter at one of our big railway stations and said: "There are six clocks in this place, and they are all different."
"Well sir," said the porter, "if they were all the same one would do!"

* * * * *

HE ASKED FOR IT

The old farmer had watched the motorist working on his secondhand car for about an hour.
"What are you looking at?" asked the motorist. "Is this the first motor car you ever saw?"
"No," was the dry reply, "but it's very much like it."

HORNBY ROLLING STOCK

GAUGE O

The Hornby Series includes a splendid range of realistic Rolling Stock. Each item is fitted with patented and exclusive automatic couplings, a special feature that places it in a class entirely of its own. There are Pullman Cars, Passenger Coaches, Guards' Vans, Tipping Wagons, Lumber Wagons, and many other types, all beautifully finished.

An attractive selection of Hornby Rolling Stock is illustrated and described on this page. Ask your dealer for a complete price list.

No. 1 BANANA VAN
An attractive model, finished in yellow and red. Price 2/9

***No. 2 PASSENGER COACH**
Suitable for 2-ft. radius rails only. First-third or Brake-third. Price 7/6

MEAT VAN
This is a very realistic model. Available lettered L.M.S. only. Price 1/9

No. 1 MILK TRAFFIC VAN
Fitted with sliding doors. Complete with milk cans. Price 2/11

BARREL WAGON
This is another interesting model of a type of wagon used in France and other European countries. Price 2/6

No. 1 TIMBER WAGON
Beautifully enamelled in yellow and red. Price 1/6

No. 1 SIDE TIPPING WAGON
Excellent design and finish. Lettered "Robert Hudson Ltd." Price 2/-

FIBRE WAGON
This is an interesting model of a type of wagon used in France and other European countries. Price 1/3

***OPEN WAGON "B"**
Similar to Hornby Wagon No. 1 but fitted with centre tarpaulin-supporting rail. Price 2/-

***GUNPOWDER VAN**
Finished in red. With opening doors. Price 2/9

No. 1 LUMBER WAGON
Fitted with bolsters and stanchions for log transport. Price 1/6

No. 2 SALOON COACH
Realistic in design and beautifully finished. Two types are available: L.N.E.R. (as illustrated) enamelled brown, and L.M.S. enamelled maroon. Suitable for 2-ft. radius rails only. Price 9/6

WINE WAGON DOUBLE BARREL
An attractive model artistically enamelled in red and green. Price 4/6

SNOW PLOUGH
With revolving plough. Price 3/9

COVERED WAGON (French Type)
This wagon is fitted with frame and sheet. Lettered "Nord" Price 2/6

BITUMEN TANK WAGON "COLAS"
Finished in blue. Price 3/6

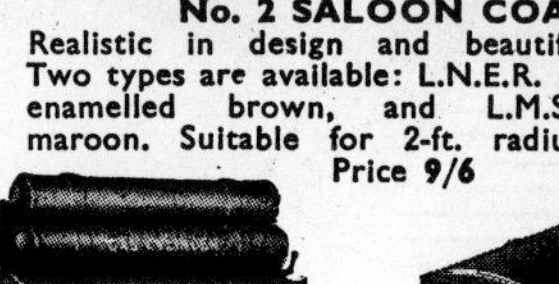

GAS CYLINDER WAGON Price 1/11

***FLAT TRUCK**
Complete with Container. Price 2/-

CONTAINERS
L.M.S.R. (Furniture), L.N.E.R. (Goods), G.W.R. (Insulated), S.R. (Ventilated). Price 6d. each

No. 1 PETROL TANK WAGON "B.P."
Finished in yellow. Price 2/-

OIL TANK WAGON "MOBILOIL"
Finished in battleship grey. Price 2/-

COAL WAGON
Similar to Hornby Wagon No. 1. Fitted with an embossed representation of coal. Price 2/3

No. 1 ROTARY TIPPING WAGON
Finished in orange. Price 2/6

***FLAT TRUCK**
Without Cable Drum. Price 1/6
Complete with Cable Drum. Price 1/9

CABLE DRUM
(British Insulated Cables Ltd.). Price 3d.

***REFRIGERATOR VAN**
Beautifully enamelled. Fitted with opening doors. Price 2/9

CHOCOLATE VAN "CADBURY'S"
This van is beautifully enamelled in blue with white roof. Price 2/9

No. 2 TIMBER WAGON
Beautifully enamelled in green and red. Suitable for 2-ft. radius rails only. Price 2/6

No. 2 SPECIAL PULLMAN COACH
As supplied with No. 2 Special and No. 3 Pullman Train Sets. This splendid coach is perfect in detail and finish. Suitable for 2-ft. radius rails only. Price 13/-

FISH VAN
This is a distinctive model. Available lettered N.E. only. Price 1/9

No. 0 MILK TRAFFIC VAN
An attractive model. Available lettered G.W. only. Price 1/9

**In L.M.S., N.E., G.W. or S.R. lettering.*

Manufactured by MECCANO LTD., BINNS ROAD, LIVERPOOL 13

NEXT MONTH: ON THE FOOTPLATE OF "THE ROYAL SCOT." PUBLISHING DATE: 1st JANUARY

MECCANO MAGAZINE

Editorial Office:
Binns Road, Liverpool 13
England

Vol. XXI. No. 12
December, 1936

With the Editor

Christmas Greetings

When this issue reaches my readers Christmas will still be some three weeks away, but as the next issue will be dated 1937 I now wish all my readers A Very Merry Christmas. And as the *"M.M."* is always passed round every household it enters, I extend my good wishes also to fathers and mothers, big brothers, and the uncles who come in so handy at Christmas as providers of good things!

Last December I got into serious trouble. "Spanner," "Tommy Dodd" and the rest of my staff—including "Pawl" the office boy—invaded my sanctum in a state of wrathful indignation and demanded to know why their good wishes also had not been conveyed to readers! This year, therefore, I add their good wishes to mine, and I take the opportunity of saying that no editor ever had more loyal and enthusiastic helpers.

The Editor and all his staff wish every reader a very Merry Christmas

Plans for the Future

All readers will be interested in my plans for the new volume that starts next month. I am not making any big changes because my correspondence shows that the present general plan of the *"M.M."* is definitely popular. But while thus retaining the main features I have in hand schemes for extensions and improvements that will add greatly to the interest of the Magazine. I will deal in more detail with these schemes next month, but I may mention now that in response to widespread requests I propose to extend very considerably the series of articles under the heading *"How Things Are Made,"* to include a wide variety of products. Other articles will deal with the life story of a famous motor car, a famous motor cycle, a famous bicycle, and so on. A new series of splendidly-illustrated articles on the production of various metals and minerals will be commenced, and the recently-introduced feature *"Something to Think About,"* which has proved even more popular than I anticipated, will be continued.

In short, the *"Meccano Magazine"* next year will be more interesting than ever before.

A Serial Story

Now I come to one feature of outstanding importance. In the past the *"M.M."* has been entirely without fiction, with the exception of a very occasional short story. Next year I am going to break new ground by commencing a serial story. But this is by no means an ordinary story. It does not deal with school life or wild and sensational adventures; it is the story of a boy's life, from the time when he leaves school to take up an apprenticeship in a large engineering works, to the day when, as a thoroughly-qualified engineer, he becomes a partner in a London firm of consulting engineers. The story is written by a well-known engineer who adopts a pen name for the occasion; and it gives a graphic description of the boy's everyday life as he passes from shop to shop in the works in the course of his engineering training. So far as I am aware no such story has ever been written, and I can assure my readers that they will find it fascinating and packed with really thrilling incidents.

Tributes to Mr. Frank Hornby

I felt sure that many readers would write to express their regret at the passing of Mr. Frank Hornby, but I was not prepared for the immense number of letters that did in fact reach me. These came from all parts of the world and were written in many different languages. It was particularly interesting to learn that the news of Mr. Hornby's death was announced by radio in Holland, and from a correspondent in that country I have received a copy of a song commemorating his life's work that was broadcast in the programme of the A.V.R.O., or Alg. Vereen. Radio Omroep, from the Hilversum station. This song, composed by Mr. H. Hollander, sketches the merits of Meccano, the foremost of all toys for boys, and expresses the gratitude to its inventor of generations of boys whose lives have been made happier by playing with Meccano outfits, and who owe their success in their careers to the interest thus aroused.

Full Speed Ahead!

Boiler and Engine Rooms of the "Queen Mary"

By George Steel

THE *"Queen Mary"* has now won the Blue Riband of the Atlantic and is hailed as the fastest and most wonderful liner in service. Every day news items concerning the great ship's movements are flashed across the world; the decorations and magnificent proportions of her public rooms have been amply described and illustrated; and the swimming pools, squash racket courts, shopping centre, children's playgrounds and other marvels of this floating city have all received their fair share of attention. Of all the myriad features that go to make up this wonder vessel, however, the most important have been seen by few of her passengers. These are the boiler and engine rooms, where the men on whom every knot depends work unceasingly. The engineers and firemen must perform their tasks efficiently before the propellers of the giant liner can turn half a revolution, or her huge rudder can move through a single degree. They also hold the key to practically every necessity and luxury of life on board; and a cook cannot even switch on an electric stove unless they have first supplied the necessary power.

Looking aft in the after engine room of the "Queen Mary." We are indebted to the courtesy of John Brown and Company Limited, for the illustrations to this article.

Unremitting watchfulness throughout every minute of the 24 hours of every day is absolutely essential to the smooth and safe running of the *"Queen Mary,"* and the responsibility of the Chief Engineer and his staff is truly colossal. Engineer officers in charge never leave their posts when the engines are running, and at sea they are on duty for four hours, with eight hours off duty, all round the clock. If an engineer is allotted the four hours from eight p.m. to midnight he will also be on duty from eight a.m. to 12 o'clock midday during the daytime. In port the Chief Engineer arranges hours and duties for his engineer officers as may be necessary or convenient, and the regular sea watches of "four on and eight off" are not maintained.

When on duty every engineer officer and electrician has a thousand and one tasks to carry out. To begin with the four propellers are driven by four sets of turbines, each set consisting of four turbines coupled to a huge totally enclosed gear wheel. These turbines require a host of smaller auxiliary machines to enable them to run, and the temporary failure of any one of these could lead to, if not a serious breakdown, at least a very appreciable drop in speed. To prevent this, almost all of these auxiliaries are duplicated, and in an emergency a standby set would be immediately brought into use.

The forced lubrication system, which is of such paramount importance, requires a total of 12 powerful pumps, three to each set of turbines, and each capable of delivering 36,000 gallons of oil per hour. To the average motorist who thinks of lubricating oil in pints and quarts, or perhaps occasionally buys a five-gallon drum, this will give some idea of the enormous quantities required to operate these modern symbols of marine power and speed. In addition, the motorist need not worry overmuch about the cooling of his lubricating oil. The *"Queen Mary"* requires two oil-coolers for each set of turbines, however, and a centrifugal pump with a capacity of 1,850 gallons per minute supplies cooling water to each pair.

Four sets of strainers are installed between the forced lubrication pumps and the oil-coolers to trap and collect every particle of dirt and sediment. Turning a handle is all that is necessary to completely remove any accumulation of foreign matter in the lubricating oil, and this can be done without shutting off the supply for a moment. All the turbine bearings, thrust blocks, gear case pinions and other moving parts must be supplied with a continuous flow of cool oil under high pressure, and many of the delivery pipes are so arranged that the valves can be padlocked in the open position, to prevent any possibility of stoppage of the oil supply to vital parts. In addition, every bearing is fitted with a temperature gauge, and readings are constantly being taken and checked.

The *"Queen Mary's"* engine room is literally a forest of gauges. Hundreds of tell-tale dials are visible everywhere, telling at a glance their vital stories of pressure or temperature. Some work only a foot or so from their bases; others are arranged for remote reading, so that the engineers on watch at the control stations, maybe 100 ft. or so away, are constantly in touch with conditions in the engine and boiler-rooms at any moment throughout the 24 hours.

The control stations themselves present a bewildering

yet most imposing array of shining wheels, levers, valves, clusters of gauges and indicators of various types. Prominent among them are the huge hand-wheels, nearly a yard in diameter, which control the admission of steam to the high-pressure turbines. Secondary sets of wheels admit steam to the astern turbines. The astern master valve cannot be opened until the ahead valve is closed, but astern steam is frequently admitted while the turbines may be still moving ahead.

The electric telegraphs, which transmit orders from the bridge, are in positions in which they can easily be seen. Each is fitted with a metallic-sounding gong, and is arranged for instantly repeating the order. Blackboards arranged in convenient positions are used for chalking up each variation and the condition of a multitude of matters, so that each engineer coming on watch can tell at a glance just how things stand, without having to enquire or investigate for himself. A desk is provided in the centre of the control station where particulars of every order from the bridge, with the time and date it was given and other important details, are entered in the engine-room log, in which it is possible to trace the complete history of every voyage at the end of each trip.

The starting platform in the "Queen Mary's" forward engine room.

Standing at the control stations, one is struck with a most uncanny sense of enormous power that seems to vibrate through the very air. Pent-up energy is evident on every side. Power, relentless and terrible, yet absolutely controlled, seems to be the keynote of the *"Queen Mary's"* engine-room. The turbines themselves, their steel covers gleaming dully under the bright lights, seem to be brooding, fretful and watchful, waiting for the touch of human hands to unleash their vast power. White-jacketed steam pipes, some of them thicker than a man's body and others the thickness of one's arm, tell of high-pressure steam. Miles and miles of piping and wiring lead everywhere, the copper pipes shining like gold. All curve and turn out of sight, each one performing its predetermined task, carrying oil, water, steam or electric current to a thousand different places.

The boilers of the "Queen Mary" have white painted steel fronts and, as our illustration shows, the boiler rooms are light and airy.

Even when the main engines are silent, the regular beat of a pump, or the distant muffled hum of the turbo-generators still give one that sense of being in the presence of dormant power, all the more insistent because of the bright lighting and white enamelled steel walls. Brilliant lighting indeed is a feature of the engine-rooms, and there it is hard to realise that one is deep down in the bowels of a ship, well below the water line. There are no dark corners, and every part of the machinery is as visible as if it were in a well-designed modern factory with glass roofing.

This applies also to the boiler-rooms. There are 24 main boilers, all with white painted steel fronts. The steam pipes too are covered with a pure white insulating material to retain heat, and the general effect is one of extreme lightness and airiness. Double-inlet fans to the number of 32 supply air for forced draught. The actual apparatus that sprays the oil fuel under pressure into the furnaces consists of 12 oil-burning units, each comprising an electric rotary pump, duplex suction strainers, discharge strainers, and a heater the purpose of which is to warm up the heavy fuel oil in order to make it thinner and more easily sprayed on to the flames. Four displacement pumps of 100 tons per hour capacity are fitted for transferring the oil fuel from the huge storage tanks to the settling tanks, and oily ballast strainers free bilge and tank water from oil before it is pumped overboard.

The foremost boiler-room is quite separate from those containing the main boilers. It houses three cylindrical boilers supplying superheated steam for the hotel generators, and saturated or ordinary steam for the various ship services. Two air compressors supply 300 cu. ft. of compressed air per minute, while four fans are constantly at work delivering 200,000 cu. ft. of ventilating air per minute to each engine-room. Seven turbo-generators, each with its own condensing and forced lubrication equipment, supply the *"Queen Mary's"* 578 electric motors, which have a total of about 17,818 h.p. They range from the smallest circulating pump motors of $\frac{1}{2}$ h.p. to the 292 h.p. motors operating the anchor and warping gear.

It is essential in a marine steam turbine installation to condense the immense volume of exhaust steam and return it to the boilers in the form of hot water. The *"Queen Mary's"* four main condensers are cooled by sea water circulated through them by eight powerful pumps, each capable of dealing with 25,000 gallons per minute. Water extraction pumps then pass the condensed steam through coolers on its way to the feed pump suction.

New Flying Boats for Imperial Airways

Preparing for the Great Empire Air Scheme

NEXT year promises to be one of the most important in the history of British commercial aviation. Preliminary flights over the North Atlantic route will be carried out, in preparation for a regular service that will connect this country with the air mail systems of Canada and the United States. In addition the great Empire air scheme by which mails in bulk are to be borne from England along the main Empire routes without any extra fee, will come into operation.

Under this scheme passengers will be able to travel to South Africa or Australia without change of aircraft. This will be an immense improvement, as at present air travellers to either of those distant termini have to journey from Paris to Brindisi, on the Mediterranean coast of France, by train, and subsequently have to transfer at several points to aircraft more suitable for the ensuing section of the route. At present the air services along the Empire air routes operate only during the day, and the passengers have to sleep overnight in hotels, or in rest houses established by the company, at the stopping places chosen as the termini of each day's journey. The night flying to be introduced under the new scheme will dispense with this great inconvenience, for the aircraft employed will be equipped with sleeping accommodation.

"Canopus," the first of the 28 Empire flying boats for Imperial Airways, taking off at Rochester. Photographs on this page and the upper one on the opposite page by courtesy of "Flight."

By flying during the night as well as in the day, it will be possible to cover much greater distances at economical speeds than under the present arrangements. It now takes 6½ days to reach Calcutta by air, for instance, but under the new scheme the time will be reduced to four days. A flight from London to Singapore under present schedules takes 8½ days, but it then will be possible in 5½ days. Going further, the air journey from Croydon to Sydney, Australia, will be done in only eight days instead of the 12½ now required. These striking reductions do not represent the ultimate improvement that will be achieved, for schedules will continue to be speeded up progressively as improvements are effected in ground organisation, eventually shortening the flying time by another 1 or 1½ days.

It is for this new scheme that Imperial Airways have under construction a fleet of 28 flying boats and 12 landplanes. In this article we are concerned only with the flying boats, as none of the huge monoplanes, which were referred to briefly in the January 1936 "*Air News*" pages, is yet completed. The flying boats are being produced by the well-known firm of Short Brothers (Rochester and Bedford) Ltd., the builders of the flying boats "*Scipio*" and "*Satyrus*" employed for several years past on the Mediterranean section of the Empire air routes. Up to the present three of the new aircraft, named "*Canopus*," "*Caledonia*" and "*Centaurus*" respectively, have left the stocks. "*Canopus*" completed its test flights in September, and afterward received the luxurious internal equipment. The boat began its career last month, when it was put into service on the Mediterranean section already mentioned. "*Caledonia*," now undergoing test flights, has been selected for experimental long-distance flights that have been planned with a view to obtaining data for actual Atlantic flights. As a preliminary to this important research work it will probably undertake a 2,500-miles flight around the coast of Britain early next year. "*Centaurus*" has also gone into service in the Mediterranean.

This broadside view of the new flying boat shows the deep two-deck hull to advantage.

The exterior views of "*Canopus*" on these pages convey a good idea of the great size of this and the other new Empire flying boats. It is 88 ft. 6 in. in length and is 24 ft. in height from the waterline to the top of the hull, and the wing span is 114 ft. These dimensions show that the machine is slightly larger than the Short "*Scipio*" already mentioned. "*Canopus*" is a high wing monoplane of the cantilever type, that is, the projecting wings are not additionally supported near their tips by any external bracing, and it is of all-metal construction. Structurally the machine differs in many respects from previous Short practice. The "backbone" of each wing is a low "box" spar of almost rectangular cross-section, and the leading and trailing edge portions of the wing are attached to this spar. Landing flaps are fitted along part of the trailing edge of each wing. The petrol tanks are placed inside the wings, and are thus well clear of the passenger quarters in the hull. This isolated and lofty situation minimises the danger of the machine catching fire if ever a forced landing had to be made upon land. A large metal float is suspended in a fixed position beneath each wing and near its tip, by three pairs of struts.

The framework of the massive hull consists of a long series of vertical straight-sided "rings" spaced only a short distance apart and connected by about 50 continuous horizontal stringers. This framework, like that of the wings, is covered externally by metal sheeting. There are two decks in the hull. The foremost compartment of the upper deck is, of course, the cockpit, or "control room" as it is called, with side-by-side seating for the Captain and the First Officer. The curved front wall of the cockpit consists chiefly of a large and almost hemispherical window that provides an exceptionally fine and unobstructed view in all directions except directly behind and straight down. When the flying boat is upon the water, the pilots can observe the surface of the latter up to 15 ft. from the bows, without craning forward. The cockpit is provided with the most modern types of navigational instruments, and includes an automatic pilot and "blind flying" equipment.

Another picture of "Canopus" in the air. The great wing span is very evident.

Immediately behind the cockpit is the wireless operator's cabin, and to the rear of this is a long mail compartment in which about three tons of mail can be stowed. Arrangements have been made for dealing with mail while the boat is in flight, and the ship's clerk has an office in this compartment. The upper deck is continued behind the junction of the wings with the hull, and the rear portion consists of a roomy hold in which the bedding is stored, and a baggage hold to which access is obtained from below through a hatch in the floor. This completes the accommodation on the upper deck.

Inside the blunt nose of "*Canopus*" is a compartment where the mooring ropes and other relative equipment are stored. A gangway at one end of the room leads to the cockpit almost overhead. The second compartment on the lower deck is the Smoking Cabin, which has accommodation for seven passengers during the day and four at night. A little farther back, and separated from the Smoking Cabin by the passageway from the main entrance of the flying boat, is the kitchen, and adjoining it is a gangway leading to the mail compartment and clerk's office on the upper deck. The Midship Cabin is the smallest of the four passenger cabins, and accommodates only three people during the day. When converted into a sleeper at night, however, there is provision for four people, as in the case of the other cabins. It is followed by the largest, or Promenade Cabin, and the After Cabin, which seat eight and six people respectively. The flying boat thus has seating for 24 passengers during the day, and sleeping accommodation for 16 at night. The remaining available space in the stern of the hull is used as a mail, freight and baggage hold.

View of part of the Promenade Cabin, with the After Cabin in the background. Photograph by courtesy of Imperial Airways Ltd.

The interior decoration and fittings of the passenger quarters of the "*Canopus*" make this flying boat the most luxurious air liner in the world. Great care has also been taken in designing the passenger cabins to ensure that they shall be as quiet as possible, and the noise of the powerful aero engines reaches them only as a very low hum. A special heating and ventilating plant enables an ideal temperature to be maintained, and the air to be changed frequently.

"*Canopus*" has four Bristol "Pegasus X" engines, and these are fitted two on each side of the hull in streamlined cowlings that project from the leading edge of the wings. These cowlings have controllable flaps so that the amount of air admitted for cooling the engines can be varied as required. The "Pegasus X" is a 9-cylinder air-cooled and supercharged engine of the radial type, and is so compact that it is only 4 ft. 6 in. in diameter. It can develop 900 h.p., with a total weight of little more than 1 lb. per horsepower. Each engine has nearly 166½ sq. ft. of cooling area, and during a 13½-hours' flight this will dissipate 260 b.h.p. in heat energy, or sufficient to drive an express locomotive from London to Carlisle. Over 70 different kinds of materials are used in building a "Pegasus" engine, and during production the majority of the components are submitted to about 20 different inspections and tests.

The total of 150 "Pegasus" aero engines being produced by the Bristol Aeroplane and Motor Co. Ltd., for the fleet of Empire flying boats, comprises the largest order of its kind ever placed for British air line equipment.

The high standard of comfort and efficiency attained in the "*Canopus*" will be repeated in the other boats.

Homeward Bound

Up the Thames on a Cunard White Star Liner

(*concluded*)

By O. S. Nock, B.Sc., D.I.C.

At the point where I broke off last month the North Goodwin Light was abeam, and now I come to the progress of the "*Georgic*" up the Thames. This vessel, and her sister ship the "*Britannic*," are the largest ships that ever come into the Thames. From the Elbow buoy, which lies just off the North Foreland, until the mouth of the river is reached at the Nore lightship, it is just like threading one's way through a maze, and with a vessel of such size consummate skill is needed on the part of the Pilot. The channels are not merely shallow, in places the navigable waterway is less than 50 yards wide. Then, although a ship responds instantly to the helm, some time elapses before she is on her new course, and that time depends on the currents and the wind. Throughout this highly intricate stage the Pilot must anticipate the courses that will be required, for even the smallest misjudgment might easily run the ship aground.

For me it was a wonderfully fascinating experience. Earlier in the evening, when one of the officers was explaining the estuary, I had made a rough sketch map showing the channels and the whereabouts of sand banks, and now it added greatly to the enjoyment of the trip to be able to pick out the various lights. Their very names add a rare touch of distinction—South Edinburgh buoy; Knock John; the Knob Bell; Shivering Sand. The conditions were very favourable, for on a clear and brilliant night such as this the buoys can be picked out more easily than in broad daylight.

The Cunard White Star motor liner "Georgic." Photograph by courtesy of Cunard White Star Limited.

After passing the Elbow we turned a little to the north-west and headed for the Tongue lightship. I noticed that Mr. Anderson was giving all the courses in degrees rather than by compass points such as "North-west by north ¾ north"; the Thames estuary requires very fine adjustments of the helm, and his voice came "Three-five-five," then "Three-five-oh," and so on as we veered round. The sea was now fairly alight with flashing buoys. On our port bow there lay the Shingles, a group of pebble ridges where seals play at low tide, and our course lay just to the north-east of them through the South Edinburgh channel. It is the sharp turn round the N.E. Shingles buoy that is the trickiest piece of all, for here the ship has to be pulled round through an angle of about 45 degrees in a very short distance. The Shingles lie almost in a direct line between Margate and Clacton-on-Sea, and almost due east of Shoeburyness.

This entry to the London river, and the approach to Southampton, are a very striking contrast to the conditions on the other side of the Atlantic. At one time the approach to New York was by just such another winding course, but, with the characteristic American boldness that has produced skyscrapers and other marvellous feats of engineering, a deep waterway was blasted out of the solid rock, and now the biggest ships can sail straight into port up the famous Ambrose channel. West of the Shingles our course became more direct. We were steaming now in a south-westerly direction down the Knob channel and then, passing through the Oaze Deep, we gradually veered round on to a course almost due west, and at last were heading straight for the mouth of the river.

It was not yet 5 a.m. Mist was coming with approaching dawn; the lights of the ship threw a soft ghostly sheen on to the water, and as yet there was not a glimmer of daylight. We were not due at Tilbury landing stage till 9 a.m. The arrival times of these ships have to be arranged to suit the tides, for it is only during the hour before and after high water that they can be got into dock. As a consequence they berth at Tilbury on a flowing tide, and of course must be moored with their bows pointing downstream. It was just about slack water as we approached the Nore lightship, and if we had gone straight up the river there would not have been sufficient depth to swing the ship round off Gravesend. So the Captain decided to anchor for a while, off the Nore. It was just 5.30 a.m. and daylight was gradually coming. A cold greenish light was spreading over the sky from the north-east, but the stars still twinkled overhead and the mast lights shone brightly. The telegraph bell rang sharply; then the voice of one of the officers speaking down to the engine-room—"The ship is at anchor. We shall be getting under way again at 7.15 a.m." I went below to my cabin and snatched an hour's sleep.

* * *

At 7 o'clock the sun was up, and the whole estuary was bathed in a soft rosy light. On our port bow not half a mile away was the Nore lightship, but beyond that there was nothing to be seen, for the mist reduced visibility to less than a mile. There was hardly a breath of wind, and the only sound was that of heavy grating as the windlass hauled up the anchor chain. It was a little after 7.15 when we were under way. We might have been in the open sea, yet Southend was barely three miles away to the north, and right opposite, somewhere in the mist, lay Sheerness at the mouth of the Medway.

From the Nore there is a dredged channel that leads into Sea Reach but the buoys are as much as a mile apart and we were literally feeling our way up this morning, for in the grey light that followed sunrise it was most difficult to sight the buoys. Here too we first encountered the Thames barges. These broad, blunt-nosed craft are most picturesque with their rich brown sails, and are usually so well laden that their hulls are only just above the water. Tacking across to catch what wind there is, they slip out of the mist and plough their way right across the dredged channel. At last some land was discernible, the flat marshes of Canvey Island just to the west of Southend. Near the river bank the land was a rather wan greenish-yellow in the filtered sunlight, and inland it quickly faded into the mist. The water was a foaming muddy green. But by the time we passed Thames Haven, and the Cliffe marshes stretched far along the south bank, the sun was getting some power. The river could be seen ahead curving round in the first of its sharp bends, and the hills lying to the south of Gravesend were looking very beautiful in the haze of distance.

There is almost a right-angled turn to the south when entering The Lower Hope, as this next reach is called, and all the time the river is getting narrower. We could see Gravesend now, some four miles away across the marshes, and the river making another meandering curve in order to get there. The yellow funnels of Orient liners lying in Tilbury docks gleamed in the sunshine, and as we turned into Gravesend Reach the river was alive with shipping. Several merchantmen were lying up on the south side, there was a beautiful schooner, an old man o' war now used as a training ship, and more sailing barges picking their way amongst all.

Now the pilot cutter was putting out to meet us, and three tugs with full steam up were manœuvring into position. The River Pilot's job is done on arrival off Gravesend, and his place is taken by a Mud Pilot for the final stage up to the London docks. Mr. Anderson remained on the bridge till the very last minute; then, with the "*Georgic*" practically at a standstill, and the cutter alongside, it seemed only a matter of seconds after he had gone before the Mud Pilot was up aloft and had taken over. One look over the port wing of the bridge, and he had summed up the whole position. In a trice his directions were following each other like lightning—"Half back, Port; full ahead Starboard."—"Stop Port"—"Half ahead Starboard"—"Hard a'Port"—"Full ahead Starboard" . . . With two tugs at the bow and one at the stern the ship was being slowly swung round in the river, and all the time the Pilot's orders and the acknowledging rings on the telegraph came with never flagging rapidity. The helm had now been taken by the Dock Pilot, who also had come on board at Gravesend. So, at a little after 9 o'clock, we were alongside Tilbury landing stage.

The "Georgic" about to enter the lock leading to King George V Dock, London. The entrance gates are just opening as the tug pulls the bows of the liner round.

But although business was quickly finished, and we were ready to start up the river at 10.30, we should have to have gone at a dead slow pace in order not to arrive at the dock too early. We could not remain alongside, as a Union-Castle liner was expected from South Africa, and so, with the tugs still in attendance, we anchored out in the river till noon. We were just leaving the berth when the "Castle" boat was sighted coming up The Lower Hope, and as we lay out in the river we had a magnificent view of her as she came up, swung, and berthed at Tilbury. It was the "*Dunvegan Castle*," one of the company's very latest motorships, and her beautiful lines called forth much admiration from the officers of the "*Georgic.*" The sun was now brilliant, and with her pale mauve hull, cream superstructure, and the characteristic red and black funnel, she certainly looked glorious.

Looking aft from the top of the forward funnel as the "Georgic" passed up the Thames just above Northfleet.

The hour before noon passed very quickly; ships were passing all the time, a big P. and O. liner was stealthily moving berth over in Tilbury docks, and then, just before the hour, the Pilot was on the bridge again, as dynamic as ever. "Rise and shine!" he sang out to the tug skippers below; the telegraph bell rang once more, and soon the "*Georgic*" was under way. I witnessed the last stage of the voyage from a truly marvellous point of vantage—the top of the forward funnel! But it isn't a funnel as such, at all; the whole of the exhaust from the engines passes up the after funnel, and the forward one accommodates the wireless cabin and the officers' smoke room.

As we set off up the river two tugs went on ahead to be ready to help us to get into dock. The wind was coming from the south-west now, and the belching chimneys of Northfleet cement works were spreading a veil of thick white smoke over the whole scene. Just beyond here the river swings abruptly to the north and then as sharply back again in a V-shaped bend round the Swanscombe marshes. Once clear of the cement works the atmosphere became brilliantly clear, though the sky was a hard steely blue and big banks of thundery cumulus cloud were coming up. The town of Dartford lay to the south now, lying some distance back in a fold of the hills, and ahead of us on the north bank was Purfleet. The scene is quite countrified here, and Purfleet especially is a pretty little village with some picturesque houses on the waterfront. Almost opposite is the mouth of the River Darent. There is another V-shaped loop, to the south this time, through Erith. As we rounded the bend, the heights of Shooters Hill and Bexley Heath lay across the marshes to the south, and right ahead the now overcast sky blended with a far flung greyness that hung across almost the whole horizon; beneath that pall was London.

Of the many approaches to this, the mightiest city on earth, none can compare with the river for sheer majesty. By air it is singularly unimpressive, and on land, whether by road or rail, one quickly becomes lost in a labyrinth of suburbs. But the Thames is an artery of commerce the like of which exists nowhere else; one can feel the nearness of a great city, this grimy meandering waterway could not but lead to something tremendous. Two gigantic electric pylons towered one on each bank; framed in the gap between them was the amazing Ford motor works; Woolwich lay to the south-east, East Ham to the north, and out of the grey smoky distance some details of dockland could now be distinguished. Although the scene before us was a merest fraction of the whole, sailing up on a tall ship like the "*Georgic*" gives an extraordinarily vivid impression of London's vastness.

And now at last journey's end was in sight. Excepting Tilbury, the King George V Dock to which we were bound is the easternmost limit of the Port of London, and as we passed Beckton Gas Works, that very extensive and remarkably equipped factory of the Gas, Light and Coke Company, the docks were revealed behind, a veritable forest of masts and funnels. Yet this was only the merest fringe of the port. Two more tugs were waiting at the dock entrance, steel hawsers were attached fore and aft, and the "*Georgic*" was slowly swung round towards the lock gates. The wind was now catching us broadside, and when we moved slowly up towards the entrance the ship drifted to starboard and the tug at the bow looked like getting jammed against the wall; but very gradually, by judicious pulling and pushing, the ship was coaxed smoothly into the lock.

One of the busiest highways hereabouts crosses over the inner gates by means of a lifting bascule bridge. The road leads to the Woolwich ferry, and motor lorries, bicycles and red London buses were passing over in a continuous stream. Beyond the bridge, in the Albert Dock alongside, and westward as far as the eye could see, were ships—ships from every corner of the globe, ranging from passenger liners like the big P. and O. "*Naldera*" to every kind of cargo boat; and their funnels formed a perfect kaleidoscope. Then, when all was ready for us to enter, this dockland highway staged a very good imitation of a West End traffic jam right across the bascule bridge, just to give us a real London welcome as it were! This event called forth some exceedingly pithy comments from the bridge of the "*Georgic,*" where "Harry," the Dock Pilot, had taken over, but it is all part of the day's work. Another characteristic that must seem odd to a stranger is the way in which barges are allowed to drift about in the docks and river, blocking the fairway alike for collier or Transatlantic liner. And sure enough, when the bridge was at last lifted and we were entering the dock, two heavily laden coal barges were lying right in front of our berth. "Harry" was beside himself. "Go on," he bawled to one of the tug skippers, "Get 'em out 'er the way!" The tug nosed the barges aside, and then the "*Georgic*" was manœuvred into position abreast of the berth. Two tugs, one at the bow and one at the stern, pushed us broadside up to the quay, and in this quietly impressive way the voyage ended.

Swamps Turned Into Farmland

Dredging Creeks and Rivers

THERE are many parts of England where the land is flat and low-lying. Areas of this kind are found in parts of Yorkshire and Somerset, and particularly in the Fen district in East Anglia. where much of the land is actually below sea level. It is almost impossible for surface water to drain away naturally from land of this kind, which readily becomes flooded after heavy rain, and for centuries artificial channels have been dug in order to drain it and to make it fit for growing crops of various kinds. Where the land is below sea level it has been necessary to lift the water into drainage canals in order to carry it away to the sea. In the Fens windmill pumps were formerly used for this purpose, and numbers of these are still to be seen there. In modern times large electrical and Diesel driven dumping stations have been established, and many of these have to be brought hurriedly into operation in times of heavy rainfall.

Important drainage works were carried out 300 years ago by Cornelius Vermuyden, a far-sighted Dutch engineer who came to this country in 1621. Vermuyden drained the Hatfield and Bedford levels, two great swamp areas near the mouth of the Ouse and in the Fens respectively. He also carried out similar schemes in other parts of the country that brought thousands of acres into cultivation that otherwise would have remained water-logged swamps. Many of the systems he devised are still in active operation.

A Priestman Floating Grab Dredger at work on the River Don, in Yorkshire. The grab has a capacity of a cubic yard and the machine dredges 75 cu. yds. per hour. On the bank of the river is a 35-ton Priestman "Lion" Diesel Dragline mounted on creeper tracks. Photograph by courtesy of Priestman Bros. Ltd., Hull.

In later years drainage work was neglected for long periods, with the result that much land was becoming useless for farming purposes. In 1930 an Act was passed giving power to the Ministry of Agriculture to form Catchment Boards to deal with the drainage areas of all the main rivers, and very soon efforts to improve the artificial channels and natural rivers were begun. Work of this kind involves dredging and excavating on a scale far beyond the capacity of hand labour. Many of the operations indeed would have been impossible if suitable machinery had not been available.

The illustration on this page shows two suitable types of dredger working on the River Don, Yorkshire, in the area of the Ouse (Yorks.) Catchment Board. In the foreground is a floating grab dredger, and beyond it on the river bank can be seen a dragline mounted on creeper tracks.

The floating grab dredger in the illustration can be used either to dredge material from the bed of a river, or to rake out or clean small creeks. When it is employed for dredging, the material is deposited on the banks, or is loaded into barges to be towed away for disposal elsewhere. Sometimes it is spread over an adjacent field, but more frequently it is used to form flood banks to prevent the river from overflowing after heavy rains or extremely high tides.

This floating dredger has many unusual features designed to suit the peculiar conditions in which it has to work. Its height had to be kept down to 10 ft. 6 in. because of a bridge under which it had to pass. Its overall length could not exceed 53 ft. 6 in., and its draft had to be limited to 4 ft. 6 in. and its beam to 14 ft. to enable it to pass through certain locks in the area in which it works. An ingenious scheme was devised by Priestman Bros Ltd., Hull, the makers of the dredger, in order to give it the necessary stability when at work. This consists of attaching floats to the sides of the vessel, and these of course are taken away when the dredger has to pass through locks that restrict its size.

The vessel is operated by means of a Diesel engine. Its jib is 50 ft. long and the grab picks up about ½ cu. yd. of mud. When the material scooped up from the bottom of the river is being discharged into barges, however, a section of the jib is taken out, shortening it to about 30 ft. A larger grab holding a cu. yd. is used with the shorter jib.

Raking, or cleaning out small creeks, is an interesting operation for which this floating dredger is specially designed. The creeks are found on the tidal portion of the Ouse, where they are formed by surface water draining into the main river from small channels on agricultural land in the immediate neighbourhood. The raking is done from about half flood to half ebb tide, that is when the water is deepest.

The rake is dropped over the stern in the creek and the vessel drawn towards the middle of the river by means of a rope which has been previously made fast to an anchor. As the rake, which is attached to the vessel, is hauled, it scoops the mud down the creek into mid-stream to be carried away by the tide. A winch and wire ropes are used for drawing the vessel backwards and forwards, the power for this operation being derived from the main propelling engine.

Where the banks are suitable, draglines mounted on creeper tracks are usually employed for deepening and widening rivers or drainage channels. One of these machines is seen at work in the background of our illustration. The bucket is dropped or thrown out into the river, and is then drawn towards the machine by means of a wire rope. It scoops up the mud as it is hauled along and when full it is hoisted by a second rope and the jib is slewed, when an ingenious mechanism tips the bucket and discharges the material. This generally is used to form a flood bank.

Formerly machines of this type were driven by steam, but of late years the practice has been to use Diesel engines. The excavators themselves vary according to the nature of the work, and jibs up to 70 ft. in length are used where wide rivers have to be dredged.

Machining a 58-Ton Forging

How Slots are Cut in a Giant Rotor

OUR cover this month shows a planing machine cutting slots in the rotor of a large alternator. The purpose of the slots is to accommodate copper coils or windings through which the current generated passes.

The production of a huge rotor of this kind is work of great engineering interest. The one shown on our cover was made from a single solid forging weighing 58 tons, and when it was finished its weight was still 43 tons, 15 tons of metal having been removed in the machining operations, including slot cutting. Its total length, including the shaft, is 30 ft. and the cylindrical portion alone is 14 ft. long.

This rotor forms part of a 50,000 kVA turbo-alternator that is driven by a steam turbine of 55,000 h.p. and generates current at 6,600 v. When it is in service every particle on its main cylindrical surface is whirled round at a speed of 240 m.p.h., or four miles a minute. This gives rise to powerful centrifugal forces, and for this reason it is necessary to subject every rotor of this kind to careful inspection and testing. In one of these tests a hole is bored right through the centre of the rotor and its shaft from end to end, so that the metal in its interior can be inspected by means of a special instrument that is a combination of telescope, a periscope and a microscope. In addition pieces of the material employed in making it are tested in order to make sure that the steel of which it consists is of the quality required. Finally the rotor, complete with its coils and the rings that retain their ends, is run at a speed 20 per cent. above that at which it will rotate when it is actually set to work. This is what is known as the over-speed test. It is carried out in a special testing house with heavy concrete walls and ramparts of sandbags, in order to prevent damage if the rotor should give way under the immense forces acting upon it. This of course is scarcely likely, as an ample margin of strength is allowed, but only when a rotor has passed satisfactorily through this and other tests is it put into operation.

Packing the copper coils or windings in the slots of the rotor of a turbo-alternator. Photograph by courtesy of Metropolitan-Vickers Electrical Co. Ltd.

The machine on which the slots for the windings are cut has a table 26 ft. long and 10 ft. wide. This weighs 30 tons and when the rotor is in position on it, the total weight is equal to that of five double-decked tramcars. In spite of this huge weight, an electric motor controlled by automatic switch gear drives the table forward at a speed of from 30 ft. to 60 ft. a minute when the cutting tools are at work, and returns it in readiness for a new cut at twice this speed. Cone-shaped rollers rotating in oil baths in the slides serve to lubricate the moving parts by carrying oil to the bearing surfaces of the table. Two of these rollers, one on each of the slides, can be seen on our cover.

The tools that cut out the slots are carried in holders that can be mounted on the side columns of the machine or on the cross slide, as required. They are capable of being set at any angle, and a small motor is mounted on the top of the cross beam in order to enable them to be moved easily and quickly. The tools cut through the metal at high speed, and a stream of cooling liquid, consisting of an emulsion of oil and water, is poured over their edges in order to prevent them from becoming too hot. This liquid can be seen running out of the slots that are being machined.

An interesting feature is the manner in which the rotor is turned round when one pair of slots have been machined, and another pair are to be cut. The operator slackens off the tie bolts that hold the work rigidly on the table, and turns the rotor through the necessary angle by means of screw jacks. The tools are then set to cut the new slots radially, that is along lines radiating from the centre line of the rotor shaft, and the tie bolts are again tightened before beginning operations. The greatest accuracy is necessary in work of this kind, for the coils or windings to be placed in the slot must not move when the rotor is running at high speed in the finished alternator. The rotor indeed is so carefully balanced that it will remain stationary in any position when the shaft is supported on two horizontal parallel knife edges, and it runs at full speed without vibration of any kind.

Even larger rotors than that shown on our cover are now made. A notable example is that of the 105,000 kW turbo alternator installed by the Metropolitan-Vickers Electrical Co. Ltd. in the Battersea Power Station. This is the largest generating unit in Europe, and was described and illustrated in the *"M.M."* for August of this year. The rotor of this alternator weighs 82 tons, and is made in three pieces held together by means of links of high tensile steel shrunk into position after being expanded by heating.

Puzzle Your Sharp-Eyed Friends

Home Made Magic that Needs no Skill

By Norman Hunter (From Maskelyne's Mysteries)

FIRST of all, let me repeat the advice I have given previously—try every trick over in private before you attempt to perform it in front of an audience. You cannot expect to do even the easiest trick smoothly and convincingly first time, but once you have got the hang of it by a few rehearsals, you will find you can do it more or less without thinking about it. This leaves you free to devote your attention to making the trick amusing and bringing out its chief points.

Now for the first mystery.

DEMON DICE

The dice are large ones, about two or three inches square. Two are black with white spots, and one is white with black spots. You stack them on an inverted glass tumbler, with the white die in the centre, and throw over them a large handkerchief. Then "Hey presto!" The audience see a mysterious movement of the dice under the covering handkerchief. When the handkerchief is whisked off there are only the two black dice left; the white one has vanished from between them. You then stroll over to a hat, which you have previously shown empty, turn it over, and out falls the missing white die.

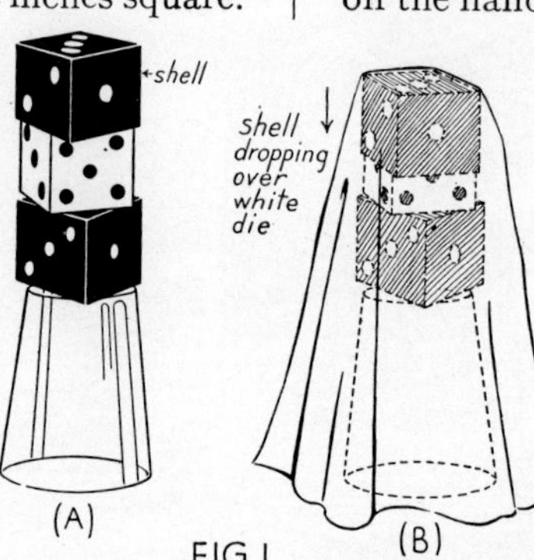

FIG. 1

How it is done. Of the three dice that the audience see, one of the black ones is a hollow sham. Actually it is a cardboard case that fits snugly but easily over the white die. You can make the whole apparatus easily enough. All you need are a few wooden cubes, children's picture blocks will do nicely; some thin cardboard and some paper. Cover one of the cubes with black paper and stick white paper discs on it to represent a die. Cover two more cubes with white paper and stick black spots on them. Then make a cardboard case to fit over the cubes, and cover this with black paper and spot it to look like a black die.

You will notice that you have one solid black die, one shell black die, and two solid white dice. You will also require a good-sized coloured handkerchief, a hat, and a glass tumbler.

To start with, one of the white dice is inside the shell, so that there appear to be two black and one white dice. In handling them you will of course be careful not to expose the white side of the black shell. Show the hat empty and casually put the three dice inside, saying that this is a very compact trick because all the apparatus can be carried in your hat. Now take the dice out again; first the solid black die, then the solid white die, and finally the black shell, leaving the second white die in the hat. The audience have seen you put three dice into the hat and take three dice out of it, so that they naturally conclude that the hat is empty.

FIG. 2 — Red Ace; Red Ace; Right hand takes away bottom half of pack.

Put the hat on one side and stack the dice on an inverted glass. The solid black goes at the bottom, then the white, and the black shell, open side downward, is placed on top. The dice are not stacked quite square, otherwise the shell would slide down over the white die. The shell is placed slightly cornerwise on the white die.

Now throw the handkerchief over the dice. Hold one corner of the handkerchief, and give the top die, which is the shell, a tap with one finger. Tap it just hard enough to square it up with the white die. The black shell will at once slide down over the white die, so that when you draw off the handkerchief the white die has seemingly vanished from between the two black ones. Turn over the hat and the duplicate white die falls out.

Fig. 1 will explain the way in which the shell drops over the white die.

Here is a very simple, but exceedingly baffling card trick.

THE AFFECTIONATE ACES

From a pack of cards you remove the four aces. The pack may be examined to prove that no duplicate aces remain hidden in it. The red aces are placed one at the top of the pack and one on the bottom, while the two black aces are put in the middle of the pack.

"The aces in a pack are very fond of one another," you remark. "See how they come together again when separated!" You show that the black aces are still in the centre of the pack, but the red aces are now with them, having left their positions on the top and bottom of the pack.

How it is done. At first glance this sounds like a trick that needs exceedingly twiddly fingers, but actually it is quite easy.

When you put the red aces on the top and the bottom of the pack, this part of the trick is quite genuine. The deceptive part comes when you cut the pack for the black aces to be placed in the centre. Instead of lifting the top half off the pack to make the cut, you lift the bottom half. To do this you must grip a packet of cards at the bottom of the pack and draw them out sideways. The audience, not knowing what you are going to do, will not suspect that the pack has been cut in any but a straightforward manner. Now have the two black aces placed on the presumed lower half of the pack. As this is really the top half of the pack, the black aces go on top of the red ace that is already there. When you bring the two halves of the pack together, the other red ace, which is on the bottom of the other packet, comes immediately above the black aces. Thus the four aces are brought together in the centre of the pack, and the trick is done

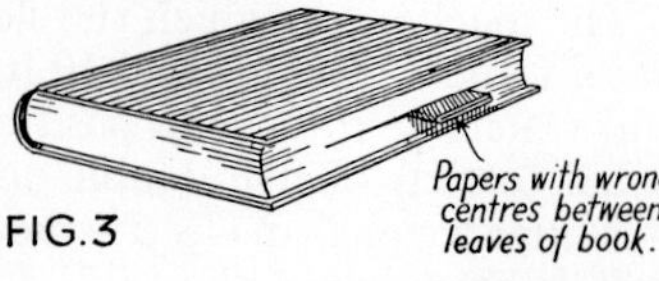

FIG. 3

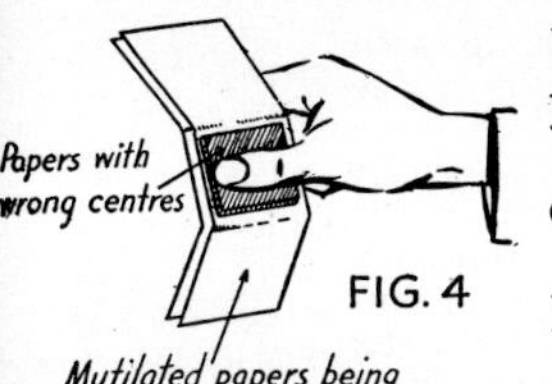

Mutilated papers being folded forward.

before the audience realise that you have started to do it.

Reference to Fig. 2 will make everything clear.

A good trick to follow this I will call

THE TRAVELLING ACES

The four aces are shown and placed openly on top of the pack, which is left in full view while an envelope is shown to be empty and sealed. This envelope is then enclosed in another slightly larger, which in turn goes into a third larger still. Each envelope is marked by a member of the audience.

You now take the pack and deal off cards from the top. The aces are no longer there, and when the three envelopes are opened the missing aces are discovered inside the smallest one. And the marks on the envelopes prove them to be the ones originally sealed up empty!

How it is done. For this trick you will need four aces taken from another pack with backs of the same pattern as those you are using. You also want four envelopes, a nest of three and a duplicate of the smallest envelope. To prepare, place the four extra aces in one of the small envelopes and put this envelope into the middle sized envelope.

To perform, hand the four aces for inspection, and while attention is drawn to them, quietly turn the halves of the pack face to face. Take back the aces and place them openly on top of the pack. As you turn to put the pack on the table you will find it quite easy to turn the pack over. To the audience nothing unusual has been done, but of course when you next deal cards from the top of the pack you are really dealing from the opposite side, and therefore the aces are no longer there.

FIG.8 Hollow rock appears to be the inside of the case

Now for the envelopes. Take the smallest empty envelope and ask someone to seal it. Place it into the next larger envelope, but immediately draw out the envelope containing the aces, saying: "To make everything quite fair I should like someone to mark the envelope in some way, say with his initials." Of course it is the envelope containing the aces which is thus marked, but the audience having no knowledge of the exchange have no reason to suspect anything. The larger envelope is then sealed and marked and enclosed in the third envelope. When the envelopes are opened you ask the person who marked the outer one to verify his mark, open it, and hand you the one inside. You have this mark verified, open it yourself, and draw out the marked envelope containing the aces. This you can safely hand to a member of the audience to open while you calmly screw the other envelopes into a ball and drop them safely out of the way, thereby hiding all evidence of how the mystery was accomplished.

As a change from card tricks here is an easy version of a very effective stage trick.

THE PECULIAR PAPERS

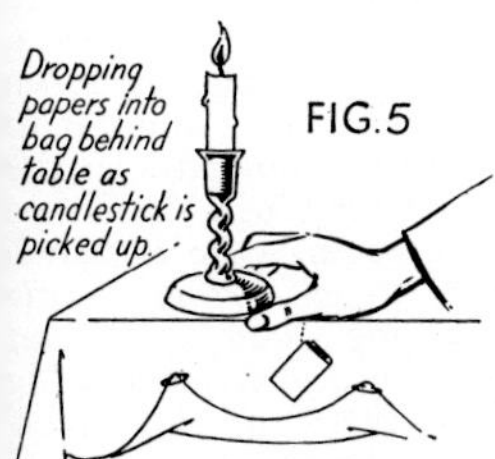

You have two sheets of tissue paper measuring about twelve inches square. One is blue and the other yellow. You cut a roughly circular piece from the centre of each, fold all the papers together, and warm them over the flame of a candle to restore them. But the trick goes wrong, and when the papers are unfolded the yellow piece has a blue centre and vice versa. Saying that you didn't warm them long enough, you strike a match and set fire to the papers. As they burn down you blow the ashes away, and immediately unfold the papers, completely restored, one piece entirely blue and the other entirely yellow.

Closing match box pushes papers into hand

How it is done. To begin with you have the two papers with the wrong centres folded into a small packet and inserted between the leaves of a largish book. The book rests on your table with its back to the audience, as shown in Fig. 3. You show the blue and yellow papers, and with a pair of scissors cut a roughly circular piece from each. Now lay these two circular pieces on the book, allowing them to hang over the back a little. Show the mutilated sheets and push your hand through the holes to prove that the papers are really cut. Pick up the two cut-out discs, and in doing so pick up behind them the folded papers from the book. Place the mutilated sheets in front of the cut circles, and fold the papers forward into a packet pretty much like the packet you have concealed. See Fig. 4.

Hold the two packets in your hand as one, and let the audience see that you have nothing concealed in your hand. Take the packet of wrong centre papers in your left, leaving the others concealed in your partly closed right hand. With this hand pick up the candlestick, the candle having been lighted before the commencement of the trick. It stands near the back of the table, and as you pick it up you drop the concealed papers into a little pocket made by pinning up the rear portion of the tablecloth (Fig. 5).

You now proceed to warm the visible papers over the flame of the candle, blow out the candle, and open out the papers. Of course the audience see at once that the wrong centres have been restored, and the result is a good laugh. Explaining that you didn't warm the papers enough, you draw them out into a sort of rough spill and pick up a box of matches. The drawer of the matchbox is pushed half out, and in the space so formed in the outer case is concealed a packet composed of two plain papers, a blue and a yellow, identical with those you first used. Strike a match and light the papers in your hand. As they begin to burn close the matchbox and so automatically thrust the folded papers into your hand, where you keep them concealed (Fig. 6). As the papers burn away, blow the ashes into the air and instantly unfold the two restored papers.

If you like you can vary the finish of the trick, and instead of producing the papers restored you can produce a large sheet, two feet square, composed of alternate stripes of blue and yellow. Or again you can produce blue and yellow silk handkerchiefs.

Here is a quick and very easy trick.

SEASIDE ROCK

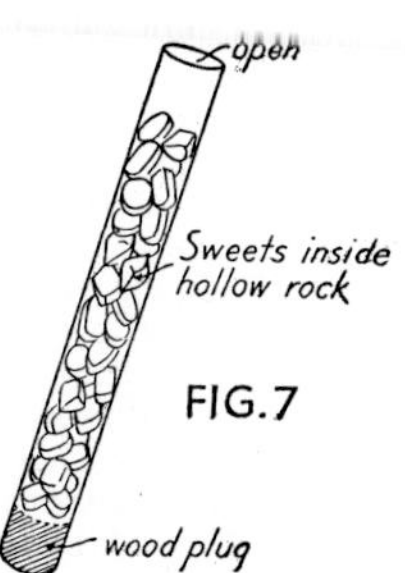

You show a stick of seaside rock and its cardboard case. The case is obviously empty. You put the rock into the case, throw it into the air, catch it, open the case, and instead of the rock a shower of little sweets pour out. The missing rock is produced from your pocket.

How it is done. The cardboard case is quite unprepared, but the stick of rock

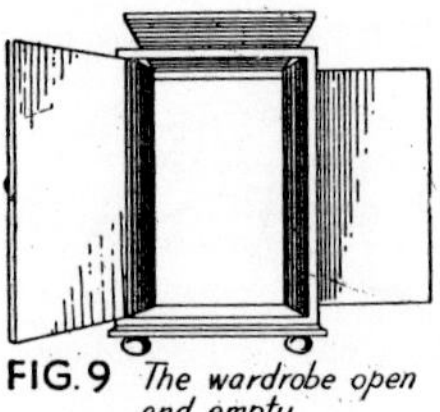

FIG. 9 *The wardrobe open and empty*

is really a cardboard tube, closed at one end and painted to resemble a stick of rock. It must fit snugly and fairly tightly into the cardboard case. The best way to arrange things is to buy a stick of rock in a tubular case. Use the rock as a mould to roll a tube from thick paper, gluing the paper well down. Insert a little piece of wooden rod in one end and paint the hollow fake to look like the real rock. Fill the hollow rock with small sweets and put the real rock into your pocket. Fig. 7 shows the hollow rock ready prepared.

Performing, show the false stick of rock and make it quite clear that the case is empty. Push the hollow stick into the case, solid end down. Put on the lid, throw the case into the air, and take the lid off. Pour out the sweets, and the case can again be shown empty because the inside of the hollow rock will look like the inside of the case. See Fig. 8. Finish by producing the real rock from your pocket, and give it to someone in the audience if you feel generous. If you like, instead of changing the rock to sweets you can fill the hollow rock with little flags, or a string of ribbons of different colours, or indeed anything of a suitable nature that will go into it.

The next trick is another very easy one, but the effect is most magical. I call it

THE UN-CUTTABLE RIBBON

You have a length of ribbon examined, also a pair of scissors. Taking the ribbon near the centre you proceed to cut a piece off. The audience see the cut piece fall off, yet, by simply rubbing the ribbon with your fingers, you cause it to be restored and everything can be examined again.

How it is done. All you need for this trick are a pair of scissors and about three yards of ribbon. Cut a piece about two inches long from one end of the ribbon. Now for the whole secret. The scissors used for the trick are fairly large ones, but they are blunt. They will cut paper, but they will not cut the fabric of the ribbon.

FIG. 11 *The production.*

Fold the little piece of ribbon and have it in your waistcoat pocket. Give out ribbon and scissors to be examined. Secure the short piece of ribbon from your pocket and conceal it in your right hand. Take the long ribbon by the centre in the same hand, pressing the short piece against the long one. Hold the two together, and with the scissors apparently cut the ribbon. The scissors merely pinch the two pieces of ribbon together, and as you instantly open the blades of the scissors, the little piece of ribbon will flutter to the floor, having apparently been cut from the long piece. The rest of the trick is merely a matter of making passes and looking as mysterious as possible before you show that the ribbon is whole again.

Another version of the trick makes use of a piece of paper, and no short piece of ribbon is needed. Fold a sheet of thickish writing paper down the centre, lay the middle of a length of ribbon along the fold, and bring the sides of the paper together, making a sort of sandwich of the ribbon. Take your scissors—they are blunt as before—and boldly cut across the centre of the paper, thus apparently cutting the ribbon as well. Hold the two sides of the paper as you cut, or better still get two members of the audience to hold the paper, one on each side. Then put down the scissors and slide the two halves of the cut paper away from the middle, revealing that the ribbon has become restored. The scissors, being blunt, will not cut through the ribbon, but they will cut the stiff paper quite easily.

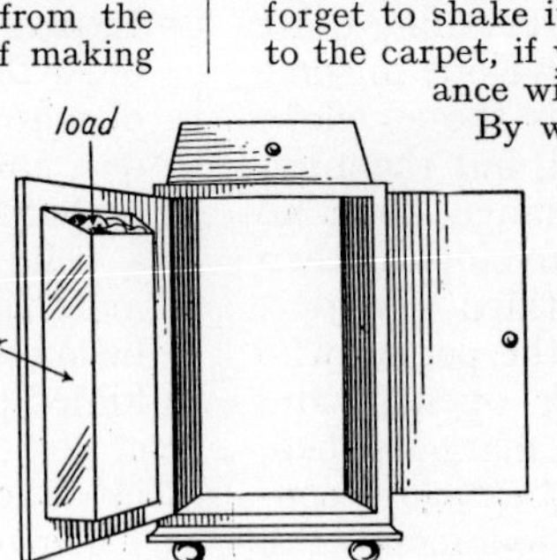

FIG. 12 *The Secret. Back view of wardrobe.*

Now let us have one of those showy tricks in which no end of unlikely articles are produced apparently from nowhere.

CONJURER'S WARDROBE

The wardrobe is a miniature affair measuring about fifteen inches high by nine inches wide and five inches deep. You can make it easily from plywood, and decorate it with mouldings, etc., to suit your fancy. It has a door back and front, and the top is hinged like a lid. Four feet are fitted to raise it above the table and allow a clear view underneath.

The wardrobe is first opened as shown in Fig. 9, and the audience are allowed to see right through. The doors and top are closed and all sides of the wardrobe are shown. There is evidently no place for concealing even a handkerchief, yet when the conjurer opens the lid he takes out dozens of flags, some on long staves, coloured goblets, dozens of yards of paper ribbon, bunches of flowers, paper garlands, and to finish up with a shower of confetti which alone makes a pile as big as the wardrobe.

FIG. 10 *The wardrobe closed*

How it is done. The wardrobe is made exactly as it appears. The front door is hinged on the opposite side to the back door. Inside the back door is fitted a box made of thin wood or tin. This box is an inch smaller all round than the door, and the sides slope inward away from the door. The top of the box is open. This forms the container for the load of articles to be produced, of which more in a moment.

When the load compartment has been packed with things, the wardrobe is closed and placed on the table. To present the trick, open the back door first, that is most important; then open the front door, and finally the lid. As you will see from Fig. 12, the load is entirely concealed behind the back door but the cabinet appears to be empty. The fact that something may be hidden behind the back door never occurs to anyone because they think they see both sides of both doors as the cabinet is opened and closed.

Having shown the cabinet empty, rattle a stick inside or put your hand through to prove the absence of mirrors, close the doors. This time you close the lid first, then the front door, and the back door last. In this way the load is concealed the whole time. Pick up the wardrobe and show all sides of it, put it down, open the lid and take out the articles.

Now for the actual things to be produced. Silk handkerchiefs of course are excellent, as they can be packed into small space. So are silk flags. To make flagstaffs, take strips of tough brown paper and roll them up, paste the ends down, and pull them out from the centre. They will form quite rigid-looking poles, and they can be closed into very little space. Attach the flags to these poles by sewing a few rings along one side of each flag. Fasten one corner of the flag to a wooden knob glued into the inside of the roll, and let the rings drop down over the pole as it is drawn out.

The goblets are ordinary cream cartons, painted different colours, and some gold and silver. A dozen will nest together in little more space than that occupied by one, and the inside goblet can be filled with handkerchiefs. The bunches of flowers are imitation ones, made from feathers and obtainable at most drapery shops. The confetti is put into the container first and packed down tight. If this is done the confetti when shaken out loose at the finish will make a large pile, even though it occupies only an inch or two when rammed into the container. Don't forget to shake it out on to a tray or sheet of paper and not on to the carpet, if you want to retain the popularity your performance will, we hope, create for you.

By way of a change we will end with a trick that is really a sort of joke, but it makes an amusing surprise.

NAME THE BOTTOM CARD

You take several cards and lay them face upward on the palm of your hand, allowing the audience to see what each card is, and reading the names aloud. Suppose they are the four of clubs, the queen of hearts and the ten of diamonds. You show them again and ask someone to name the bottom card. Of course he will say it is the four of clubs, that card having been quite obviously placed at the bottom of the heap. "No," you say, "I am afraid you are wrong. The bottom card is the queen of hearts."

You then proceed to work up a little argument by trying to persuade someone to say that he agrees with you and that the bottom card is the queen. Naturally, the more you try to persuade, the more the audience will insist that you are wrong. You then quietly lift up all the cards, saying: "I am right, the *bottom* card is the queen of hearts." And so it is. Under the bottom card you have previously hidden a miniature patience card, and this miniature card is of course the queen of hearts. The laugh is on the audience.

In conclusion, let me emphasise that, if at all possible, the same trick should not be repeated before the same audience. In order to distract the attention of the audience at critical moments in the performance of a trick a few jokes and witty sayings should be selected and memorised. Even when the greatest care is taken it is always possible for some little thing to go wrong during a trick, and if the conjurer can keep on talking there is a better chance of remedying the mistake without the audience noticing that anything has occurred. A situation of this kind is bound to arise now and then even with professional conjurers.

Boring Woodhead Tunnel

A Pioneer Railway Engineering Feat

TO ordinary travellers tunnels are perhaps the least attractive features of a railway. Often enough, just when they are enjoying a picturesque country scene, or an attractive view of hills and mountains, their train plunges into the blackness of one of these underground bores, through which it roars and clanks, while unpleasant fumes invade their compartments unless they hasten to close the windows.

Yet railways without tunnels are almost unthinkable, and on at least one occasion a tunnel was purposely introduced in the course of a railway in order to give passengers the thrill of travelling through it. This happened when the Canterbury and Whitstable Railwas was built in the early days of railways. It is said that the promoters of the railway insisted on a tunnel, and George Stephenson was called in to plan a route "with a nice tunnel in it" in place of the level and easy line previously selected by the surveyor.

An unusual view of the castellated buildings of Woodhead Station photographed from the top of the embankment at the mouth of Woodhead Tunnel. The two photographs on this page are by A. Phillips, Ashton-under-Lyne.

To a railway enthusiast a tunnel is always of interest, especially when it is a long one that represents a triumph of engineering achievement. The Woodhead Tunnel on the Manchester and Sheffield line of the Great Central section of the L.N.E.R. is an example of this. It is the longest on the L.N.E.R. system and, apart from the London tubes, there are only three longer railway tunnels in the British Isles. From end to end it measures 13 yds. more than three miles, and it was built almost a century ago, when Sheffield and Manchester were being connected by rail. It is remarkable that a tunnel of this size should have been planned in the pioneer days of railway construction, when the powerful drills and explosives used by the engineers of to-day were not available. The task of constructing it was the most formidable that railway engineers had then been called upon to face.

In spite of the example set by the promoters of the Whitstable and Canterbury Railway, railway engineers do not seek opportunities for making tunnels. When it is necessary to pass through high ground, a cutting is made if possible, but it is cheaper to tunnel if the depth is greater than about 75 ft. The purpose of Woodhead Tunnel was to enable the new railway to penetrate the Pennine Range between Woodhead and Dunford. Most tunnels have a single bore, but in this case separate tunnels were provided for the up and down tracks respectively. The boring of the down tunnel began in 1838 and was completed in 1845, when single line working was then brought into operation. Two years later the second bore was begun, and this was opened for traffic in February, 1852.

The double bore of Woodhead Tunnel seen from the station. One of the observatories used for making the line of the tunnel during construction can be seen above the tunnel on the left.

The first step towards the construction of a tunnel is the setting out or surveying of the centre line over the route to be followed. Observation towers, or observatories, as they are called, are then built at prominent points along the line. A typical tower is about 30 ft. in height, and circular stairs lead to the top, where there is a heavy stone block carrying a bronze plate on which the actual centre line is engraved. The sites of the towers are carefully chosen so that they command a view of the whole of the ground under which the tunnel is to run, and the necessary observations are made through openings in their walls. With the line they mark as a guide, the tunnel can then be driven into the hillside with such accuracy that workings from both ends eventually meet with almost uncanny precision.

Some of the observation towers built for the construction of Woodhead Tunnel still stand. One of them can be seen from the platform at Woodhead Station, as shown in the lower illustration on this page. A rough track drained by ditches was constructed over the moor to connect the observation points with five places where vertical shafts were sunk to the line of the tunnel. The average depth of these shafts was 515 ft., and their purpose was to enable several working faces to be opened out at the same time in order to speed up the task of boring. Gunpowder was used for blasting, and the holes in which it was placed were made by driving drills into the rock by means of heavy hammers. The tunnel passed through sandstone and millstone grit, a very hard rock, and altogether it was necessary to use over 150 tons of gunpowder in blasting a way through. The material broken away at each face was removed to the foot of the shaft from which tunnelling operations in that heading were being carried on, and was then hauled to the surface by means of gearing driven by steam engines. This of course was not necessary in dealing with the spoil from the headings driven from the ends of the tunnel.

Work necessarily proceeded slowly in comparison with tunnelling operations in modern times. The men engaged underground had only lamps and candles to guide them, and difficulties were caused by water flowing in, nearly 2,000 million gallons being pumped out before the tunnel was finished. A stone lining was built, and it is probable that the material required was brought from a large quarry near one of the shafts, down which it was lowered.

The position of the tunnel added to the difficulties of the work, for it is far removed from populous centres and throughout the years of construction the several hundred men engaged in it had to be housed in stone huts that were thatched or roofed over with flagstones. Remains of some of these camps can still be seen on the moors under which the tunnel passes.

After almost 100 years of service, Woodhead Tunnel is still an important link between the east and west of England.

Recent Record Flights

Miss Jean Batten, the well-known New Zealand airwoman, has flown from England to New Zealand in the record time of 11 days 1 hr. 25 min. This 14,000-mile flight involved the crossing of the Timor and Tasman Seas. Miss Batten reached Australia in the record time of 5 days 21 hrs., and efforts were made there to persuade her not to attempt the perilous flight across the Tasman Sea to New Zealand, as her machine, a Percival "Vega Gull," is of the single-engined type. Miss Batten was determined to continue by air to her native land, however. After waiting several days for favourable weather she eventually took off from Richmond, New South Wales, and accomplished the long sea crossing of 1,200 miles in about 8½ hrs.

Flights across the Atlantic Ocean have long since ceased to be a novelty, or to have any real value, but the recent fast crossing by air made by Mr. J. Mollison deserves mention. Mr. Mollison took off from Harbour Grace, Newfoundland, on 29th October and landed at Croydon airport next morning, having covered the distance of 2,300 miles in the record time of 13 hr. 17 min. His machine was a Bellanca single-engined monoplane. Mr. Mollison has now flown across the Atlantic three times, and is the only airman to have done so in aeroplanes.

The non-stop flight from Burban, California, to Columbus, Ohio, a distance of 1,986 miles, made by Mr. R. N. Buck, a young American airman, has been recognised by the Federation Aeronautique Internationale as a new world record for light aircraft. The time taken for the flight was 17 hr. 50 min., and the distance covered was 177 miles greater than the previous record, set up by two French pilots in 1932.

Airways Round The World

An aeroplane equipped as an experimental wireless laboratory, and ground wireless stations fitted up in big motor lorries, are being used in tests to determine the best positions for wireless stations across the Rocky Mountains section of the proposed trans-Canada air mail service. The mobile ground-stations move to different points along the mountains and then communication is established with the "flying laboratory" overhead. In this way practical tests can be made as to any abnormal effects that the existence of the many mountain peaks might have on the working of regular airway wireless beacons.

The Canadian Minister of Transport has announced that air mail services on the prairie sections of the trans-Canada route will be in operation next spring. Later in the spring it is intended to inaugurate the sections across the Rockies to Vancouver, and to have the entire air mail service across Canada in regular operation by July. This service will provide a vital link in the system of Empire airways, and in long-distance air transport round the world. When it is in operation loads flown across the Atlantic from England can be taken on to the Western Coast of North America, and then by flying-boat services across the Pacific to Hong Kong and the chief seaports of Australia. From these Pacific services there will be connections with the main air routes from China and Australia to India, Egypt, Africa, and England.

* * * *

Doncaster Airport now has a short wave wireless station to help wireless-equipped aircraft approaching the airport, when they come within the controlled zone, an area of five miles around the airport.

The new Westland Army Co-operation monoplane. This type has been adopted as standard equipment for the R.A.F.
Photograph by courtesy of Westland Aircraft Ltd.

Air Race from New York to Paris

An air race across the Atlantic Ocean from New York to Paris will be held on 21st May next year. This date has been chosen because it is the 10th anniversary of Lindbergh's historic solo flight from New York to Paris. The race will be flown in accordance with the rules of the International Aeronautical Federation, and as there are few restrictions, an interesting and representative range of machines should be entered. Any type of landplane will be eligible, but seaplanes and flying boats will not be allowed to compete. The machines taking part will have to carry distinctive markings on their engines, wings and fuselages, in order to render identification easy, and each will have to be equipped with a wireless transmitting and receiving set not more than 125 lb. in weight. The total number of the crew that can be carried will be limited only by the capacity of the machine.

The first prize in this Atlantic air race will be £5,000 and one half the entrance money, and the second and third prizes will be £3,000 and £2,000 respectively. The distance to be covered is about 3,645 miles, and the time limit of 40 hr. decided upon, means that the competing aircraft must fly at an average speed of at least 90 m.p.h. to keep within that time. The French Air Ministry intend to enter three machines for the race.

A Flying Motor Car

Flight and road tests are being carried out by the United States Bureau of Air Commerce with a new Pitcairn "Autogiro," fitted with a Pobjoy "Cascade" supercharged engine of 110 h.p. The machine is designed to fly through the air at 115 m.p.h., and to travel along a road at 25 m.p.h. When not in use the rotating wings can be folded along the top of the fuselage, which has a saloon body similar to that of a motor car. When the "Autogiro" is on the ground, the drive of the engine can be diverted from the airscrew to the landing wheels by means of a clutch mechanism, and the machine can then be steered and handled like a motor car.

More Aerodromes

A fine airport was completed recently at Bordeaux. The main building faces an extensive landing area and is of reinforced concrete, and owing to the soft nature of the ground it is built upon a foundation of 102 columns sunk down to firm soil. The central part of the building has three storeys, and a conspicuous feature of it is a tower 37 ft. in height, in which are the control and meteorological observation rooms. There is a powerful beacon on the roof of the tower.

A new aerodrome has also been opened at Ypenburg, close to the Hague. The equipment includes hangar accommodation for about 30 light aeroplanes, excellent repair shops and full night landing facilities. The aerodrome is only about 4½ miles from the Pynacker air route beacon, where the air routes from Amsterdam to Paris and London diverge.

An aerodrome is to be established at La Villiaze, in the Channel Islands, where a suitable site has been bought by the States of Guernsey authorities for £35,000.

Winter Airship Service to South America

The German airship *"Hindenburg"* has proved as reliable in service as the *"Graf Zeppelin,"* and has now crossed the Atlantic ocean about 26 times. The vessel has made 10 visits to Lakehurst, New Jersey, the terminus in the United States of the Zeppelin North Atlantic service, and also has flown to South America several times. On every trip the *"Hindenburg"* has carried a full load of passengers.

Until the resumption of the North Atlantic service next spring the two Zeppelins will maintain a weekly service between Frankfurt and South America.

Honouring Australian Air Pioneers

A striking memorial to Sir Charles Kingsford Smith and Mr. C. T. P. Ulm, two Australian air pioneers, is to be erected at the southern head of Sydney harbour. It will take the form of a huge copper terrestrial globe, surmounted by a replica of the *"Southern Cross,"* Kingsford Smith's famous monoplane.

Another method being adopted in Australia to keep fresh the memory of the country's air pioneers is that of naming important airports after them. For instance, Darwin airport has been renamed Ross Smith airport, and that at Mascot, Sydney, is to be known in future as the Kingsford Smith Aerodrome. Certain other Australian airports are to be renamed shortly.

New American Flying Boat

A large flying boat capable of carrying up to 36 passengers has been built by the Douglas Company, of America. It is 95 ft. in span and 70 ft. in length. The Wright "Cyclone," series "C," engine fitted in it enables it to attain a top speed of 185 m.p.h. It will have a crew of four, consisting of the pilot, assistant pilot, wireless operator, and stewardess.

The Cierva C.30 "Direct-control" Autogiro descending vertically. This machine has long rotor blades and can take off after only a short run along the ground. Photograph by courtesy of Cierva Autogiro Co. Ltd.

Imperial Airways Progress

The Annual Report of Imperial Airways shows a steady increase in the amount of traffic carried and the mileage flown. During the year ended 31st March 1936, the total number of passengers carried on the company's European services was 54,272, as compared with 48,642 during the previous 12 months. On the Empire routes the number was 8,505, an increase of 1,402 over that of the previous working year.

Four new services were started during the year. They were the London-Brindisi and London-Budapest services, and those linking up Khartum with Kano and Penang with Hong Kong. In October this year the Khartum-Kano line was further extended to Lagos, Nigeria.

The total number of the company's aircraft now in active service is 38, including the two new flying boats recently introduced on the Mediterranean section.

The huge Zeppelin shed at Friedrichshafen, in which the airship "Hindenburg" was built. Another Zeppelin, the LZ.130, is now under construction there. Photograph by J. M. S. Risk.

"Burnelli" Aeroplane to be made in Great Britain

A British version of the American "Burnelli" high wing monoplane is to be produced by the Scottish Aircraft and Engineering Co. Ltd., and the first machine will probably be completed in about five months' time.

The "Burnelli" is of all-metal construction, duralumin being chiefly used, and carries two pilots and 14 passengers. The machine differs from a normal aeroplane in having a very short fuselage, which is only large enough to contain the pilot's compartment, passenger cabin and a small baggage compartment. The fuselage is of aerofoil or wing section, thus contributing to the lift of the machine, and the curve of its underside is continued in specially-shaped booms which carry the tail unit. The two engines are carried in large nacelles that project from the front of the fuselage, a very unusual arrangement.

Test Flights Over North Atlantic

The Deutsche Luft Hansa recently completed a series of experimental flights across the North Atlantic, designed to provide data on which to work out a reliable trans-Atlantic air service between Germany and the United States. The flights have been carried out by two Dornier flying boats called *"Zephyr"* and *"Aeolus"* respectively, with the assistance of the depot ship *"Schwabenland,"* which was withdrawn from the company's South Atlantic air route specially for the purpose.

On the westward experimental flights the flying boats were catapulted from the depot ship off Lisbon, and flew by way of the Azores and Bermuda. The *"Schwabenland"* had then to hasten across the Atlantic, and start the aircraft off on their return flights. The return trips were not made immediately, as the machines also carried out experimental coastal flights between New York and Nova Scotia. On one westward trip they omitted the call at Bermuda, and flew from the Azores direct to New York. The long return flight to the Azores was also accomplished non-stop.

New Internal Air Services

Air Dispatch, the air transport company operating the early morning newspaper service between London and Paris, are planning two new internal air services. One of them will link Croydon with Portsmouth, Bournemouth, and Torquay. The other service will be between Croydon and Aberdeen.

A Modern "Flying Dutchman"

Amsterdam to London by K.L.M.

By O. S. Nock, B.Sc., D.I.C.

AMSTERDAM, 5.45 p.m. From the steps of the K.L.M. office I watched the city workers going home, some on foot, some by tram, but the majority pedalling quietly along on bicycles. It seemed incredible that I was due at Croydon in less than three hours! But the splendid aeroplanes of the K.L.M. put a girdle across the sea faster by far than any phantom ship in the legends of the "*Flying Dutchman*," and in a time of 2 hrs. 5 min. from airport to airport manage to put in a ten-minute stop at Rotterdam as well.

A smart bus painted in the same colours as the company's aircraft, dark blue and light blue, left the Leidscheplein in the heart of the city at 5.55 p.m. The initials K.L.M., by the way, stand for Koninklijke Luchtvaart Maatschappij, for which the literal English translation is "Royal Air Traffic Company"; but the name that has been officially adopted throughout the world is the well-known one of Royal Dutch Air Lines. A run of some twenty minutes brought us to Schiphol Airport, about six miles to the south of Amsterdam. The setting is as perfect a Dutch landscape as could be imagined. The country is dead flat in every direction, and well below sea level; a big canal runs north and south between high banks; a little to the north is a picturesque group of red-tiled cottages, and behind them a windmill with sails whirling round in the stiff wind.

The cockpit of a Fokker F.XII, the type of K.L.M. air liner in which the author flew from Amsterdam to London. Photographs by courtesy of Royal Dutch Air Lines.

The airport building is a characteristic piece of modern Dutch architecture. In all recent buildings, even the humblest dwellings, the windows are huge, and at Schiphol the spacious room that faces the aerodrome and combines the functions of restaurant and waiting room is glazed almost from floor to ceiling. Passengers are kept informed by loudspeaker of the times of arrival of aircraft and in every case the information is repeated in several languages. The machine by which I was going to travel provides one link in the "Rome Air Rapide" service. Rome is left at 10.25 a.m., Milan at 1.5 p.m., though of course the 24-hour clock is in use on the Continent and the time is thus 13.05. Calls are made at Frankfort and Cologne and the aeroplane is due at Schiphol at 18.15. But on our arrival by bus there was no sign of the German machine, and in a few minutes the loud speakers told us she was 40 minutes late. That meant that we should not get away until about 19.15, that is 7.15 p.m.

The time passed quickly. Over in the shed on the south side of the aerodrome were two of the mightiest K.L.M. machines. One was the Fokker F.36 4-engined monoplane, flagship of the company; this carries 32 passengers and has a cruising speed of 163 m.p.h. The other was one of the famous Fokker-Douglas D.C.2 machines that are used on the Far Eastern service from Amsterdam to Batavia and all over Europe; it was one of these twin-engined monoplanes that put up such a magnificent performance in the England-Australia race in 1934. Their cruising speed is no less than 190 m.p.h.! Our machine was the "*Ysvogel*," a handsome Fokker F.12 three-engined monoplane. This type carries 14 passengers and has a cruising speed of 125 m.p.h. The name Ysvogel means, literally, a bird from the river Y, on which Amsterdam is situated; it is what we know in England as a Kingfisher.

Soon after our arrival an aeroplane operating a Dutch internal air service arrived; this was a handsome 3-engined Fokker of class F.20 named "*Zilvermeeuw*." This was quite similar in appearance to the "*Ysvogel*," but a rather faster machine. All these Fokker types have a strong family likeness having the wings above the fuselage; in this way they differ from the Fokker-Douglas machines which have the wings below the fuselage and engines, the former being curved very slightly upward towards their extremities.

Our delayed start was in some ways most fortunate, for about 7 o'clock—or still being on the Continent I should say 19.00 hours—there developed the most astonishing atmospheric phenomena I have ever witnessed. A violent thunderstorm came up from the North Sea; the western sky darkened to the colour of indigo, and then, as the disturbance neared the coast, it divided and the main storm passed northward towards the Zuider Zee. But it was the smaller detached portion that produced so sensational an effect. The clouds, black as night, slowly clustered in the form of a "mackerel sky"; but the scales, instead of being soft white on a blue ground, were black showing patches of ominous yellow between. The wind then blew each of these black masses out like the sails of a ship and the lower ones drooped until they seemed to touch the horizon.

When the sky was at its strangest a roar overhead announced the approach of a big aeroplane. It was not the connection from Germany we were awaiting, but a beautiful Belgian monoplane from Brussels; its silver-white paint and the gay colours of the Sabena company's flag stood out with startling effect against the dark sky. This machine had scarcely landed when the great Junkers monoplane that we were expecting flew overhead, bringing with it some passengers from Milan to London. It bore the name "*Paul Billick*," was painted in the distinctive grey and black livery of the Deutsche Lufthansa, and carried of course a huge swastika on the tail. Seen together, the three machines, Belgian, Dutch, and German, made a striking group.

Then a noticeably Dutch voice on the loudspeaker—"The aeroplane for London will leave in a few minutes." Baggage and mails had been loaded, we took our seats, and at exactly 7.15 p.m. the "*Ysvogel*" took off. My seat was right forward on the port side and almost abreast of the port engine; in this type the wings are above the fuselage so that there is a clear view below past the engine. The landing space at Schiphol is very extensive, and after taxi-ing into position we took off in almost a direct line for Rotterdam. Due no doubt to the air currents caused by the thunderstorm, the going was a bit bumpy at first, and the rain rattled like hail on the windows; but flying quite low we were soon right out of the storm.

The Dutch countryside is fascinating enough when viewed from a canal boat or a train, but it is not until seen from above that its full wonder is revealed. Then the amazing network of canals and dykes is spread out like a map. From the sea run great waterways along which ocean-going ships can pass; their level is much above that of the surrounding country and their course is preserved by massive embankments. From these main arteries there branch off the smaller canals; these are lowered by locks to ground level and it is along their banks that numerous busy little towns are built. The land between these smaller canals is drained by an intricate network of dykes, which incidentally take the place of hedges in dividing field from field.

We were soon flying over Amstelveen. This little town seems literally surrounded by water; the red roofs and tall church tower looked very beautiful against the limpid blue of the canals, and just to the south were what seemed like extensive watercress beds. We crossed the railway from Leiden to Utrecht, which is lined on both sides with big dykes, and just beyond, an isolated windmill made, as always, a charming picture. Then for a while we were flying near a wide arterial road. A big programme of road building is in progress just now in Holland, and in all this new work a separate track is being provided for bicycles. Cycling is immensely popular, and by this means a much safer and more enjoyable run is ensured, and at the same time the main highway is left clear for fast traffic.

The rain had ceased some little time ago, the sky was clearer, and right ahead of us the horizon was bounded by a deepish blue haze of great beauty. The dyke-drained fields gave place for a while to slightly higher ground that was covered with a patchwork of yellow and purple squares, the latter dotted with numerous darkish objects that I later discovered to be small ricks very similar to those seen in the Scottish highlands. Alongside a big canal were seven dismantled windmills all in a row. Much to the regret to all lovers of beauty a great number of these fine old mills all over Holland are suffering the same fate, and vigorous steps are having to be taken to ensure that some of the finest examples are preserved. It would be a tragedy indeed if these beautiful windmills, which are such a characteristic feature of the Dutch landscape, were allowed to ruin now that so many of them have been rendered obsolete by the coming of more modern machinery. We crossed the railway from The Hague to Gouda along which a streamlined Diesel-electric train was speeding; over Moerkapelle, where there are acres of glass-houses, and then the fair view was obscured in a storm of rain.

Aerial view of Schiphol Airport, Amsterdam, one of the most important airports in Europe.

Out of the mist loomed Rotterdam; whole suburbs of attractive-looking flats on the outskirts, a delectable park, and ahead, through the smoky haze that hung over the city, the several channels of the river Maas appeared as winding ribbons of silver. Still flying dead straight we got a bird's-eye view of the Central station, where a westbound electric train was just leaving for The Hague; and so out over the river for a really superb view of the port of Rotterdam. From above, the dock area looks like one vast lake intersected only by numerous slender jetties and wharfs; ships were everywhere, and a little way up the river was the big three-funnelled Holland-America liner "*Statendam.*"

A Fokker F.XII air liner in the air. This triple-engined machine has a cruising speed of 125 m.p.h., and carries 14 passengers.

Rotterdam airport is on the island of Ysselmonde just across the river from the city. It is a vast open plot by the waterside. Brightly coloured barges were moored along the banks near by; we circled round banking steeply, passing over a gaily painted windmill, and made a smooth landing at exactly 7.40 p.m. It is a little under 40 miles from Amsterdam, so that our average speed, including climbing and the descent, was nearly 100 m.p.h. over this short distance. We should have travelled even faster but for a stiff wind off the sea. No time was wasted over the stop and in five minutes we were off again—next stop Croydon.

Rotterdam lies on the northern shore of that extraordinary delta by which the Rhine and the Maas enter the sea. There are a dozen large islands, on one of which is the airport, and many smaller ones, all as flat as the proverbial pancake. As we headed for England the evening sun was just breaking through, and the islands, misty grey shapes outlined by silvery threads of water, were flecked with patches lighted by the sun. In one place a group of red roofed houses would stand out brilliantly; farther away a line of sand dunes shone pale gold. We were flying much higher now, nearly 4,500 ft., and well beneath us a few light clouds went racing by, momentarily veiling the scene below. The wind was directly head-on, and blowing at a steady strength of 30 m.p.h. reduced our land speed to 95 m.p.h.

Soon after leaving Rotterdam we crossed the Old Maas river, then we passed over Voorne, and so approached the island of Over Flakke. Across the estuary known as the Brouwershaven Gat lay the island of Schoewen, a veritable patchwork quilt of brown and yellow looking fields. We flew right along the southern shore of Over Flakke, and even from this height the town of Stellendam stood out in very clear detail; a little farther westward the land lying below sea level was protected by a stout embankment. Sickle-shaped mudbanks stretched across the estuary, and the farther shore of Schoewen was lost in the haze of the setting sun.

We were travelling with hardly a tremor. From where I sat I could see through into the cockpit, and there the navigating officer, earphones to his head, was constantly consulting charts, making calculations, and always scanning the route ahead. Once he came through to see that we were all comfortable and to check the temperature of the cabin. From where I sat the pilot was hidden from view. Most of the passengers were either reading or asleep; the atmosphere was cosy in the extreme, and looking out at times it seemed as though we were scarcely moving.

Just after eight o'clock we passed over the western end of Over Flakke. To the south, the coast of Schoewen was one long line of sand dunes. We were too high to see much detail; fields glowed in the sunshine, a few clouds scudding beneath us were tinged with pink, and there was only the vaguest hint of another estuary to the south of the island. Although we were doing a good steady 95 m.p.h. we seemed merely to be drifting slowly out over the sea. The sky overhead was calm and beautiful—an astonishing contrast to the fury of the storm that had swept over Amsterdam only an hour before—and at 8.15 p.m. the sand dunes of Schoewen, our last glimpse of Holland, blended into the haze of evening.

But about five minutes later I sighted land again far to the south; this was the island of Walcheren, the southern extremity of the Maas delta. It was only a dim grey line and was soon lost to view. The sky was overcast again, though very calm; visibility was not more than about four or five miles, and in the pervading greyness the sense of motion vanished almost entirely. Somewhere ahead in the misty haze lay England. I had not plotted the course beforehand and I fell to wondering where we should first strike land. There was hardly a stir in the sea below; not a sign of a ship—and this one of the busiest waterways in the world! For half an hour we flew with scarcely a movement from the plane. Only the clouds altered their form.

At 8.50 p.m. there were definite signs of a change. Long balloon-like clouds came floating along level with us, there were one or two very slight tremors—nothing approaching a bump—and then quite suddenly the clouds swept beneath us; they were light vapoury things, frequently parted to show the sea below, but for a few moments it was quite eerie. Then as we shot clear, there ahead was a tiny point of light. In all my travels I never remember being quite so thrilled as by this, the first sight of England again, and there was real excitement in trying to spot where we were. Our approach was tantalisingly slow; the clouds raced across once more and hid the view and for a few minutes it was raining in torrents. But when the sky cleared we were near enough to see the shape of the coast; the land ran out to a blunt nosed point, and curved away southward in a sweeping bay. My first guess was right; we were heading straight for the North Foreland, and the light I had seen was Ramsgate.

One of the Douglas D.C.2s of K.L.M. at Schiphol airport. The photograph shows the Queen of Holland greeting Prince and Princess Axel of Denmark.

In a few minutes we could pick out the twinkling lights of the harbour. The light that I had first seen and taken to be a lighthouse is a powerful beacon for aircraft, placed high on the cliffs. At 9.13 p.m. we passed over the coast. It was still daylight, but Ramsgate was brilliantly illuminated with fairy lights; just inland a glowing light in the Southern Railway station revealed a locomotive being got ready for the road. Away to the south the coast could be seen stretching towards Sandwich and Deal; from still farther afield came the flashes of lighthouses and lightships, on the Goodwin Sands, along the coast, and, most powerful of all, the tremendous aerial beacon at Lympne.

From the island of Over Flakke, where we crossed the Dutch coast, to passing over Ramsgate, we had averaged 96 m.p.h. The wind, although not boisterous, was consistently steady and strong and had slowed us down very considerably—indeed it was already clear that we should not keep time. The booked speed is a little over 105 m.p.h., so that this type of machine would have a good margin of power in reserve on a quiet day; it was no doubt the rough weather prevailing all over Europe that had made the connecting plane so late in arrival at Amsterdam.

A striking photograph of Rotterdam as seen from the air. The fine buildings in the centre and foreground are the Town Hall and the General Post Office.

In the waning light the English countryside looked extraordinarily beautiful; green park lands, a winding river, miles of dark luxuriant woods made a great contrast to the last glimpses of Holland. Now Canterbury lay to the south; we were flying lower now, and among the twinkling lights there were just enough daylight to pick out the towers of the Cathedral. We were over the coast again near Whitstable, where a roundabout at a road crossing showed up very plainly. We overtook an express train heading for London; the fire door of the engine was open and from above it looked like a huge bonfire moving along. Everywhere one looked seemed an intense green, rendered more vivid still in the approaching darkness. The cabin of the *"Ysvogel,"* now that the lights were put on, was cosier than ever. The outside world seemed completely shut

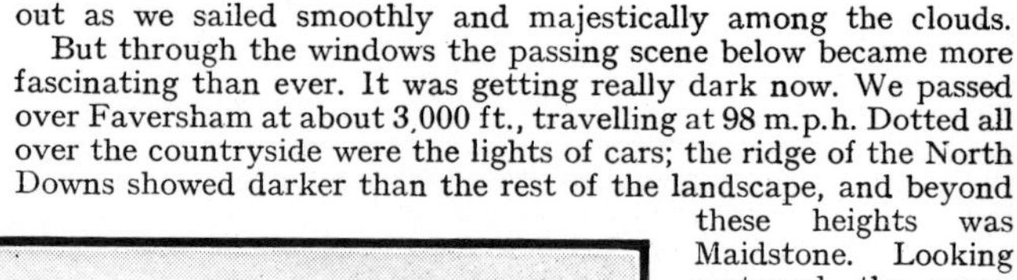

out as we sailed smoothly and majestically among the clouds.

But through the windows the passing scene below became more fascinating than ever. It was getting really dark now. We passed over Faversham at about 3,000 ft., travelling at 98 m.p.h. Dotted all over the countryside were the lights of cars; the ridge of the North Downs showed darker than the rest of the landscape, and beyond these heights was Maidstone. Looking eastward the scene was simply entrancing. The fields below were that vivid dark green of nightfall; in the distance they blended with the blue of the sky, where the rising moon shone amid a huge bank of white cumulus cloud. From far out in the blue came the imperious stabs of yellow light from Lympne beacon.

Once across the Medway it grew too dark for landmarks to be recognised. We passed over a big main road on which the headlamps of cars returning from the coast formed an endless chain of lights as far as the eye could see; there were flashing lights away to the south-west that probably came from Gatwick airport, and all the time we were gradually coming down to a lesser altitude. We crossed the valley of the Darent, recognisable by its roads and railways, at about 1,500 ft., and now right ahead of us was the red beacon of Croydon Airport.

A few minutes more and we were nearly overhead. Lights were everywhere; buses, trams, and even bicycles could be distinguished clearly. Threading its way through all was a chain of brilliant arc lights along the Brighton road, and now right below was the landing ground, its extent marked by a ring of small red beacons. We circled right round, all the time gently descending, but after turning once the control tower flashed a series of red danger signals to us; another machine had just landed and was not quite clear. The engines were put on again, we rose ever so slightly and circled right round again, and this time the control flashed green. Powerful headlights at the end of each wing were put on, we skimmed over the buildings, and came down so gently that the exact moment we touched the earth was really difficult to judge. Floodlighting the front of the control tower with our headlamps we coasted smoothly in and came to rest a few minutes before 10 o'clock.

The Control building clock showed only 9.40 p.m. During the flight I had completely forgotten that Amsterdam time is twenty minutes in advance of that of Greenwich. Although our actual flying time from Rotterdam to Croydon was 2 hrs. 13 min. we had been travelling westward with the sun, and by the clocks at each end had taken only 1 hr. 53 min.

The scene on arrival at Croydon was a fitting climax to this enthralling journey. A big Imperial Airways liner, one of the "Hannibal" class, had just arrived and shone like silver in the beam of our headlights. In the darkness ahead was a huge Junkers monoplane, while the red flashes of the tall beacon, the cheery shouts of the ground staff, and the brilliance of the moonlight night left an extraordinarily vivid impression of journey's end.

Puzzle No. 1

In each of the 10 vertical columns in Fig. 1 place words of four letters, leaving blank the middle horizontal row numbered 11. Clues to the 10 words are given below.

When this has been done, the name of an English city is to be written in the row numbered 11, and if the puzzle has been solved correctly, all the four-letter words in the vertical columns will then become words of five letters. The clues are as follows: 1. Trimming braid; 2. Part of the face; 3. Mud; 4. Used on roofs; 5. Farm buildings; 6. Fish; 7. Seed; 8. One who employs; 9. Set rotating; 10. Colour.

1	2	3	4	5	6	7	8	9	10
11									

Fig. 1.

Puzzle No. 2

In the brackets in each of the following lines insert the names of well-known towns in the British Isles, so as to make the sentences complete.

1. "Can you tell me where this road ( )?" the motorist asked the yokel.
2. "I will send in your ( ) you like," said the maid to the caller.
3. I have im( ) him its importance.
4. Nobody seems to like my cake, for there's ( ).
5. The Duke has just built a ( ) near here.
6. There was a ( ) where he had been standing in his muddy, wet boots.
7. Out ( ) is cultivated than in this country.
8. The seaman commenced to ( ) the seams of the boat.
9. He rang the ( ) and loud, but the ( ) from the ( ) could still be heard.
10. "Do you ( )," enquired a customer of the wine merchant.

Puzzle No. 3

A boy was given a piece of paper shaped somewhat like a Bishop's mitre as shown in Fig. 2, and was asked to cut it into four parts, each of these to be of similar shape. After a few experiments the boy managed the task successfully. Take a piece of paper and try this puzzle yourself.

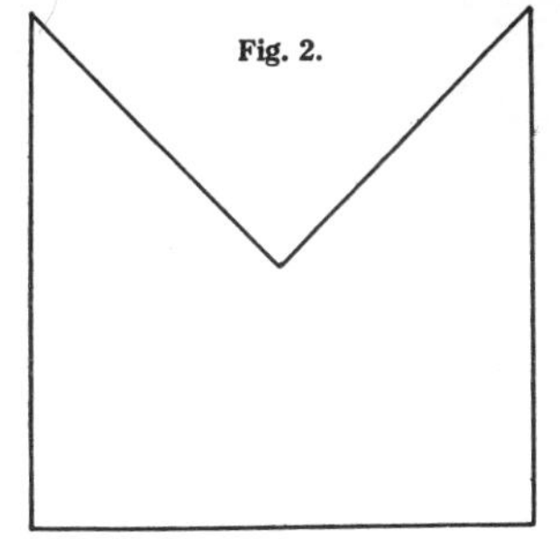
Fig. 2.

Puzzle No. 4

Starting at the letter M in the top left-hand corner of the alphabetical maze shown in Fig. 7, the reader is invited to trace his way through the maze until he reaches the tail of the "S." This should be done in less than one minute.

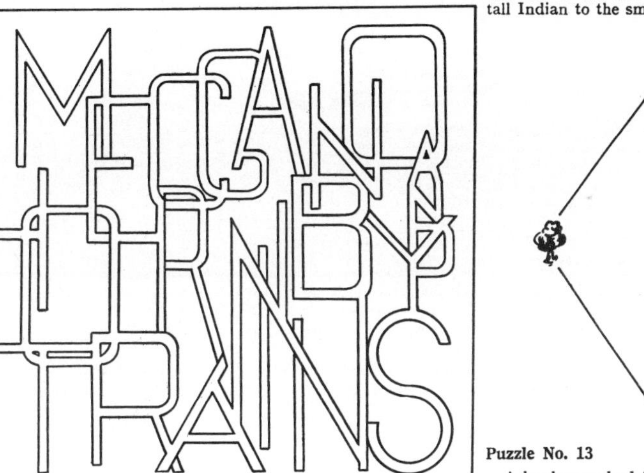

Fig. 7.

Puzzle No. 5

The letters ABCD, in that order, represent the year in which a King of England was born, each letter standing for a figure.

A and B together equal the total of C and D; A and C together equal B; A and D together are half C; C is three times the value of D.

What is the name of the King referred to?

Puzzle No. 6

A pilot boarded a ship in a river. As he climbed the ladder up the ship's side he noticed that three rungs of the ladder were under water. He stayed aboard for three hours, during which time the tide rose at the rate of 1 ft. per hour. The rungs of the ladder were 9 in. apart. How many rungs were under water when he left the ship?

Puzzle No. 7

Study the drawing of a key shown in Fig. 3 for 15 seconds; then cover it over and endeavour to draw it from memory.

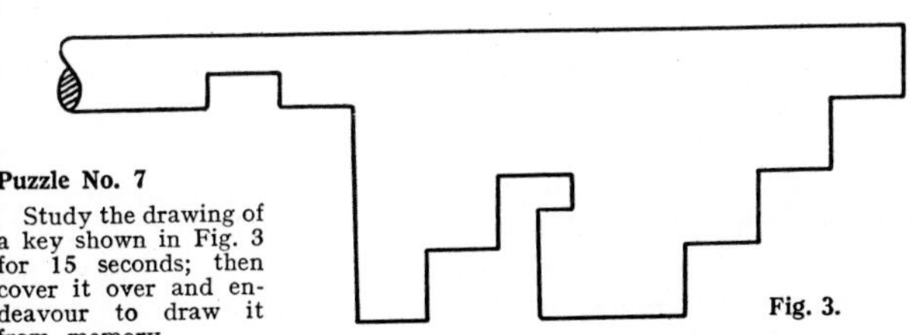
Fig. 3.

Puzzle No. 8

How many triangles are there in Fig. 4?

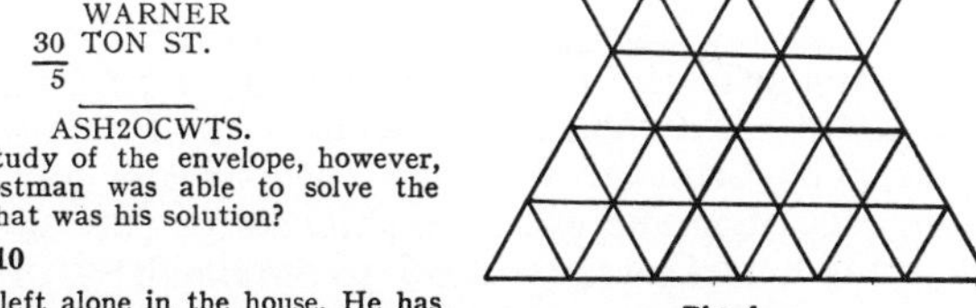
Fig. 4.

Puzzle No. 9

A letter addressed as shown below was received at a certain Post Office:

WARNER
30 TON ST.
5
ASH2OCWTS.

After a study of the envelope, however, a smart postman was able to solve the mystery. What was his solution?

Puzzle No. 10

A boy is left alone in the house. He has only one match, and he wants to light his bicycle lamp, the gas stove and the fire. Which would a discriminating boy light first?

Puzzle No. 11

A man bought a piece of linoleum 6 ft. × 3 ft., which he required to cover a floor 9 ft. × 2 ft. To do this he cut the linoleum in to two pieces that together exactly covered the floor. What was the size and shape of each piece?

Puzzle No. 12

A tall Indian and a little Indian were walking down a road. The small one was the son of the tall one. What relation was the tall Indian to the small Indian?

Fig. 5.

Puzzle No. 13

A landowner had four trees, planted one at each corner of a diamond-shaped field, as shown in Fig. 5. He bought five more similar trees and planted these in such a way that the nine trees made ten rows, each containing three trees. In what positions did he plant the new trees?

Puzzle No. 14

During manœuvres a message in code was sent by the Admiral to test the ability of the midshipmen. Here is the message:

"THIS LOT GIVE A DIM SYNOPSIS USEFUL TO NEW RANGE FINDER."

The midshipmen deciphered it with ease. Can you?

Puzzle No. 15

A man was asked "How old is your brother?"

"Two-thirds of his age," was the answer, "is just five-twelfths of mine; and I am nine years older than him."

What was the age of each?

Puzzle No. 16

Fig. 6 shows a farmhouse surrounded by eight fields, in each of which four men are at work, making a total of 32 men. The house has four windows, one in each side, so that when the farmer looks out of any of the windows he can see 12 men at work. One day an additional labourer is given a job, making a total of 33 employees. The farmer then re-arranges them in the fields so that he can still see 12 men only through each window. What was the new arrangement?

Supposing the farm work increases, and it becomes necessary to take on additional labour, how many more men could the farmer employ without disturbing his curious requirement?

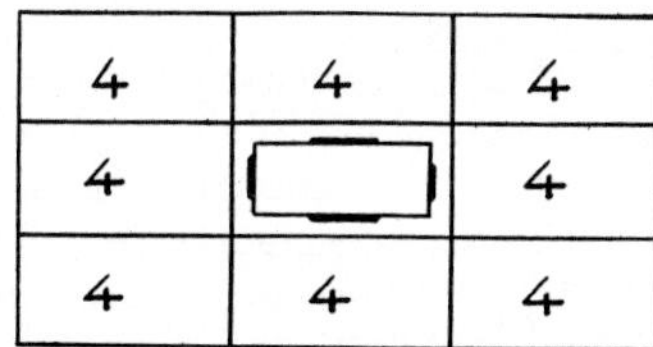

Fig. 6.

The Story of the Steamship *"Edina"*

A Wonderful Veteran of the Seas

By A. R. Prince

THE vessel illustrated on this page is the *"Edina,"* which was launched from the yard of Barclay, Curle and Co. Ltd., Glasgow, on 5th May, 1854. The *"Edina"* is still in service in Australian waters, although she has passed her 82nd birthday, and is believed to be the oldest ship in service in the southern hemisphere. Her record indeed has only been surpassed by two vessels.

The *"Edina"* has had an adventurous life. On her first commission in the British Mercantile Marine she traded for about eight months between Leith, Hull and Hamburg. The Crimean War had then broken out, and in February 1855 she was requisitioned for transport duty, carrying horses and provisions to the Black Sea. Later her passenger accommodation was enlarged and she was able to convey 40 officers and some nurses to the Crimea. It is reported that on her last trip in this service she rammed and sank a Russian vessel.

The "Edina" leaving Melbourne on her daily run to Geelong and back. This vessel was launched in 1854, and is believed to be the oldest ship in regular service in the southern hemisphere.

For five years after reverting to peaceful occupations the *"Edina"* was engaged in ordinary trading; then came her removal to Australian waters. She left Leith for Melbourne on 23rd November, 1862, and arrived in Hobson's Bay on 7th March, 1863, having taken 104 days for the trip, which was made entirely under canvas. The vessel then had three masts, and was square rigged on the foremast. She was really a large steam yacht in build, and her fine yacht-like lines can still be distinguished.

Soon after her arrival at Melbourne, gold was discovered in Otago, New Zealand, and she was diverted to carry miners and prospectors eager to share in the rush. She made exceptionally quick passages that earned her a great reputation. Her average time from Melbourne to the Bluff, in the South Island of New Zealand, was 5½ to 6 days, and on one trip she carried 350 passengers, later returning with 60 passengers and 20,000 oz. of gold.

When the Otago gold rush subsided, and the New Zealand trade began to wane, the *"Edina"* returned to the service between Melbourne and western district ports, and in this she continued until 1873. Then she was bought by Howard Smith and Sons, now the Australian Steamships Pty. Ltd., and was sent to Queensland after an extensive overhaul. She traded on that coast until 1879, when she returned to Melbourne and was placed out of commission for 12 months. During this period she was greatly altered to suit the Geelong trade, into which she was about to enter. Her hull and rig underwent extensive changes, a poop was built at the stern and two masts were removed, so that when she made her first trip across Port Philip Bay to Geelong she was almost a new vessel in appearance.

Later her owners decided to install new engines and boilers, and again the vessel underwent a transformation, for her hull was completely gutted, and she emerged from her temporary retirement with two masts. For a time she traded on the Queensland coast, and was brought back to compete with the *"Courier,"* a new vessel entering the Geelong trade, and the two were keen and worthy rivals for many years. Soon after the *"Edina"* re-entered the Geelong trade, Captain Forbes was placed in command. This was the beginning of a long association between master and ship, for Forbes remained in command for 40 years, being relieved in 1922 by Captain Moxey.

The old ship's career in service in Port Philip Bay has not been without excitement. She collided with the *"Manawatu"* in 1898, and the latter vessel was sunk, but the *"Edina"* was only slightly damaged and was beached. No lives were lost in this disaster. Nearly 15 months later she crashed into the *"Excelsior,"* one of her rivals, during a heavy fog. The *"Excelsior"* sank in deep water, and this time the *"Edina"* also was badly damaged, but her fiddle bow saved her from sinking.

Just before the Great War the veteran was relieved by a fine new passenger steamer, the *"Mourilyan,"* and was laid up. Her days were by no means over, however, in spite of her age and long service, and in 1917 she was brought out and completely overhauled, with the result that she looked like a new steamer. She seemed to bear a charmed life, for in 1928 she escaped with little damage when again concerned in a serious collision in which she sank a steam tug.

In spite of her many overhauls and alterations, the *"Edina's"* external measurements have never been altered since the day she was built, but she has had three pairs of boilers and two sets of engines, and still speeds along at 10 knots. The figurehead that once adorned her prow was a fine example of handicraft. Unfortunately she lost it soon after her gold rush days, for it was splintered to fragments when the steamer *"Dandenong"* drove into her bows while she lay at anchor at Warrnambool, Victoria, riding out a gale.

To-day the wonderful little craft still occupies a place in the active class at Lloyds, and performs her daily run from Melbourne to Portarlington and Geelong and back, a round trip of 80 miles, with the regularity of a clock.

Berthing Ships on Dry Land

How Trawlers are Hauled Ashore for Repairs

AT various periods throughout its career every ship undergoes inspection to ensure that its hull is in good condition. In the case of a large ocean liner or cargo vessel the inspection is carried out in a dry dock into which the vessel is towed by tugs. The dock gate is then closed and the water in the dock is pumped out. As the water is removed the vessel gradually settles on a row of keel-blocks laid along the floor of the dock, and is held upright by means of stout timbers or "shores" placed between the sides of the hull and the dock walls. When all the water has been pumped out from the dock a thorough inspection of the hull can be made and any necessary repairs carried out.

As it is a very expensive operation to operate a dry dock, small vessels such as fishing trawlers and coasting steamers requiring inspection or repairs are frequently simply drawn up out of the water on to slipways. In special cases each slipway is provided with side-slipping or traversing arrangements, by means of which vessels can be accommodated in berths on each side of the main slipway. Berthing ships in this manner is quite simple. The main slipway rails are laid on a gradient of about 1 in 12, and are carried on a timber way-beam that is supported partly on piles and partly on concrete foundations. The vessel is first floated over a cradle that is run down the slipway until it is submerged. The cradle consists of eight carriages on wheels. The vessel is blocked up on it in the usual manner, and it is hauled up the slipway by means of a winch until its wheels rest on the traverser, which also consists of a number of wheeled carriages. The cradle is then locked to the traverser, the haulage ropes are disconnected, and cradle and ship are pulled to one of the side berths.

A trawler being berthed on the Centre Slipway at Grimsby Fish Docks. It is carried on bilge and keel blocks mounted on a travelling cradle, and is hauled by a powerful winch operated from the engine house in the background.

The vessel is then transferred from the cradle to berth blocks laid on the ground. This is done by wedging up the berth blocks and easing off the cradle blocks until the vessel is supported entirely by the former. The cradle and traverser are removed and are then available for dealing with another vessel. A clear space of 4 ft. is left between the keel and the ground, and as only the keel-blocks and bilge-blocks remain under the vessel there is as little obstruction as if the vessel were in a dry dock.

Slipways with side-slipping arrangements such as those described have been constructed at several fishing ports, including Fleetwood and Grimsby, for the purpose of hauling trawlers ashore. The cradle of the slipway at Fleetwood is constructed of steel and consists of eight separate carriages connected by movable links. Each carriage carries two keel-blocks and two bilge-blocks, and is mounted on 12 double-flanged cast steel rail wheels. The keel-blocks are of cast steel with oak caps, and are hinged at one end. Their free ends are lifted when necessary by means of hydraulic rams, each of which is capable of raising a load of 35 tons.

The traverser consists of eight carriages. These are constructed of steel and each is mounted on 16 wheels, which run on two rails at right angles to and below the level of the main slipway rails. Four of the traversing carriages are provided with stud link traversing chains, which are adjustable to allow each to take its fair share of the strain. These chains pass from one side of the traverser over driving sprockets on the traversing gear, which is placed at one side of the slipway site, and are then brought back through pipes underground to the other side of the slipway, where they pass round idler sprockets and then back to the opposite side of the traverser. The cradle and traverser were constructed by John M. Henderson and Co. Ltd., Aberdeen, for the L.M.S. Railway.

Three slipways built in a similar manner have been constructed at the Fish Docks at Grimsby. These are known as the East, West and Centre Slipways, and in this case all the drives are carried out through hydraulic gears supplied by The Variable Speed Gear Ltd., of London. The winches were supplied by John M. Henderson and Co. Ltd.

The largest of the three slipways at Grimsby is the East Slipway, the powerful winch of which is capable of hauling vessels up to 1,080 tons out of the water at the rate of 10 ft. a minute. The winch is driven by a motor of 185 b.h.p. and the maximum pull of its drum is 140 tons. When the pull exerted is reduced to 35 tons the speed of hauling is increased to 40 ft. per min. The length of haul is about 450 ft. The traversing carriage is operated by an electric motor of 90 b.h.p. and under load moves at a speed of nine feet a minute.

The West and Centre Slipways are intended for berthing vessels up to 660 tons.

The side-slipping slipways referred to are covered by patents held by Messrs. Henderson and Nicol, Civil Engineers, Aberdeen.

Motor Yacht's New Engines

The illustration on this page shows the motor yacht *"White Lady,"* which has recently been converted to run on oil fuel. She was formerly fitted with three 125 h.p. petrol engines, but these have been replaced by two A.E.C. 6-cylinder 100 h.p. marine units, which were installed by The Ferry Engine Co. Ltd., of Woolston, Southampton. Trials have shown that the change to oil engine propulsion was justified, for the two new engines give the vessel a steady speed of almost 12 knots, while with the three petrol units, developing 175 h.p. more, she could not attain a speed of more than 14 knots. The small difference in speed is made up for by the great saving in fuel costs.

The *"White Lady"* has an overall length of 75 ft., a beam of 13 ft. 6 in., and a moulded depth of 8 ft. 2 in. The captain's cabin and accommodation for the crew are forward, while aft is the owner's cabin, and two others. The wheelhouse is well forward on the deck level, and in it the engine controls are grouped round the wheel. A new form of Lockheed hydraulic control is normally used, but there are standard telegraphs for use in case of emergency.

The motor yacht "White Lady," which is fitted with twin A.E.C. 100 h.p. 6-cylinder marine oil engines, travelling at speed of nearly 12 knots. Photograph by courtesy of The Associated Equipment Co. Ltd., Southall.

"No. 552"

The formal contract for the construction of the new express liner, *"No. 552"* at the Clydebank yard of John Brown and Co. Ltd., was signed in October last, and work has now commenced. It is expected that her gross tonnage will be 2,000 higher, and her length 12 ft. to 18 ft. more than the corresponding figures for the *"Queen Mary."*

The order for the hull castings of the liner has been placed with Wm. Beardmore and Co. Ltd., of Parkhead, Glasgow. These castings will be of exceptional dimensions and include the cast steel stern and stern frames, cast steel shaft brackets, and the rudder. The steel required for the hull is being supplied by Colvilles Ltd. The new liner will be laid down on the same stocks as those on which the *"Queen Mary"* was built, and the keel box is now under construction. The shaping of the keel frames and plates will take about four months.

Recent Additions to Our Life-boat Fleet

A new twin-screw motor life-boat has recently taken up her station at Yarmouth, Isle of Wight. This craft, named *"Yarmouth,"* is the first built by the Royal National Life-boat Institution to have twin-screw Diesel engines, each of those installed developing 40 h.p., and together giving a speed of 8¼ knots. Enough fuel oil is carried to enable the vessel to travel 237 miles at full speed without refuelling.

The new life-boat is of the Watson cabin type, and has a length of 46 ft., a breadth of 12 ft. 9 in., and in service, with crew and gear on board, she weighs 19¾ tons. The hull is divided into seven watertight compartments, and is fitted with 142 air-cases. The engine room is a watertight compartment, and each engine is itself watertight, so that it can continue running even if the engine-room is flooded. The vessel carries a crew of eight, and in rough weather can take 95 people on board. She has a line-throwing gun and an electric searchlight, and has electric light throughout.

The Civil Service has presented a new life-boat of the Watson cabin type to the Royal National Life-boat Institution, and the vessel has been named *"Civil Service No. 6."*

Four motor life-boats of the light "Liverpool" class have been laid down by the Royal National Life-boat Institution. This type of boat is for use at stations where it is necessary to launch from a carriage on an open beach. Three of the boats will be stationed at Peel, in the Isle of Man, Blackpool and Kilmore respectively.

Research Ship for British Admiralty

A contract has been placed by the Admiralty with Philip and Son Ltd., of Dartmouth, for the construction of a new research vessel. The *"Research,"* as she will be named, will be built chiefly of teak. She will have a displacement of 650 tons, and will be rigged as a brigantine. Bronze bolts will be used for fastening together the wooden frames and planking of the hull, and the anchors will also be of bronze, while gunmetal will be used in other places where metal is necessary. The ship will be fitted with an auxiliary Diesel engine specially constructed by Petters Ltd., Yeovil, so that practically all magnetic metals will be eliminated.

The reason for the use of wood and other non-magnetic substances is that the vessel is to be used for magnetic investigations, and it is vital that no part of the ship should contain properties likely to interfere with the research. The vessel also will be used in the carrying out of oceanographic surveys.

The construction of the *"Research"* is expected to occupy two years, and to cost £100,000. Her complement will number 31, including the scientific staff.

The World's Fastest Tankers

The world's fastest tankers are Japanese and have a light ship speed of nearly 19 knots, and a loaded speed of nearly 18 knots.

The average speed for the ordinary commercial tanker still stands at 11½ knots loaded, and the speed record for vessels of this type so far has been held by the fleet of the Anglo-Saxon Petroleum Company Ltd. This speed has been bettered by the 14,930-ton Dutch tanker *"Basilea,"* built by Kockums, for Camillo Eitzen and Co. This is a ship of advanced design, and is stated to have reached a speed of 13½ knots in fully loaded condition.

* * * *

Statistics compiled by the Transatlantic Passenger Conference show that 421,018 persons travelled between the coasts of the United States and Europe between 1st January and 16th September of this year, compared with 387,109 in the corresponding period of 1935, an increase of 33,909.

An Attractive 24 ft. Motor Launch

The upper illustration on this page shows a motor launch recently built and fitted out by Saunders-Roe Ltd., of Cowes, I.O.W. It has an overall length of 24 ft., a beam of 6 ft. and a depth amidships of 3 ft. 3 in. The hull is constructed entirely of double skin mahogany.

The motor installed is a 6-cylinder Chrysler Crown, which develops 53 h.p. at 1,600 r.p.m. and 92 h.p. at 3,000 r.p.m. It runs on petrol, and this is housed in a tank under the seats in the after cockpit. An electric starter is fitted.

The launch has a forward cockpit for the helmsman, in which car-type steering gear is fitted on the port side. All controls are arranged within easy reach of the helmsman, who is sheltered behind a glass windscreen fitted in gun-metal, chromium plated frames. The stem band of the vessel is of polished brass, chromium plated, and the boat is finished in white and chromium.

A 24 ft. motor launch travelling at speed. Photograph by courtesy of the builders, Saunders-Roe Ltd., Cowes.

A French Sailing Vessel for Southern Seas

The lower illustration on this page shows the three-masted sailing vessel *"Oiseau-de-Iles,"* which is fitted with an auxiliary engine and is in service in the South Seas. The vessel has been built by the Soc. An. des Anciens Chantiers Dubigeon, Nantes-Chantenay, for the Compagnie Francaise des Photosphates de l'Océanie, and is intended for transporting passengers and cargo between Papeete, Tahiti and other South Sea islands.

The vessel has a length of 133 ft., and a cargo-carrying capacity of 250 tons. The hull is divided into five watertight compartments, and the double bottom carries water ballast. She is fitted with a lead keel, and this renders her very stable when running under sail. The wooden masts reach a height of about 110 ft. above the deck. In the fore part of the vessel are the crew's quarters and the cargo hold, while the officers' cabins, three passenger cabins and the wireless room are aft.

The auxiliary machinery consists of a Sulzer Diesel engine that develops 370 b.h.p. at 300 r.p.m. Alone it gives the vessel a speed of 9 knots, though this can of course be bettered by the use of the sails and the Diesel engine together. The bronze propeller can be uncoupled from the engine when the vessel is proceeding under sail. The auxiliary machinery consists of a 34 kW electric generator, a 15 kW auxiliary generator, an electrically-driven auxiliary air compressor, and three electrically-driven pumps for general service, fuel and fresh water. A refrigerating plant is also provided.

Union-Castle Liner's New Record

The Union-Castle liner *"Stirling Castle"* recently created a new record for the passage from Capetown to Southampton, completing the voyage in 13 days 9 hrs. 13 min. Her actual steaming time was only 13 days 5 hrs. 43 min., as there was a delay of over 3 hrs. at Madeira.

Great Ports Becoming Busier

The amount of shipping using the Port of London during the year ending December 31st, 1935, totalled 59,762,150 tons. During the first seven months of the year, 35,733,192 tons entered and cleared the Port. This is an increase of 5 per cent. on the corresponding figures for last year.

The inward and outward shipping on the Clyde for the year ending 30th June, 1936, amounted to 14,309,455 tons.

Floating Bridge for Isle of Wight

A new chain-driven floating bridge for service between East and West Cowes has been completed by J. Samuel White and Co. Ltd. The bridge is 108 ft. long and is used for the conveyance of passengers and motor vehicles. It is propelled by means of two driving wheels operating on stationary cross-river chains. The wheels are turned by oil-electric machinery comprising two 27 h.p. oil engines directly coupled to 15 kW dynamos. The main propulsion motor has an output of 40 h.p.

The "Oiseau-de-Iles," a sailing vessel fitted with an auxiliary Sulzer Diesel engine, which is in service in the South Seas. Photograph by courtesy of Sulzer Bros. (London) Ltd., London.

The *"City of Benares"*

A new liner, the *"City of Benares,"* recently made her maiden voyage. This vessel, which has a gross tonnage of 11,081 tons, has been built by Barclay, Curle and Co., of Glasgow, for the Ellerman Line's City fleet. She is the first of the Company's vessels to have two funnels, and she has accommodation for 219 passengers, all in one class. It is believed that a sister ship will be under construction in 1939, when the City Line records its centenary.

World's Largest Whaler

The largest ship in the whaling trade is the *"Terje Viken,"* built in Germany for the service of United Whalers Ltd. She was built at the Deschimag yard, on the Weser, and has a gross tonnage of 20,638, with a deadweight carrying capacity of 29,000 tons, and a displacement at that loading of 43,000 tons. She has a length of 633 ft., a beam of 80 ft., and a loaded draught of 38 ft. Her propelling machinery comprises a twin-screw arrangement of triple-expansion engines, designed for a speed of about 12 knots. The cylinders are 22 in., 36¼ in., and 58¼ in. diameter, with a stroke of 39½ in., and they exhaust into Bauer-Wach low-pressure turbines. Steam is raised in six oil-fired, single-ended Scotch boilers.

Great Russian Canal Scheme

A scheme is now in operation that will provide a direct waterway from the Black Sea to the Baltic. This will establish direct river communication between such large and important cities as Kiev, Leningrad, and Moscow, and in addition will irrigate 250,000 hectares of arid land in the Ukraine and Crimea. The Lovat River will form the main link in the new river system, and the depth of the waterway will not be less than 1.7 m., or nearly 7 ft., throughout its entire length. Reservoirs will be built on the Upper Dnieper and its tributaries to ensure the water supply necessary to obtain this depth, and the bed of the Dnieper River from Orsha to Dnepropetrovsk will be deepened.

Waterway between Montreal to New York

An international commission is studying the possibility of a deep-water route between the St. Lawrence and Hudson rivers to link up the harbours of Montreal and New York. Shallow-draught vessels are at present able to travel from Montreal to New York by way of the St. Lawrence, Lake Champlain, and the Hudson River, and the commission has to consider whether the commerce between the two countries would justify increasing the depths in the canals to 20 ft. or 25 ft. The construction of a proposed shortened route would lessen the distance between the two cities by over 1,200 miles, and lengthen the navigation season of the Port of Montreal by thirty days.

* * * *

Two new oil-electric ice-breakers are being built in Russia. The ships will be named the *"Kirov"* and the *"Kuibyshev,"* and have a displacement of 8,330 tons.

Building with Concrete

Lasting Structures with Steel Reinforcement

REINFORCED concrete is rapidly becoming the leading building material of our time. The progress that has been made in the application of this material during the last few years is due largely to its great adaptability and relatively low cost, and also to the fact that a reinforced concrete structure can be erected in very much less time than is possible with other materials, such as stone and brick. Another great point in its favour is the ease with which decorative work can be carried out, for the material lends itself readily to moulding in almost any form.

In addition to its wide-spread use for constructing all kinds of public buildings, concrete is now an accepted material for the building of bridges, highways, viaducts, power stations and water reservoirs. It is also being increasingly used in the construction of open-air and enclosed swimming baths and bathing pools, and is particularly suitable and economical for this purpose, as it is designed to offer resistance to the side pressure met with in this kind of work.

The fine diving stage at the Scarborough bathing pool. It is built entirely of reinforced concrete. For the illustrations to this article we are indebted to The Trussed Concrete Steel Co. Ltd., London.

Concrete consists of a mixture of coarse and fine rock or sand particles, called aggregate, cement and water. The cement acts as mortar and when it hardens binds the aggregate to produce a solid mass. The best mixture is one in which there is enough cement to coat every particle, and to fill the spaces or voids between the grains of sand or larger particles of aggregate.

The old method of using large volumes of mass concrete had the disadvantage of excessive weight and cost. The fact that the tensile strength of concrete is low largely caused this state of affairs. Reinforced concrete has remedied this, as the steel reinforcement is added to supply the deficiency of tensile strength and is designed to be placed in the position and in the correct quantity required adequately to resist the tensile forces in any type of structure. This innovation allowed the building of structures in reinforced concrete which were impossible in mass concrete. In addition, the type of structure previously built in mass can now be erected in reinforced concrete with great economy of material, size and cost. Reinforced concrete in which steel rods or mesh is used should not be confused with encased structural steelwork in which steel joists are first built into a complete frame and then encased in concrete for fire protection.

In another method, known as the "Hy-Rib" system, the reinforcing material is made to serve a dual purpose. In this case the reinforcement is in the form of steel mesh sheets strongly ribbed. These sheets can be curved if necessary, and besides giving additional strength to the finished work, they also assist the builders in the early stages of construction, for they are so designed that the wet concrete is retained against their surface. By their use a sound and lasting concrete structure that is able to withstand high pressure is readily assured.

This type of reinforcement is particularly valuable in the construction of roofs and in similar work. The upper illustration on the opposite page is an example of its use for this purpose. It shows a concrete roof under construction at the Kemsley Mills, Sittingbourne, Kent, the world's largest paper mills, and part of the "Hy-Rib" steel mesh is visible. By using Hy-Rib 24,000 sq. ft. of flat roofing were constructed there without the need for timber shuttering. The curved ends of the Hy-Rib sheets rested upon the lower flanges of the steel beams, thereby providing the centering for the joist casing. In work of this kind the wet concrete is poured on to the sheets, levelled, and left to set. A certain amount trickles through the steel mesh and forms a "key" on the underside, to which plaster is added to make a smooth even finish for the ceiling.

In the construction of a concrete building or other structure the plastic cement is moulded to the required shape by pouring it into forms or moulds, which are known as "shuttering." These are generally made of timber that has been suitably treated to prevent the concrete from sticking to them when it hardens. In the case of a large structure it is customary to pour the concrete into the assembled forms down chutes radiating from pouring towers to different parts of the building site. These towers are sometimes carried up to great heights, and hoists raise skips of concrete to be poured down the chutes, the nozzles of which can be swung round to the point at which the material is to be placed. During pouring the concrete is worked evenly into all parts of the forms by spading.

One of the most interesting applications of reinforced concrete is in the construction of water towers. A very good example of work of this kind is the giant water tower at Caister-on-Sea, Norfolk, shown in the lower illustrations on the opposite page. This forms part of the water supply system of Great Yarmouth, and is the largest of its type in England.

From the ground to the top of the domed roof of the tank the height of this immense tower is 161 ft. 9 in. The concrete tank is divided into two compartments, the outer one of which holds 647,000 gallons of water, while the inner compartment has a capacity of 137,000 gallons. The total capacity of the tank therefore is 784,000 gallons of water, weighing approximately 3,500 tons, and the whole of this tremendous weight, together with that of the tanks themselves, is supported by the single concrete shaft, which has an internal diameter of 51 ft.

A firm foundation of course was necessary for such a massive structure. The ground at the site of the tower consists of about 2 ft. of soil over a layer of yellow clay 6 ft. in depth, under which is a bed of very compact sand and soft sandstone which extends to a depth of 45 ft. Into this three concentric rings of reinforced concrete piles 14 in. square were driven sufficiently deep to penetrate 5 ft. 9 in. into the compact sand, nearly 14 ft. below the surface, and on top of them a circular ring of concrete 9 ft. 6 in. wide by 3 ft. thick was constructed to form a base for the main shaft.

A concrete roof in course of construction at the Kemsley Paper Mills, Sittingbourne, showing sheets of ribbed steel mesh reinforcement in position.

The shaft itself has 12 sides, and up to a height of 20 ft. 6 in. its walls are 2 ft. thick. Above this level they are splayed back to a thickness of 12 in. thick. The concrete forming them is reinforced with vertical steel bars on each face, with horizontal bars outside them, and these were taken well into the adjoining side walls in order to ensure adequate hold.

At a height of 108 ft. 9 in. above the ground the shaft is capped by a stout concrete collar 21 in. wide and 4 ft. 3 in. deep, which encircles the bottom of the tank. Above this is an inverted cone that contains approximately 570 tons of concrete and 47 tons of reinforcement, and in turn has resting on it a further collar that is circular inside and 12-sided outside. This forms the base for the outer tank wall, which at its lowest level is 21 in. thick, and becomes thinner in a series of steps of 2 in., its thickness at the top being 7 in. The roof of the tank is in the form of a dome of 79 ft. span, which rises 12 ft. in the centre and is 6 in. thick throughout. A stout concrete wall divides the tank into two separate compartments.

A particularly interesting part of the constructional work was the supporting of the shuttering used for forming the overhanging part of the tank. This portion of the work is 113 ft. above ground level and no outside scaffolding was used, the whole of the necessary support being obtained from the completed portion of the shaft itself. In making this part and the outer sides of the tank practically continuous concreting was required, and altogether 570 tons of concrete were poured. This great weight was supported on temporary or "false work" built out from the shaft and consisting of trussed timber cantilevers. These were fixed to the shaft and provided support for other timbers shaped to give the correct form or profile for the cone shuttering, which was made up in specially designed panels.

The concrete used in building the tower was produced by two mixers, which served two skip hoists placed opposite each other on the centre line of the tower. The mixture for the tank was made up of 1 part of specially fine ground cement, 1½ parts of fine aggregate and 3¾ of coarse aggregate. No waterproofing compound of any kind was used, and the results have been entirely satisfactory.

Access to the tanks is given by a steel staircase that is arranged in seven flights and leads to a gallery platform immediately below the upper windows of the shaft of the tower. From there a short staircase rises to a second cross gallery leading to an access shaft 6 ft. in diameter. The cross gallery is suspended from steel hangars fixed to connections that were cast in the bottom of the tank during construction. A vertical ladder up the access shaft leads to the valve platform, and also to the roof, and the tanks themselves can be entered when necessary by means of galvanised iron ladders.

Water is delivered to the tower from a pumping station at Ormesby about 3 miles away, through a 24 in. cast iron pipe, which passes up inside the tower shaft. A special valve is fitted so that the supply pipe can be made to serve also as the delivery pipe from the tank. A 15 in. diameter overflow pipe is provided alongside the supply pipe, and the inner tank supply and delivery pipe is connected through the division wall to that for the outer tank. Wash-out pipes of 6 in. diameter lead from the lowest level of each of the tanks and are connected to the overflow pipe. All the valves are operated from the valve platform, which is 2 ft. above the highest water level.

England's largest concrete water tower of its type at Caister-on-Sea, Norfolk. The smaller illustration shows the shuttering used to give the correct form to the concrete during erection.

The tower was built to the instructions of the Chief Engineer to the Great Yarmouth Water Works Company, and the design and construction of the tower were entrusted to The Trussed Concrete Steel Company Ltd., London.

Another interesting example of unusual concrete work is the diving stage illustrated on the opposite page. This has been erected at Scarborough and is constructed entirely of specially mixed concrete with steel reinforcement.

Cigarette Cards

The Story of a Popular Collecting Hobby

By I. O. Evans

UNTIL about fifty years ago there were no cigarette cards, at any rate in Great Britain. In those days cigarettes were not sold in the stout card packets we have to-day, but in flimsy packets of paper. To keep the cigarettes from being crushed, little slips of cards were inserted, just big enough to go into the packets. These "stiffeners," as they were called, were at first blank. Then, in 1887, W. D. and H. O. Wills hit on the idea of using them for advertisement. They began by printing wording on them; then they used a representation of a packet of "Gold Flake"; and from this they went on to pictures of tins, and then to showcards and posters. At last, in 1895—perhaps they had found that people were collecting their little advertisement cards—they put on pictures of general interest. One of the first series they issued was "Ships"; another was "Soldiers and Sailors of all Nations"; another was "Kings and Queens." The "cigarette cards"—they still call them "stiffeners" in the trade—proved very popular, and soon other firms were issuing them. Nowadays we have a large number of new series every year.

"BRIGHTON BELLE" ELECTRIC EXPRESS

CHURCHMAN'S CIGARETTES

THE "QUEEN MARY" LAUNCHED

It is surprising how many of these little cards are issued. The distribution by one of the larger tobacco firms of cards dealing with a popular subject may run into hundreds of millions of one series. Thousands of series have been issued, and though not all of these have been so very big, the total of cards that have been printed must amount to billions. Many of these are thrown away, many are treasured for a time and then lost; but very many have found a home in the albums and cases of collectors.

Of the many subjects that have been put "on the cards," those dealing with the different branches of engineering are very popular. Ships, as we have seen, were among the first subjects dealt with, and they have been favourite subjects right down to the present day, when a special issue has been produced to commemorate the launching and the first voyage of the "*Queen Mary*." "Famous Steamships," "Life on Board a Man-of-War," "Life on a Liner," "The Evolution of the Steamship," "Ships of all Ages," "Strange Craft," "The Story of Navigation," "The Rig of Ships"—these are a few of the series that deal with navigation, from coracles and birch-bark canoes to the submarine, the dreadnought, and the transatlantic liner.

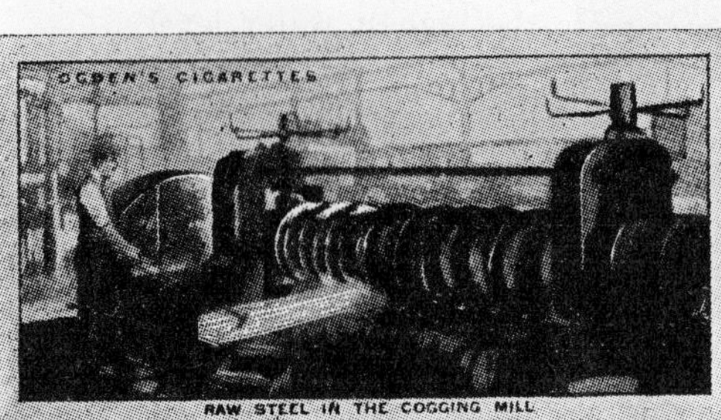

RAW STEEL IN THE COGGING MILL

Railways, too, have been the subject of many a series. "Landmarks in Railway Progress," "Wonderful Railway Travel," "Famous Expresses," "Engineering Wonders"—these deal with the history and romance of the railroad; while "Modern Railways" reminds us of present-day locomotive engineering, "Construction of Railway Trains" gives us an insight into the work of the building sheds, and "Model Railways" recalls our own small-scale experiments as railway engineers.

For shipping and railways information was ready to hand, but aeroplanes were a new thing, and at first one or two mistakes were made in describing them. Two cards had their descriptions interchanged, so that the famous Blèriot monoplane, the first to fly the Channel, is described as a triplane, and an Avro triplane, with three planes in its tail and wings instead of one or two, appears as a monoplane! As aviation progressed, however, its record on the cigarette cards progressed also, and there appeared sets illustrating "Speed, Land, Sea and Air," "The History of Aviation," "Types of Aeroplanes," and "A Day on the Airway."

ASSEMBLING & SCREWING CARRIAGE DOOR

Other branches of engineering also are dealt with, including "Modern Inventions," "Famous Inventions," "Engineering Wonders," "Motor Cars." So are science, "Scientific Inventions and Discoveries," and art, "Statuary" and "World's Masterpieces." The handyman will welcome a set on "Tools and How to Use them," and for Scouts there have been no less than five series, including not only general troop work, but hints on most of the badges and illustrations on natural history.

Sport is naturally another favourite subject. Recently series have been issued dealing with "Famous Footballers," "Cricket, Tennis, and Golf Celebrities," "Football Teams," "Races—Historic and Modern," and "Boxing Lessons." Film stars appear on a large number of series. When the cigarette cards first came out the cinema had not "arrived," but music-hall artists and famous actresses were just as popular as the film stars are to-day.

Natural history interests many of us, and whatever branch of it we like we shall find sets to suit us—"Feathered Friends," "Butterflies and Moths," "Birds and their Eggs," "A Kodak at the Zoo," "British Trees and their Uses," "Garden Life," "Life in Ponds" and "Streams" and "Constellations." For lovers of outdoor scenery are sets showing "Beauty Spots of Great Britain," and "Glorious Britain." Many parts of the Empire, and some foreign countries, have had sets, or parts of sets, devoted to them, and there have also been series with an historical interest.

Every important event has brought forward its own series of cards. Several appeared relating to the Boer War, and during the Great War there came out a number of sets, "V.C. Heroes," "Celebrities of the War," "Army Corps and Divisional Signs," "Women on War Work." There have been sets dealing with the Gods and Goddesses of ancient myth, with "Scottish Clans," "Famous Escapes," "Eastern Proverbs," "Interesting Door-Knockers," nursery rhymes, characters out of *"Robin Hood," "Lorna Doone," "David Copperfield," "The Swiss Family Robinson,"* and the adventure stories of Conan Doyle. Indeed, it would be hard to say what subject has not been turned into a series of cards!

When so many cards are produced, it is only natural that some of them should show mistakes. Such cards, as soon as the publishers know about them, are replaced by corrected issues; for this reason there are only a few of them to be had, and collectors seek them anxiously and are willing to pay more than usual for them. Some of these misprints are quite amusing. One card shows a picture of the last French Emperor, Napoleon III; on the back is the story of how Winston Churchill escaped from the Boers! Among the "Famous Characters of Fiction" illustrated on the cigarette cards was Uncle Tom, the negro slave—a rare misprint shows him with a black face but with white hands and feet!

In America cards were issued earlier than in Britain. Canada, India, and South Africa have produced their own series; so have lands so far apart as Belgium and China. Germany has issued many fine series, but recently it has devoted them all to spreading the ideals of Herr Hitler and his Nazis. In Italy a set is being issued on "Hints during Air-raids"; a complete set of the cards can be exchanged for a gas-mask. More peaceful is Holland, which has produced beautiful pictures of Natural History subjects. A serious book on the cactus plant has, instead of the ordinary illustrations, spaces where cigarette cards on the subject are to be gummed in! From Siam we get some interesting sets, including cards that show views and others that have cock fighting scenes and pictures of giants on them.

The L.M.S.R. Mobile Cinema

The L.M.S.R. make considerable use of films for educating their staff in the various subjects connected with the operation of their huge railway concern. These films are made on L.M.S.R. premises, with employees acting as "extras," and give members of the staff accurate knowledge of subjects that would otherwise be lost to them owing to the fact that they seldom have opportunities of learning anything about the company and its activities outside their own particular sphere. For instance, porters and clerks are able to become familiar with many of the intricacies of the building of a modern locomotive or coach, branches of railway work with which they do not come into contact.

In the past these educational films have been exhibited in halls at various centres on the system, but the inconvenience of this arrangement has led to the introduction of the L.M.S.R. mobile film theatre. This was introduced last month, and is a former L.N.W.R. coach converted for its present use at the L.M.S.R. Carriage and Wagon Works at Wolverton. It represents the first attempt to take purely instructional films direct to the staff at the place of their employment, and is claimed to be the first railway vehicle of its kind in the world to be equipped with a standard 35 mm. professional projector. Its introduction marks a further step in the development of the use of films for educational purposes.

The L.M.S.R. Mobile Film Theatre. This has seating capacity for 52 persons, and is now touring L.M.S.R. centres, exhibiting films showing various branches of railway working.

Many of the films to be shown in this theatre have been prepared to demonstrate to the staff the right and wrong methods of carrying out work in various branches of railway activity. These films are to be shown to the employees at railway stations and goods depots throughout the country. One film deals in a simple and straightforward manner with the many problems connected with the efficient handling of trains at stations. Much valuable time is lost, especially at stations of the larger and busier type, when the loading and unloading is not carried out as quickly as possible, but lost time can be regained if the work of the station staff is efficient. The first part of the film deals with the wrong methods. This is followed by scenes showing how operations ought to be carried out, and better and more correct working should be the result of this effective demonstration. Other films in the series deal with salesmanship and work at goods depots.

The mobile theatre was demonstrated at Euston, and commenced its tour at Birmingham last month. It will continue touring until 18th June, by which time it will have visited 68 stations and depots, according to the present schedule, and will have given a total of 572 performances.

The theatre is self-contained and has a seating capacity for 52 persons. The seats are arranged to hold four in a row, and the floor is raised from the front to a height of 15 in. at the back, so that every member of the audience has an uninterrupted view of the screen. Power for the projectors, and for lighting and heating, is obtained from a motor generator set driven by a high-speed Diesel engine. The engine is fitted with a governor and maintains the steady speed of 1,500 r.p.m. Sufficient fuel oil to last a week is carried, and this is stored in tanks in the roof of the coach. The oil is fed from the tanks to the engine by gravity.

The equipment in the operating box includes two projectors, one of which is for use with sub-standard 16 mm. silent film, while the other is for projecting full size 35 mm. sound film, such as is used in a modern cinema theatre. The 35 mm. machine is a Phillips Transportable. The illumination is given by a 750 watt. incandescent lamp, and the machine is equipped for playing gramophone records.

Skeletons in the Bath Room

How Sponges are Harvested from the Sea

By Harold J. Shepstone, F.R.G.S.

HOW many of us, when we sponge ourselves down in the bath room, realise that we are making use of a skeleton, or rather of the skeletons of countless thousands of creatures. "A sponge," says Professor Huxley, "is a kind of sub-aqueous city, where the people are arranged about the streets and roads in such a manner that each can easily appropriate his food from the water as it passes along." The fact is, the sponge is something of a zoological wonder. Originally it was looked upon as a plant, but in reality it is a very low form of animal life. It is almost at the bottom of the zoological ladder, and takes the form of a jelly-like mass, which separates itself from the shell or skeleton when the sponge is lifted out of the water and squeezed.

In its native state the sponge also is the home of numerous small sea creatures. Dr. A. S. Pearse tells how he studied the occupants of sponges at the Marine Biological Station at Tortugas, an island off the coast of Florida. He secured a sponge, about the size of a large washtub, and placed it in a container so that no animals would be lost. He cut it into thin sections, as one would slice a loaf of bread. Each slice was then carefully examined and the animals picked out, placed in bowls, and counted under a reading glass of considerable magnifying power. When the count was completed, Dr. Pearse learned that this particular living hotel had housed 17,128 guests, which meant that there were approximately two animals to every cubic inch of its volume.

Among this great host of creatures were five fishes, each about an inch in length, having exceedingly slender bodies well adapted to life in the canals of the sponge. Annelid worms to the number of 229 were taken from the canals and, embedded in the tissues of the sponge, were 38 barnacles, which were in direct connection with the sea through surface holes. Of the animals that had taken up their abode in this single sponge, small shrimps were by far the most numerous, however, the count registering 16,352.

The sponge fishing fleet of the Bahamas. About 400 schooners and sloops are engaged in the sponge industry of these islands.

Even when all animal life has been removed from a sponge and it is nothing more than a skeleton, its animal nature has not been entirely destroyed. This is easily proved by subjecting a small piece to a flame. It does not burn brightly, but it leaves a small, charcoal-like residue when entirely burnt up. All the time that it is burning it gives off a smell very similar to the burning of hair, a result that is seldom observed in the burning of vegetable matter.

When we say "sponge," we are inclined to think of the familiar article used for the toilet and bath. As a matter of fact, there are about 2,000 different kinds of sponges, and they vary considerably in size, from a pin's head to several feet in height. They are of various shapes and colours, and even the so-called bath variety shows considerable differences in quality.

While sponges are to be found all over the world in every sea, they develop better and reproduce more freely in some beds than in others. Until fairly recently they were regarded as peculiar to the waters of the Mediterranean. Then it was discovered that sponges were as common as mussels on the reefs between Florida and the Bahamas. The result was the establishment of a sponge industry in these islands that in some respects promises to rival that of the Mediterranean.

The spongy skeleton adheres very firmly to the sea bottom, or the rocks on which it grows, and how to obtain it uninjured is a problem which the fishermen have endeavoured to solve in various ways, including diving, dredging, and harpooning or hooking.

Diving is the oldest and, from the merchant's point of view, the safest and most profitable method, and it has been practised round about the Greek Islands, Sicily, the Levant, and the north of Africa for ages. There are 6,000 men now employed in the Levant sponge-fishery alone, and about the same number are at work in other parts of the Mediterranean. These Greek divers are trained to their task almost from infancy, and become gradually accustomed to working under water and to enduring pressure so great that less than half of it would mean death to an untrained man.

These undressed divers work from boats. On arriving over the beds where sponges are known to exist, the diver takes a length of rope. One end is made fast to the boat, while a large white stone is tied at the other end through a hole that has been drilled in it. Picking up the stone, the diver fastens it loosely to his chest by giving the line a turn or two round his body, and without more ado plunges overboard.

A second or two later he is upon the sea bottom, where, if the water is clear, he uses the white stone as a landmark. He leaves go of the rope and wanders round, always able to find his way back as long as he can see the stone. As often as not there is trouble going on at the bottom, however; a fight among the ground-fish, or a dolphin poking about after molluscs, makes the water as thick as a London fog, and in some grounds even the man's own movements are sufficient to cloud everything. The diver then dare not let go of the rope, but must carry the stone about with him. Hurriedly tearing off the sponges that lie to his hand, he stuffs them into a net-bag slung from his shoulder, and gives a couple of jerks to the rope. He and the bag and the stone are then swiftly hoisted up. Although sharks are plentiful in these waters, it is seldom that a diver is attacked, the splashing and shouting being sufficient as a rule to frighten them away. If a shark becomes too venturesome it is liable to be shot, for a gun is carried in every boat for that purpose.

On reaching the surface, the diver is hauled into the boat to get his breath while the next man goes down. I have seen it stated that whenever these fellows come up from the sea floor, blood flows from their mouths, ears, and noses. How many gallons of blood do the authors of such a statement suppose a man can afford to lose in the course of a day? As a rule, a Mediterranean diver expects to bleed in this manner only when he goes down for the first time after being away from such work some months, as, for instance, on the first day of the season, and then only once. What is more, the divers regard this as not only a healthy sign, but as a proof that they are fit for their work. Indeed, if any man should find that bleeding does not then occur, he will not attempt another descent that day, nor will he start regular work until he has bled.

From five to 10 fathoms is the usual depth to which these naked divers descend, though a few will venture to 13 and even 15 fathoms. The brief time which they are able to remain under water at these depths is of little use for such hard and lengthy work, however, and the effort seems almost to rob them of the power to wrench the larger sponges free from their natural moorings. The average time spent on these descents is 80 seconds, but a few can remain down for as long as 3½ minutes.

Sponges grow at varying depths, much below 10 to 15 fathoms. To secure those at depths between 15 and 50 fathoms professional divers are employed, and as they are supplied with air they can remain below for some time. As soon as such a diver reaches the bottom, he takes from his shoulders a coil of thin cord which he has brought down with him. This is known as the "track-line." Perhaps one end is weighted; if not, he ties it to whatever fixture he can find, and then sets off on his travels to the end of his tether, which is a fairly long one. He lets the trackline run from his hand as he goes, stopping every now and then to gather the finest and largest sponges he can see, and packing them as closely as possible in the net-bag that hangs over his shoulders. When his bag is full, or he finds he cannot remain down any longer, he carefully fastens his bag and even ropes it to his body, and then gives the "pull-up" signal—one long sustained pull till the hauling begins. The reason for tying the bag to the diver's body is to prevent its getting entangled with his lines while he is being hauled up.

Hooking sponges in the Bahamas. The fisherman detects the presence of a sponge by means of a bucket with a magnifying glass in the bottom.

As these men gather sponges, so they keep a watchful eye on possible submerged treasures. The waters off Greece, Sicily and Cyprus are looked upon as the oldest if not the richest submarine treasure grounds in the world, and many valuable articles have been recovered by the sponge gatherers. Sometimes the diver brings up a "surprise packet" on speculation. I knew one Mediterranean diver who, with great trouble and at some risk, succeeded in taking on board a mysterious iron box, that suggested at least deeds, if not banknotes, jewels, and bonds. When he came to open it in the presence of an admiring and expectant crew, he found nothing but a ruined silk hat and a dozen collars. To add insult to injury, the collars were a size or two too small for every man on board!

In very deep water, that is below 50 fathoms, sponges are gathered by dredging. This method is used only in the winter months, because then the equinoctial and autumn storms have had plenty of time to tear up the seaweed that otherwise would fill up the dredge, or hamper the movements of the gear. In any case, dredging is not regarded as eminently satisfactory, as it is inclined to damage many of the sponges.

The dredge used is a somewhat formidable-looking affair, resembling an immense packing-case 3 ft. high and about 18 ft. square. It is open at the top, and has a large net-bag hanging from the bottom. The meshes of the net are 4 in. square, and are made of camel's-hair cord as thick as a man's finger. This unwieldy apparatus is thrown overboard on a good sponge-ground and towed gently along like a trawl. It is then hauled up, the sponges are taken out, and the dredge is dropped overboard again.

Along the east side of the Adriatic Sea sponges are found at almost all depths. Those close to the surface are obtained by means of a kind of hooked harpoon, resembling in design a three-pronged rake. The fishermen detect the presence of the sponge by means of a spy-glass. This is nothing more than a bucket with a fairly powerful magnifying glass in the bottom through which the fishermen locates the sponge. In the Adriatic the use of the spy-glass is made easier in a very ingenious, if simple manner. Every boat carries a small supply of pebbles, and, when the look-out man wishes to inspect the ground, he dips four or five of these in oil and tosses them one by one in a curved line in front of the boat. Each pebble, as it sinks, scatters tiny drops of oil all the way down, and these help to clear the water, and thus afford a less obstructed view. When he detects the presence of a sponge, the fisherman proceeds to tear it loose with his rake. This task calls for skill if the sponge is to be obtained whole. The aim is to slide the rake immediately between the rock and the root of the sponge, and then to wrench the prize off bodily and bring it to the surface.

Hooking is the method employed by the fishermen of the Bahamas, where the sponges are not only close to the surface, but also are very plentiful. Every week a fleet of schooners sets off from Nassau to the sponge fishing grounds. The principal ones are the Great Bahama Bank and the Little Bahama Bank, lying off the islands of Andros and Abaco respectively. The former, known as "The Mud," is 200 miles in length and 64 miles in width, and the latter, known as the "Southern Mud," has a length of 143 miles, and is 10 to 38 miles wide. There are also smaller grounds, the whole covering several thousand square miles in extent, and forming what is believed to be a virtually inexhaustible source. Many varieties of sponges are obtained from these grounds.

Each schooner carries one or more two-men dinghies or dories, which are like those used by the Newfoundland codfishers and are manned largely by negroes. While the ships lie at anchor the little boats pull about over the reefs, the sponge-hooker lying over either stern or bows, and snatching at everything that looks promising.

After a week of good "catches," the fleet returns and lands its cargo. The sponges are first thoroughly rinsed and squeezed until every particle of gelatinous animal matter has been got rid of. They are then exposed to the air for a day or two, after which they are thrown into a "crawl," a crude wooden tank of water, and left to clean themselves. There they remain for about a week, when they are taken out and trodden vigorously by bare-footed men till they are once more squeezed as dry as possible. They are then passed to the warehouse, where they are again washed, clipped, sorted out according to size and quality, and compressed into bales ready for transport.

A sponge clipper at work at Nassau, in the Bahamas.

Some 400 schooners and sloops are engaged in the industry. The voyages are undertaken on shares, the owner receiving one-third of the net profits and the remainder being divided between the captain and the crew. Sponge fishing is the principal industry of the Bahamas, and every year sponges worth from £110,000 to £152,000 are exported from the islands.

Attempts are now being made to improve and develop the sponges of the Bahamas by artificial propagation. Sponges are developed from very small egg cells, about 1,000 of which would be required to form a line an inch in length. A very small creature is developed from the egg. This swims about freely for a time before settling down and beginning to grow into the sponge with which we are familiar, and ordinary small sponges actually consist of several individuals having their fibres closely interlocked with each other.

For the past few years biologists have been growing sponges on the reefs of the Bahamas with encouraging results. Various methods of production have been tried, and subdivision also has been practised. When a piece is cut off a sponge, it continues to grow, and sponges have been divided into sections of about two inches in length and replaced in the sea, with the result that in 12 to 18 months they have increased to 25 or 30 times their original size. Furthermore, these artificially-propagated sponges have no roots, and are much more robust than those grown naturally.

Fine Performance by L.N.E.R. "Pacific"

On the last day of the summer service *"The Flying Scotsman"* completed yet another successful season with a remarkable run from Edinburgh to London. During the last fortnight in September the train stops at Newcastle for five minutes in both directions, though still completing the journey between the two capitals in 7¼ hours. As a consequence, the locomotive work involved is considerably harder than during the non-stop period, but the stop enables passengers to join and leave the train at Newcastle, and obviates the necessity of carrying two engine crews for the whole distance, as the locomotives are re-manned at Newcastle. Although the same engine works right through from Edinburgh to London when the Newcastle stop is made, there is of course no need to use a locomotive fitted with a corridor tender, and so during this last fortnight of the summer service several hitherto unfamiliar engines have put in an appearance at Edinburgh. On this last day the engine was No. 4474, *"Victor Wild,"* and the load throughout from Edinburgh to London 445 tons tare, 480 tons with passengers and luggage.

On a through run of this length it might be imagined that the engine would require nursing somewhat in the early stages, but so confident are the drivers of the staying power of their locomotives that the start from Edinburgh is invariably very brisk. On this occasion indeed, the train was three minutes early before it was 30 miles away from Edinburgh. Dunbar, 29.1 miles, was passed in 31 minutes, and after a very fine climb of the Cockburnspath bank with a minimum speed of 27 miles per hour up the 1 in 96 grade, Grant's House, 41.2 miles from Edinburgh, was passed in 47 minutes. After this the running became rather easier, but in spite of a long slowing to 30 miles per hour for permanent way repairs, and a slack for pit fall troubles near Cramlington, the 124.4 miles from Edinburgh to Newcastle were completed in 139¾ minutes, 4¼ minutes early.

The London driver who took over at Newcastle again started very briskly and was three minutes early at Northallerton, but after a long spell at 70 m.p.h. across the plain of York, where for 22 miles speed averaged 69 m.p.h., matters were taken rather more easily, and the three minutes in hand allowed to gradually slip away until the train was just on time through Grantham. But in these days an express train that does not exceed 80 m.p.h. on the magnificent racing stretch from Stoke Summit down to Peterborough is a rare phenomenon, and sure enough on this occasion there was a fine spell at 84 m.p.h. in the neighbourhood of Essendine.

After Peterborough, passed a minute early, the running was magnificent, especially considering that the engine had now been going hard for over 320 miles, and after a most brilliant finish with a minimum speed of 60 m.p.h. up the five mile rise from Hatfield to Potters' Bar, *"The Flying Scotsman"* reached King's Cross three minutes early.

On this run the total running time from Edinburgh to London was only three minutes over seven hours, and had the journey been made non-stop it could easily have been completed in that time, giving an average speed for 393 miles of 56.2 miles per hour. We are indebted to Mr. O. S. Nock for these details of *"Victor Wild's"* splendid work.

L.M.S.R. 4-6-0 locomotive No. 5018 about to leave Blair Athol Station. This illustration is a prize-winning photograph by D. F. Forbes, Edinburgh, H.R.C. No. 14092.

Television at Waterloo

The Southern Railway have introduced regular television programmes at Waterloo Station, where the programmes broadcast from Alexandra Palace will be shown in the Waiting Room opposite No. 16 Platform. There will be two shows daily, from 11 a.m. to 12 noon and from 3 p.m. to 4 p.m. respectively, except on Saturdays, and admission is free to railway ticket holders.

Brilliant Running on S.R.

In 1905 Mr. Dugald Drummond, first locomotive engineer of the London and South Western Railway, built some very big four-cylinder 4-6-0 engines with driving wheels of 6 ft. diameter for mixed traffic work. These have gone through several stages of rebuilding, in the last of which, about 15 years ago, they were converted to two-cylinder propulsion; but throughout their career most of them have been stationed at Salisbury for working heavy goods traffic between there and Southampton. In the peak periods they are very frequently called upon for express duties, however, and on a recent occasion No. 333 of this class was provided to work the up *"Atlantic Coast Express"* from Exeter to Salisbury.

As far as Sidmouth Junction the load was one of only 10 coaches, weighing 345 tons gross, and No. 333 made light of it, getting up to 69 m.p.h. as early as Broadclyst and not falling below 39 m.p.h. up the four mile climb at 1 in 100-135 past Whimple. Sidmouth Junction, 12¼ miles, was reached in 17¾ min. instead of the 19 min. allowed. There three more coaches were added, bringing the load up to a total of 450 tons. On the tremendous ascent at 1 in 90 through Honiton speed fell to 22¾ m.p.h., but approaching Seaton Junction 83½ m.p.h. was attained, a remarkable achievement with 6 ft. wheels!

Beyond there speed rose and fell with the usual frequency over this steeply graded switchback, the speeds recorded being 37½ m.p.h. at Hewish, 75 at Crewkerne, 69 at Yeovil, 28 at Milborne Port, 68 at Templecombe, and 29 at Semley. The 52½ miles from Honiton Summit to Semley Summit were run at an average speed of 53 m.p.h., and with a fast descent to Salisbury, with a top speed of 74 m.p.h. at Dinton, the 75.8 miles from Sidmouth Junction were completed in 90¼ min., an average speed of 50.3 m.p.h.

This run was timed by Mr. O. S. Nock.

* * * *

Driver W. Sparshatt, driver of *"The Flying Scotsman"* and *"Silver Jubilee"* trains has retired from the footplate. Among his many notable performances was the maximum speed of 108 m.p.h. attained with an unprepared "Pacific," No. 2750 *"Papyrus."*

New Signal Box at Waterloo

The last stage of the S.R. track and signalling improvement scheme between Waterloo and Surbiton was completed when the new electric signal box at Waterloo Station was opened recently. The first part of the scheme was introduced last May, when the "Fly-over" at Wimbledon and the revised track layout at Waterloo were brought into use, together with the colour-light signalling between Vauxhall and Malden, and in June the colour-light signalling between Malden and Surbiton was completed.

This new box, which is built almost entirely of concrete, stands at the side of the track, in marked contrast to the former existing "A" box, which dominated all the tracks into Waterloo for 44 years. It contains 309 levers, each about 8 in. long, and controls an area that formerly required six signal boxes with a total of 499 levers. Four illuminated track diagrams over the lever frames show when the various sections of track are occupied.

The new box gives control of 44 colour-light signals, 62 floodlit shunting signals, and 34 route indicators, point machines and position light junction indicators. Telephones have been installed at 27 positions, so that drivers can communicate with the signal box when they are detained at a signal, and loud speaker equipment is provided between the box and the down sidings at Waterloo.

The total length of the wire used in the circuits controlled from the signal box is 110 miles, and in addition there are 30 miles of telephone wires.

L.N.E.R. to Build 121 More Locomotives

The L.N.E.R. have this year placed in service no less than 4,802 new wagons, 593 new coaches, and 739 new containers. New locomotives now in service number 56, including the sister engines to *"Cock o' the North."*

During 1937 the L.N.E.R. are to construct 121 new locomotives. These will include 14 "Silver Link" Pacific engines, a further 11 engines of the "Green Arrow" mixed traffic type, and 32 "Sandringhams" for service on main line and secondary passenger trains. In addition 38 freight locomotives, 20 tank engines of the 2-6-2 type, and six shunting engines are to be built.

L.M.S.R. Locomotive News

New engines continue to be delivered from Crewe and Derby, and also from the contractors. At the present time Derby Works are busy on the construction of 2-6-4 tanks, while Crewe Works are turning out Class 5X taper boiler 4-6-0s. Locomotives being delivered from contractors include 4-6-0 mixed traffic engines, 2-8-0 freight engines and 2-6-4 passenger tanks.

Among engines condemned are 4-6-0s Nos. 10451, 10457, 25662, *"Anzac,"* 25675, *"Sphinx,"* 25708, 25784, 25830, 25843 and 25844, in addition to Nos. 5284, *"Ambassador,"* 5315, *"Delamere,"* 5379, *"Woodcock"* and 25299, *"Vesuvius,"* and No. 14327, all 4-4-0s. No. 12479, the sole survivor of the former Furness Railway 0-6-0 goods class, has now been withdrawn from service.

The up South Coast "Daylight Express" leaving Kiama, New South Wales. This photograph secured a prize for R. B. McMillan, Melbourne, H.R.C. No. 9592, in a recent Photographic Contest.

Passenger tank engines to be condemned include 4-6-2 No. 6974, 4-4-2 No. 6827, 0-6-4 No. 2036, and the two engines, 4-4-0 No. 15028 and 0-4-4 No. 1376.

S.R. and G.W.R. Station Improvements

The S.R. are carrying out extensive alterations to Richmond Station. Both the "up" and "down" platforms are being lengthened, and the platforms serving the "district" trains of the L.P.T.B. also are being extended. A new footbridge will connect all platforms, and a car park with accommodation for 45 cars will be provided. The scheme entails the re-modelling of the goods yard and the construction of a new goods shed.

New and old forms of road transport side by side at York Station. Prize-winning photograph by H. W. West, Newport, Mon., H.R.C. No. 99.

A scheme announced by the G.W.R. provides for the complete rebuilding and enlargement of the existing Station buildings at Leamington Spa. Longer and wider platforms are to be built and the two existing main and bay line platforms will be raised to the standard height.

The "up" main line platform will be 650 ft. in length, 360 ft. of which will be under cover. The "down" main line platform will be 23 ft. longer and will have a covered length of 480 ft.

King's Cross to Edinburgh in Six Hours

In July next year the L.N.E.R. are to introduce a new streamlined train between King's Cross and Edinburgh that will cover the 393 miles in 6 hrs., a reduction of 1 hr. 15 min. on the time now taken by *"The Flying Scotsman,"* at present the fastest train making this journey. The average speed of the new train will be 66 m.p.h., and this will be the highest ever maintained over such a distance in this country.

By permission of the King, the new train will be named *"Coronation."* It will be additional to the present services, and will make only one stop, at Newcastle.

Another new train with an average speed of 68 m.p.h. is to be inaugurated by the L.N.E.R. between London and Leeds. It will be timed to cover the distance of 186 miles in 2 hrs. 45 min., or 25 min. less than the present best time of 3 hrs. 10 min.

Streamlining on Canadian Pacific Railroad

The Canadian Pacific Railroad have introduced four new lightweight semi-streamlined trains, three of which are now in service between Montreal and Quebec, Toronto and Detroit, and Calgary and Edmonton respectively.

The new trains are hauled by 4-4-4 streamlined engines of the "Jubilee" class, which are said to be capable of 110 m.p.h. The boiler pressure of these locomotives is 300 lb. per sq. in. and their driving wheels are 6 ft. 8 in. in diameter. The total weight of engine and tender is 191 tons, of which 80 tons is the weight of the tender. A noteworthy feature is that with the exception of the drivers, all the wheels run on roller bearings.

Caprotti Valve Gear for L.N.E.R. Locomotives

The L.N.E.R. are to fit two further B3 4-6-0 passenger engines with Caprotti valve gear. The class to which these engines belong was introduced by the Great Central Railway for express passenger train services and is popularly known as the "Lord Faringdon" class. Two of these engines were fitted with this valve gear eight years ago and they have since given excellent service, running an average of 53,000 miles a year. The decision to equip a further two engines has been prompted by the satisfactory saving in coal consumption.

Manchester-Sheffield Electrification

The electrification of the main line between Manchester (London Road) and Sheffield will probably be commenced at an early date. When the scheme is completed the average speed of passenger trains will be increased from 40 m.p.h. to 50 m.p.h., while that of the electric goods trains will be increased to 40 m.p.h. The overhead power system will be employed and 88 electric locomotives are to be built.

Airmen Return to School

"Finishing Classes" for Empire Flying Boat Crews

ON the fringe of the great London airport at Croydon one finds a very remarkable "school" in operation. Looking out from its windows, you see big air liners arriving or departing at the neighbouring airport; while a glance round the class-rooms of this "school" shows you a number of keen-eyed, athletic-looking young men, sitting at desks listening to lectures, or carrying out tests with wireless or other technical equipment. These young men who have temporarily gone back to school are aeroplane pilots. No novices, these. All of them are qualified airmen, holding their official licences as commercial pilots. And all of them have spent long periods up in the air.

Why, then, have they gone back to school?

The answer is that these young aviators—all of them picked men—are in special training for air work of a kind more onerous and exacting than any they have undertaken hitherto. They are to form the crews of the great new fleet of Imperial Airways flying boats—28 in number—with which next year the amplified mail scheme is to be inaugurated whereby letters in bulk, without any form of flying surcharge, are to be air-borne between England and distant parts of the Empire.

Airmen studying engine mechanism at the Imperial Airways Instruction School. The illustrations to this article are by courtesy of Imperial Airways Ltd.

As air liners grow bigger and bigger, the crews who handle them have to become correspondingly more expert. Seventeen years ago, when civil flying began, all that pilots were called upon to fly were tiny two-passenger machines, driven by single engines developing about 360 horse-power. There was no wireless equipment in commercial aircraft in those days. Scientific aerial navigation, with its many instruments, had not yet been introduced upon the airways; and commercial night-flying had still to come. Everything was primitive—in its earliest infancy.

And now see the difference between those days and the present time. In contrast to the small low-powered machines of 1919, our new Empire flying boats will be driven by four powerful motors developing a total of 3,000 horse-power. They will carry three tons of mails; their big passenger saloons will be equipped with sleeping-berths as well as with day accommodation; and when fully-loaded they will weigh just on 18 tons. Real "liners of the air," these great new craft! By night as well as day they will devour distance across the Empire, being capable of speeds of just on 200 miles an hour.

The men who handle these new clippers of the clouds will need, in addition to their work as pilots, to be experts in all questions affecting wireless and aerial navigation; while they will need also to be fully qualified in such matters as ground engineering, maintenance, and overhaul. This explains the existence of the "school" which Imperial Airways are operating. It is, in effect, a "finishing school" for pilots—a school in which experts impart to these young airmen all the scientific and technical knowledge that now appertains to commercial flying in bad weather as well as in fine, and in the hours of darkness as well as by day.

It is really two kinds of navigation that these young airmen of Empire have to master. They have to learn to handle and steer their great flying boats through the air, and they have also to learn to manœuvre them on the surface of harbours or rivers, and to bring them up to their moorings like ships of the sea. This means learning all about tides and currents, and the movements of surface craft in busy ports. They need, in fact, to be seamen as well as airmen—these young pilots who will be flying our new marine aircraft along the main trans-Empire routes.

Lessons in the class-rooms at the "finishing school" are varied by a great deal of practical and experimental work in workshops and test-rooms. Pupils go across to the machine-shops at the airport and gain practical insight into all the modern phases of air-liner maintenance and overhaul. They have completely-equipped wireless installations at their disposal. With these they can, as required, reproduce the conditions of actual flying, exchanging routine signals and experimenting in direction and position-finding. They are also able to listen-in to the day-to-day wireless signalling that is in progress between the control tower at Croydon and air liners actually in flight on the Continental routes. Another change from the lecture rooms takes place when pilots go down to Hamble, near Southampton, for practical instruction in the handling of big, multi-engined flying boats.

It is astonishing, when one visits this pilots' school, to find how varied and extensive is the knowledge that must be acquired by a modern air-line "skipper." Meteorology, of course, is an important subject. The pilot must learn all he can about the mysteries of that ocean of the air through which he will be navigating. He has to learn to read and interpret weather maps; to follow the movement of low-pressure systems and of anti-cyclones and cloud formation; to grasp immediately the significance of the wireless weather reports that will be at his disposal not only when he is on the ground, but which also will be flashed to him when he is passing high through the air.

One of the courses of lectures to which the pilots listen deals with the very intricate subject of international air legislation. Commercial air liners have not yet a freedom of the air corresponding to the freedom of the sea granted to the world's mercantile marine. Each nation claims complete sovereignty of the air above its territory, with the result that the operation of long-distance international air lines becomes a matter of delicate negotiations and reciprocal agreements, with many restrictions in regard to prohibited areas and adherence to specified corridors when passing above certain territory. With all such matters of international air law, as it exists at the present time, the air-line pilot must acquaint himself thoroughly.

An airman schoolmaster explaining to future crews of Imperial Airways air liners how a course is set. He is using a compass and a wooden outline of an aeroplane in making his meaning clear.

Another big and important subject is that of regular commercial night-flying. Chains of aerodromes along the Empire routes are now to be equipped with the latest types of flood-lights and other illuminations. Intermediate airway beacons, each flashing skyward its identifying signal, are being established along the main long-distance routes. Special illuminated wind-indicators, telling a pilot the strength and direction of the wind as he glides down to make a night landing, are also being placed on main and intermediate alighting-grounds. It is a special technique that is growing up in connection with commercial night-flying, and with every phase of this new aspect of his art the air captain must acquaint himself.

Then he has to make a study of course and distance calculations, and of the whole theory of aeronautics. He has to become familiar with aircraft compasses, and with "homing" devices that guide him to airports. He has to make a study of aero engines, and of their methods of construction, operation, maintenance, and overhaul. He needs to know all about the control systems of the air liners he will pilot.

This novel view, taken through the ring of a direction-finding aerial, shows airmen at the School studying wireless installations.

It takes a pilot from 12 to 15 months to pass through all the various classes at this aerial finishing school. By the time he has absorbed all the specialised instruction that is imparted to him he is not only an expert in handling big modern aircraft, but he has obtained also a knowledge of navigation, meteorology, wireless, and airway engineering that will prove invaluable to him in his work as an air-line skipper on the great trunk routes that now connect the Homeland with distant parts of the Empire. Britain's great mercantile marine, with its captains who rove the world, has created for itself a splendid tradition of service and of technical skill; and it is the determination of our young flying skippers to build up just as fine a reputation and tradition for the British mercantile air service.

Apart from air captains and first-officers, the amplified Empire air-mail scheme is calling for increases in the highly skilled wireless staffs. In addition, therefore, to the pilots who are entering the service of Imperial Airways, specially chosen wireless operators are being drafted from the marine service to that of the air, and in the airway school are being given the additional coaching necessary to enable them to pass their examinations for obtaining—as air-liner wireless men—the aviation equivalent of the official certificate held by ocean-liner operators.

From the earliest days of civil aviation, when the first experiments were being made with wireless telephony between aeroplanes and ground stations, wireless has played a vital part in the operation of commercial air services. From pioneer stations operating on the continental routes, the wireless network has grown until it now stretches link by link from England to Egypt, Africa, and India, and on thousands of miles to China and Australia.

As a part of the improved ground organisation for the big new Empire air scheme, many developments and improvements are taking place in wireless communication. Throughout the Empire air lines approximately 40 new wireless stations are being established; while both on the ground and in the air the equipment will embody the latest devices evolved by scientists and technicians. The wireless installations now being fitted in the new Empire flying boats are, it is claimed, the most modern and efficient ever constructed for use in commercial aircraft. One feature of these improved installations is that a direction-finding apparatus is embodied in the main set, and is not a separate piece of equipment as has been the case hitherto. By the use of this direction-finding equipment the wireless operator will be able to tune-in to ships or shore stations, and plot out the air-liner's position at any time during a flight. He will be in constant touch with one or other of a chain of ground stations, and thus will be able to obtain the latest information as to weather conditions ahead.

For the information in this article we are indebted to Imperial Airways Ltd.

Waterwheel Alternators for New Zealand

The photograph on this page shows the stator of one of two giant waterwheel alternators built by the Metropolitan-Vickers Electrical Company for the Arapuni power station in New Zealand. The alternators are rated at 24,000 kVA, 11,000 volts, and are believed to be the largest electrical machines of which construction has yet been undertaken by British manufacturers.

The yoke, or outer frame, is just over 26 ft. in diameter and weighs nearly 18 tons. It is of welded steel construction and to facilitate transport was made in four sections, with special arrangements to ensure that when the sections were assembled they would fit into exactly circular form without any packing.

The core is of laminated electrical steel and also was assembled in four sections, so that the stator when wound and completed could be divided for shipping, the coils spanning the joints being removed for this purpose. The total weight of copper in the stator winding of each machine is nearly five tons.

The Arapuni power station, in which these generators will be installed, is one of the three main power stations in the North Island of New Zealand. Its output is supplied principally to the city of Auckland, but a considerable amount of energy is also supplied to other towns and to farms in the northern area. In addition the station is connected by a 110,000 volt transmission system with the Waikaremoana Power Station, in the east of North Island, and the Mangahao Power Station in the south.

A Boat for Use on London's Reservoirs

The Metropolitan Water Board have acquired an unusual type of boat for use in distributing chemicals required in treating the water in certain London reservoirs. The boat is in the form of a punt 20 ft. in length and 7 ft. in beam, and is driven by a 12 h.p. four-cylinder internal combustion engine. It has a maximum speed of between 6 and 7 m.p.h., but as it is sometimes necessary to travel very slowly, a variable-pitch propeller is fitted by means of which the speed can be reduced to one mile per hour. At the bow and stern are conveyors operated by electric motors obtaining current from a dynamo driven from the main engine. The conveyors are supplied with the necessary chemicals from hoppers situated in the centre of the boat, and these are fed into the water as the boat travels along.

The boat will be used on several London reservoirs, and a special trailer carriage has been provided for transporting it from place to place as required.

A Post Office on Wheels

In order to facilitate communication to and from important sporting events in various parts of the country the Postmaster General has introduced a special mobile post office. The vehicle consists of a Morris-Commercial tractor unit, which hauls a Kwikfiks semi-trailer attachment that is fitted with a Duple body 22 ft. long and

The stator for one of two 24,000 kVA, 11,000 volt alternators, for a large power station in New Zealand. These alternators are believed to be the largest yet built by British manufacturers. Photograph reproduced by courtesy of Metropolitan-Vickers Electrical Co. Ltd., Manchester.

7 ft. 6 in. wide. The body is divided into three compartments. At the rear are two telephone call offices provided with folding doors, and in the centre, which is the main business compartment, there is a desk for three postal clerks and a teleprinter machine for telegrams. Telegrams are dispatched and accepted, telephone calls made, stamps sold and letters and parcels received and registered. An external writing ledge is provided on one side for the convenience of customers, who when transacting business are sheltered by a collapsible awning.

At the front of the body is a compartment for storing equipment, including duck boards, which are laid around the vehicle when it is working in fields. On the off side, behind the serving windows, are automatic stamp machines and a letter chute, which leads to a mail bag inside the vehicle.

In order that the staff may carry out their duties in conditions as near normal as possible, the drawer and shelf accommodation usually provided in ordinary post offices has been installed.

Electric current for operating the equipment is provided by a generator driven from the gear box.

Electricity at the Zoo

Reptile dens and crocodile pools floodlighted and heated by electricity are now a feature of the London Zoo. In the reptile house 75 large dens and 27 small dens are treated in this way, and in some of them tubular electric heaters are concealed in the rocks to provide properly warmed resting places for the inmates.

In each of the large dens eight 1,000 W circular reflector heaters are fitted above the front windows, and these maintain a temperature of between 75 and 80 deg. F. The water in the pools is kept at 70 deg. F. by eight 250 W thermostatically controlled heaters, and as a substitute for sunshine on dull days eight 300 W tungsten lamps are fitted near the roof. These are provided with special glass that permits the passage of ultra-violet rays. If the temperature in any den rises above the required figure, a red lamp is illuminated in the keeper's room, and a green light shows if the temperature falls too low. A bell in the curator's office also gives warning of undesirable changes in temperature.

World's Highest Turntable Fire Escape

What is believed to be the highest turntable fire escape in the world is now in the service of the Hull City Police Fire Brigade. When fully extended the escape reaches to a height of 150 ft. Power for travelling and for extending the ladder is provided by a 115 h.p. engine, which gives a road speed of 50 m.p.h.

When the ladder is to be extended the road springs are locked by the operation of levers, and four quick-acting jacks are then drawn out of the chassis and extended. The jacks are mounted on the ends of cantilever arms and project well beyond the rear wheels to provide a wide and steady base. The ladder is in six lengths and is extended and withdrawn by means of wire ropes and winding gear. The full extension can be made within half a minute of the arrival of the machine at the scene of a fire.

The escape was made by Leyland Motors Ltd., and all the controls are centralised to enable one man to operate it.

A Giant Oil Tanker

On page 315 of the June 1936 issue of the "*M.M.*" we described and illustrated the chassis of a giant tank lorry that has been built for carrying oil from the Iranian oil fields for distribution in Teheran. The lorry is now in service, and the upper illustration on this page shows the vehicle in its finished state. It was built by Straussler Mechanization Ltd., of London, and has an overall length of 25 ft. 10 in. and a weight of 12 tons. It is fitted with a Straussler V-eight engine that develops 150 b.h.p., and each of its eight road wheels is independently mounted to provide the flexibility necessary for travelling over uneven desert surfaces and rough mountain roads.

Flexibly mounted road wheels to facilitate passage over rough surfaces are an important feature of this giant petrol tank lorry, which has been built for service in the Iranian Oilfields. Photograph by courtesy of Straussler Mechanization Ltd.

Camera that Photographs Lightning

In order to obtain information regarding lightning and its effects a special observatory has been built at Pittsfield in the United States of America. It is equipped with a periscope and a high-speed camera that has a range of 20 miles.

The outside of the structure is coated with aluminium paint and the inside with black. It is 14 ft. in diameter and in the centre of it is the periscope, which is topped by a crystal sphere. Lightning flashing in any direction is reflected in the silvery surface of the roof, and thence in the crystal, from which it is reflected to the eye-piece of the periscope by a mirror set at an angle in its dark-walled tube. The camera is placed underneath the periscope platform, and is provided with a moving strip of film and 12 lenses, which are so arranged that it is possible to record lightning discharges occurring at all points round the observatory.

As the instrument is exposed to the weather when in use, adequate protection against the rain had to be provided for the lenses. This is accomplished by surrounding the camera with a curtain of compressed air, which issues from a perforated ring placed above the camera. The air curtain shuts out all but the heaviest downpours.

A New Use for Cellophane

Cellophane is now being used to insulate the windings of electric motors. The material used for this purpose is in the form of ribbon from 1/32 in. to ½ in. in width, and is so thin that the assembly takes up much less space than is required when other insulators are employed. The ribbon is wound round the wire by means of ingenious machines working at very high speed, and a special adhesive holds the turns in place.

A further advantage possessed by cellophane is that it resists high temperatures better than other insulating materials, and it is said also to dissipate the heat generated in the windings more quickly.

German Island Joined to the Mainland

The island of Ruegen, in the Baltic Sea, which is famous for its holiday resorts and bathing beaches, has now been joined to the mainland of Germany. The connection is formed by a dam 1½ miles in length from the city of Stralsund to a small island, the final link being a bridge of nine spans covering the final 550 yards. Part of the bridge is hinged, and can be raised to allow the passage of ships.

A road and a railway have been built on the dam, which has cost about £2,575,000, and besides giving easy access to Ruegen, the new works will shorten the journey from Berlin to Sweden by about two hours.

Sinking concrete foundations in the bed of the Zambesi River to support the piers of the world's longest railway bridge that is continuously over the water. The bridge was fully described in the "M.M." for July 1936.

Sark to have New Harbour

Sark, one of the Channel Islands and well-known to holiday makers, is to have a new harbour. At present the only landing place is at Le Creux. It is reached through a narrow opening between the sea walls, but in rough weather channel ships are unable to negotiate the passage and passengers are landed by means of tenders.

It is expected that the new harbour will cost about £45,000. It is hoped that this capital outlay will be amply repaid by harbour dues, and that an increased number of visitors will be attracted to the island.

A Great Hydro-Electric Scheme

A further stage towards completion of the great Cauvery-Mettur irrigation and hydro-electric scheme in India was reached recently when the foundation stone of the power house was laid. The Cauvery-Mettur project provides for the irrigation of 1,000,000 acres of existing rice fields in the delta of the Cauvery River, and of over 300,000 acres of new plantations. It has involved the construction of a great dam just over a mile in length, which has created a huge reservoir with a storage capacity of 93,000 cu. ft. behind it. The building of the dam was fully described in the "*M.M.*" for August 1934. In addition to supplying water for irrigation purposes this reservoir will also provide water power for driving huge turbines in the new power station that is now being constructed, and which when completed will supply electric current over an area of 25,000 square miles, with a population of 12,000,000.

The power-house, a steel-framed structure, will be situated at the foot of the dam on the left bank of the Cauvery River, and the equipment will include three great turbines, each capable of generating 15,000 h.p. The transmission and distribution lines radiating from the station together will be nearly 900 miles long.

A New B.B.C. Transmitter

In order to provide a satisfactory radio service for listeners in the north of Scotland, the British Broadcasting Corporation have put into commission a new transmitting plant at Burghhead on the coast of the Moray Firth. The new station is designed on similar lines to the North Ireland Regional Station, and is provided with a 500 ft. single mast anti-fading aerial. The normal power supply is taken from the mains of the Grampian Electricity Supply Company, and the power delivered to the aerial is 60 kW. The new station transmits on a wavelength of 391.1 metres, which is the same as that of the Scottish Regional transmitter at Westerglen, to which it is tuned and linked by a land-line.

From Kenya to Rhodesia by Car

An Adventurous Tour in Tropical Africa

By S. T. R. Hemsted

VERY few people have made the journey from Nairobi, Kenya Colony, to the Victoria Falls in an ordinary car using petrol; so it was no wonder that we were laughed at when we said we were going to the Victoria Falls and back in under five weeks in one that depended for its motive power on charcoal! With but little preparation we set out full of optimism to spend our Christmas holidays at the Falls, however, intending to be back in Kenya sometime in the third week of January. The distance from Nairobi to the Falls is about 4,200 miles, and on the way there are only about 1,000 miles of road that can be described as fit for "all weather" use.

Our eventful journey was made in a Buick of high horse power that is ideally suited for conversion into a "charcoal burner." The additional apparatus fitted to it for this purpose consists of two large tanks, one at each side of the car on the running board. The off-side tank produces the gas. It is first filled with good quality charcoal, and in its base a fire is lighted, the draught being provided by the suction of the engine, which has first to be started on petrol. A small quantity of water is allowed to drip continuously on the burning charcoal. This forms carbon monoxide, a combustible gas, which is passed through a pipe to the bottom of the near side tank. There it rises through many layers of sisal tow, and in passing through these it is cleansed and made ready to pass direct to the engine.

Making ready for the adventurous journey described in this article. The car runs on gas produced by allowing water to drip on burning charcoal.

The gas enters the cylinders through the ordinary induction pipe, and it is important that it should be mixed with the right quantity of air. The amount of this supplied is controlled by a wheel on the dashboard, which opens and shuts a valve on the induction pipe. The better the quality of the charcoal, the greater the quantity of air required. If the charcoal is good and running conditions are favourable, one could not wish for a better form of locomotion, but in bad conditions the apparatus can be the most trying in the world.

We set out with an enormous load, which included 16 bags of charcoal. In addition we had three tents and food for four weeks, together with tools, cameras and other baggage. We also took with us a native boy, whose chief task was to keep the charcoal burning apparatus clean, for the whole arrangement has to be cleaned thoroughly every day to maintain it in good running order, and this is a very dirty job.

We left Nairobi at dusk with the fire going well, and decided to make a night run to Arusha, in Tanganyika. We had gone scarcely 30 miles when we ran into thick mist and mud. The heavy car got hopelessly stuck, and our first night was spent in freezing cold, although we were almost on the Equator, for we were at an altitude of over 8,000 ft. We spent a horrible night trying to free the car, and did so only after 18 hours' hard work, in which we wasted three bags of our precious charcoal, spread on the road in order to give the wheels sufficient grip. Then the furnace was started and we went as far as Kajiado, in the centre of the Kenya Game Reserve, where we made a really first-class camp in a beautiful spot.

Next day we had an uneventful run to Arusha, with snow-capped Kilimanjaro towering above us. At Arusha we were eyed with curiosity and disapproval, as on the way to the Police Station we sunk right through a culvert. We had to unload everything, and the help of the majority of the inhabitants was necessary before the car was extricated.

We were already considerably behind schedule, and decided to make a night run to Dodoma, the next important centre on our route. We worked out a special organisation for long runs involving night driving. One of the party slept as best he could in the back of the car with the native and luggage, while another drove, with the third helping him. Two men were necessary to keep the car running. One was in charge of the charcoal apparatus, adjusting the supply of water to meet the varying road conditions or to allow for differences in the quality of the gas, and changing over to petrol when this was needed. The other drove the car, a task that required considerable skill and nerve over new country. If we went down a long hill with the engine acting as a brake in the ordinary manner, then we had no gas left at the bottom. This would cause considerable delay, as it was some time before the fire could be re-lighted and the car could be put into running condition again. Our usual procedure in these circumstances therefore was to put the gear lever in neutral, and advance the hand throttle so that the engine was roaring. The car would then free-wheel down the hill with the fire burning well, while the driver had to rely entirely for control on the brakes.

Travelling in this manner over the so-called Cape to Cairo Road at night was in many places beyond a joke. The fire would cast an uncanny glow on the opposite bank, and natives who saw us dashed away in fright into the bush. Often the fire would blow out enormous cinders and sparks, causing even greater panic. As each bag of charcoal was burnt, after a run of about 70 miles, we all changed round and began another shift. About midnight we usually stopped to light an enormous fire, which was often placed in the middle of the road, and to enjoy a good meal.

At Dodoma we bought more fuel, and also cleaned the whole apparatus, a task that was exceedingly tiring in the heat. The road from there through Tanganyika is wonderful, yet passes through districts that must be among the loneliest in tropical Africa. For mile after mile we scarcely saw a soul, black or white, until we arrived near Iringa, a small town situated in the Central Highlands.

A section of the main Capetown to Cairo road that is typical of a stretch 400 miles in length. In other parts the road is strewn with debris in the rainy season.

The next few days, including Christmas Day itself, passed uneventfully, except for terrific tropical thunderstorms, and the fact that we left the very good road behind us as we crossed into Northern Rhodesia. We were then making for Abercorn, the capital of this territory, and to reach it took three more days of travel through the pouring rain. The water soaked our charcoal, and it was only with very great difficulty that we could get the car to go at all. This is not surprising, for in effect we were trying to run the engine on steam. We dared not use our spare two gallons of petrol, which we kept in reserve in a small tank on the roof, for that was required for starting or when going through thick mud; and when at length we drifted into Abercorn, we found the town more or less deserted and even the hotel was closing down.

We were now very much behind time, and therefore decided to try another night run. This led to disaster. We left Abercorn in the evening, and after using up our first two bags of charcoal, we were still driving over very bad road in a thick forest. Soon after midnight we took a wrong track in the dark and found ourselves going down a very steep hill. Suddenly we realised that there was a river at the bottom, and to our horror saw that there was no bridge. We just managed to stop the car by running it into a ditch at the side, where it tilted over on its side at a very steep angle. Then came a violent explosion, and in a few seconds the roof and off side of the car were ablaze, and burning fiercely. The angle at which our car was perched had caused our precious reserve of petrol to flow out of its tank, down the side of the car and into the furnace.

A halt for a rest under a magnificent baobab tree in Tanganyika.

Fighting the fire in the darkness was a terrible task, but by smothering it with earth from the track we eventually quelled it. Our side curtains, mosquito nets, one suitcase and two rugs had been burned irretrievably, and it took us the whole of the next two days to get the car going again.

Two days later we were faced with another problem. Our charcoal was ruined by the rain, and the engine simply would not run on it. We could not buy more fuel, so the only thing we could do was to sit down and make it. None of us knew anything about its manufacture, and we had nothing but a spade, a pocket knife, and a panga, or long native knife, with which to set to work. Something had to be done, however, so we collected an enormous pile of wood and made a roaring fire. Out of this we picked likely-looking embers and ash by hand, and tried to induce the engine to run on this, but nothing on earth would persuade it to do so.

We next dug a pit and filled it with wood, which we kept burning steadily all through the night. Next morning we found a considerable quantity of good charcoal in the bottom of the pit. To our delight, the car went quite well on this, but it took us over seven days to cut down and collect the wood to make eight bags of charcoal.

This was the finish as far as I was concerned, for by this time it was essential for me to get back to Kenya. We therefore made for Mpika Aerodrome, on the main Imperial Air Route. There I booked a seat on the Atalanta aeroplane flying north, and in it reached Nairobi in one day. By road we had taken over five weeks to complete the same journey in the opposite direction.

My two companions and the native boy from Kenya were determined to complete their adventurous journey, and went on to Victoria Falls and Bulawayo. They then crossed into Portuguese East Africa and travelled north through Nyasaland. There they came upon the main road in the wet season, and in one part of it they took over 30 days to cover a distance of only 60 miles. Their difficulties were many and varied. Bridges were down and new ones had to be made to enable the car to cross; the grass grew so high on the side of the road that they could not see above it, and they were nearly bitten to death by mosquitos. Their food and money came to an end, and practically their only food for three months was mahinde, or maize, for which they depended on the generosity of the natives. When at length they arrived back in Kenya, they had taken more than seven months on their tour.

HORNBY CL

Boys! they're j

Hornby Trains—the name spells ma thousands of boys of all ages. It means mi railways for every home; railways comple all types of locomotives, coaches and stations, signals, and all the accessori make a real railway so full of interest. house electric lighting supply is alte current the whole railway can be o electrically. The latest Hornby 20-volt locomotives fitted with automatic reve be started, stopped, controlled for spe reversed entirely from the side of th without any manipulation by hand from t To add a final touch of realism, many

Hornby Train Sets are available at pr 4/11 to 6

A sel HORN

ELECTRIC MODELS

EM120 (20-volt) or EM16 (6-volt) Locomotive (non-reversing) ... ... P
EO20 (20-volt) Locomotive (reversing) ...
E120 (20-volt) Tank Locomotive (reversing) ...
E120 (20-volt) Special Tank Locomotive (automatic reversing) ... ...
E220 (20-volt) Special Tank Locomotive (automatic reversing) ... ...

A Selection of
HORNBY ELECTRIC TRAIN SETS
(20-volt and 6-volt)

EM120 (20-volt) or EM16 (6-volt) GOODS TRAIN SET (non-reversing). Price 15/-

EM320 (20-volt) or EM36 (6-volt) TANK GOODS TRAIN SET (reversing). Price 24/-

HORNBY No. EO20 (20-volt) PASSENGER TRAIN SET (reversing). Price 30/-

HORNBY No. E220 (20-volt) MIXED GOODS TRAIN SET (automatic reversing). Price 47/6

HORNBY No. E120 (20-volt) SPECIAL PASSENGER TRAIN SET (automatic reversing). Price 47/6

HORNBY No. E320 (20-volt) RIVIERA "BLUE" TRAIN SET (automatic reversing). Price 67/6

HORNBY No. E320 (20-volt) PULLMAN TRAIN SET (automatic reversing). Price 72/6

You can run this train for yourselves, boys! Just think of the fine fun you could have with a train like this. The locomotive is the popular Hornby No. 2 Special Tank drawing two No. 2 Brake Third Coaches.

MECCANO LTD. - B

K TRAINS

like real trains

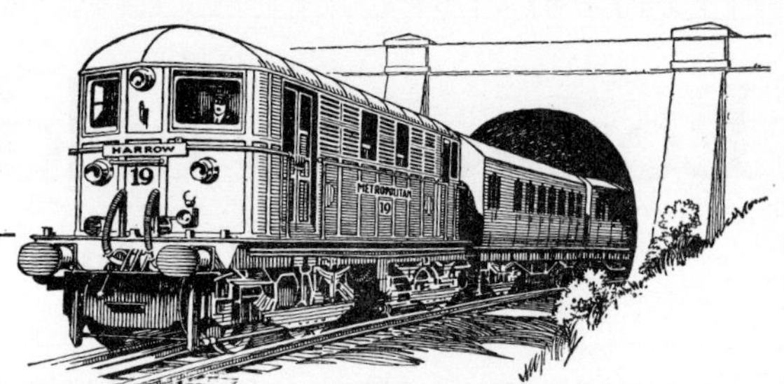

ies can be brilliantly illuminated by tiny lamps. All this is done with perfect y means of a Meccano transformer, a apparatus that automatically transforms ns current down to the low voltage re- or the railway. The Hornby 6-volt Electric tives can be run from a 6-volt Accumulator. there is a splendid range of Hornby ives fitted with clockwork motors. re extremely powerful, and capable of heavy trains at high speed over long s. With these fine locomotives there is to fear overwinding; the springs are nbreakable.

15/– to 75/– for Electric models and models.

ge of
TIVES

-volt) Special Locomotive (automatic ng) ... ... Price 37/6

CLOCKWORK MODELS

comotive (reversing)	Price	4/6
Locomotive (reversing)	,,	7/6
comotive (reversing)	,,	10/6
cial Locomotive (reversing)	,,	27/6

Here is another splendid Hornby Train that you can play with at home! The Flat Truck next to the No. 2 Special Tender Locomotive carries one of the new Hornby Goods Containers, which are exact replicas of the containers now in general use on all British railways.

AD - LIVERPOOL 13

A Selection of HORNBY CLOCKWORK TRAIN SETS

MO CLOCKWORK PASSENGER TRAIN SET (non-reversing). Price 5/6

MO CLOCKWORK MIXED GOODS TRAIN SET (non-reversing). Price 6/11

No. O "SILVER JUBILEE" CLOCKWORK PASSENGER TRAIN SET, L.N.E.R. (non-reversing). Price 7/6

HORNBY No. O GOODS TRAIN SET (reversing). Price 17/6

HORNBY No. 1 PASSENGER TRAIN SET (reversing). Price 25/–

HORNBY No. 2 TANK PASSENGER TRAIN SET (reversing). Price 40/–

HORNBY No. 3C PULLMAN TRAIN SET (reversing). Price 62/6

Longer Working Days for Plants

Growing Strawberries by Electric Light

THE working day of plants is comparatively short, except in prolonged spells of fine weather in the middle of summer, when the Sun shines brightly on them for long periods. They are then hard at work building up organic substances from carbon dioxide, water and the mineral salts absorbed from the soil by their roots, and they grow rapidly and well. Their growth is fitful and unsatisfactory, however, when rain and clouds shut out a large proportion of the light they should receive.

Unfortunately weather is too variable, especially in a climate such as that of Great Britain, to make it certain that plants are always given the light they need. Every gardener knows this, whether he grows flowers and fruit for his own enjoyment, or is a commercial grower on a large scale. The electrician is now coming to the rescue with efforts to provide plants with the light they need to keep them at work, and indeed to lengthen their working hours by turning their nights into days. The right kind of light must be chosen, for any artificial light that is ample for seeing purposes may not suit plant growth. The long waves of light that we know as red rays are necessary, but unfortunately when used alone they cause plants to grow too quickly, and it is necessary to provide also blue and ultra-violet rays in order to prevent plants from becoming "leggy," to use the expressive description of the gardener.

A special electric discharge lamp used to stimulate the growth of plants. The illustrations to this article are reproduced by courtesy of the Electrical Development Association.

Within the last few years experiments have been made with plants grown in greenhouses fitted with electric lamps of various kinds, and some very striking and promising results already have been achieved. For instance, during the winter of 1933-4, trials were made in Holland with ordinary electric lamps, but it was found that the plants placed in their light grew tall and weak, because the radiation from them consisted almost entirely of infra-red rays. Neon tubes with special reflectors therefore were substituted, and young cucumber plants illuminated by these regularly from 10 o'clock at night until 6 o'clock next morning grew more rapidly and formed stronger roots than similar plants that were not exposed to artificial light. Strawberries were grown with great success in greenhouses fitted with these lamps. Some of the plants were gassed with carbon dioxide, and it was found that this aided growth. Flowering plants also seemed to welcome the extension of their working day that lighted greenhouses gave them. For instance, star of bethlehem was found to flower 14 days earlier with treatment of this kind, and with other plants it was discovered that the stronger the light the earlier the flowering period.

In this country a special floodlighting lamp has been introduced by The General Electric Company Ltd. for plant irradiation, as this treatment is called. The lamp gives a red light, and under its influence cucumber plants have grown so well in their early stages that on planting out they have yielded fruit 10 to 14 days earlier than similar plants grown from seeds sown at the same time, but not irradiated. The plants gave the same yield, whether treated with light or not, but there is a great advantage in the saving of time effected by the use of the special lamps. It was found that the best results follow extending the working day of the plants by about six hours.

Even more remarkable results have been achieved in experiments in the United States, where interest in this subject is very great. There it has been found that the most practical artificial light for this purpose is that given by the gas-filled tungsten filament lamp. Many plants have been made to bloom earlier, especially those that flower normally in late spring and early summer, which can now be made to blossom in winter; and in one particularly interesting series of experiments plants were grown in an air-tight house which was supplied with carbon dioxide in the form of "dry ice," the well-known solid form of this gas now used so largely for cooling purposes.

The electrician is attacking the problem of growing better plants and bringing them along more quickly in other ways. These range from straightforward heating of greenhouses by electrical means, to heating the soil in which plants are grown, the provision of warm water for plants kept in frames or greenhouses, the sterilising of soil, and even the vaporisation of naphthalene and other substances to kill the pests that hinder growth and make plants sickly. Electricity can be used also to add new beauty to a garden at night by means of floodlighting. Miniature waterfalls and fountains can be kept running even in times of drought by the use of pumps that circulate the water; and the drudgery of cutting large lawns can be avoided by using electrically driven mowing machines.

The most obvious use for electricity is in directly heating frames and greenhouses. There are several types of apparatus that can be used by the owner of a greenhouse. He can fit a tubular heater, or he can suspend special cables that radiate heat to the air surrounding them. Another method consists of installing a small electrical boiler, the hot water from which is circulated through piping in exactly the same manner as in the case of a greenhouse heated by means of a coke boiler.

One great advantage of heating of this kind is that there is no smoke or fumes to cause damage to the plants. The heating is readily controlled by means of switches, and the temperature can be kept constant by installing a thermostat. The heating apparatus then responds instantaneously and in robot fashion to the demands made upon it.

Every gardener knows that many plants grow all the better for what he calls "bottom heat." The old-fashioned way of providing this was to make up a bed of manure and rotting leaves, which slowly warmed up owing to the chemical changes taking place within it. This is a task that requires skill and experience, and also is dirty and somewhat unpleasant. The electrical way is to sink special heater cables at a suitable depth in the soil. These radiate heat steadily, and it is not necessary to go to the trouble of turning the heating material over from time to time, or of renewing it fairly frequently, as with the old-fashioned method.

A remarkable contrast. The tomato plants on the right are growing in electrically heated soil, and are more vigorous than those on the left, which are not supplied with bottom heat.

Soil heating cables are designed to give fixed temperatures, such as 50 deg. F., 60 deg. F. or 70 deg. F., and merely require connecting up through a main switch to the electric supply. A standard cable is 10 yds. long and is rated at 200 watts. This length is suitable for a garden frame measuring 6 ft. by 4 ft. As in the case of electric heaters for greenhouses, the cable can be fitted with a thermostat or automatic switch to keep any required temperature in the soil in which it is laid. A separate thermostat also can be used. This can be set to any desired temperature, and so the frame in which it is fitted can be used for various purposes.

Making an electric hot bed with a cable of this kind is very easy, for the cable is simply buried in a layer of sand underneath the soil in the frame. The purpose of the sand is to give even distribution of the heat that it produces, and this is prevented from escaping too quickly by side insulation in the form of ashes or fine clinker. A layer of wire netting is placed above the cable before the soil is put into position, so that the electrical apparatus is protected against damage from spades or other gardening tools while the soil is being turned over or removed.

One interesting use to which hot beds of this kind has been put is in growing lettuce and other salad materials in frames in early spring. They also can be used for rooting slips or cuttings, germinating seeds or forcing plants, as well as for excluding frost from frames in winter.

Borders in greenhouses can be heated by means of electric cables of this kind sunk in them, and in particular this method can be used in raising crops of tomatoes. The upper illustration on this page shows the remarkable effect of using a soil heating electric cable. Two rows of tomato plants seen in it were set out at the same time alongside each other, one in an ordinary bed and another in an electrically heated one. The plants supplied with bottom heat are remarkably vigorous and healthy, and this is not mere growth, but all-round progress, for the plants growing in the heated soil yielded more fruit and did it more quickly than those given ordinary treatment.

We have grown accustomed to the idea of wiring a house for electric light and power, but that of wiring a garden seems as yet a little novel. Actually there is no difficulty in this, and the cost is by no means excessive. The cable can be buried from 2 ft. to 2 ft. 6 in. in the ground, and the line taken by it should be permanently marked in some manner, so as to ward off over-vigorous gardeners.

An electric hot water system in a small greenhouse. On the right is a thermostat that maintains a constant temperature.

The chief cost of wiring a garden in this manner is that of digging a trench, and no garden enthusiast would hesitate to do this work himself in view of the novelty of the plan and the excellent results to which he can look forward. If a buried cable cannot be used, a rubber covered one can be slung overhead. The sides of fences provide places to which it can be attached, and paths can be crossed by means of arches that are put to good use in supporting growing plants.

The keen gardener looking for means of improving his garden naturally is attracted by electricity, which can help him in so many ways, because it is clean and simple to use. The cost of course is a matter of importance. Fortunately additions can be made one by one, each costing perhaps only a few shillings, so that a whole garden can be electrified in a comparatively short period without an extensive first cost. The running costs depend on the temperatures that are to be maintained in the frames and greenhouses.

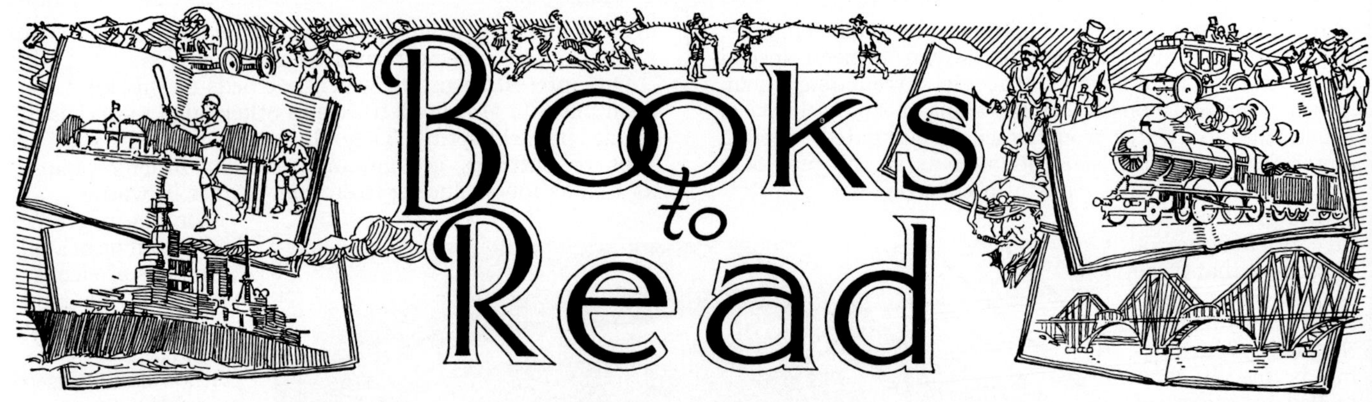

Here we review books of interest and of use to readers of the "M.M." We can supply copies of these books to readers who cannot obtain them through the usual channels. Order from Book Dept., Meccano Limited, Binns Road, Liverpool 13, adding 1/- for postage to the price. Postage on different books varies, but any balance remaining will be refunded.

"The Animal's World"

By Doris L. Mackinnon, D.Sc. (Bell. 7/6 net)

This well-written book is one that will appeal to all "*M.M.*" readers. It tells, simply but with scientific accuracy, how animals live; how they move, breathe and eat, and how they get news of their own particular world through their eyes and other sense organs. In its pages we meet animals with which we are all familiar, and others that are strange and curious in their way of life. We read of the silkworm with breathing holes along its side like the portholes of a ship; of the lattice window of an insect's eye; of the eight ears of the jelly-fish. We learn why a sleeping bird does not fall from its perch; how a camel stores food and water; how flies are able to walk on the ceiling, and how snakes propel themselves along by manipulation of their ribs.

Perhaps the most interesting chapters are those that deal with the childhood of animals, and show how the various creatures grow up, and live together in families or tribes. We are told how they talk to one another, why they differ so widely in their behaviour, and how they protect themselves against their enemies in the unceasing struggle for existence. In short, the author shows us the animal world from the inside, and gives us a fascinating glimpse of the actual living machinery. The whole scheme is completed by an account of the plants without which there would be no world of animals at all, for there would be nothing for them to feed on. In return, many plants depend upon the animal world for their continued existence. For instance, the earth-worm benefits the plant to a remarkable degree. This book also tells many interesting stories of even closer partnership between plants and animals, and in doing so reveals why honeysuckle and certain other plants smell sweeter in the evening, and explains why red clover would not produce seed in New Zealand until bumble-bees also were taken there.

The book is very fully illustrated by a series of excellent photographs, together with many well-prepared drawings.

A mole-rat showing his front teeth. From "The Animal's World," reviewed on this page.

"Strange Sea Shells"

By A. Hyatt Verrill. (Harrap. 10/6 net)

There are few people whose interest is not at once aroused at the sight of a collection of shells. These are often so attractive in colour, and present so many contrasts in size and form, that they are popular both with those who live by the sea and with those whose homes are far inland. Yet the full extent of their fascination is not sufficiently realised. Mr. Verrill makes this clear by his strange but true stories of sea shells from all parts of the world. His book is not a mere description of the shells that can be found on various coasts, but a romantic story of strange creatures of the sea, and of their homes. In it we read of a shell-fish that can jump, of others that are astonishingly fragile but can bore through the hardest rocks, and of one with a shell richly decorated in yellow and red that has a poisoned barb more deadly than the fangs of a rattlesnake. Another of the strange creatures that live in shells has eyes with no pupils and lenses, and yet can see excellently.

Of the shells themselves, the author describes one that has on it music—or at least lines, spaces and dots that look like music! Another shell of which the full story is told is so rare and valuable that it has actually been counterfeited. Descriptions are given of a wonderful array of beautifully coloured shells of all shapes that will delight and surprise readers. The oyster receives its share of attention, and an account is given of the making of an oyster farm and of the gathering of the harvest from it. How pearls are produced provides another interesting story, and the range of the book is extended to many strange creatures of the sea, such as squids and octopuses, that are associated in some manner with shells.

The book will be found of absorbing interest, especially by those who themselves have collected shells, for the author's practical knowledge and long acquaintance with these creatures of the sea are evident on every page. An excellent coloured frontispiece shows some of the strangest and most attractive of shells, and in addition there are many drawings in the text.

"Smiler Jim" and Other Stories

By Robert Harding (R.T.S. 2/6 net)

The scene of Mr. Harding's first story is set in the East which he knows so well and has used to advantage in earlier thrillers. "Smiler Jim" is in the Secret Service and is sent out on the dangerous mission of discovering the mystery of the Valley of Death, in the heart of the Arabian Desert, with the knowledge that if he fails it is likely that the whole of Arabia will be deluged in blood. He falls into the hands of an unscrupulous chief, but he succeeds in foiling the plot that had threatened danger to the country.

The remaining stories in the volume deal with adventures with wild elephants in India, escapes and fights in the desert, and with thrills in the wilder parts of Canada and at home on the Norfolk Broads.

"Twenty-Six South Sea Stories"

By Arthur Russell. (R.T.S. 3/6 net)

We are accustomed to expect stories crammed with lively doings and exciting adventures from Mr. Russell, and his latest collection is worthy of his reputation. The yarns deal with peril and romance in the South Seas, and introduce the reader to Mr. Harley Derham, a secret service agent, Bully Hargreaves, a notorious "blackbirder," and a host of pirates, cannibals, treasure-seekers and gun-runners. Some of the stories deal with savage life among the natives, and in others wireless, aeroplanes and modern scientific inventions figure prominently. A coloured frontispiece and four plates illustrate the book, which is a mine of interest for those who revel in stories of pluck and daring.

"Photography"

By D. E. K. Mees, D.Sc. (Bell. 7/6 net)

Dr. Mees is one of the greatest authorities on photography. He has been Director of Research and Development of the Eastman Kodak Company since 1912, and as he knew well many of the pioneers of modern photography he is fully qualified to tell his readers all about it. They will not be disappointed by his book, for it gives a complete background to photography and is a mine of practical information based on life-long experience and study.

The first chapter tells the story of the beginnings of photography and traces its history down to present times, contrasting the clumsy methods used by enthusiasts of 50 years ago with the simple and easy manner in which photographs can now be taken by cinematograph and ordinary cameras that can be carried in the pocket. How the cameras, plates and films they use are made is next explained, and an interesting sidelight on the popularity of photography is given by the information that 20,000 people are employed in the industry, which every year absorbs about 500 tons of pure silver. Modern photographic methods are then described, followed by chapters on what happens when a plate is exposed and is subsequently developed and fixed. The reproduction of tone values by photography is particularly well dealt with, and every amateur photographer who follows Dr. Mees' account of this subject should be able to improve his own photographic work.

Other chapters deal with the cinematograph, including the making of animated cartoons, the photography of coloured objects, and photography in colours, in which keen interest is now being taken. Finally comes a chapter on the widely different uses that have been made of photography.

Excellent use is made throughout of ingeniously planned diagrams that help readers to understand the explanations of photographic processes given by the author, and a remarkable series of 30 full page plates, several of which are in colours, add greatly to the attractions of the book.

"The Riddle of Dr. Milverson" and " 'Ferret' of the 'Omnipotent' "

By Captain Oswald Dallas

(R.T.S. 2/6 net)

Captain Dallas is an old hand at writing a thrilling and exciting story, and these volumes are characteristic of him. The first deals with the efforts of Billy Milverson to find his father, who had disappeared shortly before the school holidays. The search leads the boy into a succession of wild adventures, in which an old soldier and two midshipmen, known as the "Ferret" and the "Owl," give him stalwart assistance in unravelling the mystery. The two midshipmen re-appear in *" 'Ferret' of the 'Omnipotent,' "* a breezy yarn, full of both humour and adventure, in which the heroes fall into one scrape after another.

"The Boys' Own Annual"

(R.T.S. 10/6 net)

This year's *"Boys' Own Annual,"* the 58th of the series, maintains the high standard and varied interest of its predecessors, although its price has been reduced to 10/6. As usual, it contains a good selection of serials and short stories, all by well-known writers and full of thrills and adventures. The general articles are particularly good, and cover a very wide range of subjects, from the assault on Mount Everest to flying, lighthouses and lightships, and other matters of great interest to all boys. There are more dog yarns, a feature continued from last year's volume; and articles on games and sports, hobbies, and how to make things complete a fine volume, which contains four coloured plates and many other illustrations.

Putting nitrocellulose into a mixer during the production of photographic film base. This illustration, and the one below, are from "Photography," reviewed on this page.

An assistant holding the signal board before a scene is shot while making a moving picture. The board gives the date, the picture number and other details.

"The Schoolboys' Annual"

(R.T.S. 3/6 net)

The contents of this Annual are extremely varied and attractive, and practically every feature in it will appeal strongly to boy readers. It contains a range of stories of school life and adventure and daring in all parts of the world, and other attractions include articles on sports and hobbies. There are several coloured plates, in addition to illustrations in black and white.

"The Modern Book of Aeroplanes and Airships"

By W. H. McCormick. (A. and C. Black. 5/- net)

This book is a companion volume to the *"M.M."* Editor's *"Modern Book of Lighthouses, Lightships and Life-boats,"* which was reviewed last month. It deals in a vivid and comprehensive manner with the conquest of the air, telling the story of Man's efforts to fly from the very earliest days of balloons right down to the present time.

It is a little difficult for the modern boy to realise the daring of the pioneers who first left the surface of the ground in crude balloons filled with hot air, but the thrilling character of the ascents of the Montgolfiers and other early aeronauts is well conveyed in the account given by the author of their achievements. How these eventually led to the development of the modern rigid airship is fully explained, and the stories are told of great and hazardous flights in famous airships, including R.34, the British vessel that in 1919 made the first crossing of the Atlantic by air.

From the airship the author turns to the aeroplane. After explaining how the aeroplane originated in the gliding experiments of Lilienthal and others, he tells the story of the Wrights, the first men who actually flew in a heavier-than-air machine that was under control. Their triumph in spite of misfortune is thrillingly described, as are the daring flights of pioneers such as Roe in this country, and Latham and Blèriot, the famous French airmen whose exploits attracted so much attention.

At this stage of development came the Great War, and the author shows how the demand for machines for special purposes, such as fighting, bombing and photography, led to remarkable advances in design. The following years saw the production of bigger and faster machines, and also of unusual and ingenious types intended to give greater safety and stability in the air. The most important of these unusual machines is the Autogiro, the latest type of which actually rises vertically into the air. The part played by the engine in these developments is not overlooked, and descriptions are given of the highly efficient power units installed in modern aeroplanes. Then follows a chapter describing the aeroplane in flight. This is short, but gives a remarkably detailed and accurate picture of the actions of the pilot of machines while taking off, flying and landing.

The remaining sections of the book are devoted to modern flying in all its branches. The author first shows how the network of airways is gradually spreading over the world, and then describes famous flights and air races. The excitements of Schneider Trophy Contests, King's Cup Air Race and the MacRobertson Race are well described, and a final chapter tells how airmen use wireless to find their way.

The book is well illustrated by means of photogravure illustrations. D.G.

FROM OUR READERS

These pages are reserved for articles from our readers. Contributions not exceeding 500 words in length are invited on any subject of general interest. These should be written neatly on one side of the paper only, and they may be accompanied by photographs or sketches for use as illustrations. Articles that are published will be paid for at our usual rates. Statements contained in articles submitted for these pages are accepted as being sent in good faith, but the Editor takes no responsibility for their accuracy.

A Trip on an Austrian Cable Railway

When staying at Innsbruck recently I decided to go up the cable railway that leads almost to the summit of the Hafelekar, a mountain 7,644 ft. high. The first part of the journey is made by funicular railway, and it was a wonderful experience to see Innsbruck appearing to grow smaller and smaller as the car crawled slowly up the slopes.

About 20 minutes after starting the train stopped at the village of Hungerburg, where we changed to a cable car. As the accompanying illustration shows, this is a small box-like compartment suspended from pulleys running on one stout wire rope and hauled up by means of another. It was a thrilling, and rather fearful sensation, to look out of the windows and to see the tops of the pine trees slipping past beneath us. This part of the ascent occupied about ten minutes and brought us to Seegrube, a small station at a height of 6,239 ft., where we changed into an even smaller cable car that took us within about 30 ft. of the summit of the mountain.

From this great height I obtained wonderful views of Innsbruck and the surrounding country. The snow lay thickly around. It was dry and powdery and I thoroughly enjoyed a snowball fight with other passengers in which I took part. Coming down the mountain was even more thrilling than going up, as the ground beneath us seemed to rush up to meet us at a terrific rate. G. A. Barry (Ayr).

Cars travelling up and down the Hafelekar cable railway, near Innsbruck, in the Austrian Tyrol. Photograph by courtesy of the Innsbrucker Nordkettenbahn.

St. Catherine's Lighthouse

St. Catherine's Lighthouse is on the rocky south coast of the Isle of Wight, and is one of the most important in this country. When I visited it, I was shown a plumb line hanging from the top of the tower. The pointed end of the weight is not now exactly over the mark made for it, which shows that the structure has moved a little to one side since it was built.

There is a small fixed red light about half way up the lighthouse. This is equipped with lenses, but is much less powerful than the main light at the top of the tower, although it can be seen from a distance of 16 miles. Its beams fall upon dangerous rocks known as the Atherfield Ledge.

A flight of very small steps leads to the main light, with its vast prismatic lenses that concentrate the rays of light into central beams. The light is very powerful, and St. Catherine's can be recognised by its quick white flashes, each lasting only one-fifth of a second, which occur every five seconds. The revolving mechanism that intercepts the light to form the flashes is operated by clockwork. It weighs $2\frac{1}{2}$ tons, but is so finely constructed that the pressure of my finger caused it to revolve as it floated on its bath of mercury.

While I was in the lighthouse the fog siren was being tested. When this is working every blast is recorded, so that there can be no dispute as to whether it was really operating if any wreck or accident occurred. Two blasts, one high and one low, are given in quick succession every minute.

In the migrating season thousands of birds are attracted by the light. Formerly these obstructed the beams by flying round when unable to find a resting place, and for this reason special perches have now been fixed below the light for them.

E. Mackerness (Old Stratford).

The Sexton and the Robin

When I was looking round a churchyard in the New Forest district, I was told by the sexton that he regularly fed a robin, which came to him whenever he called it. I was greatly interested and walked with him to the place where the bird spends most of its time. It could not then be seen, but the sexton made a curious humming and whistling sound, and presently it appeared and flew on to a rail. When the sexton placed a small piece of cheese between his lips the bird flew up and took it.

I was very eager to take a photograph showing the robin flying up to the cheese, and did so with an exposure of a five-hundredth of a second. J. H. Vickers (Oxford).

A Lisbon Landmark

The Torre de Belem, shown in the photograph reproduced on this page, is a fortress tower standing like a sentinel on the left bank of the Tagus, where it forms an excellent landmark for vessels approaching Lisbon. It was built during the 15th century, and provides an excellent example of the manner in which rivers may change their courses. When it was erected Portuguese mariners were able to sail round it; and in 1497 it witnessed the departure of Vasco da Gama on the great adventure that resulted in the discovery of the sea route to India, an event that is commemorated by a monastery built near it in honour of the great explorer. To-day the tower is stranded high and dry on a sandy beach, for the river now flows in another channel.

Belem is a suburb of Lisbon and is easily reached by tramcar or electric train. Visitors to the tower are shown round by a soldier from the neighbouring fort and are well rewarded for their trouble. The view from the upper tower is very fine, and the subterranean dungeons also are interesting, for they are dark and grim, and one can imagine the unpleasant sensations of those who were confined in them when the tower was used as a state prison, about 100 years ago. T. Brooks (Halifax).

The Torre de Belem, a Portuguese fortress tower built over 400 years ago. Photograph by T. Brooks, Halifax.

A Coal-mine Rescue Station

At Wakefield there is a rescue station built and maintained by the coal owners of the West Riding of Yorkshire. The object of the station is to train teams of men in the art of rescue work in pits in which there has been a disaster of some kind, and I was very pleased to have the opportunity of inspecting it.

The chief feature of the station is an exact reproduction of the galleries of a coal-mine. These wind about under the concrete floor of the station itself. They have low roofs, and in them are long low tunnels, only about 2 ft. in height, that give the men in training practice in crawling along in narrow spaces. There are also obstacles such as beams and sandbags over which they have to climb. Here and there, laid on a sandy floor or propped up in dark corners, are dummy figures dressed like miners, and the rescue men are trained to find them and carry them out into pure air. Gas masks and special helmets are worn in the galleries, and these sometimes are filled with smoke in order to make rescue practice more realistic and difficult.

The men are taught the use of artificial breathing apparatus, how to handle hose pipes and fire extinguishers, and the methods by which gassed or drowning people are revived, either by artificial respiration or with the aid of oxygen.

I was particularly interested in a large van, fully equipped with rescue apparatus, that is always in readiness to be despatched to a coal-mine at which an accident has occurred. It carries two dozen sets of breathing apparatus, placed in special lockers, together with ambulance requirements, fire extinguishers, oxygen apparatus, stretchers, clothing, blankets, and in fact anything that is likely to be needed. In addition it has space for a crew of about a dozen men, and before seeing it I would not have believed that so much equipment could have been stowed in so small a space.

T. E. W. Smith (Halifax).

A robin flying up to take a tit-bit from the lips of the sexton of a New Forest church. Photograph by J. H. Vickers, Oxford.

The Mandi Memorial Stones

The State of Mandi, in India, lies among the Himalayas about 150 miles east of Lahore. It has had a long and interesting history, which finally resulted in a treaty between the British and the Rajah of Mandi in 1846.

The state is chiefly agricultural, but in late years it has come into prominence on account of the fact that one of the largest hydro-electric schemes in the world was put into operation there in March 1932. This now supplies current to an area in the Punjab that is about as large as Great Britain. The capital is Mandi, which was founded in 1527 and stands at the junction of the rivers Bias and Mala.

There are many temples and places of interest in the state, and of these the Memorial Stones erected just outside the capital on the banks of the river Mala are perhaps the most outstanding. These stones have been set up in memory of various Rajahs of the State. They vary in height from 2 ft. to 12 ft., but all are of about the same width and thickness. Their surfaces are elaborately carved with portraits of the Rajahs they commemorate, their wives, and certain of their retainers, who were burned with their bodies. At one time it was the custom for the wives of the Rajahs to be burned in this manner on the deaths of their husbands, but sutti, as this custom is called, was abolished by the British Government. The most recent of the stones illustrating the custom shows that 20 wives were burned with the Rajah in whose memory it was set up.

The tops only of some of the stones are visible, the rest being buried beneath the dust of ages. The largest stones are those erected in memory of ruling princes, and to the left and right of these respectively are smaller ones commemorating their daughters and sons who did not succeed to the throne. J. Mullen (Simla).

Life-boat Launched by Tractor

Power Unit that can Work in the Sea

LAUNCHING a life-boat is an exciting and sometimes difficult task, for usually it has to be accomplished with the utmost speed in a raging storm, and often in inky darkness. Nothing must go wrong on such occasions as these, for if it does the lives the life-boat has been provided to save may be lost, and the rescuers themselves may be in danger.

Where the condition of the beach permits, a life-boat is launched on a carriage that runs down launching ways into the sea. At stations where permanent launching ways cannot be built, it is mounted on a special carriage that is hauled by men or horses into the sea to a sufficient distance to enable the boat to be floated off. The beaches at many life-boat stations around our coasts are not smooth stretches of sand, however, but accumulations of treacherous mud patches, rocks and loose shingle, and at these places it is usual to employ a special tractor to haul the life-boat carriage to the sea. Tractors have been in use for this purpose for many years, and the Royal National Life-Boat Institution, which controls and maintains the life-boat service in this country, is now experimenting with a new machine of the type illustrated on this page. This tractor was built by Roadless Traction Ltd., Hounslow.

The Royal National Life-boat Institution's new tractor, designed for launching life-boats, continues to work even when partly submerged in the sea. The illustrations on this page are reproduced by courtesy of Roadless Traction Ltd., Hounslow.

What is required of a tractor for the life-boat service can best be realised by following the course of an actual launch. The life-boat is mounted on its carriage with its stern facing forward. The tractor is coupled up and proceeds along the beach to the spot selected for the launch, hauling the life-boat after it, and there it actually enters the sea, in which it may be submerged to a depth of 3 to 4 ft. It is then turned so as to face up the beach, bringing the bow of the boat towards the open sea. It is next uncoupled and turned round on the beach, so that it can push the life-boat farther out until the carriage is submerged to the required depth. When doing this the tractor itself generally is almost under water. Two ropes are attached to a launching platform at the front end of the tractor, and are passed round pulleys at the front, or seaward end of the carriage, finally being brought back and attached to the stern of the life-boat. As the tractor then travels up the beach, the life-boat is pulled off the carriage into the sea.

In severe storms the tractor is not merely partly under water, but also is swept and battered by heavy seas, and shingle or floating debris may be thrown violently against it. The machine must be very robust and entirely waterproof in order to withstand such severe treatment. All delicate working parts of the mechanism must be enclosed and adequately protected, for the entry of sea water might result in the loss of the entire tractor, apart from making the launching of the life-boat impossible.

Complete sealing is provided in the new tractor. Every opening through which water might pass, even in the stormiest weather, is closed and all parts of the power unit and steering mechanism that require it are protected against the action of water by some form of sealing device. Some of them are closed in by casing connected to the air intake pipe of the engine, the top of which stands 7 ft. 6 in. above the ground level.

A front view of the new R.N.L.I. tractor showing the girder tracks and the grid of the launching platform, which can be raised when not in use.

The tractor has to work on treacherous and difficult ground, from wet sand to thick mud. Wheels would not give a sufficient grip in all conditions, and the machine therefore is mounted on rubber-jointed girder tracks, 18 in. in width, which are driven through a gear-box and clutch.

The launching platform and the buffer arrangement for pushing the carriage into the sea to the required depth forms an extension at the front of the main frame of the tractor. A grid is provided for a man to stand on, and when not in use this can be folded back against the radiator.

Automatic Brakes for Trailers

Controlled and Operated by Compressed Air

THE brake gear of a modern road vehicle is one of its most important mechanisms. It is not only required to stop the vehicle in which it is fitted, but also must be capable of bringing it to a standstill in a very short distance at a moment's notice in emergencies. Brakes operated by pedals and hand levers usually are fitted in light vehicles, and these are efficient for their purpose, provided they are properly designed and adjusted. Much greater pressure than the muscular power a driver can exert are required on the brake drums of larger vehicles, such as heavy transport lorries and buses, and these usually are fitted with power-operated brakes.

One of the most interesting power brake systems makes use of compressed air. This is the Westinghouse brake, which is suitable for use on vehicles of all kinds. The layout of this brake on a four-wheeled motor lorry is shown in the lower illustration on this page. The air required for the application of the brakes is stored under high pressure in a special reservoir, or air bottle, from which it is released when braking is necessary. It then passes into cylinders, one for each wheel, where it acts on pistons that are connected to the levers operating the brake shoes, and its action is controlled through a valve operated by means of a pedal placed conveniently near the driver's foot.

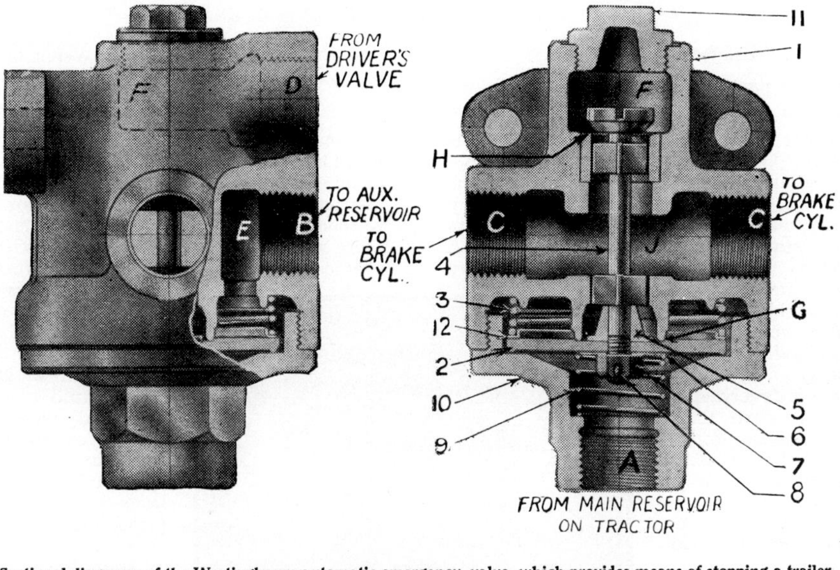

The reservoir is filled by a compressor that in a motor vehicle is driven either from the gear box or from an auxiliary shaft of the engine. When the reservoir is full, with the pressure of air within it at its highest, an automatic device stops the entry of more air and at the same time relieves the compressor of its load. This device also restarts the action when the pressure drops below an arranged figure, so that a full supply of compressed air is always ready for use. The use of the reservoir is an important feature of the Westinghouse apparatus, for it provides the driver with a reserve of energy upon which he can draw at any moment, even if his engine stalls when going uphill, or in the event of an unintended run-back. A gauge on the instrument board shows at a glance whether the pressure in the reservoir is correct.

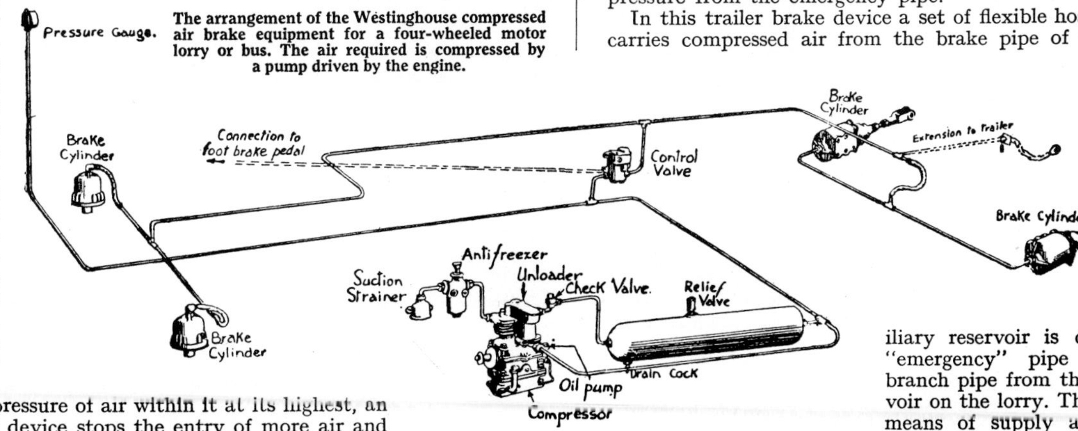

When the driver presses on the brake pedal, the control valve is opened to allow compressed air to pass from the reservoir to the brake cylinders. There it pushes out the pistons connected to the brake levers, and these apply the shoes to the drums. The greater the pressure exerted on the pedal, the greater the force with which the brakes are applied. When the brakes are to be released, the driver simply removes his foot from the pedal. The air in the cylinders then escapes, thus taking the pressure off the brake shoes.

There is no difficulty in fitting this brake to an electric trolley bus, for the compressor can be driven directly from an electric motor supplied with current from the trolley line. An electric governor cuts off the current supply of the motor when the maximum air pressure is reached in the reservoir, and automatically restarts compression when the pressure falls.

The increasing use of heavily loaded trailers behind motor lorries has created the need for a power brake that will keep the trailer under control, and prevent it from overrunning the vehicle ahead of it, and that also will stop it automatically if it breaks away. Westinghouse automatic brake equipment has been introduced for this purpose. It works from the compressed air reservoir of the lorry to which the trailer is attached, and provides a powerful brake that comes into operation immediately the air couplings between the vehicles are parted, or when an accident of any kind causes loss of air pressure from the emergency pipe.

In this trailer brake device a set of flexible hoses and couplings carries compressed air from the brake pipe of the lorry to the fittings on the trailer. A small auxiliary air reservoir and an emergency valve also are included. The auxiliary reservoir is connected by an "emergency" pipe coupling to a branch pipe from the main air reservoir on the lorry. Thus there are two means of supply available for the application of the trailer brakes. One is the compressed air released in the lorry brake pipes when the driver presses the pedal; the other is the air stored under pressure in the special reservoir on the trailer.

The emergency valve is the key to the automatic application of the trailer brakes. Normally a double-action valve allows compressed air from the lorry connection to enter the brake cylinders when the brakes are applied. If the trailer breaks away the valve moves in such a manner that openings through which air could be lost are closed, and compressed air from the auxiliary reservoir then applies the brakes.

Sectional diagrams of the Westinghouse automatic emergency valve, which provides means of stopping a trailer if it breaks loose from the lorry hauling it. The working of the valve is explained in this article. Photographs by courtesy of Westinghouse Brake and Signal Co. Ltd.

The arrangement of the Westinghouse compressed air brake equipment for a four-wheeled motor lorry or bus. The air required is compressed by a pump driven by the engine.

By P. A. Tent

Separating Fine Dust from Gases

The problem of removing fine particles of dust from gases is one with which the engineer is often confronted, and the illustration on this page shows an ingenious separator designed to solve this problem. The gases to be purified enter through the opening seen on the left in our illustration and are whirled at high speed round the circular chamber into which it leads. The comparatively heavy solid particles are flung to the outside of this artificial whirlpool by centrifugal action, and there escape through narrow openings into a special compartment in which they settle, and from which they can be removed from time to time.

This simple plan is remarkably efficient, but in special cases a double cyclone action is provided, and in addition baffle plates are placed in the path of the gases in such a manner that part of the dust is deposited on them. The double cyclone is particularly useful for gases that contain a large proportion of dust and dirt. Tests show that 90 per cent. of even the finest dust is removed rapidly and easily by the use of this separator, and as much as 99 per cent. of the particles measuring a four-hundredth of an inch or more across is stopped by it.

The separator shown in our illustration is employed to remove fine ash from the gases from a mechanically-fired boiler plant, and is capable of dealing with 7,400 cu. ft. of gas a minute. Other separators of this type are used for taking dust out of gases from cement kilns, and foundries and furnaces of all kinds.

An Inventor's Exhibition

The great event of the year in the inventor's world is the Exhibition organised by the Institute of Patentees. The 12th Exhibition of the series was a worthy successor to its predecessors, and showed that our inventors are as ingenious and enterprising as ever. In his address on opening the Exhibition, Lord Askwith, President of the Institute of Patentees, remarked on the decline in the number of patent applications made for the year ending September 1936, in comparison with the number in the previous year. The drop was from 25,726 to 25,176 and was so slight that it cannot be regarded as evidence of lack of inventive spirit. The President suggested that the increase in employment was responsible for it. This is reasonable, for many of those who would have been working out details of possible patents no doubt have not had time for activity of this kind. It is curious to find that unemployment leads to an increase in inventive activity, in view of the complaint that machines are displacing men in industry.

A feature of the Exhibition was the increase in the number of domestic and labour-saving devices. These included a new electric machine for washing plates and dishes, which rinses them first with hot water and then with cold water before leaving them to dry under cover. Some of the domestic inventions were shown by women inventors. Among these were toasting forks with two or more sets of prongs, a dust-bin with a sliding lid and an adjustable cinder sifter that is particularly suitable for use in flats and large buildings, and a saucepan in which milk falls back into the pan like a fountain when it rises instead of boiling over.

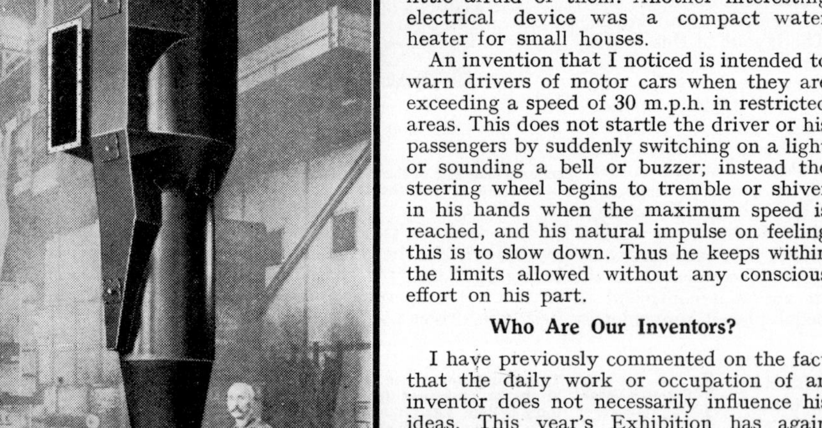
A single cyclone dust separator for removing ash from the flue gases of a mechanically fired boiler plant. Photograph by courtesy of Sulzer Bros. (London) Ltd.

Hand Torch with a Rear Light

Another simple but practical invention that attracted attention was a hand torch that provides a light in the rear as well as the main beam. Torches of this kind should be particularly useful in country districts on roads without paths, for motorists would then be warned of the presence of pedestrians carrying them. In addition there were a two-speed gear for bicycles in which the changes are effected automatically, and a simple fuse box for household use. In the latter a blown fuse is ejected by simply inserting a new one and pressing a button. The device is shock-proof, and will be appreciated by those who are not familiar with electrical gadgets and are perhaps a little afraid of them. Another interesting electrical device was a compact water heater for small houses.

An invention that I noticed is intended to warn drivers of motor cars when they are exceeding a speed of 30 m.p.h. in restricted areas. This does not startle the driver or his passengers by suddenly switching on a light or sounding a bell or buzzer; instead the steering wheel begins to tremble or shiver in his hands when the maximum speed is reached, and his natural impulse on feeling this is to slow down. Thus he keeps within the limits allowed without any conscious effort on his part.

Who Are Our Inventors?

I have previously commented on the fact that the daily work or occupation of an inventor does not necessarily influence his ideas. This year's Exhibition has again shown the truth of this. Inventors represented in it range from auctioneers and architects to butchers, schoolmasters, doctor and company directors. It is perhaps natural that a hotel proprietor should invent an improved cash till, but it is a little surprising to find that a coal merchant should invent an insect trap, an insurance broker should produce a loom darning appliance, and a vinegar maker should be responsible for apparatus to indicate the speed of a motor car. The wide range of occupations represented in the Exhibition is a further proof of the fact that man above all is an inventive being, always thinking and striving to produce new things.

Lenses to Fit on the Eyeball

An invention that promises to be a real boom is the contact eye lens, which is fitted to the shape of the eyeball and worn under the eyelids. A pair of these serve the same purpose as eyeglasses or spectacles, but are far more efficient and less unsightly. They are also safer, for they are protected naturally by the eyelids. They are therefore practically unbreakable and may be worn by people without danger taking part in games. An instance is on record in which the face of a man wearing contact glasses was badly torn in a motor car accident, while his eyes were uninjured.

The idea of contact eye lenses is by no means a new one. They were suggested 100 years ago, but it is only recently that improvements in the art of grinding lenses have made them practicable. They take a little more time to adjust than ordinary spectacles, but are comfortable to wear once the correct curvature and fitting have been secured, and provide complete correction for various defects of vision. One particularly interesting advantage they possess is that as in effect they form part of the eye itself, they do not reflect stray light into the eyes of their wearers.

A New Idea in Vice Design

The vice is one of the fundamental tools of the engineer, and while many changes have been made in its design, either to improve its working or to adapt it to special uses, revolutionary alterations have been rare since it came into general use. The new vice shown in the lower illustration on this page marks a distinct break. It is known as the "Versa Vice" and its important feature is that the work it holds rests upon a solid platform. The jaws therefore have merely to hold articles in position instead of having to grip them tightly enough to support their weight.

As the illustration shows, the jaws of the vice work in slots in a body that has a smoothly machined top. They are closed and opened by means of a hand-wheel, which acts in the same manner as the usual hand lever of an ordinary vice. Unlike the jaws of the latter, however, they can be raised within certain limits to any convenient height above the top of the body, so as to accommodate work of different sizes. The height is regulated by the use of a knob that is provided with projections to enable a good grip to be obtained.

An ingenious tyre lifting dog that is used both for lifting tyres and for stacking them. Photograph by courtesy of Joseph Booth and Bros. Ltd., Rodley.

The body of the vice is a rectangular cast steel box with flanges for bolts to hold it down to the working bench. The surface table or plate, on which the work rests, is carefully finished and is exactly parallel with the bottom flange, and the jaws are made of high tensile steel, with hardened steel faces having cross-cut grooves. Work can be set up very quickly, as the operator merely raises or lowers the jaws to the desired position. The sides of the body also are machined square to the base and surface plate, so that the vice can be bolted to knee plates to enable the jaws to grip shafts that have to be drilled or otherwise machined when in a vertical position.

The combination of a working table that provides support, and jaws that grip securely without straining or distorting objects between them, makes the Versa Vice one that can be used not only by engineers for all classes of work, but also by jewellers, watch-makers, engravers and electrical instrument makers. The most delicate electrical instruments and even watches can be held firmly in position for work to be done on them without damaging them in any way by the pressure of the jaws.

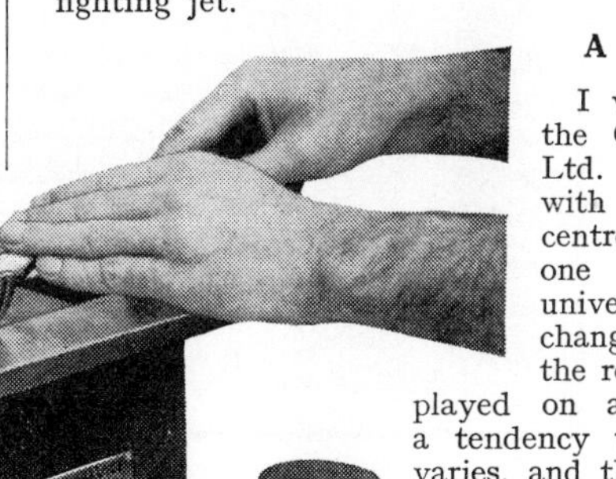

The Versa Vice in use in a motor garage. The jaws of this vice merely hold work in position instead of gripping it tightly enough to support it. Photograph by courtesy of William Frost and Company, Newcastle-upon-Tyne.

An Electric Lifting Dog

The ingenious lifting dog shown in the upper illustration on this page is designed for handling steel tyres rapidly and easily, whether they are hot or cold. It is electrically driven and is suspended from an overhead crane, its operation being controlled from the crane cage. It has three lifting links, which are expanded and contracted by levers operated by a central screw, which is driven through reduction gearing by an electric motor. A shock-absorbing clutch is fitted so that no damage is done to the working parts when the dogs come into contact with the tyre that they are about to lift, and a permanent resistance included in the motor circuit prevents injury of any kind due to overloading when contact is made.

The dogs have double heads, so that they can grip a tyre either on the outside or on the inside, and they automatically centre themselves. The machine is very precise in its action, and is used not only for handling the tyres as they come from the mill, but also for stacking them.

Sometimes it happens that a stack of tyres is built up askew. It is then easy to straighten out the pile by simply lowering the lifting dogs inside it, extending them to come into contact with the lowest tyre, and then winding them out.

Fighting Waterfront Fires

Fire fighting is a field in which the inventor is always at work, either to speed up the attack on a fire in order to prevent it from securing a firm hold, or to extinguish it more quickly and with less damage from water. The difficulties of approaching fires also is in the mind of inventors, and in Oregon, in the United States, trials have been made of a device to enable firemen to cope with burning warehouses or other buildings alongside docks, which often set firemen difficult problems. This takes the form of a small metal boat, about 3 ft. in length, equipped with an electric pump that throws a powerful jet of water through a nozzle in its deck. Another jet below the waterline propels the boat, which carries no crew, but is controlled from a distance. The rudder is guided by means of ropes or cables so that the boat can be directed to any position, from which good use can be made of its fire-fighting jet.

A Gramophone Improvement

I was interested to find that the Columbia Graphophone Co. Ltd. are now making records with a twelve-sided hole in the centre, instead of the circular one that until now has been universal. The purpose of this change is to make sure that the records will not slip. Records played on automatic radiograms have a tendency to do this; and the pitch varies, and the tone of the reproduction is spoiled, if there is a slip of only a fraction of an inch. The new form of centre hole has overcome this difficulty completely, and the records incorporating it can be played with precision and perfection of tone.

Developing Fingerprints

Inventors join in the campaign against crime in many forms, and chemical knowledge was used by one in America who has worked out an interesting method for developing fingerprints. These usually are detected by dusting suspected articles with a powder that adheres to surfaces which have been made slightly greasy by the pressure of a finger or thumb. Prints on polished table tops and on certain other kinds of surface cannot readily be made visible in this manner, but the new method is successful in the most difficult cases.

The plan followed is to blow iodine fumes over the surface to be examined. This is easily done by means of a small glass vessel containing glass wool. On blowing down a rubber tube fitted at one end of this vessel, iodine fumes are blown out at the other, and the quantity can be increased by warming the tube with the hand. When a print is found a small sheet of silver is pressed against it for a few seconds and then exposed to sunlight. When this is done the iodine print is transferred to the silver, on which it can be preserved if it is protected from a strong light.

Meccano Suggestions Section

By "Spanner"

(365 and 366) Two Meccano Torsion Springs (A. Allen, Swansea, and W. Forbes, Newcastle)

Motor car engineers have recently brought to perfection a system of springing that is entirely different from the leaf-type cantilever and semi-elliptic springs usually incorporated in both light cars and heavy commercial vehicles. In this system the springs, instead of making use of compression forces, depend for their working on torsional strains, and it is claimed that they are considerably cheaper to fit and more reliable in operation. There are certainly fewer moving parts under strain, but unavoidable complications are nevertheless necessary in other directions.

As is the case in many other branches of engineering, Meccano model-builders have kept up to date, and as will be seen from Figs. 365 and 366, A. Allen (Swansea) and W. Forbes (Newcastle) have built excellent reproductions of the latest additions to motor car engineering. These are both back-axle torsion springing arrangements, but the first is for rear wheel drive and the second for front-wheel drive cars. A. Allen, who submitted the first model, has made good use of Boiler Ends and Universal Couplings in reproducing one of the first torsion sprung rear-axles ever applied in actual practice. The differential of this gear is identical with that fitted in the Motor Chassis, Super Model Instruction Leaflet No. 1a, and the complete assembly can readily be incorporated in that model. A Coupling 1 carries the inner ends of a 2″ and 1½″ Rod. Each of these Rods has bolted to it a ¾″ Contrate Wheel, one of which is indicated at 2, and in addition the 2″ Rod has loosely mounted on it a 1½″ Contrate 3. This last part carries two 1″ Threaded Rods that are locked in opposite holes by means of two nuts each. The outer end of each Threaded Rod has screwed on to it a Collar, and when both of these are in position a short Rod is passed through their plain holes and also through the centre plain hole of the Coupling 1. Grub-screws are used to lock this short Rod in position in the Collars.

Fig. 365

Two ¾″ Pinions 4 are now added, and these are free to rotate on Pivot Bolts that are screwed into opposite tapped holes of the Coupling 1. These Bolts are screwed into the Coupling until they grip the Rod passing through the centre plain hole.

The complete differential gear is enclosed by two Boiler Ends 5 that are joined together by means of three 2″ Strips. Two further Boiler Ends 6 are now passed over the 2″ and 1½″ Rods already mentioned, and are kept in position by securing the ends of two Universal Couplings on their extremities. These Couplings are shown at 7 in Fig. 365. Two 1″×½″ Angle Brackets are now bolted to each of the Boiler Ends 6, and are pivotally attached to further Flat Brackets on the Boiler Ends 8. These last-mentioned Angle Brackets, indicated at 9, are linked up to the Flat Brackets on the Boiler End 6 by ⅜″ Bolts on the shanks of which are carried three Nuts and two Washers. On the opposite side of each Boiler End 8 to the 1″×½″ Angle Bracket, a Threaded Coupling 10 is fitted, and in the end plain hole of this part is gripped a 6″ Threaded Rod. Two Grub-screws are used for this purpose, and if the springs are intended to support a great weight, flats must be filed on the end of the Threaded Rod.

The unoccupied ends of both Threaded Rods are gripped in further Threaded Couplings as shown, and these Couplings are fixed by means of ⅜″ Bolts to a transverse Girder bolted to the main frames of the chassis. At this end of the Threaded Rod flats must be filed if heavy loads are to be supported.

The outer ends of the Universal Couplings 7 carry 1½″ Rods that are journalled in the bosses of Double Arm Cranks bolted to the Boiler Ends 8. The outer ends of the Rods carry the Road Wheels. One of the 2″ Strips of the differential casing has secured to it two 1″ Triangular Plates, the outer holes of which accommodate ½″ Bolts. By means of these Bolts the differential casing is attached to two transverse Angle Girders of the chassis frame, and on their shanks two Collars are placed for spacing purposes. These Collars are indicated at 11.

The second torsion spring arrangement, submitted by W. Forbes, is shown in Fig. 366. This is a much simpler arrangement than that just described, and as already mentioned it is only suitable for front-wheel drive chassis. The main frames of the chassis are bridged at their rear ends by a channel section girder, the end holes of which carry securing bolts for the Socket Couplings 1. Each of these Socket Couplings accommodate a Coupling 2 as shown, and this latter part is free to rotate. In its longitudinal bore is gripped one end of a short length of Hornby Control Wire. Both ends of this wire must first be flattened slightly by hammering, and its inner end is gripped tightly in a Collar 4. This Collar is attached to the channel girder by means of a bolt.

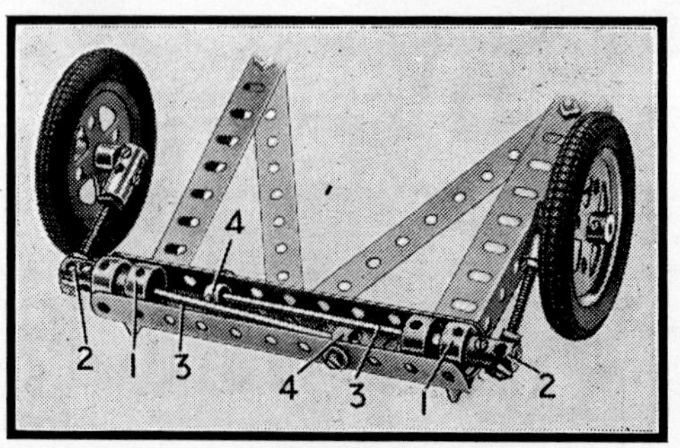

Fig. 366

The Coupling 2 has screwed into its outer tapped hole a 2″ Threaded Rod that is locked in position by means of two nuts. The unoccupied end of the Threaded Rod has passed on to it a locking nut and a Threaded Coupling, which are turned in opposite directions on the Rod until they grip each other securely. A short Rod is mounted in the end plain hole of the Threaded Coupling, and on this the road wheel is free to rotate. The wheels are held on the Rods by Collars and are spaced from the Couplings by Washers so that they run smoothly.

In actual practice the mechanism is entirely enclosed in a strong steel tube, and if in the Meccano model it is desired to follow this plan as closely as possible, the frame can be closed by means of a third Angle Girder, which would cover the Rods 3.

(367) Automatic Overload Release (K. Anderson, Birkenhead)

In actual practice most cranes are fitted with a mechanism that makes it impossible to lift a load greater than that for which the crane was designed. These overload mechanisms vary considerably in design and application, and a model of one type, shown in Fig. 367, was recently submitted by K. Anderson (Birkenhead). This model is simple to construct, and is suitable for fitting into any fixed radius jib crane and gantry crane. It is not suitable for cranes capable of operating at varying radii, because no compensation to equalise load and radius is incorporated. The framework consists of three $3\frac{1}{2}'' \times 2\frac{1}{2}''$ Flanged Plates bolted together in the manner shown in the illustration. The two Plates that are arranged vertically are bridged at their upper ends by two $2\frac{1}{2}''$ Strips.

The driving shaft 1 carries a 1″ Sprocket Wheel and a $\frac{1}{2}''$ Pinion 2, this last part meshing with a 57-teeth Gear wheel 3 that is free on the Rod 4. This Gear is spaced away from the framework by a Collar, minus grub-screw. On the outer end of the Rod 4 is mounted a 1″ loose Pulley with Dunlop Tyre, and also a Bush Wheel 3. The Bush Wheel is gripped on the Rod and is held against the Dunlop Tyre by half a Compression Spring 6. A spring loaded clutch is formed in this way between the 57-teeth Gear 3 and Bush Wheel 5.

A Worm 7, on the end of the Rod 4, meshes with a $\frac{1}{2}''$ Pinion on a Rod 8, and this carries a 1″ Sprocket Wheel that is connected to the winding barrel of the crane. When the Sprocket on the Rod 1 is rotated in an anti-clockwise direction, when looked at from the mechanism side, the driven shaft 8 is turned in a similar

Fig. 367

direction. If a load is placed on the shaft 8, the worm 7 tends to screw itself round its $\frac{1}{2}''$ Pinion, and this slides the Rod 4, thus disengaging the clutch. The clutch may be held in its disengaged position by the Pawl 9.

(368) Simple Constantinesco Gear (A. W. Marshall, Kings Lynn)

On two previous occasions Meccano models of the Constantinesco Torque Converter have been described in the "*M.M.*," but both of these were fairly complicated and made use of a considerable number of Meccano parts. They were therefore beyond the scope of many model-building enthusiasts. Mr. Marshall (Kings Lynn) has now designed a successful clockwork operated gear of this type, and as will be seen from Fig. 368 it is extremely compact.

A No. 2 Clockwork Motor is attached by a $3\frac{1}{2}''$ Angle Girder to a $3\frac{1}{2}'' \times 2\frac{1}{2}''$ Flanged Plate that forms the base. The driving spindle of the Motor carries a Coupling that is mounted in position by passing the spindle through a centre plain hole. This part forms a crank, and in one of its end tapped holes is screwed a $\frac{3}{8}''$ Bolt. This Bolt is locked in position by a Nut, and carries on its shank three Washers for spacing purposes and also a 1″ Triangular Plate 1. One hole of the Triangular Plate accommodates a 7/32″ Bolt, the shank of which is screwed into one of the threaded holes of the Collar 2.

The Rod 3 on which the Collar 2 is secured is gripped at its upper end in the longitudinal bore of a Coupling 4, that is pivotally mounted on a 1″ transverse rod. Two $1\frac{1}{2}''$ Strips 5 are mounted on this Rod, together with the ends of two $2\frac{1}{2}''$ large radius Curved Strips 6 and 7. These four Strips are secured in position by means of two Collars as shown in the photograph. The lower end of the Rod 3 has mounted on it a Bush Wheel 8 that forms a support for two Worms that are held in position by means of $\frac{3}{8}''$ Bolts.

Fig. 368

The upper holes of the $1\frac{1}{2}''$ Strips 5 carry a $1\frac{1}{2}''$ Rod, and on this Rod, between the $1\frac{1}{2}''$ Strips, are mounted eight Washers. Two Collars are next added, and one end of the $1\frac{1}{2}''$ Rod is gripped in the boss of a Crank 9. This Crank is bolted to a Flat Trunnion that in turn is bolted to one of the side plates of the Motor. Each end of the Strips 6 and 7 is lock-nutted to a Crank. The two Cranks are indicated at 10 and 11, and both bosses of these parts point inward towards the Motor. They are arranged on opposite sides of a 1″ Gear that is free to turn on the driven Rod 12.

(369) Off-Set Pawls

(A. Smiler, Leicester)

One of the difficulties associated with ratchet-operated mechanisms in Meccano models is that of obtaining a very small rotary movement for an equally small reciprocating movement of the driving mechanism. This can be overcome to a great extent by making use of large diameter Gears, having a great number of teeth, but unfortunately the necessary space is not always available. This problem has been solved successfully by A. Smiler (Leicester) who has conceived the idea of using two or more off-set Pawls. A simple two-pawl arrangement is shown in Fig. 369 and no doubt many Meccano model-builders will find use for the idea.

A Ratchet Wheel is mounted, together with two 2″ Strips, on the driving shaft, and the unoccupied ends of the Strips are joined together by a 1″ Threaded Rod. This Rod has locked on it two Flat Brackets, each of which forms a connecting point for a Pawl, without boss. This Pawl is mounted on a lock-nutted bolt, and is held in contact with the Ratchet Wheel by means of a short length of Spring Cord. One end of the Spring Cord passes through the unoccupied hole of the Pawl, and the other end is fastened round the 1″ Threaded Rod already mentioned. By sliding the lock-nutted bolts carrying the Pawls in the slotted holes of the Flat Brackets the tips of the Pawls can be off-set for half the distance between two teeth of the Ratchet Wheel.

Fig. 369

(*Continued from previous column*)

of each Crank is fitted with a Pivot Bolt, lock-nutted in position and carrying on its shank a Pawl. This Pawl is held in contact with the 1″ Gear already mentioned by means of a light spring or short length of elastic.

Miscellaneous Suggestions

Under this heading "Spanner" replies to readers who submit interesting suggestions regarding new Meccano models or movements that he is unable to deal with more fully elsewhere. On occasion he offers comments and technical criticisms that, he trusts, will be accepted in the same spirit of mutual help in which they are advanced.

M.192. M. Howes, Stockport, has discovered that a 2″ Tyre mounted on a 2″ Pulley, forms an admirable gear wheel when used in conjunction with a $\frac{1}{2}''$ Pinion. The treads of the Tyre are the exact pitch of Meccano Gears and form good teeth for light drives.

In Search of New Models

Snow Scenes for Christmas

AT this time of the year every model-builder is intent on the joys of the Christmas season, and looks forward eagerly to the good time he is going to have during the holidays. His thoughts of course are reflected in his model-building, and it is only natural that he should search for subjects that seem in some way to be closely connected with Christmas. There is no difficulty in building up novel and interesting models. At Christmas we always think of snow scenes of various kinds, and our minds turn to winter sports, such as skating and sledging. These of course figure largely among our Christmas models, and although the season is traditionally a merry one, there is no reason why the model-builder should not even go further, and represent a real snow blizzard, with a dog team fighting its way through at the command of their owner.

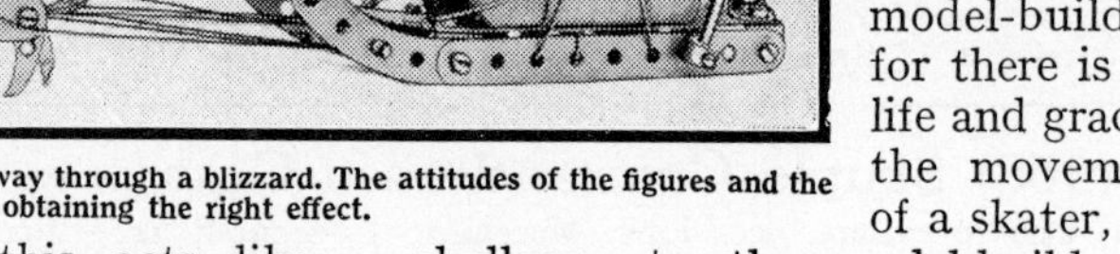

Fig. 1. A Meccano impression of an Alaskan dog team fighting its way through a blizzard. The attitudes of the figures and the dogs play an important part in obtaining the right effect.

The majority of the models of this kind that will be built will be of the humorous type. The old joke of the fat man performing involuntary gymnastics on a slide, to the great amusement of a group of small boys, is not perhaps really funny. It never seems to become out of date, however, and there is no reason why keen model-builders should not show their skill and ability by reproducing such a scene in Meccano. There should be no difficulty in making such a figure work, moving his arms and legs in a ludicrous manner, and a successful model of this kind will always interest and amuse all who see it.

Christmas of course is never complete without a yule log! In the lower illustration on this page we show a reproduction in Meccano of the traditional countryside task of bringing in the log that is to give a cheerful blaze, and thus do its share towards increasing the happiness of everyone. The log shown of course is too large for the boys who are trying to haul it along, but that does not matter very greatly in a pictorial model such as this.

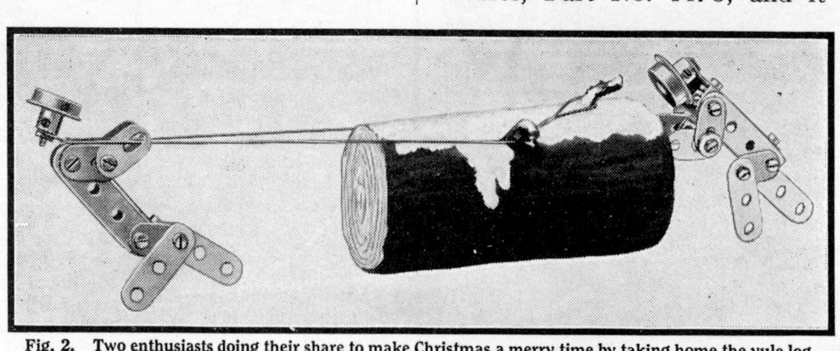

Fig. 2. Two enthusiasts doing their share to make Christmas a merry time by taking home the yule log.

A boiler covered with brown paper forms a good log. The short branches can be moulded in plastic wood, but if this material is not available, putty, wax or some similar substance will do quite as well. Thick white paint is used to represent the snow, which of course necessarily adorns all yule logs, according to Christmas tradition.

It is the attitudes of the two figures that give character to this model. A mere reproduction of a large log with two Meccano figures standing beside it would not be interesting, but the scene becomes attractive as soon as some form of motion or action is introduced. This is a point that should be kept in mind in making miniatures of all Christmas scenes, and indeed in a very wide range of scenic models.

We are assuming that there will be snow at Christmas, and if there is real Christmas weather there also will be skating. This immediately suggests excellent subjects for model-building, for there is real life and grace in the movements of a skater, and this acts like a challenge to the model-builder to reproduce it.

The upper illustration on the opposite page is an excellent example of a skating scene in Meccano. In a model of this kind the skates of course should show up well, in order to make the subject clear at the merest glance. Care therefore should be given to their construction in order that there may be no possibility of mistaking them for something else! Each of the skates in the model shown is made from two Pawls without bosses, Part No. 147C, and it will be seen that this construction is effective. The bodies of the skaters are built up of Curved Strips, and the way in which their arms have been joined together plays an important part in giving life and vigour to the scene.

This model is only an illustration of what can be done in this direction, and those who are on the look out for really novel subjects could show a novice learning to skate, or perhaps depict a break through the ice, with some skaters disappearing into the water and others falling in various ungraceful attitudes.

Sledging is as useful as skating to the model-builder in search of scenes of life and action. It is not necessary to go into details on how these should be constructed, for models of this kind have already been described in the *"M.M."* and model-builders themselves will have no difficulty in reproducing features of sledges of various types with which they are familiar.

The representation of sledges can be extended to include models similar to that shown in the upper illustration on the opposite page. This of course is serious sledging work, and not mere fun. The dogs hauling a heavily-laden sledge have an arduous task, especially if the snow over which they have to pass is soft. Then the sledge drags, their feet sink deep into the snow and they strain hard at the traces as they try to make good time.

The model illustrates these features well, and also suggests that a severe snowstorm is raging, for the man in the foreground is seen to be leaning forward as though he is struggling against a blizzard. The required attitude is given to the figure of the driver by adjusting the position of the legs and his right arm. One hand is raised to his brow in what is evidently an attempt to shield his eyes from the bitterly cold wind and clouds of drifting snow-flakes.

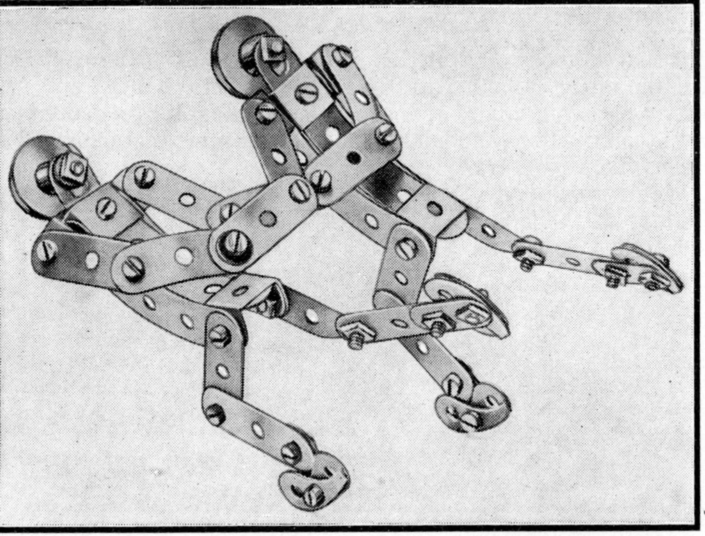

Fig. 3. The speed and grace of skaters on smooth ice is well suggested in this model.

The sledge and the stance of the man behind it are equally well portrayed, and play their part in completing the picture. The load on the sledge and the whip lash are the only parts of the model that are not Meccano parts. The former is simply a bundle of paper and the lash is a piece of stout copper wire.

The reindeer and sleigh that forms the subject of the model shown in Fig. 4, represent a more pleasurable form of sledging. The scene is typical of northern Europe, and the weather conditions are better than those of the model previously described. Reindeer are not familiar creatures outside Lapland, and model-builders can only work from photographs in trying to reproduce scenes in which they take part, but so many photographs have been reproduced in books and magazines that this offers no difficulty.

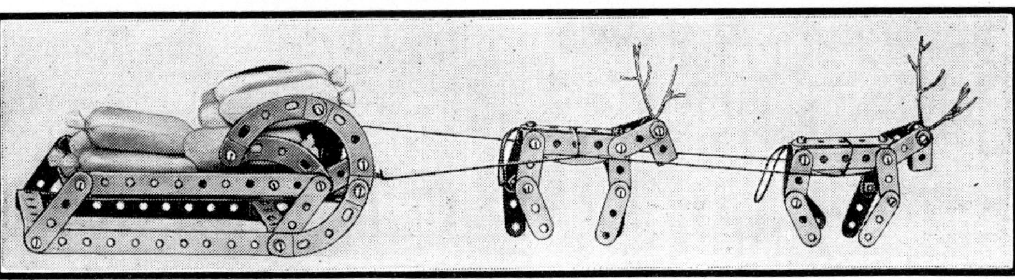

Fig. 4. The Meccano reindeer hitched to the sleigh in this scene seem eager to be off.

The sleigh is totally different from that used in northern Canada and Alaska. It can be readily distinguished by its large curved runners, and in the model it will be noticed that these form one of the main features. The only part of the model that cannot be reproduced with ordinary Meccano parts are the antlers of the reindeer, and as these must be copied fairly accurately to obtain the right effect, it is permissible to use wire or some other non-Meccano part. In the case of the model shown, Hornby control wire was used and the pieces were joined by soldering.

The model-builder who designed the scene shown in Fig. 4 had before him a drawing showing Santa Claus with his team of reindeer drawing a sleigh, and he had thoughts of making a real Christmas model by including that famous figure. This is not a very easy task, but possibly some model-builders may like to try it, and it would be interesting to see the results of the efforts of those who set out to accomplish this feat.

The models dealt with so far are outdoor in character, but it should not be overlooked that there are many indoor scenes worthy of reproduction in Meccano. The well-known demonstration model of a dance band points the way to a series of humorous models that give scope for ingenuity. These are not difficult to build. The figures of the conductor, dancers and instrumentalists are easily constructed, chiefly of Curved Strips, and the introduction of a boiler end to act as an abbreviated skirt gives a good effect. The necessary movement is given by mounting the figures on Rods passing through the platform on which they perform, and the Rods are raised and lowered by means of Eccentrics. The antics of dancing figures with hinged arms and legs can then be made very amusing, and the fun is increased when those who see the models try to find out how they work. Some of the figures might be made to strike small bells producing different notes, and there are opportunities for excellent effects in this suggestion.

Many other things that happen at Christmas and New Year parties also form good subjects for Meccano models. A group of people making merry at a well-laden table would be attractive when reproduced in miniature, especially if a touch of caricature were introduced into the make-up of the figures themselves, or into the actions they are made to perform.

Another interesting suggestion is to build models showing lively games in progress. The best type of game of course is one in which some regular movement is maintained. For instance, musical chairs lends itself well to reproduction, for the figures taking part in it can be made to pass slowly round the line of chairs placed in readiness for them, and a trip movement that would cause some of these figures to fall on to the chairs, and others to collide with each other, would give model-builders an opportunity of showing their skill.

It is not necessary that the figures in a model of this kind should seat themselves with the precision that experts at the game show. A much better effect is obtained by presenting a scene of confusion when the movement stops, and by allowing the figures simply to drop on the chairs in a haphazard manner, suggesting frantic efforts to avoid being left out of the game.

A final suggestion for humorous models of a type that would be appreciated at Christmas is to visit picture houses where good cartoons are being shown. The figures in the cartoons often are suitable for reproduction in Meccano.

Christmas Holiday Competitions

Prizes for Models of All Kinds

Building a Meccano model is indeed good fun, but the pleasure is greatly enhanced if the model is built with a definite aim in view. That is why we are continually urging model-builders to take part in the competitions announced each month in the *"M.M."* This month we are organising two competitions, one of which is designed specially for models built from the larger Meccano Outfits, while the other provides a splendid opportunity for those who possess only small Outfits to win prizes.

In the first of these competitions valuable prizes are offered for the best models of buildings of all kinds. The reproduction of houses, castles, churches and similar structures affords an interesting change from the construction of mechanical models, and provided that care is taken to choose suitable Meccano parts, really good work can be done in this direction. Architectural model-building also gives ample scope for originality in choice of subject and for the competitor to exercise his artistic abilities.

Several fine examples of architectural models have been illustrated in the *"M.M."* from time to time, and competitors should have no difficulty in finding good subjects that can be reproduced with the parts at their disposal.

The prizes in this contest will be awarded for originality of subject, neatness of construction and realism of the completed model. Any type of building may be chosen for modelling, but if possible a well-known structure, such as a famous castle or church should be selected.

Prize-winning models from recent Meccano Competitions. The penny farthing bicycle was built by G. Hudson, Doncaster, and the petrol tank lorry by L. Defries, Streatham, London.

Illustrations of suitable subjects are quite easy to obtain and photographs of many fine buildings that would be excellent for reproduction have been published in the *"Meccano Magazine."* Any size of Outfit may be used, and models of the more simple architectural subjects will receive just the same consideration as large models. Mere size alone will not ensure success for a model.

After the model is completed it is only necessary to obtain an illustration of it. This may be either a photograph or drawing, but a photograph is best if it is possible to obtain one. This need not be a professional photograph, a small "snap" will do provided that it is clear and sharp in detail. Readers who wish to photograph their models themselves and possess only simple box cameras will find many useful suggestions in the article "How to Photograph Competition Models," which appeared on page 648 of the November 1936 issue of the *"M.M."*

The competition is open to readers of all ages, living in any part of the world and there will be one section only. Each competitor must state his age, name and full address on the back of his entry and if the model is a large and complicated one a short description of its construction should be prepared. This, together with the photograph or drawing should be enclosed in an envelope addressed Christmas "Architectural" Competition, Meccano Ltd., Binns Road, Liverpool 13. The closing date for entries both Home and Overseas is 27th February, 1937.

The prizes to be awarded in the competition are announced in the panel at the foot of this page. Successful competitors will be notified by letter.

Christmas "Simplicity" Model-Building Contest

In this contest owners of even the smallest Meccano Outfits can compete on level terms with the more fortunate possessors of the more ambitious sets, and we hope that every Meccano boy who reads this announcement will decide to send in an entry. Prizes will be awarded to Meccano model-builders who succeed in constructing the most ingenious and realistic models from the smallest number of parts. Competitors may choose any subject they like for their models and the more unusual and interesting this is the better the chance of winning a prize.

When the model is completed the competitor should obtain either a photograph or a good drawing of it. He should then write his age, name and address on the back of the illustration and send it to "Christmas Simplicity Model-Building Contest," Meccano Ltd., Binns Road, Liverpool 13. The actual model must not be sent.

The competition will be divided into two Sections: A, for readers of all ages living in the British Isles, B for readers of all ages living Overseas. The prizes to be awarded in each Section are listed in the panel at the foot of this page. The closing date for Section A is 31st December, 1936, and in Section B, 27th February, 1937.

Prizes offered in these Competitions

"Architectural" Competition

1st, Meccano or Hornby Products value £5/5/–.
2nd, Meccano or Hornby Products value £3/3/–.
3rd, Meccano or Hornby Products value £2/2/–.

"Simplicity" Competition

The Prizes in each Section are:

1st, Meccano or Hornby Products value £2/2/–.
2nd, Meccano or Hornby Products value £1/1/–.
3rd, Meccano or Hornby Products value 10/6.

There will be also a number of consolation awards in each competition.

Model-Building Competition Results

By "Spanner"

"Merchant Ship" Contest

The prizewinners in the "Merchant Ship" Contest, which was announced in the June issue of the "*M.M.*" are as follows:

1st Prize, Meccano or Hornby products value £5/5/–: A Bunce, Harpenden. 2nd, products value £3/3/–: J. Willems, Hoboken, Antwerp. 3rd, products value £1/10/–: M. Drynan, Wallington, Surrey.

Products value 10/–: J. Nie, Shanghai; C. Turner, Exeter; R. Jones, Rochford, Essex; R. Cooper, Ringmer, Nr. Lewes; P. Cockram and W. Stewart, Shoreham-by-Sea.

Some idea of the great range covered by the entries in this competition is given by the illustrations on this page, which show three of the many different types of vessels that were reproduced by competitors. The judges found great difficulty in deciding the model most worthy of First Prize. The final choice lay between a fine model of the Flettner rotor ship "*Barbara*," which was submitted by A. Bunce, and a splendid reproduction of the steamship "*The City of Hope*" entered by J. Willems. Both models are really interesting and realistic, but after careful consideration the judges decided to award First Prize for the rotor ship. They were influenced in reaching their decision by the fact that this model is the better example of good Meccano construction and also is evidence of its builder's endeavour to find an original subject for his entry. The model sent by Willems is more elaborate in detail, and generally is an excellent piece of work, but showed too much reliance on the use of bent or otherwise mutilated parts for obtaining realistic effects. From this standpoint "*The City of Hope*" is inferior to the model rotor ship. By the exercise of a little ingenuity realism usually can be achieved without altering parts in any way.

For the benefit of those readers who possess back issues of the "*M.M.*," it may be mentioned that the principle of the Flettner rotor ship was dealt with on page 487 of the issue for August 1926. Although this kind of ship has not proved successful commercially, it forms an interesting type for model-ling in Meccano and provides constructional problems that call for considerable model-building skill for their satisfactory solution. In Bunce's model each rotor is made from four boilers, bolted together and strengthened by means of a Rod, which passes through their centres. The hull is made entirely from Flat Plates, and the various sections of the superstructure are made from Strips and Angle Girders.

The model of "*The City of Hope*" is remarkable for its detail work, but is less interesting than Bunce's model from the average model-builder's point of view because few owners of Meccano Outfits wish to mutilate their parts to the extent adopted in its construction. I congratulate Willems on his patience in reproducing in his model even the smallest details of the prototype. His representations of the davits and life-boats, winches, bollards and derricks are all very good indeed and faithfully reproduce the corresponding features of the vessel.

The entry that won Third Prize is the fine full-rigged sailing ship illustrated on this page, and I was greatly impressed by the realistic effect that its builder, M. Drynan, had managed to obtain. The model is intended only to show the chief characteristics of a vessel of this type, and it is not based on any particular ship. Photographs were submitted showing the model both with bare-rigging and with sails set as in the illustration reproduced here, and in my opinion, this is one of the best efforts at reproducing a ship of this kind that I have seen. There is one direction in which I think some improvement could be made, however. The masts are constructed from Strips, and I think that such parts are too heavy for the purpose. Rods undoubtedly would be more suitable.

The model shown in the centre illustration on this page won one of the smaller prizes and was built by R. Cooper. As a whole the model can scarcely be regarded as original, either in design or subject, but several portions attracted the judges on account of their interesting construction. For example the life-boats are made from $4\frac{1}{2}'' \times 2\frac{1}{2}''$ Flexible Plates bent to U shape, the corners being bolted together in pairs to form the bow and stern.

Britain's Blue Riband liner the "*Queen Mary*" was chosen by many boys as the subject for their entries, and one of the best of these is the model sent by J. Nie. It possesses a very stout hull built up from Strips. The upper decks are made from Flat Girders. This system of construction provides an interesting change from the usual method, in which Flat Plates are used, and was adopted by several other competitors. Unfortunately the stern of the vessel is not quite correct in outline and might have been more faithfully reproduced if large radius Curved Strips had been used. The funnels are represented by Boilers covered with coloured paper, the forward funnel being fitted with two bolts to represent sirens. The rigging and the wireless aerials are a little too thick in comparison with the masts.

All these models won prizes in the "Merchant Ship" Competition. The sailing ship was built by M. Drynan, Wallington, Surrey, and the oil tanker by R. Cooper, Ringmer. The rotor ship on the left won First Prize for A. Bunce, Harpenden.

Another good model of the "*Queen Mary*" was constructed by P. Cockram and W. Stewart jointly. In this model a great amount of trouble has been taken to reproduce the deck fittings of the vessel correctly. The forward ends of the upper decks are stepped back as in the actual vessel, and a neatly built workable anchor winch is fitted in the bows. The masts are built up with Rods, and unfortunately they appear rather thin in comparison with the general dimensions of the ship. The funnels are fully stayed, and the forward funnel has two Cranks to represent sirens. The ventilators are made from Couplings mounted on a Rod, with a Flanged Wheel for the cowl; I think a more realistic appearance would have been obtained by making them in box-form with Double Brackets. This system of construction would follow more closely the method adopted on the actual ship. The bridge is neatly constructed with Strips and Plates and the forward ends of the main decks beneath it are neatly moulded to reproduce the bow-shape construction adopted in the actual vessel.

Lifting Bridge "Errors" Competition

In this contest, which was announced in the issue of the "*M.M.*" for July 1936, readers were asked to make lists of all the errors they could discover in a small model of a vertical lifting bridge, an illustration of which accompanied the announcement. The most complete lists were submitted by the following competitors, and they have been awarded prizes as indicated.

Section A (for competitors living in the British Isles)

1st Prize, Meccano or Hornby products value £2/2/–: L. Willis, London, S.E.13. The 2nd and 3rd Prizes have been combined and divided equally between Miss L. J. Slater, Portsmouth, and W. Raybould, Jun., Bloxwich, each receiving goods value 15/9.

Products value 5/–: F. Phillips, Chadwell Heath; G. Askew, Horsham; N. Ferry, Timperley; F. Grace, Whitchurch; A. Thomas, Mollington.

Section B (for competitors living Overseas)

1st Prize, Meccano or Hornby products value £2/2/–: J. Rodriguez, Montreal. 2nd, products value £1/1/–: B. Wood, Berea, Johannesburg. 3rd, Products value 10/6: J. Capelli, Buenos Aires.

Products value 5/–: Nyi Kyih Vung, Shanghai; G. Milling, Lindsay, Ontario; J. Nie Shanghai; J. Smith, Melbourne; T. Ellis, Bombay.

New Outfit Models

A Greek Galley and a Target

PUMPING ENGINE models have often been described and illustrated in the "*M.M.*," but the engine shown in Fig. 1 justifies the appearance of yet another model of this kind. Although this is a simple one, built with Outfit G, it is one of the neatest that have ever been designed.

In building the model, construction should be commenced with the base as shown in Fig. 1. The cylinder, which is represented by a Boiler, is next secured in position. This is done by bolting a $4\frac{1}{2}'' \times 2\frac{1}{2}''$ Flexible Plate on opposite sides of the Boiler, and joining these to the two $3\frac{1}{2}'' \times 2\frac{1}{2}''$ Flanged Plates which are fastened to the Flexible Plates 9, by means of Angle Brackets. A washer should be placed on the shank of each bolt, between the $4\frac{1}{2}'' \times 2\frac{1}{2}''$ Flexible Plates and the Boiler, in order to leave sufficient room to enable the Boiler Ends to be pushed into position.

Fig. 1. A neat working model of a Pumping Engine, operated by an Electric Motor and built with Outfit G.

Two $12\frac{1}{2}''$ Angle Girders and two pairs of $2\frac{1}{2}''$ Cranked Curved Strips are now bolted to the $12\frac{1}{2}'' \times 2\frac{1}{2}''$ Strip Plates of the base, and the $12\frac{1}{2}''$ Angle Girders are bridged by five $3\frac{1}{2}''$ Strips located as shown. The $3\frac{1}{2}''$ Strips support a $2\frac{1}{2}'' \times 2\frac{1}{2}''$ and a $5\frac{1}{2}'' \times 2\frac{1}{2}''$ Strip Plate, and the latter forms the base for the crosshead slides. These are made by bolting two $5\frac{1}{2}''$ Angle Girders together in the form of a channel girder, and then bolting two further $5\frac{1}{2}''$ Angle Girders to this, so that a girder with a cross-section like a Double Bent Strip is formed. Two Trunnions are bolted to one end of the Girder, and two $1\frac{1}{2}''$ Strips to the other, and the two sets are connected across their free ends by Double Brackets. The Double Brackets are spanned by a $5\frac{1}{2}''$ Strip, and the tops of the Trunnions are supported by means of $1'' \times 1''$ Angle Brackets 10. The pairs of $2\frac{1}{2}''$ Cranked Curved Strips previously mentioned each have a Flat Trunnion and a Double Bent Strip bolted to them. The Double Bent Strip should be on the inner side.

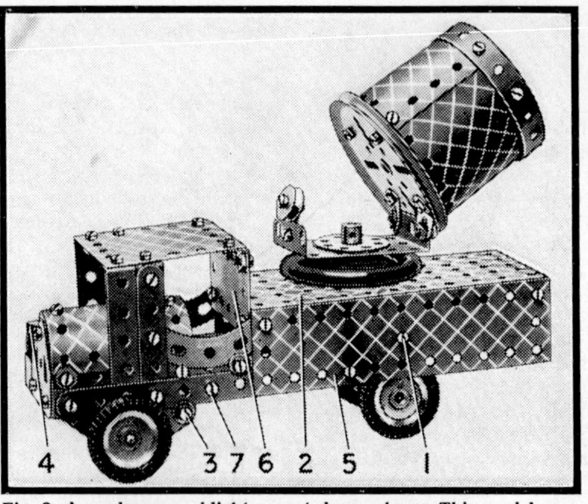

Fig. 2. A modern searchlight mounted on a lorry. This model can be built with Outfit C.

Construction of the mechanism is now commenced. A 2″ Rod forms one part of the crankshaft, and this has a Crank secured on one end. A $3\frac{1}{2}''$ Rod is used for the part of the crankshaft that supports the large flywheel, and also carries a 2″ Pulley 1, a Worm, a 2″ Sprocket and a Crank. The Crank is coupled to the first Crank by a $\frac{3}{4}''$ Bolt, which is held firmly in position by means of nuts. On the Bolt are two $4\frac{1}{2}''$ Strips 12, spaced by four washers, and bent slightly as shown in the illustration so that they pass on either side of the crosshead slides. The Strips 12 are extended by $5\frac{1}{2}''$ Strips 3, overlapped four holes, and the free ends of these are secured to the centre tapped holes of a Coupling by $\frac{3}{8}''$ Bolts, on which are Collars. An $11\frac{1}{2}''$ Rod is used for the Piston Rod, and this passes through the centre holes of the Boiler Ends, and is secured in the Coupling. Further Couplings are placed on the Rod as indicated.

Pairs of $1'' \times 1''$ Angle Brackets 11 are bolted to the Flanged Plate, which is held in place at the rear of the cylinder by a $2\frac{1}{2}'' \times 1\frac{1}{2}''$ Flanged Plate 8 and $5\frac{1}{2}''$ Strips, and these form bearings for $3\frac{1}{2}''$ Rods 5 that support Bush Wheels and are held in position by Spring Clips. One Bush Wheel has a 3″ Strip and a Coupling secured to it, and the other has a Flat Bracket and a Coupling. In each case the Couplings are pivotally connected by Flat Brackets 4 to Collars that are carried on vertical Rods, which slide in $2\frac{1}{2}'' \times \frac{1}{2}''$ Double Angle Strips inside the model and represent the piston rods of the pumps. The two pumps are connected by a system of pivoted Strips, as shown in the illustration.

The model is driven by an E6 Electric Motor, which is mounted inside the model on $3\frac{1}{2}'' \times \frac{1}{2}''$ Double Angle Strips held in place by Bolts 6 and 7. The only reduction gearing, fitted between the Motor side plates, consists of two stages, each of ratio 3 : 1 and using a 57-teeth Gear and a $\frac{1}{2}''$ Pinion. The final shaft of the reduction gear carries a $\frac{3}{4}''$ Sprocket Wheel, which is connected by Chain to a 1″ Sprocket 2 carried on a Rod that is journalled in the frame of the model. A second 1″ Sprocket on the same shaft drives the 2″ Sprocket 1.

Parts required to build the model Pumping Engine: 16 of No. 2; 2 of No. 2a; 5 of No. 3; 3 of No. 4; 2 of No. 5; 2 of No. 6a; 7 of No. 8; 4 of No. 9; 7 of No. 10; 2 of No. 11; 12 of No. 12; 6 of No. 12a; 1 of No. 13; 1 of No. 15b; 5 of No. 16; 3 of No. 17; 1 of No. 20a; 2 of No. 24; 1 of No. 26; 2 of No. 27a; 1 of No. 32; 4 of No. 35; 156 of No. 37; 3 of No. 37a; 22 of No. 38; 2 of No. 45; 2 of No. 48a; 4 of No. 48b; 1 of No. 51; 2 of No. 52; 3 of No. 53; 8 of No. 59; 2 of No. 62; 6 of No. 63; 4 of No. 90a; 20″ of No. 94; 1 of No. 95; 2 of No. 96; 1 of No. 96a; 1 of No. 109; 1 of No. 111; 3 of No. 111c; 2 of No. 126; 2 of No. 126a; 1 of No. 162; 2 of No. 189; 2 of No. 191; 1 of No. 193; 1 of No. 195; 2 of No. 197; 1 E6 Electric Motor.

The model shown in the second illustration is built with Outfit C, and represents a lorry carrying a huge searchlight, forming a mobile unit for such purposes as detecting aircraft at night. In building it two 5½"×1½" Flexible Plates 5, are first bolted to the side flanges of the 5½"×2½" Flanged Plate 2, and a 2½"×1½" Flexible Plate 6 is secured in place as shown. One of the bolts holding each of the large Flexible Plates 5 in position carries also a 2½" Cranked Curved Strip. A 5½" Strip is bolted to the lower edge of 5, and at the front of the model a 2½"×½" Double Angle Strip connects these together.

While the 2½" Double Angle Strip is being placed in position, Cranked Curved Strips that represent the front springs are fixed in place. The free ends of these are clamped firmly by the washers on Bolts 3. A "U" Section Curved Plate (Part No. 199) is held in place by a Double Angle Strip, and on the near side of the lorry this is clamped to a 3½" Strip by washers. The space on the offside of the bonnet is filled in by two Trunnions 4.

Fig. 3. A galley of the type used by the early Greeks reproduced with the aid of Meccano Outfit C.

The front axle is a 3½" Rod journalled in the centre holes of the Cranked Curved Strips that form the front springs; and the rear one is a 2" Rod journalled in a 1½"×½" Double Angle Strip that is bolted to a ½" Reversed Angle Bracket. This in turn is fixed to a 2½"×½" Double Angle Strip fastened in place by bolts 1. The "searchlight" is made by bending two 5½" Strips into a circle, and bolting two 2½" Flexible Plates and a 4½"×2½" Strip Plate to them. The whole assembly is fastened to a 3" Pulley by means of four Angle Brackets.

Parts required to build the model Lorry and Searchlight: 2 of No. 2; 1 of No. 3; 2 of No. 5; 3 of No. 10; 8 of No. 12; 2 of No. 12c; 1 of No. 16; 1 of No. 17; 1 of No. 18a; 1 of No. 19b; 4 of No. 22; 1 of No. 23; 1 of No. 24; 62 of No. 37; 2 of No. 37a; 5 of No. 38, 1 of No. 48; 6 of No. 48a; 1 of No. 51; 1 of No. 52; 4 of No. 90a, 1 of No. 111c; 1 of No. 125; 2 of No. 126; 2 of No. 126a; 2 of No. 187; 1 of No. 188; 2 of No. 189; 3 of No. 190; 1 of No. 191; 1 of No. 199; Four 1" Tyres not included in Outfit.

The C Outfit model shown in Fig. 3 represents a Greek Galley. Its construction is simple and should be commenced by bolting together a 12½" and a 5½" Strip with an overlap of three holes. At their free ends the 12½" Strips are connected by a Double Bracket, and the bolts holding the Double Bracket in place are used to secure 2½" Curved Strips in position. The 5½" Strips form the bows of the galley. They are bent slightly and bolted together through their fourth holes. A 12½" Strip is now attached to the second hole of each of the 2½" Curved Strips that form the stern, and these are connected to the lower 12½" Strips at their centre points by Flat Brackets, and at their free ends by 2½" Cranked Curved Strips 2 and also by Flat Brackets.

At the stern, two 5½" Strips are bolted to the Curved Strips on each side, and the upper ends of the Curved Strips are joined by a Double Bracket. A 2½" Strip is next curved slightly, and after being pushed beneath the upper Double Bracket is bolted to the lower one.

The gunwales of the galley are secured in place to the upper 12½" Strip by Angle Brackets. The deck work is now commenced. The deck amidships consists of two 2½"×2½" Strip Plates, two 2½"×1½" Flexible Plates, and a Flat Trunnion at the stern end. Four ½" Obtuse Angle Brackets are used to fill in the pointed portion in the stern.

The raised portion of the bows is now constructed, and is joined to the hull by two 2½" Strips, and to the projecting 2½" Curved Strips 2 by Angle Brackets 3.

The mast is composed of a 5" Rod, which is secured to the deck by a Bush Wheel and has a 1" fast Pulley secured by its setscrew as near to its upper end as possible. This leaves sufficient room to place a second 5" Rod in the boss of the Wheel, and the whole is held rigid by cord-bracing. The method of fitting the sails, rigging and oars will be clear from the illustration.

Parts required to build the Greek Galley: 4 of No. 1; 8 of No. 2; 9 of No. 5; 4 of No. 10; 2 of No. 11; 5 of No. 12; 4 of No. 12c; 2 of No. 15b; 1 of No. 16; 1 of No. 22; 1 of No. 24; 58 of No. 37; 8 of No. 38; 1 of No. 40; 5 of No. 48a; 1 of No. 51; 4 of No. 90a; 1 of No. 126a; 1 of No. 176; 2 of No. 188; 2 of No. 190.

Fig. 4 shows a shooting target built with Outfit C, and consists essentially of a large sheet of plywood that is held upright by a frame of Strips as shown. The rotor that supports the four cardboard "ducks" is mounted on a 5" Rod 5 that is journalled at one end in the frame and at the other end in a Double Bent Strip bolted to the baseboard. The Double Bent Strip should be about half an inch lower than the bearing in the frame so that the Rod 5 is slightly inclined. The "ducks" are bolted to 2½" Strips 3, each of which has two ½" Angle Brackets 2 bolted in its second hole, and the pairs of Angle Brackets are pivotally attached to Double Brackets bolted on the arms of the rotor. Angle Brackets 6 bolted to the Strips 3 keep the ducks upright when they are in the firing position, but do not prevent them from falling over when they are hit. It will be found that the ducks will fall over automatically when they reach the position occupied by that at 7, but they will be returned to an upright position when they reach the position shown in the front view of the model.

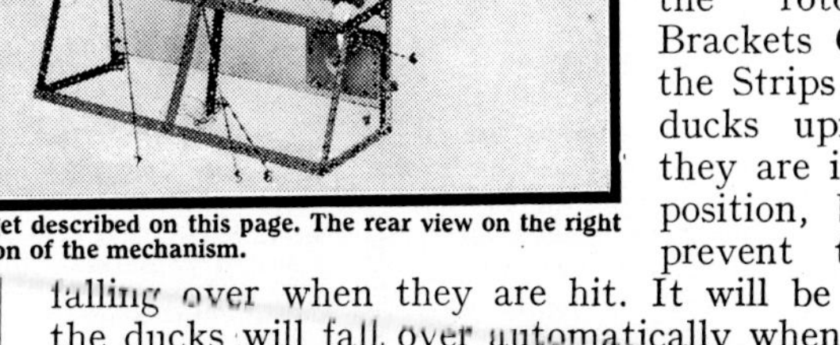

Fig. 4. Front and rear views of the fine Outfit C target described on this page. The rear view on the right shows the construction of the mechanism.

A No. 1 Clockwork Motor is used to drive the model and is bolted to the plywood so that the key shaft is left projecting to enable the Motor to be wound. A Rubber Driving Band, bearing directly on its driving spindle is prevented from slipping off by a 1" fast Pulley 4, and drives a 3" Pulley on the rotor spindle.

Parts required to build the Shooting Target: 6 of No. 1; 8 of No. 2; 2 of No. 3; 8 of No. 5; 4 of No. 8; 4 of No. 11; 12 of No. 12; 2 of No. 12a; 1 of No. 15; 1 of No. 19b; 2 of No. 22; 1 of No. 24; 78 of No. 37; 11 of No. 37a; 11 of No. 38; 1 of No. 45; 2 of No. 48a; 5 of No. 111c; 2 of No. 126a; 1 of No. 186; No. 1 Clockwork Motor.

A Merry Christmas!

A Merry Christmas to all members of the Guild and to Meccano clubs throughout the world. It always seems to me that Christmas means more to Meccano boys than to others, for they enjoy all the usual fun of this season, and in addition have the pleasure of taking part in Christmas festivities organised by the clubs to which they belong.

The Christmas season is a break in ordinary club affairs that is doubly welcome. On the one hand it marks the end of the first winter session's keen model-building. It brings with it Social Evenings and Exhibitions to which parents and friends are invited, and at which everybody present, whether a member or a visitor, has a really happy time and learns to appreciate the advantages of belonging to a live organisation. On the other hand, it is also a preliminary to even better times in store. Enthusiasm is greatly increased as a result of Christmas festivities, especially if the passing of this season has resulted in an addition to the resources of members. New members also come in at this time of the year, and new and lasting friendships are formed that add to the general enjoyment of club life. All this can be turned to good advantage, and Christmas not only can be a merry time in itself, but it also can be made to add to the enjoyment of club life in general.

Welcoming New Members

Most clubs keep the prospect of new members well to the fore, and so far this session there has been an unusually large number of recruiting campaigns. These have been very successful, but members should not rest satisfied with the results achieved so far. Instead they should continue with greater zest to try to interest boys in club life, for during the Christmas month many boys make their first acquaintance with Meccano, or have their interest in model-building increased by the addition of new parts or Accessory Outfits to their stock. Every club member should keep a keen look out for possible recruits of this kind. He will find them among his friends, or at school, and he should do his best to persuade them to join. The most satisfactory plan is to invite them to a meeting, at which they can be introduced to the Leader and other officials, and can see for themselves what good times Meccano boys have.

A point of great importance in developing a really good club spirit is that it is not enough merely to introduce a recruit. The member who persuades a boy to join his club should continue to keep an eye on him in order to see to it that he becomes thoroughly at home and is made familiar with every branch of club activity. Fussiness of course should be avoided, but a display of real friendliness should go far towards turning a recruit into a really valuable member, who will be keenly interested in the welfare of the club as a whole as well as in his own pleasures and hobbies.

Meccano Club Leaders

No. 86. Mr. G. N. Chaplin

Mr. G. N. Chaplin is Leader of the Regent Street Central School (Heywood) M.C. This club was affiliated in April, 1930, and is now one of the largest in the Meccano Guild. Model-building is actively carried on, and Lantern Lectures are a special feature of the club programme.

A Novel Attendance Indicator

Originality is one of the strong points of the Exeter M.C. The latest example of the enterprise of this club is in connection with club-room activities, and takes the form of an indicator that reveals at a glance the attendance at the last meeting, and the totals since the beginning of the month and the beginning of the year. These three items of information are given on separate dials, each having a short arrow acting as a finger.

The indicator was designed and made by a member of the club and its installation created a sensation. A graph showing how the attendance figures compare with those of a year ago also is posted up for members to see, and this practical record, which is always before their eyes at meetings, has stimulated their enthusiasm to such an extent that attendance records are being made almost every week.

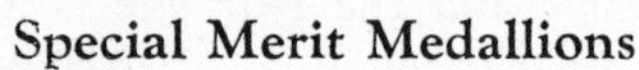

Special Merit Medallions

I hope that nominations for Special Merit Medallions earned during the first Winter session will be forwarded to me as soon as possible, to enable me to publish in an early issue of the "*M.M.*" my usual list of awards made during the past year. Nominations must be made by the Leader of the club, and the awards should be made to the members who have done most during the session to advance the interests of the club. Many Leaders like to present Special Merit Medallions and other prizes at Exhibitions or social meetings held during the Christmas and New Year holiday season. Those who wish to do so should give me notice in good time, for the Medallions must be suitably engraved before being despatched from Headquarters.

I should like to mention again, for the benefit of new Leaders, that two Merit Medallions are allotted every session to each club, and that there are no restrictions in regard to the nature of the services for which awards may be made. Those who earn a Merit Medallion value it highly because it comes from the Headquarters of the Guild and is awarded with the knowledge and approval of Mr. Roland G. Hornby, President.

Proposed Clubs

Attempts are being made to establish Meccano Clubs in the following places, and boys interested should communicate with the promoters whose names and addresses are given below:

HYTHE—J. E. N. Chappell, Millfield House, London Road, Hythe, Kent.

INVERLOCHY—G. Irvine, 11, Battlefield Crescent, Inverlochy Village, Fort-William.

WESTCLIFF-ON-SEA—H. G. Collard, 122, Hildaville Drive, Westcliff-on-Sea.

Plymouth M.C.—The club celebrates its 10th birthday shortly, and the programme for the event includes a concert, club outing, party and lantern shows, in addition to an Exhibition of record size. The Meccano section are constructing a dockside scene as their chief display, and a smaller dock scene incorporating Dinky Toys is another attraction. Mr. J. S. Stephens, a local gentleman who is very interested in club activities, has consented to be a Vice-President of the club. Club roll: 63. *Secretary:* R. G. Symons, 47, Lisson Grove, Mutley, Plymouth.

St. Giles' Cathedral (Edinburgh) M.C.—The club is now firmly established in its new quarters, and members are delighted with the improved facilities. The club-rooms are open on four afternoons and six evenings a week. The afternoon sessions are for members who live a considerable distance out of the city, and enable them to use the club-rooms immediately after school. An intensive recruiting campaign is proving very successful, and it is anticipated that the desired membership of 300 will be attained before the close of this session. Club roll: 100. *Secretary:* H. W. Govan, 18, Ravelston Park, Edinburgh, 4.

Old Charlton M.C.—An enjoyable visit has been paid to the works of Hovis, the well-known flour millers. A Debate on the topical subject "*Are Speed Records Beneficial?*" ended in favour of such records. Club roll: 21. *Secretary:* W. R. Bailey, 62, Rectory Grove, Woolwich, S.E.18.

Todmorden Road Central School (Burnley) M.C.—A very interesting Lantern Lecture on "*The Lake of Geneva*" has been given by Miss Davenport. Model-building has been the chief activity recently, and at one meeting a competition was held, in which each member had to construct an original model from a certain number of Meccano parts. The contest was won by a new member, who built an excellent model of an Ice Yacht. A lecture on "'*Q' Boats*" was much enjoyed. Club roll: 30. *Secretary:* L. Hinton, 4, Thirlmere Avenue, Burnley.

St. Stephen's (Saltash) M.C.—Several model-building meetings have been devoted to constructing models of Carts, and this unusual subject has produced some excellent results. Good models of a Bristol "Bulldog" and a D.H. "Leopard Moth" have also been built. An interest is being shown in model shipbuilding, but not much has yet been done in this direction. Games provide an occasional and popular variation in the club programme. Club roll: 10. *Secretary:* B. Braund, 9, Homer Park, Saltash.

Claremont Avenue (Kenton) M.C.—Two "Simplicity" model-building contests have been held. The winning model in the first contest was a clever model of a microphone, and in the second an electric fan. Games have been played on several occasions. Club roll: 16. *Secretary:* G. Turton, 5, Brookfield Crescent, Kenton, Harrow.

Barnard Castle School M.C.—Preparations are in hand for an Exhibition. There is a considerable demand for a Wireless section, and the formation of this is being considered. It is hoped to play a series of football matches during the winter. Club roll: 15. *Secretary:* S. W. Telfer, The School, Barnard Castle, Co. Durham.

Exeter M.C.—The club-room has been painted and re-decorated, and the equipment re-arranged so as to provide more room for the members. Very great interest is being taken in model shipbuilding, and wooden models of 81 naval vessels have been built. The Monday evening serial reading, by the Leader, of one of the well-known "William" books has provided much amusement. It has been suggested that this should be followed by the story of the club, which was formed in 1917. Attendance at meetings has been well maintained, and shows a higher average than last year. Model-building activities have continued unabated, and models completed have included locomotives, aeroplanes, ships, motor vehicles and cranes. Club roll: 31. *Secretary:* E. Ashwood, 188, Pinhoe Road, Exeter.

Fraserburgh M.C.—The Exhibition has been postponed for a few weeks. It will include Meccano models, a Hornby layout, and a section devoted to model aeroplanes. The event is being well advertised, and a large attendance is expected. Club roll: 29. *Secretary:* W. J. Dawson, Phingask, Fraserburgh.

Sid Vale M.C.—Some very enjoyable rambles have taken place, and have included visits to the top of Peak Hill and tramps across the moors. On one occasion thick mist descended while the party were on the high moorland, but they managed to keep together and returned safely. Club roll: 20. *Secretary:* L. R. J. Gliddon, Sheffield House, Sidmouth.

Wednesbury M.C.—Recent outings have included a visit to the local pumping station of the South Staffordshire Water Works Company, where the party were greatly interested to see the powerful pump at work. During a visit to the new Central Fire Station at Birmingham members were allowed to inspect the many modern types of fire fighting apparatus there, and witnessed a demonstration of the latest type of city fire alarm. The Patent Shaft and Axletree works at Wednesbury also have been visited. There members watched the rolling of iron bars, looked through blue glasses into the furnaces, and saw one of the smaller furnaces being tapped. Occasionally Games Evenings are held, and are always very popular. An intensive recruiting campaign is to be carried out. Club roll: 20. *Secretary:* A. L. Morgan, 17, Cobden Street, Fallings Heath, Wednesbury.

Members of the South Parade Modern School (Cleckheaton) M.C. This club was affiliated in September 1934. In addition to excellent model-building programmes, successful Exhibitions have been held. Our photograph shows members' preparations for a Carnival. Photograph by J. Hardill, Cleckheaton.

AUSTRALIA

Maylands M.C.—The Exhibition attracted over 200 visitors. The chief feature of the display was a large-scale Meccano Harbour, laid out in the form of the letter "U." The sea was realistically represented by cellophane, and cotton wool made effective spray. The models displayed in the harbour included a miniature of H.M.S. "*Revenge*" and two battle cruisers, and on the quayside were a high speed coaler and various types of cranes. There was also a dock railway. A recent Lecture dealt with "*The History of the Aeroplane.*" The club-room is to be extended so that the many boys waiting to join the club can be accommodated. Club roll: 32. *Secretary:* M. Thomson, 13, Kennedy Street, Maylands, West Australia.

Melbourne M.C.—A Reading Night has been held, several members bringing engineering books and reading interesting extracts. The leader also brought along a large selection of railway literature for the use of members. Meetings have been devoted chiefly to model railway operations, and on one occasion a talk explaining the operation of a semaphore signal worked by a solenoid was listened to with keen interest, as this type of signal is used on the club layout. A Meccano model of a mail bag catcher built by one member attracted much attention. Club roll: 10. *Secretary:* L. Ison, 8, Hayes Street, Northcote, Victoria, N.16.

CANADA

Montreal Y.M.C.A. M.C.—Many interesting models have been built, and members are rapidly becoming more skilful in adapting their Meccano parts to different uses. The Leader constructed an excellent Meccano Motor Chassis and demonstrated it to members. Visits have been paid to local factories, and an enjoyable trip was made to Mount Royal, where a picnic was held. Club roll: 9. *Leader:* Mr. J. Rodriguez, 1900, Tupper Street, Apt. 4, Montreal, P.Q.

Peterborough (Ontario) M.C.—This club is now divided into two groups, a junior one called "Eccentrics," and a senior one known as "Gears." Meetings have been held regularly, and model-building activities have been supplemented by talks on Meccano construction. Tobogganing and other activities have given variety to the programme. Club roll: 10. *Leader:* R. Borland, 744, George Street, Peterborough.

Rosemount M.C.—This club has resumed activities under the leadership of Mr. Ernest Rawlings, and an attractive model-building programme is being planned. Club roll: 17. *Secretary:* L. H. Tompkins, 5706, 4th Avenue, Rosemount, Quebec.

INDIA

Ranjit (Lahore) M.C.—During the summer most club activities have been out-of-doors. One group of members has visited the hydro-electric power station at Jaginder Nagar. Model-building, stamp collecting and fretwork are the chief activities of the club, and preparations are in hand for an Exhibition. Club roll: 20. *Secretary:* S. Harbhajan, 689, Krishna Bazar, Gowalmandi, Lahore.

Rawalpindi M.C.—This recently-affiliated club is making good progress. An excellent club-room, fitted with electric light, has been obtained, and meetings are held fortnightly. Model-building and fretwork are the chief hobbies, and the President has given talks on these subjects. An active interest is also taken in photography and stamp collecting. All the members are very enthusiastic, and a steady increase in membership is anticipated. Club roll: 10. *Leader:* Mr. Ismail H. Lotia, Bakery Road, Rawalpindi.

NEW ZEALAND

Christchurch M.C.—Model-building and Hornby Train operations have been the chief features of indoor meetings. On one occasion each member was given a box of Meccano parts and asked to build the best model he could with them in the short time available. Some excellent and surprisingly varied models were produced, and included various types of cranes and guns, a motor truck, Roman chariot, and a Chinese rickshaw. The first, second and third prizes in the Meccano competition organised by the Canterbury Winter Show authorities were won by the members of the club. During school holidays a visit was paid to the Addington Railway Workshops, and Cycle Runs have also been enjoyed. Club roll: 23. *Secretary:* L. W. Best, 28, Circuit Street, Strowan, Christchurch.

SOUTH AFRICA

Malvern M.C.—A special Exhibition in aid of charity resulted in a profit of nearly £65. It was opened by Mr. T. A. M. Huddle, a member of the Johannesburg City Council. The Exhibition Hall was decorated in Eastern style by one of the members, and every stall had a background showing some Eastern scene. Club roll: 85. *Secretary:* B. Saunders, P.O. Box 8, Cleveland, Johannesburg.

Unaffiliated Club

AUSTRALIA

Charters Towers M.C.—There has been considerable model-building activity, and outstanding models recently completed have been a pithead gear and a fire engine. Club roll: 3. *Secretary:* R. McLean, Marion Street, Charters Towers, Queensland.

How to Choose a Hornby Train Set

The M8 Complete Model Railway Set packed in a strong cardboard box.

AT this time of the year large numbers of boys take up Hornby Railways for the first time. Running a Hornby Railway is one of the most fascinating pursuits in the world. One of its greatest attractions is that a miniature railway can be started on a comparatively small scale, and can be extended as its owner becomes more expert and tries to make his operations more and more like those carried out on real railways. With this in mind, a little guidance in the choice of a Hornby Railway to begin with is useful, and the various possibilities are explained simply and clearly in this article.

One of the first things to consider when buying a Hornby Train Set is the amount of space available. This is important because Hornby Rails are made to give two sizes of layout, one in which the radius of curves is 1 ft. and another in which the radius is 2 ft. If sufficient room is available there should be no hesitation in choosing 2 ft. radius track, for then there would be no difficulty in using any locomotive or coach in the Hornby Series. Where the width of the space to be used is less than 4 ft. 6 in., it is advisable to lay track of 1 ft. radius. This restricts the choice of trains to some extent. The smaller locomotives and rolling stock can be used, but larger engines, such as the 20-volt Automatic Reversing Locomotives, will not run on the small circles. Generally it may be said that a circle of 1 ft. radius track requires a space of 2 ft. 6 in. sq., and one of 2 ft. radius a space of 4 ft. 6 in. sq.

This illustration shows a suitable and interesting arrangement for the M9 Model Railway Set.

When this point has been settled, there comes the all-important question of the motive power to be used. Both clockwork and electric engines are available. The latter are simple to run, and there is no danger whatever with them. If the electric mains supply is Alternating Current, the ideal plan is to instal an electric layout on which to run 20-volt locomotives. Current should be supplied through a Meccano Transformer, which reduces the mains voltage to 20 volts, which is safe and suitable for railway working. All that is necessary is to connect the Transformer to a convenient source of power on the one hand, and to the track on the other. The cost of running such a railway is low, the current consumption being about equal to that of a 60-watt lamp.

Hornby locomotives of 6-volt type also are available, with Transformers to reduce mains current to the required voltage. Wherever possible the 20-volt system should be chosen, however, for this is electrically more efficient, and has the added advantage that the wonderful Hornby Automatic Reversing Locomotives are available in it. These can be started, stopped, controlled for speed, and reversed without any handling of the levers in the cabs, operations being completely controlled from the lineside. These locomotives are not available in the 6-volt system.

Where no mains current is available, or where the supply is Direct Current, those who wish to install a Hornby Electric Railway must make use of the 6-volt system, with a 6-volt accumulator as the source of power. An accumulator of good quality and with a capacity of 20 amps. should be used. The cost of re-charging is about 1/– and satisfactory operation can be obtained, although this source of current is not so convenient as Alternating Current mains with a Transformer.

Finally there is the clockwork system. The Hornby Clockwork Locomotives have been brought to a state of perfection. They are now the strongest and best pulling engines of their type in the world, and are specially suitable for operating by time-table.

Even when the points already considered have been dealt with, the prospective owner of a Hornby Train Set will find himself confronted with a bewildering variety of wonderful products, in which there are locomotives of various sizes and types, together with a splendid array of rolling stock of all kinds. All four railway groups are represented in true colours, and a decision has to be made as to which of these shall be used on the miniature railway to be built up. Fortunately this usually is an easy problem to deal with, for most boys have their favourite groups, and are eager to reproduce these on their own layouts. Whatever their choice, they can settle down to fascinating railway working, and can make their layouts larger and more interesting, by adding accessories.

The well-known Hornby E220 Special Electric Train Set. L.M.S. Locomotive No. 1185, Standard Compound Class.

Hornby Railway Progress in 1936

By "Tommy Dodd"

The new S.R. Ventilated Containers shown in this illustration are being hauled by a Hornby No. 3C Locomotive "Lord Nelson," fitted with the smoke deflectors mentioned in the article.

EVERY year the range of products in the Hornby Series grows larger, and this year has been particularly noteworthy in this respect. The additions have included rolling stock, track components and accessories, all of which have been introduced with the purpose of adding to the realism of Hornby railway working, and a brief summary of them will be of interest.

First of all come the Containers. These are perfect replicas in miniature of those used by the four great railway groups, each of which is represented by one that is characteristic of important traffic on it. For instance, the L.M.S.R. is represented by a Furniture Container, "K.61," coloured in the familiar red of that company; and the L.N.E.R. container reproduces one used for goods generally, and is coloured brown. The G.W.R. and S.R. examples are respectively an Insulated Container enamelled white with black lettering, and a Ventilated Container in aluminium finish with green lettering. All are fitted with lifting tackle on the roof, and have a very effective appearance while being slung or when loaded on Hornby Flat Trucks and included in goods trains.

A new No. 1 Petrol Tank Wagon "Esso." This replaces the now obsolete "Pratts" wagon.

The new High Capacity Wagons will certainly make a strong appeal to all Hornby railway owners. There is an increasing tendency in railway working to make use of larger wagons, and the addition of this form of rolling stock to the Hornby Series will enable miniature railway owners also to follow this practice. The Hornby L.N.E.R. High Capacity Wagon represents the well-known 50-ton brick wagon that is particularly associated with the brick traffic from the Peterborough district to King's Cross. The G.W.R. 40-ton wagon for locomotive coal and the L.M.S.R. 30-ton wagon for similar duties are the other examples reproduced in the Hornby system, and each of the two miniatures is finished in correct colour and with appropriate lettering.

Other interesting rolling stock additions are two Tank Wagons, one for "Esso" petrol and the other for "Royal Daylight" oil. The "Esso" Tank Wagon replaces the now obsolete Pratt's Tank Wagon and is coloured in the familiar buff; the "Royal Daylight" wagon is coloured bright red as in actual practice. The Trolley Wagon fitted with Cable Drums is another attractive production. There are two Cable Drums on each Trolley Wagon, held in place by ropes. The Drums are miniatures of those used by British Insulated Cables Ltd. One of them makes an excellent load for a Flat Truck, and this combination is available in the Series.

To the Hornby electric track have been added Electric Points on a solid base. Both right-hand and left-hand points, known as ESPSR2 and ESPSL2 respectively, are available, and there is no fear of their switches moving while a train is travelling over them. These Points cannot be used with Hornby Double Track owing to the shape of the base; but those who wish to connect sidings or branch lines to double track can obtain special Points in which the lever is placed on the inside of the curve. The special Points with reversed switch sleepers are also useful in cases where sidings are being laid, and the lever of the standard Points would foul a nearby track.

The Automatic Circuit Breaker introduced early in the year has already amply proved its value to owners of both 6-volt and 20-volt Hornby Railways. It is almost uncanny in its action. Whenever a "short" occurs, whatever the cause, there is a click, and the little red push button at the top of the circuit breaker springs upward. When the cause of the trouble has been found and matters have been put right, the button is simply pressed down again and train operation can be resumed immediately. This accessory saves the time and the trouble involved in winding lengths of fuse wire round terminals.

The "Royal Daylight" Oil Tank Wagon.

The appearance of the MO Locomotive has been greatly improved by the addition of piston rods. Originally these were not fitted to this engine, and the change has been made without adding to the cost. Another interesting feature is that smoke deflectors have been added to the Hornby L.M.S.R. "*Royal Scot*" and S.R. "*Lord Nelson*" of the E320 and No. 3C types, and also to the Nord Riviera "Blue" locomotive. Those fitted to the Hornby Nord engines are characteristic of the peculiarly-shaped wind shields used on French engines. The deflectors of the English type engines also are representative of those used in real practice. Illustrations of Hornby engines fitted with smoke deflectors were reproduced in the May "*M.M.*"

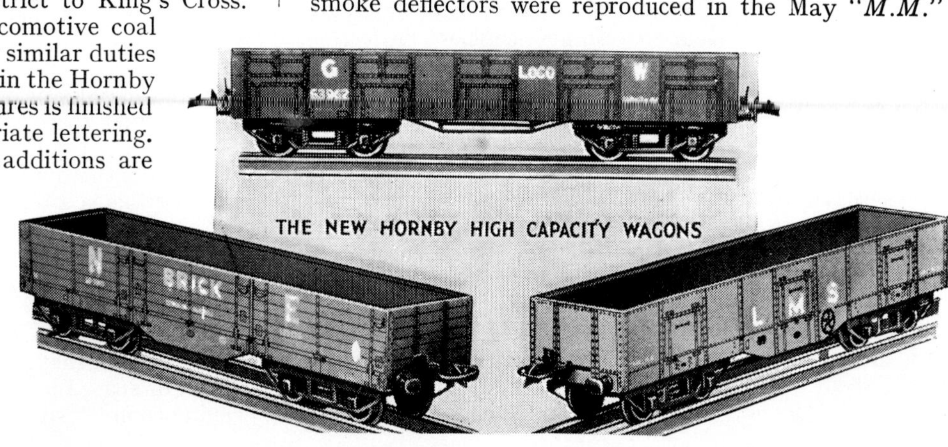

THE NEW HORNBY HIGH CAPACITY WAGONS

ENGINE SHEDS ON HORNBY LAYOUTS

ENGINE SHEDS play a very important part in the work of a railway. In a very real sense they are homes for locomotives, which are housed in them when not on duty and there receive the care and attention that is required to keep them in running order. On coming off duty, the engines themselves are cleaned, their fireboxes are cleared of ash and clinker, and the boiler tubes are blown out. The tenders are filled with coal and water, the fires are re-lighted and steam is raised, the working parts are oiled and greased, and everything generally is prepared for work before they again leave the sheds for another spell of duty. In addition much of the lighter repair work needed is carried out.

To the miniature railway enthusiast, an engine shed of course is wonderfully attractive, for there he can see locomotives of various classes, often in interesting stages of preparation for duty, and he can learn something of the inner details of railway life. He knows how necessary engine sheds are in ensuring locomotive efficiency, and naturally includes similar engine accommodation in his own layout in order to secure realism, and also because it is as useful to him as its counterpart is in actual practice. Hornby Engine Sheds are splendid storage places for Hornby engines, protecting them from dust and dirt when they are not in use. Their inclusion also adds greatly to the interest of miniature railway working, and it is no exaggeration to say that a Hornby Railway cannot be considered complete if an engine shed is not included.

There is no difficulty in providing engine accommodation on a Hornby Railway, whether clockwork or electric, for suitable engine sheds are available for the different locomotives included in the Hornby range. For the smaller locomotives the No. 1 Engine Sheds can be used. These have double track, and the No. E1E Shed, which of course has electrical track, is wired for electric lighting. Two of these sheds have double doors at each end, thus reproducing a feature of real railway practice that enables locomotives to be run right through the sheds, either in actual working, or for coaling or other purposes. The No. 1A Shed has doors only at one end, again as in many of the engine sheds in use on British railways.

All these engine sheds will accommodate any locomotive and tender with an overall length not exceeding $8\frac{3}{4}$ in. For larger locomotives, that with their tenders are not more than $17\frac{1}{2}$ in., there is a similar range of sheds available. Each of these has double track, and the No. E2E Shed is fitted with electric wiring for lighting in addition to its electrical track. Thus sufficient shed accommodation to house the locomotives used on a Hornby layout can readily be arranged.

An excellent arrangement for an engine shed on a Hornby layout. The tracks leading to the shed can be connected to the main line in a simple manner.

The next thing is to decide where the engine sheds required are to be placed. This requires a little consideration if the best use is to be made of these accessories. In actual practice sheds are placed as near stations as possible, in order to avoid long runs, with perhaps complications in working, when the engines are on their way to and from their homes. This arrangement should be followed on model railways. If a layout has two termini, an engine shed could quite rightly be placed at each, and the locomotive stock could then be divided, part being placed in each shed. Space and other considerations sometimes make it impossible to plan a layout of this kind. Only one terminal may be provided, or it may be that with a continuous track there is simply one main through station. In each case the position of the engine shed accommodation is easy to settle, for it should be near the principal station, whether this is a terminus or not.

The most important thing in deciding upon the actual site is then the rail connection that can be made to the main line. This should be as direct as possible, so that engines going to their sheds or returning to the stations for duty are not compelled to reverse several times on the way. Another point that should be taken into account is the provision of space for the inclusion of a turntable. When an engine completes its turn of duty, and the coaches it has hauled have been shunted into the sidings, it is usually run backward on its way to the shed, and it must be turned before it is sent out for its next turn of duty. The turntable can conveniently be included in the track leading direct to the shed, so that locomotives arriving for rest and attention are turned round immediately.

A useful method of incorporating engine sheds in a layout is that illustrated on this page. The accommodation provided is connected to the main line by means of left-hand points with reversed switch sleepers. A cross-over enables engines on each of the tracks of the main line to be run to the engine shed sidings without difficulty, and the sheds themselves are reached over the turntable. This is placed where it is most useful, serving both sheds directly, and at the same time space is saved by the arrangement adopted.

Activity in a Hornby Engine Shed. In this illustration a Hornby No. 2 Special L.M.S. "Compound" locomotive is being prepared for the day's duties.

Where two engine sheds are used together in order to accommodate a comprehensive range of locomotives, they can be placed side by side, but in another excellent plan, which is particularly useful on layouts where space at the side of the track is limited, they are joined end to end so as to make a long and narrow engine shed. If there is sufficient room, it is better to place them side by side, for then each locomotive can be taken into its shed or brought out with a minimum of shunting, so that time is saved in the complicated operations to be carried out.

Yet another suitable arrangement is that shown in the lower illustration on this page, to which reference has already been made. In this the sheds are placed separately in convenient positions, and each can easily be reached by means of a simple branch from the main line that passes over a turntable. In this layout other sidings are provided on the right. These can be used for engines off duty for short periods, or can be brought into use in connection with the layout itself as goods sidings. Wagons laden with locomotive coal can conveniently be shunted there while waiting their turn to be unloaded. If they are not required for these purposes they can be made to lead into a small terminal station, which would be a useful addition to the layout and also would add to the realism of the scene by placing the engine sheds and a station in association with each other.

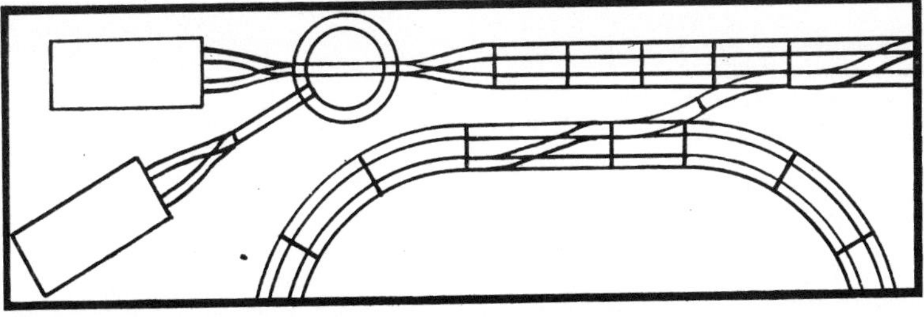

A useful method of including an engine shed on a Hornby layout. The shed sidings are connected to the main line by means of left-hand points with reversed switch sleepers.

In regard to these arrangements, each layout of course must be dealt with on its own merits, but those who are planning the addition of engine sheds to their layouts will find some very useful examples in "Hornby Layouts—One Hundred Suggestions." Other interesting schemes are to be found in the descriptions of special layouts and of the railways of Hornby Train enthusiasts that are included from time to time in the Hornby Railway Company pages of the "*M.M.*" Many of these are designed to suit special circumstances, and those who are planning Hornby Railways for themselves, or extending their existing railways, can obtain many useful hints from them. For instance, on page 663 of last month's Magazine is a diagram showing a simple and useful engine shed layout in connection with a busy terminal station.

Good use also can be made of Hornby engine sheds for the storage of the Rail Gauge, Winding Keys, Shunter's Pole and other accessories that are required in miniature railway working. These should be kept at hand in order that they can be found at a moment's notice in emergency, and a convenient place in which to keep them is alongside the track in the engine shed.

It has already been pointed out that in actual practice locomotives coming off duty receive attention and are prepared for their next turn of duty in the engine shed. This is a practice that Hornby Railway owners could follow with advantage. When their engines finish duty they should be run light to the shed, and on arrival should be examined and given any little adjustment that may be necessary. By following this plan miniature railway enthusiasts not only have the satisfaction of carrying out operations in a really workmanlike manner, but also ensure long life and high efficiency in the working of their engines.

Clockwork locomotives do not require much attention. The mechanism must be kept free from dust, which can be removed by washing out the motor with a small paint brush dipped in petrol. Fresh lubricating oil of course should be applied when the petrol has evaporated, and all the moving parts of the engine, including the couplings, the axle bearings and the piston rods and crossheads, should be lubricated slightly. The leaves of the spring should have graphite grease applied between them.

Different treatment is needed by an electric locomotive. It would be harmful to wash its mechanism out with petrol, but the gears of the electric motor are outside the side plates, and therefore can be cleaned without difficulty. The commutator and brushes must be kept free from oil in order to keep the engine working at its best. The former can be cleaned from time to time by wrapping a piece of fine emery paper round the end of a match stick, and inserting this in the plain hole at the side of the motor below the commutator shaft while the driving wheels are revolved slowly by hand. This is the most effective method of cleaning the commutator.

Branch News

Wimborne Grammar School.—Better meetings are now being arranged, and the rules are being strictly enforced, with excellent results. The track engineer has relaid much of the Branch track. Attendances have been excellent, and more satisfactory train operation has followed the introduction of a better signalling system. Secretary: R. S. Partington, The Grammar School, Wimborne, Dorset.

Glengorse (Battle).—Regular track meetings have been held, and have proved very enjoyable. More rolling stock could be used with advantage, and it is hoped to overcome this difficulty as the number of members increases. Three enthusiasts have already joined the Branch, and it is hoped shortly to enrol others. Secretary: P. Ballard, Glengorse, Battle, Sussex.

Islington.—The central feature of the recent Exhibition was a large Hornby Train layout, and other attractions included two ½-in. scale model locomotives, chemical demonstrations and a cinema show. Objects made by members on Hobbies Nights also were on view. At ordinary meetings track operations continue to be successful, and games have been enjoyed as a diversion. An interesting Lantern Lecture on *"Railways"* was given by the Secretary. A visit has been paid to the King's Cross Locomotive Running Department, where members saw the *"Green Arrow"* and the *"Silver Link,"* the whistle of which greatly interested members. Secretary: S. H. Gardener, 3, Tiverton House, Pleasant Place, Canonbury, London, N.1.

Chorlton-cum-Hardy.—The appearance of the Branch layout has been improved by the addition of miniature scenery, including an aerodrome, farm, road, and fields represented by cotton wool dyed green. A new train, the *"Scarborough Flier,"* was introduced at a recent track meeting. The Chairman is constructing a new main line station and its incorporation in the layout is eagerly awaited. It is hoped that more Hornby enthusiasts will join the Branch. Secretary: G. Gill, 56, Highfield Road, Chorlton-cum-Hardy, Manchester.

Elmside (Exeter).—At track meetings timetable and "open service" operations are undertaken alternately. Trains are run to the wishes of individual members when "open service" running is carried out. A topical feature is the introduction of driving tests for members. This step should speed up operations and increase efficiency. A model Navy has been built, and naval manœuvres in miniature have provided interesting meetings. Secretary: K. Brewer, 18, Comins Road, Exeter.

St. Giles' Cathedral (Edinburgh).—Members are now settling down in their new quarters, where they attend on the nights that suit them best. As a result the weekly attendance figures have greatly increased. The track has been laid and now all points, with two exceptions, are controlled from lever frames. A new colour-light signalling apparatus is being installed, together with automatic system for electrically operating signals from the points. Station and shed building has commenced, and it is hoped to complete the layout by the New Year. On the electric railway, a burrowing junction has recently been completed. The sight of a train suddenly diving under the baseboard and reappearing again causes much amusement. Recruiting is to be carried on with increasing vigour, the aim being a membership of 300. Secretary: H. W. Govan, 18, Ravelston Park, Edinburgh, 4.

Fishponds (Bristol).—Official positions are given to members taking part in track operations, who retain them for a month. The Branch locomotives have been tested for speed and strength. Goods and passenger train working have been carried out. Both G.W.R. and L.M.S.R. passenger trains are run, and for this reason two superintendents have been appointed. Timetable working is rigidly enforced. The Secretary has given a talk on *"Goods Traffic, Its Control and Handling."* This was followed by members telling railway stories. A Hornby 2E *"Bristol"* Station was presented to the Branch by the Chairman. Work is in hand on an electric railway for suburban train operation. Secretary: A. N. Ewings, 154, Thingwall Park, Fishponds, Bristol.

Members of the Whitgift School H.R.C. Branch No. 67. Chairman, Mr. F. Broadbent, B.A.; Secretary, A. F. Jordan. This Branch was incorporated in September 1929, and has made excellent progress during recent years. The varied programme includes visits to places of railway and general interest, as well as track meetings and lantern lectures.

AUSTRALIA

Melbourne.—Important alterations and extensions have been made to the Branch layout, and a bridge has been incorporated. High speed trains are now run successfully on the improved track. During operations, members hold various positions, such as those of drivers and signalmen, for periods of half-an-hour, and changes are then made. This arrangement allows members to become proficient in all phases of operation. A visit was paid to the Meadmore Model Co., Elswood, where members were very interested in a large model electric layout, with streamlined locomotives, and accessories, including colour-light signals. Secretary: L. Ison, 8, Hayes Street, Northcote, N.16, Victoria.

An Attractive Exhibition

Hornby Railway Company members and Hornby Railway enthusiasts in Acton, London, W.3, and district, are invited to the New Membership Exhibition of the Acton Branch. This will be held at 35A, Birkbeck Grove, Acton, W.3, on 4th and 5th December. It will be opened at 7 p.m., and admission is free.

Branches in Course of Formation

The following new Branches of the Hornby Railway Company are at present in process of formation and any boys who are interested and desirous of linking up with this unique organisation should communicate with the promoters, whose names and addresses are given below.

London—E. Fields, 2, Longstaff Crescent, Wandsworth, S.W.18.

Seaham Harbour—D. Smith, Police Station, Seaham Harbour, Co. Durham.

Branches Recently Incorporated

313. Lostock Gralam—A. Milligan, Wincham Hall, Northwich.

314. Copthorne School—J. M. Workman, Copthorne School, Crawley.

Join the Hornby Railway Company and become eligible for the competitions announced on this page.

H.R.C. COMPETITION PAGE

Join the Hornby Railway Company and become eligible for the competitions announced on this page.

A MYSTERY LOCOMOTIVE CONTEST

H.R.C. members are keen critics of locomotive designs. They appreciate the good points of the engines of different railways, and are particularly interested in the outstanding features that distinguish those of each class. At times most of them have suggested improvements of various kinds, and many must have tried to work out the result, in regard to either performance or appearance, that would follow the incorporation in certain locomotives of parts that are peculiar to others. This is a fascinating pursuit that has given rise to many fierce arguments among railway enthusiasts.

How an entirely new locomotive design may be evolved by taking parts from existing British locomotives, and combining them into a single engine, is well shown by the composite locomotive illustrated on this page. It is not easy to see at a glance that this engine is an imaginary one, for the parts of which it is supposed to be made are fitted together so skilfully that even the keenest of H.R.C. members could be excused if at first they imagined it to represent a new class.

We are sure that all will revel in the detective work of tracing the origin of each part, and thus explaining how the composite engine has been built up. In our competition this month therefore we ask members to identify each portion, and to state from which class of locomotive it comes.

In the entries the names of each of the parts should be given, together with the class and wheel arrangement of the engines represented by them in the composite, and solutions should be as brief as possible, provided that the information given is sufficient to enable the locomotives mentioned to be definitely identified. Competitors must use one sheet of paper for their entries, and their solutions must be written only on one side of the paper.

The Contest will be divided into the two usual sections, Home and Overseas, and in each of these there will be awarded three cash prizes to the respective values of 21/–, 15/–, and 10/6. Several consolation prizes will be awarded.

Envelopes containing entries should be marked *"H.R.C. Christmas Contest"* in the top left-hand corner. Entries from competitors in the Home Section should be posted to reach Headquarters at Meccano Ltd., Binns Road, Liverpool 13, not later than 31st December. The closing date for Overseas competitors is 31st March, 1937.

Railway Jokes Contest

December is the most jovial time of the year, when everybody is in the best of humours and good jokes are told and funny stories exchanged around the fireside. We hope that all H.R.C. members will share to the full in the pleasures of this merry season, and as we should like to join with them in part of their enjoyment, we are asking them to tell us the best railway joke or story of those that are sure to be told when they meet other railway enthusiasts.

Entries in this contest should be snappy and original, as well as funny. There will be three prizes consisting of products manufactured by Meccano Ltd. to the values of 21/–, 15/– and 10/6 respectively in each section, Home and Overseas, and in addition there will be a number of consolation prizes.

Envelopes containing entries should be marked *"H.R.C. December Joke Contest"* in the top left-hand corner and posted to reach Headquarters at Meccano Ltd., Binns Road, Liverpool 13, on or before 31st December. The closing date for entries in the Overseas Section is 31st March, 1937.

August "Mystery Stations Contest" Solution

No competitor was successful in gaining full marks in this contest. The First Prize was awarded to W. Lobb (11765), Broadley, Rochdale, whose entry had only one error.

The correct solution is as follows: LIME STREET (Liverpool), NEW STREET (Birmingham), FORSTER SQUARE (Bradford), CITADEL (Carlisle), CASTLE (Lancaster and Northampton), ST. ENOCH (Glasgow), WOODSIDE (Birkenhead and Aberdeen), GENERAL (Chester, Perth, Cardiff, Neath, Shrewsbury, Port Talbot, and Cymmer), WAVERLEY (Edinburgh), VICTORIA (London, Sheffield, Manchester, Nottingham, Swansea), FRIARY (Plymouth), PARAGON (Hull), TEMPLE MEADS (Bristol), WESTLAND ROW (Dublin), LONDON ROAD (Manchester, Nottingham, Leicester, Wellingborough, Brighton and Guildford), PRIORY (Dover), WELLINGTON (Leeds), BANK TOP (Darlington and Burnley), BANK QUAY (Warrington), PADDINGTON (London), KIRKGATE (Wakefield), FENCHURCH STREET (London).

COMPETITION RESULTS

HOME

October "Sharp Eyes Contest."—First: P. W. Gifford (48393), Winton, Bournemouth. Second: C. E. Wrayford (6039), Moretonhampstead, Devon. Third: N. C. Ferry (47001), Timperley, Ches. Consolation Prizes: D. Earle (41617), Wembley Park, Middx.; J. T. Fraser (2267), Exeter; J. L. Makin (30933), Penwortham, Preston; E. R. Dudley (37680), Carshalton, Surrey; D. Blackburn (49069), Kingsbury, London, N.W.9; L. J. Slater (49094), Cosham, Portsmouth.

October "Questions Contest No. 8."—First: G. L. Wilson (2478), Wormit-on-Tay, Fife. Second: J. L. Makin (30933), Penwortham, Preston. Third: K. W. Ashberry (14344), Cambridge. Consolation Prizes: M. Firth (26337), Huddersfield; J. C. Button (10335), Crewe, Ches.; R. Dace-Brown (623), Clapham Park, London, S.W.4; C. Howarth (11554), Broadbottom, Ches.; A. T. Royle (39381), Pendleton, Salford 6; A. R. Eves (35403), Boston, Lincs.

OVERSEAS

July "Errors Contest."—First: R. Pearson (29199), Richmond, Australia. Second: I. Brough (9112), Preston, Australia. Third: R. A. Wragg (7913), Bandikui, Rajputana, India. Consolation Prizes: A. Rodan (48081), Southland, New Zealand; R. Myburgh (37538), Claremont, S. Africa; W. B. Moore (20918), Toronto, Canada; J. A. Rodriguez (3647), Montreal, Canada.

July "Railway Photo Contest."—First: M. C. Lupton (43423), Elgin, S. Africa. Second: P. N. Roy, Calcutta, India. Third: H. Bennett (10615), Auckland, New Zealand.

SETS (POSTAGE EXTRA)

10 Australia	... 2d.	5 Fiji Is.	... 3d.
1 „ Jubilee	1d.	1 „ Jubilee	4d.
5 Barbados	... 2d.	5 Gold Coast	... 3d.
1 „ Jubilee	4d.	10 „ „	... 6d.
4 Bermuda	... 3d.	1 „ Jubilee	2d.
1 „ Jubilee	4d.	3 Grenada	... 2d.
5 Brit. Guiana ...	3d.	1 „ Jubilee	2d.
1 „ Jubilee	2d.	5 Hong Kong	... 2d.
10 Canada	... 2d.	10 „ „	... 5d.
3 „ Jubilee	4d.	1 „ Jubilee	3d.
4 Cayman Is.	... 6d.	20 India ...	... 6d.
1 „ Jubilee	3d.	4 „ Jubilee	6d.
10 Ceylon	... 2d.	5 Jamaica	... 2d.
1 „ Jubilee	2d.	10 „	... 5d.
5 Cyprus...	... 3d.	1 „ Jubilee	2d.
10 „ ...	... 6d.	5 Kenya ...	... 3d.
1 „ Jubilee	3d.	1 „ Jubilee	3d.

J. RUSSELL

23, Shanklin Drive, Westcliff-on-Sea

ABYSSINIA

A timely offer, which should not be missed, of a superb MINT set of 30 diff. stamps from this mysterious country, mostly 1917-31 issues (cat. over £1), with scarce AIR STAMPS, COMMEMORATIVES, PICTORIALS, ETC. Price 5/- only, secure them while you can. We offer superb collections of any country at bargain prices. Full lists FREE.

NORRIS & CO. (Dept.M), NORWOOD, LONDON, S.E.19

100 DIFFERENT STAMPS FREE to applicants for ½d. approvals.—Cox, 14, Broadmead Ave., Worcester Park.

Triangular, Octagonal and Rectangular Pkt. Free!!

Stamps of unusual shapes are always attractive and greatly increase the interest in your collection. This splendid packet of 34 different includes a beautiful new triangular stamp from Liberia, a large diamond stamp from Thessaly, and a rectangular map stamp of Cocos Islands, a large submarine Telephone issue, Turks and Caicos Isle, N.Z. Fantail Bird, set oblong Japan, and to the first 250 applicants, short sets from Hyderabad, Spain, New South Wales (100 years), and U.S.A. (including Roosevelt). Just send 2d. postage requesting approvals and free Catalogue.

LISBURN & TOWNSEND (M.M.), LIVERPOOL, 3

FREE WONDERFUL 1936 OFFER 25 NEW ISSUES AND NOVELTIES

Including **Andorra** (1935), fine new **Cayman Islands** (map of Islands), obsolete Austria, China, Denmark, **Gwalior** Service, Hungary (Statesman Szechenyi), new **Kenya** (Kavirondo Cranes), **Roumania** (new portrait of King Caroll), and many others. I will send this collection **absolutely free** to all stamp collectors sending 2d. postage (abroad 4d.).

G. P. KEEF, Willingdon, EASTBOURNE

THE "DIAMOND" PACKET IS THE ONLY PACKET

OF UNSORTED STAMPS ON THE MARKET with 15 years' reputation behind it. It contains approx. **1,000 UNSORTED STAMPS** from Convents abroad. **MANY RARE STAMPS** have been found in it. 1 pkt., 1/6; 3 pkts., 3/9; 5 pkts., 6/-. All post free inland. Colonies 3d. per pkt. extra. Foreign, 6d. extra.

Ask your stationer for the "Diamond" packet.

SPECIAL: TURKS IS. JUBILEES complete set, used or unused, 5/6.

O. NERUSH (Dept. A), 68, TURNPIKE LANE, HORNSEY, LONDON, N.8

THE 'SHIP' PACKET

This marvellous packet is offered under cost as an advertisement, **45 different stamps each with a ship on it.** A regular armada. **GABOON**, New Issue **SENEGAL** (Canoe), wonderful flotilla of caravels from **DENMARK** (complete set), **NEW CALEDONIA, IVORY COAST, COSTA RICA**, a fleet of **7 CHINESE** junks usually sold at 10d., **TRINIDAD & TOBAGO, MAURITIUS, SOUTH WEST AFRICA, NEWFOUNDLAND, U.S.A., B. GUIANA**, set of **S. AFRICA, GREECE, POLAND, INDO-CHINA, FRENCH OCEANIA**, etc. Price **4½d.**, postage 1½d. (abroad 3d. extra). Purchasers of this packet asking for approvals receive **FREE** set of **3 SPAIN** (Columbus, each with his ship on it). Senders of addresses of stamp collectors receive **FREE** set of **6 VENEZUELA** or **6 PERSIA, 100 BRITISH COLONIALS 1/-, 20 AIRPOST 6d., 6 TRIANGULARS 6d., 50 PERSIA 4/-, 2 ASTRID** (mourning stamps) **2½d., VOLUMES OF B.O.P. CHEAP.**

H. C. WATKINS (M. Dept.), Granville Road, BARNET

FREE FOUR of the **FINE TRIANGULAR STAMPS** recently issued by various countries, **FREE** to applicants for Approvals enclosing 2d. (abroad 4d.) for Postage.

DECEMBER SPECIALS

3 Bahamas	... 3d.	1 Malta Jubilee	... 2d.
4 Barbados	... 3d.	4 Negri Sembilan, mint ...	... 6d.
3 Basutoland	... 4d.	6 New Guinea	... 9d.
4 Bechuanaland ...	5d.	1 N.Z. Air, used ...	2d.
4 Queen Astrid	... 10d.	3 N.Z. Air, 1d., 3d., 6d. mint	... 1/3
3 Belgian Olympic Games...	... 9d.	4 Pahang, mint	... 6d.
6 Belgian Congo ...	3d.	4 Papua Ann., cpte	1/3
5 Bijawar	... 10d.	4 Perak, mint	... 6d.
5 British Honduras	6d.	12 Porto Rico	... 7d.
2 British Somali ...	3d.	2 Raratonga	... 4d.
2 Brunei ...	... 2d.	7 San Marino	... 5d.
5 Cayman Islands	4d.	4 Selangor mint ...	6d.
3 Chili Airmails ...	3d.	9 Soloman Ids., ½d. to 1/- mint	... 3/6
3 China, Postage Due ...	... 2d.	5 Timor	... 3d.
3 Chinese Turkestan	2d.	3 Tonga ...	... 4d.
1 Cyprus Jubilee...	2d.	7 Transjordan	... 8d.
5 Hejaz-Nejd	... 6d.		

15 Different Mozambique Company, **AIR ONLY**, Price 1/10.

All Orders Postage Extra.

A BONUS of 25 best quality sorting envelopes will be given free to purchasers of not less than 2/6 worth, and a BONUS of 50 ditto., a good assortment of sizes, will be presented to all purchasers of not less than 5/- worth from this advertisement.

EDWARD SANDELL, 10, Evelyn Grove, Southall, Mx.

All Business by Post.

The NEW "TRANSPORT" Packet

Contains a wonderful assortment of 44 foreign and colonial stamps including the following which depict various means of transportation. **Tunis** (water carrier), **Senegal** (bridge and boats), **Mauritania** (crossing desert) **Mid. Congo** (train and bridge), **Sth. Africa** (ship), **Germany** (aeroplane), **Austria** (horseman), **Indo China** (boat), **Mozambique** (aeroplane), **Gaboon** (raft), **Greece** (bridge and liner), **St. Pierre and M.** (trawler). **Fr. Guinea** (native carriers), **Dutch Indies** (Steamboat), **Madagascar** (native transport), **Brazil** (aeroplane), **Belgium** (train), **Roumania** (aeroplane), **Newfoundland** (steamship). **Fr. Morocco** (camels). **Price 6d.** All purchasers asking for approvals will receive large Ceylon pictorials free.

BURDOCK & FLURY,
4, MARLBOROUGH ROAD, LONDON, S.W.19.

SOUTH-WEST AFRICA PACKET FREE!

This wonderful pictorial packet contains the following issues: South-West Africa (Gom-pauw Bird, as illustrated), Jugo-Slavia (**Boy King**), **Vatican** (**beautiful Lawyers Congress commemorative**), Guadeloupe (Sugar Mill), Oceania (Native fishing), **Austria** (**Mint Parliament commemorative**), St. Pierre (Lighthouse), and new **Australia Telephone commemorative.** To obtain this fine gift **ABSOLUTELY FREE** simply request approvals and include 2d. postage. (No approvals sent abroad.) Price of packet alone, **9d.**

MICHAEL HERBERT (M.M.), 8, WOODSTOCK ROAD, WALTHAMSTOW, LONDON.

CHRISTMAS PRESENT NEWS.

COLONIAL STAMPS OF THE NEW REIGN

Arrangements have been completed for the despatch of

FIRST-DAY COVERS OF KING EDWARD VIII from each of the 64 Dominions and Dependencies as and when issued on the day of issue. Ensure genuine postmarks by having, delivered by your own postman by nearly every delivery for months, the new stamps direct from all parts of the Empire.

PRICES:

½d., 1d., 1½d. (and where issued 1d.) from each of 64 Colonies	£1 10 0
As above, but to 3d. value	£4 0 0
Complete set to £1 value...	£100 0 0

Prices for intermediate values, single Colonies, and single Cover on application. All Covers will be registered, except the £1 10 0 set, and not more than four stamps will be used on any one cover. Covers will be of exclusive souvenir design.

WHICH COLONY WILL BE NEXT?

It is no longer possible to have first day covers posted from the British Post Offices in Morocco. October 26, 1936, was the date of issue. Do not miss any more.

Orders should be placed at once for unused stamps of King Edward, also. These will be delivered on the day after issue.

ARCHIBALD F. McQUARRIE,
161a, Strand, London, W.C.2, England
TEL.: TEMPLE BAR 8642.

PICTORIAL COLONIALS ONLY

I specialise in Brit. Col. approvals and will send you an absolute bargain selection of pictorials (Jubilees if required). Do you want current, recent or what issues? **R. F. EMBLEY, 39, Cross St., St. Annes-on-Sea, Lancs.**

ONE THOUSAND STAMPS ON APPROVAL

From which you may select any 100 for 3/-.

This selection is not made up of the very commonest varieties, but contains stamps catalogued at 1/- each or more. (I do not sell less than 100.)

H. HARDY, "Hoyland," Potter Heigham, Norfolk.

ODDS AND ENDS

M—MINT U—USED

7 Bermuda ½d. to 6d.	M	2/2	1 Canada 1935 Air	U	8d.
1 Can. "Ottawa Air"	U	10d.	9 Cyprus ½p. to 9p.	M	4/3
6 Canada "Jubilee"	U	2/3	9 St. Lucia ½d. to 1/-	M	3/9
11 Canada Current Set	U	3/-	4 Straits Jubilee	M	2/9
3 Canada Coil	U	3d.	4 S. Rhodesia	M	2/9

Cash with order—Postage extra.

H. L. Gomm, 41, Upper Cranbrook Rd., Redland, Bristol, 6

BOYS! Why pay more? My Approval Selections are famous for real rock-bottom prices and the numbers of bargains are sure to amaze you. Thousands of fine stamps from ½d. to £1 each. Write now.

B. MAX CAMPBELL,
HALDON AVENUE, TEIGNMOUTH, DEVON.

11 Morocco and Tangier, King Edward VIII, Mint	1/-
6 Liberia 1936 Triangular Air, Complete Mint	1/2
4 Japan 1936 National Parks, Complete Mint	7d.
55 U.S.America different, Used	9d.

Post 1½d. extra. Selections from 4 a 1d. (30 for 6d.)

J. R. MORRIS, 9, Audley Road, Folkestone, Kent.

RARE RHODESIA (cat. 4/6), or 500 stamp mounts free to approval applicants. Good discount.—Winter, 89, Cobham Road, Seven Kings.

ALL BRITISH COLONIAL APPROVALS

Fine **BRITISH COLONIAL PICTORIAL SETS OF CAYMAN ISLANDS** and **GAMBIA FREE** to all Collectors sending 2d. in stamps and requesting **ALL BRITISH COLONIAL APPROVALS. BRITISH COLONIALS ONLY** on approval at bargain prices, including **JUBILEE** and **NEW PICTORIAL ISSUES,** West Indies, East and West Africa, Cyprus, Iraq, Newfoundland, Papua, and many other fine Colonials. (No stamps sent Abroad.) **C. H. SHAW (Dept. M.12), 95, CHRISTCHURCH AVENUE, KENTON, HARROW.**

See also other stamp advertisements on pages 744 and 746

THE STORY OF THE MOTOR CAR IN STAMPS

IN recent articles we have pointed out how interesting it is to collect stamps with designs that illustrate some special subject. There is a wide choice of subjects of this kind, for in whatever direction a collector's interests may lie, he can find stamps connected with them.

Stamp collectors among Meccano and Hornby Train enthusiasts are particularly well placed in this respect, for there are many stamp with designs illustrating the different branches of engineering. Pictures of ships, locomotives, aeroplanes and bridges are comparatively common features of modern stamps, and even the construction of roads has been well illustrated. In addition there are certain branches of engineering to which only a few stamps have been devoted. The story of the motor car provides an example of this kind, for there are less than a dozen stamps that deal directly with it. There are, however, other stamps connected with this subject that might well be included in a small collection, and the limited number of stamps to be acquired makes it easy for a collector with small resources to obtain a set that is complete.

It is difficult for modern boys to realise the days when motor cars were novelties, for they are accustomed to seeing highways crowded with cars and lorries of various makes. Yet 20 years ago cars were still rare, and only 10 years before that mechanically propelled vehicles were limited to a speed of 3 m.p.h., and even then had to be preceded by a man carrying a red flag. In those days motor cars were called horseless carriages. This was an apt description, for they closely resembled the carriages of that time, as is shown in our illustration of the 4c. stamp from the United States Pan-American Exhibition Series of 1901. This stamp is of particular interest, as it was the first to show a motor car in its design.

When we turn to other motor vehicle stamps, we find that they do not include reproductions of private motor cars in their designs. There are several showing commercial vehicles, however. For instance, the 50 h. stamp from the Bosnia and Herzegovina issue of 1906 and the 15 c. United States parcel post issue of 1912 both show Post Office vans of the times at which they were issued. These vans have high bodies, solid tyres, and spoked wheels, and are in striking contrast with the modern van shown on the 10 k. express delivery stamp issued in Russia in April 1932, and illustrated on this page. Another type of van is to be found on the United States 20c. special delivery stamps of 1925, also illustrated. This is not so modern as the Russian example, but represents a great advance on the vans shown in the two early stamps to which reference has been made.

Among the more interesting modern developments of the motor car has been the construction of vehicles suitable for travel across difficult country. The introduction of creeper track has played a great part in this, for cars fitted with it can travel over soft sand, in which ordinary wheels would sink, and as a result motor vehicles have penetrated into the Sahara Desert. A reminder of this is the 1 fr. design of the Child Welfare series issued in Tunis in February 1928. This stamp was issued to mark the opening of a motor service across the Sahara Desert from Tunis to Lake Chad, and shows one of the vehicles specially designed for the arduous conditions met with on its desert journeys. The stamp is illustrated in the bottom left corner of this page.

Another specialised form of motor vehicle that will provide stamps for the enthusiast making a special collection in connection with this subject is the agricultural tractor. Examples of this type of motor vehicle again come from Russia, where of course great efforts have been made to develop tractors for agricultural work in the immense wheat growing districts. A 5r. value was issued in August 1923 to commemorate an agricultural exhibition at Moscow, and the 10k. value of the 1929 Industrial Loan Propaganda issue also showed heavy agricultural tractors at work. Yet another tractor design from Russia is the 15k. value of the 1933 series commemorating the 15th Anniversary of the revolution of 1917. It is interesting to see that these tractors are fitted with rubber creeper tracks. Winter conditions in Russia are too severe for metal tracks. In 1930 experiments therefore were made with rubber tracks, and it was found that ice and snow do not cling to the joints and clog the mechanisms.

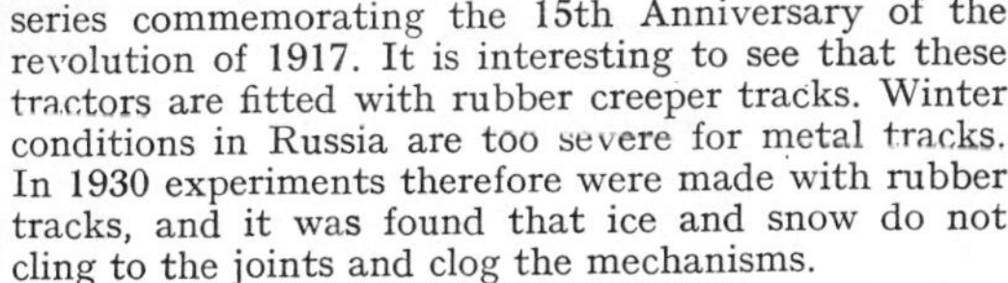

As would be expected in view of the immense extent of country devoted to the growing of wheat and other cereals, Canada also can provide an example of a stamp showing a tractor, and this is the best of its kind that has yet appeared. The stamp is the 20c. value, issued in 1930, and shows a tractor with creeper track hauling a modern reaper and binder.

A stamp collection illustrating the development of the motor vehicle would not be complete without including the two stamps issued by Germany in February last to commemorate the 50th anniversary of the invention of the motor car. These two stamps, issued during the holding of the 1936 Berlin Motor Show, bore portraits of Gottlieb Daimler (6 pf.) and Karl Benz (12 pf.), the famous motoring pioneers.

Daimler was working in a factory devoted to the manufacture of gas engines, when, in 1884, he designed a light compact engine in which petrol was used as fuel. In 1885 he fitted this engine to a bicycle and later to a "motor carriage." Karl Benz was the first to apply the petrol motor to light and practical road vehicles. His first car was produced in 1885 and its engine was rated at ¾ h.p. The car had three wheels and was capable of 6½ m.p.h.

Designs illustrating pedal and motor cycles would be interesting inclusions in this collection. The 5k. stamp from Russia's Express Delivery series illustrated on this page is an example. It was issued in 1932 as a companion to the 10k. stamp already mentioned.

MAKE SURE OF A HAPPY XMAS
By Getting Your STAMPS, ALBUMS, etc.
from STANLEY GIBBONS LTD.

WRITE FOR NEW 1937 FREE LISTS NOW

104 pages giving full details of all our Stamp Albums, Catalogues, Books and Accessories, and particulars of hundreds of fine Stamp Bargains — just what you want to help you choose your Christmas Stamp Gifts.

Two Gift Suggestions

1. **THE "NEW IDEAL" BRITISH EMPIRE ALBUM.** Just published. 384 pages with a separate space for every British Empire Postage Stamp from 1840 to the end of King George's reign. A unique book! Price only **12s. 6d.**
Postage extra, U.K. 8d., Abroad 1/11.

2. **GIBBONS' PRICED CATALOGUE 1937.** Best and most detailed catalogue—essential to every keen collector who wishes to keep right up-to-date with his collecting. 1812 pages, 108,740 items listed, 22,883 new prices in this latest edition. Price **15s.**
Postage extra, U.K. 6d., Abroad 1/3.

STANLEY GIBBONS LTD., Dept. S.15, 391 Strand, London, W.C.2

Parcels of unsorted Stamps

"WORLD"

GUARANTEED UNPICKED

Many good stamps are to be found and there is always the chance of a real "Find" being made.

Sold by weight only —CANNOT BE BEATEN FOR SHEER VALUE.

½ lb. (abt. 2,000 stamps) ... **2/6** Post Free
1 lb. („ 4,000 „) ... **4/6** „ „
2 lb. („ 8,000 „) ... **7/6** „ „

Abroad—add 6d. per ½ lb. Extra for postage

SAMPLE ¼ lb.—**1/6** Post Free. (*Abroad 1/10*)

PHILIP J. DYKE
35, Buckleigh Ave., Merton Park, S.W.20

SPECIAL XMAS OFFERS

FREE To genuine approval applicants, and to purchasers of any of the under-mentioned packets: Set of 9 Georgia **Complete to 5 Roubles;** 15 Colonial **Jubilees** (Different) 1/6; 20 at 2/3; 25 at 3/-. 30 **Commemoratives,** all different, Colonial and foreign 1/3. 9 **Ceylon.** 2c.—30c. K.G. Pictorials fine used 1/-. 60 **British Colonials** (Only Pictorials, Comms. and Jubilees) 3/3. 100 **Persia** 2/9. 100 **French Colonials** 1/6. Cash with order—postage extra.

T. R. Hughes, 'Ibis Cottage,' Long Park, Amersham.

LIBERIA TRIANGULAR AIRMAIL

FREE. For 30 days (abroad 60 days) we offer our special gift packet including new **Liberia Triangular Airmail** and **King Edward VIII Morocco** free to applicants for our Approval Sheets. Write for a selection. You need not purchase any unless our prices tempt you.

Department 254

ERRINGTON & MARTIN
LONDON, E.9, ENGLAND

New Greek Air Mail FREE

along with 25 other different stamps. Say whether British Colonial or Foreign preferred—to applicants sending 2d. in stamps and requesting our Booklets of Stamps. Special discounts allowed.

The BRAMLEY STAMP CO.,
TOWN END, BRAMLEY, LEEDS.

BIG XMAS SURPRISE

As a special XMAS surprise to you we are giving a monster gift collection of stamps FREE. Included in this wonderful lot you will find beautiful **BELGIUM** mourning issue of the tragic Queen Astrid; obsolete **ABYSSINIA** showing one of the old Emperors; **PALESTINE** printed in three languages, fine **ROUMANIA** Air Stamp and pictorial **SOUTH AFRICA;** bi-coloured **FINLAND; FRENCH COLONIALS;** attractive late King Fuad of **EGYPT;** historic **AUSTRALIA** comm.; quaint **IRAN** of Riza Shah Pahlavi; scarce provisional **ANDORRA; SALVADOR;** several stamps of countries from which you may not have got any (**BARANYA, DECCAN, HYDERABAD, SCHLESWIG, etc.**); old **CAPE OF GOOD HOPE** showing 'Hope' and Table Bay; a set of pictorials from an **INDIAN NATIVE STATE; CYPRUS** and **NIGERIA** issues that will be withdrawn in a few months; **DANZIG; DENMARK; GOLD COAST** depicting old Castle; unusual 'Child Welfare' from **MEXICO;** pictorial **NEWFOUNDLAND** showing Twin Hills and Tors Cove; an Air issue from **BRAZIL,** and others. All good stamps, all different and ALL FREE to you if you send 2d. stamp and request one of our 'Grey' booklets of stamps on approval. Our Price Lists of 'Albums and Accessories' and 'Single-Country Packets' sent free on request.

WINDSOR STAMP CO. (Dept. M.), 59, LEE ROAD, BLACKHEATH, S.E.3.

He Who Hesitates is Lost

All George V current colonials will very shortly be obsolete. Don't leave it until it is too late. Here's your chance to get them before they become scarce. Buy an Empire Packet, guaranteed to contain only unsorted British Colonials sent out exactly as received from Banks, Trading Stations, and other Outposts of the Empire.

An Empire Packet is the cheapest and best way to fill up the gaps in your British Colonial Collection, includes Silver Jubilees, Commemoratives, New and Obsolete Issues, and heaps of other attractive stamps, 100 for 1/–; 250, 2/–; 500, 3/9, 1,000, 7/3.

All Post Free (Abroad 3d. extra).

I am giving to all purchasers of 3/9 and over a Queen Victoria Labuan stamp cat. 2/6. Remit by Postal Order only.

K. HUMPHRIES (Dept. M.),
East Wittering Road, East Wittering, Chichester, Sussex.

MINT AUSTRALIA, KENYA, 20 British Colonials and Peru, catalogued 3/6, free to approval applicants. Postage 2d.—P. R. Lincoln, High Road, Potters Bar.

---

47 different ITALY inc. Commems, 2d. only. Swell approvals. We pay postage both ways.—LGS, 3, Houndsden Road, London, N.21.

DID YOU GET

the free set I offered last month? This month you have the choice of two, Exhibition Set or Red Cross Set. Write for approvals, a postcard will do and say which set you want. NO POSTAGE REQUIRED.

C. A. MASTERS, BROADSTONE, DORSET

STAMP WALLET

FREE (Size 5¼″×3¾″), fitted with **PERFORATION GAUGE,** etc., and containing **LIBERIA AIR MAIL (TRIANGULAR),** set of **ROUMANIA (AVIATION), BELGIUM** (Antwerp and Brussels Exhib.), free to Approval applicants enclosing 3d. (Abroad 6d.) for postage and packing.

A. B. LEWIS, Dept. C.6,
16, Cricklewood Lane, London, N.W.2.

THE VERY THING

stamp collectors require is our Exchange Stamp Pocket Wallet. Made in Rexine, covered in Leatherette, and contains two gussetted compartments. Free stamps given with each. Can also be used for exchange Cigarette Cards. Send Postal Order (not stamps) for **7d.** to

J. R. MATTHEWS LTD.,
22, Charterhouse Square, London, E.C.1.
Established 1860.

LINER STAMPS

ALBUM. 650 different Stamps, Pictorials, Ships, Birds, Animals, Airs, Triangles, 1,000 Mounts, Tweezers. Lot 8/6, post 6d. Smaller lot 5/–. Fine Gifts. Approval Selections.—M.S.P., 55, High St., Battersea, London, S.W.11.

See also other stamp advertisements on pages 742 and 746

Stamp Gossip

and Notes on New Issues

Winter Charity Stamps

The annual Austrian Winter Relief charity stamps were issued early last month, and consisted of a set of four most interesting allegorical designs as follows: 5gr., St. Martin's Cloak; 12gr., succouring the sick; 24gr., St. Elizabeth distributing bread; 1 schilling, the Fire of Charity.

Four of the values for the German "Winterhilfe" (winter relief) series appeared in September last, and bore designs illustrating the great new motor road from Munich to the Swiss Frontier. We illustrate the 3 pf. value which shows a general view of the road as it sweeps through pine forests and over mountains. An interesting feature of this new road, incidentally one that is common to all the great arterial roads recently constructed in Germany, is its great width of nearly 150 ft. A grass verge in the centre divides the road into two separate tracks and, as our illustration shows, cross roads are carried over on bridges so that traffic on the main road may flow unhindered.

The remaining designs of the September issues were as follows: 6pf., a bridge over the river Saale; 12pf., an alpine stretch of the road; 25pf., the bridge over the river Mangfall. A further five stamps for the series appeared at the end of October and bore designs as follows: 4pf., the Munich Motor Road; 5pf., the Nuremberg Memorial; 8pf., Deutschland Hall, Berlin; 15pf., the Fuhrerhaus, Munich; 40pf., an exterior view of the Munich Art Gallery.

The annual Luxemburg charity issue was due to be placed on sale on the first of this month. This set comprises six stamps each bearing a portrait of Wenzel I, Duke of Luxemburg (1353-1383). This issue will remain on sale until 31st January next.

A Mexican Motor Road

The opening of the new motor road between Mexico and Laredo has been commemorated in Mexico by the issue of six special stamps, three for general postage and three for air mail use.

We illustrate the 10c. air stamp which shows a view of the Tasquillo Bridge over the Rio Tula, one of several bridges in the course of the road. The remaining designs are as follows: Postal stamps; 5c., a symbolical map; 10c., the Matalote Bridge; 20c., a general view of a stretch of the road. Air stamps: 20c., the Rio Corona Bridge; 40c., Guayalejo Bridge.

Czecho-Slovakian Pictorials

The recently issued Czecho-Slovakian pictorial series is one of the most attractive scenic sets that we have seen. It contains nine stamps, ranging in value from 1.20k. to 10k.

We illustrate two of these, the 4k. and 10k. values. The 4k. shows a view of Podebrady in Bohemia. The statue in the foreground commemorates George of Podebrady, one of the most famous of the old-time Czech kings, who reigned in the middle of the 15th century. In the background is the king's castle. The 10k. stamp shows a pretty riverside view of the Danube at Bratislava. The castle on the hillside was built rather more than 600 years ago and was the home of the Hungarian kings. It was destroyed by fire in 1811, and has remained in its ruined condition ever since.

The remaining designs are as follows: 1.20k., Castle Palanok, near Mukacevo in Carpathian Ruthenia. The site has been a military fortification from very early days and the castle shown in the stamp dates from 1360. 1.50k., Banska Bystrica, an old Slovakian mining town. 2k., the castle of Zvikov in Bohemia. The castle is perched on a rocky eminence between the Vltava and Otava rivers. It dates from the 12th century. 2.50k., the castle of Strecno in Slovakia. 3k., the castle Hruba Skala. 3.50k., the Slavkov Castle in Moravia. 5k., the Masaryk Square at Olomouc in Moravia.

* * *

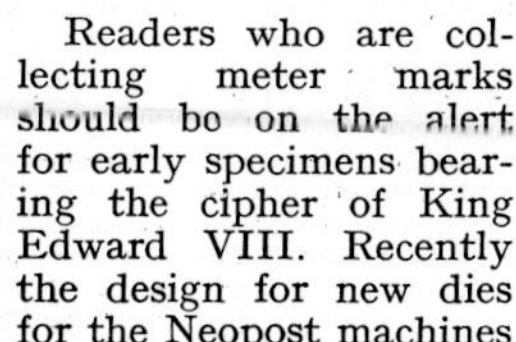

The 1937 Paris International Exhibition has been preceded by the issue of a short series of six postage stamps, values 20c. to 1f.50. The four lower values bear a design depicting a herald sounding a fanfare at the opening of the Exhibition. The two higher values, the design for which is illustrated on this page, bear an allegorical design showing a curtain being drawn back across the globe typifying the Exhibition's revelations of world wonders.

Edwardian Meter Marks

Readers who are collecting meter marks should be on the alert for early specimens bearing the cipher of King Edward VIII. Recently the design for new dies for the Neopost machines was passed and plates are in preparation for fitting on to existing machines.

The general features of the King George dies have been retained, but the size of the crown has been reduced and the *E 8 R* cipher introduced. The key letters and meter numbers in the new dies will be rather larger than in the old ones.

Callao Commemoratives

The centenary of the establishment of the Province of Callao has been celebrated in Peru by the issue of a set of 12 commemorative stamps featuring various aspects of the history and life of the Port of Callao and the Province.

We illustrate the 2c. value the design on which gives an excellent picture of the caravel *"San Cristobal,"* which played a prominent part in the battles along the coast at the time Peru was fighting for its independence from Spanish dominion.

The remaining designs are as follows: 4c., La Punta Naval College; 5c., Plaza de la Independencia; Callao; 10c., aerial view of Callao; 15c., Callao Docks; 20c., a plan of Callao; 35c., the locomotive *"La Callao"*; 50c., portrait of D. Jose de la Mar, the first President of Peru; 1s., the mail-boat *"Sacramento"*; 2s., D. Jose de Velasco; 5s., Fort Maipu. The 10s. is probably the most interesting of the whole series. It shows a plan of the fortifications at Real Felipe, built by the Spaniards in 1770. The borders of the stamp are formed by two old-time cannons mounted on a representation of the battlements of the fort extending across the foot of the stamp. The stamp is one of the most interesting pictorial designs of 1936 and it is unfortunate that at the time of going to press a specimen of the stamp was not available for illustration on this page.

Colonial King Edward Stamps

The Crown Agents for the Colonies announce that all Colonies will issue new stamps, bearing a portrait of King Edward VIII, about the date of the Coronation in May next. The stamps will be of standard size with a design showing a three-quarter profile vignette of the King's head in a circle, placed toward the top left-hand corner of the stamp, with the Imperial Crown at the top right-hand corner. The name of the Colony will appear beneath the vignette. The duty tablet will be placed in the bottom right-hand corner, and the denomination will be inscribed in words across the base.

We thank Stanley Gibbons Ltd. for their courtesy in loaning the stamps from which the illustrations on this page have been made.

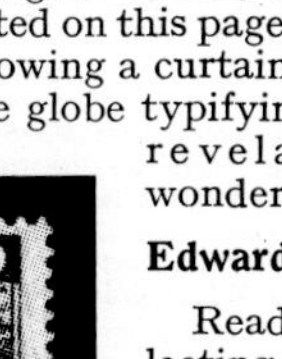

ITALY

1st July, 1936. Set of 5 fine pictorials commemorating the birth of the poet Horace, showing Athlete, the Capitol, Medallion, etc. The set of picked used copies, **10d.**

CAYMAN ISLANDS

Set of 3 unused K.G. pictorials, showing Map, Cat Boat, and Booby Birds, free to genuine applicants for approvals enclosing 2d. postage. Three stamps that are worth having.

CANADA

A fine used set of 50, various issues, including Ottawa Conference, Jubilees, Confederation, 1932 Provisional, Cartier commemorative, coil stamps, etc. A splendid lot, **2/-.**

R. D. HARRISON - ROYDON - WARE

SIX EDWARD VIII NEW ISSUES FREE

Set of six different Mint King Edward stamps from Morocco Agencies, Spanish Zone, French Zone, Tangier, free.

This superb gift will make a really fine start for your Edward collection.

Write to-day, just request approvals and enclose 2d. for postage.

K. HUMPHRIES (Dept. M.N.),
E. Wittering Road, E. Wittering, Chichester, Sussex.

CHOOSE YOUR OWN FREE GIFTS!

Write now for my List of over **100 DIFFERENT FREE GIFTS** and see how you can add these fine stamps to your collection. To all genuine applicants for my **MODERN APPROVALS** I will present free **A GRAND PACKET OF 26 DIFFERENT BRITISH COLONIALS** including the beautiful **MINT CAYMAN IS. 1935 PICTORIAL** (Cat Boat) and soon to be obsolete. **KING GEORGE ISSUES,** etc., etc. **TO FIRST 250 APPLICANTS** I will also send Free the **MINT PAPUA COMMEMORATIVE** illustrated. Send 2d. postage, etc. (6d. Abroad).

CAMPBELL (M), 71, MANOR RD., TANKERTON, KENT

CHEAP APPROVALS

My beautiful Approval Selections are ideal for filling those vacant spaces. Pictorials, Colonials, and hard to get items. Selections from 4 a 1d. Free Gift Bi-coloured Persia all applicants.

A. V. TAPP,
108, CHESTERFIELD RD., BRISTOL

XMAS BUMPER GIFT—FREE

LAST MINUTE SENSATION—KING EDWARD VIII Colonial included

A luxury Xmas present from **GLOBE-TROTTER** for every stamp collecting reader of "Meccano Magazine" who sends 2d. postage, requesting approvals. A packet of beautiful stamps—a feast to delight the lucky recipient, including Historic **PICKARD BALLOON STAMP,** illustrating Pickard's stratosphere exploring balloon, **Mozambique and Roumanian Air Mails,** Pictorials from **Belgian Congo** (Native Huts), **Trinidad, British Guiana** (Native), **Silver Jubilee,** two mint **Belgian 1919 (Tin Hat)** stamps, **Equador** (Map), large **Persia, Syria** (Mosques), **Palestine, Kenya** (Mint), selection of **Six striking African pictorials,** and others. Act now—write for your free gift now—remember **GLOBE-TROTTER** approval selections are famous for sensational value. Ask for particulars of **FREE** stamps every 14 days!

GLOBE-TROTTER, 17, WINCHESTER ROAD, BIRCHFIELD, BIRMINGHAM.

MINT PICTORIALS

(Postage Extra)

5 Egypt Airs ...	7d.	3 △ Liberia Airs	6d.
6 Bermuda ½d.-3d.	1/5	4 △ Mozambique	6d.
9 Bermuda ½d.-1/6	5/-	3 China	8d.
4 Gibraltar 1d.-3d.	1/-	2 Vimy Ridge ...	2/-
5 Ascension ...	1/-	6 Mongolia ...	9d.

Packet of **40 BRITISH COLONIALS 6d.**

A. LUCAS, 60, PARK STREET, BRISTOL.

AN AMAZING XMAS OFFER

Our final **FREE GIFT** for 1936 is definitely the **BIGGEST** and **BEST** we have ever presented. We have been able to include the latest new issue from the **MOROCCO AGENCIES** (King Edward VIII), together with a large assortment of superb **PICTORIALS** including **ST. LUCIA, NIGERIA, BRITISH GUIANA, NEWFOUNDLAND, ALGERIA** (set of three), **IRAN, TANGANYIKA** and **GERMANY,** and many attractive items such as **PERAK,** Siam, Mozambique, and Jugo-Slavia. **FREE** and **POST FREE,** just a P.C. requesting approvals to:

THE UNIVERSITY STAMP CO., 1, PLANTATION ROAD, OXFORD

The ST. KITTS Packet

Contains a **Fine mint ST. KITTS-NEVIS 'War Stamp' pictorial;** Large **AIR MAIL** Pictorials from **INDO-CHINA; U.S.A.** and **CHILE; Windsor Castle JUBILEE Pictorials** from **CEYLON, TANGANYIKA** and **JAMAICA;** Large **VATICAN STATE Pictorial** Commem.; **Obsolete ABYSSINIAN** Pictorial; a Liberian **TRIANGULAR** Air Mail Commem.; Large **BR. NYASALAND** Pictorial; China **Sun Yat Sen; Canada JUBILEE (Princess Elizabeth).** Also the **Beautiful QUEEN ASTRID Mourning** stamp. 1/- only (Postage 1½d. extra). Purchasers asking for our **BARGAIN** appros. will receive a **LARGE SPANISH TRIANGULAR** Commem. **FREE!** **THE PUKKA STAMP CO., 27, NORMANDY AVENUE, BARNET.**

SPECIAL CHRISTMAS OFFERS

25 Abyssinia, all pictorials, animals, birds, etc....	3/6
13 Liberia, 1908, elephants, monkeys, birds, lizards, etc. A very rare set ...	3/6
3 North Borneo, 1888, fine large stamps. Cat. 4/-	1/2
8 North Borneo, 1889, the scarce used set. Cat. 5/5	1/3
17 Persia, 1915 Coronation, wonderful set, stamps having silver frames ...	1/9
9 Nyassa, 1924 Triangular set ...	1/7½
25 different Silver Jubilee, includes many scarce	2/6
1,000 different, All the World, wonderful value	3/6

Free Price List of Jubilees, Pictorial and Commemorative at bargain prices on application. **WRITE TO-DAY!** This month to all genuine applicants for my Approvals I am presenting a free set of Colonial Stamps priced at over 5/-.

DERRICK PARKEN,
GREENWITH, PERRANWELL, TRURO, CORNWALL.

IMPROVED

THE "MYSTIC" PACKET

1000 UNKNOWN UNUSUAL UNSORTED 1/6

(Over 200 diff. guaranteed.)

Stamps on paper, etc. Just as received from Convents, Missions, Banks, etc. Guaranteed unpicked. Chance of a FIND in every lot. Send to-day for your treasure hunt to-morrow. 3 for **4/3,** 6 for **8/-. Abroad 1/9** pkt. **FREE!** 25 Br. Cols. including the new reign issues to approval applicants. Enclose postage. Overseas 3d. Also **FREE EXCHANGE.**

ASTLEY & CO.
(M), LOWHILL, WOLVERHAMPTON

ZOO PACKET (USUAL PRICE 1/-) FREE

to all genuine applicants for approvals sending 3d. to cover postage (both ways). Illustrated list of albums and accessories free.

C. Fawcett, 36, Flaxley Rd., Selby

Clearance Sale of Stamps

A large stock irrespective of catalogue value has been made up into packets. Mint and used Pictorials, Commemoratives, Air Mails, Jubilees, etc., etc., are included in these wonder packets. Never again will such value be offered. Post free, cash with order. 250 for **1/6.** 500 for **2/6.** 1,000 for **4/6.**

R. F. Farrington, 61, Penge Rd., London, S.E.25

"WORTH WHILE"

Your Christmas Present—5/- for 2/-

100 Superior BRITISH COLONIALS, 2/- Post Free. JUBILEES, COMMEMORATIVES, PICTORIALS, etc. I usually sell this packet for 5/- which contains such good stamps as New Zealand **JUBILEE 1d., 2½as.** Indian **JUBILEE,** Nigeria 3d., Australia sheep, Bridge and Sturt Comms., Iraq, Feisal, Gold Coast ½d. to 3d., Western Australia Swan, Mauritius, Palestine, etc.

100 such Colonials for 2/-. Truly a gift.

MONEY BACK IF NOT SATISFIED.

Ask to see some **"WORTH WHILE"** Approval Sheets. **"WORTH WHILE"** sheets for stamps **WORTH WHILE**

JOS. H. GAZE,
21, ATWOOD ROAD, DIDSBURY, MANCHESTER.

FREE! EXHIBITION PACKET

containing 50 different stamps including **Antwerp 1894 Exhibition, Brussels 1896 Exhibition, Schleswig Plebiscit, Russia,** set of **Austria** (all mint), Canada, Chili, Jamaica, etc., together with 250 mounts, handy duplicate book, and perforation gauge. Request approvals which contain the new **Edward VIII** Morocco Agencies Stamps. 25% discount. Enclose 2d. postage. Beginner's outfit containing 80-page Album, 100 different stamps, swap pocket case, 500 mounts, Tweezers, duplicate book, and magnifying glass, 2/8.

A. R. Dickie (Dept. M), 23, Winscombe Cres., Ealing, W.5

Approvals: ½d.—3d. Postcard brings good selection. B. Purcell, 59, Highbridge Road, Aylesbury.

100 diff. Stamps Free to approval applicants, good discount.—Gosling, 21, Powling Road, Ipswich.

Free. 5 Iraq and Nigerian Pictorials with approvals. Postage 1½d.—G. Kingsmill, New Barnet, Herts.

GOOD SELECTION ½d. and ½d. approvals. Generous discount.—Mann, 206, Abbey Road, Kirkstall, Leeds, 5.

APPROVALS—Better class only—competitive prices—no gifts.—Edward Lord, Grafton Road, Keighley.

100 Different Stamps Free to Approval applicants. Liberal discount.—Cuthbert, Newsham Lane, Broughton, Preston.

SEND FOR OUR

"ZOOLOGICAL" PACKET

Containing a selection of 45 Foreign and British Colonial Stamps, much better than those usually found in packets of this class, including the following pictorials: **Kenya** (Cranes), **South Africa** (Springbok), **Tchad** (Panther), **Turkey** (Wolf), **Poland** (Eagle), **Madagascar** (Zebus), **Cameroons** (Cattle), **Australia** (Sheep), **Hungary** (Turul) also (Eagle), **Fr. Indo-China** (Ox), **Barbados** (Sea-Horses), **Finland** (Lion), **Epirus** (Eagle), **W. Australia** (Swan), **New Zealand** (Kiwi) also (Fantail), **Mauritania** (Oxen), **Fed. Malay States** (Tiger), **Sweden** (Lion). **Price 6d.** Ask for approval sheets and receive **Andorra** pictorials **Free.**

BRETT & CO.,
201, Uxbridge Road, West Ealing, London, W.13.

FREE SETS of STAMPS

6 Cuba or 6 Imperial China or 6 Straits Settlements or 6 old French, etc. Just send stamps value 2d. and ask for my Approval Sheets containing some high value stamps at low prices and with progressive discounts. State which set of stamps desired to be sent free.

P. ILLINGWORTH,
TRANMERE PARK, GUISELEY, near LEEDS.

10/- Post Paid. Loose-Leaf Stamp Album, Morocco-grained Cloth Cover, 100 Ruled Sheets and 1,000 Stamps, all different. **Auntie Dot, 244, Fawcett Rd. Portsmouth.**

600 BRITISH COLONIALS on approval. Pick at ½d. each.—Sanders, 90, Newlands Avenue, Southampton.

C. V. Fairweather for approvals; British Colonials a speciality.—70, Betchworth Rd., Seven Kings, Essex.

WHEN WRITING TO ADVERTISERS

Readers are urged to observe the following points when writing to advertisers:

1. **Mention the "M.M." and any special reference number quoted in the advertisement. This helps the advertisers to give prompt attention.**
2. **See that the full amount of the price and any postage is included. It is unfair to expect advertisers to fulfil their undertakings promptly if short remittances are sent.**
3. **Give your full address.**
4. **Enquiries concerning advertisements or advertisers should be addressed to:**
   THE ADVERTISEMENT MANAGER
   MECCANO MAGAZINE, Binns Road, LIVERPOOL 13

FREE. 40 Zoological Stamps to applicants for our superior Approvals. Good discount and bonus.—M. Riley, 10, Stricklands Road, Stowmarket, Suffolk.

See also other stamp advertisements on pages 742 and 744

Competition Corner

ADVERTISEMENT "JIG-SAW" CONTEST

The advertisements in this month's *"M.M."* will be almost as important to most of our readers as are the Editorial pages. Christmas presents will be selected this month and the advertisement pages display a host of interesting toys, games and novelties calculated to gladden the heart of any boy.

In repeating the "Advertisement 'Jig-Saw' Contest" that has proved so very popular in recent December numbers, we feel sure that our readers will find the problem of sorting out the advertisements represented in the accompanying picture a most amusing occupation, and it will be a profitable one for those who are successful in winning prizes.

The illustration consists of fragments that have been cut from advertisements appearing in this issue of the *"M.M.,"* and our readers are invited to discover the advertisements from which the fragments have been taken. Some of the pieces will be readily traceable, but others will prove not quite so easy. We hope indeed that they will tease our lynx-eyed readers more than a little, for it is a very long time since we succeeded in setting a puzzle that could not be solved by more than a few of our readers!

In their solutions competitors must give the names of the advertisers concerned, and it should be noted that when an advertiser has more than one advertisement in this issue, the number of the page from which the fragment is taken must be stated in the entry.

Prizes of Meccano products to the value of 21/–, 15/–, 10/6 and 5/– respectively will be awarded to the senders of the four most accurate lists in order of merit. In addition there will be a number of consolation prizes.

Entries for the competition must be addressed to "Jig-Saw Advertisement Contest," Meccano Magazine, Binns Road, Liverpool 13, and must be forwarded to reach this office not later than 19th December. The winners will be advised by post on 21st December and their prizes will be despatched to arrive on Christmas Day.

Another set of prizes, of the same value and to be awarded in similar conditions, will be allotted to the Overseas section, which is reserved for entries from readers living outside Great Britain, Northern Ireland, the Irish Free State and the Channel Islands. Entries for the Overseas Section should be mailed to arrive not later than 31st March, 1937.

Christmas Shopping Contest

Eleven years ago we held a contest in which readers were asked to imagine that they had been given £10 to spend on Christmas presents for themselves. The entries in this contest were very interesting and we should very much like to know if there has been any change since 1925 in our readers' ideas of what they would do with such a sum. This month, therefore, we are arranging a similar contest.

We want every reader to imagine that he has been given a £10 note and told to buy for himself the Christmas present he would like most of all. The money must be spent amongst advertisers in the December *"M.M.,"* but Meccano products must not be included in the list of purchases. Readers may buy as many articles as they wish provided that the whole sum is spent, and brief notes should be added to explain their reason for each purchase.

There will be two sections in this contest—Home and Overseas—and in each prizes of Meccano products to the value of 21/–, 15/–, 10/6 and 5/– will be awarded.

Entries should be addressed "Christmas Shopping List, Meccano Magazine, Binns Road, Liverpool 13," and must be sent to reach this office not later than 31st December. Overseas closing date, 31st March, 1937.

December Drawing Contest

This month we announce the third of the monthly drawing and painting competitions that we are holding throughout the winter. Competitors may select any subject they like for their entries in this contest, and full details of the conditions and the prizes offered were given on page 607 of our October issue. New readers who are unable to obtain copies of the October issue can obtain full details from the Editor.

Entries in this month's competition must be addressed "December Drawing Contest, Meccano Magazine, Binns Road, Liverpool 13." The closing date is 31st December. Overseas section 31st March, 1937.

COMPETITION RESULTS

October Crossword Puzzle.—A large number of readers succeeded in submitting an all-correct solution to this contest, and in making their awards the judges were compelled to take into account the neatness and novelty of presentation of these entries. The solution will appear in the February issue.

The awards were as follows: 1. J. A. Ryde (Carshalton). 2. E. Burns (Wembley Hill). 3. H. McLachlan (Edinburgh 10). 4. N. F. Bartrum (Warminster). Consolation Prizes: B. Hardie (Bristol, 9); G. H. Marsh (Tipton); R. Richards (London, E.5); A. Russell (Harrow); R. P. and J. C. Walford (Newton Abbott).

October Drawing Contest.—First Prizes: Section A, D. V. Gibbs (Dundee); Section B, J. S. Taylor (Burnley). Second Prizes: Section A, A. Marsh (Coventry); Section B, J. Laing (Bramley). Consolation Prizes: A. R. Eves (Boston); A. Gilliard (Stroud); W. D. Hall (London, N.12); W. R. Phillips (North Thoresby); J. P. Tyrrell (Teddington).

OVERSEAS

July Photo Contest.—First Prizes: Section A, L. W. Humm (Geraldine, N.Z.); Section B, K. Harris (Kowloon, Hong Kong). Second Prizes: Section A, H. Bennett (Auckland, S.W.2); Section B, M. V. Nathan (Conjeevaram).

July Sketchograms.—First Prizes: Section A, J. R. Dingle (Halifax, N.S., Canada); Section B, R. Torre (Buenos Aires). Second Prizes: Section A, S. D. Kurlawalla (Bombay); R. L. Lawson (Cape Province, S.A.).

News for the World of 8113 A.D.

What will the world be like in the year 8113 A.D.? That we cannot know, but a scheme has been set on foot in America to store records and articles that will give the people of that far distant time a complete picture of our civilisation. It is proposed to place these in a stainless steel vault in the basement of Oglethorpe University, Georgia, and the year 8113 has been chosen for the opening of the vault because it is as far in the future as the first authentic date in history is in the past. If the vault survives the ravages of the 6177 years it is intended to last, the future inhabitants of the world will find in it books and newspapers, photographs, models of machinery, gramophones and cinematograph films that will show them exactly how we live to-day. The vault has an excellent chance of survival, for the buildings in which it is placed are fireproof and their foundations are on solid granite bed rock.

Earthquake, famine, or some other form of disaster may devastate the country round about the vault, or may even destroy the greater part of the Earth's population, so it may be left to a race practically undreamed of to open it, if they know of its existence, or to discover it by excavation. No doubt the archæologists of the future then would gloat over it as do those of to-day over finds in ancient Egypt or Mesopotamia.

MORE BOOKS TO READ

(Continued from page 719)

"Aeroplanes"; "The Modern Ship"; "Railways"

By R. Barnard Way and N. D. Green
(Wells, Gardner. Each 3/6 net)

These three books are the first of "The Modern How-it-Works Series," the object of which is to explain the mysteries of modern science and engineering to those who are not experts, yet wish to know the why and wherefore of it all. All are simply written and easy to follow with the aid of the many useful drawings provided, and each is provided with a coloured frontispiece.

A locomotive hauling coaches from the train ferry across the Baltic Sea on the arrival of the vessel at Gjedser, Denmark. Photograph by J. M. S. Risk.

The first book is typical of the series. In it the authors explain how an aeroplane flies and how it is constructed. The airscrew and the engines are then dealt with in a general but satisfying manner, and other chapters are devoted to the instruments that a pilot uses, the different types of aeroplanes, including the Autogiro and experimental machines, and the airways of the future.

The volume on the modern ship also covers a wide range, from the design and building of a ship to its operation at sea. Tankers, dredgers, submarines, train ferries and other special types of vessel are dealt with in addition to liners and cargo boats, and there are sections on the control of ships, instruments, and anti-rolling devices.

Railways are equally well described in the third volume, which is packed full of interesting information. It begins with an account of the work of building a railway, from the engineer's survey to the laying of the track, and passes on to the construction of the permanent way. The safety of railway working is next considered in a chapter devoted to signalling, and the authors then turn to the locomotive and rolling stock. The volume ends with an account of electrical railway equipment.

Adventure Stories

(R.T.S.)

"Companions of the Bush," by H. Allen Beard (2/- net) relates the exciting adventures of an English boy and his two Australian friends, who show their worth in many strange and difficult situations. In one particularly thrilling episode they join in the chase and capture of a bush-ranger. Throughout the action is swift and the story entertaining.

Charles Kingsley's masterpiece, *"Westward Ho!"*, is still a favourite with boys, and is here reprinted in convenient form (2/6 net), with a coloured frontispiece, and numerous pen and ink sketches in the text.

Charles Letts's Diaries for 1936

Letts's ever-popular *"Schoolboy's Diary"* for 1937 shows an interesting change. It has been revised to make it suitable for boys up to 14 years of age, and a new edition, with the name *"The Public Schools Diary,"* has been introduced for older boys, students and university undergraduates.

In addition to the usual diary portion *"The Schoolboy's Diary"* contains an excellent atlas and nearly 60 pages of text, in which valuable information is given about professions and qualifying examinations, school sports records, and language helps and arithmetical tables. The diary is published in cloth at 1/-, and can be obtained also in leather cloth, with pencil and maps, at 1/6, and in leather with pencil, maps and pockets at 2/6.

"The Public Schools Diary" gives valuable information on similar subjects of a more advanced character, together with notes on motor law and driving tests, and there is also an excellent sectional atlas of the British Isles. The diary is published in leather cloth, with pencil and maps, at 1/6, and in leather, with pockets, pencil and maps at 3/-.

Charles Letts's *"Wireless Diary"* is an excellent little publication, the diary portion of which is supplemented by 75 pages of text. These pages include a list of the chief long, medium and short wave stations, useful hints on the maintenance and repair of wireless receivers, and a section on television. This diary is obtainable in cloth at 1/-, and in leather, with pencil, at 2/6. The pages of the *"Motor Cycling"* Diary have provision for keeping daily mileage records, and the text includes notes on road law, licences and taxation, and a very useful first-aid section. Other features are a distance table and a list of famous British hills, with their location, gradient and length. The diary is published in cloth at 1/-, and in leather, with pencil, at 2/6.

The diary pages of Letts's *"Boy Scouts' Diary"* contain excellent nature notes, and other sections are packed with useful information on signalling, ropes and knots, first aid, and other subjects of interest to Scouts, Rover Scouts and Wolf Cubs. It is published in art cover, without pencil, at 9d.; with pencil, at 1/-, and in leather case, with pockets, at 2/6.

Brown's Boy Scout Diary

(Brown, Son and Ferguson Ltd. 1/-)

The 1937 issue of this excellent diary contains all the features that have made previous editions so valuable to Scouts. There are details of the qualifications of each type and class of Scout, and an illustrated list of proficiency badges. Other sections deal with signalling, camping and first aid, and there are useful notes for Sea Scouts, together with illustrations of types of sailing ships.

Minibrix Model-Building Competition

Competition enthusiasts among our readers will find an interesting opportunity to try their skill in the Minibrix Model-Building Competitions, brief details of which are given in our advertisement pages. Two competitions are to be held, a winter one to close on 1st March and a summer one to close on 1st June, and prize money to the value of £100 is offered for the best models constructed throughout with Minibrix.

Full details of the competition and an entry form can be obtained from the Minibrix Competition Department, Premo Rubber Co. Ltd., Petersfield, Hants. Readers should mention the *"M.M."* when writing.

Billiards in the Home

Billiards is one of the most fascinating of indoor games, and the small tables manufactured by E. J. Riley Ltd. make it available for every home, however small. The firm's products include several that can be placed on an ordinary dining table, and others that are both dining and billiards tables. Whatever its size, a Riley model is not a toy, but a perfect replica of the full-size table supplied to all parts of the world.

E. J. Riley Ltd. of Deal Works, Accrington, or Department 3, 147, Aldersgate Street, London, E.C.1, will be glad to send an attractive art list of their billiards tables to any *"M.M."* reader who is interested.

Skybird Displays

Model aeroplane enthusiasts among our readers will find many displays to interest them in the big stores this Christmastide. Outstanding among these will be the Skybird Aeronautical Model Department that was recently opened at Selfridges, London, by Sir Harry Brittain and Mr. C. W. A. Scott.

The principal feature of this Department is an exhibition of models illustrating aeroplane development from the period of the Great War to modern times. There is also a complete model of the civil airport at Gatwick built entirely with Skybird units. The model includes a representation of the unique Martello Air Station, hangars, and the adjoining S.R. Station.

THE QUICKEST WAY

Mrs. Rideout: "What lovely fleecy clouds: I'd like to be up there sitting on one of them."
Mr. Rideout: "All right, you drive the car."

* * * *

Two small London boys were gazing at the window of a butcher's shop decorated for Christmas. Presently one of them pointed to a number of hams hanging from a large holly branch.
"Look, Tom," he said. "Look at them 'ams a-growing up there."
"Get away," said the other. "'Ams don't grow."
"That's all you know about it," said the first scornfully. "Ain't you ever 'eard of a 'am-bush?"

* * * *

A selection of books suitable for Christmas presents: "Murder," by Mustapha Coffin; "How I Swam the Channel," by Francis Neare; "Bad Bargains," by Magot Dunn; "The Poet," by E. Auta B. Shot; "The Speedster," by Will. E. Skidd; "The Crooked Staff," by Harold Bentit; "Spring-heel Jack," by Eros High.

* * * *

A certain young fellow named Bertie
When his boots got all dusty and dertie,
Used to walk in the rain
Till he'd cleaned them again,
But he caught cold and died when aged thertie.

* * * *

A little girl's account of the children who mocked Elisha ended:
"And Elisha said to the children, 'If you make fun of me, I will set my bear on you, and it will eat you all up.' And they did, and he did, and it did."

* * * *

On his return from his first dancing lesson Bobby was asked how he liked it.
He replied: "Aw, it's easy. All you have to do is turn round and keep wiping your feet."

* * * *

"Hello, Jack. What are you doing?"
"I've built a shed out of my own head."
"Out of your own head?"
"Yes, and there's plenty of wood left for a dog-kennel."

* * * *

"I told the doctor about my absent-mindedness."
"What did he say?"
"Asked for his fee in advance."

* * * *

Lieutenant: "The enemy are as thick as peas. What shall we do?"
Captain: "Shell 'em! Shell 'em!"

* * * *

Diner: "This lobster has only one leg!"
Waiter: "Yes, sir. It lost the other in a fight."
Diner: "Well, take this back and bring me the winner."

* * * *

A NEW TRUNK LINE

Airman (after landing in a tree) to farmer: "I was trying to make a new record."
Farmer: "You did. You're the first man to climb down that tree before climbing up it."

OUTLOOK UNPROMISING

First Caddie: "What's your man like, Charlie?"
Second Caddie: "Left-handed, and keeps his change in his right-hand pocket."

* * * *

A certain young fellow named Vaughan
Took his dog for a stroll on the laughan,
But the pup, strange to say,
Went the opposite way,
And didn't return till next maughan.

* * * *

Teacher: "You missed class yesterday, didn't you?"
Boy: "Not at all, sir, not at all."

* * * *

FOR LUCK

Footpad: "Seeing as it's a noo moon, 'ow about turning yer money over?"

* * * *

"You say you served in the Great War?" said the restaurant manager, as he sampled the new cook's first soup.
"Ay, sir. Officer's cook for two years an' wounded twice."
"You're lucky. It's a wonder they didn't kill you."

* * * *

Enthusiastic House Agent (displaying catalogue): "This is a house without a flaw."
Prospective Customer: "Gosh! What do you walk on?"

* * * *

"Did you call on Mr. Smith about the bill?"
"I did."
"And what did you find out?"
"Mr. Smith."

* * * *

Outfitter: "Yes, sir, here are the boots for your Polar expedition. By the way, were you satisfied with the boots we supplied you with for your last expedition?"
Explorer: "They were the best boots I ever tasted."

* * * *

Pedestrian (to boy leading skinny pup): "What kind of a dog is that, my boy?"
Boy: "This is a police dog."
Pedestrian: "It doesn't look like a police dog."
Boy: "No, it's in the secret service."

* * * *

Tramp: "Yes lady, I had to give up work because I couldn't make both ends meet."
Lady: "What was your work?"
Tramp: "I was a contortionist."

* * * *

Old Gardener: "This yer ole sundial 'as stood 'ere for fower 'undred years."
Fair Tourist: "You don't say! And does it still keep fairly good time?"

* * * *

Judge (after explaining point of law to prisoner): "Now, what would it be termed if I were to strike you in the street and steal your watch?"
Prisoner (old lag): "Suicide, yer 'onour! Suicide!"

* * * *

Teacher (after reading John's essay on electricity): "I see here a reference to 'elastic current.' What do you mean by that?"
John: "'Elastic current' is the Scotsman's unit of electricity."

EASY MONEY

Willie: "I wish I were the gas."
Father: "Why, Willie?"
Willie: "Because every time it goes out it gets a penny."

* * * *

Young Doctor: "I'm afraid I made a mistake in filling in a death certificate to-day."
Old Doctor: "How was that?"
Young Doctor: "I absent-mindedly signed my name in the space left for 'cause of death'."

* * * *

Printer's error: "At 60 miles an hour the express dashed into the cow and literally cut it into calves."

* * * *

A man went up to a railway porter at an important station and said: "There are half a dozen clocks in this place, and they are every one different."
"Well, sir," said the porter, "if they were all alike, one would do!"

* * * *

The chemist was in a bad temper. He had told his assistant to have a sign painted for the outside of his shop, and on seeing it, was furious.
"You're a fool," he said.
"But the sign is beautifully done," said the other.
"It may be," replied the chemist, "but who is going to trade here when our sign reads: 'In making up prescriptions, we dispense with care'."

* * * *

Two tramps found a bottle of wine and retired to a secluded spot to make the best of their good fortune. By the time the bottle was empty both were fit for anything.
"Bill," said one. "I'm going to buy the Johannesburg goldfields."
"But, my dear fellow," replied Bill, with a patronising wave of his arm, "I don't care to sell."

* * * *

Angry editor to reporter: "What do you mean by inserting the expression 'Apple sauce' in parenthesis in my speech?"
Reporter: "Apple sauce? Great Scot, man, I wrote 'Applause'."

* * * *

Humble Guest: "Er—have you ever walked in your sleep, sir?"
Rich Man: "Certainly not. I may have motored."

* * * *

Some men were at work in a large cable pit when an inspector shouted down, "How many of you are there down below?"
"Five," came the answer.
"Well, I want half of you here to give a hand right away!"

* * * *

Teacher: "'I have went.' Is that sentence wrong, Johnny?"
Johnny: "Yes, Ma'am."
Teacher: "Why is it wrong?"
Johnny: "Because you ain't went yet."

* * * *

NOT HIS FAULT

Irate Landowner: "Hi! Can't you see that sign 'Private Property'? Why don't you keep off?"
Horseman (hanging on to runaway horse for dear life): "Don't tell me, tell the horse!"

INDEX

Vol. XXI

Jan.—Dec., 1936

Aeroplanes:—Ag-4 "Crusader," 273; B.A. "Eagle," 142; B.A. "Swallow," 90; Boulton Paul "Overstrand," 200; Bristol 130, 200; Caudron "Aiglon," 519; Caudron "Fregate," 518; Caudron "Luciole," 519; Caudron "Simoun," 519; Cierva Direct-Lifting Autogiro, 558; D.H. "Dragonfly," 334; D.H. 86A Express Air Liner, 335; D.H. "Hornet Moth," 90; Douglas D.C.3 Air Liner, 578; Fairey "Fantome," 395; Fairey "Firefly," 395; Gloster "Gauntlet," 394; Gloster "Gladiator," 395; Handley Page "Heyford," 201; Miles "Merlin," 90; Potez 54, 202
Aircraft Carrier, How Operated, 324
Airmen Return to School, 708
Air News, 18, 88, 142, 202, 272, 322, 378, 444, 502, 578, 630, 690
Airports:—Heston, 144; Le Bourget, 262; Rangoon, 502
Airships:—"Hindenburg," 20, 272
Air Trips:—Amsterdam to Croydon, 692; Belfast to Liverpool, 448
Altitude Record, Sq. Leader Swain Creates New, 623
Anderton Boat Lift, 442
Atlantic Flights, Record, 579
Autoflex Drive Unit, 17

Banana, Story of the, 318
Beam Engines, Historic, 30
Bells, Removing a Peal of, 192
Bidston Observatory, Work of, 132
Black Forest, Afoot in the, 606
Books to Read, 28, 96, 160, 216, 248, 336, 396, 524, 584, 642, 718, 748
Brakes:—Bendix Servo, 149; Westinghouse Automatic for Trailers, 723
Bridges:—Antwerp Bascule, Two Giant, 75; Blowing up a Brick Arch Railway, 516; Brisbane, 260; Building Great, 434; Clifton Suspension, Centenary of, 498; Famous, 130; Little Belt, Denmark, 100; Lower Zambesi Railway, 382; Triborough, N.Y., 616
Bristol Axial Engine, 157

Cable, Laying the Bass Strait, 556
Centrifugal Oil Separators, 362
Cigarette Cards, 702
Clipper Ships of the Pacific, 496
Clock, Interesting Moving Figure, 32
Coaling Large Steamships, 16
Coal Transport in the Midlands, Early, 422
Competition Corner, 65, 126, 186, 246, 306, 363, 423, 487, 551, 607, 671, 747
Competitions, Hornby Railway Company, 58, 120, 180, 240, 300, 360, 420, 484, 544, 604, 665, 741
Concrete Structures, Modern, 700
Conjuring Tricks for Christmas, 686
Cranes and their Work, Floating, 190
Cruising:—Holidays on Great Liners, 375, 570
Crusaders' Castles in the Holy Land, 266
Crushing Machinery, Powerful, 517
Crusoe's Island, Romance of, 70

Diesel Engines for Racing Cars, 104
Differential Unit, Worm Gear, 167

Editor, With the:—British Railways in 1935, 1; Aviation during 1935, 1; Petrol from Coal, 1; Tunnelling Triumphs, 69; King George V, 129; Record Flight of Flt. Lt. T. Rose, 189; An Impression of the "Queen Mary," 189; Duke of Bridgwater and his Canal, 249; Worsley's Unique Clock, 249; Death of A. M. Ampère, 309; "Hindenburg's" Record Flights, 309; Mrs. Mollison's England–Cape and Back Flight, 309; Speeding Up Railway Services, 369; Day Trips by Air, 369; Sir Henry Wellcome, 493; Southampton–Capetown Sea Record, 553; Frank Hornby, 613
Electric Generator, Europe's Largest, 430
Electric Light and Heat Stimulates Plant Growth, 716
Electro-Magnets in Industry, 250
Engineering News, 10, 80, 140, 260, 386, 508, 624, 710
Excavators:—Cableway Draglines, 456; Carryall Scraper, 351; For Work Under Water, 392; Priestman Floating Grab Dredger, 722; Super Trench, 197

Fire Brigades:—Calling the, 526; L.M.S.R. Works, 588
Fire Fighting Machines, Modern, 78
Fireside Fun, 67, 127, 187, 247, 307, 368, 428, 492, 552, 609, 674, 749
Flame Cutting and Profiling Machines, 36
Footplate Runs:—On Irish 2-6-0s, L.M.S.R. (N.C.C.), 4; Belfast to Glasgow, L.M.S.R., 72; Perth to Inverness, "Highland Mail," L.M.S.R., 254; London to Leicester, L.N.E.R. (G.C. Section), 312; London to Folkestone, S.R., 440; Belfast to Cookstown, L.M.S.R. (N.C.C.), 504; Newcastle to Edinburgh, L.N.E.R., 374; Dublin to Belfast, G.N.R., 560; In Holland, 620
Footplate Terms Explained, 506
From Our Readers, 38, 102, 164, 222, 282, 344, 404, 466, 528, 586, 640, 720
Flying Boats:—Clipper Ships of the Pacific, 496; Imperial Airways New Empire, 680; Test Flying Giant Clippers, 432
Furnaces:—Electric, 183, 622

Gears and Gear Units, Making, 82
Gold Digging in East Africa, 210
Grain Discharging from Ships, 500
Gravel Washing and Grading Plant, 146
G.W.R.:—1936 Programme, 92; Record Summer Service, 327

Hacksaw Blades, Making, 342
Heston Airport, 144
Hornby, Frank, 613, 614
Hornby Railway Company, Branch News, 59, 121, 181, 241, 301, 361, 421, 485, 545, 605, 664, 740
Hornby Railways, Special Articles:—Hints for Hornby Railway Owners, 53; New Lighting System for Hornby Accessories, 57; Dinky Toy Road Service, 117; Development of Realistic Layouts, 176; Running an Electric Railway, 236; Circuit Breaker for Electric Layouts, 237; Realistic Layout in Canada, 296; Smoke Deflectors for Hornby Locomotives, 297; Laying An Outdoor Miniature Railway, 356; Using the Two-Train Transformers, 357; Hornby Tank Wagons and their Uses, 416; Extending a Hornby Railway, 480; Hornby Signals and their Uses, 481; Kensington Model Railway, 540; Containers for Hornby Railways, 541; Preparing for Winter Activities, 600; New Hornby High Capacity Wagons, 601; Passenger Trains on Hornby Railways, 660; Cable Drum Transport in Miniature, 661; How to Choose a Hornby Train Set, 736; Hornby Trains in 1936, 737
How Things Are Made:—Cotton Driving Ropes, 626; Gears and Gear Units, 82; Hacksaw Blades, 342; Pencils, 258; Seamless Steel Poles, 446; Spun Iron and Concrete Pipes, 580
How to Get More Fun, H.R.C. Articles:—Electric Railway Operation, 54; Passenger Train Formation, 118; Joint Railway System, 178; Special Freight Working in Miniature, 238; Running Suburban and Local Services, 418; Summer Services on Hornby Railways, 482; L.M.S.R. (G.S.W.R. Section), 542; Container Traffic on Hornby Railways, 602; Station Working on Hornby Railways, 662; Engine Sheds on Hornby Layouts, 738

Iceland, A Holiday in, 563
Iraq Pipeline, Engineer's Journey to the, 26

Lathe, Wickman High Speed, 156
Life-boats, R.N.L.I. Motor, 6
L.M.S.R.:—Electrification of Wirral Railway, 213
L.N.E.R.:—Cinema Coach, 703; Developments, 212, 515; Main Line Electrification, 383; Marshalling Yard at Hessle, 206
Locomotives:—C.N.R. Streamlined, 514; Cleaning, 507; Development on French Railways, 136; G.E.R. "Claud Hamiltons," 24; G.S.R. (Ireland) "Single Wheeler," 101; G.W.R. "Earl" Class, 514; L.M.S.R. "British Legion," 23; L.M.S.R. "Jubilee" class, 139; L.N.E.R. (G.N. Section) Long Lived Express "Atlantics," 86; L.N.E.R. "Green Arrow," 452; Old Locomotives and Where to Find Them, 628; South African Railways New Engines, 270

Machining a 58-Ton Forging, 685
Maoris:—Wood Carving, 435; In New Zealand, 554
Meccano Competition Models:—Arch Bridge, 112; Argentine Railway Station, 113; "Bluebird," 49; B.S.A. Three-Wheeler Car, 596; Dance Band, 353; Dock Scene, 477; Gear Mechanism, 597; Mangle, 537; Motor-Cycle and Sidecar, 233; Naval Gun, 536; Sailing Ship, 352; Searchlight, 537; Sideboard, 173; Skeleton, 413; Small Motor Breakdown Lorry, 173; Tap, 477; Tramcar, 49; Windmill Pump, 48; Wool Carding and Condensing Machine, 233
Meccano Dinky Toys, Fun with, 42
Meccano Games, Amusing, 40
Meccano Guild, Club Notes, 50, 114, 174, 234, 294, 354, 414, 478, 538, 598, 659, 735
Meccano Guild, Secretary's Notes, 51, 115, 175, 235, 295, 355, 415, 479, 539, 599, 658, 734
Meccano Model-Building Contest Results, 49, 117, 173, 233, 293, 353, 413, 477, 537, 597, 657, 731
Meccano Models for Club Exhibitions, 230, 271
Meccano Models, New:—Aeroplanes, 108, 594; Arch Bridge, 535; Barometer, 650; Bicycles, 408; Breakdown Crane, 475; Bridges, 168; Bucket Dredger, 46; Caterpillar Tractor, 474; Chemical Balance, 594; Christmas Models, 728; Cinematograph Camera, 595; Clock, 653; Coal Handling Crane, 595; Countryside Models, 532; Cruising Yacht, 224; Deep Sea Diving Suit, 534; Dog Team, 729; Early Motor Car, 411; Electric Roundabout, 105; Engines, 286; Greek Galley, 733; Lamp, 650; Locomotives, Unusual, 592; Lorry with Searchlight, 733; Meccano in the Home, 650; Motor Ice Yacht, 535; Motor Launch, 534; Paddle Steamer, 654; Pile Driver, 225; "Pterodactyl" Aeroplane, 655; Pumping Engine, 732; Quayside Unloader, 110; Railway Signals, 593; Reindeer Sleigh, 729; Roundabout, 105, 284; "Royal Scot," 291; Seaside Models, 470; Shooting Target, 733; Six-Wheeled Lorry, 170; Skaters, 728; Spinning Mule, 652; Steamships, 44; Submarine, 655; Tail-less Aeroplane, 654; Tank, 475; Telescope, 170; Theatre, 289; Train Ferry, 474; Wall Clock, 531; Watermills, 348; Windmills, 348; Workshops, 228; Wright Biplane, 410
Mechanical Handling of Freight, 177
Model-Builders, With the, 43, 166, 288, 407, 530, 653
Motor Boat's Record Grimsby-Southampton Run, 443
Motor Car Trip from Kenya to Rhodesia, 712

Natural History:—Birds:—Marvels of Migration, 76
Nature at Work and Play, 436
Newfoundland Banksmen, 672
Night Flying: Guiding the Pilot, 204

Of General Interest, 154, 332, 462, 572, 646
Orange Growing in Palestine, 370
Our Busy Inventors, 724
Our Wonderful World, 264, 400, 520

Photography, 321, 424, 488, 648
Pipeline 248 Miles Long, 566
Pipes, Spun Iron and Concrete, Making, 580
Poles, Making Seamless Steel, 446
Post Office Speaking Clock, 458
Puzzles Pages, 68, 695

Railway News, 22, 92, 150, 212, 276, 326, 382, 450, 514, 568, 536, 706
Railways:—Barmen-Elberfeld Overhead, Germany, 12; Building a Railway Footbridge, 215; Cinema Coach, L.M.S.R., 703; Development of Smoke Deflectors, 14; Facts about British, 257; Facts about Railway Wheels, 84; Garden, For Passenger Traffic, 280; Kitchen Cars, 562; Midland and Great Northern Railway, 635; Mountain Railways of Switzerland, 316; Rail Car with Pneumatic Tyres, 271; Railway Electrification Developments, 314; Railway Working in Holland, 620; Sleepers, How Prepared, 152; "Walschaerts-Beames" Valve Gear, 214; Wimbledon Fly-Over, 391
Ray-Controlled Crossing, 403
Refractories in Industry, Importance of, 208
Rivers and Waterfalls, Strange, 94
Road and Track, 194, 340, 438, 574
Road-Breaker, Warsop Self-Contained, 196
Road Construction Machinery, 220
Road, Penyclip Viaduct, 2
Road Testing Machine, 499
Royal Air Force, 618

Salvaging Ships, 198
Sand Rivers of the Zambesi Valley, 274
Sea Trips:—Holyhead to Dun Laoghaire, R.M.S. "Cambria," 310; Glasgow to Ardrishaig, R.M.S. "Lochfyne," 372; Liverpool to Dublin, S.S. "Lady Leinster," 512; Mid-Channel–Havre-Thames, M.V. "Georgic," 632, 682
Shale Oil Industry in Scotland, 638
Shipping News, 268, 454, 564, 698
Ships:—Berthing on Dry Land, 697; "Columba," Passing of the, 308; Dredger "Manga," Suction, 33; "Duntroon," 269; How Launched, 134; "Kala-kala," Streamlined Ferry, 148; Machinery of the "Queen Mary," 678; Motor Boat's Record Grimsby–Southampton Run, 443; Oldest in Southern hemisphere, "Edina," 696; Power Boat for Timor Sea, 268; "Queen Mary," 189, 252, 678; Refloating Sunken Ships, 198; "Royal Ulsterman" and "Royal Scotsman," 455; "Stirling Castle," 269, 553, 699; Southampton-Capetown Record, 553, 699; "William Muir," Veteran Forth Paddle Steamer, 453
Snow Scenes at Hollywood, 634
Something to Think About, 402, 486, 550
Sponges, The Story of, 704
Stamp Articles 61, 123, 183, 243, 303, 365, 489, 547, 611, 667, 743
Steam Tramway Systems, 464
S.R.: Portsmouth Electrification, 276; Progress of Engineering Works, 150
Subsoil Lifting Machine, 37
Suggestions Section:—Aeroplane Modifications, 346; Automatic Dragline Bucket, 591; Automatic Overload Release, 727; Automatic Reversing Gear, 226; Balance and Lever Movement, 347; Bell Striker or Clock Escapement, 227; Bendix Pinion, 226; Clock Escapement, 473; Constantinesco Gear, 727; Electrically-operated Radial Engine, 346; Four-Cylinder Solenoid Engine, 590; Four-Wheel Steering Mechanism, 591; Gearless Reduction Drive, 227; Intermittent Motion, 473; Lightning Arrester, 347; Miscellaneous, 227, 473, 727; Novel Display Mechanism, 473; Off-Set Pawls, 727; Photographic Devices, 472, 590; Remote Control, 106, 107; Retractable Undercarriage, 227; Simple Free Wheel, 591; Torsion Springs, 726; Voting Contest, 107, 347
Sussex Iron Industry, 468
Swamps Turned into Farmland, 722

Tank Lorry for Iranian Oilfields, Straussler, 315, 711
Test Flying Giant Clippers, 432
Testing Steels for Hardness, 270
Television by Cathode Ray, 330
"Things to Come," 510
Tides, Recording and Predicting, 132
Tombs in Central America, 576
Tractor for Launching Life-Boats, R.N.L.I., 684
Traffic Signals in Miniature, 162
Trailer, New Dyson 65-ton, 251
Tramcar, The Story of, 380
Tunnels:—Severn, 494; Dartford-Purfleet, 624; Woodhead Railway, 689

Variable Speed Controller, 350

Waterfalls, Strange Rivers and, 94
Watt, Bi-Centenary of James, 8
Welding Machinery, Electric, 328
Winders for Gold Mines, Electric, 406
World's Queerest Jobs, 376

York Railway Museum, The Fascination of, 388

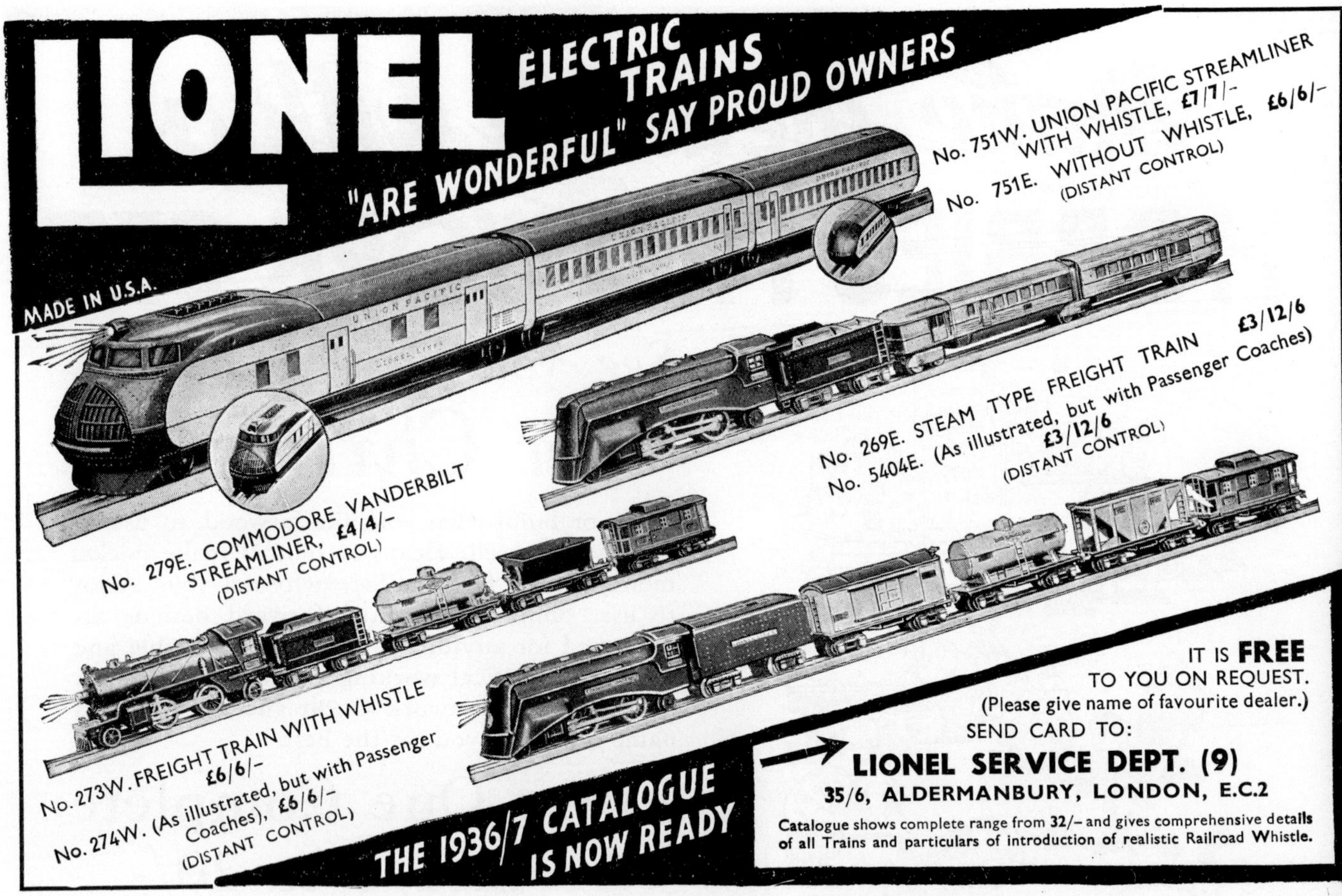

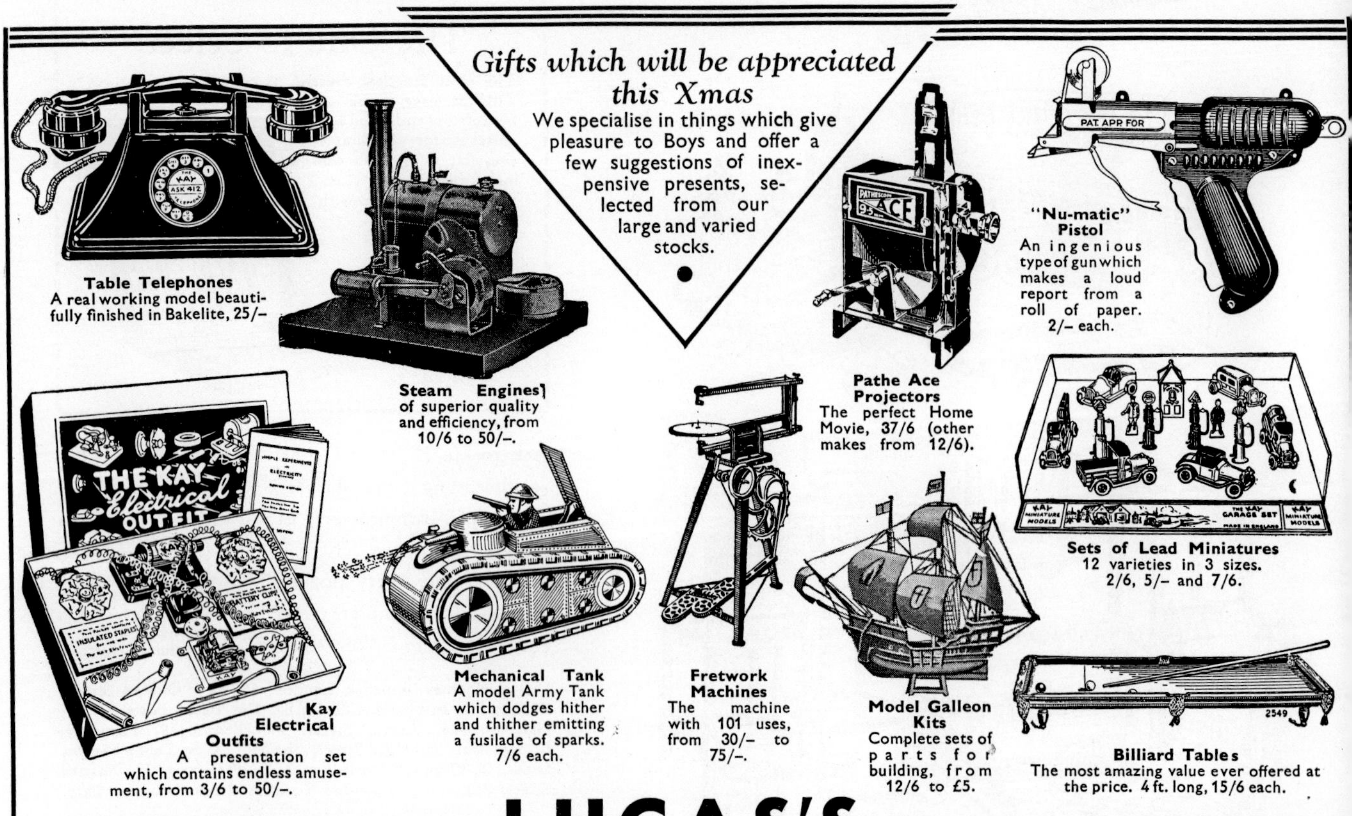

OWN A MODEL OF EYSTON'S FAMOUS RACING CAR

Certificate

1st February 1934

I Hereby Certify that I have examined the clockwork toy "MAGIC MIDGET" manufactured by Lines Brothers Ltd., and that I consider it to be a true and faithful scale model of the famous M.G. MAGIC MIDGET on which I have broken so many baby car records and which was the first baby car to attain a speed of two miles a minute.

(Signed) George Eyston

This is a real scale model of Captain Eyston's record-breaking M.G. Magic Midget—the first Baby car to do over 120 m.p.h.: Eyston, himself, has certified it to be a perfect replica. It looks a speedy car—and it is. Try the Magic Midget out against your friends' racers.

The Magic Midget has an all-steel body with a powerful clockwork motor, rubber wheels with polished aluminium disc. Length 16 *in. Price* **10/6**

Made by the makers of TRI-ANG TOYS under the Supervision of Capt. G. Eyston

MAGIC MIDGET

See the Magic Midget at your toyshop.

LINES BROS. LTD., TRI-ANG WORKS, LONDON, S.W.19

BOND'S

MARKLIN 0-4-0 TANK LOCO
Very Powerful Shunting Tank Loco for **accumulator working only.** Self-reversing.
Price, **Gauge "O"** ... ... 10/6 Postage 9d.
(List Price 16/6)

MARKLIN 4-4-0 EXPRESS LOCOS
Very Powerful Electric Mechanism for **accumulator working only.** Self-reversing.
Price, **Gauge "O"** ... ... **16/6** Postage 9d.
(List Price 28/6)
Price, **Gauge "1"** ... ... **34/-** Postage 1/-
(List Price 63/-)

MARKLIN 4-6-4 EXPRESS TANK LOCO
The most Powerful Clockwork Tank Loco made. Fitted **Speed control,** brake and reverse.
Price, **Gauge "O"** ... ... 30/- Postage 1/-
(List Price 55/-)

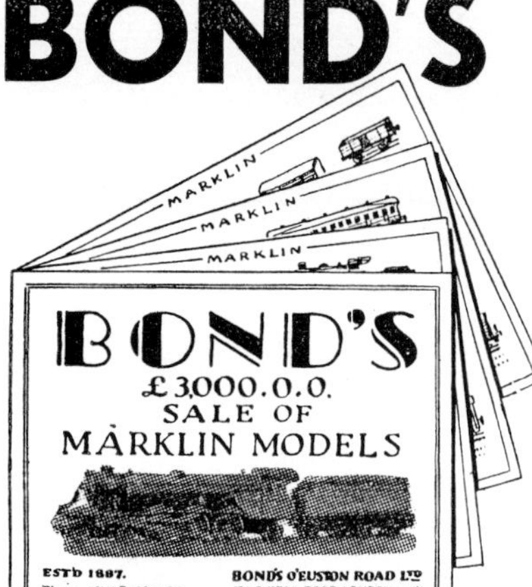

Great Sale of MARKLIN Clock-work, Steam and Electric Locomotives, Coaches, Trucks, etc., for Gauge "O" and Gauge "1."
Nearly all of these Models are being sold at about half the original cost. Send for our Special Free Marklin Catalogue, and be sure to get one of the bargains before stocks are sold out.

MARKLIN 4-6-0 EXPRESS LOCO
A very powerful and long running clockwork Loco, with **speed regulator.**
Price, **Gauge "O," 34/-** Postage 9d. (List Price 63/-)

MARKLIN 0-4-0 TANK LOCOS
Powerful Steam Loco, reversing, piston valve cylinders.
Price, **Gauge "O"** ... ... **18/9** Postage 9d.
(List Price 37/6)
Price, **Gauge "1"** ... ... **33/-** Postage 1/-
(List Price 57/6)
Tender Locos similar to above.
Price, **Gauge "O"** ... ... **15/-** Postage 9d.
(List Price 30/-)
Price, **Gauge "1"** ... ... **28/6** Postage 1/-
(List Price 51/-)

MARKLIN COACHES
All Metal Coaches and Luggage Vans, very strong, mounted on bogies.
Short Coaches, Gauge "O" ... 3/- Postage 6d.
(List Price 4/6)
Gauge "1" ... **5/-** Postage 9d.
(List Price 7/6)
Long Coaches, Gauge "O" ... **5/6** Postage 9d.
(List Price 9/6)
Gauge "1" ... **7/6** Postage 9d.
(List Price 14/6)

Bond's can supply all **Parts** and **Materials** for Model Railways, Boats and Aeroplanes, also all **Tools** to make them with. Send for Bond's Illustrated General Catalogue, **6d.** post free.

Established 1887. **BOND'S O' EUSTON ROAD LTD., 254, EUSTON ROAD, LONDON, N.W.1.** 'Phone: Museum 7137.

Portsmouth to Waterloo on the Footplate

A Farewell to Steam Traction

By a Railway Engineer

DURING the past few years the London-Portsmouth main line of the Southern Railway has witnessed some of the finest work ever done by 4–4–0 locomotives, not only in these islands but anywhere in the world. Here the "Schools" class engines have reached the very zenith of their achievements. Compared with some of the fast schedules operated on the Northern lines, the crack timing of 90 minutes for the 73.6 miles from Waterloo to Portsmouth Town does not seem exciting at first glance, but the route followed is very difficult.

On leaving the West of England main line, at Woking Junction, the line to Portsmouth strikes off due south, and at high altitudes crosses both the North and South Downs before reaching the coast. There are many miles of toilsome ascent at 1 in 80, but worse even than this are the numerous speed restrictions permanently in force. In addition to the severe slowings necessary at Clapham Junction, Woking, Guildford, and Havant, speed has to be very much restrained on some of the steepest descents owing to the numerous curves. Apart from the main line between Clapham Junction and Woking, the only part of the route where engines can be really "let go" downhill is in the deep trough between the North and South Downs, and this stretch is often the scene of thrilling travelling. Yet over such a road as this the "Schools" class locomotives regularly take trains of 350 to 400 tons on the fastest timings.

S.R. 4-4-0 locomotive No. 938, "St. Olave's," of the "Schools" class. This photograph indicates the massive yet handsome proportions of these remarkable engines, which are the heaviest and most powerful 4-4-0s in the British Isles. Photograph by courtesy of the S.R.

But the days of steam traction over this difficult course are numbered, and electrification will be completed this month, in time to handle the vast holiday traffic to and from the Isle of Wight. However much one regrets the superseding of steam locomotives—and in this case regret is made all the keener by the very competence of the "Schools"—this route is pre-eminently suited to electric traction. The great accelerative power of multiple-unit trains will be invaluable in recovering speed from the numerous slacks, and their hill-climbing ability will make for a much more even pace over the steep ups and downs.

The locomotive work done daily is of an extraordinarily high standard; and when recently I was privileged to ride on the footplate from Portsmouth to London the performance rose to heights of brilliance that I have never known equalled with a 4–4–0 engine. The load was right up to maximum, eleven coaches of the very latest stock weighing 360 tons tare; and by the time we left Portsmouth Town station every single seat was taken, making the total load up to 395 tons. The engine was No. 925, *"Cheltenham."* Driver Stares and Fireman Hall of Fratton shed were in charge, and when I joined them at Portsmouth Harbour the former did not seem very happy about things. Almost his first words to me were, "I'm afraid we're not going to do too well." He told me that, in addition to all the regular speed restrictions, no less than four engineering slacks were in force, and I must admit that with such hindrances in store timekeeping seemed out of the question.

We were not due away for 20 minutes, but the time passed quickly. From its elevated position, high above the quayside, Portsmouth Harbour station commands an extensive outlook, and this particular morning I found it irresistibly fascinating. Over the roofs at the dockyard entrance the slender rigging of H.M.S. *"Victory"* rose almost alongside the massive forward tripod of H.M.S. *"Hood,"* and at the quay wall, berthed just astern of the giant battle-cruiser, was the Royal yacht *"Victoria and Albert."* The harbour was alive with ships of all kinds, and lying far up the water, seen against the grey chalk of Portsdown Hill, was the sinister outline of H.M.S. *"Rodney."* By now the S.R. paddle steamer *"Southsea"* was coming through the narrow entrance from Spithead, laden with returning holiday-makers from the Isle of Wight. She was quickly alongside, and soon hundreds of passengers were hurrying for the train. At 10.9 a.m., dead on time, we got the *"right away."*

In response to the driver's skilful touch *"Cheltenham"* made a most impressive start. Sharply curving at first, the line rises at 1 in 87 out of the Harbour station, and then the grade eases to 1 in 245. On this awkward stretch we steadily gathered speed, and so reached the Town station, nine-tenths of a mile, in $3\frac{3}{4}$ minutes. A few minutes standing while many more passengers entrained, and then we were right away indeed, next stop Waterloo. From the moment of starting Driver Stares fixed the cut-off at 29 per cent., and so it remained all the way to London. Never before have I made a run on which no adjustment whatever has been made to the reversing gear; but a still more unusual feature, and one that is an astonishing tribute to the power of the "Schools," is that the driver never used anything but the first valve of the regulator. So that in the description that follows, when I write of regulator openings I am referring always to the first port; the main regulator was not once opened throughout the journey.

We got away from Portsmouth Town in great style and were through Fratton, 0.8 miles, in under two minutes; but then almost immediately came the first slack for permanent way repairs, a long slowing to 15 m.p.h. past Portsmouth aerodrome. We had scarcely regained any speed when Farlington Junction signals were sighted at danger; we crawled up, they just cleared in time, and then Bedhampton "distant" threatened us. Once more we scraped through without having to stop, and *"Cheltenham"* was put to it with some vigour; again it was of no avail, for there was a slow train just ahead, and Havant signals were "on." We crept towards the station, until at last the other train had got clear down the coast line; then we got the road. But by reason of these checks we had taken just over 14 minutes to pass Havant, 7.2 miles out, and were already $4\frac{1}{2}$ minutes late.

Driver Stares now fully opened the first valve, and the engine picked up in magnificent style. From the coastal plain the line rises steeply to the crest of the South Downs near Buriton, and on grades varying between 1 in 150 and 1 in 120 *"Cheltenham"* worked up to 41 m.p.h. From the beautiful wooded country near Rowlands Castle we forged our way up among the hills; speed rose to as much as 45 m.p.h. near Idsworth Crossing, and then we came on to the heaviest part of the ascent—first a mile at 1 in 100, and then nearly two miles at 1 in 80 up a deep valley between Heald Down and West Harting Down. The engine was going grandly, and after the first mile we were still doing 40 m.p.h.; Stares shouted across: "We're alright; she'll do it on the first valve." And *"Cheltenham"* did indeed! After a bank almost as steep as Shap, we came over the top at

25 m.p.h.; but in spite of this splendid climbing we had taken 28 minutes to pass the summit, only 15.6 miles out of Portsmouth.

Buriton however saw the end of slow travelling. In the short tunnel just beyond the crest of the bank Stares brought the regulator back to three-fifths, and the engine dashed away down the falling gradient at such a pace that barely three minutes after leaving the tunnel we were flying through Petersfield at 75 m.p.h. Further acceleration was stayed a moment while we rushed a brief mile rising at 1 in 273, and then once more No. 925 raced away until, at the foot of the bank, near Stodham Crossing, she touched 84 m.p.h.

A Portsmouth express ready to leave Waterloo. The locomotive is "Schools" class No. 931, "King's-Wimbledon." Note the route-indicating discs, the upper one carrying the number of the particular duty on which the engine is engaged.

The climb over the North Downs begins at once; two miles at 1 in 80 checked but little the whirlwind stride of *"Cheltenham,"* and up Liss bank speed did not fall below 52½ m.p.h. Stares had no need to touch the regulator, and with the first valve still only three-fifths open we fairly stormed over the easier part of the climb, past Liphook, going 56 to 64 m.p.h. all the way. The last two miles up to Haslemere summit are at 1 in 100; the western slopes of Hindhead lay on our left, speed began to fall off, but within a mile of the top we were still doing 56 m.p.h. Haslemere station was passed at 50, and we breasted the summit just beyond at 48½ m.p.h.—a really wonderful performance. Over the complete nine miles of ascent, four of which are at 1 in 100, or steeper, we had averaged exactly 60 miles per hour.

Although the regulator was now practically closed, we began the descent towards Guildford in dashing style; the track is winding, however, and several slight touches of the brake were necessary to keep the speed from rising too high. *"Cheltenham"* was a fine riding engine, and although she bucked a certain amount on reverse curves, her motion was as nothing compared to the fiery behaviour of, say, a Great Northern "Atlantic" at speed. We galloped merrily downhill at 70 m.p.h. in the shadow of the Surrey Highlands.

Farther down the bank we got up to 74 m.p.h., but our gay progress was brought to an end approaching Witley, where a 30 m.p.h. slack was in force on account of drainage work under the track. Directly we were over the site Stares opened the first valve fully, and in two miles *"Cheltenham"* had accellerated from 30 to 65 m.p.h.! Further caution was needed through Godalming, however, where the railway winds in serpentine fashion through a narrow glen between the hills. Speed was eased to just under 60 m.p.h., and I had to hang on tight while *"Cheltenham"* bucketed round the curves; but once through Farncombe we went ahead again. Near Peasmarsh Junction another out-of-course slowing was necessary, over a lengthy stretch where relaying was in progress; and instead of doing 70 or so, we ran cautiously at 15 m.p.h. alongside the lush meadows of the Wey valley.

A Portsmouth express hauled by No. 930, "Radley," in beautiful surroundings near Haslemere. The conductor rail for electric traction, to be inaugurated this month, can be seen alongside the running rail.

We had scarcely recovered any speed from the slack when the signals of Guildford threatened us, but after running very cautiously through the long tunnel we got a clear road once more and passed through the station in 57¼ minutes from Portsmouth, 43.3 miles. In spite of the checks at Witley and Peasmarsh we were only 2¼ minutes late. With the first regulator full open we now got away in great style; Worplesdon was passed at 66 m.p.h., and although Woking Junction "distant" was at danger when first sighted it was almost immediately pulled off, and after a careful slowing to 30 m.p.h. round the curve on to the main line, we went ahead in more brilliant style than ever.

Stares did not open out beyond three-quarter regulator, and yet over the gentle ups and downs of the main line the engine developed some really astonishing speed. Less than three miles beyond Woking Junction we were doing 67, and a moment later were tearing past Brooklands race track at 71½ m.p.h. The rise past Weybridge into Oatlands cutting was taken just as though it did not exist; and beyond Walton, on a grade no steeper than 1 in 529, *"Cheltenham"* reached the truly thrilling rate of 77 m.p.h. With such a load as 395 tons this would have been good going for a "Pacific," let alone a 4–4–0! So we passed Hampton Court Junction, 60.3 miles from Portsmouth, in 74¾ minutes, only a little over a minute late.

Sweeping up the rise at 1 in 378 past Surbiton without going below 71 m.p.h., we were running at 72½ m.p.h. on the dead level beyond when the last of the engineering slacks was encountered, a slowing to 20 m.p.h. at the west end of Malden station. But from this check we picked up so brilliantly that, reading my watch approaching Clapham Junction, I wondered whether even yet we might not just scrape into Waterloo on time. From the Malden check we had passed Wimbledon at 53 m.p.h., Earlsfield at 62, and were through Clapham Junction, 69.7 miles from the start, in just 85 minutes. With no further checks we could easily have finished in 91 minutes, or perhaps a trifle less, but as we swung into the straight, colour light signals ahead showed successively double-yellow, single yellow, and red. Stares drew up very slowly, but we were brought to a dead stand at Queens Road, 71 miles from Portsmouth in 87¼ minutes.

At the very instant we stopped the signal cleared. We were not at rest for more than 5 seconds, and then we got away in good style, leaving Nine Elms goods yard on the left and rising high above the house tops towards Vauxhall. The Thames was now close at hand, and across the water were the Houses of Parliament; we neared the terminus. At the time of my trip the vast scheme of re-signalling, with colour light signals, that has so completely revolutionised traffic working in the approaches to Waterloo, was not complete, and within half a mile of journey's end we were yet again brought down to walking pace by adverse signals. However, a second dead stop was just avoided, and passing slowly under the great "A" signal box that used to span nearly all the approach tracks, we stopped at Waterloo in 93¾ minutes from Portsmouth.

By this magnificent running Stares had actually gained nearly a minute on booked time between Havant and Waterloo, in spite of three permanent way checks, one dead stand, and two other delays from adverse signals. In fact the net time for the 73.6 mile run works out at 82 minutes—a remarkable average of 54 m.p.h. It is fortunate to be able to set on record so peerless an example of "Schools" performance; it forms indeed a wonderful farewell to steam on the Portsmouth line.

These pages are reserved for articles from our readers. Contributions not exceeding 500 words in length are invited on any subject of which the writer has special knowledge or experience. These should be written neatly on one side of the paper only, and should be accompanied if possible by original photographs for use as illustrations. Articles published will be paid for. Statements in articles submitted are accepted as being sent in good faith, but the Editor takes no responsibility for their accuracy.

Colonel Lindbergh in Iraq

Colonel Charles Lindbergh, the famous American airman, accompanied by Mrs. Lindbergh, left England last February on an air tour of Europe and the Middle East in his special Miles "Hawk" aeroplane, which is capable of nearly 200 m.p.h. They reached the border of Iraq on 17th February at about 2.30 p.m., passing over Rutbah, a station in the desert, halfway between Damascus and Baghdad. At about 4.30 p.m., when they were within a short distance of Baghdad, they encountered a severe thunderstorm. Visibility was reduced to less than 200 yds., and they were unable to find the Baghdad airport, with the result that they were compelled to return to Rutbah, after making a detour of nearly 600 miles.

Colonel Lindbergh returning to his special Miles "Hawk" aeroplane at Basrah airport, after completing the necessary formalities. Photograph by A. Kouyoumdjian, Baghdad.

They stayed overnight at Rutbah and left next morning for Basrah, where they landed after a flight of 4½ hrs. They stayed only half an hour, but before they resumed their flight I was able to obtain several interesting photographs, one of which is reproduced on this page. From Basrah they went on to India.
A. Kouyoumdjian (Baghdad).

A Trip on the Bergen-Oslo Railway

While on a visit to Norway I travelled by rail from Bergen to Oslo. I am sure that the scenic grandeur of the country through which this line passes is unexcelled in any other part of Europe.

The distance from Bergen to Oslo is about 280 miles and the railway journey takes between 12 and 13 hrs., according to weather conditions. I left Bergen one morning at 8 o'clock in a train consisting of a first, a second and a third class coach and a restaurant car. Immediately after leaving the station we plunged into a series of tunnels and proceeded at a slow speed in the darkness. Suddenly the train emerged into dazzling sunlight, with a sheer drop of 200 ft. from the line to a fiord below. Green fields and pine-covered hills were to be seen on all sides. The farmsteads dotted here and there had grass roofs and carved gables, and the bright red paint of their numerous out-houses emphasised the freshness of the country in which they stood. Soon the train drew into Voss station, and the passengers alighted for a snack at the restaurant.

On resuming our journey the track became steeper and the speed of the train dropped. Trees and shrubs became less abundant, farms disappeared, and on nearing Finse the engine had to plough its way through deep snow. The temperature was 20 deg. F. below zero, and the atmosphere was very bracing. There another stop was made, and on resuming the journey at an altitude of about 4,000 ft. we passed Hardangejöklen, a mountain towering another 2,000 ft. higher. Then we plunged into numerous snowsheds.

Voss station, one of the main stopping points on the Bergen–Oslo railway. Photograph by G. Willis, London.

Finally we reached Gulsvik and there began the descent. Trees and other forms of vegetation reappeared, homesteads came into view and mountain streams raced past as we ran briskly down the beautiful valley of Hollingdal, the engine pounding its way through dense forests on to Roa. Here the line turned south towards Oslo and soon we changed the darkness of the wooded hills for the lights of this ancient city.
G. Willis (London).

In the South Seas

The Cook Islands, about 26 miles north-east of New Zealand, are inhabited by Polynesians. One of the most interesting of these islands is Atiu, which is distinguished from the others by being fringed by the reef that surrounds the group, but is some distance from the shores of the others and entirely detached from them.

While on a visit to Atiu I saw the schooner *"Tiare Taporo"* loading copra, or dried coconut kernels. The name of this vessel means "lemon blossom." The water was too deep for anchorage, so the schooner cruised to and fro, using her auxiliary engine, while the bags of copra were carried by the natives through the surf to the edge of the reef, loaded into surf-boats, and rowed out to the schooner. Often a big wave would sweep the natives off their feet, but this only caused great amusement.

A schooner loading copra at Atiu, one of the Cook Islands. Photograph by L. Franzman, Christchurch, N.Z.

Atiu is connected with an interesting episode of the Great War. The *"Seeadler,"* a German raider, was wrecked on a reef in the South Seas, and had to be abandoned. Count von Luckner, her commander, sailed hundreds of miles in a hastily rigged life-boat, and put in at the island on his way to the Fiji Islands, where he was captured.

L. Franzman (Christchurch, N.Z.).

A South American Railway

I travelled recently by railway in Columbia, and had quite an eventful journey. The railway is about 80 miles long, and the service on it, which has been in operation for about three years, shortens the journey between Bogota, the capital, and the Atlantic coast by an appreciable distance. Before it was built goods were carried part of the way by rail and part by mule.

The railway is built in difficult country, among mountains, where rainy weather causes many landslides. For this reason it is not unusual for a train to be held up a dozen times in a single journey while the track is cleared. There are many sharp curves in the line, and the difficulties sometimes lead to derailments. All engines carry a supply of jacks, wedges and other implements for use in such emergencies. During my own journey on this railway the train was stopped several times by landslides, and on one occasion there was a locomotive derailment. The lower photograph on this page shows the crew levering the engine back on to the track.

A scene on a Columbian railway. Members of the train crew levering a derailed locomotive back on to the track. Photograph by W. B. Smith, Bromborough.

W. B. Smith (Bromborough).

A Visit to Hadrian's Wall

The great wall of stone built by the Emperor Hadrian about 1800 years ago across the narrow neck of the British Isles in order to keep back the savage Picts is a wonderful monument of Roman thoroughness that amply repays the time devoted to a visit.

The wall stretched from the Tyne to the Solway Firth, and many parts of it are still standing to-day. The two main features of interest are the forts or camps at Chesters and Housesteads. The former contains one of the most important collections of Roman antiques in this country, and many interesting facts about the actual building of the wall have been obtained from the inscriptions on the stones taken from it. Excavations have revealed the remains of granaries, ventilated floors, barracks, a general's house and baths; and such things as drainage gutters, the path worn by chariot wheels, and the still firm walls bear witness to the lasting nature of Roman building.

The Roman camp at Housesteads, some distance further west, is even better preserved, and shows the skill of the Roman builders to a much greater extent. In a small museum many interesting altars with well preserved inscriptions can be seen.

The wall between these two forts is only of medium height and it gives some idea of the amount of labour that must have been expended on its construction. For quite a few miles the wall runs along the side of the road, a ditch and rampart being on the other side. The entire wall was 73 miles in length, and there were believed to be 23 forts or stations at intervals along it, in addition to smaller places called mile-castles and watch towers.

The rampart to the south of the road ends when it reaches the edge of the tidal waters at the head of the Solway Firth, but the wall was built for some distance further, along the estuary. This was in order to prevent raiders from the North crossing the tidal flat at low water, or making their way over the Firth in small boats.

It is not known how long the wall stood in its entirety. Most of it disappeared eventually because mediæval builders treated it as a quarry, removing the stones for use in the erection of churches and farmhouses.

L. W. Peck (Thornaby-on-Tees).

"Riding The Cab" of a U.S. Freight Engine

A Day's Run on the *"Sturtevant Patrol"*

By A. C. Kalmbach

THE slowest train on any American railroad is what is known as the "way freight," the workhorse of the iron road; and the most interesting train ride I've ever had was "riding the cab," that is to say on the footplate, of the engine of such a freight train. This journey took 11 hours for the 60 miles from Galewood Yards in Chicago to Sturtevant, a small junction town on the line to Milwaukee, and the railroad was the Chicago, Milwaukee, St. Paul and Pacific, popularly known as the "Milwaukee Road."

On arrival at the starting point of my trip I looked over toward the dozens of yard tracks alongside the main line. The *"Sturtevant Patrol,"* on which I had permission to ride, was one of a dozen or more freight trains all made up, but as yet without locomotives. The caboose, a car with open platforms, has seats and desks inside and has a "cupola," which may be described as a kind of conning tower, for observing the train. It is the travelling office of an American freight train, and there is one at the rear of every regular freight. In the caboose of the *"Sturtevant Patrol"* I presented my credentials to Conductor Edward Bailey, the man in charge of the train. The standard American train crew consists of five men; the "engineer" or driver, the fireman, the front-end brakeman, who rides in the locomotive cab on freight trains and assists in switching work, the rear-end brakeman who rides in the caboose, and the conductor. The brakemen were introduced as Earl Johnson and Paul Penning.

No. 7200, the locomotive on which the trip described in this article was made. The engine is of the 2-8-0 or "Consolidation" wheel arrangement, and is a typical example of the older motive power in use on local duties.

Our time to go was 9.30 a.m., and about five minutes earlier a clink of couplings pushed together and a jolt in the caboose announced that an engine had been coupled on to our string of cars, making them into a train. The locomotive was No. 7200, an old one of the 2–8–0 type, built in 1912 by the American Locomotive Company, with Engineer Daniel Evans and Fireman Abraham Deihl in charge. White flags placed in sockets on each side of the boiler front indicated that we were an "extra," that is a train not running on a regular schedule. We took our train number, as all American extras do, from the locomotive and our direction, becoming *"Extra 7200 west."*

Freight cars being loaded at a country depot. The simple design and construction of this is typical of many similar buildings in the United States.

We were within that section of line known as "yard limits," and so could enter the main line without specific orders, looking out only for regularly-scheduled passenger trains. An upward swing of the conductor's arm from the caboose was our "highball," or starting signal, and after a routine test of the air brakes Evans put the reverse lever down in the forward corner, released the brakes, and eased out the throttle or regulator.

A switch tender or pointsman stepped from his shanty and opened the switch leading to the main line. This was not an important enough point to have a tower, or signal box, and interlocking with switches operated by power or rodding. Scarcely half a mile further on we bounced across the tracks of the intersecting St. Charles Air Line, one of the dozens of connecting railroads which criss-cross Chicago, tieing together the trunk lines and transcontinental railroads that terminate in this city.

At the "wye" or points leading to the main line an interlocking signal stopped us and we waited until train No. 5 for Milwaukee sped by. Green flags on the front of the boiler of its engine indicated that a second section was following, but the towerman handed a "fistfull of tissue paper" up to Engineer Evans, giving him his running orders. The first one said "Second 5, run 3 hr. 10 min. late," so we knew we had that much time before the second section came. The timetable showed one hour and a half before the next regular train, No. 21, so on the lifting of the signal we pulled out onto the main line and our real work of picking up, setting off, and "switching," or shunting freight vehicles began.

The train consisted of only 23 cars or wagons at the start, but was varied in composition, including box cars or goods vans of lumber and general merchandise, several tank cars of oil or gasoline, that is, petrol, open gondola cars of coal, and a flat car loaded with farm machinery. Then back at the rear next to the caboose was the "way car," filled with small lots of freight that were not enough to make carload shipments and so would be individually unloaded at the proper stations.

Stops were so frequent that our usual running speed between them was only 20 m.p.h. The first stop was at Forest Glen, about four miles from the point where we entered the main line. There I learned that we had much more work to do than the mere dropping of freight cars and the picking up of other loads or empty cars. Evans stopped the train with the way car right in front of the station, and the rear-end brakeman and the conductor started unloading the small freight. The first two cars behind the engine were consigned to Forest Glen, and so while the rear-end men were busy, the front-end brakeman uncoupled these cars and they were pulled ahead of the siding switch and backed in.

Conductor Bailey then said to the engineer, "The agent wants you to run up to the lumber yard and move a car they're unloading." We crossed to the other main track, ran up it a few hundred yards to a siding leading into a large lumber yard, and while the brakeman unlocked and opened the switch Bailey explained to me that at each local station we were under orders from the stationmaster, or agent. In this instance the lumber yard owner had telephoned the station that he wanted the switching done, and the agent ordered us to do it. Later the agent would send a bill to the lumber yard for our services.

We didn't pick up the several empty cars in the station yard, but started right up the line for the next stop, Morton Grove. "This is Monday, our busy day," explained Fireman Deihl, "and so we're only doing necessary work. We'll pick those empty cars up on our way back to-morrow, when we have more time."

The track ahead stretched out straight and clear, a perfect speedway for the Milwaukee-bound passenger flyers, which skim over it at 80 to 90 m.p.h. We didn't skim, however; instead we just plugged along up to Morton Grove Station. There two empty coal cars were to be picked up; they were placed so that they came ahead of us when the engine entered the siding where they were standing. How could we get them behind the engine where they belonged in the train? A "flying switch" was the answer. We coupled up to them and backed toward the siding points, gathering speed until just before the points Evans made a sudden brake application and Johnson at once lifted the uncoupling bar. Then, with opened throttle, we gathered speed while the cars lagged behind. Brakeman Penning threw the points between locomotive and cars, and these were switched on to the main line, in a position where we could back on to them from the siding. Again and again through the day this flying switch method was used to transpose cars and engine.

An interesting view of a typical freight train operation in the United States, showing a G.N.R. train of this kind entering the yard at Seattle. Photograph by W. Hendry, Vancouver.

The work at Morton Grove finished, we pulled ahead two miles to Golf. Beyond this small suburban station the railroad and state were building a bridge to eliminate a dangerous highway crossing. The station agent asked us to run up to the construction work and help unload and shift some cars of gravel being used for the concrete. We pulled up on the construction siding, and because it was nearly time for passenger train No. 21 to come up the main line, we pulled our train into the siding with us, and carefully locked the switch after us. Had we left it set for the siding the automatic block signals on the main line would have indicated "*caution*" two miles away, and "*stop*" at the signal nearest the switch.

Several cars of gravel were moved to better positions, some full cars were substituted for empties, and several nearly-empty bottom-discharging cars were shaken free of their remaining contents by the simple process of leaving the throttle partly open and continuously pulling the reverse lever from one end of the quadrant to the other. While this work was going on, No. 21 passed and we were then free to unlock the switch, back on to the main line and proceed to Glenview, where there was the usual routine station and private siding switching and unloading to be done.

Rear view of a caboose, or "travelling office," of a freight train. Windows in the raised portion of the roof enable the conductor to observe the running of the train.

It was nearly lunch time and we had been on the road some three hours. As we plugged out of Glenview, engineer and fireman agreed that we had better go in the siding up at the brick factory a short distance along and eat lunch at a restaurant there while "Second 5" and No. 101, the "*Hiawatha*," went by. The crack "*Hiawatha*," streamlined steam speedster of the Chicago-Minneapolis service, soon flashed by with its 430-ton train at about 100 m.p.h. We pulled out of the siding, leaving two loaded cars consigned to that point, and went on to Deerfield. At Deerfield we had a considerable amount of switching work to do, and several loaded cars to pick up. By now the cars we had been picking up exceeded in number those we had left behind, and our load had grown to 34 cars.

Eventually we reached Roundout, a junction point with a branch line and also with the Chicago Outer Belt Line. There we spent more than an hour shunting cars around on yard tracks; the empties left were to be picked up by an evening train and taken into Chicago, the loads allocated to the proper tracks for transfer or pickup by through trains.

We had a car of flour for delivery at a macaroni factory four miles down the branch line at Libertyville, so we had to arrange for train orders to permit us to go off the main line. The conductor went up in the interlocking tower and the towerman telephoned the dispatcher at Milwaukee. Running orders were then issued allowing us to travel over the single track branch to Libertyville and back. But not until we had waited for No. 139, a suburban passenger train.

Leaving caboose and train at Roundout we started off for Libertyville with the locomotive and the car of flour, all five of the crew and myself in the cab. The ride was fast and rough, for this old "Consolidation" type engine was not built for smooth travelling. The car of flour was left at an unloading platform and two empties were picked up by the "Dutch switch" method, using a favourable grade to let a car coast into position behind the engine.

Back at Roundout we found it was nearly six o'clock. when regular hours expired and overtime started for the crew. So Conductor Bailey figured that, since we had 30 miles still to cover, we had better do only the necessary work and leave the odds and ends for the next day. After waiting 10 minutes for No. 9 to pass us, we started off for Gurney, seven miles away, to pick up a car of stock. Stock must be watered at regular intervals, and the railroad company is responsible for it under very strict federal law while it is in the company's charge. There we also had to unload several hundred pounds of miscellaneous farm implements from the way car.

Meanwhile Bailey had told the trainmaster by telephone of our intention to cut the work short in order to save overtime. As we had only half an hour before No. 11, a through passenger train, was due, the crew decided to go to Ranney, 13 miles ahead, where the siding switches were power-operated from a tower and it was easy to "go in the hole," or clear the main line by getting in a siding.

With time short our only really good show of running all day was on the 13 miles to Ranney, which were covered in just 25 minutes. The reverse lever was hooked up almost to mid-gear and the throttle was kept about half open. Between watching signals Fireman Deihl spent all his time with the fire, and kept the gauge on the mark at 180 lb. We had just pulled into the siding at Ranney when the headlight of No. 11 appeared. This is a named train, known as "*The Sioux*," running out to the country along the Missouri River in South Dakota, and carries Pullman sleepers in addition to the usual coaches, diners, and baggage and mail cars.

As we pulled out of the siding, ahead of us stretched the 10-mile tangent to Sturtevant. The three-unit Sturtevant home signal grew closer and closer, and the centre light changed to green; we slowed down to move gently over the switches into the Sturtevant yard.

Engineer and conductor went through the formality of signing the train register in the station to prove their arrival and time of arrival. Then they uncoupled the caboose, pushed it up a slight rise in the yard track, and let it coast back and into a small stub track in a quiet location, a perfect Dutch switch. Regular sleeping car berths came down from the ceiling and the caboose was ready to serve as the night's lodging place for the crew.

BRAIN-WAVE

"Yes," the teacher explained, "quite a number of plants and flowers have the prefix 'dog.' For instance, the dog-rose and the dog-violet are well known. Can you name another?"

There was silence, then a bright boy put up his hand.

"Please, miss," he called, "collie-flower."

* * * *

Hiker: "What do you often find at the end of a long tramp?"

Farmer: "His feet."

* * * *

Teacher: "Now, if I subtract 25 from 37, what's the difference?"

Willie: "That's what I say. Who cares?"

* * * *

A man went to a doctor and complained about seeing spots in front of his eyes. He was advised to get glasses.

Later he met the doctor, who asked if his eyes were improving.

"Yes," said the man. "The glasses are great. I can see the spots plainer now."

* * * *

A boy applied for a job. "Have you any ambition"? asked the manager.

"Ambition?" replied the boy, "I shall never rest until I am in that chair."

* * * *

Mother: "You didn't ask for a second piece of cake at the party, did you, Sonny?"

Jack: "No, Mummy; I just asked Mrs. Green for the recipe so that you could make some like it, and she gave me another piece without my asking for it."

* * * *

Jack: "Teacher said that I'm likely to go down in history."

Father: "That's fine, my boy."

Jack: "But he said I should do better in geography, arithmetic, and English."

* * * *

Schoolmaster: "When and where did William the Conqueror land in Britain?"

Dense pupil: "Don't know, sir."

Master: "What? Don't know when William the Conqueror landed? Hastings, 1066."

Pupil: "Oh, I thought that was his telephone number."

* * * *

"I lost half-a-crown this morning, George."

"That's bad luck. Hole in your pocket?"

"No—the man who dropped it heard it fall."

* * * *

"Tommy, what is a synonym?" the teacher asked.

"A synonym," said Tommy, "is a word you use when you can't spell the other one."

* * * *

Patient: "All that's troubling me now, doctor, is my breath."

Doctor: "Well, don't trouble about that. I'll give you something that will take it away."

* * * *

Keeper: "Hi! Keep away from that elephant!"

Small Boy: "Garn, I'm not 'urtin' him!"

* * * *

Tommy: "Gee, dad, there's a man at the circus who jumps up on a horse's back, slips underneath, catches hold of its tail, and finishes up on its neck."

Dad: "That's easy! Why, I did all that the first time I was on a horse."

* * * *

"Thank you for the presents, auntie."

"Oh, they are nothing to thank me for."

"That's what I thought, but mother told me to thank you all the same."

* * * *

A meek little man was in court for a minor offence.

"Were you ever in trouble before?" asked the Judge.

"Well, er-er," was the hesitating response, "I kept a library book too long once, and was fined threepence."

* * * *

"I've been trying to think of a word for two weeks."

"How about fortnight?"

HONEST

Farmer Brown: "Some dogs have more intelligence than their owners."

Willum: "You're right there, sir, I've got one of that sort myself."

* * * *

Diner: "I say, waiter, bring my hat."

Waiter: "It's on your head, sir."

Diner: "Don't bother, then—I'll look for it myself."

"A little over zealous, are we not, Ramsbotham?"

(*By courtesy of "The Storyteller."*)

(*Block reproduced by courtesy of "The Railway Gazette."*)

Freddie: "How many of these sweets do I get for a penny, please?"

Assistant: "Oh, six or seven."

Freddie: "I'll have seven, please."

* * * *

Master (looking up sternly from his desk): "Did I hear you laugh, Willie?"

Willie: "Please, sir, I was smiling when the smile burst."

* * * *

Judge: "I've lost my hat."

Lawyer: "That's nothing. I lost a suit here yesterday."

* * * *

Manager of football team: "I've found the very man we want. Eye like a hawk, body like a bullock, speed of a racehorse, kick like a mule."

Captain: "It's a forward we want, not a farmyard."

SALESMANSHIP

Urchin: "Have you got a match, please?"

Gentleman: "No, I haven't!"

Urchin: "Well, here you are, sir. Penny a box!"

* * * *

Landlady: "A professor formerly occupied this room, sir. He invented an explosive."

New Lodger: "Ah! I suppose those spots on the ceiling are the explosive."

Landlady: "No; they're the professor."

* * * *

She: "Are these field glasses high powered?"

He: "Rather! When you look at something less than ten miles away it looks as if it's behind you."

* * * *

Estate Agent: "There's not a flaw in the entire house."

Customer: "But what do you walk on?"

* * * *

"Why did you rob this man in broad daylight?"

"Well, you see, all my dates for night work were filled up!"

* * * *

The new recruit passed an officer without saluting.

"Here, my man," called the officer, "do you see this uniform I'm wearing?"

"Yes, sir; and just look at this thing they gave me."

* * * *

Teacher: "So you are the boy who wrote on the board, 'Teacher is a fool'?"

Tommy: "Yes."

Teacher: "Well, at least I am glad you have told me the truth."

* * * *

Teacher: "George, who defeated the Philistines?"

George: "I don't know, I only follow the first league teams."

* * * *

Plumber (at 'phone): "What's that? A leak in the water pipe? Well keep yer 'and over it. And just 'ang on a minute and I'll tell yer what day I can come."

* * * *

Taxi-driver: "Say, mister, the brakes won't take; I can't stop the car!"

Passenger (anxiously): "For goodness sake stop the meter, anyway."

* * * *

Tourist (in French restaurant): "I want some mushrooms."

Waiter: "Pardon. I not understand."

Taking a paper the tourist drew a sketch of a mushroom.

The waiter beamed with intelligence and rushed to execute the order. In a few minutes he returned with—an umbrella!

* * * *

Magistrate: "So you broke into a tobacconist's shop just to get a sixpenny cigar. Then what were you doing at the safe?"

Prisoner: "I was putting in the sixpence."

* * * *

An old lady who had been making a call from a telephone kiosk for the first time had given the operator a deal of trouble. At the end of the conversation she apologised profusely to the operator and added, "I have put sixpence in the slot for yourself."

* * * *

There was a young fellow named Lee,
Who fell from a very high tree:
His nose hit the ground
With a musical sound
And broke a large boulder in three.

* * * *

Passing through a village street a recruiting sergeant met a young farmhand delivering milk.

"Now, my lad, wouldn't you like to serve the King?" asked the recruiting sergeant.

"I would, mister," replied the other, "but I can only let him have a quart at night an' a pint in the morning."

HIGH PERFORMANCE SAILPLANE

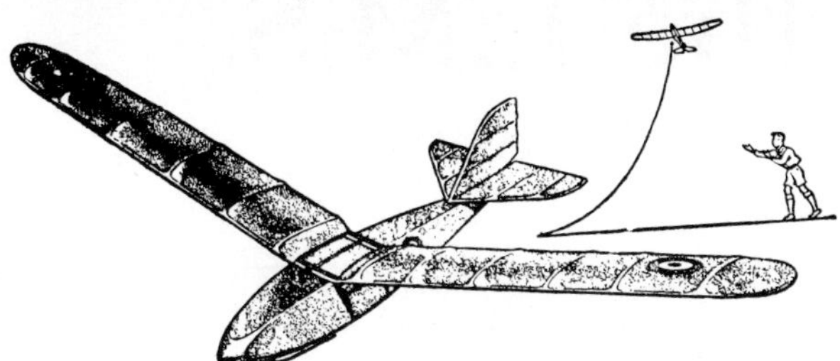

This splendid model from the **SCUD** range performs exactly like a full-scale Sailplane. It is the only British-made machine of its type made, and when correctly trimmed and under suitable weather conditions has soaring flight of up to ten minutes. This is definitely the machine for the enthusiast and will provide hours of instructive flying. **No propeller to wind. Nothing mechanical to go wrong.** Totally enclosed fuselage, mainplane and tail unit double surfaced, covered jap silk and doped silver. Skid under-carriage. Includes new catapult launching gear. Gliding angle in calm air, 1 in 15. Span 38". Price **17s. 6d.**

SEND NOW FOR ILLUSTRATED CATALOGUE DESCRIBING OUR 1937 RANGE

Stocked by leading dealers throughout the kingdom

SCUD MODELS LTD.
Lovaine Crescent Model Works, Newcastle-upon-Tyne

● ALL GAUGE 'OO' RAILWAYMEN

will be interested in our new series of lineside models. In addition to essential models such as stations, goods depots, etc., we are making many new ones as standard productions, including factory, power station, advertisement hoarding, village inn, sand and cement depot, etc., etc. Every building is a hand-made copy of the real thing, built by expert workmen with years of experience.

● GAUGE 'O' EXPERTS AND THOSE MODEL ENTHUSIASTS WHO ARE NOT SO KEEN ON RAILWAYS, BUT WANT MODEL FARM YARD BUILDINGS, BARRACKS, ARMY HUTS OR EVEN SANDBAGS AND GUN EMPLACEMENTS—ALL ARE CATERED FOR.

Write for our free catalogue and price list. Ask your local dealer to show you the latest HUGAR Models.

THE MODELS RANGE IN PRICE FROM 6D. TO 22/6

HUGAR MODELS LIMITED
SOUTH STREET, EPSOM, SURREY

The amazing popularity of the "OO" gauge TWIN TRAINS in England has prompted us to go into the question of a "Scale Model" in gauge "OO," and, in collaboration with the Southern Railway, this model of the latest Southern Electric stock, used on the new London-Portsmouth line, has been produced.

The outfit is a most attractive one consisting of a Third-Class Model Motor Coach (7" long) working off 14 volts a.c. and 12 volts d.c., two Bogie Coaches (6¾" long, First-Class Corridor and Brake Third), Oval Track 28" x 42½", Controller, complete with automatic cutout, Lubricating Oil, Connections and Book of Instructions.

In special presentation box, with label designed by the Southern Railway. Price **55/-.**

Additional Coaches available. Brake Third, or Restaurant Car, **3/6** each.

For Rails, Points and other accessories, see the BASSETT-LOWKE TWIN TRAIN FOLDER, TT/17, free and post free. Gauge "OO" booklet F.B.17 also free.

6d. large catalogues. **A.17.** Model Railways. **B.17.** Model Engines. **S.17.** Model Ships.

BASSETT-LOWKE LTD.
NORTHAMPTON London: 112, High Holborn, W.C.1 Manchester: 28, Corporation Street

114 m.p.h. on the L.M.S.

"The Coronation Scot's" Great Runs

By a Railway Engineer

THE L.M.S. streamlined era began most auspiciously on Tuesday, 29th June, when *"The Coronation Scot"* made a trial run from Euston to Crewe and back. The Editor of the *"M.M."* and I were privileged to travel by the train on this notable occasion, and to witness the attainment of the highest railway speed yet recorded in the British Empire—114 m.p.h. The record was however wrested from the L.N.E.R. streamlined engine *"Silver Fox"* only by the slender margin of 1 m.p.h., and the very closeness of the figures has made inevitable the keenest discussion on the relative merits of the rival engines.

Shortly after the event two young enthusiasts in hot debate on the subject appealed to me, and both, I fear, were a little taken back by my answer. The conditions on different lines are so dissimilar that one cannot possibly judge the relative merits of the rival engines on two isolated spurts such as these; but wherever run, speeds of over 110 m.p.h. bespeak a superbly designed locomotive. Although the two types differ considerably in principle, in detail, and last but not least in the shape of the streamlined casing, the honours are just about even when it comes to actual performance on the road.

At the same time the trial of *"The Coronation Scot"* was a very remarkable affair. Up till then the L.M.S. had never once claimed a maximum speed of 100 m.p.h. or more, although I believe it had been slightly exceeded on certain braking trials; whereas the L.N.E.R. have registered successively 100, 108, 112½, and finally the 113 m.p.h. of *"Silver Fox."* To break the record at the very first attempt was no mean achievement on the part of *"Coronation"* and her crew, and it was the result of a perfectly astounding acceleration in which speed rose from 85 to 114 in just eight miles!

The L.M.S. "Coronation Scot" near Queen's Park on the down run during the trial trip described in this article.

But I am discussing the results before the run itself. A load of eight coaches was taken, 263 tons tare and 270 tons with passengers. Nearly all the highest officials of the L.M.S. were on board, including Mr. W. A. Stanier, Chief Mechanical Engineer and designer of the engine and train, and Mr. F. A. Lemon, Works Manager at Crewe, under whose supervision the engine was built. *"Coronation"* was manned by Driver T. Clarke, best known of all L.M.S. enginemen to *"M.M."* readers, and Fireman Lewis, of Crewe; while with them on the footplate rode Mr. R. A. Riddles, Principal Assistant to the Chief Mechanical Engineer, and Inspector Miller of Willesden.

The special—"W.700" was our official designation—was booked to start at 9.50 a.m. but before we got away there was just time to go up on to the footplate and have a good look round. The cab arrangements are very similar to those of the "Princess Royals"; there is the same splendid view ahead from the cab glasses, though it seemed unusual to look out past a huge sloping blue wall. By far the most interesting feature of the cab fittings is the Hasler speed indicator, which is fixed just over the top of the reversing gear, right in front of the driver. This is of the Teloc type, and not only indicates the speed at any moment, but also the time the engine has been at work and the distance covered.

We made a beautiful start. *"The Coronation Scot"* went out of Euston with the smooth quiet efficiency of an electric train, and, accelerating in remarkable style up such a gradient, we topped Camden bank at exactly 30 m.p.h. Then, after taking the salute of crowds of waving, cheering enginemen as we passed Camden Sheds, Driver Clarke set about things in earnest. But although the acceleration out of Willesden was totally unlike that of any other train, it was not until we were through that junction that *"Coronation"* began to develop some real pace. We were then doing 65, but two miles farther on we were up to 76, and from that the engine steadily accelerated to 82 m.p.h. up the long, 1 in 335 rise past Harrow. Watford, 17½ miles, was passed in the unprecedented time of 17 minutes, at 87½ m.p.h., and speed then settled down to a steady 80 to 81 m.p.h., on the ascent to Tring. There was a momentary drop to 79 in Northchurch tunnel, but apart from that we never went below 80 all the way up. Schedule time for the 31.7 miles from Euston to Tring was 30 minutes, but on passing the summit we were already 2¼ minutes early.

From this point onward the special schedule was fairly closely observed and the speed became rather more moderate. At several places, such as Linslade tunnel and through Wolverton, considerable reduction of speed had to be made on account of curves, and there was the usual 40 m.p.h. slack through Rugby; but on the other hand the Polesworth colliery district, which used to necessitate a 30 m.p.h. slowing on account of subsidences, is now de-restricted since the taking over of the pits by the railway company. The pace descended from the 80-85 m.p.h. order to a general average of 72-77, and caused the Editor to remark jokingly: "This is a very slow train!" And slow the pace seemed after that brillant start, although in point of fact we covered the 101.9 miles from Tring to Stafford in 82¼ minutes, an average of 74.5 m.p.h.

During this period I was very interested to observe how the exhaust steam was being thrown high over the carriage roofs. We were travelling in the front coach, and a time of fairly easy running was one in which some beating down of the steam might have been expected, especially as we were travelling against a stiff breeze on a day of somewhat humid atmosphere.

When *"Coronation"* first appeared, the shape of her streamlined casing was the subject of considerable comment. On the L.N.E.R. the external front-end of the "Silver Links" was specially constructed of a wedge shape in order to throw the exhaust clear; it is indeed more an aerodynamic device to create the air currents necessary for smoke deflection than true streamlining. It is for this reason that the same shaped front was applied to the latest Mikado engines, as in their case the advantages of streamlining as such would be negligible at the moderate speeds run over the Edinburgh-Aberdeen route. *"Coronation,"* however, is truly streamlined, that is her front end is designed to provide the least possible resistance to passage through the air. It was certainly very successful on the test runs, but it will be interesting to see what happens on such stretches as from Shap down to Carlisle, where the engine will be running for miles with the regulator in the drifting position, and scarcely any blast.

Now we were approaching the climax of the run, and it was not merely a wonderful demonstration of locomotive ability, but was also a piece of first-rate stage management. We rode gently round the curve at Trent Valley Junction, doing only 30 m.p.h.–10 m.p.h. under the speed limit—and went through Stafford five minutes early, having run the 133.6 miles from Euston in 110 minutes. Then, without a sound from the engine, we recovered speed in most leisurely style, passing Great Bridgeford at only 58½ m.p.h. At Norton Bridge, however, now just ahead, there is a speed limit of 60 m.p.h.

We waited almost impatiently for Norton Bridge to be cleared, and after we were over the junction there was still not a sound from the engine. But then, quite stealthily it seemed, things began to happen; my stop-watch readings for the quarter-miles lessened rapidly, and although we were climbing a very gradual incline, 1 in 650, we were soon doing 80 m.p.h. A steepening of the grade to 1 in 398 made no difference now, the pace went on quickening until we swept over Whitmore summit at exactly 85 m.p.h. There was now just a suspicion of a purr from the engine, it might have been the exhaust and might not; but be that as it may, the next few minutes were simply electrifying.

Passing Kenton on the up run, from Crewe to Euston. The speed at this point was 96 m.p.h.

It was all over so quickly that one formed no lasting impression. I was dimly conscious of the coach swaying gently from side to side; of the wheel beats coming faster and faster; of the Editor sitting opposite waiting almost breathlessly for me to call out the result of each stop watch reading; all the time my face was glued to the window sighting and clocking the whizzing mile-posts. Madeley, 2.6 miles beyond Whitmore, was passed at 97 m.p.h.; another mile and we were over the hundred; and from that, faster and faster, until I clocked two successive half-miles in precisely 16 seconds—112½ m.p.h.! Then we were tearing past Crewe sorting sidings, braking hard, and a moment later were at rest in the station. As soon as possible I was in the next compartment to compare watches with the official L.M.S. observers and that most expert of train timers, Mr. Cecil J. Allen. Our readings agreed to the nearest tenth of a second!

There is however always a possibility of a peak speed occurring between two stop-watch readings, and on this evidence the speed had almost certainly touched 113 m.p.h., and so tied with *"Silver Fox's"* record. On this trip it actually happened so, only the peak was higher than we first thought. When the chart on the speed recorder of the engine was examined, the top speed was shown clearly and indisputably to be 114 m.p.h.! In the thrill and excitement of record-breaking, however, what was perhaps the most astonishing feat of all was overlooked—we accelerated from 85 to 114 m.p.h. in *less than eight miles!* In view of these staggering feats of speed the fact that we made the fastest run ever known from London to Crewe was of incidental interest only; the 158.1 miles were completed in 129¾ minutes, an average of 73 m.p.h. from start to stop.

Apart from the record-breaking finish of the down journey, the finest running occurred on the return trip; there were no easy spells this time, and but for the observance of service slacks speed was maintained at or about 90 m.p.h. for the whole distance. From the various slowings there were some truly amazing accelerations, and the run is not only by far the fastest that has ever been made in this country over such a distance, but it also carries off the world record for steam traction in this respect.

We started away from Crewe in thrilling style, and up the 1 in 177 gradient of Madeley bank went merrily at 74 m.p.h.; hitherto we should have considered 60 m.p.h. brilliant here, even on such a celebrity as the *"Liverpool Flyer."* Before Norton Bridge 90 m.p.h. was reached, braking to 75 for the junction seemed like a severe slack for adverse signals, and we were through Stafford 24½ miles in a shade under 21 minutes. Passing over Trent Valley Junction at 30 m.p.h., Driver Clarke then treated us to an almost uncanny acceleration, for we entered Shugborough tunnel, 3¼ miles beyond the junction, at 81 m.p.h. We braked hard to 71 in readiness for the curve at Colwich, and then came a tremendous spell of sustained high-speed running.

We reached 90 m.p.h. at Rugeley, 92½ through Lichfield, an easing to 78 past the Polesworth collieries, and then, after a rapid acceleration on the up grades beyond, we had the unique experience of having to slacken severely for the curve through Atherstone. It was the same at several other points on the route, places that up to now have never been considered as "curves," but which require careful negotiation at such speeds as *"Coronation"* was now making. It took just four miles of level track for the engine to recover from 71 to 90 m.p.h.; Nuneaton, 60.9 miles from Crewe, was passed in 48½ minutes, and after a burst at 93½ beyond Shilton we were through Rugby in under the hour, the 75.5 miles having been wiped off in the remarkable time of 59½ minutes.

The 40 m.p.h. speed restriction through Rugby was most carefully observed, and then record-breaking was renewed with a vengeance. After a lightning acceleration to 75 m.p.h. up the rise to Kilsby tunnel, we were soon travelling at 90 m.p.h. again; indeed there was not one single piece of level or favourable road where we did not reach or exceed the ninety rate.

Back at Euston after covering the 158.1 miles from Crewe at an average speed of 80 m.p.h.

The running over the last 60 miles was a fitting climax to the day's proceedings. Over Castlethorpe troughs at exactly 100 m.p.h.; up the gentle rise past Bletchley going 89–93 m.p.h., and then a steady 87 m.p.h. up to Tring. At King's Langley speed was up to 99, and after easing to 84 through Watford tunnel *"Coronation"* wound up with a joyous 96 m.p.h. approaching Wembley. Sweeping through Willesden Junction at 85 m.p.h., we were still doing 80 at Kilburn, but the brakes were on hard when we entered Primrose Hill tunnel, and we emerged at a bare 40 m.p.h. to receive the cheers of Camden shed. So down the bank and into Euston, to complete the 158.1 miles from Crewe in the truly record time of 119 minutes.

During that amazing last lap the 57.4 miles from Blisworth to Willesden were reeled off in 38 minutes 26 seconds, an average of 89.8 m.p.h. throughout; while for 151 miles, from Betley Road to South Hampstead, speed averaged just 83 m.p.h.!

It only remains to add that the engine was in perfect trim on arrival. As for the bearings and moving parts, well, I felt the left-hand outside big-end, and the piston rod; they were both dead cold. A superb locomotive performance, and one of which Mr. W. A. Stanier, the men who built the engine, and Driver Clarke and Fireman Lewis have every reason to be proud.

Inventions of the Future

Power from the Wind and the Sun

By I. O. Evans

THERE is one important respect in which our civilisation is different from that of our ancestors, and this is in the use of energy. The people of old had few sources of power. They used windmills and waterwheels, but on a very small scale, and only for driving simple machines such as hammers, that could be attached to them. They had no means at all of transmitting power from place to place, and the greater part of their work had to be carried out by animal or human toil.

To-day the labour of beast and man plays a comparatively small part in our work, and for almost all our more important tasks we make use of machines. In place of the galley with its lines of toiling rowers we have the steamship, and the horse-driven coach has given way to the locomotive and the petrol-driven car. Mechanical harvesters reap and thresh the corn, steam-navvies dig into the ground; and we are continually reading that a new machine has been invented to perform some difficult task previously carried out by hand.

The Shuman-Boys solar heater at Meadi, near Cairo, Egypt. The parabolic mirrors reflected the Sun's rays on long thin tubes or boilers, and the power output of the plant was about 55 h.p.

To drive these machines we have one great source of power, the fuel we derive from the earth. Apart from a few machines worked by river or by wind, we drive them by burning petrol, oil, or coal. There may be unknown sources of these yet to be discovered, hidden by the tropical forests or buried beneath the Antarctic snows, but supplies are bound to be limited, however great they may be. What is to happen when we have exhausted them? Without fuel or something to replace it, our civilisation would come to a tragic end. Great cities would perish for lack of food if there were no mechanical transport, and if civilisation of any sort were to last it would be an agricultural one depending on human and animal muscle like the civilisations of the past, unable to support a population as great as that of to-day.

This is a very tragic prospect, but fortunately there are other sources of energy to which we could turn. First, we could distil fuel from the rich plant-growths of the tropical forests, a store that replaces itself every year. Very likely these would not meet all our needs, but they might be able to supply whatever engines there may be that have to depend on liquid fuel.

We have already begun to replace fuel as an energy source by the use of electricity generated by rivers and waterfalls. The waters of these drive great water turbines that spin dynamos to supply with electricity the railways and cities of a whole countryside.

A suggestion for a wind power plant. Funnels at the top of a tower 500 ft. high would concentrate the wind on a turbine.

Just as the old-fashioned waterwheels have given place to these huge water-turbines, so we may be able to find better means of using the power of the wind than the crude windmills of our ancestors. A vertical cylinder rapidly rotated in a strong wind is pressed powerfully to one side. Such rotor cylinders have been successfully used for driving ships, and attempts are being made to use them for generating power on land. A number of the rotors might be mounted on trucks running on a circular track. The thrust of the wind would then drive them round the track, and they could be geared to dynamos at its centre.

Winds near the ground are inconstant. Those further aloft are much more steady, and plans have been made for immense wind-motors raised far into the air on towering lattice-work masts. A mast 500 ft. high would carry a huge funnel with an opening 80 ft. across, turned to face the wind by means of rudder-like vanes. The funnels would concentrate the wind on to turbines, so that even the slightest breeze would have considerable effect, while stronger winds and gales would produce a great power indeed.

Even in the old days attempts were made to use the tides as a source of power, paddle-wheels being turned by them and made to drive millstones. Nowadays we neglect the tides completely as sources of power, but later we might attempt to make use of them. For example, they could be used to raise and lower huge floating rafts, geared to machinery on the land. They could be harnessed by dams across river estuaries, and made to drive turbines as they flowed in and out. It is calculated that a barrage across the Bay of Fundy, off the coast of North America, would make available energy of 100,000,000 h.p., and plans have already been made for using the tides in this neighbourhood to generate electric power.

There are other ways of getting energy from the sea that would be even more titanic in scale. The waters of the Mediterranean evaporate in the sunshine more rapidly than they are replaced by the rivers that feed it, with the result that there is a steady current flowing through the Straits of Gibraltar. A barrage across the Straits, provided with immense turbines, would give great power, but would interfere with sea traffic. A more ingenious plan is to dig a channel from the Mediterranean to the Quattara Depression, a valley in northern Africa with a floor several hundred feet below sea level. The water would at once rush in to convert the valley into a lake. Soon, however, it would evaporate in the fierce heat of the tropical Sun, and there would be a steady flow of water down the channel. It would merely be necessary to instal turbines in this to produce a source of power that would never be exhausted.

The heat of the Earth itself also is a possible source of energy, for it comes to the surface in usable form at volcanoes and hot springs. The heat of Mount Etna has already been tapped on a small scale, and doubtless the process could be used in other volcanic regions. Volcanoes have done so much damage that it is pleasant to think they can be turned to useful purposes instead.

Even where there are no volcanoes the Earth's heat can still be used. Our coal-mines are unpleasantly warm, and as they are bored deeper their temperature increases. The suggestion has been made that two shafts should be sunk, each to a depth of about two miles, and joined by a horizontal gallery. Cold water pumped down the one shaft would emerge at the other almost at boiling point, ready to give off steam in a low-pressure boiler and so to drive engines and generate electric power.

A helicopter invented by the Marquis of Pescara making a trial flight. The two great lifting airscrews rotate in opposite directions. It rises vertically from the ground and flies at an excellent speed.

In this country it sounds almost ironic to talk about using the heat of the sunshine! Other lands, however, are more favoured in this respect than ours, and there solar heat would form a very reliable source of energy. Solar motors have been tried in Arizona, and also in Egypt. In these the heat of the Sun is concentrated by a number of mirrors on to a boiler, raising steam from water pumped into it. In one method the mirrors are ranged on a circular framework, which is gently turned so that they always face the Sun. In the other they are curved to form a trough, concentrating the Sun's rays on tubes through which water flows. This is a method by which we could make use of the most arid desert, converting the Sahara itself into a valuable source of energy for our needs.

Other possible schemes involve the use of the strange "cosmic rays" which fall on the Earth from space, and of the energy of the atoms, the tiny particles of matter of which everything is supposed to consist. A further possibility is the use of photo-electric cells, which convert the Sun's light into electric current, and tiny motors driven by light have been constructed. There is plainly no need to despair of finding sources of energy when our fuel supplies show signs of getting low.

The jungle traveller, which is capable of 15 m.p.h. on land, and 8 m.p.h. on water. It carries a crew of three and is intended for use in rough and unexplored country.

We are accustomed to a countryside that would seem very surprising indeed to our ancestors, with its arterial roads, its railways, its coal mines thrusting their galleries below the ground and its aeroplanes darting overhead. The people of the next century may equally be accustomed to a countryside that would astonish us by the absence of coal mines, steam trains or factory chimneys vomiting clouds of smoke. Lofty wind-towers may rise above it, and the mirrors of sun-motors may gleam here and there, while great barrages with their turbines may close the river mouths. By such methods electricity will be generated, to be transmitted by overhead cables or underground to be used in countless ways. The world will then use as much energy as it needs, but it will be cleaner, healthier and pleasanter than that in which we live.

These new sources of energy will involve modifications of our present methods of transport. For the most part, our engines, cars, ships and aeroplanes carry supplies of fuel with them. We are already beginning to electrify the railways, and this process is likely to continue. For road cars, ships and aeroplanes we may be able to devise improved accumulators that will store sufficient current for long journeys, or we may be able to broadcast energy that moving vehicles on land or on sea or in the air will be able to "receive" and use.

For certain purposes, especially in exploration, craft will be needed that are able to travel equally by land or by sea. There are already floating tanks that can swim across rivers, but these are needlessly clumsy for ordinary peaceful purposes. In the United States experiments are now being made with a "jungle traveller" that will cross broken country on tractor-like caterpillar treads, and will float on water, propelling itself by means of paddles or a screw. This strange-looking craft is shown in the lower illustration on this page. With its "crew" of three, weighing two tons, it travels at 15 m.p.h. on land and 8 m.p.h. on the water, and it should be very useful for exploring the river valleys and jungles of South America.

There are further improvements yet to hope for, in the design of aircraft, apart from the rocket propulsion mentioned recently in the *"M.M."* There is great need of some method of enabling aircraft to rise and sink vertically, and to hover motionless in the air. For this purpose we may at last be able to devise a practical helicopter, lifted by a screw revolving above it. A machine of this kind that has actually flown is shown in the upper illustration on this page. By further research and experiment no doubt the difficulties of helicopter flight will be overcome, and we shall then have a machine that will be able to rise from the flat roof of a house, an ordinary garden, the deck of a ship, or even the body of a huge transatlantic superplane.

Surface transport will not be abandoned, but will undergo many changes. For instance, railway trains will be speedier, and may run suspended from tracks fixed on pylons instead of taking up valuable space on the ground. Mountain ranges will be pierced by tunnels, and there also will be tunnels under the English Channel and other narrow waterways. These tunnels will be available for motor cars. These also will be speedier and simpler than those of to-day, and they will run on arterial roads properly planned to take them, and on which there will be none of the tragic accidents that are now so common.

Similarly we may hope for advances at sea with larger and steadier ships, wireless beams giving visibility through fog and other novel devices to prevent collisions, and surer means of navigation.

Hornby "*Princess Elizabeth*" in Service

Miniature "Heavy Traffic" Conditions

MORE realistic miniature railway working than ever before has become possible since the introduction of the splendid Hornby scale model locomotive "*Princess Elizabeth,*" which was described in detail in the May "*M.M.,*" and of the new Hornby Corridor Coaches described by "Tommy Dodd" on page 495 of this issue. The running of the new engine, and its management when in traffic, especially at the head of heavy trains made up with the new coaches, is the subject of this article.

The Hornby "*Princess Elizabeth*" is a treasure that will be well cared for by its owners, and will give wonderful service if the directions packed with it are followed. Like a real engine about to take up regular duties, it should be carefully "nursed" before any heavy work is undertaken so that all the bearings become run in and all traces of stiffness are removed. Before it goes out on service it should be examined to see that the wheel treads and collector shoes are clean. The careful "driver" will take special care to see that the armature shaft and axle bearings are properly lubricated, and that the rods and motion of the engine are given a tiny drop of oil at each joint so as to ensure perfectly free running. The Meccano "K" type Oil Can is just the thing for jobs like this, as the flow is controlled by the push button exactly as with a full-size oil can. It is fascinating to go round the engine in this way, as a real driver does with his full scale locomotive, before it proceeds to the station or siding to pick up its train.

The Hornby "Princess Elizabeth" at the head of a heavy express consisting of the new No. 2 Corridor Coaches. The engine is arousing the keen interest of waiting passengers!

"*Princess Elizabeth*" is exactly what is wanted for hauling miniatures of "*The Royal Scot,*" "*The Night Scot*" or "*The Mid-day Scot.*" It is itself a miniature of the real engines used on these famous expresses, and its efficient six-coupled motor has a remarkable capacity both for hauling heavy loads and for continuous high-speed running. Long non-stop runs therefore present no difficulties, and the greatest fun will be obtained if a layout is planned to represent the line from Euston to Glasgow, and heavy expresses are run over it with few calls, and with perhaps a stop to change crews, as in the case of "*The Royal Scot.*" A long non-continuous line of course is best for this working. Sufficient space is not always available for this, but the thrill of long sustained running at high speed can be obtained with a layout on which terminal stations representing "Glasgow" and "Euston" are placed on extensions of the main line, which consists of an oval or circular track.

There are many other trains that can be worked realistically in miniature by means of the Hornby "*Princess Elizabeth.*" For instance, the new locomotive can be used for the "10.40 a.m. Liverpool" from Euston and for the lighter but faster up 5.25 p.m. "*Liverpool Flyer,*" which completes the journey to Euston in 3 hr. 20 min. The haulage of the 10.10 a.m. "*Merseyside Express*" from Lime Street, Liverpool, to Euston also is a "Princess" turn.

For all these trains the new Hornby Corridor Coaches are ideal. They are fitted with free-running bogies and supplied with corridor connections. The latest destination-board practice of the L.M.S. has been faithfully reproduced on them above the windows, and the trains can be appropriately named to add to their general attractiveness.

Another interesting turn for a "Princess" is not a mile-a-minute uxury express, but a much less imposing fish train! This is the "1.55 p.m. Fish" from Aberdeen, an important freight train that is booked at high speed from Aberdeen to London (Broad Street) in order to catch the market at Billingsgate, and is hauled sometimes by a "Princess." Thus there is plenty of excuse, so often necessary in miniature, for running a goods train with even such a splendid locomotive as the Hornby "*Princess Elizabeth.*"

In miniature it is not always possible to have more than one engine of any particular type in service, so that in many cases "*Princess Elizabeth*" will be the only engine of its kind on the line. It will appear therefore on practically every heavy express train of importance. Such intensive use of the locomotive is a parallel of present-day L.M.S. operating practice, for the capacity of modern locomotives is such that the greatest possible use is made of them in traffic, and long mileages are run in the course of a very short time.

A turn involving what is perhaps the largest mileage covered in 24 hours is regularly undertaken by the L.M.S. 4-6-2 "Princesses." This is the haulage of the down "*Royal Scot*" from Euston to Glasgow, a distance of 401.4 miles, on one day, the return being made the same night with the up "*Night Scot.*" Thus one engine runs over 800 miles in approximately 21 hours. The Hornby "*Princess Elizabeth*" is ideal for such workings because its motor is designed for long continuous running.

New American Diesel-Electric Locomotive
Baltimore and Ohio Streamline Design

A DIESEL-ELECTRIC locomotive that is the most powerful of its type to be operated in the east of the United States has recently been introduced on the Baltimore and Ohio Railroad. Remarkable progress has been made in the United States during recent years in the development of locomotives of this type. The fastest train in the world, the *"Super Chief"* of the Atchison, Topeka and Santa Fé Railroad is hauled by a twin unit Diesel-engined locomotive, and the appearance of the Baltimore and Ohio engine marked the completion of regularly-scheduled Diesel-electric operation between the Atlantic and Pacific coasts.

The new locomotive is shown in the accompanying illustration and is the first of several ordered by the Baltimore and Ohio line. Its first run in service was made on a heavy Pullman train bringing passengers from western and south western districts to Jersey City. Until the delivery of the remaining engines of the class it was used to haul the famous streamline *"Royal Blue"* express between New York and Washington, and on the completion of its first run on this service it was met as the train approached Washington by the first American-built locomotive *"Tom Thumb,"* which was constructed for the Baltimore and Ohio Railroad in 1829. The oldest and the newest of American locomotives then moved side by side into the Union Station, Washington, showing in a striking manner the progress of over 100 years of railroad development.

One of the giant 3,600 h.p. Diesel-electric locomotives of the Baltimore and Ohio Railroad. They will be used for hauling the "Capitol Limited" between Washington and Chicago. Photograph by courtesy of the Baltimore and Ohio Railroad.

The new locomotive is of the twin unit type, each unit being provided with two 900 h.p. Diesel power plants so that the total output of the whole locomotive is 3,600 h.p. The twin units are coupled for operation from the driving compartment of the leading vehicle. Each runs on two six-wheeled bogies in which special means have been employed to ensure smooth riding and stability in rounding curves. The outer axles of each bogie truck have an electric traction motor geared directly to them, the centre axles being idlers and necessary for weight carrying purposes only.

Each of the 900 h.p. plants consists of a Diesel engine with the necessary arrangements for its fuel supply, cooling and lubrication. A power generator and exciter, a generator for charging batteries and the necessary electrical controlling gear are included. In addition each locomotive unit carries a fuel tank of 1,200 gallons capacity, and a 1,100-gallon water tank for supplying the steam boiler that is carried for train heating purposes. Each main generator supplies direct current at 600 volts to the 450 h.p. traction motors mentioned previously. These generators also are used for engine starting purposes, and then they receive energy from the battery through separate contactors provided for this purpose. The cooling of each engine is effected by means of water-cooled radiators suspended from the roof. The air for radiator cooling is taken through grilled openings in the sides of the vehicle and is forced out through the radiator assemblies by fans.

As the illustration shows, the driving cab is situated slightly behind the nose of the locomotive, which has been shaped to reduce wind resistance at high speeds and to provide the widest possible outlook for the driver. Safety glass is used for all the cab windows, and those in front have special windshield wipers and a hot air defrosting arrangement in order to secure the maximum visibility for the crew in all conditions. Comfortable seats are provided for the men, the driver being accompanied by a helper, or "fireman," as he would be on a steam locomotive.

The main locomotive throttle is situated in the cab of the first unit, although the second one is equipped for independent operation for yard movements, such as turntable manœuvres, that may necessitate the separation of one unit from the other. The throttle, the reverse lever and the brake handle control all the movements required of the locomotive, and any movement of the throttle is relayed electrically to each power plant. An electro-pneumatic device actuates the engine speed governor of each engine to regulate the speed and output of each individual plant.

The second locomotive of this type to be delivered was exhibited at Atlantic City alongside the remarkable new Baltimore and Ohio steam locomotive *"George H. Emerson."* These two locomotives are seen in the illustration on page 454 of this issue. The wheel arrangement of the steam engine is 4–4–4–4, there being leading and trailing four-wheeled trucks with two four-coupled units between them, each unit being driven by a separate pair of cylinders. The engine has a water-tube boiler carrying a pressure of 380 lb. per sq. in. and a special design of superheater developed in the company's own shop.

A Hornby "Schools" Class Locomotive

Splendid New Model of S.R. "*Eton*"

THE recent introduction of the magnificent Hornby 4–6–2 "*Princess Elizabeth*" has now been followed by another splendid addition to the locomotives of the Hornby Series. This is a handsome model of the S.R. 4–4–0 No. 900, "*Eton*," the pioneer engine of the famous "Schools" class. These locomotives probably are the most popular to be seen in the area served by the Southern Railway. The special purpose of their design, their handsome yet massive appearance and the work that they do all appeal strongly to the imagination, and there also is a special interest in their names, for each is named after a famous English public school.

As the photograph on this page shows, the new model bears a striking resemblance to the real engine and reproduces all its more prominent features. It is available for electric and for clockwork railways. The electric model is provided with a 20-volt motor that incorporates the famous Hornby Remote Control, which means that it can be started, stopped, controlled for speed and reversed without any handling of the locomotive itself. The clockwork movement is the well-tried No. 2 Special mechanism, which gives great hauling power and the maximum length of run.

The splendid new Hornby S.R. locomotive No. 900, "Eton," described in this article. The design of this handsome miniature locomotive follows closely that of the real engines of the popular "Schools" class.

The general design of the engine is very pleasing. The massive boiler with its characteristic fittings, the smoke deflectors at the front end and the typical cab all combine to give the effect of the real "*Eton*" in miniature. The amount of detail incorporated is remarkable. For instance, all S.R. model railway owners will be delighted to see that it carries miniature route-indicating discs. Most readers know that the S.R. do not make use of the British standard headlamp code, and that route-indicating discs are carried on their locomotives because of the complexity of their tracks. The miniature discs provided with the Hornby "*Eton*" locomotive enable owners of S.R. layouts to follow this practice exactly. The brackets for these discs at the front of the new locomotive are correct in number and position. Thus there is one on each side of the smoke-box door, a feature peculiar to S.R. practice and made necessary by the number of indications that have to be provided for, and there are in addition the usual three brackets above the buffer beam and one below the chimney.

The front of the model reproduces exactly the characteristic S.R. smoke-box, and smoke deflectors, or "down-draught" plates as they are termed officially, give the model an up-to-date appearance. The shape of the real plates is followed exactly, and the miniature deflectors even incorporate the two small slots in the front edge that provide hand-holds for the enginemen when passing round the front of the engine.

The chimney and dome are of squat modern design and the Ross Pop safety valves are smart little fittings finished in polished brass. There is a considerable amount of polished brasswork about the engine, and this adds to the smartness of its appearance. For instance, there are the clack boxes, one on each side of the boiler behind the smoke-box, by means of which the feed water from the injectors is introduced into the boiler of the real engine. These are modelled in a very realistic manner, as the photograph shows, and each is complete with a length of feed pipe that disappears below the footplate. From the characteristic steam turret and whistle mounting in front of the cab the whistle itself projects forward horizontally; and the two steam pipes that pass downward on each side follow the characteristic contours of the real ones.

A striking external feature of the design of the real "Schools" is the setting-in at an angle of the upper part of the side sheets of the cab. This was necessary owing to the restricted loading gauge of the Hastings route, for which the engines were primarily designed. This feature is reproduced effectively in the new Hornby locomotive and results in a very distinctive appearance. The cab is of the modern side-window type as fitted to the engines of the "Schools" class. It includes a die-cast fire-box back that projects into the cab, in which the regulator and various other fittings are represented. The fire hole door also is shown in relief.

The finish of the Hornby "Schools" class locomotive is splendid. Standard S.R. practice is followed, and the engine is attractively lined out in black and white. A smart detail that adds a splash of colour is the small oval number plate with its red background on the cab side. The nameplates, on the leading splashers, are particularly striking, the name "*Eton*" standing out well in gold letters on a red background. The edge of the nameplate also is in gold to represent the polished brass of the original.

The tender is of standard No. 2 Special design and incorporates the main features of modern S.R. six-wheeled tenders. It is fully fitted up internally with the appropriate division plates, sloping coal space, water filler and brake handles.

Stamp Gossip

and Notes on New Issues

Coronation Stamp Error

We wonder how many of our readers have noticed a curious feature in the Orb shown on the G.B. Coronation stamp.

Comparison with authentic pictures of the King's and Queen's Orbs used at the Coronation ceremony reveals that the stamp orb differs from them both in that it shows a band of precious stones running

vertically from the encircling band to the foot of the Cross at right angles to the Cross. In the real Orbs the vertical plane of this half-circle is the same as that of the Cross.

Comparison of the Orb on the British stamps with that shown in the design for the Crown Colonies stamp immediately shows the error if, as *"Gibbons Stamp Monthly"* says, it is an error, for there is just a chance that this portrayal is one permitted by convention. The Orb is depicted in this style in the 1876 Orb watermark of Great Britain and in the 1935 Silver Jubilee stamps of India.

French Railway Pictorials

The 13th International Railway Congress, which has been held this year in Paris, has been marked by the issue of two commemorative stamps, bearing designs that will be of interest to all railway enthusiasts among our readers.

Both stamps are illustrated here. The 30c. shows a modern electric locomotive, while the 1 f. 50 provides a striking impression of a streamlined "Pacific" type locomotive.

* * * *

An interesting special stamp, exclusively for use on letters posted in Czecho-Slovakia for destinations within the countries of Czecho-Slovakia, Jugo-Slavia and Roumania, has just been issued.

The principal feature of the design shows Prague Cathedral, but more interesting points are three linked rings at the foot, signifying the Little Entente formed by the three countries, and the label at the head which reads *"Ceskoslovensko—Petite Entente."*

A short while ago overprinted stamps were issued in Roumania to serve in the same way for mail posted in Roumania.

Empire Mails by Air

In a stamp article in the March 1930 issue under the title *"Airways are Mail-ways,"* we made the forecast that the time was rapidly coming "when all mails will be carried by air over both land and sea, except on the shortest journeys." As the years have passed, one country after another has adopted air transit as standard for its first-class mail. For quite a long time all European mail originating in Holland has been sent forward by air, and a great part of Britain's inland letter mail is now air-borne.

The greatest step forward, however, has been the decision that in future all letters passing between South Africa and Great Britain shall be carried by air without extra charge. At first this service is bound to call for a fairly substantial subsidy, but it is expected to become self-supporting within a comparatively short time.

It may be taken for granted that the success of this scheme will inevitably lead to similar arrangements for the Indian, Malayan, Australian and New Zealand mails. The carriage of Canadian and U.S.A. European mails by air as a result of the establishment of a regular trans-atlantic air service also is a possibility of the very near future.

A Stamp Photographic Contest

Readers who are camera enthusiasts, as well as stamp collectors, will be interested in a photographic competition promoted by *"Gibbons' Stamp Monthly"* for photographs illustrating the title *"The Young Philatelist."*

A specially interesting feature is that the prizes, consisting of stamp goods to be chosen from Messrs. Stanley Gibbons' catalogue, will range from two guineas upward, according to the number of entries. The photographs must have been taken by the entrants and the closing date is 30th September. Full details of the competition are given in the July issue of *"Gibbons' Stamp Monthly"* and interested readers who have difficulty in obtaining a copy of that issue should apply to the Editor, *"Gibbons' Stamp Monthly,"* 391, Strand, London, W.C.2.

* * *

Australia is to mark the 150th anniversary of the founding of the State of New South Wales, which falls in October next, by the issue of three commemorative stamps, 2d., 3d. and 9d. denominations.

The stamps are to appear on 12th October and a special first-day cover will be published for stamp collectors' use.

Danish Silver Jubilee Issues

The Silver Jubilee of King Christian X of Denmark, which was celebrated during our own Coronation week in May last, has been marked by the issue of a short set of four commemorative stamps.

We illustrate the 5 öre value, which has for its design a view of Marselisborg Castle, the royal summer residence, which lies close to the city of Aarhus in Jutland. In the foreground there is a racing yacht, representative of the King's yachting interests.

The design for the 10 and 30 öre values, also reproduced here, shows King Christian riding on horseback in the streets of Copenhagen. This undoubtedly will be the most popular design of the series, if only because it illustrates the King's democratic way of life. He is frequently seen moving alone about the streets of his capital.

The remaining stamp of the series, the 15 öre value, shows a view of Amalienborg Palace, King Christian's Copenhagen residence.

The Jubilee was marked in Iceland by the issue of a series of three stamps, 10, 30 and 40 aur values. Each of these stamps bears a portrait of King Christian.

Colombian Anniversary Stamps

The 400th anniversary of the founding of the city of Bogota, Colombia, will be celebrated next year, and a short series of three commemorative stamps is to be issued to mark the occasion.

One of the stamps will bear a composite design showing Jimenez de Quesada, the founder of Bogota, and the Indian ruler of the territory at the time of the conquest by Spain. The portraits will be flanked by a representation of a coffee plant on the left and of a maize plant on the right, symbolic of two of the country's principal crops. In the centre, between the two portraits, there will be a representation of an ancient Indian stone idol with a cross rising behind it.

The other two designs will show views of ancient and modern Bogota respectively.

* * * *

Readers in the United States of America will be pleased to learn that there is every prospect of the relaxation of the present American regulations prohibiting the reproduction of U.S.A. stamps in publications produced in the U.S.A.

A Bill now pending in Congress seeks to abolish the regulation.

Holiday Bargains

During the next few weeks many of our readers will be taking a cruising holiday. They alone, perhaps, among holiday-making stamp enthusiasts will have their stamp collections actively in mind, for they may find excellent opportunities of acquiring new specimens.

A word of advice therefore may be useful to them. They should buy stamps only from post offices and obviously reputable stamp shops, not from itinerant

vendors. The stamp journals last autumn contained many letters from stamp collectors who had bought from such vendors, only to find that they had been "stung," packets of stamps that had been offered as "bargains" containing little else but rubbish.

Interesting odd lots occasionally are to be found in out of the way places both at home and abroad, however, and holiday makers will find it worth while to keep their eyes open for such lots. Four years ago, we found a bargain in a general shop in a village on the North Wales coast.

We had asked for a picture postcard view of a particular spot. The shopkeeper "thought she might have an old one" and started rummaging among some packets in a box. As she turned the packets over we saw three very soiled packets of stamps. On enquiry we found that they had been in stock since before the war. There had never been any demand for them and we were offered them for 2d. each, although their price was really 6d.

The sequel to this story should have been the discovery in the packets of several Cape Triangulars and Sydney "Views." There was nothing quite so thrilling as that, but there were many useful stamps that helped to make those packets the best sixpennyworth we ever bought.

U.S. Navy and Army Issues

This month we are able to illustrate the 5c. values in the United States parallel series of Army and Navy commemoratives.

The 5c. Army stamp shows composite views of the buildings at the West Point

Military Academy. The Navy stamp is, perhaps, the more interesting, for it shows naval cadets in old time and modern uniform.

* * * *

Stanley Gibbons Ltd. ask us to remind our readers of the importance of placing their orders early for the new season's catalogues that are to be published on 1st September.

Egypt's King Farouk Issues

The rush of British Coronation issues has tended to obscure the forthcoming Egyptian issues bearing the portrait of King Farouk, an event that is the more interesting to stamp collectors by reason of the great philatelic interests of the late King Fouad.

The new stamps, ranging in value from 1 mil. to 20 mils., are to appear on the first of this month. The design shows a squared-up portrait of King Farouk in morning dress and wearing the fez. The straight edges bordering the portrait are carried out to the edge of the stamp, and the corners, printed with plain ground in the same colour as the portrait background, are left blank. The top and side panels have a plain ground contrasting with the principal colour of the stamp and bear the wording *"Postes d'Egypte"* in Roman characters at the foot and in Arab script at the head. The figures of value, also in Roman and Arabic numerals, are placed level with the King's forehead on each side of the stamp. The design is very effective and strikes an entirely new note in stamp design.

Incidentally Egypt has in preparation four series of commemorative stamps to mark the forthcoming Cotton Congress, the Abrogation of Capitulations Conference, and the Ophthalmic and Wireless Congresses.

New South West Africa Issue

Readers who are forming collections of stamps illustrating transport methods,

will welcome the new South West African 1½d. issue, illustrated here.

The design of this stamp, it is officially explained, is intended to show the three modern methods of mail transport, by sea, land and air. As usual in the stamps of South West Africa and the Union of South Africa, the inscriptions are bilingual, alternate stamps bearing inscriptions in Afrikaans and English.

* * * *

We are indebted to Mr. L. T. Chapman of Christchurch for a souvenir cover commemorating the official opening of the new Chief Post Office at Dunedin, N.Z., on 14th April last.

All mail posted from this office on that day bore the special cancellation mark "Opening of New Chief Post Office, Dunedin, 14. Ap. 37.

* * * *

The King George VI issues for Mauritius and Nyasaland are in preparation. We understand that the designs will be the same as those of the existing series, with the substitution of the portrait of King George VI for that of King George V.

Several other colonies contemplate using existing designs for their King George VI stamps, and we cannot help thinking that this is indeed a pity. Imagine what a page of an album will look like with two such sets following one another! At first sight, both sets will look monotonously alike.

India's New Stamps

It is expected that four of India's new series of stamps bearing the portrait of King George VI, the 3p., 6p., 9p. and 1a values, will be placed on sale this month. In many ways these stamps will be entirely different from previous Indian issues, although the King-Emperor's portrait will continue to be the principal feature.

The new stamps will have the King-Emperor's portrait in the centre as the principal feature, but otherwise the designs will differ considerably from previous Indian types. Instead of being contained in an oval, the portrait will be framed by a pointed arch, symbolic of the country's characteristic architecture. The portrait will show head and shoulders in order that more of the beauty of the Imperial robes may be displayed.

The value tablets will appear at the foot of each side of the arch surround. The corners left at the top by the sweep of the arch will be filled by a lotus bud emblem, with a small amount of scroll work of varying form.

The designs for the high values have been forwarded to London for inspection by the King. These will follow previous styles very closely, but it is intended to use rather richer and more distinctive colourings.

* * * *

The centenary of the foundation of Athens University has been celebrated in Greece by the issue of a 3 drachmae commemorative stamp. The design, illustrated here, shows a figure of Minerva the Goddess of Wisdom and Industry, and in the background a Greek temple, from which rays of light are bursting, presumably to represent the Dawn of Learning.

Danube Centenary Stamps

The centenary of the Danube Steam Navigation Company, celebrated in June last, has brought three commemorative

stamps from Austria. In each case one of the popular steamers plying on the Danube has been chosen for illustration, and we show here the 12 gr. value with a picture of the steamer *"Maria Anna."*

The other designs are as follows: 24 g. the *"Franz Schubert"*; 64 g, the *"Oesterreich."*

We thank Stanley Gibbons Ltd. for their courtesy in loaning the stamps from which the illustrations for our stamp pages have been made.

Electrifying the Pennsylvania Railroad

A Notable Main Line Conversion

By Edward T. Myers

THE greatest single railway electrification programme that has yet been carried out completely at one time is that of the Pennsylvania Railroad, in the United States of America. This includes a total of approximately 310 route miles and 1,030 track miles, and has involved the main line of the Company from New York to Washington, together with those branch lines and yards along this stretch that were not already operated electrically.

The reason for this great programme of main line electrification was the desire to improve both the freight and the passenger services of the railway. With steam operation the tracks between New York and Washington, a distance of 224.8 miles, were being used practically to capacity in the operation of long-distance traffic. Since the electrification was inaugurated, the accelerations and general improvements that have been made to the through services have had the effect of making this section probably the busiest high speed main line in the world.

An express on the electrified main line of the Pennsylvania Railroad, hauled by one of the 3,750 h.p. locomotives of class P-5. The illustrations to this article are reproduced by courtesy of the Pennsylvania Railroad.

The scheme for electrification was decided upon some years ago. Studies were made that covered not only the generally known advantages of electric traction, but also the whole industrial and transportation situation in the United States. The probability was not lost sight of that by 1950 the metropolitan area around New York would extend considerably farther both west and east than at present, and that it would contain perhaps 30 million people.

In 1928, the company planned to make the change slowly, but early in 1931, the late General W. W. Atterbury, then President of the Pennsylvania Railroad, in the face of the growing depression in business and the increasing need for employment, announced that the programme would be speeded up. General Atterbury pointed out that prices were at such a level that the improvements could be contracted for at exceptionally favourable rates. He argued that at a time of reduced traffic the work could proceed with much less interference from the movement of passing trains.

For many years electric locomotives have pulled Pennsylvania trains through the tunnels under the Hudson River into the magnificent Pennsylvania Station in New York. Older *"M.M."* readers no doubt will remember the article in the August 1928 issue describing a run on the famous *"Congressional Limited,"* in which reference was made to the change-over from steam to electric locomotives at "Manhattan Transfer," New Jersey. Passengers on trains from the west who wished to go to what is known as "downtown" New York, instead of continuing to the main station, also have in the past changed at Manhattan Transfer, in their case to the Hudson and Manhattan Railroad.

The change from steam to electric power is now made much farther west, so that there is no longer need for a stop for this purpose at Manhattan Transfer before entering the tubes under the Hudson River. Passengers for the Hudson and Manhattan line now transfer at a new and architecturally splendid structure in Newark, New Jersey. This new station is the terminus of a new city underground railroad, or "subway," and provides facilities for buses, taxicabs, and private cars. Included with the station improvements at Newark is a bridge over the Passaic River. This is to carry the tracks used by through trains on their way to and from the Pennsylvania Station in New York.

In Philadelphia, in the autumn of 1930, the company opened one of the most modern and complete electrified suburban stations in the world. This is situated near the old Broad Street Station, which had been the focal point of Pennsylvania passenger traffic in the city for 50 years, and all suburban trains were then moved there from Broad Street. Before the opening of this new downtown suburban station, the Pennsylvania Railroad built a concrete arch bridge across the Schuylkill River and constructed on the west bank of the river the first or northern wing of its great new passenger terminal. This new wing, known as the 30th Street Station, serves as the West Philadelphia stop for all suburban trains. The new main building of the Pennsylvania Station takes a leading place among the great passenger terminals of the world.

In Baltimore a programme of tremendous magnitude was put in hand. This includes the construction of two new through tunnels practically parallel to those now in use, and the reconstruction of the latter, and altogether

The new and the old forms of motive power on the Pennsylvania Railroad. On the left is one of the new streamlined electric locomotives of class GG-1 that were specially designed for hauling the fastest and heaviest expresses between New York and Washington. On the right is a "Pacific" steam locomotive of class K4S.

these now afford four express tracks under and through the city. Several outlying grade crossings are eliminated under the new arrangement.

Alternating current of 11,000 volts and 25 cycles is employed. This is the system that has been used for years in the Philadelphia suburban zone. After a great deal of study, the engineers of the Pennsylvania Railroad have concluded that it is best adapted for the heavy-traction trunk line work on the Pennsylvania Railroad. It has dominated electrifications carried out in the Eastern States, with the exception of those of the New York Central and the Lackawanna lines; and it has been used with success in Europe, in Germany, Switzerland and Sweden.

In the Philadelphia and New York suburban zones, which were electrified long before the present programme was taken in hand, the multiple unit type of train already in use is still retained. For through services on the main line it was decided to employ separate electric locomotives, however, and with the assistance of the electrical manufacturing companies several new types of locomotives have been developed. In designing these the chief aims have been to secure the maximum interchangeability of parts, a minimum cost of maintenance, and the simplest methods of manufacture.

The type of heavy-duty passenger locomotive first designed for the new services is known as class P-5. The engines of this class are designed for high speeds, and are capable of 90 m.p.h. They are of the 4-6-4 wheel arrangement, with three pairs of driving wheels 6 ft. in diameter and a four-wheeled bogie truck at each end. They are 62 ft. 8 in. in length, with a weight of over 167 tons, and are composed of three distinct parts, known as the chassis, deck, and cab units respectively, each of which must be completely equipped before the three are assembled to form a complete locomotive.

The new locomotives could not have been built with motors of the types that were available at the beginning of the electrification programme. New motors therefore were designed for the purpose, and there is one for each pair of driving wheels. They fit between the wheels instead of above the frames, so that the dummy axle, or jack shaft, driving the coupled wheels through side rods that were common on earlier electric locomotives are eliminated. The jack shaft arrangement is unsatisfactory for high speed service on account of vibration. The class P-5 locomotive develops 3,750 h.p. or 22,300 lb. tractive power, at 63 m.p.h.

An electric train of the type used in the Philadelphia and New York suburban zones of the Pennsylvania Railroad.

Another class of passenger locomotives is known as 0-1. This has two pairs of driving wheels, each pair driven by two motors, with two four-wheeled bogie trucks, one at each end of the engine, giving the 4-4-4 wheel arrangement. The 0-1 class locomotive develops 2,500 h.p. at 63 m.p.h.

Since the completion of the electrification throughout, streamlined electric locomotives have been introduced for express trains. These giants are rated at 4,620 h.p. and have a tractive effort at starting of 72,000 lb. They have the 4-6-6-4 wheel arrangement, the chassis of each engine being formed of two articulated units. These locomotives are classed 99-1 and are probably the most powerful high-speed passenger engines in the world.

For freight service, only one type of engine is used. This is the 2-8-2 class L-6, which has four pairs of driving wheels and leading and trailing two-wheeled trucks.

Some Railway Engineering Feats

Historic Bridges, Viaducts and Tunnels

By H. J. Locke

THE building of streamlined locomotives and coaches for special services, the breaking of speed records and the running of many hundreds of additional trains to and from all parts in connection with national events and Bank Holidays, are facts that keep the British railways perpetually in the public mind. The railways have welcomed and assisted in the development of travel by air. The drone of the aero engine cannot still the fascination of the locomotive whistle, however, and the steam locomotive remains industrially essential and at the same time humanly thrilling.

Much is heard of the mechanical engineering triumphs of the railways. Little is known of the work of the civil engineer. All over the country there can be seen examples of the mighty engineering tasks that have been accomplished to carry railway tracks across valleys, rivers and even arms of the sea. Many of these stand as perpetual monuments to the courage and skill of the engineers who undertook this pioneer work, in some cases 100 years and more ago.

The Forth Bridge, which was opened as long ago as 1891, bears tribute to the skill, daring and courage of the men who built it. It cost £3,000,000 to construct, and its three towers rise 361 ft. from sea level, more than the height of St. Paul's Cathedral. It needed 54,000 tons of steelwork and 6,500,000 rivets before the bridge could carry the railway metals across the Firth of Forth. It is built on the cantilever principle, and including the north and south approach viaducts constructed on the shores of the Forth it measures 1½ miles in length.

Another wonderful structure, which was built in 1850 by that great engineer, Robert Stephenson, is the Britannia Tubular Bridge that carries the L.M.S. line across the Menai Strait in North Wales. The basis of the design of the bridge was the use of two continuous rectangular tubes of wrought iron. Each of these is 1,510 ft. long and some 4,680 tons in weight, and three supporting towers were set up in the middle of the straits to carry the two main spans, which are 459 ft. across. The tubular bridge is the principal connecting link with Holyhead for the Royal Mail steamer service to and from Ireland. It has safely carried the *"Irish Mail"* trains between the mainland and the Isle of Anglesey since its opening 87 years ago.

The handsome mouth of Box Tunnel on the G.W.R. This tunnel was so disliked in the early days of railways that timid passengers used to leave the train at one end, journey "overland" by coach, and rejoin the railway at the other end.

Away in the West Country across the River Tamar is the beautiful Royal Albert Bridge at Saltash, built in 1859 by the world-renowned engineer, Isambard K. Brunel, whose name appears on the end of the bridge. This was Brunel's masterpiece, and over it G.W.R. metals pass from Devon into Cornwall. It is 2,230 ft. long and is made up of two main spans and 17 land spans. The main spans are each 455 ft. in length and weigh 1,060 tons. The bridge is 110 ft. above high-water level and took four years to build. The opening ceremony was performed on 3rd May, 1859, by the Prince Consort, after whom it was named the "Royal Albert Bridge."

Hundreds of other lesser-known bridges and viaducts have been constructed by railway engineers, and each plays a vitally important part in the daily working of our great railways. Indeed the L.N.E.R. route to Scotland is often referred to as the "Great Bridges Route." It includes the Forth Bridge previously mentioned, and also the Tay Bridge, across the Firth of Tay. In addition there are Welwyn Viaduct, the Nene Viaduct at Peterborough, the Trent Bridge at Newark, a swing bridge at Selby, Durham Viaduct, the King Edward VII Bridge at Newcastle and the Royal Border Bridge at Berwick, all of which are crossed on the northbound run of *"The Flying Scotsman."*

The task of boring railway tunnels has been no less arduous than that of erecting bridges and viaducts, yet perhaps even less has been heard of the trials, hardships and ultimate triumphs of the men engaged on their construction. Perhaps the greatest feat of railway tunnelling in this country was the construction of the Severn Tunnel, which is the longest under-water tunnel in the world. It is 4 miles 628 yards in length, and at its deepest part is 138 ft. below high-water level. The tunnel cost nearly £2,000,000, and took thirteen years to build. Its opening for traffic in 1886 reduced the railway journey time between Cardiff and Bristol and London by an hour, and paved the way for the great industrial development of South Wales.

The second longest railway tunnel in Great Britain is on the L.M.S. line at Totley in Derbyshire, and is 3 miles 950 yards in length. The third longest tunnel is also owned by the L.M.S. This is at Standedge and is 3 miles 60 yards long. The only other railway tunnel in this country over 3 miles long is on the L.N.E.R. line between Manchester and Sheffield at Woodhead in Derbyshire. This tunnel is 3 miles 13 yards in length. Altogether there are 1,042 tunnels on the British railways, of which 45 are between one and two miles long. Five of them have a length of between two and three miles.

Brunel's masterpiece, the Royal Albert Bridge at Saltash, under construction. One of the main spans is in position, and preliminary work towards the raising of the other is in hand. Photograph by courtesy of the G.W.R.

When tunnels were first built on the railways difficulty was sometimes experienced in getting passengers to go through them for fear that the sides or roof would collapse. Box Tunnel on the G.W.R. was one that was particularly disliked, and at one time trains used to stop at one end to allow passengers to travel by coach to the other end, where the trains took them on again! The fear and dislike of travelling through tunnels was soon overcome when passengers realised that they were perfectly safe and were in fact a boon in shortening a journey.

Just as all railway bridges and all track, trains, and other equipment are regularly inspected by experienced men, so are railway tunnels. Tunnels that are near other borings under the Earth, such as coal mines, get even more than their regular share of inspection. Railway gangers patrol the permanent way each day and are responsible for inspecting any tunnels on their particular section of line. By means of instruments with which they are supplied they are able to tell immediately if there is any likelihood of trains fouling the roof or walls, and in the event of any serious fault being found, the tunnel is immediately closed to traffic.

The entrance to the Britannia Tubular Bridge across the Menai Straits. Each of the stone lions guarding the portal weighs 80 tons. Photograph by courtesy of the L.M.S.

In addition to this daily inspection, a special inspection of every tunnel is made two or three times a year by the railway engineers with the aid of a specially-constructed tunnel van. This van has a semi-circular gauge with projecting metal spikes built up on its roof. If any part of the roof has dropped, no matter how slightly, the gauge indicates the spot immediately as the van passes through the tunnel. Bright lights are focussed on the roof, and the spikes are very closely watched by the engineer in charge of the train. If any faults are found, these are carefully marked and repairs are carried out without delay by the engineering staff.

It is not generally realised that tunnel construction does not necessarily involve boring. When a tunnel is to be built fairly near the surface and the ground above is clear, it is often built by what is known as the cut-and-cover method. This involves the making of a cutting, similar to the many railway cuttings all over the country, and then the building of the tunnel lining in the cutting. When this lining is complete the cutting is filled in again over the top, leaving the tunnel enclosed.

The cut-and-cover method was employed for the construction of London's first underground railway, the Metropolitan, which was opened in 1863 from Bishop's Road to Farringdon Street. Another interesting London cut-and-cover tunnel, which is passed over by many thousands of people every summer, but is not very well known, carries the L.N.E.R. line into Marylebone beneath Lord's Cricket Ground. It actually passes under a corner of the famous ground, which had to be opened up at the time of its construction for the former Great Central Railway. When the tunnel was completed the opening was refilled and the turf replaced in position.

In some places it has been found desirable by a railway company to convert a tunnel into a cutting. This of course is done only when the tunnel lies near the surface, and reconstruction becomes necessary owing to the difficulty of keeping the tunnel in good repair, or on account of widening operations that involve additional tracks. The Chevet cutting on the L.M.S. was once a tunnel. Its reconstruction is of comparatively recent date and it is a good example of a "changeover" from tunnel to cutting. Another tunnel that also has been opened up is the former Cofton Tunnel, on the L.M.S. This was situated at Barnt Green, near Birmingham, on the Midland route to Bristol, and was demolished in three lengths by explosives.

Preparing a Railway Timetable

How the Paths of Trains are Worked Out

By Christopher Cowan

TO many people railway timetables are complete mysteries, and few of those who make use of them regularly have any idea of how they are prepared. The figures in them and on the time sheets of the railway companies represent a state of constant activity all over the system, for they give a complete record of the movements of every regular train.

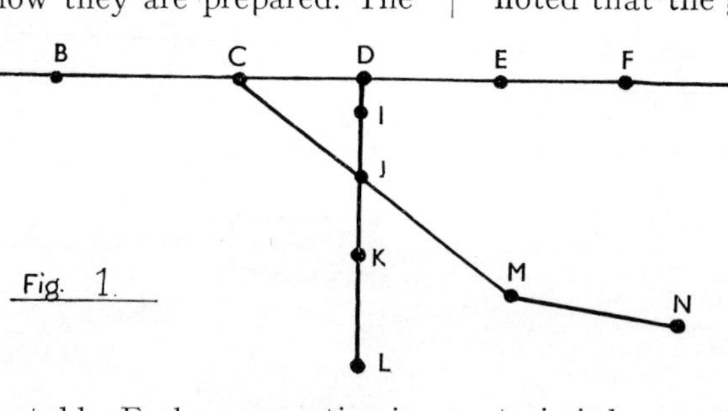

Naturally the greatest care is taken in the preparation and printing of a timetable. Early preparation is necessary, for a single change in the timing of one train may necessitate the alteration of connecting services throughout the greater part of a system. Suggestions from the public for an altered or additional service here or there have to be weighed up. The possibilities of the better use of locomotives and coaching stock without impairing the service afforded must be considered; also any new or special features that are to be introduced.

The "path" of each train has to be worked out with its correct timing at every point of importance, such as signal cabins, junctions and stations. This is done by preparing a chart, which shows graphically the path of each train so that its position at any given moment can be seen. How this is carried out can be seen by reference to the accompanying illustrations.

Fig. 1 shows an imaginary railway system in diagram form. This consists of three lines, A to H, C to N, and D to L. We will suppose that we have to arrange for the running of five trains over this system, and in order to keep things as simple as possible we will deal with down trains only. Our first train is to be an express from A to H, stopping only at the junctions C and D. In connection with this there is a branch train from C to N, and this connects also with another train from J to L. The other two trains are a stopping service from A to N, and a connecting service from C to H.

In order to show graphically the movement of each of these trains we prepare a chart as shown in Fig. 2. On this the various stations of each route are shown vertically, and are spaced proportionately to their distance from each other. The intervals of time are marked off horizontally. In this case three hours will be sufficient. It will be noted that the graph is really in three separate sections. This is because our imaginary system is supposed to be made up of three routes, as shown in the diagram in Fig. 1. In actual practice a graph of this system would be enough to show a whole day's working, together with local speed variations due to gradients or other causes.

We will make our first train leave the terminus A at 10 a.m. If the speed of the train is known the journey time can be calculated, having regard to conditions on the route, and the appropriate arrival and departure points at the junctions C and D can be arrived at. These points are now connected, and the line marked "No. 1" shows graphically the working of the trains. As the connecting trains from C to N and from J to L run over different sections of the line they cannot be shown on the same diagram. Trains "No. 2" and "No. 3" therefore are shown on separate sections of the chart, each distinct run having a separate section. Thus if there had been 20 branch lines, we should have needed 20 sections to our graph.

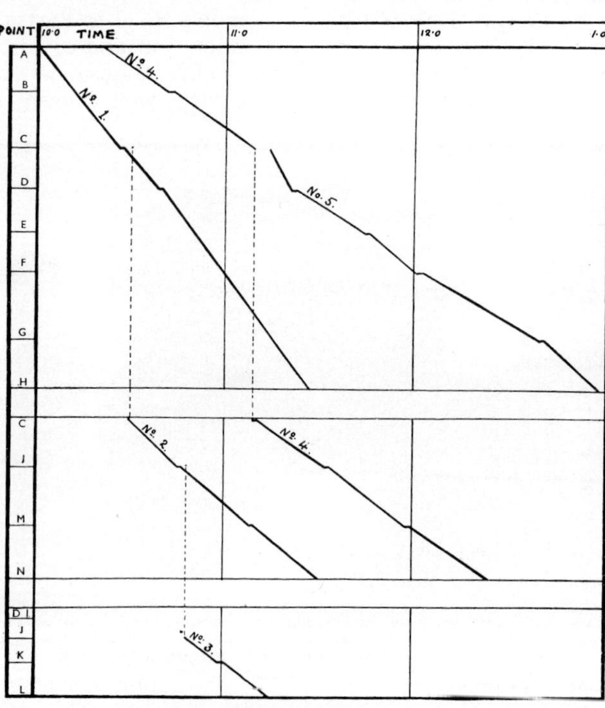

Fig. 2. The chart on which are plotted the paths of down trains on the railway shown in Fig. 1.

It may be wondered what happens when a train leaves one section of the line for another. This is indicated on the graph by a dotted line from one section to another, joining the two corresponding points. Thus train "No. 4" runs from A to C in the top portion of the diagram, and reappears again in the second portion, where its path from C to N is traced. As station C is common to both lines it appears on both graphs.

After we have plotted our trains it is a simple matter to draw up a finished timetable. In plotting the times of our trains we may find two lines on the graph meeting or coming close together. It is then necessary to re-adjust our timing according to the features of the line. The great advantage of the graph system is that it shows exactly where such conflicting paths occur, and we can immediately see the effect of any adjustments.

With such a visual control of our entire system, it is a simple matter to arrange for special trains, or duplicate working, or any other emergency in passenger or goods traffic operation that is demanded of a busy railway.

LIONEL ELECTRIC TRAINS

MADE IN U.S.A.

LOOK AT THESE WONDERFUL NEW **LIONEL** MODELS, WHISTLING, REVERSING, SWITCHING BY REMOTE CONTROL

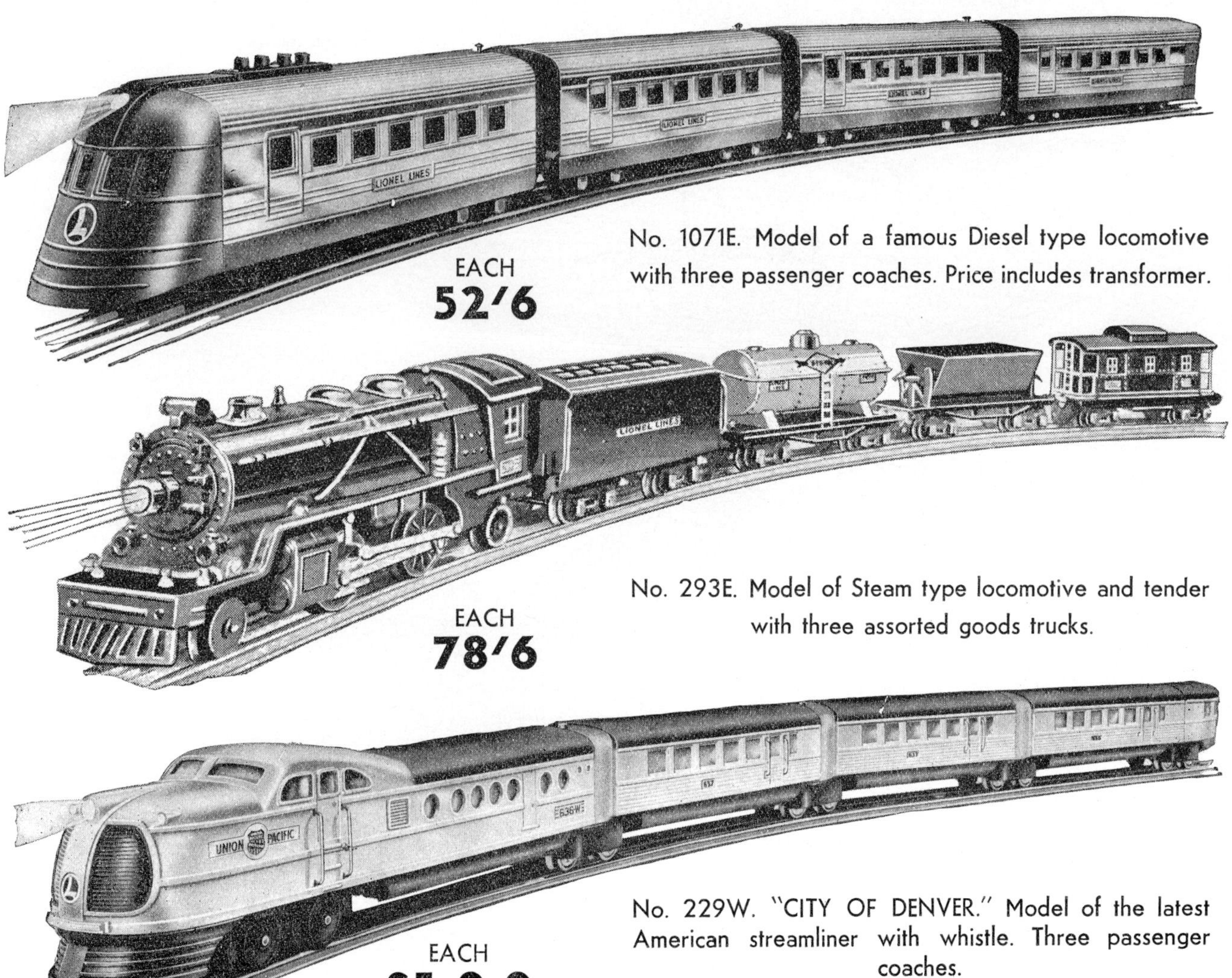

No. 1071E. Model of a famous Diesel type locomotive with three passenger coaches. Price includes transformer.

EACH **52/6**

No. 293E. Model of Steam type locomotive and tender with three assorted goods trucks.

EACH **78/6**

No. 229W. "CITY OF DENVER." Model of the latest American streamliner with whistle. Three passenger coaches.

EACH **£5-0-0**

FREE

Write for Beautifully Illustrated Catalogue of Steam Type Trains and many other fine Models.

To **LIONEL SERVICE DEPT. (17)**

35/36, Aldermanbury, LONDON, E.C.2

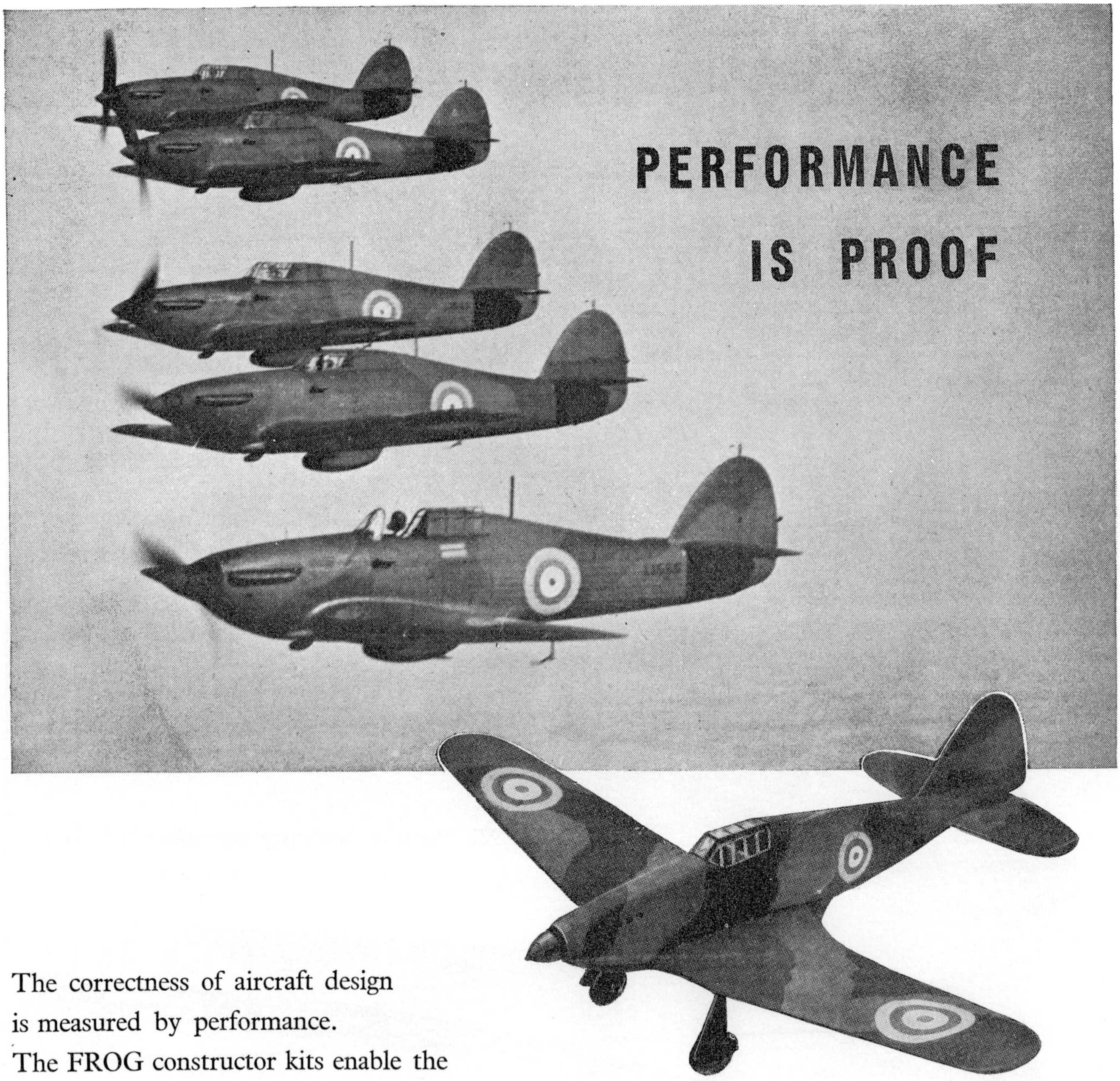

PERFORMANCE IS PROOF

The correctness of aircraft design is measured by performance. The FROG constructor kits enable the enthusiast to build a model with both high performance and excellent appearance. Constructor kits from 1/6 to 21/-. See them at your local toyshop or post the coupon below.

HAWKER HURRICANE **1'6**

NO TOOLS REQUIRED · ALL PARTS CUT TO SHAPE · INSTRUCTIONS EASY TO FOLLOW · EXCELLENT PERFORMANCE

MODEL AIRCRAFT

Covered by World Patents granted and pending.

Made in England by International Model Aircraft Ltd.

OBTAINABLE AT ALL GOOD TOYSHOPS AND STORES Sole Concessionaires:

LINES BROS. LTD., MORDEN ROAD, MERTON, S.W.19

FROG Trade Mark Regd.

COUPON *Please send me your "Frog" coloured leaflet with particulars of the "Frog" Flying Club and how to obtain handsome enamelled "Frog" Pilot badges.*

To Lines Bros. Ltd. (Dept. 5), Morden Road, London, S.W.19

NAME...

ADDRESS...

PLEASE WRITE IN BLOCK LETTERS 10'38

A Famous Streamlined Locomotive

On the Footplate of "*Sir Nigel Gresley*"

By a Railway Engineer

FEW locomotives have captured popular fancy to a greater degree than the Class "A4" "Pacifics" of the L.N.E.R. They were the first fully streamlined engines to be built in this country, and although the shrouding covered up a great deal of the motion, and so took away much of the fascination inherent in the sight of powerful machinery in motion, the striking novelty of the outer casing and its queer shape gave a touch of mystery to the engines. Great things were expected of them, and when, barely a month after being turned out of Doncaster works, "*Silver Link*" attained 112½ m.p.h., their fame was assured. But because their wonderful reputation was made primarily on "*The Silver Jubilee*" express, many people got the impression that they were high-speed engines pure and simple, and that on the heavy Anglo-Scottish expresses they were little superior to the "Pacifics" and "Super-Pacifics" that had preceded them.

Now that the type has been multiplied, the majority of the East Coast expresses are regularly hauled by "A4s," and their performances with 500-ton loads are in some ways even more impressive than the spectacular feats achieved with the more moderately weighted streamlined trains. The first additions to the original four silver engines were turned out in standard L.N.E.R. green, and these were followed by the five "Dominion" engines, in Garter blue, for the "*Coronation.*" But there is a degree of inconvenience in having silver, green, and blue engines, as they cannot always be confined to their own special services; to secure the maximum interchangeability blue was adopted for all the "A4s."

On a recent journey by the 5.45 p.m. express from King's Cross to Darlington I was privileged to ride on the footplate for part of the run; our engine was the best known of the whole stud, No. 4498 "*Sir Nigel Gresley.*" Even in the quietest traffic periods the 5.45 p.m. is a difficult train to work, as some of the intermediate timings are very tight, and the load out of King's Cross is rarely less than 14 coaches. But ordinarily this includes a portion for Hull, so that the load is lightened by two or three coaches north of Doncaster. On the occasion of my trip, however, traffic was so heavy that the Newcastle portion alone consisted of 15 coaches. The Hull coaches were run separately as a second portion, and so there was no respite whatever on the northern section of the run. The actual load was 474 tons tare, and 510 tons with passengers and luggage. No. 4498 was in charge of Driver Burfoot, of King's Cross shed, who, as I described in the "*M.M.*" for September 1937, made such a splendid run on the trial spin of the "*Coronation*" express last year; his run it will be remembered included a top speed of 109 m.p.h. On my trip his mate was Fireman Pearce.

"Sir Nigel Gresley" at the head of the 5.45 p.m. Newcastle express from King's Cross on the run described in this article. This photograph and the lower one on the opposite page are by Mr. E. R. Wethersett.

The exterior of a locomotive may be streamlined or not, but there is no changing the cab. Riding on the footplate and looking out through the front glasses one is scarcely conscious of the streamlining, except to note how efficiently that peculiar wedge-shaped front throws the exhaust steam clear of the cab. The "A4s" have the standard Gresley regulator, with two handles, one on either side of the cab, and also the vertical column reversing gear; this latter is a beautifully easy appliance to manipulate, requiring none of the brawn needed with some older pattern lever gears. Bucket seats for the driver and fireman were first fitted on the "A4s," but now all the L.N.E.R. "Pacifics" have been so equipped. Apart from the canopy that covers the air-pocket between the engine and the front of the tender, there is scarcely any difference between the layout of the fittings on the "A4s" and on the ordinary "Super-Pacifics" of Class "A3." The streamliners, however, are all fitted with a recording speedometer. This appliance is mounted underneath the fireman's seat, in which position it can be read after dark quite easily in the light of the fire.

The schedule for the King's Cross–Grantham stage, 114 minutes for 105.5 miles, is not exceptionally hard by present standards, and we suffered a number of traffic delays. But after adverse signals at Potter's Bar and Welwyn North had made us two minutes late, there came a fine sprint, in which the 43.1 miles from Hitchin to Fletton Junction were reeled off in 34 min. 24 sec., at an average speed of exactly 75 m.p.h. We were going well too on the long climb to Stoke, but then came further delays, at Little Bytham and Corby. Fortunately we had a little time in hand, and with a smart recovery from the last of the signal checks we ran into Grantham just on time.

But it was from Grantham northward that the capacity of the engine was shown in so superb a light. Only 50 minutes are allowed for the 50.5-mile run to Doncaster, and with a permanent speed restriction to 55 m.p.h. through Retford, where speed normally would be 80 m.p.h. or over, it needs some very smart work with a 510-ton load. We made a beautifully clean start, and by the time we breasted the second mile post out of Grantham, and the beam from the colour-light signal at the entrance to Peascliffe Tunnel grew into a piercing shaft of green light, No. 4498 was linked up to 15 per cent. cut-off. This is just one-fifth of full gear, yet it was the normal running position for most of the trip.

Just inside the tunnel the descent to the Trent Valley begins. We emerged accelerating quicker than ever. Barkston, 4.2 miles out, was passed at 62 m.p.h., Hougham at 75; and even now that the regulator was pushed back a little we knocked up a merry 82 m.p.h. past Claypole. In spite of this favourable length the initial timing of 15 minutes for the 14.6 miles from Grantham to Newark takes some doing, and we swept through at 79 m.p.h. only 13 sec. to the good. We were easing, too, for the passage over Muskham troughs. Water was picked up at just over 70 m.p.h., and then, with the regulator full open again, "*Sir Nigel Gresley*" buckled to it with tremendous vim.

There was a time, not so many years ago, when 60 m.p.h. was considered good going on the level with any load much over 400 tons; but nowadays there seems no limit to what we may expect from the "A4s." Here, across the dead flat of the Trent Valley, No. 4498 accelerated from 70 to the astonishing speed of 77½ m.p.h. in a little over four miles. We began the rise to Askham Tunnel in wonderful style; in the first mile or so the drop in speed was barely perceptible, but the driver was taking no chances. When half-way up the first 1 in 200 pitch cut-off was advanced to 20 per cent. This took us through Dukeries Junction at the unusually high rate of 62 m.p.h.—after four miles of climbing—and now, although the grade was easing slightly, cut-off was further advanced, to 25 per cent., to take us over the final hummock past Markham signal box.

A cut-off of 25 per cent., if used continuously with a wide open regulator, would be moderately hard going on a big engine, but these short spells, judiciously timed, made very little extra demand on the boiler, and yet were saving whole minutes in running. For the response of No. 4498 to the longer cut-off was really startling, and we stormed over Markham summit at 64 m.p.h. The gear was quickly linked up to 15 per cent. again, and almost as quickly we were racing downhill at 82 m.p.h.; but steam was shut off now, and

L.N.E.R. No. 4498 "Sir Nigel Gresley," the hundredth Gresley "Pacific" locomotive to be built. A splendid Gauge OO model of this engine is introduced in the new Hornby-Dublo Railway System described on page 554. Photograph by courtesy of the L.N.E.R.

Burfoot, with an occasional glance at the speedometer, was making gentle applications of the brake in readiness for the slack through Retford. We came down well below the limit, to a little under 50 m.p.h., and passed through the station, 33.1 miles from Grantham, in 30¾ minutes.

Then we streaked away to 75 m.p.h. on little easier than level road near Scrooby troughs. The 3-mile rise to Piper's Wood was taken flying. At Bawtry, half-way up, there came again that magic turn of the reversing screw, and with cut-off thereby increased from 15 to 20 per cent. *"Sir Nigel Gresley"* took his big load of 510 tons fairly sailing over the summit at 67 m.p.h. We touched 77½ m.p.h. on the down grade through Rossington, and were past Black Carr Junction, 47.7 miles from Grantham, in exactly 44 minutes. Steam was shut off now, and slowing all the time we ran past miles of sidings and seemingly endless coal trains. At the locomotive running sheds, over on our right, in the dusk one recognised the familiar shapes of "Atlantics," "Pacifics," "Green Arrows," streamliners and many more. A minute later we were entering Doncaster station to stop in the brilliant time of 48¾ minutes, a start-to-stop average speed of 62¼ m.p.h. over the 50.5 miles from Grantham.

There is little respite on the next section especially as we were continuing without any reduction in load. For 10 miles the line is dead level, and here it was extremely interesting to note just how rapidly the engine gathered speed. Burfoot linked up, bit by bit, his adjustments being made in inverse ration to the rise in speed. Two miles out we were doing 50 m.p.h.; in another two speed was up to a mile a minute, and in ten miles from Doncaster we attained a full 75 an hour. In the next four miles, although the country remains as flat as the proverbial pancake, there are three little hummocks, where the railway crosses in succession the Knottingley and Goole Canal, the line from Hull to Wakefield, and the River Aire.Each of these involves a modest rise above the level of the surrounding country, and the longest adverse pitch, three-quarters of a mile at 1 in 270, pulled us down to 71½ m.p.h. But once to the dead flat again north of Templehirst *"Sir Nigel Gresley"* developed the finest bit of speeding on the whole trip by attaining 79 m.p.h.

A train of new vehicles provided for "The Flying Scotsman" service this year, hauled by "Sir Nigel Gresley." This photograph was taken on a special run before the new train went into regular service.

So we passed Brayton Junction, 17.0 miles from Doncaster, in the remarkably short time of 17 min. 35 sec. Approaching Selby signals were against us, but in response, it seemed, to our musical chime whistle, the "distant" was pulled off, and the check did not cost us more than half a minute in running, as we were in any case preparing to slow down for the usual 30 m.p.h. slack.

In passing, it is interesting to note the variety of signals met with on this run. In the Southern Area the old Great Northern somersault type are rapidly being replaced by standard upper quadrant semaphores; there are colour lights at many points, and here, in the North Eastern area, the very distinctive lower quadrant signals of the former N.E.R., which work in a slot in their wooden post, are much in evidence.

We were through Selby, 18.4 miles from Doncaster, in 20¼ minutes, and then with regulator wide open and the valves cutting off at 35 per cent. we roared out across the swing bridge over the Ouse and round the great curve beyond. A backward look from the footplate revealed a seemingly endless chain of lighted windows as our 15-coach train came winding round behind us. In the meantime Burfoot was linking up step by step, and by the time we swung over Barlby Junction, not more than three-quarters of a mile beyond Selby, No. 4498 was working on 15 per cent. cut-off once more. This stretch of road is definitely against the engine. There is nothing that could be termed a "bank," but a succession of short lengths graded at 1 in 222, 1 in 228, or so come one after the other, and culminate in the 2-mile rise at 1 in 390 to the second crossing of the Ouse, at Naburn swing bridge.

Four miles beyond Selby we were doing a mile a minute. Escrick was passed at 66 m.p.h., and we cleared Naburn bridge at 70 m.p.h. The slowing up for York, however, begins a full 2 miles out, with the preliminary slack over Chaloner's Whin Junction. We were past this point, 30.2 miles from Doncaster, in 32½ minutes, but as we neared the great gantry that spans the tracks by Holgate excursion platforms our own particular signal showed red, until we were within a hundred yards of it. Then the arm was pulled off, and there flashed up an illuminated letter M. This was one of the new multiple-lamp route indicators, recently installed, that aptly foreshadow the coming resignalling of York station throughout with colour-light signals. We ran gently through to the north end of the station, and in spite of the final check, and the slight one at Selby, drew up in 36¾ minutes from Doncaster, just inside the sharp 37-minute booking. Our net time for the 32.2 mile run was 35¾ minutes, and considering that this particular schedule is designed for a train-load of about 400 tons No. 4498 had done splendidly indeed.

On the last stage I travelled in the train, a contrast indeed in smoothness and comfort. After stowing away my overalls and cleaning up generally I resumed timing, to find that No. 4498 and her crew were carrying on in the same brilliant style. We were doing 70 m.p.h. in just ten miles from York, and against the faintly rising nature of the road attained a full 75 an hour at Sessay. Then unfortunately there came a very bad signal check, approaching Thirsk, which cost us nearly 5 minutes in running. Nevertheless speed was recovered well, and with a glorious sprint over the final 14 miles from Northallerton, the 44.1 miles from York to Darlington were completed in 47¾ minutes, less than a minute outside schedule. Our net time indeed was not a second over 43 minutes, and as I waved farewell to the enginemen, and watched the train leave for Newcastle, I felt that one could scarcely wish for a finer example of British locomotive performance. My mind went back to a previous trip behind *"Sir Nigel Gresley,"* which I described in the *"M.M."* for August of this year. Then this splendid engine regaled us by a glorious burst of speed between Grantham and Peterborough, touching 94 m.p.h. and continuing for 10 miles at an average of 89.8 m.p.h. with a 510-ton train.

TRICKS TO AMUSE YOUR FRIENDS

ONE of the most fascinating branches of photography is the production of humorous "trick" or "fake" prints. The variety of results it is possible to obtain even with the most simple cameras is almost endless, and as all the work can be carried out indoors, photography of this kind is particularly suitable for the long winter evenings.

Probably the most mysterious photographic trick is the "Headless Man." The illustrations on this and the opposite page reveal the idea and the means by which the illusion is produced, and the photography can be carried out with a box camera. The assistance of two friends is necessary. The only other requirements are two large white sheets, one to serve as a background and the other to be wrapped around one of the sitters, and a small white cloth to cover the head and neck of the other sitter.

The two sitters should be of similar build, since any marked difference will lead to incongruity in the finished result. One must be swathed from the neck downward in a white sheet, while the other, whose head is covered with the smaller white cloth, holds the former's head in his hands.

The "Headless Man." The gruesome photograph on the right can be produced with any kind of camera, and how the mystifying trick is carried out is revealed by the accompanying drawing.

The negative should be slightly over-exposed, and as an image of sharp contrast is wanted development must be prolonged until a considerable degree of density has been built up in the negative. The prolonged development, coupled with over-exposure, will blot out the shadow detail in the "shroud."

Prints showing a man shaving himself or extracting one of his own teeth are other examples of humorous photographs that can be produced on similar lines; while a photograph of a headless man engaged in trimming off with scissors one or two curves in his neck is also within the scope of this model.

Another popular trick photograph is the "ghost" picture. Prints of this kind are very easily made, and even the simplest box camera will give good results. Let us suppose that it is desired to photograph a friend with a "ghost" standing behind him. First the scene is arranged as required, and then the friend and the "ghost," who is covered from head to foot with a white sheet, are placed in their respective positions. A photograph is taken, giving only one-half the full exposure required. The "ghost" then walks out and the second half of the exposure is given, the sitter keeping perfectly still between the two exposures. The negative will then show the sitter and the scene properly exposed, and only a thin transparent image of the ghost will appear in the view.

A photograph showing a person "imprisoned" in a bottle is an amusing photographic trick that is easily produced with a camera having a focussing screen. A clear glass bottle is placed against a dark background such as a piece of brown paper, and focussed to a large size upon the ground-glass screen. Next, four pieces of stamp paper are stuck on the screen to mark the inside portion of the bottle. A plate is then exposed to get a picture of the bottle, but is not developed.

Next the person who is to appear in the bottle is placed against a black background, and the figure is focussed so that it comes within the area marked by the stamp paper on the screen. The undeveloped plate is replaced in the camera, and given a second exposure. When the plate is developed in the usual way the figure will appear to be standing inside the bottle. The secret of success is to have the backgrounds dark and the sitter in light clothes.

The "man in a bottle' 'trick and many others may also be done by a process known as "double" or "combination" printing. Combination printing is most frequently used to put in a more suitable background to a portrait or to place figures in landscapes, and readers will find this process a great help in the production of "mystery" photographs. For example, suppose that it is desired to transplant a photograph of a friend, taken against an unsightly brick wall, into the foreground of a beautiful landscape photographed on another occasion. All that is required is some daylight printing paper and red water-colour paint, or some of the special opaque mixtures sold for blocking out negatives.

Obviously it would be absurd to transfer a figure lighted from the left into a view lighted from the right, so care must be taken that both pictures are lighted from approximately the same angle.

Assuming that the negatives pass this test, work is commenced on the portrait negative, which we will call "A," the landscape negative being labelled "B," for identification purposes. First, everything except the portrait on "A" is painted out, a very fine-pointed brush being used to preserve the outline of the figure. Sufficient colour must be laid on to render the blocked-out portion equally dense in every part. As soon as the paint is dry an ordinary P.O.P. contact print is made. This will show the figure against a plain white background. The next step is to paint over the figure on the print, so that it is completely protected from light action while the remainder of the print is being made. As P.O.P. is sensitive to daylight, it is advisable to carry out this operation in artificial light, care being exercised to ensure accuracy in exactly covering the outline, overlapping either way being avoided.

How to arrange the sitters in producing the trick photograph reproduced below.

The paper bearing the painted-over figure is now placed in contact with negative "B," and a print is made of the same depth of tone as the figure. The print now shows a landscape with a paint-covered figure, and a little rinsing under the tap will quickly remove the paint. The print is now toned and fixed and there should be nothing to indicate that it is other than an untouched print from one negative. Your friend will be greatly mystified to find himself photographed in a place where perhaps he has never been!

Another "Headless Man" picture easily produced by the method shown in the illustration at the top of this page.

Another highly amusing photographic trick is the production of a print showing a person or object severely distorted. The most simple method of working, and one that does not necessitate the making of a negative specially for the purpose, is as follows. A suitable negative, preferably a full length portrait, is selected and then soaked in water until the gelatine emulsion is softened. It is then left to dry until all water drops on the surface and back of the negative have evaporated. Then while the emulsion is still soft, the negative is held over a moderately warm flame such as that from a small gas jet turned almost "off." The gelatine will soon begin to melt, and the negative should then be tipped and twisted about so as to divert the flow in the desired direction. For instance, the gelatine on which is the image of the person's legs may be run sideways slightly, while his head may be separated from the body by a lengthy neck! When the desired effect has been obtained the negative should be laid in a horizontal position and left to cool. If a film negative is used, care must be taken to prevent it from becoming ignited, and in this case it is best to melt the gelatine by the heat from an electric light bulb.

A photograph of a person with a gigantic head and a little body is another amusing trick that never fails to command a laugh. Many variations of this trick will, of course, suggest themselves, and the method of working is practically the same in every instance. The most simple method is known as the "paste-on" process. No special equipment is necessary and suitable existing prints can be used. Two photographs of the same person are required. One of these should be a "close-up" showing the person's head on as large a scale as possible. The other must be a full length portrait, and should be taken at some distance so that it is on quite a small scale. The best results will be obtained with photographs that are lighted from the same angle, and if special photographs are taken for the purpose this point should be carefully watched.

The large head from the close-up print is carefully cut out and pasted in position on the small body of the other print. The joined-up prints should be as nearly as possible similar in tone, and the picture to be pasted on should be made on thin paper, so that the edges of the cut-out will not be visible. The effect is greatly improved by a little careful pencil shading on the combination print to hide any signs of the joint.

If a camera with double extension is available to permit copying, the combined print should be photographed. Prints from the resulting negative will be found even more effective than the original combination print.

To render the description simple we have confined ourselves to a very straightforward example of a combination print, but endless scope is provided by this method for the production of different types of humorous subjects. Other examples are "Grandpa vaulting a pillar-box," a boy riding a bicycle on the sea, or even a Rugby footballer making a gallant leap six yards into the air to prevent a "drop" at goal from crossing the bar. A slightly different procedure is required in the case of "Vaulting Grandpa." A print of this kind would require three exposures and three printings—first a portrait of Grandpa; second, a chum vaulting a small table or other fairly wide object; and third, a street scene including a pillar-box. Grandpa's head would have to be superimposed upon the vaulter's shoulders, and the latter pasted in turn over the pillar-box. Other good trick photographs can be produced by combining two or more of the foregoing suggestions.

It should be remembered that success in trick photography is attained not so much by the use of special apparatus as by imagination and careful planning. The subject is full of fascination and provides a good training in the working of various photographic processes.

MERSEY MODELS

STEAM ENGINES (From 12′6 to 47′6)
and WORKSHOP MODELS (From 2′6 to 10′6)

Mersey Models are obtainable from all the large stores and leading toy shops. Send for name and address of your nearest dealer.

You can build Mersey Models into Meccano models, or fit extra gearing made from Meccano parts (securing by screws to the wood base), as the gear wheels and axle rods are of the same standard as Meccano.

Send for fully illustrated catalogue. (Free)

MODEL GRINDSTONE
True to detail and moulded throughout in Bakelite.
Price **2/6**
(Postage and packing 6d.)

MODEL PRESS. Small Power Press, with ⅛ in. plunger and die. Attractively finished with plated table. Can be driven by any of our steam-engines or by our Electric Motor. Price **5/6** (Postage and packing 6d.)

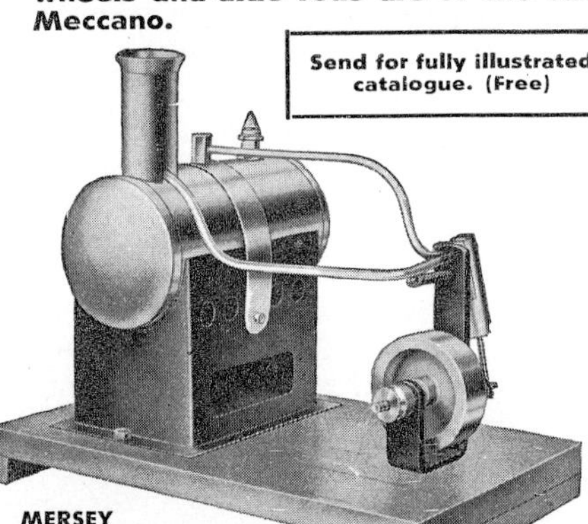

MERSEY MODEL No. 51
Price 12/6
(Carriage and packing 9d.)

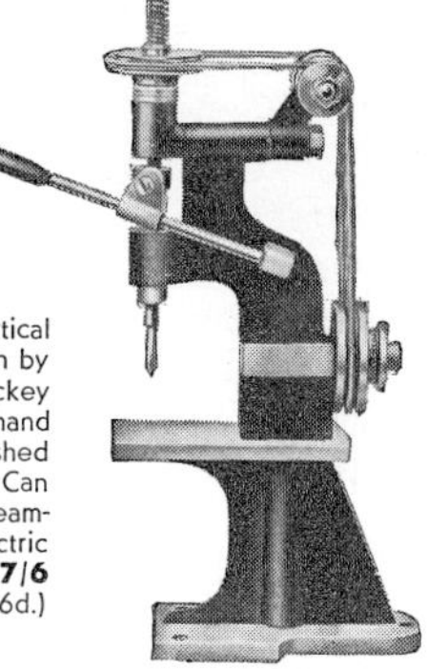

MODEL DRILL. Vertical High Speed Drill, driven by spring belt over jockey pulleys, operated by hand lever. Attractively finished with plated pulleys, etc. Can be driven by any of our steam-engines or by our Electric Motor. Price **7/6** (Postage and packing 6d.)

MODEL LATHE. This ⅜ in. Centre Model Flat-bed lathe is fitted with headstock, tailstock and slide rest. The latter can be operated at any angle. Drive is by two-speed V Pulley. Can be driven by any of our steam-engines or by our Electric Motor. Plated finish. Price **10/6** (Postage and packing 6d.)

MODEL CIRCULAR SAW. This model is of sturdy design and has an adjustable table. Can be driven by any of our steam-engines or by our Electric Motor. Price **4/6** (Postage and packing 6d.)

Sole Manufacturers: **MERSEY MODEL CO. LTD., Cooper's Buildings, Church Street, LIVERPOOL 1**

"WILCO" FAVOURITES

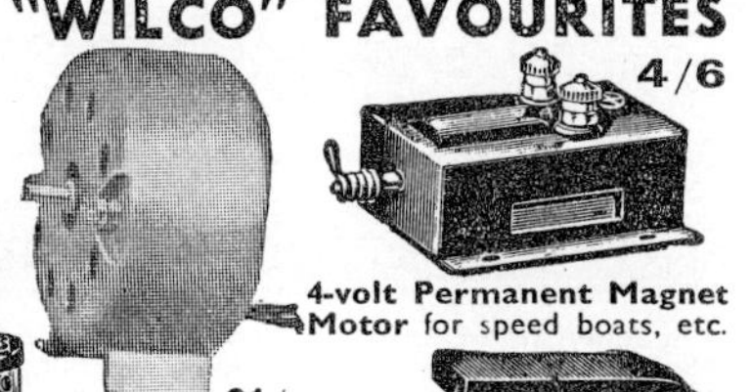

21′6 Complete with Rear Lamp

'Wilco' Cycle Dynamo Set This beautiful all chromium set has our standard ball bearing, easy running dynamo, and the headlamp is fitted with 2 bulbs, both of which work from dynamo or battery and are controlled by a rotary switch on lamp. A fully guaranteed set that you will be proud to own. Other models from **14/9** to **23/9.**

21/- A first class A.C. Motor, 200/250 volts. Self-lubricating bearings, silent running and excellent for Meccano model driving, also geared type for cine-projectors, etc

4/6 **4-volt Permanent Magnet Motor** for speed boats, etc.

2′9 Post 4d **Ideal 4-volt Motor** for Meccano models and speed boats, base plate drilled for easy mounting.

Ironclad Geared Motor. 4-6-volt. Very powerful indeed and will work from batteries or off A.C. mains through a "Wilco" Transformer.
Price **9′6** Post 6d. (un-geared)
Price **12′6** (as illus.) Post 6d.

Miniature Fittings. Complete with bulb, flex and clip for battery. 1⅛" to 2⅜" high. Each **1′-** Post 2d.

"WILCO" Low Voltage Transformer—with speed regulator, reduces 200-250 vt. A.C. to 2-8 volts. Capacity 3 amperes. Will drive small motors perfectly Price **15′6**

Price **14′6** Post 6d
Our best Dynamo will light up your Models or Railway with SIX 3.5-volt Bulbs.

200/250-vt. A.C. **Geared Mains Motor 30′-** Just right for driving models.

3/-. Post 4d. **Shocking Coil.** Operates from a Standard dry battery Other models up to 45/- each.

44 page Catalogue Entirely Revised. Full of Good Lines. 4d. Post Free.
L. WILKINSON, "Electric House," 204, Lower Addiscombe Rd., CROYDON

BRITAIN'S DEFENCE IN SCALE MODELS

Complete A.A. GUN Detachment	... ...	price 4/6
Complete SEARCHLIGHT UNIT	... ...	price 4/–
MODERN TRENCH LAYOUT	... ...	price 5/–

Sets of Figures, ARMY, TERRITORIAL, R.A.F. and Civilian. AIRPORT Buildings, HANGARS, etc., and all accessories to 1/72nd scale.

SKYBIRDS

WARTIME and MODERN AIRCRAFT.
Complete Models or Constructive Sets. All to scale in this WORLD FAMOUS Series.
LATEST ADDITIONS: The BLACKBURN "SKUA."
Constructive Set price **1/6.** Completed model **12/6.**
SKYBIRDS "MAMMOTH" Hangar price **10/6.**
If unable to obtain from local agents, write:
"SKYBIRDS" (Desk B.) **3, ALDERMANBURY AVE., LONDON E.C.2.**

The New "*Twentieth Century Limited*"

Luxury Trains for Famous American Service

THE "*Twentieth Century Limited*" of the New York Central Railroad, which is shown on our cover, is one of the most famous of the world's great trains. It has run between New York and Chicago since June 1902. In its early days it covered the distance of 960 miles between the two cities in 20 hours, its average speed being nearly 49 m.p.h. It was then said that the experiment of running a train over such a long distance at this high speed could not be maintained, as neither the rolling stock nor the track would be able to stand up to the treatment they would receive, but the train was immediately successful and grew more and more popular.

To begin with there were only five coaches, carrying 27 passengers, but the train soon grew to enormous dimensions, and on rush days had to be run in sections. New and more luxurious rolling stock has been introduced from time to time, more powerful engines have been designed to haul it, and the journey time has been reduced step by step until to-day the "*Twentieth Century Limited*" takes only 16 hrs. for its long journey. Every day sections leave New York in the east and Chicago in the west in the evening, and run through the night over the water-level route of the railway along the shores of the Great Lakes and the banks of the Hudson River, reaching their destinations at breakfast time on the following morning.

The streamlined "Twentieth Century Limited" on its 16-hour run between New York and Chicago. The train is headed by one of the streamlined "Hudson" locomotives described on this page. Photograph by courtesy of the New York Central System.

The reduction to 16 hrs. for the time between New York and Chicago was made in June of this year, when streamlined locomotive giants and new coaches were introduced. Altogether 62 coaches and 10 streamlined locomotives were built for this purpose in order to allow the operation between the two great cities of four sections. From front to rear each complete train appears like a smooth, jointed metallic tube on wheels. In its first month of operation there was a great increase in the number of passengers travelling by it, and equal interest was shown by onlookers. Every night thousands of motorists made special trips to crossings to see it speed by at 80 m.p.h., and in the cities through which it passes seeing the "*Century*" go by is a recognised diversion.

Between New York and Harmon, a run of 46 min., the train is hauled by an electric locomotive, for steam locomotives do not work into New York City. For the rest of the journey, between Harmon and Chicago, the most modern of steam locomotives are employed; sleek grey giants, streamlined and finished generally to match perfectly the rolling stock. How striking in appearance these engines are is shown in our cover illustration—prepared from a photograph kindly supplied by the New York Central System—and from the photograph on this page. They have the sheet metal "prow" or apron that is a popular fitting on American streamlined locomotives, and this rises up to a bulbous boiler front on which is a characteristic fin in which the headlight is centred. The cylinders, wheels and motion are all exposed; there is no mystery about these parts of the engine, for utility has made the shrouding of the working parts inadvisable.

The chimney is not visible externally, but is contained within a trough-shaped casing running the length of the boiler top. Smoke deflection is provided for by means of louvred openings at the front end of this casing; these openings can be seen in the illustration on this page.

The wheel arrangement of the engine is the 4–6–4 or "Hudson" type introduced into the United States by the New York Central in 1927. Since that time engines of this type have given splendid service on the "*Century*" and other main line trains. They are simple in general design and robust in construction, as is characteristic of most American locomotive types. Two cylinders only are fitted, but these in conjunction with the vast boiler provide sufficient power for the haulage of the heaviest and the fastest expresses. The locomotives have aluminium-finished driving wheels. The fin already mentioned is of aluminium with a special satin finish.

The new "*Twentieth Century*" trains are made up of from 13 to 16 coaches of weights varying from 57 to 67½ tons empty. All the underframes, sides, ends and roofs of the new vehicles are of "Cor-Ten" steel, assembled as far as possible by welding. This form of construction, together with the use of aluminium alloy for various parts, gives the new coaches a weight of little more than two-thirds of that of the older all-steel stock previously used.

There are no open berths in the sleeping coaches, where the accommodation consists of what are known as "roomettes," bedrooms, compartments and drawing rooms. The "roomettes" are private sitting rooms by day and bedrooms by night, with every modern comfort for their occupants. A greater novelty is provided by the duplex compartments, an ingenious "upstairs and downstairs" arrangement of rooms on two levels, in each of which is a sofa that becomes a bed by night. The dining cars also are specially luxurious.

How Geographical Globes Are Made

Reproducing the World on Glass Spheres

By K. J. Schaub

WHETHER in London, New York, Capetown, Bombay or Berlin, few people rotating a globe on their desks, seeking some definite spot on the many-coloured sphere, have any notion where the globe comes from.

In Lichterfelde, a suburb of Berlin, there is a factory that produces geographical globes for the whole world, with the 5,000 names on each, translated into 24 different languages. It is a long, laborious process from the first dab of paint to the finishing touch.

Famous scientists are studying day in, day out, examining and noting every change undergone by Mother Earth. Here a town has been renamed; there near the South Pole new land has been discovered; here again an important canal has been cut, and there new frontiers have to be taken into account.

Gluing a map section on a glass globe. There are 12 sections to each globe, and they are illuminated by an electric lamp placed inside it.

Political events can alter the whole cartographical face of the earth in a night. A short time ago, for instance, Manchukuo in Asia was made an independent state and had to be given a national colour of its own on the map. Ethiopia, as part of the Italian Empire, had to be re-coloured in the same hue as Italy, and forthcoming editions will portray Austria in the same colour as Germany. The recent frontier changes in Czecho-Slovakia also will be shown in due course by the globe maker.

One of the most essential foundations of globe manufacture has long been the sub-division of the map of the world into 12 equal segments. These ellipse-shaped sections of map are printed in 24 different grades of colour, and these when put together later on will form the multi-coloured surface of the globe.

The globes have diameters varying from 5 in. to about 3 ft. 6 in. The core consists of papier maché and iron in the smaller models and of steel and aluminium in the larger ones. The papier maché is shaped into hemispheres by means of hydraulic pressure, and these are afterwards placed together to form the complete globe.

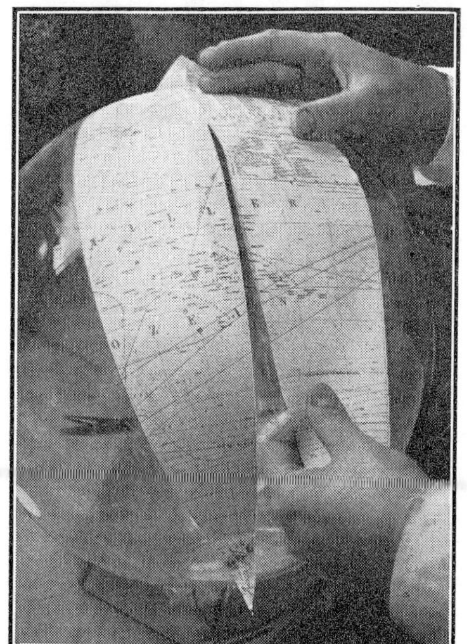

Fitting two of the 12 map sections together. The greatest accuracy is necessary in this work.

Next begins the deft work of expert gluing girls. The 12 map sectors are carefully cut out and glued in succession to the pressed globe. This sounds very simple, but to watch this work is to get quite a different impression of the difficulties involved. It is a question of accurately fitting frontier to frontier, river to river and degree to degree. Not a crease must be made. The sectors must not be even a fraction of an inch too narrow or too wide, for with the 12 sections this would cause too large an error, and in the end the last piece of map would not meet its neighbours, or would overlap them.

Eventually each globe is set up on its North-South Pole axis, and the many-coloured sphere is ready in its final make-up. The globes are next washed in warm water, coated with ordinary edible gelatine, and finally painted all over with oil lacquer. They are then ready to begin their journey across the world.

Two new inventions have recently taken their place in this workshop. One is the extremely practical, so-called light globe. In this case the globe is not made of cardboard or aluminium, but of glass, and it is lit from within by means of an electric light bulb. The internal lighting makes the map particularly clear and colourful.

The second invention is the "Great Globe." This is a masterpiece of workmanship, with a diameter of over 3 ft. Nearly three years of scientific work were required in order to reproduce the Earth in this size for the first time. This impressive picture of the world indicates not only the political configuration, but also the river and mountain systems. There is also the whole traffic network of the world, including caravan routes, steamship lines, railway lines and air routes, and finally all the large radio stations are shown. Furthermore this map also marks deserts and the limits of pack ice.

When the idea of constructing such a mighty globe was first mooted the manufacturers pondered for a long time whether it would be possible to find a purchaser. To-day so many orders have been received from all over the world that the firm does not know which to supply first. Not only scientific institutes and political organisations, but also many private individuals have purchased these globes.

How the Locomotive Works

1. Steam-Raising and Superheating

By a Railway Engineer

A LITTLE thrill goes through the group of onlookers as departure time comes. Then—*"Right Away!"*—the driver gives a sharp tug at a slender-looking rod; there is a hiss as the sanding valves open, a first explosive burst of the exhaust, and they are off. Fascinating, is it not? The steam locomotive is the embodiment of power, especially if, just as it is getting under way, there comes a slip, the wheels spin round, and with a thunderous roar, a great column of exhaust steam goes high in the air. In spite of its fascination, however, the steam locomotive remains one of the least understood of machines, and at the Editor's request I have prepared a couple of articles which, it is hoped, will make clear the principles on which it works.

The upper illustration on the opposite page shows a longitudinal section through the boiler and fire-box of a typical locomotive. Considering first of all the fire-box end, it is perhaps not generally realised that what is externally visible is not the actual fire-box but only an outer shell. The fire-box proper, which on British locomotives is usually made of copper, is surrounded, except on the underside, by a jacket of water; this not only produces extremely rapid boiling of the water, but also prevents the fire-box walls from getting unduly hot. The locomotive fire-box has got to burn coal at a tremendous rate. Imagine burning two hundredweight of coal every hour on a space as big as an ordinary household grate, and you have some idea of the rate of combustion in the engine of a fast express!

To burn coal at this rate it is of course essential to have an ample supply of air. As will be seen from the diagram, this air is provided from two sources; one is through the front damper into the ashpan, and so up through the fire-bars, and the other through the fire-box door. A large grate helps in the burning of the coal, for the fire can be spread more thinly over the surface, and the air can pass up from the ashpan more freely. The speed of the engine would naturally cause air to pass through the dampers and the ashpan, but a very powerful system of forced draught is in action all the time the regulator is open. The exhaust steam, shooting through the smoke-box to the chimney creates a partial vacuum in the smoke-box, and this produces a powerful draught from the fire-box to the front end all the time the cylinders are exhausting.

In the fire-box itself this strong current of air has to be carefully directed to provide the air just where it is wanted, so that complete burning of the fuel takes place over the whole area of the grate. The air-stream entering through the front damper, and thence up through the ashpan, is directed by means of an arch built of firebricks, which spans the full width of the fire-box. The directions imparted to the air-streams by this brick arch are shown in the sectional diagram. On reaching the backward end of the arch the air is swept round by the draught from the smoke-box and joins the direct stream from the fire-box door. A further study of the diagram shows another valuable function of the brick arch; it draws all the air-streams together so that they impinge upon the tube system exactly at right-angles to the tube-plate. Thus there is a minimum of resistance at entry.

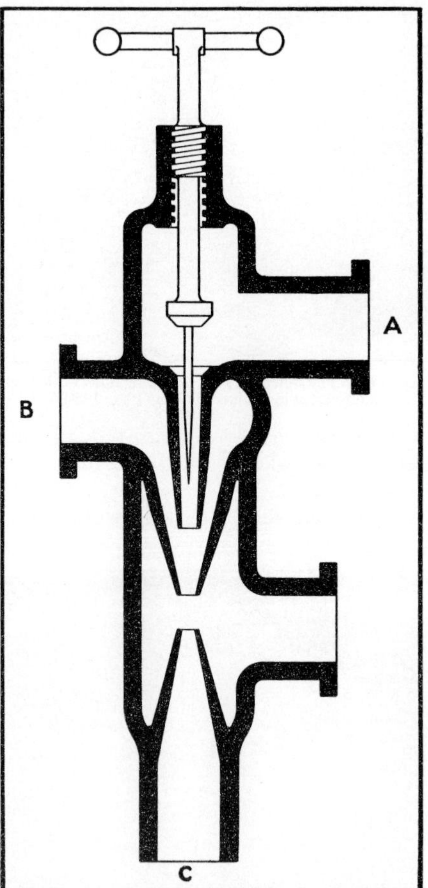

Diagram showing the principle of operation of the injector. A represents the steam inlet, B the entry of the water supply and C the delivery outlet. The other opening, unlettered, is the overflow.

This brings me to the boiler proper. It is often thought that steam locomotives are fitted with a water-tube boiler; this is not the case. The water is contained in the cylindrical drum, and it is the hot gases, hot air, and fumes from the fire that pass through the tubes. In a locomotive boiler the tubes act as flues. There is a very large number of these tubes; on the standard non-streamlined "Super-Pacifics" of the L.N.E.R. for example there are 121 tubes, each just under two inches in diameter inside. The outside of every flue tube is in direct contact with the water. Steel is an excellent conductor of heat, and as the tubes are only $\frac{1}{16}$ in. thick the intense heat of the flue gases rushing through inside is very easily transferred to the water. The outside surface area of the tube is accordingly termed heating surface.

The more tubes there are the more readily will the water be boiled, though there comes a point in any locomotive design where the crowding of more tubes into the boiler in order to obtain more heating surface will defeat its own object, by offering too restricted a passage for the flue gases. The steaming ability of a boiler depends almost entirely upon the draught. It is easier to maintain a powerful draught through a comparatively small number of large tubes than through a great number of small ones, and although the heating surface of the two boilers may be exactly the same the one with the larger tubes will steam much more freely.

A very striking illustration of this point is afforded by the original L.N.W.R. "Claughton" class 4–6–0s, and the three-cylinder reconstructed "Claughtons" of the modern L.M.S. "Patriot" class. The original class had 149 tubes the internal diameter of which was 1.667 in., and, as an old driver once expressed it to me, the engines were often "shy to steam." In the rebuilds the number of tubes is reduced to 140, and the internal diameter is increased to 1.917 in. It is of course well known that the "Patriots" are wonderfully free-steaming engines.

The steam that collects at the top of a locomotive boiler is termed "saturated steam." The vapour rising from the surface of the boiling water carries with it innumerable particles of moisture, and although the pressure may gradually be built up to, say, 200 lb. per sq. in., the steam still remains saturated. In this state it is often called "wet" steam. Modern practice however is universally in favour of using steam that is not merely dry, but is heated above its natural temperature of formation. After the steam has collected at the top of the boiler, either in the dome or in the perforated pipe used on certain types, it is led back into the boiler to be superheated, that is heated above the temperature at which the water naturally boils. I should explain here that whereas under atmospheric conditions water boils at 212 degrees F., when it is boiled under pressure, as in a locomotive boiler, the temperature at which boiling takes place is much higher; at 200 lb. per sq. in. water does not boil until 380 degrees F. is reached.

The steam is carried through a series of special tubes, and to accommodate these a re-arrangement of the flues is necessary. In the case of the L.N.E.R. non-streamlined "Super-Pacifics" there are, in addition to the 121 small flue tubes previously mentioned, 43 large tubes, and these contain the superheater tubes, or elements as they are called. Saturated steam enters a tube at the front end of the superheating system; it is then conducted, as the diagram shows, right back to the fire-box end of the boiler, and then to the front again. In the process the steam is made hotter and hotter until it finally emerges at a temperature of about 700 degrees F. As just explained, the temperature of saturated steam under a pressure of 200 lb. per sq. in. is only 380 degrees F., so that the degree of superheating attained is quite large. The steam is then absolutely dry—a searing, scorching gas, which, unless the greatest care is taken with the lubrication system, will play havoc with cylinders and valves. Saturated steam is far easier to deal with in this respect, for the moisture in it acts as a natural lubricant.

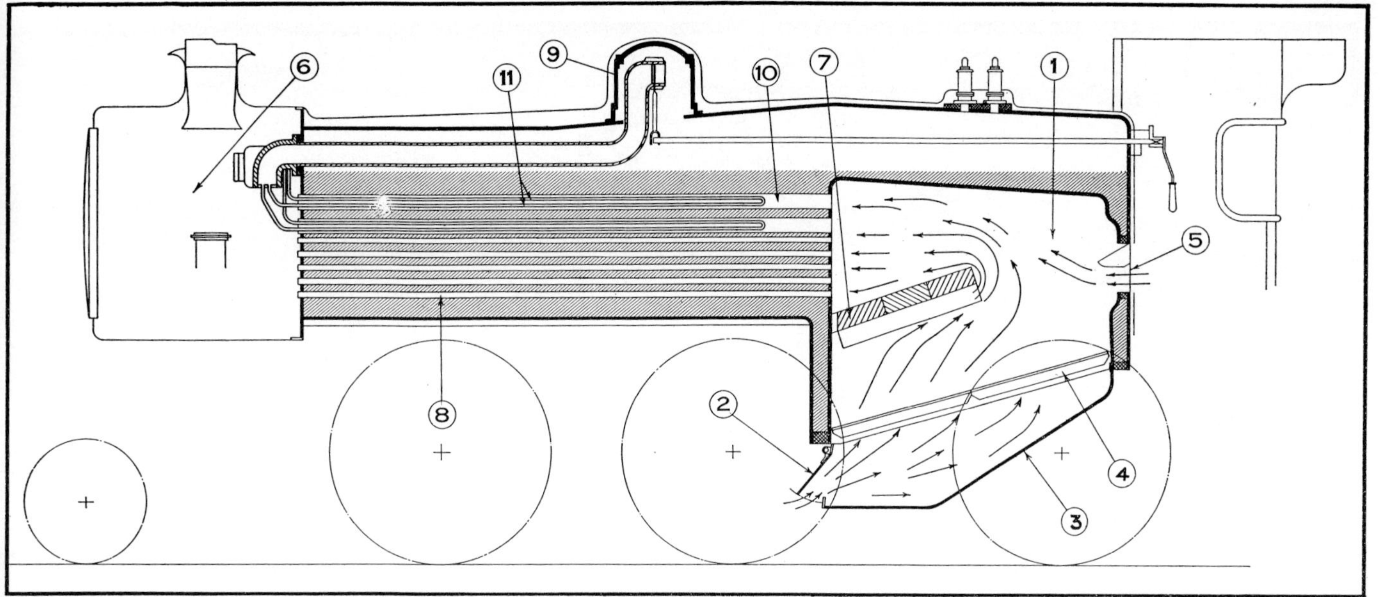

Sectional view of a locomotive boiler and fire-box. The numbers indicate different parts as follows: 1. Inner fire-box, 2. Front damper, 3. Ashpan, 4. Fire-bars, 5. Fire-box door, 6. Smoke-box, 7. Brick arch, 8. Small tubes, 9. Dome (inner), 10. Large tubes, 11. Superheater elements.

In view of this considerable disadvantage, it may well be asked "Why use superheated steam at all?" Another point that is not generally realised adds further weight to the question; superheated steam at, say 200 lb. per sq. in., however much hotter and drier it is, can exert no more force on the pistons than saturated steam at the same pressure. The great advantage of superheated steam, and one that far outweighs any difficulties experienced in the mechanical working of the locomotive, lies in the greater volume of steam obtained from the same amount of coal. Supposing a cubic foot of saturated steam at 175 lb. per sq. in. is superheated to 670 degrees F.; the pressure is kept constant, as in a locomotive boiler, and in consequence the steam expands under the additional heat, just as would steel. That cubic foot of saturated steam would become no less than 1½ cubic feet of superheated steam. This means that to produce the same volume of steam only two-thirds of the amount of water used in a saturated engine needs to be boiled, and of course less coal needs to be burned.

Off to the South! A Gresley "Pacific" locomotive makes the first few puffs of its journey and forms an impressive sight as it leaves Waverley Station, Edinburgh

It would thus seem that by superheating one gets something for nothing; actually of course some of the heat from the flue gases, which would otherwise have been used for evaporation of the water is used in heating the steam that is passing to and fro through the superheater elements. This amount of heat has been found to be practically negligible in proportion to the greatly increased volume of steam obtained. The superheating elements are of necessity placed along the middle of the flue tubes, and here of course the hot flue gases are of little or no value for heating the water; it is the gas immediately in contact with the flue tube walls that provides most of the heating. So what would otherwise be waste heat is utilised for superheating, and this of course is the secret of the great increase in efficiency.

A point that will probably have occurred to readers by this time is "How is the boiler kept full of water?" On the earliest locomotives a simple pump was used, driven off the crosshead; and that method had, of course, the serious drawback that replenishment of the boiler ceased when the engine stopped, as for example during the time of standing at a station. It was a Frenchman, Henri Giffard, who made the wonderful invention of the injector. The diagram on the previous page illustrates the principle upon which the injector works. The pipe A is connected to a steam supply, which can be controlled from the footplate; the pipe B is in direct communication with the water tanks. When steam is turned on through pipe A its passage through the gap where the water pipe joins in creates a partial vacuum and sucks water through the pipe B. The steam then continues through the narrowing cone and, as in the nozzle of a turbine, greatly increases its speed of flow. But it is now thoroughly mixed with cold water sucked in from the tender tank. This mixing causes the steam to condense, and the jet changes into one of hot water travelling at high speed into the delivery pipe at C. The power of this jet is great enough to lift the non-return, or "clack" valve and force a steady stream of hot water into the boiler against the normal working pressure.

Almost all modern locomotives are fitted with two injectors, one using live steam and the other putting some of the exhaust steam to very good purpose. The exhaust steam injector is one of the most ingenious appliances ever invented. Not only does it make use of what would otherwise be waste steam from the exhaust for feeding the boiler, but it also acts as a feed water heater. Working on a steam pressure of no more than 15 lb. per sq. in. one of these marvellous injectors can feed water into the boiler against a pressure of 240 lb. per sq. in.; not only this, the water enters the boiler at nearly 200 degrees F. At such a pressure the boiling point of water is 390 degrees F., so that by means of the exhaust steam injector the water is half-way to boiling point before it even enters the boiler! On fast express runs it is usual to keep the exhaust steam injector on all the time, and to use the live steam injector as a reserve of power when the engine is working especially hard and the water in the boiler is being evaporated very rapidly.

(To be continued)

The Winter Timetables

The winter timetables introduced last month show considerable saving in time on those of last winter. On the G.W.R. high-speed trains cover 2,207 miles at a speed of a mile a minute and over. This is an increase of 91 miles over the corresponding figure last year. Faster services are provided from Paignton and Torquay, Weston-super-Mare, Bristol, Bath and Plymouth to Paddington, and the new timetable includes 3,644 miles to be covered daily by the G.W.R. streamlined railcars.

"The Royal Scot" of the L.M.S. system is 25 min. faster than last year and the total saving on the whole of the L.M.S. system is 825 min. affecting a total of 237 trains. The fastest train is the 6.20 from Birmingham to Euston which covers the 65.0 miles from Rugby to Watford in exactly 60 min. The next fastest train is the *"Liverpool Flyer,"* the 5.25 from Lime Street, which runs from Crewe to Euston, a distance of 158.06 miles, at a speed of 64.08 m.p.h. *"The Coronation Scot"* is the third fastest train, the run from Euston to Carlisle being made at an average speed of 63.42 m.p.h.

The L.N.E.R. winter trains cover 3,392 miles per week more than last year. Improved services are provided in East Anglia, and faster journeys from Yarmouth and Lowestoft to London are included. The early morning service from Glasgow and Edinburgh to King's Cross is accelerated by 10 min.

The new Southern Railway timetable retains the whole of the electric expresses running during the summer, including four trains per hour from London to Brighton and four trains per hour to Portsmouth.

L.M.S. Diesel Train

In September the L.M.S. brought into service the experimental streamlined Diesel-driven light passenger unit, which has undergone several service tests. The train is driven by six 125 h.p. Leyland Diesel-hydraulic traction units and is capable of a maximum of 75 m.p.h.

The train makes three trips daily from Cambridge to Oxford and two from Oxford to Cambridge, with additional short trips from Bletchley to Cambridge and Oxford to Bletchley, making a total mileage of 462 daily. Including stops at Sandy, Bedford and Bletchley, the 77 miles between Cambridge and Oxford take $1\frac{3}{4}$ hours. The highest booked average speeds are 53.3 m.p.h. from Bletchley to Bedford, and 52.1 m.p.h. from Oxford to Bletchley.

The Largest Wagon in Britain

The L.N.E.R. are to build a special trolley wagon that will be capable of carrying a dead load of 120 tons. This will be the largest and heaviest single freight-carrying unit in Great Britain. It will have at least 12 pairs of wheels and will be so arranged that by the use of cantilevers its load capacity can be increased at will up to 150 tons. The wagon will be used for the conveyance of such exceptional loads of machinery as stators and turbines. It will be specially adapted for running over the lines of continental railways, thus avoiding the need for unloading and reloading for shipment.

A 0-6-0 shunting or "switching" locomotive of the Toronto, Hamilton and Buffalo Railway. The New York Central System and the C.P.R. have joint interests in this line. Photograph by H. McMichael, Waterford, Ontario.

Kid Gloves for Railwaymen

Strange to relate, one of the largest and most varied collections of gloves in England is to be found, not in an outfitter's shop, but at the Swindon Stores of the G.W.R. Gloves of all kinds are housed there, from the smart kid gauntlets worn by the company's chauffeurs to the specially tested rubber gloves worn by men doing high tension electrical work. There are gloves for locomotive builders, for those who reduce to scrap-iron a veteran that was once pride of her driver's heart, and for the diver on the river bed surveying the piers of a bridge. Most of the gloves are designed to give protection from fire and electricity, sharp metallic edges and biting acid. They are all useful, but rarely elegant.

A Brisk Run Behind *"Sir Daniel Gooch"*

Last month we announced that one of the latest engines of the G.W.R. "Castle" class has been named *"Sir Daniel Gooch,"* after the celebrated first Locomotive Superintendent of the company and designer of the broad-gauge engines. It was a happy thought to bestow such an honoured name upon one of the "Castle" class, for to the speed and haulage power of the modern type is brought some of the romance always associated with broad-gauge days.

As might be imagined the new *"Sir Daniel Gooch"* is a speedy runner. As an example, on a recent up run on *"The Bristolian,"* despite very rough weather, some fine speeding was done. Adverse signals caused a loss of $1\frac{1}{2}$ min. at the start, so that it took nearly 13 minutes to pass Stoke Gifford East Box, only 6.1 miles out. But after that *"Sir Daniel Gooch"* got going in great style and hauled his 225-ton load over the 72.9 miles on to Tilehurst in $58\frac{1}{2}$ min. A steady 60 m.p.h. up the 1 in 300 to Badminton was followed by a joyous 90 at Little Somerford, and east of Swindon speed lay between 80 and 85 m.p.h. for nearly 30 miles of level road. Reading would have been passed comfortably ahead of time, but heavier trains, normally well ahead of the flyer, had not been able to battle so successfully with the wind, and a series of slight delays prevented a punctual arrival in London. The net time for the 117.6 mile journey from Bristol to Paddington was only $102\frac{3}{4}$ minutes, however; a fine performance.

This run was timed by Mr. O. S. Nock.

G.W.R. Increase Use of Loud-Speakers

The loud-speaker installations at Paddington, Birmingham (Snow Hill), Cardiff and Newport Stations have proved so successful in directing passengers to trains during rush periods that the G.W.R. are to install similar equipment at Torquay.

A second portable loud-speaker unit will also be in use this winter at G.W.R. stations where large sports crowds are anticipated.

* * * *

L.N.E.R. locomotive No. 4806 has been named *"The Green Howard"* by Major-General H. E. Franklyn, D.S.O., M.C.

New Australian 4-6-0s

The upper illustration on this page shows one of a new series of locomotives that has been introduced in Australia. Except for their larger tenders these engines are identical with the C36 class of the New South Wales Government Railway System. The tenders in use are the largest in service in Australia. The new engines are used on the Trans-Australian line between Kalgoorlie (Western Australia) and Port Pirie Junction, a distance of 1,108 miles. The engines are changed once during the run, at Cook, which is approximately the half-way point of the journey.

At 85 per cent. boiler pressure the tractive effort of the new engines is 30,500 lb. Their length over buffers is 81 ft. 3 in. and the total weight of the engine and tender in full working order is 205 tons 10 cwt. The tender capacity is 12,000 gallons of water and 17½ tons of coal.

One of the new "C" class 4-6-0s with 12,000 gallon tenders delivered to the Commonwealth Railways. These engines are for working Trans-Australian expresses between Port Pirie Junction and Kalgoorlie. Photograph by T. Watson, Sydney, Australia.

L.M.S. Notes

The L.M.S. ran 11 special trains carrying a total of over 5,000 passengers to Glasgow for the launching of the new Cunard White Star liner *"Queen Elizabeth"* on 27th September.

The Garratt locomotives Nos. 4967–4999 have been renumbered 7967–7999 in order to provide for prospective class 5P5F 4–6–0s.

All-steel wagons of 16 tons capacity are being built for Imperial Chemical Industries traffic. There will be 50 of them, and they will be used for the conveyance of light soda ash in bulk.

The L.M.S. print five tons of tickets each week, representing five million pieces of cardboard. The annual coal consumption of the company is five million tons, a total that keeps 18,000 miners busy all the year round.

Nearly 15,000 L.M.S. employees will attend evening classes this winter at the company's expense. Various aspects of railway work will be taught at these classes.

"The Coronation Scot" leaving Euston in charge of No. 6223, "Princess Alice," one of the blue streamlined 4-6-2s. Photograph by J. P. Wilson, Nottingham.

New L.N.E.R. Luxury Train

Last month the L.N.E.R. placed in service a new train between Liverpool Street and Harwich (Parkeston Quay). It is known as the *"Hook Continental"* and consists of 11 coaches having seats for 84 first and 240 second class passengers. In accordance with usual practice for Continental services, two Pullman Cars are attached. The *"Hook Continental"* leaves Liverpool St. at 8.15 a.m. and the up train commences at 6.20 a.m. arriving at Liverpool Street at 7.53.

Improving L.N.E.R. Locomotive Depots

The last stages of the work in connection with the improvements at the L.N.E.R. locomotive depot at Lincoln are now in hand and a contract has been placed for the extension of the general stores, in which spare locomotive parts and materials will be kept. A new locomotive depot is being constructed at Darnall, near Sheffield, in connection with the Manchester and Sheffield electrification scheme. This depot will provide accommodation for both steam and electric locomotives. Work is to be commenced almost immediately, as it is desirable that this depot in particular should be ready for the changeover which, according to present schedules, should take place in about two years.

At Darlington, where the depot is being completely modernised, a contract for the rebuilding of the locomotive sheds has already been let. This depot has associations with the earliest public railway in the country, and when complete will be one of the most up-to-date on the L.N.E.R. A mechanical coaling plant, new engine disposal pits, up-to-date repair equipment, new offices and a new mess room are all included in the scheme. The present turntable is to be replaced by one of 70 ft. diameter, which will be able to deal with the largest engines at present in use.

* * * *

L.M.S. Film Units have commenced their tour of the system and 100,000 members of the L.M.S. staff are expected to visit them.

G.W.R. Station Improvements

G.W.R. engineers are at present busy changing Brunel's famous arch roof at Paddington. The old arrangement of a series of hipped sky-lights that extend from the centre of each of the four spans like fishbones is being altered. The new glazing now being fitted to the bay that covers No. 1 platform follows the curve of the roof and admits more light and air. This bay is 700 ft. in length and the work will involve the use of 29,000 sq. ft. of glass and 95 tons of steel work.

The cleaning of the roof will in future be much easier and quicker, as new gangways are being provided, together with a water supply with stopcocks at every 40 ft. The cleaners will work from movable platforms mounted on ball-bearing wheels, which will run on rails stretching the whole length of each side of the bay.

At St. Davids, Exeter, the G.W.R. are carrying out the first instalment of their comprehensive scheme of improvements. This part of the scheme provides for the complete remodelling of the station building on the down side, the widening of the station approach side by 11 ft. for a distance of 170 ft., and the erection of a canopy covering for cars, 350 ft. in length and running along the whole front of the building. The present architectural features of the station will be retained and the new work will be faced with stone to match, so that the completed building will be in harmony with the Cathedral City.

Traffic Speed-Up at Holyhead

With a view to speeding-up the handling of newspapers and merchandise between trains and steamers at Holyhead, the L.M.S. are to instal conveyors. The conveyor on the quay will include a portable section of belt 43 ft. long and 3 ft. wide, adjustable for all conditions of the tide and with speed variable up to a maximum of 200 ft. per min. Each of the three steamers working between Holyhead and Kingstown will be fitted with a separate distributing conveyor, which will be stored on the ship's deck when not in use.

L.M.S. Centenary Exhibition at Birmingham

Last month the L.M.S. arranged for the "Century of Progress" Exhibition held at Euston to be repeated in Birmingham. Historic locomotives and coaches were on show and a collection of relics and models were exhibited at the City Art Gallery.

The World's Giant Silk Moths

Cocoons Brought to England by Air

By L. Hugh Newman

THE silk-producing insects of the world form one of the largest family of moths, and their life histories are extraordinarily interesting. Most of them have on one or both pairs of wings distinct "eye" spots that undoubtedly serve as warning colouration. All the moths in this family have large plump bodies that would make a tasty meal for any insect-eating animal or bird. When they are at rest, with forewings drooped down over the hind wings, the spots are covered; but immediately the insects are disturbed they raise and expand their wings and thus expose the spots, which give the impression that some animal has awakened and opened its huge eyes!

An Atlas moth drying its wings shortly after emerging from its silk cocoon. These giant moths from the Himalayas often require a whole night for this, and in the meantime they hang motionless from a twig, as shown in this illustration.

Apart from our old friend the silkworm moth, the silk moth most commonly reared in this country is the oak silk moth, the scientific name of which is *Telea polyphemus*. This richly coloured moth is a native of North America, where it is bred commercially for its pure white silk. Its larvæ feed on oak leaves, and are possibly the most beautiful in the world. They are really quite hardy, and thrive in our climate. When the caterpillars are full grown they have lovely apple-green coloured skins, flecked all over with gold and silver "spots," which glint in the sunlight with superb effect as though studded with jewels. They have the strange habit of inflating their heads at any sign of danger. This action makes them look grotesque, and apparently has an alarming effect on any bird that settles near them with an eye to a nice juicy meal, as they are seldom attacked in the wild.

These moths spend the winter as pupæ inside cocoons, and emerge in May or early June. The eggs are deposited on the underside of an oak leaf, and it has been found that the tiny caterpillars when just hatched welcome a varied menu of food in the form of green leaves. They flourish and grow fat on the leaves of the willow, plum, hawthorn, pear or apple, but those of the elderberry are their favourites.

Another silk moth from North America is one that has the picturesque English name of the robin moth. It is very lovely to look at, for it has a prettily banded body, and the "eye" spots on the wings are of rich brown, shading to pink and cream. It naturally feeds on much the same kind of food as the oak silk moth, and so in this case the difficulty of feeding the caterpillars, which sometimes makes it impossible to breed foreign insects in England, presents no difficulties. The caterpillars themselves are sturdy-looking creatures, greenish-blue in colour, with pink "prickles," or tubercles as we call them, all over their bodies. They do not look anything like the caterpillars we see in this country, and for this fact alone it is interesting to breed them, and to watch them develop through their successive stages until they eventually emerge as glorious moths.

An Indian moon moth, photographed a few hours after emerging from the pupa, brought to this country by air mail.

Of the foreign insects we can easily breed in our own gardens, the simplest to deal with, and at the same time the most beautiful, are the two moon moths, one a native of India and the other of North America. Visitors to the Insect House at the London Zoo no doubt have seen these lovely pale-green moths, with long sweeping tails, fluttering about in the little glass houses specially heated and lighted for them.

The large dark-brown cocoons of this moth should be kept indoors in a warm room away from frost. About the middle of April strange scratching and "picking" noises suddenly may be heard. These are made by the struggling moth trying to get out of its cocoon. Now is the time for quick action. In the wild state the cocoon would be exposed to a steamy atmosphere and would be fairly soft, so that the moth inside would be able to push its way to liberty. A cocoon kept in the manner described is hard and tough, however, and therefore should be soaked in a basin of tepid water for a few minutes. An airing cupboard backing on to a water tank in the bathroom is the best place of all to stand the cage when the moths are emerging. Then there will be none of the crippled moths that are obtained when the cocoons are not treated properly.

It is a revelation to watch one of these moon moths actually emerge. First of all the strange "picking" noises are heard, and then careful watch reveals a damp patch appearing at one end of the cocoon, where the moth has pressed an alkaline gland on the top of its head against the side of the hollow dome. When this alkaline liquid has softened the gum that holds the silk threads together, the moth inside commences to "tease" the fibres apart by using its head as a battering ram. It seems that the moth actually needs this violent exercise, for on more than one occasion I have "helped" a moth out when it seemed to be "stuck," or too exhausted to get out by itself, and in each case the lovely tapering tails have never developed properly.

The oak silk moth, a native of North America that thrives in Great Britain. The caterpillar is apple green, flecked with gold and silver spots.

The time these giant moths take to expand and dry their wings is amazing. Some of the largest wait a day or more before they fly. Moon moths usually take about four hours to unfurl their wings, but sometimes one that is apparently a cripple in the evening will prove to be perfect next morning.

It is worth while clearing out a box room or an attic in order to give these moths plenty of space to fly and pair, and they will not spoil their wings so badly if ceiling and walls are draped with muslin. They appear to have to learn to fly. At first they have a curious way of jerking their wings in one sharp flip, which shoots them into the air like a shuttlecock, only to fall clumsily down to the floor again. Each moth will do this a dozen or more times before it flies properly, and then it looks like a great white bat.

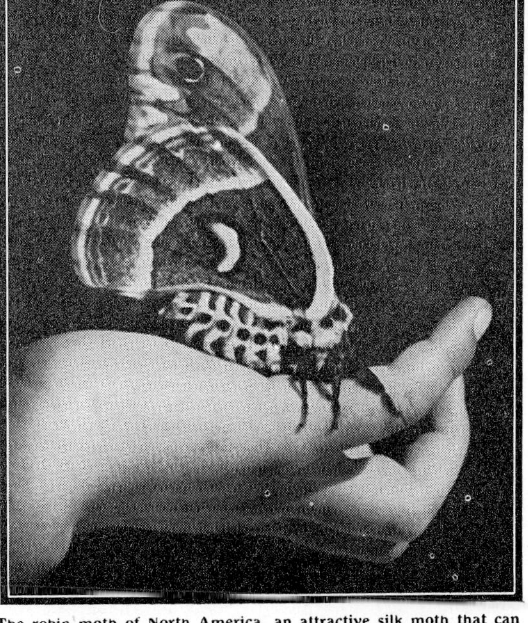

The robin moth of North America, an attractive silk moth that can be reared from cocoons bought in Great Britain.

Of the two moon moths, one from India, and the other from the United States, the former is the best to breed over here, as the caterpillars will feed on a variety of foods, including leaves of the walnut, hawthorn, plum, apple, nut, and wild cherry. The American moth will only feed on walnut, and is smaller when it is bred in captivity. Both take their names from the crescent marks in the centre of each wing.

The tiny caterpillar of the Indian moon moth on first hatching from the egg is red and black, but after skin casting it takes on a green shade and a number of "warts" appear on its body. Very soon the caterpillar grows as thick as the thumb, and the "warts" turn bright yellow and become larger, crowned with magnificent tufts of hair. By about the end of August they should begin to spin their cocoons, rather large, flexible, brownish balls of silk.

It is from India that the largest moths in the world come to us, in the form of live pupæ of the Atlas moth sent over by air mail in November or December. Natives are employed to go out into the jungle and collect the cocoons, which in districts where the insects are common are dotted about among the foliage like plums on a plum tree. As a matter of fact these balls of brown silk do not look unlike plums! They are packed in specially constructed boxes, made of a very light but strong wood, and despatched by the first possible air liner carrying mail to this country.

A collector of my acquaintance tells me that these giant insects look more like ungainly birds than moths as they fly up and down the lower slopes of the Himalayas. I know they can grow to an enormous size. A female I once bred out myself in a greenhouse measured just under a foot across the wings, and I believe that even larger specimens have been caught in the wild.

Most people favour breeding this moth indoors on cut food in a large breeding cage, as the caterpillars are inclined to be delicate, resenting cold winds, damp, and any change in temperature. The best place for the cage is in the window of a room facing south, with a stove or open fire burning day and night if possible; and the feeding caterpillars should be given fresh boughs of their favourite food every day so that they keep healthy and free from disease. The larvæ will feed on oak, plum, apple, beech, and barberry, but I have always found they do best on willow, which they prefer. Breeders must be patient when they receive their cocoons, as the moths emerge over a long period, commencing soon after Christmas and continuing right into the Summer. In order to get pairings and obtain eggs, it is best to keep the cocoons fairly cool so that they won't emerge before the trees are in leaf.

NOTE: The author of this article will be glad to give further information and advice on the rearing of silk moths to any reader who writes to him at The Butterfly Farm, Bexley, Kent. THE EDITOR.

RAILWAY DEVELOPMENT IN STAMPS

PROBABLY most of our readers are familiar with the story of the development of railways. We wonder how many of them have sought to tell the story with the aid of postage stamps. Few stamp stories are so complete, yet so simple to compile. There are only slightly more than 130 stamps in the complete series, but these cover effectively the whole story from Stephenson's days to modern streamlined giants.

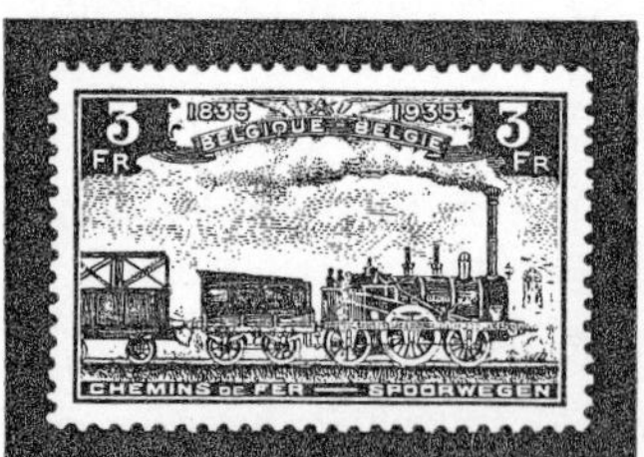

Stephenson's *"Rocket"* unfortunately is not to be found in the collection, but it has excellent deputies in the *"Austria,"* shown on the 12 gr. value of Austria's railway centenary commemorative issue of 1937, and the *"Eagle"* built in 1835 for the Bavarian Railways, illustrated on the 60 pf. value of Germany's railway centenary issue of 1935. The first of these stamps is illustrated here. Both locomotives actually were built in England by Robert Stephenson and Company.

The other stamps in these Austrian and German series showed modern steam and electric locomotives, the most interesting being the famous *"Flying Hamburger"* express, a streamlined articulated Diesel engined railcar unit, which at the time of issue of the stamp was the fastest train in the world, covering the run between Berlin and Hamburg at an average speed of 77.4 m.p.h. This train is shown on the 25 pf. of the German series. The 25 gr. Austrian stamp showing a modern steam locomotive is illustrated on this page.

"Le Belge," one of the Belgian State Railway's earliest locomotives, was shown on the higher values of the Belgian 1935 parcel post issue, one of which, the 3 fr., is illustrated on this page. This engine was slightly later in type than *"Austria"* and *"Eagle."* Another design in this series showed a Diesel railcar unit.

The earliest railway stamp design appeared on a 1c. stamp issued in 1860 by New Brunswick. The locomotive shown on this stamp was a wood-burning engine with a 4–4–0 wheel arrangement. Its outstanding features were a tremendous spark-arrester fitted to the chimney, a necessary item of equipment since the railway ran through virgin forests, and a high railing along the running plate, presumably to enable the driver to take a walk around his engine without risk of falling off.

The 5m. value of Egypt's 1933 International Railway Congress issue provides an excellent illustration of the next stage of the development of locomotive design, marked by the introduction of inside cylinders, coupled driving wheels and a cab for the locomotive crew. The engine shown on it is typical of those serving the Egyptian Railways in 1852, and three other excellent designs in the same series show engines of 1859, 1862 and 1932.

Stamps of the American continent are rich in railway designs, one of the most outstanding of which shows a Stirling "single-wheeler" on the 3c. value of Uruguay's 1895 issue. This was of exactly the same type as the famous G.N.R. locomotives that hauled *"The Flying Scotsman"* 50 years ago, described in the August *"M.M."*

Other splendid American railway stamps are a "wood-burner," similar in type to the New Brunswick stamp already described, seen on the U.S. 3c. issue of 1869, and the "mail train" design on the 5c. value of the U.S. 1912 parcels post issue. The latter shows a mail train travelling at full speed about to pick up a sack of mail at a wayside station.

This picture is so splendid an impression of a locomotive at speed that it is a pity the wheel-arrangement is not clearly defined. The leading wheels are apparently the same size as the drivers, and as the connecting rod is partially obscured, we are left in doubt as to whether the arrangement is 4–4–2 or 2–6–2. The 3c. value in the same series showed a postal sorting clerk at the door of a mail van, placing a sack of mail in readiness for delivery into a lineside collecting apparatus.

The 2c. value from the U.S. 1901 series showed a splendid picture of an express train of Pullman cars being hauled by one of the then up-to-date 4–4–2 "Atlantic" type passenger express engines.

Newfoundland's 5c. 1928 tourist publicity issue showed a picture of a 4–6–2 "Pacific" locomotive hauling the cross-country express from St. Johns to Port-aux-Basques.

A typical C.P.R. locomotive is shown on Canada's 1927 20c. Special Delivery stamp but the illustration is a composite picture showing the development of mail delivery services within the Dominion, and the locomotive is too small a feature to be considered a first-class railway picture.

Among South American stamps the best railway specimen is to be found on the 1c. value of Ecuador's 1908 issue celebrating the 25th anniversary of the opening of the Guayaquil-Quito Railway. This is a really splendid locomotive "portrait" and shows a 4–4–0 engine equipped with a pilot or "cowcatcher," a headlight in front of the chimney and a bell.

Salvador showed an early type of 4–4–0 engine on a 3c. stamp issued in 1896, while Honduras featured a still earlier type, complete with cowcatcher, spark arrester and headlight in its 1898 series.

There are no British stamps illustrating home railways but India provides an excellent view of an express passenger train on the 4 a. value of its current issue, and South-West Africa shows a mail train in the design of the current 1½d. value.

There is not sufficient space here to deal with all of the stamps available, electric locomotives for example, but the Editor is compiling a complete list, and will send a copy to any reader who cares to apply.

LOOK! Just like a Real Movie Show –

- **BRILLIANT LIGHTING**
- **FINEST QUALITY LENSES**
- **EFFICIENT MECHANISM**

Here is the finest HOME ENTERTAINMENT the whole family can enjoy. Very reasonably priced, the "BINGOSCOPE" Projectors provide all the atmosphere of the "Cinema"; they are easy to run, give clear flickerless pictures and the films are non-inflammable.

There are plenty of interesting and amusing films from which to choose.

Get BINGOSCOPE now for the Christmas Parties. Stocked by leading Dealers and Toy Shops.

In case of difficulty write to:
L. REES & CO. LTD., Dept. M.M., 12, New Union Street, London E.C.2.

BINGOSCOPE

RESISTANCE

B.4 25/-

MADE IN ENGLAND

FILMS

Mickey Mouse and Cartoons, including Popeye, Betty Boop and Donald Duck.
8 ft. 1/-; 15 ft. 1/6; 30 ft. 3/9; 60 ft. 6/6

Pathescope Comedy Films
Specially selected stories, full of fun and excitement.
8 ft. 1/-; 15 ft. 1/6; 30 ft. 3/6; 60 ft. 6/-

RANGE OF MODELS

B.1. 5/- Battery Model, lighting from 3-cell flashlamp battery.

B.2. 10/6 }
B.3. 17/6 } Lighting from 5-cell dry battery or accumulator.

B.4. 25/- Mains Model. A.C. or D.C. 100 to 250 volts. Complete with flex, adaptor and reliable metal resistance.

FOR USE WITH 9.5 m.m. NON-FLAM FILMS.

10/6
BATTERY MODEL

BINGOSCOPE

How the Locomotive Works

2. Cylinders, Valves, and Valve Gear

By a Railway Engineer

IN last month's *"M.M."* I described the general layout of the boiler and fire-box of a steam locomotive, the method of raising steam, and the working of the injectors by which the boiler is kept full of water. I now come to the equally vital part of the locomotive where the energy of the high-pressure steam is changed into mechanical work.

The rate at which the boiler and fire-box can raise steam depends of course upon the rate at which coal is fired. For any particular fire-box however there comes a point beyond which the coal cannot be burned economically—there is not enough air—and this rate limits the output of the locomotive. A consumption of about 40 lb. of coal per minute is an average figure to-day with fast express trains, and for purposes of explanation I will assume that this rate is kept up throughout the run; steam-raising is thus uniformly rapid all the time.

When a locomotive is started up steam can be kept on for practically the whole of the piston stroke; on account of the slow speed steam is not taken from the boiler at a very high rate, and such working can be continued until a speed of about 10 or 15 m.p.h. is attained. But as the engine accelerates and the rate of using steam rapidly increases, the steam supply to the cylinders must be lessened otherwise the boiler would not be able to supply the demand. This lessening of the supply is done by causing the admission valve to close earlier in the piston stroke. The moment that the admission valve closes is called the point of "cut-off." In most modern locomotives the cut-off when working in full gear takes place after the piston has travelled 75 per cent. of its stroke, though on the majority of Sir Nigel Gresley's engines the full-gear cut-off is 65 per cent.

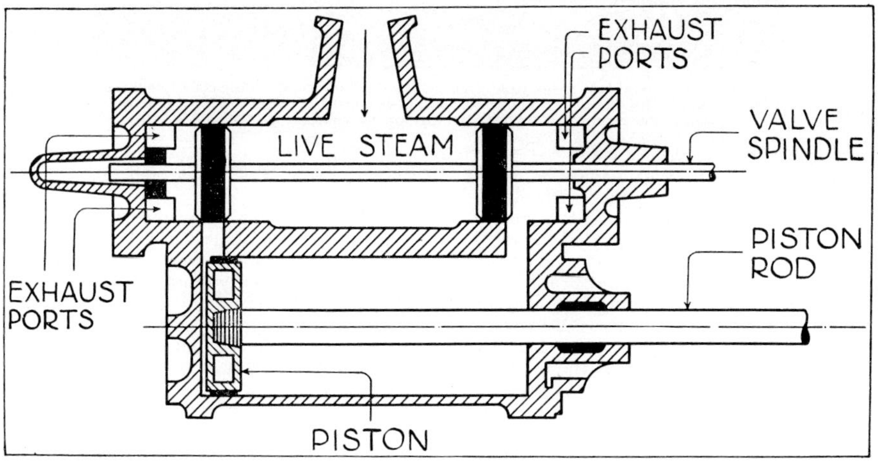

Section of a locomotive cylinder and valve chest showing the path of the steam in and out of the cylinder. The piston is about to commence its backward stroke, the rear port being already open to exhaust.

Now by the time a locomotive has attained 15 m.p.h. the cut-off will have been reduced to about 60 per cent., and then assuming that the train is accelerating along a level road, it is a case of reducing cut-off in direct proportion to the speed. At 30 m.p.h. the pistons will be moving twice as fast as at 15 m.p.h., and in order to keep the amount of steam taken from the boiler at a constant figure only half the amount used at 15 m.p.h. should be allowed to enter the cylinders; in other words the cut-off should be 30 per cent. By a proportionate reduction as the engine accelerates to full express speed the cut-off would be reduced to 15 per cent. by the time 60 m.p.h. is attained.

In actual practice the cut-off is reduced by steps rather than continuously, and in such a case as I have described the driver would probably adjust his gear from 60 to 50 per cent. at one movement, then 50 to 40, and more gradually thereafter. But the whole process of "notching-up," as it is called, is governed by the necessity of keeping the rate of steam consumption more or less constant. This essentially practical consideration is in itself quite sufficient reason for working at short cut-offs when running at high speed, but there is in addition the equally important matter of thermal efficiency entering into it. Indeed one cannot study the working of the steam locomotive without marvelling at the way in which the functioning of its various processes dovetail together into one remarkably complete and harmonious power plant on wheels.

When an engine is running with cut-off taking place at 15 per cent. of the piston stroke, a small amount of steam occupying just over one-sixth of the total volume of the cylinder is imprisoned. The natural tendency of high-pressure steam is to expand and the only way it can expand is by pushing the piston. In so doing the steam loses pressure until at the end of the stroke, when the exhaust valve opens, it is at very little more than atmospheric pressure. In order to use as little live steam from the boiler at each stroke the locomotive engineer aims at getting as much work as possible done entirely by the expansion of the steam. To do this, and so work at the earliest possible cut-off, high boiler pressure is necessary; otherwise the steam would be expanded and cooled to such a degree that condensation would take place in the cylinder.

I have explained why it is necessary gradually to lessen the amount of steam passing into the cylinders as a locomotive works up to speed. There is another method which, as a practical measure, is just as effective as adjusting the point of cut-off, that is by partly closing the regulator. By so doing, however, not only is the amount of steam passing from the boiler to the cylinders lessened, but its pressure also is reduced. The actual regulator valve is like a sliding door that works at right-angles across a passage-way; when the door is partly closed a considerable restriction is caused and the steam that passes on does so at reduced pressure. When it reaches the cylinder this medium-pressure steam is not nearly so effective, and the admission valve has to be kept open longer so as to make the point of cut-off later and so gain more power.

The mere fact that when working with the regulator only partly open steam has to be admitted for a longer period of the stroke would seem to indicate a more extravagant use of the steam; actually however the explanation is not quite so simple. Such steam as passes through the restricted opening of the regulator valve not only loses pressure but in so doing increases its volume; for example, if the regulator is closed to such a degree that steam is entering the cylinders at 140 lb. per sq. in. against a boiler pressure of 220 lb. per sq. in. every cubic foot of steam taken from the boiler would become 1½ cubic feet after passing through the regulator. But a driver who worked in this way would need at least double the "cut-off," say 30 per cent., of that of his friend who worked with a wide-open regulator, and he would use about 20 per cent. more live steam from the boiler.

Readers who have followed the series of articles describing footplate trips will no doubt recall several occasions when famous types of locomotive were handled on the long cut-off method, with the regulator only partly opened; in view of my last remarks about the relative efficiency of this way of driving they may probably wonder whether the enginemen on such occasions were doing as well as they might. The modern locomotive is extraordinarily sensitive to slight variations in its mechanism; these usually affect the steaming in some way or other, and of course it is useless to go on working the engine in the theoretically correct manner if she will not steam. I once rode on one of a very famous class of British locomotives; normally 15 to 20 per cent. cut-off, with full regulator gave excellent results, but this particular engine would not steam at all if she was linked up below 33 per cent. Drivers quickly find out what adjustments of the various controls give the best results, and very often quite unorthodox methods give magnificent performance on the road.

So far I have referred only to single-expansion locomotives, in which all the cylinders take live steam from the boiler, and all exhaust to the atmosphere. With the exception of the famous Midland compounds of the L.M.S. there are very few double-expansion locomotives in this country, but on the continent of Europe they are probably in the majority. Live steam from the boiler is admitted to the high-pressure cylinders; there it is only partially expanded, before exhausting into the intermediate steam chest, or receiver as it is called. From the receiver it is admitted to the low-pressure cylinders, expansion is completed, and it is then exhausted to the atmosphere. On a locomotive having a boiler pressure of 200 lb. per sq. in., the pressure of steam entering the low-pressure cylinders will be somewhere about 65 lb. per sq. in.

Inside the smoke-box of L.M.S. No. 6220 "Coronation." Steam passes to the cylinders through the large pipes at the side of the smoke-box and is exhausted through the blast pipe shown below the chimney extension. Photograph by courtesy of the L.M.S.

It is now time to say something of the ingenious mechanism by which the point of cut-off is adjusted, the reversing gear. For modern locomotives, at any rate in this country, the Walschaerts valve gear is more used than any other, and as it is usually fitted outside the movements of its various members are easier to study than those of gears such as Joy's, or the Stephenson's link motion, which are usually found between the frames. At the best of times the Walschaerts valve gear looks an extremely complicated mechanism, and even when a locomotive is moving slowly the functions of the individual rods are not easy to see.

The to-and-fro motion of a locomotive valve is a combination of two distinct movements, and once these two are separated from each other the valve gear mechanism becomes quite simple to understand. The first of those motions is a constant quantity backwards and forwards, no matter in what position the reversing screw may be; it is also exactly "in phase" with the motion of the piston rod, that is it changes from forward to backward motion at the same instant. Now when a locomotive is running in mid-gear, that is with the reversing lever half way between the full forward and full reverse positions, this "in phase" movement is the only movement that the valve possesses. Referring now to the diagram on this page, the rod N is motionless when the engine is in "mid gear," for although the curved link K is oscillating about its central pivot the sliding block is also in a position that coincides with that pivot. I will however explain more fully the actuation of the link K later on.

To the end of the piston rod A, moving in and out of the cylinder E, is connected the crosshead B; this latter has rigidly fixed to it a downward extension piece Q. From the extremity of Q is pivoted a system of two links, P and Q, both of which are free to move at all the joints. It will be noted that link O is also connected to the valve spindle G, at a point below its connection to the rod N. Now the upper extremity of link O is connected by a pin joint to the rod N, which latter is at rest; the reciprocating motion of the piston and crosshead imparts a large oscillating motion to the lower extremity of link O, but since the upper end is fixed, by the immobility of rod N, only a very small motion is given to the valve spindle G. It will naturally be asked, why it is necessary to move the valve spindle at all when the engine is in mid-gear: it is here that the mechanical construction of the valves and cylinder ports have to be taken into account.

On the previous page is a longitudinal section showing the arrangement of a piston valve and the cylinder that it supplies with steam. The piston is shown at one end of its stroke and the valve at the same end of the cylinder as the piston is just covering the steam port. The piston is about to move from left to right, but it is clear that if the valve were moved ever so slightly in the reverse direction steam would be admitted to the cylinder. But the engine is still in mid-gear, and therefore the valve travels in the same direction as the piston. The extent of its travel can be seen by referring to the port at the opposite end of the cylinder, for the valve at that end must move just far enough to the right to bring its steam face directly in line with the right hand steam port. In the position shown, of course, the portion of the cylinder to the right of the piston is open to exhaust. The portion of the valve motion derived from the crosshead is therefore revealed as that necessary to give the exhaust opening at each stroke, and to bring the valves just to the point where any further motion would admit steam.

The other component is now easy to follow. If the block L is moved either way from the mid-position of the link K, the fore-and-aft oscillating motion is given to the rod N and this motion becomes super-imposed upon the mid-gear movement of the valve spindle. The block L is by the way shifted by means of the reversing gear in the cab. Turning the reversing wheel, or moving the lever, pushes or pulls the rod T; this acting through the bell-crank S, which is pivoted at U, raises or lowers the die-block by means of the link R. The farther from the mid-position of the link that the die-block is raised the greater will be the motion imparted to the rod N, and consequently the longer will the valve be open to admit steam into the cylinder.

Space does not allow me to describe in detail the other valve gear most commonly used in this country, Stephenson's link motion, but though it differs considerably in detail and in action the net result is very much the same; in both gears the valve travel is shortened as the engine is linked up. Until comparatively recent times the mechanism fitted to most locomotives was such that as the valve travel was shortened, due to linking up, so also were the port openings lessened both for admission of steam, and for exhaust. Thus, when running fast on a fairly short cut-off, quite an amount of throttling took place due to the restricted entry to the cylinder. Such throttling naturally tends to slow up the engine.

Diagram of Walschaerts valve gear. The functions of the various parts indicated by letters are described in this article.

But the effect of a restricted entry to the cylinders is nothing like so serious as that of a restricted exhaust. When the steam has been expanded and is at very little more than atmospheric pressure it flows much less readily than when entering the cylinder, when the pressure may be 200 lb. per sq. in. or more. At high speeds the exhaust steam has literally to be pushed out of the cylinders, and unless the exhaust ports are large, and the passages leading to the blast pipe carefully designed and free from sharp bends quite a lot of the engine's power may be frittered away. In some tests made not so many years ago on a famous British locomotive it was found that when running at 70 m.p.h. just one-third of the total power developed by the engine was spent in getting the steam in and out of the cylinder, that is half as much power as it took to haul 10 heavy bogie coaches along! By making the total travel of the valves longer the exhaust opening can be improved and in most locomotives of to-day the full exhaust port opening is obtained even though the engine is running fully linked up, at 15 per cent. cut-off, or less.

Such are the essential factors in the functioning of the steam locomotive. There are other appliances, such as feed-water heaters, and mechanical lubricators which help to improve performance, but they rank as accessories rather than vital components.

Puzzle Your Sharp-Eyed Friends

More Conjuring for Christmas Parties

By Norman Hunter (From Maskelyne's Mysteries)

IN this article I am going to describe a few tricks that are simple to carry out, but will be found very effective. Those of my readers who wish to perform them will have no difficulty in making or contriving the few pieces of apparatus necessary, and with a little practice will be able to mystify their audiences completely.

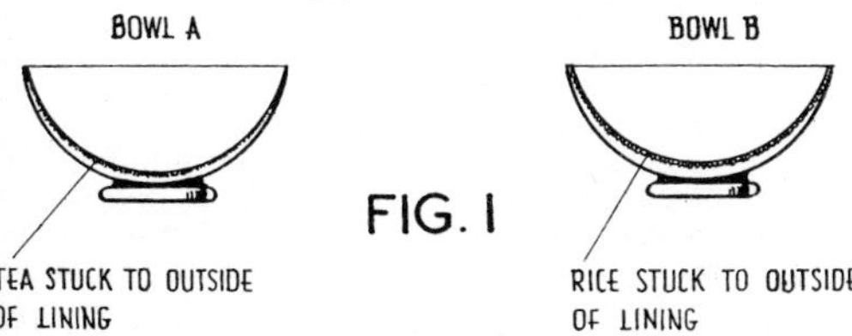

FIG. 1

CHANGING TEA INTO RICE

To start off with here is one of those effective tricks in which two things change places. In this case the things are a bowl of rice and a bowl of tea. Two bowls are shown to be empty. One is then filled with rice and one with tea. A plate is laid over each bowl and they are turned upside down. A black handkerchief is laid over the bowl of tea and a white one over the bowl of rice.

"By changing the places of the handkerchiefs," you say, "I make the contents of the bowls change places too. Watch." You pick up the handkerchiefs and change them over so that the white one is on the bowl of tea and the black on the bowl of rice. You then lift the bowls. Out of the bowl in which you put the tea pours the rice; the bowl you filled with rice now contains the tea. Both bowls may be handed for examination.

The Secret. You will need four tin or aluminium bowls; get shallow ones if you can. Cut two of them down with metal cutting shears until they will fit snugly into the other two bowls. All four bowls should of course be of the same size. Now stick rice all over the outside of one of the cut down bowls and stick tea all over the outside of the other cut down bowl.

To prepare for the trick, put some tea into one of the bowls and press the tea covered cut-down bowl into it. Do the same with rice in the other bowl. Fig. 1 shows a sectional view of the bowls. The bowls may now be shown quite freely and will appear empty, the fact that the insides are rather shallower than the outsides will not be noticed. Be careful to mark the bowls so that you know which contains tea and which the rice.

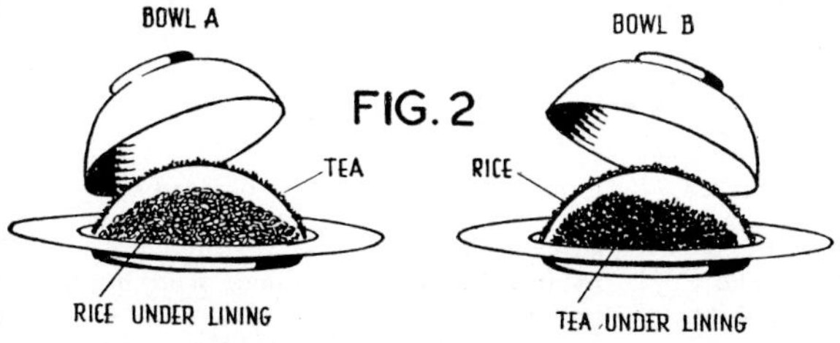

BOWL A — TEA — RICE UNDER LINING
BOWL B — RICE — TEA UNDER LINING
FIG. 2

Into the bowl containing tea pour some rice until it is level full. In the same way fill the bowl secretly prepared with rice, using tea for the purpose. Place a plate over each bowl and invert them. The by-play with the handkerchiefs is only for effect. In lifting the bowls you leave the linings behind. These cover the heaps of rice and tea and make them look like the opposite commodity. The loose rice and tea which was between the bowl and lining pours out and effectively disguises the presence of the linings. (Fig. 2.)

To make the trick easy to work, the linings should be trimmed so that they are an easy but not too loose fit. They can be held in place by the fingers during the first part of the trick, and will remain on the plates of their own accord at the finish. At the end of the trick the bowls can of course be examined.

A LANTERN MYSTERY

Next comes a showy little item very suitable for finishing a performance. Having produced a lot of coloured silk handkerchiefs and flags, you drop them on to a tray; then, picking all the silks up in a bunch, you change them instantly into a large, lighted Japanese lantern.

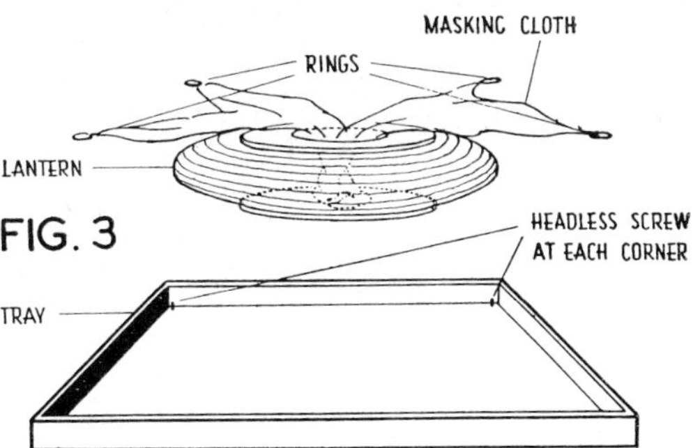

FIG. 3

The Secret. The whole secret is in the tray. This is square and just large enough to take the lantern when folded. Cover the top of the tray with a piece of patterned material such as cretonne. Now cut another square of the same material and sew a tiny metal ring to each corner. Drive a small screw into each corner of the tray and cut off the heads of the screws. The finished square of material should be of such a size that when the four rings are slipped over the four screws the cloth is stretched tightly over the tray.

Now for the lantern. Get one made of fabric if you can; it will last longer than a paper one. Take off the deep rim at the top and fasten in place a flat ring cut from a piece of thin plywood. Take off the bottom of the lantern and put in its place a flat disc of plywood. Close the lantern, and to the centre of the bottom disc, on the inside, fasten the centre of the square of fabric you have prepared. On top of this fasten a simple spring clip. To help the lantern to open quickly you can also screw a flat piece of lead to the bottom.

Figs. 3 and 4 explain very clearly the way in which the lantern is concealed. To set the trick, first fold the lantern and pull out the square of cloth all round. Place the folded lantern on the tray and slip the rings over the screws. The tray will then appear empty, and the lantern will be hidden under the cloth as in Fig. 4. The clip alone will be visible.

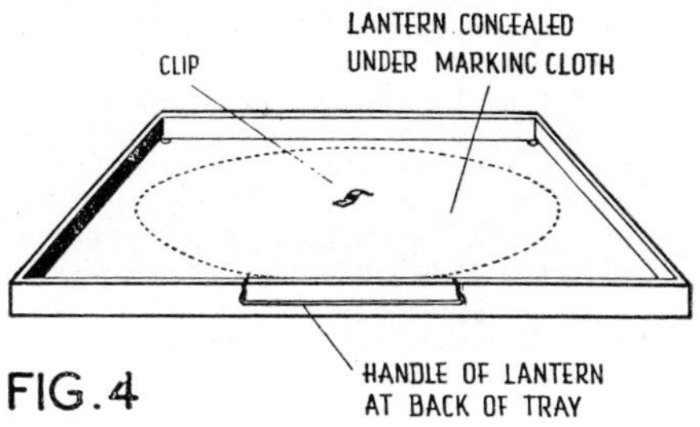

FIG. 4

In performing the trick lay the silks on the tray, and as you put the last one down tuck them all into the clip. Now pick up the lantern by the handle, which projects through slits cut in one side of the tray as shown in Fig. 4. The weighted base of the lantern will cause it to open, swallowing the square of masking material and all the silks.

The lighting of the lantern is simple. Get an electric torch and solder the case to the top of the handle of the lantern. Remove the lens and bulb. Attach a length of flex to a bulb holder containing a bulb and connect this to the torch case. Put the bulb on the end of the flex into the folded lantern before fastening the masking cloth down. When you pick up the lantern all you have to do is to switch on the torch in the ordinary way, and the lamp in the lantern will light.

STAMPS THAT FLY

Now for a trick with a novel touch about it. A trick with postage stamps.

"Everybody knows you have to stick stamps on a letter if you want it to go by post," you say, "but not everyone knows it is the flying ability of the stamps that actually transports the letter." When the laughter has died down after this "calm whopper" you pick up a large knife and show both sides of the blade. You then stick three stamps, or rather three squares of coloured paper to represent stamps, on each side of the blade. There is a red one in

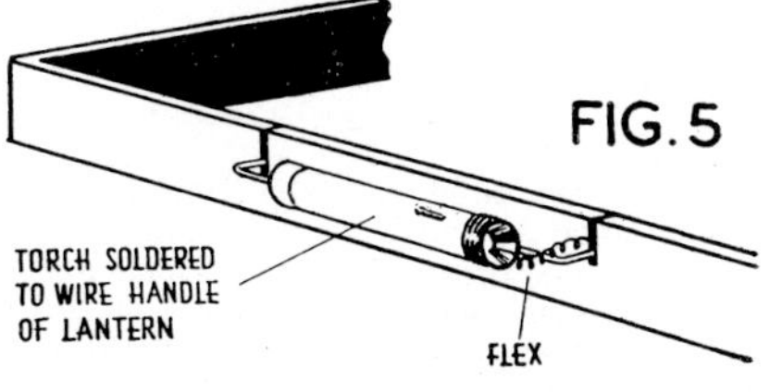

FIG. 5

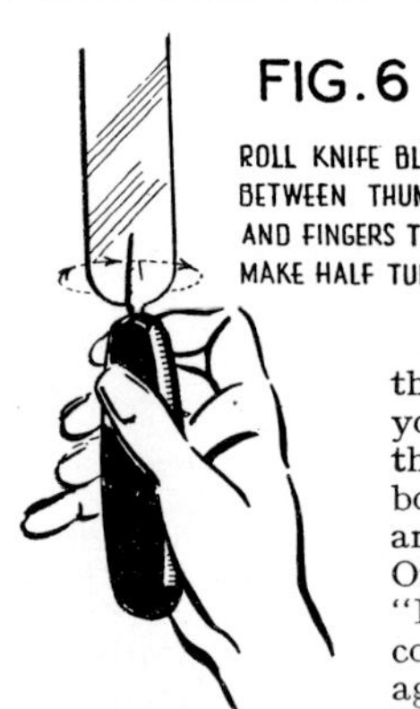

the middle, a blue one on one side and a green one on the other side. You show both sides of the knife with the six stamps on the blade. "Postman" you shout. Instantly the papers vanish and both sides of the knife are shown blank. Once again you cry "Postman!" and back come the stamps again.

The Secret. You can get just the right kind of knife for this trick at the sixpenny stores; a pastry knife, which has a flat blade and a nice round handle. The whole secret of the trick consists in giving the knife a peculiar twist while showing both sides of it.

Have a saucer of water handy. Pick up the knife and show both sides of it. Take a paper square, dip it in the water and stick it in the centre of the blade. Show both sides of the blade. Now take another red square and apparently stick it on the plain side of the blade. Actually just as your hand reaches the knife you roll the handle round in your fingers and stick the second red square above the first. Now to show that there is a red square on each side of the blade, exhibit the side with the paper on, then with a swinging-over movement of your arm apparently show the other side of the blade. In making the swing-over movement with your arm, roll the handle of the knife in your fingers again. You will then find that you are still showing the same side of the blade, although to the audience it appears as if you have shown both sides. Practise this move, because it is the key to the whole trick. Fig. 6 will show you how to make the twirl with the knife.

Now using the same method stick the green and blue squares on the knife, sticking both green ones on the same side, then both blue ones, one above the other. You can then show that there are apparently six stamps

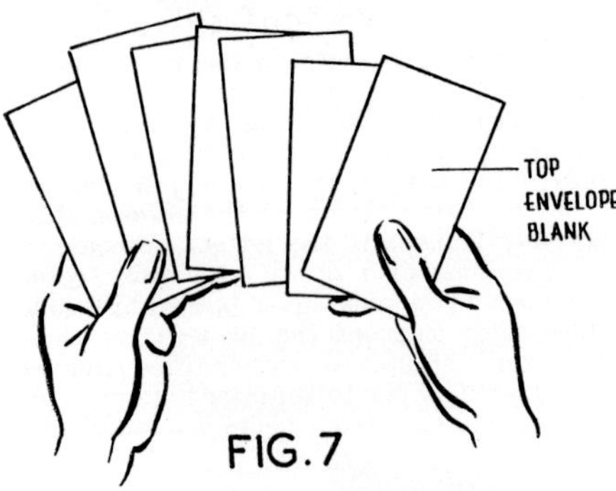

FIG.7

HOLDING THE ENVELOPES SO THAT THE STAMPS ARE HIDDEN

on the knife, three each side. The trick is now as good as done. On the shout "Postman!" you quickly flick the knife over; then, using the twirl again, show both sides of the knife apparently plain. To make the stamps come back, reverse the movements.

A TRICK WITH ENVELOPES

Here is another trick with stamps that will work very well in conjunction with the one I have described above. Neatly performed it is a profound mystery.

You have six envelopes and a pencil. Going to six members of the audience, you ask each one to write his or her name on

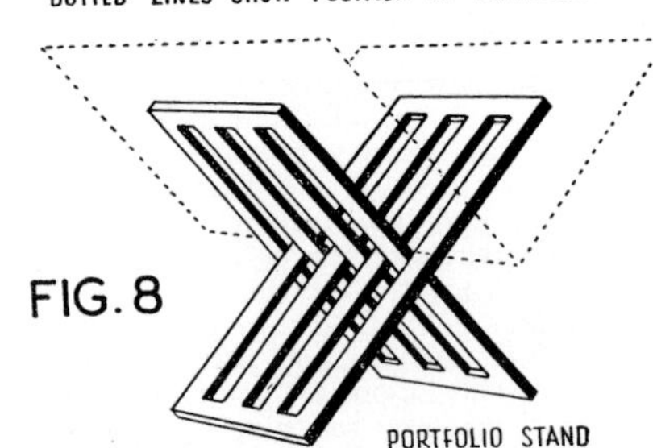

FIG.8

one envelope. You put the envelopes on a glass tumbler in full view while you vanish the six stamps as already described.

"This is useful when you forget to stamp your letters" you say, "You can send the stamps on to catch up the letters."

Going to the envelopes you pick them up one at a time. Each now has a stamp in the top right-hand corner, and each also bears the genuine signature of the person who marked it.

The Secret. You have seven envelopes instead of six. Six of them have stamps, or rather coloured paper labels, stuck on them. The seventh is plain. The plain envelope is on top of the pile. Show the pile of envelopes, then fan them out as shown in Fig. 7. Thanks to the top one being plain they will all appear plain. Do not deliberately say that the envelopes are not stamped and the audience will accept them as plain. Now go round and have the envelopes signed, but keep your hand over the top one so that this does not receive a name. As you return to your table slip this envelope below the others. Doing the business with the knife and stamps next will cause the audience to forget the envelopes, and when later on they are shown them bearing stamps they will remember only having signed them and will have assumed them to be plain.

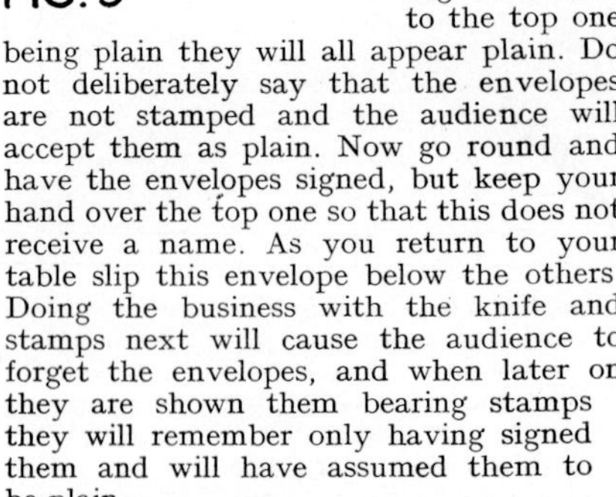

FIG.9

THINGS FROM NOWHERE

After that I think we might try one of those popular tricks in which the conjuror produces a host of articles apparently from nowhere. You begin by showing a portfolio, one of those affairs like the two covers of a book, usually employed for holding sketches and papers of different kinds. You open it and show that it is empty. You then put it on a small stand on your table, a mere skeleton affair, and instantly take out of it flags, handkerchiefs, ribbons and so on.

The Secret. The stand has no trick about it, being used simply to hold the portfolio. It is a sort of miniature easel as shown in Fig. 8. The portfolio itself is easy to make but awkward to describe. If you look at Figs. 9 and 10 you will get a good idea of its construction. Briefly speaking it is composed of three boards instead of two. The front is plain and solid. The back is a mere framework, the centre having been cut out. Between these two boards is another of the same size having attached to its back a wedge shaped compartment.

The articles to be produced are packed into this compartment, and the portfolio, opened out, is placed on the stand. The ends of the portfolio are provided with gussets of thick paper or book binders cloth so that it is not possible for the audience to see into the portfolio through the ends. There are two gussets at each end, one between the front of the portfolio and the movable centre board, the other between the centre board and the back. It will now be clear that whether the portfolio is opened at part A (Fig. 11) to show it empty, or at part B to allow the articles to be produced, there is always a gusset at each end for masking purposes. These gussets should be made the shape of half a circle so that the portfolio may be opened out sufficiently to show it

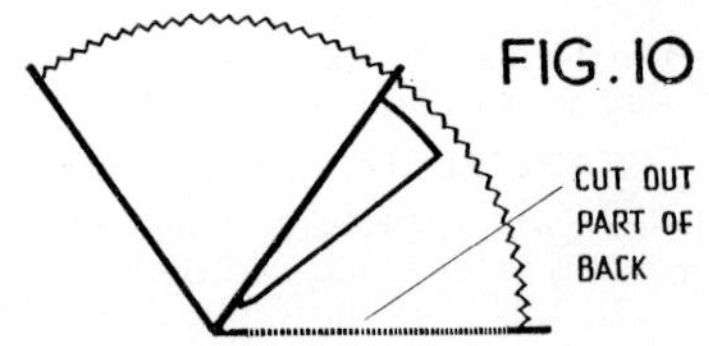

FIG.10

empty without making it necessary for you to tilt it and expose the secret compartment.

When you show the trick, take the portfolio off the stand and open the front part. It will appear quite empty and flat, the secret compartment being at the back. You then close it and put it back on the stand, opening it again at the back part. All you then have to do is to take out the articles already packed into the secret compartment.

It only remains to suggest how to present these tricks effectively, and this will offer no difficulty to the amateur conjuror if he practises them. The essence of conjuring is rapid movement at exactly the right moment, and it would obviously be courting disaster to try out these or any other tricks without rehearsal.

Another great help is a flow of easy talk, the purpose of which is to distract the attention of members of the audience. I have suggested suitable patter for some of the tricks described, and this can easily be extended by the inclusion of jokes or

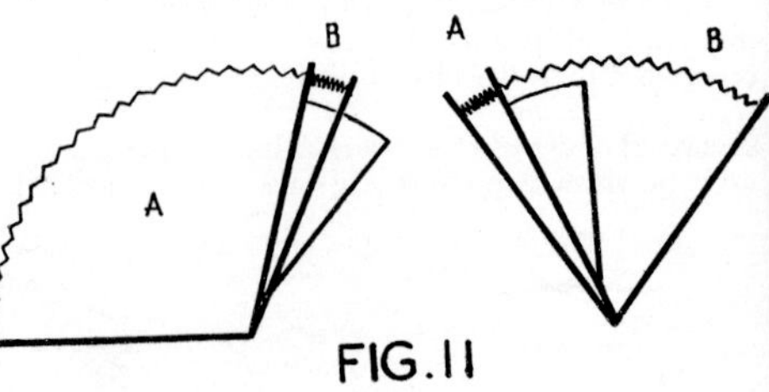

FIG.11

humorous stories, or perhaps of comments on certain members of the audience. The entertainer may even arrange for a confederate in the audience, who might be instructed to start an argument at a critical moment to attract attention while the conjuror makes some rapid movement in connection with his trick.

Finally let me warn those who give a conjuring entertainment against repeating their tricks before the same audience.

Fun with Hornby-Dublo Clockwork Trains

Running Operations on a Simple Layout

LAST month we dealt with the running of Hornby-Dublo Electric Trains, and described typical operations made possible by their remarkably efficient and positive system of Remote Control. This month we consider the running of Hornby-Dublo Clockwork Trains, and in order to show what fun can be obtained we illustrate on this page a specimen layout, the rails of which occupy a space 6 ft. by 3 ft., and describe typical operations that can be carried out on it with passenger and goods trains.

The layout is an extension of the oval system of rails contained in the Hornby-Dublo Train Sets, to which points and other rails have been added. The main line is oval in form, and has a running loop laid parallel to one side of the oval. From the opposite side two dead-end branch lines turn off inside the main track, and as shown in the upper illustration these can serve a standard Main Line Station and a Goods Depot respectively. Additional stations can be provided alongside the main line, but the exact arrangement of these can be left to the individual model railway owner. The double track formed by the main and loop lines, for instance, could be made to serve a double-road station made up of two Main Line Stations, or a Main Line Station and an Island Platform. Alternatively the loop road need not serve a platform, but can be used simply as a passing loop, or for running-round purposes. The addition of a station outside the track will increase the width of the space required by five inches.

A scene on the layout described in this article. The goods train is being shunted into its siding, in order to clear the main line for the running of the express, which is ready to leave the Main Line Station in the centre of the layout.

In the series of operations to be described we will assume that we are fortunate enough to possess two trains, one passenger and one goods, made up as shown in the upper illustration. The braking and reversing of Hornby-Dublo Clockwork Locomotives is performed by means of levers, which project through the cab roof in the case of the streamlined express locomotive "*Sir Nigel Gresley*," and are found in the bunker of the Tank Locomotive. It is very good fun, however, to see if we can make our clockwork engines stop just where we want them to, without having to touch them to apply the brake. On a given layout it is possible after a certain amount of experimenting to arrange this with great accuracy by varying the number of turns of the key that are given to the engines. Actually, as each twist of the hand when winding moves the key through half a revolution only, it would be more correct to refer to half-turns.

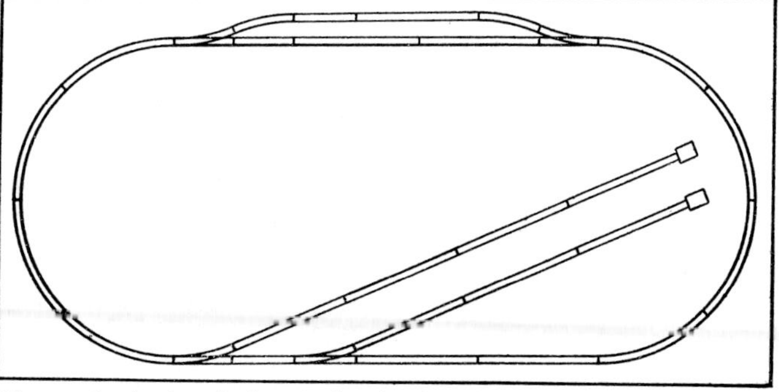

Diagram showing how the layout referred to is made up. The rails only are shown, as the positions of the accessories can be left to individual choice.

We will assume that at the commencement of operations our passenger train, consisting of a Two-Coach Articulated Unit, is standing alongside the terminal station platform, with the locomotive already attached. Similarly the goods train, consisting of an 0–6–2 Tank, two Wagons, two Vans and a Brake Van, is in the goods road alongside the Goods Depot previously referred to. The first train movement can be run by the express from the terminus to the passing station. If we give the locomotive 11 or 12 half-turns of the key, assuming that it is unwound at the start, we will find that it will leave the terminus and make three full circuits of the track. It can then be diverted into the loop road if this is served by a platform, or it can be run straight into a stop on the parallel track.

Possibly the locomotive will run a little too far. In that case the run should be made again, giving the motor from an unwound state a little less than the number of half-turns of the key given on the first run. For instance if 12 half-turns prove too much it is not a bad plan to count the "clicks" of the ratchet after the eleventh half-turn; if "11 and two clicks" is not enough, then an additional "click" on the next run will probably be just right. Judgment must be exercised as to the exact point at which to stop winding, but after a little experience it is not difficult to give just the right amount of "wind."

While the express is at rest we can wind up the locomotive of the goods train and despatch it for a trip round the main line. We must not forget to set the points at each end of the loop road, as one or other of the tracks is occupied by the passenger train. With about the same number of turns of the key as we gave the passenger locomotive, the goods train will run from the siding, make three circuits of the track, and finally come to rest on the loop. The goods train can now be left refuged while the passenger train proceeds on its way. This train can stop at the intermediate station after one, two or three circuits, the number of turns of the key being varied according to requirements.

It is now the turn of the passenger train to wait at the station. We can therefore despatch the goods train, but in order to avoid delay to the express we will imagine that the goods train is bound for the goods yard. If we wind the Tank Locomotive to the extent of two half-turns of the key and three "clicks" of the ratchet the train will run forward round the main line until it is just past the points leading to the goods road. On reversing it will be found that the locomotive still has sufficient energy to propel the train into the siding. The express can now be despatched as before. When it has reached the end of its run we can uncouple the Tank Locomotive from the wagons in the siding, and if we then give it just over two half-turns of the key it can be run round the track to couple on to the rear of the passenger train. After coupling up, the engine is reversed and then the express locomotive is reversed also. The two engines between them, without any further winding, will move the train out backward from alongside the platform round the main line until the points leading to the inner station are reached.

The Tank Locomotive can be used in this way, as it adds to the variety of operations, and it is not correct in any case even for empty passenger trains to be backed over considerable distances along the main line. The Tank Locomotive by now will probably be run down, but after being detached from the train the slightest amount of "wind" will be sufficient to carry the engine into the goods siding again. The passenger locomotive can then be made to back its train alongside the platform of the inner station once more in order to commence a further round of duty. For this purpose it is only necessary to turn the key for about three "clicks" of the ratchet.

The trains are now in the same positions as they were when we commenced operations. A great deal more variety is possible than the necessarily simple operations that have been described in this article. Individual Hornby-Dublo Train owners will all have their own favourite schemes and we should like to hear about them.

THE TOWER OF EMPIRE

The illustration on this page shows a fine model of the Tower of Empire at the recent Glasgow Exhibition. The model was built by A. Cant, Glasgow W.3, and stands 4 ft. high. Readers who compare the drawing of the actual tower that appeared on page 139 of the March 1938 "*M.M.*" with the accompanying illustration of the model will realise the excellent proportions of the latter, and the skilful manner in which the external appearance of this famous tower has been reproduced.

The framework of the model is composed entirely of Meccano Angle Girders and Strips, and the outer covering consists of thin cardboard painted silver and sea blue. The tower is illuminated by 13 4.5 volt lamps, the current for which is supplied by a Transformer. When viewed in a darkened room the illuminated model is very impressive.

MODEL-BUILDING HINTS FROM READERS

In the hundreds of letters that I receive each week from model-builders all over the world, I regularly find details of time-saving dodges and useful model-building hints that the writers have discovered in the course of their experiments. For example, A.D. Muff, Canterbury, New Zealand, mentions a dodge that he finds useful in assembling intricate gear-boxes. Sometimes, he says, it is a little difficult to place Pinions, Collars, etc. in the required places, but the trouble can easily be overcome by screwing a length of Screwed Rod into the boss of the part and then using the Rod as a handle with which to manœuvre the part into its allotted position. Readers who are building models of complicated gear-boxes particularly will appreciate the practical value of this suggestion, but every model-builder will find good uses for Muff's method.

A. Forsyth, Blackpool, tells me that he often uses a pea bulb for illuminating interiors of models under construction. In order to make the lamp more manageable the wires carrying the current are sheathed in a length of Spring Cord. Forsyth also finds that a Handrail Coupling forms a useful pulley of small diameter for use at the end of a shaft. The Cord or Driving Band is passed around the neck of the Coupling between the boss and the head. If a pulley of this kind is used in conjunction with a 3″ Pulley a driving ratio of approximately 10 : 1 is obtained.

Large diameter pulleys are needed for building pit-head gear and similar models, and J. Purley, Devonshire, has devised an extremely neat method by which these can be made. For the rim of each pulley 28 Curved Strips are required. These are bolted together to form two complete circles, each Curved Strip overlapping its neighbour by three holes. The two last Curved Strips must be forced together to allow the last bolt of each ring to be inserted, with the result that all the Curved Strips take up an angle of about 30 deg. to the plane of the wheel. The two rings therefore can be placed together to form a large pulley with a V-shaped groove. The sides of the rim are fastened together by End Bearings, the arms of which are opened out to the required angle. Approximately 16 End Bearings are required to give a good effect, and in their bosses 8″ Rods are locked to form the spokes. The inner ends of the Rods are splayed out like the spokes of a bicycle wheel, and are fastened by Collars to two Face Plates mounted on a central Rod. The wheel can be made to rotate truly on its axle by adjusting the tension of the individual spokes.

A MODEL ROAD JUNCTION

Lars Linder, Stockholm, an enthusiastic model-builder who competes regularly in "*M.M.*" contests, finds pleasure in experimenting with Dinky Toys in conjunction with Meccano. Recently he built a clover leaf road junction, of the type that is now becoming popular on the Continent and in America. The framework of the model is built up from Strips and Angle Girders, but the roadways are represented by cardboard. In the cardboard slots are cut, through which jut four 1″ Rods attached to carriages below the roadways. Dinky Toys Vehicles are placed over the Rods, and are pulled along by means of an endless belt of Sprocket Chain attached to the carriages below, thus giving the effect of vehicles moving under their own power. The Sprocket Wheels around which the Chain is passed are driven by an Electric Motor.

AN INGENIOUS AIR SPEED INDICATOR

Instruments used in the navigation of aircraft make good subjects for Meccano models, and recently G. S. Pearce, Wellington, decided to make a demonstration model of an air speed indicator. Pearce's instrument is quite simple in construction, but is capable of indicating air speeds to within one to two miles per hour of the correct reading. He tested it by holding it out of the window of his father's car while travelling at various speeds, and marked out the scale to correspond with the readings given by the speedometer of the car.

The indicator is a small box-like structure built up from Meccano Flat Plates and Angle Girders, on top of which is the calibrated cardboard scale, which is held in place by two Strips. A 5½″ Strip is used for a pointer, and is pivoted on a short Rod passed through two Angle Brackets bolted to the top of the casing of the instrument. A 2″ Slotted Strip is bolted to the lower end of the 5½″ Strip, so that the two parts overlap two holes.

An 8″ Rod is journalled horizontally in the sides of the casing, and at one end, outside the casing, it carries a Designing Table (Part No. 107). This is a piece of wood approximately 6″ square, at the centre of which a Bush Wheel is bolted. An End Bearing is fitted on the other end of the 8″ Rod and is connected by two Driving Bands, or pieces of strong elastic, to a fixed part of the instrument. At its centre, inside the casing, the Rod carries a Collar, and into this is screwed a bolt that passes also through the slot of the 2″ Slotted Strip. Any movement of the horizontal Rod therefore is transmitted to the pointer working in front of the scale.

To use the instrument it is placed with the Designing Table facing forward, so that this is forced backward. The air pressure on the Table is proportionate to the speed at which the instrument is carried ahead, and a direct reading is given on the scale.

The Tower of Empire at the Glasgow Exhibition has been the subject of many good Meccano models, one of the best of which is the fine example constructed by A. Cant, Glasgow W.3, shown in this illustration.

SLIDING GEAR-BOX SHAFTS

A correspondent recently set our model-building staff an interesting problem. He wished to build a model in which a shaft had to slide to and fro while rotating, and he could not see how it was possible to keep the shaft connected to the main gear train while it was sliding backwards and forwards. The idea of filing a flat on the shaft so that the gear could remain stationary did not appeal to him, because the shaft would be spoiled for future use.

The solution suggested by our model-building staff is as follows. The gear is left loose on the shaft and into its boss is screwed a 1″ Screwed Rod. The latter is locked in position by a nut, and a 3½″ Rod is fixed firmly to its end by a Collar. The Rod is arranged so that it is parallel with the main shaft, and a Coupling is then fitted over the ends of the main shaft and the 3½″ Rod. One of the grub screws is tightened up to lock the Coupling on the main shaft, but this is left free on the 3½″ Rod.

With this arrangement the shaft can be moved backwards and forwards freely within the limits set by the 3″ Rod, and no matter what position it is in the drive is still taken from the gear train.

A SIMPLE MACHINE FOR WINDING SOLENOIDS

After reading the paragraph describing the use of solenoids that appeared on "*With the Model-Builders*" page in the October "*M.M.*" S. Johnson, Shoreditch, set to work to design a machine for winding his own solenoids. The one he built is of very simple construction, but works quite satisfactorily. It is built up on a base consisting of a 5½″×2½″ Flanged Plate, to which two sets of Architraves are bolted 3½″ apart to form the bearings for a small Crank Handle and a 3½″ Screwed Rod. A Meccano Bobbin is mounted at the centre of the Screwed Rod, and is locked in position by two nuts. At one of its ends the Screwed Rod carries a ¾″ Sprocket Wheel, which is connected by Sprocket Chain to a 1½″ Sprocket Wheel on the Crank Handle. The reel carrying the wire is fitted loosely on the shaft of the Crank Handle.

In order to prevent the wire from running too quickly off its reel, the latter is provided with a friction brake consisting of a Strip tensioned by means of a length of Spring Cord.

LOW FRICTION BEARINGS FOR VERTICAL SHAFTS

While building a model clock recently, T. Lomas, London, discovered that several vertical shafts were introducing an undue amount of friction into the mechanism. The shafts concerned were journalled in holes in Meccano Plates and were supported by Collars bearing on the Plates. He decided to try to reduce the friction as much as possible and in the course of his experiments to this end designed two interesting new bearings specially suitable for shafts that have to be journalled in a vertical position.

One of the bearings consists of a Coupling, into one end of which the plain shank of a Threaded Pin is pushed. The Threaded Pin is fastened in position by its threaded portion and the shaft bears upon its rounded end.

The other bearing is built up by fitting a Steel Ball into one end of a Socket Coupling and fixing it in position by a Grub Screw. A Collar is pushed into the other end of the Socket Coupling and the bearing is then ready for mounting.

A SIMPLE TYPE OF CLUTCH

A Meccano clutch need not be of the friction disc type that is so often used in motor chassis models. There are other simple types of clutches for various purposes, all of which can readily be built up from Meccano parts. For instance, a clutch device for preventing damage to a driving Motor due to overloading can be built up from an Angle Bracket and a Spring Clip. The Angle Bracket is bolted to a 57-teeth Gear loose on its Rod. The Clip is pressed on the Rod so that its wings engage the Angle Bracket.

AHOY for CHRISTMAS!

SHIP MODELS from a WONDER CATALOGUE

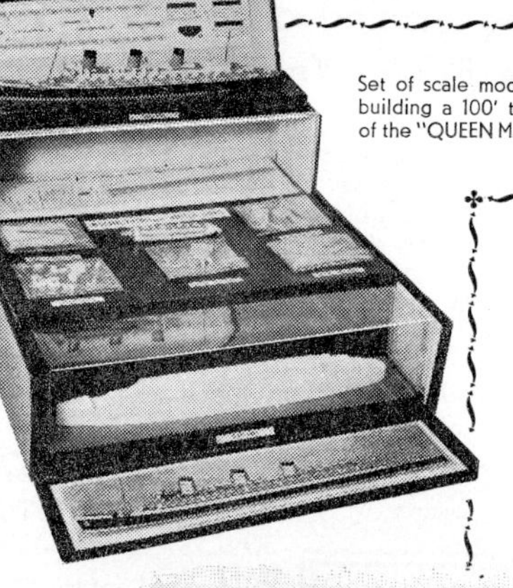

Set of scale model parts for building a 100' to 1" model of the "QUEEN MARY," **12/6**

IOLANTHE II—the super motor boat. 27½ in. long. Clockwork or electric **42/-**

BASSETT-LOWKE'S Model Shipyard is the most famous in the world. Ships of every type, size and price are constructed there—yachts, motor boats, scale ships from tugs to ocean greyhounds like the R.M.S. "Queen Mary."

If you like building things choose a set of parts from the many illustrated in their catalogue, old-time ships, streamline speed boats, or attractive little waterline ships like those illustrated.

There are fittings and deck parts, too, for the boy who wants to give his own boat that "finishing touch," so write now for

S.17. COMPLETE MODEL SHIP CATALOGUE **6d.** post free

The famous "Great Britain," first screw steamer to cross the Atlantic, built from a 50' to 1" set of parts, costing **12/6**

The "Pilot Lugger"—a practical sailing boat, steady and reliable. 24" long. **£2-15-0**

Those interested in building these waterline sets should write for **WB.17** booklet 1d.

BASSETT-LOWKE LTD., NORTHAMPTON

LONDON: 112, High Holborn, W.C.1 **MANCHESTER: 28, Corporation Street**

CYCLISTS—*Increase your light!*

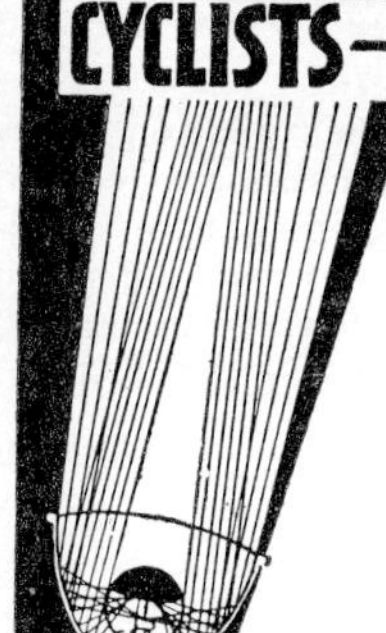

TRE VITA (TREMENDOUS VITALITY)

DOUBLE REFLECTOR BULBS OF AMAZING BRILLIANCY

TRY THIS SIMPLE TEST:

Connect an ordinary cycle bulb to a battery, without a reflector, and notice the short distance the rays travel. This proves that the rays need your reflector to make the forward beam. Now consider how the rays which do not reach your reflector are lost, and you will realise why Double Reflector Bulbs which throw these rays back upon your reflector, give you a "Light of Amazing Brilliancy."

DYNAMO HEAD LAMP BULBS
With 15 mm. Double Reflector Balloons and M.E.S. Caps.

Ref.	Volts.	Amps.	Watts.	Price.
751	4	.3	1.2	7½d.
752	4	.35	1.4	7½d.
753	4.5	.3	1.35	7½d.
754	4.5	.35	1.575	7½d.
755	4.5	.4	1.8	7½d.
759	6	.25	1.5	7½d.
760	[illegible]	[illegible]	[illegible]	[illegible]
761	6	.35	2.1	7½d.
762	6	.4	2.4	7½d.
763	6	.45	2.7	7½d.
764	6	.5	3	7½d.
765	6	.55	3.3	7½d.
770	Special Bulb for Lucifer 6V. 12-Pole			7½d.

BATTERY HEAD LAMP BULBS

Ref.	Rating.	For Use with	Balloon	Price
140	2.5V. 0.3A.	One Large Twin Cell	11½mm.	6d.
141	2.5V. 0.3A.	Cycle Lamp or Torch	15 mm.	6d.
142	3.8V. 0.3A.	One Normal 3-Cell	11½mm.	6d.
143	3.8V. 0.3A.	or one Box 3-Cell Cycle Lamp or Torch	15 mm.	6d.
144	5.5V. 0.3A.	Two Large Twin Cell Cycle Lamp or Torch	15 mm.	7½d.
145	8V. .15A.	Two Normal 3-Cell Cycle Lamp or Torch	15 mm.	7½d.

See Double Reflector Bulbs actually demonstrated in Cycle Lamps.

Read the original reports of the National Physical Laboratory proving the OUTSTANDING SUPERIORITY both of TUBA and of DOUBLE REFLECTOR BULBS.

BATTERY SAVER BULBS

Tre Vita Battery Saver Bulbs consume more than 40% less current than any other Cycle Bulbs. Over 120 burning hours from each Twin Cell Battery. Despite such Lower Consumption, and Longer Life, their precision manufacture secures Brighter Light, enabling the easy reading of typewriting at a distance of 25 yards.

Ref.	Volts.	Amps.	Balloon	For Use with	Price
129	2.5	.06A	12 mm. Flat	One Large Twin Cell	6d.
124	2.5	.06A	11-12 mm. Ball	One Large Twin Cell	6d.
130	2.5	.06A	15 mm. Ball	One Large Twin Cell	6d.

Obtainable from Halfords and leading Cycle Dealers or Post Free. Catalogues Post Free.

VITALITY BULBS (Props.: Wartburg Lamps Ltd.) **RYLAND ROAD, LONDON, N.W.5**

There's no difference—

—YOU RUN A REAL RAILWAY

● PURCHASE IN CONFIDENCE

Whether you are interested in locomotives only or complete railways you can be certain that Milbro products will give you the same utterly reliable service that is expected of the great railway groups in this country. Send 6d. for your copy of the 100 page catalogue to

Perfect in every detail, built to precision limits by skilled craftsmen. Milbro locomotives and railway accessories are as real as their prototypes. They are the experts' choice every time.

MILBRO TRUE-TO-SCALE *replicas for reliability*

MILLS BROS. (Model Engineers) LTD.
St. Mary's Road, SHEFFIELD

London Showrooms:
2, Victoria Colonnade, Victoria House, Southampton Row, W.C.1

TAKE UP THE MODEL HOBBY

RESOURCE — INITIATIVE — FUN — ALL PLAY THEIR PART in the making of a Model Railway, the running of a Model Engine, the sailing of a Model Yacht!

The "real" thing! At the time of going to press our locomotive factory was busy assembling models of this latest L.M.S. locomotive, so we are showing a photograph of the actual 4–6–2 "Duchess of Montrose." The model in clockwork or electric a.c. or d.c. (ready before Christmas), will cost **£8 8 0**

The peak of the Bassett-Lowke range illustrated—the latest L.M.S. Pacific "Duchess of Montrose," from the 1938 "Duchess of Buccleugh" class; the L.N.E.R. "Empire of India," a model for the moderns; the L.M.S. Compound, most popular of our inexpensive 4-4-0 types; L.N.E.R. "Arsenal," hand made and exquisitely finished; our 0-6-0 "wonder-value" Goods Locomotive, either in L.M.S. or L.N.E. colours; while the Bassett-Lowke all-steel bogie coaches are the best value on the market to-day!

The L.N.E.R. "EMPIRE OF INDIA" in garter blue, a superb model, with every detail of the original faithfully reproduced. In this series of "super" scale model streamliners, the red and gold "Duchess of Gloucester" has just been added, and others are the L.N.E.R. "Silver Link," and "Dominion of Canada," and L.M.S. "Coronation." Clockwork or electric. Price **£12 12 0**

L.M.S. COMPOUND. The designers of the model have reproduced to the full the shapely and characteristic outline—the deep buffer beams, foot plating over the coupled wheels and high-sided tender—of this popular L.M.S. type. The model does not require large curves and is the ideal inexpensive locomotive for you.

Price	Clockwork	**£1 12 6**
6–8 d.c.	(Junior Permag)	**£1 17 0**
8–10 d.c.	(Spur Drive)	**£2 10 0**
20 v. a.c.	Motor	**£2 2 6**

L.N.E.R. "MELTON HALL," No. 2838—a model of one of the most "capable" classes on L.N.E. metals to-day—the 3-cylinder 4–6–0s—first of which was the "Sandringham" class designed by Sir Nigel Gresley. A model of the "Arsenal," No. 2848, is also available.

Price. Clockwork, or electric, a.c. 20 volts, or d.c. 8-10 volts **£7 18 6**

PASSENGER ROLLING STOCK. Good news for enthusiasts, these coaches have been reduced to 11/6 each and are available in all companies' colours in both 1st class corridor and corridor brake thirds. They can be fitted with Bassett-Lowke's special bogie No. 612/0, which gives exceptionally easy running, at an extra cost of 5/– per vehicle.

0–6–0 GOODS LOCOMOTIVE—a wonderful value engine in either L.N.E.R. or L.M.S. colours. In clockwork **28/6.** Junior d.c., 6-8 volts, **35/–.** Spur drive, d.c., 8-10 volts, **42/–,** or a.c., 20-volts, **39/–**

REDUCTIONS

In their COMPLETE MODEL RAILWAY CATALOGUE, A.17 (out this November), Bassett-Lowke Ltd. show interesting new productions but they also show reductions in the cost of several accessories, including their famous STEEL PERMANENT WAY, both ready laid and in parts.

This is wonderful news, because the fine quality of the track is unaltered.

Sheradised steel permanent way laid on battens is now 2/– per length curved or straight (electric 2/3), points 9/– each (electric 11/6) and parallel points 11/6 (electric 14/6), and other prices reduced accordingly.

In parts their slide-on chairs and keyed chairs are down in price, and they have introduced a neat new centre rail chair, used with running rail section, at 3/– per 100.

Just Out!

BASSETT-LOWKE GAUGE O SCALE MODEL RAILWAYS

3d

PRICE 3D

A wonderful new publication, fresh from the presses, devoted entirely to Gauge "O" railways. Fully illustrated in two colours and over 40 pages. You must send for a copy! Ask for G.R.17. Price 3d.

Also ask us to include our free Railway Booklet TT.17.

A.17. MODEL RAILWAYS from gauge "OO" to 9½ ins. (New edition out this November.) **6d.** post free.

B.17. (In two sections). B.1. Engines, Boilers and Fittings. **3d.** post free. B.2. Castings, Materials and Fittings, **3d.** post free.

S.17. Model Ships and Ship Fittings. **6d.** post free. See page xi for announcement.

BASSETT-LOWKE LTD., NORTHAMPTON

LONDON: 112, High Holborn, W.C.1 **MANCHESTER: 28, Corporation Street**

MERSEY MODELS

BRITISH MADE THROUGHOUT

You can build Mersey Model Steam Engines into Meccano models or fit extra gearing made from Meccano parts (securing by screws to the wood base), as the gear wheels and axle rods are of the same standard as Meccano.

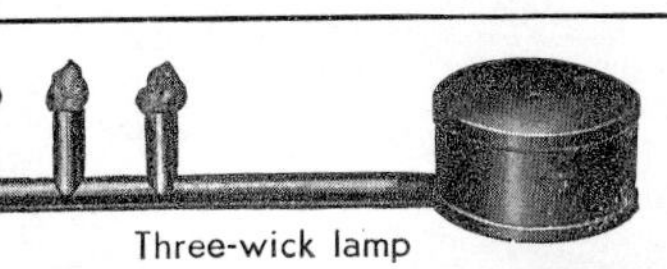

Three-wick lamp

M.M.C. Packed Piston

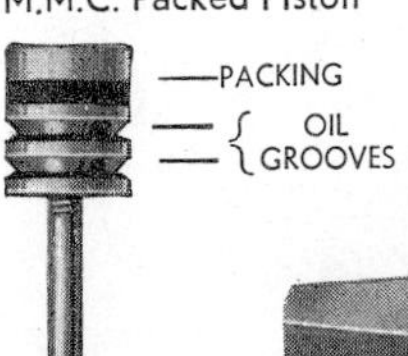

MERSEY MODEL No. 52R
21/6

PRICE LIST

Model 51. Single speed	**12/6**
Model 52. Single speed	**16/6**
Model 52G. Two speeds, non-reversing	**19/6**
Model 52R. Single speed, reversing (as illustrated above)	**21/6**
Model 52GR. Two speeds, reversing	**24/6**
Model 53. Single speed*	**25/6**
Model 53G. Two speeds, non-reversing	**28/6**
Model 53R. Single speed, reversing*	**31/6**
Model 52GR. Two speeds, reversing*	**34/6**
Model 54. Twin cylinder, single speed*	**37/6**
Model 54R. Twin cylinder, single speed, reversing†	**42/6**
Model 54D. Twin cylinder, with dynamo	**47/6**
Model 55. Three cylinder, single speed*	**45/6**
Model 55R. Three cylinder, single speed, reversing*	**49/6**

*With countershaft as illustrated in Model 54R below
†As illustrated below

MODEL GRINDSTONE True to detail and moulded throughout in Bakelite. Price **2/6** (Postage and packing 6d.)

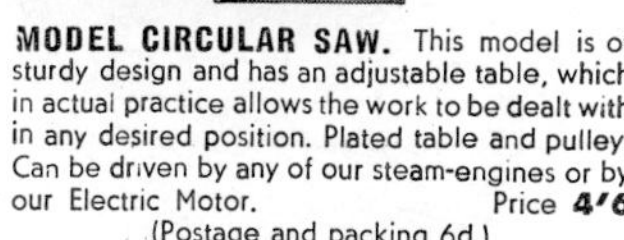

MODEL CIRCULAR SAW. This model is of sturdy design and has an adjustable table, which in actual practice allows the work to be dealt with in any desired position. Plated table and pulley. Can be driven by any of our steam-engines or by our Electric Motor. Price **4/6** (Postage and packing 6d.)

SHOCKING COILS. No. 1. This well-designed induction coil works successfully even with flash lamp battery. It has silver contact points and moulded bakelite base. The "shock" can be regulated to the desired strength by the pull-out solenoid. Price **5/-** Postage and packing 6d.)

No. 2, as above, but fitted with resistance or loading coil for weakening the circuit and connected to a three-way switch (as illustrated). Price **6/6** (Postage and packing 6d.)

MODEL PRESS. Small Power Press, with ⅛ in. plunger and die. Attractively finished with plated table, etc. Can be driven by any of our steam-engines or by our Electric Motor. Price **5/6** (Postage and packing 6d.)

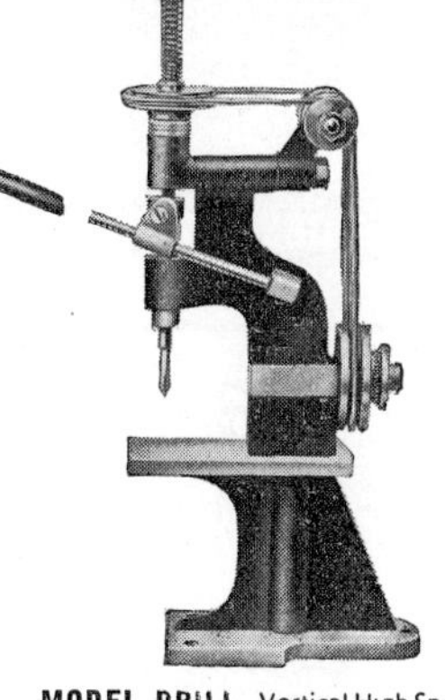

MODEL DRILL. Vertical High Speed Drill, driven by spring belt over jockey pulleys, operated by hand lever. Attractively finished with plated pulleys, etc. Can be driven by any of our steam-engines or by our Electric Motor. Price **7/6** (Postage and packing 6d.)

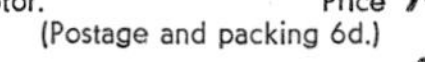

MERSEY MODEL No. 54R
42/6

MODEL LATHE. This ¾ in. Centre Model Flat-bed Lathe is fitted with headstock, tailstock, and slide rest. The latter can be operated at any angle. Drive is by two-speed V Pulley. Can be driven by any of our steam-engines or by our Electric Motor. Plated finish. Price **10/6** (Postage and packing 6d.)

Mersey Models are obtainable from all the large stores and leading toy shops. If you have any difficulty send for name and address of your nearest dealer.

Sole Manufacturers:

MERSEY MODEL CO. LTD., Cooper's Buildings, Church Street, LIVERPOOL 1

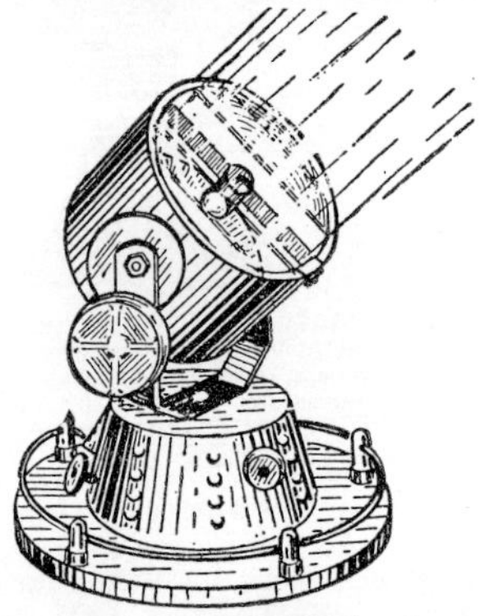

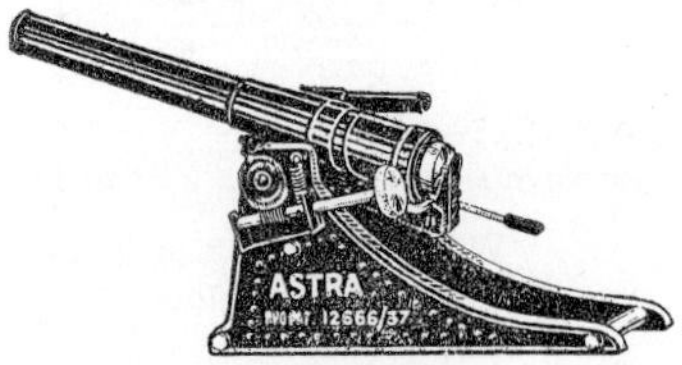

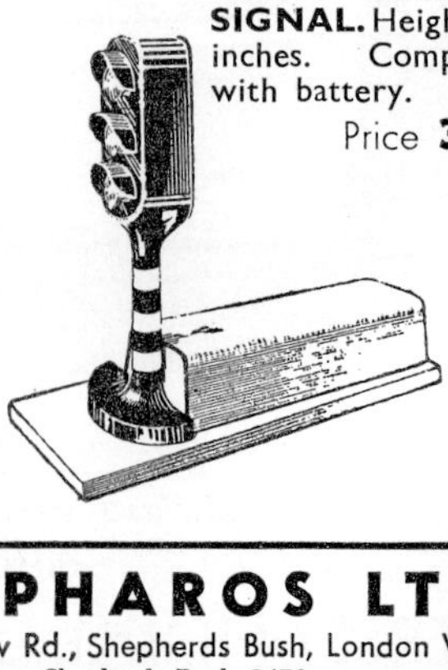

Photography

Lakes and Ponds

By A.R.P.S.

MOST of us live near parks or open spaces where there is a lake or pond that can be visited almost at any time, and so I have selected lakes as my subject for this month's talk.

There are many natural sheets of water which offer good opportunities for the picture hunter at any time of the year, but at this season those opportunities are perhaps better than at any other, for the reason that the tree foliage is not so heavy, and generally the lighting is softer.

It is a mistake to take a view with the camera facing across the lake, usually the result shows too much water. A better effect will result if you can find a satisfactory bend in the bank or side of the lake, and include a clump of trees or bushes with their reflections, while a portion of the lake occupies the remainder of the film. If there happens to be a small island or a pair of swans, search for a position where these can be included in the picture.

The inclusion of figures on the bank requires care. Figures will often spoil a picture by being too prominent. If you have two friends with you, and it is possible for one to be sitting and the other standing, you may get a good result, but do not attempt to expose with both standing.

Artificial lakes, those with built-up banks, do not lend themselves well for picture making, and so it is necessary to survey the scene in order to find a place where little of the bank will be included. Perhaps you will alight on a point where there is an overhanging tree obscuring the stone wall of the edge.

Artificial lakes are often used for model yacht racing, and many excellent "shots" can be obtained. The time to expose is a few seconds after the start, when all the models are away from the shore and under way. Watch them in your view-finder and be sure to wait until they have separated. It is possible to be in a position where you can get them in a very pleasing line all heeling over with the wind, making their sails look very pictorial. Avoid including the owners of the boats. For this subject you can allow a good stretch of water in the foreground because the centre of interest is the group of models.

Do not be too keen on a small stop. I would suggest F8, and with a Selo H.P.3 film give 1/200th or for F11, 1/100th. If you are taking racing models you will require a larger stop, say F6.8, and give 1/500th.

If you have not started developing by the time method, do so with your next film; I am certain you will be pleased with the results. It is the surest and most successful way.

The Swan Pool. Photograph by J. Zammit, Valetta, Malta, G.C. The upper photograph is by G. F. Webb, Swindon, Wilts.

A Polish Officer's Dublo Layout

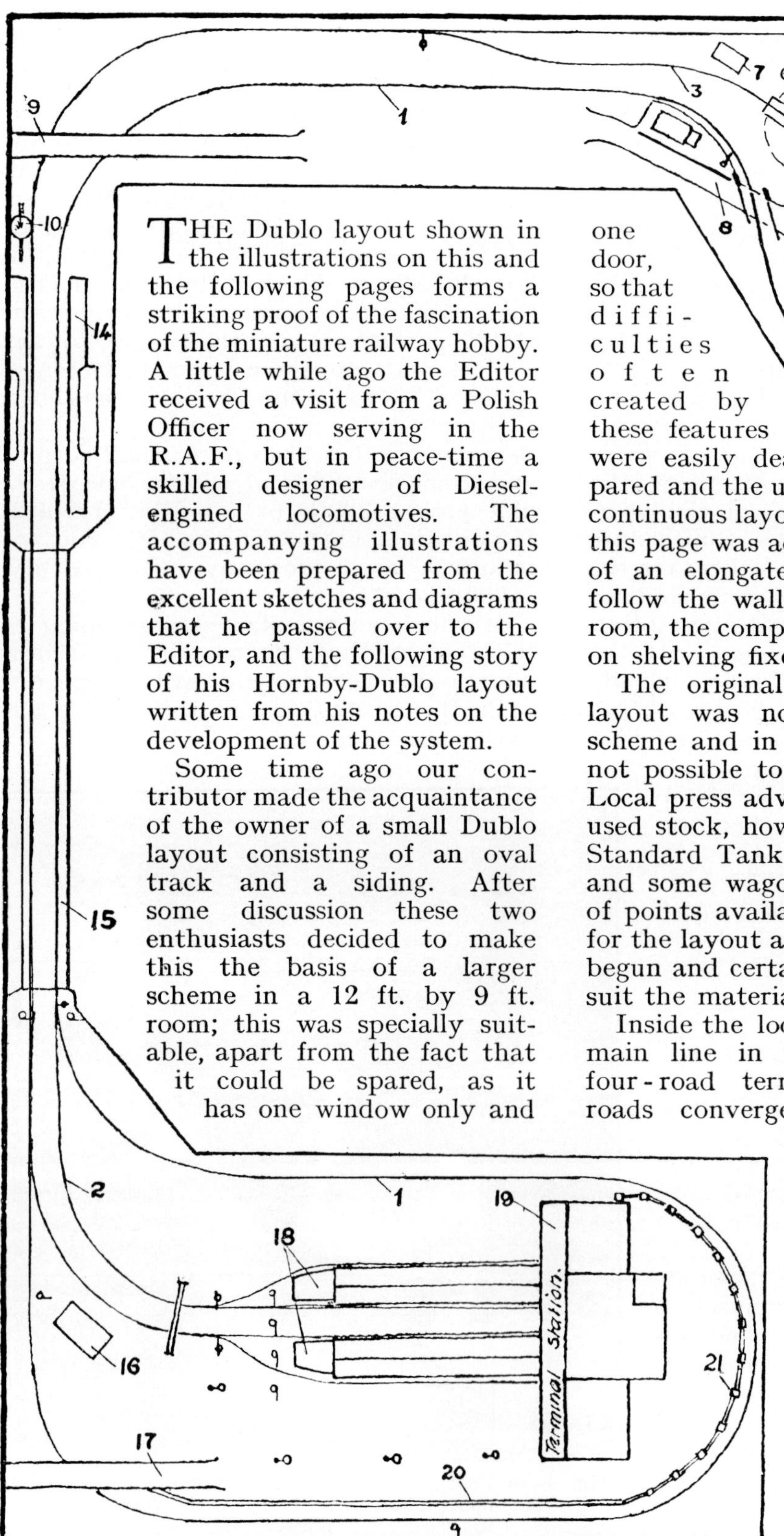

THE Dublo layout shown in the illustrations on this and the following pages forms a striking proof of the fascination of the miniature railway hobby. A little while ago the Editor received a visit from a Polish Officer now serving in the R.A.F., but in peace-time a skilled designer of Diesel-engined locomotives. The accompanying illustrations have been prepared from the excellent sketches and diagrams that he passed over to the Editor, and the following story of his Hornby-Dublo layout written from his notes on the development of the system.

Some time ago our contributor made the acquaintance of the owner of a small Dublo layout consisting of an oval track and a siding. After some discussion these two enthusiasts decided to make this the basis of a larger scheme in a 12 ft. by 9 ft. room; this was specially suitable, apart from the fact that it could be spared, as it has one window only and one door, so that difficulties often created by these features were easily dealt with. Plans were prepared and the unusually interesting form of continuous layout shown in the diagram on this page was adopted. In effect it consists of an elongated oval track adapted to follow the walls of the three sides of the room, the complete system being laid down on shelving fixed for the purpose.

The original equipment of the small layout was not sufficient for the new scheme and in wartime conditions it was not possible to obtain any new material. Local press advertisements provided some used stock, however, including two Dublo Standard Tank Locomotives, rails, points and some wagons. Although the number of points available was really not enough for the layout as planned, track laying was begun and certain details were modified to suit the material in hand.

Inside the loop at the lower end of the main line in the diagram is placed a four-road terminal station. The four roads converge into two beyond the platform ends, and join the main track where there is a narrowing down of the baseboard to lead to a 40 in. bridge. The length of track from this point onward through the passing station is laid down to the normal Dublo double-track standards and has the appearance of an ordinary two-track main line. Passing on under a concrete type bridge, the line swings to

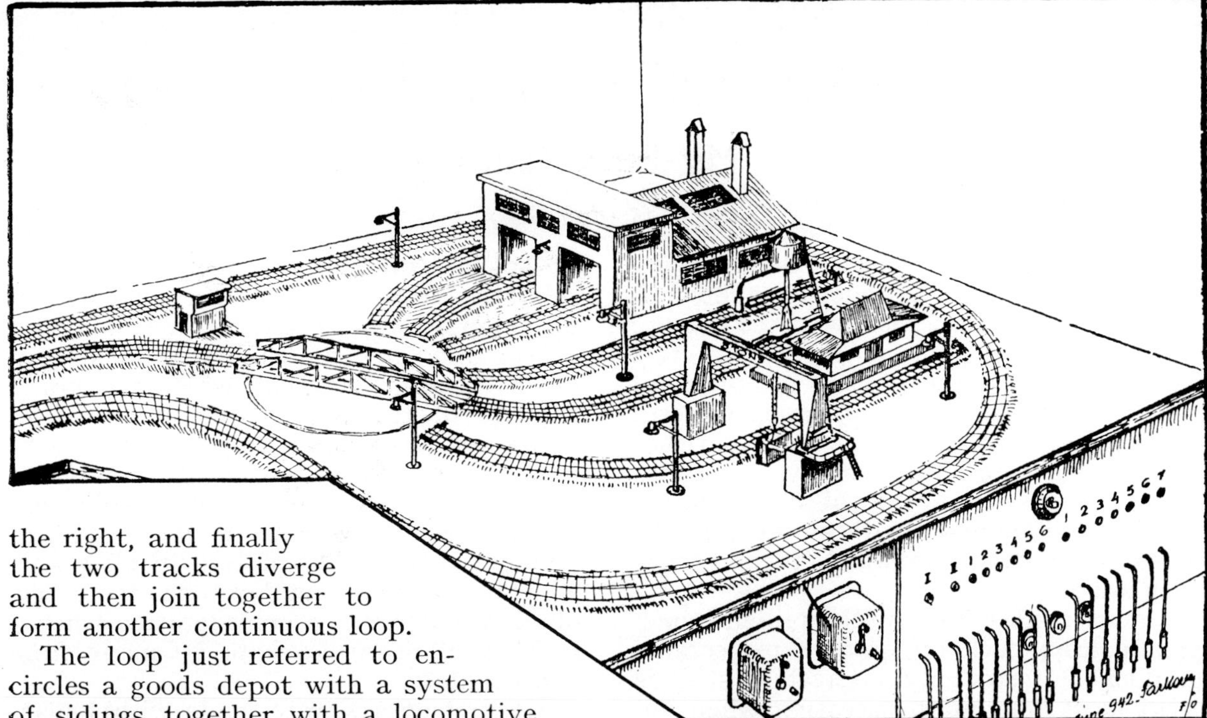

the right, and finally the two tracks diverge and then join together to form another continuous loop.

The loop just referred to encircles a goods depot with a system of sidings together with a locomotive shed and tracks. All these roads radiate from a turntable, which provides the means of transferring engines or wagons from one line to another, this arrangement being adopted owing to the small number of points available. Access to the turntable from the main line is gained in the usual way by means of points as shown. The actual details of this end of the line are well shown in the illustration on this page.

The railway is electrically operated and is divided into two main sections each governed by a standard Controller. The division between the two sections occurs at the passing station, and makes it possible for trains to be stopped automatically on passing from one section to the other, if the same Controller is switched off. In addition, various other tracks, such as the platform lines at the terminal, and the goods yard and engine depot roads, form separate sections to which current is only supplied through connections at the switchboard or control panel. For this purpose plug and socket connections are arranged on the panel, the whole arrangement being compact and efficient.

The terminal station itself is a typically modern structure, having the usual station buildings and offices at the inner end of the platform. Windows and doors are cut out and properly modelled, the window openings being glazed with cellophane, and the building and the outside premises are electrically lighted. The platforms are roofed, not by all-over arched roof, but each platform having its own roof supported by columns running down the centre. This arrangement keeps the trains in full view all the time and is very effective.

Owing to the shortage of purchased track materials, the lines serving the terminal station were home-made. At the end of the curved approach from the main line the tracks are spanned by a signal bridge, also home-made, as was the signal cabin, from which train movements in and out of the station are supposed to be controlled. Another interesting feature close by is the overbridge crossing the main line and leading down to the station yard as shown in the plan on page 170. This bridge was made of plywood 4 mm. thick and painted to represent old stone construction. From it a fence runs alongside the main line as far as the curve passing the terminal station frontage. This represents a net fence, the net being actually cut from a Christmas stocking.

Key to the Plan on the previous page:

1, Main lines; 2, Lines to terminus; 3, Siding to turntable; 4, Engine roads; 5, Goods roads; 6, Turntable; 7, Signal box; 8, Level Crossing; 9. Concrete bridge; 10, Water tower; 11, Engine shed; 12, Goods depot; 13, Overhead crane; 14, Passing station; 15, Steel bridge; 16, Junction box; 17, Stone bridge; 18, Terminal platform; 19, Terminal building; 20, Net fence; 21, Wall.

Forty-Five Years of Railway Photography

I.—My Early Cameras

By H. Gordon Tidey

IT will, no doubt, be conceded that every small boy, from the age when he first begins to take notice, is fascinated by the locomotive, and one imagines that this has been so ever since the inception of railways. As he grows up he either loses his interest or else retains and nourishes it, in which case he eventually becomes a "Railwayist"—an object of never-ending wonder (not unmixed with amusement) to those who have discarded their earlier allegiance.

I must confess that at the present time, and looking back on quite a respectable number of years, my interest is still as great as it was on the occasion when, on giving my Mother the slip, I was eventually found on the platform at Norwood Junction intently studying the "innards" of a Stroudley D1 class 0-4-2 tank! As I was then aged about six it is hardly to be supposed that my investigations suggested any marked improvement on these capable little engines, which to this day remain such a monument to the genius of their designer William Stroudley.

It occurs to me that after so many years, of which much of my spare time has been given to the photography of trains in motion and locomotives, a review of some of my experiences may be acceptable to readers of the "*M.M.*," of which the study of railways forms an important section.

In very early days I felt the urge to record, by means of photography, the thrilling spectacle of a crack express, hauled by a locomotive which, in those days, was kept in spotless condition, with all the splendour of clean paint and burnished brass and steel work. Not having the means at my disposal to acquire an apparatus at all suitable to such exacting work, I wasted much time and expensive material in fruitless endeavours before realising that I must modify my ambitions and keep within the capabilities of such outfits as I could afford. The miniature camera was then unheard of, although at the present time (and for those who can afford it) it has been developed to an extent which renders it capable of turning out work second to none, and the results can be enlarged to any reasonable size provided a first-class lens is fitted to the camera. However, my personal preference is for a camera giving a picture of ½-plate or 6 by 4 size, which, although cumbersome to carry, obviates enlarging, a consideration when a number of prints have to be made from one negative.

My first efforts were made with ¼-plate box cameras of various sorts, most of which were loaded with plates in sheaths, and had shutters operated by elastic bands or springs, giving an exposure which was at all times problematical. The changing of plates, although worked on a system which had every appearance of being reliable, was actually in practice very much the reverse, usually allowing several plates to fall down at one operation, with the result that one never actually knew how many remained, nor which of those released had been exposed. Needless to say, my results with these cameras, of which I had several at different times,

L.N.W.R.: Up Liverpool express hauled by 4-cylinder compound 4-4-0 "Empress." On right is a 2-4-0 "Dreadnought" class 3-cylinder compound.

were not up to reproduction standard, although I can remember they afforded me quite a lot of enjoyment.

The first really efficient instrument I owned was one known as a "Cyclist's Gem." This was a hand camera fitted with a focussing front and a rapid rectilinear lens working at F8, and had a spring shutter giving speeds which were alleged to be 1/25, 1/50 and 1/100. This, of its kind, was really a very useful little instrument, with which I managed to turn out some quite passable results, the highest shutter speed being fast enough to render a train, if not travelling faster than about 45 m.p.h., sufficiently sharp for ordinary purposes. It must of course be remembered that, in those days, a plate of 250 H & D was an "ultra rapid," whilst a lens of a larger aperture than F8 was a luxury far beyond the capacity of pocket possessed by the average small boy. On glancing through some of the work I turned out during this period I am invariably surprised at the quality of the results, when taking into account the limitations of the camera, coupled with slowness of lens and plates. No doubt the secret lies in the fact that these slow plates had a vastly greater latitude, and therefore did not suffer so much owing to inevitable under-exposure.

G.N.R.: 4-2-2 "Stirling" single No. 1007.

I was perforce content with this outfit for a considerable time, but after much consideration, coupled with a lengthy period of rigid economy (helped out by relatives), I next purchased a simple tripod camera, having the luxury of a focussing screen and dark slides, and a metal shutter of the revolving type, the motive power being an elastic band. One advantage of this was that two or more bands could be used to give a faster exposure, but there was naturally no means of telling the length of such exposure, and one could only judge by experiment how many bands were necessary, the number of course varying according to the speed of the train. I cannot remember ever achieving any greatly improved results with this outfit, although I got through a very considerable amount of material.

It would be, I suppose, about 1904 that I took the plunge, and went in for my first ½-plate set. This was a Sanderson Tripod Camera, having a Thornton Pickard roller blind shutter fitting on the front of the lens, and having a marked tendency to jump off under the stress of the discharge, chiefly because I had screwed up the controlling spring in order to obtain maximum speed. The change over to half-plate opened my eyes to the fact that, owing to the larger size, a far greater shutter speed was necessary, because a small amount of movement in the image appeared to be intensified out of all proportion. For this reason it was only a short time before I realised the necessity of a further outlay, and purchased a second-hand focal plane shutter, only to find that in order to take advantage of the speed which such a shutter gives, a faster lens was a vital need. (Continued on page 214)

L.N.W.R.: Manchester train hauled by "Dreadnought" class 3-cylinder compound "Vesuvius."

New Electric Shunting Locomotives—

(*Continued from page 182*)

of the locomotive is the height of the trolley wire; this comes down to a minimum of 8 ft. above the rail. It was accordingly necessary to place the driver's cabin at the end and to bucket it by cutting away the locomotive frames, thus allowing of low side entrance.

These locomotives operate on a two-mile siding, each handling a train of 30 tubs which total about 65 tons. With this load a speed of 8 m.p.h. is obtained on the level and 6 m.p.h. up the maximum gradient of 1 in 48. The maximum speed is limited to 14 m.p.h.

This description is reproduced from "The Metropolitan-Vickers Gazette" by courtesy of the Editor.

Forty-Five Years of Railway Photography—

(*Continued from page 185*)

I then purchased a Goerz "Dagor" working at F6.8, and with this combination I turned out some of my first really passable work.

It was shortly after acquiring this set that I was at York, and took the opportunity to have a shot at the up "*Newcastle-Sheffield Flier,*" then the fastest timed train in the kingdom, with its scheduled speed of over 61 m.p.h. from Darlington to York. Having pitched the tripod on a suitable spot on the low embankment, I proceeded to focus, of course with a cloth, when I became aware of a confused buzzing sound at my feet, and on glancing down was horrified to find myself absolutely surrounded by wasps. I had pitched that tripod right on top of a thickly populated wasps' nest, and the inhabitants were showing their not unnatural resentment in no uncertain fashion. Well, I seized the cloth and made tracks along that rough and sloping embankment at a pace which put the "*Newcastle Flier*" right in the shade! By wielding the cloth furiously I managed to escape without a single sting, but it was only the imminence of the time at which I expected the "*Newcastle Flier*" which gave me sufficient courage to retrieve my apparatus, and you may be sure I wasted no time in getting away again.

I should like to make it quite clear that I do not wish in any way to discourage any young enthusiast who has perforce to make use of a camera not fitted with a focal plane shutter and large aperture lens. My own experience and that of many others (such experience having been bought with many years of experimenting, plus much waste of material), is that, provided one is prepared to recognise, and make allowance for, the limitations of such an outfit, it is possible to turn out quite passable work. The main point to bear in mind must always be that the ordinary front lens shutter, as fitted to such cameras, is quite useless for trains at high speed, and even were it sufficiently fast, no lens with a smaller aperture than F6 would give sufficient exposure with a higher shutter speed than about 1/200 sec.

There are, however, many large stations having an overbridge in the very near vicinity, and if one does not object to a high viewpoint, quite good results can be obtained from such as the trains will not only be travelling quite slowly but will also usually give very impressive exhaust effects. An exposure of about 1/50 sec. will generally be ample, in sunshine. There are also many heavy gradients throughout the country on which trains frequently drop to as slow a speed as 30 m.p.h., and these furnish quite fair game for such an apparatus.

In addition to this, many opportunities for shots will occur from station platforms, such as engines standing at adjoining platforms, or coaling and watering in yards, which are often situated within reach of a platform. If one makes such a camera a constant travelling companion it will be found that it is quite possible to form quite a comprehensive collection.

The three illustrations are all from negatives made by the "Cyclist's Gem" camera referred to on page 185, and will, I think, bear out my statement that trains at speed were quite a feasible proposition, in a good light and with the quickest exposure available.

EDITOR'S NOTE—Readers should bear in mind that this article refers to peace-time railway photography, and that such work is practically impossible under present restrictions.

(*Next month: "My two Reflex cameras"*).

The Diesel Engine Locomotive—

(*Continued from page 191*)

working, together with a further indirect saving of approximately £180, making a total saving of £910 in 12 months.

The upper illustration on page 191 shows a number of Diesel engines for locomotives at various stages of construction in the shops of a well-known British manufacturer. These are eight-cylinder single-acting 2-cycle engines developing 300 b.h.p. at 1,200 r.p.m. They weigh 2.16 tons each, have frames of welded steel construction, and an overall length of 7 ft. 4 in.

All Diesel engines are, of course, thoroughly tested before leaving the manufacturer's works, and the last illustration on page 191 shows one such engine coupled up to a dynamometer on the test bed. This particular engine is for a 170 b.h.p. 0–6–0 shunting locomotive ordered by the L.M.S. railway.

(*Next Month: "From Power Unit to Driving Wheels"*).

William Hedley— (*Continued from page 195*)

and the staithes. After the strike the keel thus equipped was used for some years in towing ships.

After leaving Wylam, about 1826, Hedley took over various collieries and devoted himself to developing them and increasing their efficiency. At Callerton colliery he introduced improvements in the pumping machinery.

Hedley died at Burnhopeside Hall, near Lanchester, Durham, on 9th January 1843.

The "Methuen Park Railroad"

A Layout in a Limited Space

THE illustrations on this and the following page are of an interesting system the official title of which is the *"Methuen Park Railroad."* This is not based on American practice as the title might lead one to suppose at first but it is chosen because the owner, Mr. F. Appleton, of London N.W.1, prefers the term "railroad" which was frequently used in this country in the early days to describe what we nowadays invariably call a "railway."

The 0-4-2 tank locomotive of the "Methuen Park Railroad" described in this article. The engine was built by Mr. F. G. Appleton, the owner of the layout.

Although the system as it is to-day was commenced only two and a half years ago as a distraction from wartime activities it had its origin in quite the earliest days of Hornby trains, and the first engine was one of the popular "Zulu" Tanks of those days. Even before that Mr. Appleton had been a "Meccano boy" for some years, so that he has had a considerable experience of the products of the well-known Factory in Binns Road! At that time of course clockwork engines only were the rule in the Hornby System, and the "Zulu" was later supplemented by various typical brass-domed Hornby locomotives of that time.

After some development, as in the case of quite a few model railways 20 years or so ago, the attractions of radio and then motor cycling ousted the railway and the original stock was disposed of. However, another start was made some six years ago and an electrically-operated miniature railway had reached a promising stage of development when it was abandoned because its operation was not appreciated by the tenants of the flat below! The trials of many miniature railway owners, especially in the larger gauges, are surely in proportion to the difficulties experienced by the promoters of real railways over 100 years ago!

So after a lapse of time the present layout was commenced, a removal in the meantime making matters more favourable in that a separate room became available, although this is of somewhat restricted dimensions. A space of 10 ft. by 6 ft. is not unduly large for a gauge 0 layout, so that the system has a definite "branch line" character, but is none the less interesting on that account. The line is laid on a raised structure 3 ft. high so that it is at a convenient height for handling. Boards 1 in. thick form the base so that a firm foundation for the track is assured.

Naturally the layout is a simple one and only one station, named *"Methuen Halt,"* is included. This has a single platform and is situated alongside the single track main line which, having to make the most of the space available, is oval in form. In passing the station platform and its approaches the main line has a loop taken off it and by means of various points connections are made to sidings serving a goods platform and a small shed with Platform Crane and loading gauge at one end of the room. At the other end of the room it has been found possible to include a small locomotive shed, access to this being gained by means of a turntable. A water tower and two engine roads complete the "Locomotive Department." These features are all outside the main oval and are concentrated on one side of the system; along the opposite side the line runs through a long tunnel the main purpose of which is to carry the track past a desk and other items. Curiously enough, as is the usual way on model railways, any minor mishaps such as buffer-locking and so on that may occur invariably happen in this tunnel! Actually these occasions are infrequent, but to deal with them the top of the tunnel is made removable.

The track is composed of small scale permanent way material and is electrified, the current being 20 volts fed to the centre rail. The line is ballasted throughout with fine limestone chippings as obtainable from "bird shops" and it is merely laid in position, not glued or otherwise "fixed" as is sometimes done. As long as the ballast is kept "within bounds" by a wood strip alongside the track or by the presence of a miniature board fence or other scenic feature, the fact that it is not fixed to the baseboard is of advantage if there are alterations or repairs to be made to the track. Ballast spilled on the floor is however not popular with the Home Authorities as many readers may have found out.

Signalling has not progressed a great deal in extent but what there is has been well done. Two aspect colour-light signals are used, an accumulator being employed to supply the necessary current, so that

"Methuen Halt" showing the overbridge and light signals.

A home-built bogie timber wagon is included in this illustration.

the installation is on quite modern lines. The individual signals have all been constructed at home and are wired to contacts at the points so that the operation of the latter automatically changes the signal aspect. An interesting point is that there are several "dolls" or dwarf signals suspended from the footbridge that spans all tracks about half-way along the platform at "*Methuen Halt*." This position gives them an unusual and realistic appearance, being a change from the more or less standard arrangement of having a cluster of signals on a gantry or bracket post structure.

The overbridge incidentally leads from the station platform over the lines to a car park that has recently been provided just outside the tracks. This we are told has been made specially for the convenience of regular passengers who live a fair way from the station. Most of them must do because so far there have been no "housing developments" in the neighbourhood, although a notable lineside feature is a miniature "Tudor Cottage" with leaded windows. This is a most effective piece of scenery that was built at home and its charm is increased by the fact that it can be lit up when required; naturally it has a most attractive appearance. Electric lighting is also provided in the station yard and elsewhere by means of lamp standards. There is in fact enough illumination on the railway itself to make night operations possible in a realistic manner, the light in the room being then turned out.

The district served by the line is "country" in character, but it is slowly being developed so that increased passenger and goods traffic is to be expected. Actually goods developments, as measured by the recent increases to the "Company's" freight stock, have made necessary an extra siding, and this meant lengthening the station footbridge, so that altogether it was quite an involved job.

Lineside items in the neighbourhood of the station include a fogman's hut, and there is a signal cabin so placed that the "box-man," to use a railway term, has a good view of the whole of the operations carried out at the station and in the adjacent sidings. Miniature figures add a realistic touch to the platform and railway premises generally, and local milk traffic is well catered for by a number of platform trolleys and a "regiment" of churns. Hornby Hedging and Trees add a welcome touch of green to the surroundings. The car park at the station usually accommodates a fair number of Dinky Toys Motor Cars; other street features include "A.A." and "R.A.C." call-boxes and there are in addition G.P.O. letter and telephone boxes. In the goods yard freight items include Cable Drums and Miniature Containers and various other loads, all of which are handled by means of the Platform Crane referred to previously.

The rolling stock is not numerous as yet, but no doubt as traffic grows there will be greater activity in the "Company's shops." A prominent vehicle in passenger traffic operations is a bogie Hornby Pullman. In addition to its normal use it is employed at periods of slack traffic as part of a "pull and push" train which makes an ideal unit for typical branch or local work. Among the freight wagons are several from the Hornby range, including various special-purpose vehicles, such as a Cement Wagon, and a "United Dairies" Milk Tank for through milk traffic in bulk. Each of these has had additional details put on. Home-built items include a goods brake of the pattern used on the former G.N.R. and a very effective bogie wagon, or "*Macaw*" as the G.W.R. code would describe it, for timber traffic and other long loads.

The locomotive stock is varied, pride of place being taken by a Hornby G.W.R. "*County of Bedford*" Locomotive. This has had certain additional details put on by the owner of the layout, including a dummy crosshead-driven vacuum pump, reversing rod from the cab to a point ahead of the front splasher, brackets for spare lamps, and so on. This engine has the reputation of being a most reliable performer. Another locomotive, built at home, is what may be described as a 0-4-4 version of the well-known L.N.E.R. "N2" class tanks. These of course have the 0-6-2 wheel arrangement, but the model follows their general lines and details, including the condensing pipes and the flat-roofed cab with rounded "eaves."

The "works" of the third engine, a 0-4-2 tank, are nearly 20 years old, and survive from one of the old Hornby No. 2 Locomotives! Bearings are worn but the mechanism, which is of course a clockwork one, still works well and the engine has a fine turn of speed.

A freight train passing "Methuen Halt," with the Hornby "County of Bedford" at its head.

On this system very realistic results have been attained by concentrating attention on a single station, with its yard, goods depot and so on. Where a good length is available but not much width, a "station" system instead of a "main line" system can provide a great deal of fun. A "layout on a shelf," more or less, has distinct possibilities, and we hope to go into the idea more fully at some future date.

In the Cab of "The Flying Scotsman"

By Edward H. Livesay

ONE morning a good many years ago a little boy stood on the up platform of Potters Bar station, 13 miles out of King's Cross on the Great Northern Railway. Suddenly, like a Jack-in-the-box, an engine burst out of the black mouth of Potters Bar tunnel, tossing a plume of white above it. The spellbound child caught a fleeting glimpse of a sleek, green engine with bright steel rods flashing to and fro beside a great driving wheel, and behind, a cavalcade of brown, curved-roof carriages streaming by in a haze of dust, to disappear down the line towards Hatfield. Excited litter sprang up from the ballast behind the swaying guard's van, to be tossed, tumbled and sucked along, whirled high in the air before giving up its mad chase after the speeding train and settling wearily down again between the shining metals. The station went to sleep once more, and the little boy trotted home, well pleased. It was 17th May 1895; he had seen *"The Flying Scotsman"* in full flight to Edinburgh, with a Stirling 8-ft. single at its head.

The scene changes. It is no longer Potters Bar station in the nineties, but King's Cross locomotive shed on 24th August 1938. The little boy is as fond of locomotives as ever, and has come to the shed to make close acquaintance with L.N.E.R. streamlined "A4s," on one of which he will be riding to Edinburgh next day with *"The Flying Scotsman."*

As you will have guessed, I was that little boy, and when going through the shed with Mr. Simpson, the Assistant Superintendent, looking at "A4s" and "Atlantics" being groomed and lit-up, he said "There's an engine outside you might like to see—'Old No. 1,' a Stirling single. She's been brought out of the Locomotive Museum at York and put into running order, and is taking an excursion train to Cambridge this morning." And there she stood, with the sunlight glinting on her glossy paint and polished brass, a picture in green and gold, looking as immaculate as she must have done when fresh from the paint-shop in 1870.

"Would you like to go round to King's Cross station on her footplate—she's just pulling out?" Mr. Simpson needn't have asked! Climbing up into the cab, I looked round. What a bleak, bare little shelter, after the comfort and complexity of the American cabs I had been riding in only a few weeks before! Why, there seemed hardly anything there! Surely they couldn't have put everything back when they let her out of the Museum? But they had—engines were simpler in those days, and enginemen were not used to luxury; and controls and fittings were simpler too. There was a pull-out regulator, a reverse lever, brake valve, water and steam gauges, injector, whistle and blower handles, but little else, except sanding and damper handles. There were two tip-up seats, or shelves rather; a modern concession, certainly not fitted when the engine first appeared. The cab was little more than an exaggerated weather-board, so narrow, low and open. Enginemen were a tough lot in those days. Many claimed they didn't like cabs—they made them soft! Fancy driving *"Lord of the Isles,"* say, Gooch's famous broad gauge 8-footer, in mid-winter, at 70 m.p.h., with no protection at all, not even a weather-board, or "spectacle-plate" as it was sometimes called. Yet those old-timers did it, and thrived on it apparently.

The last touches having been given to her immaculate perfection, No. 1 came to life, and with cylinder cocks squirting steam and water moved off with stately gait out of the Yard, with the crew plus an Inspector and myself on the footplate. It was fascinating actually to be riding a Stirling 8-footer after all these years! Out on to the main line near Belle Isle Box, we then backed down through smoky Gasworks Tunnel into King's Cross and on to the waiting train of "period" brown teak coaches, also resurrected for the occasion. The platform was crowded with enthusiasts, all anxious to greet the old veteran, and if possible travel behind her to Cambridge. I would have done this too had I thought of the excursion in time, but the preparations for the *"Flying Scotsman"* run had put the affair clean out of my mind, and every seat was booked. However, the little trip on her footplate had been a greater treat and privilege than Cambridge and back behind her, so after taking a snap or two I watched her pull out, to add a few more miles to the 1,400,000 already chalked up during her active life.

"The Flying Scotsman" of 1888, put in order for special half-day trips in 1938. The engine is G.N.R. 4-2-2 No. 1, the famous Stirling single-wheeler. Photograph by courtesy of the L.N.E.R.

Next day the *"Flying Scotsman"* trip brought me back to the shed again to pick up No. 4491, *"Commonwealth of Australia."* First came introductions to her two crews; one English, Taylor and Floyd, and the other Scottish, Maguire and Kinnear, after which I stood aside to watch the final touches being given to lubricators, fire and so on—coal and water had been taken on already. Floyd was busy in the cab, and Taylor, with an oil-can, on the ground. Time was up, so we piled into the cab and followed yesterday's trail round into King's Cross, No. 10 Departure platform, finding the usual little crowd of well-wishers gathered to watch *"The Flying Scotsman"* off on her 392-mile non-stop run to Edinburgh.

9.45 a.m., and 15 minutes to train time. Maguire and Kinnear retired to the compartment next the van reserved for the off-duty crew; I took a snapshot and put a few queries to Taylor before settling down

L.N.E.R. "Commonwealth of Australia," the locomotive on which the footplate trip described in this article was made. Photograph by courtesy of the L.N.E.R.

in Floyd's bucket seat, which he said he wouldn't be wanting for a while. I felt quite a thrill of anticipation at the treat in store for me that sunny summer day. Floyd, watching from the cab door, caught the wave of the Guard's green flag, and with a laconic "Right away!" turned inboard and busied himself with injector and shovel. Taylor reached forward, pulled the regulator, and with cylinder cocks viciously hissing, on the stroke of 10 a.m. "*Commonwealth of Australia*" moved away from the platform into the sooty mouth of Gasworks Tunnel with her 500-ton load behind her and 392 non-stop miles in front of her.

Picking up speed rapidly, in spite of a brief slip on the 1 in 107 gradient in the tunnel, quickly checked with sand, we ran through Hornsey, four miles from the start, at rising 50 according to the Flaman speed recorder tucked away under my seat. The acceleration continued up the long 13-mile bank, through tunnel after tunnel—seven in that distance—until we roared through Potters Bar and over the the top at 60. My childhood treat in reverse! *Then* I had watched "*The Flying Scotsman*" from the platform—*now* I saw the blurred station buildings stream by from the cab. Was there a little boy standing there, or was it only my memory playing tricks?

Down through Hatfield we rushed, and out on to the many-arched Welwyn viaduct, shortly afterwards picking up water from Langley troughs, the first of six refreshers taken en route. Very simple. Floyd stood ready at the handle, and at a hail from Taylor that we were over the trough, round it whirled, down went the scoop, and in a matter of seconds a thousand gallons or so were up in the tank.

On the completion of the trip, at Waverley, Edinburgh. From left to right the figures are Taylor, Maguire, the author, Floyd and Kinnear.

By this time I had become used to my surroundings, differing somewhat as they did from those on the North American engines with which I was most familiar. The cab was very well arranged and free from draught and heat, save right in front of the firedoor, which was generally kept open, rather to my surprise. Though the cab was less roomy than those across the Atlantic—the British loading-gauge is 9 ft. by 13 ft. 3 in. as against 10 ft. 6 in. by 15 ft. 6 in.—it was in no way cramped, and the bucket seat was very comfortable. The engine's riding was admirable, and the balance of the 3-cylinder 120-deg. drive so good that the motion was imperceptible.

I was thoroughly enjoying the novelty of spinning along over perfect British track when we swept through Stevenage, and began the long descent to Sandy. Floyd shouted in my ear: "We'll be going pretty fast soon—watch the Flaman!" Bending down, I saw the hand was moving steadily across the dial, and I could feel the beautiful engine accelerating. From its action it was enjoying things as much as I was. Like a race-horse extending itself in a swinging gallop over springy turf, No. 4491 was doing just what she was intended to do—she was showing her heels, and speed was rising steadily—70–80–90, and we roared through Arlesey with a crash of sound flung back from the station buildings and footbridge as it flicked overhead. Sitting snug in Floyd's seat, looking ahead through the strip of safety glass by the open window or down at the ballast streaming by beneath, I felt a glow spread through me, and I gloried in the song of the wind as it swept past.

Floyd's job was much easier than I had thought it would be. Instead of the firing being of the "little and often" kind, it seemed more the "good deal and seldom"; 20 or 30 shovelfuls would be followed by a 10-minute rest. Most fuel was placed at the back of the box, to shake down towards the front, and as this method seemed quite simple I pleaded permission to try my hand at firing, which was readily granted; he passed the shovel to me with a smile. I wanted to be able to say I had fired "*The Flying Scotsman*"! I had fired on threshing-engines on the prairie, in the stokehole of the cruiser "*Rainbow*" during the First War, and in minesweeping trawlers too, and "*Commonwealth of Australia*" would be another scalp at my belt. But it proved a painful business, and after one or two essays I gave it up. Thinking the cab was going to be hot—it wasn't—I had donned nothing but overalls, and when I turned to fill the shovel the fierce heat from the fire-door struck right through and scorched me. It was agony—I was being roasted to make a fireman's holiday.

Here was another familiar stretch—the embankment beside the Ouse, nearing Huntingdon, where I had learnt to swim long years ago. We roared through the station, from which I had watched the 8-footers nose and lurch over the points outside just as we were doing, and go flying up the 1 in 200 bank to Abbots Ripton. An easy bit for some miles followed, through Peterborough and over Werrington troughs, these making a second contribution to our water-tank, and shortly after the long Stoke bank was reached, down which so many spectacular speeds have been recorded, including "*Mallard's*" 126 m.p.h. Over the top at Stoke Box, and it was down, down almost continuously for over 20 miles through Grantham and Newark to Muskham troughs.

After a cautious negotiation of York's curved station the "change of watch" took place, near Tollerton, 198 miles from London. Maguire and Kinnear, now in working rig, came on to the footplate, and after exchanging a few casual remarks on conditions with Taylor and Floyd, the latter pair retired to the compartment reserved for enginemen off-duty, "to clean, dinner and get their heads down," as the Navy has it. The up "*Flying Scotsman*" flashed by near here, and I noticed how little air disturbance occurred, thanks to the streamlining, which evidently flings the air upward more than sideways. Again I tried firing, this time under Kinnear's tuition, but again it was a failure—I could not stand that roasting. Part of my anatomy was already nicely browned; I did not want it overdone.

Hour after hour "*Commonwealth*" jogged along at 65–70 m.p.h.; it was all the schedule called for. For 100 miles or so right from Retford nearly to Durham the profile is extraordinarily easy, and she made light of her job. Past Darlington, with Stephenson's "*Locomotion No. 1*" on her pedestal, the first engine to haul passengers on a railway; on to Durham, with its glorious Cathedral and Castle dominating the city, the fascinating run continued; fascinating not only from a locomotive enthusiast's viewpoint, but also from a scenic angle. There was nearly always something of interest to note both inside and outside the cab, and I enjoyed every moment. The tender-corridor came in very useful, being used several times to break any possible monotony of a seven-hour non-stop run.

Little has been said about speed, regulator, cut-off, and so on; there is no need to give a log as alterations were so seldom made to the controls. The regulator was kept wide open, and the cut-off generally left at 15 per cent. only lengthened slightly up gradients. The load was only moderate for an "A4," as was the average speed. I should say that even a less experienced driver would get all that was called for out of No. 4491. She was just playing with her job, spinning along tirelessly, effortlessly, up hill, down dale and on the level, no doubt right on schedule or a trifle ahead of it. I don't think we were checked by signals once.

Closing on Newcastle, the route became more and more tricky. "*The Flying Scotsman*" snaked round curve after curve, clicking over a maze of points, crossings and junctions. Not a high speed stretch, this, which is why the "*Silver Jubilee*" does most of its spectacular running south of Darlington. Out over the Tyne we rumbled, on to the King Edward bridge, high above the river, looking down on the grimy docks and building-slips that line its banks. At Killingworth stood Stephenson's ivy-covered cottage, close to the track; then we began to run out of smoke and grime into unspoilt country, and the farther north we went the lovelier it became. Gradients stiffened, though they see-sawed and were mostly short, until at Alnmouth we hit four miles of 1 in 170, and I saw Maguire reach for the reverse handle. The exhaust note deeepened; it had generally been practically inaudible. Falloden flashed by, with a level crossing and a "Halt," where the Grey family have—or had, at any rate—the right to "Flag" any train they want to catch. Lucker trough gave No. 4491 another drink, the sixth since leaving London, and she sped on like a giant refreshed.

We swept out on to the many-arched granite Royal Border Bridge, across the Tweed, through Berwick station, and almost at once struck another four-mile bank of 1 in 190. I sniffed the air. What was it—heather? Yes! There was the boundary board—I was in Bonnie Scotland at last! Grant's House is at the top of the long pull from Berwick; over the peak there is a four mile drop at 1 in 98, the Cockburnspath bank, the stiffest gradient between London and Edinburgh with the exception of a mile of 1 in 78 up into Waverley. Speeding down this, and through the little tunnel near the top—the last had been Askham, near Retford, 219 miles back—the coast came into sight again, and was followed to Dunbar, where the lines turn inland. Running on into Edinburgh, with the fire burning thin and pressure dropping, we came to a stand in Waverley at 4.57 p.m. three minutes ahead of time. The 392 miles from King's Cross had been covered non-stop in 417 minutes, at an average of 56.2 m.p.h.

The former G.N.R. 4-2-2 No. 1, the famous single-wheeler preserved in York Museum and put in running order again for special purposes in 1938.

Returning to London next day, with the same engine and the same crews, the run was just as pleasant and uneventful. Taylor almost promised some real speed down Stoke bank, but on getting there we were a little ahead of time, so nothing spectacular was possible. "*The Flying Scotsman's*" non-stop reputation has to be upheld at all costs: even as it was, we found distant signals against us once or twice south of Hatfield; brakes would begin gently rubbing and the warning arms were approached cautiously, with everyone apprehensive of a stop. But always they would drop just in time to prevent this disaster, off would go the brakes, and the exhaust would begin streaming over our heads again. "*Commonwealth of Australia*" came to rest in King's Cross at 4.55, five minutes early; I went round to the shed with her, to be greeted with laughter in the Superintendent's office: "You look as if you've been working!" "So I have—that's why we got in five minutes ahead of time!" "Well, there's lots of hot water. What did you think of it all?" "Splendid—couldn't have been better!" Verily, that was the only possible judgment to pass on this, my first run on a British express locomotive.

Engineering Notes

New Dam Protected Against Earthquakes

On the Santa Eulalia River, about 50 miles east of Lima, Peru, a great dam is being constructed, and one of its most interesting features is that it is designed to withstand earthquake shocks. The structure is sited at a point where the river flows through a crack in the mountains caused by an earthquake. The chasm is about 1,300 ft. long, 500 ft. deep, and from 18 ft. to 65 ft. wide, and the dam is being built on a solid concrete base that reaches down to solid rock 55 ft. below the bed of the stream and up between the walls of the chasm to a height of 90 ft.

One of the many wartime activities of L.M.S. workshops. Rail-mounted 12 in. howitzers leaving one of the works after renovation. This photograph and that below are reproduced from "Carry On," by courtesy of L.M.S.R.

The structure will be known as the Autisha Dam, and in shape is rather like a butterfly, with the wing sections separated by a space 6 in. wide and 10 ft. long. The manner in which this space is closed is the key point in the design, and in the event of an earthquake occurring in the area, it will permit the two wing sections to move without cracking. On the upstream side of the dam the gap between the wings is blocked by a length of iron pipe filled with concrete, which rests against two vertical beams set in the face of the dam and will be forced into the gap by the pressure of the impounded water behind it. At the centre of the 10 ft. gap is a shaft, on the downstream side of which is a V-shaped copper expansion joint that closes the space between the two wing sections on that side. The purpose of this flexible sheath is to prevent the passage of any water that may seep past the concrete pipe.

The work is being done in two stages. When the first is completed the dam will rise 256 ft. above the river-bed and will hold back behind it about 396,300,000 gallons of water. It is expected, however, that the demand for water will steadily increase, and provision has been made for the height of the dam to be increased by 72 ft., which will create a total storage capacity of 2,377,530,000 gallons. The water under a head of 915 ft. will be used to drive an electric power plant to develop 30,000 kW.

How the L.M.S. Workshops Went to War

It was revealed recently that 44,000 workers in L.M.S. Railway workshops have been building tanks, guns, aeroplanes and other war equipment, in addition to carrying on their normal work of building and repairing locomotives and rolling stock for the L.M.S. lines.

At the outbreak of war in 1939 the L.M.S. had already begun production of wings for Hawker "Hurricanes." Since then the works have turned out wings for "Typhoons" and "Horsa" gliders and have repaired hundreds of planes damaged in combat. The very intricate and specialised work of making gun mountings has also been successfully tackled, and 250 17-pounder guns, and 500 carriages for 25-pounder field guns have been built. Other gun work included the renovation of 23 last war 12 in. howitzers, 51 carriages and limbers for 9.2 howitzer bodies, the manufacture of 13,000 gun and aperture sights for American Lewis guns, and many thousands of rifle butts.

For the Navy L.M.S. workshops have produced among other items over 8,000 assault boats and 2,000 shields of bullet proof steel for protection from low-flying aircraft.

During the dark days of Dunkirk nearly 700 tradesmen's motor vans were converted at great speed into armoured vehicles known as Armadillos, which were intended for the protection of airfields in the event of enemy landings in this country. During the first three years of the war the workshops turned out 642 tanks, comprising Centaurs, Matildas, Cruisers and Covenanters, and also provided thousands of spare parts for each type.

Shell machining and cartridge case reforming have also been carried out extensively.

War Vehicles Shipped in Parts Across the Atlantic

Since the war started 300,000 American and Canadian vehicles have been shipped across the Atlantic in millions of parts and assembled by men of the British, Canadian, and United States Forces. The work was begun in 1940 by the Mechanisation Branch of the Ministry of Supply, and by May of last year 39 plants employing 100,000 workers were involved in the task. Maximum weekly output of 6,537 assembled vehicles was reached in April 1944.

One of the Armadillos referred to on this page. It is one of 677 made in L.M.S. workshops at the time of Dunkirk.

"The International Limited"

By Edward H. Livesay

"THE *International Limited*" of the Canadian Railway is so named because it runs between Montreal and Chicago. The distance covered is 849 miles, during which it makes at least 20 stops, taking 17 hrs. 45 min., and thus averaging 48 m.p.h. This is a very good performance, and better than it appears at first sight, as it involves passage under the Detroit river between Canada and the States, coupled with electric haulage through the tunnel; that is from Sarnia, Ontario, to Port Huron, Michigan, a distance of three miles. The double change from steam to electricity and back again, and slow travel through the tunnel, take 30 min. We will not attempt to describe the whole journey, but will confine ourselves to the first section only, from Montreal to Toronto. These two cities are the largest in Canada, Montreal having a population of over a million, and Toronto one approaching that number. Naturally a good train service is provided between them, over three routes, two being Canadian Pacific, both single track from Glen Tay, 144 miles out of Montreal, and the third, Canadian National, double tracked throughout. It is the last that comes into this account.

There are no trains in Canada like the non-stop British expresses, such as, say, "*The Flying Scotsman*," "*Coronation Scot*" or "*Cornish Riviera*." The only trains that do bear some resemblance, in being day services, minus sleeping cars, are the two "Pool" trains running in both directions between Montreal and Toronto, 329 miles, but there the similarity ends, 10 stops being made en route, as against one by the "*Coronation Scot*" and none by the other British trains I have named. Comparison shows that the Canadian engine has far the heavier task. Though both average and maximum speeds are up to British standards, the weight of the train is far greater. In all cases the maximum speed is restricted; to 80 m.p.h. in Canada, 90 in Great Britain.

What is a "Pool" train? It is one run jointly by the Canadian National and Canadian Pacific Companies, which share or "pool" the receipts. A few years ago the two companies indulged in cut-throat competition for the lucrative traffic between Montreal and Toronto, with the result that it ceased to be lucrative for either. For instance, timing was cut until in 1931 the C.P.R. ran a train over the first Division, Montreal, to Smiths Falls, 124 miles, at an average speed of 68.9, making it the fastest train in the Empire at that time. The C.N.R., not to be outdone, built five special "high-wheel" engines for "*The International.*" No. 5704, the engine on which I travelled, is one of these. And so things went on.

This didn't pay. Trouble was sure to result sooner or later, probably a wreck; and as profits had gone, both railways came to see the folly of it, agreed to "pool" the traffic, and fixed the time at 6½ hrs. "*The International*" is a "pool" train only as far as Toronto; it leaves the C.P.R. Windsor Station, takes the C.N.R. route, is hauled by one of the C.N.R. special engines, runs into the Union Station in Toronto, and is made up of stock of both companies.

You will probably like to know something of the chief differences that would strike you if you came to Canada and found yourself alongside No. 5704, which will be hauling "*The International*" on the run we are going to take. Some of these features apply to American locomotives in general. The first thing sure to impress you would be the greater size of the engine, chiefly in height and length, and from this many other structural and operational differences arise. The rail gauge, or distance between the metals, is exactly the same on both sides of the Atlantic, 4 ft. 8½ in., but the "loading gauge" is more generous in North America, so the boiler, the real source of an engine's power, can be bigger and higher, and the cylinders that utilise the power larger. No. 5704 stands 15 ft. 3 in. in height, and is 10 ft. 6 in. wide, or about 24 in. by 18 in. larger in cross-section than the average British express engine.

Joining No. 5704 at the C.N.R. Turcot Locomotive Depot, I was introduced to the crew, Enginemen Barden and Peachey, climbing on board to look round the cab. The picture will give you a good idea of what a Canadian cab looks like. It was of the "vestibule," all-enclosed pattern, and had four seats, the two spare ones being of the "drop" variety. The hanging throttle-lever is right in front of the driver (engineer in Canada), with the reversing gear air-operated, the brake controls, and the brake and exhaust-pressure gauges. On the other side are the fireman's gauges, pressure, steam-heat, etc., and the group of five little wheels concern

The Canadian National Railway "International Limited," a run on which is described in this article. The illustrations to the article are reproduced by courtesy of the Canadian National Railways.

the five steam jets blowing the fuel into the four corners and centre of the fire-box, the engine having mechanical stoking. A 2-cylinder reversible engine under the cab drives a worm-conveyor bringing the coal forward from the tender, lifts it on to a shelf inside the fire-box, just below the door, whence it is blown by the five steam jets, the operation of which can be seen through the row of holes below the door.

But we must get on with the run. No. 5704's colour-scheme is very handsome, light green, with a darker green running-board picked out with red and gold, red number-plate, and black side-plates. Like all Canadian engines, she is well kept, and starts out from the roundhouse spotless and shining. She pushed the nine cars round into the C.P.R. Windsor Station over a long and rather twisty route; they weighed about 625 tons, a light load in the enginemen's view, but four more were to be added at Brockville.

We got away promptly at 3 p.m.; no green flag here, an air whistle in the cab gives two blasts, sounded by the Conductor (Guard), after he has handed up the "Train Orders" and boarded the train. The two suburban stops disposed of, at Westmount and Montreal West, the real run began, and at Dorval we switched over to the C.N.R. double track main line, and were soon roaring along at 75 m.p.h.

I parked myself on the drop seat behind the fireman, right in the door, trying to keep cool, without much success, seldom leaving it except to get at the drinking-water can, packed with ice in the engineer's locker. There was a long spell of high speed after St. Annes, 70–80, and the riding was good, yet it was much harsher than on the Gresley or Stanier Pacifics. It felt hard, as if the springs were stiffer, as no doubt they were, to compensate for the greater weight on the axles. Possibly the track was not so perfectly kept as it is in Britain; in fact, I am sure it wasn't! Yet it was good, with heavy steel; it must be, to take these heavy engines pounding over it at 80.

In the cab of a locomotive of the C.N.R. "5700" Class.

Barden had forecast very high speed with this train, mentioning a probable figure that made me smile inwardly, as I had made a point of enquiring about this, and had been officially told that 80 was supposed to be the limit, and nothing over that was likely to be done. Nor was it; that is approximately 80, I won't swear to a mile or two. Near Rivierre Beaudette, when we were doing a cool 80! I saw Barden take out his watch, so I followed suit. He studied it for a while, I studied mine. Came a hail: "There you are, a mile in 45 seconds, 90 m.p.h. "Whoa! Come off the roof, that's only 80!" from me. "Eighty? How do you get that way? Mile in 45 seconds is 90!" "Sorry, 80!" We had quite a confab about this, but there, I don't believe Barden really thought it was 90, he was surely too old a hand to make such a bloomer. No, he was pulling my leg.

We had left Montreal West three minutes late, but at Cornwall, the first stop, were a minute ahead, and had averaged 63.8 from St. Annes. Water was taken very quickly, due to a big filler-pipe; then came immediately a steep 1 in 93 incline, the "Hog's Back," the engine accelerating all the way up, and passing over the top at 50. You could certainly hear that exhaust! A harsh roar, and the fire-box a blinding mass of dazzling white flame. It was fascinating to watch the mechanical stoker. No need to be worried at seeing the fireman sweating and swearing in tropic heat, breaking his back and his heart behind a shovel. Peachey just sat in his seat, making an occasional visit to the fire-door to step on a treadle, and see the door fly open if he wanted to peek inside, turning a little injector-wheel, or adjusting the jets or feed occasionally. I too peeked inside frequently, watching the fuel falling ceaselessly on to the shelf, to be picked up by the invisible jets of steam and whirled to a fiery death in that raging box.

I thought of Smith, the fireman on "*King William III*," the engine on which I had made a footplate trip with "*The Cornish Riviera*" when I was in Britain. Smith went through an almost ceaseless cycle of operations—fill scoop, open fire-door flap, discharge scoop, close flap and so on. How he would have liked to be in Peachey's shoes, and have had the benefit of mechanical stoking and a pneumatic treadle-operated fire-door.

Of course Peachey was hot, but not from toil. We all were, though I was probably the coolest of the trio in the cab, sitting right in the door, with my legs outside, while the enginemen were in "hot seats" close to the backplate. Everything about the cab was bone dry, and the deck (footplate) was often drenched with water, yes, and the backplate too, Peachey just sprayed everything inside the cab indiscriminately, including me. However, I didn't mind; I was only wearing a suit of filthy overalls, grimed with the accumulated dirt of many trips on all sorts and conditions of locomotives. A little water might even wash some of it off. The speed was as high as ever, 75–80.

Prescott was passed O.T., and here I caught sight of the St. Lawrence, a streak of blue and silver through the trees, and the air got cooler; the afternoon was wearing on. Then came the Brockville stop, and the crew changed. It is a "Division" point, at each of which "ground crews" seize on the engine, apply grease-guns to nipples about the motion, clean the ashpan, and so on. A 73 sq. ft. grate lets a lot of ash through! The 58 miles from Cornwall had been covered in 53 minutes, 65.7 m.p.h. Four cars were added here, bringing the train weight up to 950 tons, so it will be seen that, as the speed would be as high as ever, No. 5704 was going to be extended a little, in the hands of the new crew, Enginemen Clare and Taylor. Getting away again, a stop was made just beyond the station for coal, several tons being taken on in three minutes from a very efficient coal-stage.

Finally clearing Brockville, we settled down once more, in less trying temperature, running through rougher country, round a lot of curvature and through many rock cuttings. But the speed remained high, the 80 limit being often reached, but not exceeded. No. 5704 was really putting her best foot foremost now, hauling the 950-ton load with tremendous vim. The stoker was grinding away vigorously, sending a continuous stream of fuel into the ravenous fire-box, and keeping the pressure well up in the sixties (two-hundred-and, of course). No. 5704 was doing well, I thought, though Barden had said his regular engine was plenty better, I have heard that sort of remark before from engine men!

Drifting steam naturally gave no trouble; the air was hot, and the tremendous blast in any case carried the exhaust high above the cab. The engineer's window was of the "Kent" revolving pattern, which seemed to me to keep the glass quite free from smuts and smears. This "clear vision" device is simply a circular disc revolving at high speed in contact with a scraper, so nothing has a chance to settle on it. Approaching Kingston, the next stop, there was another steep ¾-mile incline at 1 in 98, which could not be "rushed," and the 950-ton load called for full regulator plus the booster, which was kept in gear for some distance. It cuts out automatically when the engine is "notched up" and is not intended to remain driving at over 12 m.p.h.

This trip was pretty noisy; the engine was working hard, and everything was wide open; one had to shout to make oneself heard. This gets boring after a time, to both parties, and when the whistle chimed in simultaneously it was positively maddening, generally resulting in interjections with no bearings whatever on the conversation. Its long drawn-out bellow always seemed to join in when one wanted to say something in a hurry, or worse still, after one had begun, and felt disinclined to stop.. The law enforces its sounding at every level-crossing, and as these occur every mile or so its ill-timed, blatant intercessions were only too frequent, quite spoiling the rhythm of an interesting chat. The bell, fitted on all N. American engines, as it was on English ones too a century and more ago before the whistle was invented, is always rung in city limits, but not at level-crossings, or "grade-crossings," as they are called out here. It wouldn't "carry" well enough, or act as a strong enough deterrent to jackasses "beating the train to the crossing."

I have seen this game played myself; here is an instance. We were entering the town of Peterborough at about 40 m.p.h., and I was sitting in the fireman's seat, looking idly out of the window, when I saw a car rapidly speeding towards us and the crossing that we should be reaching in a few seconds. Watching it, and subconsciously noting where our respective movements would bring us together—it would be at the crossing if we both kept on—I expected the car to slow up and stop. Suddenly, with a thrill, I realised it was not going to stop, it was going to "beat the train to the crossing!" It looked impossible; I felt certain there was going to be a smash. But lo and behold, there was no smash, and looking across the cab through the other window I saw the car disappearing up the road in a cloud of dust.

C.N.R. 4-6-4 locomotive No. 5704, on the footplate of which the "outward" run described in this article was made.

It had been so close a call that if the car had had another coat of varnish it would have been scratched; the driver had missed death by a fraction of a second. I shouted across to the engineer: 'I have often heard about that sort of thing, but never thought I should see it from the cab. I suppose that fool is quite proud of himself." "It was a woman!" he said, disgustedly. Of course he hadn't seen the car at all until it suddenly flashed out on his side; modern high-pitched boilers cut off all the engineer's view of the other side.

By this time we were nearing Belleville, another Divisional point, still roaring along at high speed, lurching and rolling, the harsh ceaseless snarl of the exhaust and the grinding of the coal-conveyor sounding above the rumble of the wheels. Very different this from the almost effortless swaying flight of "*The Coronation Scot*" and "*Flying Scotsman!*" I thought of those beautiful engines, spinning along hour after hour in an atmosphere entirely free from any sense of stress or strain, except perhaps up Shap and Beattock, and could not fail to mark the contrast. No. 5704 was being thrashed, but nevertheless seemed to "take it." American engines expect to be thrashed on occasion, and they are. The fireman doesn't mind; he just speeds up the conveyor a little! Before getting into the station another water-stop was made; we were using a good deal of fuel too, naturally, hauling a 950-ton train at high speed, 114 lb. a mile, or a ton every 19 miles. There may have been some special reason for the coaling-stop, as actually the 20 tons carried should theoretically be enough to run No. 5407 from Montreal to Toronto.

At Belleville the usual "servicing" was done, and the third and last crew, Enginemen Crozier and Henricks, took over. In Canada crews never do over 150 miles running at a stretch, between two Divisional points, at least they never have in my experience. Setting off on the last lap, we were soon bowling along again at the same pace, with Lake Ontario in the picture on the left, the Sun, a ball of fire, sinking lower in a turquoise sky. The silvery waters of the great inland sea were having their effect in the cab; it got quite shivery, a complete contrast to the suffocating heat earlier in the afternoon, as a gentle breeze blew off the surface of the lake. The speed now; on straighter track, seemed higher than ever; I had to stand up to make notes in my pad, which is always the case, I find, when an engine's actions are a bit turbulent, to get some spring in my knees. Otherwise if I try to write sitting down I can't read my own notes!

Yes, it was fast travelling along here, the average to Port Hope, a "flag" stop, or one made at a "halt" or to set down a passenger or two, being 63.9. Off again to Oshawa, where the great General Motors plant is located, humming full blast on war work, the stop only lasting a minute, and we were away on the last lap. I cannot say I was sorry; I had had pretty well enough of it! I had been nearly six hours in that thunderous cab, and the heat in the early stages of the trip had taken it out of me. I wanted to get to Toronto, have a hot bath, follow it with a cold shower and go to bed, and the sooner the better. The engine may have wanted a rest too, she had certainly earned it. But she had a tough assignment to tackle as a finale, the very heavy 7-mile Port Union-Scarboro bank of 1 in 100, which is followed by a similar drop into Toronto. It was taken manfully with the regulator two-thirds open and 40 per cent. cut-off. In this country I have seldom seen "full-regulator" short cut-off running indulged in, for technical reasons that have no place in this article. Deflector-plates beside the smoke-box certainly were not wanted here; the exhaust sounded deep, angry and harsh, shooting high above the chimney before reluctantly curling back over the train. The speed fell to 20 near the top, and she slipped once approaching it, for which she cannot be blamed, with the 950-ton train and booster out of action; it cannot be used at much over 12 m.p.h. But of course No. 5704 made the grade all right. We banged over the summit, and ran easily down the opposite side through the suburbs of Toronto, coming to a stand in the fine Union Station dead on time at 9.30 p.m.

"*The International Limited*" had covered the 334 miles from Montreal in 390 minutes, making eight stops, and had averaged 51.4 m.p.h. Very good work indeed, I think you will agree, with a load that began at 625 tons and ended at 950 tons.

The Short "Shetland"

Largest British Flying Boat

By John W. R. Taylor

JUST as the name of "Hawker" is always associated with high-speed fighters and the name of "Handley-Page" with big, reliable air liners, so has the name "Short" become almost synonymous with "flying boat" in the British aircraft industry. Consequently, the announcement of a new Short flying boat—the "Shetland"—was certain to attract a good deal of interest at the present time, when attention is focussed on the aircraft being prepared in Britain and America for use on the post-war airlines.

The firm of Short Brothers has the distinction of being the oldest established aircraft company in the world, and in the last 37 years has made many notable contributions to aviation progress. For instance, in 1909 Short No. 2, piloted by the present Lord Brabazon, was the first all-British aeroplane to make a flight of one mile in a closed circuit. In the next year came the Short "Tandem-Twin," the world's first multi-engined aircraft. Then, from the Short factory at Rochester, came in 1912 the first aircraft fitted with folding wings, in 1915 the first aircraft to sink an enemy ship by torpedo, in 1920 the first British all-metal aeroplane, in 1924 the first all-metal flying boat, and, more recently, the "Stirling," the first of the R.A.F.'s four-motor monoplane bombers. The Empire and "Sunderland" flying boats have an unparalleled record of reliability and service, and have carried the flag of British air transport all over the world during the war years.

The "Shetland" certainly carries on the fine traditions of its famous forerunners. Quite apart from the fact that it is the largest British aircraft flying, its top speed of 267 m.p.h. makes it the world's fastest flying boat and it has a maximum range of no less than 4,650 miles—the distance from London to Bombay. It was originally designed, in co-operation with Saunders-Roe of Cowes, for long range patrol and reconnaissance duties with the R.A.F., to succeed the "Sunderland"; consequently the prototype is fitted with fore and aft gun-turrets. But these are being removed, and production machines will have finely-streamlined hulls, bearing a distinct family likeness to the Empire boats.

The "Shetland" is a very impressive aeroplane with a wing span of 150 ft. and a loaded weight of 58 tons. Its four Bristol "Centaurus" engines give a combined power output of more than 10,000 h.p. A good idea of its size is given by the fact that the tip of its single fin is almost ten feet higher than the average house. But in spite of all this Short test-pilots, who have flown more than 5,000 miles in the "Shetland," are very enthusiastic about its handling qualities. The flight deck for the pilots, navigators, flight engineer and wireless-operator is very spacious and beautifully laid out, with the result that all knobs, dials, levers and "gadgets" needed to fly this great aeroplane seem to be in exactly the right place, and the large Perspex canopy gives an unrestricted horizontal field of vision through 360°.

The passenger accommodation is no less spacious and well-planned, and up to 70 passengers can be carried in real comfort on the two decks. Normally, however, provision will be made for 40 day passengers and 24 sleepers. There are three main cabins on the lower deck, complete with dressing rooms and toilet facilities. On the upper deck is the dining saloon, a cocktail bar, kitchen and two mail or freight compartments. The "Shetland" opens up new possibilities on the Empire air routes, for it can carry a payload of 13¼ tons for 2,076 miles at 188 m.p.h. Finally, for those who like comparisons, although its wing span is 50 ft. less than that of the Martin "Mars," the "Shetland's" loaded weight is only some 10,000 lbs. less than that of the American flying boat, and its maximum payload is approximately the same.

Another view of the Short "Shetland," Britain's largest flying boat.

The Atomic Bomb

Atom Splitting as a Source of Power

THE greatest sensation of the World War undoubtedly was the sudden appearance on the scene of the atomic bomb, a comparatively small affair as bombs go, but capable of destruction to an extent previously undreamed of. It was only the application of atomic energy in warfare that was sudden, however; the atomic bomb had been foreseen, and its successful use followed on concentrated research and hard work by Allied scientists extending over five years.

To understand exactly what the atomic bomb is and does, it is best to go back to the first authentic case of atom splitting in 1919. By that time it was already well known that the atom, long thought to be the smallest particle of matter that could exist, is in reality built up of still tinier particles, called the proton and the electron, the first of which has a positive electric charge, while the second has a negative one. In the picture that has been formed of a typical atom, the protons, with a number of electrons, are concentrated in a central nucleus, and the rest of the electrons are grouped round it, so that the greater part of the space occupied by the whole atom is empty.

The 90 or more elements that we know are built up of various numbers of protons and electrons distributed in this manner, and most of them, including hydrogen, oxygen, nitrogen, carbon and metals such as lead, tin, copper and iron, seemed then about as permanent as anything could be. A few were known to break up of their own accord, however, shooting out electrified particles and generating a certain amount of heat in the process. The best known of these radioactive elements, as they are called, is radium, and another metal that behaves in a similar way is uranium, a comparatively rare element that until recently has been found useful chiefly for giving glass a yellow colour.

With this in mind efforts were made to break up atoms that were not radioactive, and the first real success came to Lord Rutherford in 1919. The plan that he followed was to shoot charged particles at nitrogen, the well-known gaseous element that forms about four-fifths of the atmosphere. This was a queer kind of shooting match, for, as we have seen, the nitrogen atoms forming the targets are mostly space, and only one in about 45,000 of the tiny particles used as bullets or shells managed to hit the mark, the positive nucleus; the rest passed harmlessly through. The few that did reach their target chipped off pieces of the nitrogen nuclei.

From that time onward efforts at atom splitting became a regular pursuit of scientists. As bullets or shells they used many different kinds of tiny particles, shot out at high speeds from radioactive materials and from other sources, and eventually pressed into this service an entirely new kind of particle discovered in 1932 by Prof. Sir James Chadwick, one of the scientists behind the production of the atomic bomb. This particle is a strange one, for unlike the proton and electron it has no electric charge at all. This makes it the more penetrating, for it can approach the centre of an atom without being electrically repelled, and it was soon found to be extremely effective. The name given to it, one that suggested its lack of electrical charge, was "neutron," and neutrons play a vital part in the explosion of the atomic bomb.

There is no space here to go fully into the various kinds of "guns" used in these atomic bombardments, but two are worthy of special mention. One of them was used by Drs. Cockroft and Walton in 1932. As bullets they used the nuclei of hydrogen atoms, to which they gave tremendous speed by applying very high electric voltages. The nuclei were then shot at the metal lithium, which disintegrated under their attack and was transformed into helium, thus achieving the transmutation dream of the alchemists. The second atomic gun is the cyclotron, developed by Professor Lawrence, an American scientist. In this the charged particles used as bullets are whirled round and round spirally in a narrow channel between two electro-magnets until they attain very high speeds. Cyclotrons are large and costly, and so far few have been constructed. The one we illustrate is at Liverpool University.

Pioneers in atom splitting. In the centre is Lord Rutherford, who first broke up an atom artificially in 1919. On his left is Dr. J. D. Cockroft and on his right Dr. E. S. Walton, who in 1932, transformed the metal lithium into helium by an atom-splitting process.

One reason for the persistence of the atom splitters is that in the process a vast amount of energy is released. In a sense the splitting of any atom is an explosion, for at the moment of disintegration this energy is released at once. In this the action is similar to what happens when a quantity of T.N.T., or trinitrotoluene, is shocked into violent explosion by means of a detonator, for the particles of this explosive are instantaneously broken up, and a large quantity of energy is released that immediately makes its presence known by the terrific roar and blast. In the case of an ordinary explosive the energy released is that holding the constituent atoms together, but when an atom is split the energy set free actually comes from the destruction of a part of the atom itself, and is far greater in proportion

The cyclotron at Liverpool University. This machine gives high speeds to charged particles by whirling them in a spiral course under the influence of two powerful electro-magnets, and the particles are then used for atomic bombardments. Photograph by courtesy of the Physics Department, University of Liverpool.

to the amount of matter involved.

The discovery of some means of splitting atoms and releasing this energy therefore would provide us with a wonderful source of power. The energy that would be derived from a cupful of ordinary water if the atoms in it could be split up would be more than sufficient to drive "*Queen Mary*" across the Atlantic, a task that at present calls for the burning of vast quantities of oil.

At first there seemed little prospect of our ever being able to make use of atomic energy, for the simple reason that more energy had to be put into the splitting process than could be got out of it, while success was only attained in dealing with quantities too minute to be visible. Then all at once an astonishing discovery was made. This concerns the metal uranium, to which we have already referred as a radioactive element. In a series of experiments in which this element was bombarded by neutrons it was found that in the residue there were atoms of barium, which have a weight of about half that of the atoms of uranium. Previous scientific artillery bombardments had merely chipped off tiny bits of various atoms, but here was a case in which a heavy atom actually broke up into two parts of about equal size.

Then the further discovery was made that in the splitting more neutrons are actually set free, shot out of the atom breaking up at speeds comparable to that of the neutrons that brought about the change. In other words, the bullets in this shooting match make others immediately they strike the right targets, and their number is continuously being increased. It was soon seen that shooting a neutron into a mass of uranium would start a chain action. It would break up one atom, and the neutrons then released would be capable of breaking up more; this would continue, and atom splitting would spread like wildfire through the mass, releasing energy on an explosive scale.

This was rather alarming. It was reassuring to find that uranium itself does not behave in this way, for a form of the metal, an isotope as scientists call it, with an atomic weight of 235 against the 238 of ordinary uranium, was discovered to be responsible. This is usually known as U235, and it is present in the uranium that we know to the extent of little more than half of one per cent. Still the prospect was sufficiently disturbing to make some of the scientists who were carrying out these experiments suspend their activities until they had learned more about it.

This was the position when the war broke out. From that moment there was no news of any developments until the first atomic bomb was exploded over Hiroshima but in the meantime many Allied scientists and industrialists had been secretly at work, and enormous sums of money had been spent in experiments and in erecting plant for the production of atomic bombs.

The first step was to find some way of extracting from uranium the small proportion of U235 that it contains. Isotopes have the same chemical properties, and separating them is a difficult and laborious task. One way of doing it is to give them an electrical charge and shoot them out in a magnetic field, the effect of which is to sort them out according to their masses; but this is a terribly slow way and not easy to adapt to the production of more than minute quantities. The plan was discussed, but a form of diffusion seems to have been used in making the atomic bombs dropped on Japan. This can be used for gases and liquids. How it works is best illustrated by imagining a mixture of the two well-known gases hydrogen and carbon dioxide, the first of which is much lighter than the second. If such a mixture is placed in a porous vessel, made say of unglazed earthenware, both gases will make their way through the pores of the material and escape, but the hydrogen will do this more quickly than the heavier gas, and so the first fraction of the mixture diffused in this way will be richer in hydrogen than the original one.

Then came the task of making the bomb itself. The quantity of U235 to be used had to be worked out carefully, for in a very small amount the chance of the neutrons produced by the breakup of some of the atoms hitting the centres of others is very small and the chain effect would not be produced. Some, if not all, would escape, and the only way to make sure that there would be collisions is to increase that amount of U235. By doing this a critical size is eventually reached when a sufficient proportion of the neutrons produced would be effective in making the atomic break-up spread at high speed throughout the mass. *(Continued on page 434)*

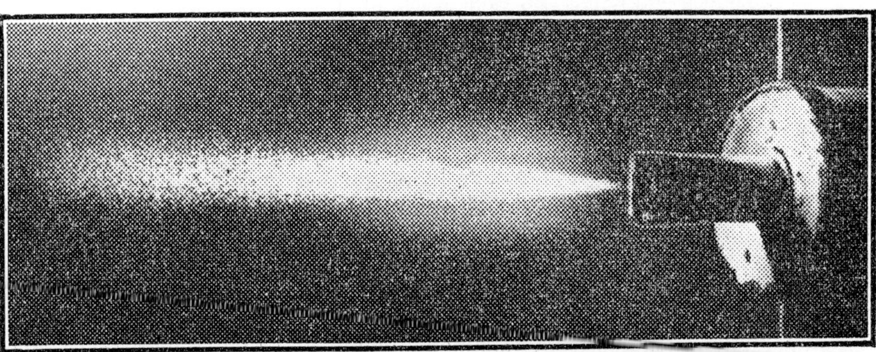

The beam of particles shot out by the Liverpool University cyclotron.

The British Civil Air Fleet—

(*Continued from page 404*)

and should do much to establish British prestige on the Atlantic run. But it will be superseded later by the "Tudor" II which has a much larger fuselage, with accommodation for twice as many passengers.

The "Hermes" is very similar in general layout to the "Tudor" and is approximately the same size, with a wing span of 113 ft. and a loaded weight of 31 tons. It can be fitted out with bunks for 16 "sleeper" passengers, comfortable armchairs for 34 day passengers, or up to 50 smaller seats. There is no doubt that it will carry on the fine tradition of the old Handley Page "Hannibal" biplane, whose remarkable safety record and luxurious accommodation won for Imperial Airways each year more passengers in and out of this country than all other European airlines put together. But whereas the "Hannibals" plodded along at a steady 98 m.p.h. the "Hermes" will cruise at well over double that speed.

All the skill, care and experience that have been put into British warplanes in the last six years will go into the designing and construction of our new airliners, and will ensure that British airlines, the world's first, will once again be the world's best.

The Atomic Bomb—

(*Cont. from page 413*)

An atomic bomb must have in it at least this critical amount of U235. Such a mass would be very unstable. The release in it of one neutron that penetrated into the nucleus of an atom would start off the chain reaction and the whole mass would explode almost instantaneously. How it was arranged that the atomic bomb used in Japan should explode at exactly the required moment has not been revealed at the time of writing, and this seems to be the greatest secret of the new weapon, for the general behaviour of U235 and the way to extract it from ordinary uranium are well known to scientists.

It is difficult to imagine how much energy goes into the atomic bomb explosion, even when we bear in mind the enormous devastation that the two bombs dropped on Japan caused. We all know what a 10-ton R.A.F. bomb can do; from descriptions and from photographs of bomb damage in German cities, and from this we might be able to form some idea of what would happen if a bomb containing 8,000 tons of ordinary explosive were dropped. Yet the stupendous effect of an ordinary bomb of this size would be no greater than that of an atomic bomb containing only 1 lb. of U235.

There is another way of looking at it that will help us to realise what happens when an atomic bomb explodes. After all, atom splitting is not new, and in fact we ourselves throughout the whole history of life on the Earth have been dependent on atom splitting for warmth, and indirectly for food and clothing. But these atoms are in the interior of the Sun, the warmth and light of which come from continuous atom splitting on a colossal scale that keeps the Sun at a temperature of millions of degrees. Fortunately for us the Sun is a long way off, so far away that the heat and light produced by these atomic explosions are just comforting to us. But when the first atomic bomb exploded over Hiroshima the effect was as if a miniature of the Sun, a ball of matter the temperature of which rose suddenly to 10 million deg. C. or more, with a correspondingly huge rise in pressure, had been suddenly created on Earth. The blinding, blasting effect of this terrific outburst of energy can well be imagined.

So far as is known only one other element could possibly be used in making an atomic bomb, and this does not really exist! The paradox is explained by the fact that the element does not occur in the Earth, but is an artificial one made by smuggling an extra neutron into the atom of uranium by bombardment. Its name is plutonium. Making it is a costly and laborious business, so it seems that only U235 can be used for the present, and this too is rare and extremely costly to isolate. Whether we shall ever learn the secret of splitting the atoms of more common elements, the break up of which keeps the Sun going, remains to be seen.

It seems lamentable that the first real use made of what can only be described as a scientific triumph should be a mission of destruction, and it is hoped that atomic energy will in future find peaceful applications that will be for the benefit of all mankind. Before we can make any approach to this, however, it will be necessary to find some means of harnessing the terrific power that atom splitting can give us by slowing down the process and so robbing the change of its explosive character.

At present the greatest hope of doing this is given by what is known as the uranium pile. In this, uranium mixed with graphite is bombarded by neutrons, with the result that plutonium is formed. If this is hit by neutrons, it will break up, shooting out more neutrons, just as U235 does, but the graphite spreads the materials apart so that the extra neutrons shot out of the plutonium escape instead of spreading the break up through the rest of this element. After a time the bombardment is stopped. The plutonium is then separated from the uranium and is mixed with graphite in a smaller pile that can be used as a source of energy, the graphite being used in sufficient proportion to slow down the chain reaction.

The Boeing C-97, shown above, is the transport counterpart of the B-29 "Superfortress" heavy bomber, and is in service with Air Transport Command of the U.S.A.A.F. The civil version of this machine is known as the Model 377 "Stratocruiser." Photograph by courtesy of the Boeing Aircraft Company, U.S.A.

The "Meteor's" Record—(*Continued from page 411*)

world speed record and, consequently, in co-operation with Glosters, started preparing for a record attempt.

The only modifications made to the "Meteor" were the removal of its guns and aerial masts, slight structural strengthening near the control surfaces, the filling in of all holes and the application of a high-gloss surface finish. In addition, longer nacelles were fitted to improve the air supply to the engines.

The rest of the story is now history. Piloted by Group-Capt. H. J. Wilson, the "Meteor" set up a record that will not easily be beaten.

Back again at last

THE BEST KIT IN THE WORLD.

Every part is in the Kit, correct to shape, scale and detail. No carving or shaping is required. With these Kits you can build a whole squadron of perfectly detailed 1/72nd scale models in less time than it takes to build one machine with any other Kit. This range of models include, retractable undercarriages, radial engines, pilot's seat, rockets with beams, guns, injection moulded crystal clear cabins, astra domes, ball turrets, etc., insignia paint and cement.

Price Including Purchase Tax.

017 P	Spitfire I. ...	... 5/6	105 P	Mustang	... 6/1
109 P	Spitfire XII	... 5/6	113 P	F.W. 190	... 5/6
048 P	Hurricane	... 5/6	115 P	Hellcat ...	... 7/4
060 P	Me. 109 ...	... 5/6	062 P	Miles Magister I	4/11
			107 P	Thunderbolt ...	6/1

TO THE TRADE

Are you on our mailing list? If not please write to us, enclosing three trade references—

THERE IS NOTHING TO COMPARE WITH A 'PENGUIN' KIT

MADE BY

INTERNATIONAL MODEL AIRCRAFT LTD. · MORDEN RD. · MERTON · LONDON · S.W.19.

The Gallant Malta Convoy

By Denis Rebbeck, M.A., M.Inst.N.A., A.M.I.Mech.E.

IN August 1942, when the position of Malta was critical, food for the population and petrol for the "Spitfires" became the paramount necessity. In consequence, a fleet of ships, among the finest in the Merchant Navy, was collected and dispatched with naval protection. It was fully appreciated by all concerned that the naval protection was far from adequate, particularly as regards air cover. In this convoy were three of the latest and fastest motor cargo vessels of the Shaw Savill fleet, the "*Waimarama*," illustrated on this page, the "*Wairangi*," and the "*Empire Hope*." These ships had been built by Harland and Wolff Limited, and were completed in 1938, 1935 and 1941 respectively; they were all of 12,000 tons, and had come to be known as "Empire Food Ships," having been designed specially for the Anglo-Australasian Trade. All three were sunk in that gallant convoy.

The "*Empire Hope*" was first attacked by high-level bombers on the morning of 11th August, but escaped. In the evening the attacks were renewed. Submarines were about throughout the night, and on the following day the attacks made by high-level and torpedo bombers were continuous.

On the evening of the 12th massed attacks were concentrated on the "*Empire Hope*," and 18 near misses were scored in half an hour. These damaged the engines and made the vessel a sitting target, but she continued to fight back gallantly. The gun crews were blown out of the gun positions more than once, but each time they crawled back to their guns. Some of the crews were even blown overboard, but they swam back to the ship to continue their barrage.

Two direct hits then set the ship on fire. One fire ignited the cargo of kerosene; another started in the hold containing explosives. Near by was stowed a large quantity of bagged coal and this was thrown upward by the force of the explosion, the dust being driven deeply and painfully into the men's skins. Some of the lifeboats were half full of coal dust as they hung at the davits, but they were all got safely away, and in spite of all that the crew had been through the only casualty was one broken wrist.

The end of the "*Waimarama*" was sudden and tragic. On the morning of 13th August she was hit by three or four bombs on and near the bridge, and bridge and everybody on it disappeared completely. The petrol cargo on board caught fire and the vessel was soon ablaze from end to end, going down within four minutes and leaving the sea around her aflame with burning petrol. H.M.S. "*Ledbury*" made gallant attempts to rescue the survivors, but most of them, including the Captain, were lost.

On the morning of 12th August, the "*Wairangi*," when a mile and a half from Cape Bon, was hit by a torpedo fired from an enemy M.T.B. The main engines stopped and the inflow of water was found to be beyond the capacity of the pumps. As it was hopeless to attempt to tow her in face of constant attacks, she was scuttled so as to prevent the ship and her cargo of munitions from falling into the hands of the enemy. Her entire crew were saved by the destroyer "*Eskimo*."

Photography

Action Portraits

By E. E. Steele

I ENJOY immensely taking pictures of people in action, even if they are only doing commonplace things. Sometimes they are aware that a photograph is being taken, but usually they know nothing about it because the camera is hidden except for the moment when the exposure is made.

The old lady about to fill her bucket was rather suspicious although I had planned to take the photograph unbeknown to her. The background of hollyhocks and the pump was attractive, and seemed to provide an ideal setting for the old-fashioned cottager. It is best to place yourself at the right distance and face the other way while you make

"Good and tight!"

the necessary adjustments to your camera, setting the shutter and the distance—already set permanently with the simple box camera—and then keep it behind your back until all is right for making a rapid exposure. I did this, but made my shot a trifle too early.

The photograph of the farm labourer is the kind you can often get by merely keeping your eyes open when out in the country. I was cycling along, looking for something to photograph, when I noticed the preparation for the new gate. It was an easy matter to pass the time of the day with the workman, bring out the camera and suggest a picture, asking him to give a good pull on the spanner while the exposure was made. This provided for a natural expression and a genuine feeling of action. The lens was not stopped down, so that the background is kept soft and subdued. This is often useful in portraiture, where a sharp background can detract from the portrait itself.

The photographer needs to be resourceful to obtain some photographs, as illustrated by my friend in the wheelbarrow. We were out cycling one day when the

The opportunist.

horse chestnuts were in flower, and he particularly wanted a photograph, but these flowers, on their tall, showy spikes, bloom out of reach when a close-up is required. A glance up the road revealed a road-mender's barrow, which was pressed into service, and made the photograph possible. My picture was made when my friend was focussing his camera, quite unaware that a photograph was being made.

Country woman in typical setting.

Photography

Moving Trains

By "Shed Superintendent"

ANY reader who possesses a camera with a shutter that can be set to give an exposure of 1/100th second will find that interesting pictures can be obtained of moving trains from angles other than the conventional three-quarter head-on view.

One method consists of swinging the camera, to take a broadside view of an engine or part of a train as it passes. The accompanying illustration of the front of a Royal train engine was taken in this manner. The art of correct swing needs a little practice. The camera is best used at eye level, and the rate of swing of the camera must correspond with the movement of the train, in order to give a sharp picture of the train against a blurred background. The swing must follow through, and must not be stopped at the moment of exposure.

The photographer should stand well back from the line, at the same time making sure that as little foreground as possible is included, since this will also appear blurred by the camera movement. It is also advisable to choose a site, such as a junction, where the train is not going at full speed.

Decorations on the front of a G.W.R. engine hauling the Royal Train.

Another method is to take pictures out of the window of a moving train. The photograph of the driver of the "*Cornish Riviera*" was taken from the window of a local train near Reading which was proceeding in the same direction on the adjacent line, and the difference in the speeds of the two trains at that particular moment was so slight as to make this picture quite a simple matter. The photographer can stand at an open window—preferably in the corridor—without exposing himself to danger by putting his head or the camera outside the carriage. He should take up an easy stance on his feet, taking care not to lean against the structure of the coach, which would have the effect of transmitting vibrations to the camera.

The driver of the "Cornish Riviera." Taken from the window of a slow train.

The photograph just referred to is of particular interest as recording a fleeting glimpse of the normal routine of the cab—the driver at his window, his mate busy with his scoop-like firing shovel. It would be difficult, if not impossible, to get such a picture in any other way. We hope that many readers will try this scheme during the summer and send in their results with a view to publication if suitable.

"Queen Mary" in Service Again

AFTER steaming 569,543 miles on transport service during the war, during which she carried 765,429 Servicemen across the oceans, the *"Queen Mary"* has now returned to the North Atlantic service. She made her first post-war voyage in this capacity on 31st July, 10 years after the keel of her sister ship *"Queen Elizabeth"* was laid down. The two *"Queens"* should have taken up the transatlantic service together in 1940, but the war intervened, and only now have the two great vessels taken up their joint task. There was a historic moment in the last week of July, when the *"Queen Mary,"* anchored off Cowes on the completion of her trials, was passed by the younger vessel returning from New York to Southampton, a meeting that was celebrated by triumphant greetings from their sirens.

"Queen Mary" reached Southampton from Halifax at the end of her last trooping voyage in September of last year, and a few days later 1,500 workmen from John Brown and Co. Ltd., Clydebank, her builders, swarmed aboard and began to dismantle troop fittings, removing the maze of standee berths, temporary wooden bulkheads and other special equipment as a preliminary to reconstructing and restoring the interior of the vessel. Scaffolding was erected and the decks resounded to the noise of hammers chipping and scaling paintwork. In the meantime many and varied tasks were undertaken above decks.

The 32 motor lifeboats were removed to the yard of John I. Thornycroft Ltd. at Northam for overhaul, the davits were dismantled and boat winches overhauled. One interesting task was the reconversion of the deck rails, on which thousands of troops had carved their names or initials. These were all scraped and planed ready for repolishing, except for one length that is to be preserved in the United States.

At one stage the vessel was moved into the King George V graving dock at Southampton, where the four 35-ton propellers were removed, the tailshafts were drawn and the underwater part of the hull was scaled and painted with anti-fouling composition, of which 3,000 gallons were required. At the same time a special composition, known as "Aranbee Fairing," used to smooth down the irregularities of overlapping plates, was inspected and renewed where necessary. The use of this composition has greatly lessened friction by reducing the resistance of the hull when the vessel is steaming at speed.

The giant machinery of the *"Queen Mary"* also was overhauled. She has 24 main water tube boilers, and these were thoroughly inspected and their thousands of tubes examined. The casings of the giant turbines were lifted and every detail was carefully scrutinised, while the great lengths of shafting inside the ship were inspected. The auxiliary machinery, consisting of pumps, electric generators, refrigerating compressors and a host of items of electrical equipment, was taken apart, and all worn parts were replaced, everything being restored to its original condition.

Dinky Toys No. 52a Cunard White Star Liner "Queen Mary."

Helicopters at Work

By John W. R. Taylor

THE most important news about helicopters is that at last they are being put to work. At the moment only the Sikorsky S-51 and Bell 47 are available for commercial service, but they are doing jobs that no other type of aeroplane could do. This makes up somewhat for their high initial cost—£17,000 in the case of the S-51.

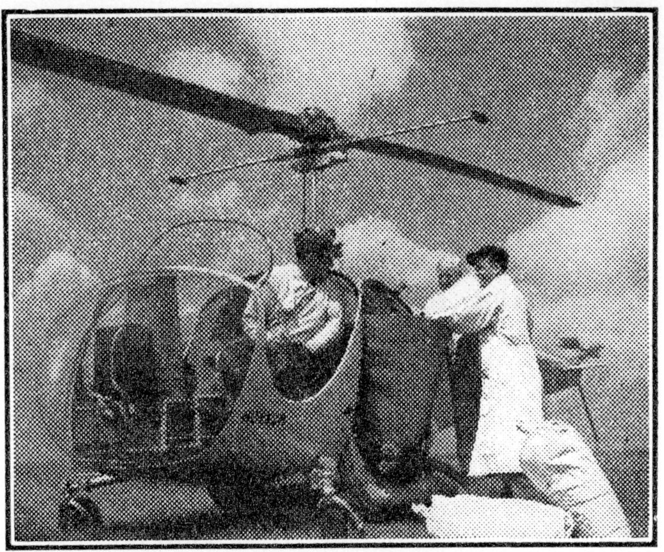

Loading agricultural dust into one of the two 220 lb. capacity hoppers of a Bell 47 crop-dusting helicopter.

Down on the Farm

Some jobs are merely stunts, like the lady trapeze artiste who performed her act on a trapeze slung under a Bell 47; but others are very practical. For instance, the Argentine has been suffering increasingly in recent years from swarms of locusts, which caused the loss of more than £6,000,000 to the corn crop alone in 1946. Every method of combating the plague failed until last year, when a Buenos Aires firm obtained 11 Bell 47 crop-dusting helicopters, filled their hoppers with anti-locust dust and flew them straight into the swarms. The results were astonishing, up to 98 per cent. of the pests being killed in some attacks, the first time the locust plague had ever been effectively halted.

In Canada, Airspray Limited of Toronto have used similar aircraft to spread D.D.T. and rotenone dust over crops of potatoes, beans, corn, tomatoes, onions and tobacco. This work proved most effective, for the down-thrust from the rotor beat the dust past the top layer of leaves, reaching those underneath.

Dusting is only one way in which the helicopter can be useful to the farmer. In California the hoppers of Bell 47s have been filled with corn for aerial crop sowing, while a Sikorsky machine belonging to R.A.F. Coastal Command, operating from Thorney Island, trawled a fine net after it with the object of collecting samples of insects blown across to this country from the Continent. British agricultural experts were particularly anxious to discover if the Bean Aphis arrives in this way.

Another "farm" use has its drawbacks, for it is doubtful if the "cowboy" films of the future will be as exciting if, as is suggested, the cowboys sell their horses and roam the range by helicopter to count cattle, locate strays or to get from their ranch to town quickly in rough country.

Man-hunts, Real and Make-believe

Talking of films, R.K.O. Studios in Hollywood recently shot a series of chase

The helicopter in action. It can cover a 60 ft. swath in one pass, and dust between 100 and 200 acres an hour. The photographs on this page are reproduced by courtesy of Bell Aircraft Corporation, U.S.A.

sequences from the air, pursuing fleeing bandits with a camera mounted in a Bell 47. Ten hours of flying produced 12 complete sequences for "*Your Red Wagon,*" resulting in a saving of £2,500 in production time and equipment.

In a sterner role, the helicopter has proved itself useful for real police duty both in Britain and America. An S-51 was used last year by the Norfolk County police during the hunt for the escaped Polish criminal Stanislaw Zborowski, near Thetford. In Connecticut, U.S.A., another S-51 was used to control traffic swarming to and from the annual Yale-Columbia-Pennsylvania boat races. Working in conjunction with 30 patrol cars, the aerial "cop" in his 'copter was able to sort out traffic jams quickly, and even call up a breakdown lorry to an accident.

Sikorsky S-51 helicopter showing how it could be used to lower an engineer on to a buoy at sea, for maintenance work. The S-51, with a "Leonides" engine, is being built in this country by Westland Aircraft Ltd., to whom we are indebted for this photograph.

Another helicopter joined an expedition sent out by the Lundberg-Ryan Air Exploration Company to survey and open up new mineral and oilfields in Northern Canada. Hans Lundberg hopes to prove to the Canadian Government that geographical survey by helicopter can accomplish in 10 years what it would take 100 years to do by the ordinary methods.

An obvious job for the helicopter is to deliver mail quickly between post offices or from post office to airfield. Experiments carried out in America in 1946–7 proved an unqualified success, and plans are in hand for large-scale use of helicopters by the American Post Office. Similar tests in Britain were delayed by lack of suitable equipment, but flights are now being made by an experimental B.E.A. Helicopter Unit carrying mails in the Bristol-Yeovil-Poole area. Later the tests will be extended to other parts of the country, and may well lead within a few years to a regular helicopter mail service in this country.

Helicopters to the Rescue

Helicopters are already in full-time service with the American Fleet, replacing destroyers for such tasks as delivering mail, for communications duties and spotting. But one of their chief duties will be to rescue "ditched" aircrew—for as a rescue 'plane the helicopter is in a class by itself, ashore or afloat. They have already proved their worth at sea, both in the Pacific and Mediterranean, where several Naval pilots have been snatched from the sea after forced landings.

Ashore, dozens of people have been rescued by helicopters from regions as far apart as the Arctic Circle and the tropical jungle of Brazil. When a forest fire swept over the rugged mountains near Los Angeles, two helicopters rescued 20 trapped fire-fighters, transported 250 more to fire fronts with no road access, and delivered a ton of supplies each day to them.

The most famous helicopter rescue occurred in September 1946, after a "Skymaster" had crashed in thick fog, 25 miles from Gander Airport, Newfoundland. Twenty-five miles is six minutes flying time, not far, but in this case 25 miles of thick spruce forest and bog. It was obviously impossible to carry the 18 survivors to safety through the forest; the only hope was by helicopter. It was not a forlorn hope; 24 hours after two Sikorsky aircraft reached Gander all the injured were safe in bed.

The story sounds simple written like that. But it does not tell of how the first helicopter to reach the scene of the accident sank up to its fuselage in the ooze and was only saved by the prompt action of its pilot, who put the rotors into climbing pitch and hovered above the ground while timber for a landing stage was flown out from (*Continued on page 176*)

"Bath Abbey," of the Western Region "Castle" class fitted to burn oil fuel. The illustrations to this article are by courtesy of the Western Region.

Oil Burners in the Western Region

OUR cover this month, reproduced by permission of the Editor of the "*British Railways Western Region Magazine,*" shows the conversion of a Western Region engine from coal to oil-fuel. In the recent renewal of experiments in the oil firing of steam locomotives the G.W.R. made the first move a year or two ago by the conversion of some of their big 2-8-0 mineral engines. Now, under the Government programme referred to in the November 1945 "*M.M.*," work is proceeding also on the other main lines, with the object of putting into service a total of 1,217 oil-burning engines.

In this conversion scheme the London Midland, Eastern, North Eastern and Southern Regions are concentrating on fitting up heavy freight engines, with some mixed-traffic types. But the Western and Southern Regions intend to deal with express types as well, and No. 5079 "*Lysander*" shown in the cover illustration is one of 25 "Castles" included in Swindon plans. In addition 84 of the useful "Hall" class are being dealt with, and the first of these was No. 5955 "*Garth Hall,*" illustrated in the "*M.M.*" in August 1946. So there will be 109 Western Region oil-burning 4-6-0s when the programme is completed; and the 18 big 2-8-0s included in the earlier scheme will have been increased to 63.

Piping of the oil from the tender fuel tank to the burner in the fire-box means additional connections between the engine and the tender. The ends of these can be seen peeping out of the upper slotted opening below the cab floor of "*Lysander.*" The larger one in the centre carries steam to the heater provided in the tender to keep the fuel oil in the correct condition for easy flowing by gravity from the tender to the fire-box. The group of little hand wheels near the man working on the left side of the cab control the steam supply for burner cleaning purposes, for the tender heater and for the auxiliary blower, and also the burner steam that atomises the oil. The fuel regulator and other fittings are close by, for the Western Region fireman rides on the left-hand side of the cab.

The fuelling arrangements at depots have to be fairly elaborate, and the depots have to be strategically placed in relation to the mileages involved in the engine's regular runs. Storage tanks at refuelling depots have to be filled, and they receive their supplies by means of rail tank wagons. These wagons have steam heating coils to make possible the pumping of the fuel from them to the ground storage tanks. A steam-driven duplex pump located in a pump house at the depot performs this work, and engines are refuelled by means of the same pump from the ground storage tanks. These tanks and the pipelines in the depot are steam heated, and thermostatic control ensures the maintenance of the correct temperature.

The lower illustration shows the typical 26,000 gallon storage and refuelling plant at Swindon. This has overhead arrangements for filling the tender tanks by means of special standpipes designed to avoid leakage or overfilling. A neat detail is the electric light fitted by the fuel outlet; it is controlled automatically by the movement of the standpipe arm. The earlier depot and tender arrangements provide for the connection of the fuelling pipe below the tender body.

The largest locomotive oil storage and refuelling plant in this country is at Old Oak Common, Western Region. This has a capacity of 352,000 gallons. A Western Region tender tank holds 1,700 gallons, or sufficient for about 250 miles of main line running.

The refuelling plant for oil-burning locomotives at Swindon, showing one of the overhead filling standpipes in use.

Oil for Britain

IV. Chemicals from Petroleum

THE products of crude petroleum may be simply divided into four classes. The first and most important of these contains all the compounds which are derived from the crude by *Refining*. That is, they are compounds which were in the crude when it left the well, and they are yielded by the separation and purifying processes—distillation, solvent extraction, chemical treatment—described in the last two articles. A brief list of the typical main products of petroleum refining is as follows:

The four articles in this series were prepared by the Public Relations Department of Manchester Oil Refinery Limited, to whom due acknowledgment is made.

(*a*) Straight run gasoline, once used as motor fuel but now almost always employed in conjunction with additives, or blended with other types of gasoline (see below) before being employed as a fuel for I.C. engines, because the anti-knock properties of *straight* gasoline are inadequate for modern I.C. practice.

(*b*) White Spirit, and other light fractions used as solvents in such applications as dry cleaning, the extraction of oils and fats, and in the rubber, paint and printing industries.

(*c*) Kerosene, whose chief use is as a fuel for tractors, cookers, lamps, heaters, etc.

(*d*) Gas Oil, used as Diesel engine fuel; for making the familiar "oil gas" of Town Gas Works, and as fuel for modern brick kilns or other relatively small furnaces such as those employed in domestic heating installations.

(*e*) Paraffin Wax, for candles, cosmetics, polishes, wax proof paper, etc.

(*f*) Medicinal liquid paraffin, with whose applications the reader is no doubt familiar!

(*g*) "Technical White Oils." These must be of sufficient purity to be employed in food manufacture, and are also used in cosmetics, agricultural sprays in the textile industry and as light lubricating oils.

(*h*) Transformer Oils, whose high stability and freedom from impurities render them ideal for electrical insulation in transformers and switch gear.

(*i*) Lubricating Oils, which will be well known to the mechanically minded readers of the "*M.M.*"

(*j*) Asphaltic bitumen, used in road making, the preparation of roofing materials, plastics, etc.

This short list shows the widespread way in which just one class of petroleum products enters into our daily lives at every point.

Hydrocarbon Synthesis Pilot Plant at the Baton, Rouge, Louisiana, refinery of the Standard Oil Company of New Jersey, U.S.A.

The second class of petroleum products are those which were originally produced as by-products from the treatment of petroleum fractions, but which have now assumed an importance of their own. Some arise during the refining of petroleum, whilst others are formed by special treatment of refined oils. In this class we may also place the *petroleum aromatic extracts*, which occur during the solvent extraction of distillates as outlined in the last article.

It would be impossible to give here a complete list of all the products in this class. Those manufactured by Manchester Oil Refinery include: *fat-splitting agents*, derived during the acid treatment of liquid paraffin and used in soap manufacture; *water-soluble petroleum sulphonates* (in liquid or powder form for use as wetting agents and cleansers) derived during the oleum treatment of technical white oils; *Oil-soluble petroleum sulphonates*, which arise during the manufacture of white oils and liquid paraffin, and the range of *petroleum aromatic extracts*, used largely in the rubber, paint, printing ink and foundry trades in place of rosin or linseed oil.

Part of the distillation unit of the oil-soluble sulphonates plant at Manchester Oil Refinery.

The third class of petroleum products are the synthetic gasolines. After World War I straight run gasoline production was found to be quite inadequate to satisfy the ever increasing demand for petrol, and petroleum technologists began to look about for methods of converting more plentiful petroleum products, such as natural gas, topped crude (*i.e.*, crude containing no gasoline) gas oil, etc., into gasoline. At the same time methods were being developed to improve the anti-knock qualities of natural and synthetic gasolines, and all these processes may be considered under the general heading of synthetic gasolines.

In considering the development of gasoline production, it is important to understand the influence of engine design on fuel specification. The efficiency of a petrol engine increases as its compression ratio is raised. Consequently, the tendency in petrol engine design has been towards higher compression ratios; but in any particular case, if the compression ratio is raised beyond a certain figure the engine begins to "knock" and to develop less power. The use of higher compression ratios demands improved fuels with better "anti-knock" properties. The anti-knock value or *octane number* of a fuel is a measure of its tendency to knock when employed in a special test engine having a variable compression ratio. The development of fuels with ever-higher octane numbers has been an important aim of synthetic gasoline research during the past twenty years.

The first process to be considered is the straightforward cracking operation, developed mainly between the years 1925–1935.

Cracking in theory is very simple. A feed stock of topped crude, kerosene gas oil or other heavy petroleum fraction is subjected to heat and pressure, upon which the large, high-boiling hydrocarbons split up and reform into smaller hydrocarbons of lower boiling point. Also, the yield contains *unsaturates* and *aromatics* not present in the charge, and, in particular, the *paraffins* are more *highly-branched* (see second article in this series, in the February 1948 "*M.M.*"), which means that the gasoline will have good anti-knock properties. In this way, part of the feed stock is converted into gasoline with a satisfactory anti-knock value.

In practice, the feed stock is first fractionally distilled along with the cracked products from a previous cycle, so that any light ends in the feed may be removed, and any heavy ends in the yield retained, and the heavy ends from this distillation pass through a tube still to the reaction chamber, where, at a temperature of from 800° F. to 1,000° F. and a pressure between 100 to 500 lb. per sq. in., cracking takes place. From the reaction chamber the cracked products pass eventually back to the fractionating column. The light ends after fractionating form the yield, and consist of cracked gasoline, and *olefinic* gases (see February "*M.M.*") evolved during the process, about which more will be said below. The total yield of cracked gasoline, and the gasoline : gas ratio of the yield depend on the cracking conditions and, in general, the more severe the conditions, the higher the anti-knock value of the gasoline, but the smaller the yield in proportion to that of the gases.

A similar process is employed to improve the anti-knock value of the straight run gasoline distilled direct from crude; in this case the operation is termed "Thermal Reforming" and the yield consists of higher-octane gasoline together with (as previously), olefinic gases.

There also exist many variations of these processes employing catalysts, which make possible yields of much better-quality gasoline under considerably easier conditions of temperature and pressure; these operations are termed "catalytic cracking."

A corner of the Research Laboratories at Manchester Oil Refinery.

It has been mentioned that, during cracking operations of the above type, large volumes of olefinic gases are produced, and it was natural, that toward the middle of 1930s, methods of converting these olefinic gases into yet more gasoline, should have been developed. The general name for such processes is *polymerization*. Polymers are hydrocarbons having equal ratios of hydrogen to carbon atoms—such as Ethylene (C_2H_4) and Propylene (C_3H_6) and, in general, polymerization converts the lighter olefinics, such as Ethylene and Propylene, into their heavier polymers having formulæ such as C_6H_{12}, C_7H_{14}, etc. In actual fact, the chemistry of the process if much more complex than this, and to consider polymerization in more detail would land us in very deep water.

As with cracking and reforming, polymerization may be thermal or catalytic, although thermal polymerization as such is becoming obsolete.

Yet another process for the production of gasoline is Alkylation, in which a paraffinic gas such as *iso*-butane (Branched chain butane

$$\begin{array}{c} CH_3 \\ | \\ CH_3{-}CH{-}CH_3 \end{array}$$

see page 42, February "*M.M.*") is united with an olefinic gas such as butylene, yielding a gasoline of very high anti-knock rating suitable for aviation spirit.

As we have seen, there is an abundant supply of olefinic gases from cracking, but, although there is a good supply of *normal* (straight chain) Butane ($CH_3{-}CH_2{-}CH_2{-}CH_3$) evolved during the production of gasoline by any of the cracking processes, there is insufficient *iso*-butane. Hence the necessity of converting normal to *iso*-butane. The latter process is termed *isomerization*, and isomerization and alkylation are employed on other hydrocarbon gases as well as butane and butylene, to yield high octane aviation spirit. If the reader has managed to follow all this without confusion, he will have a good idea of the process employed in the production of present day petrol—perhaps the most important of our chemicals from petroleum.

The fourth and final class of petroleum chemicals are the hydrocarbon "bricks" which form the raw materials of our modern chemical industries. Until recently, all but a few of these "bricks" were obtained from coal-tar, but to-day, developments are taking place in petroleum chemistry which will make a complete range of basic chemicals available from petroleum.

In the first place, there is a large chemicals industry forming around the olefinic gases alone, and more particularly around ethylene, propylene and butylene.

Explosives, lacquers, synthetic rubbers, alcohols, artificial silks, plastics, glycerine, drugs, anæsthetics and many other products are, or can be, based on the olefines—either alone or in (*Continued on page 176*)

A Miniature Cinema

The upper illustration on this page shows a tiny cinema owned by Mr. G. M. Starling, Meccano and Hornby Train dealer, of Dereham, Norfolk. The cinema was constructed before the war, when an old store room was converted for the purpose. It then seated seven people, and was believed to be the smallest in the world. It has now been enlarged and holds 20. Shows are given twice a week and admission is by invitation; a collection is taken at each showing and is given to the R.S.P.C.A.

The miniature cinema owned by Mr. G. M. Starling, Dereham, Norfolk, by whose courtesy this photograph is reproduced.

The colour scheme of this interesting cinema is pink and green, and the screen curtains are controlled electrically from the projection room, as are the coloured lighting effects and the dimmers. The motor that moves the curtains drives through Meccano gearing. Two 16 mm. sound projectors are installed.

Mr. Starling hopes to make local news reels again soon.

A MODEL RAILWAY EXHIBITION

Readers living in Edinburgh and District will be interested in a model railway exhibition arranged by Mr. E. Dove, Nottingham, that will be held at Leith Links from 22nd to 27th May. The working models to be shown include a 10¼ in. gauge reproduction of the *"Coronation Scot,"* a model G.W.R. "Hall" of the same gauge and many others of the greatest interest, all of which have been built by Mr. Dove. The proceeds of the Exhibition are being devoted to the work of the Soldiers, Sailors and Airmen's Families Association.

Oil for Britain—(*Continued from page 160*)

conjunction with *aromatics*. In addition, countless most important organic substances are synthesized from aromatics alone, the chief of which are perhaps the "coal tar" dyestuffs. The aromatics have been derived hitherto mainly from coal tar, but a new process of great significance has now been developed which will produce from Kerosene, Gas oil or other distillates, a full range of both aromatics and olefines in one operation. This operation is termed the "Catarole" process (for the CATalytic production of AROmatics and OLEfines) and a plant to operate it is at present under construction at Partington near Manchester. Details of this process will in due course form the subject of a special article in the *"M.M."*

The last two illustrations in the present article are reproduced by courtesy of Manchester Oil Refinery Ltd.

* * * *

In these four brief articles, an effort has been made to present the reader with an overall picture of the petroleum industry as it stands to-day, with special emphasis upon oil refining in Britain. The industry is continually expanding and, as has been shown, there is almost no aspect of modern living which does not depend on it. Ambitious young chemists and engineers will find enormous and exciting possibilities in the World of Petroleum.

Helicopters at Work—(*Continued from page 147*)

Gander. Nor does it tell of the skill and gentle precision needed to land a helicopter on a platform with only 18 in. of room to spare, carrying a passenger with a broken neck. Only when such details are filled in can the real value of a helicopter rescue service be appreciated. As the Editor of *"The New York Times"* wrote: "The helicopter, fragile child of air science, did the trick that nothing else could accomplish. The ingenuity of man has seldom won a quicker or more thrilling victory over the wilderness."

The "Chipmunk" primary trainer aircraft built by the Canadian factory of the de Havilland Enterprise, by whose courtesy this photograph is reproduced. This type of trainer has been demonstrated very successfully in this country.

The "*Mammoth*"

Merseyside's Giant Floating Crane

THE floating cranes that are used in estuaries and harbours have many features of outstanding interest. They are usually of immense power, ready to take over almost any lifting task involved in the construction of harbours and docks, the building of ships and the loading of vessels. They are notable too on account of their range and the variety of their applications. A floating crane can travel anywhere where there is depth for it, and to see one of these giants moving slowly and majestically along such waterways as the Mersey and Thames Estuaries is a very thrilling sight, especially if it is carrying one of the huge and spectacular loads for which these cranes have been designed.

The floating crane shown on our cover is a splendid example of this type. It is the 200-ton crane "*Mammoth*" of the Mersey Docks and Harbour Board, to whom we are indebted for the photograph on which the cover is based and also for the illustrations reproduced on these pages. This is capable of slewing or turning round through a complete circle—the rotating weight is over 600 tons—and the jib can be moved up and down over a wide angle, so that it can be used in an extensive range of positions. The crane structure is mounted on a pontoon 154 ft. long and 88 ft. 6 in. in beam, and it is so placed that the greatest outward reach of the jib is either over the side of the pontoon or over its stem. An advantage of this is that the crane can deal with lifts in narrow entrances and in restricted places. Its ability to deal with heavy loads over the gates of the large graving docks of the Mersey Docks and Harbour Board system makes it of great value in ship repairing.

The scope of the crane indeed is exceptional in regard to height of lift and radius of action. It is capable of lying alongside the largest vessel afloat and delivering loads up to 60 tons from the hold of the vessel on to the quay, or in the reverse direction. The height of the lifting blocks used in lifts of this weight ranges from 115 ft. to 197 ft., according to the position of the jib.

Details of the lifting powers of the "*Mammoth*" are interesting. Loads of 60 to 200 tons are handled by two 100-ton lifting blocks fixed on the crane jib, and a load of 200 tons, the maximum, can be dealt with at a radius of from 95 to 110 ft., which gives a clear overside and overstem distance of from 50 ft. 9 in. to 65 ft. 9 in. The radius is greater for loads of 60 to 150 tons. The speed of lift for all these heavy loads is 3½ ft. per min. and the height of the lifting blocks above water ranges from 98 to 170 ft.

With loads of 60 tons or less, which can be handled by two 30-ton blocks on a trolley that can be moved along the full length of the jib, the speed of lift is 16½ ft. per min., and the radius of action is increased to 120 to 185 ft. The trolley speed is 12 ft. per min. With loads of all magnitudes the lifting blocks can be

The Mersey Docks and Harbour Board floating crane "Mammoth," preparing to lift a 75-ton ex-R.A.F. launch aboard the Houlder Line steamship "Elstree Grange" for shipment to Buenos Aires. The cradle in which the launch was lifted added 10 tons to the weight raised.

used singly when the weight to be lifted is half the maximum.

All these crane movements are electrically operated, and are under precise control at all speeds. For each there is a separate electric motor, and there are 10 of these, all interchangeable.

The hull of the vessel is divided into 18 compartments. On the after part of the deck is an area of about 300 sq. yds. that is specially strengthened, so that it can receive in safety heavy loads in transit. The illustration on this page demonstrates the use of this space. In it the crane is seen lifting railway coaches from the quayside on to the deck of the vessel, from which later they will be transferred to the steamer transporting them overseas.

The crane is driven by two sets of triple expansion marine type engines, working at a pressure of 150 lb. per sq. in., each of which can be uncoupled from the propeller shaft of the vessel and used for driving generating plant that provides the current for the crane movements. A separate steam-driven generator furnishes the energy for lighting the vessel, which can be done very effectively in order to make work at night possible.

The *"Mammoth"* is a striking feature when seen in the docks on Merseyside, with its giant jib towering over the great ships and warehouses; and it is even more impressive when it is seen making its stately way, at its speed of nearly 5 m.p.h., on the waters of the estuary, especially when it is carrying some giant load. On one occasion it carried part of a lock gate weighing 190 tons across the Mersey. This was the gate of the Alfred Dock, Birkenhead, which required strengthening and repairing and was removed to the Brunswick Dock, Liverpool, for this purpose. When the necessary work had been completed the two halves of the gate were taken across the river in turn without difficulty. On each occasion the half gate was swung from the dock wall to the deck of the floating crane, where it rested in an improvised cradle during its voyage.

The *"Mammoth"* also played an important part in the removal and replacement of bridges connecting the floating stages of the Wallasey Ferries at Egremont and New Brighton. Some years ago a bridge weighing 152 tons was placed in position at New Brighton with its aid. Later an existing bridge was removed for reconstruction, and the rebuilt bridge, weighing 110 tons, was taken by the floating crane down the Mersey from the place where it was fabricated, and lifted into position. In work of this kind the state of the tide has to be taken into consideration, the connection being made at the moment when the tide has risen to its full height.

Railway coaches for export being lifted from the quayside to the deck of the "Mammoth," ready to be transferred to the vessel in which they were to travel overseas.

During one of the many air attacks on Merseyside during the war, a bomb hit the deck of the *"Mammoth"* while she was in the Birkenhead docks and she sank, with her giant jib still towering above water. Salvaging the vessel presented a very difficult problem. To make it easier to raise the pontoon it was decided to remove the jib. For this purpose two travelling steel towers 100 ft. in height were erected, and on these two powerful derrick cranes were mounted for use in dismantling the structure. Then the pontoon itself was raised and repaired, after which the cranes on their towers were employed in rebuilding the jib. This work was carried out by Sir William Arrol and Co. Ltd., Glasgow.

Electric Power from Volcanic Steam

By V. Burton

Where engineers are trying to harness Iceland's volcanic steam. Photographs, Polar Photos.

A FEW miles from Reykjavik, the capital of Iceland, a jet of steam is spurting to a height of 250 ft. from the blue volcanic rock, with a roar so deafening that it is impossible to stay near it for more than two or three minutes. "We're going to harness it," Icelands' engineers tell you, "and put it to work for us in industry."

About two years ago I watched them make the first tentative borings into the great bed of steam that lies beneath Iceland's volcanic rocks. Since then, the predominant sound at Krisuvik, the site of the borings, has been the chug-chug of the engine that operates the drills. Slowly the engineers bored through the rock, cutting an initial hole the size of a soup plate until the tip of the eight-inch drill reached a depth of 760 ft.

"Then things began to happen," one of the engineers says. "From beneath our feet came a roaring rumbling sound, like that when our volcano Mt. Hekla erupted. There was a moment's suspense. Then we started to run—and only just in time, for the jet of steam that roared up flung the one-ton boring machinery so high that in crashing it smashed through a bed of concrete 28 in. thick."

Steam and sulphurous fumes escaping from fissures in Iceland's volcanic mountain region.

Now the job is to harness this man-made geyser and make it provide power for the factories and homes of Reykjavik, a city of 55,000 people.

"Iceland is a poor country," you are told. "We have no coal or timber or oil, and it costs us a lot in foreign currency to import fuel. Yet under our feet there's enough steam to blow the island sky high. We're boring for it."

In Italy, engineers have harnessed volcanic steam for industrial purposes, and there it is producing some 300,000 kilowatts annually. In New Zealand too, volcanic steam is being used experimentally to drive turbines. But the Icelanders have no previous experience to help them. They have sent engineers to Italy to pick up what they can, but even so they are working largely in the dark—feeling their way to the background noise of roaring steam.

Lava pools near where borings are being made to extract volcanic steam for the generation of electric power.

The jet that screams from the rocks at Krisuvik will yield enough electricity to provide the needs of a medium-sized town, and the drills are now boring for further supplies of steam.

Meanwhile, the Icelanders are working out how they are going to harness the jets. It will not be just a case of capping them as one caps an oil gusher, and then controlling the flow of steam. The present jet represents some 90 tons of steam an hour, but it is not all pure steam. It contains water, and it will be necessary to extract this before the steam reaches the machinery it is to drive. Experiments towards the solution of this problem are being made now, and when they are concluded a power station will be built near the jets.

Mount Hekla is connected by underground channels with the site where Iceland's engineers are boring for steam. When the volcano erupted in 1947 lava welled up beneath a farmhouse near the site.

In the meantime the engineers are working in sub-zero temperatures, with the wind sweeping down from the white flanks of the mountains and across the contorted lava formations, drilling for further supplies of steam. Already the second boring has reached a depth of 500 ft. "We only have another couple of hundred or so feet to go before we hit the steam bed," they say, "and then we'll have to run again!"

The harnessing of volcanic steam would mean a very great deal to the economy of Iceland. For the Icelanders have built up an important herring by-product industry. They are producing valuable herring oil and fertiliser, and the factories of Reykjavik, and of Akureyri, the island's second city, are working at full blast.

"There are all the herrings in the sea necessary to the extension of our new industry," the Icelanders say. "All we need now is the additional power to extend it. That from our waterfalls is not sufficient, and it seems we're walking on our latent power—volcanic, superheated, roaring steam in unlimited quantities. Sometimes it comes roaring up through the earth naturally. We're going to harness it."

Boeing's Atom-Bombers

By John W. R. Taylor

ON 8th February 1949 a sleek silver warplane took off from Moses Lake A.F. Base in Washington State and raced non-stop across the entire 2,289-mile span of the United States to Andrews Air Force Base, Maryland, in 3 hr. 46 min., at an average speed of 607 m.p.h. Such a record would have been spectacular if set up by the latest sweptwing jet fighter or high-speed research aircraft. In fact, it was achieved by a sixty-ton six-engined bomber—the Boeing XB-47 "Stratojet."

This flight proved to the world that Boeings were still in the forefront of big 'plane development, for the "Stratojet" is no high-speed freak. On the contrary, its great power and speed are intended primarily to enable it to carry the atomic bomb quickly, at very high altitude, to any target within 1,200 miles of its base, drop the bomb accurately, and then return home safely. From nose to tail it incorporates every up-to-the-minute design feature and piece of equipment needed to make it America's finest bomber; yet its story really began 36 years ago, when "Bill" Boeing built his first stick-and-string seaplane in a tiny hangar on the shores of Lake Union, Seattle.

The photograph above shows the Boeing XB-47 "Stratojet" bomber. For our illustrations and that on which our cover is based we are indebted to the Boeing Airplane Company, U.S.A.

At that time, construction of an aircraft like the "Stratojet" would have seemed an almost impossible undertaking. It still does, and would be but for the fact that "Bill" Boeing's little hangar has grown into one of the world's biggest aircraft factories, with an equally vast "branch office" at Wichita, Kansas, staffed by designers and engineers whose experience of building big, complex aeroplanes is second-to-none in the world.

Not all Boeing aeroplanes have been big. The earliest genuine Boeing design was the little B.1 flying boat of 1919, the first aircraft ever to carry commercial air mail in North America. The machine that put the young company on its feet was the PW–9 fighter of 1923, more than 100 of which were supplied to the U.S. Air Service. They were racy little biplanes, with a top speed of 160 m.p.h., and each fitted with a 440 h.p. Curtiss D–12—the engine that made possible the earliest really streamlined U.S. and British fighter 'planes. Then came the American switchover to radial engines, which produced the aggressive "Wasp"-powered Boeing P–12 fighters, so popular in Hollywood flying films in the '30s, followed in turn by the P–26 when the monoplane returned to fashion in 1933.

But by that year work had started on an aeroplane destined to make the words "Boeing" and "bomber" almost synonymous — the B–17 "Flying Fortress." When the first XB–17 flew on 28th July 1935 it was far from being an aerial fortress. Its defences consisted of just five machine guns, carried on pivot-mountings; and although its four 750 h.p. engines produced a top speed of 250 m.p.h., it was obviously no match for the new 300 m.p.h. eight-gun fighters being built in Europe. To make matters worse, it crashed within three months of its first flight, because somebody forgot to remove before take-off some pins that locked the tail controls to prevent damage by gusts of wind while the aircraft was on the ground.

Fortunately, Army Air Corps experts had seen enough of the XB–17 by then to

The earliest genuine Boeing design was the little B.1 flying boat of 1919 seen here. On the right is the nose of one of the big Boeing "Stratofreighters" of to-day.

realise that, with more powerful engines and more guns, it might well be made into an offensive weapon of tremendous power. So they ordered 13 improved Y1B–17 "Fortresses" in 1936, then 39 turbo-supercharged B–17Bs in 1938 and finally, during World War II, over 12,600 more B–17s, built by Boeing, Douglas, Vega and a host of sub-contractors. They dropped between them nearly half of all the bombs loosed on Europe by U.S. bombers, and shot down more than two-thirds of all the enemy fighters destroyed over Europe by U.S. bombers. To supplement their guns, they added the new tactic of high-altitude flying to their defences, dropping bombs from heights up to 30,000 ft., out of range of many enemy guns and fighters. Simultaneously, in 1944–5, the "Fort's" big brothers, the B–29 "Superfortresses," were busy delivering 96 per cent. of all the bombs dropped on Japan in World War II, finishing up with the two atom-bombs that brought the war to a close.

Meanwhile the time was ripe for yet another big change in warplane design, for the advent of jet power had begun to make even the mighty B–29, with its 10-ton bomb load and 12 guns, look old-fashioned. Boeings replaced it by the even more powerful B–50 "Superfortress," and at the same time developed a civil counterpart, the "Stratocruiser," as flagship for the world's airlines. Behind the scenes they started work on the XB–47 "Stratojet," no mere jet-engined development of the "Superfortress," but a completely new sweptwing atom-bomber with a score of untried design features that would make it as revolutionary as the first 1935 "Fortress."

It was no easy task. The jet-propelled aircraft that emerged from World War II were fast. A British Gloster "Meteor" had proved that conclusively by lifting the World's Absolute Speed Record from 469 m.p.h. to 606 m.p.h. in one jump. But increased power and speed had introduced tremendous new problems. Chief of these was "compressibility," the building up of shock waves that could batter an aeroplane to pieces as it approached the speed of sound, which is 660 m.p.h. at 30,000 ft. German scientists had proved that the effects of compressibility could be postponed by sweeping back wings and tail surfaces. So, determined to make their XB–47 the world's fastest bomber, Boeing designed it as a perfectly streamlined fuselage carried on narrow,

Boeing YB-17A bomber, the first four-engined aircraft fitted with turbo-superchargers for improved performance at height.

sharply sweptback wings. Nor were the wings merely sweptback: they were made razor thin, to reduce drag to a minimum, and so flexible that they droop when the aircraft is on the ground and curve up at the tips during flight. This flexibility, gained without sacrificing strength, enables the wing tips to "ride the bumps" while the fuselage rides far more smoothly than a conventional 'plane.

To avoid breaking up airflow over the wings, Boeing designers slung the XB–47's six 4,000 lb. thrust General Electric J–35 jet engines underneath in pods. The problem of how to retract undercarriage wheels into the thin wings was solved by making them retract into the fuselage instead! The idea of having two pairs of main wheels under the fuselage, with small "balancer" wheels at the wing tips, was tried out on a converted "Marauder" bomber, proved successful and adopted for the XB–47. Finally, in case even 24,000 lb. of thrust proved insufficient to lift the bomber from the runway with a full load, 18 rockets were fitted in the rear fuselage to provide a further 20,000 lb. thrust. As a result, a few weeks after the original XB–47 prototype made its first flight on 17th December 1947, it began a series of startling, almost vertical climb tests, trailing a cloud of smoke from its rockets.

A flying view of the Boeing XB-47 "Stratojet" bomber.

The second XB–47 flew on 21st July 1948, and two months later the U.S. Air Force ordered the type into full production at Wichita, adding that they wanted the first production B–47A within 18 months. They got it, on 1st March 1950, and have since received enough B–47As to form at least one complete squadron.

Some idea of what this achievement has involved can be gained from the few statistics that are not secret. For example, construction of a B–47 involves 3,464,000 man-hours and the two prototypes cost nearly £4¼ million. This compares with 138,000 man-hours and about £125,000 for the first "Fortress."

To produce the B–47 it was necessary to design and build more than 60,000 separate jigs and tools, of which the wing jig alone required the drilling of some 15,000 bolt holes to an accuracy of .0005 in. Finally, the bomber itself has to be built up from more than 52,000 different kinds of parts, not including rivets and engine components. The result is a "medium" bomber, able to fly at more than 600 m.p.h. at very high altitudes, with up to 10 tons of bombs.

The first prototype XB–47 was re-engined with six 5,200 lb. thrust General Electric J–47 jet engines in the Autumn of 1949, and production B–47A and B–47B "Stratojets" differ little from this aircraft, except that the 'Bs carry external fuel tanks under their wings and can be equipped for mid-air refuelling, to increase their combat radius to 1,500 miles. They are the finest bombers in service to-day with any air force.

Boeings never believe in resting on their laurels, however, and already they have produced a much larger, eight-engined bomber on the same lines, named the XB–52 "Stratofortress." Its weight is nearly double that of the B–47A and its prototype cost anything up to £27 million.

Riding a Southern Main Line Diesel

By S. C. Townroe, A.M.I.Mech.E.

THE Southern Region main line diesel-electric locomotive, No. 10201, was on show at the Festival of Britain last year, and I expect many *"M.M."* readers took the opportunity of inspecting it. The locomotive is of the 2–6–6–2 type, or "1 Co-Co 1." Its power unit is a 1,750 H.P. English Electric Company 16-cylinder diesel engine, and it has traction motors on each of its six driving axles. Altogether it weighs 135 tons, and its tractive effort is 31,200 lb. Both No. 10201 and the sister engine No. 10202 were built at Ashford Works.

While No. 10201 was still in the Festival, in September last year, No. 10202 was put into service on the Southern Region West of England line, working two round trips to Exeter every twenty-four hours, six days a week. This working included the night mail train from Waterloo to Exeter, and the fast 7.30 a.m. train from Exeter to London.

The photograph at the head of the page, by G. O. P. Pearce, shows Southern diesel-electric No. 10202 at the head of the up 12.40 p.m. leaving Bournemouth Central for Waterloo. This picture was obtained on the first day of intensive working by a diesel-electric locomotive between Waterloo and Weymouth.

By April of this year, this engine had completed over 75,000 miles on these duties without any serious trouble. It had done the work of two steam locomotives daily, and in six months had run a mileage that a steam locomotive would not cover in less than eighteen months. The timekeeping was excellent and the drivers spoke highly of the comfort and ease of control.

The loads did not generally exceed 11 coaches on the West of England line during the Winter. As it was intended to use the second engine on the more heavily-loaded Bournemouth and Weymouth trains, commencing this Spring, there was some speculation whether the diesel-electrics would manage trains of 13 coaches on the fastest trains, such as *"The Royal Wessex."* I should explain that the gear ratios of the traction motors were designed for high-speed services, and not for the heaviest trains, so at present the gearing is on the high side.

I was delighted to have the opportunity of riding on No. 10201 on the first day it worked *"The Royal Wessex,"* which leaves Waterloo at 4.35 p.m. and is allowed 55 minutes to pass Worting Junction, $51\frac{1}{4}$ miles. With long stretches of gradient at 1 in 330 and speed restrictions in the London suburban area, the time allowance is not generous for a train exceeding 450 tons in total weight. The day was 1st April, and Driver Jack Attfield, of Bournemouth, was anxious that the engine should not make an April fool of him by dropping precious minutes, as he usually keeps time to the minute!

The engine was already nicely warmed up, as it had done a trip to Weymouth and back already since the early morning, and the fuel tanks had been filled with

1,100 gallons of oil in readiness for another 270-mile trip. To supply the steam-heating boiler 880 gallons of water also had been taken on.

Sharp at 4.35 p.m. Driver Attfield got the *"Right-away"* and he brought the controller handle gently round to notch 3. The engine let forth a typical diesel roar as it took the weight of the thirteen coaches, and as we rounded the curves leaving Waterloo the ammeter needle on the control panel flickered momentarily, indicating that slight slipping was occurring at the driving wheels. A touch of the trigger to operate the air sanding gear corrected this.

Passing Queen's Road the speed had crept up to 45 m.p.h., but instead of the series of green colour-lights that we expected to see ahead, we were brought to a dead stand outside Clapham Junction, and then diverted to the local line. Evidently, something unusual had happened. As we passed Earlsfield we saw the culprit—a steam locomotive broken down in the section.

At Raynes Park the diversion lights told us that we were switching back to the main line again, which involved a reduction to 20 m.p.h. at the crossover. Consequently we were 5½ minutes down on schedule at Hampton Court Junction. Jack grimly told his fireman to "stoke up the fire" and held the controller handle to notch 8, the full power position, where it was to stay for the next 38 miles.

West Weybridge was passed at 68 m.p.h., but we did not reach that speed again until Farnborough, for the long rising gradient to milepost 31 brought our pace down to a minimum of 56 m.p.h. at the summit. Inspector Frank Thornton came through from the engine-room to the driving compartment to tell us that the engine was running sweetly at 750 r.p.m., at a comfortable temperature and with no signs of distress. In the cab we could hear little more than the rush of air beating against the windows, but with the engine-room door open we knew we were working on a "growler," as the Americans call their diesels!

Over the 14½ miles from Farnborough to Basingstoke our speed averaged 71 m.p.h. and when the signal box at Worting Junction came in sight, we peered at our watches to see how far we were off schedule. Only three minutes late! So we had regained 2½ minutes on the most difficult part of the journey. At that rate we stood a chance of reaching our first stop, Winchester, on time, but we were baulked by a speed restriction of 15 m.p.h. at Waltham, where the permanent-way men had laid some new lengths of flat-bottom rail a few days before. For six miles we cruised at 80 m.p.h. until it was time to apply the brakes approaching Winchester, and we came to a stand two minutes behind time.

Starting from Winchester, the seven miles to Eastleigh were run in eight minutes and we reached the next stop, Southampton Central, in 15¾ minutes against the 17 minutes allowed. Thus brought within three quarters of a minute of right time, we felt that the handicap of the unexpected delay at Clapham Junction had been overcome. Four minutes are allowed at Southampton. With a steam engine this is barely enough to take sufficient water for Weymouth, but the diesel ignores wayside water-columns! At Brockenhurst, we were safely on time, but the awkward curve at that station is no easy place to start a long train and the control handle had to go to notch 6, causing the engine to emit an extra loud growl, before we moved. At Bournemouth Central eight coaches were detached and No. 10201 purred on toward Weymouth. We had timed *"The Royal Wessex!"*

Diesel-electric No. 10201, on which the author rode, nearing Eastleigh with a train from Weymouth to Waterloo.

A Talk with Stirling Moss

By the Editor

SITTING comfortably in a pleasant lounge talking to Stirling Moss was one of the most enjoyable experiences of my life. Stirling knows what he is talking about when his subject is motor car racing and motor car rallies, and it is thrilling to listen to his stories of the cars he has driven and the successes he has gained. There is nothing dramatic in his conversation, as one usually understands the term, but all the time there is the feeling that here is a master of his trade giving his listeners well judged and mature comments.

I had not talked long to Stirling before I discovered that in his boyhood days he had been a Meccano enthusiast and a reader of the Magazine. I had already felt assured on this point, so I was scarcely surprised when he told me. It seemed only natural somehow that a master of mechanism should have had an introduction to it through Meccano, and it was equally natural that such an enthusiast should be a regular *M.M.* reader. He seems to have been a car enthusiast before he took up Meccano, for I gather that he became interested when he was only six, while he actually drove a small Austin when he was 11. He had been familiar with cars from his very earliest days, for his father had raced himself, and his mother had taken part in car trials. It is not surprising therefore to find that he badly wanted a car when he was only 15, a car that he could not only drive himself but could use in races of some kind.

Stirling Moss is congratulated at the end of one of the many races in which he scored a victory.

Unfortunately this was forbidden, but he did become the owner of a three-wheeled Morgan when he was 15. This was followed first by an M.G. and then by a B.M.W. sports car when he could drive on the road. Next year came his start in the racing world, when he sold his B.M.W. and with the proceeds bought a Cooper 500. This was the car in which Stirling rose to fame as a racing driver. It was his own car, entered in races by himself and even at his first race meeting he secured a third place in the event for which he entered. This in itself was a wonderful start, but more was to follow, for after that "firsts" became the rule.

At this time Stirling was only 18, and his remarkable successes were very impressive, even to those who knew how he had grown up with cars and had become a skilful driver, and also one who knew every corner of the racing game, both on and off the track. When he was telling me about his early races, however, there was no special elation in his voice. He spoke simply as one who had studied every detail of the career to which he had set himself. Looking back on his career on road and track it is clear that he has earned his successes by the close attention he has given to every detail and the care he takes to keep himself perfectly fit. In all his races he just set out to run as fast as his car would allow and to finish as high as he could, whatever the opposition. He showed this very early when he drove H.W.Ms. in Continental races against experienced drivers in faster cars at a time when Ferraris were sweeping the field.

"You were young to take part in races in which no doubt veterans of the track were competing" I remarked. "Did you ever feel nervous?"

Stirling seemed slightly interested in this himself.

Moss taking his Kieft through the paddock bend at Goodwood to win the Earl of March Trophy race.

Looking back over the reports of that last day of last year's Monte Carlo Rally I recalled that of the crew of the winning Sunbeam-Talbot it was Stirling Moss who was chosen to drive the car on the treacherous surface, and his control and timing throughout were masterly. He may have been right in saying that the result was pure luck. That was typical of him—but the luck was the kind that falls to the expert.

This brought me to an important question that I had determined to ask Stirling, a short one that is likely to arouse a lot of discussion. It was this. "What qualities should a racing driver possess?"

The answer to this question might have been a very long one, but a very brief one came immediately.

"He must have the feel of his car" replied Stirling. "It goes without saying that he must be familiar with every detail of it and that he must possess good judgment of speed and distance. But above all he must be absolutely at one with the car, so that he controls its every movement with the same speed (*Continued on page 52*)

"I only remember being nervous on one or two occasions," he said after a moment's thought. "One of these was at one of the earliest meetings in which I took part. It had been raining heavily and the course was wet and slippery, and it was very easy to get into a skid."

"It doesn't seem to have disturbed you very much" I said.

"Actually it taught me a great deal, and never since have I felt nervous even in the most difficult conditions when I have been driving a car that I knew and that was completely reliable."

"A Sunbeam-Talbot in the 1952 Monte Carlo Rally, for instance," I suggested. "On that last circuit particularly driving must have been very difficult with a road covered with ice and snow."

"Perhaps you are right" he said. "The surface was bad and it was necessary to keep very closely to the average speed laid down for the circuit, but I was lucky. Anything might have happened on that road, and fortunately I was able to keep the car going on schedule, and we got round without mishap."

Stirling Moss and his co-driver John Cutts in one of the cars of the official Sunbeam-Talbot team on the Stelvio Pass during the 1952 Alpine Trial, in which the team won 11 major awards. The pass climbs to a height of 9,042 ft. Photograph by courtesy of Sunbeam-Talbot Ltd.

The Bristol Britannia—(*Continued from page 6*)

small-scale Britannia control surfaces were flight tested on a Bristol Freighter.

As a result of all this care and skill, the Britannia can be regarded as a thoroughly practical aircraft only five months after its first flight. Already B.O.A.C. have ordered five more, equipped to carry 20 tons of cargo instead of passengers at rates which will compare favourably with surface transport. And they have taken over one of the Ministry prototypes to bring their passenger-carrying fleet of Britannias to 26. Overseas airlines, including Qantas, Aerovias Guest of Mexico and Tasman Empire Airways may soon decide to re-equip with Britannias, and there are persistent rumours that R.A.F. Coastal Command and the Royal Canadian Air Force are interested in a militarised version for long-range over-water patrol.

This is only a start, for Britannias will not be in full service for another couple of years, and will then have many years of development ahead of them. Almost certainly, loaded weight and payload will soon be increased, making them even more attractive economically; and more powerful, economical engines like the Rolls-Royce Conway or Napier Nomad may make them even more attractive militarily. So the Britannia, like the Comet and Viscount, is a British air liner of which we can be very, very proud.

The Television Microscope—

(*Continued from page 7*)

make these stand out, and to give the contrast that is necessary if they are to be examined and studied thoroughly. The use of stains, which in most respects have proved very efficient, has disadvantages of its own. With televised microscopy specimens can be made to stand out clearly without staining, so that these undesirable results are avoided, and the slow or rapid movements of material under a microscope can easily be watched on the television screen.

The use of this new method in the study of microscopic living things is only just beginning, and there is no doubt that the new tool will provide wonderful aid in probing more deeply into the structure of materials.

A Talk with Stirling Moss—(*Continued from page 11*)

and certainty that he can control his own actions."

This interested me very greatly. Every racing car has its own individuality. In racing it is not enough to be skilful with clutch, gear-box and brake. The racing driver must know instinctively what to do and when to do it, just as he knows how and when to move his own limbs in running a race himself.

In his youngest days Stirling was a horseman, skilled in jumping, and apparently the same skill that he developed there has played a great part in the control of the very highly strung cars that he has driven at speed and around curves in the motor car world. Today he flies for relaxation and pleasure, so he is accustomed to speed in more spheres than one, and no doubt he will be as successful in the air if occasion arises as he has been on land.

Stirling's triumphs on the racing track, and in endurance tests and rallies have been legendary and I need not present readers with a list of them. They would take up more space than I could spare anyway! But I would like to remind readers of his outstanding achievement in the International Alpine Rally in July of last year, when he was a member of the Sunbeam-Talbot team that won the Manufacturers' Team Prize for the best team irrespective of size, class or nationality, and secured other awards in what has been described as the toughest rally in the world, for car and man. I have already spoken of his part in the 1952 Monte Carlo Rally. This month he is taking part in the 1953 Rally, again in a Sunbeam-Talbot, and in this he will carry the best wishes of every reader of the *M.M.*, all of whom have followed his career with the most intense interest.

New Meccano Models—(*Continued from page 39*)

is supplied with the *Magic* Motor) fixed on a $1\frac{1}{2}''$ Rod, mounted in the tail boom, and a $2\frac{1}{2}''$ Strip bolted to a Rod and Strip Connector on the Rod represents the tail rotor.

The Brighton Works Terrier, originally L.B.S.C. No. 35 Morden built in 1878. The engine is resplendent in the yellow Stroudley livery, with the copper chimney cap that formerly distinguished Brighton passenger locomotives. Photograph by H. C. Casserley.

The top of the fuselage is completed by two $2\frac{1}{2}''$ Strips 11, curved to shape and attached to the sides by Obtuse Angle Brackets, A $5\frac{1}{2}''$ Strip 12 is also curved and is fixed at the nose to an Obtuse Angle Bracket. Strip 12 is supported at its rear end by a $5\frac{1}{2}'' \times 1\frac{1}{2}''$ Flexible Plate bolted between the sides.

The curved top of the tail boom is formed by two $5\frac{1}{2}'' \times 2\frac{1}{2}''$ Flexible Plates 13, two $1\frac{11}{16}''$ radius Curved Plates 14 and a U-section Curved Plate 15. These parts are curved to the required shape and are fixed to the sides of the boom.

The main rotor blades are made by bolting four $12\frac{1}{2}''$ Strips to a Bush Wheel fixed on the upper end of the axle driven by the Motor. The $12\frac{1}{2}''$ Strips are arranged in pairs, each pair being made from two Strips overlapped seven holes. The blades are completed by $5\frac{1}{2}''$ Strips 16 arranged as shown in Fig. 3.

EXHIBITION OF RAILWAY PHOTOGRAPHY

Readers in Lancashire and Cheshire who are interested in railway photography will be glad to know that the splendid Railway Photographic Exhibition held in London last October, and referred to on page 480 of the *M.M.* for that month, will be showing at the Liverpool College of Art, Hope Street, Liverpool 1, from Monday 5th January to Saturday 10th January inclusive. The hours of admission will be: Monday to Friday inclusive, 5.30 p.m.–8 p.m., and on Saturday, 1.30 p.m.–8 p.m. Admission will be free, and a Catalogue, price 1/–, will be on sale.

This Exhibition has been organised by the Railway Correspondence and Travel Society in association with the Railway Photographic Society.

Engine Nicknames

by R. S. McNaught

LIKE all other persons and things we hold in affectionate regard, railway engines have always been liable to get nicknames. From all I can gather, it is a habit very much confined to the British, who however do not hesitate to apply it to engines belonging to other people. This was noticeable when the original British Expeditionary Force—the Old Contemptibles—found itself on the Continent at the outset of the 1914–18 War. Somebody then spotted, with incredulous glee, the old-fashioned Belgian engines, which had huge square smokestacks like nothing else on rails; they were instantly dubbed Souvenirs, and the name stuck for ever.

To have some idea at least of the nicknames attached by time-honoured usage to various classes of locomotives is a very useful asset to any railway enthusiast, and should by no means be looked upon as a frivolous touch to our hobby. When one comes to look into the matter, it is obvious that in almost the majority of cases the "unofficial" name gives a clue to the usefulness or the popularity of the class concerned.

Our heading illustration shows a Cauliflower, one of the L.N.W.R. 0-6-0s that were given this name because of the fancied resemblance to this useful vegetable of the coat-of-arms on the driving wheel splashers. British Railways Photograph.

There are many instances in this sphere where a single word speaks volumes. For example, could there be a better name than Mourners for the little Webb 0–6–2 tank engines of the former London and North Western line? It does not require the eye of an expert to decide that these engines have never been liable to set up speed records, whatever their other qualities; and these must be many, for the class has kept going years beyond what might have been expected.

It must be thoroughly understood that in writing of "nicknames" we are dealing only with what may be best described as "informal but generally-accepted titles which have never appeared either on name plates or in official records." Thus, Royal Scot is not a nickname for that class; on the other hand Baby Scot definitely is a nickname for the smaller type, originally derived from Crewe Claughtons, which are known officially as Patriots.

Very occasionally an exception to the rule turns up, however. A good recent example is to be observed in the standard General Purpose class of the Eastern Region. These are officially B 1's or Antelopes. But one of them, its original number 8306, came into service with the splendid name *Bongo*, and this was too good a thing to miss. So to-day few of the men refer to the class as anything but Bongos, whether you like it or not. Apparently the unofficial name was not liked in official circles, for after a works visit for overhaul No. 61005, as she now is, returned to service minus name plates. But they have since been restored!

After all, the B1's are excellent engines within their limits, and who could really dislike a Bongo?

The origin of nicknames is often one of the most intriguing mysteries. Obviously they must start with one particular person, most probably some foreman, fitter, or driver closely associated with a new engine right at its advent. I cannot trace many instances of nicknames contrived after a machine has been in service any length of time. If the name is apt it sticks and soon spreads, and thus achieves a kind of unofficial sanction wherever the newcomer works. In due course it appears in print, probably first of all in one of the journals of the various railway enthusiasts' clubs or societies. Then it finds its way into the old-established monthlies, and finally into the spotters' notebooks, and then it would be difficult indeed to forget or change it.

A Peacock 4-4-0 of the former Midland and Great Northern Joint Railway. These engines were built by the well-known firm Beyer, Peacock and Co. Ltd., of Manchester.

This process was easy in the case of a compact railway of the pre-grouping era, but even then I have often wondered, for instance, how soon after they issued from Crewe Works the stalwart 18 inch goods class—the official description—were talked of at Camden and Carlisle as Cauliflowers! This celebrated nickname of course arose from the innovation of adorning the engine's middle splasher with the coat of arms of the owners, which from a distance of a few yards looked singularly like that pleasant vegetable! Did the crew of the first 18 inch goods to surmount Shap say to the interested motive power workers at Carlisle Shed: "Well, here's the new model, and the chaps at Crewe call them Cauliflowers, so you call them the same?"

Do nicknames have any practical value in railway working? The answer is, "Yes, quite a lot," because they are invariably time-savers and very handy as such in the boisterous and noisy conditions of the job. It is a lot easier for a running shed foreman, with safety-valves roaring away in his immediate vicinity, to shout across several sets of metals to a spare crew "Get that Jenner off the coal stage quick" than "get that ex-Great Northern goods engine . . ." or even "get No. 10 . . . .6 off the stage." I would go further and say that the majority of the men know the engines only by their class nicknames, and whether the latter are frivolous, affectionate, or even the reverse of complimentary, they play a vital part in the everyday activities of shed, goods yard, or station.

I can recall watching some shunting operations at a station in which a Great Western 2-cylinder passenger engine was taking part—a grand old type now nearing extinction. To mere spectators at the platform end like myself, she was a Saint, and if we called her a Lady or even a Court we were also right, for the several groups form but one general class. But to the shunters, signalman, and inspector supervising the shunting, she was the

A Highflyer, or in other words a Lancashire and Yorkshire 4-4-2 as turned out from Horwich Works just over 50 years ago. The tall slender boiler and the big long-striding coupled wheels account for the nickname. The class became obsolete in 1934. British Railways Photograph.

Bristol engine, for their working timetables ordained that the engine from an incoming Bristol express should perform this regular shunting operation before proceeding to shed to turn and be serviced. But to the enginemen their steed was definitely a 29, and by no other name, even their official ones, were these famous engines known, whether Saints, Ladies, or Courts. Perhaps 29 can hardly be classed as a nickname as it was derived from the running numbers of the series from 2901 onwards, but on the whole the G.W.R. standardised types led to fewer unofficial titles than on most other lines.

In the earliest days, the genesis of nicknames can be seen in the first lumbering Wylam Dillies, and Puffing Billy itself was scarcely likely to appear in its owners' records as such. As time went on and various firms set up in the new and very lucrative business of engine-building, their products, which of course were of their own design, were dubbed accordingly. Thus we find mention of Bury's, Sharpies, Vulcans or Peacocks, which are not difficult to identify. The same idea has been extended in more modern times; at the turn of the century some Brighton engines built in Glasgow were always called Scotchmen—a horrible name to the purist—and even in Southern days a batch of the well-known King Arthurs were similarly referred to as Scotch Arthurs. In many quarters, incidentally, they are regarded as the pick of all the Arthurs.

It would be impossible within the scope of a single article to give anything like a comprehensive list of nicknames of the past and the present, but I will group a small selection of perhaps the best known into the sections in which they naturally fall.

I will begin with the most celebrated of all engine classes to carry a nickname, and that in itself probably the most apt ever bestowed upon a class of engines. I refer of course to the one and only Stroudley Terriers. It is true that to their drivers and firemen these great little machines were always the Rooters, but in their native Sussex the two terms are synonymous, and if you ever owned a terrier worth the name, you would know whether they are rooters or not! For such small engines to have found for themselves an honoured place in the Hall of Fame is a very remarkable thing, and of course some of them are still very much on the go. If you turn to page 52 you will see a fine picture of one of these famous engines.

An L.N.W.R. Webb Compound 0-8-0 coal engine with the piano-front casing prominent ahead of the smoke-box. Many of the class were converted to superheated simple engines. British Railways Photograph.

A long list could be compiled of names with a whimsical turn derived from celebrities of the period. In its early days the Premier Line, the old L.N.W.R., had its Bloomers, both Large and Small, which must have caused the raising of many a prim Victorian eyebrow. The same company's men were once promised marvellous new compounds that were to conquer Shap and dispense with double-heading for ever. Actually they got the duddest and most sluggish of all Mr. Webb's creations, the 4–6–0 1400 Class four-cylinder compounds, and promptly called them Bill Baileys after the hero of a music hall song of the day.

Some feature or look, good, bad or unusual, is perhaps the most common source of a locomotive nickname. The L.N.W.R. Piano-fronts were a good example of this. They were given a curved box at their front ends to enclose part of the low pressure cylinder—they were compound engines—and this irresistibly suggested the curved lid over the case of a piano. Actually they were ungainly mineral engines. The L. and Y. Highflyers provided another instance. They were 4–4–2s that had unusually large coupled wheels, which gave them a long striking appearance, and tall slender boilers.

More examples of these nicknames will be given in a further article next month.

Two Bells

By John W. R. Taylor

WHEN we talk about the pioneer days of flying, we usually mean the 1903-12 era, the days of the Wright brothers, Santos-Dumont, Curtiss, Farman, A. V. Roe and Bleriot, when every flight was an adventure.

We have come a long way in 50 years—so far that no place on earth is more than a day's journey from London in a Canberra bomber. But we have had to pay a high price for progress.

Vertical Take-off. — **A start has been made with helicopters, which are already operating into city centres. Here is one of Sabena's Sikorsky S.55s at Brussels Heliport. Photograph by courtesy of Sabena.**

In those old pioneer days, crashes were merely a part of the process of learning to fly. A few people were killed, usually because their frail stick-and-string aeroplanes broke up in the air. More often, airmen were able to step out of the wreckage, brush themselves down, build another, improved, aeroplane in a few days, and try again.

One reason was that their aeroplanes had what we call a low wing loading. The 1903 Wright biplane, for example, weighed 750 lb., complete with pilot, and had a wing area of 510 sq. ft. Thus, every square foot of wing surface had to lift a load of only 1½ lb. The comparable wing loading of a Stratocruiser air liner is over 80 lb. per sq. ft.

Now, a 'plane with a low wing loading and adequate power can take off very quickly. Its wings develop so much lift, and it weighs so little, that it will leave the ground after a short run, and at quite a low speed. The Wright biplane reached only 31 m.p.h. in full flight and took off after a run of 40 ft.

By comparison, the average heavily-loaded modern air liner will not leave the ground until it has reached a speed of well over 100 m.p.h., and needs a take-off run of anything up to 1½ miles. As a result, aerodromes like London Airport need two-mile long concrete runways, extending over hundreds of acres of good farming land.

There is an even more unpleasant consequence of high landing and take-off speeds. If anything goes wrong—and the majority of aircraft accidents *do* occur during take-off and landing—the crash at around 100 m.p.h. will obviously be far more serious than the 30 m.p.h. crash of a lightly-loaded aeroplane.

For years, the late C. G. Grey, famous editor of *The Aeroplane* and contributor to *Meccano Magazine*, pleaded for "aircraft that would land slowly and not burn up in a crash". But the public demand speed, and airlines must make money. The inevitable result is the sort of air liners we have today.

This does not mean that air travel is unsafe. On the contrary. In Australia, which is one of the most air-minded countries in the world, the accident rate is such that if a baby was put aboard an air liner on the day it was born, it could expect to keep flying day and night until it reached the age of 93 before becoming due for an accident.

Nevertheless, designers and scientists all over the world are beginning to turn their attention more and more to ways of dispensing with miles of concrete runway.

The main reason is that they have to ensure that their countries would not be left defenceless if all airfields were destroyed in the early stages of an atomic war; and the results so far are of more use to military aviation than to the airlines. But civil flying is bound to benefit in due course from all the millions of pounds, dollars, francs and roubles being spent in research.

High wing loading. The Boeing Stratocruiser. Photograph by courtesy of Pan American World Airways System.

The new aircraft that have evolved from this research are often of fantastic shape. Last year we had the Convair XFY-1 and Lockheed XFV-1 vertical take-off fighters, which stand on their tail and climb away vertically, their propellers working like helicopter rotors. Then we had the even more weird Rolls-Royce "Flying Bedstead", which demonstrated a way to take off vertically without all the complications of sitting on one's tail.

The Bell XV-3 Convertiplane, the two rotors of which are mounted at the wing-tips.

Another type of vertical take-off aircraft —the helicopter—is of course already well established. In its present form, it is tremendously expensive to operate and comparatively slow. But from it are being developed convertiplanes, which will take off as helicopters and convert into semi-fixed wing aeroplanes for cruising flight. Such an aircraft will be the 44-seat Fairey Rotodyne helicopter, due to fly early next year.

Another, which was completed in February of this year, is the American Bell XV-3. It works on entirely different principles from those of the turboprop-engined Rotodyne, because its two rotors, which are mounted at the ends of 30 ft. span fixed wings, are designed to tilt forward through 90 deg. after take-off, so that they act as forward facing propellers for cruising flight.

Conversion from rotor to propeller is said to be a smooth, gradual operation, taking 10 to 15 seconds. Surprisingly, it has no effect on the 'plane's attitude. In fact, the pilot can stop or reverse the conversion at any point, whilst maintaining steady, stable flight.

The result is an extremely promising design, because the XV-3 can rise vertically, hover or fly forward, backward or sideways without any difficulty, and can manoeuvre and land in confined areas even under gusty wind conditions. It can, in short, do anything that a helicopter will do, and, as an aeroplane, should have a forward speed of over 175 m.p.h., which is considerably faster than the present international speed record for helicopters.

The four-seat Bell XV-3 has been built

to test the practicability of tilting rotor designs for Army observation, reconnaissance, ambulance, liaison and rescue aircraft, as well as for future large cargo and assault transport projects. It is powered by a 450 h.p. Pratt and Whitney R-985 piston engine, mounted behind the cabin, and is at present undergoing extensive tied-down ground tests before starting its flight testing.

A second revolutionary new Bell aircraft was announced on 3rd February, just one week before the XV-3. It is called the VTOL (vertical take-off and landing) aircraft and works in much the same way as the Rolls-Royce "Flying Bedstead", in that it uses the thrust of a pair of downward-pointing jet engines to raise it off the ground. But, as can be seen from the photograph on this page, it looks far more like a conventional aeroplane than does the Rolls-Royce machine.

The VTOL is a hybrid, with the fuselage of a glider, the wings of a standard lightplane, and the skid undercarriage of a Bell 47 helicopter. It was built as quickly as possible, at the company's own expense, to prove the practicability of direct jet-lift. The only official help concerned the two 1,000 lb. thrust Fairchild J44 turbojets, which were supplied by the U.S.A.F. and are of the type used to power pilotless target aircraft.

Another revolutionary Bell type, the VTOL (vertical take-off and landing) aircraft. It was built to prove the practicability of direct jet-lift.

Loaded weight of the single-seat VTOL is about 2,000 lb.; it is 21 ft. long and has a wing span of 26 ft. Its big advantage, compared with "tail-sitters" like the XFY-1 and XFV-1, is that its fuselage remains horizontal at all times, eliminating the need for special ground handling equipment and making take-off and landing less uncomfortable for its pilot. After take-off, the engines are simply rotated through 90 deg. to a horizontal position, and the VTOL then performs just like any other jet 'plane, with all its lift coming from the fixed wings.

It was rolled out of Bell's Niagara Falls factory in January 1954, after which its pilot, David Howe, spent several months familiarising himself with its controls and equipment. Not until 16th November did he attempt to lift it off the ground; but the caution was worthwhile, because he found he was able to master completely the control techniques within 40 sec. of take-off on the first flight. Soon afterwards, he flew the aircraft a distance of nearly half a mile, staying up for two minutes; and he has since made many more successful flights, although he had not attempted to rotate the engines in the air to the horizontal cruising position at the time this article was written.

Control at low speeds is achieved in much the same way as on the "Flying Bedstead", by ejecting compressed air through nozzles at the wing tips and tail, the compressed air being supplied by a Palouste turbine mounted behind the cockpit. To bank to the left, for example, compressed air is ejected from the starboard wing-tip to thrust that wing up. Once a reasonable forward speed has been reached, this system of control gives way to conventional ailerons, rudder and elevators, both systems being worked by normal cockpit controls.

Test pilot Howe finds nothing strange in travelling vertically up and down because, before joining Bell, he spent five years with the Otis Elevator Company, who make and install lifts in buildings. He is also a very experienced fixed wing pilot, having destroyed nine enemy aircraft as a fighter pilot with the U.S.A.A.F. in Europe during the war. Later he graduated from the U.S.A.F.'s test pilot school at Edwards Air Force Base, California. (Cont. on page 342)

Two Bells—*(Continued from page 310)*

The aircraft he now flies, and the XV-3, look strange in an age of super-streamlined, supersonic jets. But they are among the first of a new generation of aeroplanes that should be safer and more versatile than any we know today. We are only at the "Wright brothers stage" of this new era of flight, and Rolls-Royce, Bell and Fairey are the pioneers. The convertiplanes and VTOLs of the future will be as different to the XV-3 and "Flying Bedstead" as the Comet is different to the Wright biplane; and they may well bring true the old dream of safe, cheap, convenient flying for everyone.

MECCANO MAGAZINE

Registered at the G.P.O., London, for transmission by Canadian Magazine Post.

EDITORIAL AND ADVERTISING OFFICES:
LIVERPOOL 13, ENGLAND.
Telegrams: "Meccano, Liverpool."

Readers' Sales and Wants. Private advertisements (i.e., not trade) are charged 1d. per word, minimum 1/-. Cash with order. Readers' advertisements are published as soon as possible; inclusion in the first issue after receiving them cannot be guaranteed.

Advertisements of goods currently manufactured by Meccano Ltd. cannot be accepted.

READERS' SALES AND WANTS

SALES

"M.M.s" December 1951–December 1953 (except January 1952), also "Amateur Photographers", 30th April 1952–29th December 1954. All 4d. each or offers for part lots. Excellent condition.—Hadlow, Colwall Green, Malvern, Worcs.

"M.M.s" complete sets, years 1951, 1952, 1953, 1954. All in good condition, 6/- each year.—R. Matthews, 291 Chester Road, Streetly, Staffs.

"M.M.s", very good condition, January 1939–December 1941; 1942, May–September, November; 1943, January, February, June, August–December; 1944, January–March, May, June, July–November; 1945, complete; 1946, January, March–November; 1947, complete; 1948, January–November. Offers to—R. Towse, 24 Marshall Street, Newland, Hull, Yorks.

Perfect condition "M.M.s", "Trains Illustrated" and "S.R." Magazines. All 1946–1954. Offers—Scrace, 114 Rushams Road, Horsham, Sussex.

Good condition. "M.M.s" 1942–1954 complete, £4. "Trains Illustrated", No. 1 to December 1954 (December 1953 missing), £4. Also Railway Books. S.A.E. for list.—Palk, 59 Couchmore Avenue, Esher, Surrey.

A good assortment of Trix Rails and Rolling Stock, two-thirds cost price. Excellent condition. S.A.E. for list.—Blundell. 56 Alcester Road, Studley, Warwickshire.

Graham-Farish Transformer-Controller. As new, £1. —J. Beenstock, 49 Singleton Road, Salford 7, Lancs.

3,400 Stamps worth £33, now for sale at £28.—G. A. Phillips, Primrose Cottage, London Beach, St. Michaels, Tenterden.

Hornby gauge 0 Electric Rails and Points. S.A.E. for list.—D. Abbott, 29 Priory Road, Newbury, Berks.

Hornby gauge 0 Electric Train, Accessories, Goods and Passenger.—K. Haden, 18 Saburnam Road, Wednesbury, Staffs.

"M.M.s" January 1944–March 1950 inclusive, offers?—D. Warren, 2 Church Road, West Ewell, Surrey.

"M.M.s" 1946–1952 inclusive. Unbound: 1946 3/6, 1951 5/-, 1952 5/-. Bound: 1947 5/-, 1948 5/-, 1949 5/-, 1950 6/-, or 30/- the lot. All in good condition.—T. Lynton, 6 Chichester Place, Brighton 7.

Pre-war Hornby Clockwork Stock: Standard Compound 4-4-0, Tender, Passenger Brake Van, Milk Van, Double-track Crossover, £3.—Salter, 50 Pinewood Avenue, New Haw, Weybridge, Surrey.

"The New Educational Library" Odhams, £12/12/-. New this year, will take £9/9/- or nearest offer.—Evans, 75 Gwynedd Avenue, Townhill, Swansea.

Hornby gauge 0, 2 ft. radius Electric Track, 43 Rails, four Points, 12 Trucks (four Bogie), lot 25/-. Plus carriage.—Baxter, 15 Balmoral Avenue, Beaumont Park, Huddersfield.

"M.M.s", 72 copies from January 1942–December 1947. All copies in clean uncut condition. Offers please. Complete collection of 1,400 Foreign and Colonial stamps, all in clean condition. Offers please. Adana high speed No. 1 Printing Press, printing area $3\frac{3}{4}$ in. × $2\frac{5}{16}$ in., two Chases, Wood Furniture, four sets of Ink Rollers, Instruction Book, etc. Trial arranged if required. Price £3/10/- or offers. Enquiries for "M.M.s", stamps and Adana to—Dolman, 34 The Ridgeway, London W.3.

"M.M.s" April 1944–May 1953, four missing. £2/10/-. All in very good condition.—Calladine, 136 Brookhill, Stapleford, Notts.

"M.M.s" February 1950–December 1952. Good condition, 15/- or near offer.—Evans, 10 Northern Road, Swindon, Wilts.

WANTS

Meccano Part No. 129 (Toothed Segment).—Advertiser, St. George, 45 Brookland Rise, London N.W.11.

Apparatus and Chemicals. Send price list to G. Ramsay, 10 Centaurus Road, Christchurch, New Zealand.

Obsolete Dinky Toys, all kinds. Please send list and full particulars to—J. Holmes, 181 Royal Parade, Parkville, Victoria, Australia.

"M.M.s" 1946–7 complete and January 1949, unbound, clean.—Streetly, 45 Engayne Gardens, Upminster.

January 1929 and February 1933 back number "M.M.s" urgently required by Overseas reader to complete collection. Replies to—Box MM90.

Geared Roller Bearings 167 complete and Meccano No. 2 Clockwork Reversible Motor in good condition, also Standard Mechanisms, Pre-war large Outfit Instructions, How to Use Meccano Parts, Books of Prize Models, New Meccano Models, Super Model leaflets.—J. R. Jeffery, Hollerith Office, Box 14, State Mines, Transvaal, South Africa.

Pre-war Dinky Toys, Aeroplanes, especially Flying Boats.—B. Paget, 204 Daventry Road, Coventry.

Meccano Super Model Leaflets required. Complete set or separate. Fifty per cent. above published price offered.—Geoffrey Myers, Colwall Green, Malvern, Worcs.

Two Roller Races 192 teeth, or Geared Roller Bearing, Manual 4–7, Book of New Models, How to Use Meccano Parts.—Box No. 86.

Super Model Leaflet No. 37. Any condition. State price.—Green, 91 Bradshaw Road, Honley, nr. Huddersfield.

Small Motor Car Cards inside Kellogg's Cornflake packets, about 1948, preferably coloured. State price, condition and numbers available.—Warner, 7 Marsvid Avenue, Drayton, Portsmouth.

The "Deltic"

The World's Most Powerful Diesel-Electric Locomotive

LAST December railway enthusiasts throughout the country were startled by the sudden appearance on British railways of a powerful diesel-electric locomotive named the *Deltic*. This was built at the Preston works of the English Electric Company Ltd., a firm that has produced many fine engines of similar type for use on railways in British Dominions and in other parts of the world. It ran trials locally in the Liverpool area, and then between Liverpool and Preston, and its striking appearance, with its performance, suggested that here was something of a kind that would be seen on British railways for many years to come.

The *Deltic* locomotive is described by its makers as the most powerful diesel-electric railway engine in the world. It is a very large one, with a total length over buffer beams of 64 ft., and a height from rail level of 12 ft. 10½ in. Its weight in running order is 106 tons.

From this it is easily gathered that the *Deltic* is a massive engine, and when it is seen on the line there is no doubt left in the minds of the beholders as to its immense power and capabilities. As prepared for its trials, it was also very striking in appearance. The main colour was bright blue, with grey roof and underworks, and striking gold lining on its cab front and sides.

The locomotive owes its power to the development of a new lightweight diesel engine by D. Napier and Son Ltd., from which the locomotive indeed got its name. It is fitted with two of these Deltic power units, each with its own main and auxiliary generators, cooling system, silencer, etc.

The *Deltic* engine generates one horse power for every six pounds of its weight, and the two engines of the locomotive give it a total of 3,300 h.p. It is of the Co-Co type, which means that its bogies have three axles, each with its own motor, this being indicated by the capital letters C, the o's showing that there are no other axles.

The picture at the top of the page shows the diesel-electric locomotive "Deltic," the most powerful engine of its kind in the world, at the head of a train near Preston, on the London Midland Region of British Railways. Our illustration is reproduced by courtesy of the English Electric Company Ltd., makers of the locomotive.

The new locomotive has been designed to have a maximum speed of 90 miles an hour and at the same time to possess the best possible characteristics for hauling loads of various sizes. The claim is made for it that it could reduce the timing of the fastest present-day run from London to Edinburgh by 30 minutes, allowing for the same speed restrictions and operating margins.

A glance at the picture of the locomotive shows that the superstructure consists of a long central compartment, with a driving

(Continued on page 189)

The "Deltic"—(*Continued from page 203*)

cab at each end, each cab having the characteristic nose end in front of it. The two power units are in the central compartment, with an automatic oil-fired boiler in the centre of the locomotive between them, which provides heat for the train hauled by the engine. Between the power units there is also a storage battery, principally used for starting the engine.

For normal work in railway service the two power units of the locomotive will run together. They are controlled simultaneously, and the engine turning power or torque is automatically adjusted to suit the load and speed. Changeover switches are provided so that either power unit can drive all six traction motors, so that with only one power unit in operation the tractive effort of the locomotive is not affected, but it will then operate at approximately half the maximum speed.

"The Overland"

A Trip on a Famous Australian Train

By H. G. Forsythe

LUXURY, speed and efficiency are the highlights of *The Overland*, one of Australia's finest trains, which runs daily in both directions between Melbourne and Adelaide. Its coaches of gleaming stainless steel and maroon are hauled by diesel-electric locomotives, and it represents the last word in modern rail travel.

The picture on this page shows *The Overland* at Adelaide Station a few minutes before setting out on its 483-mile overnight journey to Melbourne. Two of the South Australian Railways new "900" Class diesel-electric locomotives head the train. These locomotives are immensely powerful. Each has a maximum tractive effort of 54,000 lb., weighs 120 tons, is 66 ft. long and can travel at speeds up to 74 m.p.h. *The Overland* weighs anything up to 600 tons and in the first sixty miles of its journey it has to pass over the Mount Lofty Ranges, where a ruling grade of 1 in 45 is encountered.

The illustration at the head of the page shows "The Overland" in Adelaide Station, South Australia, ready to begin its 483-mile run to Melbourne, Victoria. Photograph by courtesy of South Australian Railways.

A journey in *The Overland* is an experience not easily forgotten. The coaches, built in South Australian Railways workshops at Islington, have been designed to provide the maximum possible comforts for the traveller. The average accommodation on the train is for 350 passengers. There are "Roomette," "Twinette" and ordinary types of sleeping compartments for 120; First and Second Class sitting up coaches for 174; and a special "Roadside" coach providing accommodation for 56 passengers desiring to travel between any of the intermediate stations. The whole train is air-conditioned, being beautifully cool in summer and pleasantly warm in winter. Above all, the air-conditioning keeps out every trace of dust, and the passenger arrives at his destination, after the overnight journey, feeling as fresh and clean as when he left home.

The "Roomette" and "Twinette" cars are especially luxurious. The "Roomette" compartments can be made up for day or night use. Each individual compartment has its own temperature control, washing facilities and ample wardrobe space, and iced water is provided in Thermos flasks. There is a small cupboard in which you can

Driving controls of a South Australian Railways 1,760 h.p. Class "900" diesel-electric locomotive. Locomotives of this type haul "The Overland" over the South Australian section of its journey. Illustration by courtesy of the English Electric Co. Ltd.

put your shoes for cleaning by the Conductor, and you can even have a shower bath on this train. Each of the "Twinette" compartments has its own private shower and toilet. In all compartments a large landscape type window gives a wonderful view of the countryside in daylight hours.

The sitting up cars too are extremely comfortable. The First Class cars have a centre aisle and seat 48 passengers. They have aircraft type adjustable seats, that can be moved to any position at the push of a button. Adjustable footrests also add to the comfort of passengers. The Second Class cars, while seating more passengers, also have adjustable reclining seats.

Let us imagine we are taking a trip on *The Overland*. At 7 p.m. exactly we pull smoothly out of Adelaide Station. Accelerating rapidly as we pass through the suburbs, we are in the foothills of the Mount Lofty Ranges almost before we have had time to settle down in our comfortable lounge seat. Now we are climbing in earnest. Such is the smooth hauling power of the diesel-electric locomotives that it is hard to realise that in the first twenty miles we have already climbed over 1,000 ft. At Mount Barker Junction, 31 miles from Adelaide, the elevation is 1,320 ft. above sea-level. Now it is getting quite dark and we shall not be able to see much more of the magnificent mountain scenery. Another 30 miles and we are out of the mountains and are crossing the Murray River at Murray Bridge. The railway bridge spanning the river here is 1,880 ft. long.

The time is now almost 10 o'clock and nearly time for bed. If we have a sleeper all we have to do is to lower the bunk, which is balanced, almost finger-light, and we have a comfortable ready-made bed awaiting us.

After Murray Bridge long stretches of flat barren country lie before us.

"The Overland" is seen in this picture running through the Victorian countryside, hauled by two Victorian Railways "B" Class diesel-electric locomotives. These locomotives are in charge of the train for the 287-mile journey between Serviceton and Melbourne. Photograph by courtesy of Victorian Railways.

Inside a South Australian Railways Class "900" diesel-electric locomotive, showing the English Electric 16-cylinder V type diesel engine. The generator in the foreground supplies current to the four traction motors. Photograph by courtesy of the English Electric Co. Ltd.

Here *The Overland* picks up speed, rolling on through the night, with its powerful headlight blazing, until at 2 a.m. we reach Serviceton, on the Victoria–South Australia Border, 196 miles from Adelaide. Here engines and crew are changed.

Two Victorian Railway "B" Class diesel-electrics are now in charge for the remaining 287 miles to Melbourne. These engines are not quite as powerful as their South Australian counterparts. They have a tractive effort of 40,000 lb., weigh a few tons less and are slightly shorter. But the big reserves of power available in the "900" Class locomotives are not needed for the run through Victoria, although the line still passes through stretches of difficult country. For instance there is the 1 in 48 Ingliston Bank past Ballarat, but nothing as severe as the sustained gradients and sharp curves of the Mount Lofty Ranges is encountered.

The "B" Class locomotives are capable of high speeds, their maximum being 83 m.p.h. In practice, however, *The Overland* is rarely allowed to exceed 60 m.p.h. because of the nature of the track and the country through which it passes.

Soon after leaving Ballarat, at 7.15 in the morning, the conductor brings in a breakfast tray. He reminds us too, in case we have forgotten, to change our watches, for Victorian time is half an hour ahead of that of South Australia.

Now we can settle down to enjoy the scenery provided by the fertile Victorian countryside, but all too soon we are approaching the outskirts of Melbourne and at 9 a.m., just thirteen and a half hours after setting out from Adelaide, we arrive at Spencer Street Station, Melbourne's main line terminus.

The average speed for the whole journey of nearly 36 m.p.h. may seem slow to those who are used to high speeds over relatively short distances in Great Britain. But in difficult country, and with 15 scheduled stops, it is quite an achievement.

"The Overland" near Mount Lofty Station, hauled by one of the 222-ton "500" Class 4-8-4s used in the Mount Lofty Ranges before the diesel-electrics were placed in service.

Farewell to Flying Boats

By John W. R. Taylor

IT is always sad to see any aircraft reach the end of its useful life and be sent off to the scrap-heap; but the farewell ceremony held at Pembroke Dock in South Wales on 31st January this year was particularly moving. It marked not only the disappearance from service of the last home-based Sunderland flying boats, but the approaching end of all R.A.F. flying boat activities. Only No. 205/209 Squadron, based at Seletar, Singapore, still flies Sunderlands, and no replacements are being built or even designed.

There has never been a time in the history of the Royal Air Force when it has been without water-based aircraft. Even in the 1914–18 War the Royal Naval Air Service—which was combined with the Royal Flying Corps to form the R.A.F. in April, 1918—had its squadrons of big twin-engined Curtiss 'boats. Re-designed at Felixstowe by John Porte and fitted with Rolls-Royce engines, they fought gallant actions against German submarines in the North Sea and even shot down three Zeppelins.

Between the two world wars flying boats were the aircraft traditionally used by the Royal Air Force for "showing the flag," and many great flights were made. On one of them, in 1927, four Supermarine Southamptons flew 28,000 miles in formation from Plymouth to Singapore, round Australia, back to Singapore, on to Hong Kong and then back once more to Singapore. Except for a faulty primus stove and a few barnacles, the only trouble was caused by tar oozing from refuelling lighters in the tropics and marking their immaculate white hulls.

The picture at the head of this page shows K4774, the very first Sunderland of 1937.

The 1930s were the golden years of flying boats, when they not only flew with the R.A.F. but were chosen by Britain's national airline, Imperial Airways, to operate *all* services throughout the Commonwealth.

With their Short Empire 'boats, Imperial Airways set standards of performance, reliability and comfort that gave them undisputed leadership in the air. And when the R.A.F. asked in Specification R2/33 for a new patrol-bomber flying boat, it was logical for Short's to base their design on the Empire 'boat.

Militarisation of the design was not easy. More powerful engines had to be fitted. Then the whole interior had to be re-designed to accommodate gun positions, bombs, radio and other fighting equipment instead of luxury seating for passengers. At the same time, the design of the hull was improved.

One of the main problems was to find a place for the bombs and depth charges, because performance would have suffered if they had been hung under the wings, and it was not considered practicable to cut holes for bomb-doors in the bottom of the hull. In the end, it was decided to carry the bombs inside the fuselage on racks which could be slid out on rails under the wings when the target was approached.

The result looked very different from an Empire 'boat and surprisingly "fierce," with a two-gun turret on the blunt nose, a four-gun tail turret and two open single-gun positions in the top of the fuselage behind the wing. It seemed a big, sturdy, reliable machine and it was, with a loaded weight of 44,600 lb., a span of 112 ft. 10 in., four 1,010 h.p. Bristol Pegasus 22 engines and sufficient fuel to fly 2,600 miles at 178 m.p.h. with a two-ton payload.

Such performance was excellent at that time and the R.A.F. ordered the aircraft into large-scale production as the Sunderland 1—a decision for which they later had good reason to be thankful.

Although the prototype did not fly until 1937, production 'boats were in service a year later, the first squadron to receive them being No. 230 which was, with No. 201, also the last unit to fly Sunderlands in the U.K. in January of this year. And by the time war started in 1939 Coastal Command had 39 Sunderlands, plus two twin-engined Lerwicks, and 59 veteran biplane flying boats of doubtful value.

It was not long before the Sunderlands were in action. In fact, they were the first aircraft mentioned by name in an Air Ministry communique in World War II.

They earned this honour on 18th September, in 1939, when three of them picked up a radio message that the s.s. *Kensington Court* had been torpedoed by a German submarine and was sinking. When they arrived at the scene of action, they found 34 survivors crowded in two lifeboats.

Despite a heavy swell, two of the Sunderlands were put down near these boats, while the third circled overhead in case the submarine re-appeared. Unfortunately, the lifeboats could not approach the aircraft in such a sea, or they might have smashed against the hulls and caused serious damage; but this did not deter the aircrews, who organised a shuttle service with rubber dinghies and eventually took off and returned safely to their base with 21 rescued seamen in one 'boat and 13 in the other.

Bearing in mind that the civil Empire flying boats carried only 17 passengers, the addition of such a load to a crew of seven and heavy operational equipment might have seemed hazardous. But on later occasions Sunderlands carried far bigger loads when they were sent to Norway, Greece, Crete and the Far East to rescue soldiers and civilians from the advancing enemy. The record was probably held by the crew that flew to safety no fewer than 87 men in a single trip—six of them in the toilet—an achievement which necessitated a take-off run of about five miles!

Sunderland flying boat on convoy patrol during World War II. Note the camouflage and beam guns. Imperial War Museum photograph.

Other exploits by Sunderland crews included what must be an all-time record for duration of a single operational sortie. Normally, these 'boats could remain on patrol for 14–16 hrs., on anti-submarine convoy escort and reconnaissance duties far out over the Atlantic and Indian Oceans. But Air Cdre. "Kelly" Barnes and his crew are said to have stayed out for seven days on one occasion.

It appears that they became bored after a few hours of patrol, with nothing hostile in sight, and decided to alight in mid-ocean in the hope that the situation might improve. With plenty of food and drink in the galley and room to go for a walk in the big hull, they suffered little inconvenience.

Eventually, they resumed their patrol, alighted again on the calm sea, and continued doing this until they decided it was time to go home.

All this may sound good fun; but, in general, the war was a grim one for the flying boat crews of Coastal Command. Their most consistent enemies were boredom and the strain of watching constantly for a tiny periscope or a tossing lifeboat in a vast emptiness of ocean, which led one pilot to believe he saw a motor-cyclist riding along 450 miles out to sea from the Irish Coast.

Any change from the monotony was normally unpleasant, because the enemy feared the ever-watchful Sunderlands and did their best to destroy them. Often, a single 'boat was pounced upon by a swarm of enemy fighters; but the battle was not one-sided.

In April 1940, for example, a Sunderland was attacked by six powerfully-armed Junkers 88 twin-engined fighters while escorting a convoy to Norway. The first two Ju.88s came in with guns blazing, were engaged by the flying boat's beam and rear gunners and promptly retired to safety. Five minutes later, the other four enemy machines dived on the Sunderland. The rear gunner held his fire until the first was within 100 yards, then opened up with his four machine-guns and the Ju.88 crashed in flames. The next was damaged so badly that it crashed in Norway and, after trying unsuccessfully to drop bombs on the flying boat, the rest made off.

A few weeks later, the same aircraft was attacked by four Messerschmitt Me.109 fighters, one of which it shot down. As a result, the Germans soon had such a healthy respect for the Sunderland's ability to defend itself that they called it the "Flying Porcupine."

One of Coastal Command's last Sunderland Mk.5's, powered by 1,200 h.p. Pratt and Whitney engines, and weighing 65,000 lb. The underwing blisters accommodate search radar. Photograph reproduced by courtesy of "Flight."

There are countless other stories of Sunderlands in action in World War II—of how they guided surface vessels to the aid of torpedoed seamen; of the pilot who dived his crashing aircraft into the submarine that had shot it to ribbons; of the crew that ran out of fuel far from land, rigged up a sail consisting of the cockpit awning fixed to a dinghy oar and radioed that they were sailing home at one knot and were scheduled to arrive in three days' time; and of many other exploits, both grim and gay.

Suffice it to say that they played an outstanding part in keeping open our Atlantic life-line in World War II, and that, afterwards, a Sunderland was the only craft able to carry a doctor to the stricken H.M.S. *Amethyst* while she lay still at the mercy of the Communist Chinese guns that had shelled her in a region devoid of airfields; and also that a Sunderland squadron from Hong Kong was the only R.A.F. unit that could be sent into action in the first three months of the Korean War, because no airfields were available for landplanes.

Remembering all this, it is difficult to believe that only 721 Sunderlands were

(*Continued on page 259*)

Farewell to Flying Boats—*(Continued from page 218)*

built, in Mk. 1, 2, 3 and 5 versions, and that the last came off the assembly line as long ago as October, 1945. Seldom has so much been achieved by so few aircraft, and even when the last of them are retired by No. 205/209 Squadron, and by the Royal New Zealand Air Force and French Naval Air Service with whom they still fly, many people will remember with affection the might, majesty, domination and power of the last and greatest of Britain's wonderful military flying boats.

Space Notes

J. Humphries, B.Sc.(Eng.), A.M.I.Mech.E., A.F.R.Ae.S.

Rocket Motors

The gases to drive a rocket motor along are produced by burning a "propellent" mixture in a combustion chamber, and the substances burnt can be either solid or liquid. Although the gases produced are usually similar, solid motors and liquid motors, as they are called, are vastly different in construction.

A solid propellent is often a mixture of a fuel and an oxygen-carrying substance, known as an oxidant, which when ignited will continue to burn until it is all used up. Such a propellent is stored in the combustion chamber. This type of rocket is then very simple in construction. It is just a tube full of propellent, closed at one end and with a nozzle at the other, usually with an electrically-operated igniter rather than the more familiar blue touch-paper.

The liquid motor is a different proposition altogether. Here the fuel — perhaps petrol or kerosene — and the oxidant—maybe liquid oxygen or nitric acid—are stored in separate tanks and must be fed into the combustion chamber in a carefully controlled manner in just the right proportions and at the correct rate to give the required thrust. The liquid motor therefore is a complex device of pipes, control valves, injectors and pumps.

This rocket uses propellents at such a vast rate—for the same thrust a rocket uses them at about 15 times the rate that an equivalent turbojet uses fuel—that the choice of method for injecting them into the combustion chamber is very important. The simplest method is to apply a gas pressure to the tanks, as shown in Fig. 1; this forces the propellents through the control valves into the combustion chamber. The drawback of this system is that the tanks must withstand a high pressure, 400 lb./sq. in. or more, and consequently become very heavy if large quantities of propellent are to be carried. So this arrangement is normally used only for small rockets designed to run for a short time, such as anti-aircraft rockets.

A lighter system used for large rockets, particularly those which have to run for more than about

In the picture at the top of the page a 100 ft. shock tube is seen. Above is the Oriole, a high altitude research vehicle described on the opposite page. Photograph, Avco Research Laboratory.

half a minute, is shown in Fig. 2. Here the propellents are fed by means of pumps and can therefore be stored in lightweight unpressurised tanks. Centrifugal pumps driven by a small turbine and running at high speeds are normally used. The gas for driving the turbine can very conveniently be obtained by decomposing high concentration hydrogen peroxide, which produces a mixture of steam and oxygen at high temperature. This usually means carrying an extra tank of peroxide which makes the motor more complex, and it is now quite common practice to provide a gas generator that uses the main propellents, but burns them in the right ratio to produce a gas at about 500 deg. C. that can conveniently be used to drive the turbine.

Shock Tubes

Some very unconventional methods have been evolved for solving the unconventional problems met with in developing long range missiles and satellites. A very few years ago nothing was known about the aerodynamics of flight at altitudes above 20 miles and speeds greater than a Mach number of 10. Experiments with conventional wind tunnels, blowing air round by means of a fan, were quite out of the question, but one of the most useful pieces of equipment recently devised for investigating these extreme conditions is the "shock tube" seen in the picture on the opposite page. Nothing could look much less like a conventional wind tunnel.

The shock tube consists basically of a long tube, from one to four inches in diameter, at one end of which is a small pressure chamber known as a "driver". Pressure can be built up very rapidly in the driver, either by suddenly opening a valve connected to a high pressure gas bottle or by igniting in it a mixture of combustible gases. The driver is separated from the tube by a burster disc which is carefully designed to fail at a given pressure—this can be anything up to 10,000 lb. sq. in. When the disc breaks the high pressure gases rush into the tube, which is filled with a gas at low pressure, and form a shock wave across the tube.

This shock wave travels down the tube at extremely high speed, with a Mach number of 10 to 25, and is followed by the driver gases. A model placed in the tube is subject to this extremely high speed flow from the time of arrival of the shock wave to the time of arrival of the driver gases. This duration increases with length of tube so that most shock tubes are very long. The one shown is 100 ft. long, but even so the testing time is only 300 millionths of a second! To make any measurements at all during such a short time interval special electronic recording instruments have to be used.

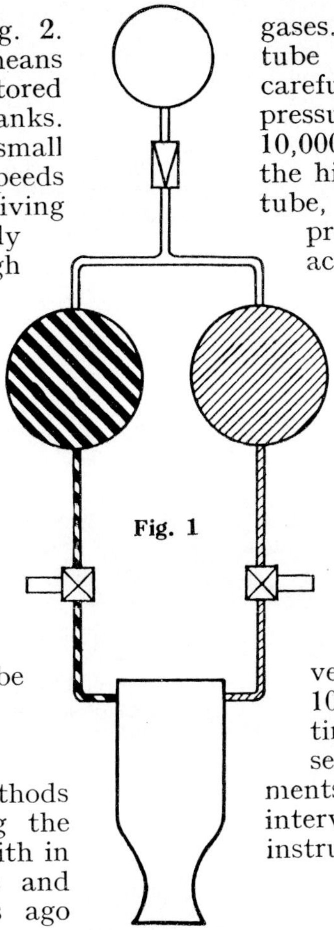

Fig. 1

Diagrams showing the working of pressurised gas, above, and turbo-pump liquid, below, propellent motors. Photograph, University of Maryland.

Fig. 2

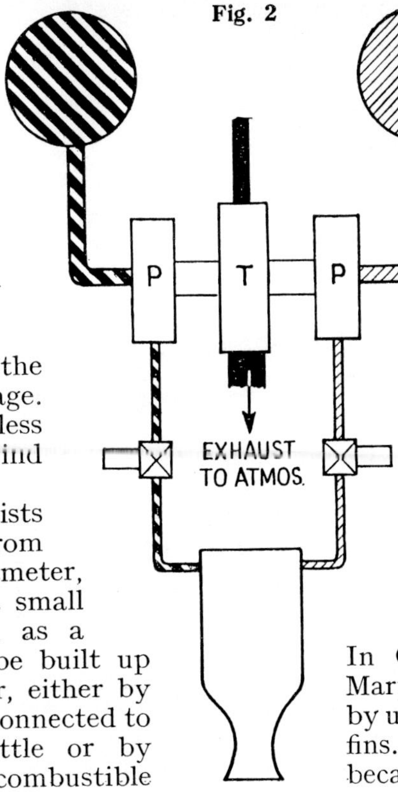

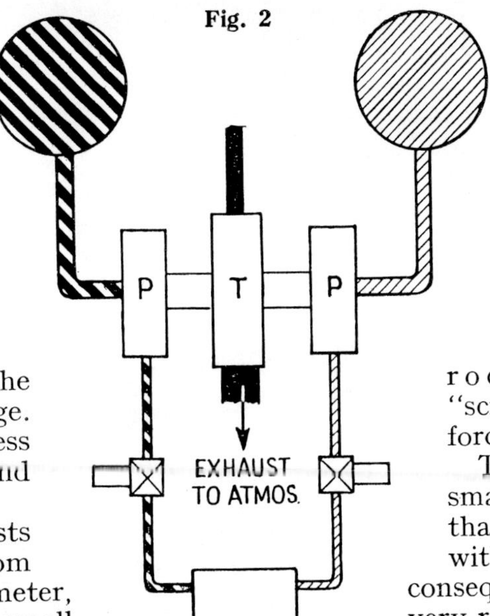

Oriole

One tends to think of upper atmosphere research with rockets as being a very expensive business to be undertaken only by government organisations. In general this is true, but during the past few years Professor S. F. Singer of the University of Maryland has developed several small research vehicles propelled by surplus solid propellent rockets which he has "scrounged" from the armed forces.

The major problem with the smaller research rockets is that their drag compared with their weight is high and consequently they are slowed up very rapidly by the air after the rocket motor has finished firing. In Oriole, the latest product from Maryland, the drag has been reduced by using a very slender vehicle with no fins. It achieves aerodynamic stability because its centre (Cont. on page 406)

Space Notes—*(Continued from page 365)*
of gravity is placed very far forward. The "sting", which carries the instruments, is placed on top of a Loki booster rocket. This booster fires for 0.8 sec., and then the string continues by itself to reach a peak altitude of 80-120 miles. The total cost to the University is £100 per vehicle.

Manned Rocket Volunteer

Recently the U.S. Congress appointed a Committee on Astro-nautics and Space Exploration, and various experts have been called to it to give their views. One of these was Dr. Wernher von Braun, who is in charge of the Explorer satellite programme. He proposed the launching of a 150-mile altitude man-carrying rocket as a preliminary to a manned satellite. Major D. G. Simons, who set an altitude endurance record last August with a 32-hour 102,000 foot balloon flight, has volunteered to be the first passenger.

Back from the Sea

Salvaging a Seventeenth Century Warship

By Trevor Holloway

ON 10th August, 1628, large crowds gathered on the landing stage in front of the King's palace at Stockholm, in Sweden, to bid God-speed to the finest ship of the Swedish Home Fleet as she set out on her maiden voyage. She was the *Vasa*, a 48-gun, three-decker ship of the line, stoutly built and finely decorated, and she made a fine sight as she was warped out from the quay. According to the records, the sea was calm, with a light south-westerly breeze gently billowing her sails. It was a festive day, indeed, and in addition to her full complement of 350 officers and men, there were a number of their relatives and friends aboard.

With top and mizzen sails set, the *Vasa* headed slowly towards open water. When clear of the cliffs that shelter the harbour to the south, her sails filled. Then suddenly, to the dismay of all who watched her progress, she was seen to heel over. A few minutes later she sank into 18 fathoms of water, and some 40 of her crew and passengers perished.

During the summer of 1959, just 331 years after the disastrous August day, the first serious attempt to raise the *Vasa* began. Its successful conclusion will form the final chapter to an exciting story that began two years earlier, when salvage experts and research workers met to determine how best the exacting task should be tackled. The discoveries so far made indicate that the *Vasa* was an impressive and, for the period, an extremely powerful vessel, equipped in the latest manner and richly decorated, as was customary in those days. But as to her appearance when ready for action, or the reason for her tragic loss, nothing is known.

When the *Vasa* finally reaches the surface—and there is little doubt she will—new light will be cast on the history of naval sailing ships and their development. At the present time, Nelson's flagship *Victory* is the oldest preserved, and indisputably identified, naval vessel in the world. She was launched at Chatham in 1765 and commissioned in 1788; but she was altered many times before retiring from active service in 1812, so the *Victory* we see at Portsmouth today is not truly representative of naval design in the days when she was built.

The ship about which this article is written is the "Vasa", which rested in the mud of the bed of the Baltic Sea for 331 years. In the picture at the head of the page wooden articles found in her are being carefully brushed with polyglycol to prevent their drying out too quickly. This photograph, and that on page 7, are reproduced by courtesy of Atlas Copco.

The *Vasa*, on the other hand, was commissioned more than a century before the *Victory* was launched. Furthermore, she has lain preserved from rot. In addition, her timbers are known to be worm-free, for the boring teredo, or shipworm, does not exist in Baltic waters.

Operations began when a team of specially trained divers went down to make preliminary investigations. They found the *Vasa* lying some 100 ft. down in pitch darkness, half buried in clay and covered from stem to stern in silt and mud that had protected her. Had the vessel sunk off the English coast, the divers would have had little difficulty in gaining a good idea of the vessel's appearance, but the waters of Stockholm harbour are dirty brown and so clouded that the 200-watt mercury vapour lamps used could only penetrate a few feet. The moment the divers started work and disturbed the slime, visibility dropped to nil.

This meant that divers have had to work by sense of touch. They groped about with their hands, and on returning to the surface were interrogated by experts about what they had felt, rather than seen. Piece by piece this jig-saw of information has been catalogued, and hundreds of sketches have been made, based on the divers' reports. In this way a general picture of the *Vasa's* hull has been built up, and it will be a matter of exciting interest to see just how accurate the sketches prove to be when her mighty oaken hull breaks surface some time during the next two years.

The salvage method employed in raising the vessel was to pass a series of steel cables under the vessel, and make these fast to two lifting pontoons on the surface. Before the salvage ship arrived on the scene the divers had the extremely hazardous task of boring six tunnels, each about 22 yards long, under the hull, through which to pass the specially designed steel cables attached to the lifting pontoons.

The first "lift" took place on 20th August of last year, and since then sixteen further "lifts" have been made. Each time the vessel was raised about 16 ft. and towed a little farther inshore until she grounded again. This process of lift and tow will continue until the *Vasa* comes to her final resting place in the Galavaret dock. It is slow work, for each time the vessel grounds she settles down into 10 ft. of tenacious bottom clay.

Operations were suspended towards the end of September last, and will be resumed again in spring of this year. At present the *Vasa* is lying in eight fathoms of water a short distance from the shores of Kastell Holmen, the naval depot at the entrance to Stockholm's inner harbour.

It was fortunate that the vessel was found to be lying on an even keel, for this fact made raising operations less difficult. The success achieved so far in clearing silt and slime, and freeing the vessel from the clay in which she was embedded, would not have been possible without compressed air. Fortunately, the Atlas Copco concern, specialists in compressed air techniques and equipment, has its headquarters just outside Stockholm, and has given its help to the Swedish Neptun Salvage Co., which placed its leading experts at the disposal of the *Vasa* Salvage Committee.

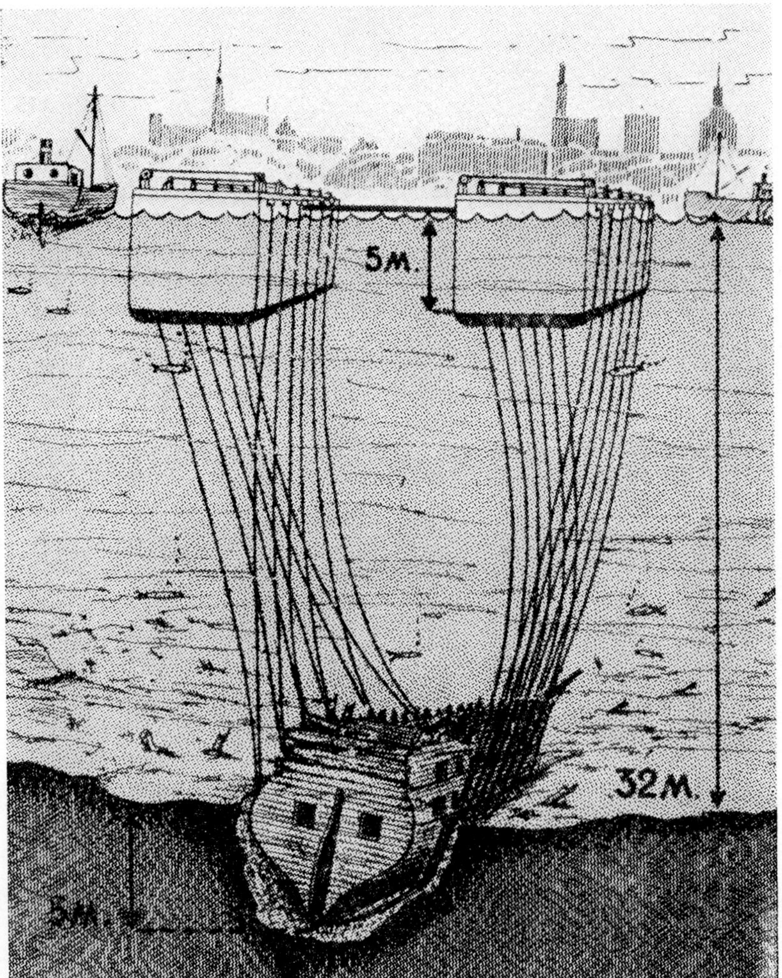

How the "Vasa" was lifted from the bed of the Baltic. "Dagens Nyheter" Illustration, sketch by Rune Almquist.

Compressed air is required for a number

Compressed air for use in the salvaging of the "Vasa" came from this Atlas Copco compressor.

of purposes, among them providing the divers with their air supply. Sweeping away the solid sediment is another, and this is then pumped to the surface, carrying with it any other solid matter it contains. Careful sifting and inspection of this suspended matter have already resulted in numerous valuable finds, and it is vital that no scrap of evidence, however small, shall escape examination.

Failure of the compressed air system would not only be disastrous from a salvage point of view, but could well have fatal consequences for the divers working in the cold and murky water below. Owing to the high standard of the equipment, and the fine work of the compressed air team, there has not been the slightest failure during two years of operation.

Next spring, when work is resumed, divers using high pressure air and water lines will start ridding the hull of the three centuries' accumulation of silt and mud with which it is filled. During this mammoth "rinsing-out" operation a great many Atlas Copco compressed air driven tools will be employed, with the firm's Arpic, a portable barge-mounted compressor, providing the vital air supply. The rinsing and removal of ballast is expected to occupy the whole of the summer working season this year until low temperatures and ice hazards once more bring work to an end. All being well, the *Vasa* will be in dry dock by the spring of 1961.

Exciting discoveries have been made each time the divers have gone down. Up to now more than 730 interesting and historically important articles of all shapes and sizes have been recovered, many of which are already on show in the Stockholm Museum of Naval History.

It is a matter for regret that the swirling dark brown waters above the *Vasa* have ruled out any possibility of filming operations. Had the water been clear, a first-class documentary film would have been possible, but all that film and TV cameras have managed to capture has been shots of less exciting work on the surface. But the cameras will have an exciting time when the *Vasa* appears above the surface for the first time.

The Salvage Committee are confident that much will be learned of ship decoration and wood carving of the early seventeenth century. A foretaste has been the salvaging of the *Vasa's* imposing figurehead, a two-ton lion rampant some 16 ft. high. It was brought to the surface last summer and its condition suggests that the timbers of the wreck are still first-class.

At any rate, the lion was positively awe-inspiring as its head broke the surface of the water. Foam dripped from a still crimson mouth and the golden locks of the mane glistened in the sunlight—after 331 years in a watery grave!

"FUN WITH TOOLS"

By William Moore and Robert Cynar
(Edmund Ward, Price 11/6)

To most of us tools mean work, but boys will find from this book that they can provide real enjoyment. The fun of course is that enjoyed by those who love to make things, and it is rightly pointed out that it is the greater if the thing made looks like the product of a skilled worker. This undoubtedly will follow careful adherence to the various rules for using simple tools laid down in the book, and anyone interested in such work cannot fail to find in it something that they would like to make. A jig-saw puzzle, a game, a bird feeding table, even a milk bottle carrier and a picnic box, these and many other things are described and illustrated, with full instructions for making them.

Living on a Railway Tunnel

By J. B. Ashby

AFTER reading the article in a recent issue of the *Meccano Magazine* about a railway station built on a bridge, I was reminded of something even more extra-ordinary—a house on the entrance to a railway tunnel.

The house is built above the North entrance to Clayton Tunnel, which is a few miles north of Brighton on the main London–Brighton line. It now belongs to British Railways, but was built in the days of the former London, Brighton and South Coast Railway. It was originally a pay office for the labour force constructing the tunnel, and at one time the chief ganger of the tunnel maintenance gang used to live there. After being empty for some years, it is again occupied, this time by a Southern Region passenger guard, his wife and two children.

The house consists of four main rooms, two bedrooms, a kitchen and living room. There is no bathroom because of the problem of surplus water getting into the tunnel. There is a safety fence at the rear of the house and this fence has a padlocked gate so that the children cannot be in any danger of straying over the tunnel edge.

The good lady of the house let me have a look round. The little house was spotlessly clean; even the windows did not appear to get dirty, in spite of the passage of trains below. On the mirror in the living room was a list of the trains on which her husband was working that day, and as the train came into the tunnel or went out of it, his small daughter would wave to her father from the window.

Nowadays, of course, most of the trains are electric and there is very little noise when a train passes through and the vibration is scarcely discernible. In the summer there are of course more steam trains and specials running to Brighton through the tunnel. There is, however, rather more noise when gangs are at work in the tunnel.

The occupants have lived there for several years and like being there very much. There is a pleasant little garden at the rear of the house, which is shown in the picture above. The look out over the track is to the right.

At the time of my visit the occupier's son was having a bedroom built in one of the towers, with access through a loft ladder in the kitchen.

ENGINES TO MEND

Railway engines, like all other machines, require maintenance and repair if they are to continue to do their jobs properly. Apart from heavy overhauls, carried out at a principal works, locomotive maintenance and repair is done at motive power depots and their associated sheds. At these places engines stand cold and stiff—there is nothing quite so dead as an engine not in steam—while fitters, boilersmiths, and other "sheddies" minister to their ailments.

The pictures above and below show some of this shed repair work being executed. In the lower illustration, Spitfire *of the W.R. Castle class is standing partly supported on jacks and packing, and minus*

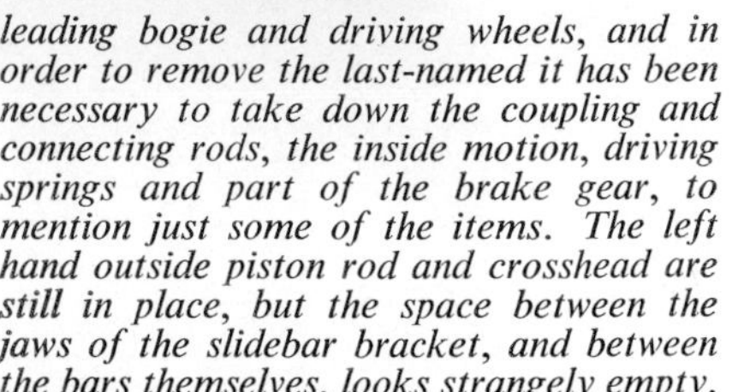

leading bogie and driving wheels, and in order to remove the last-named it has been necessary to take down the coupling and connecting rods, the inside motion, driving springs and part of the brake gear, to mention just some of the items. The left hand outside piston rod and crosshead are still in place, but the space between the jaws of the slidebar bracket, and between the bars themselves, looks strangely empty.

It is possible that the driving wheels and their crank axle have been removed for the sort of attention that is being given to the journals of a crank axle in the top picture. Here, the crank axle of the driving wheels from an E.R. three-cylinder Pacific locomotive is shown being skimmed up in the wheel lathe at King's Cross Motive Power Depot. **—Leslie Norman**

This picture of a Castle undergoing repairs, and the photograph at the top of this page, are by H. G. Forsythe. The picture on the right is by R. S. Greenwood.

A Railway Miscellany

Railway semaphore signals are often seen with large crosses on their arms. This is to indicate that those particular signals are not in use and are not to be obeyed. Usually, one finds there is an alteration to the signalling scheme in progress when signals are thus cancelled. If it is merely the replacement of an old signal by a newer one then, by working at a quiet period, railway engineers can bring the signal into use without delay. The photograph

ALTERING SIGNAL SCHEMES

below shows the scene at Rochdale East Junction on the day when the connection between the main ex-L & Y line across the Pennines and the Rochdale to Bacup branch was removed. The Rochdale-Bacup branch lost its passenger services in 1947 and is now worked only as far as Facit by one or two freight trains a day. When the connection was removed, access to the branch for freight trains was possible only from the down goods line, and much of the signalling at the junction had to be altered.

The crosses are being removed from the arms of a shunting signal. This type of signal may include several arms mounted one above the other for simplicity. The topmost arm indicates the road which is furthest left, and the lowest arm that on the extreme right.

As soon as the crosses had been removed from the semaphore arms, the signalman tested the working of the signal, setting up

the various routes through his turnouts and seeing that the correct arms came "off" when he pulled the appropriate levers. In the siding adjoining is a work train typical of that accompanying permanent way gangs. **—R. S. Greenwood**

A GIANT OF THE SEAS

Innovations on the Canberra

By K. Slader

The launch of the 45,000-ton P. & O. passenger liner "Canberra" at the Belfast yard of Harland and Wolff, Ltd. Photograph: P. & O. S. N. Co.

THE largest ship ever to serve the route from the United Kingdom to Australia, and thence across the Pacific to the west coast of America. That will be the proud claim of the intriguing new P. & O. passenger liner *Canberra* when, in the middle of next year, she makes her maiden voyage across the world. A ship designed for the convenience of passengers she will be a floating exhibition of British creative achievement.

She was launched on March 16 at the Belfast yard of Harland and Wolff, Ltd., by Dame Pattie Menzies, G.B.E, wife of the Australian Prime Minister. Now in the fitting-out basin *Canberra* is still in a far from complete state, yet already many unusual features are exhibited by this 45,000-ton ship.

The bugbear of the naval architect, weight aloft, is being countered by two bold devices. One is that the superstructure is being made of aluminium and in all about 1,000 tons will be used on board. It gives a saving in weight of almost double that figure, and can be compared with 13,500 tons of steel used on the shell alone. Unusual, too, is the position of the lifeboats. Instead of being on the upper deck, which is the conventional place, they are on the promenade deck, three decks nearer the water.

A SYMBOLIC NAME

Giving their reason for choosing the name Canberra for the new ship, her owners say, "The name Canberra was chosen because it symbolises the part which the P. & O. Lines have played in the development of Australian trade, and commerce overseas, for the last century, and the growing importance in world affairs both of Australia and her capital city Canberra. Happily the name means 'The Meeting Place' in the language of Australia's Aborigines, and this ship will be the meeting place of the peoples of the world."

On the upper decks, the twin streamlined smoke stacks, an outstanding characteristic of the ship, will be placed well aft so that any smuts from the oil burners are thrown clear of the deck.

Passengers will be able to sit at ease on the upper deck, snugly screened from the wind as the ship moves swiftly along at $27\frac{1}{2}$ knots.

There is ample space for deck games and there are four swimming baths on board, one of which is reserved for the crew. *Canberra* also carries a theatre two decks high. Not only can wide screen stereophonic films be shown, but live shows also can be produced. Television will be installed in some public rooms, the hospital and a number of first-class cabins. Telecine programmes will be shown at sea on closed circuit television; in port, local programmes will be picked up.

Boys and girls alike are carefully catered for, with two play rooms containing games, toys, tricycles, and pedal cars, as well as mechanical toys, dolls and dolls' houses. Leading off from the first-class play room is a nursery, and also a room provided with drawing boards, pencils and paper for those who fancy something a little more serious.

Miniature wheel-house

Outside is the playground with a chute and merry-go-round and in one corner is a space rocket, with a real periscope, through which one can see all that happens on the deck above.

The tourist class play room has a miniature wheel-house with its own wheel, astern of a binnacle complete with cover and a real compass. There is also a locomotive, with tender big enough for riding on, running two-thirds the length of the forward bulkhead.

A teenage room is also to be found on board. This

This sketch shows the proposed Teenagers Room—Tourist class, designed by John Wright, A.A.dip. Hons., A.R.I.B.A. Photograph by courtesy of P. & O. S. N. Co.

has been nicknamed the "rumpus room", and is equipped with soda fountain, juke box and indestructible floors and walls. It is soundproof, too!

This fine new ship has accommodation for 530 first-class passengers, and 1,685 tourist-class, while her crew will total close on 1,000.

The huge observation lounge built high up in the bridge tower—one of the new features in "Canberra"—is seen under construction. Central Press picture.

Rolling will not present any obstacles as two sets of stabilizers have been fitted. These are small fins housed below the water line inside the vessel. When required for use they can be run out into position and operated by being inclined to the direction of travel. The leading edge on one side is inclined upwards, and on the other side downwards, causing the ship to heel towards the latter. They are operated by a gyroscope in such a way that the angle of heel exactly counteracts the angle of roll. When stabilizers were first fitted to big ships it was found that an immediate and considerable lessening of crockery bills was one advantage!

There will be natural lighting in many of *Canberra's* inside cabins, as well as the outboard ones. This is made possible by incorporating verandahs in the layout, and it will also give a sea view to many more cabins than is usual. Plastics are to be used extensively, and will replace paint internally, except in a few places, as well as being used as a deck covering. Many cabin fittings will

The streamlined smokestacks of "Canberra", set aft, are clearly seen in this impression of the new vessel by J. Stobart, S.M.A. Photograph: P. & O. S. N. Co.

be made of plastic to blend with the modern decorations.

Some of the items to be found in all cabins will be two-programme radios, special taps supplying iced water, and air conditioning.

Loading and unloading of the cargo will be through the ship's side, instead of through hatchways in the upper deck, giving more room for passengers, for there is no cargo handling gear on deck and, of course, no hatches. A movable platform can be loaded with anything from a small parcel to a car and conveyed from the quayside up to the cargo opening, into the ship and along to the point of discharge.

Passengers' luggage will be loaded on to one of two conveyor belts. One goes to an elevator where bags required on voyage are taken to the appropriate deck; the other takes bags straight down to the baggage room, where they are stored by the baggage room conveyor. All these work on the push button principle and will greatly reduce the waiting time of passengers seeing their luggage aboard.

Engine room TV link

The engines are turbo-electric, and are designed to create a shaft horse-power of 85,000. The boilers are directly below the smokestacks, and the engine room is immediately ahead of the boilers. This means that most of the ship is well away from the noise of the engines.

The chief engineer of a large liner often wishes to be in two (or more) places at once. Seated in his office on board the *Canberra* he will be able to see what is happening in any one of the four machinery compartments simply by turning a knob, for he is connected to them by an internal television circuit. This is particularly valuable in an emergency, or in fog, when the watertight doors are closed.

Manœuvring in a confined space has been simplified by installing bow propellers working in a transverse tunnel, allowing the bows to be swung easily to port or starboard even when the ship is travelling too slowly to respond tc the rudder position.

The *Canberra* is truly "a ship that shapes the future" as her owners so proudly proclaim. May God protect all who sail or serve in her.

THE TRAMWAYS OF HUDDERSFIELD

By Roy Brook

This is a well-produced history of a British tramway system of the medium sized category. Huddersfield has had horse, steam and electric trams, the system commencing in 1883. The inevitable electrification began in 1900, and the trams served the town until 1940. At its maximum extent, there were 140 trams operating over 39 miles of route.

The book contains 120 pages, printed in large clear type. There are numerous illustrations, and route maps showing track arrangements, of the system in three different stages of development. Routes and tickets are also dealt with, all contributing to an interesting story.

Copies can be obtained from the author, R. Brook, of 12 Hawthorne Terrace, Crosland Moor, Huddersfield, price 10/– post free. Profits from the sale will be donated to The Tramway Museum Society, to aid their Museum project at Crich, Derbyshire. **J.W.G.**

The House That Downing Built

FEW—if any—of the world's residences can boast of such international fame as No. 10 Downing Street, the official home of Britain's Prime Minister. To add to its distinction, architects and builders are now carrying out a costly reconstruction to make the building safe and prevent it from collapsing.

The rebuilding will not greatly affect the interior; the Cabinet room and other famous parts of the house will remain unchanged.

By
LESLIE E. WELLS

There can be few London buildings on which more money per foot of frontage has been spent. So shoddy was its original construction that almost every decade has produced a repair bill of several thousand pounds.

Curiously enough, the 250-years-old houses in Downing Street owe their origin to the enterprise of a man who was a traitor to his cause, Sir George Downing, whom his contemporary, Samuel Pepys, described as "a parfidious rogue". He was the nephew of the Governor of Massachusetts, and was one of the first graduates of Harvard University, where he tutored for a time before returning to England to become Scoutmaster, or Chief Intelligence Officer, in Oliver Cromwell's army.

* * * *

With the Restoration of Charles II, Downing—a whole-hearted turncoat—made his peace with the king, and, in return for betraying the names of three of the men who signed Charles I's death warrant (one of them was Downing's old colonel), was granted a baronetcy and the lease of the land on which Downing Street now stands. The land was parcelled out into building plots, and most of the gardens and pleasant walks disappeared.

The site of No. 10 remained undeveloped until the first house was built there in the reign of Elizabeth I. It was from this house in 1605 that the occupier, a Court official and magistrate, was called to the cellar adjoining the House of Lords to arrest Guy Fawkes, sitting on his kegs of gunpowder. Thus was the Gunpowder Plot frustrated.

The house was known until 1825 as No. 5 and was subsequently occupied successively by Lord Lichfield (a Jacobite), Count d'Auverquerque (William III's Master of the Horse), and Baron Bothmar (the Hanoverian Minister).

* * * *

Then, in 1731, George II offered it to Sir Robert Walpole, his Prime Minister, as a gift. He accepted on condition that it became the perpetual residence of the First Lord of the Treasury.

Walpole lived in the house for some years (his son, Horace Walpole, one of our great letter writers, dates more than one letter from No. 10—"I am willing to enjoy this sweet corner while I may", he says in one of them—and up to 1834 it was the practice for most First Lords of the Treasury to take up residence there on their appointment.

After 1834, although No. 10 was used as an office and for receptions, First Lords of the Treasury did not always live there. Lord Melbourne, Sir Robert Peel. Palmerston and Lord John Russell continued to occupy their former London homes. Lord Beaconsfield did not move to Downing Street until his party returned to power in 1877, and Gladstone never used No. 10 as a home until 1880. Since then each Prime Minister, on coming into

WHERE THE CABINET MEETS

The historic Cabinet Room (right) and (above) the famous front door of No. 10. These pictures are reproduced by courtesy of the Ministry of Works and the Radio Times Hulton Picture Library respectively.

(Left) The Prime Minister's study on the first floor: Ministry of Works picture. (Bottom, left) This old print shows No. 10 in the days when it was the office of the First Lord of the Treasury. (Right) The house as it is today. The two last-named illustrations are by courtesy of Radio Times Hulton Picture Library.

office, automatically takes up residence in this historic house.

No. 10 is a three-storeyed house with a basement. The front door, with its well-polished lion's-head brass knocker, leads into a hall paved with squares of black and white marble; a double door gives on to a corridor leading to the Cabinet Room at the back of the house, and there is a passage which joins No. 10 to No. 11, the residence of the Chancellor of the Exchequer. The Cabinet Room—40 feet long by 20 feet wide—has panelled walls, a carved grey marble mantel, tall book-cases and folding doors which open on to a terrace. The long table, covered with worn baize, seats 22 people and it is here that the Cabinet meet for their deliberations. The only picture in the room is Van Loo's portrait of Walpole.

The bookcases hold a remarkable library. Each volume has been presented, with an autographed bookplate, by a Cabinet Minister. If possible, Ministers present their own works; Sir Winston Churchill is one who has had no difficulty here. Some may find other choices significant. Sir Stafford Cripps chose William Morris; Lord Hewart, Aristotle; Lord Thurso, Izaak Walton; Sir Hartley Shawcross, Coleridge; Lord Jowett, Keats.

Above the Cabinet Room and secretaries' offices are a series of State rooms. In 1945, Lord Attlee found them "not very suited to family life in the present age" and retreated to a flat on the top floor. Other tenants of No. 10 have delighted in their elegance, particularly in Soane's dining-room and Kent's furniture.

* * * *

No. 10 has two dining-rooms and two drawing-rooms. One of each is used only for official occasions—the oak-panelled State dining-room has received the Queen and other royalty entertained by the Prime Minister of the day. The private rooms are, of course, for the personal use of the Premier and his family. The bedrooms are unexpectedly and delightfully homely with their sloping attic ceilings. There are three bathrooms with coloured porcelain baths and basins.

The kitchen is in the basement and so, too, is the most impressive object in the house. Here, in beautifully-cut letters, is a tablet that tells us:

"*In this room during the Second World War His Majesty the King was graciously pleased to dine on fourteen occasions with the Prime Minister, Mr. Churchill, the Deputy Prime Minister, Mr. Attlee, and some of their principal colleagues in the National Government and various high commanders of the British and United States Forces.*

"*On two of these occasions the company was forced to withdraw into a neighbouring shelter by the air bombardment of the enemy.*"

It is certain that whatever reconstruction is carried out No. 10 will always retain its glorious history and cherished tradition, and will continue steadfastly to cope with the many problems imposed by a swiftly-changing world.

The Amazing Story Of A Tropical Phenomenon

ROADS—FROM A LAKE

By

LESLIE E. WELLS

ONE of Nature's strangest creations is the Asphalt Lake in tropical Trinidad. Popularly known as Pitch Lake, it has supplied, during the past 100 years or so, millions of tons of asphalt which has surfaced many of the roads of the world. Yet, for all this, the quantity of the asphalt in the lake shows no visible signs of diminishing. It is a vast and almost inexhaustible storehouse of wealth.

Trinidad Lake asphalt was used in the U.S.A. more than 80 years ago as a road-surfacing material. In some parts of the world there are surfacings more than 50 years old, and, in spite of greatly increased traffic, especially during World War II, they are still in excellent condition.

The greyish-black mass that forms the lake lies at the highest part of La Brea Point, about threequarters of a mile from the sea and about 140 feet above it. It is roughly circular in shape—about 1,700 feet in diameter—and the deposit actually being worked consists of about 75 acres.

The depth of the lake was a matter of speculation until attempts were made to reach the bottom by means of borings. Several attempts failed because the pipe or casing used was carried so far from the vertical at a depth of about 150 feet, by the motion of the asphalt, that further operations were abandoned. However, in 1925 a new method was tried using a movable derrick of the oil well type. A three-inch pipe, with the lower end closed by a wooden plug, was lowered into the asphalt with a one-inch steam line inserted to carry steam to the bottom of the pipe. As the asphalt was melted the pipe sank, aided by rotation from the derrick platform, and additional lengths were added until the bottom of the lake was reached. These sounding operations were continued across the lake in two directions so as to obtain an idea of the depth. The cross sections indicate that the lake is bowl-shaped and has a maximum depth at the centre of 285 feet.

By mechanical means

Although many people imagine pitch to be sticky and soft, most of the pitch lake is as hard as the asphalt blocks into which it is refined. There are danger areas, however, towards the centre, where the pitch has a molasses-like appearance and never hardens. To walk on one of these patches would mean a horrible death for the victim, for he would be slowly sucked under until he suffocated.

Until comparatively recently mining was done entirely by employing manual labour, and every pound of asphalt had to be dug out with a pickaxe. Today, however, practically every operation is done by mechanical means. Huge ditcher machines are used for extracting the asphalt and loading it into dumper cars. These then take their load to a ramp at the side of the lake from which point a train carries the material to the refinery.

The long trenches left by the ditcher fill up after a day or so with pitch which moves in from the sides and wells up from below. This hardens, forming a new crust, so that the process of ditching can start all over again.

Asphalt, on being loaded into the railway trucks, is usually wet and is honeycombed with gas cavities up to an inch or more in diameter, resembling a Gruyere cheese.

When the trucks arrive at the refinery they are emptied into huge tanks holding about 100 tons each. They are fitted with high pressure steam coils and a number of perforated pipes in the bottom for the introduction of dry steam, used for agitating the mass of asphalt during melting.

When the steam is passed through the coils, the crude asphalt gradually melts and water it contains is driven off as steam. At this stage the perforated agitation pipes are opened to assist the melting operation and keep the mineral matter, present in the asphalt, in suspension, thereby producing a uniform product.

After about four hours the operation is complete and the asphalt is drawn off from the bottom of the tank, passed through a fine screen to remove extraneous vegetable matter, and run into barrels ready for shipment.

Victims of the lake

Sometimes this limitless lake claims for its own any object that may have been carelessly left on the surface; at other times some fossil, or some long-lost treasure that had vanished many years before, is brought to the surface. Numerous bone fragments and teeth identified by paleontologists as belonging to the mammals of the Pleistocene Period (Glacial or Ice Age) have been uncovered. These fossils prove that such beasts once lived in Trinidad, and roamed the wild country in prehistoric times when the lake was in a semi-fluid state. Attempting to walk upon the surface, they were engulfed.

Frequently, fossils come to the surface. This is possible because the lake is con-

The picture at the top of the page shows railway trucks being loaded with asphalt ready for transport to the refinery. Illustrations to this article are reproduced by the courtesy of The Trinidad Lake Asphalt Company Limited.

stantly shifting in waves or currents. The motion is very slow, yet anything placed on the surface will change its position from day to day.

Appeared—then vanished

In view of this movement, an interesting event occurred in 1928 when a tree, believed to have been buried in the asphalt for more than 5,000 years, appeared and disappeared all within a month.

The tree came through the surface in an upright position and continued to rise until its trunk stood six feet above the surface. Workmen sawed pieces from the top for souvenirs. It continued to rise until it had reached a height of ten feet, when it began to sink back into the asphalt, and in a few days it had completely disappeared.

How did this strange lake originate? Speculations are many, but the most widely accepted theory is that it took form during a period of earth movements which resulted in numerous earth faults. This, in turn, allowed a stream of petroleum and gas to meet a stream of mud. The two united to force an outlet in the crater of an extinct volcano and gradually filled it. In time, the oils in the crater basin evaporated and left the deposit of asphalt.

Today, as road-paving material, Pitch Lake asphalt is used by nearly every country in the world and, although the demand is on the increase, the supply is not likely to give cause for alarm for many hundreds of years to come.

Asphalt being tipped into huge tanks where it is refined by having the water and gas driven off by a simple dehydration process.

Ditches that have been left by the ditcher machine. These fill up after a day or so.

An Illuminated Car Badge

Thousands of cars will be wearing a new look this summer, says the R.A.C. The cars will belong to R.A.C. members who are displaying badges from a complete new range of Club emblems now available. The new badges will also be seen on private goods vehicles, motor-cycles and scooters.

Most striking development is the first-ever illuminated badge to be offered to its members by any national motoring club. The silver-and-blue Elizabethan badge, already so well-known to motorists and two-wheeler riders, is lit by a festoon 3-watt, 12-volt lamp, connected to the side-lamp circuit.

Over three feet of wiring is supplied with the badge, together with a simple wiring diagram applicable to most present-day cars, including those several years old.

The badge, which is available from all R.A.C. Offices and Service Centres, takes only a few minutes to fit. It costs 12s. 6d.

Associate Members of the R.A.C. have the choice of the new illuminated badge, the existing Elizabethan badge or another newcomer, a de-luxe nickel-and-chromium-plated brass badge, with chromium-plated fittings, which costs 25s. Full Members of the R.A.C. also have a new badge embodying the best features of previous emblems. The other new R.A.C. badge is for private goods vehicles.

ROAD SAFETY NOTES

LONGER days, better weather . . . and hiking and biking ahead.

This is the time when everyone wants to get outside, the younger ones to play; the older ones to walk or ride. Unfortunately, so many, in their enjoyment of these pleasures, forget the ordinary, simple rules of "roadmanship"; things such as kerb drill (which is just as important to older people as to youngsters) and using the roads with consideration for other people's safety as well as one's own.

If you are going out walking in the country, where often there are no pavements, don't walk with your back to the traffic—walk on the right-hand side where you can see what's coming. Keep well in to the side, so that traffic does not have to swerve to avoid you.

When you are cycling, never ride more than two abreast and ride in single file when the road is narrow or busy. If there is a cycle track, use it. Remember it is better to be safe than sorry, and simple, commonsense precautions help so much.

Photographers' Page

CLOSE-UP photography is fascinating, but it has its dangers. The greatest of these is limited depth of field. When you are working close to your subject, the zone of sharpness is only an inch or two at best. The smallest possible aperture, therefore, should be used to get as much depth of field as you can. Small apertures help, too, to reduce distortion caused by some supplementary lenses, especially those not made primarily for photography, e.g. spectacle lenses.

When photographing models—Hornby-

H. G. Forsythe Writes About:

CREATING REALISM

A close-up picture of Hornby-Dublo "Bristol Castle" on the layout of Richard Lewis of Langley, Bucks.

Dublo Trains, for instance—try to position your subject so that it is broadside on to your camera, or nearly so. This helps to keep as much of your subject as possible in focus.

Choice of viewpoint

For utmost realism choice of viewpoint is important. A good rule is to place your camera as near as possible at the same relative height as it would be if you were actually photographing the real thing. Look at our picture (above) of *Bristol Castle*. If this had been a real railway scene, the camera man would have been standing in an elevated position which overlooked the line.

The second photograph shows how the picture was taken. The camera was fitted with a 2 dioptre supplementary lens and the distance between camera and subject is shown being set by the use of a Meccano Distance Gauge, which you make yourself. The gauge consists simply of two $12\frac{1}{2}$ inch Perforated Strips bolted together. At one end a short Perforated Strip is bolted on by means of an Angle Bracket. At the other end a Slide Piece and a $6\frac{1}{2}$ inch Axle can be moved to any desired position depending on the supplementary lens in use. Distances can be measured accurately on the Distance Gauge, when making it up, and the appropriate holes marked. In this example the Slide Piece and Axle are at the 20 inch position. By now you will see how very useful Meccano can be to photographers—a point to bear in mind at Christmas time.

Mount camera firmly

Exposure for close-ups out of doors in good weather is no problem, but indoors artificial light must be used. It is possible to use ordinary household lighting, a reading lamp, for instance. A good place for a single light is fairly high up behind the camera position. Shadows cast by a light from there give a "sunlight" effect. A 75-watt lamp three feet from your subject needs an exposure of between one and two seconds at *f* 11 when using a medium speed film. The camera must be mounted firmly on the Camera Stand, or on a tripod, for such long exposures and, if possible, a cable release should be used.

Below (left): Richard Lewis using a Meccano Distance Gauge sets the distance between the camera and his subject in preparing to take a picture. His camera is mounted on the Meccano Camera Stand described last month. (Right) This shot of a Meccano model tram was taken by artificial light, using a 1 dioptre supplementary lens.

RAM-JETS

WHEN we think of long-range ballistic missiles, orbital vehicles or space vehicles we usually assume that they must be propelled by rockets. And yet, the first part of their journey is through the atmosphere and a considerable weight could be saved by using oxygen from the air instead of carrying it.

The only air-breathing engine light enough to be of practical use in this respect is the ram-jet. In its simplest form, air is taken in through an intake and is compressed solely by the forward motion of the vehicle. Fuel is injected and burnt and the resultant gases are expanded through an exhaust nozzle to produce thrust. A very simple device, as you can comprehend—the only moving part is the fuel pump—so why hasn't it been used? Well, one of its main drawbacks is that it will only work efficiently at very high speeds — preferably supersonic. Again, it is not very adaptable to a wide range of operating conditions. In other words, a ram-jet designed to work, say, at Mach 2, at an altitude of 30,000 feet, will not work happily, if at all, under conditions widely differing from these.

One of the major problems is that of maintaining combustion; if the air velocity is too high, the density too low or the fuel-air ratio not quite right, then the flame will go out. Many types of "flame-holder" have been tried, but none has so far been successful over the range of conditions that would be required for a first-stage booster.

A 36-in. diameter hyperjet engine capable of delivering 250,000 lb. thrust. Photograph by courtesy of Marquardt Corporation.

Over the last few years the American firm Marquardt has been developing a composite engine comprising a ram-jet "wrapped round" a rocket. The rocket provides high thrust for take-off and low-speed operation.

Space Notes

BY

J. HUMPHRIES, B.Sc.(Eng.), A.M.I.Mech.E., A.F.R.Ae.S.

This ram-jet is different in one important respect from a conventional one—the flame is stabilised not by a conventional mechanical flame-holder, but by the rocket flame itself. The rocket produces so much heat that it ensures that the ram-jet fuel is vaporised and burnt. The fuel is a boron compound. This is a very high energy fuel and is also used in the rocket. The illustration on this page shows a "hyperjet", as Marquardt calls these combined engines, capable of producing 250,000 lb. of thrust. This type of unit might well be used as the basic first stage engine for future space vehicles.

LOCKHEED SPACE STATION

The wheel-like satellite shown in the top illustration on page 7 has been designed by the Aerospace Division of Lockheed Missiles. It is intended to house a staff of ten in complete independence of the earth for six months. Laboratories would be housed in the hub; living and recreational quarters in the rim. Power would be supplied by a shielded nuclear source placed at the end of a boom.

The components would be fired as individual units into space, on pre-calculated orbits, and there assembled. For assembly an astrotug would be used. This is a small vehicle specially designed for construction work and manned by a crew of two or three. It would be capable of supporting its crew for several days.

The astrotug is a completely independent working vehicle and personnel need not leave it in space-suits in order to work on the project of assembling the space station. The tug consists of two double-walled pressure vessels with an overall length of about 20 feet and an inside diameter of nine feet. Swivelling rocket nozzles are arranged for manoeuvring. On the forward end are four mechanical manipulator arms with interchangeable "hands" for such jobs as gripping, welding, hammering and cutting. Hands can be changed by remote control from inside, and viewing ports provide uninterrupted observation.

Radar aerials, searchlights, and other equipment necessary to the tug's work are mounted externally. Main controls and instruments, including radar, radio, computers, control and navigation consoles, are duplicated in each of the two compartments as a safety measure.

Men working in space-suits would be able to apply only very small forces and could work for limited periods of time. With the Lockheed astrotug, personnel could carry on the work in comparative safety and comfort with maximum efficiency. A special re-entry vehicle, shown in our third illustration, has been designed for ferrying to and from the earth. Tugs themselves would remain floating in orbit indefinitely, being re-provisioned as fresh relief crews arrive.

LIFE BEYOND THE EARTH

As soon as Man realised that the points of light in the sky were other worlds he wondered if there were life on them. For centuries philosophers—and more recently science-fiction writers—have discussed the problem, but until quite recently there has been no attempt to contact such life, if it exists. In looking for alien life it is natural

(Above): A 10-man permanent scientific space station. (Left): Two-man ferry vehicle for transporting personnel to space station. This illustration, and that at the top of page 6, are by courtesy of Lockheed Missiles.

On the other hand, the surface of Mars is well-known and the presence of markings which looked artificial and were known at one time as canals led certain astronomers to deduce that intelligent life had existed at some time on Mars. This theory is now discredited, but seasonal colour changes indicate that some form of vegetation may live on Mars. Again, there is no oxygen, and it is hard to believe that intelligent life could evolve without it.

When we leave the solar system we find we are unable to observe the planets of other suns. Present day earth-bound telescopes could not detect them. It is possible that a giant moon-based telescope (where there is no atmosphere to interfere with viewing) could detect giant planets, the size of Jupiter, around the nearer stars but would not enable us to see any detail nor even to detect smaller planets of a size more likely to support life.

The closest sun-like stars likely to have life-bearing planets are Epsilon Eridani, at a distance of 10.8 light-years and Tau Ceti at 11.8 light-years. If they have planets, and they support intelligent life, our only way of detecting the inhabitants is by radio.

Scientists at Cornell University have argued that any other beings in the universe who are as intelligent as ourselves will already have reached the same conclusions and may be sending out radio waves aimed at other intelligent life. The frequency used must be one that can penetrate atmospheres readily, say between one and 10,000 megacycles per second. It should also be a frequency that will be known to every scientific observer in the universe.

The most likely frequency, according to the scientists, is 1420 megacycles, which is one of the radio emission lines of neutral interstellar gas. It is reasonable to expect that sensitive receivers for this frequency would be developed early in any civilisation's investigation of radio astronomy.

At the National Radio Astronomy Observatory in West Virginia scientists have for some time been listening in to this frequency in the hope, so far unfulfilled, of detecting alien signals. This work may, one day, lead to our first contact with extra-terrestrial intelligences.

to look close to home first, in our own solar system. The only planets on which intelligent life might conceivably exist are Venus and Mars.

Recently, the discovery of water vapour on Venus has made the possibility of life there rather more likely. However, oxygen has not been detected and radio studies indicate a surface temperature of over 600 degrees F. In addition, the surface is perpetually covered in cloud and nothing is known of its surface features.

OLYMPIA EXHIBITION

The main theme of the British Transport exhibit at the National Schoolboy's Own Exhibition, at Olympia, from January 1 to 13 is "Careers on British Railways". There will be a special information counter with a display of photographic prints and colour transparencies illustrating various railway occupations. Push-button and static models of railway locomotives and rolling stock, and of British Road Services vehicles, will also be on view.

British Transport films will be screened in a cinema on the stand, and, at the end of each performance, the audience will be invited to take part in a prize quiz on the films they have seen. The winners will have the opportunity of participating in the final contest on the last day of the exhibition.

There will also be a British Railways and British Road Services information counter.

* * * *

The **"Ian Allan Book of Railways"** (6/6d.) is a re-issue of favourite stories selected from the *Locospotters' Annuals* Nos. 1–3 by the same publishers. The subjects have been well chosen and include a topical reference to the type 5 diesels recently introduced on the East Coast route. The Night Ferry, Royal travel and an account of the sharp competition between rival routes for the Plymouth traffic in the early days of this century provide pleasing variety. A ride with the guard of a goods train makes another story, while steam locomotive enthusiasts will welcome the account of the Stanier 4–6–2s of the West Coast route. There is, in addition, a particularly interesting section entitled "Night Mail", with a footplate adventure thrown in for good measure. There are plenty of pictures, several in colour.

The Mile-A-Second Aeroplane

AIR NEWS

By John W. R. Taylor

MANY people scoffed when North American Aviation said they were designing an aeroplane to fly at 3,600 m.p.h., or a mile a second. The unofficial speed record then stood at 2,148 m.p.h., set up by Captain Milburn Apt a minute or two before he crashed and was killed in the rocket-powered Bell X–2 research aircraft, in 1956. To advance nearly 1,500 m.p.h. in a single jump seemed far too optimistic, and few pilots envied Scott Crossfield, who was chosen to make the first test flights in the new aeroplane, known as the X–15.

The main requirements were for an engine able to thrust the X–15 to more than five and a half times the speed of sound, and an airframe that would not melt or break up if the air flowing past it heated the skin to a temperature of 1,200 deg. F.

The Reaction Motors Division of Thiokol Chemical Corporation began work on a huge, single-chamber rocket engine that would develop a thrust of 57,000 lb., running on ammonia and liquid oxygen propellents. North American built the airframe mainly of titanium and stainless steel, with an "armour" skin of heat-resistant Inconel X nickel alloy steel.

When it was completed, the X–15 looked more missile than aeroplane, with a 50 ft. long bullet-shape fuselage, stubby wings spanning only 22 feet, and dart-like tail. As its engine was expected to consume the propellents at the rate of about five tons a minute at full power, North American decided to save fuel by launching the aircraft in mid-air, at a height of about 40,000 feet, from a Stratofortress bomber.

* * * *

Three X–15s were built, and Scott Crossfield made the first powered flight in one of them on September 17, 1959. At that time, the aircraft was fitted with two smaller rocket-motors, as the 57,000 lb. thrust XLR99 engine was not ready. A speed of over 1,300 m.p.h. was reached in a shallow climb to 50,000 feet. Further flights followed, and on November 15, 1960, Crossfield made the first flight with the XLR99 installed, clocking nearly 2,000 m.p.h. even with the engine throttled back to its lowest power and with the air-brakes extended.

The X–15 research aeroplane shown in captive flight with the B–52 carrier 'plane. Note the stubby wings of the X–15 which is capable of fantastic speeds. Picture by courtesy of National Aeronautics and Space Administration.

* * * *

Since then, almost every flight has raised either the unofficial speed or height record. The planned mile-a-second was first achieved by Major Robert White of the United States' Air Force, who recorded 3,603 m.p.h. on June 23, 1961. On November 9, he beat this with 4,093 m.p.h. Earlier, on October 11, Major White had climbed to a record height of 217,000 feet, or more than 41 miles.

These exploits of the X–15 have been overshadowed by Russian and American space-flights. This is a pity, because you and I are far more likely to travel in supersonic airliners, made safer by lessons learned with the X–15, than in Sputniks and space-ships.

A STEP NEARER

The long-awaited B.E.A. helicopter service between London, Paris and Brussels, which might halve present journey times, has been brought a step nearer by the news that Westland Aircraft have obtained a licence to build the Boeing-Vertol 107 in England.

Able to carry 25 passengers at a speed of 155 m.p.h., the 107 is the best aircraft of its kind in the world and has already been delivered to New York Airways. The American version has two 1,250 h.p. General Electric CT58 shaft-turbine engines; the Westland-built 107s will almost certainly be powered by de Havilland Gnomes, which are British-built versions of the CT58.

The roomy cabin of the Boeing-Vertol 107 is similar to that of a fixed-wing airliner, with eight rows of seats which run in pairs on the port side and in single units on the starboard side of a central aisle. There are overhead luggage racks, and a roll-out baggage container in the underside of the rear fuselage.

PHOTOGENIC PODS

A favourite subject for the cameras of passengers travelling by Boeing 707 jet-liner is the view of two of the engine pods suspended under the wing, as seen from windows at the front of the cabin.

To take full advantage of the free publicity offered by all this amateur photography, B.O.A.C. have now painted their name on each side of the support struts for the engine pods.

Left (top): This Lockheed Vega, built 32 years ago, is being used to test U.S. radar ground equipment. (Below): The Lockheed Starfighter for Germany which got cold treatment at a United States' Air Force base in Florida. The climatic hangar also duplicated rain and humidity conditions found virtually anywhere in the world. Both these illustrations appear by courtesy of Lockheed.

FLYING ON THE GROUND

A few years ago, I was invited by B.O.A.C. to sample the first American-built flight simulator brought to this country. I sat in a dummy cockpit, complete down to the last dial and lever, and had to "fly" it under radio instructions from somebody outside, relying on the instruments to tell me how fast and high I was flying, whether I was straight and level, and so on. The whole thing became so realistic after a time that I forgot I was on the ground and became quite worried when the instructor told me to come in to land—something I had never attempted in a real aeroplane on instruments.

Since then flight simulators have become normal training aids, used by almost all air forces and airlines. They enable aircrew to learn quite a lot about how to handle a new aeroplane without any danger, especially as the instructor can introduce faults such as an engine failure, brake failure, or radio interference just to make things more difficult for the men under training.

* * * *

The latest simulators are very elaborate, with tape-recorders to provide sound effects such as the squeal of brakes and the noise of a faltering engine. Every movement of the controls is reflected by the needles on several instruments, just as in a real aircraft.

Now, the realism is being carried a stage further by means of a development known as "Terravision", produced by General Precision Systems of Aylesbury, Bucks. This projects a closed-circuit TV picture of an airfield on to a screen which can be seen by the pilot during take-off and landing, so that he sees exactly the view that he would get from the flight deck of a real aeroplane. The result is so realistic that even experienced captains have been known to forget that they are in a simulator after half an hour's "flying".

The R.A.F. is to use "Terravision" attachments on its flight simulators, beginning with the simulator for the new Argosy transport.

"TENNIS NET" SAVES LIVES

When next you pass by an R.A.F. fighter station, you will probably notice something that looks like a giant tennis net slung across the end of the runway. Attached at each end by steel cables to brake drums, it is, in fact, a barrier to stop any jet aircraft that might get into trouble during take-off or landing. When an aircraft hits the barrier, the nylon net wraps round the wings, the cables and brake drums take the strain and the aircraft is brought to a halt with negligible damage and with no injury to the pilot or aircrew.

Built in Sweden, the barrier has been in service at R.A.F. stations in Germany since 1958 and has already been used there to stop ten Hunters, five Swifts, a Meteor, a Vampire and a Canberra. Another 30 aircraft have been stopped by the barrier at airfields in Britain, when they failed to take off properly, or "overshot" on landing due to a brake failure or for some other reason. The barrier normally lies flat on the ground, but can be raised in three seconds by an electric signal from the control tower in an emergency.

VETERAN VEGA

Radar was unknown when the Lockheed Vega monoplane illustrated at the top of this page made its first flight 32 years ago; yet it is in use today to test new U.S. radar ground equipment for the simple reason that it is the best aeroplane for the job.

The Vega is made almost entirely of wood, so that it forms a very difficult target for the radar to detect, and has a good performance, with a top speed of 180 m.p.h. and ceiling of 20,000 feet. To test the radar to the full, the few metal parts that were used originally have been replaced, where possible, by wood or fibreglass components, and the propeller now has blades of laminated wood instead of aluminium.

FLORIDA FREEZE

In spite of the snow and icicles, the photograph of a Lockheed Starfighter on this page was taken in Florida on a hot summer's day. The explanation is that the aircraft is inside the big climatic test hangar at Eglin Air Force Base, where all U.S. combat aircraft are taken to ensure that they will continue to work in whatever part of the world they have to fly.

The Starfighter, one of a number being built for the German Air Force, spent two months inside the hangar in temperatures ranging from plus 120 deg. to minus 65 deg. F. It was also deluged with rain and exposed to prolonged humidity. At regular intervals, engineers went inside to check that, in spite of everything, its engine would still start, its wheels retract, its hood open, its control surfaces work properly and all the other components do their job just as well as if the aircraft were newly off the assembly line.

H. G. FORSYTHE DESCRIBES THE RAILWAYS OF JAMAICA. HE CALLS THEM . . .

"THE FRIENDLIEST LINE IN THE WORLD"

THE Port Antonio train was, as usual, late—very late, but nobody seemed to mind. At Darling Spring Halt, in the heart of Jamaica's lush green countryside, the friendly crossing keeper told me, "The afternoon train goes through anytime between four and six". I was there to photograph that train. I hoped it would arrive while the light was still good; luckily, it did. With a rumble and a roar and an ear-splitting whistle it thundered out of a tunnel, a fine old Canadian-built 4–8–0 at its head. The train consisted of two box cars and three coaches, two second class, one composite 1st and 2nd. They were old coaches—built at least 60 years ago—made of wood with platforms and steps in the American Old West style.

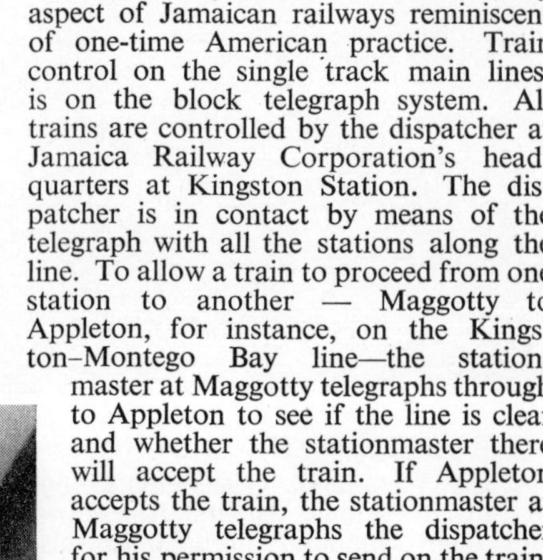

Those elderly coaches are not the only aspect of Jamaican railways reminiscent of one-time American practice. Train control on the single track main lines, is on the block telegraph system. All trains are controlled by the dispatcher at Jamaica Railway Corporation's headquarters at Kingston Station. The dispatcher is in contact by means of the telegraph with all the stations along the line. To allow a train to proceed from one station to another — Maggotty to Appleton, for instance, on the Kingston–Montego Bay line—the stationmaster at Maggotty telegraphs through to Appleton to see if the line is clear and whether the stationmaster there will accept the train. If Appleton accepts the train, the stationmaster at Maggotty telegraphs the dispatcher for his permission to send on the train. If all is well, the stationmaster then makes out a clearance card to give the driver of the train. Trains are not allowed to move without appropriate cards.

Signalling at stations is done by hand-held flags or lamps. Often, trains are held up outside stations while stationmaster, staff and a boy or two round up and chase away various livestock which are grazing near the line or may have strayed on to it.

At busy stations there is an additional safety precaution—the Pilotman. There is only one Pilotman at each centre and trains are not allowed to move in the station area unless he is

At Kingston Motive Power Depot steam locomotive No. 55 (above) is turned by hand outside the Roundhouse. Left: View from the cab of an English Electric diesel-electric locomotive, looking back along the train in the mountain section of the Kingston–Montego Bay line. All the illustrations are by the author

aboard. He is, in fact, a living "staff". This practice originated in England many years ago. As traffic increased the live member of the railway staff who acted as Pilotman was replaced by the token, or "staff", for single-line working, hence the origin of the name.

Other responsibilities of the Pilotman include setting and locking the points for incoming trains before walking up the line to meet them.

The Jamaica Railway Corporation, like most other railways, is in the process of dieselisation. Latest additions to stock include some specially-designed Metropolitan-Cammell diesel-hydraulic railcars powered by Rolls-Royce engines. There is also a small stud of very efficient 750 h.p. English Electric mixed traffic Bo-Bo diesel-electrics.

I made an exciting footplate trip on one of these on the 113-mile Kingston to Montego Bay line, passing through some of the most difficult mountain sections in the world. The summit of the line at Greenvale is only 1,705 feet, but to get there the line has been literally hacked out of the mountain side. With incredibly sharp curves and 1 in 30 gradients the line is a challenge even to the best motive power.

We had approximately 200 tons behind us, and once or twice the diesel almost ground to a stop on the sharp curves as she climbed, with the ammeter reading close to overload limit. On through the hills we struggled not far from the mysterious district of "Look Behind". It was hot work, too. On several occasions along the route the water for the cooling system had to be replenished.

Goods traffic on the J.R.C. includes bananas, sugar cane, alumina, jute, oil and a host of other commodities. Forming a unique feature of mixed trains on market days are the special market cars—modified box cars fitted with seats and windows. These dual-purpose vehicles carry passengers as well as the goods, such as farm produce and poultry, they are taking to market.

Let us imagine we are on the 2 p.m. Port Antonio mixed train a few minutes before leaving Kingston Station. The oil-fired 4-8-0 has just backed down from the shed and is coupled on to the box cars up front. A shriek on the whistle, lots of shouting from the guard and station staff, and we're off!

Through the yards we go, but almost at once we slow for a stop at Greenwich Farm Halt. Here, it seems, there is a little delay. Someone rushes past carrying an iron bedstead to load into one of the box cars; there is a lot more shouting. Off again and soon we come to open country and at 40 m.p.h. are passing through the great Caymanus Estate, where we see sugar cane growing up on either side.

Next stop is Gregory Park. On the passing loop is the diesel railcar from Montego Bay. Here we see the station-master hand the clearance card to our guard who, in turn, passes it to our driver.

Further on we come to Spanish Town. One time Jamaica's capital, the town is now an important railway junction. Here we branch off northwards along the Rio Cobre Gorge towards Bog Walk. Now the scenery becomes truly magnificent as

(*Continued on page 217*)

Top: The diesel train from Montego Bay arrives at Kingston Station. These Metropolitan-Cammell railcars are the latest thing on Jamaican railways. Right: At Kingston, the Jamaica Railway Corporation has well-equipped workshops. Here two steam locomotives are undergoing heavy overhaul.

"The Friendliest Line in the World"—

(*Continued from page 199*)

flatlands give place to hills and we begin to climb. We plunge through tunnels hewn in solid rock and, every so often, catch glimpses of the river far below.

At Bog Walk chickens flutter off the line as we approach. Here our engine does a little shunting and some passengers change trains. On a siding a little railcar, full of school-children, waits to go to Linstead.

Then we really take to the hills. Our engine tackles 1 in 30 inclines with thunderous exhaust. Trees growing picturesquely right over the line get their topmost leaves blasted off as we pass beneath. On the downgrades we seem to fly along, lurching on the bends with the ring and shriek of flanges hard against guide rails in our ears.

Harewood Halt, Richmond, Highgate, Albany. Familiar names but what different countryside! Through banana plantations, past tall coconut palms, breadfruit trees, mangoes and bamboo, the train moves on.

At every station there is much activity. Stops are always longer than scheduled, but who cares?—there is so much to see. We are a bit late but we'll get there just the same.

There is no dining car on the train, but at every station there is fruit in plenty to buy, and on board there is always an unofficial "refreshment officer". Somehow he manages to serve every conceivable soft drink *on ice*, yet he can provide hot patties, too. These are like Cornish pasties, but are filled with curried meat.

Now we are leaving the hills and for the last 25 miles our route lies along the coast. Sometimes the line is built right along the water's edge and, if we are lucky, we may see a fine sunset over the Caribbean Sea. We reach Annotto Bay, Windsor Castle, Buff Bay, St. Margaret's Bay, then, at length, Port Antonio, our terminus and the end of our never-to-be-forgotten trip on the friendliest line in the world.

RAILWAY NOTES

Contributed by R. A. H. Weight

Engine With A Wonderful History

I AM sure that readers of the *M.M.* were delighted to hear the news that the locomotive *Flying Scotsman*, which is not to be confused with the famous Anglo-Scottish express train whose centenary was recently celebrated, is not to be broken up, but will be available from time to time for hauling special trains. Most readers in this country will know that Mr. A. F. Pegler, who is a business executive and a member of the Eastern Region Board, purchased the *Flying Scotsman* locomotive for £3,000. She will be maintained at Doncaster on his behalf after restoration to her original condition as L.N.E.R. 4472. The engine's B.R. number was 60103.

The locomotive *Flying Scotsman*, which entered service early in 1923, was the third Gresley Pacific to be built, its predecessors being *Great Northern* and *Sir Frederick Banbury* which were completed before the Great Northern Railway was merged into the L.N.E.R. group. The *Flying Scotsman* became extremely well-known both at home and overseas, as she was a shining and prominent exhibit through the 1924–5 seasons at the vast British Empire Exhibition at Wembley. After taking part in the making of the film *Flying Scotsman*, which was made on the Stevenage–Hertford line and was shown in cinemas over a wide area, she was one of several Pacifics to be equipped with the new, unique, corridor tenders allowing drivers and firemen to be changed half-way in the course of the 393-mile, world-record, non-stop run between London and Edinburgh inaugurated on May 1st, 1928. The non-stop run became a summer feature in both directions until 1961—apart from the war years and just afterwards—the schedules becoming increasingly faster.

No. 4472 made the first northbound run in 1928 and the venture aroused great interest. I was one of a huge party of officials, sightseers and photographers who watched her initial departure on the famous occasion.

Flying Scotsman also made the first northbound journeys in several succeeding seasons, and I well remember that of 1933 which is depicted in one of the illustrations on this page. I watched the train from my home—at that time my "recording station" for engine numbers, times, and

Above: The "Flying Scotsman" at the start of the first London–Edinburgh non-stop run of the 1933 season. Photograph by courtesy of British Railways, Eastern Region.

The end of the story. Class A3 4-6-2 locomotive No. 60103 "Flying Scotsman" about to make its last run in B.R. service, at the head of the 1.15 p.m. London–Leeds express. The engine took the train as far as Doncaster. Photograph by S. Creer.

R.C.T.S. Special en route from Brighton to London Bridge via Dorking, seen near Shoreham. The train is headed by K class 2–6–0 locomotive No. 32353, built in 1921. The illustrations on this page are by S. C. Nash.

loads—which was situated about five and a half miles out from King's Cross.

In 1934, when streamlined high-speed expresses and also the A4 Pacific design were under consideration, *Flying Scotsman*, hauling a four-coach special test train, achieved the amazing time of only 2 hr. 32 min. along the 186 miles from King's Cross to Leeds. She was handled on that occasion by my late friend Driver Sparshatt who was ably assisted by Fireman Webster. The non-stop return trip took only five minutes more, although two more carriages were added, making a load of 205 tons.

While descending Stoke Bank, south of Grantham, No. 4472 attained the first authentic British record of 100 m.p.h., the maximum speed being recorded precisely by instruments in a dynamometer car next to the engine. Careful precautions were taken to ensure clear signals throughout, and speed restrictions were then considerably fewer than is usual today.

Commencing a few years after the record run, 51 Pacifics of the first two series numbered 2543–82; 4471–81; (lately B.R. 60044–83; 60102–12) were gradually merged into the A3 class, with boilers having a higher steam pressure and increased superheating surface, and with cylinders slightly smaller in diameter than originally, thus making them even finer performers throughout the East Coast route. More recently double blast pipes and chimneys were fitted, and trough-type smoke deflectors were added to a number of them, including *Flying Scotsman*. Some people thought that the latter features rather spoilt the handsome appearance of a noble class.

Although the A4 Pacifics and, during the last few years, Deltic and other large diesels, had taken over many of the chief express duties, A3s have often proved to be highly capable performers almost to the end—and some are still running.

In the very cold weather of last January *Flying Scotsman*, making what was announced as her "last revenue-earning journey", hauled a substantial load on the 1.15 p.m. express from King's Cross. With her new owner on the footplate she attained a maximum speed of 90 m.p.h. and reached Doncaster five minutes before time.

'MID SNOW AND ICE!

The exceptionally long and severe winter, with its blizzards, heavy snowfalls and continuous frosts, taxed all transport services to the utmost and brought a good many to a temporary standstill. On a few exposed or high sections of British Railways trains were engulfed by snowdrifts, and in the worst cases were only freed after the combined efforts of determined men aided by locomotives, snowploughs and shovels.

Alternative routes to those blocked by snow were improvised so that limited long-distance and other services could be maintained as far as possible, even during the worst conditions. On one occasion, for instance, *The Royal Scot* travelled from Glasgow via Dumfries to Carlisle, then on to Newcastle and along the East Coast route to King's Cross, instead of to Euston. During this bad weather, unusual steam and diesel locomotives were noted, sometimes in odd combinations. Many found themselves in difficulties because of the oil, water, brake gear and heating apparatus being frozen. Water troughs were frozen solid; many points, signals, tunnels and electrified tracks were severely affected by ice, as were most of the passenger and freight rolling stock.

Yet such was the good work achieved by the railways that for thousands of people travel to and from work or school was almost normal.

THE DISAPPEARING 4–4–0

During the first part of the present century, 4–4–0 locomotives were an ever-present sight on many a British railway. They were built in many sizes and types for handling all kinds of trains, from the express to the more humble "perishable". For instance, the large and powerful Midland Railway, and the less extensive South Eastern and Chatham Railway (respectively merged in 1923 into the L.M.S. and Southern groups) relied entirely upon 4–4–0s in working the principal passenger services. So, to a more modest extent, did a number of the old-time companies such as the Furness, North Staffordshire, Cambrian and Great North of Scotland.

Bigger and gradually more powerful six-coupled express or mixed traffic locomotives, and 2–6–2 or 2–6–4 tank engines sounded the knell of the 4–4–0, apart from some secondary or stand-by duties.

The S.R. "Schools", introduced as late as 1930, probably ranked as the biggest and most powerful 4–4–0 class in the world. Designed for the London–Tunbridge Wells–Hastings service, involving steep gradients, sharp curves and restricted clearances in tunnels, they served as a successful mainstay until complete dieselisation in 1958. Years ago they performed splendidly on the Waterloo–Portsmouth and Bournemouth expresses. Since that time they have been employed in many secondary and cross-country duties and were finally in use around the Central and Western Divisions.

No B.R. 4–4–0s now remain in regular service, although a selection are being preserved for exhibition. Locomotives so preserved will be restored to their original livery—indeed some have already been so treated—and some will occasionally haul special trains.

Excursion to Farnborough, September 10, 1961, in connection with Air Display. The locomotive is Schools class No. 30905 "Tonbridge".

A CUP FINAL —OLD STYLE

KENNINGTON 90 years ago was very different from the Kennington of today. Then it was part of rural England, and its peace was never disturbed by the hooting of motor horns and the rumblings of buses. Occasionally a hansom cab or two might be seen, and now and again one could hear the blast of a post-horn announcing the passing of a stage coach.

The Oval was different, too, and far from being one of the sacred homes of cricket it marked the scene of what might be regarded as the first Cup Final.

By

Geoffrey J. Matson

This took place on March 16, 1872, and caused no small amount of consternation among the few people living in the district. Dozens of hansoms and private landaus—more than they had ever seen on one day before—rolled up throughout the morning, and eventually there were a thousand spectators crowded into the Oval ground. It was a very exclusive attendance, for at that time football was scoffed at by the masses, and only met with favour in the public schools and a few of the most exclusive clubs.

* * * *

There had been no knock-out contest to decide who should meet for this first Cup Final, it was merely a game played between two football teams for a "cup". The teams taking part were the Wanderers—made up of old members of the public schools and universities—and the Royal Engineers.

The players had no set position on the field as they have today. Each team consisted of a goalkeeper, a back, a half-back and eight others who wandered about just as they liked. The dress, too, compared with today's standards, was very unorthodox. Each man wore a pair of long, white flannel trousers, the bottoms of which were tucked into the top of his socks, a white shirt, a small "pill-box" cap, and brown boots fitted with ugly iron spikes. The goalposts were of wood, and instead of a wooden crossbar a length of tape was stretched from upright to upright.

* * * *

Fireside Fun

It was the custom in an Irish village for visitors to offer a half-witted lad a sixpence and a copper penny and the village fool always took the penny, because, it was believed, it was the larger.

One day an English visitor asked him, "Why do you always take the penny, John? Don't you know the sixpence is worth far more?"

"Sure, man, I know that," replied the fool, "but I wance took the tanner and they would niver try me again."

A shipyard worker was teaching a woman riveter what to do.

"I'll hold the rivet," he said, "and when I nod my head, you hit it with the hammer."

She did.

He left a widow and three children.

* * * *

Said the countryman about his neighbour with large feet, "He'd a bin a tall 'un if 'e 'adn't 'ad ower much turned up at the bottom."

* * * *

"Patrick," said the priest, "whisky is your worst enemy."

"But, Father," said Pat, "wasn't it only last Sunday you were telling us to love our enemies?"

"It was," said the priest, "but I didn't say anything about swallowing them."

"Go back—the engine's caught fire!"

Jack: "Listen you, I'm a boxer. I box guys and lay 'em out."

Mike: "Yeah? Well, I'm an undertaker. I lay 'em out and box 'em!"

* * * *

Judge (during dispute over an eight-day clock): I award the clock to the plaintiff.

Defendant: Then what on earth do I get?

Judge: You get the eight days.

RIDE (AIR CUSHION) HIGH with the HOVERCRAFT!

TODAY'S MOST ADVANCED WORKING MODEL AS DEMONSTRATED ON TV, NEWSREELS AND PUBLICISED ON RADIO AND IN THE PRESS

Traverses flat land or reasonably calm water on a cushion of air like a real Hovercraft. Easy to assemble, all plastic kit with the most magnificent set of step-by-step instructions, including 15 large photo-illustrations. Also cement, accessories, and **FREE BP Fuel Dispenser.** Recommended suitable ·8 c.c. glow-plug engines: AM 049, "Cobra" and FROG 049. Overall size of model: Length, 17 in., Width, 11 in., Height to top of rudders, 4 in.

Kit price **£2 2s.** Also made-up model (complete with motor) **£7 5s.**

MOBO HOVERCRAFT *See it now at your model shop!*

Each box contains free BP Fuel Dispenser and fascinating detailed account of BP Fuel-research work on real Hovercraft development.

Designed and made by the JETEX Division of

D. SEBEL & CO. LTD. West Street, Erith, Kent
Telephone: Erith 33020 Telegrams: SEBELCO, ERITH

Competition Page

How Many Errors Has Our Artist Made?